W9-DDG-837

THE BEST PHYSICS PROGRAM FOR ALL YOUR STUDENTS

#1 Physics Text in the Nation

GLENCOE

McGraw-Hill

Helps Students Achieve Their Full Potential

Physics: Principles and Problems is a unique balance of concisely developed concepts supported by an appropriate amount of math and everyday applications. This winning combination helps all your students *achieve their full potential* and promotes higher physics enrollment.

Fundamental concepts are developed clearly in a narrative style that motivates and helps your students relate physics to their everyday world. Math is appropriate to support the concepts while it remains unintimidating for your students.

Objectives

- display an understanding of the difference between solids and liquids on a microscopic level.
- discuss properties of solids such as elasticity.
- display an understanding of the origin of thermal expansion; be able to solve problems using linear thermal expansion; state some examples of applications and difficulties caused by thermal expansion.

13.2 THE SOLID STATE

What is the difference between a liquid and a solid? Solids are stiff. You can push them. Liquids are soft. Can you rest your finger on water? No, it goes right in. Of course, if you "bellyflop" into a swimming pool, you recognize that a liquid can seem rather solid. Scientists have recently found that, under certain laboratory conditions, solids and liquids are not so easily distinguished. The researchers have made clusters containing only a few dozen atoms, suggested by the computer images in Figure 13–16. These clusters can be both liquid and solid at the same temperature. Study of this strange state of matter may help scientists to invent new, useful materials in the future.

a 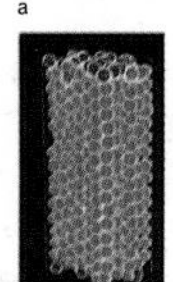
b 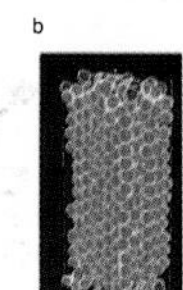
c 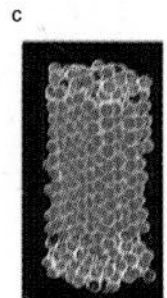
d 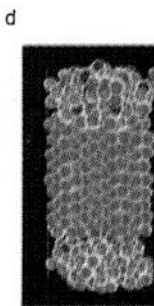

FIGURE 13–16. The difference in crystal structure between a solid and a liquid is not great. Solids have a long-range order, while the order in liquids is short range.

Solid Bodies

The particles in a true solid are fixed in a crystal lattice.

When the temperature of a liquid is lowered, the average kinetic energy of the particles is lowered. As the particles slow down, the cohesive forces become more effective, and the particles are no longer able to slide over one another. The particles become frozen into a fixed pattern called a **crystal lattice**, Figure 13–17. Despite the forces that hold the particles in place, the particles do not stop moving completely. Rather, they vibrate around their fixed positions in the crystal lattice. In some solid materials, the particles do not form a fixed crystalline pattern. Their positions are fixed, but the pattern is variable. These substances have no regular crystal structure but have definite volume and shape, so they are called **amorphous solids**. Butter, paraffin, and glass are examples. They are often classified as very viscous (slow-flowing) liquids.

FIGURE 13–17. The solid form of water, ice, has a larger volume than an equal mass of its liquid form (a). The crystalline structure of ice (b).

a 

b 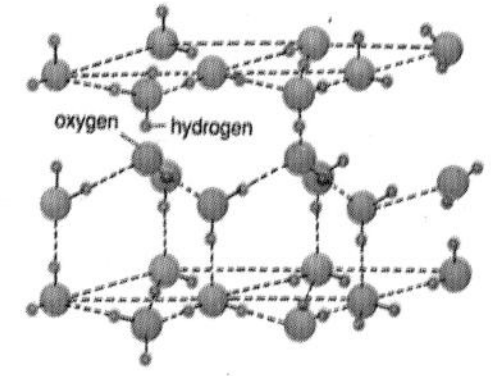

PROBLEM SOLVING STRATEGY

The choice of axes does not affect the final solution of a problem.

In resolving force, velocity, or displacement vectors, choose the direction of the component axes according to the specifics of the problem. Since the choice of axes will not affect the results, choose the set that simplifies the solution. Quite often you will want one axis to represent a horizontal, or right-left direction, and the second axis a vertical, or up-down direction. In other problems, one component is in the east-west direction, while the other is in the north-south direction. Be sure to specify the positive direction for each axis.

Example Problem

Resolving a Velocity Vector Into Its Components

A wind with a velocity of 40.0 km/h blows toward 30.0°, Figure 6–10.

a. What is the component of the wind's velocity toward 90°?
b. What is the component of the wind's velocity toward 0°?

Given: v = 40.0 km/h, 30.0° **Unknowns:** v_{90}, v_o

Solution:
Toward 0° and 90° are positive. Angles are measured from 0°. To find the component toward 90°, v_{90}, use the relation

$$\sin 30° = \frac{v_{90}}{v}.$$

Then, $v_{90} = v(\sin 30.0°)$
$= (40.0 \text{ km/h})(0.500)$
$v_{90} = 20.0$ km/h at 90.0°.

To find the component from 0°, v_o, use the relation

$$\cos 30° = \frac{v_o}{v}.$$

Then, $v_o = v(\cos 30°)$
$= (40.0 \text{ km/h})(0.866)$
$v_o = 34.6$ km/h at 0.0°.

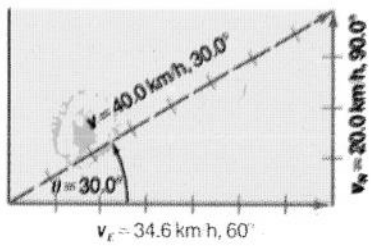

v = 40.0 km/h, 30.0°
θ = 30.0°
v_N = 20.0 km/h, 90.0°
v_E = 34.6 km/h, 60°

FIGURE 6–10. Use with the Example Problem.

Practice Problems

11. A heavy box is pulled across a wooden floor with a rope. The rope makes an angle of 60° with the floor. A force of 75 N is exerted on the rope. What is the component of the force parallel to the floor?
12. An airplane flies toward 149° at 525 km/h. What is the component of the plane's velocity
...toward 180°?
...f 72 N along the handle of a lawn mower ...n. Find the horizontal component of this ... held at an angle with the lawn of
c. 30.0°.
... an angle of 305° from east. Find the east-...nponents of this walk.

Use your calculator to find the angle θ whose tangent is 50.0/90.0, called the arotan.

Keys	Result
50.0 ÷ 90.9 =	0. 555. . .
shift tan	29. 1

arotan 50.00/90.00 = 29.1°

Problem Solving Strategies provide valuable insight into solving the chapter problems. **Example Problems** teach your students not only the solution but also the means by which to achieve the solution. **Practice Problems** support each math concept and provide an opportunity for immediate feedback.

Engaging Everyday Applications, Exciting Labs and Interesting Special Features Illustrate How Physics Principles Apply to the Student's World

Labs, labs, and more labs demonstrate daily applications of physics and provide the hands-on experience you want for your students. *You* choose from full-page **Physics Labs** or unique "quickie" **Pocket Labs**. Both are designed to help clarify common physics misconceptions.

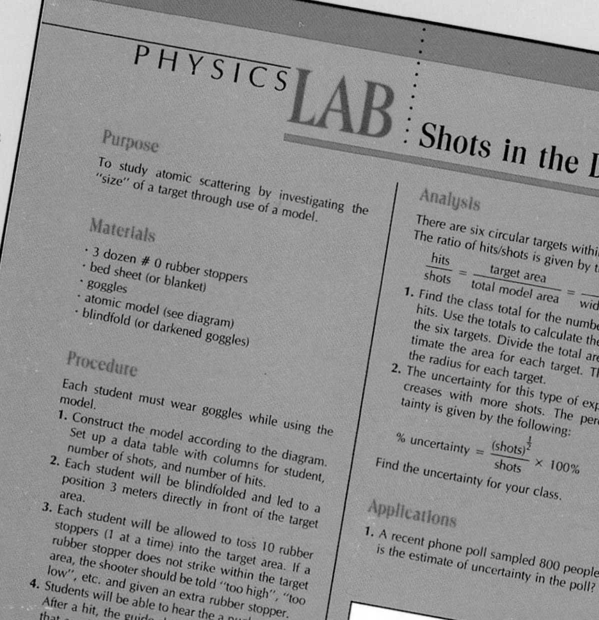

PHYSICS LAB: Shots in the Dark

Purpose

To study atomic scattering by investigating the "size" of a target through use of a model.

Materials

- 3 dozen # 0 rubber stoppers
- bed sheet (or blanket)
- goggles
- atomic model (see diagram)
- blindfold (or darkened goggles)

Procedure

Each student must wear goggles while using the model.

1. Construct the model according to the diagram. Set up a data table with columns for student, number of shots, and number of hits.
2. Each student will be blindfolded and led to a position 3 meters directly in front of the target area.
3. Each student will be allowed to toss 10 rubber stoppers (1 at a time) into the target area. If a rubber stopper does not strike within the target area, the shooter should be told "too high", "too low", etc. and given an extra rubber stopper.
4. Students will be able to hear the a nuclear "hit". After a hit, the guide should instruct the shooter that another hit cannot be counted on the same target and the shots should be moved around.
5. After a student finishes her throws, she will be the guide for the next student "shooter".
6. After serving as guide, each student should record her initials and the number of hits on the chalkboard.

Observations and Data

1. Record each student, the number of shots, and the number of hits.
2. Did the students with more hits have better data?

Analysis

There are six circular targets within the target area. The ratio of hits/shots is given by the following:

$$\frac{\text{hits}}{\text{shots}} = \frac{\text{target area}}{\text{total model area}} = \frac{6\pi r^2}{\text{width} \times \text{height}}$$

1. Find the class total for the number of shots and hits. Use the totals to calculate the total area for the six targets. Divide the total area by 6 to estimate the area for each target. Then calculate the radius for each target.
2. The uncertainty for this type of experiment decreases with more shots. The percent uncertainty is given by the following:

$$\%\ \text{uncertainty} = \frac{(\text{shots})^{\frac{1}{2}}}{\text{shots}} \times 100\%$$

Find the uncertainty for your class.

Applications

1. A recent phone poll sampled 800 people. What is the estimate of uncertainty in the poll?

POCKET LAB

FOOT PRESSURE

How much pressure do you exert when standing on the ground with one foot? Is it more or less than air pressure? Estimate your weight in newtons. **Hint:** 500 N = 110 lb. Stand on a piece of paper and have a lab partner trace the outline of your foot. Draw a rectangle that has about the same area as the outline. Calculate the area in square meters. Use the definition of pressure to estimate your pressure. $P = F/A$

Physics and society

COMPUTER VIRUSES— DANGEROUS ENEMIES OR FRIENDLY HAZARDS?

Many solid state components are found in computers. The micro computers that we use at home or in school are the devices that we most depend upon to do vital things for us.

PCs, school, and office computers can be afflicted by computer viruses. A computer virus is a piece of software that modifies other programs in such a way as to include a part of itself on the other programs. Most computer viruses invade PCs on a floppy disk brought to the PC. The floppy disk is said to be "infected." The hard disk, or hard drive, of a computer then becomes infected by the floppy disk.

Some computer viruses have been called "friendly." For example, in 1987 a German student developed a program that sent a Christmas message over a German computer network. This virus typed out a greeting on a person's printer and then forwarded a copy of itself to everyone on that person's mailing list. Because of the way computers are linked in networks, the virus linked up to IBM's international network within hours. The IBM company quickly took steps to safeguard its network link with passwords so that such an event could not happen again.

Other computer viruses are definitely "unfriendly." A virus known as the Pakistani brain virus destroyed every file with which it came in contact.

Computer viruses may affect specific kinds of computers, such as Apple Macintosh computers or Commodore Amiga computers. One computer virus affecting Macintosh computers may have originated in Canada and then made its way into a computer game. Whoever used the game picked up the computer virus without knowing it.

Most of the computer viruses have affected home computers and small businesses up to now. Computer users have to be careful about using someone else's software or getting programs from unknown sources. Also, it is necessary to keep clean backups of syst[illegible] case the system be[illegible] fected by using [illegible] floppy disk.

Engineers have [illegible] detection kits for t[illegible] and safeguarding [illegible] puter viruses. Th[illegible] "antivirus" prog[illegible] eradicate existi[illegible] antivirus progra[illegible] one strain of co[illegible] not other strai[illegible] may be more d[illegible] on the way. Security consul[illegible] tants even warn that there are possibilities for blackmail or sabotage.

DEVELOPING A VIEWPOINT

Read about computer viruses and come to class with answers to the following questions.

1. In your opinion, should friendly computer viruses be tolerated? Why or why not?
2. Suppose that an unfriendly computer virus was produced that could destroy all the data in the computers at your bank. How could your bank safeguard its financial data against such a virus?
3. In what ways could computer viruses be used as a weapon for national defense?

SUGGESTED READINGS

Greenberg, Ross M. "Know Thy Viral Enemy." *Byte* 14, 275–280, June 1989.

Kerr, Susan. "A Secret No More." *Datamation* 35 (13), 53–55, July 1, 1989.

Marshall, Eliot. "The Scourge of Computer Viruses." *Science* 240, 133–134, April 8, 1988.

608 Solid State Electronics

Special features like **Physics and Society** do more than simply reinforce concepts. They help students understand and appreciate the myriad ways physics relates to the real world outside the classroom.

Teach Physics the Way You Want With Our Unique Wraparound Teacher Edition

The Teacher Wraparound Edition makes it easy for you to meet your teaching goals. Everything you need to teach, reteach, check for understanding, and expand upon key concepts is conveniently located right at your fingertips.

Preceding each chapter is a complete **Planning Guide** designed to give you a quick, yet comprehensive overview of all chapter features, program components, and supplemental activities and materials.

CHAPTER 3 Describing Motion: Velocity

PLANNING GUIDE (5 class sessions)

CONTENTS	TEXT FEATURES	TEACHER RESOURCE PACKAGE	OTHER COMPONENTS
3.1 How Far and How Fast?, pp. 41–49 (2 Class Sessions) • Position and Distance • Average Velocity • Finding Displacement from Velocity and Time • Position-Time Graphs • The Slope of a Position-Time Graph	**Physics Lab:** The Car Race, p. 50 **Physics and Technology:** 3-D Computer Graphing, p. 47 **Pocket Lab:** Joggers Speed, p. 45 **Problem Solving Strategy:** Conversion Factors, p. 45 **Concept Review**, p. 49	**Study Guide:** How Far and How Fast? **Physics Lab Data Sheet:** The Car Race **Reteaching Master:** Using a Reference Point	**Laboratory Manual:** Lab 3.1 Uniform Motion **Physics Skill Master 12**
3.2 New Meanings For Old Words, pp. 51–57 (3 Class Sessions) • Positive and Negative Velocities • Instantaneous Velocity • Velocity-Time Graphs • Relativity of Velocity	**Pocket Lab:** Bowling Ball Displacement, p. 52 **Concept Review**, p. 54	**Study Guide:** New Meanings For Old Words **Critical Thinking Master:** Positions Along a Roller Coaster **Enrichment Master:** Graphing Relative Velocity **Transparency Worksheet:** Position vs Time: uniform velocity—uniform acceleration	**Transparency 3:** Position vs Time: uniform velocity—uniform acceleration **Physics Skill Master 13**
Chapter Review, pp. 57–67	Summary Key Terms Reviewing Concepts Applying Concepts Problems Using a Graphing Calculator	**Vocabulary Review** **Chapter Test**	**Test Bank**

6.1 GRAPHICAL METHOD OF VECTOR ADDITION

All of the **Laboratory Options** are conveniently located at the beginning of each chapter for quick, easy reference to the chapter's hands-on activities.

Laboratory Options

STUDENT EDITION

Physics Lab

Pinhole Camera	334

Pocket Labs

A Matter of Perception	333
An Illuminating Matter	335
Soap Solutions	340
Light Polarization	342

TEACHER EDITION

Activities

Demonstration	330, 340
Discovery	332, 339
Cooperative Learning	339

LABORATORY MANUAL

Light Days	Lab 16.1
Polarization of Light	Lab 16.2

Three-Step Teaching Cycle

Strategies for teaching key concepts within each chapter are provided within Focus, Teach, and Close. Within the three-step teaching cycle are cooperative learning strategies, reteaching techniques, enrichment exercises, and unique ways to check for understanding. All are designed to enhance your individual teaching style.

Practical Assessment Options Throughout Each Chapter

Assessment Options

Portfolio Assessment
Extension Project 1, TWE, p. 328b
Enrichment, TWE, p. 332
Critical Thinking, TWE, p. 335
Portfolio Assessment, TWE, pp. 333, 338
Enrichment, TWE, p. 341

Performance Assessment
Extension Project 2, TWE, p. 328b
Pocket Labs, pp. 333, 335, 340, 342
Physics Lab, p. 334
Pocket Lab Assessment, TWE, p. 342

Content Assessment
Self Assessment: Practice Problems, pp. 332, 336
Assessment, Critical Thinking, TWE, p. 334
Convergent Question, TWE, p. 342
Concept Reviews, pp. 336, 342
Chapter Review, pp. 343–345
Supplemental Problems, pp. 699–700

Group Assessment
Activities for group assessment occur with Cooperative Learning and lab activities.

Assessment Options at the beginning of each chapter help you quickly locate and select the assessment strategies — from traditional to innovative — that best meet your needs.

Assessment

Performance

To further assess students' understanding of parallel circuits, ask if the current in the first resistor changes when you connect the second, third, and fourth resistors in parallel. Have them predict the answer and then devise a method of testing it. Have them explain how to connect an ammeter so it measures the current through just one resistor. [You must disconnect one lead from the first resistor from the point where the two, three, and four resistors join. Connect one lead of the ammeter to this point and the other lead to the resistor lead you disconnected. That is, it should be in the location of one of the meters …ing 20 A in Figure 23–8, …n the location of the meter …ing 60 A.]

Assessment

Critical Thinking

In order to further assess students' understanding of free fall, ask them to cite examples of near weightlessness. Besides space shuttle photos and videos, they should mention the highest point in a trampoline jump, the discrepant event on page 164, and the change in weight when an elevator accelerates.

Performance and **Critical Thinking Assessments** offer ways to evaluate areas of student performance that are difficult to assess by traditional means. Many of these are linked to the lab experiences in the Student Edition.

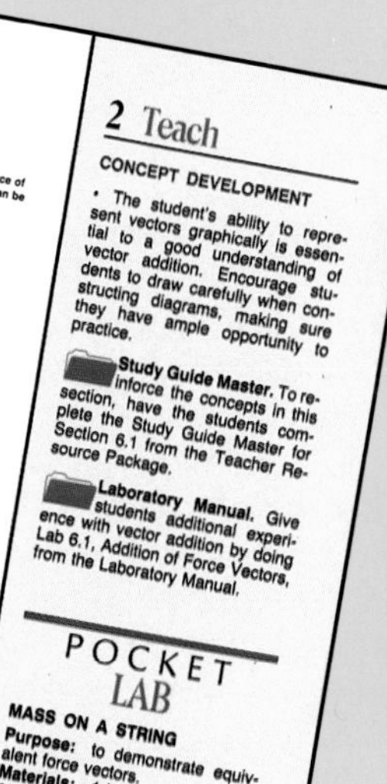

2 Teach

CONCEPT DEVELOPMENT

• The student's ability to represent vectors graphically is essential to a good understanding of vector addition. Encourage students to draw carefully when constructing diagrams, making sure they have ample opportunity to practice.

Study Guide Master. To reinforce the concepts in this section, have the students complete the Study Guide Master for Section 6.1 from the Teacher Resource Package.

Laboratory Manual. Give students additional experience with vector addition by doing Lab 6.1, Addition of Force Vectors, from the Laboratory Manual.

POCKET LAB

MASS ON A STRING
Purpose: to demonstrate equivalent force vectors.
Materials: 1-kg mass; string; 20-N spring balance.
Outcome: The reading on the balance should be 9.8 N. Even with a longer string the reading should be about 9.8 N (plus the extra weight of the string).

• Imagine walking along one edge of a 50-meter square then turning 90° and walking 50 meters along a second side of the square. Now how far are you from where you started? [71 me…

Multicultural Connections … show how all peoples and cultures contributed to the knowledge of physics. Explains how diverse cultures use physics to solve common problems.

Interdisciplinary Connections … show how physics connects to other sciences such as medicine, biology, and chemistry, as well as to other subjects.

Demonstrations
Some are simple, some are more elaborate, but all offer you ways to help students experience physics principles in action.

A Newly Formatted Teacher Resource Package Provides Options for Every Step of Your Lesson Plan

Physics: Principles and Problems provides valuable support material to help reinforce the chapter concepts and create a positive, stimulating environment for learning.

Reinforcement and Enrichment

Study Guide
promotes comprehension as the students read their text.

Vocabulary
reinforces all the key terms discussed within the text.

Reteaching
uses alternative teaching strategies to explore the chapter concepts.

Critical Thinking
encourages the use of critical thinking skills in solving problems.

Enrichment
allows your students to go beyond the content discussed in the chapter.

Hands-On Learning

Lab Worksheets
contain the questions and data tables for all of the in-text labs.

Physics Skills
provide the essential skills needed to complete many of the math and lab activities.

Lab Manual
gives you additional labs for each chapter. They are designed for different levels of involvement so that you can easily adapt them to your classroom's needs.

Assessment

Evaluation
provides everything you need to check your students' understanding of the program objectives.

Instructional Aids

Transparency Masters
include blackline reproductions and student worksheets for each of the program's full-color transparencies.

Supplemental Lessons
offer complete lessons on special topics not discussed in the textbook. They include one each on gas laws and relativity and two on rotary motion.

Lesson Plans
include a complete teaching plan for every lesson in an easy-to-use format.

Problems and Solutions Manual
is a comprehensive resource that contains all the in-text problems and their solutions.

Transparency Package
includes over 45 full-color transparencies in a three-ring binder with a resource book of blackline masters and student worksheets for each transparency.

English/Spanish Glossary
provides definitions of all the important physics terms in Spanish.

Additional Program Components Provide Maximum Teacher Support

Technology

Computer Test Bank

features 180 algorithm-based problems that allow you to generate an almost infinite number of review and test problems. It also includes a wide range of short answer and essay questions.

Science and Technology Physics Videodisc

which features many video reports produced and narrated by TV's "Mister Wizard," lets students catch a glimpse of real scientists exploring current problems and technological developments.

Lab Partner

is a user-friendly, powerful software package that allows the triple option of displaying, manipulating, and graphing experimental data. Features include on-line help systems, easy-to-use spreadsheet functions, and simple graphing of any data set.

Videodisc Correlation

provides a barcode correlation of more than 1000 images in Optical Data's Physical Science videodiscs to all chapters of the text. Videodiscs are available directly from Optical Data:

30 Technology Drive
P.O. Box 4919
Warren, NJ 07060

Glencoe Science Professional Development Series

Cooperative Learning Resource Guide

helps you turn almost any classroom situation into an opportunity to put the effectiveness of group learning to work.

Alternate Assessment in the Science Classroom

uses a variety of performance-based tasks and skills assessments to help you measure student mastery of important thinking processes and skills.

Here Are The Tools to Meet All Your Challenges

Concepts are presented clearly, concisely, and visually. Real-world applications help students see the physics in their everyday lives. Built-in labs allow students to experience physics firsthand. Mathematics is integrated but not intimidating. Teacher Classroom Resources provide options for every step of your lesson plan.

Product	ISBN
Student Edition	0-02-826721-4
Teacher Wraparound Edition	0-02-826722-2
Teacher Classroom Resources	0-02-826723-0
Laboratory Manual-SE	0-02-826724-9
Laboratory Manual-TE	0-02-826725-7
Problems & Solutions Manual	0-02-826726-5
Transparency Package	0-02-826727-3
English/Spanish Glossary	0-02-826728-1
Study Guide–SE	0-02-826729-X
Computer Test Bank-Apple	0-02-826730-3
Computer Test Bank-IBM	0-02-826731-1
Computer Test Bank-Macintosh	0-02-826733-8
Science and Technology Physics Videodisc	0-02-826135-6
Laser Disc Correlation Booklet	0-02-826732-X
Vocabulary Review	0-02-826734-6
Enrichment	0-02-826735-4
Reteaching	0-02-826736-2
Critical Thinking	0-02-826737-0
Physics Skills	0-02-826738-9
Study Guide	0-02-826739-7
Lab Worksheets	0-02-826741-9
Transparency Masters	0-02-826742-7
Evaluation	0-02-826743-5
Lesson Plans	0-02-826747-8
Supplemental Lessons	0-02-826748-6
Lab Partner Software- IBM	0675-17271-3
Lab Partner Software- Apple	0675-02487-0
Alternate Assessment in the Science Classroom	0-02-826429-0
Cooperative Learning in the Science Classroom	0-02-826430-4

For more information contact your nearest regional office or call 1-800-334-7344.

1. Northeast Region
Glencoe/McGraw-Hill
15 Trafalgar Square #201
Nashua, NH 03063-1968
Phone: 603-880-4701
Phone: 800-424-3451
Fax: 603-595-0204

2. Mid-Atlantic Region
Glencoe/McGraw-Hill
P.O. Box 458
Hightstown, NJ 08520-0458
Phone: 609-426-5560
Phone: 800-553-7515
Fax: 609-426-7063

3. Atlantic-Southeast Region
Glencoe/McGraw-Hill
Brookside Park
One Harbison Way, Suite 101
Columbia, SC 29212
Phone: 803-732-2365
Phone: 800-731-2365
Fax: 803-732-4582

4. Southeast Region
Glencoe/McGraw-Hill
6510 Jimmy Carter Boulevard
Norcross, GA 30071
Phone: 404-446-7493
Phone: 800-982-3992
Fax: 404-446-2356

5. Mid-America Region
Glencoe/McGraw-Hill
936 Eastwind Drive
Westerville, OH 43081
Phone: 614-890-1111
Phone: 800-848-1567
Fax: 614-899-4905

6. Great Lakes Region
Glencoe/McGraw-Hill
846 East Algonquin Road
Schaumburg, IL 60173
Phone: 708-397-8448
Phone: 800-762-4876
Fax: 708-397-9472

7. Mid-Continent Region
Glencoe/McGraw-Hill
846 East Algonquin Road
Schaumburg, IL 60173
Phone: 708-397-8448
Phone: 800-762-4876
Fax: 708-397-9472

8. Southwest Region
Glencoe/McGraw-Hill
320 Westway Place, Suite 550
Arlington, TX 76018
Phone: 817-784-2113
Phone: 800-828-5096
Fax: 817-784-2116

9. Texas Region
Glencoe/McGraw-Hill
320 Westway Place, Suite 550
Arlington, TX 76018
Phone: 817-784-2100
Phone: 800-828-5096
Fax: 817-784-2116

10. Western Region
Glencoe/McGraw-Hill
709 E. Riverpark Lane, Suite 150
Boise, ID 83706
Phone: 208-368-0300
Phone: 800-452-6126
Fax: 208-368-0303
Includes Alaska

11. California Region
Glencoe/McGraw-Hill
15319 Chatsworth Street
P. O. Box 9609
Mission Hills, CA 91346
Phone: 818-898-1391
Phone: 800-423-9534
Fax: 818-365-5489
Includes Hawaii

Glencoe Catholic School Region
Glencoe/McGraw-Hill
25 Crescent Street, 1st Floor
Stamford, CT 06906
Phone: 203-964-9109
Phone: 800-551-8766
Fax: 203-967-3108

Canada
McGraw-Hill Ryerson Ltd.
300 Water Street
Whitby, Ontario
Canada L1N 9B6
Phone: 905-430-5000
Phone: 800-565-5758
Fax: 905-430-5020

International
McGraw-Hill, Inc. International Group
Princeton-Hightstown Road
Hightstown, NJ 08520
Phone: 609-426-5934
Fax: 609-426-7917

DoDDS and Pacific Territories
McGraw-Hill School Publishing Company
1221 Avenue of the Americas
13th Floor
New York, NY 10020
Phone: 212-512-6128
Fax: 212-512-6050

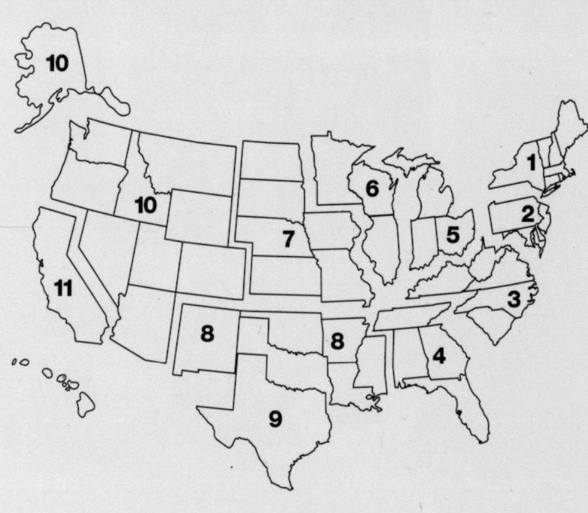

GLENCOE
McGraw-Hill
P.O. BOX 508
COLUMBUS, OHIO 43216

SC 90897-3 3/95

TEACHER WRAPAROUND EDITION

Merrill

Physics

Principles and Problems

GLENCOE

McGraw-Hill

New York, New York   Columbus, Ohio   Mission Hills, California   Peoria, Illinois

A Glencoe/McGraw-Hill Program

Merrill Physics: Principles & Problems

Student Edition
Teacher Wraparound Edition
Problems and Solutions Manual
Teacher Resource Package
Transparency Package
Laboratory Manual:
Student and Teacher Editions
Study Guide, Student Edition
Lesson Plan Booklet
English/Spanish Glossary
Computer Test Bank

Authors

Paul Zitzewitz
Professor of Physics
University of Michigan-Dearborn
Dearborn, Michigan

Robert Neff
Physics Teacher
Suffern High School
Suffern, New York

Mark Davids
Physics Teacher
Grosse Pointe South High School
Grosse Pointe Farms, Michigan

Kelly Wedding
Teacher-Scientist
Technical Education Research Center
Cambridge, Massachusetts

Content Consultants

Craig Kramer
Physics Teacher
Bexley High School
Bexley, Ohio

Donald Wilke
Physics Teacher
Worthington High School
Worthington, Ohio

Multicultural Consultants

Karen L. Muir, Ph.D
Department of Social and
Behavioral Sciences
Columbus State University
Columbus, Ohio

Gloria Craig Letts
Science Supervisor
Columbus Public Schools
Columbus, Ohio

ISBN 0-02-826722-2

Send all inquiries to: **Glencoe/McGraw-Hill**
936 Eastwind Drive,
Westerville, Ohio 43081

Printed in the United States of America.

3 4 5 6 7 8 9 10 11 12 13 14 15 QPH/MC 03 02 01 00 99 98 97 96 95

Table of Contents

TEACHER GUIDE

STUDENT TEXT

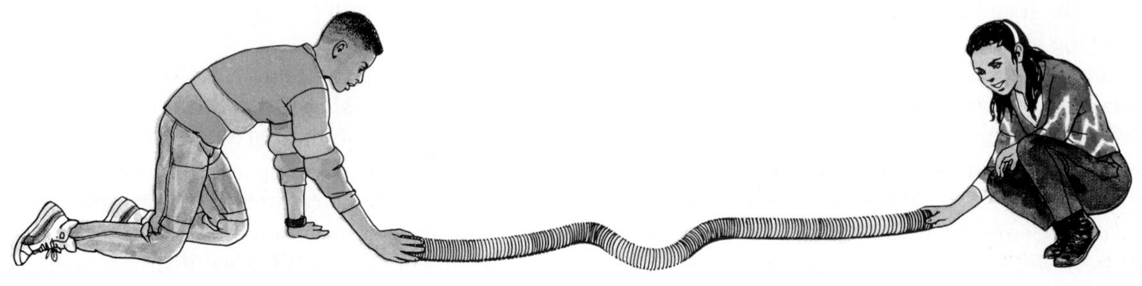

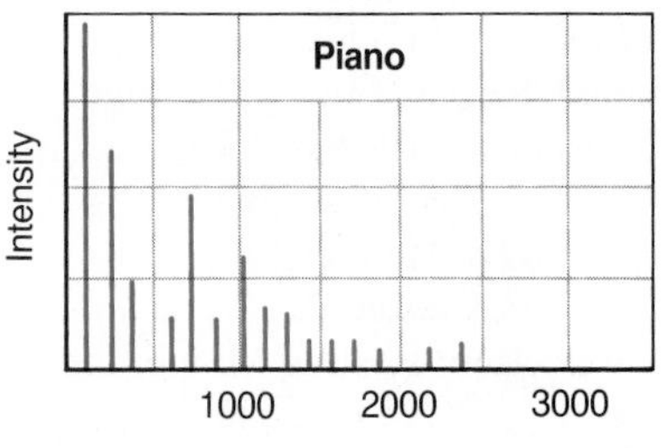
Piano
Intensity
1000
2000
3000
Frequency (Hz)

AC
DC
ON
OFF

Features of Student Edition

Chapter Opener

Each chapter opens with a striking full-page photograph illustrating a concept introduced in the chapter. The accompanying question further intrigues the student, and, more importantly, gives an indication of how the concepts in the chapter apply to "real" life. The chapter introductory paragraph refers to, but does not answer, the question. The question itself is answered at the appropriate place in the chapter, with the answer highlighted for the student.

The Concept Check in the margin lists terms and concepts from previous chapters that are important for a good understanding of the current chapter. The Concept Check not only helps prepare the student to better understand the new material, but also reinforces the unity and continuity of physics.

Teaching Blocks

Each chapter is divided into 2-4 major sections, with student objectives set in the margin at the start of the section. Each major section is subdivided into smaller, single-concept sections. This structure makes it easier for students to organize material and gives them a better insight into the hierarchy of topics. By dividing material into logical topics, it also gives teachers more clear-cut options when material must be skipped.

Each major section ends with a Concept Review containing four conceptual questions, designed to give students immediate feedback concerning the understanding of new concepts. The last Concept Review question asks students to use critical thinking in applying concepts discussed in the block to a real life situation.

Intext Features

Each chapter contains either a Physics and Technology or a Physics and Society feature.

Each Physics and Technology feature presents a technological advance appropriate to the chapter and includes a suggestion for further investigation.

Physics and Society features deal with some physical concept in the chapter that has precipitated a societal issue. Background material is presented and students are asked to develop a viewpoint after discussing the issue.

These features are designed to make the student aware of the place of physics in the world and to reinforce the importance of being scientifically literate in order to make informed decisions.

Physics Lab

Each chapter contains a 1-page lab that focuses on rectifying a common student misconception about the physics presented in the chapter. The lab can be done in less than one class period and is relatively easy to set up. By being part of the text, the labs are readily available and will help teachers fulfill any laboratory requirements. Since the labs are aimed at common misconceptions, they provide ideal hands-on opportunity for student unteaching and reteaching. They are also structured to give the teacher additional opportunities to point out everyday applications of physical principles.

Pocket Labs

Each major section includes at least one easy-to-do minilab that provides additional hands-on motivational or discovery activities to enhance conceptualization of physics principles. The Pocket Labs also offer teachers additional opportunities to include laboratory activities in their curriculum.

Example Problems

Each new type of problem or equation is introduced with an Example Problem to provide students and teachers with completely worked models of the equations introduced in the text.

Immediately following most Example Problems is a set of Practice Problems using the concept introduced in the example. Complete solutions to these drill exercises are found in Solutions Appendix A. These problems are designed to provide immediate reinforcement and feedback whenever new quantitative concepts are introduced.

Problem Solving Strategies, placed before appropriate Example Problems, are designed to introduce and focus students' attention on specific techniques needed to solve problems using the concept being presented. They also alert the teacher that special review or additional instruction may be needed.

Margin Features

Student Notes

Blue student notes are placed in the margin for students to use to direct their study.

Help Wanted

These are short features describing some less obvious physics-related career opportunity to the student, as well as to indicate how many jobs require a knowledge of physics.

F.Y.I.

F.Y.I.s are bits and pieces of physics trivia designed to grab students attention. They might include "quotable" quotes, unusual concept applications, or interesting information about the concept being discussed.

Connections

Connections show how physical principles underlie many of the seemingly unrelated facets of society. They also offer the teacher additional examples of applications of physics concepts.

Chapter Review

Each Chapter Review will be made up of six sections:

Summary statements, organized by major section, act as a review guide for students.
Key Terms is a list of bold-faced terms appearing in the chapter to provide students with a convenient vocabulary review.
Reviewing Concepts present non-math factual questions to test students' knowledge of new ideas introduced in the chapter.
Applying Concepts ask the student to use critical thinking skills by applying the facts and theories presented in the chapter to explain some every day phenomenon.
Problems are mathematical questions, organized by major section. Within each section, the items will be arranged from simple drill problems using the equations introduced in the chapter to more difficult problems requiring critical thinking and often including concepts introduced in previous chapters. The easier problems give teachers additional items to check basic understanding of equations presented. the more challenging items check not only understanding of new material, but the assimilation and integration of this material with previously learned concepts.

Thinking Physic-ly These are "brain-expanding" application questions asking students to explain some everyday occurrence. These questions will serve as chapter closure for the students.

Appendices

A. Practice Problem Solutions contains complete solutions to all intext Practice Problems. These step-by-step solutions provide students with immediate feedback and allow them to work independently.

B. Supplementary Problems provide 22 pages of supplemental problems, arranged chapter-by-chapter, that can be assigned as needed by the teacher. This appendix answers a widely-expressed teacher need by providing both students and teachers with an easily accessible source of additional problems whenever they are required.

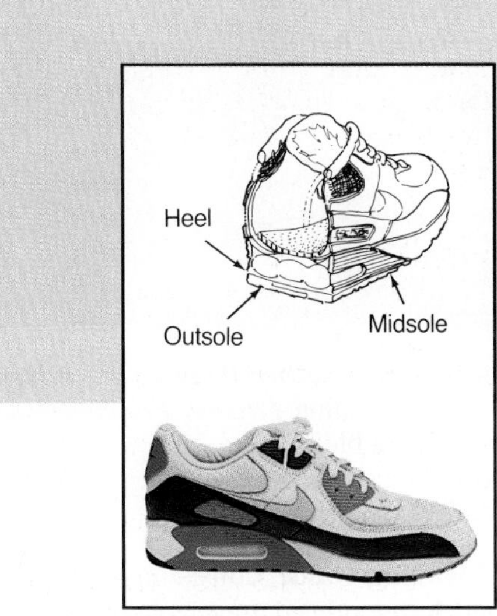

Features of Teacher Edition

The *Teacher Wraparound Edition* is designed to make teaching ***Physics: Principles and Problems*** as easy as possible.

Interleaves

A **Planning Guide,** consisting of two pages of **planning charts,** precedes each chapter. The Guide lists by major divisions all materials available in the *Student Edition*, the ***Teacher Resource Package,*** and other components, including the ***Laboratory Manual,*** and the ***Transparency Package.*** **Extension Projects** for extended study, **Science Fair Activities,** and **Student Readings** are suggested. **Supplementary Materials** for the teacher are listed, including commercially available software, audiovisuals such as films, filmstrips and slide sets, and books and magazine articles. **Activity and Demonstration Materials** are listed for each Physics Lab, Pocket Lab, and demonstration in the chapter. Finally, **Problem Correlations Tables** coordinate all Practice Problems, Chapter Review Problems, and Supplementary Problems to the major section for which they are appropriate, with the more difficult problems indicated.

Wraparound Margins

All other teacher material is located in the margin alongside the student page. At the beginning of each chapter, a short **Overview** summarizing **theme development** and calling out common **misconceptions** is provided. The key terms, a list of **laboratory options,** and **tips for using the chapter-opening photo** are included in the chapter introduction. The teaching materials for the body of the chapter is organized to follow the format of the student edition. Each major sections starts with **Preparation,** containing an **Overview** and a **Bridging** section. **Focus** provides a discussion idea, a demonstration, or other simple activities you can use to direct student attention to the concepts to be learned. Each text page includes **Teaching Suggestions** and a selection of **Background Enrichment, Challenge, Demonstration,** and **Teacher FYI** ideas. A **Checking for Understanding** with a **Reteaching Suggestion** and an **Extension** activity are included in each major division to aid you in presenting more difficult concepts. **Guided** and **Independent Practice** suggestions plus **Cooperative Learning** activities prepare students to work on their own without teacher supervision. The material in each major division ends with a close section. This feature provides you with a summarizing activity and a correlation of all text questions and problems appropriate to the section. Information for teaching each **Investigation** and **Pocket Lab** is included in the margins where these activities occur. Objectives process skills developed, time allotment, preparation notes, and tips on teaching the activity are included. **Answers** to all Practice Problems, Chapter Review items, and Supplementary Problems are given in the teacher margin adjacent to the problem. Opportunities for using alternative assessment methods are presented in the **Portfolio Assessment, Performance Assessment,** and **Critical Thinking Assessment** options appearing throughout the margin material.

Supplementary Materials

Teacher Resource Package

The *Teacher Resource Package* includes a variety of options for meeting a range of student needs. The easy-to-use ***Booklets*** offer flexibility and convenient access to all material. The Booklets include:

1. **Vocabulary Review Masters** - vocabulary review for each chapter.
2. **Study Guide Masters** - cover all major concepts from each text section.
3. **Reteaching Masters** - provide additional reinforcement on some concepts within the chapter.
4. **Critical Thinking Masters** - designed for more motivated students.
5. **Enrichment Masters** - provide opportunities for students to apply information from the chapter to a new situation.
6. **Transparency Masters** - copy masters of the 47 full-color transparencies, 47 transparency worksheet masters, plus teaching strategies for the transparencies.
7. **Physics Skill Masters** - aid students in acquiring physics science skills.
8. **Supplemental Lessons** - four complete lessons, 2 on rotary motion, one on the 9 gas laws, and one on relativity; selected tables and charts for easy duplication.
9. **Laboratory Worksheets** - provide data tables and the Analysis and Applications questions with answer spaces for Physics Labs.
10. **Evaluation Masters** - 4 section tests correlated to student objectives.
    Semester Evaluations - two 4-page semester tests.

Reduced answer pages are provided whenever appropriate within each booklet.

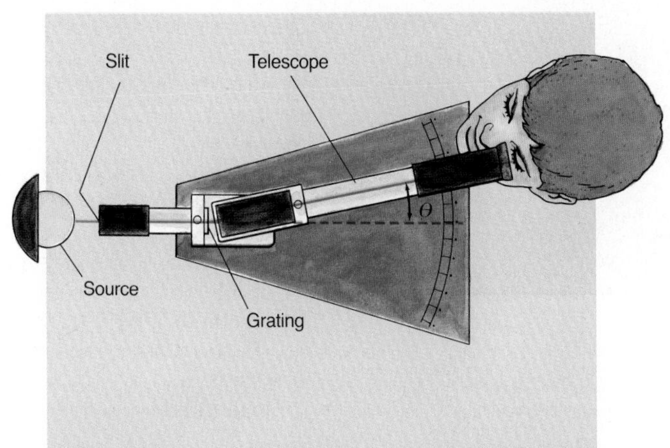

Laboratory Manual

The ***Laboratory Manual*** is a learning-through-doing program of activities. Based on the philosophy that scientific knowledge is acquired through individual activity and experimentation, the manual consists of many varied laboratory activities designed to reinforce concepts presented in ***Physics: Principles and Problems.*** Several of the labs or extensions are designed for use with Labmaster Software.

Test Bank Software

The ***Test Bank Software*** provides you with a tool to design a test from a bank of questions. Program features include selection of sections to be tested, objectives to be tested, number of questions for each section, total number of questions on a test, inclusion or exclusion of specific questions, and multiple test forms. Teachers may also add their own questions or modify existing questions.

Color Transparencies

The ***Transparency Package*** contains 47 full-color transparencies, **Teacher Guide,** and **a transparency worksheet** for each transparency. All of the transparencies explain concepts covered in the Student Edition—some also extend material introduced in the text. Overlays on some transparencies make it easier to demonstrate complex ideas.

Problems and Solutions Manual

The manual contains a comprehensive listing of energy problems in the student text, Practice Problems, Chapter Review Problems, and Supplemental Problems. Each problem statement is followed by a complete solution for that problem, including art work.

Study Guide SE

This is a consumable version of the Study Guide Booklet contained in the Teacher Resource Package.

English-Spanish Glossary

This supplement presents an English-Spanish and Spanish-English version of the glossary in the student text.

Lesson Plan Booklet

This booklet contains complete lesson plans for every major section of the student text plus references to all program components.

Philosophy

Physics: Principles & Problems is designed to help students with a wide range of backgrounds and abilities to learn physics. Students will learn only if they become involved in the subject. In the first chapter students are given a challenge to build a tower that will bring out their creativity and ability to work with others. Each chapter of **Physics: Principles & Problems** begins with a full-color photograph that poses a question to be answered in the text. The book employs a lively writing style, colorful and useful photographs and illustrations, hand-on and minds-on activities called **Pocket Labs,** and applications that relate physics to everyday life. Problems frequently involve examples from sports, and numbers have been carefully chose to be realistic. A career that uses a topic introduced in the chapter is described as **Help Wanted** advertisement. Physics is not an isolated, impersonal activity, so the text mentions people who have made contributions in the past, as well as the present practitioners, and each chapter includes a feature describing an interaction between physics and either technology or society.

Chapters are grouped into five major units, Mechanics; Properties of Matter, Waves, Sound, and Light; Electricity and Magnetism; Modern Physics. While a brief introduction to rotational motion is included in the textbook, two supplementary chapters are in the ***Teacher Resource Package*** for those teachers interested in a thorough development. Gas laws are also included in the ***Teacher Resource Package*** rather than the textbook. Music is featured in the chapter on sound, and applications of light such as rainbows and corrective eyeglasses are discussed in the chapter of light. Modern Physics includes a chapter on Solid State Electronics that features experiments using inexpensive light-emitting diodes to produce student interest and learning. The final chapters will give students enough knowledge of the quark model of matter to understand the debates over building the next generation particle accelerators.

Physics: Principles & Problems strikes a balance between emphasizing the principles and concepts of physics and the solution of problems. Each chapter starts with a list of concepts needed from previous chapters. Concept review questions include one question that tests critical thinking skills. In the chapter review are key words from the chapters, as well as questions that review the concepts and others that challenge students to apply them. The teaching of problem solving begins with the presentation of a model **Example Problem.** The given and unknown quantities are isolated, the basic equation or equations presented, and a concise solution presented. Several **Practice Problems** follow, with solutions given in an appendix. The chapter review contains more problems, and the more difficult ones are marked.

Mathematical methods of laboratory measurements scientific notation and significant digits, algebraic manipulations, and graphical representation are gathered in the second chapter. Students are encouraged to experience physical results in a different way by means of graphs throughout the book. Six exercises or graphical calculators are included to illustrate methods of using these inexpensive tools to deepen student understanding.

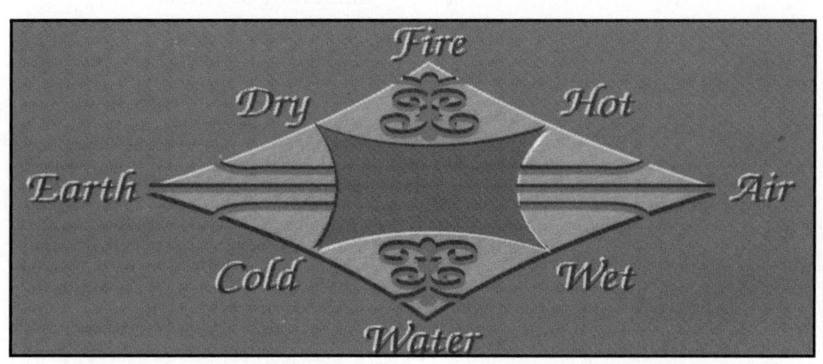

Themes Matrix

The themes of science are broad unifying ideas that integrate the major concepts of many disciplines. They are an important part of any teaching strategy because they help students see the importance of truly understanding concepts rather than simply memorizing isolated facts. Themes help students see connections between physics and other science courses.

The table below shows a matrix of the five content areas and themes adapted from *Project 2061,* "Science for All Americans" (American Association for the Advancement of Science). These themes occur not only in physics, but the other sciences, mathematics, technology. By calling attention to the themes as they recur, you will help your students understand how the principles they are studying will be useful not only later in this course, but in their other studies as well.

MATRIX OF THEMES AND CONTENT

CONTENTS	THEMES					
	Systems definitions, boundaries feedback	**Constancy** stability & equilibrium, conservation & invariancy, symmetry	**Patterns of Change** trends, cycles, randomness and chaos	**Scale** range of size, sensitivity to scale scale	**Models** physical, conceptual, matematical	**Nature and Values of Science** world view, scientific inquiry, scientific enterprise, values and attitudes
Ch 1-2	Definitions of systems (Ch 1) Feedback (Ch 2)	Invariancy (Ch 2) Uncertainty of measurment (Ch 2)	Variables and their relationship (Ch 2)	Range of size (Ch 2) Sensitivity to scale size (Ch 2)	Use of models (Ch 1) Mathematical models	World view (Ch 1) Scientific inquiry and enterprise (Ch 1) Values and attitudes (Ch 1) Scientific inquiry and process (Ch 2)
Mechanics (Ch 3-11)	Force Systems (Ch 5) Newton's law (Ch 5) Vector systems and boundaries (Ch 6) Momentum in closed systems (Ch 9) Machined, mechanical advantage and feedback (Ch 10) Energy systems (Ch 11)	Constant velocity and acceleration (Ch 4) Projectile motion (Ch 7) Symmetrical motion (Ch 4,7) Force stability (Ch 5) Vector equilibrium (Ch 6) Equilibrium in simple harminic motion (Ch 7) Invariance and constancy in motion (Ch 3-5,8) Constancy of momentum (Ch 9) Constancy of energy (Ch 11) Conservation of momentum (Ch 9) Conservation of energy (Ch 11)	Velocity and position (Ch 3) Graphs (Ch 3) Changes in motion (Ch 4,5) Forces and motions (Ch 5,8) Cyclical motion (Ch 7,8)	Graphs (Ch 3) Forces, scale (Ch 5,8)	Motion, position, distance (Ch 3) Acceleration (Ch 4) Forces (Ch 5,6) Vectors (Ch 6) Projectile motion (Ch 7) Gravitation (Ch 8) Momentum (Ch 9) Machines, work, power (Ch 10) Kinetic and potential energy (Ch 11)	Graphical methods (Ch 3) Newton's laws (Ch 5,8) Vector methods (Ch 6) World view (Ch 5,8,11)
Materials (Ch. 12,13)	Thermal systems (Ch 12) Fluids and hydraulics (Ch 13) States of matter (Ch 13)	Thermal stability and equilibrium (Ch 12) Conservation of energy (Ch 12) Invariance of matter (Ch 13) Fluid/pressure symmetry (Ch 13)	Randomness (Ch 13) Chaos (Ch 13) Entropy (Ch 13) Change of state (Ch 12,13)	Temperature scales (Ch 12) Scales of order (Ch 13) Capillary action (Ch 13) Surface tension (Ch 13) Crystals, liquids, states of matter (Ch 13)	Kinetic-molecular theory (Ch 12) Thermal energy and temperature (Ch 12) Evaporation and condensation (Ch 13) States of matter (Ch 13)	Heat engines, technology (Ch 12) Hydraulics (Ch 13)

MATRIX OF THEMES AND CONTENT

CONTENTS	THEMES					
	Systems definitions, boundaries feedback	**Constancy** stability & equilibrium, conservation & invariancy, symmetry	**Patterns of Change** trends, cycles, randomness and chaos	**Scale** range of size, sensitivity to scale scale	**Models** physical, conceptual, matematical	**Nature and Values of Science** world view, scientific inquiry, scientific enterprise, values and attitudes
Waves (Ch14-19)	Waves and boundaries (Ch 14-17,19) Sound waves (Ch 15) Light waves (Ch 16) Light rays, reflection, refraction (Ch 17) Mirrors, lenses images (Ch 18) Light, diffraction and interference (Ch 14,19)	Symmetry of wave motion (Ch 14-19) Reflection and refraction (Ch 14,17,18) Mirrors, objects and images (Ch 18) Lenses, objects and images (Ch 18) Speed of light (Ch 16)	Cycles in wave motion (Ch 14,15,19) Reflection and refraction (Ch 14,17,18) Diffracton and interference (Ch 14,19)	Frequency and wavelength (Ch 14,15,16,19) Decibel scale (Ch 15) Diffraction effects (Ch 14,19)	Longitudinal and transverse waves (Ch 14,16) Droppler shift (Ch 15) Polarization (Ch 16) Reflection and refraction (Ch 14,17,18) Mirrors and lenses (Ch 18) Light diffraction and interference (Ch 19)	Sound, music, instruments (Ch 15) Light, color, illumination (Ch 16) Optics, technology (Ch 17-19)
Electricity and Magnetism (Ch 20-26)	Electric charges and charge transfer (Ch 20,21) Electric fields (Ch 21,26) Electric circuits (Ch 22,23) Magnetic fields (Ch 24,25,26)	Electric charges and charge transfer (Ch 20,21) Conservation of electric charge (Ch 20-23) Symmetry: in electric charges (Ch 20) in electric fields (Ch 21,26) in electric circuits (Ch 22,23) in magnetic fields (Ch 24-26) Equilibrium: of charged bodies (Ch 20,21) in electrical circuits (Ch 22,23) of electrical fields and forces (Ch 21,26) of magnetic fields and forces (Ch 24-26)	Changing electric fields (Ch 21,26) Changing magnetic fields (Ch 24-26) Energy cycles in electrical circuits (Ch 22,23)	Electrical charges and forces (Ch 20) Electric field strength (Ch 21) Magnetic field strength (Ch 24) Electromagnetic waves and spectrum (Ch 26)	Electrical charges (Ch 20,21) Electric field lines (Ch 21) Electric circuit diagrams (Ch 22,23) Magnetic field lines (Ch 24-26)	Uses of electricity (Ch 20,22-24) Development of electromagnetism (Ch 24-26) Generation and tranmission of electricity (Ch 22,25)
Modern Physics (Ch 27-31)	Atomic energy levels and boundaries (Ch 27-29) Nuclear systems and reactions (Ch 30,31) Electron motion and energy bands (Ch 29) Quantization of energy (Ch 27,28)	Duality of waves and particles (Ch 27,28) Symmetry of light emission and absorption (Ch 27,28) Symmetry in nuclear reactions (Ch 30,31) Stability of nuclei (Ch 28,30) Particles and antiparticles (Ch 30) Conservation, nuclear reactions (Ch 30,31) Equilibrium in photoelectric effect (Ch 27) Constancy of spectra (Ch 27,28) Conservation of energy and momentum (Ch 27)	Uncertainty principle (Ch 27) Randomness in radioactive decay (Ch 28,30) Nuclear reactions (Ch 30,31) Probability in the quantum theory (Ch 28)	Size scale of atoms, nuclei, and quarks (Ch 28,30) Scales of energies (Ch27,28,30,31) Scales of fissions, chain and fusion reactions (Ch 31) Radioactive half-lives (Ch 30) Range of nuclear forces (Ch 31)	Quantum model of atomic structure (Ch 27-31) Nuclear equations (Ch 30,31) Electron gas model of conductors (Ch 29) Band theory of electrical conduction (Ch 29) Fundamental particles and the quark model (Ch 30)	Development of atomic theories (Ch 27-30) Application of spectroscopy (Ch 28) Nuclear technology and applications (Ch 28,29,31) Laser technology (Ch 28) Electronic devices (Ch 29) Nuclear bombardment techniques (Ch 30)

Misconceptions

How do students learn physics? Decades ago, many teachers taught as though students were empty vessels into which one could pour the pure wisdom gained by humans over centuries. It is now well understood that students come to the physics class with firmly-held beliefs about how the world works that they have formed themselves. The most common example is the (mis)understanding of forces and motion that is much closer to Aristotle than it is to Newton. Even though this understanding, which we may call the student's world-view, is at variance with the understanding of the teacher and the scientific community, the student has developed his world-view over a period of time and found it to be consistent with everyday life. Students interpret lectures, material read from books, and even demonstrations and experiments in the light of this world-view. Since what we say in class is interpreted by the student in light of his or her own world-view, a student may internalize an idea in a form completely different from what we intend.

Aristotelean views of motion are only one example of what are variously called preconceptions, misconceptions, naive conceptions, or alternative conceptions. Whatever they are called, they are extremely persistent. And, why shouldn't they be? They have served the student well to this point. Nevertheless, they are a barrier to learning in physics and the other sciences. How can they be replaced? Research has shown this process to be a difficult task. Reading, hearing lectures, and even solving problems often have little effect on intuitive beliefs. Hands-on experiences guided by the teacher by means of questions seem to be more effective. The end result should be that students adjust and correct their own understanding of the world around them. Knowledge has not been delivered to them, rather they have created their own knowledge.

To help you guide students to create their own knowledge, at the beginning of each chapter in the Teacher's Edition you will find a list of common misconceptions about material in the chapter, and known difficulties are highlighted. The "Pocket Lab" in each teaching block is designed to give hands-on experience, and the Concept Review Questions at the end of the block give feedback on the level of understanding. Further, the Laboratory in each chapter is designed to address misconceptions, as are many of the Reviewing Concepts and Applying Concepts questions in the Chapter Review material.

Multicultural Connections

''Multicultural education is an idea stating that all students, regardless of the groups to which they belong, such as those related to gender, ethnicity, race, culture, social class, religion, or exceptionality, should experience education equality in the schools.''—James Banks

American classrooms reflect the rich and diverse cultural heritages of the American people. Students come from different ethnic backgrounds and different cultural experiences into a common classroom that must assist all of them to learn. The diversity itself is an important focus of the learning experience.

Diversity can be repressed, creating a hostile environment; ignored, creating an indifferent environment; or appreciated, creating a receptive and productive environment. Responding to diversity and approaching it as a part of every curriculum is challenging to a teacher, experienced or not. The goal of science is understanding. The goal of multicultural education is to promote the understanding of how people from different cultures approach and solve the basic problems all humans have in living and learning. ***Physics: Principles and Problems*** addresses this issue. In the **Teacher Wraparound Edition,** information is provided about people and groups who have traditionally been misrepresented or omitted. The intent is to build awareness and appreciation for the global community in which we all live. By providing these opportunities, ***Physics: Principles and Problems*** is helping meet the five major goals of multicultural education:

1. promoting the strength and value of cultural diversity
2. promoting the human rights of and respect for those who are different from oneself
3. promoting alternative life choices for people
4. promoting social justice and equal opportunity for all people
5. promoting equity in the distribution of power among groups

Two books that provide additional information on multicultural education are:

Banks, James A. (with Cherry A. McGee Banks) *Multicultural Education: Issues and Perspectives*. Boston: Allyn Bacon, 1989.

Banks, James A. (with others) *Curriculum Guidelines for Multiethnic Education*. Washington D.C.: National Council for the Social Studies, 1977.

Problem Solving

Negative student attitude toward problem solving is probably one of the biggest hurdles physics teachers must overcome. Unfortunately, students may enter your classroom with several of the following misconceptions about problem solving.

- The way to solve a problem should be obvious when you first read a problem.
- No trial and error or "playing around" with different approaches to a problem is allowed.
- There is only one "right" way to solve a problem.
- You can't change a problem to make it simpler.
- Problem solving always proceeds in a linear, logical manner.
- Guessing and hunches are not allowed.

When faced with a problem, most novice focus their attention on getting the "right" answer. Similarities among problems are rarely seen. Instead, each problem is looked upon as a completely new, unique situation. Often, choosing a starting point is the biggest obstacle. When introducing problem solving in your classroom, you may want to present the following general plan as one way to attack a problem.

1. **Verbalize the problem**–state the problem out loud and believe that you can solve it.
2. **Define the problem**–analyze the information provided and determine what you know and what you need to know in order to solve the problem.
3. **Explore**–brainstorm strategies for organizing the given information and finding out what you need to know.
4. **Plan**–decide on a strategy or group of strategies and list steps and substeps to the strategies.
5. **Carry out** the plan.
6. **Assess**–decide what was done, determine if you are closer to solving the problem, and why or why not.

As students become more proficient at problem solving, this six-step approach may become cumbersome, and many steps will be combined.

Once students have an overall plan, they can begin to develop their own strategies for problem solving. A strategy is an organized approach to a problem that breaks down the task of obtaining and organizing information into stages. Having a group of strategies to choose from will help students over the initial panic felt when faced with a problem. Several strategies are listed below.

- Construct a table, graph, or figure.
- List all possible solutions.
- Look for a pattern.
- Talk to an expert.
- Act out the problem.
- Make a model.
- Guess and check.
- Work backwards.
- Make a drawing.
- Solve a simpler or similar problem.

It is important to remember that students' attitude toward problems solving is a big factor in their success or failure. No matter how many models or strategies are provided, if students think they're no good at solving problems, they will probably fail. Talk about problem solving as an important skill. Use the words "problem solving" often and consistently to describe the problem solving process. Finally, focus on progress in using the process, rather than in attaining the correct outcome.

0 5 10 15 20 25 30

Laboratory Rationale

Experimental data form the bedrock of science and so have a special place in science teaching. Students need first hand experiences with the physical world. These experiences can range from regular laboratory experiments to a heightened awareness of the way the world around us operates.

Laboratory work can be an exciting part of your total course. Try to look on the laboratory as a valuable tool to gain student interest, even though it takes a good deal of effort to make the laboratory run smoothly. Experimentation gives another advantage. It makes your physics course different from other, non-laboratory courses your students take—a change of pace.

To those of you who are teaching your first physics class, the laboratory part of the course may seem overwhelming. No one develops a complete laboratory program the first year. Build on the strength of your available equipment and try to develop a few good experiments.

To round out laboratory experiences, use demonstration experiments. Many examples in which the whole class works from the same data can be found in the teacher edition. These demonstrations offer valuable opportunities to illustrate correct procedure and techniques. Try to use student input and assistance freely.

Scattered throughout the textbook are many suggestions for short, quick Pocket Labs that use a minimum of equipment. When using these, you might make students responsible for their organization and execution.

Assessment

Performance: ***Physics: Principles and Problems*** provides numerous opportunities to observe students performing both in informal and formal settings. The Physics Labs, Pocket Labs, and Pocket Lab Assessments allow you to evaluate students' understanding of concepts and process skills as well as their ability to handle lab equipment. Additional opportunities for assessment are found in the **Laboratory Manual.**

Group Assessment: ***Physics: Principles and Problems*** provides many opportunities for cooperative learning. The Physics Labs and Pocket Labs, as well as additional suggestions for cooperative activities throughout the teacher margins, provide many opportunities to observe group processes and products.

Portfolio Assessment: A portfolio is a way a student can collect and present a limited selection of work products that best demonstrate his or her growth and progress in scientific attitudes, processes, and knowledge. The portfolio is not meant to be a complete collection of all worksheets and assignments for the grading period, but can be a collection of students' best work. At the conclusion of each chapter, students can select their best work from that chapter. It might, for example, be a lab report including data, graphs, analysis, and conclusions. An essential element in portfolio development is the composition of a submission letter that explains why the student selected that particular piece of work and evaluates it in terms of his or her own progress. Every chapter of ***Physics: Principles and Problems*** contains questions and problems, projects, enrichment activities, labs, and library research opportunities that result in products suitable for portfolio inclusion. In addition many of the projects suggested in the **Teacher Resource Package** produce suitable work examples.

Content Assessment: In the foreseeable future, students will be required to pass pencil-and-paper tests to exit high school and to enter college, trade school, or other training programs. Every chapter of ***Physics: Principles and Problems*** contains numerous strategies and checkpoints for evaluating student mastery of science concepts. For the formal content assessment, a 4-page chapter test is provided for each chapter. If your individual assessment plan requires a test that differs from the Chapter Test, or if you would like several versions of the same test, customized tests can easily be produced using the **Computer Test Bank.**

35 40 45 50 55 60 65 70

Laboratory Safety

The physics laboratory is a safe place to experiment if you are careful. You must assume responsibility for the safety of yourself and your neighbors. Here are some safety rules to help guide you in protecting yourself and others from injury in the lab:

1. The physics laboratory is to be used for serious work.
2. Do not perform experiments that are unauthorized. Always obtain your instructor's permission.
3. Study your laboratory assignment before you come to the lab. If you are in doubt about any procedure, ask your instructor for help.
4. Use the safety equipment provided for you. Know the location of the fire extinguisher, safety shower, fire blanket, and first aid kit.
5. Report any accident, injury, or incorrect procedure to your instructor at once.
6. Smother fires with a towel. If clothing should catch fire, smother it with a blanket or coat or quench it under a safety shower. NEVER RUN.
7. Handle toxic, combustible, or radioactive substances only under the direction of your instructor. If you spill acid or another corrosive chemical, wash it off immediately with water. Never taste any chemical substance or draw poisonous materials into a glass tube with your mouth. Keep combustible materials away from open flames.
8. Place broken glass and solid substances in designated containers. Keep insoluble waste material out of the sink.
9. Use electrical equipment only under the supervision of your instructor. Be sure your instructor checks electric circuits before you activate them.
10. When your investigation is completed, be sure to turn off the water and gas and disconnect electrical connections. Clean your work area. Return all materials and apparatus to their proper places.

FIRST AID IN THE LABORATORY

REPORT ALL ACCIDENTS, INJURIES, AND SPILLS TO YOUR INSTRUCTOR IMMEDIATELY.

YOU MUST KNOW: safe laboratory techniques,
where and how to report an accident, injury, or spill,
location of first aid equipment, fire alarm, phone, school nurse's office.

SITUATION	SAFE RESPONSE
burns	flush with cold water
cuts and bruises	treat as directed by instruction included in your first aid kit.
electric shock	provide person with fresh air, have them recline in a position so that their head is lower than their body; if necessary, provide artificial respiration.
fainting or collapse	See electric shock.
fire	turn off all flames and gas jets; wrap person in fire blanket; use fire extinguisher to put out fire. DO NOT use water to extinguish fire, as water may react with burning substance and intensify fire.
foreign matter in eyes	flush with plenty of water, use eye wash bottle.
poisoning	note the suspected poisoning agent, contact your instructor for antidote; if necessary, call poison control center.
severe bleeding	apply pressure or a compress directly to the wound and get medical attention immediately.
spills, general acid burns	wash area with plenty of water; use safety shower; use sodium hydrogen carbonate, $NaHCO_3$ (baking soda)
base burns	use boric acid, H_3BO_3

Organization Guide

The Organization Guide for *Physics: Principles & Problems* is designed to help you arrange your physics course within the framework of a single academic year. This table suggests time allotments and the use of laboratory experiments to plan a complete physics program. Using this guide you can gear the study pattern of each class to suit the needs and abilities of the students.

The suggested time allotments are those needed for class lecture time, Laboratory work and testing will require extra time. You can best determine these needs, because laboratory needs can vary from school to school.

It is a major goal of this text that students achieve a thorough understanding of each topic before proceeding to new material. To quote Sir Isaac Newton, "It is better to achieve a little with certainty than a great deal that one is not sure of."

ORGANIZATION GUIDE

Chapter	Section	Class Sessions	Suggested Laboratory Experiments PL - Physics Lab LM - Lab Manual
1		1	PL p. 10 LM 1.1
2	2:1	2	LM 2.1
	2:2	2	LM 2.2
	2:3	1	PL p. 28; LM 2.3
	2:4	1	
3	3:1	2	PL p. 50; LM 3.1
	3:2	3	
4	4:1	2	PL p. 70; LM 4.1
	4:2	3	LM 4.2
5	5:1	2	LM 5.1
	5:2	4	PL p. 98; LM 5.2
6	6:1	2	LM 6.1
	6:2	2	PL p. 114;
	6:3	2	LM 6.2
7	7:1	3	PL p. 140; LM 7.1, 7.2
	7:2	2	
8	8:1	3	PL p. 158; LM 8.1
	8:2	3	
9	9:1	1	LM 9.2
	9:2	5	PL p. 182; LM 9.1
10	10:1	3	
	10:2	2	PL p. 204; LM 10.1, 10.2
11	11:1	3	PL p. 225,
	11:2	3	LM 11.1
12	12:1	3	PL p. 249; LM 12.1
	12:2	3	

ORGANIZATION GUIDE

Chapter	Section	Class Sessions	Suggested Laboratory Experiments PL - Physics Lab LM - Lab Manual
13	13:1 13:2	3 3	PL p. 271; LM 13.1
14	14:1 14:2	3 3	PL p. 292; LM 14.1, 14.2
15	15:1 15:2	3 2	PL p. 313, LM 15.1, LM 15.2
16	16:1 16:2	2 3	PL p. 334; LM 16.1 LM 16.2
17	17:1 17:2	4 2	PL p. 352; LM 17.1, 17.2
18	18:1 18:2	3 3	LM 18.1 PL p. 379; LM 18.2
19	19:1 19:2	3 1	PL p. 399; LM 19.1 LM 19.2
20	20:1 20:2	2 4	PL p. 412, LM 20.1
21	21:1 21:2	2 4	PL p. 430, LM 21.1
22	22:1 22:2	3 3	PL p. 456; LM 22.1 LM 22.2
23	23:1 23:2	3 3	PL p. 479; LM 23.1, 23.2
24	24:1 24:2	4 3	PL p. 501; LM 24.1, 24.2, LM 24.3
25	25:1 25:2	3 3	PL p. 522; LM 25.1 25.2
26	26:1 26:2	3 2	LM 26.1 PL p. 543
27	27:1 27:2	3 2	PL p. 562; LM 27.1, 27.2
28	28:1 28:2	4 2	PL p. 579; LM 28.1
29	29:1 29:2	3 2	PL p. 604 LM 29.1, 29.2
30	30:1 30:2	3 3	PL p. 623; LM 30.1
31	31:1 31:2	2 4	LM 31.1; PL p. 650

Equipment List

Classroom items such as paper, pencils, and water, and building equipment such as a piano are not included in the list below. Numbers in parentheses following the equipment items are quantities for one set-up. Numbers in the right hand column refer to chapters. Refer to the interleaf pages in front of each chapter for a more detailed list.

D=demonstration **K=Pocket Lab** **L=Physics Lab**

Item	Chapters
alpha source on needle	30(K)
aluminum foil	24(D)
aluminum rings	25(D)
aluminum rod	15(D)
ammeter	22(K), 22(L), 23(K), 24(K), 25(K), 29(K), 31(L)
amplifier, mini audio (Radio Shack #277-1008)	25(L), 26(K)
aquarium	17(D), 17(K)
atomic model	28(L)
balance	2(K), 2(L), 9(D), 13(L), 21(K)
balloons	13(D), 20(K)
balls, steel, 0.5 cm-2 cm	4(K), 4(L), 11(K), 21(K), 21(L), 24(K), 25(K), 26(L), 27(L), 28(K)
battery, flashlight	29(D)
battery, 9 V	25(L), 26(K)
battery, 1.5 V	24(D)
battery-powered car (or physics bulldozer)	3(L), 4(L), 6(L), 25(L)
beakers, 100-mL, 250-mL, 1000-mL	12(L), 12(K), 13(L), 13(K), 17(K), 27(K)
beans	4(D)
bottle, nonmetallic, juice, 12 oz	2(K)
bottle, dropping	17(D)
bowling ball	3(K), 5(K)
box, clear plastic	17(D)
bubble level, small	4(K)
bulb, 120 W	27(K)
burned out light bulbs	13(D)
buzzer (sonalert)	15(D)
C-clamps (2)	9(L), 15(D)
calculator	7(K), 17(K), 18(K)
camera	18(K)
cart, 1 kg	5(K), 11(L)
clay	18(K), 18(L), 19(K), 19(L), 21(L), 26(K), 26(L)
cloud chamber	30(K)
coat hangers, metal	15(D)
coil, induction, AC	
coil of wire	25(K)

Hammer
Tuning fork
Air column
Water

compass	24(D)
copper tubing, 1/2 inch (1 m)	25(K)
cord, heavy	6(K), 7(D)
corks	31(D)
croquet mallet	7(D)
cups, foam or paper	8(K), 12(K), 22(D)
cups, polystyrene	12, 17(D)
D-cell, 1.5 V	22(K), 24(L)
diffraction gratings	19(K), 19(L), 28(D), 28(K)
dish, semicircular plastic	17(L)
dominoes (10)	15(K)
dropper	12(K)
dry ice	30(K)
electrical leads	31(L)
electroscope	20(K)
eyeglasses, several pair	18(K)
farad capacitor	22(D)
film can with top	13(L)
film cans (with a resistor inside)	22(L)
filter material, red, green, and blue	27(K)
filter, polarizing	16(K)
filter, red	16(K)
fishing line	3(L), 4(L)
flashbulb, AG1B	25(D)
flashlight bulb	22, 25(D)
flashlight	16(D), 27(K)
flicker bulb	24(D)
floor tile (3 pieces)	2(L)
fluorescein (10 g)	27(K)
foam ball	15(D)
foam, plastic, 25-cm square	21(K)
food coloring	8(K), 12(K)
frequency generator	15(K)
friction board	6(D)
fur	20(K), 20(L)
galvanometer	25(D), 25(K)
gas discharge tubes	28(K)
gas discharge power supply	28(K)
Geiger counter	30(K)
Genecon (or efficient DC motor)	25(K)
generator, electrostatic	21(D)
glass sheet	24(D)
glass brick	19(D)
goggles, safety	11(K), 12(L), 13(K), 28(L)
golf ball	17(K)
graduated cylinder, 1000-mL	15(L)
graph paper	2(L), 17(L), 26(L), 30(L)
heater, immersion	22(D)
heater	12(D)

high-voltage source	28(D)
hot plate or bunsen burner	12(L), 18(D)
immersion oil	17(D)
iron filings	24(D)
jumping disks	13(K)
laboratory cart (2)	4(K), 9(K)
laboratory cart with spring mechanism	11(K)
lamps and sockets, miniature	22(K), 23(K), 25(K)
laser	17, 19(D), 19(K)
lead sheet	12(D)
LED, bi-color	29(L)
LED, green	29(L)
LED, red	29(D), 29(K), 29(L)
lens, concave, large diameter	18(L)
lens, convex, large diameter	18(K), 18(L)
Leyden jar	21(D)
light bulb (non-frosted) in fixture, 40 Watt	16(L)
light source	18(D)
light bulbs (of different wattage) and boxes	16(K)
light bulb with power supply	18(K)
light bulb and socket (3)	23(D), 24(D), 26(D)
light, straight filament, 40 W	19(L)
liquid graphite	20(L)
magnet, cylindrical	25(D)
magnet, permanent, strong (neodymium)	24(D), 25(L), 26(K), 26(L), 30(K)
magnets, horseshoe	24(D), 24(K), 25(D)
magnets, horseshoe, neodymium (2)	25(K)
magnets, bar	24(D)
magnets, disk	24(K), 24(L), 31(K)
magnet wire, #26 or #28, (1 m)	24(L)
magnetic compass	24(K)
mallet, rubber	15(D)
marble, glass, large	12(D), 26(L)
marbles, glass, 12 mm (4)	28(K)
masses, assorted	5(D), 5(L), 6(D), 6(K), 7(D), 8(K), 10(K), 11(L)
metersticks	2(K), 4(K), 5(D), 6(D), 6(L), 7(D), 9(D), 10(L), 11(D), 11(K), 14(L), 15(K), 16(K), 19(L)
metronome	3(L)
microscope	17(D)
mirror, convex	18(K)
mirror, makeup	18(K)
mirror, plane	17(D), 18(K)
mirror, concave	18(D), 18(K)
motor, miniature DC	25(K)
movie screen	19(K), 28(D)

nail, small, #2 finishing	16(L)
nail, large, #8 common	16(L)
nail, 2-3 cm	18(L)
needle	13(K)
oscilloscope	24(D)
paper clips	6(D), 13(K), 24(K)
paper, colored	1(L)
peg board	16(D)
pen, felt-tip	3(L), 17(L), 19(D)
pens, colored marking	27(L)
photocell	31(L)
pie pan, 22-cm aluminum	20(L), 28(K)
piece of screen	19(K)
pith ball material	20(L)
pith balls	15(D), 20(D), 21(K)
plastic drinking glass	20(L)
plastic soda bottle	13,17(D)
plastic drinking glasses	7(D)
plastic strip, corrugated	28(D)
plastic foam insulation, 30 cm x 30 cm block	20(L)
plastic fishing bob	7(D)
plate glass	18(D)
Plexiglass tube	16, 24(D)
power supply, AC, low voltage	25(L)
power supply, DC, variable, 0-12 V	19(K), 20(D), 22(D), 22(K), 22(L), 23(D), 23(K), 23(L), 24(D), 24(K), 29(K), 29(L)
prism	17(D), 28(D)
protractor	6(L)
radio, battery-powered	26(D)
record	19(D)
resistor, 200-400Ω	29(D)
resistor, 470Ω	29(K), 29(L)
resistors, 1Ω, 5Ω , 15Ω and 10-W ratings	22(K)
resistors, identical, 330Ω or 470Ω , 1/2 W (3)	23(K)
ring stand	13(D), 15(D), 16(D)
ripple tank	19(D)
rope	6(K), 9(K)
rubber stoppers, #0 (3 doz)	28(L)
ruler, with center groove, 30 cm	2(K), 2(L), 11(K), 13(K), 15(K), 17(L), 18(L), 19(L), 21(L), 26(K), 26(L), 31(L)
sandpaper	24(L)
scissors	1(L)
screw eyes or hooks	7(D)
set of dominoes	31(D)
skateboards (2)	9(K)
slide whistles	15(D)
slide, photographic, 35 mm	28(D)
slide projector	28(D)
soap bubble wand	16(K)
socket wired with dimmer switch	27(K)
softball	7(K), 7(L), 9(D)

solenoid, iron or air core	25(K), 25(L)
spectrum discharge tubes	28(D)
sponge ball	16(K)
spoon	17(K)
spring scales, 10 N	6(K)
spring scales, 20 N	5(K), 5(L), 6(D), 8(K), 9(D), 9(K), 9(L), 10(K), 11(L), 13(L)
spring, coil	14(K), 14(L)
stick, pine	13(D)
stopwatches	3(K), 4(D), 4(K), 4(L), 6(L), 7(K), 7(L), 9(K), 9(L), 10(L), 11(L), 12(K), 12(L), 14(L), 25(K)
straw, plastic	3(L), 4(L), 20(L), 21(K)
string	6(D), 6(K), 7(D), 8(D), 8(K), 8(L), 10(K), 15(D), 25(L)
stroboscope	4(D)
Styrofoam section	5(K)
suction-cup darts	8(D)
tape, masking	3(L), 5(L), 9(L), 11(L), 16(L),25(L), 26(L)
tape, transparent	1(K), 1(L), 4(D), 4(K), 4(L), 7(D), 11(K), 19(K), 19(L), 20(L), 24(L), 30(K)
tape recorder	15(K)
telephone pickup coil (Radio Shack #44-533)	25(L), 26(K)
tennis ball	17(K)
test tubes	13(D), 18(D)
thermistor	29(K)
thermometers	12(D), 12(K), 12(L)
thread	13(D), 20(L), 21(K)
thumbtacks (2)	8(L)
transparent plastic container	24(D)
transparent sheets	19(D)
tube, glass, hollow	15(L)
tuning fork hammer	15(L)
tuning forks	15(D), 15(L)
U-channel	4(K), 4(L), 27(L)
Van de Graaff generator	20(D)
voltmeter	22(D), 22(L), 25(K), 29(L), 31(L)
wagon	4(D)
watch glass	20(D)
wires, connecting	2(L), 22(K), 22(L), 23(D), 23(K), 24(D), 24(D), 25(K), 29(K), 29(L)
wood blocks	6(D), 9(L)
wood board	20(D)
yarn, (2 m)	14(K)

Suppliers

Audiovisual materials for purchase or rental may be obtained from the following distributors. All materials should be ordered months in advance, with alternate choices of dates for their use.

A list of university audiovisual distributors is included for your convenience. All audiovisual materials can be obtained from one of these suggested sources. The first reference is a good general source of information on physics audiovisual materials.

Audiovisual Resources

"A Potpourri of Physics Teaching Ideas," edited by Donna Berry, Published by the American Association of Physics Teachers.

AAPT
5112 Berwyn Road
College Park, MD 20740-4100

Bergwall Productions, Inc.
839 Stewart Ave.
Garden City, NY 11530

Collier-Macmillan School
and Library Services
866 Third Ave.
New York, NY 10022

Ealing Film Loops
BFA Educational Media
2211 Michigan Ave.
Santa Monica, CA 90404

Ealing Film Loops
Cambridge, MA 02140

Education Development Center
39 Chapel St.
Newton, MA 02160

Educational Material and
Equipment Co.
46 Lafayette Ave.
New Rochelle, NY 10801

Encyclopaedia Britannica
Educational Corporation
425 North Michigan Ave.
Chicago, IL 60611

Handel Film Corp.
8730 Sunset Blvd.
West Hollywood, CA 90069

Learning Corporation of America
1350 Avenue of the Americas
New York, NY 10019

Metrologic Instruments, Inc.
P.O. Box 307
143 Harding Ave.
Bellmawr, NJ 08031

Pyramid Films
P.O. Box 1048
Santa Monica, CA 90406

Ross Books
P.O. Box 4340
Berkeley, CA 94794

Thomas Alva Edison
Foundation
21000 West Ten Mile Road
Southfield, MI 48075

Time-Life Multimedia
100 Eisenhower Drive
Paramus, NJ 07652

WVIZ-TV
4300 Brookpark Road
Cleveland, OH 44134

University Rental Services

The University of Arizona
Film Library
Tucson, AZ 85719
(602) 621-3282

University of Illinois
Visual Aids Service
1325 South Oak
Champaign, IL 61820
(217) 333-1360

Indiana University
Audio Visual Center
Bloomington, IN 47405
(812) 335-2103

Kent State University
Audio-Visual Service
Kent, OH 44242
(216) 672-3456

Syracuse University
Film Rental Center
1455 E. Colvin
Syracuse, NY 13210
(315) 479-6631

Washington State Univ.
Audio-Visual Center
Pullman, WA 99164
(509) 335-4535

Equipment

Arbor Scientific
P.O. Box 2750
Ann Arbor, MI 48106-2750

Carolina Biological Supply Co.
2700 York Road
Burlington, NC 27215

Central Scientific Co.
11222 Melrose Avenue
Franklin Park, IL 60131

Fisher Scientific Co.
4901 W. LeMoyne
Chicago, IL 60615

Flinn Scientific Inc.
P.O. Box 219
Batavia, IL 60510

LaPine Scientific Company
6001 S. Knox Avenue
Chicago, IL 60629

McKilligan Supply Corporation
435 Main Street
Johnson City, NY 13790

Nasco
901 Janesville Avenue
Fort Atkinson, WI 53538

Pasco Scientific
10101 Foothills Blvd.
P.O. Box 619011
Roseville, CA 95661-9011

Sargent-Welch Scientific Co.
7300 N. Linder
Skokie, IL 60077

Sargent-Welch Scientific of Canada, Ltd.
285 Caryray Drive
Weston, Ontario, Canada M9L 1P3

Science Kit and Boreal Labs
777 E. Park Drive
Tonawanda, NY 14150

Ward's Natural Science Establishment, Inc.
P.O. Box 1712
Rochester, NY 14603

Evaluation Form

We want your opinions!

We at Glencoe Publishing feel that with the 1992 edition of Merrill's **Physics: Principles & Problems,** we have produced a quality textbook program«but the final proof of that rests with you, the teachers who have had the opportunity to put our materials to use in your classrooms. That's why we would very much appreciate it if you would take the time to respond to any of the parts of this questionnaire that are appropriate for you. In doing so, you will be letting us know how good a job we've done and where we can work to improve.

Please note: 1) you need not have used all of the program components to respond to this questionnaire;
2) we encourage you to give us your honest and most candid opinions.

Excellent				Poor	**Student Text**
5	4	3	2	1	Format
5	4	3	2	1	Readability
5	4	3	2	1	Approach
5	4	3	2	1	Organization
5	4	3	2	1	Factual accuracy
5	4	3	2	1	Coverage of physics principles
5	4	3	2	1	Thoroughness of concept development
5	4	3	2	1	Visual impact
5	4	3	2	1	Treatment of new terms
5	4	3	2	1	Graphs
5	4	3	2	1	Problems
5	4	3	2	1	Illustrations
5	4	3	2	1	Glossary

Excellent				Poor	**Teacher Wraparound Edition**
5	4	3	2	1	Teachability
5	4	3	2	1	Planning Guide
5	4	3	2	1	Demonstration
5	4	3	2	1	Performance Objectives
5	4	3	2	1	Teaching aids
5	4	3	2	1	Chapter materials
5	4	3	2	1	Problem Correlations
5	4	3	2	1	**Problem & Solution Manual**

Excellent				Poor	**Supplements**
5	4	3	2	1	Teacher Resource Package
5	4	3	2	1	Laboratory Manual SE
5	4	3	2	1	Laboratory, Physics, TE
5	4	3	2	1	Transparency Package
5	4	3	2	1	Study Guide, SE
5	4	3	2	1	Test Bank Software
5	4	3	2	1	English-Spanish Glossary
5	4	3	2	1	Lesson Plan Booklet

School Information

1. Grade level of students	9	10		11	12
2. Total number of students enrolled in that grade	1–50	51–100		101–200	200+
3. Total number of students enrolled in physics	1–50	51–100		101–200	200+
4. Average class size	25 or less	26–30		31–35	41 or more
5. Total school enrollment	1–200	201–500		501–1000	1000+
6. Locale of school	rural	small town		suburban	large city
7. Ability level of class	below average		average		above average
8. Appropriateness of text for your class	easy		about right		difficult
9. Number of years text used	1	2	3	4	5
10. May we quote you?			yes		no

Please feel free to attach an additional sheet to make further comments.

Name __________________ Date __________________

School __________________ City __________ State __________ Zip ________

FOLD

CUT

FOLD

NO POSTAGE
NECESSARY
IF MAILED
IN THE
UNITED STATES

BUSINESS REPLY MAIL

FIRST CLASS PERMIT NO. 284 COLUMBUS,OHIO

POSTAGE WILL BE PAID BY ADDRESSEE

GLENCOE PUBLISHING CO.
Editorial Director, Science Dept.
936 EASTWIND DRIVE
WESTERVILLE, OHIO 43081

Merrill

Physics

Principles and Problems

Authors

Paul W. Zitzewitz
Professor of Physics
University of Michigan-Dearborn
Dearborn, Michigan

Robert F. Neff
Physics Teacher
Suffern High School
Suffern, New York

Mark Davids
Physics Teacher
Grosse Pointe South High School
Grosse Pointe Farms, Michigan

Content Consultants

Robert B. Clark, Ph.D.
Professor of Physics
Texas A & M University
College Station, Texas

Patrick Kenealy, Ph.D.
Professor of Physics
California State University
Long Beach, California

GLENCOE
McGraw–Hill

New York, New York   Columbus, Ohio   Mission Hills, California   Peoria, Illinois

A Glencoe/McGraw-Hill Program

Merrill Physics: Principles & Problems

Student Edition
Teacher Wraparound Edition
Problems and Solutions Manual
Teacher Resource Package
Transparency Package
Laboratory Manual:
Student and Teacher Editions
Study Guide, Student Edition
Lesson Plan Booklet
English/Spanish Glossary
Computer Test Bank

Authors

Paul W. Zitzewitz is Professor of Physics at the University of Michigan-Dearborn. He received his B.A. from Carleton College and M.A. and Ph.D. from Harvard University, all in physics. His research director at Harvard was Nobel laureate Norman Ramsey. Dr. Zitzewitz has taught physics to undergraduates for 19 years, and is an active experimenter in the field of atomic physics with over 50 research papers.

Robert F. Neff has taught physics for 26 years at Suffern High School, Suffern, New York. He received his B.S. from Kenyon College and his M.S.T. from Cornell University. Mr. Neff has made frequent contributions to *The Physics Teacher* magazine and is a long time editor of one of its monthly columns. Mr. Neff has presented workshops on physics demonstrations to physics teachers across the country.

Content Consultants

Robert B. Clark, Ph.D.
Professor of Physics
Texas A & M University
College Station, TX

Patrick Kenealy, Ph.D.
Professor of Physics
California State University
Long Beach, CA

Reviewers

Harold H. Baumer, Science Dept. head, Emmerich Manual High School, Indianapolis, IN
Alex Domkowski, Physics teacher, Saint Mary's Hall, San Antonio, TX
Lloyd W. Harrich, Physics teacher, San Ramon Valley High School, Danville, CA
David P. Koch, Physics teacher, The Hockaday School, Dallas, TX
Emma Jean McClendon, Physics & Physical Science teacher, W.H. Adamson High School, Dallas, TX
Dan Myers, Physics teacher, Waurika High School, Waurika, OK
Julia Davis Pearson, Mathematics & Physics teacher, Clinton Central Jr/Sr High School, Michigantown, IN
Robert A. Sporman, Physics teacher, Kearsley High School, Flint, MI
James E. Teague, Science Dept. chairperson, Los Angeles Baptist High School, Sepulveda, CA
Kelly A. Wedding, Teacher-Scientist, Technical Education Research Center, Cambridge, MA
Margaret M. Wiedower, Science chairperson & teacher, Academy of Our Lady of Peace, San Diego, CA

ISBN 0-02-826721-4

Send all inquiries to: Glencoe/McGraw-Hill
936 Eastwind Drive,
Westerville, Ohio 43081

Printed in the United States of America.

4 5 6 7 8 9 10 11 12 13 14 15 QPH/MC 03 02 01 00 99 98 97 96 95

TABLE OF Contents

MECHANICS

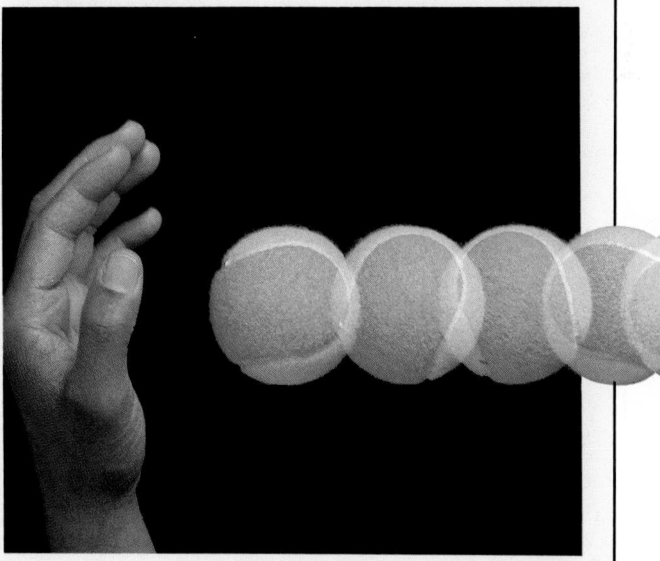

Physics Labs

iv

STATES OF MATTER

WAVES AND LIGHT

v

Pocket Labs

vi

ELECTRICITY

vii

Features

Problem Solving Strategies

Using Your Calculator

Using a Graphing Calculator

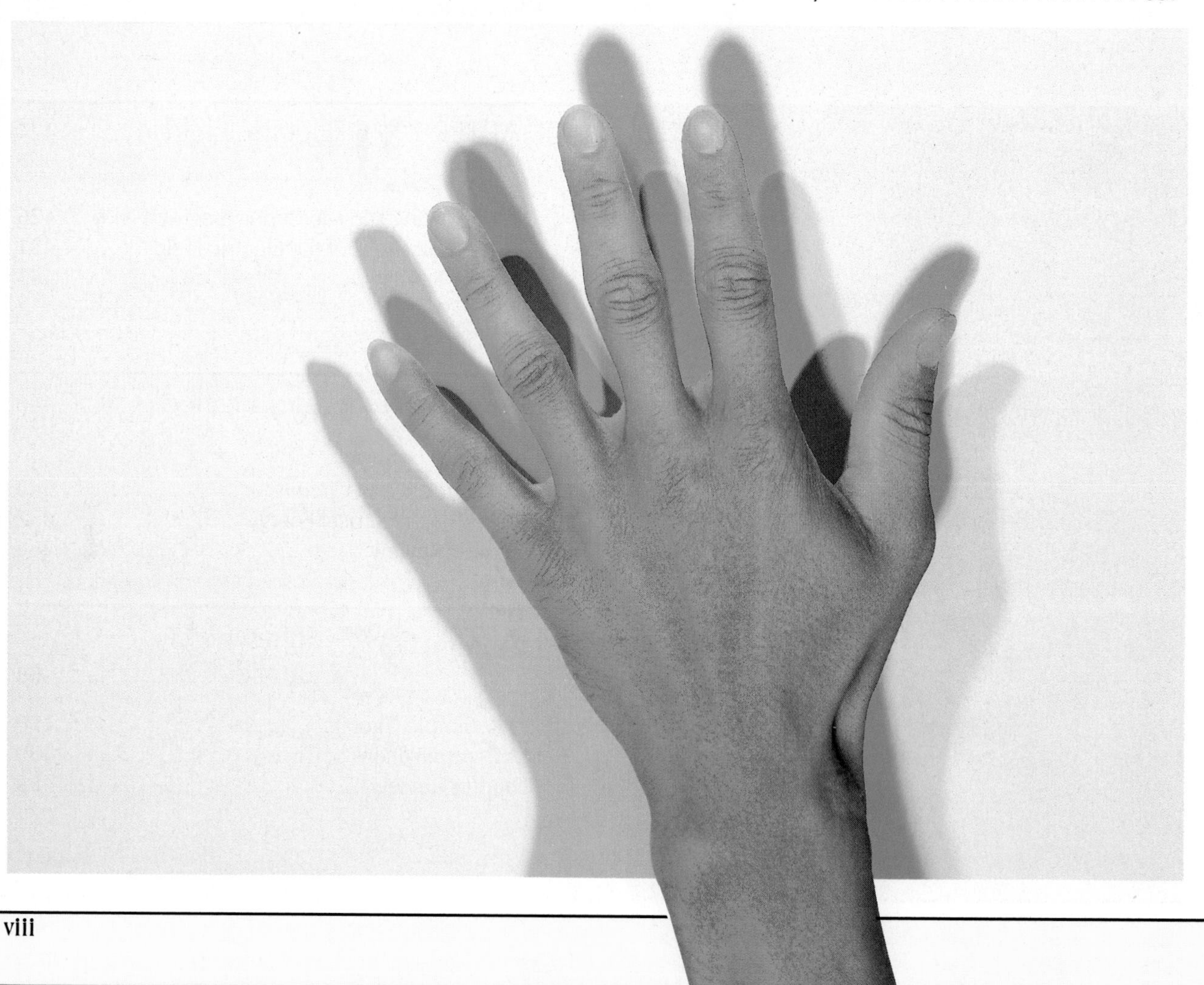

viii

MODERN PHYSICS

ix

Features

Physics and Society

Physics and Technology

x

Features

Connections

Careers

xi

Dear Students,

Physics is much more than equations and numbers. Physics is about what happens in the world all around you. It is about the colors in a rainbow, about the sparkle and hardness of a diamond. It is involved with walking, running, bicycling, driving a car, or directing an interplanetory probe. The principles of physics are evident in toys, in ball games, in musical instruments, and in giant electrical generators.

Look at the photos at the beginning of each chapter. They are examples of physics all around you. Physics, you will find, deals with the way nature behaves - with what are called natural laws. Many of the technological advances of civilization have resulted from understanding these laws. Studying physics might make it possible for you to help advance both science and technology. You may even find yourself in a career that uses the results of physics. In any case, as a citizen with a knowledge of physics, you will be better able to help solve the difficult questions that technology poses for our society.

You will find that physics is a human activity, an exciting adventure. You will learn a little about the men and women from many countries who, over the years, have helped us to understand the world around us. You can join the adventure as you begin to understand the world around you.

Paul W Zitzewitz

xii

Get the Most out of Physics

Physics is all about the world around you. An example is popping the cork on a bottle of a carbonated beverage.

A question will be posed in each chapter. Do you know the answer to this one?

CHAPTER 13 States of Matter

Bottled Cloud

Janet was helping her parents prepare for a dinner party. As she popped the cork on a bottle of sparkling grape juice, a small cloud formed around the bottle's mouth. The cloud surprised Janet's mother. What explanation did Janet give her mother?

Chapter Outline

13.1 THE FLUID STATES
- Pressure
- Fluids at Rest—Hydrostatics
- Fluids in Motion—Hydrodynamics
- Liquids vs Gases
- Surface Tension
- Evaporation and Condensation
- Plasma

13.2 THE SOLID STATE
- Solid Bodies
- Elasticity in Solids
- Thermal Expansion of Matter

Concept Check

The following terms or concepts from earlier chapters are important for a good understanding of this chapter. If you are not familiar with them, you should review them before studying this chapter.
- force, Chapter 5
- work, kinetic energy, potential energy, Chapter 11
- temperature, thermal energy, heat, Chapter 12

You have lived with the three common states of matter all your life. You breathe air, drink and swim in water, and build with solid objects. In general, you are familiar with most of their properties. Yet, there can be some surprises. The photo shows a bottle that contained cold, sparkling grape juice. Carbon dioxide gas is dissolved in the liquid. When the cork is removed, the pressure in the bottle suddenly drops. The result is a beautiful display of the states of matter.

265

The **Concept Check** is a reminder of what you should know before you start the new chapter. If you do not feel comfortable with the ideas listed, review them before starting the new chapter.

The answer will be somewhere in the chapter.

Bottled Cloud

in diameter. A cloud of these droplets is called a fog. Fogs often form when moist air is chilled by cold ground. Fogs can also be formed in your home. When a carbonated drink is opened, the sudden decrease in pressure causes the temperature to drop, condensing the water vapor and forming the fog seen when Janet opened the bottle of sparkling grape juice.

Plasma

If you heat a solid, it melts to form a liquid. Further heating results in a gas. What happens if you increase the temperature still further? Collisions between the particles become violent enough to tear the particles

xiii

Study for Mastery

Objectives

- show an ability to add vectors by the graphical method; recognize that the order of vector addition does not matter.
- recognize the independence of perpendicular vector quantities.

The resultant i... ingle vector that could repres... um of several vectors.

6.1 GRAPHICAL METHOD OF VECTOR ADDITION

A vector quantity can be represented by an arrow-tipped line segment. The length of the line, drawn to scale, represents the magnitude of the quantity. The direction of the arrow indicates the direction of the quantity. This arrow-tipped line segment represents a vector. Just as we can represent a vector graphically, we can add vectors graphically. They also can be represented in printed materials in boldface type, ***A, B***.

Vector Addition in One Dimension

Suppose a child walks 200 m east, pauses, and then continues 400 m east. To find the total displacement, or change in position of the child, we must add the two vector quantities. In Figure 6–1a, *A* and *B*, drawn to scale, are vectors representing the two segments of the child's walk. The vectors are added by placing the tail of one vector at the head of the other vector. It is very important that neither the direction

Physics involves ideas, or concepts. The list of **Objectives** will guide your study. Read the section quickly. Make note of all boldfaced terms. Skip equations and example problems. Don't worry if you don't understand the material now. The words and ideas will be more familiar the next time you read them.

CONCEPT REVIEW

1.1 The order in which you add vectors does not matter. Mathematicians say that vector addition is commutative. Which ordinary arithmetic operations are commutative? Which are not?
1.2 Two boys push on a crate. One exerts a 400-N force, the other a 300-N force. The resultant force on the crate is 600 N. Explain.
1.3 What is the largest resultant force the two boys in question 1.2 could exert on the crate? What is the smallest resultant force?

Read the section again, more slowly this time. Pay attention to definitions. Use the **Concept Review** questions to check on your understanding. You may need to read the section again.

CHAPTER 6 REVIEW

SUMMARY

- The resultant is the sum of two or more vectors.
- To add two vectors graphically, place the tail of the second vector at the head of the first vector. Draw th... vector t...
- The res... be foun...
- A vector can be resolved into two perp... components.
- Vectors at any angles may be added b... their components, adding all vertical a... zontal components separately, and the... the resultant.

Turn to the **Chapter Review.** Check the **Key Terms.** Review the **Summary** statements and compare them with the **Objectives** you read at the beginning of the section.

KEY TERMS

resultant
trigonometry
sine (sin)
cosine (cos)
tangent (tan)
components
vector resolution
equilibrium
equilibrant force

REVIEWING CONCEPTS

1. What method is used to add vectors graphically?
2. A vector is to be added graphically to a second vector. Which of th... to the first vector: mov... its length?
3. In your own words, w...

12. A book is on an inclined plane.
    a. Describe two convenient co... the weight of the book.
    b. How are the magnitudes of th... nents related to the angle of th...

APPLYING CONCEPTS

1. A vector drawn 15 mm long repr... locity of 30 m/s. How long shoul... vector to represent a velocity of 2...
2. If a vector that is 1 cm long repre... of 5 N, how many newtons do... ...me ...

resu... of 3 ...e res...

THINKING PHYSIC-LY

Weight lifting or "pumping iron" has become very popular in the last few years. When lifting a barbell, which grip will exert less force on the lifter's arms: one in which the arms are extended straight upward from the body so they

Reviewing Concept questions refer to the text. **Applying Concepts** questions require you to think of new ways to apply the ideas in the chapter. Extend your thinking by **Thinking Physic-ly!**

xiv

Solve Problems Successfully

Many ideas in physics are best described by using math. Most useful applications of physical principles often depend on quantitative relationships among variables.

PROBLEM SOLVING STRATEGY

When solving problems, use an orderly procedure.

1. Read the problem carefully. Try to visualize the actual situation. Make a sketch if necessary.
2. Identify the quantities that are given in the problem.
3. Identify the quantity that is unknown, the one you have to find.
4. Select the equation or equations that will relate the given and unknown quantities.
5. Make sure the equations can be applied to the problem, that is, is the acceleration constant?
6. Rewrite equations as needed to solve for the unknown quantity.
7. Substitute the given values including proper units into the equation and solve. Be sure your answer is in the correct units.
8. Make a rough estimate to see if your answer is reasonable.

Problem Solving Strategies are scattered throughout the book. They are helpful hints for working different kinds of problems. **Example Problems** use those hints to show you methods you can use to solve the **Practice Problems.** To help you be successful, complete solutions for all Practice Problems are in **Appendix A. Problems** in the **Chapter Review** will give you further practice.

Example Problem

Flight of a Tennis Ball

A tennis ball is thrown straight up with an initial velocity of +22.5 m/s. It is caught at the same distance above ground from which it was thrown. **a.** How high does the ball rise? **b.** How long does the ball remain in the air?

Given: v_i = +22.5 m/s, **Unknowns: a.** d **b.** t

Solution:

a. At the top of its flight, the instantaneous velocity of the ball is zero. Thus, the final velocity for the upward part of the ball's flight will be zero. Therefore, we know v_i, g, and need d. Use the equation $v_f^2 = v_i^2 + 2gd$, solving it for d.

$v_i^2 + 2gd$ or $2gd = -v_i^2$.

m/s²) / m/s²) = +25.8 m.

sitive), so d = +25.8 m.

now that the times required for the rising and ht will be the same. That is, the time to rise Thus, we know v_f and g but need t. Use = 0, we solve for t, obtaining

$= \frac{-22.5 \text{ m/s}}{-9.80 \text{ m/s}^2} = +2.30$ s.

Practice Problems

27. If you drop a golf ball, how far does it fall in ½ s?
28. A spacecraft traveling at a velocity of +1210 m/s is uniformly accelerated at −150 m/s². If the acceleration lasts for 8.68 s, what is the final velocity of the craft? Explain your results in words.
29. A man falls 1.0 m to the floor.

Appendix A
Solutions for Practice Problems

$IMA = \frac{d_e}{d_r} = \frac{33.0 \text{ m}}{16.5 \text{ m}} = 2.00$, so

$efficiency = \frac{1.74}{2.00} \times 100\% = 87\%$

15. $eff = \frac{W_o}{W_i} \times 100\% = \frac{F_r d_r}{F_e d_e} \times 100\%$, so

$d_e = \frac{F_r d_r (100\%)}{F_e (eff)}$

$= \frac{(125 \times 10^3 \text{ N})(0.13 \text{ m})(100\%)}{(225 \text{ N})(88.7\%)}$

$= 0.81$ m

b. The work is that of 60 000 100-megaton bombs.

4. a. Since $W = \Delta KE = \frac{1}{2}mv^2$, then $v = \sqrt{2W/m'}$.

If $W' = \frac{1}{2}W$,

$v' = \sqrt{2W'/m'}$

$= \sqrt{2\left(\frac{1}{2}W\right)/m'} = \sqrt{\frac{1}{2}}v'$

$= (0.707)(100 \text{ km/h}) = 70.7$ km/h

b. If $W' = 2W$,

$v' = \sqrt{2}\,(100 \text{ km/h})$

$= 141$ km/h

Using Your CALCULATOR

Calculators can be used to evaluate equations. Note that each of the factors in the denominator must be divided into the numerator.

$$d = \frac{v_i^2}{2g}$$

22.5 [x²] [+/-]   -506.25

[÷] [2] [÷] [9.80] [+/-] [=]   25.829082

d = 25.8 m

You will find calculating tips and shortcuts in the **Using Your Calculator** features in the margin beside many of the **Example Problems.** If you like using a graphing calculator, you will enjoy the **Using a Graphing Calculator** exercises in some of the **Chapter Reviews.**

XV

Experiment with Physics

The ideas of physics must always be tested against the natural world. To find out how the world works, you must do some experiments.

Try the **Pocket Labs.** They are quick activities that give you hands-on experiences with new ideas introduced in a section of the chapter.

POCKET LAB

ENERGY IN COINS

Would your car require more or less stopping distance when it is loaded with passengers, luggage, and so on? Explain. A short activity will aid in answering the question. Lay a ruler on a smooth table. Place two quarters against the edge of the ruler. Momentarily push the two quarters at the same speed across the table and then stop the ruler. Choose two quarters that slide the same distance before stopping. Now tape another coin on top of one quarter to increase its mass. Again push the coins with the ruler. Does the stopping distance depend upon the mass? Explain why?

Pay attention to **Safety Symbols.** Look for them. They will alert you to possible dangers in your laboratory experiences.

The **Physics Labs** will help you develop valuable skills in gathering and analyzing data, of communicating your results to others, and of applying those results by answering questions.

PHYSICS LAB: Heating Up

Purpose

To discover how the temperature increases with a constant supply of thermal energy.

Materials

- hot plate (or bunsen burner)
- 250-mL pyrex beaker
- water
- thermometer
- stopwatch
- goggles

Procedure

1. Turn your hot plate to a medium setting (or as recommended by your teacher). Allow a few minutes for the plate to heat up. While heating water wear goggles.
2. Pour 150 ml of room temperature water into the 250-mL beaker.
3. Measure the initial temperature of the water. Keep the thermometer in the water.

Analysis

xvi

Think Physic-ly

How does the study of Physics apply to the rest of your life? **Want Ads** describe careers that use some of the concepts you will learn in your study. **Connections** illustrate how the ideas of physics influence almost every area of your life. In an **FYI**, you might find a poem, an amusing anecdote, or a bit of physics trivia. **Physics and Technology** features present an interesting application of physics. The **Physics and Society** features present a discussion of a social or environmental concern that involves some application of physics. You will find that Physics applies to all of your life.

F.Y.I.

Small insects have large sur-ace areas and low weights. They quickly reach terminal ve-ocities of only a few centimeters per second. An ant can fall from a fifty-story building and walk away unharmed after hitting the sidewalk.

HELP WANTED

PHYSICISTS

Budding, young "Newtons and Einsteins" are needed on the research and development team of a large corporation. A doctorate in Physics (or a Masters degree and an ...rd of accomplishment) ...e will consider various ...alization that can pro... ...pplications for our ma... ...nics, communication, ...ivisions. The ability to ...ently and as a part of ...sential. For information ...titute of Physics, 335 ...reet, New York, NY 10017

HELP WANTED

ELECTRONIC EQUIPMENT REPAIRERS

The ability to test, troubleshoot, and repair a variety of equipment requires knowledge of products, test equipment, safety measures, electrical schematics, and service manuals. In addition, you must be able to communicate effectively to represent the company to customers. Good manual dexterity and color vision, as well as vocational/technical school or military training, are also musts. Your job performance will determine yo... ties. For ... Electron... 604 No...

BIOLOGY CONNECTION

The cheetah runs at a maximum speed of 60-63 mph. Its rate of acceleration is awesome—from a starting speed of 0 to 45 mph in two seconds.

Physics and technology

AERODYNAMIC HELMETS

In the 74th Indy 500, Arie Luyendyk drove an average speed of 185.984 mph (297.5 km/h) to win. His maximum speed was greater than 220 mph (352 km/h). At these speeds, drivers complain that their heads are buffeted se-

creating an area of low pressure; the higher pressure below the helmet pushes it upward. Simpson Race Products Company found a way to break up the airflow over the helmet through the use of pressure-relief ducts and stall strips. The Simpson helmet has two gill-like outlet ducts and two ripple strips on each side of the top of the helmet. The ducts allow low-energy airflow out of the helmet to mix with the faster moving air over the top, thus

helmet won the 1990 Schwitzer Award given by the Society of Automotive Engineers for innovation and excellence in race car design. Besides its improved aerodynamic qualities, the helmet has a new liner that provides better protection and it improves airflow to cool the driver's head.

- What other applications might this improved helmet have?

Physics and society

WEAK ELECTROMAGNETIC FIELDS—A HEALTH CONCERN?

Alternating currents, such as those in household wiring, produce electric and magnetic fields. The very low AC frequency is call Extremely Low Frequency, or ELF. The many sources of ELF electric and magnetic fields include power lines, home wiring, electric

Recently, however, experiments have shown that cells are sensitive to even very weak ELF fields. They can affect flow of ions across cell membranes, synthesis of DNA, and the response of cells to hormones. Abnormal development of chick embryos has been seen. The experimental results, however, are very complex. Some effects of ELFs occur only at certain frequencies or amplitudes. Others occur only if the fields are turned on or off abruptly. Finally, for most environmental health hazards the larger the exposure, or dose,

ELF? Some studies found small increases in leukemia, breast cancer, and brain cancer. Studies of users of electric blankets have shown no effects on men, but increases in cancers and brain tumors in children whose mothers slept under electric blankets while pregnant. Studies to find the causes will take years and may not have conclusive results. In the meantime, what should be done?

DEVELOPING A VIEWPOINT

Read articles about ELFs and

Chapter 1

What Is Physics?

CHAPTER OVERVIEW

Theme Development: This opening chapter, particularly important to the comfort and attitude of the science learner, introduces the student to the nature and values of physics. Themes of defining systems and use of models—both tools of inquiry—are introduced.

MISCONCEPTIONS

Students typically view science as much more rigid than it really is. Imagination and creativity aren't generally seen as playing a big role in science though history shows that the best scientists have been exceptionally creative. Furthermore, many people are under the impression that there is a specific, defined scientific method. In fact, there are as many scientific methods as there are scientists.

Laboratory Options

STUDENT EDITION

Physics Lab

The Paper Tower	10

Pocket Lab

Falling	6

TEACHER EDITION

Activities

Cooperative Learning	6, 6
Discovery	9

LABORATORY MANUAL

Bubble Up	Lab 1.1

CHAPTER

1 What Is Physics?

Super Ideas?

The floating block is a small magnet held up against the force of gravity by the disc of superconducting material under it. This disc is made of material that must be cooled well below zero by liquid nitrogen. Such a material was unknown only a few years ago. How did physicists discover superconductivity and develop these new materials?

Objectives

- be able to state what physics is.
- appreciate the importance of creativity and collaboration in science.
- recognize the roles of theory and experiment in physics research.
- understand that, while there is no single "scientific method," there are common methods used by all scientists.

What is physics? What do you think when you see the word *physics*? Do you see equations? Do you hear people saying how hard it is? The atomic bomb? Or do you see people? Albert Einstein with wild hair and no socks? Men in white coats?

Yes, physics has a certain reputation. Yes, physics does make use of mathematics as a powerful language. But, physics also involves concepts, ideas, and principles expressed in ordinary words. Yes, the atomic bomb was built with the aid of many physicists. But, the electricity that lights our homes and schools and brings us radio, television, CDs, and computers was also developed by physicists. Physics also helps athletes train more efficiently and have better equipment so that new records are set.

Of course, Albert Einstein was a physicist. But, so are many women and men who are not super-geniuses, who could easily be your next door neighbor—or you.

The goal of this course is not to make you a physicist. It is to give you an idea of the way physicists view the world; to have the satisfaction of understanding and even predicting the outcome of the activities occurring all around you; to know enough about physics so you can have a rewarding career in a technological world; to be able to make informed decisions as a citizen in an increasingly complex age; to learn to ask questions.

Someone once said, "Professional baseball players and physicists love their work. Others just go to work." We hope you will feel like a physicist about this class.

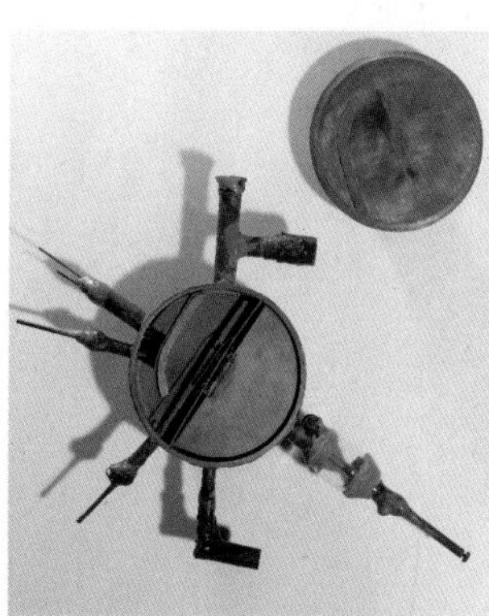

FIGURE 1–1. Shown here is the first operating cyclotron, used to study subatomic particles. It was built in 1930 by E.O. Lawrence. It has a circumference of about 13 inches. In contrast, the proposed superconducting Super Collider will be about 52 miles in circumference, and can give particles 100 million times more energy.

3

Introducing The Chapter

Super Ideas

Using The Photo: Superconductivity was certainly the scientific splash of the late eighties. Though superconductivity isn't the spectacular subject it once was, important developments continue to be made. Broadening applications for superconductors include the manufacture of practical superconducting wires and films, as well as the ongoing use of industrial superconductors in atomic research and medicine. You might want to make the topic one that students will follow throughout the year as an example of the growth and development of a scientific problem.

To answer the chapter opener question, refer students to page 6.

Multicultural Connections

Many inventors were not scientists in the formal sense. Charlotte Smith spent much of her life helping women inventors receive credit, patents, and royalties for their inventions. An example of the problem was the case of Ellen Eglin, an African American domestic servant who invented the clothes wringer. Ellen sold the rights to the invention for only $18.00, a tiny fraction of the money made by the person who bought the rights. In 1891, Charlotte Smith founded a short-lived magazine, "The Woman Inventor." She worked the rest of her life trying to keep other women from suffering the fate of Ellen Eglin.

Assessment Options

Portfolio Assessment
Portfolio Assessment, TWE, p. 5
Answers to Developing a Viewpoint, p. 7
Portfolio Assessment, TWE, p. 9
Answer to Thinking Physic-ly, p. 11

Performance Assessment
Pocket Lab, p. 6
Physics Lab, p. 10
Using Lab Skills, p. 11

Content Assessment
Convergent Question, TWE, p. 9
Concept Review, p. 9
Chapter Review, p. 11

Group Assessment
Activities for group assessment occur with Cooperative Learning and lab activities.

PHYSICS: THE SEARCH FOR UNDERSTANDING

Preparation

OVERVIEW

This section presents physics as a growing and developing branch of scientific inquiry. It also shows how scientific investigation can be a valuable application for human creativity.

BRIDGING

Students will respond to this section based on their individual knowledge of scientific advances. In general, material in this section will also connect with what students may have heard in the past about how scientists conduct their work.

1 Focus

DISCREPANT EVENT

Invite a guest speaker from a local business that employs people who are scientifically or technically trained. Have the speaker discuss personal scientific work and careers in science.

Enrichment Master. With this section, use the Enrichment Master, Thinking Creatively, from the Teacher Resource Package.

ENRICHMENT MASTER

Use the Enrichment master for Chapter 1 with this section.

TRANSPARENCY

Use Transparency 1 with this section

STUDY GUIDE MASTER

Use the Study Guide master for Chapter 1.

F. Y. I.

Discovery consists of seeing what everybody has seen but thinking what nobody has thought.

—Albert Szent-Györgyi 1893–1986

Physics: The Search for Understanding

Physics is the branch of knowledge that studies the physical world. Physicists investigate objects as small as atoms and as large as galaxies. They study the natures of matter and energy and how they are related. How do they do this study? Physicists and other scientists are inquisitive people who look at the world around them with questioning eyes. Their observations lead them to search for the causes of what they see. What makes the sun shine? How do the planets move? Of what is matter made? More often than not, finding explanations to the original questions leads to more questions and experiments. What all scientists hope for are powerful explanations that describe more than one phenomenon and lead to a better understanding of the universe.

Sometimes the results of the work of physicists are only of interest to other physicists. Other times their work leads to devices, such as lasers, calculators, or computers, which change everyone's life. As an example of how physics works, let's look at the recent history of a field of physics which has produced some of the most important scientific advances of the last few years, "high temperature" superconductivity.

In September 1986, two Swiss scientists working for IBM Corporation announced that they had discovered a new superconducting material that worked at temperatures as "high" as −243°C, 30° above absolute zero, the lowest possible temperature for matter. Until that time, materials were only superconducting at temperatures close to absolute zero, −273°C. This temperature is theoretically the lowest temperature possible. The new material was a ceramic, a glass-like material that does

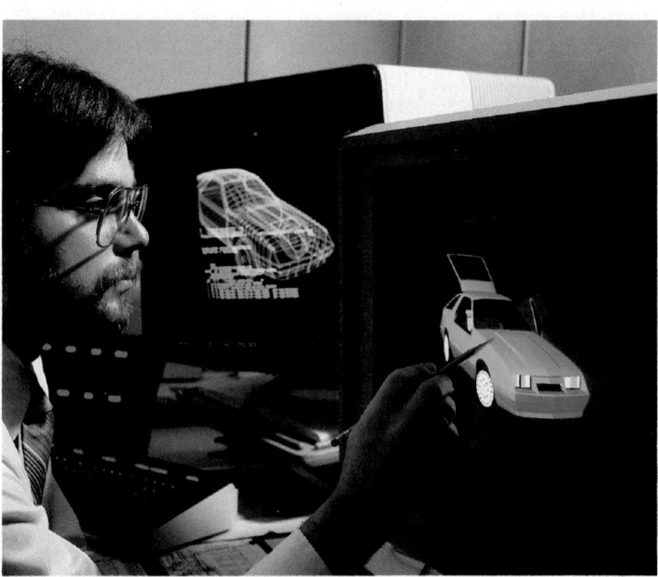

FIGURE 1–2. Physicists don't always work in labs, and the results of their studies are important not just to other physicists.

TEACHER 

Many seemingly unrelated professions rely on a good knowledge of physics. Physicians, physical therapists, and sports trainers use biophysics or biomechanics to understand how systems in the body work together and how movement occurs. Engineers and architects apply physics to materials and the way they build and design structures. Forensic science frequently relies on mechanics to determine what occurred at the scene of a crime or an accident. Have your students come up with other examples.

FIGURE 1–3. Superconducting materials are very quickly finding uses outside of physics. Medical diagnostic equipment, like the MRI instrument shown here, is an example.

HELP WANTED

PHYSICISTS

Budding, young "Newtons and Einsteins" are needed on the research and development team of a large corporation. A doctorate in Physics (or a Masters degree and an extensive record of accomplishment) is required. We will consider various areas of specialization that can provide creative applications for our materials, electronics, communication, and medical divisions. The ability to work independently and as a part of the team is essential. For information contact:

American Institute of Physics, 335 East 45th Street, New York, NY 10017

not normally conduct any electricity. Even though superconducting metals had been discovered in 1911, this development was exciting because earlier superconductors worked at temperatures very difficult to reach and maintain. In 1973, a metal alloy had been found that worked at 23° above absolute zero, but in the next 13 years no further progress had been made.

Within weeks after the discovery was announced, researchers in the United States, China, and Japan had repeated the experiments. That fall, scientists tried different materials and increased the temperature to 52°, then 77°, then 90°, then, in February 1987, to 98° above absolute zero (−175°C). In March 1987, three thousand physicists jammed a hotel ballroom for eight hours to hear reports of experiments. In July 1987, President Ronald Reagan held a press conference to watch a demonstration of superconductivity and to announce a United States effort to apply the new developments. By the end of the same year, high school students had made superconductors that worked above −196°C.

Physicists and engineers have dreamed of many exciting applications for superconductors. Superconducting wires could carry electricity to cities from distant power plants without energy loss. They could be used in magnets that make nuclear fusion possible, that allow high-speed trains to "float" above the track, that could detect oil and minerals in Earth, or pinpoint diseased body tissue. Superconductors might make possible smaller, faster, more powerful computers. Until recently, the problem has been that superconductors worked at such low temperatures that they had to be cooled by liquid helium. Liquid helium is very expensive (more than $5 per liter) and difficult to store. The new superconductors can be cooled with liquid nitrogen, which costs about the same as soda pop. Now some of the dreams may be possible. But first the new materials, now as brittle as glass, must be modified so they can be made into flexible wires. Even more exciting would be the development of materials that are superconducting at room temperatures.

FIGURE 1–4. Wires made of superconducting materials. The ability to produce flexible materials will allow many exciting applications for superconductors.

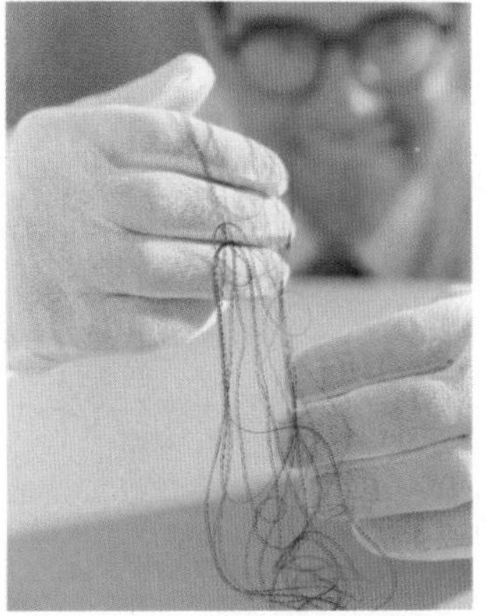

2 Teach

CONCEPT DEVELOPMENT

Study Guide Master. To reinforce the concepts in this section, have the students complete the Study Guide Master for Section 1.1 from the Teacher Resource Package.

- Before assigning this chapter, you might have the students write a paragraph or two on what they think science is all about. Then at the end of the year, have them answer the same question again and compare the two.
- There are many interesting ideas about scientific method. The American physicist and philosopher of science, P.W. Bridgeman, said: "I like to say that there is no scientific method as such, but that the most vital feature of the scientist's procedure has been merely to do his utmost with his mind, *no holds barred.*"
- A good reference about the scientific enterprise—which includes some good demonstration ideas—is K.C. Cole's book, *Sympathetic Vibrations: Reflections on Physics as a Way of Life.*
- A current scientific problem for which information is readily available is the greenhouse effect. The issue shows the interplay of measurements and theory, and, because it has chemical and biological aspects, demonstrates the fundamental inseparability of all the sciences.

Assessment

Portfolio

Throughout the year you may want to have your students research special issues relating science and society. These issues should be challenging, relevant, brief, and require a value judgment. An example would be a recent proposal to develop thermal energy in Hawaii that would require building roads and other support structures in wilderness areas.

Connect to MEDICINE

The instrument in Figure 1–3 is a Magnetic Resonance Imaging (MRI) machine. The MRI provides a way of "seeing" inside a person without using dangerous radiation. The patient is placed inside a large electromagnet, which causes the nuclei of the hydrogen atoms in the body to point in one direction. The body is bathed in a weak radio signal of varying frequency that can change the direction of the hydrogen nuclei. Computers analyze the location of the changing atoms and present the results as an image. What are the advantages and disadvantages of using superconductors in the magnet? [With no resistance, there is no energy loss, and so the magnet requires less energy to run. Ordinary superconductors must be cooled with liquid helium, which is expensive. High-temperature superconductors would require less expensive refrigeration.]

CONCEPT DEVELOPMENT

ACTIVITY

Cooperative Learning: Have students share their personal experiences with practicing scientists, engineers, and other technically trained people. If they protest that they don't know any scientists remind them of their contacts with medically trained people.

Critical Thinking Master, Teacher Resource Package. You may wish to have students complete the Critical Thinking Master, Superconductivity, with this section.

Cooperative Learning: Have students separate into discussion groups to discuss the differences between science and technology. Questions to consider include: What is the moral role of scientists as they do research? (Many scientists were in a moral dilemma as they worked on the Manhattan Project.) When did the "right to die" become an issue? What will happen as the percentage of older people increases in our society? Why has the state of the environment suddenly become such a big issue? Have students make a list of positive and negative contributions of science.

POCKET LAB

FALLING

Purpose: to discover how the motion of a falling object depends on surface area and mass.
Materials: 1 sheet of paper; 5 pennies; 10-cm tape.
Outcome: The ball of paper hits first because it has less air resistance. The four pennies hit at the same time as the single penny. Aristotle was wrong. If Aristotle was correct, the four pennies should have fallen faster and reached the ground first.

FIGURE 1–5. Trial and error is an important part of any scientific method.

Super Ideas?

How did these discoveries occur? The original discovery, in 1911, was made by the Dutch physicist Heike Kamerlingh Onnes. Kamerlingh Onnes was an experimental physicist, one who worked in a research laboratory, often inventing and building the equipment he needed to carry out his experiments, and then using insight, knowledge, and imagination to interpret the results. Many times the results had no immediate practical applications. Onnes had built new kinds of refrigerators that could reach previously unexplored low temperatures. He then studied the properties of gases, liquids, and solids at these new temperatures. He anticipated that mercury would become a better electrical conductor when the temperature was lowered. What totally surprised him was that *all* resistance disappeared when mercury reached 4° above absolute zero!

For over forty years after 1911 no one had developed a complete explanation of how materials could conduct electricity without loss. That is, there was no theory of superconductivity. In 1957, three American theoretical physicists, John Bardeen, Leon Cooper, and Robert Schrieffer, presented a theory, called the BCS theory, that explained how superconductors work. Theoretical physicists use mathematics and, especially today, computers to construct a framework of explanations called a theory that explains experimental data and predicts new results. Theoreticians also need insight, imagination, and creativity. The work of theoreticians in superconductivity is not finished, because no theory can yet explain how the new superconducting materials work.

We still have much to learn about the interactions of matter and energy. Sometimes experimental results come before the theoretical explanations. In other cases, a theory predicts the result of an experiment that has not yet been done. Often physics has important applications to other sciences. Superconducting magnets are an important part of devices used by chemists to learn the structure of molecules, by biologists to trace molecules through cells, and by physicians to find brain tumors.

POCKET LAB

FALLING

Aristotle argued that heavy objects fall faster than light objects. Galileo stated that light and heavy objects fall at the same rate. What do you think? Tear a sheet of paper in half. Crumple one half so that it is in the shape of a ball. Hold the half sheet in one hand and the ball in the other. Drop them from the same height at the same time. Describe what you observed. Explain the results. Predict which will fall faster: four pennies taped together or a single penny. Try it. Was Aristotle correct? Explain.

Transparency Package. Use Transparency 1 and accompanying worksheet, Petals Around the Rose, to reinforce the concept of scientific problem-solving.

CRITICAL THINKING

Use the Critical Thinking master for Chapter 1 with this section.

Physics and society

RESEARCH DOLLARS

How are scientific discoveries made? Although some important scientific discoveries are made "by chance," most are the result of years of carefully directed work called research. With the exception of a few people who study science as a hobby, most scientists get paid to do research in their scientific field. Some scientists are professors at universities. Teaching students is only part of their job. Much of their work consists of doing research—that is, exploring ideas, creating hypotheses, performing experiments, and publishing findings. Many other scientists also work for government-funded laboratories or for private companies.

Physicists call the current theory, or explanation, of the fundamental building blocks of matter the "Standard Model." According to this theory, the basic components from which all matter is made are the particles called quarks and leptons. The giant particle accelerators at Fermilab near Chicago and the LEP in Switzerland are used to make particles collide at very high energies. Physicists study the results of these collisions to test predictions of the Standard Model.

Further research is needed to understand the nature of the quarks and leptons themselves. This new research, however, will require the construction of a larger, more powerful particle accelerator known as the Superconducting Super Collider (SSC). It is estimated that the SSC will cost more than 7 billion dollars to build.

It is difficult to measure the value of SSC research. Although it is expected to contribute significantly to our understanding of the natural world, SSC research offers no immediate practical application benefiting human society. Many people believe government money would be better spent improving the quality of human life in direct ways such as finding a cure for AIDS or reducing pollution. Some scientists are concerned that financing the SSC may take money away from important scientist research in other disciplines such as biology, medicine, chemistry, and other branches of physics.

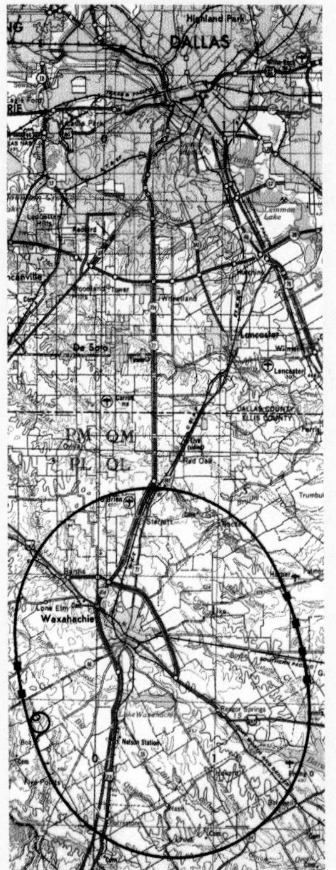

DEVELOPING A VIEWPOINT

1. Some of history's most important scientific discoveries had at first no apparent practical application. Can you think of some examples? What is the practical significance of understanding the essential composition of matter?

2. Should our government support basic research like the SSC project? Would money be better spent on applied research such as finding a cure for AIDS?

3. Earlier particle accelerators, built for basic physics research, led to new methods of treating cancer and to more advanced computers. What basic research in other areas of science has led to totally unexpected results?

SUGGESTED READINGS

Dawson, John M. "Plasma Particle Accelerators." *Scientific American,* March 1989, pp. 54–61.

"The Supercostly Supercollider." *The Economist,* January 27, 1990, pp. 87–88.

Irvine, John and Ben R. Martin, Phoebe Isard. "Investing in the Future: How Much Governments Pay for Academic Research." *Physics Today,* September 1990, pp. 31–38.

Physics and society

Answers To DEVELOPING A VIEWPOINT

1–3: PRO: Optical microscopes can be used to study entities 1000 times larger than atoms. The building blocks of matter, though, are 10 000 times smaller than atoms. To study these building blocks, scientists bombard them with high-energy particles. By generating extremely high-energy particles, the SSC will enable physicists to study subatomic particles much smaller than the ones previously studied. Unlike nuclear power plants that turn mass into energy, collision energy (created by particle accelerators) turns energy into the mass of new particles. By replicating the Big Bang, physicists hope to explain the origin and formation of matter and mass.

The construction and operation of the Superconducting Super Collider south of Dallas (see map) will create approximately 2000 high-tech jobs with an annual payroll of $270 million. In recent years in the United States, physical science research funding has dropped considerably below that of Japan and the major Western European countries. Thus, the United States is significantly behind in its investment in physical science research. Many people believe that the SSC is critical to maintaining U.S. leadership in particle physics research.

CON: Initially estimated to cost $5.9 billion to build, the latest design of the SSC is now expected to cost at least $10 billion. Physicists cannot guarantee that the SSC will run as predicted until it is actually put to the test. The construction of the SSC will require a level of mechanical precision that could increase its cost even further above those estimates.

Research is currently underway to develop smaller, less costly, more powerful particle accelerators using plasma gas of dissociated positive ions and electrons. These plasma accelerators could make standard particle accelerators obsolete in the not-too-distant future.

Teacher Resources: Goodwin, Irwin. "HEPAP and Its Subpanel Approve Redesign and Higher Cost of SSC." *Physics Today,* February 1990, pages 67–68.
Newton, David E. and Seiznick, Irwin L. "Difficult Decisions: The Superconducting Super Collider." *The Science Teacher,* January 1990, pages 35–39.
Zitzewitz, Paul. *Physics: Principles and Problems.* Glencoe, Columbus, 1995, Chapters 27, 28, and 30.

LABORATORY MANUAL

Use Lab 1.1 with this section.

CONCEPT DEVELOPMENT

Critical Thinking: Ask students which American companies they think have the largest scientific research programs. [IBM, General Electric, AT&T, General Motors, Xerox, Ford, and Kodak are among the companies with large research establishments.]

CHECKING FOR UNDERSTANDING

Ask students what the ultimate test is for scientific theories. [Comparison with the way the real world actually works.]

RETEACHING

This would be a good point at which to discuss your own favorite example of the scientific process at work. If it can be a modern example, so much the better. Or, you might ask students a question such as "Where does the Earth's atmosphere end?" [Answering this question resembles tackling a scientific problem. First, what do we mean by *atmosphere?* Do we have the data necessary to answer the question? For what purpose are we asking the question? For example, do we mean *atmosphere* in the sense of where it is possible to grow plants or for people to breathe? Our answer will depend on how we define *atmosphere.*]

Reteaching Master, Teacher Resource Package. Use the Reteaching Master for Chapter 1, The Role of Chance in Experimentation, with this section.

EXTENSION

Have interested students look into how the scientific enterprise is organized: What are the major professional societies in physics and what are their main functions? [The major professional society in physics is the American Institute of Physics (AIP), which provides services for ten member societies. The main function of these societies is communication, via meetings and publications.]

Laboratory Manual. Give students additional experience with the nature of physics by doing Lab 1.1, Bubble Up, from the Laboratory Manual.

F. Y. I.

A strategy is an organized approach to a problem that breaks down the task of obtaining and organizing information into stages. Strategies can be the "bridge" in solving problems. Several strategies are listed below.

- List all possible solutions.
- Look for a pattern.
- Construct a table, graph, or figure.
- Make a model.
- Guess and check.
- Work backwards.
- Make a drawing.
- Solve a simpler or similar related problem.

Science and technology constantly interact. Often new equipment, such as the refrigerators Kamerlingh Onnes built, produce further scientific results. Other times science results in new products. For example, engineers have built giant magnets and small, efficient motors and generators using superconductors. The applications of science affect the lives of everyone more and more each year. For this reason, all of us need an understanding of physics, as well as the other sciences, to make informed decisions about problems involving our rapidly changing society.

Perhaps the most surprising aspect of physics is that its results can be described by a small number of relationships, or laws. These laws often can be expressed using mathematics, which has been called the language of physics.

What and How, not Why: Scientific Methods

Starting in the fourth and fifth centuries B.C., Greek philosophers tried to determine what the world was made of. Chief among them was Aristotle, who lived around 340 B.C. Aristotle was a student of the philsopher Plato and tutored Alexander the Great, conqueror of much of the known world. Aristotle founded a school of philosophy and wrote many books, some on science. Aristotle and his followers made some observations of everyday occurrences, and then tried to draw all possible conclusions solely by logical argument. Unfortunately, they were not very interested in knowing exactly *what* happens or *how* it happens, or even *if* it happens, given different conditions. Their interests were mainly theorizing why the specific events that they observed occurred.

Aristotle believed that all matter within reach was made up of four elements: Earth, Water, Air, and Fire. Each element had a "natural place." The highest place belonged to Fire, then Air, then Water, and, at the bottom, Earth. Motion occurred because an element wanted to reach its own natural place. Thus Water bubbled up through springs on Earth. Adding Fire to Water produced steam, a form of Air, that rose. A stone (Earth) fell through both Air and Water to reach the ground. When a stone was tossed up, it was given "violent motion." When this motion ceased, natural motion took over and the stone fell.

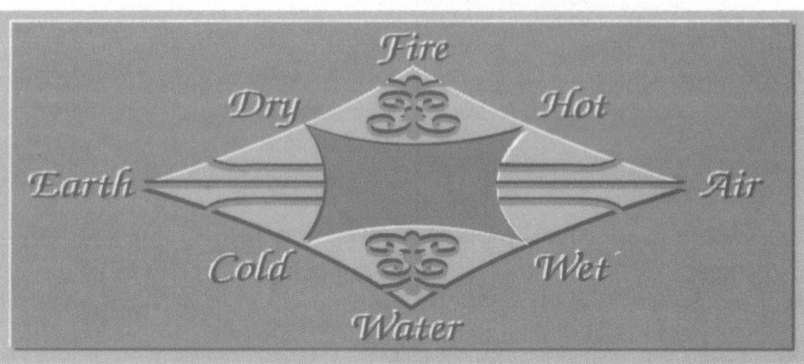

FIGURE 1–6. Aristotle believed that all "earthly" matter was composed of four elements. Each element had a particular quality associated with it.

The strict scientific method taught in other science courses does not work in physics. While a hypothesis is always on display, a great deal of physics is done on the basis of "what happens if. . . ." Many principles are theoretical and involve years of thought until the last bit of information (which may be from an entirely different field) is brought to light. Frequently when an experiment does not go as expected, a series of new concepts is developed. Things are not always as they appear! An excellent book on this subject is *Serendipity: Accidental Discoveries in Science* by Royston M. Roberts, John Wiley and Sons, 1989.

The writings of the early Greeks first came to Europe through Arabic translations in the twelfth century. Until the sixteenth century, Europeans accepted the Greek teachings as truth, with no need for verification. One of the first European scientists to claim publicly that knowledge must be based on observations and experiments rather than ancient books was Galileo Galilei (1564–1642). He questioned the belief that Earth is the center of the universe. He doubted Aristotle's views on physics, especially the idea that objects of large mass fall faster than objects of small mass. To prove Aristotle wrong, Galileo developed a systematic method of observation, experimentation, and analysis.

There is no single "scientific method." All scientists, however, study problems in an organized way. They combine systematic experimentation with careful measurement and analysis of results. From these analyses, conclusions are drawn. These conclusions are then subjected to additional tests to find out if they are valid. Since Galileo's time, scientists all over the world have used these techniques and methods to gain a better understanding of the universe. Knowledge, skill, luck, imagination, trial and error, educated guesses, and great patience—all play a part. For example, the two Swiss scientists who discovered the new superconductors said they "felt free to try something crazy." The leader of the University of Houston superconductor research group, Paul Chu, said, "We feel we have an advantage over some other groups because we are not confined to conventional thinking. We think wildly."

F.Y.I.

No number of experiments can prove me right; a single experiment can prove me wrong.
—Albert Einstein

HISTORY CONNECTION

Cultural and political activities affect the lives of scientists and their discoveries. For example, Henry Moseley, a brilliant English scientist studying X rays in Rutherford's laboratory, enlisted as a lieutenant in the Royal Engineers when World War I broke out. Rutherford tried, unsuccessfully, to get Moseley to resign to continue his research. Moseley was killed in the Battle of Gallipoli at the age of 27.

CONCEPT REVIEW

1.1 Did Heike Kamerlingh Onnes discover superconductivity trying to make a measurement agree with theory? Explain.

1.2 What is a theory in physics?

1.3 Critical Thinking: Which is a better model for scientific work, a student working in his or her basement on a project to enter in a competition, or a group of people with different talents cooperating to solve a problem?

FIGURE 1–7. The University of Houston research team working on superconductors. A group of scientists with different areas of specialization often work together to produce spectacular results.

Assessment

Portfolio

After students do the Physics Lab on page 10, have them find photographs of buildings or other structures that illustrate applications of the towers they built. Have them include a short paragraph with a history and description of the buildings chosen. Suggestions: Transamerica Pyramid in San Francisco, Sears Tower and John Hancock Tower in Chicago.

ACTIVITY

Discovery: Show a series of shapes or symbols on an overhead projector and ask students to determine a rule that enables them to predict the next shape or symbol in the series. Explain that even if their rule always worked (over a finite number of trials), it is still not necessarily the "right" one; there is always the possibility that an exception is looming in the future and a single wrong prediction can disprove their rule. (This activity is most effective if your series doesn't have a single "right" answer.)

Guided Practice: Go over the Concept Review Questions as a cooperative class activity.

INDEPENDENT PRACTICE/ EXTENSION

Refer to the Assignment Guide below for additional questions and problems for independent practice.

1:1 ASSIGNMENT GUIDE

	PRACTICE	EXTENSION
CHAPTER REVIEW p. 11		
· Reviewing Concepts	1–5	
· Applying Concepts		1–11

RETEACHING MASTER

Use the Reteaching master for Chapter 1 with this section.

3 Close

CONVERGENT QUESTION

Ask students how modern science differs from the mere cataloging of facts that people did two thousand years ago. [Today science has a theoretical structure that attempts to tie together various facts and observations into a coherent whole. Also, science has a predictive power, which a collection of facts does not have.]

CONCEPT REVIEW ANSWERS

1.1 No. He discovered it because he had invented a new technology and was investigating properties of ordinary materials with it.

1.2 A theory is a framework of explanations that explains experimental data and predicts new results.

1.3 Critical Thinking: Either model is acceptable and has produced results. Often, however, a synergistic group of people with diverse talents will produce spectacular results more quickly and more efficiently.

PHYSICS LAB

Process Skills: observing, formulating models, defining operationally, measuring, questioning.

MISCONCEPTIONS

Students often believe that physics is done by individuals working in isolation, not teams.

Lab Worksheet, Teacher Resource Package. If desired, use the lab worksheet master provided for this chapter for students to record their data.

OBSERVATIONS

1. Many of the groups will roll thin strips of paper into tubes. This geometry has good structural integrity.
2. Most groups will have different bases. A wider base gives better stability but uses more material.

ANALYSIS

1. Many groups will tend to run out of tape. Other groups will run out of time. Some groups will change plans in the middle of their construction. Some groups will build a tower that will fall over.
2. Many students will lack the necessary experience to effectively work in groups. This is a skill that needs coaching and practice.

APPLICATIONS

Most designs will exhibit several features of good architecture. The towers may be based on triangular bases. They may be symmetric. They will have folded members for strength without adding mass.

ASSESSMENT

Critical Thinking: To further assess students' understanding of building construction, ask the following question.

1. Is there a limit to how tall a building can be built? What are some of the limiting factors? [Safety as well as structural integrity must be considered. A taller tower is more subject to swaying in the wind and may pose severe safety problems in case of fire, earthquakes, and so forth. The ground under the tower must be solid enough to support the weight of the building.]

PHYSICS LAB: The Paper Tower

Purpose

To design and construct the tallest free standing tower from a single sheet of paper and 30 cm of tape.

Materials

- 1 sheet white paper
- 1 sheet colored paper
- 30-cm plastic tape
- scissors

Procedure

1. Each student will receive 1 sheet of white paper. Use the white sheet to try out various design possibilities. Think wildly.
2. Each lab group will receive one sheet of colored paper for their competition tower.
3. Before beginning with the colored paper, examine the designs of each group member.
4. Decide which aspects of each design should be incorporated into your final design. The most important aspects of a winning team are communication and cooperation.
5. Plan ahead. Set a timetable for experimentation and for actual construction. Plan on finishing at least five minutes before the end of the period.
6. Watch your time. Do not fall too far behind schedule.
7. Your tower must be free standing for at least five seconds.
8. Measure your tower before it tips over.

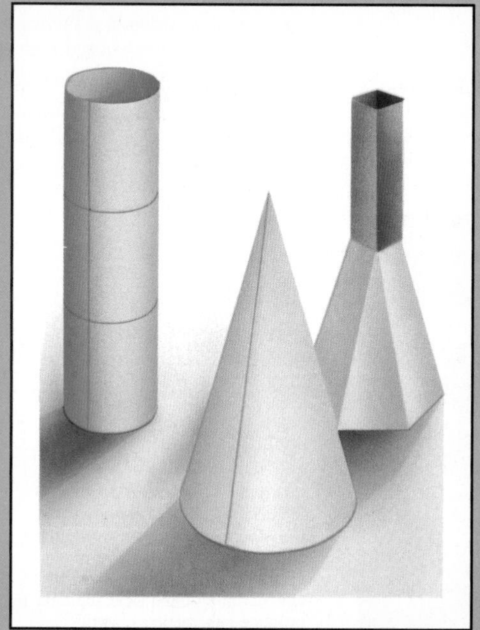

Observations and Data

1. Look at the designs from the other groups. Describe how they are similar.
2. Look at the designs from the other groups. Describe how they are different.

Analysis

1. What were the limiting factors in your tower's construction?
2. Did your group work well as a team? What could you do differently to be more effective?

Applications

1. What architectural elements have been incorporated into your design?

CLOSING CHAPTER 1

Evaluation Masters. Use to test chapter objectives.

Answers To REVIEWING CONCEPTS

1. Physics is the study of the basic physical laws that can be applied to all the sciences.
2. Mathematics is the international, clear language of science.
3. The experimental physics came first.
4. Onnes investigated superconductivity by making better equipment and lowering the temperature of gases. The others looked at the results of experiments and tried to explain how materials could become superconductors.
5. Aristotle's four elements were Earth, Water, Air, and Fire. They each had a natural place. It took "violent motion" to move them from their place, and their "natural motion" was to their proper place.

CHAPTER 1 REVIEW

SUMMARY

- Physics is the study of matter and energy and their relationships.
- Physics is basic to all other sciences.
- A knowledge of physics makes us, as citizens, better able to make decisions about questions related to science and technology.
- Scientists study problems in an organized way, using many techniques.
- Scientists are interested in knowing what happens and how it happens, but not necessarily why.
- Much scientific work is done in groups, where people collaborate with one another.

REVIEWING CONCEPTS

1. Define physics in your own words.
2. Why is mathematics important to science?
3. Which came first in superconductivity, the experimental physics or the theoretical physics?
4. Kamerlingh Onnes is considered an experimental physicist, while Bardeen, Cooper and Schrieffer are theoretical physicists. Explain the difference.
5. Assume Aristotle's four element theory is correct. How does the theory explain the motion of each of the elements?

APPLYING CONCEPTS

1. Give some examples of applications of the result of work by physicists.
2. Give examples of applications of the result of work done by physicists on superconductivity.
3. Use a dictionary to find out what aspects of nature are investigated by each of the following scientists: astronomer, geophysicist, biophysicist, astrophysicist.
4. Some of the branches of physics you will study in this course will investigate motion, the properties of materials, sound, light, electricity and magnetism, properties of atoms, and nuclear physics. Give at least one example of an application of each branch.
5. What reason might the Greeks have had not to question the evidence that heavier objects fall faster than lighter objects? **Hint:** Did you ever question which fell faster?
6. Is the scientific method a clearly-defined set of steps and procedures? Support your answer.
7. Why will the work of a physicist never be finished?
8. Why does science tend to be self-correcting?
9. Aristotle believed wood was a combination of fire, water, and earth. Use his four-element theory to explain why a wooden boat floats on water.

USING LAB SKILLS

1. In the Pocket Lab on page 6, what would happen if you dropped a steel ball and a plastic foam ball that were exactly the same size from the same height at the same time?
2. In the Physics Lab on page 10, what if your group had been given two sheets of paper? Could your tower be twice as tall? Explain.

THINKING PHYSIC-LY

It has been said that a fool can ask more questions than a wise man can answer. In science it is frequently the case that a wise man is needed to ask the right question rather than to answer it. Explain.

Answers To
APPLYING CONCEPTS

1. Student answers will vary, but may include the following: atomic bomb, electricity, CDs, computers, and the space program.
2. Student answers will vary, but may include the following: Superconducting wires could carry electricity without energy loss; make nuclear fusion possible; allow higher-speed trains; detect oil; pinpoint diseased body tissue; allow faster, more powerful computers.
3. Astronomer: person who studies the material universe beyond Earth's atmosphere; geophysicist: person who studies the physics of Earth; biophysicist: person who studies the biological structures of physics; astrophysicist: person who studies the branch of astronomy that deals with the physical properties of celestial objects.
4. Student answers will vary, but may include the following: motion—improved design of equipment such as tennis rackets and skis; properties of materials—heat pumps; light—mixing colored spotlights to make a different color; electricity—electric motors, generators; magnetism—television; nuclear physics—CAT scans and other diagnostic instruments; sound—ultrasonics.
5. Many light objects are affected by air resistance. Without controlled experiments, their everyday observations told them that heavier objects did fall faster.
6. There is no definite order of specific steps—in fact, there are almost as many approaches as there are experiments. However, whatever approach is used, it always includes close observation, controlled experimentation, summarizing, checking, rechecking, re-rechecking. . . .
7. The more questions physicists answer, the more they will have.
8. No theory is considered absolute and free from criticism. Scientists are always trying to improve any theory. New knowledge may cause theories to be modified.
9. The Earth part of the wood wants to move to its natural place below water (the stream) and make the boat sink. The Fire part wants to rise to its natural place and cause the boat to float above Air. The combination in the wood allows the boat to float.

Answers To
USING LAB SKILLS

1. Over the short distance the balls were dropped, they should both hit the ground at the same time.
2. It is unlikely that the new tower could be twice as tall. A taller tower needs a stronger base so that it doesn't fall or get crushed. This would require more material.

Answer To
THINKING PHYSIC-LY

Both activities are important. Often, however, the training, experience, and imagination necessary to know just what question to ask have provided the insight necessary to find the answer.

EVALUATION MASTER

Use the Chapter Evaluation master for Chapter 1 with this section.

CHAPTER

2 A Mathematical Toolkit

PLANNING GUIDE (6 class sessions)

CONTENTS	TEXT FEATURES	TEACHER RESOURCE PACKAGE	OTHER COMPONENTS
2.1 The Measure of Science, pp. 14–19 (2 Class Sessions) • The Metric System • Scientific Notation • Prefixes Used with SI Units • Arithmetic Operations in Scientific Notation	**Physics and Society:** To SI or Not to SI, p. 20 **Pocket Lab:** Paper Block, p. 17 **Using Your Calculator:** Scientific Notation, p. 18 **Concept Review,** p. 19	**Study Guide:** The Measure of Science **Transparency Worksheet:** Time Scale/Mass Scale	**Laboratory Manual:** Lab 2.1 Measuring Length Lab 2.2 Measuring Temperature Lab 2.3 Measuring Time **Transparency 2:** Time Scale/Mass Scale **Physics Skill Masters 1,2**
2.2 Not All Is Certain, pp. 21–26 (2 Class Sessions) • Uncertainties of Measurements • Accuracy and Precision • Significant Digits • Operations Using Significant Digits	**Pocket Lab:** High and Low, p. 25 **Concept Review,** p. 26	**Study Guide:** Not All Is Certain **Critical Thinking Master:** Direct and Indirect Measurements	**Physics Skill Masters 3,4,9,10,11**
2.3 Displaying Data, pp. 26–31 (1 Class Session) • Graphing Data • Linear, Quadratic, and Inverse Relationships	**Physics Lab:** Getting Straight, p. 28 **Pocket Lab:** Juiced Up, p. 30 **Problem Solving Strategy:** Plotting Graphs, p. 27 **Concept Review,** p. 31	**Study Guide:** Displaying Data **Physics Lab Data Sheet:** Getting Straight **Reteaching Master:** Determining Relationships from Graphs **Enrichment Master:** Straightening Curves	**Physics Skill Masters 6,7**
2.4 Manipulating Equations, pp. 31–34 (1 Class Session) • Solving Equations Using Algebra • Units in Equations	**Concept Review,** p. 34	**Study Guide:** Manipulating Equations	**Physics Skill Masters 5,8**
Chapter Review, pp. 35–39	Summary Key Terms Reviewing Concepts Applying Concepts Problems Thinking Physic-ly	**Vocabulary Review** **Chapter Test**	**Test Bank**

SUPPLEMENTARY MATERIALS

SOFTWARE	AUDIOVISUAL	BOOKS/MAGAZINES
Graphical Analysis III, Vernier (Apple II, IBM PC). *The Metric System,* Queue, Inc. (Apple II, IBM PC, Macintosh). *Physical Science 2,* Queue, Inc. (Apple II).	Videos: *Basic Math for the Study of Science,* Cabisco Mathematics (still frame). *Powers of Ten,* Pyramid. *Scientific Notation,* Cabisco Mathematics (still frame). Filmstrip: *The Nature of Science: Nothing Is Absolute,* AVNA Media.	Hooper, William. "Business Expects Schools to Teach Metrics." *The Physics Teacher,* February 1990, p. 120. Khandelwal, Govind S., and Pritchard, W. Maurice. "Teaching Units." *The Physics Teacher,* May 1990, p. 30. Mathieson, D. L. "Why Round the Answer?" *The Physics Teacher,* October 1990, p. 471.

PROBLEM CORRELATION

CONCEPTS	CHAPTER REVIEW			PROBLEMS APPENDIX
	Reviewing Concepts	Applying Concepts	Problems	
2.1 The Measure of Science				
The Metric System	1,2,3	1		
Scientific Notation			1	1
Prefixes Used with SI Units	4	2,3,4	2,**3**	2
Arithmetic Operations in Scientific Notation		7	4	3
2.2 Not All Is Certain				
Uncertainties of Measurement				
Accuracy and Precision	5,6	5,6		
Significant Digits	7,8		5,6,7	4,5
Operations Using Significant Digits			8,9,10,11,12,13,14,15	6,7,8
2.3 Displaying Data				
Graphing Data	11,12	11		
Linear, Quadratic, and Inverse Relationships	9,10,13,14,15	8,9,12	**16,**17,**18,19**	**9,10**
2.4 Manipulating Equations				
Solving Equations Using Algebra			21	11,**12**
Units in Equations	16	10	20,22,23,24,**25, 26,**27,28,**29**	**13,**14,15

ACTIVITY AND DEMONSTRATION MATERIALS

PHYSICS LAB	POCKET LAB	DEMONSTRATIONS
Page 28 3 pieces of electrical wire 2 rectangular pieces of floor tile 1 triangular floor tile balance 30-cm ruler graph paper	Pages 17, 25, 30 paper 30 cm ruler 2 meter sticks 12-oz nonmetallic juice bottle water balance	

EXTENSION PROJECTS

LIBRARY RESEARCH

1. Cartesian Coordinate System
Investigate the Cartesian Coordinate System. When and where did it originate? What was its purpose?

HANDS–ON

2. Scientific Notation
Practice estimating amounts in scientific notation. For example, the weight of a football player in newtons might be 1.0×10^3 N.

STUDENT READINGS

Barnes, George. "Food, Eating, and Mathematical Scaling." *The Physics Teacher,* December 1990.

Cadogan, Peter. *From Quark to Quasar: Notes on the Scale of the Universe.* New York: Cambridge University Press, 1985.

Cole, K. C. "Beyond Measurement." *Discover,* October 1983.

Friberg, Joran. "Numbers and Measures in the Earliest Written Records." *Scientific American,* February 1984.

Hooper, William. "Metrication Is Alive in the United States." *The Physics Teacher,* October 1990.

Chapter 2

A Mathematical Toolkit

CHAPTER OVERVIEW

Theme Development: The major theme is basic to all of science: modeling of scientific variables. Mathematical modeling often begins with measurement, and the treatment of uncertainty in measurement is introduced here. The metric system and SI units are effective for treating data quantitatively. Presentation of data by graphs is included.

MISCONCEPTIONS

Students are accustomed to treating numbers as exact and do not readily accept uncertainty in measurements. They also have trouble interpreting graphs.

KEY TERMS

accuracy
dependent variable
derived unit
fundamental unit
independent variable
inverse relationship
kilogram
linear relationship
meter
metric system
parallax
precision
prefix
quadratic equation
scientific notation
second
SI
significant digit
slope
y-intercept

Laboratory Options

STUDENT EDITION

Physics Lab

Getting Straight	28

Pocket Labs

Paper Block	17
High and Low	25
Juiced Up	30

TEACHER EDITION

Activities

Cooperative Learning	16, 17, 29, 29, 33
Discovery	22

LABORATORY MANUAL

Measuring Length	Lab 2.1
Measuring Temperature	Lab 2.2
Measuring Time	Lab 2.3

CHAPTER 2

A Mathematical Toolkit

A Graphic Display

Identify the graph that shows a linear relationship.

Physics often uses mathematics as its language. This chapter presents a collection of mathematical techniques you will find useful throughout the course. You might think of the chapter as a collection of tools that can be used when needed later.

Central to the tools is the use of graphs and equations to represent the results of many observations and experiments. Probably the most famous physics equation is Einstein's $E = mc^2$. This simple equation describes one of the most powerful concepts of physics—the equivalence of mass and energy for a particle at rest.

How do you find an equation to describe experimental results? Frequently a graph of the data gives you a clue. In this chapter you will see how data describing the distance a car travels while braking to a stop can be expressed by an equation. Thus, you will learn that one of the most powerful ways of analyzing data is to display them as a graph.

Chapter Outline

Concept Check

The following terms or concepts are important for a good understanding of this chapter. If you are not familiar with them, you should review them before studying this chapter.
- algebra and graphing techniques

Introducing The Chapter

A Graphic Display

Using The Photo: Students should be encouraged to use calculators and should get in-class practice performing the operations of this chapter. Not all calculators have the same keyboards, so allow students time to familiarize themselves with their own machines. Remind your students how quickly calculator technology has progressed in roughly twenty years—from simple four-function calculators to programmable, display calculators with graph functions. Hand-held calculators can do what it took a room-sized computer to do not so long ago!

The answer to the question about the graphing calculator can be found on page 29.

Concept Check

Students will investigate the nature of the physical world through experiments and observations. It is essential that they understand the strengths and limitations of the measurements they use. Because science also depends upon the generalization of information and knowledge, students must also be familiar with interpreting and reporting data in the form of tables and graphs.

This chapter does not have to be taught all at once. You may decide to cover only some sections now and the others when needed. Obviously you can come back to this material as many times as is necessary.

Assessment Options

Portfolio Assessment
Enrichment, TWE, p. 18
Developing a Viewpoint, p. 20
Connect to Chemistry, TWE, p. 29
Applying Concepts 4, p. 36

Performance Assessment
Pocket Labs, pp. 17, 25
Pocket Lab Assessment, p. 30
Physics Lab, p. 28
Using Lab Skills, p. 39

Content Assessment
Self assessment: Practice Problems, pp. 17, 18, 25, 33, 34
Convergent question about reporting uncertainty, TWE, p. 26
Concept Reviews, pp. 19, 26, 31, 34
Chapter Review, pp. 35–39
Supplemental Problems, pp. 688–689

Group Assessment
Activities for group assessment occur with Cooperative Learning and lab activities.

2.1 THE MEASURE OF SCIENCE

Preparation

OBJECTIVES

The objectives are listed on the student page. Remind students to preview these objectives as a study guide to this major section.

OVERVIEW

This teaching block is an introduction to the metric system, which uses SI units, and to understanding and using scientific notation.

BRIDGING

This section extends your students' previous math experience and relies somewhat on a current knowledge of the metric system.

1 Focus

DISCREPANT EVENT

Display a selection of metric measuring devices: meter stick, metric ruler, mass set, lab clock, metric bathroom scale, voltmeter, ammeter, metric balance. Have students measure with one or two of them for firsthand involvement. Obtain and use a metric wall chart from a scientific supply house.

Assessment

Portfolio

A selection of graphs produced by a student throughout the year should be placed in the portfolio to show an increase in ability to display data graphically.

Objectives

- state the fundamental SI units for time, length, and mass.
- demonstrate an ability to use scientific notation.
- identify and use common metric prefixes.
- be able to perform arithmetic operations using scientific notation.

2.1 THE MEASURE OF SCIENCE

The science of physics is based on a few principles and involves the development of concepts. The application of these principles and concepts usually involves the measurement of one or more quantities. In almost every country except the United States, the metric system is used in everyday life. The world-wide scientific community, including the United States, uses an adaptation of the metric system, the SI, to make measurements.

The Metric System

The metric system is based on powers of ten.

The **metric system** of measurement was created by French scientists in 1795. It is convenient to use because units of different sizes are related by powers of ten. An international committee determines the standards of the metric system. This committee has set up the International System of Units (**SI**). The SI is used throughout the world. SI units are emphasized throughout this text. The National Institute of Standards and Technology (NIST) keeps the official standards for the units of length, mass, and time for the United States. Because other quantities can be described using these three units, they are called **fundamental units**.

The SI unit of time, the second, is based on the oscillation time of an atom.

The standard unit of time is the **second** (s). The second was first defined as 1/86 400 of the mean solar day. A mean solar day is the average length of the day over a period of one year. In 1967, the second was redefined in terms of the frequency of one type of radiation emitted by a cesium-133 atom.

The standard SI unit of length is the **meter** (m). The meter was first defined as one ten-millionth (10^{-7}) of the distance from the north pole to the equator, measured along a line passing through Lyons, France.

FIGURE 2–1. Several countries have issued stamps to help the general public become familiar with SI units of measurement.

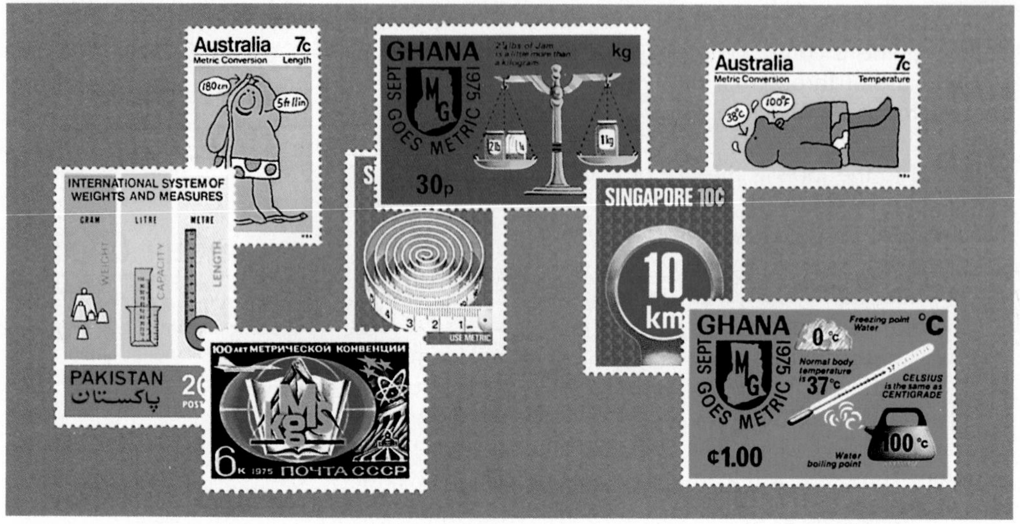

TEACHER F.Y.I.

You can get highly accurate time signals (from the U.S. Naval Observatory Master Clock) by dialing the NIST numbers, 1-303-409-7111 or 1-900-410-8463. The signals come from Boulder, Colorado. If you have a radio that will receive 5, 10, or 15 MHz, you can pick up coordinated universal time signals coming from the NIST station WWV in Colorado.

FIGURE 2–2. In ancient times, water clocks, called clepsydras, were used for keeping time. The water clock in the photograph is in the Children's Museum, Indianapolis, Indiana.

F.Y.I.

Precise measurements of length are important. Parts used in high performance car engines must be measured to 7 μm (0.000007 m).

In the 20th century, physicists found that light could be used to make very precise measurements of distances. In 1960, the meter was redefined as a multiple of a wavelength of light emitted by krypton-86. By 1982, an even more precise length measurement defined the meter as the distance light travels in 1/299 792 458 second in a vacuum.

The SI unit of length is the meter, defined as the distance light travels in a certain amount of time.

The third standard unit measures the mass of an object. The **kilogram** (kg) is the only unit not defined in terms of the properties of atoms. It is the mass of a platinum-iridium metal cylinder kept near Paris. A copy is kept at the NIST.

Two other fundamental units will be introduced as needed in the text. A wide variety of other units, called **derived units**, are combinations of the fundamental units. A common derived unit is the meter per second, or m/s, used to measure speed.

The SI unit of mass is the kilogram.

Scientific Notation

Scientists often work with very large and very small quantities. For example, the mass of Earth is about

6 000 000 000 000 000 000 000 000 kilograms

and the mass of an electron is

0.000 000 000 000 000 000 000 000 000 000 911 kilograms.

Written in this form, the quantities take up much space and are difficult to use in calculations. To work with such numbers more easily, we write them in a shortened form by expressing decimal places as powers of ten. This method of expressing numbers is called exponential notation. **Scientific notation** is based on exponential notation. In scientific notation, the numerical part of a measurement is expressed as a number between 1 and 10 multiplied by a whole-number power of 10.

$$M \times 10^n$$

In this expression, $1 \leq M < 10$ and n is an integer. For example, 2000 meters can be written 2×10^3 m. The mass of a softball is about 180 g or 1.8×10^{-1} kg.

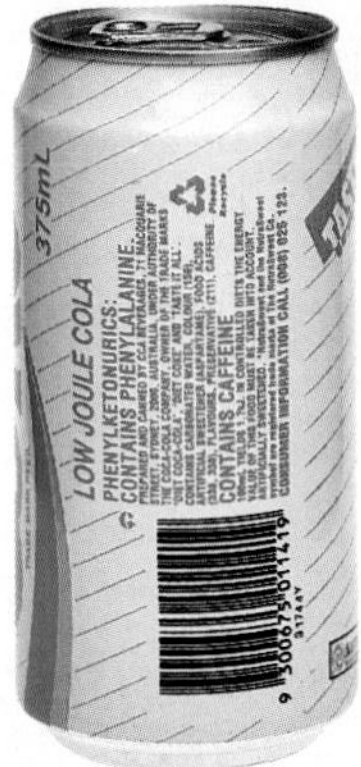

FIGURE 2–3. Most countries now use the SI unit *joule* rather than calorie for energy.

2 Teach

CONCEPT DEVELOPMENT

Study Guide Master. To reinforce the concepts in this section, have the students complete the Study Guide Master for Section 2.1 from the Teacher Resource Package.

- Do not emphasize conversion from metric to English units or vice versa. The best way to learn metric is to practice it and get direct experience with the units.
- Some teachers may remember the National Bureau of Standards (NBS), which was the immediate predecessor of the National Institute of Standards and Technology (NIST).
- The exact equivalents of the base units are included for reference but should not be memorized by the students. The important point is that the units are derived in terms of physical experiments.
- Emphasize the importance of writing every measurement with a unit. There are few quantities in physics that have no units. (Index of refraction and coefficient of friction are two that we will use in this course.)

STUDY GUIDE MASTER

Use the Study Guide master for section 2.1.

CONCEPT DEVELOPMENT

ACTIVITY

Cooperative Learning: Give students a list of objects in the room. Have students work in pairs to predict the size (length, width, height, or mass) of each object, then to measure each object in SI units.

Laboratory Manual. Give students additional experience with metric measurement and SI units by assigning one or all of the following labs, as time allows: 2.1, Measuring Length; 2.2, Measuring Temperature; 2.3, Measuring Time.

Answers To
PRACTICE PROBLEMS

Have students refer to Appendix A of the Solutions Appendix for complete solutions to Practice Problems.

1. **a.** 5.8×10^3 m
   b. 4.5×10^5 m
   c. 3.02×10^8 m
   d. 8.6×10^{10} m
2. **a.** 5.08×10^{-4} kg
   b. 4.5×10^{-7} kg
   c. 3.600×10^{-3} kg
   d. 4×10^{-3} kg
3. **a.** 3×10^8 s
   b. 1.86×10^5 s
   c. 9.3×10^7 s

Physics Skill Master, Teacher Resource Package. Assign Physics Skill Masters 1, and 2, Mathematics Assessment, and Recording Measurements, to reinforce students' understanding.

F. Y. I.

When the metric system was proposed in 1792, a 10-hour clock was included in the plan. This part of the system was never accepted and was eventually abandoned.

To write measurements using scientific notation, move the decimal point until only one non-zero digit remains on the left. Then count the number of places the decimal point was moved and use that number as the exponent of ten. Thus, the approximate mass of Earth can also be expressed as 6×10^{24} kg. Note that the exponent becomes larger as the decimal point is moved to the left.

To write the mass of the electron in scientific notation, the decimal point is moved 31 places to the right. Thus, the mass of the electron can also be written as 9.11×10^{-31} kg. Note that the exponent becomes smaller as the decimal point is moved to the right.

Practice Problems

Express the following measurements in scientific notation.

1. **a.** 5800 m **b.** 450 000 m **c.** 302 000 000 m **d.** 86 000 000 000 m
2. **a.** 0.000 508 kg **b.** 0.000 000 45 kg **c.** 0.003600 kg **d.** 0.004 kg
3. ▶ **a.** 300 000 000 s **b.** 186 000 s **c.** 93 000 000 s

A quantity written in scientific notation consists of a number between 1 and 10 followed by 10 raised to a power.

Prefixes Used With SI Units

Metric prefixes differ from one another by a power of ten.

Like our number system, the metric system is a decimal system. **Prefixes** are used to change SI units by powers of ten. Thus, one tenth of a meter is a decimeter, one hundredth of a meter is a centimeter, and one thousandth of a meter is a millimeter. Each of these divisions can be found on a meter stick. The prefixes that change SI units by a power of one thousand are most common. Thus, one thousand meters is a kilometer. Figure 2–4 shows the vast range of lengths of objects in our universe. Commonly used length units are shown.

FIGURE 2–4. Objects in the universe range from the very small to the unimaginably large.

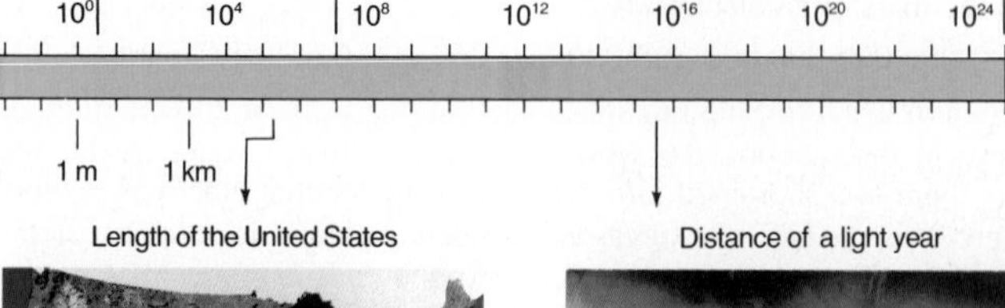

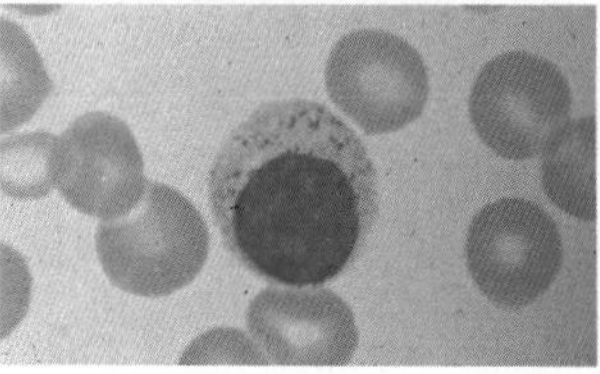
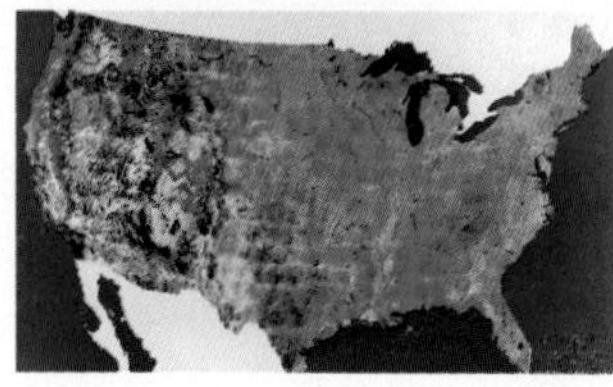
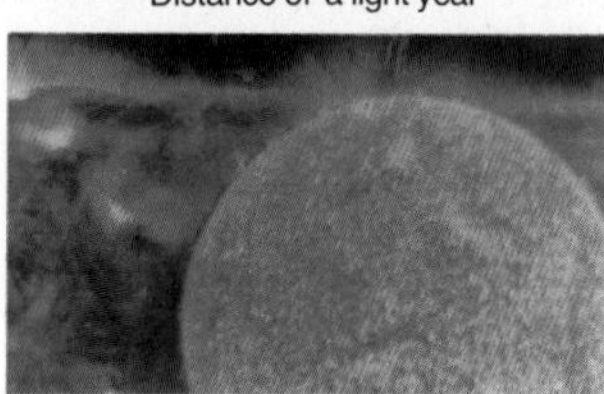

LABORATORY MANUAL

Use Labs 2.1, 2.2, and 2.3 with this section.

SKILL MASTER

Use Physics Skill Masters 1 and 2 with this section.

The metric units for all quantities use the same prefixes. One thousandth of a gram is a milligram, and one thousand grams is a kilogram. To use SI units effectively, it is important to know the meanings of the prefixes in Table 2–1.

Table 2–1

Prefixes Used with SI Units			
Prefix	**Symbol**	**Fractions**	**Example**
pico	p	1/1 000 000 000 000 or 10^{-12}	picometer (pm)
nano	n	1/1 000 000 000 or 10^{-9}	nanometer (nm)
micro	μ	1/1 000 000 or 10^{-6}	microgram (μg)
milli	m	1/1 000 or 10^{-3}	milligram (mg)
centi	c	1/100 or 10^{-2}	centimeter (cm)
deci	d	1/10 or 10^{-1}	decimeter (dm)
		Multiples	
tera	T	1 000 000 000 000 or 10^{12}	terameter (Tm)
giga	G	1 000 000 000 or 10^{9}	gigameter (Gm)
mega	M	1 000 000 or 10^{6}	megagram (Mg)
kilo	k	1000 or 10^{3}	kilometer (km)
hecto	h	100 or 10^{2}	hectometer (hm)
deka	da	10 or 10^{1}	dekagram (dag)

Example Problem

Conversion Between Units

What is the equivalent of 500 millimeters in meters?

Solution: From Table 2–1, we see the conversion factor is

1 millimeter = 1×10^{-3} meter.

Therefore,

$$(500 \text{ mm})\frac{(1 \times 10^{-3} \text{ m})}{1 \text{ mm}} = 500 \times 10^{-3} \text{ m} = 5 \times 10^{-1} \text{ m}$$

Practice Problems

4. Convert each of the following length measurements to its equivalent in meters.
a. 1.1 cm **b.** 76.2 pm **c.** 2.1 km **d.** 0.123 Mm

▶ **5.** Convert each of these mass measurements to its equivalent in kilograms.
a. 147 g **b.** 11 μg **c.** 7.23 Mg **d.** 478 mg

Arithmetic Operations in Scientific Notation

Suppose you need to add or subtract measurements expressed in scientific notation. If the numbers have the same exponent, simply add or subtract the values of *M* and keep the same *n*.

Quantities to be added or subtracted must have the same exponents.

POCKET LAB

PAPER BLOCK

Look closely at the markings on a cm scale. Would you guess that a single sheet of paper has a volume of more or less than 1.0 cm^3? Estimate the volume of a single sheet of paper to one significant digit. Record your estimate in correct scientific notation. Use the cm scale to measure the volume of a sheet of paper. (**Hint:** Measure the thickness of 10 or 20 sheets.) Record your measured value. Compare the measured value to your estimate.

CONCEPT DEVELOPMENT

- Note that the kilogram is an exception among the seven base units because it already has a prefix.
- Point out to students that the seven base units of SI (or units derived from them) can measure any physical quantity known about in science.
- Point out that raising the exponent of 10 by 1 is equivalent to multiplying by 10.
- In using powers of 10, help students remember that when the decimal is moved to the left, the exponent must increase. ("Both *Left* and *Larger* begin with *L*.") When the decimal is moved to the right, the power of ten is reduced. ("Both *Right* and *Reduced* begin with *R*.")
- Have students bring in examples of metric units printed on items they can find around the house.

Cooperative Learning: Challenge student groups to come up with mnemonic devices for remembering the metric prefixes in Table 2–1. Let students choose which ones they think are most effective.

- Design a timed quiz in which students convert from the unit with a prefix to powers of 10 with the base unit. Example: 2.0 mm (2.0×10^{-3} m); 3.0 ns (3.0×10^{-9} s); and so on. Students should be able to complete such a quiz more rapidly as the year progresses.

Answers To
PRACTICE PROBLEMS

Have students refer to Appendix A of the Solutions Appendix for complete solutions to Practice Problems.

4. a. 1.1×10^{-2} m
b. 7.62×10^{-11} m
c. 2.1×10^{3} m
d. 1.23×10^{5} m

5. a. 1.47×10^{-1} kg
b. 1.1×10^{-8} kg
c. 7.23×10^{3} kg
d. 4.78×10^{-4} kg

POCKET LAB

PAPER BLOCK

Purpose: to predict and measure a volume.
Materials: paper; 30 cm ruler; calculator.
Outcome: Most students will predict that the paper has a volume less than 1.0 cm^3. A single sheet of paper has dimensions of about 23 cm × 28 cm × 0.01 cm, or 6 cm^3.

CONCEPT DEVELOPMENT

- In working with powers of 10, use an analogy from algebra. Adding or subtracting numbers expressed in scientific notation obeys a rule similar to the rule in algebra that says you can't combine unlike terms. For example, $3x^4 + 2x^4 = 5x^4$, but $3x^4 + 4x^5$ can't be simplified.

- Negative exponents are troublesome to many students. In decimal form, negative powers of 10 yield numbers smaller than 1. Remind students that $10^0 = 1$. (They may have learned that anything to the 0 power—except 0—equals 1.) Put another way, 10^0 marks the boundary between numbers greater than 1 and numbers smaller than 1.

- Try to give your students some feeling for large (and small) powers of 10. For example, try this comparison: 10^6 seconds is about 12 days, 10^9 seconds is about 32 years, and 10^{12} seconds is about 32 000 years. The universe is believed to be *less than* 10^{18} seconds old.

Enrichment: Enrico Fermi, (about whom more is discussed in Chapters 30 and 31), was famous for this "back of the envelope" or order-of-magnitude calculations. Problems calling for order-of-magnitude estimates are called "Fermi questions." For example, how many basketballs would fit into your classroom? [approximately 5000] Make up a list of Fermi questions and present them to the class.

Answers To
PRACTICE PROBLEMS

Have students refer to Appendix A of the Solutions Appendix for complete solutions to Practice Problems.

6. a. 8×10^{-7} kg
b. 7×10^{-3} kg
c. 3.96×10^{-19} kg
d. 4.6×10^{-12} kg
7. a. 2×10^{-8} m²
b. -1.52×10^{-11} m²
c. 3.0×10^{-9} m²
d. 4.6×10^{-19} m²
8. a. 5.4×10^{-7} mg
b. 6.2×10^{-3} mg
c. 2.8×10^{-14} g
d. 7.9×10^3 m

Using Your CALCULATOR

Using a calculator simplifies performing arithmetic operations on numbers in scientific notation.

4.0×10^{-6} kg $- 3.0 \times 10^{-7}$ kg

Keys	Answer
4.0 EXP 6 +/- −	4.-06
3.0 EXP 7 +/- =	3.7-6

3.7×10^{-6} kg

$$\frac{8 \times 10^6 \text{ m}}{2 \times 10^{-2} \text{ s}}$$

Keys	Answer
8 EXP 6 ÷	8.06
2 EXP 2 +/- =	4.08

4×10^8 m/s

Example Problem

Adding and Subtracting with Like Exponents

a. $4 \times 10^8 \text{ m} + 3 \times 10^8 \text{ m} = 7 \times 10^8 \text{ m}$
b. $6.2 \times 10^{-3} \text{ m} - 2.8 \times 10^{-3} \text{ m} = 3.4 \times 10^{-3} \text{ m}$

If the powers of ten are not the same, they must be made the same before the numbers are added or subtracted. Move the decimal points until the exponents are the same.

Example Problem

Adding and Subtracting with Unlike Exponents

a. $4.0 \times 10^6 \text{ m} + 3 \times 10^5 \text{ m}$
$= 4.0 \times 10^6 \text{ m} + 0.3 \times 10^6 \text{ m} = 4.3 \times 10^6 \text{ m}$
b. $4.0 \times 10^{-6} \text{ kg} - 3 \times 10^{-7} \text{ kg}$
$= 4.0 \times 10^{-6} \text{ kg} - 0.3 \times 10^{-6} \text{ kg} = 3.7 \times 10^{-6} \text{ kg}$

Suppose you have to add a measurement made in meters to one made in kilometers. You first must convert the measurements to a common unit, then make the power of ten the same. Finally you add or subtract.

Example Problem

Adding and Subtracting with Unlike Units

a. $4.1 \text{ m} + 1.5468 \text{ km} = 4.1 \text{ m} + 1546.8 \text{ m}$
$= 1550.9 \text{ m} = 1.5509 \text{ km}$
b. $2.31 \times 10^{-2} \text{ g} + 6.1 \text{ mg} = 23.1 \text{ mg} + 6.1 \text{ mg} = 29.2 \text{ mg}$
c. $2.03 \times 10^2 \text{ m} + 1.057 \text{ km} = 2.03 \times 10^2 \text{ m} + 10.57 \times 10^2 \text{ m}$
$= 12.60 \times 10^2 \text{ m} = 1.260 \text{ km}$

Practice Problems

Solve the following problems. Express your answers in scientific notation.

6. a. 5×10^{-7} kg $+ 3 \times 10^{-7}$ kg
b. 4×10^{-3} kg $+ 3 \times 10^{-3}$ kg
c. 1.66×10^{-19} kg $+ 2.30 \times 10^{-19}$ kg
d. 7.2×10^{-12} kg $- 2.6 \times 10^{-12}$ kg
7. a. 6×10^{-8} m² $- 4 \times 10^{-8}$ m²
b. 3.8×10^{-12} m² $- 1.90 \times 10^{-11}$ m²
c. 5.8×10^{-9} m² $- 2.8 \times 10^{-9}$ m²
d. 2.26×10^{-18} m² $- 1.80 \times 10^{-18}$ m²
▶ **8. a.** 5.0×10^{-7} mg $+ 4 \times 10^{-8}$ mg
b. 6.0×10^{-3} mg $+ 2 \times 10^{-4}$ mg
c. 3.0×10^{-2} pg $- 2 \times 10^{-6}$ ng
d. 8.2 km $- 3 \times 10^2$ m

Quantities expressed in scientific notation do not need to have the same exponents before they are multiplied or divided. Multiply the values of M, then add the exponents. The units are multiplied.

Example Problem

Multiplication Using Scientific Notation

a. $(3 \times 10^6 \text{ m})(2 \times 10^3 \text{ m}) = 6 \times 10^{6+3} \text{ m}^2 = 6 \times 10^9 \text{ m}^2$
b. $(2 \times 10^{-5} \text{ m})(4 \times 10^9 \text{ m}) = 8 \times 10^{9-5} \text{ m}^2 = 8 \times 10^4 \text{ m}^2$
c. $(4 \times 10^3 \text{ kg})(5 \times 10^{11} \text{ m}) = 20 \times 10^{3+11} \text{ kg} \cdot \text{m}$
$= 2 \times 10^{15} \text{ kg} \cdot \text{m}$

Quantities expressed in scientific notation with different exponents also can be divided. Divide the values of M, then subtract the exponent of the divisor from the exponent of the dividend.

Example Problem

Division Using Scientific Notation

a. $\dfrac{8 \times 10^6 \text{ m}}{2 \times 10^3 \text{ s}} = 4 \times 10^{(6-3)} \text{ m/s} = 4 \times 10^3 \text{ m/s}$

b. $\dfrac{8 \times 10^6 \text{ kg}}{2 \times 10^{-2} \text{ m}^3} = 4 \times 10^{6-(-2)} \text{ kg/m}^3 = 4 \times 10^8 \text{ kg/m}^3$

Practice Problems

Find the value of each of the following quantities.

9. a. $(2 \times 10^4 \text{ m})(4 \times 10^8 \text{ m})$ c. $(6 \times 10^{-4} \text{ m})(5 \times 10^{-8} \text{ m})$
b. $(3 \times 10^4 \text{ m})(2 \times 10^6 \text{ m})$ d. $(2.5 \times 10^{-7} \text{ m})(2.5 \times 10^{16} \text{ m})$

10. a. $\dfrac{6 \times 10^8 \text{ kg}}{2 \times 10^4 \text{ m}^3}$ c. $\dfrac{6 \times 10^{-8} \text{ m}}{2 \times 10^4 \text{ s}}$
b. $\dfrac{6 \times 10^8 \text{ kg}}{2 \times 10^{-4} \text{ m}^3}$ d. $\dfrac{6 \times 10^{-8} \text{ m}}{2 \times 10^{-4} \text{ s}}$

▶ 11. a. $\dfrac{(3 \times 10^4 \text{ kg})(4 \times 10^4 \text{ m})}{6 \times 10^4 \text{ s}}$ b. $\dfrac{(2.5 \times 10^6 \text{ kg})(6 \times 10^4 \text{ m})}{5 \times 10^{-2} \text{ s}^2}$

CONCEPT REVIEW

1.1 Some calculators display large numbers as 1.574 E8. Express in normal scientific notation.
1.2 Your height might be given either in terms of a small unit, like a millimeter, or a larger unit, like a meter. In which case would your height be a larger number?
1.3 Describe in detail how you would measure the time in seconds needed to go from home to school.
1.4 Critical Thinking: What additional steps would you need to time your trip, using one clock at home and one at school?

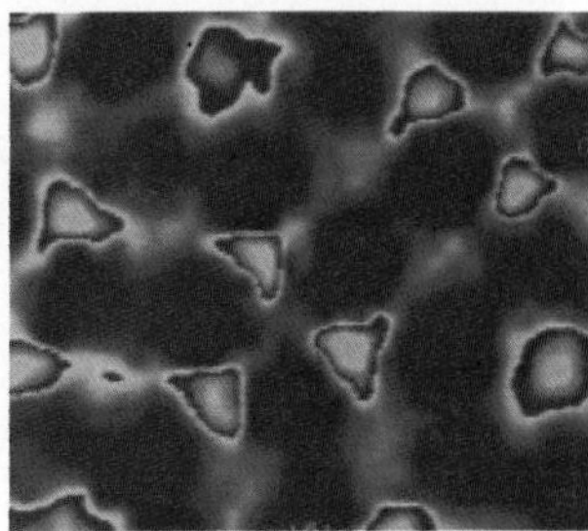

a

b

FIGURE 2–5. For extremely small measurements, such as the diameter of a red blood cell (a), and for very large measurements, such as the distance to the Andromeda galaxy (b), it is convenient to use scientific notation. Showing all the digits in numbers like these makes calculations difficult.

The product of two numbers written in scientific notation is the product of the values of M times 10 raised to the sum of their exponents.

The quotient of two numbers is the quotient of the values of M times 10 raised to the difference of their exponents.

CONCEPT DEVELOPMENT

CHECKING FOR UNDERSTANDING

In some cases, the base units mole and kilogram can refer to the same quantity. Why do you think both are used as base units? [The mole is such a powerful concept in chemistry—it enables chemists to measure many things—that it is given the status of a separate base unit.]

RETEACHING

Transparency Package. To reteach powers of ten and SI units, use Transparency 2, Time Scale/Mass Scale, and accompanying worksheet.

Guided Practice: After going over the Example Problems, have students complete the Practice Problems in class.

INDEPENDENT PRACTICE/ EXTENSION

Refer to the Assignment Guide below for additional questions and problems for independent practice.

Answers To PRACTICE PROBLEMS

Have students refer to Appendix A of the Solutions Appendix for complete solutions to Practice Problems.

9. a. $8 \times 10^{12} \text{ m}^2$
b. $6 \times 10^{10} \text{ m}^2$
c. $3 \times 10^{-11} \text{ m}^2$
d. $6.25 \times 10^9 \text{ m}^2$
10. a. $3 \times 10^4 \text{ kg/m}^3$
b. $3 \times 10^{12} \text{ kg/m}^3$
c. $3 \times 10^{-12} \text{ m/s}$
d. $3 \times 10^{-4} \text{ m/s}$
11. a. $2 \times 10^4 \text{ kg}\cdot\text{m/s}$
b. $3 \times 10^{12} \text{ kg}\cdot\text{m/s}^2$

2:1 ASSIGNMENT GUIDE

	PRACTICE	EXTENSION
CHAPTER REVIEW pp. 35–39		
· Reviewing Concepts	1–4	
· Applying Concepts		1–4
· Problems*	1, 2, 4	
APPENDIX B PROBLEMS*		
· Chapter 2, p. 688	1–3	

* Complete solutions to all Chapter Review and Appendix problems appear in the Problems and Solutions Manual.

indicated by a portable clock when you leave home. Note the time indicated by the same clock when you arrive at school. Subtract the first time from the second time. Convert hours or minutes to seconds.
1.4 Critical Thinking: Make sure the two clocks are synchronized. That is, that they show the same time. Either set your watch by the clock at school, carry the watch home and set your clock at home to agree with your watch, or use a time signal given by a radio station, for example, to set both clocks at the same time.

3 Close

CONVERGENT QUESTION

Explain how SI and powers of 10 are related. [Powers of 10 are an integral part of the prefixes used with SI.]

CONCEPT REVIEW ANSWERS

1.1 1.574×10^8
1.2 It would be a larger number in the case of the smaller unit.
1.3 Note (or write down) the time

Physics and society

Background: There are three classes of SI units: the base units, the supplementary units, and the derived units.

SI is coherent. All derived units are obtained by multiplying or dividing other units, using only "one" as the numerical conversion factor. For example,

$$1 \text{ joule} = 1 \text{ newton} \times 1 \text{ meter};$$

$$1 \text{ pascal} = \frac{1 \text{ newton}}{\text{meter}^2}.$$

SI is consistent. It is a system in which there is a minimum number of units and in which each measurable quantity has only one primary unit. For example, all lengths are stated in terms of the meter and all forces are stated in terms of the newton.

Several other units are permitted for use with the metric system. Degree Celsius is commonly used in place of kelvin, the liter instead of the cubic decimeter, and the milliliter in place of the cubic centimeter.

Answers To DEVELOPING A VIEWPOINT

1. Trade with some countries may improve because products would be standardized. Some countries require products in metric units and the U.S. could compete there. Some U.S. companies have found they can reduce inventories by going totally metric. (Cf. Sheets article.)

2. Auto mechanics may not be affected because they have had to work on metric cars for years; they have had to maintain two sets of tools. Plumbers would have to buy another set of tools, so companies that make plumbing tools would benefit. Plumbers would also have to stock metric and non-metric replacement parts. Plumbing repairs would likely be more expensive for the consumer. A bank teller might find that standard bank forms would change in size as metric paper sizes became standard. The farmer would probably need two sets of tools for farm machinery. He or she would have to rethink formulations for livestock feed and for pesticides and fertilizers. The farmer would have to know if a certain price per metric quantity is good for his or her pork or corn.

3. In a moment of crisis, a pilot or air controller who is accustomed to reporting altitude in feet is likely to make an incorrect judgment in the real altitude. For example, if altitude is 3000 meters, is this about 10 000 feet or 3000 feet or 1000 feet? The difference might mean disaster. Thus, the use of common units throughout the world means that air travel should be safer everywhere.

TRANSPARENCY

Use Transparency 2 with this section.

Physics and society

TO SI OR NOT TO SI

If you ask a German teenager how tall he is, he may answer "160 cm" or "1.60 m." Germany and most of the rest of the world use a metric system of measurement, the International System of Units (SI).

In 1875, the "Treaty of the Meter" established the International Bureau of Weights and Measures. Since then, the General Conference of Weights and Measures has handled all international matters relating to the metric system, giving it the designation SI in 1960. Only the United States, Liberia, and Burma have yet to fully adopt the SI system. Scientists all over the world use the SI system because it provides a common means of communicating data.

The use of the metric system has been legal in the United States since 1866. In 1975, Congress passed the Metric Conversion Act, which called for voluntary conversion to the metric system. Some states began using kilometers on highway signs. Some schools began to teach the metric system along with the English system. The major United States automobile makers started building metric cars.

The United States Omnibus Trade and Competitiveness Act of 1988 established the metric system as the preferred system of measurement for the United States commerce. The bill requires all federal agencies to adopt the metric system in all business dealings by 1992. Because many industries depend on government contracts, these industries will have to go metric in order to keep government business. One of the biggest holdouts against the metric system has been the aerospace industry, which uses inch/pound standards for building aircraft. Since the passage of the trade act, several aerospace companies are in the process of converting to the metric system. More consumer goods are now using metric units. Some 60% of the major United States corporations manufactured some metric products in 1989.

Use of the metric system will take some getting used to in everyday life. It will mean "counting calories" in joules. An apple, for example, contains about 150 kJ; a glass of whole milk, 540 kJ. Reading height charts may seem strange. For example, a basketball program may list the height of a center as 196 cm. Gasoline pumps will measure liters. (The liter is not an SI unit; the cubic decimeter is the SI unit of volume. The General Conference of Weights and Measures allows the use of the liter with the SI system.) If clothing manufacturers adopt the metric system, you will buy jeans in such sizes as 61W and 66L.

Many people believe that the use of the same units of measurement all over the world will improve trade among nations. It already facilitates "trade" among scientists.

DEVELOPING A VIEWPOINT

Widespread use of the metric system in the U.S. is considered by many to be necessary if the U.S. is to remain economically competitive. Read some references on the subject and come to class prepared to discuss the following questions:

1. What are some specific economic advantages to using the metric system?
2. How would changing to metric affect such jobs as an auto mechanic, a plumber, and a bank teller?
3. Air traffic controllers and pilots, except in China and the Soviet Union, report altitude in feet. Would safety be compromised if all pilots and controllers were required to report altitude in meters instead?

REFERENCES

Byrne, Gregory. "Going the Extra Meter." *Science*, 241(4872), September 16, 1988, p. 1437.

Feirre, John L. *SI Metric Handbook*. Charles Scribner's Sons, New York, 1971.

Sheets, Kenneth R. "A New Measure of Success." *U.S. News & World Report* 108(10), March 12, 1990, p. 61.

—— "The SI Unit of Pressure." *American Metric Journal* 16(5), September/ October 1988, pp. 34–35.

2.2 NOT ALL IS CERTAIN

Often several scientists measure the same quantities and compare the data they obtain. Each scientist must know how trustworthy the data are. Every measurement, whether made by a student or a professional scientist, is subject to uncertainty.

The length of a ruler can change with changes of temperature. An electric measuring device can be affected by magnetic fields near it. In one way or another, all instruments are subject to external influences. Uncertainties in measurement cannot be avoided, although we try to make them as small as possible. For this reason, it is important to clearly describe the uncertainties in our measurements.

Objectives

- recognize that all measured quantities have uncertainties.
- distinguish between accuracy and precision.
- show you can use significant digits and that you understand their use in stating the precision of measured quantities.
- use significant digits correctly when recording measured data.

Uncertainties of Measurements

All measurements are subject to uncertainties.

In addition to uncertainties due to external causes, such as those listed above, the accuracy of a measurement is affected by the person making the reading. One common source of error comes from the angle at which an instrument is read. In a car, the passenger's reading of the gas gauge and the driver's reading of the same gauge can be quite different. From the passenger's viewpoint, Figure 2–6, the needle is on the second division. From the driver's seat, the needle is above the third division. The driver's reading is more correct. The difference in the readings is caused by parallax. **Parallax** (PAR uh laks) is the apparent shift in the position of an object when it is viewed from various angles. The relative positions of the object and a reference point behind it change. Gas gauges and laboratory instruments must be read at eye level and straight on to avoid parallax errors.

Accuracy and Precision

Precision is the degree of exactness to which a measurement can be reproduced.

Precision is the degree of exactness to which the measurement of a quantity can be reproduced. For example, a student was conducting an experiment to determine the speed of light. Several trials were made that yielded values ranging from 3.000×10^8 m/s to 3.002×10^8 m/s, with an average of 3.001×10^8 m/s. This led the student to report that the speed of light is $(3.001 \pm 0.001) \times 10^8$ m/s. According to the student's measurements, the speed of light might range from 3.000×10^8 m/s to 3.002×10^8 m/s. The precision of the measurement was 0.001×10^8 m/s.

The precision of an instrument is limited by the smallest division on the measurement scale.

a

b

FIGURE 2–6. A parallax example is shown when a car's gasoline gauge is viewed from the passenger's seat (a) and the driver's seat (b). Note the apparent difference in readings.

TEACHER F.Y.I.

Not only is precision limited by the finest division on the scale of a measuring device, but for very small observations, precision depends on the physical characteristics of light itself. For example, the smallest detail that can be seen with a microscope is about the same size as the wavelength of light being used. For this reason, a microscope that could show atomic detail would require a wavelength of less than one nanometer. The scanning tunneling microscope images atoms without using light.

2.2 NOT ALL IS CERTAIN

Preparation

OBJECTIVES

The objectives are listed on the student page. Remind students to preview these objectives as a study guide to this major section.

OVERVIEW

This section teaches the contrasting concepts of accuracy and precision, the use of significant digits to handle uncertainty, and operations with significant digits.

BRIDGING

Most students understand that a distance between two points on a map, given in miles, is not accurate to within a fraction of an inch. Likewise, a fossil that is called 5 million years old today will not be called 5 million years and one day old tomorrow or 5 000 001 years old next year. Such exaggerated distinctions will help students understand the finer points concerning imprecision and uncertainty in this section.

1 Focus

DISCREPANT EVENT

Use this demonstration to illustrate and clarify the idea of significant digits. Get a piece of wood that is 1 meter long with a square cross-section. Fasten a regular meter stick to one side, leave one side unmarked, mark another side with decimeter marks and mark the last side off in centimeters. Choose something that has a length of less than 1 meter. Measure it first on the unmarked side (to one significant digit), then the decimeter side (to two significant digits), etc. Write down each measurement as you go. Students will usually appreciate that successive measurements are "better." Stress that the last significant digit is an estimate between the finest marks on the scale.

2 Teach

CONCEPT DEVELOPMENT

• Some calculators now can be set to display a fixed number of significant digits.

ACTIVITY

Discovery: Pass out rulers to students and have them measure the thickness of a page in a book by measuring the thickness of 100 pages and then dividing by 100. Record on the chalkboard the results of the measurement. Point out that each person should estimate to one hundredth of a centimeter, because the smallest division on a meter stick is one tenth of a centimeter. Point out that dividing by 100 does not change the number of significant digits because 100 refers to a count, rather than to a measurement.

• Part of the problem with uncertainty is that, outside scientific literature, uncertainties are rarely given with data. That makes it seem that such numbers are exact, which (if they are measurements) they are not.

Study Guide Master. To reinforce the concepts in this section, have the students complete the Study Guide Master for Section 2.2 from the Teacher Resource Package.

Physics Skill Master, Teacher Resource Package. Assign Physics Skill Master 3, Using the Vernier Caliper, to reinforce students' understanding.

Physics Skill Master, Teacher Resource Package. Assign Physics Skill Master 4, Propagation of Error, to reinforce students' understanding.

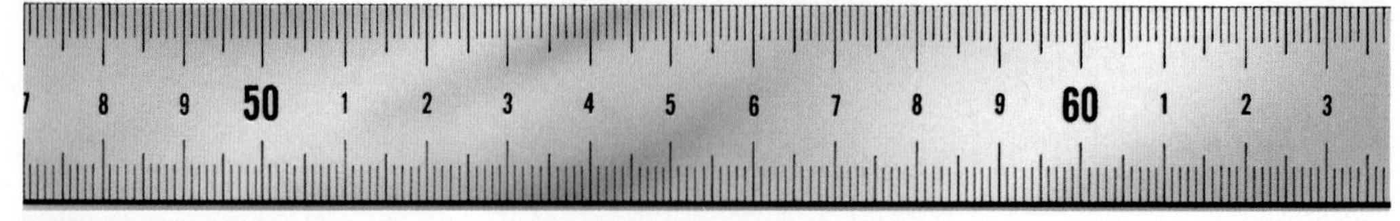

FIGURE 2–7. The meter stick contains centimeter and millimeter divisions.

The precision of a measuring device is limited by the finest division on its scale. The smallest division on a meter stick, Figure 2–7, is a millimeter. Thus, a measurement of any smaller length with a meter stick can be only an estimate. Even on a micrometer, Figure 2–8a, you can make measurements to only 0.005 mm. There is a limit to the precision of even the best instruments.

The accuracy of a measurement describes how well the result agrees with an accepted value.

Accuracy is the extent to which a measured value agrees with the standard value of a quantity. In the experiment to measure the speed of light, the accuracy is the difference between the student's measurement and the defined value of the speed of light, quoted to the same precision: 2.998×10^8 m/s. Thus, the accuracy is $(3.001 \times 10^8 \text{ m/s}) - (2.998 \times 10^8 \text{ m/s}) = 0.003 \times 10^8$ m/s. It would be possible to make a very precise measurement because the instrument is very sensitive, but have that measurement be inaccurate because the instrument was uncalibrated or because you made a reading error.

Significant digits are all the digits that are certain plus a digit that estimates the fraction of the smallest division of the measuring scale.

The accuracy of an instrument depends on how well its performance compares to a currently accepted standard. The accuracy of measuring devices should be checked regularly. They can be calibrated by using them to measure quantities whose values are accurately known. Uncertainties in measurement affect the accuracy of a measurement. Precision, however, is not affected because it is based on the smallest division on the instrument.

Significant Digits

Because the precision of all measuring devices is limited, the number of digits that are valid for any measurement is also limited. The valid digits are called the **significant digits**. Suppose you measure the length

FIGURE 2–8. The micrometer (a) and analytical balance (b) are used to obtain very precise measurements of length and mass, respectively.

a

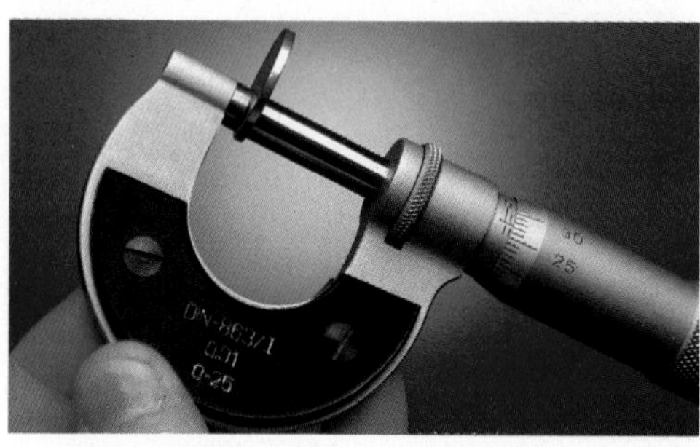

b

STUDY GUIDE MASTER

Use the Study Guide master for section 2.2.

SKILL MASTER

Use Physics Skill Masters 3, 4, 9, 10, and 11 with this section.

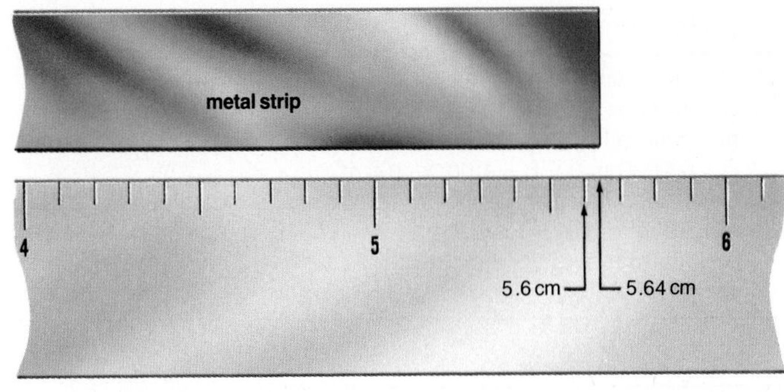

FIGURE 2–9. The accuracy of any measurement depends on both the instrument used and the observer. After a calculation, keep only those digits that truly reflect the accuracy of the original measurement.

of a strip of metal with a meter stick. The smallest division on the meter stick is a millimeter. You should read the scale to the nearest millimeter and then estimate any remaining length as a fraction of a millimeter. The metal strip in Figure 2–9 is somewhat longer than 5.6 centimeters, or 56 millimeters. Looking closely at the scale, you can see that the end of the metal strip is about four-tenths of the way between 56 and 57 millimeters. Therefore, the length of the strip is best stated as 56.4 millimeters. The last digit is an estimate. It might not be 4 but is likely not larger than 5 or smaller than 3. Your measurement, 56.4 mm, contains three significant digits. They are the two digits you are sure of, 5 and 6, and one, 4, that is an estimated digit.

Suppose that the end of the metal strip is exactly on the 56 millimeter mark. In this case, you should record the measurement as 56.0 millimeters. The zero indicates that the strip is not 0.1 millimeter more or less than 56 millimeters. The zero is a significant digit because it transmits information. It is the uncertain digit because you are estimating it. The last digit given for any measurement is the uncertain digit. *All nonzero digits in a measurement are significant.*

Zeros are often a problem. The zero mentioned in 56.0 millimeters is significant. However, a zero that only serves to locate the decimal point is not significant. Thus the value of 0.0026 kilogram contains two significant digits. The measurement of 0.002060 kilogram contains four significant digits. The final zero indicates a reasonable estimate.

There is no way to tell how many of the zeros in the measurement 186 000 m are significant. The 6 may have been the estimated digit and the three zeros may be needed only to place the decimal point. Or, all three zeros may be significant because they were measured. To avoid confusion, such measurements are written in scientific notation. In the number that appears before the power of ten, all the digits are significant. Thus, 1.860×10^5 m has four significant digits. To summarize, the following rules are used to determine the number of significant digits.

1. Nonzero digits are always significant.
2. All final zeros after the decimal point are significant.
3. Zeros between two other significant digits are always significant.
4. Zeros used solely for spacing the decimal point are not significant.

Write results in scientific notation to indicate clearly which zeros are significant.

F.Y.I.

Any error that can creep in, will. It will be in the direction that will do most damage to the calculation.

Murphy's law

CONCEPT DEVELOPMENT

• Discuss the error in this advertising statement: *Net weight before cooking, 4 oz.* (113.4 g). [Actually there are two errors here, one, the two numbers are not expressed to the same number of significant digits; and two, ounces and grams should not be equated.]

• Students may tend to confuse significant digits and decimal places. They're not the same thing, and are not usually related. Significant digits are a reasonably convenient, fast way of handling the inevitable uncertainties in data.

• Emphasize that all measurements have some uncertainty. When you use measurements in a formula, the significant digit rules help obtain a meaningful answer that takes into account the uncertainty.

• A good analogy to differentiate between precision and accuracy is the target analogy. Draw targets on the chalkboard as shown here.

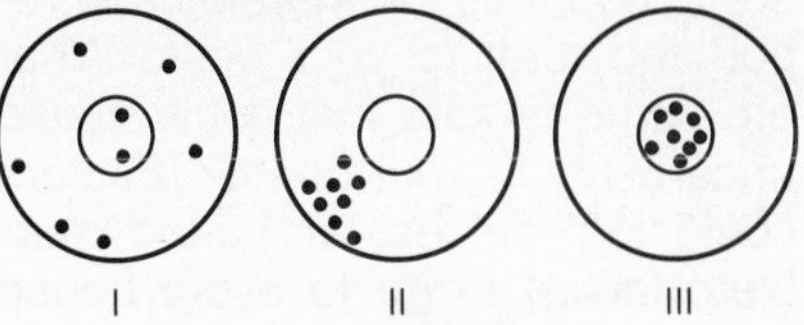

The dots represent bullet holes in the target. The first target shows good accuracy and poor precision; the second shows good precision and poor accuracy. The third represents good accuracy and good precision.

Physics Skill Master, Teacher Resource Package. Assign Physics Skill Master 9, Determining Significant Digits, to reinforce students' understanding.

Physics Skill Master, Teacher Resource Package. Assign Physics Skill Master 10, Experimental Error, to reinforce students' understanding.

The number of significant digits in a quantity ending in one or more zeros like 30 s, 60 W, or 100 km is ambiguous. We have chosen to avoid writing 30 s as 3.0×10^1 s to avoid de-emphasizing the size of the quantity. Significant digits are the result of measurements, and students should be coached to develop a sense of the precision implied in a number such as those listed above. For example, a time interval written as 30 s is probably measured to ± 1 s, so there are 2 significant digits; 100 km is ± 1 km (3 signficant digits) unless it is in a list of numbers such as 400 km, 600 km, when it is more likely ± 10 km (2 significant digits). If while teaching you find an ambiguous quantity urge students to think about the measurement process and develop an argument supporting a reasonable number of significant digits.

Answers To
PRACTICE PROBLEMS

Have students refer to Appendix A of the Solutions Appendix for complete solutions to Practice Problems.

12. **a.** 4 **b.** 3 **c.** 2 **d.** 4 **e.** 2 **f.** 3

13. **a.** 2 **b.** 4 **c.** 4 **d.** 3 **e.** 4 **f.** 3

CONCEPT DEVELOPMENT

CHECKING FOR UNDERSTANDING

Hand out metric rulers to students and have them measure a standard item, like their physics textbook cover. Record these values and discuss the differences.

RETEACHING

To reinforce the concept of measurement uncertainty, propose the following hypothetical project to your class. Imagine that you are hired to conduct a "marble survey" of your neighborhood or town. You are to count all the marbles and report the total to your boss. What are some factors that could cause uncertainty in your count? [Factors could include lost or buried marbles, failure to go to every house or apartment, disagreement over what a marble really is (for example, should your count include ball bearings?), and broken marbles. Students won't have trouble thinking of many sources of uncertainty.]

EXTENSION

There are many systems of accounting for uncertainty in measurements. They range from significant digits to percentage error to standard deviation. Look up the standard deviation system, which may be covered by your calculator's instruction booklet.

Critical Thinking: Have students look for examples of data in which the uncertainty is given. Ask about sports statistics: Is there a margin of uncertainty there? [Though there is uncertainty in all *measurements,* many kinds of statistics rely on enumeration rather than on measurement. (There is no uncertainty in the statement "He struck out three times," though there may be some dispute over the official's calls.)]

Practice Problems

12. State the number of significant digits in each measurement.

a. 2804 m
b. 2.84 m
c. 0.0029 m
d. 0.003 068 m
e. 4.6×10^5 m
f. 4.06×10^5 m

▶ **13.** State the number of significant digits for each measurement.

a. 75 m
b. 75.00 mm
c. 0.007 060 kg
d. 1.87×10^6 ml
e. 1.008×10^8 m
f. 1.20×10^{-4} m

Operations Using Significant Digits

The sum or difference of two values is as precise as the least precise value.

When you are working in the laboratory it is extremely important to remember that *the result of any mathematical operation with measurements can never be more precise than the least precise measurement.* Suppose you measure the lengths 6.48 meters and 18.2 meters. You are asked to find the sum of the two lengths. The length 18.2 meters is precise only to a tenth of a meter. The result of any mathematical operation with measurements cannot be more precise than the least precise measurement. Therefore, the sum of the two lengths can be precise only to a tenth of a meter. First add 6.48 meters to 18.2 meters to get 24.68 meters. Then round off the sum to the nearest tenth of a meter. The correct value is 24.7 meters. Subtraction is handled the same way. To add or subtract measurements, first perform the operation, and then round off the result to correspond to the least precise value involved.

Example Problem

Significant Digits—Addition and Subtraction

Add 24.686 m + 2.343 m + 3.21 m.

Solution:

$$\begin{array}{r} 24.686\ \text{m} \\ 2.343\ \text{m} \\ \underline{3.21\ \ \ \text{m}} \\ 30.239\ \text{m} \\ = 30.24\ \ \ \text{m} \end{array}$$

Note that 3.21 m is the least precise measurement. Round off the result to the nearest hundredth of a meter. Follow the same rules for subtraction.

FIGURE 2–10. When using a calculator in solving problems, it is important to note that your answers cannot be more precise than the least precise quantity involved.

A different method is used to find the correct number of significant digits when multiplying or dividing measurements. After performing the calculation, note the factor with the least number of significant digits. Round the product or quotient to this number of digits.

Example Problem

Significant Digits—Multiplication

Multiply 3.22 cm by 2.1 cm.

Solution:

$$\begin{array}{r} 3.2\,\textcircled{2}\ \text{cm} \\ \underline{2.\,\textcircled{1}\ \text{cm}} \\ \textcircled{3}\,\textcircled{2}\,\textcircled{2} \\ \underline{6\,4.\,\textcircled{4}\phantom{\textcircled{2}}} \\ 6.\textcircled{7}\,\textcircled{6}\,\textcircled{2}\ \text{cm}^2 \end{array}$$

This is correctly stated as 6.8 cm^2.

The less precise factor, 2.1 cm, contains two significant digits. Therefore the product has only two. Note that each circled digit is doubtful, either because it is an estimated measurement or is multiplied by an estimated measurement. Since the 7 in the product is doubtful, the 6 and 2 are certainly not significant. The answer is best stated as 6.8 cm^2.

Example Problem

Significant Digits—Division

Divide 36.5 m by 3.414 s.

Solution:

$$\frac{36.5\ \text{m}}{3.414\ \text{s}} = 10.69\ \text{m/s}$$ This is correctly stated as 10.7 m/s.

The number of significant digits in a product or quotient is the number in the factor with the lesser number of significant digits.

Be sure to record all measurements made during an experiment with the correct number of significant digits. The number of significant digits shows the precision of the instrument. When using a calculator, be particularly careful to record your answer with the proper number of significant digits, even though the calculator shows additional, meaningless digits, Figure 2–10.

It is important to understand that significant digits are only considered when calculating with measurements, not when counting. For example, if you add 2 pencils and 3 pencils, you will have exactly 5 pencils, with no uncertainty. Because of the uncertainty in all measurements, it is important to let anyone who is using your data know exactly how precise your values are.

Practice Problems

14. Add 6.201 cm, 7.4 cm, 0.68 cm, and 12.0 cm.

15. Subtract
- **a.** 8.264 g from 10.8 g.
- **b.** 0.4168 m from 475 m.

POCKET LAB

HIGH AND LOW

Measure the height of the tallest person and the shortest person in your lab group to the nearest 0.1 cm. Estimate the uncertainty in each measurement. Predict how tall each person would be from heel to the top of the head when lying down on the lab table. Would the values be within the uncertainty of the first measurement? Try it. Explain the results.

POCKET LAB

HIGH AND LOW

Purpose: to make measurements and estimates of uncertainty.

Materials: 2 meter sticks.

Outcome: The uncertainty of the height measurement will be in the range of 0.3 cm. When lying down, most students will stretch out by 2.0 cm. (Without the weight on the spine, it will straighten out to a measurable degree.) This difference is not within the estimated uncertainty range of the original measurement.

CONCEPT DEVELOPMENT

Critical Thinking: Can you think of instances in which uncertainty in data is ignored? For example, perhaps there are consumer products for which specific quantifiable claims are made but no possible range of values is suggested.

Physics Skill Master, Teacher Resource Package. Assign Physics Skill Master 11, Estimating Orders of Magnitude, to reinforce students' understanding.

Guided Practice: Work through the example problems on pages 24–25 in class.

Independent Practice: Assign the Practice Problems for homework and then spend some time going over them during the next class period.

Answers To
PRACTICE PROBLEMS

Have students refer to Appendix A of the Solutions Appendix for complete solutions to Practice Problems.

14. 26.3 cm (rounded from 26.281 cm)

15. **a.** 2.5 g (rounded from 2.536 g)
b. 475 m (rounded from 474.5832 m)

Answers To
PRACTICE PROBLEMS (cont)

16. **a.** 3.0×10^2 cm^2
b. 13.6 km^2

17. **a.** 2.73 cm/s
b. 0.253 cm/s

CHECKING FOR UNDERSTANDING

Have students answer the Concept Review questions out loud, and discuss their answers.

RETEACHING

Transparency Package. Reteach uncertainty in measurements with the help of Transparency 2, Time and Mass Scales.

EXTENSION

Critical Thinking Master. Assign the Critical Thinking Master for Chapter 2, Direct and Indirect Measurements.

3 Close

CONVERGENT QUESTION

• Apply the saying "A chain is only as strong as its weakest link" to the rules for using significant digits. [The chain is the result of calculating with data containing uncertainty. The piece of data with the greatest uncertainty will determine the uncertainty of the end result.]

• Why may it be considered dishonest to report data with no indication of uncertainty? [The reader may put too much confidence in the data, which can lead to mistakes.]

CONCEPT REVIEW ANSWERS

2.1 It would be more precise but less accurate.
2.2 No, it doesn't change the fineness of the divisions on its scale.
2.3 Between 181.5 and 182.5 cm.
2.4 **Critical Thinking:** It is a measure of precision. The way the question is asked can affect the accuracy.

16. Perform the following multiplications.
a. 131 cm × 2.3 cm
b. 3.2145 km × 4.23 km

▶ **17.** Perform the following divisions.
a. 20.2 cm ÷ 7.41 s
b. 3.1416 cm ÷ 12.4 s

CONCEPT REVIEW

2.1 If you have a micrometer that has been bent more than 1 mm out of alignment, how would it compare to a new, quality meter stick in precision? accuracy?
2.2 Does parallax affect the precision of a measuring instrument? Explain.
2.3 Explain in your own words the range in heights that would be implied if you reported a measurement as "His height is 182 cm."
2.4 **Critical Thinking:** Poll takers often interview people and report "1000 people were interviewed for a margin of accuracy of ±3%." Is this a measure of the precision or accuracy of the poll? **Hint:** Suppose you were interviewed by your principal about your opinions about school rules.

Objectives

- **distinguish between dependent and independent variables.**
- **be able to graph data points.**
- **understand how smooth curves drawn through data points represent the relationship between independent and dependent variables.**
- **recognize linear and direct relationships and be able to find and interpret the slope of the curve.**
- **recognize quadratic and inverse relationships.**

2.3 DISPLAYING DATA

A well-designed graph is more than a "picture worth a thousand words." It can give you more information than either words, columns of numbers, or equations. To be useful, however, a graph must be drawn properly. In this section we will develop the use of graphs to display data.

Graphing Data

One of the most important skills to learn in driving a car is how to stop it safely. No car can "stop on a dime." The faster the car is going, the farther it travels before it stops. If you studied for a driver's license, you probably found a table in the manual showing how far a car moves beyond the point at which the driver makes a decision to stop.

One state manual shows that a car travels a certain distance between the time the driver decides to stop the car and the time he puts on the brakes. This is called the "reaction distance." When the brakes are applied, the car slows down and travels the "braking distance." Table 2–2 and the bar graph, Figure 2–11, show these distances, together with the total stopping distance for various speeds. The table shows both SI quantities as well as, in parentheses, the English units used in the driver's manual.

2.3 DISPLAYING DATA

Preparation

OBJECTIVES

The objectives are listed on the student page. Remind students to preview these objectives as a study guide to this major section.

OVERVIEW

Graphical presentation of data is taught. This section includes simple forms of functional relationships—linear, direct, quadratic, inverse.

BRIDGING

To graph data correctly, students will use principles of algebra, and some knowledge of units, powers of 10, and uncertainty.

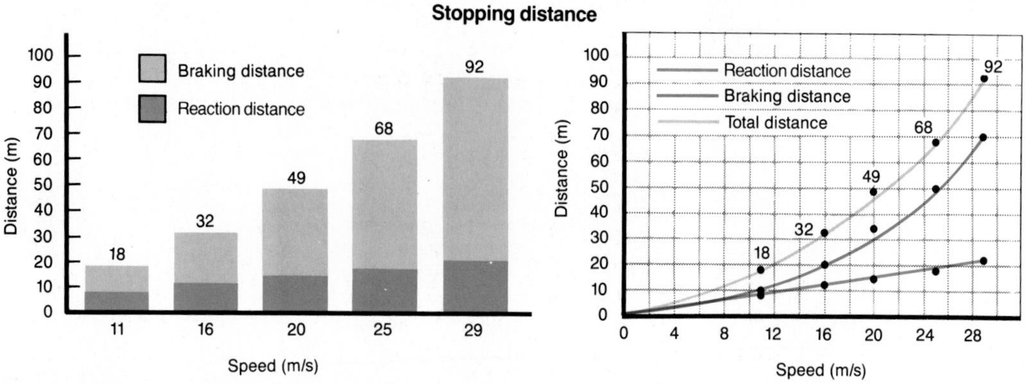

Stopping distance

FIGURE 2–11. The total stopping distance is the sum of the reaction and braking distances. Graphs (a) and (b) display the same information in two different ways.

Table 2–2

Reaction and Braking Distances vs Speed

Original speed		Reaction distance		Braking distance		Total distance	
m/s	(mph)	m	(ft)	m	(ft)	m	(ft)
11	(25)	8	(27)	10	(34)	18	(61)
16	(35)	12	(38)	20	(67)	32	(105)
20	(45)	15	(49)	34	(110)	49	(159)
25	(55)	18	(60)	50	(165)	68	(225)
29	(65)	22	(71)	70	(231)	92	(302)

The first step in analyzing data is to look at them carefully. Which variable did the experimenter (the driver) change? In our example, it was the speed of the car. Thus speed is the **independent variable**, or manipulated variable. The other two variables, reaction distance and braking distance, changed as a result of the change in the speed. These quantities are called **dependent variables**, or responding variables.

The independent variable is the one the experimenter can control directly. The value of the dependent variable depends on the independent variable.

How do the distances change for a given change in the speed? Notice that the reaction distance increases by about the same amount for each increase in speed. The braking distance, however, increases much more as the speed increases. The relationship between the distances and speed can be seen more easily if the data are plotted on a graph. To avoid confusion, you should plot two graphs, one of reaction distance and the other of braking distance.

FIGURE 2–12. Knowing when and how to apply brakes safely is an important part of a driver's test.

PROBLEM SOLVING STRATEGY

Plotting Graphs

These steps will help you plot graphs from data tables.

1. Identify the independent and dependent variables. The independent variable is plotted on the horizontal, or x-axis. The dependent variable is plotted on the vertical, or y-axis. In our example, speed is plotted on the x-axis, and distance is plotted on the y-axis.

1 Focus

DISCREPANT EVENT

Boyle's law (the volume of a gas varies inversely with the pressure put upon it) can be used to demonstrate an inverse relationship. Plug the end of a syringe and press on the plunger. Read the volume of air in the syringe. Ask students to determine the independent variable (pressure) and the dependent variable (volume). Graph the data on the board or overhead. Have students choose scale divisions on the x-axis and y-axis. Discuss errors in the experiment and how these errors would affect the data. Use this opportunity to discuss points to remember, such as titling graphs, labeling axes, and determining scale divisions.

2 Teach

CONCEPT DEVELOPMENT

- Impress upon students that graphing is a valuable technique that should be thoroughly mastered. Graphs drawn as part of the course's laboratory work will provide worthwhile practice.
- Ask students whether the data in Table 2–2 or in the graphs of the table's data convey the information in a more meaningful way. Most will answer that the graphs do.

Study Guide Master. To reinforce the concepts in this section, have the students complete the Study Guide Master for section 2.3 from the Teacher Resource Package.

2:2 ASSIGNMENT GUIDE

	PRACTICE	EXTENSION
CHAPTER REVIEW pp. 35–39		
· Reviewing Concepts	5–8	
· Applying Concepts		5–6
· Problems*	5–15	
APPENDIX B PROBLEMS*		
· Chapter 2, p. 688	4–8	

* Complete solutions to all Chapter Review and Appendix problems appear in the Problems and Solutions Manual.

TRANSPARENCY

Use Transparency 2 with this section.

CRITICAL THINKING

Use the Critical Thinking master for Chapter 2 with this section.

STUDY GUIDE MASTER

Use the Study Guide master for section 2.3.

PHYSICS LAB

Process Skills: using numbers, observing, communicating, interpreting data, measuring, predicting, defining operationally.

MISCONCEPTIONS

Many students do not understand the significance of the slopes of graphs.

Teaching Suggestions: Wires should be precut into short (5–8 cm), medium (13–16 cm), and long (20–28 cm) lengths. Floor tile can be cut in small (4–12 cm^2) and large (20–60 cm^2) rectangular pieces and medium triangles (20–40 cm^2). Store the three wires and three pieces of tile in a plastic lock bag for each group.

Lab Worksheet, Teacher Resource Package. If desired, use the lab worksheet master for this chapter for students to record their data.

OBSERVATIONS

1. Yes, the graph should pass through 0,0. (When the length of the wire is zero, the mass is zero.)
2. The graph for the tiles should also pass through 0,0.

ANALYSIS

1. The value of the mass of the object will equal zero when the length (or area) is zero.
2. Values of slope will vary depending on the type of wire and type of tile.
3. The slope of the wire graph tells the amount of mass for each cm of wire. The slope of the tile graph indicates the mass for each cm^2 of tile.

APPLICATIONS

The average weight for a certain number of tablets, for example ten tablets, is found, then the total weight of the finished tablet lot is determined. The finished number of tablets is calculated by dividing the average weight per tablet into the total weight. This procedure is used because an average lot size can be one million or more tablets.

PHYSICS LAB : Getting Straight

Purpose

To create and use graphs to estimate the mass of objects.

Materials

- 3 pieces of electrical wire with lengths between 5 cm - 30 cm
- 2 rectangular pieces of floor tile
- 1 triangular floor tile
- balance
- 30-cm ruler
- graph paper

Procedure

1. Measure the length of the three wires to the nearest 0.1 cm.
2. Measure the mass of only the longest and shortest wires.
3. Make a graph of mass (vertical) versus length (horizontal). Include the units on the graph.
4. Use the graph to predict the mass of the middle length.
5. Calculate the area of both rectangular pieces of tile. Measure their masses.
6. Make a graph of mass (vertical) versus area (horizontal) for the rectangular pieces.
7. Measure the area of the triangular piece of tile and use the graph to predict the mass.

Observations and Data

1. Does your graph of the wire mass versus length pass through the origin?
2. Does your graph of the area of the tiles versus mass pass through the origin?

Analysis

1. Explain why your graphs should pass through the origin.
2. Calculate the slope of each graph (include the units).
3. Explain the meaning of each slope.

Applications

1. In the pharmaceutical industry, how might the weight of compressed tablets be used to determine the quantity of finished tablets produced in a specific lot?

ASSESSMENT

Critical Thinking: To further assess students' understanding of building construction, ask the following questions.

1. Suppose that another lab group had longer wires than your samples. How would their graph be different? Explain. [Their graph would be more spread out than yours, but your data should fit on their line because both graphs should have the same slope and both should go through the origin.]
2. If a different lab group used a thicker wire, how would their graph be similar to yours? How would it be different? [The graph for the thicker wire would still be a straight line through the origin, but it would have a higher value for the slope.]

2. Determine the range of the independent variable to be plotted. In the example, data are given for speeds between 11 and 29 m/s. A convenient range for the x-axis might be 0–30 m/s.
3. Decide if the origin (0, 0) is a valid data point. When the speed is zero, reaction and stopping distances are obviously both zero. In this case then, your graph should include the origin. Spread out the data as much as possible. Let each space on the graph paper stand for a convenient unit. Choose 2, 5, or 10 spaces to represent 10 m/s.
4. Number and label the horizontal axis.
5. Repeat steps 2–4 for the dependent variable.
6. Plot your data points on the graph.
7. Draw the best straight line or smooth curve that passes through as many data points as possible. *Do not use a series of straight line segments that "connect the dots."*
8. Give the graph a title that clearly tells what the graph represents.

Linear, Quadratic, and Inverse Relationships

The graph, Figure 2–13, of reaction distance versus speed is a straight line. That is, the dependent variable varies linearly with the independent variable; there is a **linear relationship** between the two variables.

A Graphic Display

The relationship of the two variables shown in this graph can be written as an equation

$$y = mx + b,$$

where m and b are constants called the slope and y-intercept, respectively. Each constant can be found from the graph. The **slope**, m, is the ratio of the vertical change to the horizontal change. To find the slope, select two points, **A** and **B**, as far apart as possible on the line. *They should not be data points.* The vertical change, or rise, Δy, is the difference in the vertical values of **A** and **B.** The horizontal change, or run, Δx, is the difference in the horizontal values of **A** and **B.** The slope of the graph is then calculated as

$$m = \frac{\text{rise}}{\text{run}} = \frac{\Delta y}{\Delta x} = \frac{(20 - 0)\text{ m}}{(27 - 0)\text{ m/s}} = \frac{20\text{ m}}{27\text{ m/s}} = 0.74\text{ s}.$$

Notice that units have been kept with the variables.

The independent variable is plotted on the x-axis. The dependent variable is plotted on the y-axis.

The slope of a graph is $\Delta y/\Delta x$.

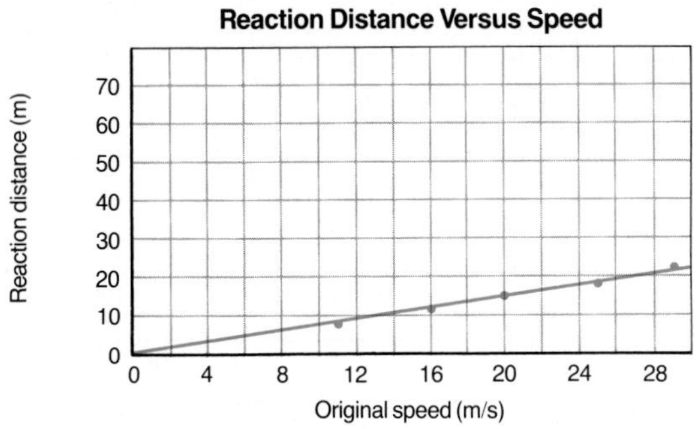

Reaction Distance Versus Speed

Reaction distance (m): 0, 10, 20, 30, 40, 50, 60, 70

Original speed (m/s): 0, 4, 8, 12, 16, 20, 24, 28

FIGURE 2–13. The graph indicates a linear relationship between reaction distance and car speed.

CONCEPT DEVELOPMENT

• It could be argued that people are more visually oriented than numerically oriented, and therefore graphs make more of an impact. Or, to paraphrase an old saying, "A graph is worth a thousand pieces of data."

ACTIVITY

Cooperative Learning: Have students bring in graphs from newspapers or magazines and evaluate them in terms of construction and usefulness.

• Emphasize that, contrary to common practice in mathematics, the grid squares on the x and y axes usually have different sizes for scientific graphs.

• An excellent reference (which is an artwork itself) on the history and development of graphs is *The Visual Display of Quantitative Information* by Edward R. Tufte, Graphics Press, Cheshire, Connecticut, 1983.

ACTIVITY

Cooperative Learning: Go around the class, having each student add a step to the process of making a graph. Remember that the order of some steps is not crucial while the order of others is; for example, axes must be divided up before data can be plotted.

Reteaching Master, Teacher Resource Package. Use the Reteaching Master for Chapter 2, Determining Relationships from Graphs.

Critical Thinking: Graphs are not always totally objective presentations of data. Particularly in advertising, graphs are frequently used to conceal or distort information. See if students can find examples from actual ads. If not, ask them to think of ways that certain information could be emphasized or underplayed on a graph.

Enrichment: Have some students learn how to use graph-generating programs on the computer. Let them demonstrate the procedure to the class.

Connect to CHEMISTRY

Graphs can be used to analyze data collected from a chemistry experiment. Explain pH if necessary. The pH measurements in the table were obtained when sodium hydroxide was added to acetic acid. Have students graph the data. Ask if there is a linear relationship between the volume and the pH. [no] Are there portions of the graph that are approximately linear? [Yes, 0–48 cm^3 and 55–100 cm^3]

Table

cm^3 acid added	pH
0	1.0
30	1.3
40	1.5
48	2.0
49	3.0
51	11.0
55	12.0
60	13.0
80	13.5
100	14.0

CHECKING FOR UNDERSTANDING

The best check is to design a short quiz in which you give the students some data and ask them to draw a graph. Make it clear beforehand what your set of rules for graphing is, especially if it differs from that presented in this section.

RETEACHING

The most difficult part of constructing graphs seems to be choosing the scale used on each axis. There are two separate decisions. First, one examines the data to see its range of values. Second, the choice of what one box stands for is constrained by several factors: convenience, the need to have a graph of reasonable size, and fitting all data on the graph.

Physics Skill Master, Teacher Resource Package. Assign Physics Skill Masters 6, Graphing Techniques, and 7, Interpreting Graphs, to reteach this section.

Guided Practice: Go over the Concept Review problems on page 31 as an in-class exercise.

INDEPENDENT PRACTICE/ EXTENSION

Refer to the Assignment Guide on page 31 for additional questions and problems for independent practice.

POCKET LAB

JUICED UP

Purpose: to learn how to use a graph for predicting.
Materials: 12-oz nonmetallic juice bottle; water; balance.
Outcome: The graph can be used to accurately predict any height of water. The graph does not pass through 0,0 because the bottle also has mass. The vertical intercept is the mass of the bottle. The slope of the graph is the value of the number of grams of water for each cm of height.

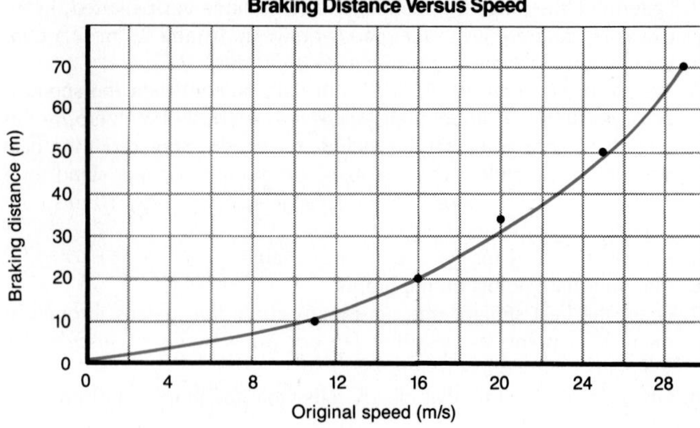

FIGURE 2–14. The graph indicates a parabolic relationship; braking distance varies as the square of the original speed.

The *y*-intercept is the value of *y* when *x* is zero.

If the dependent variable decreases when the independent variable increases, then the slope is negative.

POCKET LAB

JUICED UP

Use a sharp pencil to make marks at 2.0 cm, 4.0 cm, and 6.0 cm on the insides of a juice can. Fill the can to the 2.0 cm mark and measure the mass of the can and water on a balance. Fill the can to the 6.0 cm mark and again measure the mass on a balance. Make a graph of mass (vertical) versus height (horizontal). Predict the mass when the can has 4.0 cm of water. (**Hint:** The graph should be a straight line.) Explain why the graph does not go through 0,0. What is the meaning of the slope of the graph?

The ***y*-intercept,** *b*, is the point at which the line crosses the *y*-axis, and is the *y* value when the value of *x* is zero. In this case, when *x* is zero, the value of *y* is 0 m. For special cases like this, when the *y*-intercept equals zero, the equation becomes $y = mx$. The quantity *y* varies directly with *x*.

The value of *y* does not always increase with increasing *x*. If *y* gets smaller as *x* gets larger, then $\Delta y/\Delta x$ is less than zero, and the slope is negative.

After drawing the graph and obtaining the equation, check to see if the results make sense. The slope indicates the increased reaction distance for an increase in speed. It has units of meters/(meters/second), or seconds. Thus it is a time, the reaction time. It is the time your body takes from the instant the message to stop the car registers in your brain until your foot hits the brake pedal. Thus, the slope is a *property* of the system the graph describes.

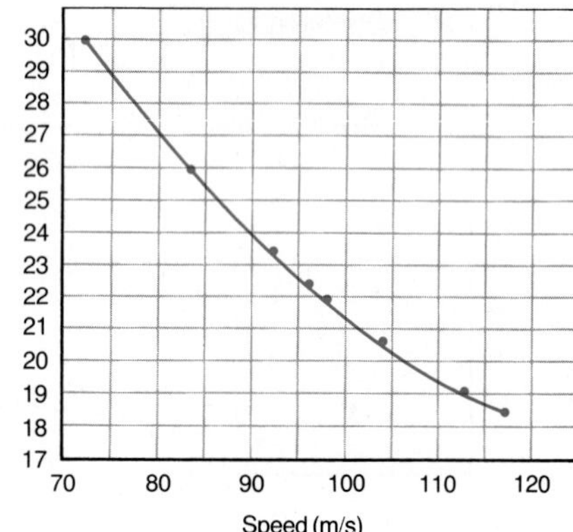

FIGURE 2–15. The graph shows the inverse relationship between the time required to travel a fixed distance and the speed.

Assessment

Performance

To further assess students' understanding of graphical relationships, have them predict the graph when using a plastic funnel with one end plugged. Use clay as a support so the funnel will stand upright. Test the predictions by repeating the Pocket Lab. [Because the funnel is larger at the top, the graph will no longer be linear. The measured mass will be smaller than that predicted by drawing a straight line between the 2-cm and 6-cm points. If three data points are used and a curved line drawn, predictions will again be accurate.]

Figure 2–14 is the graph of the braking distance versus speed, completed as suggested in the Problem Solving Strategy. Note that the relationship is not linear.

The smooth line drawn through all the data points curves upward. You cannot draw a straight line through all the points. Such graphs are frequently parabolas, indicating that the two variables are related by the equation

$$y = kx^2,$$

where k is a constant. This equation shows that y varies directly with the square of x. This equation is one form of a **quadratic relationship**. The constant k shows how fast y changes with x^2. In Chapters 4 and 5, we will discuss variables that are related by this equation, and learn why braking distance depends on speed in this way.

Some variables are related by the type of graph shown in Figure 2–15. In this case, a plot has been made of the time required to travel a fixed distance as the speed of travel is changed. When the speed is doubled, the time is reduced to one-half its original time. The relationship between speed and time is an inverse variation. The graph is a hyperbola, not a straight line. The general equation for an **inverse relationship** is

$$xy = k \text{ or } y = k \cdot \left(\frac{1}{x}\right) = kx^{-1}.$$

The parabolic relationship exists when one variable depends on the square of another.

A hyperbola results when one variable depends on the inverse of the other.

Circumference Versus Diameter

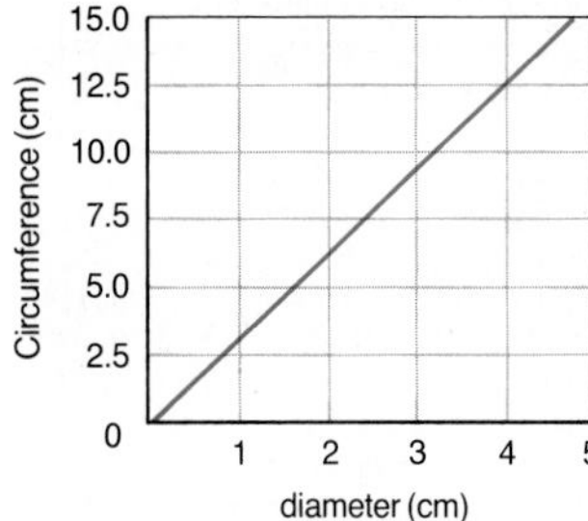

FIGURE 2–16. Use with Concept Review 3.4.

CONCEPT REVIEW

3.1 What would be the meaning of a non-zero y-intercept to the graph of reaction distance versus speed?

3.2 At what speed is the reaction distance 10 m?

3.3 Explain in your own words the significance of a steeper line, or larger slope to the graph of reaction distance versus speed.

3.4 Critical Thinking: Figure 2–16 shows the relationship between the circumference and the diameter of a circle. Could a different circle be described by a different straight line? What is the meaning of the slope?

2.4 MANIPULATING EQUATIONS

The manner in which one quantity, such as the circumference of a circle, depends on another, such as the circle's diameter, can be represented symbolically by an equation, $C = \pi d$, as well as by a graph. If we want to find how the diameter depends on the circumference, we can use rules of algebra to rearrange the equation, $d = C/\pi$.

Objectives

- **demonstrate the ability to manipulate algebraic equations.**
- **use dimensional analysis to test the validity of an equation.**

3 Close

CONVERGENT QUESTION

Explain to students that *interpolation* is reading off graph values between data points, and *extrapolation* is reading off graph values beyond data points. Ask them which process is likely to introduce more error. [Extrapolation, because it goes beyond what has actually been measured in the experiment.]

Enrichment Master. With this section, use the Enrichment Master, Straightening Curves, from the Teacher Resource Package.

CONCEPT REVIEW ANSWERS

3.1 It would mean that the car moved a non-zero distance when its original speed was zero.
3.2 Between 12 and 13 m/s.
3.3 A steeper line means a longer reaction time.
3.4 Critical Thinking: There is only one straight line. The slope is π.

2.4 MANIPULATING EQUATIONS

Preparation

OBJECTIVES

The objectives are listed on the student page. Remind students to preview these objectives as a study guide to this major section.

OVERVIEW

This section develops the process of using equations with units in physics.

BRIDGING

This section makes use of terms from algebra concerning the four fundamental operations; a few terms from simple geometry such as diameter, circle, radius, area, length, and width; and two words from everyday language, distance and speed.

2:3 ASSIGNMENT GUIDE

	PRACTICE	EXTENSION
CHAPTER REVIEW pp. 35–39		
· Reviewing Concepts	9–15	
· Applying Concepts		9, 11, 12
· Problems*	17	16, 18, 19
APPENDIX B PROBLEMS*		
· Chapter 2, p. 688		9, 10

* Complete solutions to all Chapter Review and Appendix problems appear in the Problems and Solutions Manual.

ENRICHMENT MASTER

Use the Enrichment master for Chapter 2 with this section.

RETEACHING MASTER

Use the Reteaching master for Chapter 2 with this section.

SKILL MASTER

Use Physics Skill Masters 6 and 7 with this section.

1 Focus

DISCREPANT EVENT

Solve these problems on the board using simple equations and data with units.

How long does it take sunlight to travel from the sun to Earth? Use 1.5×10^{11} m for the distance from the sun to Earth, and 3.0×10^8 m/s for the speed of light. [answer: 500 seconds]

What's the average density of Earth? Remember that density is equal to mass divided by volume. The mass of Earth is 6.0×10^{24} kg and the radius of Earth is 6.4×10^6 m. [Use Volume of a sphere $= (4/3)\pi R^3$ to get the volume, then divide to get 5.5×10^3 kg/m^3. For comparison, water has a density of 1.0×10^3 kg/m^3.]

If you need a more challenging example, estimate the volume of concrete needed for one kilometer of superhighway. [Answer: Approximately 4000 cubic meters. Of course, the answer you get will depend on your estimates.]

2 Teach

CONCEPT DEVELOPMENT

- Stress that what's being learned here is not really new, but an application of skills learned earlier in math class to scientific equations.

Study Guide Master To reinforce the concepts in this section have the students complete the Study Guide Master for section 2.4 from the Teacher Resource Package.

- Point out that when data are substituted into equations, that data should be completed *with* units. The units are then carried through and manipulated just the same as any other algebraic quantity. If students leave off units, the data become just numbers without meaning.

- Many students want to use *x* for the unknown in an equation. Discourage this practice and promote the use of whatever variable is being looked for, such as *t* or *d*. Again, using the unknown variable itself helps to give more meaning to the process.

HELP WANTED

ACTUARY

Do you love the challenge of figures and probability? A logical, analytical mind and exceptional knowledge of math and statistics are required for the position of actuary in the corporate headquarters of this major insurance company. A bachelor's degree in math, or Actuarial Science, and certification on appropriate examinations are musts. For information contact:

American Academy of Actuaries, 1720 I Street, N.W. 7th Floor, Washington, DC 20006

Solve equations for the required variable, the unknown, placing it on the left-hand side of the equals sign.

Solving Equations Using Algebra

From your graph of the reaction distance versus speed, you can obtain an equation relating the two variables. If we represent the reaction distance by *d*, the speed of the car by *v*, and the slope, which we discovered had units of time, by *t*, the equation is

$$d = vt, \text{ or } d = tv.$$

Note that this last equation has the same form, but different symbols than $y = mx$. The distance, *d*, is the dependent variable. The speed, *v*, is the independent variable. The slope, *m*, is the reaction time, *t*. You can use this equation to find *d* if you know *v* and *t*. What if, however, you know *d* and *t* and want to find *v*? You can solve the equation above for *v*. First, place the term containing *v* on the left side.

$$vt = d$$

To get *v* alone on the left side, but not change the value of the relationship, divide both sides of the equation by *t*. Thus,

$$v = \frac{d}{t}.$$

That is, the speed of the car is equal to the reaction distance divided by the reaction time. If an equation contains several factors, the same process is followed until the unknown is isolated on the left side of the equation. The steps can be performed in any sequence; just be sure you perform the same operations on both sides of the equation.

F.Y.I.

"Mathematics is the door and the key to the sciences."
Roger Bacon

Example Problem

Solving Equations

Solve the following equation for *x*.

$$\frac{ay}{x} = \frac{cb}{s}$$

Solution:

Multiply both sides by *x*.

$$ay = \frac{cbx}{s}$$

Rearrange to bring *x* to the left side.

$$\frac{cbx}{s} = ay$$

Divide both sides by *cb*.

$$\frac{x}{s} = \frac{ay}{cb}$$

Multiply both sides by *s*.

$$x = \frac{asy}{cb}$$

TEACHER 

In a fascinating application of algebra to speculation, researchers have produced what is sometimes called the Drake equation, which gives an estimate for the number of advanced technical civilizations in the universe that have the interest and capability for interstellar communication. An astronomy book would be one good source for this calculation. If you have the Project Physics Readers available, the second reader has an article called "Is There Intelligent Life Beyond the Earth?" by I.S. Shklovskii and Carl Sagan.

Example Problem

Solving Equations

Solve the following equation for x. $y = mx + b$

Solution:

Rearrange to bring x to the left side. $mx + b = y$

Subtract b from both sides. $mx = y - b$

Divide both sides by m. $x = (y - b)/m$

Practice Problems

18. Solve the following equation for b. $y = mx + b$

19. Solve the following equations for v.

a. $d = vt$ **c.** $a = \frac{v^2}{2d}$

b. $t = \frac{d}{v}$ **d.** $\frac{v}{a} = \frac{b}{c}$

20. Solve each of these equations for E.

a. $f = \frac{E}{s}$ **b.** $m = \frac{2E}{v^2}$ **c.** $\frac{E}{c^2} = m$

21. Solve the equation $v^2 = v_0^2 + 2ad$ for d.

▶ **22.** Solve each of these equations for a.

a. $v = v_0 + at$ **c.** $v^2 = v_0^2 + 2ay$

b. $y = v_0t + ½at^2$ **d.** $v = \sqrt{2as}$

PHILOSOPHY CONNECTION

French philosopher and mathematician, Rene Descartes, (1596–1650), for whom the familiar Cartesian coordinates are named, is considered by many to have introduced analytical geometry as an appendix to his famous philosophical treatise on universal science, "Discourse on the Method of Rightly Conducting Reason and Seeking Truth in the Sciences". It has been noted that Descartes considered negative numbers "false", and avoided using them.

FIGURE 2–17. Did somebody miscalculate?

Multicultural Connections

Measuring and computing physical quantities requires the use of mathematics. Our modern system of mathematics owes a great deal to Islamic mathematicians. They developed the "Arabic numerals" by building upon Hindu mathematics. By the sixteenth century, Arabic numerals had replaced Roman numerals in the West. One Islamic scholar, Abu Jafar al-Khwarizmi, invented algebra (from the Arabic word "al-jabr") during the ninth century A.D. One of his contemporaries, Abu al-Battani, developed trigonometry. Thus, the modern mathematical tools that we use to study and record physical phenomena date back more than one thousand years.

CONCEPT DEVELOPMENT

Cooperative Learning: Assign simple substitution exercises, then divide students up into pairs and have them check each other's work.

Physics Skill Master, Teacher Resource Package. Assign Physics Skill Master 5, Dimensional Analysis, to reinforce students' understanding.

Physics Skill Master, Teacher Resource Package. Assign Physics Skill Master 8, Gathering and Analyzing Data, to reinforce students' understanding.

Critical Thinking: One equation for the air resistance force, F, is $F = kv^2$, where k is a constant and v is the speed of the object. Force is measured in a unit called the newton, N. Take speed as measured in m/s. In order to make the units of the equation come out correctly, ask students what units the constant, k, would have to have. [Newtons, divided by m^2/s^2.]

Answers To
PRACTICE PROBLEMS

Have students refer to Appendix A of the Solutions Appendix for complete solutions to Practice Problems.

18. $b = y - mx$

19. **a.** $v = \frac{d}{t}$

b. $v = \frac{d}{t}$

c. $v = \pm\sqrt{2ad}$

d. $v = \frac{ab}{c}$

20. **a.** $E = fs$

b. $E = \frac{mv^2}{2}$

c. $E = mc^2$

21. $d = \frac{(v^2 - v_0^2)}{2a}$

22. **a.** $a = \frac{v - v_0}{t}$

b. $a = \frac{2(y - v_0t)}{t^2}$

c. $a = \frac{v^2 - v_0^2}{2y}$

d. $a = \frac{v^2}{2s}$

CHECKING FOR UNDERSTANDING

Have students solve the following problem: How long does it take light to travel through a piece of glass 3.0 mm thick? (Use the value 3.0×10^8 m/s for the speed of light.) [Answer: 1.0×10^{-11} s or 10 ps, from the equation $d = vt$.]

RETEACHING

Review the basic algebraic operations of addition, subtraction, multiplication, and division. Then show how the manipulation of data in an equation such as density = mass/volume uses these algebraic rules. Get students involved in working out examples as much as possible. Walk around the class to see where students are having difficulties.

Guided Practice: Go over the Example Problem and the Practice Problems that follow as a class exercise.

INDEPENDENT PRACTICE/ EXTENSION

Refer to the Assignment Guide below for additional questions and problems for independent practice.

3 Close

CONVERGENT QUESTION

The volume of the Great Pyramid of Cheops is about 2.4×10^6 m³. Have students calculate about how many buildings the size of your school would fit into this volume.

Answers To

PRACTICE PROBLEMS

Have students refer to Appendix A of the Solutions Appendix for complete solutions to Practice Problems.

23. a. 6 cm²
b. 4.50 m

24. a. incorrect
b. correct
c. incorrect

CONCEPT REVIEW ANSWERS

4.1 There are four times as many people as cars, or, for every car there are four people.

4.2 The circumference of a circle can be found by multiplying the length of its radius by the number π and then by the number 2.

4.3 $S = 20T$

4.4 Critical Thinking: $15/2\pi$ m = 2.4 m. Since $C = \pi d$, increasing C by 15 m increases πd by 15 m, which increases d by $15/\pi$ m, and thus increases the radius by half that amount. Or, think of the graph of C versus d in Figure 2–16. Move vertically a distance ΔC, and this moves to the right a distance Δd/slope = $\Delta d/\pi$. The radius of Earth is not needed.

Units in Equations

All terms in an equation should have the same prefixes of the units.

Suppose you want to find the area of a wood plank. The plank is 15.0 cm wide and 2.50 m long. If you simply multiply length times width, you get 37.5 cm · m. This is not very useful. You should first make sure all terms in an equation have the same units. In this case, change the width to 0.150 m. You will then obtain an area of 0.375 m².

Always write the units with the values in an equation.

Most physical quantities have units as well as numerical values. When you substitute a value into an equation, you must write both the value and the unit. If your answer has the wrong units, you have made an error in your solution. When a term has several units, you can operate on the units like any other mathematical quantity.

Example Problem

Operating on Units

If v = 11.0 m/s and t = 6.00 s, find d using $d = vt$. Find the units for d.

Solution:

$d = vt$ = (11.0 m/s)(6.00 s) = 66.0 (m/s) s = 66.0 m

Units provide a useful way of checking the correctness of an equation.

Note that the units on the right, meters, are the units for distance. By inspecting the units, you will often be able to tell when you have set up the equation incorrectly.

Practice Problems

23. Identify the answers to these exercises using consistent units.
a. Find the area of a rectangle 2 mm by 30 cm.
b. Find the perimeter of a rectangle 25 cm by 2.00 m.

▶ **24.** Find which of the following equations are incorrect.
a. area = (length)(width)(height) **c.** distance = (speed)(time)²
b. time = distance/speed

CONCEPT REVIEW

4.1 Write a sentence that gives the same information as the equation $P = 4C$, where P represents the number of people and C represents the number of cars.

4.2 Write a sentence giving the same information as the equation $C = 2\pi r$, where C is the circumference of a circle and r is its radius.

4.3 Write an equation using the variables S and T to represent the following sentence: "There are twenty times as many students as teachers at this school."

4.4 **Critical Thinking:** The radius of Earth at the equator is 6378 km. Imagine a stiff wire wrapped around the equator of a perfectly smooth Earth. Suppose we now increased the length of the wire by 15 m, and shaped the wire into a circle centered at the center of Earth. How far above Earth's surface would the wire be? Explain your reasoning. If any information that you did not need was given in the problem, indicate it.

CHAPTER 2 REVIEW

SUMMARY

2.1 The Measure of Science

- The meter, second, and kilogram are the fundamental units of length, time, and mass in the SI system.
- Derived units are a combination of fundamental units.
- Large and small measurements, often used in physics, are most clearly written using scientific notation.
- Prefixes are used to change SI units by powers of 10.
- To be added or subtracted, quantities written in scientific notation must be raised to the same power of 10.
- Quantities written in scientific notation need not have the same power of 10 to be multiplied or divided.

2.2 Not All Is Certain

- All measurements are subject to some uncertainty.
- Precision is the degree of exactness with which a quantity is measured.
- Accuracy is the extent to which the measured and accepted values of a quantity agree.
- For a given measurement, the number of significant digits is limited by the precision of the measuring device.
- The last digit in a measurement is always an estimate. Only one estimated digit is significant.
- The result of any mathematical operation made with measurements can never be more precise than the least precise measurement.

2.3 Displaying Data

- Data are plotted in graphical form to show the relationship between two variables.
- The independent variable is the one the experimenter changes. It is plotted on the x- or horizontal axis. The dependent variable, which changes as a result of the changes made by the experimenter, is plotted on the y- or vertical axis.
- A graph in which data lie in a straight line is a graph of a linear relationship.
- A linear relationship can be represented by the equation $y = mx + b$.
- The slope, m, of a straight-line graph is the vertical change (rise) divided by the horizontal change (run).
- The graph of a quadratic relationship is a parabolic curve. It represents an equation $y = kx^2$.
- The graph of an inverse relationship between x and y is a hyperbolic curve. It represents an equation $xy = k$.

2.4 Manipulating Equations

- When solving an equation for a quantity, you should add, subtract, multiply, or divide in order to put that quantity alone on the left side of the equation.
- Units must be included when solving problems. The units must be the same on both sides of the equation. If this is not true, the equation is wrong.

KEY TERMS

metric system	precision
SI	accuracy
fundamental units	significant digits
second	independent variable
meter	dependent variables
kilogram	linear relationship
derived units	slope
scientific notation	y-intercept
prefixes	quadratic relationship
parallax	inverse relationship

REVIEWING CONCEPTS

1. Why is the International System of Units important?
2. List the common fundamental units in the SI system.
3. How are the fundamental units and derived units related?

CLOSING CHAPTER 2

Review Summary statements and Key Terms with your students.

ASSESSMENT

Vocabulary Review Master, Teacher Resource Package. Use this master to check students' understanding of Key Terms.

Evaluation Masters. Use Parts A and B of the Chapter Evaluation Masters from the Teacher Resource Package to test qualitative chapter objectives. Use Parts C and D to test quantitative chapter objectives.

Answers To
REVIEWING CONCEPTS

1. The International System of Units allows scientists all over the world to make measurements in the same system. Thus scientists know exactly what is meant by measurements made by other scientists.
2. seconds, time; meters, length; and kilograms, mass
3. The derived units are combinations of the fundamental units.
4. a. centimeter **b.** millimeter **c.** kilometer
5. the precision of a measuring device, which is limited by the finest division on its scale
6. Student answers will vary, but could include the following.
a. 365 days in a year **b.** The length of a meter stick is 1003.9 mm.
7. The final digit is estimated.
8. a. Zeros are necessary to indicate the magnitude of the value, but there is no way of knowing whether or not the instrument used to measure the values actually measured the zeros. The zeros may serve only to locate the six.
b. Write the number in scientific notation, including only the significant digits.

Answers continue on page 36.

2:4 ASSIGNMENT GUIDE

	PRACTICE	EXTENSION
CHAPTER REVIEW pp. 35–39		
· Reviewing Concepts	16	
· Applying Concepts		10
· Problems*	20–24, 27, 28	25, 26, 29
APPENDIX B PROBLEMS*		
· Chapter 2, pp. 688–689	11, 14, 15	12, 13

* Complete solutions to all Chapter Review and Appendix problems appear in the Problems and Solutions Manual.

STUDY GUIDE MASTER

Use the Study Guide master for section 2.4.

SKILL MASTER

Use Physics Skill Master 5 with this section.

SKILL MASTER

Use Physics Skill Master 8 with this section.

Answers To
REVIEWING CONCEPTS (cont)

9. The slope of a linear graph is the ratio of the vertical change to the horizontal change, or rise over run.
10. **a.** Longer reaction distance because $d = vt$ and t is larger. **b.** Larger slope because the vertical distance increases more rapidly with speed.
11. Temperature is the independent variable; volume is the dependent variable.
12. **a.** temperature **b.** volume
13. **a.** parabolic **b.** Linear, since y is being plotted versus the square of x, not x.
14. **a.** inverse relationship **b.** direct relationship **c.** direct relationship with the square of v
15. **a.** hyperbola **b.** straight line **c.** parabola
16. Make sure that the terms on both sides of an equation have the same units, and check that the problem is set up correctly.

Answers To
APPLYING CONCEPTS

1. **a.** Student answers will vary. Two possible answers: $\frac{g}{cm^3}, \frac{kg}{m^3}$.
   b. derived unit
   c. $\frac{kg}{m^3}$
2. Student answers will vary, but could be about
   a. 1 cm
   b. 0.1 mm
   c. 3 m
   d. 1 km
3. Student answers will vary.
4. Student answers will vary, but could include some of the following.

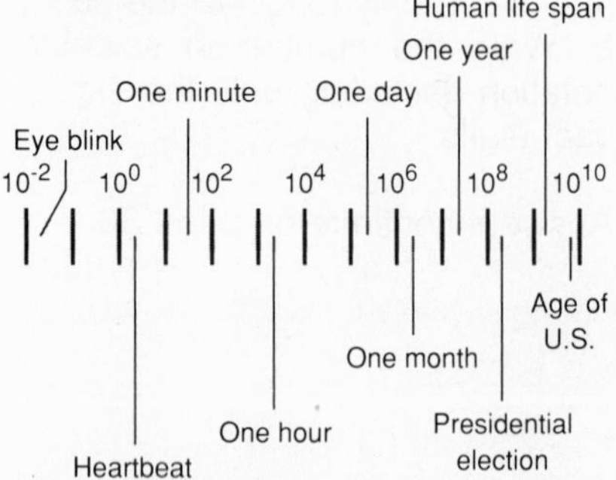

4. Give the proper name for each multiple of the meter listed.
   a. 1/100 m **b.** 1/1000 m **c.** 1000 m
5. What determines the precision of a measurement?
6. Give an example of a measurement that is
   a. accurate but not precise.
   b. precise but not accurate.
7. How does the last digit differ from the other digits in a measurement?
8. Rick recorded a measurement as 76 000 nm.
   a. Why is it difficult to tell how many significant digits there are?
   b. How can the number of significant digits in such a number be made clear?
9. How do you find the slope of a straight-line or linear graph.
10. A person who has consumed alcohol usually has longer reaction times than a person who has not. Thus, the time between seeing a stoplight and hitting the brakes would be longer for the drinker than for the nondrinker.
    a. For a fixed speed, would the "reaction distance" for such a driver be longer or shorter than for a nondrinking driver?
    b. Would the slope of the graph of reaction distance versus speed have a larger or smaller slope?
11. During a laboratory experiment, the temperature of the gas in a balloon is varied and the volume of the balloon is measured. Which quantity is the independent variable? Which quantity is the dependent variable?
12. When plotting a graph of the experiment in the previous question,
    a. what quantity is plotted as the abscissa (horizontally)?
    b. what quantity is plotted as the ordinate (vertically)?
13. A relationship between the independent variable x and the dependent variable y can be written using the equation $y = ax^2$, where a is a constant.
    a. What is the shape of the graph of this equation?
    b. If $z = x^2$, what would be the shape of the graph $y = az$?
14. According to the formula $F = mv^2/r$, what relationship exists between
    a. F and r?
    b. F and m?
    c. F and v?
15. For the previous question, what type of graph would be drawn for
    a. F versus r?
    b. F versus m?
    c. F versus v?
16. How may units be used to check if an equation is written correctly?

APPLYING CONCEPTS

1. The density of a substance is the mass per unit volume of that substance.
   a. List a possible metric unit for density.
   b. Does density have a fundamental or derived unit?
   c. What is the SI unit for density?
2. Locate the size of the following objects in Figure 2–4.
   a. The width of your thumb.
   b. The thickness of a page in this book.
   c. The height of your classroom.
   d. The distance from your house to school.
3. Make a chart of sizes of objects similar to Figure 2–4. Include only objects you have measured. Some should be less than one millimeter, others several kilometers.
4. Make a chart of time intervals similar to Figure 2–4. Include intervals like the time between heartbeats, the time between presidential elections, the average lifetime of a human, the age of the United States, and so forth. Find as many very short and very long examples as you can.
5. Three students use a meterstick to measure the width of a lab table. One records an answer of 84 cm, another, 83.8, and the third, 83.78. Explain which answer is recorded correctly.
6. Suppose Madelaine measures the speed of light to be 2.999×10^8 m/s with an uncertainty of 0.006×10^8 m/s.
   a. Is this measurement more or less precise than the example on page 21?
   b. Is it more or less accurate?
7. Why can quantities with different units never be added or subtracted but can be multiplied or divided? Give examples to support your answer.

REVIEW MASTER

Use the Vocabulary Review master for Chapter 2 with this section.

EVALUATION MASTER

Use the Chapter Evaluation master for Chapter 2 with this section.

8. Suppose you receive $5.00 at the beginning of a week and spend $1.00 each day for lunch. You prepare a graph of the amount you have left at the end of each day. Would the slope of this graph be positive, zero, or negative? Why?
9. Data are plotted on a graph and the value on the *y*-axis is the same for each value of the independent variable. What is the slope? Why?
10. The graph of braking distance versus car speed is part of a parabola. Thus we write the equation $d = kv^2$. The distance, *d*, has units, meters, and velocity, *v*, has units meters/second. How could you find the units of *k*? What would they be?
11. Think of a relationship between two variables. In baseball you might consider the relationship between the distance the ball is hit and the speed of the pitch. Determine which is the independent variable and which is the dependent variable. In this example, the speed of the pitch is the independent variable. Choose your own relationship. If you can, think of other possible independent variables for the same dependent variable.
12. Aristotle said that the quickness of a falling object varies inversely with the density of the medium in which it is falling.
    a. According to Aristotle, would a rock fall faster in water (density 1000 kg/m^3), or in air (density 1 kg/m^3)?
    b. How fast would a rock fall in a vacuum? Based on this, why did Aristotle say that there could be no such thing as a vacuum?

PROBLEMS

2.1 The Measure of Science

1. Express the following numbers in scientific notation.
    a. 5 000 000 000 000 000 000 000 000 m
    b. 0.000 000 000 000 000 000 166 m
    c. 2 033 000 000 m
    d. 0.000 000 103 0 m
2. Convert each of the following measurements into meters.
    a. 42.3 cm
    b. 6.2 pm
    c. 21 km
    d. 0.023 mm
    e. 214 μm
    f. 570 nm
3. Rank the following mass measurements from smallest to largest: 11.6 mg, 1021 μg, 0.000 006 kg, 0.31 mg.
4. Add or subtract as indicated.
    a. 5.80×10^9 s $+ 3.20 \times 10^8$ s
    b. 4.87×10^{-6} m $- 1.93 \times 10^{-6}$ m
    c. 3.14×10^{-5} kg $+ 9.36 \times 10^{-5}$ kg
    d. 8.12×10^7 g $- 6.20 \times 10^6$ g

2.2 Not All Is Certain

5. State the number of significant digits in the following measurements.
    a. 248 m
    b. 0.000 03 m
    c. 64.01 m
    d. 80.001 m
6. State the number of significant digits in the following measurements.
    a. 2.40×10^6 kg
    b. 6×10^8 kg
    c. 4.07×10^{16} m
7. Many labels give metric equivalents of English quantities. Examples are: 12 fluid ounces (9345.66 mL), 353 ft (107.59 m), 2.0 inch (50.80 mm). Report each metric equivalent using the correct number of significant digits.
8. Add or subtract as indicated and state the answer with the correct number of significant digits.
    a. 16.2 m + 5.008 m + 13.48 m
    b. 5.006 m + 12.0077 m + 8.0084 m
    c. 78.05 cm^2 − 32.046 cm^2
    d. 15.07 kg − 12.0 kg
9. Multiply or divide as indicated watching significant digits.
    a. $(6.2 \times 10^{18}$ m$)(4.7 \times 10^{-10}$ m$)$
    b. $(5.6 \times 10^{-7}$ m$) \div (2.8 \times 10^{-12}$ s$)$
    c. $(8.1 \times 10^{-4}$ km$)(1.6 \times 10^{-3}$ km$)$
    d. $(6.5 \times 10^5$ kg$) \div (3.4 \times 10^3$ m$^3)$
10. Tom did the following problems on his calculator, reporting the results shown. Give the answer to each using the correct number of significant digits.
    a. 5.32 mm + 2.1 mm = 7.4200000 mm
    b. 13.597 m × 3.65 m = 49.6290500 m^2
    c. 83.2 kg − 12.804 kg = 70.3960000 kg
11. A rectangular floor has a length of 15.72 m and a width of 4.40 m. Calculate the area of the floor to the best possible value using these measurements.

5. Length measurements are made to the smallest scale division, then the final digit is estimated. Only 83.78 cm has a digit estimated beyond the meterstick's millimeter scale.
6. a. less precise
   b. more accurate
7. Only like terms can be added or subtracted. 5 m and 1 s cannot be added; but divided, 5 m/s becomes a velocity.
8. Negative, because the change in vertical distance is negative for a positive change in horizontal distance.
9. Zero. The change in vertical distance is zero.
10. Solve for *k*: $kv^2 = d$, $k = d/v^2$. The units of *k* are $m/(m/s)^2 = s^2/m$.
11. Answers will vary according to the relationship chosen.
12. a. Lower density means faster speed, so the rock falls faster in air.
    b. Since a vacuum would have a zero density, the rock should fall infinitely fast. Nothing can fall this fast.

Answers To

PROBLEMS

Refer to Problems and Solutions Manual for complete solutions.

1. **a.** 5×10^{24} m
   b. 1.66×10^{-19} m
   c. 2.033×10^{9} m
   d. 1.030×10^{-7} m
2. **a.** 0.423 m
   b. 6.2×10^{-12} m
   c. 2.1×10^{4} m
   d. 2.3×10^{-5} m
   e. 2.14×10^{-4} m
   f. 5.70×10^{-7} m
3. 0.31 mg, 1021 μg, 0.000 006 kg, 11.6 mg
4. **a.** 6.12×10^{9} s
   b. 2.94×10^{-6} m
   c. 1.250×10^{-4} kg
   d. 7.50×10^{7} g
5. **a.** 3
   b. 1
   c. 4
   d. 5
6. **a.** 3
   b. 1
   c. 3
7. 9.4×10^{3} mL, 108 m, 51 mm
8. **a.** 34.7 m
   b. 25.022 m
   c. 46.00 cm^2
   d. 3.1 kg
9. **a.** 2.9×10^{9} m^2
   b. 2.0×10^{5} m/s
   c. 1.3×10^{-6} km^2
   d. 1.9×10^{2} kg/m^3
10. **a.** 7.4 mm
    b. 49.6 m^2
    c. 70.4 kg
11. 69.2 m^2
12. **a.** 101.6 m
    b. 584 m^2
13. 2.4×10^{2} m^3
14. 362.1 m
15. 48.2 kg
16. **a.** (a) 80 g, (b) 260 g, (c) 400 g
    b. (a) 37 cm^3, (b) 11 cm^3, (c) 7 cm^3
    c. The steepness represents the increased mass of each additional cubic centimeter of the substance.
17. **a.** Refer to the Problems and Solutions Manual.
    b. a straight line
    c. $M = mV$, where m is the slope.
    d. mass/volume; density
18. **a.** Refer to the Problems and Solutions Manual.
    b. The acceleration varies directly with the force.
    c. $F = ka$
    d. $m/s^2 \cdot N$

12. A yard is 33.21 m long and 17.6 m wide.
   a. What length of fence must be purchased to enclose the entire yard?
   b. What area must be covered if the yard is to be fertilized?

13. The length of a room is 16.40 m, its width is 4.5 m, and its height is 3.26 m. What volume does the room enclose?

14. The sides of a quadrangular plot of land are 132.68 m, 48.3 m, 132.736 m, and 48.37 m. What is the perimeter of the plot as can best be determined from these measurements?

15. A water tank has a mass of 3.64 kg when empty and a mass of 51.8 kg when filled to a certain level. What is the mass of the water in the tank?

2.3 Displaying Data

▶ **16.** Figure 2–18 shows the mass of three substances for volumes between 0 and 60 cm^3.
   a. What is the mass of 30 cm^3 of each substance?
   b. If you had 100 g of each substance, what would their volumes be?
   c. Describe the meaning of the steepness of the lines in this graph (a single word is not a sufficient answer!).

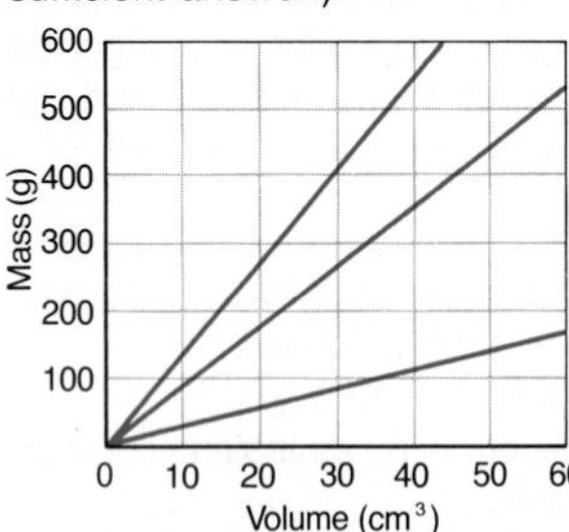

FIGURE 2-18. Use with Problem 16.

17. During an experiment, a student measured the mass of 10.0 cm^3 of alcohol. The student then measured the mass of 20.0 cm^3 of alcohol. In this way the data in Table 2–3 were collected.

Table 2–3

Volume (cm^3)	Mass (g)
10.0	7.9
20.0	15.8
30.0	23.7
40.0	31.6
50.0	39.6

   a. Plot the values given in the table and draw the curve that best fits all points.
   b. Describe the resulting curve.
   c. Use the graph to write an equation relating the volume to the mass of the alcohol.
   d. Find the units of the slope of the graph. What is the name given to this quantity?

▶ **18.** During a class demonstration, an instructor placed a 1.0-kg mass on a horizontal table that was nearly frictionless. The instructor then applied various horizontal forces to the mass and measured the rate at which the mass gained speed (was accelerated) for each force applied. The results of the experiment are shown in Table 2–4.

Table 2–4

Force (N)	Acceleration (m/s^2)
5.0	4.9
10.0	9.8
15.0	15.2
20.0	20.1
25.0	25.0
30.0	29.9

   a. Plot the values given in the table and draw the curve that best fits all points.
   b. Describe, in words, the relationship between force and acceleration according to the graph.
   c. Write the equation relating the force and the acceleration that results from the graph.
   d. Find the units of the slope of the graph.

▶ **19.** The teacher who performed the experiment in the previous problem then changed the procedure. The mass was varied while the force was kept constant. The acceleration of each mass was then recorded. The results are shown in Table 2–5.

Table 2–5

Mass (kg)	Acceleration (m/s^2)
1.0	12.0
2.0	5.9
3.0	4.1
4.0	3.0
5.0	2.5
6.0	2.0

a. Plot the values given in the table and draw the curve that best fits all points.
b. Describe the resulting curve.
c. According to the graph, what is the relationship between mass and the acceleration produced by a constant force?
d. Write the equation relating acceleration to mass given by the data in the graph.
e. Find the units of the constant in the equation.

2.4 Manipulating Equations

20. Each cubic centimeter of gold has a mass of 19.3 g. A cube of gold measures 4.23 cm on each edge.
a. What is the volume of the cube?
b. What is its mass?

21. Solve the equation

$$T = 2\pi \sqrt{l/g}$$

a. for l.
b. for g.

22. Each cubic centimeter of silver has a mass of 10.5 g.
a. What is the mass of 65.0 cm^3 of silver?
b. When placed on a beam balance, the 65.0-cm^3 piece of silver has a mass of only 616 g. What volume of the piece is hollow?

23. Assume that a small sugar cube has sides 1 cm long. If you had a box containing 1 mole of sugar cubes and lined them up side by side, how long would the line be? 1 mole = 6.02×10^{23} units.

24. The average distance between Earth and the sun is 1.50×10^8 km.
a. Calculate the average speed, in km/h, of Earth assuming a circular path about the sun. Use the equation $v = \frac{2\pi r}{T}$.
b. Convert your answer from km/h to m/s. Show all units.

▶ **25.** The radius of Earth is 6.37×10^3 km.
a. Find the speed, in km/h, resulting from the rotation of Earth, of a person standing on the equator.
b. Convert your answer to m/s.

▶ **26.** A child rides a merry-go-round horse that is 5.4 m from the center. The rides lasts 10 minutes. During this time, the ride makes 24 revolutions. Find the speed of the child in meters/second. Use the equation $v = \frac{2\pi r}{T}$.

27. Manipulate the equation $v = d/t$ and find the answers to these problems using consistent units.
a. Find the distance a bike travels in 1.5 minutes, if it is traveling at a constant speed of 20 km/h.
b. How long will it take a car to travel 6000 m if its speed is a constant 30 km/h?

28. Water drips from a faucet into a flask at the rate of two drops every 3 seconds. A cubic centimeter (cm^3) contains 20 drops. What volume of water, in cubic decimeters (dm^3), will be collected in 1 hour?

▶ **29.** Tony's Pizza Shop ordered new 23-cm pizza pans (9-inch pans). By mistake, 26-cm (10-inch) pans were delivered. Tony says that the difference is too small to worry about. As Tony's accountant, what would you say knowing materials cost about 0.25 cents per square centimeter?

USING LAB SKILLS

1. How could your measurements in the Pocket Lab on page 17 be improved?
2. Using the data from the Physics Lab on page 28, estimate the uncertainty of the length and mass measurements.

THINKING PHYSIC-LY

Three students decide to buy a $20.51 gift for a friend. Sally divides $20.51 by 3 on her calculator and gets 6.83666667 as a result. Is this a reasonable amount for each student to pay? Explain.

19. a. Refer to the Problems and Solutions Manual.
b. hyperbola
c. Acceleration varies inversely with the mass.
d. $a = c/M$
e. $kg{\cdot}m/s^2$

20. a. 75.7 cm^3
b. 1.46×10^3 g

21. a. $l = \frac{gT^2}{4\pi^2}$
b. $g = \frac{4\pi^2 l}{T^2}$

22. a. 683 g
b. 6.3 cm^3

23. 6.02×10^{18} km

24. a. 1.08×10^5 km/h
b. 2.99×10^4 m/s

25. a. 1.67×10^3 km/h
b. 464 m/s

26. 1.4 m/s

27. a. 0.50 km
b. 0.20 h

28. $0.12 \frac{dm^3}{h}$

29. Each pizza costs 30 cents more to make.

Answers To USING LAB SKILLS

1. The accuracy of the measurements could have been improved by using more sensitive instruments, such as measuring the thickness of the paper with a micrometer, which measures in μm.
2. The length is supposed to be accurate to the nearest 0.1 cm, but the wires are not straight, and students will have some difficulty in measuring this accurately. The uncertainty of the mass measurement depends on the accuracy and precision of the balance. With an electronic balance, most students will announce the answer as 0.001 grams.

Answer To THINKING PHYSIC-LY

No. Just because a calculator gives an answer to nine places, it does not mean that all places are valid. In this case, the numbers must be rounded to the nearest hundredth.

CHAPTER

3 Describing Motion: Velocity

PLANNING GUIDE (5 class sessions)

CONTENTS	TEXT FEATURES	TEACHER RESOURCE PACKAGE	OTHER COMPONENTS
3.1 How Far and How Fast?, pp. 41–49 (2 Class Sessions) • Position and Distance • Average Velocity • Finding Displacement from Velocity and Time • Position-Time Graphs • The Slope of a Position-Time Graph	**Physics Lab:** The Car Race, p. 50 **Physics and Technology:** The Sonic Ranger, p. 47 **Pocket Lab:** Jogger's Speed, p. 45 **Problem Solving Strategy:** Conversion Factors, p. 45 **Concept Review**, p. 49	**Study Guide:** How Far and How Fast? **Physics Lab Data Sheet:** The Car Race **Reteaching Master:** Using a Reference Point	**Laboratory Manual:** Lab 3.1 Uniform Motion **Physics Skill Master 12**
3.2 New Meanings for Old Words, pp. 51–57 (3 Class Sessions) • Positive and Negative Velocities • Instantaneous Velocity • Velocity-Time Graphs • Relativity of Velocity	**Pocket Lab:** Bowling Ball Displacement, p. 52 **Concept Review,** p. 57	**Study Guide:** New Meanings for Old Words **Critical Thinking Master:** Positions Along a Roller Coaster **Enrichment Master:** Graphing Relative Velocity **Transparency Worksheet:** Position vs Time	**Transparency 3:** Position vs Time **Physics Skill Master 13**
Chapter Review, pp. 57–61	Summary Key Terms Reviewing Concepts Applying Concepts Problems Using a Graphing Calculator Thinking Physic-ly	**Vocabulary Review** **Chapter Test**	**Test Bank**

SUPPLEMENTARY MATERIALS

SOFTWARE	AUDIOVISUAL	BOOKS/MAGAZINES
Kinematics, Vernier (Apple II). *Motion: A Microcomputer-Based Lab,* HRM (Apple II). *A Tutorial on Motion,* COMPress/Queue, Inc. (Apple II).	Filmstrips: *Motion: Velocity and Acceleration,* Clearvue. *Understanding Motion,* Bergwall. Video: *The Mechanical Universe and Beyond: Velocity and Time* and *Mass, Momentum, Energy,* Films Inc.	Coombs, Earl. "Demonstrating the Difference between Velocity and Acceleration." *The Physics Teacher,* November 1990, p. 546. Halada, Richard S. "The Strobe Cannon." *The Physics Teacher,* October 1990, p. 488. Payne, Mark M. "How Fast Are We Going?" *The Physics Teacher,* February 1990, p. 102. Peckman, G. D., *et al.* "If You Don't Have a Slicker, Does It Pay to Walk Quicker?" *The Science Teacher,* December 1987, pp. 35–39.

PROBLEM CORRELATION

CONCEPTS		CHAPTER REVIEW			PROBLEMS APPENDIX
		Reviewing Concepts	Applying Concepts	Problems	
3.1	**How Far and How Fast?**				
	Position and Distance	1,2	1,2	1	1
	Average Velocity	3,4	3,4	2,3,5,6,7	2,3,**4**
	Finding Displacement From Velocity and Time		5	4,9,10,**11,12**	5,6,**7**
	Position-Time Graphs			13,14	**8**,9
	The Slope of a Position-Time Graph	5,6	6,7,8,9	**15,16,**17,18, 19,**20**	10,11
3.2	**New Meanings For Old Words**				
	Position and Negative Velocities	7			
	Instantaneous Velocity	8		21,22	12
	Velocity-Time Graphs	9,10,11	10,11	23,24,**25**	**13,14**
	Relativity of Velocity			8	15

ACTIVITY AND DEMONSTRATION MATERIALS

PHYSICS LAB	POCKET LAB	DEMONSTRATIONS
Page 50 battery-powered car marking pen 2.5 m length of wide paper masking tape 5 cm length of plastic straw 3.0-m fishing line metronome	Pages 45, 52 stopwatches football field bowling ball	

EXTENSION PROJECTS

LIBRARY RESEARCH

1. Record Speed
Do some research to find out the record velocity for an automobile. Under what conditions was such a velocity attained?

HANDS-ON

2. Calculating Distance
Using a car speedometer and a timer, calculate a distance such as the length of your block. Check your results by referring to the odometer reading.

STUDENT READINGS

Bartlett, Albert A., and Lamb, J. Parker. "The Train Left the Track." *The Physics Teacher,* December 1990.

Easton, D. "The Stoplight Dilemma Revisited." *The Physics Teacher,* January 1990.

Gardner, Martin. "The Computer As Scientist." *Discover,* June 1983.

Nalence, Eugene E. "Using Automobile Road Test Data." *The Physics Teacher,* May 1988.

"3-D Graphing." *Byte,* January 1989.

Chapter 3

Describing Motion: Velocity

CHAPTER OVERVIEW

Theme Development: A study of motion introduces mathematical modeling of concepts such as position, displacement, distance, speed, time interval, and the various motion graphs. The lesson abstracts the real world into an ideal mathematical system.

MISCONCEPTIONS

Two student difficulties stand out here. One, the use of graphs and how they represent a set of data; and two, the slope concept used for determining velocity. In addition, a common misconception is that moving objects at the same point along a path have the same velocity.

KEY TERMS

average velocity
clock reading
constant velocity
displacement
distance
factor-label method
frame of reference
instantaneous position
instantaneous velocity
position
position-time graph
reference point
scalar
slope
speed
time interval
vector
velocity
velocity-time graph

Laboratory Options

CHAPTER 3

Describing Motion: Velocity

Introducing The Chapter

How Fast?

The Example Problem on page 45 shows how to figure out which race Florence Griffith-Joyner ran the fastest.

Using The Photo: Motion is everywhere, especially in sports. To specify this event's motion, careful measurement of distance and time is necessary. The calculations needed to answer the question in the caption are given on page 45.

Concept Check

Make sure students have a clear understanding of the concepts taught in Chapter 2 that are listed in the Concept Check. Students with a good grasp of fundamental and derived units, the manipulation of algebraic equations, and graphing techniques will more easily understand the principles of velocity introduced in this chapter.

How Fast?

In the 1988 Summer Olympics, Florence Griffith-Joyner won the 100-m race in 10.54 s and the 200-m race in 21.34 s. In which race did she run faster?

Chapter Outline

Take a moment to think of things that move. People walk, run, and ride bikes. Earth rotates once each day and revolves about the sun once each year. The sun also rotates with the Milky Way, which itself is moving within its local group of galaxies. Because motion is common to everything in the universe, we begin our study of physics with a study of motion.

Two of the most exciting forms of motion to watch are the 100-m and 200-m dashes. Sprinters must blast out of the starting blocks, reaching peak speed in the shortest possible time. Sometimes the race seems over almost before it has begun.

We can describe motion in three ways. The first description uses common, ordinary words in sentences. The second uses an equation involving mathematical quantities. The third uses graphs that show how these quantities change in time.

Concept Check

The following terms or concepts from earlier chapters are important for a good understanding of this chapter. If you are not familiar with them, you should review them before studying this chapter.

- units: fundamental (length and time) and derived (m/s), manipulation of algebraic equations, Chapter 2
- graphing techniques, Chapter 2

41

Assessment Options

Portfolio Assessment
Portfolio Assessment, TWE, p. 44
Connect to Biology, TWE, p. 44
Cooperative Learning, TWE, p. 51
Checking for Understanding, bulleted item two, TWE, p. 55

Performance Assessment
Pocket Labs, pp. 45, 52
Physics Lab, p. 50
Assessment, Critical Thinking, TWE, p. 50
Using Lab Skills, p. 61

Content Assessment
Self Assessment: Practice Problems, pp. 45, 47, 53, 55, 56
Critical Thinking, TWE, p. 54
Concept Reviews, pp. 49, 57
Chapter Review, pp. 57–61
Supplemental Problems, pp. 689–690

Group Assessment
Activities for group assessment occur with Cooperative Learning and lab activities.

3.1 HOW FAR AND HOW FAST?

Preparation

OBJECTIVES

The objectives are listed on the student page. Remind students to preview these objectives as a study guide to this major section.

OVERVIEW

In this first section on detailed physics, it's necessary to build up some vocabulary to describe aspects of motion. Except for instantaneous velocity and velocity-time graphs, all the words listed in Key Terms on page 41 are introduced here. Notice that although many words are familiar, they may have meanings which are somewhat different from their everyday usage.

BRIDGING

Students will find that mathematics skills they have gained from algebra—graphing data and solving equations with variables—are important to solving motion problems in physics. Manipulation of units will be useful to physics students throughout their course of study.

1 Focus

Try to ease students into this section by having them discuss the concept of speed. After all, everyone has had lots of exposure to this idea. Use a toy such as a toy bulldozer that has a manageable, constant motion. Simply let it go across your desk top once or twice, then ask what would need to be measured to determine the toy's speed. You might make a point of using more than one set of units to do the problem.

CONCEPT DEVELOPMENT

The plus-sign minus-sign method is the conventional way to designate direction. You may want to make students aware that other frames of reference are possible and acceptable.

Objectives

- **define and give an example of a frame of reference.**
- **define the concept of average velocity in a way that shows you know how to calculate it.**
- **demonstrate the ability to calculate average velocity and to solve an equation involving velocity, distance, and time.**
- **interpret and plot position-time graphs for positive and negative positions.**
- **be able to determine the slope of a curve on a position-time graph and calculate the velocity.**

3.1 HOW FAR AND HOW FAST?

Before we can study how something moves, we have to know where it is. To simplify matters, we will set up a few ground rules. First, we will only describe motion, not try to explain its causes. Second, we will begin by studying objects that move only in straight lines. Third, we will study objects as if they were point objects, not three-dimensional bodies. For example, if we describe the motion of a bicycle, we will mentally step back until the bike and its rider look like a point.

Position and Distance

Where is something? How do we locate it? Figure 3–1 is a drawing of two cars on a road. Where is car A? More precisely, what is the position of a very tiny dot on car A? First, put a scale on the drawing. To locate car A, we describe its position in terms of its relationship to some other point on the scale, like the zero mark. The scale shows the separation between the zero mark and car A is 8.0 m. That is, A is 8.0 m to the right of zero. What is the position of car B? It is 1.0 m to the left of zero.

Position is the separation between an object and a reference point.

In making zero the **reference point**, you have chosen a **frame of reference**. You could have chosen either car, some point to the left of both, to the right of both, or any other point between them. The separation between car A and the reference point would be different in each case. The **position** of an object is the separation between that object and a reference point. We will use the symbol *d* to represent position.

Distance, on the other hand, needs no reference frame. You measure the distance between two objects by measuring their separation. Car A is 9.0 m from car B no matter where you put the reference point.

A vector is a quantity that is represented by both a magnitude and a direction.

Distance differs from position in a second way. Both a distance and a direction are needed to describe position. Point **A** is 8.0 m to the right of "0." Although the direction can be described in terms of left and right, it will be more convenient for us to use plus (+) and minus (−) signs. Positive (+) directions are to the right of the reference point; negative (−) directions are to the left. Thus, the position of A is +8.0 m and the position of B is −1.0 m. Distance, on the other hand, involves only a length measurement, never direction.

A quantity, like distance, that has only a magnitude, or size, is called a **scalar** (scā-ler). Position, on the other hand, has both magnitude (size) and direction. Such a quantity is called a **vector.** We will identify many other quantities as either scalars or vectors.

Vector Conventions

- **Velocity vectors are red.**
- **Displacement vectors are green.**

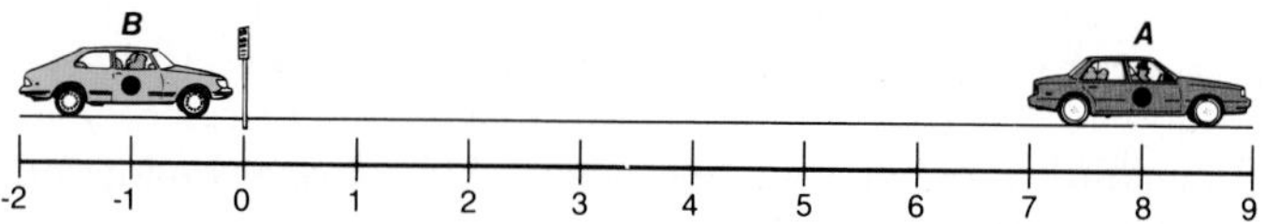

FIGURE 3–1. The position of these two automobiles is determined from a point of reference.

TEACHER F.Y.I.

Galileo was one of the first to perceive that mathematics and physics should work together to describe physical phenomena. Galileo, however, used geometry rather than algebra to describe physical phenomena.

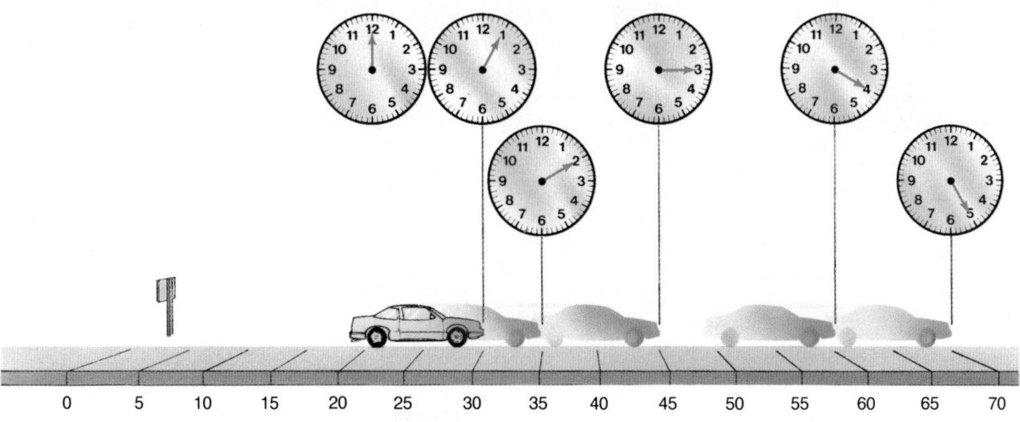

FIGURE 3–2. The change in position of car B over a 5-second period.

Average Velocity

Both car A and car B are moving, and Figure 3–1 shows their position at one particular instant. Figure 3–2 shows what would be seen if a series of photos of car B and a clock were made. We can identify the instant car B is at a certain position by the reading on a clock. We will give this **clock reading** the symbol t.

If the car continues to move, how long will it be at any one position? That is almost the same as asking "how long are the hands of the clock at any one position?" The clock reading lasts zero seconds. The moving car is located at 9.0 m at one and only one time. The position of the car is an **instantaneous position**. The moving car generates a series of pairs of instantaneous positions and clock readings, Table 3–1.

The numbers in this table can be used to find out how fast the car is moving. There is no question that between any two clock readings, a fast-moving car has a larger change in position than a slow-moving car. So first, we should define what we mean by change in position.

The change in position of an object is often called its **displacement.** To find the displacement of an object, take its position at one clock reading, d_2, and subtract its position at an earlier clock reading, d_1. We use the symbol Δd for the displacement or change in position, so $\Delta d = d_2 - d_1$. Displacement, the difference between two positions, is a vector quantity. It can either be positive or negative. In the same way, we find the **time interval** between two clock readings, $\Delta t = t_2 - t_1$.

Now, consider the ratio $\frac{\Delta d}{\Delta t}$ between the times t_1 and t_2. For the moving car data given in Table 3–1, the denominator, the time interval, Δt, is always 1.0 second. The value of the ratio $\Delta d/\Delta t$ varies from 0, between 0.0 and 1.0 second, to 15, between 3.0 and 4.0 seconds. Note that the ratio is larger when the car moves quickly than it is when the car moves slowly.

Table 3–1

Clock readings, t, in s	Positions, d, in m
0.0	30
1.0	30
2.0	35
3.0	45
4.0	60
5.0	70

An instantaneous position is the location of an object at an instant, at a single time.

2 Teach

CONCEPT DEVELOPMENT

Study Guide Master. To reinforce the concepts in this section, have the students complete the Study Guide Master for Section 3.1 from the Teacher Resource Package.

- Emphasize the difference between distance, displacement, and position.
- Ask the students what the word "magnitude" means to them. It's a difficult word to get a handle on. Review it frequently and emphasize that 10 km is a magnitude and east is a direction.
- To help students get used to everyday speeds in SI units, use the following table:

40 km/h	= 25 mi/h	= 11 m/s
80	= 50	= 22
100	= 62	= 28
120	= 75	= 33

However, the table should definitely not be memorized.

- There is a conversion trick that people from metric countries often use to convert from a speed in kilometers per hour to a speed in meters per second. The trick is simply to divide by 3.6. Can your students discover why this trick works?

Critical Thinking: Ask: Does an odometer measure distance or displacement? [distance] What do you need to measure displacement? [a map and a measuring device]

Enrichment: Make up several examples of distance versus displacement, then have students contribute some of their own examples.

Multicultural Connections

The Kalahari people of Africa hunt the fastest animal on Earth, the cheetah. How do the Kalahari catch the cheetahs? They understand that something moving at a constant speed over a long time can overtake something that can move faster, but only for a shorter period. The Kalahari chase the cheetah at a pace they can maintain for an extended period. The cheetah cannot maintain its rapid pace. When it tires, the Kalahari can catch it.

STUDY GUIDE MASTER

Use the Study Guide master for section 3.1.

CONCEPT DEVELOPMENT

- Note that average speed does not tell the whole story. For example, consider a journey with an average speed of 30 m/s. From this information can you tell if the object ever moved with a speed of 45 m/s? No! So the average speed tells you nothing about the variation of the speed during the trip.
- It's important to make the distinction between *time* and *time interval.* By time we mean a single clock reading, t. A time interval is the result of subtracting two clock readings $t_2 - t_1$ or Δt.

ACTIVITY

Discovery: As the study of physics gets started it's very important to always give students a feeling for the sizes of the units used for any quantity. That is, they should be able to relate them to their own experience as much as possible. To start this type of activity, you can mark off a four-or-five-meter-long course in the front of the room and ask student volunteers to walk normally along the course. Now, to get time, count aloud (or to yourself if you prefer) one thousand one, one thousand two, etc. With a little practice, checking yourself against a watch, you can measure things to at least a half second. Normal walking speeds will be one to two meters per second.

Assessment

Portfolio

Suggest students make a reference sheet of calculations of velocities of common objects in m/s. Examples are automobile speed limits, pitched baseballs and football passes, and runners and swimmers at their school.

The average velocity between two times is the change in position divided by the difference in the two times.

The ratio $\Delta d/\Delta t$ is called **average velocity** and is indicated by the symbol $\bar{v}$, called v-bar. The average velocity over a given time interval is the change of position divided by the time interval over which the change occurred, or

$$\bar{v} = \frac{\Delta d}{\Delta t} = \frac{d_2 - d_1}{t_2 - t_1}.$$

The units for average velocity are a distance unit divided by a time unit. Any distance unit and any time unit can be used to calculate speed. In this textbook, we will usually use kilometers or meters for distance and seconds or hours for time. For example, between 3.0 and 4.0 seconds, the average velocity of the car is 15 meters in one second, or 15 meters per second. Note: "per second" means "in one second."

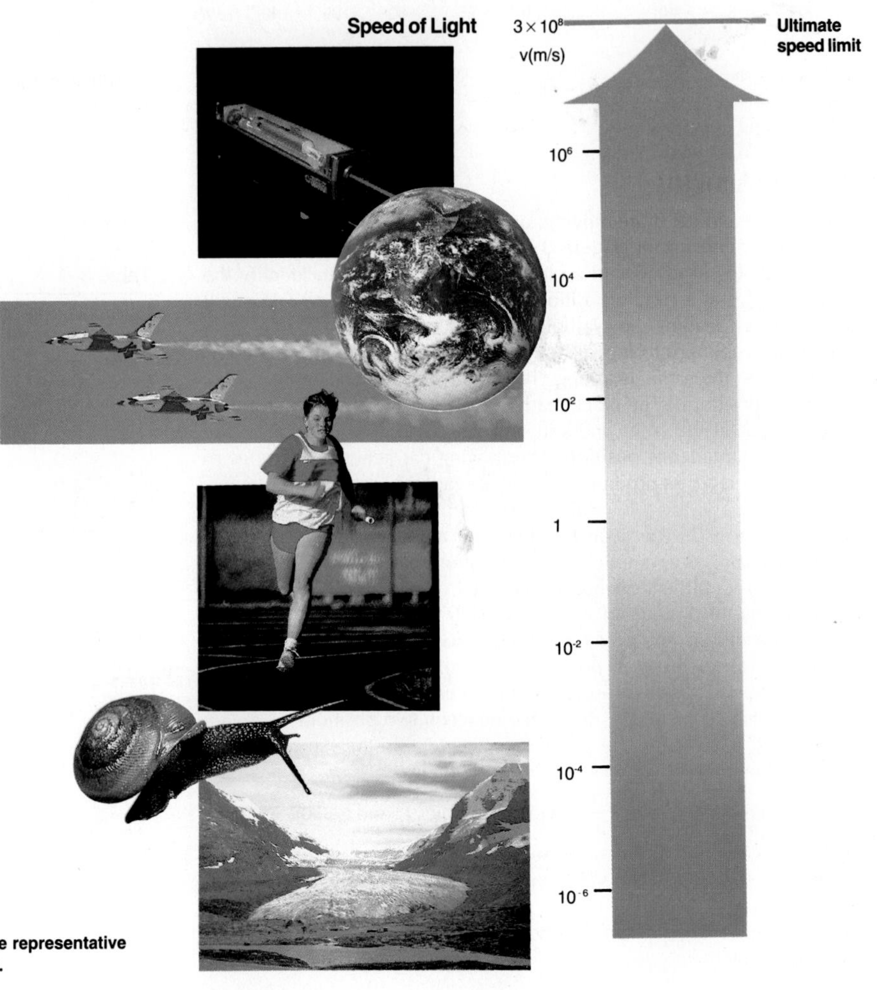

FIGURE 3–3. Some representative velocities of Earth.

Connect to BIOLOGY

How fast do animals move and plants grow? Ask students to look up the speeds animals can run, from the snail pictured to the fastest large cat. To give students practice with negative exponents, have them measure plant growth and calculate the velocity of the tip of the growing plant.

PROBLEM SOLVING STRATEGY

An easy way to change from one unit to another is by using conversion factors. To convert a velocity, given in kilometers per hour, km/h, to meters per second, m/s, you must first change kilometers to meters, then hours to seconds. The value of any quantity does not change when it is multiplied by 1. Any quantity divided by its equivalent equals one. Since 1000 m = 1 km and 3600 s = 1 h, we can make the following conversion factors.

$$\frac{1000\ \text{m}}{1\ \text{km}} = \frac{1\ \text{h}}{3600\ \text{s}} = 1$$

Therefore, to change a velocity in km/h to m/s, first multiply it by an appropriate distance conversion factor and then by a time conversion factor. For example, 100 km/h becomes

$$100\frac{\text{km}}{\text{h}} \cdot \left(\frac{1000\ \text{m}}{1\ \text{km}}\right) \cdot \left(\frac{1\ \text{h}}{3600\ \text{s}}\right) = 27.8\frac{\text{m}}{\text{s}}.$$

This method of converting one unit to another unit is called dimensional analysis, or the **factor-label method** of unit conversion. Unit labels are treated as mathematical factors and can be divided out. If the final units do not make sense, check your factors. You may find that a factor has either been inverted or stated incorrectly.

Units can be changed by multiplying by a factor of unit magnitude.

When solving problems, always include units with quantities.

Example Problem

Calculating Average Velocity

In the 1988 Summer Olympics, Florence Griffith-Joyner won the 100-m race in 10.54 s. Assuming the length of the race is measured to 0.1 m, find her average velocity in m/s and km/h.

Given: displacement, $\Delta d = +100.0$ m
time interval, $\Delta t = 10.54$ s

Unknown: average velocity, $\bar{v}$

Basic equation: $\bar{v} = \frac{\Delta d}{\Delta t}$

Solution: $\bar{v} = \frac{\Delta d}{\Delta t} = \frac{+100.0\ \text{m}}{10.54\ \text{s}} = +9.488$ m/s

$$+9.488\ \text{m/s}\left(\frac{3600\ \text{s/h}}{1000\ \text{m/km}}\right) = +34.16\ \text{km/h}$$

That is, she ran at the rate of +9.488 m in one second, or +34.16 km in one hour. In the 200-m race, Flo-Jo's average velocity was 200.0 m/21.34 s = +9.372 m/s, so her average velocity was greater in the 100-m race.

POCKET LAB

JOGGER'S SPEED

Take a stopwatch to the football field. Measure the time it takes to walk 50 m (55 yards). Calculate your average speed. Measure the time it takes you to jog, or run, the same distance. What is your average speed?

◀ How Fast?

Practice Problems

1. A high school athlete runs 1.00×10^2 m in 12.20 s. What is the velocity in m/s and km/h?
2. A person walks 13 km in 2.0 h. What is the person's average velocity in km/h and m/s?

POCKET LAB

JOGGER'S SPEED

Purpose: to permit students to calculate speed using simple data collected for distance and time.

Materials: stopwatch; football field.

Outcome: Students will take between 25 and 50 s to walk 50 m. Their average speeds will be in the range of 1 to 2 m/s. Students will take between 7 and 12 s to run/jog 50 m. Their average speeds will be in the range of 4 to 7 m/s.

Answers To
PRACTICE PROBLEMS

Have students refer to Appendix A of the Solutions Appendix for complete solutions to Practice Problems.

1. 8.20 m/s; 29.5 km/h
2. 6.5 km/h; 1.8 m/s

TEACHER F.Y.I.

A person who can estimate a time interval to within 0.5 s is considered to have an extremely accurate sense of time, or "absolute timing." Absolute timing is the ability of a person to over- or underestimate a time interval by a few fractions of a second. The error is the same amount whether the judged interval is 0.5 s, 0.25 s, or 0.13 s. If the judged time interval is greater than 0.5 s, however, the error size is not constant. From *Winston Churchill's Afternoon Nap*, J. Campbell, 1986, Simon and Schuster.

Answers To
PRACTICE PROBLEMS (cont)

3. slowest between 0.0 and 1.0 s (0 m/s); fastest between 3.0 and 4.0 s (15 m/s)

4. 2.5 m/s

CONCEPT DEVELOPMENT

• Check to make sure that students are using units along with each number they write down. Simply put, this practice helps to make sense of the numbers in a problem. Since this is a very good habit to acquire, set a good example yourself by making it a standard practice. For example, 30 by itself doesn't say much, but 30 m/s says a lot more!

• To impress upon students the need for units, develop a discussion using tangible items like money. If you claim to have 30 in reference to monetary values, people want to know 30 what? Dollars? Cents? Yachts? BMW's?

• Because of the way most physics equations are set up, speed is used in meters per second. So to give students an idea of how big meters per second are, remind them of walking speeds. Then ask for the world record in the 100-m dash. It's just under ten seconds, thus the top average speed is about ten meters per second. Knowing these two speed values will help give students a framework for judging speeds.

Guided Practice: After going over the Example Problem on this page, have students try the first Practice Problem on page 47.

Independent Practice: Assign the remaining Practice Problems (6–8) on page 47 for homework and spend time going over them the next class period.

FIGURE 3–4. This high-speed French train travels commercially at speeds close to 305 km/h. The train moves as a single unit, giving it an exceptionally smooth ride. Japanese and German railways are working on magnetically-suspended trains that can reach speeds of 480 km/h.

3. Using the data in Table 3–1, during what one-second-long time interval is the car moving slowest? moving fastest?

▶ **4.** Using the data in Table 3–1, find the average velocity of the car in the time interval between 0.0 and 2.0 s.

Finding Displacement from Velocity and Time

Any one quantity in the equation for average velocity can be found if the other two are known. For example, if the average velocity and time interval are known, then the displacement can be found by rearranging the equation.

$$\bar{v} = \frac{\Delta d}{\Delta t}, \text{ to the form, } \Delta d = \bar{v}\Delta t.$$

You can quickly check your algebra by examining the units. The quantity Δd has units meters. The quantity $\bar{v}\Delta t$ has units (m/s)s = m. This is an indication that the equation is correct.

HELP WANTED

AUTO MECHANIC

Our automotive technicians have vocational/technical school or military training; have successfully passed certification exams; own their own basic tools; and have excellent mechanical aptitude, reasoning ability, and knowledge of electronics and various automotive systems. They complete our educational programs and on-the-job training while advancing within the organization. For information contact:
Automotive Service Industry Association, 444 North Michigan Avenue, Chicago, IL 60611

Example Problem

Distance Traveled with an Average Velocity

The high-speed train in Figure 3–4 travels from Paris to Lyons at an average velocity of +227 km/h. The trip takes 2.00 h. How far is Lyons from Paris?

Given: average velocity, $\bar{v} = +227$ km/h; time interval, $\Delta t = 2.00$ h

Unknown: displacement, Δd

Basic equation: $\bar{v} = \frac{\Delta d}{\Delta t}$

Solution: $\Delta d = \bar{v}\Delta t$

$\Delta d = (+227 \text{ km/h})(2.00 \text{ h}) = +454 \text{ km}$

TEACHER 

Galileo observed the swaying of an altar lamp during a service and discovered that no matter how wide the path of the swing, the time to move from one end of the path to the other was the same. How did he time the swaying of the lamp? With his pulse!

Practice Problems

5. Suppose a car travels at a constant 10 m/s. How far would it move in 1 hour? in 1 minute? in 1 second? in 1 millisecond? in 1 microsecond? in 1 nanosecond?
6. A train leaves the station at the 0.0-m marker traveling with a constant velocity of 36.0 m/s.
   a. How many seconds later will the train pass the 1620.0-m marker?
   b. What is the velocity of the train in km/h?
7. At 1:00 P.M., a car, traveling at a constant velocity of 94 km/h toward the west, is 17 km to the west of your school. Where will it be at 3:30 P.M.?
8. ▶ Suppose the car in Practice Problem 7 started 17 km east of your school at the same time, moving in the same direction at the same velocity.
   a. Where would it be at 3:30 P.M.?
   b. When would it be at your school?

F. Y. I.

Time was invented to keep everything from happening at the same time.
Space was invented so that everything doesn't happen to you.

Anonymous

If the average velocity of an object is the same for all time intervals, then the object moves at **constant velocity**. Constant velocity is often called uniform velocity. For all time intervals, no matter how long or short, the ratio $\Delta d/\Delta t$ is constant. When describing motion with constant velocity, we can replace the time interval, Δt, by the clock reading, t. In the same way, we can replace the displacement, Δd, by d, the distance from the object's location at $t = 0$. For the special case of uniform velocity, then

$$v = \frac{d}{t}.$$

An object moves with constant velocity if its average velocity is the same for all time intervals.

Physics and technology

THE SONIC RANGER

Have you ever stood at the edge of a cliff, clapped your hands, and heard an echo? You can guess how far away the reflecting rocks are by the time it takes for the echo to arrive. Some years ago Polaroid cameras began to use this principle to focus the lens on the object to be photographed. The hand clap was replaced by a burst of ultrasound. The device is now called a sonic ranger and is used to make rapid, accurate distance measurements.

In one model, a burst of ultrasound is produced 20 times each second. A computer measures the time needed for the ultrasound to be reflected off the object and return to the ranger. This data is then used to calculate the distance from the ranger to the object. All this is done so quickly that the computer can plot the position of a rapidly moving object. It can even graph the velocity and acceleration simultaneously.

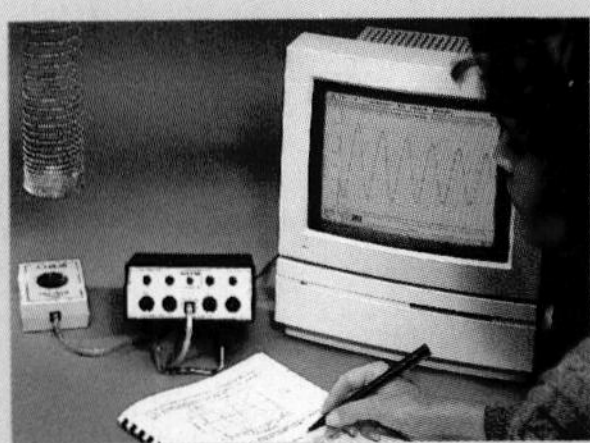

Suppose you are the object the ultrasound bounces off of. How would you move so that the sonic ranger would produce a position-time graph that is a straight line?

Answers To
PRACTICE PROBLEMS

Have students refer to Appendix A of the Solutions Appendix for complete solutions to Practice Problems.

5. 1h, 3×10^4 m; 1 min, 6×10^2 m; 1s, 10 m; 1 ms, 10 mm; 1 μs, 10 μm; 1 ns; 10 nm
6. a. 45.0 s
   b. 130 km/h
7. 250 km west of school
8. a. 220 km west of school
   b. 1:11 pm

Laboratory Manual. Give students additional experience with constant velocity by doing Lab 3.1, Uniform Motion, from the Laboratory Manual.

Physics and technology

By "walking a graph," students add another method of learning about distance, velocity, and acceleration. It complements words, equations, and graphs and is a significant aid in learning to describe motion. By walking toward or away from the sonic ranger with a constant velocity, students can produce a position-time graph that is a straight line.

Teacher Resource: Try "Precalculus Mathematics: A Graphing Approach," by Franklin Demana and Bert K. Waits, Addison Wesley. Both authors are at Ohio State University in Columbus, Ohio.

LABORATORY MANUAL

Use Lab 3.1 with this section.

CHECKING FOR UNDERSTANDING

Review the vocabulary from Key Terms used thus far, such as average velocity, distance, frame of reference, scalar, vector, and so on. Ask students to define the terms using concrete examples.

RETEACHING

Reteaching Master, Teacher Resource Package. Use the Reteaching Master, Mapping and Reference Points.

EXTENSION

Make enlarged copies of various types of motion graphs in this section to use for discussion and reinforcement. Put up simple graphs of motion and ask students to perform the situation shown. Include acceleration in both positive and negative directions.

Position versus Time	
Time (s)	Position (m)
0	100
1	360
2	620
3	880
4	1140
5	1400

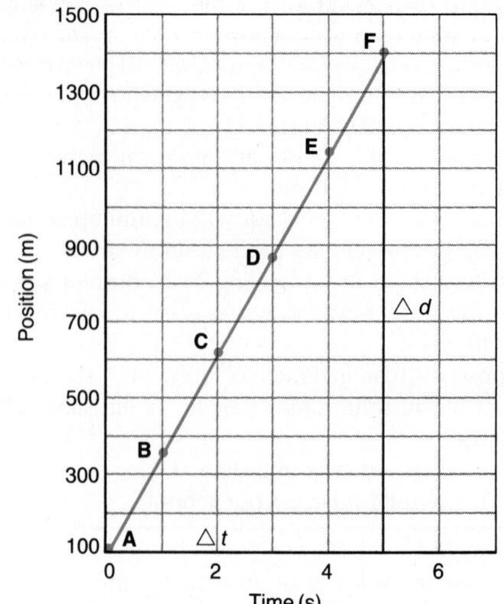

FIGURE 3–5. A position-time graph for an airplane traveling at a constant velocity.

Position-Time Graphs

A jet airplane travels at a constant velocity of +260 m/s. The equation describing the displacement, d, from its position at $t = 0$ for a constant velocity is $d = vt$. A graph that shows how position depends on clock reading, or time, is called a **position-time graph**. To make such a graph of the plane's motion, first make a table of clock readings (times) and corresponding positions of the plane. Figure 3–5 includes a table of positions for the first 5 seconds of travel, assuming the plane was located at the position 100 m from the reference position at $t = 0$ seconds. The data are then plotted on a graph with time as the independent variable and position as the dependent variable. A straight line best represents the data. This graph shows that there is a linear relationship between position and time. The y-intercept of the graph shows the position of the object at $t = 0$, in this case, 100 m.

An excellent way of learning about motion from graphs is to use your hand to model the moving object. Let the edge of your desk be the straight line along which the motion takes place. Choose the center of the edge to be the reference point, with positive position numbers to the right. In the case of Figure 3–5, your hand should move smoothly, at a constant velocity, as you count off 5 seconds. Each second your hand moves a distance that represents 260 m.

FIGURE 3–6. Once a jetliner has reached cruising altitude, it moves with constant velocity. Its speed through the air and over the ground may be different, but they both will be uniform.

The Slope of a Position-Time Graph

The velocity of an object can be found from a position-time graph. On a position-time graph, the displacement is the vertical separation of two points. A time interval is the horizontal separation. The ratio of

RETEACHING MASTER

Use the Reteaching master for Chapter 3 with this section.

displacement to time interval is the average velocity. The ratio of the vertical separation of two points on a curve, or rise, to the horizontal separation of the points, or run, is the **slope** of the curve of a graph. That is,

$$slope = \frac{rise}{run} = \frac{\Delta d}{\Delta t}.$$

You can get a more accurate slope if you use the largest possible rise and run. In Figure 3–5, the slope of the line between points **A** and **F** is given by

$$slope = \frac{rise}{run} = \frac{1400\text{ m} - 100\text{ m}}{5\text{ s} - 0\text{ s}} = \frac{+1300\text{ m}}{5\text{ s}} = +260\frac{\text{m}}{\text{s}}.$$

You see that the slope is the velocity of the airplane we used to generate the graph.

CONCEPT REVIEW

1.1 Describe the position of the period in this sentence using three reference points: one on the book, the second on your desk, the third fixed in the room.

1.2 For each of the position-time graphs in Figure 3–7 below,
 a. perform the indicated motions with your hand.
 b. write a description of the motion.

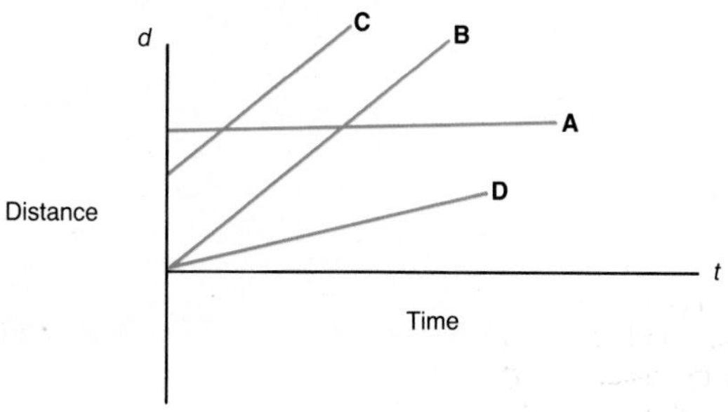

1.3 Draw a position-time graph of a person who walks one block at a moderate speed, waits a short time for a "walk" light, walks the next block more slowly, then the final block very fast. All blocks are of equal length.

1.4 Critical Thinking: Suppose that in your town positive house numbers are north of Main Street and negative numbers are south. You leave your house that is located at −800 at 9:00 A.M. You arrive at Main Street at 9:04, reach +800 at 9:08, and stop at +1600 at 9:14 A.M.
 a. Draw a position-time graph of your walk.
 b. Find your average velocity for your entire trip. (Use units of house number per minute.)
 c. Find your average velocities between 9:00 and 9:04, 9:04 and 9:08, 9:08 and 9:14. Which is largest? smallest?

F. Y. I.

Nature, to be commanded, must be obeyed.

Francis Bacon

One of the greatest pains to human nature is the pain of a new idea.

-Walter Bagehot

The slope of a line on a position-time graph is the average velocity, $\bar{v} = \frac{\Delta d}{\Delta t}$.

FIGURE 3–7. Use with Concept Review 1.2.

EARTH SCIENCE CONNECTION

The Beaufort Scale is used by meteorologists to indicate wind speeds. A wind comparable to the fastest speed run by a person is classed as 5, a strong breeze. A wind as fast as a running cheetah is classified as 11, a storm. Winds of up to 371 km/h (beyond the scale) have been registered on Mount Washington, New Hampshire.

CONCEPT DEVELOPMENT

Suppose you had a position-time graph with a vertical line. What would this mean? [You are everywhere at once, which is not possible.]

Critical Thinking: When you express speeds in different sets of units, the numbers you get change. Ask students if the actual value of the speed changes with the changing units.

ACTIVITY

Cooperative Learning: Have students make a chart of typical speeds for various things such as cars, planes, sound, baseballs, etc.

3 Close

CONVERGENT QUESTION

What would it take to have complete information about someone's motion at an instant? [instantaneous velocity value and the position]

INDEPENDENT PRACTICE/ EXTENSION

Refer to the Assignment Guide on this page for additional questions and problems for independent practice.

CONCEPT REVIEW ANSWERS

1.1 Answers will vary! Examples: 12.1 cm to left of edge of page, 35 cm to right of left edge of desk, 3.5 m from chalkboard.

1.2b. **A** remains at rest at a positive coordinate; **B** starts from origin and moves to right at constant speed; **C** starts at positive coordinate and moves to right at same velocity as **B**; **D** moves to right from origin at slower velocity than **B** and **C**.

1.3

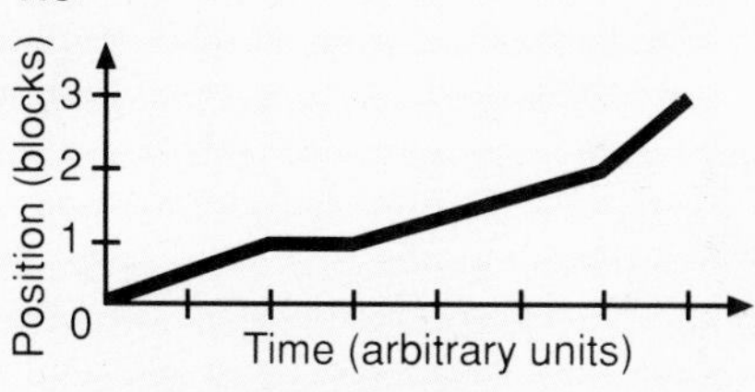

1.4 Critical Thinking: a. Assume constant velocity walking between given times.

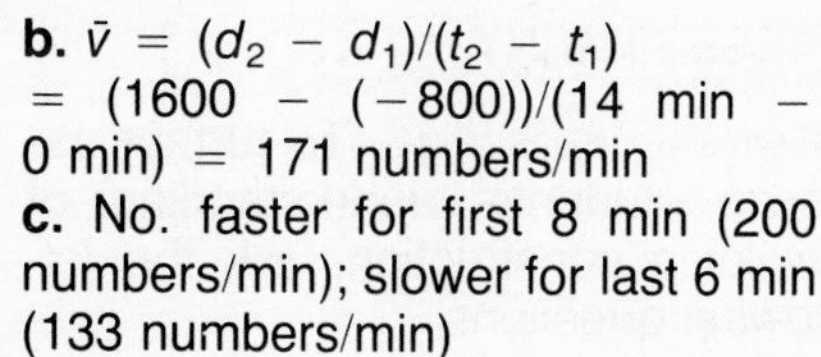
b. $\bar{v} = (d_2 - d_1)/(t_2 - t_1)$ $= (1600 - (-800))/(14\text{ min} - 0\text{ min}) = 171$ numbers/min
c. No. faster for first 8 min (200 numbers/min); slower for last 6 min (133 numbers/min)

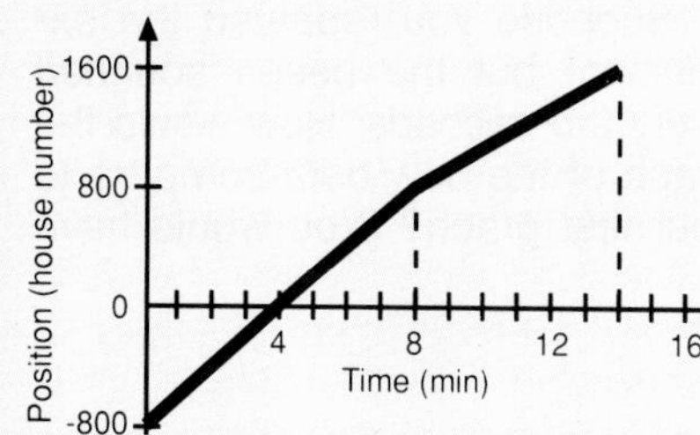

3:1 ASSIGNMENT GUIDE

	PRACTICE	EXTENSION
CHAPTER REVIEW pp. 57–61		
· Reviewing Concepts	1–6	
· Applying Concepts		1–9
· Problems*	1–7, 9, 10, 13, 14, 17–19	11, 12, 15, 16, 20
APPENDIX B PROBLEMS*		
· Chapter 3 p. 689	1–3, 5, 6 9–11	4, 7, 8

* Complete solutions to all Chapter Review and Appendix problems appear in the Problems and Solutions Manual.

PHYSICS LAB

Process Skills: using numbers, observing, classifying, communicating, interpreting, measuring, predicting, questioning, defining operations.

MISCONCEPTIONS

Many students will confuse the concepts of speed and position. Some students will believe that the car must be at zero position at zero time. Some students will believe that the car cannot be moving at zero seconds.

Lab Worksheet, Teacher Resource Package. If desired, use the lab worksheet master for this chapter for students to record their data.

OBSERVATIONS

1. The marks are evenly spaced. This means that the car moved the same amount of distance each second.
2. The values in the data table will depend on the speed of the car.
3. The points on the graph should be in a straight line.
Note 1: The graph does not go through 0,0.
Note 2: The slope of the graph is not zero at 0 s since the car is moving at the reference mark.

ANALYSIS

1. A typical slope will be 0.36 m/s. This is the velocity.
2. All groups should have a straight line graph, but each group might have a different starting point and a different slope.

APPLICATIONS

The "look" of the graph might be misleading. The group with the highest value of the slope should be the fastest.

PHYSICS LAB: The Car Race

Purpose

To make and interpret a graph of the motion of a toy car.

Materials

- battery-powered car (or bulldozer)
- marking pen
- 2.5 m length of wide paper
- masking tape
- 5 cm length of plastic straw
- 3.0-m fishing line
- metronome (or tape recorder with beeps recorded at 1.0 s intervals)

Procedure

1. Tape the short length of the plastic straw to the underside of the car.
2. Thread the fishing line through the straw and tape both ends of the line as shown below. This will prevent the car from curving.
3. Mark a reference line near the end of the paper. (See sketch.)
4. Adjust the metronome or volume of the tape recorder so students can hear it.
5. Turn the car on and start it at the end of the paper. Note: The car must be moving at full speed before it reaches the reference line.
6. Mark the position of the back of the car at every beep.
7. You should have at least five marks after the car crosses the reference line.

Observations and Data

1. Look at the spacing of the marks. What does this tell you about the motion?
2. Label the marks after the reference line 0 s, 1 s, and so on.
3. Measure each mark from the reference line.
4. Make a data table of times and displacements (measured from the reference line).
5. Make a graph of displacements (vertical axis) and times (horizontal axis).

Analysis

1. Find the slope of the graph (include units). What does it mean?
2. Should all lab groups have the same type of graph? Explain.

Applications

1. Look at the value of the slopes of at least two other lab groups. Can you predict which car is fastest?

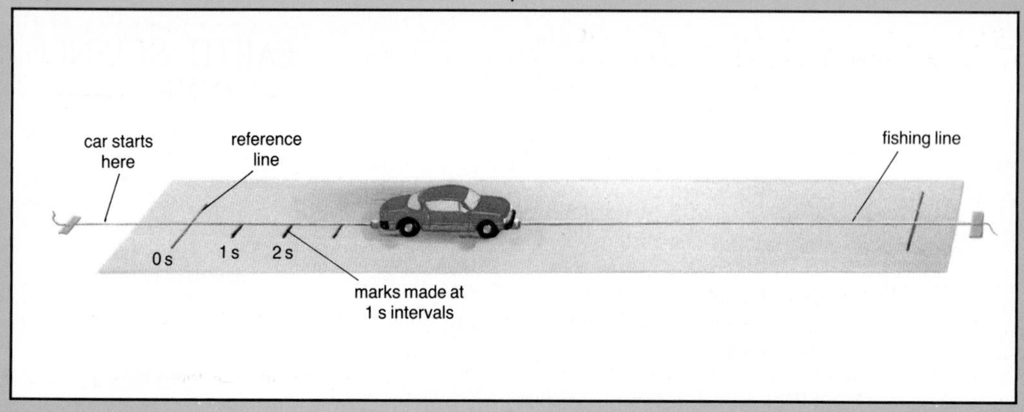

ASSESSMENT

Critical Thinking: To further assess students' understanding of building construction, ask the following questions.

1. Suppose you repeated the experiment but the beeps sounded every 2.0 seconds. How would the graph of the new data compare to your first graph? [You would have fewer data points, but the graph would still be a straight line with the same slope (velocity) as before.]

2. Use your graph to predict the time that it would take for your car to travel a distance of 2.5 m. Explain your method. [You could either extend the graph to estimate the time needed or use the velocity (slope value) to calculate the time.]

3.2 NEW MEANINGS FOR OLD WORDS

The concepts of position and velocity are not laws of nature that were discovered by scientists. Rather, they were invented or created by humans to help describe the motion of objects. We can choose a frame of reference and select a measuring scale. We can also decide which direction is positive and which is negative. In this section, we will use other tools that humans have invented to better understand motion.

Objectives

- distinguish displacement from distance and velocity from speed.
- be able to plot and interpret a velocity-time graph.
- understand the meaning of the area under the curve on a velocity-time graph and be able to calculate the displacement from such a graph.
- define and use the concept of relativity of velocities.
- define and give examples of instantaneous velocity, distinguishing instantaneous from average velocity.

Positive and Negative Velocities

Positions, as we have described them, can be both positive and negative. When we first discussed positions, we chose positive positions to be to the right of a reference point and negative to the left. Displacements, or changes in position, can also be either positive or negative. Objects moving to the right have positive displacements. Motions to the left result in negative displacements. Time intervals, on the other hand, are always positive. No one has yet learned how to make time move backward!

Imagine a ball on the +20-m line of a metric playing field. The player could kick the ball in either direction. If it moved at a constant 10 m/s, it could reach either the +10-m or +30-m line in one second. In either case, the magnitude of the velocity would be the same, but the algebraic sign would be different. **Speed** is the magnitude of the velocity. The **velocity** of an object, however, includes both its speed and the algebraic sign or direction. An object moving toward more positive positions has a positive velocity. Thus, a ball moving from +20 m to +30 m would have an average velocity of +10 m/s, while a ball moving from +20 m to +10 m would have $\bar{v}$ = −10 m/s. As in Figure 3–8, an arrow can be used to indicate the velocity of an object. Arrows that point to the right show positive velocities; arrows pointing to the left indicate negative velocities.

Average velocity can be either positive or negative.

Speed is the size or magnitude of the velocity. Speed is always positive.

Notice that an object can have a negative position but still have a positive velocity. If the ball were kicked from −47 m to −27 m in 2.0 s, it would have an average velocity of +10 m/s.

FIGURE 3–8. Will the ball be kicked with a positive or negative velocity?

3.2 NEW MEANINGS FOR OLD WORDS

Preparation

OBJECTIVES

The objectives are listed on the student page. Remind students to preview these objectives as a study guide to this major section.

OVERVIEW

Two new concepts appear in this section: instantaneous velocity and velocity-time graphs.

BRIDGING

All of the concepts and definitions from the first section are built upon here. These two sections are quite closely connected.

1 Focus

DISCREPANT EVENT

Discuss with students what the spacing would look like if an object pulling the tape through a dot timer is moving with a constant velocity. [The spaces would all be equal.] Have all students make a tape of constant velocity by pulling the tape through their timers as they walk away. They will have to move fairly quickly so the dots are easily distinguishable. Help students find a portion of the tape that shows constant velocity.

Have students mark off every fourth or fifth dot so there will be a couple of centimeters between each mark. Now have them measure from the beginning of the tape to the second mark, and so on to about eight marks. Call each interval a tic of time, and make a graph of position versus time. [The graph should be a straight line with a positive slope.]

ACTIVITY

Cooperative Learning: Students should work in threes. Put one student in a wagon with a handful of beans. The student will drop one bean every second according to the command of another student who will watch a stopwatch for 10–15 s and count out loud. Let a third student pull the wagon at a constant, slow velocity. Have students measure the distances and graph distance to time. Repeat for a faster, constant speed. What is the average speed? Why is the graph not actually linear?

POCKET LAB

BOWLING BALL DISPLACEMENT

Purpose: to have students collect displacement and time data for a rolled bowling ball, and compute the average speed.
Materials: bowling ball (1 per class); stopwatches.
Outcome: A typical data table for the bowling ball:

distance	time	average speed
10 m	2.2 s	4.5 m/s
20 m	4.6 s	4.3 m/s
30 m	7.3 s	4.1 m/s

Students will not be able to predict the time needed to roll 100 m from the average speed for 30 m because the ball is slowing down, not traveling with constant velocity.

2 Teach

CONCEPT DEVELOPMENT

Study Guide Master. To reinforce the concepts in this section, have the students complete the Study Guide Master for Section 3.2 from the Teacher Resource Package.

- The slope of a position-time graph is the velocity of an object. Have students find the slope of the position-time graph they made in FOCUS on page 51. The units for the slope will be cm/tic. Emphasize that slope always carries units with it and these units should be used to identify what the slope represents. To make a velocity-time graph, have students cut the tape into pieces by cutting at each mark. Then make a bar graph by pasting the pieces on end next to each other. Even though there is some experimental error, this velocity-time graph should look like a horizontal line since all the pieces should be about the same length.

- You may want to discuss motion that gives a negative displacement with reference to a central point.

- The abrupt changes of velocity shown on many of the graphs in this chapter do not show how the motion really occurs. An abrupt (sharp-pointed) change in velocity means that it took no time to change the velocity, which is impossible. Actually these abrupt changes should be shown as curves, indicating that it takes some time for the change in velocity to happen.

POCKET LAB

BOWLING BALL DISPLACEMENT

Take a bowling ball and stopwatches into the hallway. Divide into three groups. Have all timers start their clocks when the ball is rolled. Group 1 should stop their watches when the ball has gone 10 m. Group 2 should stop when the ball has rolled 20 m, and Group 3 should stop their clocks when the ball has rolled 30 m. Record all data on the chalkboard. Use the distance to calculate the average speed for each distance. Could the average speed for 30 m be used to predict the time needed to roll 100 m? Why?

Example Problem

Position-Time Graph for a Complete Trip

Figure 3–9 is a position-time graph for a short car trip. Find the average velocity of the car for each part of the trip.

Solution: Between points **A** and **B**,

$$\bar{v} = \frac{\Delta d}{\Delta t} = \frac{+200\text{ m}}{10\text{ s}} = +20\text{ m/s}$$

Between points **B** and **C**, the line is horizontal.

$$\bar{v} = \frac{\Delta d}{\Delta t} = \frac{+0\text{ m}}{10\text{ s}} = +0\text{ m/s}$$

The car is at rest.

Between points **C** and **D**, the position of the car decreases; the displacement is negative.

$$\bar{v} = \frac{\Delta d}{\Delta t} = \frac{-50\text{ m}}{5\text{ s}} = -10\text{ m/s}$$

The slope and velocity are both negative; the car moves in a direction opposite to its original direction. Between points **D** and **E**,

$$\bar{v} = \frac{\Delta d}{\Delta t} = \frac{-250\text{ m}}{20\text{ s}} = -12.5\text{ m/s}$$

The slope and velocity are both more negative. The velocity has the same negative value for the entire segment, even though the position at point **E** is negative. That is, the car passed its starting point. Between points **E** and **F**,

$$\bar{v} = \frac{\Delta d}{\Delta t} = \frac{+100\text{ m}}{15\text{ s}} = +6.7\text{ m/s}$$

The velocity again is positive. The car is moving again in its original direction.

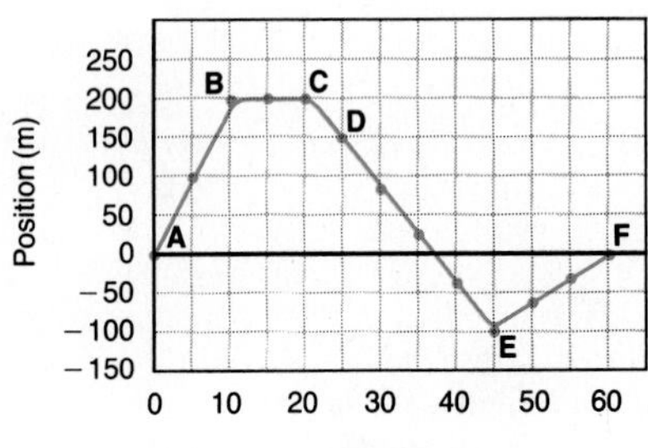

FIGURE 3–9. A position-time graph for a short car trip.

Practice Problems

9. Describe in words the motion of the four walkers shown in the four curves in Figure 3–10. Assume the positive direction is east and the reference point is the corner of High Street.

10. Sketch position-time graphs for these four motions:
  a. starting at a positive position with a positive velocity.
  b. starting at a negative position with a smaller positive velocity.
  c. remaining at a negative position.
  d. starting at a positive position with a negative velocity.

11. Find the average velocities shown in Figure 3–11.
  a. between t = 10 and 12 s **c.** between t = 20 and 24 s
  b. between t = 14 and 18 s **d.** between t = 26 and 30 s

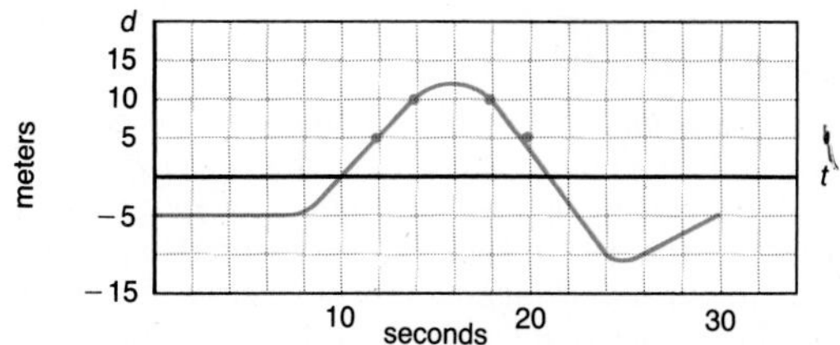
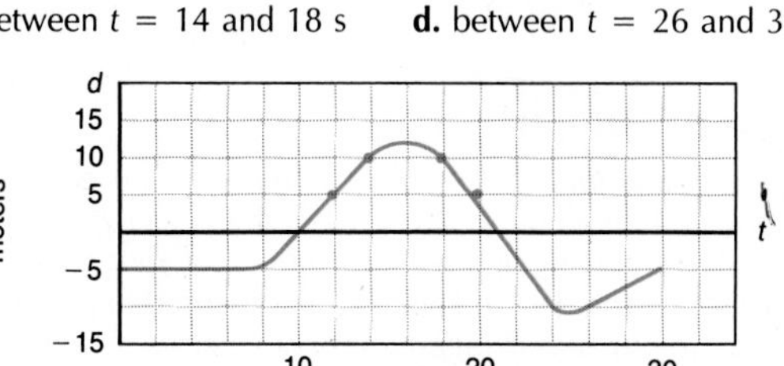

▶ **12.** Draw a position-time graph of a moving elevator. Use the first floor as the reference point and up as positive. The elevator waits on the first floor for 30 s, rises to the third floor in 20 s, stops for 30 s, then goes to the basement, which it reaches in 40 s.

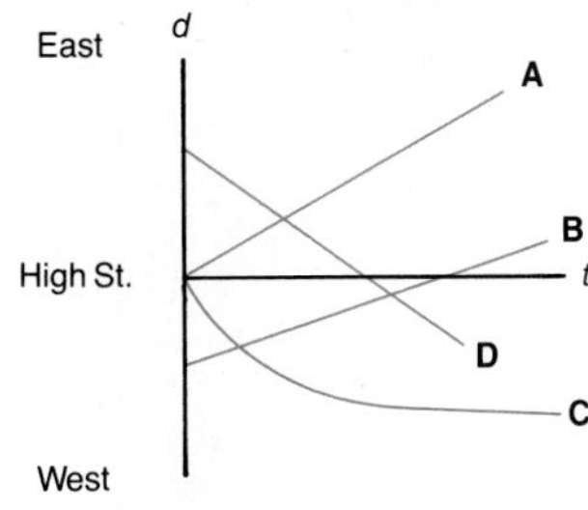

FIGURE 3–10. Use with Practice Problem 9.

FIGURE 3–11. Use with Practice Problem 11.

Instantaneous Velocity

To find the velocity of a car, you use its speedometer. Suppose the speedometer needle swings upward from 70 to 90 km/h. What is the car doing? The car is obviously speeding up. If you glance at the speedometer and see the needle at 80 km/h, what does that mean? It means that at the instant you looked, the car's velocity was 80 km/h. Its instantaneous velocity was 80 km/h. That is, if the velocity had been constant, the car would have driven 80 km in one hour.

A position-time graph can be used to find instantaneous velocity. Figure 3–12a is a position-time graph of a runner during a 100-m dash. Figure 3–12b shows the first 2.5 s of the dash. If the person had a speedometer, what would it read at 1.0 s? Start by finding the average velocity between 0.0 s and 2.0 s. The rise, the runner's displacement, is 12.5 m, while the run, the time interval, is 2.0 s. The slope of the line connecting these two points is the average velocity during this time interval, 6.3 m/s. Next, find the average velocity between 0.5 s and 1.5 s. Now the displacement is 6.8 m while the time interval is 1.0 s. The slope of the connecting line, the average velocity, is 6.8 m/s. We could continue this process, choosing the time interval smaller and smaller until the two clock readings are almost the same. We can no longer draw a line connecting the two points. We now draw a straight line that is the tangent to the curve at that point. The slope of the tangent is called the **instantaneous velocity** at that instant.

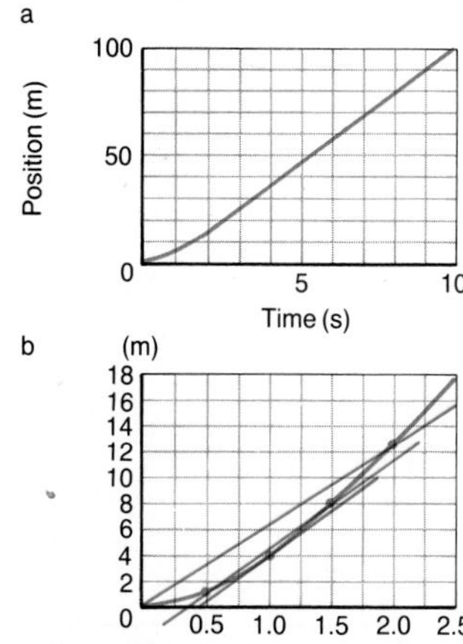

FIGURE 3–12. A position-time graph (a) can be used to find instantaneous velocities by determining the slope at various times (b).

Answers To
PRACTICE PROBLEMS

Have students refer to Appendix A of the Solutions Appendix for complete solutions to Practice Problems.

9. Refer to Solutions Appendix for graph. Walker a starts at High St. walking east at constant velocity; walker b starts west of High St. walking east at slower constant velocity; walker c walks west from High St., first fast but slows to a stop; walker d starts east of High St. and walks west at constant velocity.
10. Refer to Appendix A for graph.
11. Refer to Appendix A for graph. **a.** 2.5 m/s; **b.** 0 m/s; **c.** −3.75 m/s; **d.** 1.25 m/s
12. Refer to Appendix A for graph.

Critical Thinking Master, Teacher Resource Package. For practice in graphing movement in more than one direction, have students attempt the Critical Thinking worksheet, Positions Along a Roller Coaster.

CONCEPT DEVELOPMENT

• The idea of instantaneous velocity confuses some students. Remember, we use the word "time" to mean the same as "clock reading." Then there is time interval (Δt) which is the difference between two clock readings. Average speed (or velocity) involves a time interval, whereas an instantaneous value is at one single time. We can get instantaneous velocity only by using a graph. While the distinction between average velocity and instantaneous velocity is important, don't overemphasize it. In more advanced textbooks, the distinction between them is made using the language of calculus involving limits.

• You may have some students who are enrolled in calculus. This is a good place to point out that taking the slope is equivalent to taking a derivative.

• When finding the slope, use the curve rather than data points, and form the largest possible triangle to get a better value.

Critical Thinking: Ask students how they could use a car to measure time (using the odometer and speedometer). How many significant digits would such a time have?

CONCEPT DEVELOPMENT

Police radar is continuous-wave radar fired from a hand-held "gun." Consider having a policeman as a guest speaker to talk about how the device works, how it can be wrong, and about newer technology. In addition, the speaker could use the device to measure the velocity of an object thrown by students.

Critical Thinking: Suppose you had a velocity-time graph for which the line was vertical. Ask students what that would mean. [Something had all velocities at once—an impossibility.]

Assessment

Critical Thinking

Have students analyze the results of the Pocket Lab on page 45 with the methods developed in the Example Problem "Finding Displacement from Velocity-Time Graph." For example, ask, "If you walked at the calculated speed for 10 minutes, how far would you have gone? What if you ran?

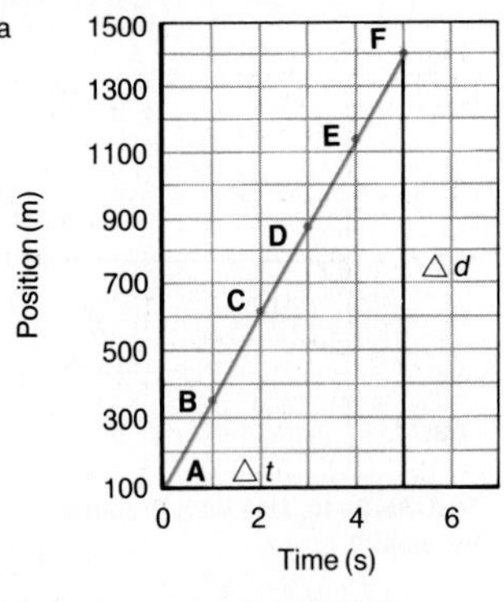

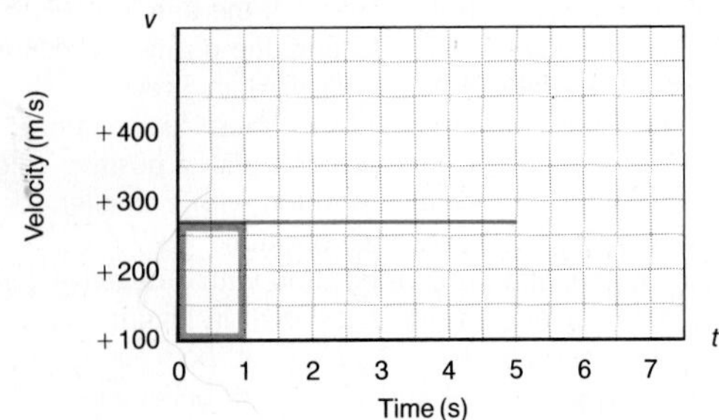

FIGURE 3–13. The velocity-time graph for an airplane moving with a constant velocity of 260 m/s.

The displacement between two times is the area under the curve of a velocity-time graph.

The instantaneous velocity is the tangent to a curve on a position-time graph.

Velocity-Time Graphs

A **velocity-time graph** is a useful new tool that can be used to describe motion with either constant or changing velocity. Again, model the motion shown in the graph with the motion of your hand along the edge of your desk. The data in Figure 3–5 were used to plot a position-time graph of an airplane flying at constant velocity. A plot of the velocity versus time is shown in Figure 3–13. Every point on the line has the same vertical value because the velocity is constant. The line is parallel to the *t*-axis.

How would you describe the motion of the runner shown in the velocity-time graph in Figure 3–14? The vertical value of any point is the instantaneous velocity at that time. During the first five seconds, the runner's instantaneous velocity increases. For the next five seconds, he runs at a constant 8 m/s, and over the last three seconds, he slows to a stop.

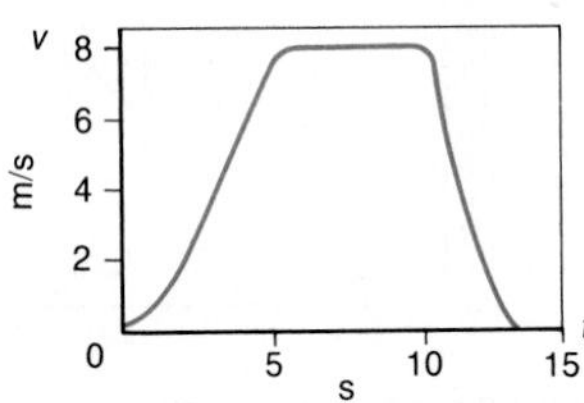

FIGURE 3–14. A velocity-time graph shows the instantaneous velocity of the runner at every instant.

Example Problem

Finding Displacement from a Velocity-Time Graph

Find the displacement of the plane whose velocity is shown in Figure 3–13 at **a.** 1.0 s. **b.** 3.0 s.

Given: *v-t* graph, Figure 3–13b; time intervals, **a.** 0.0 s to 1.0 s, **b.** 0.0 s to 3.0 s

Unknown: displacement, d

Basic equation: area under graph, $d = vt$

Solution:

Note shaded area under line in Figure 3–13b. The vertical side is velocity: $v = +260$ m/s.

a. Horizontal side is time interval: $t = 1.0$ s;
the area of rectangle under the line is

$$vt = (+260 \text{ m/s})(1.0 \text{ s}) = +260 \text{ m}.$$

This quantity is the displacement in 1.0 s.

b. At the end of 3.0 s, the area under the line is

$$vt = (+260 \text{ m/s})(3.0 \text{ s}) = +780 \text{ m};$$

the displacement of the plane in 3.0 s.

LAB WORKSHEET

Use the Lab Worksheet for Chapter 3 with this Physics Lab.

CRITICAL THINKING

Use the Critical Thinking master for Chapter 3 with this section.

STUDY GUIDE MASTER

Use the Study Guide master for section 3.2.

Thus, the area under the line on a velocity-time graph is equal to the displacement of the object from its original position to its position at time t. When velocity is constant, displacement increases linearly with time. If you plot the displacement versus time, you will get a straight line with a slope equal to the velocity.

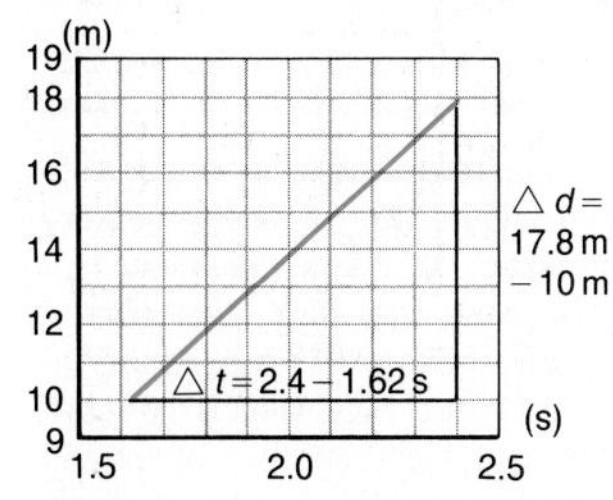

FIGURE 3–15. Use with Practice Problem 13.

Practice Problems

13. Using Figure 3–15 find the sprinter's velocity at 2.0 s.

14. Use your hand on your desk to model the motion shown by the curves in Figure 3–16a below. Describe in words the motions.

15. Figure 3–16b is the velocity-time graph of an object. What is its velocity at

a. 0 s? **b.** 1 s? **c.** 2 s?

16. Using the graph in Figure 3–16b, describe how the instantaneous velocity changes with time.

17. Sketch velocity-time graphs for the graphs in Figure 3–16c.

18. A car moves along a straight road at a constant velocity of +75 km/h for 4.0 h, stops for 2.0 h, and then drives in the reverse direction at the original speed for 3.0 h.

a. Plot a velocity-time graph for the car.

b. Find the area under the curve for the first 4 h. What does this represent?

c. Explain how to use the graph to find the distance the car is from its starting point at the end of 9.0 h.

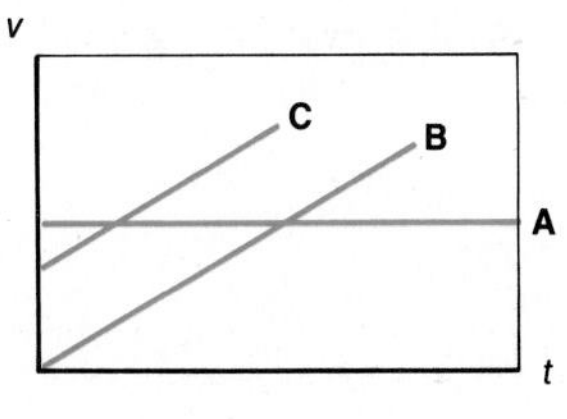

a

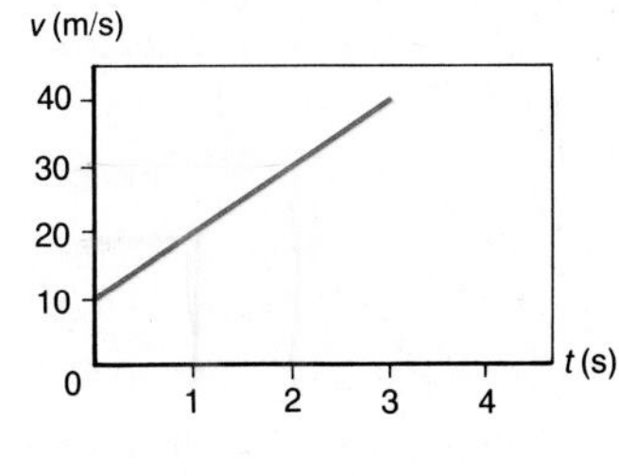

b

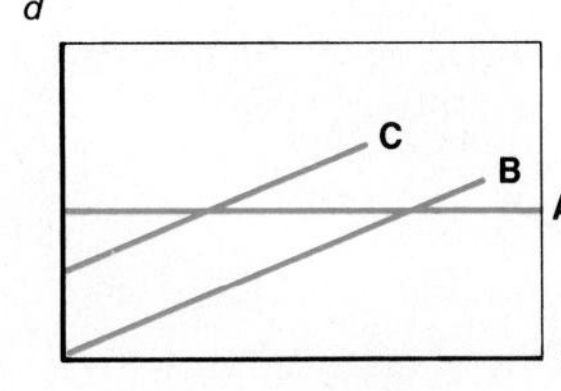

c

FIGURE 3–16. Use with Practice Problems 14, 15, 16, and 17.

▶**19.** A person drives a car at a constant +25 m/s for 10.0 min. The car runs out of gas, so the driver, carrying an empty gasoline can, walks at +1.5 m/s for 20.0 min to the nearest gas station. After the 10.0 min needed to fill the can, the driver walks back to the car at a slower −1.2 m/s. The car is then driven home at −25 m/s.

a. Draw a velocity-time graph for the driver, using seconds as your time unit. You will have to calculate the distance the driver walked to the station in order to find the time needed to walk back to the car.

b. Draw a position-time graph for the problem from the areas under the curves of the velocity-time graph.

CHECKING FOR UNDERSTANDING

• Choose a problem that starts with a data table of a motion. Guide students as they generate a graph and answer questions from the graph.

• Or, have students sketch a velocity-time graph of their favorite sport (or part of it) and then defend what they've drawn.

RETEACHING

Transparency Package. Use Transparency 3 to quiz students on details of velocity-time graphs.

EXTENSION

Have interested students find out how the sonic ranger (which was mentioned earlier) works.

Answers To
PRACTICE PROBLEMS

Refer to Appendix A of the Solutions Appendix for complete solutions to Practice Problems.

13. Refer to the Solutions Appendix for graph.

14. A moves to right at constant speed; **B** moves to right from rest at constantly increasing speed; **C** has an initial nonzero velocity to the right and continues to move to right at constantly increasing speed.

15. a. 10 m/s; **b.** 20 m/s; **c.** 30 m/s

16. Each second it increases 10 m/s.

17. Refer to the Solutions Appendix for graph.

18. a. Refer to the Solutions Appendix for graph.
b. Area is 300 km, the distance traveled in that time.
c. 75 km

19. Refer to Appendix A for graphs.

TRANSPARENCY

Use Transparency 3 with this section.

CONCEPT DEVELOPMENT

If you have computer graphing capabilities, you might still want to have students master graphing manually before you turn them loose with the computer.

Guided Practice: After going over the Example Problem on this page, have students work on Practice Problem 20.

Independent Practice: Assign Practice Problems 21 and 22 on this page for homework, then review them with students during the next class period.

Enrichment Master. With this section, use the Enrichment Master, Graphing Relative Velocity, from the Teacher Resource Package.

3 Close

CONVERGENT QUESTION

Draw two graphs of your typical trip to school, one a position-time graph and the other a velocity-time graph. Compare your graph with someone who takes a similar route to school.

INDEPENDENT PRACTICE/ EXTENSION

Refer to the Assignment Guide on page 57 for additional questions and problems for independent practice.

Answers To
PRACTICE PROBLEMS

Have students refer to Appendix A of the Solutions Appendix for complete solutions to Practice Problems.

20. **a.** 13 km/h; **b.** −13 km/h
21. 102 km/h

F.Y.I.

You're driving at a comfortable 55 mi/h when, zoom, you're passed by a speeder. How fast was the passing car going? Here's how to find out. At the instant your two windshields are aligned, start counting. When you reach a count of ten, keep counting, but note the location of the front wheels of the other car. You can use a lane stripe, concrete crack, or lamp post. When your front wheels reach the same spot, stop counting. Divide the number by 10 and multiply by your speed. For example, if you reached the spot at the count of 13, the other car was going 13/10 x 55 mi/h = 72 mi/h.

FIGURE 3–17. When the ship is traveling with constant velocity at sea, with nothing on the horizon to serve as a reference point, it is difficult to tell whether it is moving.

Relativity of Velocity

If you have ever been a passenger on a large ship, you may have noticed that once the ship reached cruising speed, you have no sense of how fast the ship is moving. You could measure the velocity of passengers walking fore and aft, just as you could when the ship is moored at the pier. You might find that they were moving at +2 m/s or −2 m/s, depending on their direction. If a person on land could see into the ship, however, that person would see the situation differently. If the ship were moving at a typical velocity of 10 m/s, then the land observer would clock the passengers moving at 12 m/s or 8 m/s. Which observer is correct? The answer is either or both. When measuring either position or velocity, you must first define your reference frame. When on the ship, you used a reference frame with a reference point fixed to the ship. The viewer on land, however, used a reference frame that moved with Earth. The reference point was fixed with respect to Earth.

Example Problem

Finding Velocity from a Different Reference Frame

A passenger on a ship is moving forward at 10 m/s. What are his velocities, as measured by an observer at rest on the shore, if the observer walks **a.** with a velocity of +2 m/s toward the front of the ship? **b.** with a velocity of −2 m/s toward the rear?

Given: velocity of ship,
$v_s = +10$ m/s
velocity of passenger,
a. $v_p = +2$ m/s
b. $v_p = -2$ m/s

Unknown: velocity of passenger relative to observer, v_o

Basic equation: $v_o = v_p + v_s$

Solution:
a. $v_o = +2 \text{ m/s} + 10 \text{ m/s} = +12 \text{ m/s}$
b. $v_o = -2 \text{ m/s} + 10 \text{ m/s} = +8 \text{ m/s}$

In 1905, Albert Einstein pointed out that this rule does not work when the velocities are near the speed of light, 3×10^8 m/s. In fact, if the passengers and people on the ground measured the speed of light emitted by a lamp, even on a supersonic plane, both groups would measure exactly the same velocity! This fact was central to Einstein's theory of relativity.

Practice Problems

20. From the reference frame of a stationary observer, a car, traveling at a constant speed of 92 km/h, is passed by a truck moving at 105 km/h.
a. From the point of view of the car, what is the truck's speed?
b. From the point of view of the truck, what is the car's speed?

▶ **21.** As you travel at a constant 95 km/h, a car that you know to be 3.5 m long, passes you in 1.8 s. How fast is it going relative to Earth?

TEACHER 

Here's more information on the student F.Y.I. Ask students if this method depends on how fast you count. Point out that, since you take a ratio of times, it could be 13 s/10 s or 13 min/10 min—there would be no change. Lead them to see that if you count too rapidly, it becomes too hard to tell the exact locations of the cars. This leads to a large experimental uncertainty. On the other hand, if you count very slowly, the other car's speed can change. This method finds the average speed, which may not be the speed of the car when it passed you.
Derivation: The distance traveled by the two cars, from the point where their positions are identical to the spot you note, are the same. Since $d = vt$, $v_{you}t_{you} = v_{other}t_{other}$, so $v_{other} = (t_{you}/t_{other})v_{you}$.

CONCEPT REVIEW

2.1 The hill people measure heights using the top of the highest peak as a reference point and down as the positive direction. Valley people use the river bottom as the reference point and up as the positive direction. If they both observed a stone falling, would they agree on its velocity? speed? displacement? distance?

2.2 Draw a position-time graph for the motion of the particle shown on the velocity-time graph, Figure 3–18.

2.3 Two people leave a lamppost at the same time. One walks east, the other west, both at the same speed. Describe the position-time and velocity-time graphs of the two people.

2.4 Critical Thinking: A policeman clocked a driver going 20 mph over the speed limit just as the driver passed a slower car. He arrested both drivers. The judge agreed, saying "If the two cars were next to each other, they must have been going the same speed." Is the judge correct? Explain in words and with a position-time graph.

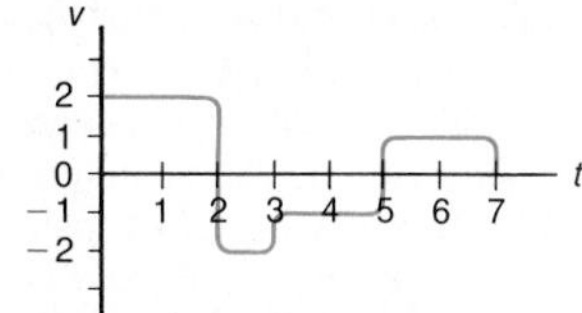

FIGURE 3–18. Use with Concept Review 2.2.

CHAPTER 3 REVIEW

SUMMARY

3.1 How Far and How Fast?

- The position of an object is its separation from a reference point.
- Displacement is a vector quantity indicating the magnitude and direction of an object's change of position.
- A scalar quantity is described completely by its magnitude, while a vector quantity requires both magnitude and direction.
- Average velocity is the displacement (change in position) divided by the time interval.
- The slope of a position-time graph is the velocity of the object.
- If the position-time graph is a straight line, the object is moving with constant velocity.

3.2 New Meanings for Old Words

- The area under the curve of a velocity-time graph is the displacement of the object.
- Instantaneous velocity is the velocity of an object at a given instant.
- A frame of reference defines a reference point from which positions are measured.

KEY TERMS

reference point
frame of reference
position
distance
scalar
vector
clock reading
instantaneous position
displacement
time interval
average velocity
factor-label method
constant velocity
position-time graph
slope
speed
velocity
instantaneous velocity
velocity-time graph

REVIEWING CONCEPTS

1. List conditions under which a football may be treated as a point. When can it not be?
2. How does a vector differ from a scalar?
3. Is displacement a vector or a scalar?
4. Is average velocity a vector or a scalar?
5. What quantity can be obtained from the slope of a position-time graph?
6. A physics book is moving across a table. Can the book have a
   a. constant speed and a changing velocity?
   b. constant velocity and a changing speed? Explain your answers.

3:2 ASSIGNMENT GUIDE

	PRACTICE	EXTENSION
CHAPTER REVIEW pp. 57–61		
· Reviewing Concepts	7–11	
· Applying Concepts		10, 11
· Problems*	8, 21–24	25
APPENDIX B PROBLEMS*		
· Chapter 3 p. 690	12, 15	13, 14

* Complete solutions to all Chapter Review and Appendix problems appear in the Problems and Solutions Manual.

ENRICHMENT MASTER

Use the Enrichment master for Chapter 3 with this section.

CONCEPT REVIEW ANSWERS

2.1 They would get opposite signs for velocity and displacement, and equal speeds and distances.

2.2

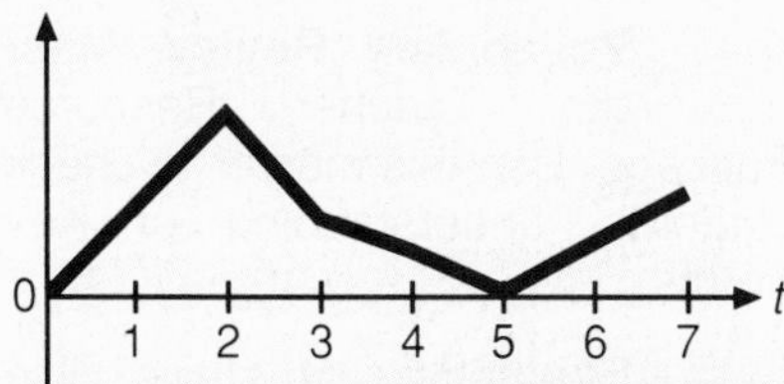

2.3 Call east the position direction and person A is the one who walks east. The position-time graph of person A is a straight line with a constant positive slope, v_A. Person B's straight line has a constant negative slope of $-v_A$. The velocity-time curve for person A is a horizontal line with a constant value of v_A; person B is a horizontal line with a constant value of $-v_A$.

a.

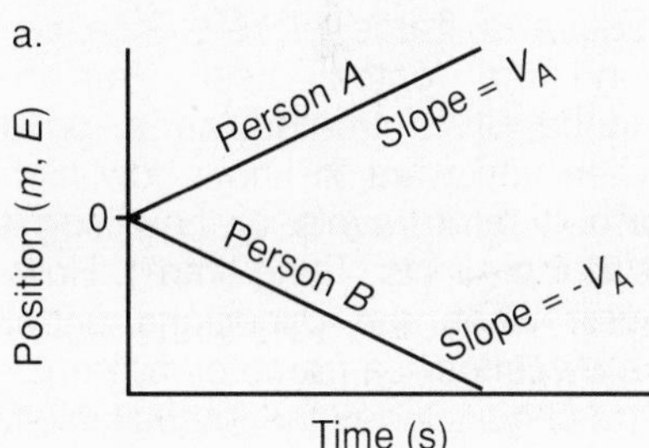

b.

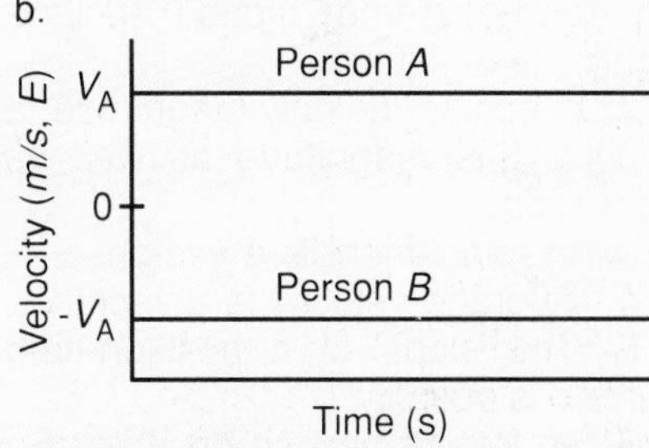

2.4 Critical Thinking: No. They had the same position, not velocity. To have the same velocity, they would have had to have the same relative position for a length of time.

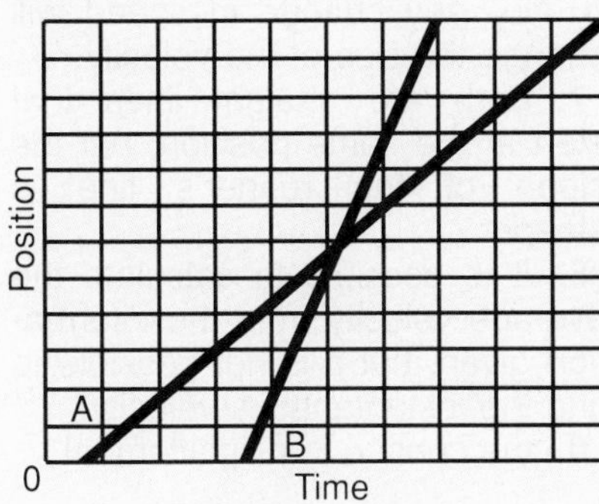

CLOSING CHAPTER 3

Review Summary statements and Key Terms with your students.

ASSESSMENT

Vocabulary Review Master, Teacher Resource Package. Use this master to check students' understanding of Key Terms.

Evaluation Masters. Use Parts A and B of the Chapter Evaluation Masters from the Teacher Resource Package to test qualitative chapter objectives. Use Parts C and D to test quantitative chapter objectives.

Answers To
REVIEWING CONCEPTS

1. A football is treated as a point when the conditions under study require a frame of reference beyond the football itself. For instance, it is treated as a point when you want to know how high or how far it travels; or, how long it is in the air (its "hang time"). However, when the conditions under study concern a frame of reference that only includes the football itself, it cannot be treated as a point. It must be treated as a football. For instance, questions about its spin or end-over-end motion include only the ball itself.

2. A scalar has only magnitude; a vector has magnitude as well as direction.

3. Displacement is a vector.

4. Average velocity is a vector.

5. The slope of a position-time graph is velocity.

6. a. Yes. If you sit on a merry-go-round and look straight ahead, you see that your direction is changing; your velocity is therefore changing. For most of the ride, your speed remains constant. Hold the book out from your body and twirl around at a constant rate.

b. No. Any change in speed will change the size of the velocity.

7. Both are straight lines that start at the same position, but the slope of the runner's line is steeper.

8. It is possible to calculate the average velocity from the information given, but it is not possible to find the instantaneous velocity.

9. the change in displacement

7. A walker and a runner leave your front door at the same time. They move in the same direction at different constant velocities. Describe the position-time graphs of each.

8. If you know the positions of a particle at two points along its path and also know the time it took to get from one point to the other, can you determine the particle's instantaneous velocity? its average velocity? Explain.

9. What quantity is represented by the area under a velocity-time curve?

10. Figure 3–19 shows a velocity-time graph for an automobile on a test track. Describe the changes in velocity with time.

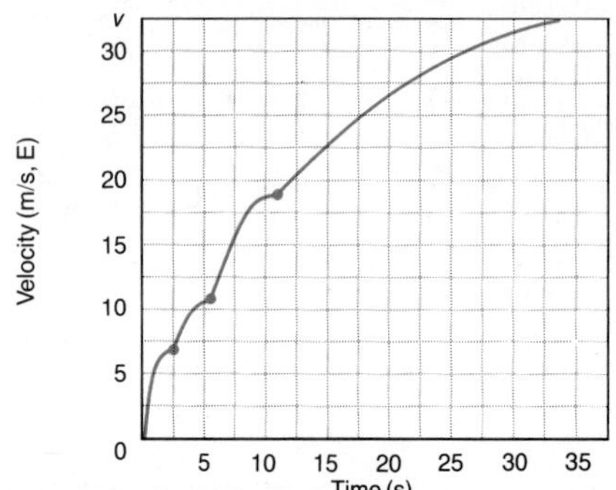

FIGURE 3–19. Use with Reviewing Concepts 10 and Problem 22.

APPLYING CONCEPTS

1. If the scale in Figure 3–1 was moved 3 m to the right, would the position of each car remain the same?

2. If the scale in Figure 3–1 was moved 3 m to the right, would the distance between the cars remain the same?

3. A NASA team oversees a space shuttle launch at Cape Canaveral in Florida and then travels to Edwards Air Force Base in California to supervise the landing. Which group of people, the astronauts or the NASA team, has the greater displacement?

4. Average velocity is $\Delta d/\Delta t$. Consider the ratio $\Delta t/\Delta d$. When is this new ratio large? When is it small? Can it ever be zero? Invent a reasonable name for it.

5. If the average velocity of a particle is zero in some time interval, what can you say about its displacement for that interval?

6. Look at Figure 3–20a.
   a. What kind of motion does this graph represent?
   b. What does the slope of the line represent?

7. Use the intervals marked on the graph in Figure 3–20b to describe the velocity of the object during each interval.

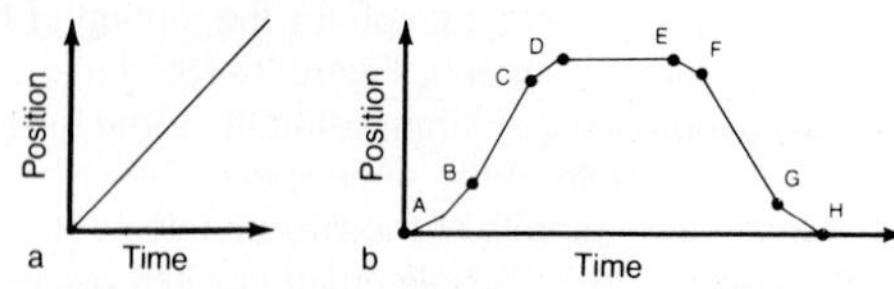

FIGURE 3–20. Use with Applying Concepts 6 and 7 (b).

8. Figure 3–21 is a position-time graph of two people running.
   a. Describe the position of runner A relative to runner B at the y-intercepts.
   b. Which runner is faster?
   c. What occurs at point **P** and beyond?

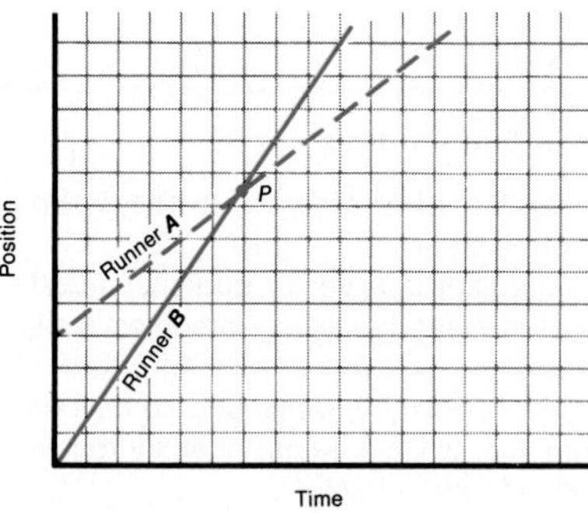

FIGURE 3–21. Use with Applying Concepts 8.

9. Figure 3–22 is a position-time graph of the motion of two cars on a road.
   a. At what time(s) does one car pass the other?
   b. Which car is moving faster at 7.0 s?
   c. At what time(s) do the cars have the same velocity?
   d. Over what time interval is car B speeding up all the time?
   e. Over what time interval is car B slowing down all the time?

10. The car starts from rest and increases its speed. As the car's speed increases, the driver shifts gears.

REVIEW MASTER

Use the Vocabulary Review master for Chapter 6 with this section.

EVALUATION MASTER

Use the Chapter Evaluation master for Chapter 6 with this section.

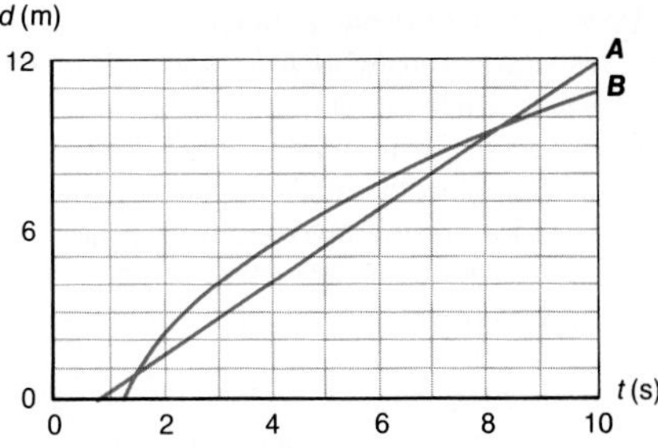

FIGURE 3–22. Use with Applying Concepts 9 and Problem 21.

10. Look at Figure 3–23a.
    a. What kind of motion does this graph represent?
    b. What does the area under the curve of the graph represent?
11. Look at Figure 3–23b.
    a. What kind of motion does this graph represent?
    b. What does the area under the curve of the graph represent?

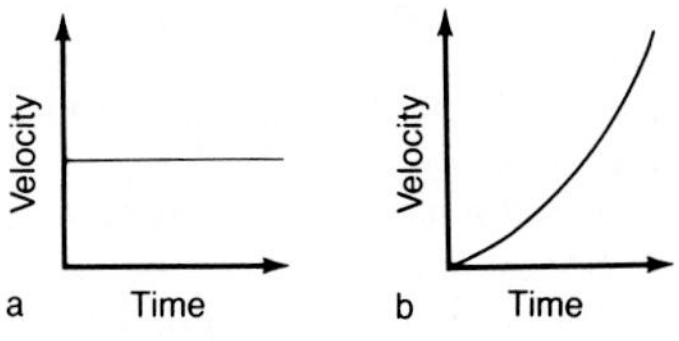

FIGURE 3–23. Use (a) with Applying Concepts 10, (b) with Applying Concepts 11.

PROBLEMS

3.1 How Far and How Fast?

1. While John is traveling along an interstate highway, he notices a 160-mile marker as he passes through town. Later John passes another mile marker, 115.
    a. What is the distance between town and John's current location?
    b. What is John's current position?
2. While John is traveling along a straight interstate highway, he notices that the mile marker reads 260. John travels until he reaches the 150-mile marker and then retraces his path to the 175-mile marker. What is John's resultant displacement from the 260-mile marker?
3. A physics book is moved once around the perimeter of a table of dimensions 1.0 m by 2.0 m.
    a. If the book ends up at its initial position, what is its displacement?
    b. What is the distance traveled?
4. Light from the sun reaches Earth in 8.3 min. The velocity of light is 3.00×10^8 m/s. How far is Earth from the sun?
5. You and a friend each drive 50 km. You travel at 90 km/h, your friend at 95 km/h. How long will your friend wait for you at the end of the trip?
6. From the list of winning times from the 1988 Summer Olympics track events in Table 3–2, calculate the average speeds for each race. Assume the length of each event is known to the nearest 0.1 m.

Table 3–2

Length of event (m)	Time (min:sec)	
	Men	Women
100	0:09.86	0:10.49
200	0:19.72	0:21.34
400	0:43.29	0:47.66
800	1:41.73	1:53.28
1 500	3:28.86	3:52.47
3 000	7:28.96	8:22.62
5 000	12:58.39	14:37.73
10 000	27:08.23	30:13.74

7. Construct a table similar to Table 3–2 listing average speeds for track events in your school, district, or state.
8. Construct an average speed table similar to Problem 6 for swimming events at your school, district, or state. Compare speeds for swimming to those for running. Explain.
9. Two cars approach each other; both cars are moving westward, one at 78 km/h, the other at 64 km/h.
    a. What is the velocity of the first car relative to (in the frame of reference of) the second car?
    b. After they pass, will their relative velocity change?

Answers To
APPLYING CONCEPTS

1. No. Car A's position would now be +5.0 m and Car B's position would be −4.0 m.
2. Yes. The distance between the cars would remain 9.0 m.
3. The space shuttle travels a greater distance (scalar quantity) around Earth in getting to Edwards Air Force Base. Its displacement (vector quantity), however, is the position of its landing point, Edwards Air Force Base, minus its starting (reference) point, Cape Canaveral, which is the same for the astronauts as it is for the NASA team.
4. The ratio is large when the object is moving slowly, and small when it is moving quickly. It can never be zero because it would have to have two positions in a zero time interval.
5. If the average velocity for a time interval is zero, the displacement for that time interval is zero. The distance may be non-zero.
6. a. The graph represents constant velocity. **b.** the value of the constant velocity
7. A–B, increasing; B–C, constant; C–D, decreasing; D–E, zero; E–F, increasing negative; F–G, constant negative; G–H, decreasing negative
8. a. Runner A has a head start by four units. **b.** Runner B is faster since the slope is steeper. **c.** Runner B passes Runner A at point **P.**
9. a. when the positions are the same, at 1.4 s and 8.2 s; **b.** Car A has a steeper slope and a larger velocity. **c.** at 4 s, when the slopes are the same; **d.** at no interval; **e.** Always, because the slope is always decreasing.
10. a. The graph represents motion with a constant positive velocity. **b.** The area under the curve represents the change in displacement.
11. a. The graph represents motion with a positive increasing velocity. **b.** The area under the curve represents the change in displacement.

Answers To
PROBLEMS

Complete solutions for all Chapter Review Problems can be found in the Problems and Solutions Manual accompanying this text.

1. a. 45 miles
b. +115
2. −85 km
3. a. zero displacement
b. 6.0 m
4. 1.5×10^{11} m
5. 1.8 minutes
6.

Length of event (m)	Speed (m/s)	
	Men	Women
100	10.142	9.533
200	10.142	9.372
400	9.240	8.393
800	7.864	7.062
1500	7.1818	6.4524
3000	6.6821	5.9687
5000	6.4235	5.0991
10000	6.1416	5.5135

7. Student answers will vary.
8. Student answers will vary.
9. a. 14 km/h, west
b. no
10. 11 m
11. a. 720 km/h
b. no
12. a. 50 km/h
b. no, 48 km/h
13. a. Refer to Problems and Solutions Manual.
b. parabola
c. 10 m
14. a. 400 m
b. 0
c. −200 m
15. a. Refer to Problems and Solutions Manual.
b.150 km, 170 km
c. 1.3 h, 1.2 h
16. Refer to Problems and Solutions Manual. Both cars arrive at 1:00 P.M.
17. Refer to Problems and Solutions Manual. 8.0 m/s
18. a. Refer to Problems and Solutions Manual.
b. 550 m
c. 300 m

10. Ann is driving down a street at 55 km/h. Suddenly a child runs into the street. If it takes Ann 0.75 s to react and apply the brakes, how many meters will she have moved before she begins to slow down?

▶ **11.** You plan a trip on which you want to average 90 km/h. You cover the first half of the distance at an average speed of only 48 km/h. What must your average speed be in the second half of the trip to meet your goal? Note that the velocities are based on half the distance, not half the time. Is this reasonable?

▶ **12.** You drive a car 2.0 h at 40 km/h, then 2.0 h at 60 km/h.
a. What is your average velocity?
b. Do you get the same answer if you drive 100 km at each of the two speeds above?

13. The total distance a steel ball rolls down an incline at various times is given in Table 3–3.
a. Draw a position-time graph of the motion of the ball. When setting up the axes, use five divisions for each 10 m of travel on the *d*-axis. Use five divisions for each second of time on the *t*-axis.
b. What type of curve is the line of the graph?
c. What distance has the ball rolled at the end of 2.2 s?

Table 3–3

Time (s)	Distance (m)
0.0	0.0
1.0	2.0
2.0	8.0
3.0	18.0
4.0	32.9
5.0	50.0

14. Use the position-time graph in Figure 3–24 to find how far the object travels
a. between t = 0 s and t = 40 s.
b. between t = 40 s and t = 70 s.
c. between t = 90 s and t = 100 s.

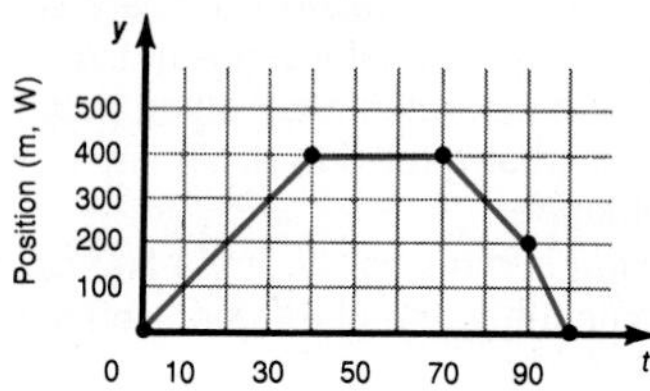

FIGURE 3–24. Use with Problem 14 and 19.

▶ **15.** Both car A and car B leave school when a clock reads zero. Car A travels at a constant 75 km/h, while car B travels at 85 km/h.
a. Draw a position-time graph showing the motion of both cars.
b. How far are the two cars from school when the clock reads 2.0 h? Calculate the distances using the equation of motion and show them on your graph.
c. Both cars passed a gas station 100 km from the school. When did each car pass the station? Calculate the times and show them on your graph.

▶ **16.** Draw a position-time graph for two cars driving to the beach, 50 km from school. Car A leaves a store 10 km from school closer to the beach at noon, and drives at 40 km/h. Car B starts from school at 12:30 P.M. and drives at 100 km/h. When does each get to the beach?

17. Plot the data in Table 3–1 on a position-time graph. Find the average velocity in the time interval between 0.0 s and 5.0 s.

18. A cyclist maintains a constant velocity of +5.0 m/s. At time t = 0, the cyclist is +250 m from point **A.**
a. Plot a position-time graph of the cyclist's location from point **A** at 10.0-s intervals for 60.0 s.
b. What is the cyclist's position from point **A** at 60.0 s?
c. What is the displacement from the starting position at 60.0 s?

19. From the position-time graph, Figure 3–24, construct a table showing the average velocity of the object during each 10-s interval over the entire 100 s.

▶ **20.** Two cars travel along a straight road. When a stopwatch reads t = 0.00 h, car A is at d_A = 48.0 km moving at a constant 36.0 km/h. Later, when the watch reads t = 0.50 h, car B is at d_B = 0.00 km moving at 48.0 km/h. Answer the following questions: first, graphically by creating a position-time graph; second, algebraically by writing down equations for the positions d_A and d_B as a function of the stopwatch time, t.
a. What will the watch read when car B passes car A?
b. At what position will the passing occur?
c. When the cars pass, how long will it have been since car A was at the reference point?

19.

Time Interval(s)	Average Velocity (m/s)
0–10	10
10–20	10
20–30	10
30–40	10
40–50	0
50–60	0
60–70	0
70–80	−10
80–90	−10
90–100	−20

20. Refer to Problems and Solutions Manual.
a. 6.0 h
b. 2.6×10^2 km
c. 7.3 h

3.2 New Meanings for Old Words

21. Refer to Figure 3–22 to find the instantaneous speed for
a. car B at 2.0 s.
b. car B at 9.0 s.
c. car A at 2.0 s.

22. Find the instantaneous speed of the car at 15 s from Figure 3–19.

23. Plot a velocity-time graph using the information in Table 3–4.

Table 3–4

Time (s)	Velocity (m/s)	Time (s)	Velocity (m/s)
0.0	4.0	7.0	12.0
1.0	8.0	8.0	8.0
2.0	12.0	9.0	4.0
3.0	14.0	10.0	0.0
4.0	16.0	11.0	−4.0
5.0	16.0	12.0	−8.0
6.0	14.0		

24. Refer to Figure 3–25 to find the distance the moving object travels between
a. $t = 0$ s and $t = 5$ s.
b. $t = 5$ s and $t = 10$ s.
c. $t = 10$ s and $t = 15$ s.
d. $t = 0$ s and $t = 25$ s.

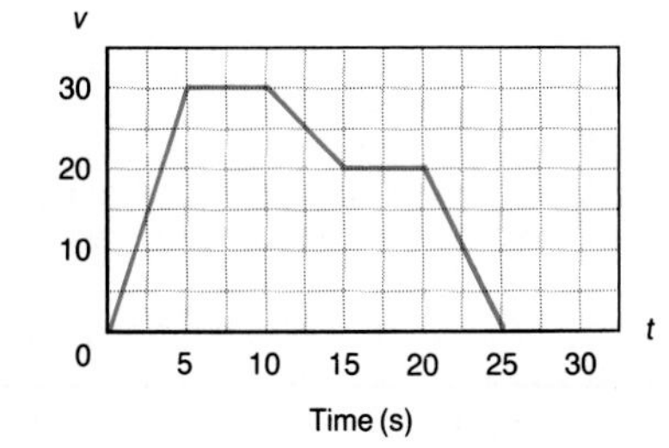

FIGURE 3–25.

▶ **25.** The velocity of an automobile changes over an 8.0-s time period as shown in Table 3–5.
a. Plot the velocity-time graph of the motion.
b. Determine the distance the car travels during the first 2.0 s.
c. What distance does the car travel during the first 4.0 s?
d. What distance does the car travel during the entire 8.0 s?

Table 3–5

Time (s)	Velocity (m/s)	Time (s)	Velocity (m/s)
0.0	0.0	5.0	20.0
1.0	4.0	6.0	20.0
2.0	4.0	7.0	20.0
3.0	8.0	8.0	20.0
4.0	16.0		

USING A GRAPHING CALCULATOR

Members of a physics class stood 25 m apart and used stopwatches to measure the time a car driving down the highway passed each person. They compiled their data into the following table:

Table 3–6

Time (s)	Position (m)	Time (s)	Position (m)
0.0	0.0	5.9	125.0
1.3	25.0	7.0	150.0
2.7	50.0	8.6	175.0
3.6	75.0	10.3	200.0
5.1	100.0		

Use a graphing calculator to fit a line to a position-time graph the data and to plot this line. Be sure to set the display range of the graph so that all the data fits on it. Find the slope of the line. What was the speed of the car?

USING LAB SKILLS

1. How could the Pocket Lab on page 52 be changed to make a better prediction of the time it would take for the bowling ball to go 100 m?

THINKING PHYSIC-LY

On some toll roads, the ticket is stamped with the time you enter the toll road and the time you exit. How can the toll taker determine if you were speeding?

21. Refer to Problems and Solutions Manual.
a. 2.3 m/s
b. 0.67 m/s
c. 1.25 m/s

22. Refer to Problems and Solutions Manual. 0.83 m/s^2

23. Refer to Problems and Solutions Manual.

24. Refer to Problems and Solutions Manual.
a. 75 m
b. 150 m
c. 125 m
d. 500 m

25. **a.** Refer to Problems and Solutions Manual.
b. 6.0 m
c. 24 m
d. 102 m

Answers To USING A GRAPHING CALCULATOR

Solution (on a Casio fx-7000G)

1. Set the calculation mode to LR2. (SHIFT MODE/)
2. Set the range values (RANGE 0 12 2 0 200 25)
3. Clear the statistical memory (Cls EXE)
4. Clear the graph (Cls EXE)
5. Enter the data ({time}, {position}; 1 DT)
6. Graph the data (Graph Line 1 EXE)
7. Trace along the line to find the change in position between 0 and 10.3 seconds (TRACE {left arrow until x = 0} X<−>Y {right arrow until x = 10.3})
8. Divide the difference by 10.3

Answer: 19.7 m/s

Answer To USING LAB SKILLS

1. If readings were extended to 40 m and 50 m, you would have a better idea of the rate at which the ball was slowing down, so it would be easier to make a more accurate prediction.

Answer To THINKING PHYSIC-LY

The toll taker knows the distance between exits and can determine the time it took you to drive between exits. If your average speed is above the posted speed limits, you were speeding.

CHAPTER 4 Acceleration

PLANNING GUIDE (5 class sessions)

CONTENTS	TEXT FEATURES	TEACHER RESOURCE PACKAGE	OTHER COMPONENTS
4.1 What Is Acceleration?, pp. 64–69 (2 Class Sessions) • Average Acceleration • Average and Instantaneous Acceleration • Velocity of an Object With Constant Acceleration	**Physics Lab:** Ball and Car Race, p. 70 **Physics and Technology:** Cushioning the Blow, p. 68 **Pocket Lab:** Uniform or Not?, p. 66 **Concept Review,** p. 69	**Study Guide:** What Is Acceleration? **Physics Lab Data Sheet:** Ball and Car Race **Reteaching Master:** Monitoring Acceleration **Enrichment Master:** Velocity of a Baseball	**Laboratory Manual:** Lab 4.1 Accelerated Motion
4.2 Displacement During Constant Acceleration, pp. 71–80 (3 Class Sessions) • Displacement When Velocity and Time Are Known • Displacement When Acceleration and Time Are Known • Displacement When Velocity and Acceleration Are Known • Acceleration Due to Gravity	**Pocket Lab:** Direction of Acceleration, p. 75 **Pocket Lab:** A Ball Race, p. 80 **Problem Solving Strategy:** Motion Problems, p. 78 **Using Your Calculator:** Solving Equations, p. 79 **Concept Review,** p. 80	**Study Guide:** Displacement During Constant Acceleration **Critical Thinking Master:** Acceleration and Escape Velocity **Transparency Worksheet:** Velocity vs Time	**Laboratory Manual:** Lab 4.2 Acceleration Due to Gravity **Transparency 4:** Velocity vs Time
Chapter Review, pp. 80–85	Summary Key Terms Reviewing Concepts Applying Concepts Problems Thinking Physic-ly	**Vocabulary Review** **Chapter Test**	**Test Bank**

SUPPLEMENTARY MATERIALS

SOFTWARE	AUDIOVISUAL	BOOKS/MAGAZINES
Fall Guy: Investigations of Falling Objects, HRM (Apple II). *Kinematics,* Vernier (Apple II). *A Tutorial on Acceleration,* COMPress/Queue, Inc. (Apple II).	Video: *The Mechanical Universe: Introduction to the Mechanical Universe* and *The Law of Falling Bodies,* Films Inc. Filmstrips: *Motion: Velocity and Acceleration,* Clearvue. *Understanding Motion,* Bergwall.	Bailey, Herbert R. "Experiments in Free Fall and Rebound." *The Physics Teacher,* February 1990, p. 100. Brody, Howard. "The Tennis Ball Bounce Test." *The Physics Teacher,* September 1990, p. 407. Crummett, Bill. "Measurements of Acceleration Due to Gravity." *The Physics Teacher,* May 1990, p. 291. Martin, D. "Encouraging Critical Thought: Alternative Problem Forms." *The Physics Teacher,* May 1988, pp. 288–289.

PROBLEM CORRELATION

CONCEPTS	CHAPTER REVIEW			PROBLEMS APPENDIX
	Reviewing Concepts	Applying Concepts	Problems	
4.1 What Is Acceleration?				
Average Acceleration	1,2		1,2	1
Average and Instantaneous Acceleration	3,4,5	1,2,4	3,4,6,**7**	2,**3**
Velocity of an Object With Constant Acceleration		3	5,8,9	4,5
4.2 Displacement During Constant Acceleration				
Displacement When Velocity and Time Are Known			10,11	6,7
Displacement When Acceleration and Time Are Known			12,13,14,21	8,9
Displacement When Velocity and Acceleration Are Known	6,7		16,17,18,19,20,22, 23,24,**25,26,**27,**28,**29	10,11,12,13
Acceleration Due to Gravity	8,9,10	5,6,7,8,9	**15,**30,31,32,**33,34,** 35,36,37	14,**15,16**

ACTIVITY AND DEMONSTRATION MATERIALS

PHYSICS LAB	POCKET LAB	DEMONSTRATIONS
Page 70 battery-powered car 1" steel ball 10 cm of tape 90 cm length of U channel short length of plastic straw 100 cm of fishing line stopwatch	Pages 66, 75, 80 U channel book tape 2 steel balls stopwatch meter stick laboratory cart small bubble level	Pages 67, 79 wagon beans stopwatch tape faucet stroboscope

EXTENSION PROJECTS

LIBRARY RESEARCH

1. The Atwood Machine
Do some research into the Atwood machine. Describe its purpose.

HANDS-ON

2. Graphing Stopping Distances
Using safe driving techniques in an empty parking lot, determine your stopping distance for initial speeds of 5, 10, 15, 20, 25, 30, and 35 mph. Graph your results. What does the graph indicate?

STUDENT READINGS

Goldman, Terry, Hughes, Richard J., and Nieto, Michael Martin. "Gravity and Antimatter [new ideas challenge independence of gravitational acceleration for mass and substance]." *Scientific American,* March 1988.

Hammer, Signe. "The Riddle of Turbulence." *Science Digest,* May 1984.

Wright, Karen. "Trends in Transportation: The Shape of Things to Go." *Scientific American,* May 1990.

Chapter 4

Acceleration

CHAPTER OVERVIEW

Theme Development: This chapter illustrates mathematical modeling of quantities, introduces the pattern of change of velocity that we call acceleration, and shows the symmetrical nature of certain kinds of motion.

MISCONCEPTIONS

Students tend to confuse speed and acceleration. They have trouble making sense of the units for acceleration. There's also a tendency to use signs inconsistently.

KEY TERMS

acceleration due to gravity
average acceleration
constant or uniform acceleration
final velocity
initial velocity
instantaneous acceleration

Laboratory Options

STUDENT EDITION

Physics Lab

Ball and Car Race	70

Pocket Labs

Uniform or Not?	66
Direction of Acceleration	75
A Ball Race	80

TEACHER EDITION

Activities

Demonstration	67, 79
Cooperative Learning	67, 79

LABORATORY MANUAL

Accelerated Motion	Lab 4.1
Acceleration Due to Gravity	Lab 4.2

CHAPTER

4 Acceleration

Demon Drop

The Demon Drop ride lasts only 1.5 seconds. How fast are you going when you are slowed to a halt? How far do you fall?

Chapter Outline

Concept Check

The following terms or concepts from earlier chapters are important for a good understanding of this chapter. If you are not familiar with them, you should review them before studying this chapter.
- graphing, slopes, Chapter 2
- manipulating algebraic equations, Chapter 2
- position and velocity, Chapter 3
- graphs of motion at constant velocity, Chapter 3

Amusement park rides thrill customers by changing the velocities of the riders quickly and in unexpected directions. The ride may be a gentle, circling carousel or a rapidly-swinging tilt-o-whirl. It may be the rapid ascents and descents of a roller coaster. For pure heart-stopping thrills, however, nothing beats the ride on the Demon Drop. Held down with shoulder bars, you stop for a moment at the top. The supports under the car are suddenly released, and you drop with close to the acceleration of gravity.

63

Introducing The Chapter

Demon Drop

Using The Photo: This type of ride has both a speeding-up phase during the drop and a slowing-down phase during the final horizontal part of the motion. Gravity provides the speeding-up force and an excellent braking system slows you down. Between these two phases there's a short bit of motion around a curve. Taken all together, a lot happens in a very few seconds!

The method for solving the chapter opener questions is outlined in the Example Problem on page 77.

Concept Check

Make sure students have a clear understanding of the concepts taught in Chapters 2 and 3 listed in the Concept Check. Students familiar with manipulating algebraic equations, position, velocity, and graphing slopes and motion at constant velocity will be well prepared to investigate the patterns of motion identified with acceleration, as introduced in this chapter.

Assessment Options

Portfolio Assessment
Portfolio Assessment, TWE, p. 66
Connect to Mathematics, TWE, p. 72
Portfolio Assessment, TWE, p. 73
Critical Thinking, TWE, p. 74

Performance Assessment
Demonstration with beans, TWE, p. 67
Pocket Labs, pp. 66, 75
Physics Lab, p. 70
Using Lab Skills, p. 85

Content Assessment
Self assessment: Practice Problems, pp. 66, 68, 69, 72, 74, 75, 77, 79
Assessment, Critical Thinking, TWE, p. 70
Pocket Lab Assessment, TWE, p. 75
Thinking Physic-ly, p. 85
Concept Reviews, pp. 69, 80
Chapter Review, pp. 80–85
Supplemental Problems, pp. 690–691

Group Assessment
Activities for group assessment occur with Cooperative Learning and lab activities.

4.1 WHAT IS ACCELERATION?

Preparation

OBJECTIVES

The objectives are listed on the student page. Remind students to preview these objectives as a study guide to this major section.

OVERVIEW

The major concept introduced in this section is acceleration and its quantitative definition.

BRIDGING

Concepts from previous chapters essential to this section include graphing (including slope), manipulating algebraic equations, velocity, position, and graphs of motion at constant velocity.

1 Focus

DISCREPANT EVENT

Ask students to imagine themselves in an automobile. Imagine further that they are blindfolded. Question: Is there any way that they could tell whether or not the car was accelerating? [Yes, by noting whether or not they had a tendency to push back into the seat or slide off the seat—in other words, the way the ride feels. Some may add they would listen for the pitch of the engine to change.]

Now assume the blindfold is removed. Ask what instrument they would look at to tell whether or not there was acceleration. [Most will answer that they would look at the speedometer to see if the reading was changing.]

Almost everyone will know the answers to these two questions, so they have a good intuitive feeling for acceleration. Now the task becomes to extend this understanding to the quantitative measure of acceleration.

Objectives

- **define average and instantaneous acceleration.**
- **be able to calculate average acceleration, given two velocities and the time interval between them.**
- **be able to calculate average and instantaneous acceleration from a velocity-time graph.**
- **be able to calculate final velocity in the case of uniform acceleration.**

Vector Conventions

- *Velocity vectors are red.*
- *Displacement vectors are green.*
- ***Acceleration vectors are purple.***

4.1 WHAT IS ACCELERATION?

The faster that the velocity of a ride changes, the greater the thrill. How fast does velocity change? The rate at which velocity changes is such a useful concept that it is given a special name, acceleration. In this chapter, as in Chapter 3, we will consider motion in only one dimension. Changes in velocity can either be positive or negative; direction will be indicated by plus or minus.

Average Acceleration

An airplane is at rest at the start of the runway, Figure 4–1; it has zero velocity. When cleared for takeoff by the tower, the pilot opens the plane's throttle. After 10 seconds, the airspeed indicator shows +30 m/s. After 20 seconds, it shows +60 m/s. When 30 seconds have elapsed, the airspeed is +90 m/s and the plane lifts off. In each 10-second interval the airplane's speed increased by 30 m/s. Thus, in each second, the velocity increased 3 m/s. The airplane has accelerated down the runway.

Let the change in velocity be Δv, and the time interval during which the velocity changes be Δt. Consider the ratio $\frac{\Delta v}{\Delta t}$. When is it large? The ratio is large when there is a large velocity change in a small time interval. The ratio is called the **average acceleration** between the two times.

Suppose an object has velocity v_1 at time t_1 and velocity v_2 at time t_2. The change in velocity is $\Delta v = v_2 - v_1$. The change takes place during the time interval $\Delta t = t_2 - t_1$. Thus, the average acceleration, the change in velocity divided by the interval of time, is given by

$$\bar{a} = \frac{v_2 - v_1}{t_2 - t_1} = \frac{\Delta v}{\Delta t}.$$

FIGURE 4–1. The air speed indicators above the runway show the velocities at the times shown below the runway.

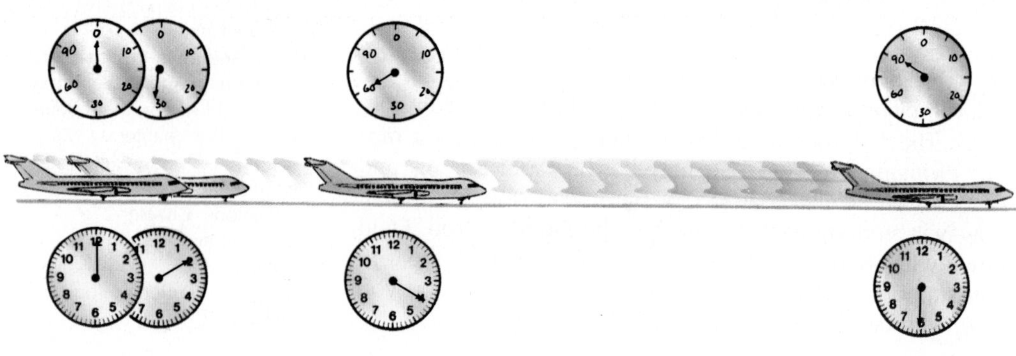

Multicultural Connections

Fireworks are an exciting part of many different celebrations or events in our country, such as the Fourth of July and baseball games. However, we would not have fireworks if the Chinese had not invented gunpowder and used it to make rockets. Although they used the rockets as weapons, they also used them to create fireworks. While some of the materials used in modern fireworks have changed, most fireworks still use the same principles first developed in China.

For a fireworks rocket to be seen, the rocket must accelerate quickly to a velocity which will carry the fireworks to the right height. What factors determine how quickly a fireworks rocket must accelerate? Some of them are the height it must reach, how quickly the fuse to the fireworks payload will burn, how quickly the rocket fuel will burn, and how much of the rocket can be used to hold fuel.

Velocity is measured in meters per second, m/s, so acceleration is measured in (m/s)/s, or m/s/s. This unit is read "meters per second per second." More often the unit for acceleration is written as m/s^2 and read "meters per second squared." In either case, acceleration tells how many meters per second the velocity changes in each second.

Just as position and velocity are vectors, numbers with both magnitude and direction, so is acceleration. In straight-line motion, acceleration can be either positive or negative. When the velocity increases, its change is a positive number and the acceleration is positive; when velocity decreases, the change is negative, and so is the acceleration.

BIOLOGY CONNECTION

The cheetah runs at a maximum speed of 60-63 mph. Its rate of acceleration is awesome—from a starting speed of 0 to 45 mph in two seconds.

Example Problem

Calculating Average Acceleration

The velocity of a car increases from 2.0 m/s at 1.0 s to 16 m/s at 4.5 s. What is the car's average acceleration?

Given: first velocity, $v_1 = 2.0$ m/s; second velocity, $v_2 = 16$ m/s; time interval, $t_1 = 1.0$ s; $t_2 = 4.5$ s

Unknown: acceleration, $\bar{a}$

Basic equation: $\bar{a} = \frac{\Delta v}{\Delta t}$

Solution: velocity change, $\Delta v = v_2 - v_1 = 16 \text{ m/s} - 2.0 \text{ m/s} = 14 \text{ m/s}$

time interval, $\Delta t = t_2 - t_1 = 4.5 \text{ s} - 1.0 \text{ s} = 3.5 \text{ s}$

acceleration, $\bar{a} = \frac{\Delta v}{\Delta t} = \frac{14 \text{ m/s}}{3.5 \text{ s}} = 4.0 \text{ m/s}^2$

Does an object with a negative acceleration always slow down? Consider the following Example Problem.

The units of acceleration are usually m/s/s or m/s^2.

Example Problem

Acceleration of a Car Backing Up

A car goes faster and faster backwards down a long driveway. We define forward velocity as positive, so backward velocity is negative. The car's velocity changes from −2.0 m/s to −9.0 m/s in a 2.0-s time interval. Find its acceleration.

Given: first velocity, $v_1 = -2.0$ m/s; second velocity, $v_2 = -9.0$ m/s; $\Delta t = 2.0$ s

Unknown: acceleration, $\bar{a}$

Basic equation: $\bar{a} = \frac{\Delta v}{\Delta t}$

Solution: velocity change, $\Delta v = -9.0 \text{ m/s} - (-2 \text{ m/s}) = -7.0 \text{ m/s}$

average acceleration, $\bar{a} = \frac{\Delta v}{\Delta t} = \frac{-7.0 \text{ m/s}}{2.0 \text{ s}} = -3.5 \text{ m/s}^2$

FIGURE 4–2. The car backing down the driveway is increasing its velocity but in the negative direction.

TEACHER **F.Y.I.**

Acceleration units often provoke student questions like this one: "I can visualize one meter and I have some experience of one second, but what is one m/s^2?" Something with an acceleration of one m/s^2 means its speed changes by one m/s during every one second time interval. For every second of travel, the velocity of a moving body increases by that amount. For example, if an object begins at rest and experiences an acceleration of 2.5 m/s/s, at the end of the first second it will be traveling at 2.5 m/s; at the end of the second second, its velocity will be 5.0 m/s; at the end of the third second, it will be traveling at 7.5 m/s; and so on.

2 Teach

CONCEPT DEVELOPMENT

Study Guide Master. To reinforce the concepts in this section, have the students complete the Study Guide Master for Section 4.1 from the Teacher Resource Package.

- If you have access to an ultrasonic ranger/detector and the software that plots the motion of an object as it moves in front of the detector, the students can see their motion as it is happening. This gives an immediate visual picture which can be very helpful.

- It's also important to be able to go from a graph to its verbal description, and from a verbal description to a graph. Here's an example: A student walks to a friend's house at a constant speed, stops to talk for a while, then runs home at a steady speed. Have students draw position-time and velocity-time graphs for this motion. You might also put some motion graphs on the board, then ask students to describe the sequence of events indicated by the graphs.

- Another example to use for motion graphing is a person speeding up from a stoplight to the speed limit, traveling at the speed limit for a while, then slowing down until reaching a stop sign.

- From the numerous graphs in this chapter you can make enlargements to use as transparencies for teaching particular concepts.

Enrichment: You may have some students who are enrolled in calculus. This is a good place to mention that taking the slope is equivalent to taking the first derivative, and finding the area under a curve is equivalent to integrating. Acceleration is the same as the second derivative of a position-time graph.

Laboratory Manual. Give students additional experience with accelerated motion by doing Lab 4.1, Accelerated Motion, from the Laboratory Manual.

POCKET LAB

UNIFORM OR NOT?

Purpose: to investigate the acceleration of a rolling steel ball on an incline to determine if its acceleration is uniform.

Materials: U channel; book; tape; steel ball; stopwatch; meter stick.

Outcome: As the steel ball rolls down the ramp, it is speeding up. The ball is accelerating. The time needed for the ball to roll 40 cm depends on the angle. A typical time might be 1.5 s. Many students will predict that the time needed to roll twice as far will be twice as much. A few students will suggest that the time needs to be more than twice. The activity will confirm that the actual time is less than twice.

Answers To
PRACTICE PROBLEMS

Have students refer to Appendix A of the Solutions Appendix for complete solutions to Practice Problems.

1. 8.0 m/s^2
2. -7.0 m/s^2
3. 3.0 m/s^2
4. a. -8.3 m/s^2
   b. half as great

Assessment

Portfolio

Include samples of acceleration problems solved graphically, such as Practice Problem 7 on page 68, or a graphical solution of Practice Problems 13 and 14 on page 72 in the portfolio. Have students accompany the graphs with written descriptions of the motion.

POCKET LAB

UNIFORM OR NOT?

Set up a U channel on a book so it acts as an inclined ramp (or make a channel from two meter sticks taped together along the edges). Release a steel ball so that it rolls down the ramp. Using a stopwatch, measure the time it takes to roll 0.40 m. Write a sentence describing the motion of the ball. Predict how much time it would take to roll 0.80 m. Explain your prediction.

Thus, the car's speed increases, but its acceleration is negative. When the car reaches the end of the driveway, the driver puts on the brakes and comes to a stop. Then, the final velocity will be less negative than the initial velocity. The acceleration will be positive, even though the car is moving slower.

Practice Problems

1. An Indy-500 race car's velocity increases from $+4.0$ m/s to $+36$ m/s over a 4.0-s period. What is its average acceleration?
2. The same race car slows from $+36$ m/s to $+15$ m/s over 3.0 s. What is its average acceleration over this time interval?
3. A car is coasting backwards down a hill at -3.0 m/s when the driver gets the engine started. After 2.5 s, the car is moving uphill at a velocity of $+4.5$ m/s. What is the car's average acceleration?
4. ▶ A bus is moving at 25 m/s. The driver steps on the brakes, and the bus stops in 3.0 s.
   a. What is the average acceleration of the bus while braking?
   b. Suppose the bus took twice as long to stop. How would the acceleration compare to the acceleration you found above?

Average and Instantaneous Acceleration

Acceleration is positive if the velocity change is positive.

In Chapter 3, velocity-time graphs were used to find the object's displacement. Now we will use them in another way. Figure 4–3 lists the velocities of a jet rolling down a runway for takeoff, and a graph of the data. As time increases, so does the velocity of the plane. The plane is accelerating. The change in velocity is the change in the ordinate, or *rise*, of the curve. The time interval is the change in the abscissa, or *run*. Average acceleration is the change in velocity divided by the time interval, so the average acceleration is given by the slope of the curve.

Acceleration is the slope of a velocity-time graph.

$$slope = \frac{rise}{run} = \frac{\Delta v}{\Delta t} = \bar{a}$$

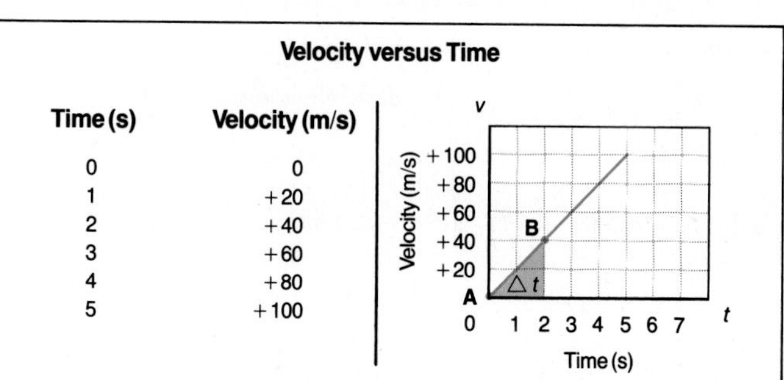

FIGURE 4–3. A velocity-time graph for uniformly accelerated motion.

STUDY GUIDE MASTER

Use the Study Guide master for section 4.1.

LABORATORY MANUAL

Use Lab 4.1 with this section.

In this case, the curve on a velocity-time graph is a straight line, and so the change in velocity is the same in each time interval. The slope is constant, as is the acceleration of the object. For the airplane in Figure 4–3, the acceleration is 20 m/s/s. Its velocity increases 20 m/s for every second.

In many cases, however, acceleration changes in time. At a given time the instantaneous acceleration is the slope of the tangent to the curve at that time. Figure 4–4 shows the change in velocity with time of an automobile. In this case, the slope, and thus the acceleration, is greatest just as the car accelerates from rest. This car's acceleration is smallest when its velocity is largest.

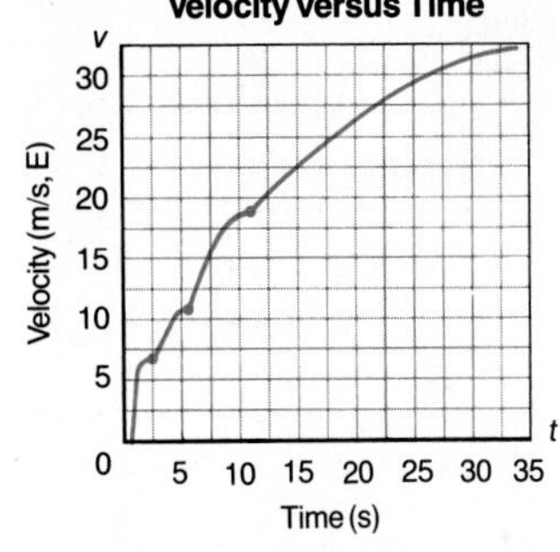

FIGURE 4–4. The changes in velocity with time of a car accelerating as the driver shifts from first to fourth gear.

Example Problem

Finding the Average Acceleration of a Runner

Figure 4–5 is a velocity-time graph of a sprinter during a 100-m dash. Find the sprinter's average acceleration between **a.** 0.0 s and 1.0 s. **b.** 2.0 s and 4.0 s.

Given: velocity-time graph

Unknown: average acceleration, $\bar{a}$

Basic equation: $\bar{a} = \frac{\Delta v}{\Delta t} = \frac{rise}{run}$

FIGURE 4–5. Use with the Example Problem.

Solution: From the graph, we get Table 4–1.

Table 4–1

Time (s)	Velocity (m/s)
0.0	0.0
1.0	7.8
2.0	10.0
4.0	10.8

Thus,

a. $\bar{a} = \frac{\Delta v}{\Delta t} = \frac{rise}{run} = \frac{7.8 \text{ m/s}}{1.0 \text{ s}} = 7.8 \text{ m/s}^2$

b. $\bar{a} = \frac{\Delta v}{\Delta t} = \frac{rise}{run} = \frac{0.8 \text{ m/s}}{2.0 \text{ s}} = 0.4 \text{ m/s}^2$

The **instantaneous acceleration** is given by the slope of a tangent to the curve on a velocity-time graph. You will find that a tangent to the curve as shown on Figure 4–5 at 1.0 s has a slope of 3.9 m/s^2.

CONCEPT DEVELOPMENT

Remember to emphasize that if the slope of a velocity-time graph is high that means the acceleration is large. Conversely, if the slope of such a graph is small, the acceleration is small.

ACTIVITY

Demonstration: Put one student in a wagon with a handful of beans. The student will drop one bean every second according to the command of another student who will watch a stopwatch for 5–10 s and count out loud. Another student should pull the wagon, making a concentrated effort to begin slowly and gradually increase the speed. Have students measure the distances and graph distance-to-time. Repeat, starting with the wagon moving rapidly, then gradually slow it down. Graph the data for this trial. If time permits, push the wagon with a sudden amount of force and allow friction to slow it down. Graph the data. Lead this into a discussion of friction and the effect of force on acceleration.

Cooperative Learning: Drawing on the practical knowledge of your student athletes, pose the following question: What is the average acceleration of a runner in the 100-m dash? [First, remember that the average speed for this event is about 10 m/s. So a runner has to get up to something like this speed during the time interval of acceleration. Suppose students say it takes 2 s to get up to top speed. Then the average acceleration would be about 5 m/s^2. More important than the actual answer is the process of estimation and thinking about this running event in the quantitative way.]

RETEACHING MASTER

Use the Reteaching master for Chapter 4 with this section.

ENRICHMENT MASTER

Use the Enrichment master for Chapter 4 with this section.

RETEACHING

Reteaching Master. Teacher Resource Package. Use the Reteaching Master, Monitoring Acceleration, with this section.

EXTENSION

Enrichment Master. With this section, use the Enrichment Master, Velocity of a Baseball, from the Teacher Resource Package.

CHECKING FOR UNDERSTANDING

Use an example like a pitched baseball which lands in the catcher's mitt. Ask students to draw a velocity-time graph of this motion. Make sure that they show the average acceleration of the pitched ball to be less than the acceleration of the ball at the catcher's mitt. Or, you might want to approach it the opposite way by putting a velocity-time graph on the board or overhead and asking for a description of the motion.

Physics and technology

CUSHIONING THE BLOW

The automobile has given people freedom, but over the years, its mass and speed have resulted in many deaths and serious injuries in collisions. To improve safety, manufacturers have installed devices either to avoid accidents or to protect occupants of a car in an accident. The latest passive restraint devices include shoulder straps that move into place automatically and air bags. These devices allow the car occupants to slow down gradually with the car instead of being thrown into the car body or into the air where their speed goes to zero very rapidly.

Air bags can be installed on both the driver and passenger sides of a car. A crash at 10 to 15 mph with its sudden acceleration, triggers sensors that activate an igniter. This decomposes sodium azide pellets, producing nitrogen gas that rushes into the nylon bag, forcing it out of its storage compartment as it inflates. The whole process takes place in less than 40 milliseconds. The air bag spreads the time over which the occupant's speed is brought to zero. Injuries to the head and chest are reduced or eliminated. The occupant forces the gas out of the cushion through holes in the bag. The bag deflates within two seconds, allowing the driver to maintain control of the car.

• Crash tests show that air bags dramatically reduce injury in frontal collisions. However, protection is poor in side impacts and in rollovers. Can you think of any other disadvantage?

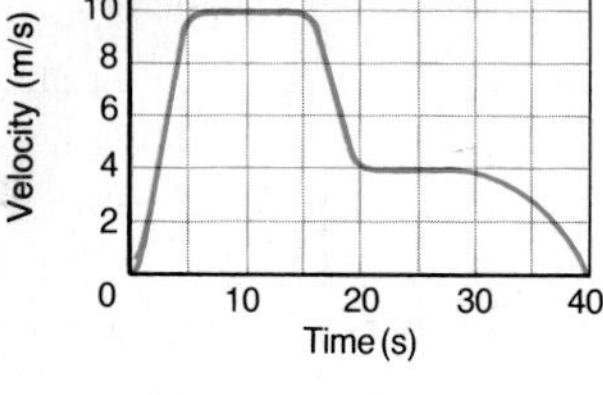

FIGURE 4–6. Use with Practice Problems 5, 6, and 7.

Practice Problems

5. Describe, in words, the velocity of the toy train shown in Figure 4–6 between 0 and 20 s.
6. Figure 4–6 shows a velocity-time graph of a toy train.
   a. During which time interval or intervals is the speed constant?
   b. During which interval or intervals is the train's acceleration positive?
   c. During which interval or intervals is its acceleration less than zero?
   d. During which time interval is the acceleration most negative?
7. For Figure 4–6, find the average acceleration during the given time intervals.
   a. 0 to 5 s c. 15 to 20 s
   b. 0 to 10 s d. 0 to 40 s
8. ▶ a. Draw a velocity-time graph for an object whose velocity is constantly decreasing from 10 m/s at t = 0.0 s to −10 m/s at t = 2.0 s. Assume it has constant acceleration.
   b. What is its average acceleration between 0.0 s and 2.0 s?
   c. What is its acceleration when its velocity is 0 m/s?

Physics and technology

In 1990, a driver-side air bag was standard on seventy-six car models. Its use is expected to jump in the next few years. Chrysler Corporation offers driver-side air bags on all the automobiles it produces in the United States. Air bags are also available as standard equipment on all Mercedes-Benz models and some BMW, Volvo, and Acura models.

Once deployed, an air bag cannot be reused. The air bag must be replaced. Depending on the extent of damage to the air bag system, such as the sensors, the replacement cost could be as much as $500.

Because it protects well only in front-end collisions, the air bag should be used along with a shoulder strap and seat belt; thus, the reason for the air bag's official name: supplemental restraint system (SRS).

Teacher Resources: Keller, Maryann N. "Putting More Air in the Airbag." *Motor Trend,* 40 (9), September 1988, page 124. Knepper, Mike. "Proper Restraint." *Home Mechanix,* 85 (737), September 1989, pages 73–77. "Which Cars Do Better in a Crash?" *Consumer Reports,* 55 (4), April 1990, pages 218–220.

Guided Practice: Go over the Example Problem on page 67, then have students work on the first two Practice Problems on this page.

Independent Practice: Assign the remaining Practice Problems on this page for homework and spend some time reviewing them with students the next class period.

Answers To
PRACTICE PROBLEMS

Have students refer to Appendix A of the Solutions Appendix for complete solutions to Practice Problems.

5. Starting from rest, it accelerates to 10 m/s in the first 5 s. It remains at this speed for 10 s, before slowing to 4 m/s over the last 5 s.

6. **a.** 5 to 15 s and 21 to 28 s
b. 0 to 6 s
c. 15 to 20 s, 28 to 40 s
d. 16 to 19 s

7. **a.** 2 m/s^2
b. 1 m/s^2
c. −1.2 m/s^2
d. 0 m/s^2

8. **a.** Refer to Appendix A for graph.
b. −10 m/s^2
c. −10 m/s^2

Velocity of an Object With Constant Acceleration

Acceleration that does not change in time is **uniform** or **constant acceleration**. In this case, the velocity-time graph of constant acceleration is a straight line. The velocity when the clock reading, or time, is zero is called the **initial velocity**, v_i. The slope of the line is the acceleration, a, so the equation that describes the curve, and thus the velocity at t, is

$$v_f = v_i + at.$$

Example Problem

Final Velocity After Uniform Acceleration

If a car with a velocity of 2.0 m/s at $t = 0$ accelerates at a rate of $+4.0\ \text{m/s}^2$ for 2.5 s, what is its velocity at time $t = 2.5$ s?

Given: $v_i = +2.0$ m/s, $a = +4.0\ \text{m/s}^2$, $t = 2.5$ s

Unknown: final velocity, v_f

Basic equation: $v_f = v_i + at$

Solution:

$$v_f = v_i + at = +2.0\ \text{m/s} + (+4.0\ \text{m/s}^2)(2.5\ \text{s}) = +12\ \text{m/s}$$

Practice Problems

9. A golf ball rolls up a hill toward a Putt-Putt hole.
   a. If it starts with a velocity of +2.0 m/s and accelerates at a constant rate of $-0.50\ \text{m/s}^2$, what is its velocity after 2.0 s?
   b. If the acceleration occurs for 6.0 s, what is its final velocity?
   c. Describe, in words, the motion of the golf ball.

10. A bus traveling at +30 km/h accelerates at a constant $+3.5\ \text{m/s}^2$ for 6.8 s. What is its final velocity in km/h?

11. If a car accelerates from rest at a constant $5.5\ \text{m/s}^2$, how long will be required to reach 28 m/s?

▶ **12.** A car slows from 22 m/s to 3 m/s with a constant acceleration of $-2.1\ \text{m/s}^2$. How long does it require?

CONCEPT REVIEW

1.1 Describe, in words, how you calculate average acceleration between two times.

1.2 **a.** If an object has zero acceleration, does that mean its velocity is zero? Give an example.
   b. If an object has zero velocity at some instant, does that mean its acceleration is zero? Give an example.

1.3 Is km/h/s a unit of acceleration? Is this unit the same as km/s/h? Explain the meaning of the two.

1.4 Critical Thinking: Figure 4–7 is a strobe photo of a horizontally moving ball. What information about the photo would you need and what measurements would you make to estimate the acceleration?

F.Y.I.

One of Galileo's contributions to the study of motion was to recognize that the correct method to use in solving a problem is to remove complicating factors, like air resistance, to make clear the important factor, the effect of Earth's gravity on the motion of bodies.

If a velocity-time graph is a straight line, the acceleration is uniform or constant.

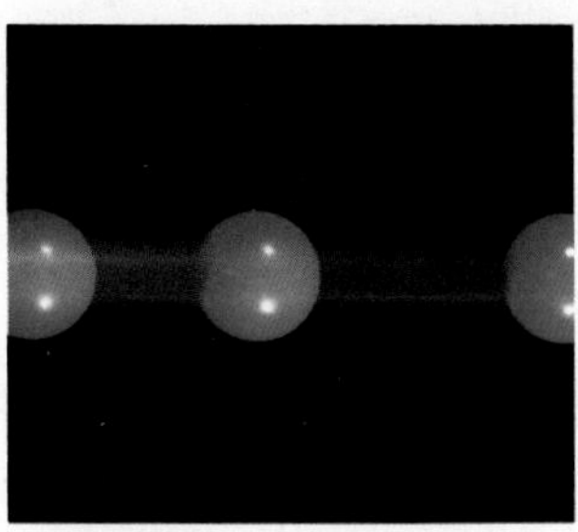

FIGURE 4—7. Use with Concept Review 1.4.

CONCEPT DEVELOPMENT

Critical Thinking: Ask students to develop a conversion factor for changing an acceleration in terms of km/h/s into m/s/s. [Multiply the acceleration in km/h/s by 0.278 to get the acceleration in m/s/s.]

INDEPENDENT PRACTICE/ EXTENSION

Refer to the Assignment Guide below for additional questions and problems for independent practice.

Answers To
PRACTICE PROBLEMS

Have students refer to Appendix A of the Solutions Appendix for complete solutions to Practice Problems.

9. **a.** 1.0 m/s; **b.** −1.0 m/s; **c.** Velocity decreases; ball rolls back downhill.
10. 116 km/h
11. 5.1 s
12. 9.0 s

3 Close

CONVERGENT QUESTION

Ask students to distinguish between velocity and acceleration by giving examples complete with proper units.

CONCEPT REVIEW ANSWERS

1.1 You find the acceleration by dividing the change in velocity of an object by the time taken to make the velocity change.
1.2 a. No. If the object has constant velocity, its acceleration is zero. **b.** No. The golf ball in Practice Problem 9 had non-zero acceleration but stopped for an instant as its direction of motion reversed.
1.3 Yes; yes. The first measures how many km/h the speed changes each second. The second measures how many km/s the speed changes in one hour.
1.4 Critical Thinking: You need to know the time between flashes and the distance scale. Measure the distance between the first two images and the distance between the last two. From these you get two velocities. Between these two velocities, a time interval of x flashes occurred. Divide the difference of the two velocities by x.

4:1 ASSIGNMENT GUIDE

	PRACTICE	EXTENSION
CHAPTER REVIEW pp. 80–85		
· Reviewing Concepts	1–5	
· Applying Concepts		1–4
· Problems*	1–6, 8, 9	7
APPENDIX B PROBLEMS*		
· Chapter 4 p. 690	1, 2, 3, 5	3

* Complete solutions to all Chapter Review and Appendix problems appear in the Problems and Solutions Manual.

PHYSICS LAB

Process Skills: observing, formulating models, communicating, interpreting data, hypothesizing, questioning, defining operationally, measuring.

MISCONCEPTIONS

Velocity and acceleration can be easily confused. They are related but distinct concepts.

Lab Worksheet, Teacher Resource Package. If desired, use the lab worksheet master for this chapter for students to record their data.

OBSERVATIONS

1. The car has constant velocity.
2. The ball changes velocity (accelerates).
3. For the first part of the race, the car goes faster than the ball. During the last part of the race, the ball goes faster. At some instant (near the middle of the race) both objects have the same velocity.

ANALYSIS

The position-time graph for the car is a simple linear relationship producing a straight line. The graph of the ball is an increasing slope with an upward curve. At the point representing halfway in distance, the slopes of the two graphs are equal. The tangent of the slope for the ball is equal to the slope for the car.

APPLICATION

It will take the policeman a period of time to reach the same speed as the speeder. During this interval the speeder is increasing the distance between the two cars. The policeman must go faster than the speeder before the gap gets smaller.

LAB WORKSHEET

Use the Lab Worksheet for Chapter 4 with this Physics Lab

PHYSICS LAB: Ball and Car Race

Purpose

To compare the motion of constant velocity to the motion of constant acceleration.

Materials

- battery-powered car
- 1″ steel ball
- 10 cm of tape
- 90 cm length of U channel
- short length of plastic straw
- 100 cm of fishing line
- stopwatch

Procedure

1. Tape the straw to the bottom of the car. Thread the fishing line through the straw and securely tape *both* ends as shown below. (The car will now be constrained to move in a straight line.)
2. Place a piece of tape on the table to serve as a reference line.
3. Turn the car on and start it behind the reference line. (See sketch.)
4. Measure the average time needed for the car to travel from the reference line to the end of the ramp (at least 3 trials).
5. Place a book or wood blocks and so on under one end of the U channel and measure the time it takes for the ball to roll down the ramp when *starting from the reference line*!
6. Adjust the height of the end of the ramp until the time it takes the ball to roll is within the 0.1 s of the time needed for the car.
7. Place the ball on the ramp at the reference line. Start the car behind the reference line and release the ball as the cart reaches the reference line.
8. Which object won the race? Was it close?

Observations and Data

1. Describe the motion of the car in words.
2. Describe the motion of the ball in words.
3. Did it appear that the objects ever had the same speed during the race? If so, then where?

Analysis

1. Set up a graph of position (vertical axis) vs time (horizontal axis).
2. Assume that the car had a steady speed. Show this motion on the graph.
3. Place a marker at the halfway point for the ball. Measure the time needed for the ball to roll halfway.
4. Assume that the ball was gaining speed (accelerating) for the entire time. Draw a smooth curve to show the motion of the ball. (**Hint:** This curve should have the same starting and ending points as the car, but also include the data point for the halfway distance.)
5. Did the two graphs ever have equal slopes (equal velocities)? Where?

Applications

1. Why does it take so long for a policeman in a parked car to catch up after you speed by him?

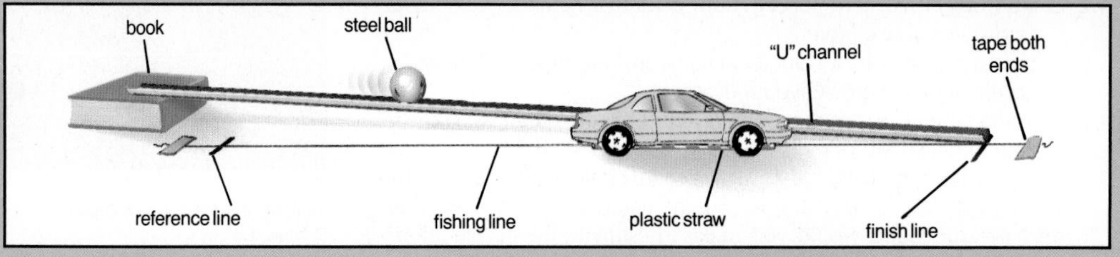

ASSESSMENT

Critical Thinking: To further assess students' understanding of acceleration, ask the following questions.

1. You assumed that the car had a steady velocity. Would you expect the car to accelerate or go faster if the track were slightly downhill? Why? Try it. [Students will be surprised to find that the velocity of the car is the same as before. The velocity of the car is controlled by the gears between the electric motor and the wheels.]

2. Assume that you have a tie race between the ball and the car. Compare the average speed of the ball to the average speed of the car. [Both objects have the same average (not instantaneous) speed. They both travel the same distance in the same time.]

4.2 DISPLACEMENT DURING CONSTANT ACCELERATION

The distance traveled by a moving object is much easier to measure than its velocity. For that reason, we will develop three equations that relate the displacement to two of the three other quantities we use to describe motion—time, velocity, and acceleration. *These equations are correct only when acceleration is constant.* Fortunately, for many types of moving bodies, including those falling due to gravity, this condition is true when air resistance is ignored.

Displacement When Velocity and Time Are Known

When an object is moving with constant velocity, its displacement can be found by multiplying its velocity by the time interval. To find the displacement if the object is uniformly accelerating, the velocity is replaced by the average velocity,

$$\bar{v} = \tfrac{1}{2}(v_f + v_i).$$

To show this, consider the velocity-time graph for an object with constant acceleration, Figure 4–8. The displacement is the total area under the curve. The total area is the sum of the area of the rectangle, $v_i t$, and the area of the triangle, $\tfrac{1}{2}(v_f - v_i)t$. The total area is the displacement, $d = v_i t + \tfrac{1}{2}(v_f - v_i)t$, or

$$\boxed{d = \tfrac{1}{2}(v_f + v_i)t.}$$

Objectives

- be able to calculate the displacement of an object undergoing uniform acceleration when you know two out of the three quantities: acceleration, time, velocity.
- be able to solve problems of the motion of objects uniformly accelerated by gravity.
- learn to use an organized strategy for solving motion problems.

Example Problem

Displacement When Velocity and Time Are Known

What is the displacement of a train as it is accelerated uniformly from +11 m/s to +33 m/s in a 20.0-s interval?

Given: initial velocity, $v_i = +11$ m/s; final velocity, $v_f = +33$ m/s; time interval, $t = 20.0$ s

Unknown: displacement, d

Basic equation: $d = \tfrac{1}{2}(v_f + v_i)t$

Solution: $d = \tfrac{1}{2}(v_f + v_i)t = \tfrac{1}{2}(+33\text{ m/s} + 11\text{ m/s})(20.0\text{ s})$
$= +4.4 \times 10^2$ m

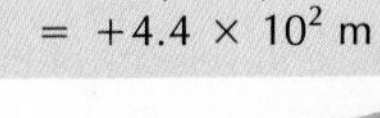

4.2 DISPLACEMENT DURING CONSTANT ACCELERATION

Preparation

OBJECTIVES

The objectives are listed on the student page. Remind students to preview these objectives as a study guide to this major section.

OVERVIEW

The major equations of one-dimensional motion with constant acceleration and the important special case of acceleration due to gravity are introduced in this section. (Note that these equations only apply when the acceleration is constant.)

BRIDGING

Facility with graphical analysis is crucial here. Most of these graphical manipulations were covered in Chapter 2.

TEACHER

So far we've discussed how position changes with time (velocity) and how velocity changes with time (acceleration). Have students describe what it would mean to have a rate of change of acceleration. [It would mean that acceleration is not constant, that it is changing. Engineers call this quantity "jerk." It turns out that a jerk during an elevator ride makes our stomachs queasy, so engineers try to minimize it.]

1 Focus

DISCREPANT EVENT

It's possible to get a good estimate of acceleration due to gravity by using very simple equipment. As mentioned in the last chapter, approximate measuring of time can be done by counting one thousand-one, one thousand-two, one thousand-three, etc. With a little practice each syllable will be about a quarter of a second. Now measure a height of 1 m from the floor. Drop a convenient object, like a ball, from this height and, by the counting method described above, time its fall. Usually it comes out about 0.5 s. So the distance covered is 1 m and the time of the fall is about 0.5 s. Using the equation $d = 1/2\ gt^2$ yields a value of about 8 m/s^2—not bad for such crude equipment! You might also ask students what the average velocity of fall is for the ball. [About 2 m/s]

Answers To
PRACTICE PROBLEMS

Have students refer to Appendix A of the Solutions Appendix for complete solutions to Practice Problems.

13. 3.6×10^2 m
14. 1.7×10^3 m
15. 6.3 s
16. 0.94 m/s

Connect to MATHEMATICS

Students will probably know equations for calculation areas of geometric forms. They may also have been introduced to the method of estimating the area of an irregular region by placing graph paper on the object and counting full and partial squares. Most likely, however, they will either have ignored the dimensions of the area or used two length dimensions. The area has a dimension that is the product of the dimension of the quantity displayed along the x-axis and that displayed along the y-axis. The areas calculated in this chapter are more abstract. In each case, the y-axis displays a rate, velocity (m/s) or acceleration (m/s^2), while the x-axis displays time. Thus, the dimension of the area is either (m/s)s = m, or (m/s^2)s = m/s.

Practice Problems

13. A race car traveling at +44 m/s is uniformly accelerated to a velocity of +22 m/s over an 11-s interval. What is its displacement during this time?

14. A rocket traveling at +88 m/s is accelerated uniformly to +132 m/s over a 15-s interval. What is its displacement during this time?

15. A car accelerates at a constant rate from 15 m/s to 25 m/s while it travels 125 m. How long does this motion take?

▶ **16.** A bike rider accelerates constantly to a velocity of 7.5 m/s during 4.5 s. The bike's displacement is +19 m. What was the initial velocity of the bike?

Displacement When Acceleration and Time Are Known

If the initial velocity, acceleration, and time interval are known, the displacement of the object can be found by combining equations already used. The final velocity of a uniformly accelerated object is $v_f = v_i + at$. The displacement of an object with uniform acceleration is $d = ½(v_f + v_i)t$.

Substitute the final velocity from the first equation into the second equation.

$$d = ½(v_f + v_i)t = ½((v_i + at) + v_i)t = ½(2v_i + at)t$$

$$\boxed{d = v_it + ½at^2}$$

There are two terms in this equation. The first term, v_it, corresponds to the displacement of an object if it were moving with constant velocity, v_i. The second term, $½at^2$, gives the displacement of an object starting from rest and moving with uniform acceleration. The sum of these two terms gives the displacement of an object that starts with an initial velocity and accelerates uniformly. For an object that starts from rest, the equation reduces to $d = ½at^2$.

You can see these relationships by looking at a velocity-time graph of uniformly accelerated motion. As you know, the area under the curve of a velocity-time graph is the displacement of the object.

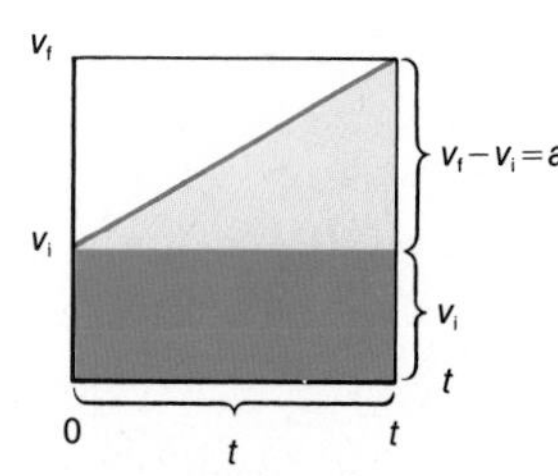

FIGURE 4–8. A velocity-time graph of uniformly accelerated motion. The shaded area represents displacement.

Look at the shaded area under the curve between time $t_i = 0$ and time t, Figure 4–8. The shaded area is made up of a rectangle with a triangle on top. The area of the rectangle is its height, the initial velocity, v_i, multiplied by its base, the time t. That is, area $= v_it$. This area is the displacement the object would have if it had the constant velocity v_i.

The altitude of the triangle is the change in velocity of the uniformly accelerated object. Since $v_f = v_i + at$, $(v_f - v_i) = at$. The base is again the time t. The area of a triangle is half the base times the altitude, or $½(at)(t) = ½at^2$. This area is the displacement the object would have if it were uniformly accelerated from rest.

The total displacement is the sum of the two areas under the curve, $d = v_it + ½at^2$.

What useful graphs could be constructed where a rate is plotted along the y-axis? What would be the meaning of the area for such a graph? [Possible answers include $/gal plotted against number of gallons, or a pay rate of $/h versus the number of hours worked. If overtime is paid at a higher rate, then this graph is not just a straight line.]

Position versus Time	
Time (s)	Position (m)
0	+0
1	+10
2	+40
3	+90
4	+160
5	+250

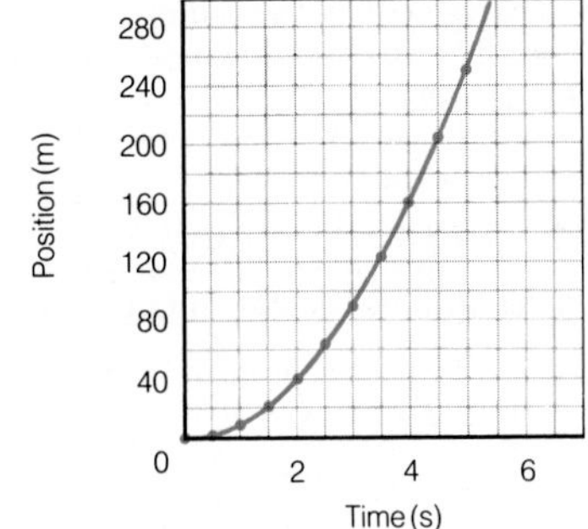

FIGURE 4–9. A position-time graph for uniformly accelerated motion.

What kind of curve is the position-time graph of an object accelerated from rest at a constant rate? Figure 4–9 includes a table of the positions of the jet plane for the first five seconds of its acceleration. The positions were found from the area under the curve of the velocity-time graph, Figure 4–3.

The data were then plotted to give the position-time graph shown. The curve of the position-time graph is half a parabola. When one quantity varies directly with the square of the other, a parabolic curve results.

As you have seen, the slope of a position-time graph is the velocity of the object. When an object's velocity is constant, its position changes the same amount each second. Therefore, the position-time graph is a straight line with a constant slope. If, however, the object is accelerated, during each second its displacement is larger than it was the second before. The position-time graph for accelerated motion is a parabola, and the slope does change. Figure 4–10 again shows the position-time graph for the jet plane. Suppose you want to find the slope of the curve at point **P**. Draw a line tangent to the curve at point **P**. The slope of the tangent line is the instantaneous velocity at point **P**. Point **P** is at the time 3 seconds. A tangent line is drawn, and

$$v = slope = \frac{rise}{run} = \frac{+270 \text{ m} - 0 \text{ m}}{6.0 \text{ s} - 1.5 \text{ s}}$$

$$= \frac{270 \text{ m}}{4.5 \text{ s}} = +60 \text{ m/s}.$$

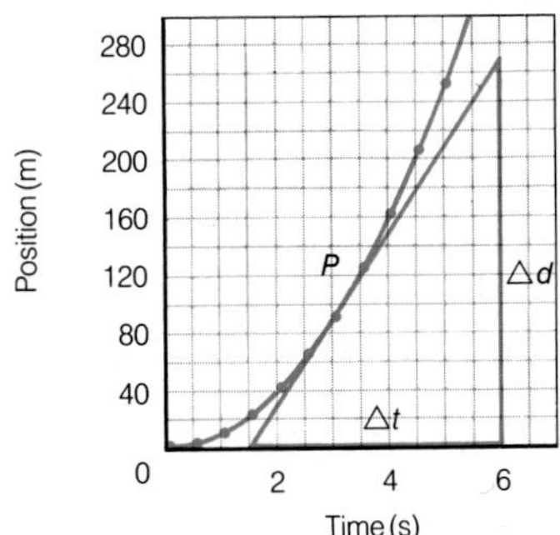

FIGURE 4–10. The slope at any point on a position-time graph indicates the velocity of the object.

2 Teach

CONCEPT DEVELOPMENT

- Acceleration can be used in a broader sense than just dealing with motion. It applies whenever the rate of a quantity changes with time. That is, things other than motions can be accelerated.

Study Guide Master. To reinforce these concepts, have the students complete the Study Guide Master for Section 4.2 from the Teacher Resource Package.

- Again, graphs are essential here. Provide graph paper freely so students can draw lots of graphs—it should become an automatic process.

Assessment

Portfolio

In some car owner manuals for more high-performance, expensive cars, there are graphs of speed vs. time as the car goes through its gears. They're usually well-labeled graphs which present real world examples of acceleration. They're particularly good for computing distance traveled by area methods and acceleration by slope methods. Similar material is also available in various monthly car magazines. Have students collect some of these graphs and do the calculations. Students should also include a written description of the motion.

STUDY GUIDE MASTER

Use the Study Guide master for section 4.2.

CONCEPT DEVELOPMENT

Remember that the application of the four motion equations is restricted to situations of constant acceleration. Motions with nonconstant acceleration are much harder to deal with.

Critical Thinking: One suggestion for propelling spacecraft is by solar sails, giant thin metal sheets pushed on by sunlight. In one article it is suggested that in one hour, starting from rest, such a sail could move a spacecraft one meter. Have students calculate the spacecraft's acceleration. [1.5×10^{-7} m/s^2]

Teacher Resource: Michael, Valerie. "Graphical Analysis." *Science Teacher.* October 1989, pages 37–40.

Critical Thinking Master, Teacher Resource Package. You may wish to have students complete the Critical Thinking Master, Acceleration and Escape Velocity, with this section.

Answers To
PRACTICE PROBLEMS

Have students refer to Appendix A of the Solutions Appendix for complete solutions to Practice Problems.

17. 1.35×10^3 m
18. 8.8 m/s^2
19. a. -11 m/s^2
b. 22 m
20. 83 m

HELP WANTED

AIR TRAFFIC CONTROLLER

If you can think fast and communicate clearly and decisively while juggling dozens of details in your mind, you might be the person we are seeking. Three years of work experience or 4 years of college and the ability to pass the Federal Civil Service Exam may qualify you to enter a training program. Advancement is based on job performance, and completion of on-the-job training programs. Knowledge of foreign languages is a plus. For information contact:
The local Job Information Center of The U.S. Office of Personnel Management

The velocity at the end of 3 seconds for an object that accelerates at $+20$ m/s^2 is $+60$ m/s, which agrees with the velocity-time graph for the jet plane.

Example Problem

Calculating Displacement From Acceleration and Time

A car starting from rest accelerates uniformly at $+6.1$ m/s^2 for 7.0 s. How far does the car move?

Given: initial velocity, $v_i = 0$ m/s; acceleration, $a = +6.1$ m/s^2; final time, $t = 7.0$ s

Unknown: displacement, d

Basic equation: $d = v_i t + \frac{1}{2}at^2$

Solution:
$$d = v_i t + \tfrac{1}{2}at^2$$
$$= (0\text{ m/s})(7.0\text{ s}) + \tfrac{1}{2}(+6.1\text{ m/s}^2)(7.0\text{ s})^2$$
$$= 0\text{ m} + 150\text{ m} = +150\text{ m}$$

Practice Problems

17. An airplane starts from rest and accelerates at a constant $+3.00$ m/s^2 for 30.0 s before leaving the ground. What is its displacement during this time?

18. Starting from rest, a race car moves 110 m in the first 5.0 s of uniform acceleration. What is the car's acceleration?

19. A driver brings a car traveling at $+22$ m/s to a full stop in 2.0 s. Assume its acceleration is constant.
a. What is the car's acceleration?
b. How far does it travel before stopping?

▶ **20.** A biker passes a lamppost at the crest of a hill at $+4.5$ m/s. She accelerates down the hill at a constant rate of $+0.40$ m/s^2 for 12 s. How far does she move down the hill during this time?

FIGURE 4–11.

Displacement When Velocity and Acceleration Are Known

We can combine the equations for final velocity and displacement to form an equation relating initial and final velocities, acceleration, and displacement in which time does not appear. First, recall the two motion equations,

$$d = \tfrac{1}{2}(v_f + v_i)t \text{ and } v_f = v_i + at.$$

The second equation is now solved for t and substituted in the first, resulting in

$$d = \tfrac{1}{2}\frac{(v_f + v_i)(v_f - v_i)}{a} = \tfrac{1}{2}\frac{v_f^2 - v_i^2}{a}.$$

Solving for v_f^2 yields

$$\boxed{v_f^2 = v_i^2 + 2ad.}$$

Example Problem

Calculating Acceleration From Displacement and Velocity

An airplane must reach a velocity of 71 m/s for takeoff. If the runway is 1.0 km long, what must the constant acceleration be?

Given: initial velocity,
$v_i = 0$ m/s
final velocity,
$v_f = 71$ m/s
displacement,
$d = +1.0$ km
$= +1.0 \times 10^3$ m

Unknown: acceleration, a
Basic equation: $v_f^2 = v_i^2 + 2ad$

Solution: $v_f^2 = v_i^2 + 2ad$, so $a = \dfrac{v_f^2 - v_i^2}{2d}$

$$= \frac{(71 \text{ m/s})^2 - 0}{2\,(+1.0 \times 10^3 \text{ m})}$$
$$= +2.5 \text{ m/s}^2$$

Consider the reverse of this problem. The plane lands going 71 m/s. It slows to a halt with an acceleration of -2.5 m/s^2. How much runway does it require? We use the same basic equation, solved for the displacement,

$$d = \frac{v_f^2 - v_i^2}{2a}$$
$$= \frac{(0 \text{ m/s})^2 - (71 \text{ m/s})^2}{2(-2.5 \text{ m/s}^2)}$$
$$= +1.0 \times 10^3 \text{ m}.$$

Notice that the displacement is the same. The motion in these two cases is said to be symmetrical. The conditions at the beginning and end of the motion are reversed, and the solutions are equivalent. Symmetry often plays an important role in physics problems.

POCKET LAB

DIRECTION OF ACCELERATION

Tape a bubble level onto the top of a laboratory cart. Adjust the level until the bubble is centered. Watch the motion of the bubble as you begin to pull the cart forward. Which way does the bubble move? The bubble shows the acceleration of the cart. Which way is the cart accelerating as it starts to move forward? Try to keep the cart moving so that the bubble returns to the center position. What direction is the acceleration of the cart now? What happens to the bubble when the cart coasts to a stop? What does that indicate about the acceleration? Predict what would happen to the bubble if you tie the string to the back of the cart and repeat the experiment. Draw a sketch of the cart and use arrows to indicate the direction of acceleration as the cart starts to move backwards.

Practice Problems

21. An airplane accelerates from a velocity of 21 m/s at the constant rate of 3.0 m/s^2 over +535 m. What is its final velocity?

22. The pilot stops the same plane in 484 m using a constant acceleration of -8.0 m/s^2. How fast was the plane moving before braking began?

23. A person wearing a shoulder harness can survive a car crash if the acceleration is smaller than -300 m/s^2. Assuming constant acceleration, how far must the front end of the car collapse if it crashes while going 101 km/h?

▶**24.** A car is initially sliding backwards down a hill at -25 km/h. The driver guns the car. By the time the car's velocity is +35 km/h, it is +3.2 m from its starting point. Assuming the car was uniformly accelerated, find the acceleration.

POCKET LAB

DIRECTION OF ACCELERATION

Purpose: to investigate acceleration of a laboratory cart using a simple accelerometer.

Materials: small bubble level; laboratory cart; tape.

Outcome: The bubble will move forward as the cart starts to move forward. This indicates that the cart accelerates in the forward direction. When the bubble is centered, the cart is not accelerating. Objects moving in a straight line at a steady speed have zero acceleration. As the car coasts to a stop, the bubble will move toward the back of the cart. The acceleration is in the direction opposite the motion. As soon as the cart starts to move in the backward direction, the bubble will move toward the back of the cart. This indicates that the cart is accelerating in the same direction as it starts to move. When the cart is moving at a steady speed, the bubble is centered. This indicates that the acceleration is zero. As the cart comes to a stop, the bubble moves toward the front. The stopping cart now is accelerating in the opposite direction.

Answers To
PRACTICE PROBLEMS

Have students refer to Appendix A of the Solutions Appendix for complete solutions to Practice Problems.

21. 60 m/s
22. 88 m/s
23. 1.32 m
24. 7.3 m/s^2

Assessment

Critical Thinking

To further assess students' understanding of the operation of accelerometers, explain that a helium balloon held in a car acts the same as the air bubble in the bubble level. Have them predict what would happen to a helium balloon in a car when the car accelerates from standing—first forward and then backward. Next predict what will happen to the balloon if the car stops—first from forward motion, then from backward. [The balloon moves in the direction of the acceleration.]

CRITICAL THINKING

Use the Critical Thinking master for Chapter 4 with this section.

CONCEPT DEVELOPMENT

A visual way of demonstrating acceleration is by using a device called an accelerometer (see Pocket Lab, p. 75). In its usual form for demonstrations, an accelerometer is two pieces of clear plastic separated by a gap of a few millimeters, with colored liquid placed in the gap. When the device undergoes an acceleration, the level of the liquid is no longer horizontal. An accelerometer can be mounted on motion carts, turntables, pendulums, etc., to show the nature of particular acceleration.

When air resistance is ignored, the acceleration of a falling body doesn't depend on mass, initial height, and initial velocity.

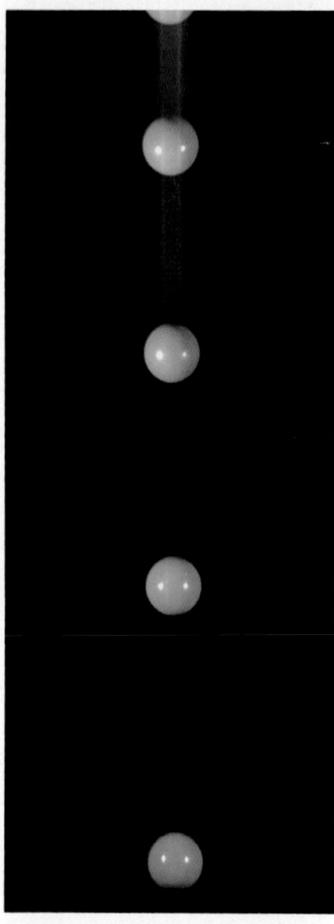

FIGURE 4–12. Strobe photograph of a ball in freefall. Images are at 1/120-s intervals.

Acceleration Due to Gravity

Galileo was the first to show that all objects fall to Earth with a constant acceleration. There is no evidence that he actually dropped two cannon balls from the leaning tower of Pisa, but he did conduct many experiments with balls rolling down inclined planes. He had previously shown that the inclined plane "diluted" gravity, slowing motion so he could make careful measurements.

We know from experiments that no matter what the mass of the object is, whether it is dropped from 1 m, 10 m, or 100 m, or whether it is dropped or thrown, as long as air resistance can be ignored, the acceleration due to gravity is the same for all objects at the same location on Earth.

Acceleration due to gravity is given a special symbol, g. Since acceleration is a vector quantity, g must have both magnitude and direction. We will choose "up" as our positive direction, so a falling object has a negative velocity. The acceleration of a falling object is also negative. On the surface of Earth, a freely falling object has an acceleration, g, of -9.80 m/s^2. Actually, g varies slightly, from -9.790 m/s^2 in southern Florida to -9.810 m/s^2 in northern Maine. It is also smaller at high altitudes; $g = -9.789$ m/s^2 on the top of Pike's Peak. We will use a typical value of -9.80 m/s^2. Thus, if a ball is dropped from the top of a building, it starts with zero velocity and in each second of fall gains a downward velocity of -9.80 m/s.

Strobe photos of a dropped ball are shown in Figure 4–12. The time interval between photos is 1/120 s. The distance between each pair of images increases. Since $v = \Delta d/\Delta t$, the speed is increasing. Because we have taken the upward direction to be positive, the velocity is becoming more and more negative.

Assuming no air resistance, all problems involving motion of falling objects can be solved by using the equations developed in this chapter with the acceleration, a, replaced by g.

$$v_f = v_i + gt$$
$$v_f^2 = v_i^2 + 2gd$$
$$d = v_i t + \tfrac{1}{2}gt^2$$

If you throw a ball straight up, it leaves your hand with a positive velocity of, say, $+20.0$ m/s. Positive velocity means it is rising. The acceleration of the ball is -9.80 m/s^2, so after 1 second its velocity is $+10.2$ m/s. After 2 seconds the velocity is $+0.40$ m/s. After 3 seconds, the velocity is -9.40 m/s. Now the velocity is no longer positive. The negative velocity indicates that the ball is no longer rising, it is falling. After 4 seconds, the velocity is -19.20 m/s, so it is falling faster and faster. See the velocity-time graph, Figure 4–13a. Let's examine what happens around 2 seconds, as shown in Figure 4–13b. The velocity changes smoothly from positive to negative at about 2.04 s. For just an instant, at the top of its flight, the ball has zero velocity.

How does the ball's position change? The position-time graph, Figure 4–13c, has a large positive slope at $t = 0$, when the velocity is large and positive. As time increases, the velocity and the slope decrease. When the slope (and velocity) is zero, the ball is at its maximum height, as shown in the detailed position-time graph, Figure 4–13d. On the

TEACHER

The stroboscope is an instrument that provides intermittent illumination of an object to study its motion, rotary speed, or frequency of vibration. It causes an object to appear to slow down or stop by producing illumination in short bursts of about 1 μs at a selected frequency.

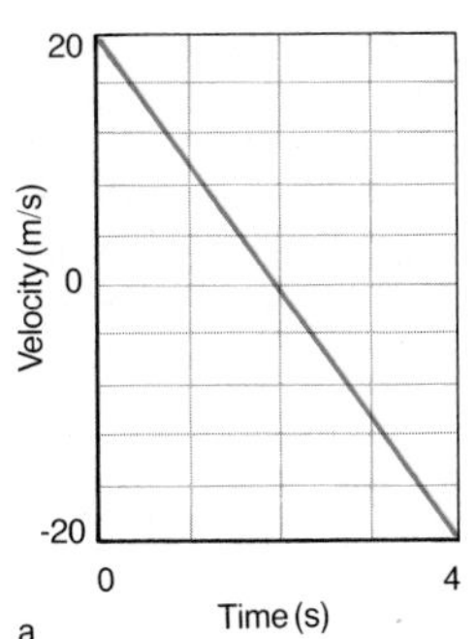

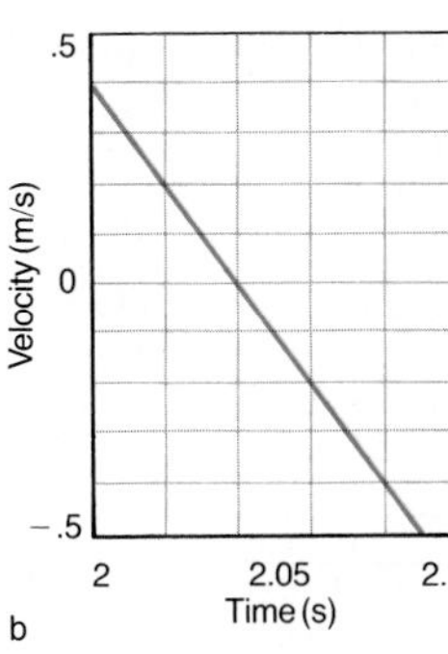

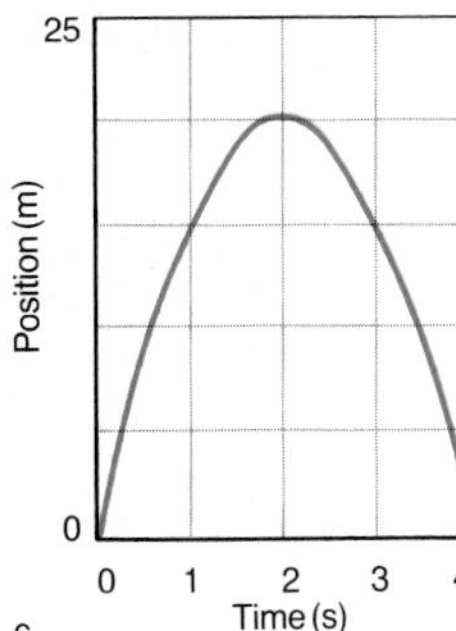

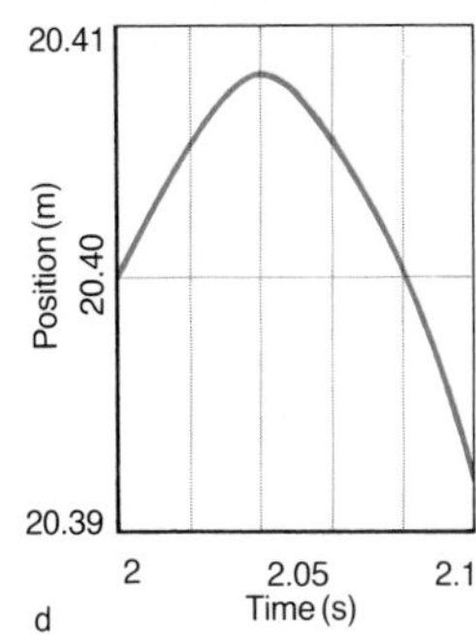

FIGURE 4–13. Velocity-time and position-time graphs for a tennis ball thrown straight up.

way down, the ball's velocity and the slope of the position-time graph are negative and become more negative. After it has fallen 2.04 seconds, the ball will be once again in your hand. It spends as much time rising as falling. It rises the same distance during the first 2.04 seconds as it falls during the final 2.04 seconds. Note that, although the total distance the ball travels is the distance up plus the distance down, the total displacement, the change in position, is zero.

Example Problem

Freely Falling Objects

The time the Demon Drop ride at Cedar Point, Ohio is freely falling is 1.5 s. **a.** What is its velocity at the end of this time? **b.** How far does it fall?

Given: acceleration of gravity, $g = -9.80 \text{ m/s}^2$; initial velocity, $v_i = 0$ m/s; time interval, $t = 1.5$ s

Unknowns: **a.** final velocity, v_f **b.** displacement, d

Basic equations: **a.** $v_f = v_i + gt$ **b.** $d = v_i t + \frac{1}{2}gt^2$

Solution:

a. $v_f = v_i + gt = 0 \text{ m/s} + (-9.80 \text{ m/s}^2)(1.5 \text{ s})$

$v_f = -15$ m/s

b: $d = v_i t + \frac{1}{2}gt^2 = 0 \text{ m/s}(1.5\text{s}) + \frac{1}{2}(-9.80 \text{ m/s}^2)(1.5 \text{ s})^2$

$= \frac{1}{2}(-9.80 \text{ m/s}^2)(2.25 \text{ s}^2) = -11 \text{ m}$

Negative displacement means that the final position is lower than the initial position.

Demon Drop

FIGURE 4–14. The thrill of the Demon Drop ride comes from being in freefall.

Practice Problems

25. A brick falls freely from a high scaffold.
   a. What is its velocity after 4.0 s?
   b. How far does the brick fall during the first 4.0 s?

▶ **26.** Now that you know about acceleration, test your reaction time. Ask a friend to hold a ruler just even with the top of your fingers. Then have your friend drop the ruler. Taking the number of centimeters

CONCEPT DEVELOPMENT

Have students with graphing calculators explore the graphs in Figure 4–13.

Laboratory Manual. Give students additional experience with acceleration due to gravity by doing Lab 4.2 from the Laboratory Manual.

Answers To
PRACTICE PROBLEMS

Have students refer to Appendix A of the Solutions Appendix for complete solutions to Practice Problems.

25. a. −39 m/s, downward
b. −78 m, downward

26. Calculate using

$$t = \sqrt{\frac{2d}{g}}.$$

TEACHER F.Y.I.

"Free fall" means that an object is free to move under the influence of gravity, not that it is released from rest.

CONCEPT DEVELOPMENT

• The importance of the material on this page can't be overstated. Table 4-2 and the nine specific suggestions in the problem-solving strategy provide a support structure, especially for those students having trouble making the shift into formal problem solving. Not only will the table help students become familiar with these motion equations but it also alleviates the "I just don't know what to do next!" syndrome.

• Describe the process by which one chooses the correct motion equation for a particular problem. This is one of the most frequently asked student questions, "But how do I know which equation to use?"

CHECKING FOR UNDERSTANDING

It is important to be able to translate each equation from Table 4-2 into intelligible English. Ask students to look at an equation and say it in words.

RETEACHING

Transparency Package. Reteach graphical analysis of uniform velocity and acceleration using Transparency 4 and accompanying worksheet.

EXTENSION

Present students with a series of motion graphs. Ask them what information can be extracted from each. Remember that finding slopes and areas adds to the information drawn from a graph. Then, using Table 4-2, show how the equations can be used to get numerical answers when data is not presented in graphical form.

that the ruler falls before you can catch it, calculate your reaction time. An average of several trials will give more accurate results. The reaction time for most people is more than 0.15 s.

Several equations for solving problems of uniformly accelerated motion have been introduced in this chapter. How do you know which one(s) to use in solving a problem? The equations are listed in Table 4–2, together with a list of the quantities related by each equation.

Table 4–2

Equations of Motion for Uniform Acceleration

Equation	Variables
$v_f = v_i + at$	v_i v_f a t
$d = \frac{1}{2}(v_f + v_i)t$	v_i d v_f t
$d = v_it + \frac{1}{2}at^2$	v_i d a t
$v_f^2 = v_i^2 + 2ad$	v_i d v_f a

Note that each equation has at least one of the four variables, d, v_f, a, or t missing. All include the initial velocity, v_i, as well as the initial time (0) and initial position (also zero).

PROBLEM SOLVING STRATEGY

When solving problems, use an orderly procedure.

1. Read the problem carefully. Try to visualize the actual situation. Make a sketch if necessary.
2. Identify the quantities that are given in the problem.
3. Identify the quantity that is unknown, the one you have to find.
4. Select the equation or equations that will relate the given and unknown quantities.
5. Make sure the equations can be applied to the problem, that is, is the acceleration constant?
6. Rewrite equations as needed to solve for the unknown quantity.
7. Substitute the given values including proper units into the equation and solve. Be sure your answer is in the correct units.
8. Make a rough estimate to see if your answer is reasonable.

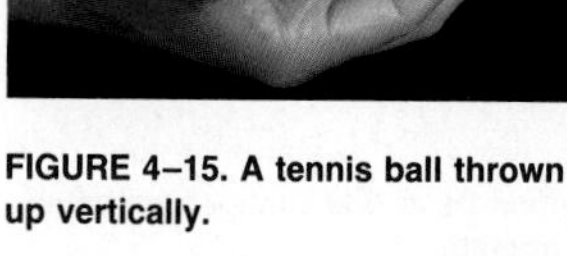

FIGURE 4–15. A tennis ball thrown up vertically.

Example Problem

Flight of a Tennis Ball

A tennis ball is thrown straight up with an initial velocity of +22.5 m/s. It is caught at the same distance above ground from which it was thrown. **a.** How high does the ball rise? **b.** How long does the ball remain in the air?

Given: $v_i = +22.5$ m/s, upward
$g = -9.80$ m/s^2, downward

Unknowns: a. d **b.** t

Basic equations:
$v_f = v_i + gt$
$d = v_it + \frac{1}{2}gt^2$
$v_f^2 = v_i^2 + 2gd$
$d = \frac{1}{2}(v_f + v_i)t$

LABORATORY MANUAL

Use Lab 4.2 with this section.

TRANSPARENCY

Use Transparency 4 with this section.

Solution:

a. At the top of its flight, the instantaneous velocity of the ball is zero. Thus, the final velocity for the upward part of the ball's flight will be zero. Therefore, we know v_i, g, and need d. Use the equation $v_f^2 = v_i^2 + 2gd$, solving it for d.

With $v_f = 0$, $0 = v_i^2 + 2gd$ or $2gd = -v_i^2$.

Thus,

$$d = \frac{-v_i^2}{2g} = \frac{-(22.5\ \text{m/s})^2}{2(-9.80\ \text{m/s}^2)} = +25.8\ \text{m}.$$

The direction is up (positive), so $d = +25.8$ m.

b. From symmetry, we know that the times required for the rising and falling parts of the flight will be the same. That is, the time to rise is half the total time. Thus, we know v_f and g but need t. Use $v_f = v_i + gt$. With $v_f = 0$, we solve for t, obtaining

$$t = \frac{-v_i}{g} = \frac{-22.5\ \text{m/s}}{-9.80\ \text{m/s}^2} = +2.30\ \text{s}.$$

Thus, the total trip time is 4.60 s.

Using Your CALCULATOR

Calculators can be used to evaluate equations. Note that each of the factors in the denominator must be divided into the numerator.

$$d = -\frac{v_i^2}{2\,g}$$

22.5 [x²] [+/-] → -506.25

[÷] 2 [÷] 9.80 [+/-] [=] → 25.829082

$d = 25.8$ m

Example Problem

Finding Displacement When Velocities and Times Are Known

A spaceship far from any star or planet accelerates uniformly from +65.0 m/s to +162.0 m/s in 10.0 s. How far does it move?

Given: $v_i = +65.0$ m/s, $v_f = +162.0$ m/s, $t = 10.0$ s

Unknown: displacement, d

Basic equation: $d = \frac{1}{2}(v_f + v_i)t$

Solution: $d = \frac{1}{2}(v_f + v_i)t$

$= \frac{1}{2}(+162.0\ \text{m/s} + 65.0\ \text{m/s})(10.0\ \text{s})$

$= +1.14 \times 10^3\ \text{m} = +1.14\ \text{km}$

FIGURE 4–16. A spacecraft accelerates vertically at takeoff.

Practice Problems

27. If you drop a golf ball, how far does it fall in ½ s?

28. A spacecraft traveling at a velocity of +1210 m/s is uniformly accelerated at $-150\ \text{m/s}^2$. If the acceleration lasts for 8.68 s, what is the final velocity of the craft? Explain your results in words.

29. A man falls 1.0 m to the floor.
- **a.** How long does the fall take?
- **b.** How fast is he going when he hits the floor?

30. On wet pavement, a car can be accelerated with a maximum acceleration a = 0.20 g before its tires slip.
- **a.** Starting from rest, how fast is it moving after 2.0 s?
- **b.** How far has it moved after 4.0 s?

Cooperative Learning: Have each student make up a quantitative motion problem, picking examples from around the room. Read them aloud or put them on the board, then let the rest of the class make judgments about how realistic the numbers in the problems are.

Guided Practice: Go over the Example Problems on pages 78 and 79, then have students work on the first two Practice Problems in class.

Independent Practice: Assign the remaining Practice Problems on pages 79 and 80 for homework. Review students' answers the next class period.

ACTIVITY

Demonstration: Adjust a faucet or other source of water so that drops come out. You'll notice that the drops at the bottom of the column are farther apart than the drops higher up. The best way to show this is by shining a stroboscope on the drops and freezing their motion. Ask your students why the drop separation gets greater.

Answer: Since the lowest drop started first, it has accelerated for the longest time. It is therefore moving fastest and has separated most from the next highest drop.

4:2 ASSIGNMENT GUIDE

	PRACTICE	EXTENSION
CHAPTER REVIEW pp. 80–85		
· Reviewing Concepts	6–10	
· Applying Concepts		5–9
· Problems*	10–14, 16–24, 27, 29–32, 35–37	15, 25, 26, 28, 33, 34
APPENDIX B PROBLEMS*		
· Chapter 4 pp. 690–691	6–14	15, 16

* Complete solutions to all Chapter Review and Appendix problems appear in the Problems and Solutions Manual.

Answers To
PRACTICE PROBLEMS

Have students refer to Appendix A of the Solutions Appendix for complete solutions to Practice Problems.

27. −1.2 m

28. −90 m/s; spacecraft reverses motion

29. **a.** 0.45 s
b. −4.4 m/s

30. **a.** 3.9 m/s
b. 16 m

31. **a.** 2.8 s
b. 37 m

32. **a.** 46 m/min/s can be interpreted as a speed change of either 46 m/min each second or 46 m/s each minute.
b. 92 m/min

c.

t(s)	v_f(m/min)
0.5	23
1.0	46
1.5	69
2.0	92
3.0	92
4.0	92
5.0	92

d.

t(s)	d(m)
1.0	0.4
2.0	1.5
3.0	3.0
4.0	4.5
5.0	6.0

POCKET LAB

A BALL RACE

Purpose: to investigate acceleration of balls due to gravity on an inclined ramp.
Materials: U channel; book; meter stick; 2 steel balls.
Outcome: Some student will predict that the top ball will gain on the bottom ball. These students are confusing velocity with acceleration. The balls increase velocity as they roll, but the acceleration depends upon the steepness of the ramp. The activity will show that the distance between the balls stays the same. Both gain the same amount of velocity per time. Both have the same acceleration on the ramp.

CONCEPT DEVELOPMENT

Have students look up in *The Guinness Book of World Records* or elsewhere the maximum acceleration that a human being has been able to survive. Problem 2 of the Chapter Review gives some typical data, but is this still the record?

Critical Thinking: In one science-fiction story the plot hinges on a device called the "Time Accelerator." Ask students what they think such a device did. [It changed the normal rate of flow of time—making, for example, travel into the future possible.]

INDEPENDENT PRACTICE/ EXTENSION

Refer to the Assignment Guide on page 79 for additional questions and problems for independent practice.

3 Close

CONVERGENT QUESTION

As passengers in an automobile, assuming they have a good stopwatch available, ask students what they would do to compute the car's average acceleration. [Watch the car's speedometer, record the speed at two times and measure the time interval between these two speeds with the stopwatch, then follow the definition of acceleration to compute the actual value.]

POCKET LAB

A BALL RACE

Assemble an inclined ramp from a piece of U channel, or two meter sticks taped together along the edges, and a book. Mark a position 40 cm and 80 cm from the top. Start one ball at the top and one ball at the 40 cm position. When the balls are released at the same instant, will the balls get closer together or farther apart as they roll down the ramp? Why? Try it. Explain what happened in terms of the velocities. What does this tell you about the acceleration of each ball? Release one ball from the top. Release the other ball from the top as soon as the first ball reaches the 40 cm mark. Do the balls stay the same distance apart? As they roll down the hill, do they ever have the same velocities? Do they have the same acceleration?

31. A pitcher throws a baseball straight up with an initial speed of 27 m/s.
  a. How long does it take the ball to reach its highest point?
  b. How high does the ball rise above its release point?

▶ **32.** A motor of a certain elevator gives it a constant upward acceleration of 46 m/min/s. The elevator starts from rest, accelerates for 2.0 s, then continues with constant speed.
  a. Explain what this statement of acceleration means.
  b. What is the final speed after 2 s?
  c. Calculate speed after 0.5, 1.0, 1.5, 2.0, 3.0, 4.0, and 5.0 s. Sketch a graph showing speed vs time.
  d. How far has it risen 1.0, 2.0, 3.0, 4.0, and 5.0 s after start? Sketch the graph.

CONCEPT REVIEW

2.1 If you are given a table of velocities of an object at various times, how could you find out if the acceleration is constant?

2.2 If initial and final velocities and constant acceleration are given and displacement is unknown, what equation would you use?

2.3 The gravitational acceleration on Mars is about 1/3 that on Earth. If you could throw a ball up with the same velocity on Mars as on Earth,
  a. how would its maximum height compare to that on Earth?
  b. how would its flight time compare?

2.4 **Critical Thinking:** When a ball is thrown vertically upward, it continues up until it reaches a certain point, then it falls down again. At the highest point, its velocity is instantaneously zero. It is not moving up or down. **a.** Is it accelerating? **b.** Give reasons. **c.** Devise an experiment to find out.

CHAPTER 4 REVIEW

SUMMARY

4.1 What Is Acceleration?

- Acceleration is the ratio of the change in velocity to the time interval over which it occurs.
- Constant acceleration is called uniform acceleration.
- The slope of the line on a velocity-time graph is the acceleration of the object.
- A velocity-time graph for a uniformly accelerated object is a straight line.

4.2 Displacement During Constant Acceleration

- Three equations relate the displacement of a uniformly accelerated object to velocity, time, and acceleration.
- A position-time graph for a uniformly accelerated object is half a parabola. Position varies with the square of the time.
- The acceleration of gravity is -9.80 m/s^2 near Earth.
- Problems of uniformly accelerated motion can be solved using one or more of the formulas in Table 4–2.

CONCEPT REVIEW ANSWERS

2.1 Draw a velocity-time graph and see if the curve is a straight line.

2.2 $v_f^2 = v_i^2 + 2ad$

2.3 a. At maximum height, $v_f = 0$, so $d = v_i^2/2g$, or three times higher. **b.** Time to fall from height found from $d = \frac{1}{2}gt^2$ or $t = \sqrt{2d/g}$. Time up and down is three times this. Therefore, time is 3 times as long.

2.4 a. Yes. **b.** Its velocity is still changing; zero velocity does not mean zero change. **c.** Take strobe photos to measure its position. From photos calculate its velocity.

KEY TERMS

average acceleration
instantaneous acceleration
constant or uniform acceleration
initial velocity
final velocity
acceleration due to gravity

REVIEWING CONCEPTS

1. A car is traveling on an interstate highway.
   a. Can the car have a negative velocity and a positive acceleration at the same time?
   b. Can the car change the direction of its velocity when traveling with a constant acceleration?
2. Can the velocity of an object change when its acceleration is constant? If you answer yes, give an example. If you answer no, explain why not.
3. What does the slope of the tangent to a velocity-time graph measure?
4. If a velocity-time curve is a straight line parallel to the *t*-axis, what can be deduced about the acceleration?
5. If you are given a table of velocities of an object at various times, how could you find out if the acceleration of the object is constant?
6. If initial and final velocities and acceleration are given, and the distance is unknown, what equation would you use?
7. Write a summary of the equations for displacement, velocity, and time of a body experiencing uniformly accelerated motion.
8. Explain why an aluminum ball and a steel ball of similar size and shape, dropped from the same height, reach the ground at the same time.
9. Give some examples of falling objects for which air resistance cannot be ignored.
10. Give some examples of falling objects for which air resistance can be ignored.

APPLYING CONCEPTS

1. Figure 4–4 shows the velocity-time graph for an accelerating car. The three "notches" in the curve occur where the driver shifts gears.
   a. Describe the changes in velocity and acceleration of the car while it is in first gear.
   b. Is the acceleration just before a gear change larger or smaller than the acceleration just after the gear change? Explain your answer.
2. Study Figure 4–4. During what time interval is the acceleration largest? smallest?
3. Solve the equation $v_f = v_i + at$ for acceleration. What is the equation you get?
4. Look at Figure 4–17, which is a position-time graph of uniform acceleration.
   a. What type of curve does this graph represent?
   b. What does the slope of a tangent line taken at any point represent?
   c. How would slopes taken at higher points on the line differ from those taken at lower points?

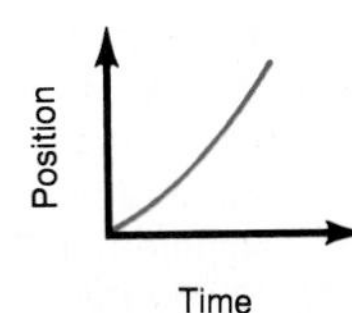

FIGURE 4–17. Use with Applying Concepts 4.

5. An object shot straight up rises for 7.0 s before it reaches its maximum height. A second object falling from rest takes 7.0 s to reach the ground. Compare the displacements traveled by the objects during the 7.0-s period.
6. Describe the changes in the velocity of a ball thrown straight up into the air. Then describe the changes in its acceleration.
7. The value of *g* on the moon is 1/6 of its value on Earth.
   a. Will a ball dropped from the same height by an astronaut hit the ground with a smaller or larger speed than on Earth?
   b. Will the ball take more or less time to fall?
8. A ball is thrown vertically upward with the same initial velocity on Earth and on planet Dweeb, which has three times the gravitational acceleration as Earth.
   a. How does the maximum height reached by the ball on Dweeb compare with the maximum height on Earth?
   b. If the ball on Dweeb were thrown with three times greater initial velocity, how would that change your answer to **a**?

CLOSING CHAPTER 4

Review Summary statements and Key Terms with your students.

ASSESSMENT

Vocabulary Review Master, Teacher Resource Package. Use this master to check students' understanding of Key Terms.

Evaluation Masters. Use Parts A and B of the Chapter Evaluation Masters from the Teacher Resource Package to test qualitative chapter objectives. Use Parts C and D to test quantitative chapter objectives.

Answers To
REVIEWING CONCEPTS

1. a. Yes. A car's velocity is positive or negative with respect to its direction of motion from some point of reference. One direction of motion is defined as positive, and velocities in that direction are considered positive. The opposite direction of motion is considered negative; and, likewise all velocities. An object undergoing positive acceleration is either uniformly increasing its velocity in the positive direction, or uniformly reducing its velocity in the negative direction.
b. A car climbing a hill and running out of gas will eventually change the direction of its velocity while maintaining a constant acceleration. If we define the direction of motion uphill as positive, then after its motor stops, the car's velocity decreases, reaches zero, and then changes its direction of motion downhill. Throughout each change in the magnitude or direction of its velocity, the car is undergoing uniform negative acceleration.
2. Yes. Drop a book.
3. The slope of the tangent to a velocity-time graph indicates acceleration.
4. When the velocity-time graph is a line parallel to the *t*-axis, the acceleration is zero.
5. Draw a velocity-time graph and see if the curve is a straight line.
6. $v_f^2 = v_i^2 + 2ad$
7. $a = \frac{v_f - v_i}{t}$
$v_f = v_i + at$
$d = \frac{(v_f + v_i)\,t}{2}$

8. All objects accelerate toward the ground at the same rate.
9. Student answers will vary. Some examples are sheets of paper, parachutes, leaves, and feathers.
10. Student answers will vary. Some examples are a steel ball, a rock, and a person falling through small distances.

Answers To
APPLYING CONCEPTS

1. a. Velocity increases rapidly at first, then more slowly. Acceleration is greatest at the beginning, but is reduced as velocity increases. Eventually it is necessary for the driver to shift into second gear. **b.** The acceleration is smaller just before the gear change because the slope is less at that point on the graph. Once the driver shifts and the gears engage, acceleration and the slope of the curve increase.

2. The average acceleration is largest in the time interval zero to one second and smallest during the last second. The instantaneous acceleration varies over each interval, starting large and decreasing. It actually becomes zero at points where pauses due to shifting gears occur.

3. $v_f = v_i + at$, so $v_f - v_i = at$, and

$$a = \frac{v_f - v_i}{t} = \frac{\Delta v}{t}$$

This is the equation for acceleration.

4. a. The curve is a parabola. **b.** The slope of a line tangent to the curve represents the instantaneous velocity at that point. **c.** The slopes would be larger at higher points, indicating larger velocities.

5. Both objects have traveled the same distance. The object shot straight up rises to the same height from which the other object fell.

6. Velocity is reduced at a constant rate as the ball travels up into the air. As the ball begins to drop, the velocity again begins to increase until it reaches the height from which it was initially released. At that point, the ball will have the same velocity it had upon release. The acceleration is constant throughout its flight.

7. a. The ball will hit the moon with a smaller velocity because the acceleration of gravity is less on the moon. **b.** The ball will take more time.

8. a. In the equation $d = \frac{v_f^2 - v_i^2}{2g}$, the relationship between d and g is an inverse one. For instance, if g increases by three times, or $d = \frac{v_f^2 - v_i^2}{2(3g)}$, d becomes 1/3. Therefore, a ball on Dweeb would rise to a height of only one-third that on Earth. **b.** With $v_f = 0$, the value d is directly proportional to the square of initial velocity, v_i. That is,

$$d = \frac{v_f^2 - (3v_i)^2}{2g}.$$

On Earth an initial velocity three times greater results in a ball rising nine times higher. On Dweeb, however, the height of nine times higher would be reduced to only three times higher because of d's inverse relationship to a g that is three times greater.

9. a. Rock B hits the ground with a greater velocity. **b.** They have the same acceleration, that of gravity. **c.** Rock B

9. Rock A is dropped from a cliff; rock B is thrown downward.
a. When they reach the bottom, which rock has a greater velocity?
b. Which has a greater acceleration?
c. Which arrives first?

PROBLEMS

4.1 What Is Acceleration?

1. Find the uniform acceleration that causes a car's velocity to change from 32 m/s to 96 m/s in an 8.0-s period.

2. Rocket-powered sleds are used to test the responses of humans to acceleration. Starting from rest, one sled can reach a speed of 444 m/s in 1.80 s and can be brought to a stop again in 2.15 s.
a. Calculate the acceleration of the sled when starting and compare it to the acceleration due to gravity, 9.80 m/s^2.
b. Find the acceleration of the sled when braking and compare it to the magnitude of the acceleration due to gravity.

3. Use Figure 4–18 to find the acceleration of the moving object
a. during the first 5 s of travel.
b. between the fifth and the tenth second of travel.
c. between the tenth and the fifteenth second of travel.
d. between the twentieth and twenty-fifth second of travel.

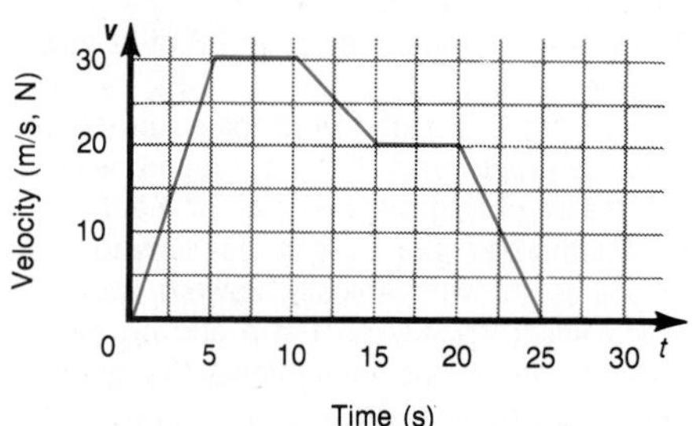

FIGURE 4–18. Use with Problem 3.

4. To accompany each of the graphs in Figure 4–19, draw
a. a velocity-time graph.
b. an acceleration-time graph.

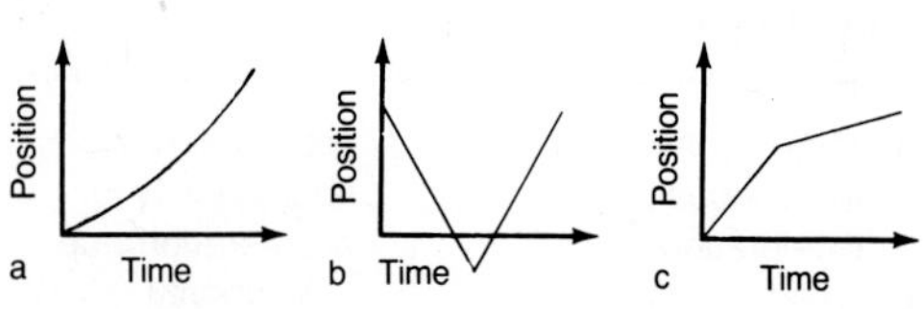

FIGURE 4–19. Use with Problem 4.

5. A car with a velocity of 22 m/s is accelerated uniformly at the rate of 1.6 m/s^2 for 6.8 s. What is its final velocity?

6. The velocity of an automobile changes over an 8.0-s time period as shown in Table 4–3.
a. Plot the velocity-time graph of the motion.
b. Determine the displacement of the car during the first 2.0 s.
c. What displacement does the car have during the first 4.0 s?
d. What displacement does the car have during the entire 8.0 s?
e. Find the slope of the line between t = 0 s and t = 4.0 s. What does this slope represent?
f. Find the slope of the line between t = 5.0 s and t = 7.0 s. What does this slope indicate?

Table 4–3

Time (s)	Velocity (m/s)	Time (s)	Velocity (m/s)
0.0	0.0	5.0	20.0
1.0	4.0	6.0	20.0
2.0	8.0	7.0	20.0
3.0	12.0	8.0	20.0
4.0	16.0		

▶ **7.** Figure 4–20 shows the position-time and velocity-time graphs of a karate expert using a fist to break wooden boards.
a. Use the velocity-time graph to describe the motion of the expert's fist during the first 10 ms.
b. Estimate the slope of the velocity-time graph to determine the acceleration of the fist when it suddenly stops.
c. Express the acceleration as a multiple of the gravitational acceleration, g = 9.80 m/s^2.
d. Determine the area under the velocity-time curve to find the displacement of the fist in the first 6 ms. Compare with the position-time graph.

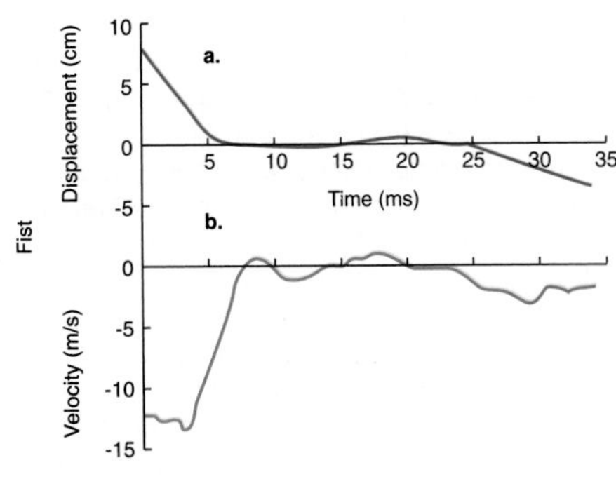

FIGURE 4–20. Use with Problem 7.

8. A supersonic jet flying at 145 m/s is accelerated uniformly at the rate of 23.1 m/s^2 for 20.0 s.

a. What is its final velocity?

b. The speed of sound in air is 331 m/s. How many times the speed of sound is the plane's final speed?

9. Determine the final velocity of a proton that has an initial velocity of 2.35×10^5 m/s, and then is accelerated uniformly in an electric field at the rate of -1.10×10^{12} m/s^2 for 1.50×10^{-7} s.

4.2 Displacement During Constant Acceleration

10. Determine the displacement of a plane that is uniformly accelerated from 66 m/s to 88 m/s in 12 s.

11. How far does a plane fly in 15 s while its velocity is changing from 145 m/s to 75 m/s at a uniform rate of acceleration?

12. A car moves at 12 m/s and coasts up a hill with a uniform acceleration of -1.6 m/s^2.

a. How far has it traveled after 6.0 s?

b. How far has it gone after 9.0 s?

13. Four cars start from rest. Car A accelerates at 6.0 m/s^2; car B at 5.4 m/s^2; car C at 8.0 m/s^2, and car D at 12 m/s^2.

a. In the first column of a table, show the velocity of each car at the end of 2.0 s.

b. In the second column, show the displacement of each car during the same 2.0 s.

c. What conclusion do you reach about the velocity attained and the displacement of a body starting from rest at the end of the first 2.0 s of acceleration?

14. An astronaut drops a feather from 1.2 m above the surface of the moon. If the acceleration of gravity on the moon is 1.62 m/s^2 down, how long does it take the feather to hit the surface?

▶ **15.** Table 4–4 is a table of the displacements and velocities of a ball at the end of each second for the first 5.0 s of free-fall from rest.

a. Use the data in the table to plot a velocity-time graph.

b. Use the data in the table to plot a position-time graph.

c. Find the slope of the curve at the end of 2.0 and 4.0 s on the position-time graph. What are the approximate slopes? Do the values agree with the table of velocity?

d. Use the data in the table to plot a position versus time-squared graph. What type of curve is obtained?

e. Find the slope of the line at any point. Explain the significance of the value.

f. Does this curve agree with the equation $d = \frac{1}{2}gt^2$?

Table 4–4

Time (s)	Displacement (m)	Velocity (m/s)
0.0	0.0	0.0
1.0	−4.9	−9.8
2.0	−19.6	−19.6
3.0	−44.1	−29.4
4.0	−78.4	−39.2
5.0	−122.5	−49.0

16. A plane travels 5.0×10^2 m while being accelerated uniformly from rest at the rate of 5.0 m/s^2. What final velocity does it attain?

17. A race car can be slowed with a constant acceleration of -11 m/s^2.

a. If the car is going 55 m/s, how many meters will it take to stop?

b. Repeat for a car going 110 m/s.

18. An engineer must design a runway to accommodate airplanes that must reach a ground velocity of 61 m/s before they can take off. These planes are capable of being accelerated uniformly at the rate of 2.5 m/s^2.

a. How long will it take the planes to reach takeoff speed?

b. What must be the minimum length of the runway?

Answers To
PROBLEMS

Complete solutions to all Chapter Review Problems can be found in the Problems and Solutions Manual accompanying this text.

1. 8.0 m/s^2

2. **a.** 247 m/s^2
b. -207 m/s^2

3. **a.** 6 m/s^2
b. 0
c. -2 m/s^2
d. -4 m/s^2

4. Refer to Problems and Solutions Manual.

5. 33 m/s

6. **a.** Refer to Problems and Solutions Manual.
b. 8.0 m
c. 32 m
d. 110 m
e. 4 m/s^2
f. 0 constant velocity

7. **a.** The fist moves downward at about -13 m/s for about 5 ms, then comes to a halt.
b. 5.3×10^3 m/s^2
c. Acceleration is about 530 *g*.
d. -8 cm; this agrees with the position-time graph, which shows a net displacement of -8 cm.

8. **a.** 607 m/s
b. 1.83 times the speed of sound

9. 7.0×10^4 m/s

10. 9.2×10^2 m

11. 1.7×10^3 m

12. **a.** 43 m
b. 43 m

13. **a.** and **b.**

Car	Velocity (m/s)	Displacement (m)
A	12	12
B	11	11
C	16	16
D	24	24

c. Displacement and velocity are numerically the same.

14. 1.2 s

15. **a.** and **b.** Refer to Problems and Solutions Manual.
c. Refer to Problems and Solutions Manual; -20 m/s, -39 m/s; yes
d. Refer to Problems and Solutions Manual; a straight line
e. -4.9 m/s^2 Slope is $\frac{1}{2}$ *g*
f. Yes

16. 71 m/s

17. **a.** 1.4×10^2 m
b. 5.5×10^2 m

18. **a.** 24 s
b. 7.4×10^2 m

REVIEW MASTER

Use the Vocabulary Review master for Chapter 4 with this section.

EVALUATION MASTER

Use the Chapter Evaluation master for Chapter 4 with this section.

Answers To
PROBLEMS (cont)

19. **a.** 5.00 s
b. 388 m
c. −93 m/s
20. **a.** 3.1×10^8 m/s²
b. 11×10^{-6} s
21. **a.** No collision
b. Refer to Problems and Solutions Manual.
c. Collision occurs.
22. 1.6 m thick
23. 29 times g
24. 2×10^5 m/s²
25. **a.** Yes. It hits the barrier.
b. 22 m/s
26. **a.** and **b.** Refer to Problems and Solutions Manual.
c. slope = 0.083 s²/m
1/slope = 12 m/s²
d. Yes, −6 m/s²

19. A rocket traveling at 155 m/s is accelerated at a rate of −31.0 m/s².
- **a.** How long will it take before the instantaneous speed is 0 m/s?
- **b.** How far will it travel during this time?
- **c.** What will be its velocity after 8.00 s?

20. Engineers are developing new types of guns that might someday be used to launch satellites as if they were bullets. One such gun can give a small object a velocity of 3.5 km/s moving it through only 2.0 cm.
- **a.** What acceleration does the gun give this object?
- **b.** Over what time interval does the acceleration take place?

21. An express train, traveling at 36.0 m/s, is accidentally sidetracked onto a local train track. The express engineer spots a local train exactly 1.00×10^2 m ahead on the same track and traveling in the same direction. The engineer jams on the brakes and slows the express at a constant rate of −3.00 m/s². The local engineer is unaware of the situation. If the speed of the local is 11.0 m/s, will the express be able to stop in time or will there be a collision? To solve this problem, take the position of the express when it first sights the local as a point of origin. Next, keeping in mind that the local has exactly a 1.00×10^2 m lead, calculate how far each train is from the origin at the end of the 12.0 s it would take the express to stop.
- **a.** On the basis of your calculations, would you conclude that there is or is not a collision?
- **b.** The calculations you made in part **a** do not allow for the possibility that a collision might take place before the end of the 12 s required for the express to come to a halt. To check on this, take the position of the express when it first sights the local as the point of origin and calculate the position of each train at the end of each second after sighting. Make a table showing the distance of each train from the origin at the end of each second. Plot these positions on the same graph and draw two lines.
- **c.** Use your graph to check your answer to part **a**.

22. Highway safety engineers build soft barriers so that cars hitting them will slow down at a safe rate. A person wearing a safety belt can withstand an acceleration of −300 m/s². How thick should barriers be to safely stop a car that hits a barrier at 110 km/h?

23. A baseball pitcher throws a fastball at a speed of 44 m/s. The acceleration occurs as the pitcher holds the ball in his hand and moves it through an almost straight-line distance of 3.5 m. Calculate the acceleration, assuming it is uniform. Compare this acceleration to the acceleration due to gravity, 9.80 m/s².

24. If a bullet leaves the muzzle of a rifle with a speed of 600 m/s, and the barrel of the rifle is 0.9 m long, what is the acceleration of the bullet while in the barrel?

▶ **25.** A driver of a car going 90.0 km/h suddenly sees the lights of a barrier 40.0 m ahead. It takes the driver 0.75 s before he applies the brakes, and the average acceleration during braking is −10.0 m/s².
- **a.** Determine if the car hits the barrier.
- **b.** What is the maximum speed at which the car could be moving and not hit the barrier 40.0 m ahead? Assume the acceleration rate doesn't change.

▶ **26.** Data in Table 4–5, taken from a driver's handbook, show the distance a car travels when it brakes to a halt from a specific initial velocity.

Table 4–5

Initial velocity (m/s)	Braking distance (m)
11	10
15	20
20	34
25	50
29	70

- **a.** Plot the braking distance versus the initial velocity. Describe the shape of the curve you obtain.
- **b.** Plot the braking distance versus the square of the initial velocity. Describe the shape of the curve you obtain.
- **c.** Calculate the slope of your graph from part **b**. Find the value and units of the quantity 1/slope of the curve.
- **d.** Does this curve agree with the equation $v_i^2 = -2ad$? What is the value of a?

27. A car moving with a constant acceleration covers the distance between two points 60 m apart in 6.0 s. Its velocity as it passes the second point is 15 m/s.
   a. What was the speed at the first point?
   b. What is the constant acceleration?
   c. How far behind the first point was the car at rest?

▶ **28.** As a traffic light turns green, a waiting car starts with a constant acceleration of 6.0 m/s^2. At the instant the car begins to accelerate, a truck with a constant velocity of 21 m/s passes in the next lane. **Hint:** Set the two distance equations equal to each other.
   a. How far will the car travel before it overtakes the truck?
   b. How fast will the car be traveling when it overtakes the truck?

29. Use the information from the previous problem.
   a. Draw velocity-time and position-time graphs for the car and truck.
   b. Do the graphs confirm the answer you calculated for the exercise?

30. A stone falls freely from rest for 8.0 s.
   a. Calculate the stone's velocity after 8.0 s.
   b. What is the stone's displacement during this time?

31. A student drops a rock from a bridge to the water 12.0 m below. With what speed does the rock strike the water?

FIGURE 4–21.

32. Kyle is flying a helicopter when he drops a bag. When the bag has fallen 2.0 s,
   a. what is the bag's velocity?
   b. how far has the bag fallen?

▶ **33.** Kyle is flying the same helicopter and it is rising at 5.0 m/s when he releases the bag. After 2.0 s,
   a. what is the bag's velocity?
   b. how far has the bag fallen?
   c. how far below the helicopter is the bag?

▶ **34.** Kyle's helicopter now descends at 5.0 m/s as he releases the bag. After 2.0 s,
   a. what is the bag's velocity?
   b. how far has the bag fallen?
   c. how far below the helicopter is the bag?
   d. what is common to the answers to Problems 32, 33 and 34?

35. A weather balloon is floating at a constant height above Earth when it releases a pack of instruments.
   a. If the pack hits the ground with a velocity of −73.5 m/s, how far does the pack fall?
   b. How long does the pack fall?

36. During a baseball game, a batter hits a high pop-up. If the ball remains in the air for 6.0 s, how high does it rise? **Hint:** Calculate the height using the second half of the trajectory.

37. A tennis ball is dropped from 1.20 m above the ground. It rebounds to a height of 1.00 m.
   a. With what velocity does it hit the ground?
   b. With what velocity does it leave the ground?
   c. If the tennis ball were in contact with the ground for 0.010 s, find its acceleration while touching the ground. Compare to *g*.

USING LAB SKILLS

1. After completing the Physics Lab on page 70, predict what would happen to the distance between two tennis balls when you drop them at the same time, but start one ball 0.5 m higher than the other. Why? Test your prediction by dropping two balls down a stair well or from a second story window while another student observes.

THINKING PHYSIC-LY

Which has the greater acceleration: a car that increases its speed from 50 to 60 km/h, or a bike that goes from 0 to 10 km/h in the same time? Explain.

27. **a.** 5 m/s
   b. 1.7 m/s^2
   c. 7.5 m

28. **a.** 1.5×10^2 m
   b. 42 m/s

29. **a.** Refer to Problems and Solutions Manual.
   b. Yes

30. **a.** −78 m/s, downward
   b. -3.1×10^2 m

31. 15.3 m/s

32. **a.** −20 m/s
   b. −20 m

33. **a.** −15 m/s
   b. −10 m
   c. 20 m

34. **a.** −25 m/s
   b. −30 m
   c. 20 m
   d. Bag is 20 m below the helicopter after 2.0 s.

35. **a.** −276 m
   b. 7.50 s

36. −44 m

37. **a.** −4.85 m/s, downward
   b. 4.43 m/s
   c. +930 m/s^2, 95 times *g*

Answer To
USING LAB SKILLS

1. The distance between the two balls would remain the same. Both balls will always be accelerating, but the accelerations are the same and the starting velocities are the same, therefore the velocities should be the same.

Answer To
THINKING PHYSIC-LY

They are exactly the same acceleration because the change in velocity is the same and the change in time is the same.

CHAPTER

5 Forces

PLANNING GUIDE (6 class sessions)

CONTENTS	TEXT FEATURES	TEACHER RESOURCE PACKAGE	OTHER COMPONENTS
5.1 Newton's Laws of Motion, pp. 88–93 (2 Class Sessions) • Forces • Newton's First Law of Motion • Newton's Second Law of Motion • The Unit of Force • Newton's Third Law of Motion	**Pocket Lab:** Bowling Balls, p. 93 **Concept Review,** p. 93	**Study Guide:** Newton's Laws of Motion **Reteaching Master:** Newton's Laws **Enrichment Master:** Inertia and "Magic" **Transparency Worksheet:** Newton's Third Law	**Laboratory Manual:** Lab 5.1 Newton's Second Law **Transparency 5:** Newton's Third Law
5.2 Using Newton's Laws, pp. 93–103 (4 Class Sessions) • Mass and Weight • Two Kinds of Mass • Friction • The Net Force Causes Acceleration • The Fall of Bodies in the Air	**Physics Lab:** The Elevator Ride, p. 98 **Physics and Technology:** Fast Pedaling, p. 103 **Pocket Lab:** Balanced and Unbalanced Forces, p. 100 **Problem Solving Strategy:** Solving Force Problems, p. 97 **Concept Review,** p. 103	**Study Guide:** Using Newton's Laws **Physics Lab Data Sheet:** The Elevator Ride **Critical Thinking Master:** Forces and Flight	**Laboratory Manual:** Lab 5.2 Friction
Chapter Review, pp. 104–107	Summary Key Terms Reviewing Concepts Applying Concepts Problems Thinking Physic-ly	**Vocabulary Review** **Chapter Review**	**Test Bank**

SUPPLEMENTARY MATERIALS

SOFTWARE	AUDIOVISUAL	BOOKS/MAGAZINES
Introduction to General Physics, Disk I: Force and Motion, COMPress/Queue, Inc. (Apple II, IBM PC, Macintosh) *Investigating Matter and Energy, MMV Force and Motion,* Queue, Inc. (Apple II, IBM PC, Macintosh) *General Physics Series Vol. III, Motion,* Cross Educational Software (Apple II, IBM PC)	Videos: *Newton's Laws of Motion: Demos of Mass, Force, & Momentum,* Queue, Inc. *The Mechanical Universe—High School Adaptation, Quad 1, Newton's Laws,* Annenberg Project, 1985.	Escobar, Carole, "Amusement Park Physics," *The Physics Teacher*, October 1990, p. 446. McFarland, Ernie, "Newton's Third Law at a Traffic Intersection," *The Physics Teacher*, May 1990, p. 315. Minstrell, Jim, "Getting the Facts Straight," *The Science Teacher,* January 1983, p. 53. Sadanand, Nanjundiah, and Kess, Joseph, "Concepts in Force and Motion," *The Physics Teacher*, November 1990, p. 530.

PROBLEM CORRELATION

CONCEPTS	CHAPTER REVIEW			PROBLEMS APPENDIX
	Reviewing Concepts	Applying Concepts	Problems	
5.1 Newton's Laws of Motion				
Forces	1	1		
Newton's First Law of Motion	2,3			
Newton's Second Law of Motion		2,3	1,4,5,**6,7,8**	1,2,**3,4**
Newton's Third Law of Motion	4	4	9,10	5
5.2 Using Newton's Laws				
Mass and Weight	5,6	5	11,12,13	6,7
Two Kinds of Mass				
Friction	7	6,7,8,9	14,15,**16**	8,9
The Net Force Causes Acceleration	8,9,10		17,18,19,**20,21**,22,23, 24,25,**26,27,28,29**	10,**11,12,13**
The Fall of Bodies in the Air	11	10,11		
Other Kinematics			2,**3**	

ACTIVITY AND DEMONSTRATION MATERIALS

PHYSICS LAB	POCKET LAB	DEMONSTRATIONS
Page 98 1-kg mass 20-N spring balance 10-cm masking tape	Pages 93, 100 bowling ball sponge or Styrofoam section 1-kg cart spring balance	Pages 88, 96 2 identical blocks or masses with hooks at both ends thread horizontal support hardcover book sheet of paper (slightly smaller than book)

EXTENSION PROJECTS

LIBRARY RESEARCH

1. Seat Belts
Through library research, explore the structure of seat belts and investigate seat belt laws. What arguments were posed for and against seat belt laws?

DISPLAY MODEL

2. Newton's Laws of Motion
Prepare a videotape or a bulletin-board display for the class of five cartoon examples where Newton's laws of motion are defied. Include an explanation of the laws being demonstrated.

STUDENT READINGS

Brancazio, Peter. "Sir Isaac and the Rising Fast Ball." *Discover,* July 1984.

Dabrowski, Jan Paul. "Analysis of a Space Shuttle Launch." *The Physics Teacher,* January 1990.

Hobson, A. "Strike 'law' from the physics books." *Physics Today,* April 1990.

Kyke, C. "How Weight Affects Bicycle Speed." *Bicycling,* April 1988.

"Newton Vindicated—Einstein Too! [experiment upholds Newton's second law of motion]." *Sky and Telescope,* May 1987.

Smith, Craig W., and West, Kenneth D. "A Science Friction Adventure." *The Physics Teacher,* May 1990.

Chapter 5

Forces

CHAPTER OVERVIEW

Theme Development: The constancy theme, particularly stability and equilibrium, is developed and expanded by the introduction of Newton's laws of motion. The laws unify a broad range of phenomena.

MISCONCEPTIONS

Students think that constant motion is caused by constant force. Newton's third law is easily misunderstood. In everyday usage the distinction between mass and weight is blurred, and the two kinds of mass—gravitational and inertial—are confused as well.

KEY TERMS

action-reaction forces
coefficient of friction
dynamics
electromagnetic force
force
friction
gravitational force
inertial mass
kinematics
Newton's first law
Newton's second law
Newton's third law
sliding friction
static friction
strong nuclear force
terminal velocity
weak force
weight

Laboratory Options

STUDENT EDITION

Physics Lab

The Elevator Ride	98

Pocket Labs

Bowling Balls	93
Balanced and Unbalanced Forces	100

TEACHER EDITION

Activities

Demonstration	88, 96
Discovery	89
Cooperative Learning	90, 91, 92, 97, 103

LABORATORY MANUAL

Newton's Second Law	Lab 5.1
Friction	Lab 5.2

CHAPTER 5 Forces

◀ Going Down

A team of sky divers can form beautiful patterns as they plummet toward Earth at high speeds. How do the sky divers control their velocities?

Chapter Outline

Chapters 3 and 4 were limited to a discussion of the study of *how* objects move, **kinematics.** Galileo devised many ingenious experiments that allowed him to effectively describe motions but not to explain them. Chapter 5 introduces the subject of **dynamics.** The study of *why* objects move as they do. Dynamics can answer such questions as, "Why do the sky divers in the photograph accelerate rather than fall at a constant rate?"

The causes of acceleration were first studied by Sir Isaac Newton (1642–1727). The connection between acceleration and its cause can be summarized by three statements known, after the man who formulated them, as Newton's laws of motion.

√ Concept Check

The following terms or concepts from earlier chapters are important for a good understanding of this chapter. If you are not familiar with them, you should review them before studying this chapter.

- dimensional analysis, Chapter 2
- velocity, Chapter 3
- acceleration, Chapter 4

Introducing The Chapter

Going Down

Using The Photo: This photograph can be used to discuss the section titled The Fall of Bodies in the Air on pages 102–103. In broad terms, sky divers maneuver to control their acceleration and hence their downward speed. By changing the cross-sectional area they present to the air, they can change the drag force on them and thus their acceleration.

Sky divers are accelerated at approximately 9.8 m/s^2 when they jump from a plane. Drag, a force due to friction from air resistance, depends on the speed of the falling object and the cross-sectional area it presents to the air. As the sky diver's speed increases, the force of drag increases, while the force due to gravity (weight) remains constant. However, the net force is zero when the force due to the weight of the sky diver and the force of drag eventually become equal. With a net force of zero on the sky diver, the acceleration is zero also. So, the sky diver travels at a constant speed, which is his or her terminal velocity. A sky diver can reach terminal velocity in about 11 seconds.

√ Concept Check

Make sure students have a clear understanding of the concepts taught in Chapters 3 and 4 that are listed in the Concept Check. Students with a good grasp of the nature of physical motion and how it is measured will more easily understand the principles of forces introduced in this chapter.

Assessment Options

Portfolio Assessment
Portfolio Assessment, TWE, p. 89
Portfolio Assessment, TWE, p. 95
Connect to Biology, TWE, p. 100
Applying Concepts 4, p. 105

Performance Assessment
Pocket Labs, pp. 93, 100
Pocket Lab Assessment, TWE, p. 93
Cardboard-balloon activity, TWE, p. 97
Physics Lab, p. 98

Content Assessment
Self assessment: Practice Problems, pp. 92, 94, 99, 100, 102
Critical Thinking, TWE, p. 95
Assessment, Critical Thinking, TWE, p. 98
Concept Reviews, pp. 93, 103
Chapter Review, pp. 104–107
Supplemental Problems, p. 691

Group Assessment
Activities for group assessment occur with Cooperative Learning and lab activities.

5.1 NEWTON'S LAWS OF MOTION

Preparation

OBJECTIVES

The objectives are listed on the student page. Remind students to preview these objectives as a study guide to this major section.

OVERVIEW

This section introduces Newton's laws, which deal with inertia, force, and acceleration. Also emphasized is the wide range of situations in which Newton's laws can be applied.

BRIDGING

Students will need to recall terms used to describe motion in Chapters 3 and 4. Remind them of the definitions for velocity and uniform acceleration.

1 Focus

DISCREPANT EVENT

Demonstration: You will need two identical blocks or masses (200–300 g) with hooks at both ends, a horizontal support, and some sewing thread. Suspend the blocks from the horizontal support with equal lengths of thread. Also attach equal lengths of thread to the bottom hooks. Without previous discussion, pull downward slowly on one of the bottom threads until the top thread breaks. Then give the bottom thread of the second block a quick jerk, breaking it. With the first block, the slow, steady force was transmitted through the weight to the top thread, so the top thread experienced the weight of the block plus the force of the pull. On the other hand, because of the inertia of the second block, the rapid application of force was not transmitted to the top thread before the bottom thread broke.

Objectives

- name the four basic forces, their relative strengths, and some familiar examples.
- state Newton's three laws of motion and display an understanding of their applications.
- be able to use Newton's second law in solving problems.
- understand the difference between net forces that cause acceleration and action-reaction pairs.

5.1 NEWTON'S LAWS OF MOTION

Isaac Newton started work on his laws of motion in 1665, but did not publish them until 1687. More than three hundred years later, his three laws still summarize the relationship between acceleration, and its cause, force.

Forces

Forces are vector quantities.

What is a force? **Force** can be defined as a push or a pull. When you hang your jacket on a coat-hook, the hook pulls upward on your jacket. If you place a coin on your palm, the coin pushes downward on your hand. These forces occur when one object touches another. On the other hand, if you drop the coin, it will fall to the ground, pulled by a force called gravity. Gravity is a force that acts between objects even when they are not touching. Sometimes forces, like that of gravity on a coin, cause accelerations; other times forces stretch, bend, or squeeze an object. All forces are vectors—they not only have magnitude but they also have direction. In fact, we define "down" as the direction gravity pulls.

Although you can think of hundreds of different forces, physicists group them all into just four kinds. The force that Newton first described, the **gravitational force,** is an attractive force that exists between all objects. The gravitational force of Earth on the moon holds the moon in its orbit. The gravitational force of the moon on Earth causes tides. Despite its effects on our daily lives, the gravitational force is the weakest of the four forces.

FIGURE 5–1. We take the interaction of forces for granted in everyday life. Electromagnetic forces between the bubble gum particles make this impressive bubble possible.

The forces that give materials their strength, their ability to bend, squeeze, stretch, or shatter, are examples of the **electromagnetic force.** These forces result from a basic property of particles called electric charge. Charged particles at rest or in motion exert electric forces on each other. When charged particles are in motion they produce magnetic forces on each other. Electric and magnetic forces are both considered to be aspects of a single force, the electromagnetic force. It is very large compared to the gravitational force.

The two remaining forces are less familiar because they are evident mainly over distances the size of the nucleus of an atom. The third force is the **strong nuclear force** that holds the particles in the nucleus together. It is the strongest of the four forces—hundreds of times stronger than the electromagnetic force. But it only acts over distances the size of the nucleus.

The fourth force is called the **weak force.** It is actually a form of electromagnetic force, and is involved in the radioactive decay of some nuclei. Electricity and magnetism were unified into a single force in the 1870s. Recently the electromagnetic force has been linked with the weak force. This suggests to physicists that all forces are different aspects of a single force. They have constructed theories called Grand Unification Theories (GUTs) and Supersymmetric theories that try to demonstrate this unification. At this time, however, the theories are incomplete and do not fully agree with experiments.

Multicultural Connections

Karate means "empty hand" and was created by Okinawans in the seventeenth century as a means of self defense when weapons were outlawed by their Japanese rulers. It can take years of work, but with careful training and preparation empty hands can break concrete blocks. A trained karateka can break a 3.8-cm thick concrete block by moving her hand at 11 m/sec to create 3069 N of force. It is hard to believe that something as soft as a hand can really break something as hard as concrete, but, in fact, the bones in the human hand can withstand up to 40 times that amount of force.

FIGURE 5–2. If the red team exerts a greater force on the rope than the blue team, the rope will accelerate toward the red team.

Newton's First Law of Motion

Suppose you place a wooden block on a carpeted floor and give it a forward push. The carpeted floor pushes backwards on the block, and the block will stop moving almost as soon as you remove your hand. If you use a smooth wooden floor instead of the carpet, the smooth surface pushes back less, and the block will slide farther. If you have an extremely smooth block and a very slippery floor, almost no backward force is exerted on the block, and it may slide at almost constant speed for a long distance without any additional pushes from you. Galileo speculated that if a perfectly smooth object were on a perfectly smooth horizontal surface it might travel forever in a straight line.

It was left to Newton, however, to develop Galileo's idea more fully. Imagine an object with no force on it. If it is moving at constant speed in a straight line, it will continue to do so. If it is at rest, it will remain at rest, because rest is a special name for zero velocity. This behavior of objects is described in **Newton's first law.** The law states that *an object with no force acting on it moves with constant velocity.*

Objects often have more than one force acting on them. Think of the rope used in a tug-of-war. The members of one team pull the rope one way, the people on the other team pull it in the opposite direction. If the two teams pull with equal strength, the rope will experience no net force, even though there are obviously forces acting on it. If one team pulls harder than the other, though, the rope will begin to accelerate.

To understand the effects of forces in two directions, we assign signs: positive for forces to the right, negative for forces to the left. All the forces pulling to the right combine to produce one large positive force. In the same way, forces to the left combine into a large negative force. If the team pulling to the right is stronger, the net force is positive. If the other team is stronger, the net force is negative. Thus, our method of finding the net force on an object is to sum all the forces, keeping track of signs. If the rope starts at rest, it does not begin to move if the net force is zero. It has a constant—zero—velocity. Thus, we state Newton's first law more carefully: *an object with no net force acting on it remains at rest or moves with constant velocity in a straight line.*

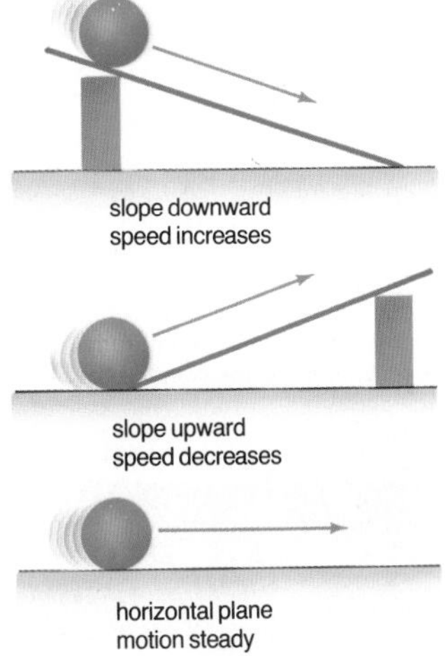

FIGURE 5–3. From observing the motion of objects on inclined planes, Galileo believed that if there were no friction, objects would continue in constant horizontal motion.

2 Teach

CONCEPT DEVELOPMENT

• The more hands-on experience students can get with motion, the better. Performing the minilab, doing experiments from the laboratory manual, or viewing demonstrations should be used liberally.

Study Guide Master. To reinforce the concepts in this section, have the students complete the Study Guide Master for Section 5.1 from the Teacher Resource Package.

Laboratory Manual. Give students additional experience with forces by doing Lab 5.1, Newton's Second Law from the Laboratory Manual.

ACTIVITY

Discovery: Let students observe firsthand the two cases described in Newton's first law. Have them use a low-friction pulley (usually they are about 10 cm in diameter and have ball bearings) clamped in a firm support. Attach masses of no more than 100 g to each end of a light string at least 1.5 m long. Have students hang this arrangement over the pulley. If the masses are not quite equal, they should be adjusted by hanging paper clips on one mass or the other.

When the two equal masses are at rest, ask students what forces act on each mass. This is the test case of the first law. Now have them give one of the masses a slight push. Point out the constant motion of the system—the uniform motion part of the first law. A well-adjusted system will show uniform motion quite nicely. Point out that the total force on the two masses is still zero.

Assessment

Portfolio

Toys present interesting examples of forces and motion. Have students collect pictures or make sketches of different motion toys, and write a description of the motions of the toys and the forces causing the motions.

STUDY GUIDE MASTER

Use the Study Guide master for section 5.1.

LABORATORY MANUAL

Use Lab 5.1 with this section.

CONCEPT DEVELOPMENT

- Emphasize that the force in the equation $F = ma$ is the unbalanced or net force. It might be good to write the word *net* on F when using the equation.
- Ask students if they can tell whether a vehicle they're riding in is moving at constant speed or accelerating. Usually they can tell the difference. Remind them that they have a built-in sense to feel acceleration, even though it may be difficult for them to determine if a moving vehicle is accelerating just by observing it.

Cooperative Learning: Have groups of students make up a pair of examples that will help them remember that $F = ma$. For instance, consider the different behaviors of a tennis ball and a bowling ball when they're both kicked with the same force.

Enrichment: Have students research Newton and find out why he didn't publish this information for 22 years.

- Help students understand net force by relating it to net income.
- Newton's second law is really a vector equation. It says that the direction of acceleration will be in the same direction as the net force.
- Newton's second law in the form $a = \frac{F}{m}$ makes it more apparent that acceleration is directly proportional to net force and inversely proportional to mass.

Newton's Second Law of Motion

Newton's first law states that if there is no net force on an object, there is no acceleration. In other words, the object moves at constant velocity. But how much will an object accelerate when there is a net force? Think about pushing a bowling ball. The harder you push, the faster the velocity of the ball will change. The larger the force, the larger the acceleration, the rate of change in velocity. Acceleration is found to be directly proportional to force.

Acceleration also depends on the mass of an object. Masses of bowling balls vary; some are small, others large. If you exert the same force on a less massive ball, its acceleration will be larger. In fact, if the mass is half as much, the acceleration will be twice as large. The acceleration is inversely proportional to the mass. These relationships are true in general and are stated in **Newton's second law:** *the acceleration of a body is directly proportional to the net force on it and inversely proportional to its mass.* Newton's second law may be summarized as

Newton's second law states that the acceleration of an object is directly proportional to the net force on it and inversely proportional to its mass.

$$a = \frac{F}{m}, \text{ or, more commonly, } F = ma.$$

If an object has a net force exerted on it, it will accelerate. Force and acceleration both have direction as well as size. The acceleration is in the same direction as the force causing it. If the force is in the positive direction, so will be the acceleration. Similarly, if the force is in the negative direction, so will be the acceleration.

According to Newton's second law, a net force on an object causes it to accelerate. In addition, the larger the mass of the object, the smaller the acceleration. For this reason, we say that a massive body has more inertia than a less massive body.

Figure 5–4 pictures a simple experiment that demonstrates Newton's second law. Lay an index card over a drinking glass. Place a penny on the card, centered over the glass. With the flick of a finger, give the card a quick horizontal push. The card moves away, but the penny drops into the glass. Why doesn't the penny accelerate with the card? The penny has more mass (we say it has more inertia), and a horizontal force is needed to accelerate it. The card is too smooth to exert much horizontal force on the penny. With very little horizontal force on it, the penny has little sideways acceleration. As soon as the card is no longer under it, however, the upward force of the card is removed. There is mostly a net downward force, the force of gravity, so the penny accelerates downward, falling into the glass.

FIGURE 5–4. A quick snap of a finger can knock the card from under a coin, allowing the coin to drop into the glass.

a

b

c

TEACHER F.Y.I.

In Figure 5–4, note that $F_{up} = W$. When $F_a > F_f$, the card accelerates horizontally (out from under the coin).

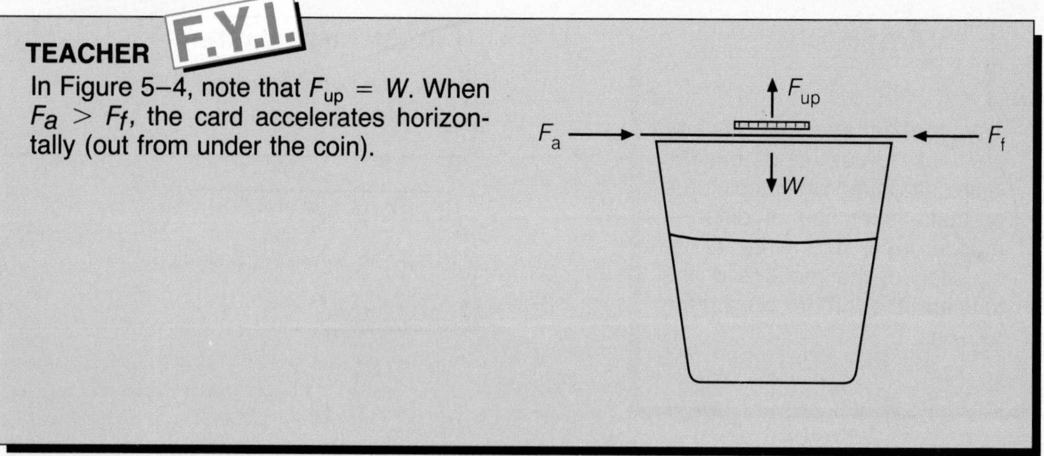

The Unit of Force

Newton's second law gives us a way to define the unit of force. A force that causes a mass of one kilogram to accelerate at a rate of one meter per second squared is defined as one newton (N). That is

$$F = ma = (1.00\ \text{kg})(1.00\ \text{m/s}^2) = 1.00\ \text{N}.$$

Newton's second law defines the newton.

Example Problem

Using Newton's Second Law to Find the Net Force on an Accelerating Object

What net force is required to accelerate a 1500-kg race car at $+3.00\ \text{m/s}^2$?

Given: $m = 1500$ kg, $a = +3.00\ \text{m/s}^2$

Unknown: force, F

Basic equation: $F = ma$

Solution:

Choose the positive direction to be in the direction of the acceleration. Now, $F = ma = (1500\ \text{kg})(+3.00\ \text{m/s}^2)$
$= +4500$ N, in the positive direction.

That is, a 4500-N force will accelerate a 1500-kg race car at a rate of $3.00\ \text{m/s}^2$. The force and acceleration are in the same direction.

FIGURE 5–5. By reducing the mass of a race car, car builders get maximum acceleration from the available force.

Example Problem

Finding Force When Acceleration Must Be Calculated

An artillery shell has a mass of 55 kg. The shell is fired from a gun, leaving the barrel with a velocity of +770 m/s. The gun barrel is 1.5 m long. Assume that the force, and thus the acceleration, of the shell is constant while the shell is in the gun barrel. What is the force on the shell while it is in the gun barrel?

Given: $m = 55$ kg, $v_f = +770$ m/s, $v_i = 0$ m/s, $d = +1.5$ m

Unknown: force, F

Basic equation: $F = ma$

Solution:

You cannot use $F = ma$ directly because you don't know a. You are given the final velocity and distance, and you know the initial velocity is zero. Since we assume that the acceleration is constant, we can find a using $v_f^2 = v_i^2 + 2ad$. The positive direction is along the gun barrel, in the direction of the velocity of the shell.

$$v_f^2 = v_i^2 + 2ad, \text{ or } a = \frac{v_f^2 - v_i^2}{2d} = \frac{(+770\ \text{m/s})^2 - 0}{2(+1.5\ \text{m})}$$

$$a = +2.0 \times 10^5\ \text{m/s}^2 \text{ (in the direction of the velocity)}$$

That is, a forward force of 1.1×10^7 N acting on a shell will increase its speed from 0 to 770 m/s over a distance of 1.5 m.

F.Y.I.

A drag racer tries to obtain maximum acceleration over a quarter mile course. The fastest time on record for the quarter mile is 4.801 s. The highest final speed on record is 301.70 mi/h.

ENRICHMENT MASTER

Use the Enrichment master for Chapter 5 with this section.

RETEACHING MASTER

Use the Reteaching master for Chapter 5 with this section.

TRANSPARENCY

Use Transparency 5 with this section.

CONCEPT DEVELOPMENT

Point out that the student will need to substitute kgm/s^2 for a newton when they want to check units in a problem.

Cooperative Learning: Have students pool information to create a table of movements that represent acceleration. They can then do a rough ranking of the items according to the amount of acceleration. (Note: The ranking step is not as important as being able to identify acceleration.)

Guided Practice: After going over the Example Problems, have students try the first Practice Problem on page 92.

Independent Practice: Assign the remaining Practice Problems on the next page for homework and spend some time discussing them the next class period.

CHECKING FOR UNDERSTANDING

Question students about Newton's laws. Ask for the laws in their own words. Ask for concrete examples of each law. Make sure that students are using the terminology correctly.

RETEACHING

Reteaching Master. Use Teacher Resource Package. Give students more experience with Newton's laws by using the Reteaching Master, Newton's Laws.

Transparency Package. Use Transparency 5 to reteach Newton's third law of motion.

EXTENSION

Explore with students an imaginary world where acceleration is *proportional* to the mass when a constant force is applied. Massive objects would then have huge accelerations.

Enrichment Master. With this section, use the Enrichment Master, Inertia and "Magic," from the Teacher Resource Package.

Answers To
PRACTICE PROBLEMS

Have students refer to Appendix A of the Solutions Appendix for complete solutions to Practice Problems.

1. 7.4 kg
2. -1.24×10^3 N
The negative sign of the acceleration slowing down the motor bike tells us that the motor bike has a velocity in the positive direction. The negative sign on the force indicates that it is directed opposite to the motor bike velocity.
3. -9.8×10^3 N; the road surface pushing against the car tires
4. a. $+1.7$ m/s^2; **b.** The upward force being given as a positive number means that the downward motion of the spider is represented as a negative velocity. The positive acceleration is opposed to this negative velocity and gives rise to a slowing of the spider.

CONCEPT DEVELOPMENT

Emphasize that the action and reaction forces act on different bodies, but that accelerating or net forces act on the same body.

Cooperative Learning: Cartoonists use a lot of motion in their drawings. Have students bring in examples, make copies or transparencies of them, and then discuss how well the motions in the drawings agree with Newton's laws.

Laboratory Manual. Give students additional experience with Newton's second law by doing Lab 5.1 from the Laboratory Manual.

Vector Conventions

- *Velocity vectors are red.*
- *Displacement vectors are green.*
- *Acceleration vectors are purple.*
- ▶ ***Force vectors are blue.***

Practice Problems

1. When a shot-putter exerts a net force of 140 N on a shot, the shot has an acceleration of 19 m/s^2. What is the mass of the shot?
2. Together a motorbike and rider have a mass of 275 kg. The motorbike is slowed down with an acceleration of -4.50 m/s^2. What is the net force on the motorbike? Describe the direction of this force and the meaning of the negative sign.
3. A car, mass 1225 kg, traveling at 105 km/h, slows to a stop in 53 m. What is the size and direction of the force that acted on the car? What provided the force?
▶ **4.** Imagine a spider with mass 7.0×10^{-5} kg moving downward on its thread. The thread exerts a force that results in a net upward force on the spider of 1.2×10^{-4} N.
   a. What is the acceleration of the spider?
   b. Explain the sign of the velocity and describe in words how the thread changes the velocity of the spider.

Newton's Third Law of Motion

Forces always occur in pairs.

If you try to accelerate a bowling ball by kicking it, you may become painfully aware of Newton's third law. As you kick the ball, your toes will feel the equal force the ball is exerting on you. If you exert a force on a baseball to stop it, the ball also exerts a force on you. These are examples of the forces described in **Newton's third law:** *When one object exerts a force on a second object, the second exerts a force on the first that is equal in magnitude but opposite in direction.*

According to Newton's third law, if you exert a small force on the ball, it exerts a small force on you. The larger the force you exert on the ball, the stronger its force is on you. The magnitudes are always equal. These two forces are often called **action-reaction forces.**

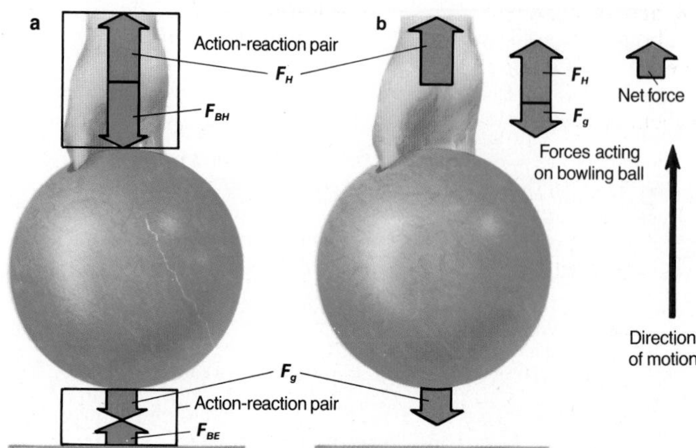

FIGURE 5–6. Each pair of action-reaction forces is equal (a). However, there is a net upward force on the bowling ball, causing it to accelerate upward (b).

3 Close

CONVERGENT QUESTION

Do this simple demonstration: Drop any kind of a ball from waist height. Allow it to hit the floor and then catch it at the top of its bounce. After students have watched this very ordinary event, ask them to describe the ball's motion in detail. This "simple" motion involves *acceleration due* to *gravity, rest, slowing down* while *hitting the floor,* and *accelerating* off the *floor.* The action provides an excellent review of Newton's laws.

Critical Thinking: NASA must use Newton's laws in complex, real world situations for firing and tracking space vehicles. Discuss some of the complicating factors they face in using Newton's laws. For example, consider the firing of a rocket. One of the chief problems is that force and acceleration are continually changing after ignition.

Let's analyze the forces involved when you pick up a bowling ball, as in Figure 5–6. When your hand exerts a force on the ball, the ball exerts a force on your hand that is the same size, but in the opposite direction. These two forces are action-reaction forces. In addition, Earth exerts a downward gravitational force on the ball, and the ball exerts an upward force of the same magnitude on Earth. As you examine the diagram, note the two equal but opposite forces acting on *two different* objects, your hand and the ball, the ball and Earth.

Why does the ball accelerate upward? After all, the force your hand exerts on the ball is the same magnitude as the force the ball exerts on your hand. Where is the net upward force that causes the acceleration? To answer that question, we need to isolate the bowling ball and examine only the forces that act on it. There are two forces acting on the ball, the force of your hand directed upward and the force of gravity pulling downward. When you lift the ball, the force exerted by your hand is greater than the force of gravity, so the ball accelerates upward. *Only the forces on the ball determine its acceleration.*

POCKET LAB

BOWLING BALLS

Hold a bowling ball in your hand. Identify the forces on the bowling ball. Are the forces balanced or unbalanced?

Place the bowling ball on a lab table. Identify the forces. Are the forces balanced or unbalanced? Place a sponge or large piece of foam on the table and the bowling ball on top of the sponge. What happens to the sponge? Does the same thing happen to the table?

CONCEPT REVIEW

1.1 Suppose you exert a force on a black block and measure its acceleration. You then exert the same force on a brown block. Its acceleration is three times that of the black block. What can you conclude about the masses of the blocks?

1.2 Describe the newton in words, without using the terms *equal, mass, accelerate,* or *acceleration.*

1.3 Can you feel the inertia of a pencil? of this textbook? How?

1.4 **Critical Thinking:** If you push forward on the back of an automobile, does that mean that its velocity has to be in the forward direction? Explain and give an example.

5.2 USING NEWTON'S LAWS

A track can only exert force on a car through the tires. This force will be transmitted only if there is enough friction between track and tires. If you have ever tried to accelerate a car on icy or wet roads, you know that the existence of friction is not guaranteed. Among the applications of Newton's laws we will explore in this section is friction.

Objectives

- **distinguish between weight and mass and use the second law to relate them.**
- **demonstrate an understanding of the nature of frictional forces and be able to use the coefficient of friction in solving problems.**
- **demonstrate an understanding of the meaning of net force and be able to calculate the acceleration that results.**
- **understand the definition of free-fall and the causes of air resistance and terminal velocity.**

FIGURE 5–7. Drag racers "smoke" or "boil" their tires before a race to increase the friction between the tires and the track.

POCKET LAB

BOWLING BALLS

Purpose: to allow students to observe balanced and unbalanced forces.

Materials: bowling ball; sponge or Styrofoam section.

Outcome: The ball is subject to a downward force (gravity) and an upward force (the hand). The forces are balanced. ($F_{net} = 0$) Again the ball has two forces acting on it (gravity and the table). Again, the forces are balanced. The sponge was compressed until the forces were balanced. The table was also compressed by the ball, but it was such a small amount that it would be difficult to measure.

CONCEPT REVIEW ANSWERS

1.1 Newton's second law indicates that, for the same force, acceleration is inversely proportional to mass. Therefore, since the acceleration of the brown block is three times that of the black, the brown block must have only one-third the mass of the black block.

1.2 Answers will vary. They should contain the idea that one newton will cause the velocity of a 1-kg object to change at the rate of 1 m per second for every second that the force acts.

1.3 Yes. Hold in your hands and shake it (accelerate it). You feel its resistance to acceleration.

1.4 Critical Thinking: No. Newton's second law says the auto's acceleration has to be in the forward direction. If it is moving backward and you push forward, you will reduce its backward velocity.

Assessment

Performance

To further assess your students' understanding of balanced and unbalanced forces, have them explore other examples of inanimate objects exerting contact forces. Examples are the chairs on which they sit and the floor on which they stand.

5:1 ASSIGNMENT GUIDE

	PRACTICE	EXTENSION
CHAPTER REVIEW pp. 104–107		
· Reviewing Concepts	1–4	
· Applying Concepts		1–4
· Problems*	1, 4, 5, 9, 10	6–8
APPENDIX B PROBLEMS*		
· Chapter 5, p. 691	1–2, 5	3–4

* Complete solutions to all Chapter Review and Appendix problems appear in the Problems and Solutions Manual.

5.2 USING NEWTON'S LAWS

OBJECTIVES

The objectives are listed on the student page. Remind students to preview these objectives as a study guide to this major section.

OVERVIEW

A small part of the wide range of situations for which Newton's second law applies is introduced here, including mass and weight, friction, and air resistance. The distinction between mass and force is central to understanding applications of Newton's second law. After all, the law ties these two concepts together. Frictional forces (and whether or not they are to be included in particular problems) are important in the correct analysis of general force problems.

BRIDGING

Prepare a chart of the weight of common objects in newtons to help students become familiar with the size of the newton. For example, a paper clip of mass 1 g, or 0.001 kg, weighs 0.0098 N. A nickel of mass 0.005 kg weighs 0.049 N. A person who has a mass of about 60 kg has a weight of 588 N.

1 Focus

Why do snow skiers wax their skis? Surfers their boards? Why do some skateboards cost a great deal more than others? Why are sports cars built with the shape they have? (streamlined) Why did Olympic athlete Jackie Joyner-Kersee wear a hood? All to reduce friction! Discuss with students their own experiences with frictional forces. Since the forces are very common, many examples should be brought out. Review the units for force and mass, stressing that having different units, they are different concepts.

FIGURE 5–8. The weight of a medium-sized apple is about one newton.

Mass and Weight

Walking home from school, you see a box on the ground and give it a good kick. If the box goes sailing, you know it has a small mass. If the box hardly accelerates at all, it must have a large mass. Suppose you pick up the box and then let it drop. It will accelerate downward. Thus, Earth must be exerting a downward force on it. The gravitational force exerted by a large body, usually Earth, is called **weight.** Weight is measured in newtons like all other forces. A medium-sized apple weighs about one newton.

The weight of an object can be found using Newton's second law of motion. On the surface of Earth, objects that have only the force of gravity acting on them fall downward with an acceleration of 9.80 m/s^2. This acceleration is so important that we give it a special symbol and write $g = 9.80$ m/s^2 in the downward direction.

The force of gravity on an object is present whether the object is falling, resting on the ground, or being lifted. Earth still pulls downward on it. The force of gravity is given by the equation $F = mg$. This force is called the weight of an object and is given the symbol W. Therefore, we write

$$W = mg.$$

The weight of an object is proportional to its mass.

On the surface of Earth, the weight of an object with a 1.00-kg mass is 9.80 N. The weight of any object is proportional to its mass. Weight is a vector quantity pointed toward the center of Earth. If we assign "up" to be the positive direction, then weight would be negative. More often we will use the word "down" instead of a minus sign (−) when direction is needed.

Weight is the gravitational force of an object.

Example Problem

Calculating Weight

Find the weight of a 2.26-kilogram bag of sugar.

$$W = mg = (2.26\text{ kg})(9.80\text{ m/s}^2) = 22.1\text{ kg·m/s}^2 = 22.1\text{ N}.$$

The direction of the weight is down.

Practice Problems

In these problems use $g = 9.80$ m/s^2.

5. What is the weight of each of the following objects?
   a. 0.113-kg hockey puck **c.** 870-kg automobile
   b. 108-kg football player

6. Find the mass of each of these weights.
   a. 98 N **b.** 80 N **c.** 0.98 N

7. A 20-N stone rests on a table. What is the force the table exerts on the stone? in what direction?

2 Teach

CONCEPT DEVELOPMENT

Hang kilogram masses on a spring scale calibrated in newtons to emphasize the relation of mass and weight. Use the concepts of mass and weight carefully. Insist that your students do, too.

Study Guide Master. To reinforce the concepts in this section, have the students complete the Study Guide Master for Section 5.2 from the Teacher Resource Package.

Answers To
PRACTICE PROBLEMS

Have students refer to Appendix A of the Solutions Appendix for complete solutions to Practice Problems.

5. a. 1.11 N; **b.** 1.06 × 10^3 N; **c.** 8.50 × 10^3 N
6. a. 10 kg; **b.** 8.2 kg; **c.** 0.10 kg
7. 20 N, upward
8. a. 7.4 × 10^2 N; **b.** 2.9 × 10^2 N; **c.** 9.1 m/s^2

STUDY GUIDE MASTER

Use the Study Guide master for section 5.2.

8. An astronaut with mass 75 kg travels to Mars. What is his weight
  a. on Earth?
  b. What is his weight on Mars where $g = 3.8\ m/s^2$?
  c. What is the value of g on top of a mountain if the astronaut weighs 683 N?

You do not really "feel" your weight. What you do feel are the forces exerted on you by objects that touch you. When standing, you don't feel the force you exert on the floor, you feel the force the floor exerts on you. The larger your weight, the larger the force of the floor on you. When sitting, you feel the force of the chair. If you do a pull-up, you feel the force of the bar on your hands. When you are at rest, or moving at constant velocity, these forces are equal in magnitude to your weight, but in the opposite direction.

Mass and weight are not the same. Weight depends on the acceleration due to gravity, and thus may vary from location to location. A person weighs a very small amount less on top of a high mountain, even though he or she has the same mass. A bowling ball with a mass of 7.3 kg weighs 71 N on Earth, but only 12 N on the moon, where the acceleration due to gravity is $1.6\ m/s^2$. If you tried to kick a bowling ball across the surface of the moon, however, it would be just as hard to accelerate as on Earth because its mass would be the same.

Two Kinds of Mass

We discussed one way of determining mass by measuring the amount of force necessary to accelerate it, that is, its inertia. The **inertial mass** of an object is the ratio of the net force exerted on the object and its acceleration,

$$m = \frac{F}{a}.$$

A second method of finding mass is to compare the gravitational forces exerted on two objects, one with an unknown mass, the other with a known mass. The object with the unknown mass is placed on one pan of a beam balance. The object with the known mass is placed

FIGURE 5–9. A beam balance allows you to compare an unknown mass to a known mass. Using an inertial balance, you can calculate the mass from the back and forth motion of the mass.

HELP WANTED

AIRCRAFT MECHANIC

We need FAA-certified airframe, powerplant, and instrumentation specialists with technical school and/or military training and appropriate experience.

Combine your understanding of the principles of aerodynamics, propulsion, hydraulics, and electronics with your ability to perform with precision under pressure.

The opportunity for advancement to the positions of supervisor or inspector with additional experience and certification is substantial. For information, contact:

Future Aviation Professionals of America, 4291 J Memorial Drive, Atlanta, GA 30032, or call 1-800-JET-JOBS

CONCEPT DEVELOPMENT

To clarify the difference between weight and mass, discuss what would happen to your weight and mass if you were on a journey to different planets. In brief, the mass of anything depends on the number and kind of atoms in it. The weight of anything depends on its mass and where it is; that is, on what gravitational forces are acting on it.

Critical Thinking: Newton started from scratch with no previous laws of motion on which to build. Ask students to imagine how Newton could have arrived at his laws. What might have been the processes he went through? Could the steps have been done quickly or not? How could Newton be confident that he was right? Answers should include such processes as observation, critical thought, and repeated experimentation. These were no doubt supported by a strong curiosity. The importance of being able to design meaningful experiments should also be emphasized. (No one gave Newton a lab manual.) Students should realize that the powerful generalizations of these laws are not the result of some sudden inspiration. They are the product of many detailed observations and painstaking analyses.

Assessment

Portfolio

Have students keep a log of examples that differentiate between mass and weight. Example: Put a bowling ball in a wagon. If you accelerate the wagon forward, the ball rolls back. If you lift the front wheels, the ball rolls back. In which case is the ball's mass important? In which case is the weight important? [mass in the first case, weight in the second]

TEACHER F.Y.I.

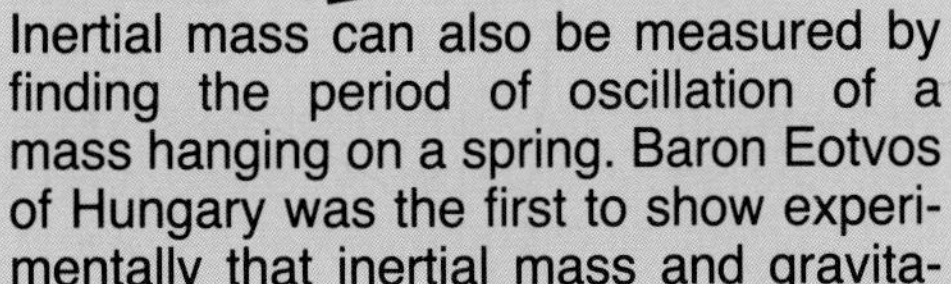

Inertial mass can also be measured by finding the period of oscillation of a mass hanging on a spring. Baron Eotvos of Hungary was the first to show experimentally that inertial mass and gravitational mass are equal to a high degree of precision. Today, most theories hold that inertial and gravitational mass are exactly the same.

CONCEPT DEVELOPMENT

- For friction studies, use a Teflon-coated cookie sheet cut into 5″ × 16″ strips fastened to a board with screws. Cover a 6″ × 3″ × 1″ block of wood on the bottom and sides with felt cloth. Show students that the force of friction is the same regardless of the size of the surfaces in contact.
- A good model or analogy for frictional force between two objects is two pieces of Velcro. On a microscopic level, two surfaces in contact do partially mesh into one another.
- Frictional forces are often advantageous or necessary. Examples of items that involve or use friction include running shoes, sandpaper, food graters, car brakes, and sand on icy roads.

Enrichment: Discuss with students why graphite is a good lubricant. Because of the way its atoms are arranged, layers of graphite can slide over one another very easily.

Critical Thinking: Ask students if there are other kinds of friction not mentioned in this section. (Rolling friction would be one.) What are some ways of reducing friction?

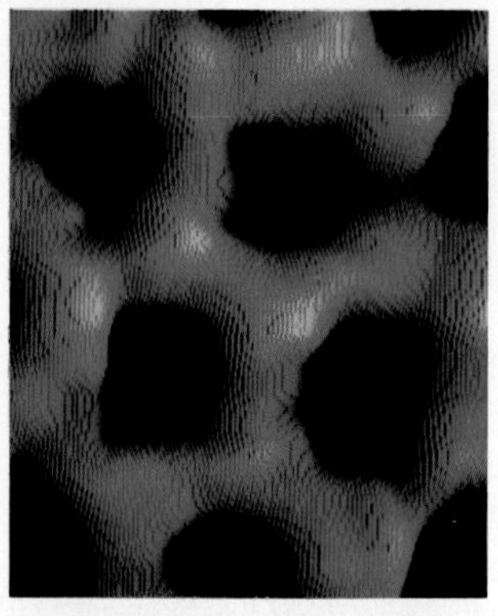

FIGURE 5–10. This photograph of a graphite crystal, magnified by a scanning tunneling microscope, reveals the surface irregularities of the crystal at the atomic level.

on the pan at the other end of the beam. When the pans balance, the force of gravity is the same on each pan. Then the masses of the objects on either side of the balance must be the same. The mass measured this way is called the gravitational mass.

Suppose you apply the same force to two different objects and find that the acceleration of one object is twice that of the other. You would conclude that the mass of the first object is half that of the second. If you put the same objects on a pan balance, you would find the gravitational force on the first object is half the gravitational force on the second. Very precise experiments indicate that inertial mass and gravitational mass of objects are equal within the accuracy of the experiments. In 1916 Albert Einstein (1879–1955) used the equality of inertial and gravitational masses as one foundation for his general theory of relativity.

Friction

Slide your hand across a tabletop. The force you feel opposing the movement of your hand is called friction. It acts when brakes slow a bike or car, when a sailboat moves through water, and when a sky diver falls through the air. If there was no friction, whenever you tried to walk, you would slip as if you were on ice. Without friction, tires would spin and cars would not move. An eraser could not grip your homework paper and remove a mistake.

Friction is the force that opposes the motion between two surfaces that are in contact. The direction of the force is parallel to the surface and in a direction that opposes the slipping of the two surfaces. To understand the cause of friction, you must recognize that on a microscopic scale, all surfaces are rough. When two surfaces rub, the high points of one surface temporarily bond to the high points of the other. The electromagnetic force causes this bonding.

If you try to push a heavy box along the floor, you will find it very hard to start it from rest, Figure 5–11. If two objects are not in relative motion, **static friction** is the force that opposes the start of motion. Static friction forces have maximum values. When the magnitude of your push on the box is greater than the maximum value of the static

FIGURE 5–11. A greater and greater horizontal force, F_a is applied to a box (a-d). An equal force of static friction acts in the opposite direction to keep the box from moving. When F_a exceeds the force of static friction, the box accelerates (e). The box will move at a constant velocity if F_a is then reduced until it equals the force of sliding friction. (f).

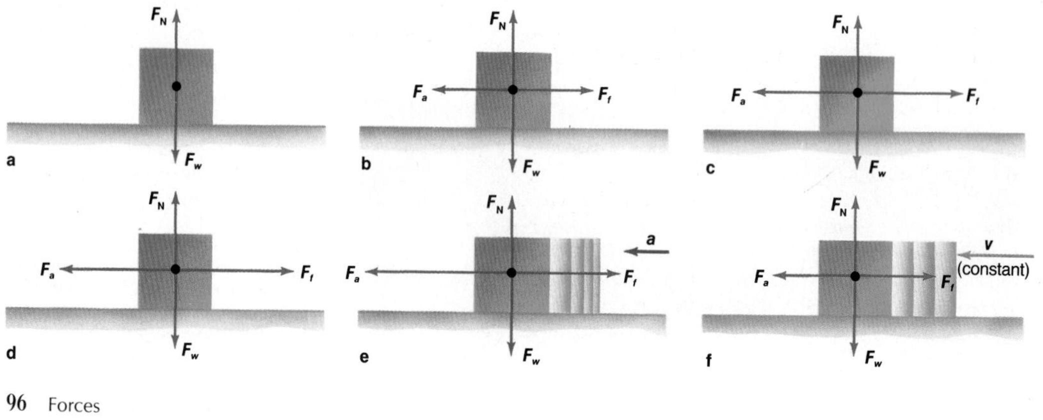

DEMONSTRATION

Purpose: to demonstrate the frictional effects of air.

Equipment: hardcover book, sheet of paper slightly smaller than the book

Procedure: **1.** Hold both the book and the sheet of paper horizontally at about shoulder height. **2.** Drop them at the same time. **3.** Lay the sheet of paper on top of the book and again drop them together. **4.** Crumple the paper and again drop the book and paper from the same height.

Results: In Step 2, the book falls faster than the sheet of paper. In Steps 3 and 4, the book and paper fall at the same rate.

Questions: **1.** Why does the paper fall so much more slowly when the book and paper fall side by side? *The ratio of surface to weight is much greater for the flat sheet of paper than for the book. Therefore, the frictional force of air re-*

friction between the floor and the box, the box starts moving. When the box starts to move, the force of friction decreases. The force between surfaces in relative motion is called **sliding friction.** The force of sliding friction is less than that of static friction. Thus, a car will stop faster if the wheels are not skidding.

How large is the force of sliding friction? Slide your book across the desk. It slows down. To keep it moving at constant velocity, you must exert a constant force that is just the same size as the frictional force, but in the opposite direction. See Figure 5–12. By measuring the force you exert, called the applied force, F_A, you can find the force of friction, F_f.

Experimentally it has been found that the force of friction depends primarily on the force pushing the surfaces together, F_N, and on the nature of the surfaces in contact. This result can be expressed as

$$F_f = \mu F_N.$$

In this equation μ (mu), called the **coefficient of friction,** is a constant that depends on the two surfaces in contact. F_N is the force pushing the surfaces together. It is called the normal force, where "normal" means perpendicular. In the example above, the normal force on the book is the force exerted by the table, perpendicular to its surface. When the book is resting on a horizontal surface, the normal force of the table on the book is numerically equal to the weight of the book (W). The normal force of the table on the book is also equal to the force of the book on the table, since they are action-reaction forces. If you use your hands to exert an extra force, F, down on the book, the force of the book on the table increases to $W + F$. By Newton's third law, the normal force of the table upward on the book also increases to $W + F$.

Notice that when we are studying the friction between two objects, such as a book lying on a horizontal table, there are two sets of forces. The first set is parallel to the surfaces that are touching. This set consists of the force that moves the object and the opposing frictional force. The second set of forces acts perpendicular to the two surfaces. The downward force may be just the object's weight, the downward force of gravity. Often, though, other forces are exerted on the object. A person might push the object down, or perhaps lift up on it. A second object might be placed on top of the first. The sum of all vertical forces is the total downward force. The other force in this set is the equal but upward force exerted on the object by the table. That force is the normal force on the object. In many cases, the coefficient of sliding friction for two surfaces in contact is very nearly independent of the amount of surface area in contact and the velocity of motion. Problems solved in this book will make this assumption.

PROBLEM SOLVING STRATEGY

When solving problems involving more than one force on an object:

1. Always start by sketching a neat drawing of the object.
2. Then draw arrows representing all the forces acting on the object.
3. Label each force with the cause of the force. Be specific. Examples are "weight," "force of string," "normal force exerted by table," "force of friction."

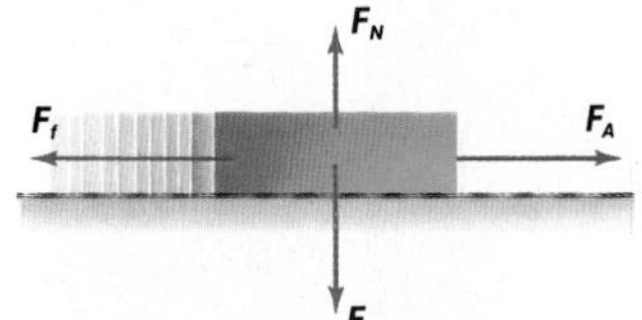

FIGURE 5–12. Four forces are shown acting on a book that is moving to the right at a constant velocity.

EARTH SCIENCE CONNECTION

The San Andreas Fault in California is a series of fractures in Earth's crust. Forces in Earth's interior cause the rocks to slide past each other in a horizontal direction. At first the forces of friction between the two surfaces are greater than the forces that cause the slide, so the rocks stretch and twist. Eventually, forces within the rocks become greater than the forces of friction, and, much like the release of a stretched rubber band, the rocks snap back in place. This movement with the resulting release of tremendous amounts of energy is an earthquake.

CONCEPT DEVELOPMENT

Use a demonstration spring scale so the class can read the scale as you pull a brick across a table. Guide students to understand that it takes much more force to get the brick started than it does to keep it moving. Starting friction is called static friction. There are different coefficients of friction for static friction.

Critical Thinking: Have students list devices that operate best when μ is high and when it is low. A discussion of sports equipment may be helpful here.

ACTIVITY

Cooperative Learning: Have students work in pairs for this activity. Each pair should cut a square of cardboard approximately 10 cm on a side and punch a hole through the center with a pencil. Then have students push the square back and forth across a table and discuss the forces acting on it. Then, blow up an ordinary balloon (round works best), twist it shut, and push the open end through the hole. Untwist the balloon and place the system on the table. If the hole is small enough (and large enough), the square will ride on a cushion of air. Slide it across the table. Discuss the forces acting on it now. What is different? What is unchanged?

Laboratory Manual. Give students additional experience with friction by doing Lab 5.2 from the Laboratory Manual.

sistance is more effective in controlling the rate of fall of the paper. **2.** Why does the paper fall at the same rate as the book in the last two demonstrations? *In Step 3, the book effectively shielded the paper from the air molecules. In Step 4, the surface area to weight ratio was reduced.* (Note: Many of the students will still hold the Aristotelian view that lighter objects fall more slowly. This demonstration should help them understand Galileo's discovery that in the absence of friction, all objects fall at the same rate.)

LABORATORY MANUAL

Use Lab 5.2 with this section.

PHYSICS LAB

Process Skills: observing, communicating, controlling variables, inferring, measuring, using numbers, interpreting data, questioning.

MISCONCEPTIONS

Most students believe that objects in motion must have a force on them to sustain that motion. Review the concept of zero velocity and emphasize that an object in motion can sometimes have a zero velocity.

Lab Worksheet, Teacher Resource Package. If desired, use the lab worksheet master for Chapter 5 for students to record their data.

OBSERVATIONS

The readings from the spring balance increase at the start of the upward ride, return to about 1 kg during the ride, decrease below 1 kg at the start of the downward ride, return to about 1 kg, then increase again as the "ride" ends.

ANALYSIS

1. When moving at a steady speed, the forces are balanced, meaning the $F_{net} = 0$. The rider will feel her normal weight.
2. When starting upward (or moving downward but slowing), the floor must push with more force than the normal weight. The F_{net} is upward and the acceleration is upward. The rider feels heavier.
3. When starting downward (or moving upward but slowing), the floor must push with less force than the normal weight. The F_{net} is downward and the acceleration is downward. The rider feels lighter.

APPLICATIONS

1. Except for the momentary "jerk" when stepping on or off of the escalator, you should feel your normal weight. The escalator moves at a steady speed. The forces are balanced.
2. The riders will feel lighter when they are accelerating downward. This occurs when the coaster is "falling" down a hill. The riders feel heavier when they are accelerating upward. This occurs as the coaster begins climbing a hill.

PHYSICS LAB: The Elevator Ride

Purpose

To determine why you feel heavier or lighter when riding in an elevator.

Materials

- 1-kg mass
- 20-N spring balance
- 10 cm masking tape

Procedure

1. Imagine you take an upward elevator ride. Write a few sentences describing when you feel normal, heavier (than normal), and lighter (than normal).
2. Imagine you take a downward elevator ride. Write a few sentences describing when you feel normal, heavier (than normal), and lighter (than normal).
3. Hold the 1-kg mass in your hand and give it an upward elevator ride. Describe when the mass feels normal, heavier than normal, and lighter than normal.
4. Hold the mass in your hand and give it a downward elevator ride. Describe when the mass feels normal, heavier than normal, and lighter than normal.
5. Securely tape the mass to the hook on the spring balance. Warning: A falling mass can cause serious damage to the foot or toe!
6. Start with the mass just above the floor and take it on an upward and downward elevator ride.

Observations and Data

1. Carefully watch the spring balance and notice how the readings change for different parts of the ride. Record your observations.

Analysis

1. Identify those places in the ride when the spring balance reads a normal value for the mass. Describe the motion of the mass. Are the forces balanced or unbalanced?

2. Identify those places in the ride when the spring balance reads a "heavier" value. Which direction is the F_{net}? Which direction is the acceleration?
3. Identify those places in the ride when the spring balance reads a "lighter" value. Which way is the F_{net}? Which direction is the acceleration?

Applications

1. Do you feel heavier or lighter when riding on an escalator? Explain your answer in terms of the motion and the forces.
2. Identify the places on a roller coaster ride where you feel heavier or lighter. Explain your answer in terms of the motion and the forces.

ASSESSMENT

Critical Thinking: To further assess your students' understanding of weight, ask the following questions.

1. Suppose that you were carrying a package as you rode on the elevator. Would there be instances when it felt lighter or heavier? Explain. [Yes. It would feel heavier during an upward acceleration and lighter during a downward acceleration.]
2. Does your weight feel different when you ride an escalator? Explain. [No, because the escalator moves at a constant velocity.]

Example Problem

Sliding Friction

A smooth wooden block is placed on a smooth wooden tabletop. You find that you must exert a force of 14.0 N to keep the 40.0-N block moving at a constant velocity. **a.** What is the coefficient of sliding friction for the block and table? **b.** If a 20.0-N brick is placed on the block, what force will be required to keep the block and brick moving at constant velocity?

a. Given: $F_A = 14.0$ N, $W = 40.0$ N, $a = 0$

Unknown: coefficient of friction, μ

Basic equations: $F = ma$, $F_f = \mu F_N$

Solution:

Draw a diagram showing the forces on the block, Figure 5–13. Because $a = 0$, the force you exert, F_A, must be equal in size to the frictional force, F_f. In addition, because the block is resting on the table and there is no other vertical force on it, the normal force equals the weight, $F_N = W$. Thus, $F_A = F_f = \mu W$ or

$$\mu = \frac{F_A}{W} = \frac{14.0\text{ N}}{40.0\text{ N}} = 0.350.$$

b. Given: weight of brick, $W' = 20.0$ N

Unknown: new applied force, F_A

Basic equation: $F_N = W + W'$

Solution:

The block exerts a larger force $(W + W')$ on the table, and so the normal force is also increased. This increases the frictional force.

$$\begin{aligned} F_A &= F_f \\ &= \mu F_N \\ &= \mu(W + W') \\ &= (0.350)(40.0\text{ N} + 20.0\text{ N}) \\ &= 21.0\text{ N}. \end{aligned}$$

Note that μ depends only on the surfaces in contact, and so is the same for the two parts of the Example Problem.

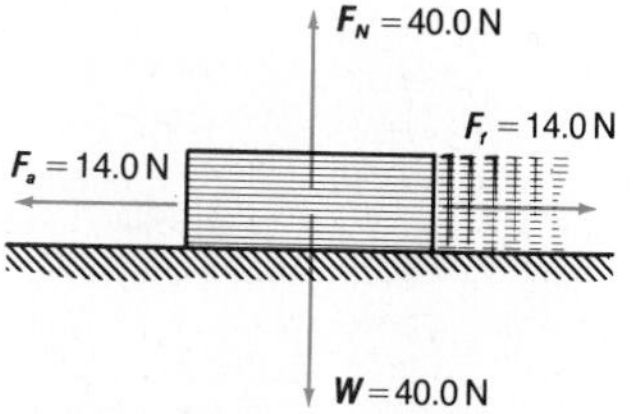

FIGURE 5–13. Use with the Example Problem.

Practice Problems

9. Suppose Joe, who weighs 625 N, stands on a bathroom scale calibrated in newtons.
   a. What force would the scale exert on Joe? in what direction?
   b. If Joe now holds a 50-N cat in his arms, what force would the scale exert on him?
   c. After Joe puts down the cat, his father comes up behind him and lifts upward on his elbows with a 72-N force. What force does the scale now exert on Joe?
10. a. A 52-N sled is pulled across a cement sidewalk at constant speed. A horizontal force of 36 N is exerted. What is the coefficient of sliding friction between the sidewalk and the metal runners of the sled?

Guided Practice: After going over the Example Problem, have students try the first Practice Problem on p. 99.

Independent Practice: Assign the remaining Practice Problems on the next page for homework and spend some time discussing them the next day.

Answers To
PRACTICE PROBLEMS

Have students refer to Appendix A of the Solutions Appendix for complete solutions to Practice Problems.

9. **a.** 625 N, upward; **b.** 675 N; **c.** 553 N, upward
10. **a.** 0.69; **b.** 84 N

LAB WORKSHEET

Use the Lab Worksheet for Chapter 5 with this Physics Lab.

POCKET LAB

BALANCED AND UNBALANCED FORCES

Purpose: to allow students to observe and measure the effects of balanced and unbalanced forces on a moving system.

Materials: 1-kg cart; spring balance.

Outcome: Students will find that only a very small force is required to keep the cart moving at a steady speed. Typical values range from 0.1 N to 0.2 N. The pulling force was enough to balance the frictional force. Almost all students will be surprised that the cart gains speed. The cart accelerates because the pulling force is greater than the frictional force. The F_{net} is the difference between 1.0 N and the frictional force.

Answers To
PRACTICE PROBLEMS (cont.)

11. a. -3.7×10^3 N; **b.** -4.9 m/s^2 F_f is constant; **c.** 92 m

12. larger; shorter distance

Connect to BIOLOGY

This chapter explains that forces must be exerted to cause the acceleration. Such forces can damage the body, either as a result of forces external to the body being applied, or forces exerted on an internal body part. Bungee jumping has become a popular pastime. It is a variation of an event practiced by people who jumped from cliffs with vines attached to their ankles. In one such jump, the person experienced a force of over 15 000 lbs (69 000 N) when the vine became taut. How does the bungee cord reduce the force on the jumper? [The change in velocity occurs over a longer distance, so the acceleration, and thus the force, is smaller.]

POCKET LAB

BALANCED AND UNBALANCED FORCES

Attach a 1-kg cart to a spring balance and pull horizontally on the cart so it moves at a slow, steady speed. What was the value on the balance? Were the forces balanced or unbalanced? Repeat the procedure except try to keep the reading on the balance at a steady value of 1.0 N. Describe the motion. Were the forces balanced or unbalanced? Estimate F_{net}.

b. Suppose the sled now runs on packed snow. The coefficient of friction is now only 0.12. If a person weighing 650 N sits on the sled, what force is needed to slide the sled across the snow at constant speed?

11. The coefficient of sliding friction between rubber tires and wet pavement is 0.50. The brakes are applied to a 750-kg car traveling 30 m/s, and the car skids to a stop.

a. What is the size and direction of the force of friction that the road exerts on the car?

b. What would be the size and direction of the acceleration of the car? Why would it be constant?

c. How far would the car travel before stopping?

▶ **12.** If the tires of the car in Practice Problem 11 did not skid, the coefficient of friction would have been 0.70. Would the force of friction have been larger, smaller, or the same? Would the car have come to a stop in a shorter, the same, or a longer distance?

The Net Force Causes Acceleration

In Newton's second law of motion, $F = ma$, the force, F, that causes the mass to accelerate is the net force acting on the mass. In Figure 5–14a, a 10 kg mass rests on a frictionless, horizontal surface. A +100-N force is exerted horizontally on the mass. The resulting acceleration is

$$a = \frac{F}{m} = \frac{+100 \text{ N}}{10 \text{ kg}} = +10 \text{ m/s}^2.$$

If the same mass rests on a rough surface, friction will oppose the motion. In Figure 5–14b, the frictional force is −20 N. The negative sign indicates that the force acts in a direction opposite the positive applied force. The acceleration of any object is the result of the net force acting on it. The net force is the vector sum of the applied and frictional forces. When you sum forces, which are vectors, you must pay attention to the signs. That is,

Friction acts in a direction parallel to the surfaces in contact and opposes the motion.

$$F_{net} = F_{applied} + F_f$$
$$= +100 \text{ N} + (-20 \text{ N}) = +80 \text{ N},$$

and the resulting acceleration is given by

$$a = \frac{F_{net}}{m} = \frac{+80 \text{ N}}{10 \text{ kg}} = +8.0 \text{ m/s}^2.$$

The direction of the acceleration is positive, in the direction of the applied force.

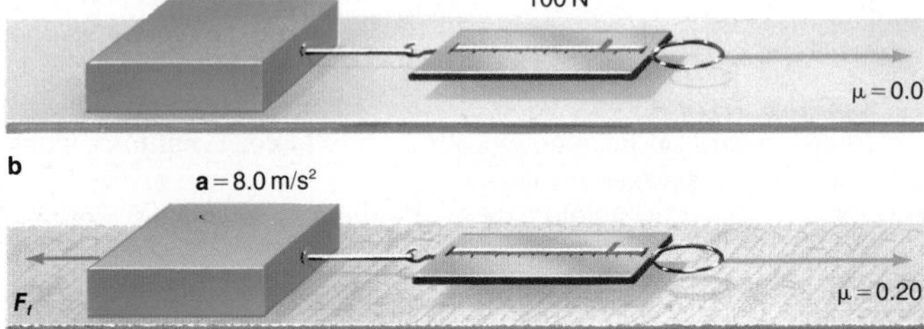

FIGURE 5–14. When acted upon by a 100-N force, the acceleration of a 10-kg mass on a frictionless surface (a) is greater than the acceleration of a 10-kg mass on a rough surface (b).

Other forces besides friction act on objects. Consider a 10.0-kg stone lying on the ground. The stone is at rest; the net force on it is zero. The weight of the stone, W, is 98.0 N in a downward direction. The ground exerts an equal and opposite force, 98.0 N, upward. The net force is

$$F_{net} = F_{ground} + W = 98.0 \text{ N} + (-98.0 \text{ N}) = 0 \text{ N}.$$

How can the stone be given an upward acceleration? Suppose a person exerts a 148-N upward force on the stone. The net force is

$$F_{net} = F_{person} + W = +148.0 \text{ N} + (-98.0 \text{ N}) = +50.0 \text{ N}.$$

The net force acting on the stone is 50 N upward. The acceleration of the stone can now be found from Newton's second law:

$$a = \frac{f}{m} = \frac{+50 \text{ N}}{10 \text{ kg}} = +5 \text{ m/s}^2.$$

The stone will be accelerated upward at $+5$ m/s^2.

FIGURE 5–15. A mass is accelerated upward if the total force exerted upward is greater than the weight.

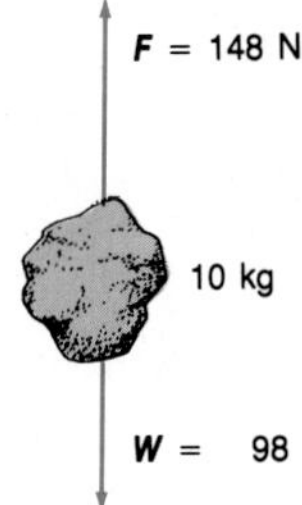

Example Problem

Forces on an Accelerating Object

A spring scale hangs from the ceiling of an elevator. It supports a package that weighs 25 N. **a.** What upward force does the scale exert when the elevator is not moving? **b.** What force must the scale exert when the elevator and object accelerate upward at $+1.5$ m/s^2? Use Figure 5–16.

Given: weight of package, $W = 25$ N
acceleration,
a. $a = 0$ m/s^2
b. $a = +1.5$ m/s^2

Unknown: upward force, F_{scale}
Basic equations: $F_{net} = ma$
$F_{net} = F_{scale} + W$
$W = mg$

Solution:

a. Because $a = 0$, $F_{net} = 0$, so
$F_{scale} = -W = -(-25 \text{ N}) = 25 \text{ N (up)}.$
Weight is 25 N down, so the scale supplies 25 N up.

b. Now $a = +1.5$ m/s^2. Therefore,
$F_{net} = m(+1.5 \text{ m/s}^2).$
We are not given the mass of the object, but we can find it from the weight, $W = mg$, so

$$m = \frac{W}{g} = \frac{25 \text{ N}}{9.80 \text{ m/s}^2} = 2.6 \text{ kg. Thus,}$$

$F_{net} = (2.6 \text{ kg})(+1.5 \text{ m/s}^2) = +3.9 \text{ N (up)}$
$F_{net} = F_{scale} + W;\ F_{scale} = F_{net} - W$
$= +3.9 \text{ N} - (-25 \text{ N}) = +29 \text{ N (up)}.$

That is, the scale exerts a larger force and thus indicates a larger weight when the elevator accelerates upward.

The net force is the vector sum of all forces acting on a body.

FIGURE 5–16. Use with the Example Problem.

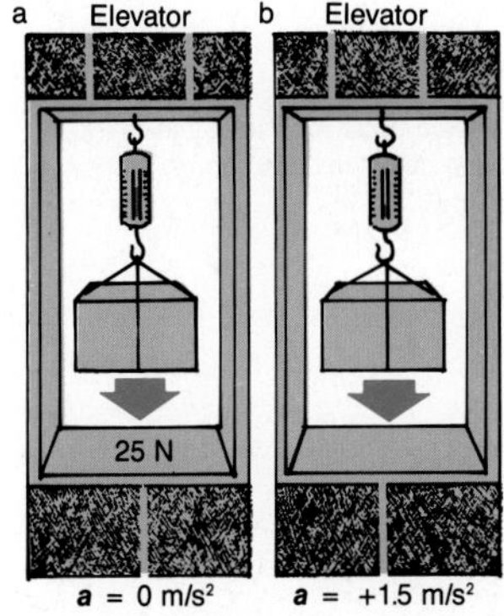

CONCEPT DEVELOPMENT

Convergent Question: Ask students if they can think of situations not covered by Newton's laws. They may suggest cases of changing forces or masses and some may know about relativistic complications at very high speeds. Basically, however, the laws cover all cases.

Critical Thinking Master, Teacher Resource Package. For further investigation of the concepts presented in this section, use the Critical Thinking Master Forces and Flight.

CRITICAL THINKING

Use the Critical Thinking master for Chapter 5 with this section.

Answers To
PRACTICE PROBLEMS

Have students refer to Appendix A of the Solutions Appendix for complete solutions to Practice Problems.

13. a. 5.0 kg; **b.** 4.0 m/s^2
14. a. 1.50 kg; **b.** −3.00 m/s^2
15. a. 20×10^6 N; **b.** 5.0 m/s^2; **c.** 7.8 km/s; **d.** It would increase.
16. $F_{appt} = 4.4 \times 10^3$ N

CHECKING FOR UNDERSTANDING

Have students respond to questions 2.1 and 2.2 of the Concept Review. Also, use testing material in TRP for this chapter or use problems and exercises from the end of the chapter to assess student comprehension.

RETEACHING

Transparency Package. Reteach Newton's third law using Transparency 5 and the accompanying worksheet.

EXTENSION

Ask students what would happen if you threw a Ping-Pong ball downward at a speed greater than its terminal velocity. (The ball would slow down until it reached its terminal velocity, and then would continue downward at that constant speed.)

INDEPENDENT PRACTICE/ EXTENSION

Refer to the Assignment Guide below for additional questions and problems for independent practice.

If you ride an elevator, you "feel" your inertial mass. When the elevator accelerates upward, you feel the added force of the floor on your feet, accelerating you up. You also feel the forces your muscles exert on your stomach; these forces may make your stomach feel strange.

Practice Problems

13. A rubber ball weighs 49 N.
  a. What is the mass of the ball?
  b. What is the acceleration of the ball if an upward force of 69 N is applied?

14. A small weather rocket weighs 14.7 N.
  a. What is its mass?
  b. The rocket is carried up by a balloon. The rocket is released from the balloon and fired, but its engine exerts an upward force of 10.2 N. What is the acceleration of the rocket?

15. The space shuttle has a mass of 2.0×10^6 kg. At lift-off the engines generate an upward force of 30×10^6 N.
  a. What is the weight of the shuttle?
  b. What is the acceleration of the shuttle when launched?
  c. The average acceleration of the shuttle during its 10 minute launch is 13 m/s^2. What velocity does it attain?
  d. As the space shuttle engines burn, the mass of the fuel becomes less and less. Assuming the force exerted by the engines remains the same, would you expect the acceleration to increase, decrease, or remain the same? Why?

▶ **16.** A certain sports car accelerates from 0 to 60 mph in 9.0 s (average acceleration = 3.0 m/s^2). The mass of the car is 1354 kg. The average backward force due to air drag during acceleration is 280 N. Find the forward force required to give the car this acceleration.

F.Y.I.

Small insects have large surface areas and low weights. They quickly reach terminal velocities of only a few centimeters per second. An ant can fall from a fifty-story building and walk away unharmed after hitting the sidewalk.

The Fall of Bodies in the Air

An object in freefall (in a vacuum) has only the force of gravity acting on it. Its acceleration is equal to *g*.

Astronauts on the surface of the moon dropped a hammer and a feather together. These objects hit the surface at the same time. Without any air, all objects fall with the same acceleration. On Earth, the acceleration is 9.80 m/s^2; on the moon it is 1.60 m/s^2.

The force of air molecules striking a moving object is called air resistance.

In air, however, an additional force acts on moving bodies. Try this experiment. Take two pieces of notebook paper. Crumple one into a ball. Now hold them side by side and drop them at the same time. The two pieces of paper obviously do not accelerate at the same rate. The flat paper encounters much more air resistance than the ball. Air resistance, sometimes called the drag force, is a friction-like force. As an object moves through the air, it collides with air molecules that exert a force on it. The force depends on the size and shape of the object, the density of the air, and the speed of motion.

Suppose you drop a ping-pong ball. Just after you drop it, it has very little velocity, and thus very small drag force. The downward force of gravity is larger than the upward drag force and the ball accelerates downward. As its velocity increases, so does the drag force. At some later time the drag force equals the force of gravity. The net force is now zero, and the velocity of the ball becomes constant. This constant velocity is called the **terminal velocity.**

5:2 ASSIGNMENT GUIDE

	PRACTICE	EXTENSION
CHAPTER REVIEW pp. 5-18–5-21		
· Reviewing Concepts	5–11	
· Applying Concepts		5–11
· Problems*	2, 11–15, 17–19, 22–25	3, 16, 20, 21, 26, 29
APPENDIX B PROBLEMS*		
· Chapter 5, p. 691	7–10	11–13

* Complete solutions to all Chapter Review and Appendix problems appear in the Problems and Solutions Manual.

TRANSPARENCY

Use Transparency 5 with this section.

Physics and technology

FAST PEDALING

The forces that work against the speed of a bicycle racer are the weight of the bike and rider, friction with the road surface and within the wheel itself, and air resistance. The bike rider's biggest battle is with air resistance. About 70% of the air resistance, or drag, that a rider encounters is caused by his own body. That's why riders maintain a crouched position during a race. The rider can further cut air resistance by wearing tightfitting clothing made from smooth fabric. New aerodynamic designs for bikes, wheels, and helmets are also being used to reduce air resistance.

To reduce weight and make acceleration easier, lightweight alloys and composite materials containing carbon fibers are being used to build strong but very low mass frames. A bike made of titanium, for example, can have a mass of less than 9 kg.

The ball bearings in the wheels cause friction. This bearing friction can be reduced by using improved bearings and lubricants.

The total effect of all these efforts may be a gain of only a few meters per kilometer. However, even that small gain can mean a big difference in a race.

· What are some ways you could reduce the rolling friction between a bike and the riding surface?

Physics and technology

The best bike design to minimize air resistance is the recumbent cycle, which puts the rider in a kind of "easy chair" position. The streamlined torpedo-like shape of some of these cycles also helps decrease air resistance.

The question to the students concerns rolling friction. The friction between the tire and road gets the cyclist started and stopped and helps him or her accelerate and corner. But as a tire rolls, the tire flattens slightly. Energy is lost as the tire deforms to match the roughness of the pavement.

Going Down

The terminal velocity of a ping-pong ball in air is only 9 m/s. A basketball has a terminal velocity of 20 m/s, while a baseball can fall as fast as 42 m/s. Skiers increase their terminal velocities by decreasing drag force. They hold their bodies in an "egg" shape and wear very smooth clothing and streamlined helmets. A sky diver can control terminal velocity by changing body shape. A spread-eagle position gives the slowest terminal velocity, about 60 m/s. By opening the parachute, the sky diver has become part of a very large object with a correspondingly large drag force. The terminal velocity is now about 5 m/s.

ACTIVITY

Cooperative Learning: Have students bring in the softer kinds of balls, such as Nerf balls or whiffle balls. Ask students why these balls are safer and less likely to do damage. (These balls are less dense. When thrown or batted, they have more surface in contact with the air, and, having less mass, their terminal velocities are therefore lower.)

CONCEPT REVIEW

2.1 A sky diver in the spread-eagle position opens the parachute. Is the diver accelerated? which direction? Explain your answer.

2.2 A weight lifter lifts a 115-kg barbell from the ground.
- **a.** How does the force exerted by the lifter compare with the weight of the barbell? Explain.
- **b.** How does the force exerted by the lifter on the barbell compare with the force exerted by the barbell on the lifter?

2.3 Suppose you put a wooden block against a wall and push horizontally to keep it from falling. Draw a diagram showing the forces on the block and the causes of those forces. Pay special attention to the normal force and the weight of the block. Are they in the same direction? Are they equal?

2.4 **Critical Thinking:** When a football defensive lineman wants to stop an opponent, he puts his shoulder into his opponent's body and lifts up. How does this affect the ability of his opponent to accelerate? Explain.

3 Close

CONVERGENT QUESTION

Consider with students why Newton's laws are still so useful more than three hundred years after their publication. Certainly the major factor is that they are a close and accurate analysis of the way nature operates. They are not statements of faddish opinion.

CONCEPT REVIEW ANSWERS

2.1 Yes, upward. The chute exerts an upward force on the diver. The resulting upward acceleration causes the diver's downward velocity to decrease.

2.2 a. The force is a bit greater initially because the barbell must be accelerated upward from zero to some constant lifting velocity. During the constant velocity part of the lift, the lifter's force equals the barbell weight. **b.** Equal and opposite. They are action-reaction forces.

2.3 Weight down, friction up; force of your hand into wall; (normal) force of wall out. Normal force is perpendicular to the weight. Weight is equal (and opposite) to friction force, which is μ times the normal force.

2.4 By lifting him, he reduces the force between the opponent's feet and the ground, reducing the frictional force that allows him to accelerate.

CLOSING CHAPTER 5

Review Summary statements and Key Terms with your students.

ASSESSMENT

Vocabulary Review Master, Teacher Resource Package. Use this master to check students' understanding of Key Terms.

Evaluation Masters. Use Parts A and B of the Chapter Evaluation Masters from the Teacher Resource Package to test qualitative chapter objectives. Use Parts C and D to test quantitative chapter objectives.

Answers To
REVIEWING CONCEPTS

1. a. gravitational force **b.** gravitational force **c.** strong nuclear force **d.** electromagnetic force

2. a. An object at rest tends to stay at rest if no outside force acts on it. **b.** Newton's first law says that the state of motion of the physics book will change if a net force acts on the book. The force from your hand is greater than any opposing force such as friction. With a net force on it, the book slides in the direction of the net force. **c.** When your hand no longer applies a force on the book, the net force on the book is now a frictional force in a direction opposite to the book's motion, so it eventually comes to a stop. **d.** The book would remain in motion if the net force acting on it were zero. For example, remove friction.

3. A large force is required to accelerate the mass of the bicycle and rider. Once the desired constant velocity is reached, a much smaller force is sufficient to overcome the ever present frictional forces.

4. The rock does pull on Earth, but Earth's enormous mass would undergo only a minute acceleration by such a small force. This acceleration would go undetected.

5. Their total mass would be the same, 3.0 kg. Their weight would be ten times greater.

6. The rock would be easier to lift on the moon. The weight of the rock on the moon is less than on Earth since the acceleration due to gravity is less on the moon. $W = mg$. There is no difference in force needed to throw the rock horizontally since the force depends only on the acceleration of the rock and its mass. $F = ma$.

7. Friction between the hand cart and carton supplies the force.

8. In both cases, the tendency of the package to remain at rest or in motion is the result of inertia. More specifically, if the frictional force between the package and the seat is not large enough to accelerate the mass of the package at the same rate as the bus is accelerating, then the bus will "outrun" the package. In the case of braking, insufficient frictional force to decelerate the package at the same rate as the bus will result in the package "outrunning" the bus.

9. No. It only means the forces acting on it are balanced and the net force is zero. (With an object hanging on a rope, the weight of the object is balanced by the tension in the rope.)

10. Yes. Its velocity changed direction, thus it was accelerated and a force is required to accelerate the basketball.

CHAPTER 5 REVIEW

SUMMARY

5.1 Newton's Laws of Motion

- All forces are vectors; they have both magnitude and direction.
- The four basic forces are the gravitational, electromagnetic, and strong and weak nuclear forces.
- Newton's first law states that an object with no net (unbalanced) force acting on it will either remain at rest or continue moving at constant speed in a straight line.
- Newton's second law states that when a net (unbalanced) force acts on an object, the resulting acceleration varies directly with the force and inversely with the mass of the object.
- Newton's third law states that forces always exist in pairs. When one object exerts a force on a second object, the second exerts an equal and opposite force on the first.
- The weight of a body is proportional to its mass.
- Weight is the gravitational force on a body.

5.2 Using Newton's Laws

- Gravitational mass and inertial mass are two essentially different concepts. The gravitational and inertial masses of a body, however, are numerically equal.
- Friction is a force that acts when two objects rub against each other.
- The magnitude of the sliding friction force is the product of the coefficient of friction and the normal force.
- Net force is the vector sum of forces acting on the body.
- A body falling in air reaches terminal velocity when the upward force of air resistance equals the downward force of gravity.

KEY TERMS

kinematics
dynamics
force
Newton's third law
action-reaction forces
weight
gravitational force
electromagnetic force
strong nuclear force
weak force
Newton's first law
Newton's second law
inertial mass
friction
static friction
sliding friction
coefficient of friction
terminal velocity

REVIEWING CONCEPTS

1. The text states that all forces can be grouped into just four kinds of forces. Name the force that best describes the following:
   a. the weakest force.
   b. the force that acts over the longest distance.
   c. the strongest force.
   d. the force that holds matter together.

2. A physics book is motionless on the top of a table. If you give it a hard push with your hand, it slides across the table and slowly comes to a stop. Use Newton's first law of motion to answer the following questions.
   a. Why does the book remain motionless before the force is applied?
   b. Why does the book move when the hand pushes on it?
   c. Why does the book eventually come to a stop?
   d. Under what conditions would the book remain in motion at a constant speed?

3. Why do you have to push harder on the pedals of a single-speed bicycle to start it moving than to keep it moving with a constant velocity?

4. Suppose you dropped a rock from a bridge into a valley below. Earth pulls on the rock and it accelerates downward. According to Newton's third law, the rock must also be pulling on Earth, yet we don't notice the Earth accelerating upward. Explain.

5. Let's say your textbooks have a total mass of 3.0 kg. What would be the mass of the books if they were taken to Jupiter where the acceleration due to gravity is 10 times that of Earth?

6. Compare the force needed to lift a 10-kg rock on Earth and on the moon. Now compare the force needed to throw the same rock horizontally at the same speed in the two locations.

7. You place a carton of books on a hand cart. When you accelerate the cart, the carton also accelerates. What supplies the force that accelerates the carton?

8. Why does a package on the seat of a bus slide backward when the bus accelerates quickly from rest? Why does it slide forward when the driver applies the brakes?

9. Suppose the acceleration of an object is zero. Does this mean there are no forces acting on it? Give an example supporting your answer.

10. When a basketball player dribbles a basketball, it falls to the floor and bounces up. Is a force required to make it bounce? Why?

11. Before a skydiver opens her parachute, she may already be falling at a velocity higher than her terminal velocity with the parachute open.

a. Describe what happens to her velocity as she opens her parachute.

b. Describe her velocity from after her parachute has been open for a while until she is about to land.

APPLYING CONCEPTS

1. Which of the four forces makes paint cling to a wall? Which force makes adhesive sticky? Which force makes wax stick to a car?

2. If you are in a car that is struck from behind, you can receive a serious neck injury called whiplash.

a. Using Newton's laws of motion, explain what happens.

b. How does a headrest reduce whiplash?

3. Should astronauts choose pencils with hard or soft lead when taking notes in space? Explain.

FIGURE 5–17.

4. According to legend, a horse learned Newton's laws. When it was told to pull a cart, it refused, saying that if it pulled the cart forward, according to Newton's third law there would be an equal force backwards. Thus, there would be balanced forces and, according to Newton's second law, the cart would not accelerate. How would you reason with this rather weird horse?

5. When people go on a diet, most say they want to lose weight. Describe some methods that would allow them to decrease their weight without decreasing their mass.

6. Drag racers often set their tires on fire to soften the rubber and increase the coefficient of friction, μ. What is the role friction plays?

7. Which creates a greater force of friction: sliding your physics book across a table on its back cover or along one of its edges?

8. Is the coefficient of friction the same between two identical surfaces in a lab on Earth and in a lab in a space colony on the moon? Explain.

9. Can the coefficient of friction ever be greater than one? less than one? Explain. What information would you need to calculate μ precisely?

10. The same object is dropped in a vacuum and then in air. Which of the parameters (distance, velocity, acceleration) vary and which remain constant during succeeding seconds of time

a. in a vacuum?

b. in air when terminal velocity from air resistance has been reached?

11. While riding in a helicopter, you drop two ping-pong balls, one filled with air and the other with water. Both experience air resistance as they fall. Which ball reaches terminal velocity first? Do both hit the ground at the same time? Explain.

PROBLEMS

5.1 Newton's Laws of Motion

1. A 873-kg (1930 lb) dragster, starting from rest, attains a speed of 26.3 m/s (58.9 m/h) in 0.59 s.

a. Find the average acceleration of the dragster during this time interval?

b. What is the size of the average force on the dragster during this time interval?

c. Assume the driver has a mass of 68 kg. What horizontal force does the seat exert on the driver?

d. Is the driver's mass in part **c** an inertial mass or a gravitational mass?

2. The dragster in Problem 1 completed the 402.3 m (0.2500 mile) run in 4.936 s. If the

REVIEW MASTER

Use the Vocabulary Review master for Chapter 5 with this section.

EVALUATION MASTER

Use the Chapter Evaluation master for Chapter 5 with this section.

11. a. The frictional force of air resistance suddenly becomes larger than the gravitational force. The velocity of the sky diver drops to that of her terminal velocity. **b.** The frictional force of air resistance and the gravitational force are equal. Their sum is zero, so there is no longer any acceleration. The sky diver continues downward at a constant velocity, her terminal velocity.

Answers To
APPLYING CONCEPTS

1. All are examples of the electromagnetic force.

2. a. The car is suddenly accelerated forward. The seat accelerates your body, but your neck has to accelerate your head. This can hurt your neck muscles. **b.** The headrest pushes on your head, accelerating it in the same direction as the car.

3. A soft lead pencil would work better because it would require less force to make a mark on paper. The magnitude of the action-reaction force pair could push the astronaut away from the paper.

4. The equal and opposite forces referred to in Newton's third law are acting on different objects. The horse would pull on the cart and the cart would pull on the horse. The cart would have an unbalanced net force on it (neglecting friction) and would thus accelerate. Moral: Never teach a horse only a little physics.

5. Free fall, move to the moon, climb a mountain. Each of these will decrease the acceleration due to gravity and weight will be lost. $W = mg$.

6. The friction of the tires on the road makes it possible for the road to exert the force on the dragster.

7. Since friction depends on the nature of the surfaces (book/table) and the force pushing the surfaces together (book's weight), both would produce identical amounts of friction.

8. No. The coefficient of friction depends on the nature of the surfaces in contact and the normal force. In the lab on the moon, F_W would be less, therefore F_N, the action-reaction partner, would be less. Therefore, μ would be correspondingly less.

Answers continue on page 106.

Answers To
APPLYING CONCEPTS (cont)

9. Yes. The frictional force is greater than the normal force. Yes. The frictional force is less than the normal force. Both the frictional force and the normal force would be needed.

10. a. Distance traveled each second increases; velocity is increasing; acceleration is constant. **b.** Distance continues to increase; velocity and acceleration both constant (acceleration is zero).

11. The lighter, air-filled Ping-Pong ball reaches terminal velocity first. Its mass is less for the same size and shape, so the frictional force of upward air resistance becomes equal to the downward force of $m \times g$ sooner. Because the force of gravity on the more massive water-filled Ping-Pong ball is larger, its terminal velocity is larger, and it strikes the ground first.

Answers To
PROBLEMS

Complete solutions for all Chapter Review Problems can be found in the Problems and Solutions Manual accompanying this text.

1. a. 45 m/s^2; **b.** 3.9×10^4 N; **c.** 3.1×10^3 N; **d.** inertial mass
2. 33.02 m/s^2; 163.0 m/s
3. No, the acceleration during the first half-second was 45 m/s^2 (problem 1) and the acceleration for the full time was 33.02 m/s^2 (problem 2).
4. -5×10^3 N, upward
5. 3.1×10^3 N
6. 6.3×10^3 N
7. 33 m
8. a. 14 m/s; **b.** 3.2×10^3 N
9. 6.6×10^{-25} m/s^2
10. -2.0 m/s^2
11. a. 95.0 kg; **b.** 929 N; **c.** 95.0 kg; **d.** 934 N; **e.** "mass-in"
12. 250 kg
13. 10.5 m/s^2, down
14. -1.13×10^4 N, opposite direction of motion
15. 0.255
16. 0.400
17. -1 m/s^2

car had constant acceleration, what would be its acceleration and final velocity?

▶ **3.** The dragster crossed the finish line going 126.6 m/s (283.1 mph). Is the assumption of constant acceleration good? What other piece of evidence could you use to see if the acceleration is constant?

4. In Chapter 4, you found that when a karate strike hits wooden blocks, the hand undergoes an acceleration of -6500 m/s^2. Medical data indicates the mass of the forearm and hand to be about 0.7 kg. What is the force exerted on the hand by the blocks? What is its direction?

5. After a day of testing race cars, you decide to take your own 1550-kg car onto the test track. While moving down the track at 10 m/s, you suddenly accelerate to 30 m/s in 10 s. What is the average net force that you have applied to the car during the 10-s interval?

▶ **6.** A race car has a mass of 710 kg. It starts from rest and travels 40 m in 3.0 s. The car is uniformly accelerated during the entire time. What net force is applied to it?

▶ **7.** A force of -9000 N is used to stop a 1500-kg car traveling at 20 m/s. What braking distance is needed to bring the car to a halt?

▶ **8.** A 65-kg swimmer jumps off a 10-m tower.
a. Find the swimmer's velocity when hitting the water.
b. The swimmer comes to a stop 2 m below the surface. Find the net force exerted by the water.

9. When you drop a 0.40-kg apple, Earth exerts a force on it that accelerates it at 9.8 m/s^2 toward Earth's surface. According to Newton's third law, the apple must exert an equal and opposite force on Earth. If the mass of Earth is 5.98×10^{24} kg, what's the magnitude of Earth's acceleration?

10. A 60-kg boy and a 40-kg girl use an elastic rope while engaged in a tug-of-war on an icy frictionless surface. If the acceleration of the girl toward the boy is 3.0 m/s^2, determine the magnitude of the acceleration of the boy toward the girl.

5.2 Using Newton's Laws

11. A 95.0-kg (209 lb) boxer has his first match in the Canal Zone ($g = 9.782$ m/s^2) and his second match at the North Pole ($g = 9.832$ m/s^2).
a. What is his mass in the Canal Zone?
b. What is his weight in the Canal Zone?
c. What is his mass at the North Pole?
d. What is his weight at the North Pole?
e. Does he "weigh-in" or does he really "mass-in"?

12. Your new motorcycle weighs 2450 N. What is its mass in kilograms?

13. You place a 7.50-kg television set on a spring scale. If the scale reads 78.4 N, what is the acceleration of gravity at that location?

14. In Chapter 4, you calculated the braking acceleration for a car based on data in a driver's handbook. The acceleration was -12.2 m/s^2. If the car has a mass of 925 kg, find the frictional force and state the direction.

15. If you use a horizontal force of 30.0 N to slide a 12.0-kg wooden crate across a floor at a constant velocity, what is the coefficient of sliding friction between crate and floor?

▶ **16.** You are driving a 2500.0-kg car at a constant speed of 14.0 m/s along an icy, but straight and level road. While approaching a traffic light, it turns red. You slam on the brakes. Your wheels lock, the tires begin skidding, and the car slides to a halt in a distance of 25.0 m. What is the coefficient of sliding friction (μ) between your tires and the icy roadbed?

17. A person fishing hooks a 2.0-kg fish on a line that can only sustain a maximum of 38 N of force before breaking. At one point while reeling in the bass, it fights back with a force of 40 N. What is the minimum acceleration with which you must play out the line during this time in order to keep the line from breaking?

18. A 4500-kg helicopter accelerates upward at 2 m/s^2. What lift force is exerted by the air on the propellers?

19. The maximum force a grocery sack can withstand and not rip is 250 N. If 20 kg of groceries are lifted from the floor to the table with an acceleration of 5 m/s^2, will the sack hold?

▶ **20.** A student stands on a bathroom scale in an elevator at rest on the 64th floor of a building. The scale reads 836 N.
a. As the elevator moves up, the scale reading increases to 935 N, then decreases back to 836 N. Find the acceleration of the elevator.
b. As the elevator approaches the 74th floor, the scale reading drops as low as 782 N. What is the acceleration of the elevator?

c. Using your results from parts **a** and **b**, explain which change in velocity, starting or stopping, would take the longer time.
d. Explain the changes in the scale you would expect on the ride back down.

▶ **21.** A 2.1×10^{-4}-kg spider is suspended from a thin strand of spider web. The greatest tension the strand can withstand without breaking is 2.0×10^{-3} N. What is the maximum acceleration with which the spider can safely climb up the strand?

22. A sled of mass 50 kg is pulled along snow-covered, flat ground. The static friction coefficient is 0.30, and the sliding friction coefficient is 0.10.
a. What does the sled weigh?
b. What force will be needed to start the sled moving?
c. What force is needed to keep the sled moving at a constant velocity?
d. Once moving, what total force must be applied to the sled to accelerate it 3.0 m/s^2?

23. A force of 40 N accelerates a 5.0-kg block at 6.0 m/s^2 along a horizontal surface.
a. How large is the frictional force?
b. What is the coefficient of friction?

24. A 200-kg crate is pushed horizontally with a force of 700 N. If the coefficient of friction is 0.20, calculate the acceleration of the crate.

25. Safety engineers estimate that an elevator can hold 20 persons of 75-kg average mass. The elevator itself has a mass of 500 kg. Tensile strength tests show that the cable supporting the elevator can tolerate a maximum force of 2.96×10^4 N. What is the greatest acceleration that the elevator's motor can produce without breaking the cable?

▶ **26.** The instruments attached to a weather balloon have a mass of 5.0 kg.
a. The balloon is released and exerts an upward force of 98 N on the instruments. What is the acceleration of the balloon and instruments?
b. After the balloon has accelerated for 10 seconds, the instruments are released. What is the velocity of the instruments at the moment of their release?
c. What net force acts on the instruments after their release?
d. When does the direction of their velocity first become downward?

▶ **27.** A 2.0-kg mass (m_1) and a 3.0-kg mass (m_2) are attached to a lightweight cord that passes over a frictionless pulley, Figure 5–18. The hanging masses are free to move. Assume the positive direction of motion to be when the smaller object moves upward and the larger mass moves downward.
a. Draw the situation, showing all forces.
b. In what direction does the smaller mass move?
c. What is its acceleration?

▶ **28.** You change the masses in Figure 5–18 to 1.00 kg and 4.00 kg.
a. What can you expect the acceleration of the 4.00-kg mass to be?
b. What is the tension force acting on the cord?

FIGURE 5–18. Use with Problems 27, 28, and 29.

▶ **29.** You then decide to replace the 1.00-kg object from Problem 28 with a 2.00-kg object.
a. What is the acceleration of the 2.00-kg object?
b. What is the new tension force acting on the cord?

THINKING PHYSIC-LY

1. Suppose you are in a spaceship in freefall between Earth and the moon. How could you distinguish between a lead brick and an ordinary brick if you were blindfolded and wore gloves?
2. Cheetahs are bigger and faster than small gazelles, but more often than not gazelles escape a pursuing cheetah by zigzagging. Exactly why does this put the cheetah at a disadvantage?

18. 5.3×10^4 N
19. No, the sack will rip.
20. **a.** 1.2 m/s^2; **b.** -0.63 m/s^2; **c.** stopping, lower acceleration; **d.** scale reads less than 836 N, reads 836 N, then reads more than 836 N
21. 0.68 m/s^2
22. **a.** 4.9×10^2; **b.** 150 N, static friction; **c.** 49 N, sliding friction; **d.** 2.0×10^2 N
23. **a.** 10 N; **b.** 0.20
24. 1.5 m/s^2
25. 4.8 m/s^2
26. **a.** 9.8 m/s^2, up; **b.** 98 m/s, up; **c.** -49 N, down; **d.** 1.0×10 s
27. **a.** Refer to Problems and Solutions Manual for Diagram. **b.** upward; **c.** 2.0 m/s^2
28. **a.** 5.88 m/s^2; **b.** 15.7 N
29. **a.** 3.27 m/s^2; **b.** 26.1 N

Answers To
THINKING PHYSIC-LY

1. Find out which brick has greater inertia by trying to change its motion: for example, pushing each sideways. The brick that required the greatest force to change its motion has the most mass—the lead brick.
2. Since the cheetahs are more massive, it takes more force to change their motion. Since speed drops to zero, and then must increase again after each "zig," the gazelles (given equal strength) can accelerate more rapidly after each change in direction.

CHAPTER 6 Vectors

PLANNING GUIDE (6 class sessions)

CONTENTS	TEXT FEATURES	TEACHER RESOURCE PACKAGE	OTHER COMPONENTS
6.1 Graphical Method of Vector Addition, pp.110–113 (2 Class Sessions) • Vector Addition in One Dimension • Vector Addition in Two Dimensions • Addition of Several Vectors • Independence of Vector Quantities	**Pocket Lab:** Mass on a String, p. 111 **Concept Review,** p. 113	**Study Guide:** Graphical Method of Vector Addition **Reteaching Master:** Analysis of Vectors **Transparency Worksheet:** Forces on an Inclined Plane	**Laboratory Manual:** Lab 6.1 Addition of Force Vectors **Transparency 6:** Forces on an Inclined Plane
6.2 Analytical Method of Vector Addition, pp. 113–120 (2 Class Sessions) • Adding Perpendicular Vectors • Components of Vectors • Adding Vectors at Any Angle	**Physics Lab:** The Paper River, p.114 **Physics and Technology:** Swaying Skyscrapers, p.117 **Problem Solving Strategy:** Vector Resolution, p. 118 **Using Your Calculator:** Trig Functions, p. 115 **Concept Review,** p. 120	**Study Guide:** Analytical Method of Vector Addition **Physics Lab Data Sheet:** The Paper River **Critical Thinking Master:** Measuring Height Indirectly **Transparency Worksheet:** Non-perpendicular Forces	**Transparency 7:** Non-perpendicular Forces
6.3 Applications of Vectors, pp. 120–127 (2 Class Sessions) • Equilibrium • Gravitational Force and Inclined Planes	**Pocket Lab:** Force Vectors I, p. 121 **Pocket Lab:** Force Vectors II, p. 122 **Concept Review,** p. 127	**Study Guide:** Applications of Vectors **Enrichment Master:** Coefficient of Friction	**Laboratory Manual:** Lab 6.2 Physics 500
Chapter Review, pp. 127–131	Summary Key Terms Reviewing Concepts Applying Concepts Problems Thinking Physic-ly	**Vocabulary Review** **Chapter Test**	**Test Bank**

SUPPLEMENTARY MATERIALS

SOFTWARE	AUDIOVISUAL	BOOKS/MAGAZINES
Vectors and Graphing, Cross, (Apple II, IBM PC). *Vector Addition II,* Vernier, (Apple II). *Vectors and Linear Motion,* Focus Media (Apple II).	Filmstrip: *Understanding Vectors,* Bergwall.	McDonald, Thomas. "Vector Racing." *The Science Teacher,* November 1984, pp. 38–45. Nelson, Jim. "Static Equilibrium." *The Science Teacher,* December 1985, pp. 20–23. Ramirez-Bon, R. "An Interesting Problem Solved by Vectors." *The Physics Teacher,* December 1990, p. 594.

PROBLEM CORRELATION

CONCEPTS	CHAPTER REVIEW			PROBLEMS APPENDIX
	Reviewing Concepts	Applying Concepts	Problems	
6.1 Graphical Method of Vector Addition				
Vector Addition in One Dimension		1,2,3,4	1,2,3,4	4,**5**
Vector Addition in Two Dimensions	1,2,3,4,6	5	5	6,7
Addition of Several Vectors	5		6,7	
Independence of Vector Quantities				
6.2 Analytical Method of Vector Addition				
Adding Perpendicular Vectors		6	8,9,**10**,11,13,14,15,16, 17,18,19,**20**	1,2,3,8,9,**10**
Components of Vectors	7	7,8,11	21,22,**23**,**24**	11,12,13,14,**15**
Adding Vectors at Any Angle			**12**,25,26,27,**28**	16,**17**
6.3 Applications of Vectors				
Equilibrium	8,9,10,11	9,10	29,30,31,32,**33**	**18**,**19**,**20**,**21**
Gravitational Force and Inclined Planes	12	12,13	34,**35**,**36**,**37**	

ACTIVITY AND DEMONSTRATION MATERIALS

PHYSICS LAB	POCKET LAB	DEMONSTRATIONS
Page 114 small battery-powered car (or physics bulldozer) meter stick protractor stopwatch single sheet of paper about 1 m x 10 m meat department butcher paper or from the art department	Pages 111, 121, 122 1-kg mass string 20-N spring balance 1-m cord 1-kg mass 10-m rope	Pages 111, 126 2 spring scales 50-g mass 2 1-kg masses square piece of cloth piece of string chalk paper clip wooden block friction board spring scale

EXTENSION PROJECTS

LIBRARY RESEARCH

1. Navigation Techniques
Through library research, investigate past and present navigation techniques. For example, how have microelectronics improved inertial guidance systems?

HANDS-ON

2. Independent Vectors
Use a large capacity spring scale and a ramp to measure the effect of changing the angle on the downhill force exerted by a loaded wagon or sled.

STUDENT READINGS

Aquirre, J.M. "Student Preconceptions About Vector Kinematics." *The Physics Teacher,* April 1988.

Browne, Malcolm W. "Slippery Skins for Speedier Subs." *Discover,* April 1984.

Crane, Richard. "Frisbees, Can Lids, and Gyroscopic Effects." *The Physics Teacher,* May 1983.

Gilmore, C.P. "Spin Sail Harnesses Mysterious Magnus Effect." *Popular Science,* January 1984.

Greenwood, Margaret Stautberg, "Inclined Plane on a Frictionless Surface." *The Physics Teacher,* February 1990.

Chapter 6

Vectors

CHAPTER OVERVIEW

Theme Development: This chapter on vectors and their mathematical manipulation illustrates mathematical modeling of motion phenomena.

MISCONCEPTIONS

Having worked mainly with arithmetical quantities up until their exposure to vectors, students want to continue to add vectors like ordinary numbers. It is also difficult for them to accept the fact that perpendicular vectors don't influence each other.

KEY TERMS

components
cosine (cos)
equilibrant force
equilibrium
resultant
sine (sin)
tangent (tan)
trigonometry
vector resolution

Laboratory Options

STUDENT EDITION

Physics Lab

The Paper River	114

Pocket Labs

Mass on a String	111
Force Vectors I	121
Force Vectors II	122

TEACHER EDITION

Activities

Demonstration	111, 126
Cooperative Learning	116, 119, 125

LABORATORY MANUAL

Addition of Force Vectors	Lab 6.1
Physics 500	Lab 6.2

CHAPTER 6 Vectors

A Weighty Subject

The slack wire supports the weight of the performer. How does the force exerted by the wire compare to the weight of the walker?

Make this challenge to some strong friends. Have them hold on to the ends of a light rope several meters long and pull until it is taut. Then challenge them to keep the rope from sagging as you hang a medium-sized bag of potatoes from its center. After all, your friends claim to be strong, and the bag doesn't weigh much. Nevertheless, they will find it impossible to keep the rope perfectly straight. Why? You will discover the answer to this question as you understand the vector nature of forces.

Chapter Outline

Concept Check

The following terms or concepts from earlier chapters are important for a good understanding of this chapter. If you are not familiar with them, you should review them before studying this chapter.
- velocity, Chapter 3
- acceleration, Chapter 4
- force, vectors, Newton's first and second laws, Chapter 5

109

Introducing The Chapter

A Weighty Subject

Using The Photo: In some ways vectors are counterintuitive, that is, our common sense doesn't always predict correct vector results. Most students would say that the force exerted by the wire equals the weight of the walker, yet the laws of vectors teach us otherwise.

To answer the chapter opener question, students will find the information they need in the Example Problem on page 122.

Concept Check

Make sure students have a clear understanding of the concepts taught in Chapters 3, 4, and 5 listed in the Concept Check. Understanding the principles of physical motion and Newton's laws will have prepared students to recognize and apply vector quantities, which are the focus of this chapter.

CONCEPT DEVELOPMENT

Many teachers find the use of arrows valuable in teaching vectors. They can be magnetic for attaching to metal blackboards, large and wooden for dramatic flair, or small for use on an overhead projector. One scheme uses an extendable curtain rod for an adjustable length vector!

Assessment

Portfolio

Have students assemble a collection of their graphical solutions of vector problems. Include problems illustrating the addition of vectors and finding vector components. Use these examples for review in later chapters when vector methods will be used again.

Assessment Options

Portfolio Assessment
Portfolio Assessment, TWE, p. 109
Focus, TWE, p. 115
Research on swaying skyscrapers, Physics and Technology, p. 117
Portfolio Assessment, TWE, p. 118
Enrichment on tires, TWE, p. 126

Performance Assessment
Pocket Labs, pp. 111, 121, 122
Physics Lab, p. 114

Content Assessment
Self assessment: Practice Problems, pp. 112, 115, 118, 120, 123, 126
Demonstration on vectors, TWE, p. 110
Pocket Lab Assessment, TWE, p. 122
Critical Thinking, TWE, p. 123
Concept Reviews, pp. 113, 120, 127
Chapter Review, pp. 127–131
Supplemental Problems, pp. 691–693

Group Assessment
Activities for group assessment occur with Cooperative Learning and lab activities.

6.1 GRAPHICAL METHOD OF VECTOR ADDITION

Preparation

OBJECTIVES

The objectives are listed on the student page. Remind students to preview these objectives as a study guide to this major section.

OVERVIEW

This section introduces vector quantities as they apply to the real world. Force vectors are added with the help of graphs, and the independence of perpendicular vector quantities is emphasized.

BRIDGING

In Chapters 3 and 4, algebraic signs gave the direction for one-dimensional motion. East was positive (+) and west was negative (−). Using these signs, what would the child's displacement be? [−200 meters]

1 Focus

- If you live in an area where sailing, skiing, surfing, or wind surfing is possible, bring in a local expert to talk about techniques which utilize the wind such as tacking or particular body positions.
- The article "Meet Your Classmates in a Vector Contest" by Raymond A. Rogoway, *The Physics Teacher*, Vol. 29, February, 1991, p. 102, suggests an interesting game used both to teach vectors and to get students to interact with one another.

Objectives

- **show an ability to add vectors by the graphical method; recognize that the order of vector addition does not matter.**
- **recognize the independence of perpendicular vector quantities.**

The resultant is the single vector that could represent the sum of several vectors.

6.1 GRAPHICAL METHOD OF VECTOR ADDITION

A vector quantity can be represented by an arrow-tipped line segment. The length of the line, drawn to scale, represents the magnitude of the quantity. The direction of the arrow indicates the direction of the quantity. This arrow-tipped line segment represents a vector. Just as we can represent a vector graphically, we can add vectors graphically. They also can be represented in printed materials in boldface type, ***A, B***.

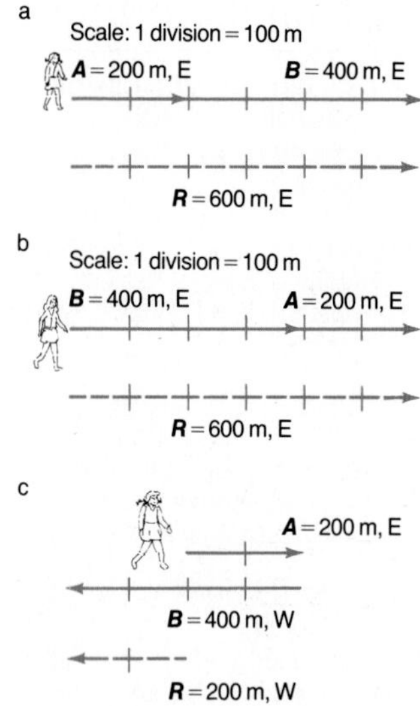

FIGURE 6–1. Vectors are added by placing the tail of one vector at the head of the other vector. The resultant, *R*, represents the sum of *A* and *B* (a). The order of addition does not matter (b). The vectors can have different directions (c).

Vector Addition in One Dimension

Suppose a child walks 200 m east, pauses, and then continues 400 m east. To find the total displacement, or change in position of the child, we must add the two vector quantities. In Figure 6–1a, *A* and *B*, drawn to scale, are vectors representing the two segments of the child's walk. The vectors are added by placing the tail of one vector at the head of the other vector. It is very important that neither the direction nor the length of either vector is changed during the process. A third vector is then drawn connecting the tail of the first vector to the head of the second vector. This third vector represents the sum of the first two vectors. It is called the **resultant** of *A* and *B*. The resultant is always drawn from the *tail* of the first vector to the *head* of the last vector.

When vectors are added, the order of addition does not matter. The tail of *A* could have been placed at the head of *B*. Figure 6–1b shows that the same vector sum would result.

To find the magnitude of the resultant, *R*, measure its length using the same scale used to draw *A* and *B*. In this situation, the total change in position is 200 m east + 400 m east = 600 m east.

The two vectors can have different directions, Figure 6–1c. If the child had turned around after moving 200 m east and walked 400 m west, the change of position would have been 200 m east + 400 m west or 200 m west. Note that in both cases, the vectors are added head to tail, and the directions of the original vectors are not changed.

Vector Addition in Two Dimensions

So far we have looked at motion in only one dimension. Vectors can also represent motion in two dimensions. In Figure 6–2, *A* and *B* represent the two displacements of a student who walked first 95 m east

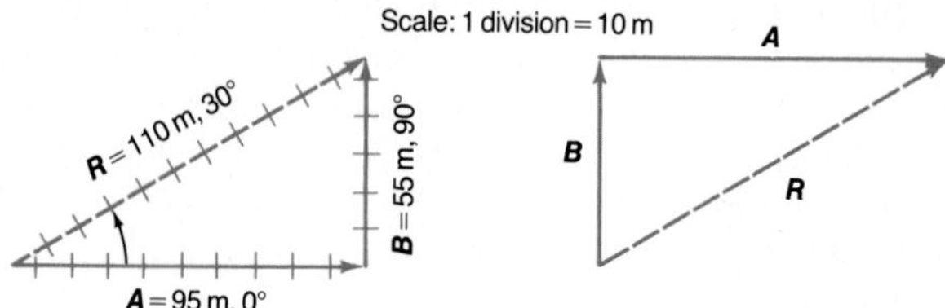

FIGURE 6–2. The vector sum of *B* + *A* is the same as the vector sum of *A* + *B*.

DEMONSTRATION

Purpose: to demonstrate how a vector diagram can represent a situation in which actual forces are balanced.

Equipment: 2 spring scales; 50-g mass; 2 1-kg masses; square piece of cloth; piece of string; chalk; paper clip

Procedure: 1. Make a 20-N weight from two 1-kg masses and one 50-g mass tied in a square piece of cloth or bag marked 20 N. Hang two spring scales calibrated in newtons above the chalkboard. Connect the scales with a piece of string and suspend the 20-N weight with a paper clip at the center of the string. **2.** Point out that the algebraic sum of the two forces shown on the scales is greater than 20 N. Ask students to relate the source of the extra force. Students sometimes add the forces like scalars and thus will not be able to account for the extra force. **3.** Mark the directions of the three forces by running a piece of chalk along the

and then 55 m north. The vectors are added by placing the tail of one vector at the head of the other vector. The resultant of *A* and *B* is drawn from the tail of the first vector to the head of the second vector. To find the magnitude of the resultant, *R*, measure its length using the same scale used to draw *A* and *B*. Its direction can be found with a protractor. The direction is expressed as an angle measured counterclockwise from the horizontal. In Figure 6–2, the resultant displacement is 110 m at 30° north of east.

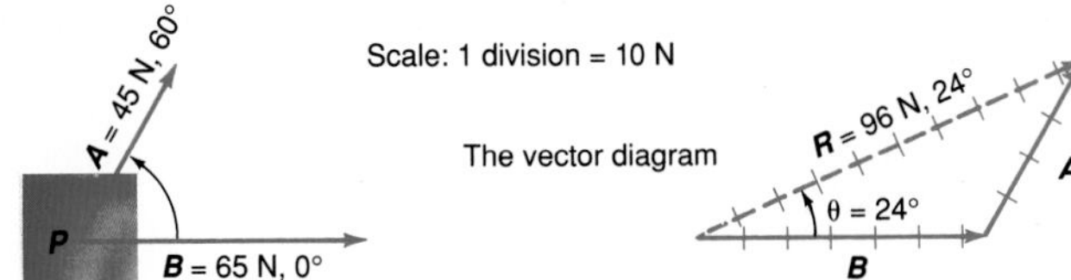

FIGURE 6–3. The resultant force of two forces acting on a point can be determined graphically.

Force vectors are added in the same way as position or velocity vectors. In Figure 6–3, a force, *A*, of 45 N and a force, *B*, of 65 N are exerted on an object at point **P.** Force *A* acts in the direction of 60°, force *B* acts at 0°. The resultant, *R*, is the sum of the two forces. Vectors representing forces *A* and *B* are drawn to scale. *R* is found by moving *A* without changing its direction or length until the tail of *A* is located at the head of *B*. The resultant is drawn from the tail of the first vector, *B*, to the head of the second vector, *A*. As before, the magnitude of *R* is determined using the same scale used for *A* and *B*. The angle is again found with a protractor. In this case, *R* is 96 N acting in a direction of 24°. A single force of 96 N acting in a direction of 24° will have exactly the same effect as two forces, 45 N at 60° and 65 N at 0°, acting at the same time.

POCKET LAB

MASS ON A STRING

Hang a 1.0-kg mass on a short string attached to a 20-N spring balance. What is the reading? Would the reading be larger or smaller if you use a longer string? Try it. What did you learn?

Addition of Several Vectors

Often, more than two forces act at the same time on the same object. To find the resultant of three or more vectors, follow the same procedure you used to add two vectors. Just be sure to place the vectors head-to-tail. The order of addition is not important. In Figure 6–4a, the three forces, *A*, *B*, and *C*, are acting on point **P.** In Figures 6–4b and 6–4c, the vectors are added graphically. Note that the resultant is the same in both sketches although two different orders of addition are used. Remember, when placing vectors head-to-tail, the direction and length of each vector must not be changed.

FIGURE 6–4. In (a) the three forces act concurrently on point P. In (b) and (c) the vectors are added graphically. The resultant is the same in both diagrams.

b
P
c
a
a

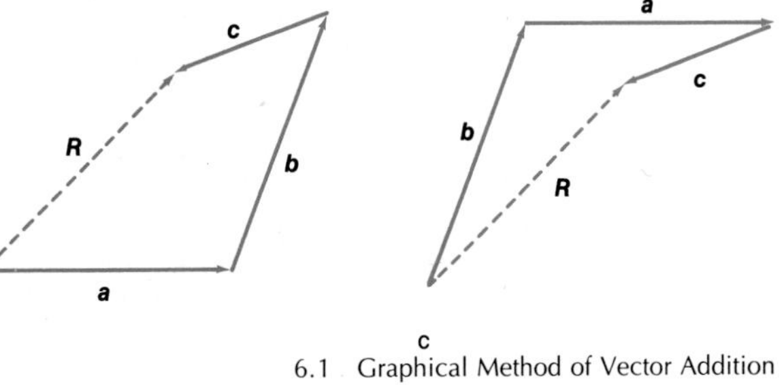

a
c
b
R
c

2 Teach

CONCEPT DEVELOPMENT

• The student's ability to represent vectors graphically is essential to a good understanding of vector addition. Encourage students to draw carefully when constructing diagrams, making sure they have ample opportunity to practice.

Study Guide Master. To reinforce the concepts in this section, have the students complete the Study Guide Master for Section 6.1 from the Teacher Resource Package.

Laboratory Manual. Give students additional experience with vector addition by doing Lab 6.1, Addition of Force Vectors, from the Laboratory Manual.

POCKET LAB

MASS ON A STRING

Purpose: to demonstrate equivalent force vectors.
Materials: 1-kg mass; string; 20-N spring balance.
Outcome: The reading on the balance should be 9.8 N. Even with a longer string the reading should be about 9.8 N (plus the extra weight of the string).

• Imagine walking along one edge of a 50-meter square then turning 90° and walking 50 meters along a second side of the square. Now how far are you from where you started? [71 meters] If students insist on answering 100 meters, ask why they would cut across on the diagonal when they're in a hurry? You can back this situation up by using a scale drawing on the board and measuring off the various lengths.

strings. Record the magnitude of the three forces. Removing the scales, strings, and weight, draw the appropriate vectors.

Results: Vector addition will show that the sum of the two scales' forces is 20 N straight up, which balances the weight down. Repeat with the 20-N weight suspended closer to one scale.

STUDY GUIDE MASTER

Use the Study Guide master for section 6.1.

LABORATORY MANUAL

Use Lab 6.1 with this section.

Answers To

PRACTICE PROBLEMS

Have students refer to Appendix A of the Solutions Appendix for complete solutions to Practice Problems.

1. **a.** 22 km; **b.** 16 km
2. 207 N, 53°, north of east
3. **a.** 34 km; **b.** 21 km, 61°, north of east

CONCEPT DEVELOPMENT

These questions will help the student learn the process of abstraction. The student must be able to read a problem description involving vector quantities and then draw a diagram of the situation.

ACTIVITY

Reteaching Master, Teacher Resource Package. Use the Reteaching Master, Analysis of Vectors, to reinforce the processes introduced in Chapter 6.

CHECKING FOR UNDERSTANDING

Have students work on the Practice Problems in class. Stress the importance of a careful diagram. Check to see that they start with a drawing.

RETEACHING

Transparency Package. Reteach the concept of independent vector quantities using Transparency 6.

EXTENSION

Students sometimes get the idea that only two forces can act concurrently on a body. Discuss situations where more than a few forces are exerted simultaneously (a plane in flight, a bridge, hanging sign in the wind, children fighting over a toy).

INDEPENDENT PRACTICE/ EXTENSION

Refer to the Assignment Guide on page 113 for additional questions and problems for independent practice.

Vector Conventions

- *Velocity vectors are red.*
- *Displacement vectors are green.*
- *Acceleration vectors are purple.*
- *Force vectors are blue.*
- ***Vector resultants are dashed lines.***

Practice Problems

Draw vector diagrams to solve each problem.

1. After walking 11 km due north from camp, a hiker then walks 11 km due east.
   a. What is the total distance walked by the hiker?
   b. Determine the total displacement from the starting point.
2. Two boys push on a box. One pushes with a force of 125 N to the east. The other exerts a force of 165 N to the north. What is the size and direction of the resultant force on the box?
3. ▶ An explorer walks 13 km due east, then 18 km north, and finally 3 km west.
   a. What is the total distance walked?
   b. What is the resulting displacement of the explorer from the starting point?

Independence of Vector Quantities

Perpendicular vector quantities are independent of one another. A motorboat heads east at 8.0 m/s across a river that flows north at 5.0 m/s. Starting from the west bank, the boat will travel 8.0 m east in one second. In the same second, it also travels 5.0 m north. The velocity north does not change the velocity east. Neither does the velocity east change the velocity north. These two perpendicular velocities are independent of each other. *Perpendicular vector quantities can be treated independently of one another.*

Scale: 1 division = 1 m/s

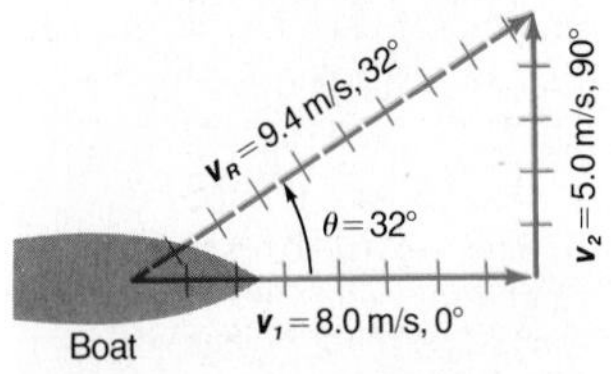

FIGURE 6–5. A boat traveling 9.4 m/s at 32° north of east can also be described as traveling both east at 8.0 m/s and north at 5.0 m/s at the same time.

In Figure 6–5, the two velocities of the boat are represented by vectors. When these vectors are added, the resultant velocity, v_R, is 9.4 m/s at 32° north of east. You can also think of the boat as traveling, in each second, east 8.0 m and north 5.0 m at the same time. Both statements have the same meaning.

Suppose that the river is 80 meters wide. Because the boat's velocity is 8 m/s east, it will take the boat 10 seconds to cross the river. During this 10 seconds, the boat will also be carried 50 meters downstream. In no way does the downstream velocity change the velocity of the boat across the river.

Perpendicular vector quantities can be treated independently of one another.

Practice Problems

Draw vector diagrams to solve each problem.

4. A motorboat heads due east at 16 m/s across a river that flows due north at 9.0 m/s.
   a. What is the resultant velocity (speed and direction) of the boat?
   b. If the river is 136 m wide, how long does it take the motorboat to reach the other side?
   c. How far downstream is the boat when it reaches the other side of the river?
5. While flying due east at 120 km/h, an airplane is also carried northward at 45 km/h by the wind blowing due north. What is the plane's resultant velocity?

Answers To

PRACTICE PROBLEMS

Have students refer to Appendix A of the Solutions Appendix for complete solutions to Practice Problems.

4. **a.** 18 m/s, 29°, north of east; **b.** 8.5 s; **c.** 77 m
5. 130 km/h, 21°, north of east

▶ **6.** Three teenagers push a heavy crate across the floor. Dion pushes with a force of 185 N at 0°. Shirley exerts a force of 165 N at 30°, while Joan pushes with 195 N force at 300°. What is the resultant force on the crate?

CONCEPT REVIEW

1.1 The order in which you add vectors does not matter. Mathematicians say that vector addition is commutative. Which ordinary arithmetic operations are commutative? Which are not?

1.2 Two boys push on a crate. One exerts a 400-N force, the other a 300-N force. The resultant force on the crate is 600 N. Explain.

1.3 What is the largest resultant force the two boys in question 1.2 could exert on the crate? What is the smallest resultant force?

1.4 **Critical Thinking:** Two unequal forces are exerted on a box. Could the net force ever be zero? What if three unequal forces are exerted? Support your argument with a diagram.

6.2 ANALYTICAL METHOD OF VECTOR ADDITION

You have seen how a vector quantity can be represented by an arrow. A vector quantity in two dimensions can also be represented by two numbers. One gives its length and the second gives the angle between that vector and a reference direction. The sum of any two vectors can be determined using trigonometry. **Trigonometry** deals with the relationships among angles and sides of triangles.

Trigonometric functions are defined in terms of one of the non - 90° angles of a right triangle. The common trigonometric functions of an angle are the **sine** (sin), **cosine** (cos), and **tangent** (tan). For the triangle in Figure 6–6a,

$$\sin \theta = \frac{\text{opposite side}}{\text{hypotenuse}}$$

$$\cos \theta = \frac{\text{adjacent side}}{\text{hypotenuse}}$$

$$\tan \theta = \frac{\text{opposite side}}{\text{adjacent side}}$$

The numerical value of the trigonometry functions can be found with a calculator or from Table D–6 in the Appendix. For example, suppose you need to build a triangular form with the dimensions shown in Figure 6–6b. You know that the hypotenuse of the triangle is 7.6 m and the side adjacent to angle θ is 3.1 m. Therefore, by using the cosine function, you can determine what size you should make θ.

$$\cos \theta = \frac{\text{adjacent side}}{\text{hypotenuse}} = \frac{3.1 \text{ m}}{7.6 \text{ m}} = 0.41$$

Therefore, from a calculator or trigonometry table, θ = 66°.

F.Y.I.

Physics Terms Made Easy
Hypotenuse: Animal like a rhinoceros but with no horn or nose.

Objectives

- understand the addition of forces and be able to solve force vector addition problems.
- recognize the applications of elementary geometry and trigonometry to vector addition and be able to solve problems using these methods.

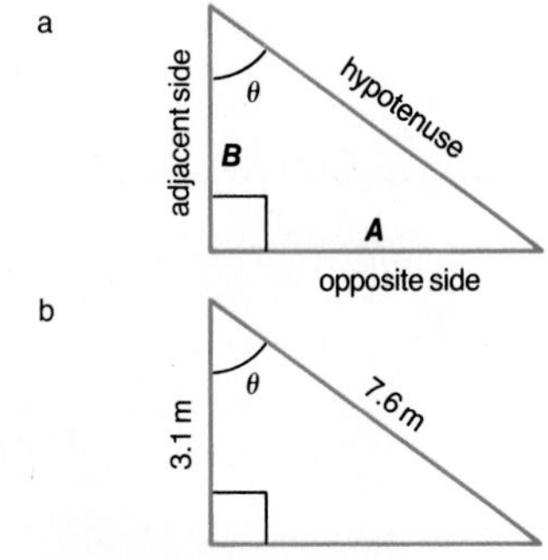

FIGURE 6–6. Vector sums can be found using the trigonometric functions of right triangles.

Answers To
PRACTICE PROBLEMS
6. 434 N, 11.5°, south of east

3 Close

CONVERGENT QUESTION

Ask students if they have ever walked or ridden a bike in a strong wind, or if they have been in a rowboat or canoe on a stream with a strong current. What happened?

CONCEPT REVIEW ANSWERS

1.1 Addition and multiplication are commutative; subtraction and division are not.
1.2 Forces are vectors, and the two boys do not push in the same direction.
1.3 700 N when pushing in the same direction; 100 N when pushing in opposite directions.
1.4 **Critical Thinking:** No; yes, if the vectors form a closed triangle.

6.2 ANALYTICAL METHOD OF VECTOR ADDITION

Preparation

OBJECTIVES

The objectives are listed on the student page. Remind students to preview these objectives as a study guide to this major section.

OVERVIEW

The process of finding vector components and then using these components in problem solution is a powerful tool.

BRIDGING

Finding vector components involves the use of trigonometry. Review or introduce trigonometry, especially if you've only used graphical analysis methods up to now.

6:1 ASSIGNMENT GUIDE

	PRACTICE	EXTENSION
CHAPTER REVIEW pp. 127–131		
· Reviewing Concepts	1–6	
· Applying Concepts		1–5
· Problems*	1–7	7
APPENDIX B PROBLEMS*		
· Chapter 6 p. 692	4, 6, 7	5

*Complete solutions to all Chapter Review and Appendix problems appear in the Problems and Solutions Manual.

RETEACHING MASTER

Use the Reteaching master for Chapter 6 with this section.

TRANSPARENCY

Use Transparency 6 with this section.

PHYSICS LAB

Process Skills: observing, measuring, inferring, predicting, defining operationally, communicating, using numbers.

MISCONCEPTIONS

Most students will believe that the motion of the river will affect the speed of the boat across the river. A pre-lab discussion will bring out the following student ideas: 1. The river causes the boat to go faster, therefore the boat will get across in less time. 2. The boat travels farther, therefore the boat will take more time to get across.

Lab Worksheet, Teacher Resource Package. If desired, use the lab worksheet master for this chapter for students to record their data.

OBSERVATIONS

1. The motion of the boat is a simultaneous combination of its own speed and the speed of the river.
2. Yes, the boat travels a greater distance than straight across in the same time, so the net speed is greater.
3. No, the same time is needed. The river does not push or pull the boat in the direction called "across the river." Therefore the motion of the river cannot affect the "across" motion of the boat.

ANALYSIS

1. The speed of the river can be determined using *velocity = distance traveled/time.*
2. The combined speed is the simple sum: ground speed = boat speed + river speed.
3. The combined speed is the vector sum: ground speed = boat speed − river speed. Note: The boat cannot go upstream when the current is faster than the boat.

APPLICATIONS

The motion of a plane is the combination of its speed through the air and the speed of the air (wind). Whenever a plane is flying at an angle to the wind, it will not be moving in the direction that it is pointing.

PHYSICS LAB: The Paper River

Purpose

To discover how boats travel on a river.

Materials

- small battery-powered car (or physics bulldozer)
- meter stick
- protractor
- stopwatch
- single sheet of paper about 1 m × 10 m-meat department butcher paper or from the art department

Procedure

1. Your car will serve as the boat. Write a brief statement to explain how the boat's speed can be determined.
2. Your boat will start with all wheels on the paper river. Measure the width of the river and predict how much time is needed for your boat to go directly across the river. Show your data and calculations.
3. Determine the time needed to cross the river when your boat is placed on the edge of the river. Make three trials and record the times.
4. Do you think it will take more or less time to cross when the river is flowing? Explain your prediction.
5. Have a student (the hydro engineer) walk slowly, at a constant speed, while pulling the river along the floor. Each group should measure the time it takes for the boat to cross the flowing river. Compare the results with your prediction.
6. Devise a method to measure the speed of the river. Have the hydro engineer pull the river at a constant speed and collect the necessary data.

Observations and Data

1. Does the boat move in the direction that it is pointing?
2. Did the motion of the water make the boat go faster?
3. Did the motion of the water affect the time needed when the boat was pointed straight across?
4. Which had more speed, the river or the boat? Explain your choice.

Analysis

1. Calculate the speed of the river.
2. Using your results for the speed of the boat and river, calculate the speed of the boat, compared to the ground, when the boat is headed directly downstream.
3. Using the results for the speed of the boat and the river, calculate the speed of the boat, compared to the ground, when the boat is headed upstream.

Applications

1. Do small propeller aircraft always move in the direction that they are pointing? Do they ever fly sideways?

ASSESSMENT

Critical Thinking: To further assess your students' understanding of velocity vectors, have them answer the following questions.

1. A boat moving at 5.0 m/s can travel across an 80-m calm pond and back in 32 s, (plus turning time). Would it need the same time to travel 80 m downstream and 80 m upstream on a river with a current of 2.0 m/s? [No. Upstream time = 80 m/3.0 m/s = 27 s; downstream time = 80 m/7.0 m/s = 11 s. Total time is approximately 38 s.]

2. A small plane requires an airspeed of 45 m/s for lift-off. Would it be better to takeoff with or against the wind? Why? (Assume a wind speed of 10 m/s) [When the plane heads into the wind, the moving air contributes 10 m/s of airspeed. The plane will "feel" the extra wind and be able to take off with a ground speed of only 35 m/s.]

Adding Perpendicular Vectors

If two vectors are perpendicular, a right angle is formed when the tail of the second vector is placed at the head of the first. The resultant vector, drawn from the tail of the first to the head of the second, is the hypotenuse of the right triangle formed by the three vectors. The length of the resultant can be calculated using the Pythagorean theorem. You can find the interior angle, θ, by using the trigonometric tangent function. In Figure 6–6, $\tan \theta = A/B$. Whenever solving vector addition analytically, draw a careful sketch of the vectors and check that your answer agrees with the sketch.

The Pythagorean theorem can be used to calculate the resultant of perpendicular vectors.

Example Problem

Finding a Resultant Velocity

An airplane flying toward 0° at 90.0 km/h is being blown toward 90° at 50.0 km/h, Figure 6–7. What is the resultant velocity of the plane?

Given: plane velocity,
$v_p = 90.0$ km/h at 0°
wind velocity,
$v_w = 50.0$ km/h at 90°

Unknown: resultant velocity, v_R
Basic equation: $R^2 = A^2 + B^2$
or $v_R^2 = v_p^2 + v_w^2$

$$\tan \theta = \frac{\text{side opposite}}{\text{side adjacent}}$$

Solution: The vector v_R is the hypotenuse of a right triangle. Its magnitude is given by $v_R^2 = v_p^2 + v_w^2$

$$v_R^2 = (90.0 \text{ km/h})^2 + (50.0 \text{ km/h})^2$$
$$= \sqrt{1.06 \times 10^4 \text{ (km/h)}^2}$$
$$v_R = 103 \text{ km/h.}$$

The angle, θ, is found from

$$\tan \theta = \frac{\text{opposite side}}{\text{adjacent side}}$$
$$= \frac{50.0 \text{ km/h}}{90.0 \text{ km/h}}$$

so,

$$\tan \theta = 0.556.$$

A calculator, or Table D–6 in the Appendix, shows that 0.556 is the tangent of 29°. Therefore, θ is 29°. The resultant velocity is

$$v_R = 103 \text{ km/h at } 29°.$$

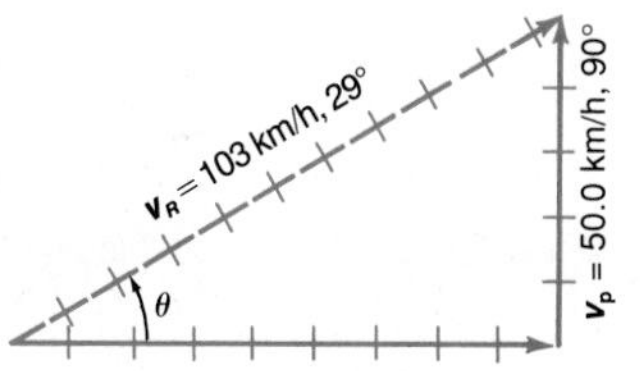

v_R = 103 km/h, 29°
v_p = 50.0 km/h, 90°
θ
v_w = 90.0 km/h, 0°

FIGURE 6–7. The vector diagram shows the approximate solution to the Example Problem.

Using Your CALCULATOR

Use your calculator to find the angle θ whose tangent is 50.0/90.0, called the arctan.

Keys	Result
50.0 ÷ 90.0 =	0. 555. . .
shift tan	29. 1

arctan 50.0/90.0 = 29.1°

Practice Problems

7. A 110-N force and a 55-N force both act on an object point **P.** The 110-N force acts at 90°. The 55-N force acts at 0°. What is the magnitude and direction of the resultant force?

1 Focus

Challenge students to come up with quick ways of showing vector quantities in action using their hands, and available materials. You're after anything that shows how vectors work, especially emphasizing direction.

2 Teach

CONCEPT DEVELOPMENT

The skill of making good vector diagrams is an important one. Whether a careful scale drawing or a rougher diagram showing relative sizes and directions of force on an object (what's called a free body diagram), the technique must be mastered.

Study Guide Master. To reinforce the concepts in this section, have the students complete the Study Guide Master for Section 6.2 from the Teacher Resource Package.

Guided Practice: Review the Example Problem in class on the board. Then have students work on the first two Practice Problems, offering individual assistance when needed.

Independent Practice: Assign Practice Problems 9 and 10 on page 116 for homework. Review the solutions in class the next day.

Enrichment: How do you add vectors in three dimensions rather than just in two dimensions? Hint: If the three-dimensional vectors are all perpendicular, then you simply add a third term into the Pythagorean theorem to get the resultant.

LAB WORKSHEET

Use the Lab Worksheet for Chapter 6 with this Physics Lab.

Answers To
PRACTICE PROBLEMS

Have students refer to Appendix A of the Solutions Appendix for complete solutions to Practice Problems.

7. 120 N, 63°

Answers To
PRACTICE PROBLEMS (cont)

8. **a.** 9.3 m/s at 24°
b. 13 s
9. **a.** 4.4 m/s at 30°
b. 11 s
c. 24 m
10. 160 km/h at 140°

CONCEPT DEVELOPMENT

Students often do not see that the two perpendicular components can be used to replace the original vector. Put another way, the two perpendicular components are equivalent to the original vector. The point of resolving vectors into components is so that we can add up many *x* (or *y*) components in standard arithmetic fashion.

ACTIVITY

Cooperative Learning: Teach students how to use a magnetic compass and have them set up a trail using distances and bearings. Then have groups trade instructions for following the trail.

8. A motorboat travels at 8.5 m/s. It heads straight across a river 110 m wide.
a. If the water flows downstream at a rate of 3.8 m/s, what is the boat's resultant velocity?
b. How long does it take the boat to reach the opposite shore?

9. A boat heads directly across a river 41 m wide at 3.8 m/s. The current is flowing downstream at 2.2 m/s.
a. What is the resultant velocity of the boat?
b. How much time does it take the boat to cross the river?
c. How far downstream is the boat when it reaches the other side?

▶ **10.** A 42-km/h wind blows toward 215°, while a plane heads toward 125° at 152 km/h. What is the resultant velocity of the plane?

Components of Vectors

A vector quantity can be resolved into its perpendicular components.

We have seen that two or more vectors acting in different directions from the same point may be replaced by a single vector, the resultant. The resultant has the same effect as the original vectors.

It is also possible to begin with a single vector and think of it as the resultant of two vectors. We usually choose two new vectors in directions that are perpendicular to each other. These two vectors are called the **components** of the vector.

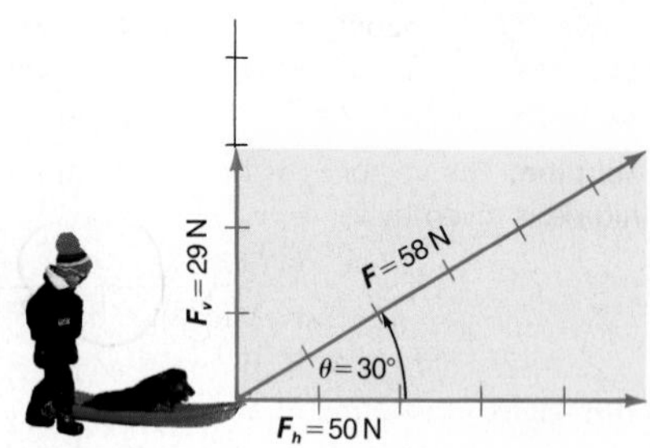

FIGURE 6–8. The force used to pull a sled can be resolved into its vertical and horizontal components.

The process of finding the magnitude of a component in a given direction is called **vector resolution**. Consider the sled being pulled in Figure 6–8. A 58-N force is exerted on a rope held at an angle of 30° with the horizontal. The rope pulls both forward and upward on the sled. The only force that pulls the sled forward is the horizontal component, F_h. The vertical component, F_v, pulls the sled upward.

Trigonometry can be used to find the magnitudes of perpendicular vector components.

The magnitudes of the horizontal and vertical components of F are found by first drawing a set of perpendicular axes, Figure 6–9. One axis is horizontal. The other axis is vertical. The vector that represents the force in the rope, F, is then drawn to scale at the proper angle. To resolve the rope force into the components F_v and F_h, draw perpendicular lines from each axis to the tip of the force vector. The magnitudes of the two components can then be measured using the scale used for F. Note that we can reverse the process, and show that the resultant of F_v and F_h is F, the original force.

STUDY GUIDE MASTER

Use the Study Guide master for section 6.2.

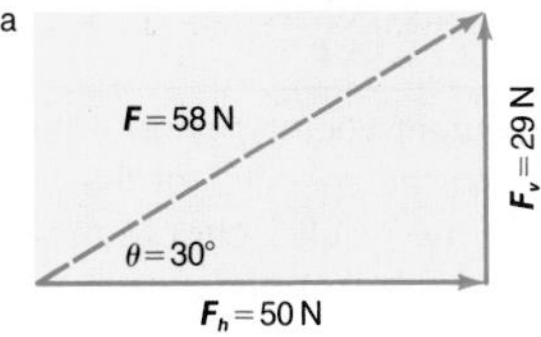

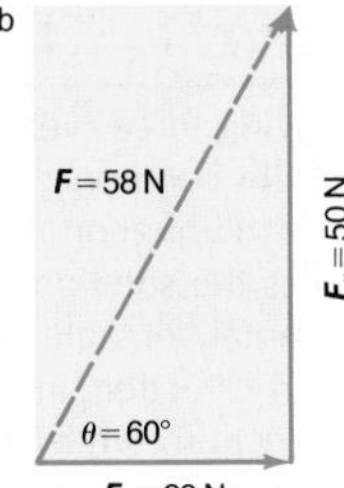

FIGURE 6–9. The magnitudes of horizontal and vertical components of a force depend on its direction.

In Figure 6–9, F_v and F_h are found using trigonometry. In this case,

$$\sin\theta = \frac{F_v}{F} \qquad \cos\theta = \frac{F_h}{F}$$

$$F_v = F\sin\theta \qquad F_h = F\cos\theta$$

The signs of F_v and F_h can be found from the vector diagram. If the value for either F_v or F_h is positive, then F_v acts upward and F_h acts to the right. If F_v is negative, it acts downward. A negative F_h acts to the left.

Suppose the person pulling the sled keeps the force constant but lowers the rope. The angle, θ, is decreased, and the horizontal component of the force is increased. The vertical component decreases. On the other hand, if the angle between the rope and the horizontal is increased, the horizontal component decreases, and the vertical component increases. Thus, the magnitude of the components change as the direction of the pulling force changes.

As the force becomes more nearly perpendicular to the direction of motion, the horizontal component approaches zero.

Physics and technology

SWAYING SKYSCRAPERS

The Sears Tower in Chicago rises 443 meters above the pavement. It is the tallest building in the world. There have been plans and models for taller buildings, to a height of more than 1.6 km. High-strength steel and concrete and new engineering designs make it possible to build tall buildings using lighter-weight structures. These less-massive buildings would be more vulnerable to wind buffeting than older buildings with heavy masonry and hundreds of steel columns.

High winds can cause upper floors of tall buildings to sway and elevators to jam. To counteract these effects, tuned mass dampers can be installed near the tops of buildings. Mass dampers may be huge blocks of concrete or large trays filled with lead. Using computer-controlled hydraulic systems, the dampers can be moved so that the resultant force of their motion dampens or reduces the motion of the building. The force exerted on the building by the damper is opposite to the motion of the building. Thus the swaying of the building is reduced.

• What factor would you measure in order to determine when a mass damper system should be put into motion?

Physics and technology

Restrained by large springs, mass dampers rest on a smooth layer of oil which reduces friction. When accelerometers detect any horizontal component over 0.003 g, a computer drives the motion of the block so that it moves in time with the building.

The building motion can be described by a sine wave, and the block is "tuned" to move 90 degrees out of phase with the building; that is, the block's sine wave starts one-fourth period after that of the building.

The hydraulic motors that accelerate the block exert forces in the opposite direction on the building. These forces reduce the swaying motion of the building. In another example, the installation of the mass damper in the Citicorp building was equivalent to adding four times the building's structural bracing. The damper has reduced the sway of the building by about 45%.

Teacher Resources: Ellis, William S. "Skyscrapers." *National Geographic.* February 1989, pages 143–173.
Gannon, Robert. "Buildings That Keep Their Balance." *Popular Science.* August 1985, pages 58–62.
Stewart, Doug. "Skyscraping." *Discover.* September 1988, pages 46–56.

CONCEPT DEVELOPMENT

Have someone whose job or hobby involves navigation (pilot, surveyor, sailor, well driller, gun sighter, hiker) make a presentation about the use of vectors in his or her profession or hobby.

Guided Practice: After going over the Example Problem, have students try the first Practice Problem on page 118.

Independent Practice: Assign the remaining Practice Problems on this page for homework and spend some time discussing them the next day.

Answers To

PRACTICE PROBLEMS

Have students refer to Appendix A of the Solutions Appendix for complete solutions to Practice Problems.

11. 38 N
12. a. 270 km/h; **b.** −450 km/h
13. a. 36 N; **b.** 55 N; **c.** 62 N
14. 8.43 km, east; 12.0 km, south

Assessment

Portfolio

Have students interested in rock climbing sketch or collect pictures of rock climbing equipment. Have the students write a report on rock climbing in which they discuss the forces exerted by the ropes, as well as the horizontal and vertical forces exerted by the rocks. What techniques does the climber use to obtain secure upward forces from the rocks? [Press hard against the rock to create a large normal force, therefore a larger frictional force, or use hooks or ropes attached to protrusions so as not to rely on friction.]

The choice of axes does not affect the final solution of a problem.

PROBLEM SOLVING STRATEGY

In resolving force, velocity, or displacement vectors, choose the direction of the component axes according to the specifics of the problem. Since the choice of axes will not affect the results, choose the set that simplifies the solution. Quite often you will want one axis to represent a horizontal, or right-left direction, and the second axis a vertical, or up-down direction. In other problems, one component is in the east-west direction, while the other is in the north-south direction. Be sure to specify the positive direction for each axis.

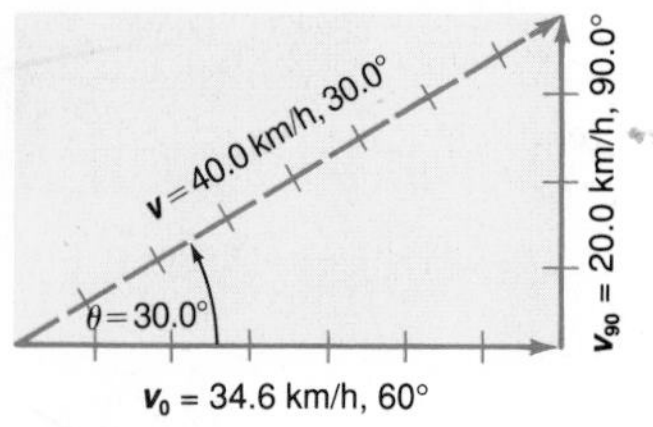

FIGURE 6–10. Use with the Example Problem.

Example Problem

Resolving a Velocity Vector Into Its Components

A wind with a velocity of 40.0 km/h blows toward 30.0°, Figure 6–10.

a. What is the component of the wind's velocity toward 90°?
b. What is the component of the wind's velocity toward 0°?

Given: v = 40.0 km/h, 30.0° **Unknowns:** v_{90}, v_0

Solution:

Toward 0° and 90° are positive. Angles are measured from 0°. To find the component toward 90°, v_{90}, use the relation

$$\sin 30° = \frac{v_{90}}{v}.$$

Then, $v_{90} = v(\sin 30.0°)$
$= (40.0 \text{ km/h})(0.500)$
$v_{90} = 20.0$ km/h at 90.0°.

To find the component from 0°, v_0, use the relation

$$\cos 30° = \frac{v_0}{v}.$$

Then, $v_0 = v(\cos 30°)$
$= (40.0 \text{ km/h})(0.866)$
$v_0 = 34.6$ km/h at 0.0°.

Practice Problems

11. A heavy box is pulled across a wooden floor with a rope. The rope makes an angle of 60° with the floor. A force of 75 N is exerted on the rope. What is the component of the force parallel to the floor?

12. An airplane flies toward 149° at 525 km/h. What is the component of the plane's velocity
a. toward 90°? **b.** toward 180°?

13. A student exerts a force of 72 N along the handle of a lawn mower to push it across the lawn. Find the horizontal component of this force when the handle is held at an angle with the lawn of
a. 60.0°. **b.** 40.0°. **c.** 30.0°.

▶ **14.** A hiker walks 14.7 km at an angle of 305° from east. Find the east-west and north-south components of this walk.

TEACHER F.Y.I.

Vector comes from the Latin word that means "to carry." In biology, a vector is an agent capable of carrying a pathogen from one organism to another.

Adding Vectors at Any Angle

Vector resolution can also be used to add two or more vectors that are not perpendicular to each other. First, each vector is resolved into its perpendicular components. Then the vertical components of all the vectors are added together to produce a single vector that acts in the vertical direction. Next, all of the horizontal components of the vectors are added together to produce a single horizontal vector. The resulting vertical and horizontal components can be added together to obtain the final resultant.

If two vectors are acting at angles other than 90° another way to determine the resultant mathematically is by using the law of cosines and the law of sines. These are discussed in Appendix E.

FIGURE 6–11. The resultant force on the log can be determined by adding the vertical and horizontal components of the rope forces.

Example Problem

Adding Non-Perpendicular Vectors

Two ropes are pulling on a log as shown in Figure 6–11. What is the net force on the log?

Given: $F_1 = 12.0$ N at 10.0°
$F_2 = 8.0$ N at 120°

Unknown: F_{net}

Basic equations: $F_x = F\cos\theta$
$F_y = F\sin\theta$
$F_{net}^2 = F_{net\ x}^2 + F_{net\ y}^2$

Solution:

Find the perpendicular components of each force, Figure 6–12.

$$F_{1x} = (12.0\text{ N})\cos 10.0° = 11.8\text{ N}$$
$$F_{1y} = (12.0\text{ N})\sin 10.0° = 2.0\text{ N}$$
$$F_{2x} = (8.0\text{ N})\cos 120.0° = -4.0\text{ N}$$
$$F_{2y} = (8.0\text{ N})\sin 120.0° = 6.9\text{ N}$$

Sum x and y components.

$$F_{net\ x} = F_{1x} + F_{2x} = 11.8\text{ N} + (-4.0\text{ N}) = 7.8\text{ N}$$
$$F_{net\ y} = F_{1y} + F_{2y} = 2.0\text{ N} + 6.9\text{ N} = 8.9\text{ N}$$

Find the magnitude of the net force.

$$F_{net} = \sqrt{F_x^2 + F_y^2} = \sqrt{(7.8\text{ N})^2 + (8.9\text{ N})^2} = 11\text{ N}$$

Find the angle of the force.

$$\tan\theta = \frac{F_y}{F_x} = \frac{8.9\text{ N}}{7.8\text{ N}} = 1.14$$
$$\theta = 49°$$

Non-perpendicular vectors can be added by resolving each into its vertical and horizontal components and summing them.

FIGURE 6–12. The forces on the log (a) are resolved into their horizontal and vertical components (b) (c) (d).

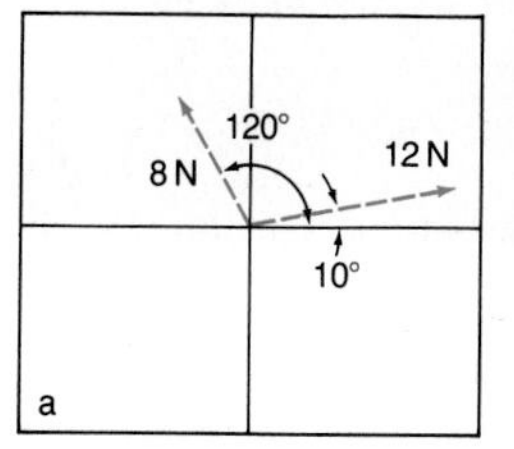

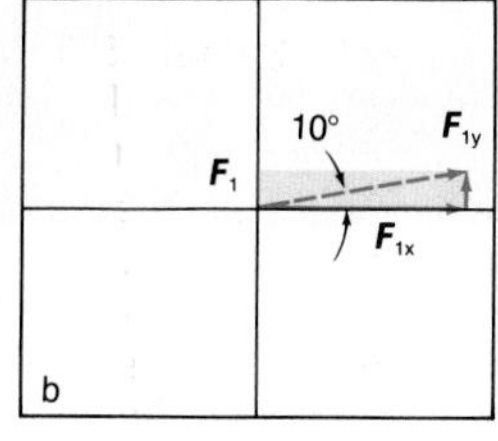

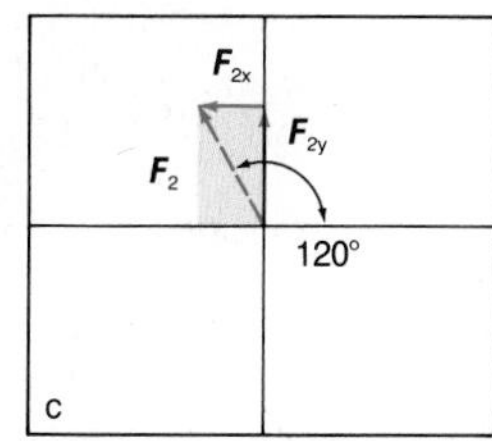

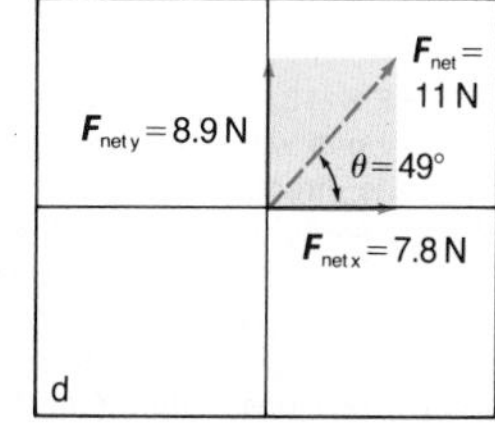

CONCEPT DEVELOPMENT

- You may find the trigonometry teacher in your school to be a great resource for this section. If you need more problems or have gifted students who need more of a challenge, that teacher should have materials. In addition, collaboration between the two of you would give the trig teacher applications for vectors (discussion of your labs) for students who are concurrently enrolled.
- Vector resolution is preferred over the law of cosines because any number of vectors can be solved simultaneously.
- Students must master vector resolution before going on; it will be used throughout this text for solving force and motion diagrams, electric and magnetic fields, etc.

ACTIVITY

Critical Thinking Master, Teacher Resource Package. Use the Critical Thinking Master, Measuring Height Indirectly, for further investigation of the application of geometry to vector addition.

CHECKING FOR UNDERSTANDING

Have students respond in class to the Concept Review questions.

RETEACHING

Transparency Package. Reteach non-perpendicular vector analysis using Transparency 7 and accompanying worksheet.

INDEPENDENT PRACTICE/ EXTENSION

Refer to the Assignment Guide below for additional questions and problems for independent practice.

CRITICAL THINKING

Use the Critical Thinking master for Chapter 6 with this section.

Answers To
PRACTICE PROBLEMS

Have students refer to Appendix A of the Solutions Appendix for complete solutions to Practice Problems.

15. 22.5 N, 337.3°
16. 27.1 N, 125°

3 Close

CONVERGENT QUESTION

Have students verbally summarize the process of vector addition. Make sure they emphasize the importance of direction.

CONCEPT REVIEW ANSWERS

2.1 $F_{TOT}^2 = F_J^2 + F_B^2$, so

$$F_B = \sqrt{F_{TOT}^2 - F_J^2} = \sqrt{(13\text{ N})^2 - (12\text{ N})^2} = 5\text{ N}.$$

2.2 equal, if the one component is zero: never shorter

2.3 East-West component is positive for vectors having angle θ such that $-90° < \theta < 90°$; negative for $90° < \theta < 270°$.

2.4 Critical Thinking: You would make the component of your velocity that is parallel to the river equal and opposite to the velocity of the river.

Preparation

OBJECTIVES

The objectives are listed on the student page. Remind students to preview these objectives as a study guide to this major section.

OVERVIEW

For force vectors, one of the most important applications is how to achieve static balance—that is, equilibrium. Whether designing a bridge, building, or highway, equilibrium is vital.

BRIDGING

Equilibrium is a force situation covered by Newton's second law. To properly understand the equilibrium of three forces, students must understand how to add up two forces.

F.Y.I.

Although Oliver Heaviside was greatly respected by scientists of his day, he is almost forgotten today. Unfortunately, his methods, such as the use of vectors to describe forces, were so successful that they were simply written into texts describing other people's work, without crediting Heaviside.

Practice Problems

15. Find the resultant force on the log in the last Example Problem if F_1 remains the same and F_2 is changed to 14.0 N at 310.0°.

▶ **16.** Three people are pulling on a tree. The first person pulls with 15 N at 65.0°; the second with 16 N at 135°; the third with 11 N at 195°. What is the magnitude and direction of the resultant force on the tree?

CONCEPT REVIEW

2.1 Joanne pulls on a trunk with a 12-N force. Bev pulls at right angles to Joanne. How hard must Bev pull to make the resultant force on the trunk 13 N?

2.2 Could you ever have a resultant vector shorter than one of its components? equal to a component? Explain.

2.3 You have chosen axes with east and north positive. Angles are measured from the east axis. For what range of angles is the east-west component of a vector positive? For which angles is the east-west component of a vector negative?

2.4 **Critical Thinking:** You are piloting a boat that crosses a fast-moving river. You want to reach a pier directly across from your starting point. Describe how you would select your heading in terms of the components of your velocity.

Objectives

- **state the requirements for equilibrium.**
- **state the meaning of equilibrant, differentiating between resultant and equilibrant.**
- **specify the proper method of resolving vectors into perpendicular components; be able to choose axes and resolve vectors graphically and analytically.**
- **be able to specify axes, resolve vectors, and solve inclined plane problems.**

6.3 APPLICATIONS OF VECTORS

Forces and accelerations are vector quantities, so it seems natural to think of Newton's laws in terms of vector equations. Newton, however, never used vectors. It was not until almost two hundred years later, in the 1880s, that Sir Oliver Heaviside, a British electrician, convinced sceptical physicists that Newton's laws were best understood using vectors. We can use the techniques for adding and resolving vectors to analyze the acceleration of objects that have several forces exerted on them.

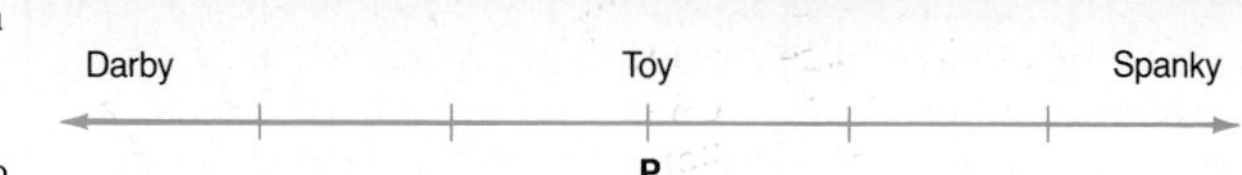

FIGURE 6–13. When Darby and Spanky pull with equal force in opposite directions, the forces on the toy are in equilibrium, and the toy does not move. The resultant force is zero (a). Two equal forces exerted in opposite directions on the toy produce equilibrium (b).

Multicultural Connections

Eskimos use equilibrant forces to build igloos. An igloo is a dome-shaped structure built of blocks of ice shaped to redirect the force of gravity. As gravity pulls the blocks closer together, each block pushes against the blocks on either side, above, and below it. This means that there are forces pushing against each block from the blocks around it. The top, center block is the most important one. Until it is in place, the top row of blocks will move because the forces exerted by the other blocks are smaller in total than the force of gravity. However, once the top block is inserted, all the blocks in the igloo will stay in place because the sum of the upward forces on each block equals the downward force of gravity on that block.

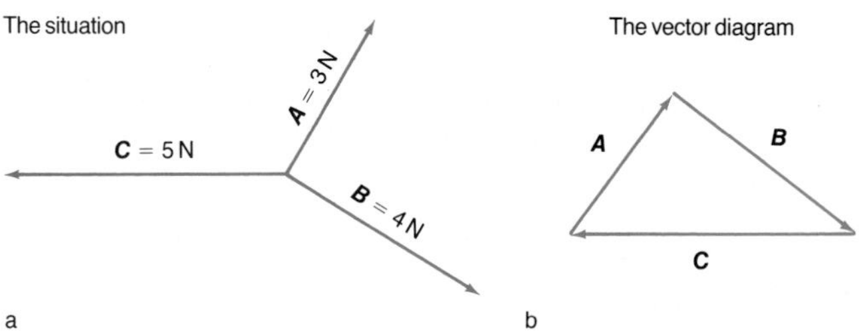

FIGURE 6–14. Forces in equilibrium give a resultant force of zero.

Equilibrium

When the net force—the net sum of all the forces acting—is zero, the object is in **equilibrium**. According to Newton's laws, the object will not be accelerated because there is no net force on it. A simple example of equilibrium is the case in which two equal forces act in opposite directions on an object, as shown in Figure 6–13. The resultant force is zero.

Equilibrium occurs when the net force acting on a point is zero.

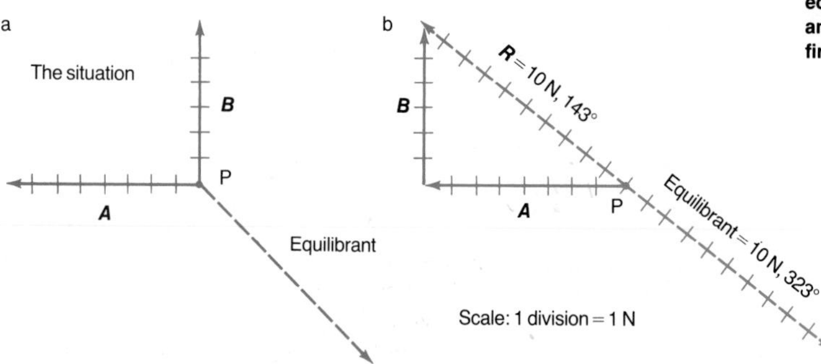

FIGURE 6–15. To determine the equilibrant of two forces acting at an angle of 90° with each other, first find the resultant of the two forces.

Figure 6–14a shows an object at point **P** with three forces acting on it. The 3-N force and the 4-N force are at right angles to each other. When the three vectors are added head-to-tail, they form a closed triangle, as in Figure 6–14b. The distance from the tail of the first vector to the head of the last vector is then zero, so the length of the resultant is zero. The length of the resultant is zero, so the vector sum is zero. Therefore, the three forces produce zero net force on point **P.** The object at point **P** is in equilibrium.

When the vector sum of forces acting at one point is not zero, a force can be applied that will produce equilibrium. This force is called the **equilibrant** (ee KWIL uh bruhnt) **force**. The equilibrant force is the single additional force that, if applied at the same point as the other forces, will produce equilibrium.

To find the equilibrant of two or more forces, first find the resultant force. The equilibrant force is equal in magnitude to the resultant, but opposite in direction. In Figure 6–15, the equilibrant force is a 10-N force whose direction is opposite to the direction of the resultant.

POCKET LAB

FORCE VECTORS I

Choose two of the largest students in your class to pull on the opposite ends of a strong 10 m long rope. Does the rope appear to be straight? Now have the smallest student attempt to push down on the middle of the rope with one finger. Is it possible for the students to keep the rope taut and straight? Explain.

6:2 ASSIGNMENT GUIDE

	PRACTICE	EXTENSION
CHAPTER REVIEW pp. 127–131		
· Reviewing Concepts	7	
· Applying Concepts		6–8, 11
· Problems*	8, 9, 11, 13–19, 21, 22, 25–27	10, 12, 20, 23, 24, 28
APPENDIX B PROBLEMS*		
· Chapter 6, pp. 691–692	1–3, 8, 9, 11–14, 16	10, 15, 17

* Complete solutions to all Chapter Review and Appendix problems appear in the Problems and Solutions Manual.

TRANSPARENCY

Use Transparency 7 with this section.

STUDY GUIDE MASTER

Use the Study Guide master for section 6.3.

1 Focus

A ball carrier and a tackler have collided and are still moving toward the goal line. How does a second tackler decide how to stop this motion? That is, what kind of information does the second tackler use to produce equilibrium?

2 Teach

CONCEPT DEVELOPMENT

- *Only* so-called translational motion is being discussed here. That is, motion where the whole object moves from one place to another place. We're simplifying these objects by considering them to be points.
- No net force on an object does not necessarily mean that the object will not be moving. An object experiencing no net force will have a constant velocity, which may or may not be zero.

Study Guide Master. To reinforce the concepts in this section, have the students complete the Study Guide Master for Section 6.3 from the Teacher Resource Package.

POCKET LAB

FORCE VECTORS I

Purpose: to compare forces represented by perpendicular and nonperpendicular vectors.
Material: 10-m rope.
Outcome: Most students will agree that the rope is straight, although a few may notice that it really isn't. The small student can easily push down on the rope. The large students are pulling horizontally and cannot provide enough upward force to balance the small downward force.

CONCEPT DEVELOPMENT

In trying to find an equilibrant, students will often just get the resultant of the two vectors and call the resultant the equilibrant. Remind them that the equilibrant is a vector of the same magnitude but opposite direction compared to the resultant.

POCKET LAB

FORCE VECTORS II

Purpose: to demonstrate nonperpendicular components of vectors.
Materials: 1-m cord; 1-kg mass.
Outcome: When the hands are pulled together each hand exerts an upward force of 4.9 N. As the hands are moved apart, the force increases because only the vertical component of the string force contributes to lifting the mass. It is not possible to pull hard enough to make the cord perfectly straight. The hands must exert an upward force to balance the downward force of 9.8 N.

CHECKING FOR UNDERSTANDING

Review the Example Problem in class, and draw a diagram on the board. Ask students to explain in their own words why the two ropes can never be totally horizontal.

RETEACHING

Demonstrate to students how three vectors producing equilibrium form a closed triangle when they are added. Then explain that obtaining the equilibrant this way (by determining the third side of the force vector triangle) produces the same equilibrant as the method of first finding the resultant and then drawing the opposite of the resultant.

EXTENSION

Enrichment Master. With this section, assign the Enrichment Master for Chapter 6, Coefficient of Friction, from the Teacher Resource Package.

A Weighty Subject

Sometimes the equilibrant is exerted by two or more forces. For example, in the chapter-opening photo, the upward force that balances the weight of the performer is provided by the cable. The force exerted by the two ends of the cable can be found by following the method in the example below.

FIGURE 6–16. Use with the Example Problem.

Example Problem

Finding Forces When Components Are Known

A sign that weighs 168 N is supported by ropes *a* and *b*, Figure 6–16, that make 22.5° angles with the horizontal. The sign is not moving. What forces do the ropes exert on the sign?

Given: The sign is in equilibrium.
weight of sign, W = 168 N (down)
angles ropes make with horizontal, 22.5°

Unknowns: forces of rope *a*, A
forces of rope *b*, B

Basic equations: In equilibrium, net force is zero,

$$A + B + W = 0.$$

For any force, F

$$F_h = F\cos\theta,\ F_v = F\sin\theta.$$

Solution:

Choose a coordinate system with horizontal and vertical axes. The direction of W is down, so the direction of $A + B$ is up.

The sum $A + B$ has no horizontal components, so the horizontal components of A and B, A_h and B_h, have equal magnitudes.

Now, $A_h = A\cos 22.5°$ and $B_h = B\cos 22.5°$.

Since $A_h = B_h$, the magnitudes of A and B must be equal.

The magnitude of the sum of the vertical components of A and B equals the magnitude of the weight of the sign, 168 N. That is,

$$A_v + B_v = 168\text{ N}.$$

Since $A_v = A\sin 22.5°$ and $B_v = B\sin 22.5°$ and $A = B$,

$$A_v = B_v.$$

Thus, $$A_v = B_v = 1/2(168\text{ N}) = 84\text{ N}$$

and $$A = \frac{A_v}{\sin 22.5°} = 220\text{ N}$$

$$B = A = 220\text{ N}$$

The force in each rope is larger than the weight of the sign. Try different angles. As the angle between the ropes and the horizontal increases, the horizontal components of the forces become smaller. When the ropes are vertical, the horizontal components are zero, and each rope exerts only half the weight of the sign, 84 N. Note that since the forces exerted by the ropes must always have vertical components adding to 168 N, the ropes can never be totally horizontal.

POCKET LAB

FORCE VECTORS II

Tie two loops in the ends of a strong cord that is about 1 m long. Hold a loop in each hand as a classmate carefully hangs a 1-kg mass on the string. Start with your hands together and slowly move your hands apart. Try to make the cord straight. Is it possible? How are the forces acting?

Assessment

Critical Thinking

While ropes can support only forces that pull (tension), wood and metal can also support pushing (compressive) forces. Extend the results of the Pocket Lab to the forces exerted when a person stands on the top of a ladder. He or she exerts a downward force (weight) on the top. What are the magnitude and direction of the forces exerted by each leg on the ground? Are there other forces exerted by parts of the ladder? [Assume each leg makes an angle θ with the vertical. The force exerted by each leg is 1/2 $W/\cos\theta$ along the direction of the leg. The brace that keeps the legs from spreading exerts an inward force 1/2 $W/\sin\theta$ on each leg.]

Practice Problems

17. A net force of 55 N acts due west on an object. What added single force on the object produces equilibrium?
18. Two forces act on an object. One force is 6.0 N horizontally. The second force is 8.0 N vertically.
    a. Find the magnitude and direction of the resultant.
    b. If the object is in equilibrium, find the magnitude and direction of the force that produces equilibrium.
19. A 62-N force acts at 30.0° and a second 62-N force acts at 60.0°.
    a. Determine the resultant force.
    b. What is the magnitude and direction of the force that produces equilibrium?
20. Two forces act on an object. A 36-N force acts at 225°. A 48-N force acts at 315°. What would be the magnitude and direction of their equilibrant?
21. The sign in the last Example Problem is now hung by ropes that each make an angle of 42° with the horizontal. What force does each rope exert?
22. ▶ The people who hung the sign decided to raise it higher by pulling the two ropes more horizontal. They increase the force on each rope to 575 N and keep the angles equal. What angle does each rope make with the horizontal now?

FINE ARTS CONNECTION

Vectors have direction.

Gravitational Force and Inclined Planes

The gravitational force acting on an object is directed toward the center of Earth. The object's weight, *W*, can be represented by a vector directed down. *Down* is the direction an object falls.

Figure 6–17 shows a trunk resting on an inclined plane. To analyze the forces acting on the trunk, the weight of the trunk, *W*, is resolved into two components perpendicular to each other. When doing inclined plane problems, we may choose one axis along the incline, and the second axis perpendicular to it. Thus, we have one component, $F_{\parallel}$, the parallel force, that acts parallel to the incline. The second component, $F_{\perp}$, called the perpendicular force, acts perpendicular to the incline.

When solving inclined problems, it is convenient to choose a set of axes perpendicular and parallel to the plane.

FIGURE 6–17. Using an inclined plane does not require less work, but often makes a job easier.

CONCEPT DEVELOPMENT

Critical Thinking: What motion situation would a closed triangle of three velocity vectors indicate? How about three acceleration vectors?

Guided Practice: After reviewing the Example Problem on page 122, have students work on the first two Practice Problems. Review their answers in class.

Independent Practice: After going over Practice Problems 17 and 18 in class, assign the remaining Problems (19–22) for homework.

Answers To
PRACTICE PROBLEMS

Have students refer to Appendix A of the Solutions Appendix for complete solutions to Practice Problems.

17. 55 N, due east
18. **a.** 10.0 N, 53°; **b.** 10.0 N, 223°
19. **a.** 120 N, 45°; **b.** 120 N, 225°
20. 60 N, 99°
21. 126 N
22. 8.4°

ENRICHMENT MASTER

Use the Enrichment master for Chapter 6 with this section.

CONCEPT DEVELOPMENT

It sometimes helps to use a "pick up and move" method to teach inclined planes. Use colored bits of transparent plastic for vectors (colored presentation folders are an inexpensive alternative) and cut out vectors. Draw the inclined plane problem on the overhead and use these vectors to produce the vector diagram as in Figure 6–18. Pick up the component down plane $F_{\parallel}$ and place it head-to-tail for the other two. Students will then see the right triangle produced, as well as the value of the angle.

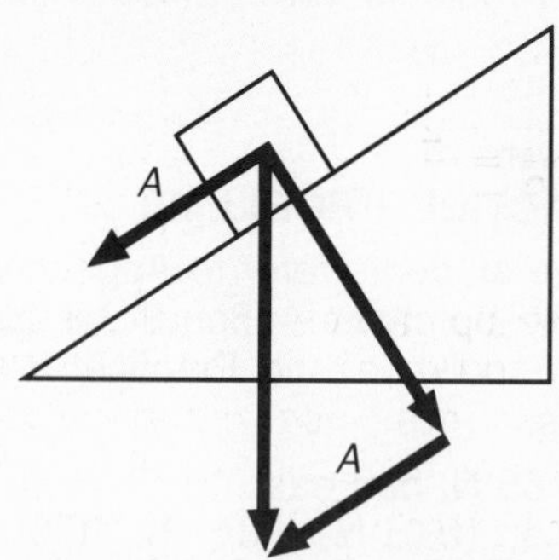

Enrichment: Discuss static friction with students. As theta increases for a plane, the object will eventually begin to slide as the down-the-plane component overcomes the frictional force. The angle at which the slide begins is:

$$\tan \theta = F_f/F_N = \mu \text{ static.}$$

It is then relatively simple to determine the coefficient of static friction using an inclined plane.

Connect to BIOLOGY

The human body provides many good illustrations of the vector nature of forces. Ask a student volunteer to hang from a chinning bar with hands directly above shoulders. Each hand now supplies an upward force of half the student's weight. Next, have the student spread his or her hands as far apart as comfortable. It should soon be obvious that the arms have larger forces on them. If the student's weight is W, how large are these forces? [Use the analysis on page 125 of the TWE to show that 1/2 $W \cos \theta/2$ gives the force exerted by each arm T, where θ is the angle between the arms.]

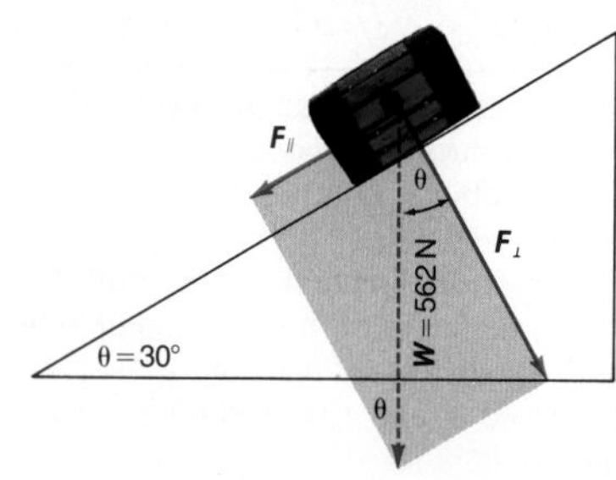

FIGURE 6–18. The weight vector *W* is resolved into two components. One component acts parallel to the plane. The other acts perpendicular to the plane.

Look at the right triangle formed by the surface of the incline and its horizontal and vertical sides. It is similar to the right triangle formed by W, $F_{\perp}$, and $F_{\parallel}$ because the corresponding sides are mutually perpendicular. Therefore the angles are equal. If θ and W are both known, a vector diagram similar to Figure 6–18 can be drawn, and the force W resolved into the components $F_{\parallel}$ and $F_{\perp}$. You can calculate the values of $F_{\parallel}$ and $F_{\perp}$ using either graphical or trigonometric methods.

Example Problem

Finding $F_{\perp}$ and $F_{\parallel}$

A trunk weighing 562 N is resting on a plane inclined at 30° from the horizontal, Figure 6–18. Find the components of the weight parallel and perpendicular to the plane.

Given: weight, $W = 562$ N
plane angle with respect to horizontal, $\theta = 30.0°$

Unknowns: perpendicular component, $F_{\perp}$; parallel component, $F_{\parallel}$

Solution:

Resolve weight into components perpendicular and parallel to plane.

$$\sin \theta = \frac{F_{\parallel}}{W}; \text{ so, } F_{\parallel} = W \sin \theta. \qquad \cos \theta = \frac{F_{\perp}}{W}; \text{ so, } F_{\perp} = W \cos \theta.$$

$$F_{\parallel} = +(562 \text{ N})(\sin 30.0°) = +(562 \text{ N})(0.500) = +281 \text{ N}$$

$$F_{\perp} = +(562 \text{ N})(\cos 30.0°) = +(562 \text{ N})(0.866) = +487 \text{ N}$$

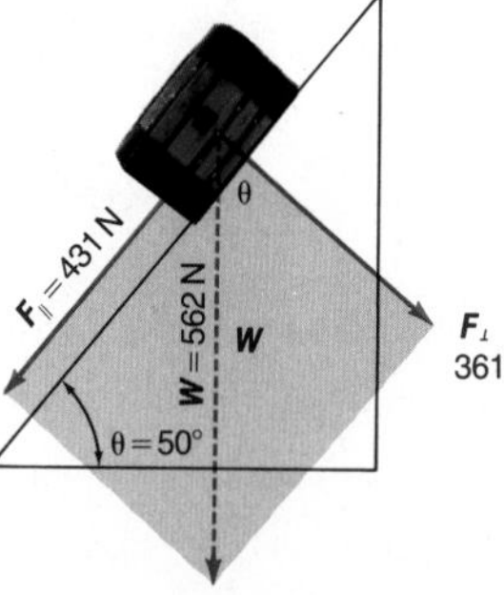

FIGURE 6–19. As the angle of the incline increases, the component of the weight acting parallel to the plane increases. The component that acts perpendicular to the plane decreases.

The directions of the two components are shown on Figure 6–18. Note that as the incline in Figure 6–19 becomes steeper, $F_{\parallel}$ becomes greater and $F_{\perp}$ becomes smaller.

What other forces act on the trunk besides the force of gravity? The inclined plane exerts an upward force perpendicular to its surface, the normal force, F_N. Since the trunk has no acceleration perpendicular to the plane, all forces in that direction must be balanced. Therefore,

$$F_N + F_{\perp} = 0$$
$$F_N - W \cos \theta = 0$$
$$F_N = W \cos \theta.$$

If there is no friction between the trunk and the plane, the only force on the trunk along the plane is the parallel component of its weight, $F_{\parallel} = W \sin \theta$. According to Newton's second law, the acceleration,

$$a = \frac{F}{m} = \frac{W \sin \theta}{m}.$$

But, $W/m = g$, so the acceleration of the trunk is $a = g \sin \theta$. As the plane becomes more horizontal, the acceleration approaches zero. When the plane is tilted more vertically, the acceleration approaches closer to $g = 9.80 \text{ m/s}^2$.

Example Problem

Finding Acceleration Down a Plane

The 562-N trunk is on a frictionless plane inclined at 30.0° from the horizontal. Find the acceleration of the trunk. What is its direction?

Given: weight of trunk, $W = 562$ N; angle of plane, $\theta = 30.0°$

Unknown: acceleration down the plane, a

Basic equations: $F = ma$; $W = mg$; $F_{\parallel} = +W \sin \theta$

Solution:

Find net force on trunk.

$F_{\parallel} = +W \sin \theta = +mg \sin \theta$

Find acceleration.

$$a = \frac{F}{m} = \frac{+W \sin \theta}{m} = +g \sin \theta$$

$$= +(9.80 \text{ m/s}^2)(0.500)$$

$$a = +4.90 \text{ m/s}^2$$

The acceleration is down the plane.

Usually there is friction between the inclined plane and the object on it. The resolution of weight on an inclined plane can be used to measure the force of friction or the coefficient of static friction between the two surfaces. Put a coin on one of your textbooks. Now slowly lift the cover. The coin will remain at rest until the cover reaches a certain angle. Then the coin begins to accelerate down the book.

The downward force along the cover is the parallel component of the coin's weight, proportional to sin θ. As the cover angle is increased, the parallel component of the weight increases. It is balanced by the static friction force. Static friction can never be larger than μF_N, so when the force along the cover exceeds the frictional force, the coin starts to move. Once the coin starts to move, static friction is replaced by sliding friction, which is a smaller force. The coin, with a non-zero net force on it, accelerates down the book. If you measure the angle of the cover when the coin first begins to move, you can determine the coefficient of static friction. Try different objects and books. Which combination has the greatest coefficient of static friction? the least?

HELP WANTED

SURVEYOR

If you love the kind of precision work that is normally found only in a lab but are also lured by the great outdoors, our firm has the perfect position for you. Not everyone has the knack for visualizing three dimensionally and expressing it two dimensionally. That skill, along with good eyesight, physical fitness, and some job-site mobility, are musts for success as a surveyor. A solid educational background including 1 to 4 years of college, extensive on-the-job training, and licensure are also required. Opportunity for advancement to supervisory positions is excellent. For information contact:
American Congress on Surveying and Mapping, 210 Little Falls Street, Falls Church, VA 22046

FIGURE 6–20. By reducing friction between the slide and the slider, water adds excitement to a water slide.

CONCEPT DEVELOPMENT

When an object hangs from the middle of a string, there is a simple formula for finding the tension in the string. The formula is

$$T = \frac{W}{2 \cos \theta/2}.$$

This formula is derived as follows:

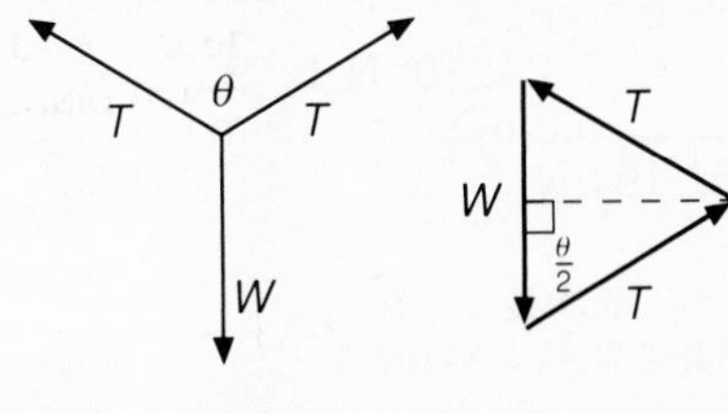

$$\cos \frac{\theta}{2} = \frac{\frac{W}{2}}{T} \qquad T = \frac{W}{2 \cos \frac{\theta}{2}}$$

As θ approaches 180°, the tension goes to infinity. Another interesting derivation is to show that the coefficient of friction is equal to tan θ where θ is the angle at which an object slides down a plane at constant speed. The derivation is as follows:

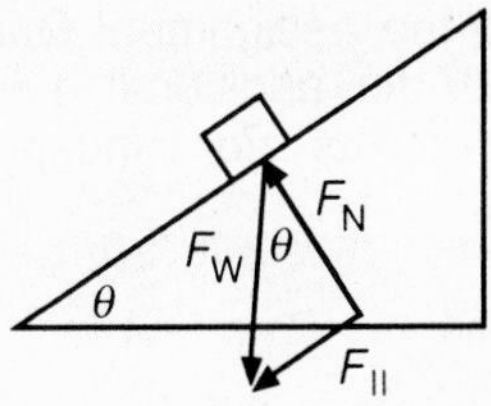

$F_N = F_W \cos \theta \qquad F_{\parallel} = F_W \sin \theta$

If block slides at a constant speed, $F_{\parallel} = F_f$.

$$\mu = \frac{F_f}{F_N} = \frac{F_W \sin \theta}{F_W \cos \theta}$$

$$\mu = \tan \theta$$

Point out that physical conditions dictate the directions of the components. Component forces are the result of real agents: ropes, planes, gravity, friction, and so on.

Note that in Chapter 5, F_N was equal to the weight, but here on the incline it is only related to weight by $F_N = W \cos \theta$.

Guided Practice: Discuss the Example Problems on pages 124, 125, and 126. Have students try the first Practice Problem on page 126 in class.

Independent Practice: Assign the remaining Practice Problems (24–26) for homework and spend time discussing them the next day.

Answers To

PRACTICE PROBLEMS

Have students refer to Appendix A of the Solutions Appendix for complete solutions to Practice Problems.

23. a. 229 N, 513 N; **b.** Perpendicular force is less and parallel force is greater on the 66° incline.

24. a. 7.1×10^3 N; **b.** 9.7×10^3 N

25. a. 5.8 m/s^2; **b.** 19 m/s; **c.** no

26. 191 N

CHECKING FOR UNDERSTANDING

Have students respond in class to the Concept Review questions on pages 126 and 127.

RETEACHING

Transparency Package. Reteach vector resolution with the help of your transparent vectors (see page 124) and Transparency 6.

INDEPENDENT PRACTICE/ EXTENSION

Refer to the Assignment Guide on page 127 for additional questions and problems for independent practice.

3 Close

CONVERGENT QUESTION

Why is so much time spent on the special case of vectors in balance? What is the wider importance of such situations?

Enrichment: Have students research the coefficient of friction for tires—old, new, racing, off-road, and so on. They could also find the coefficient of friction for tires on various road conditions.

CONCEPT REVIEW ANSWERS

3.1 The hill exerts the equilibrant force F_E.

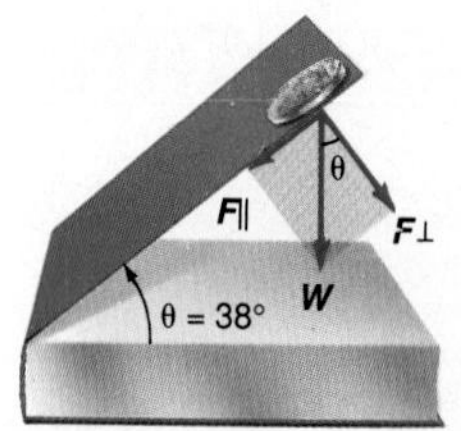

FIGURE 6–21. Use with Example Problem.

Example Problem

Finding the Coefficient of Static Friction

A coin placed on the cover of a book just begins to move when the cover makes an angle of 38° with the horizontal, Figure 6–21. What is the coefficient of static friction between the cover and coin?

Given: angle of inclined plane, $\theta = 38°$

Unknown: μ

Basic equations: maximum static friction,
$F_f = \mu F_N$
$F_\perp = W \cos \theta$
$F_\parallel = W \sin \theta$

Solution:

Because the coin stays on the book cover, the forces perpendicular to the cover are equal in magnitude.

$$F_N = F_\perp = W \cos \theta$$

As long as the coin is not moving, the forces parallel to the book cover are equal in magnitude.

$$F_f = F_\parallel = W \sin \theta$$

When motion is just ready to start, friction is at its maximum.

$$F_f = \mu F_N$$

Thus, $W \sin \theta = \mu W \cos \theta$.

This means that $\mu = \sin \theta / \cos \theta = \tan \theta$. In this case, $\mu = \tan 38° = 0.78$.

FIGURE 6–22. Use with Concept Review 3.1.

Practice Problems

23. The 562-N trunk is placed on an inclined plane that forms a 66° angle with the horizontal.
 a. Calculate the values of $F_\perp$ and $F_\parallel$.
 b. Compare your results with those given above for the same trunk on a 30° incline.

24. A car weighing 1.2×10^4 N is parked on a 36° slope.
 a. Find the force tending to cause the car to roll down the hill.
 b. What is the force the car exerts perpendicular to the hill?

25. The brakes in the car in Practice Problem 24 fail, and the car starts to roll down the hill. Assume there is no friction.
 a. What is the acceleration of the car?
 b. After it has moved 30 m, how fast is it moving?
 c. Could a sprinter run this fast?

▶ **26.** The roof on a house rises 1.00 m over a horizontal distance of 3.50 m. A 71.0-kg roofer stands on the roof. Is the frictional force that keeps the roofer from slipping equal in magnitude to $F_\perp$ or $F_\parallel$? What is its magnitude?

DEMONSTRATION

Purpose: to introduce the advanced concept, coefficient of friction.

Equipment: wooden block, friction board, spring scale

Procedure: 1. Push the block so that it begins to slide on the friction board. Raise the friction board until the component of the block's weight along the plane balances the frictional force, and the block slides down at a constant velocity. **2.** Using the weight of the block, you can calculate the force parallel to the plane and the force perpendicular to the plane with the spring scale.

Results: The force that is parallel equals the frictional force, and the force that is perpendicular equals the normal force. You can find the coefficient of friction between the block and the plane using $f = \mu F_N$.

CONCEPT REVIEW

3.1 Figure 6–22 shows the shoe of a hiker who is climbing a hill. The two components of the force the person exerts on the shoe are shown. On a copy of the figure, draw the equilibrant force on the shoe that keeps the shoe in equilibrium. What exerts that force?

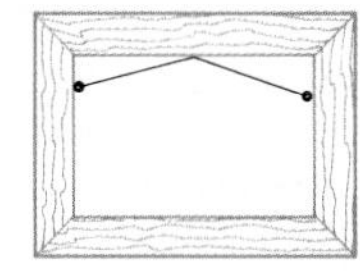
a

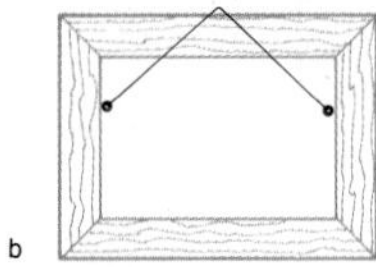
b

FIGURE 6–23. Use with Concept Review 3.2.

3.2 Your mother asks you to hang a heavy painting. The frame has a wire across the back, and you plan to hook this wire over a nail in the wall. The wire will break if the force pulling on it is too big. You don't want it to break. Should it look like the Figure 6–23a or 6–23b? Explain.

3.3 The snow under the skier in Figure 6–24 is so slippery that you can ignore friction. Copy the drawing and draw vectors showing the forces on the skier and the resultant force. Identify the cause of each force.

3.4 Critical Thinking: The skier in the problem above suddenly runs into rough snow. As a result of the force of the snow, the skier moves with constant velocity. Add a vector representing this force on your drawing.

FIGURE 6–24. Use with Concept Review 3.3, 3.4.

CHAPTER 6 REVIEW

SUMMARY

6.1 Graphical Method of Vector Addition

- The resultant is the sum of two or more vectors.
- To add two vectors graphically, place the tail of the second vector at the head of the first vector. Draw the resultant vector from the tail of the first vector to the head of the second vector.
- The resultant of several concurrent vectors can be found by the same procedures used for adding two vectors.
- Perpendicular components of vector quantities are independent of each other.

6.2 Analytical Method of Vector Addition

- Perpendicular vectors may be added analytically by using the Pythagorean relation and the definition of the tangent of an angle.
- A vector can be resolved into two perpendicular components.
- Vectors at any angles may be added by finding their components, adding all vertical and horizontal components separately, and then finding the resultant.

6.3 Applications of Vectors

- When no net force acts on an object, it is in equilibrium.
- The equilibrant is the single force that is equal in magnitude and opposite in direction to the resultant of several forces acting on a point. This produces equilibrium.
- The weight of an object on an inclined plane can be resolved into two perpendicular components. One component, $F_{\parallel}$, acts parallel to the plane; the other component, $F_{\perp}$, acts perpendicular to the plane.

3.2 Figure 6–18a; because $F = W/\sin\theta$, and θ is larger.

3.3 F_N is the normal force of the slope on the skier. F_W is the force of gravity on the skier, the skier's weight.

3.4 Critical Thinking: The friction force, F_f, is equal in magnitude but opposite in direction to the resultant force, F_R.

CLOSING CHAPTER 6

Review Summary statements and Key Terms with your students.

ASSESSMENT

Vocabulary Review Master, Teacher Resource Package. Use this master to check students' understanding of Key Terms.

Evaluation Masters. Use Parts A and B of the Chapter Evaluation Masters from the Teacher Resource Package to test qualitative chapter objectives. Use Parts C and D to test quantitative chapter objectives.

6:3 ASSIGNMENT GUIDE

	PRACTICE	EXTENSION
CHAPTER REVIEW pp. 127–131		
· Reviewing Concepts	8–12	
· Applying Concepts		9, 10, 12, 13
· Problems*	29–32, 34	33, 35–37
APPENDIX B PROBLEMS*		
· Chapter 6, pp. 692–693		18–22

* Complete solutions to all Chapter Review and Appendix problems appear in the Problems and Solutions Manual.

TRANSPARENCY

Use Transparency 6 with this section.

REVIEW MASTER

Use the Vocabulary Review master for Chapter 6 with this section.

EVALUATION MASTER

Use the Chapter Evaluation master for Chapter 6 with this section.

KEY TERMS

resultant	components
trigonometry	vector resolution
sine (sin)	equilibrium
cosine (cos)	equilibrant force
tangent (tan)	

REVIEWING CONCEPTS

1. What method is used to add vectors graphically?
2. A vector is to be added graphically to a second vector. Which of the following may you do to the first vector: move it, rotate it, or change its length?
3. In your own words, write a clear definition of the resultant of two or more vectors. Do not tell how to find it, but tell what it represents.
4. Does anything happen to the forces that produce the resultant force? Do the original forces disappear?
5. How is the resultant force affected when force vectors are added in a different order?
6. Why are vectors *A* and *B* in Figure 6–25 considered to represent different forces?

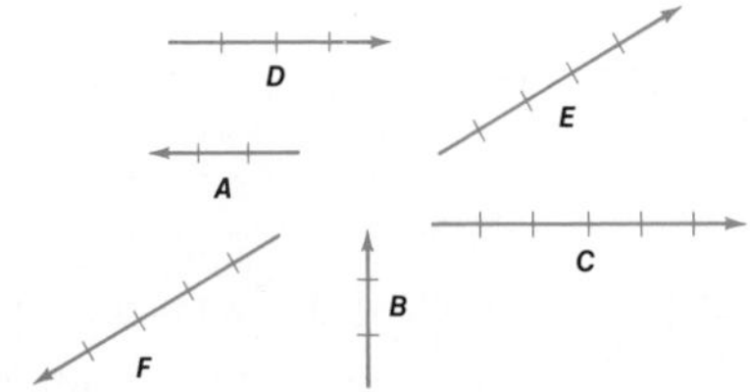

FIGURE 6–25. Use with Reviewing Concepts 6 and Problems 2, 5, 6.

7. We have often set up "vertical" and "horizontal" axes. How could you do this in the real world? How could you find the vertical when you are on a hill?
8. What is meant about the forces acting on a book if we state that the book is in a state of equilibrium?
9. How can the equilibrant of two or more forces be found?
10. Can an object in equilibrium be moving? Explain.
11. What is the sum of three vectors that form a triangle? Assuming that the vectors are forces, what does this imply about the object on which the forces act?
12. A book is on an inclined plane.
    a. Describe two convenient components of the weight of the book.
    b. How are the magnitudes of these components related to the angle of the incline?

APPLYING CONCEPTS

1. A vector drawn 15 mm long represents a velocity of 30 m/s. How long should you draw a vector to represent a velocity of 20 m/s?
2. If a vector that is 1 cm long represents a force of 5 N, how many newtons does a vector 3 cm long, drawn to the same scale, represent?
3. What is the largest possible resultant force of two forces with magnitudes of 3 N and 4 N? What is the smallest possible resultant? Draw a sketch to demonstrate your answers.
4. Two dogs pull on a toy. One pulls with a force of 10 N, the other with a force of 15 N.
    a. In what relative directions can the dogs act to give the toy the smallest acceleration?
    b. Can they ever result in zero acceleration?
5. Two vectors are originally parallel. How does the resultant vector change as the angle between the two vectors increases to 180°?
6. A right triangle has two sides *A* and *B*. If $\tan \theta = A/B$,
    a. which side of the triangle is longer if $\tan \theta$ is greater than one?
    b. which side of the triangle is longer if $\tan \theta$ is less than one?
    c. what does it mean if $\tan \theta$ equals one?
7. Gayle is pushing a lawn spreader across her lawn. Can she increase the horizontal component of the force without changing the force that she is applying to the spreader handle? Explain.
8. The transmitting tower of a TV station is held upright by guy wires that extend from the top of the tower to the ground. The wires make a 30.0° angle with the tower. The force along the guy wires can be resolved into two perpendicular components. Which one is larger?
9. What is the net force that acts on an object when it is in equilibrium?
10. When stretching a clothesline or a strand of wire between two posts, it is relatively easy to pull one end of the line hard enough to remove most of the slack. However, it is almost always necessary to resort to some mechani-

Answers To
REVIEWING CONCEPTS

1. Vectors are added head to tail. The resultant is drawn from the tail of the first vector to the head of the last vector. The head of the resultant vector coincides with the head of the last vector added.

2. You may move it, but you cannot rotate it or change its length.

3. The resultant is a single vector that can replace two or more vectors. It has the same effect as the sum of the original vectors.

4. No. They are still there. The object acts as if just one force, the resultant force, is acting on it.

5. It is not affected since vectors can be added in any order.

6. Vectors A and B could represent two forces that have the same size, but different directions.

7. Hang a weight on a string. The string defines the vertical direction. An object also falls vertically. Horizontal is perpendicular to this direction.

8. When two or more forces act concurrently on an object and their vector sum is zero, the object is in equilibrium.

9. Find the resultant of the forces. The equilibrant will be the same size, but the opposite direction of the resultant.

10. Yes. Newton's first law permits motion as long as an object's velocity is constant. It cannot accelerate.

11. The vector sum of forces forming a closed triangle is zero. If these are the only forces acting on the object, then the net force on the object is zero and the object is in equilibrium.

12. **a.** One component is parallel to the inclined plane and the other is perpendicular to it. **b.** $F_{\parallel} = W \sin \theta$. $F_{\perp} = W \cos \theta$, where W is the weight of the book.

Answers To
APPLYING CONCEPTS

1. 10 mm

2. 15 N

3. largest resultant: 3 N + 4 N = 7 N; smallest resultant: 4 N − 3 N = 1 N

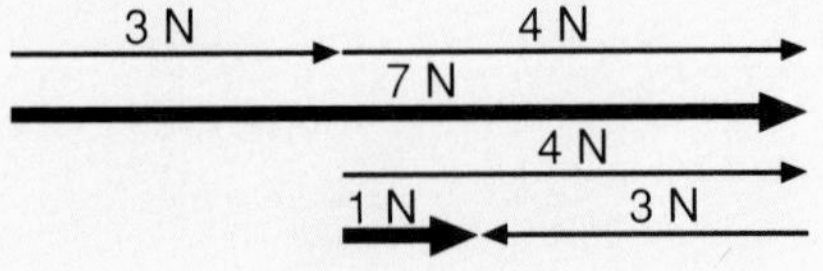

4. **a.** opposite directions; **b.** No. Two unequal forces can never add to zero.

5. As the angle between two parallel vectors increases, the resultant vector decreases.

6. **a.** side A; **b.** side B; **c.** Side A and side B have the same length.

7. Yes. Lower the handle to make the angle between the handle and the horizontal smaller.

8. the component perpendicular to the ground

9. The net force is zero.

10. When stretching a clothesline or strand of wire between two posts, there is no perpendicular component upward to balance the weight of the clothesline or wire. All the force exerted is horizontal to the weight. Stretching it to remove the last of the slack is an attempt to reduce the flexibility of the clothesline or wire and to increase the internal forces holding the line together; hence the need for superhuman strength.

cal device that can exert a greater-than-human force to take out the last of the slack to make the line completely horizontal. Why is this true? Disregard any stretching of the line.

11. Bill is trying to get a car unstuck from mud using a long line of strong rope. Which method would allow the greater force to be exerted on the car? Why?
    a. Bill ties one end of the rope to the car and pulls on the other end.
    b. Bill ties one end on the car and the other to a tree, then stands about halfway between the two ends and pushes on the rope perpendicular to it.
12. The weight of a book sliding down a frictionless inclined plane can be broken into two vector components: one acting parallel to the plane, and the other acting perpendicular to the plane.
    a. At what angle are these two components equal?
    b. At what angle is the component parallel to the plane equal to zero?
    c. At what angle is the component parallel to the plane equal to the weight?
13. A student puts two objects on a physics book and carefully tilts the cover. At a small angle, one object starts to slide. At a large angle, the other begins to slide. Which has the greater coefficient of static friction?

PROBLEMS

6.1 Graphical Method of Vector Addition

1. What is the vector sum of a 65-N force acting due east and a 32-N force acting due west?
2. Graphically find the sum of the following pairs of vectors in Figure 6–25.
    a. *D* and *C*
    b. *A* and *D*
    c. *C* and *A*
    d. *A* and *C*
    e. *E* and *F*
3. a. What is the resultant of a pair of forces, 100 N upward and 75 N downward?
    b. What is their resultant if they both act downward?
4. An airplane normally flies at 200 km/h. What is the resultant velocity of the airplane if
    a. it experiences a 50-km/h tail wind?
    b. it experiences a 50-km/h head wind?
5. Graphically add the following pairs of vectors in Figure 6–25.
    a. *B* and *D*
    b. *C* and *E*
    c. *D* and *E*
6. Graphically add the following vectors in Figure 6–25.
    a. $A + C + D$
    b. $D + E + B$
    c. $B + D + F$
7. Three forces act on point **P**. Force *A* has a magnitude of 80.0 N and is directed at 60.0°. Force *B* has a magnitude of 70.0 N and is directed at 0.0°. Force *C* has a magnitude of 40.0 N and is directed at 315°.
    a. Graphically add these three forces in the order $A + B + C$.
    b. Graphically add these three forces in the order $C + B + A$.
    c. What is noted about the solutions in each case?

6.2 Analytical Method of Vector Addition

▶ 8. You head downstream on a river in a canoe. You can paddle at 5.0 km/h and the river is flowing at 2.0 km/h. How far downstream will you be in 30 minutes?

9. You walk 30 m south and 30 m east. Draw and add vectors for these two displacements. Compute the resultant.

▶ 10. A ship leaves its home port expecting to travel to a port 500 km due south. Before it can move, a severe storm comes up and blows the ship 100 km due east. How far is the ship from its destination? In what direction must the ship travel to reach its destination?

11. A hiker leaves camp and, using a compass, walks 4 km E, 6 km S, 3 km E, 5 km N, 10 km W, 8 km N, and 3 km S. At the end of three days, the hiker is lost. By drawing a diagram, compute how far the hiker is from camp and which direction should be taken to get back to camp.

▶ 12. Three forces act simultaneously on point **J**. One force is 10.0 N north; the second is 15.0 N west; the third is 15.0 N 30.0° east of north. Determine the magnitude and direction of the resultant force.

13. Diane rows a boat at 8.0 m/s directly across a river that flows at 6.0 m/s.
    a. What is the resultant speed of the boat?

11. Method *b.* Vector consideration shows that if the rope is nearly straight, the car and tree provide forces that are much greater than the driver force.

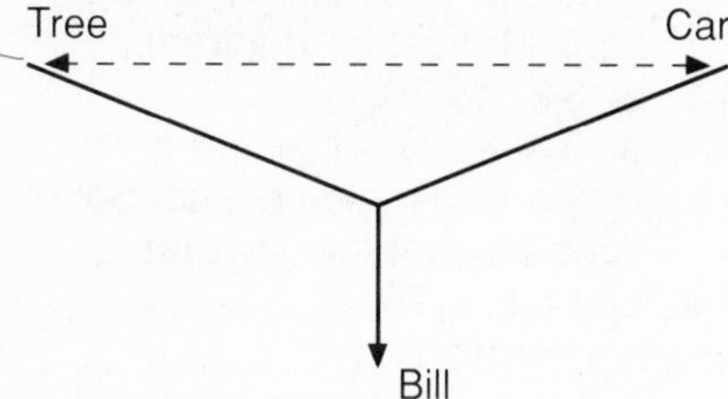

12. a. 45°; **b.** 0°; **c.** 90°

13. The one that begins to slide at the larger angle has the greater coefficient of static friction.

Answers To
PROBLEMS

Complete solutions for all Chapter Review Problems can be found in the Problems and Solutions Manuel accompanying this text.

1. 33 N, east; Refer to Problems and Solutions Manual.

2. Refer to Problems and Solutions Manual.

3. a. 25 N, upward; **b.** 175 N, downward

4. a. 250 km/h, in direction of plane; **b.** 150 km/h, in opposite direction of plane

5. Refer to Problems and Solutions Manual.

6. Refer to Problems and Solutions Manual.

7. a. Refer to Problems and Solutions Manual for diagram. **b.** Refer to Problems and Solutions Manual for diagram. **c.** Each gives same resultant, about 144 N at 16°.

8. 3.5 km; Refer to Problems and Solutions Manual.

9. 42 m, 315°; Refer to Problems and Solutions Manual.

10. 509 km, 259°; Refer to Problems and Solutions Manual.

11. 5 km, 307°; Refer to Problems and Solutions Manual.

12. 24.2 N, 108°; Refer to Problems and Solutions Manual.

Answers continue on page 130.

Answers To
PROBLEMS (cont)

13. **a.** 10 m/s, 53° (from bank); **b.** 30 s; **c.** 1.8×10^2 m
Refer to Problems and Solutions Manual for diagram.
14. **a.** 34°; **b.** 90 s; **c.** 5.4×10^2 m; **d.** 90 s
Refer to Problems and Solutions Manual for diagram.
15. 230 km/h, 76°
16. 1.1×10^2 N, 37°
Refer to Problems and Solutions Manual for diagram.
17. **a.** 4.1 m/s, 67° (from bank); **b.** 63 s; **c.** 1.0×10^2 m
18. 16 m/s^2, 67° (up from horizontal)
Refer to Problems and Solutions Manual for diagram.
19. **a.** 65 m/s; **b.** 58°
Refer to Problems and Solutions Manual for diagram.
20. 158 km/h, 18° west of south
Refer to Problems and Solutions Manual for diagram.
21. F_h = 65 N; F_v = 65 N
22. 108 N
Refer to Problems and Solutions Manual for diagram.
23. **a.** 2.2 m/s^2; **b.** 340 N, up
Refer to Problems and Solutions Manual for diagram.
24. 13 N
25. 79 km, 47°
26. **a.** 110 N; **b.** 107 N; **c.** 97 N; **d.** 81 N; **e.** +30 N
27. 279 N, up
Refer to Problems and Solutions Manual for diagram.

b. If the stream is 240 m wide, how long will it take Diane to row across?
c. How far downstream will Diane be?

14. Dave rows a boat across a river at 4.0 m/s. The river flows at 6.0 m/s and is 360 m across.
a. In what direction, relative to the shore, does Dave's boat go?
b. How long does it take Dave to cross the river?
c. How far downstream is Dave's landing point?
d. How long would it take Dave to cross the river if there were no current?

15. Kyle is flying a plane due north at 225 km/h as a wind carries it due east at 55 km/h. Find the magnitude and direction of the plane's resultant velocity analytically.

16. Sue and Jenny kick a soccer ball at exactly the same time. Sue's foot exerts a force of 66 N north. Jenny's foot exerts a force of 88 N east. What is the magnitude and direction of the resultant force on the ball?

17. Kym is in a boat traveling 3.8 m/s straight across a river 240 m wide. The river is flowing at 1.6 m/s.
a. What is Kym's resultant velocity?
b. How long does it take Kym to cross the river?
c. How far is Kym downstream when she reaches the other side?

18. A weather station releases a weather balloon. The balloon's buoyancy accelerates it straight up at 15 m/s^2. At the same time, a wind accelerates it horizontally at 6.5 m/s^2. What is the magnitude and direction (with reference to the horizontal) of the resultant acceleration?

19. A descent vehicle landing on the moon has a vertical velocity toward the surface of the moon of 35 m/s. At the same time, it has a horizontal velocity of 55 m/s.
a. At what speed does the vehicle move along its descent path?
b. At what angle with the vertical is this path?

▶ **20.** Kyle wishes to fly to a point 450 km due south in 3.00 hours. A wind is blowing from the west at 50 km/hr. Compute the proper heading and speed that Kyle must choose in order to reach his destination on time.

21. Dan applies a force of 92 N on a heavy box by using a rope held at an angle of 45° with the horizontal. What are the vertical and horizontal components of the 92-N force?

22. Beth, a construction worker, attempts to pull a stake out of the ground by pulling on a rope that is attached to the stake. The rope makes an angle of 60.0° with the horizontal. Beth exerts a force of 125 N on the rope. What is the magnitude of the upward component of the force acting on the stake?

▶ **23.** A 40-kg crate is pulled across the ice with a rope. A force of 100 N is applied at an angle of 30° with the horizontal. Neglecting friction, calculate
a. the acceleration of the crate.
b. the upward force the ice exerts on the crate as it is pulled.

▶ **24.** Joe pushes on the handle of a 10-kg lawn spreader. The handle makes a 45° angle with the horizontal. Joe wishes to accelerate the spreader from rest to 1.39 m/s in 1.5 s. What force must Joe apply to the handle? Neglect friction.

25. Tammy leaves the office, drives 26 km due north, then turns onto a second highway and continues in a direction of 30.0° north of east for 62 km. What is her total displacement from the office?

26. Find the magnitude of the resultant of a 40-N force and a 70-N force acting concurrently when the angle between them is
a. 0.0°. **b.** 30.0°. **c.** 60.0°. **d.** 90.0°. **e.** 180.0°.

27. Three people attempt to haul a heavy sign to the roof of a building by using three ropes attached to the sign. Abby stands directly above the sign and pulls straight up on a rope. Eric and Kim stand on either side of Abby. Their ropes form 30.0° angles with Abby's rope. A force of 102 N is applied on each rope. What is the net upward force acting on the sign? See Figure 6–26.

FIGURE 6–26. Use with Problem 27.

▶ **28.** A river flows toward 90°. Mark, a riverboat pilot, heads the boat at 297° and is able to go straight across the river at 6.0 m/s. See Figure 6–27.

a. What is the velocity of the current?

b. What is the velocity of the boat as seen from the river bank?

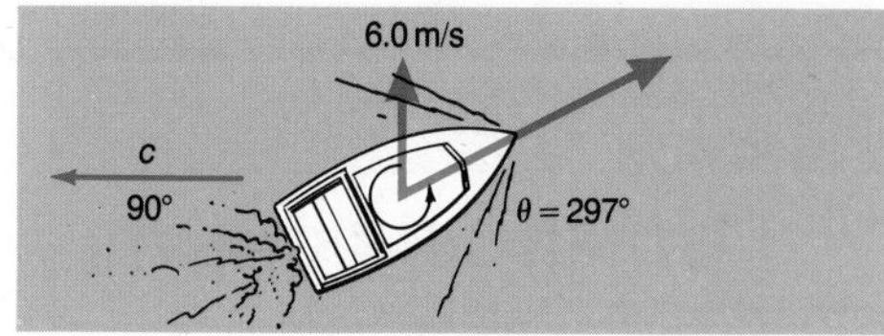

FIGURE 6–27. Use with Problem 28.

6.3 Applications of Vectors

29. An object in equilibrium has three forces exerted on it. A 33-N force acts at 90°, and a 44-N force acts at 60°. What is the magnitude and direction of the third force?

30. Five forces act on an object: the first, 60 N at 90°; the second, 40 N at 0°; the third, 80 N at 270°; the fourth, 40 N at 180°; and the fifth, 50 N at 60°. What is the magnitude and direction of a sixth force that produces equilibrium of the object?

31. A street lamp weighs 150 N. It is supported equally by two wires that form an angle of 120° with each other.

a. What is the tension of each of these wires?

b. If the angle between the wires is reduced to 90.0°, what new force does each wire exert?

c. As the angle between the wires decrease, what happens to the force in the wire?

32. Joe wishes to hang a sign weighing 750 N so that cable A attached to the store makes a 30.0° angle as shown in Figure 6–28. Cable B is attached to an adjoining building. Calculate the necessary tension in cable B.

FIGURE 6–28. Use with Problem 32.

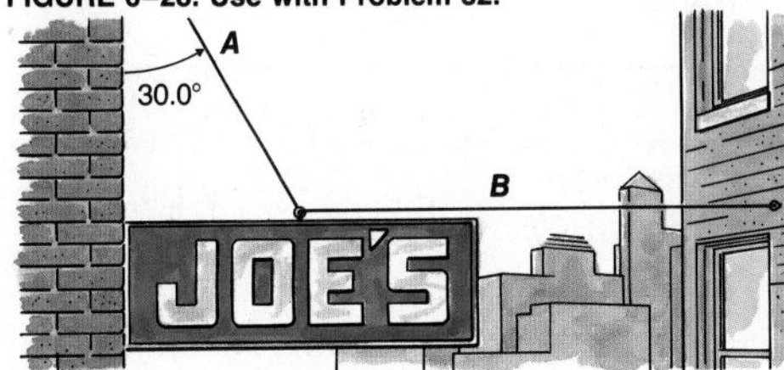

▶ **33.** Rachel pulls her 18-kg suitcase at a constant speed by pulling on a handle that makes an angle θ with the horizontal. The frictional force on the suitcase is 27 N and Rachel exerts a 43-N force on the handle.

a. What angle does the handle make with the horizontal?

b. What is the normal force exerted on the suitcase?

34. You place a box weighing 215 N on an inclined plane that makes a 35.0° angle with the horizontal. Compute the component of the gravitational force acting down the inclined plane.

▶ **35.** You slide a 325-N trunk up a 20.0° inclined plane with a constant velocity by exerting a force of 211 N parallel to the inclined plane.

a. What is the component of the trunk's weight parallel to the plane?

b. What is the sum of your applied force, friction, and the parallel component of the trunk's weight? Why?

c. What is the size and direction of the friction force?

d. What is the coefficient of friction?

▶ **36.** What force would you have to exert on the trunk in Problem 35 so that it would slide down the plane with a constant velocity? What would be the direction of the force?

▶ **37.** A 2.5-kg block slides down a 25° inclined plane with constant acceleration. The block starts from rest at the top. At the bottom, its velocity reaches 0.65 m/s. The length of the incline is 1.6 m.

a. What is the acceleration of the block?

b. What is the coefficient of friction between the plane and block?

c. Does the result of either **a** or **b** depend on the mass of the block?

THINKING PHYSIC-LY

Weight lifting or "pumping iron" has become very popular in the last few years. When lifting a barbell, which grip will exert less force on the lifter's arms: one in which the arms are extended straight upward from the body so they are at right angles to the bars, or one in which the arms are spread so that the bar is gripped closer to the weights? Explain.

28. **a.** 12 m/s, 90°; **b.** 6.0 m/s, 0°
29. 74 N, 253°
30. 34 N, 223°
31. **a.** $T_1 = T_2 = 150$ N; **b.** $T_1 = T_2 = 106$ N; **c.** decreases toward 75 N
Refer to Problems and Solutions Manual for diagram.
32. 433 N, right
Refer to Problems and Solutions Manual for diagram.
33. **a.** 51°; **b.** 1.4×10^2 N, up
Refer to Problems and Solutions Manual for diagram.
34. 123 N
Refer to Problems and Solutions Manual for diagram.
35. **a.** 111 N; **b.** zero, constant velocity; **c.** 100 N, down plane; **d.** 0.327
36. 11 N, up plane
37. **a.** 0.13 m/s^2; **b.** 0.452; **c.** no

Answer To
THINKING PHYSIC-LY

Only the force perpendicular to the barbell contributes to lifting it. A grip in which the arms are extended straight forward from the body, so that all the force exerted is perpendicular to the bar, will exert less force on the weightlifter's arms. Spreading the arms so that the bar is gripped closer to weights reduces the component of force perpendicular to the bar. The lifter must exert more total force for the perpendicular component to equal the force exerted when the arms are perpendicular to the bar.

CHAPTER

7 Motion in Two Dimensions

PLANNING GUIDE (5 class sessions)

CONTENTS	TEXT FEATURES	TEACHER RESOURCE PACKAGE	OTHER COMPONENTS
7.1 Projectile Motion, pp. 134–141 (3 Class Sessions) • Independence of Motion in Two Dimensions • Objects Launched Horizontally • Objects Launched at an Angle	**Physics Lab:** The Softball Throw, p. 140 **Pocket Lab:** Where the Ball Bounces, p. 135 **Problem Solving Strategy:** Projectile Motion Problem, p. 137 **Problem Solving Strategy:** Check for Reasonable Answers, p. 139 **Concept Review,** p. 141	**Study Guide:** Projectile Motion **Physics Lab Data Sheet:** The Softball Throw **Reteaching Master:** Horizontal and Vertical Components of Motion **Transparency Worksheet:** The Trajectory of a Projectile	**Laboratory Manual:** Lab 7.1 Projectile Motion Lab 7.2 Range of a Projectile **Transparency 8:** The Trajectory of a Projectile
7.2 Periodic Motion, pp. 141–150 (2 Class Sessions) • Circular Motion • Changing Circular Motion: Torque • Simple Harmonic Motion	**Physics and Technology:** Centrifuges, p. 149 **Pocket Lab:** Target Practice, p. 145 **Pocket Lab:** Tick-Tock, p. 149 **Concept Review,** p. 150	**Study Guide:** Periodic Motion **Enrichment Master:** The Gyroscope Effect **Critical Thinking Master:** Mechanical Resonance	
Chapter Review, pp. 150–153	Summary Key Terms Reviewing Concepts Applying Concepts Problems Using a Graphing Calculator Thinking Physic-ly	**Vocabulary Review** **Chapter Test**	**Test Bank**

SUPPLEMENTARY MATERIALS

SOFTWARE	AUDIOVISUAL	BOOKS/MAGAZINES
Projectile Motion, EME (Macintosh). *Circular Motion,* Cross (Apple II, IBM PC). *Harmonic Motion Workshop,* High Technology (Apple II).	Films: *Frames of Reference,* PSSC. *Free Fall and Projectile Motion,* PSSC. *Experiments in Space: Projectile Motion,* Ealing Film Loops.	Frank, Michael T., and Kluk, Edward. "Equations of Motion on a Computer Spreadsheet: The Damped Harmonic Oscillator and More." *The Physics Teacher*, May 1990, p. 308. Keefer, Robert K.F. "So What Else Can You Do with a Ballistic Pendulum?" *The Physics Teacher*, October 1990, p. 495. van den Berg, Daday and Ed. "A Launcher for Projectile Motion." *The Physics Teacher,* October 1990, p. 477. Van Hise, Y. "Physics With Fizz." *The Science Teacher,* September 1987, pp. 54–57.

PROBLEM CORRELATION

CONCEPTS	CHAPTER REVIEW			PROBLEMS APPENDIX
	Reviewing Concepts	Applying Concepts	Problems	
7.1 Projectile Motion				
Independence of Motion in Two Dimensions	1,2	1	**1**	1
Objects Launched Horizontally	3	2,3	2,3,4,**5,6,7**	**2**,3,4,5
Objects Launched at an Angle		4,5	**8,9,10,11,12**	6,**7**,**8**,9
7.2 Periodic Motion				
Circular Motion	4,5,6,7	6,7	13,14,15,16,17, **18,19,20**	**10,11,12,**13
Changing Circular Motion: Torque	8	8,9		14
Simple Harmonic Motion	9,10,11,12	10,11	21,**22**	15,**16**

ACTIVITY AND DEMONSTRATION MATERIALS

PHYSICS LAB	POCKET LAB	DEMONSTRATIONS
Page 140 softball stopwatch paper pencil calculator	Pages 135, 145, 149 golf ball stopwatch 1.0-m string rubber stopper with hole steel nut	Pages 142, 143, 146 large jar plastic fishing bob string water tape 4 pieces of heavy cord—1.5 m each 30-cm x 30-cm of stiff cardboard 2–4 plastic drinking glasses croquet mallet several screw eyes or hooks mass

EXTENSION PROJECTS

LIBRARY RESEARCH

1. Harold Edgerton
In the library, find examples of Harold Edgerton's work with stroboscopic photography. What have scientists learned from his photos?

HANDS-ON

2. Projectile Range
(outdoor activity) Using a slingshot and a protractor, fire a golf ball and determine the effect of angle on the range (horizontal distance).

STUDENT READINGS

Beach, John E. "Centripetal Force on a Turntable." *The Physics Teacher*, February 1990.

Brancazio, Peter. "Getting a Kick Out of Physics." *Discover,* November 1984.

Dobrowski, Jan Paul. "Analysis of a Space Shuttle Launch." *The Physics Teacher,* January 1990.

Hanson, Michael. "The Flight of the Boomerang." *The Physics Teacher,* March 1990.

Price, Channon P. "Teacup Physics: Centripetal Acceleration." *The Physics Teacher,* January 1990.

Strange, Curtis. "Curtis in Control: You Can't Play Golf Until You Have Control Over Your Swing and Over Yourself." *Golf Magazine,* November 1988.

Chapter 7

Motion in Two Dimensions

CHAPTER OVERVIEW

Theme Development: The theme of symmetry is important to this chapter, as projectile motion shows symmetry about the highest point in an object's path. Though circular motion shows strong symmetry, centripetal force and simple harmonic motion both develop the patterns of change theme because of their cyclic nature.

MISCONCEPTIONS

The difficulty of accepting the independence of perpendicular vector components comes up again in the motion of projectiles and in circular motion. Students may have the idea that objects constrained to follow a curved path will tend to remain on a curved path when no longer constrained. Another sticking point is this: For projectile motions, why isn't acceleration zero at the top of the motion when the velocity is zero?

Laboratory Options

STUDENT EDITION

Physics Lab

The Softball Throw	140

Pocket Labs

Where the Ball Bounces	135
Target Practice	145
Tick-Tock	149

TEACHER EDITION

Activities

Discovery	135
Cooperative Learning	137
Demonstration	142, 143, 146

LABORATORY MANUAL

Projectile Motion	Lab 7.1
Range of a Projectile	Lab 7.2

KEY TERMS

amplitude
centripetal acceleration
centripetal forces
mechanical resonance
pendulum
period
projectile
range
simple harmonic motion (SHM)
torque
trajectory

CHAPTER 7 Motion in Two Dimensions

$V_x + V_y$

After adjusting the strobe light, Jamahl and Stacey watched the water droplets spraying into a sink. Jamahl was surprised to see the drops spread apart as they fell into the sink. Stacey said she could explain it. What explanation would she give?

The graceful arch of the water drops in the photo on the facing page illustrates motion you have probably seen many times. The flight of baseballs, basketballs, and golf balls follows the same path. Mathematically, the curve is a parabola. Newton's laws of motion are all that are needed to understand how objects like water drops and golf balls move.

Chapter Outline

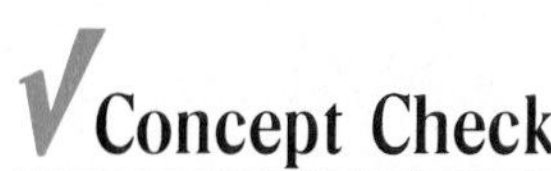

Concept Check

The following terms or concepts from earlier chapters are important for a good understanding of this chapter. If you are not familiar with them, you should review them before studying this chapter
- velocity, Chapter 3
- acceleration, Chapter 4
- motion of falling objects, Chapter 5
- resolution of vectors, Chapter 6
- independence of vector quantities, Chapter 6

Introducing The Chapter

$V_x + V_y$

Using The Photo: Vertical and horizontal motions are clearly shown here, but most students won't think to divide up the motion this way. The parabolic trajectory is also apparent. From clues about the photo's scale, ask students to estimate how often the strobe light flashed. Have students refer to page 137 for help answering this question.

Concept Check

Make sure students have a clear understanding of the concepts taught in Chapters 3, 4, 5, and 6 listed in the Concept Check. Students with a good grasp of the principles of physical motion, falling objects, and vectors will have an important context for understanding the concept of two-dimensional motion presented in this chapter.

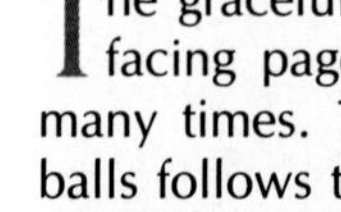

Assessment Options

Portfolio Assessment
Portfolio Assessment, TWE, p. 136
Enrichment on amusement park rides, TWE, p. 143
Answer to Physics and Technology, p. 149
Thinking Physic-ly, p. 153

Performance
Activity, TWE, p. 135
Pocket Labs, pp. 135, 145, 149
Pocket Lab Assessment, TWE, p. 149
Physics Lab, p. 140

Content
Self Assessment: Practice Problems, pp. 136, 139, 145, 149
Checking for Understanding, TWE, p. 138
Assessment, Critical Thinking, TWE, p. 140
Concept Reviews, pp. 141, 150
Chapter Review, pp. 150–153
Supplemental Problems, pp. 693–694

Group Assessment
Activities for group assessment occur with Cooperative Learning and lab activities.

7.1 PROJECTILE MOTION

Preparation

OBJECTIVES

The objectives are listed on the student page. Remind students to preview these objectives as a study guide to this major section.

OVERVIEW

The motion of projectiles exemplifies motion in accord with Newton's laws, especially Newton's second law. Analysis of such motion assumes that perpendicular components are independent, allowing separate analysis of the vertical and horizontal parts of the motion.

BRIDGING

Previously introduced chapter concepts in use here include vector components, independence of perpendicular vector components, and Newton's second law.

1 Focus

The general idea of a projectile's path can be shown by using a toy Ping-Pong ball gun to fire balls at various angles. Because of their rather low speed, students can see the path easily.

2 Teach

CONCEPT DEVELOPMENT

- Ask why the projectile moves horizontally and what force makes it move vertically. Emphasize that there is only a vertical force on the projectile in the absence of air resistance.
- Point out to students that if an observer moved to the right at the correct speed, the ball projected horizontally in Figure 7–1 would appear to fall straight down.
- Demonstrate this in front of the class by dropping a pen while walking rapidly. Ask students to watch the path of the pen relative to your body. It should land straight down by your foot. Repeat the procedure, having them watch the path of the pen from where you released it to where it lands.

Objectives

- **show that you understand the independence of vertical and horizontal velocities of a projectile by solving problems of projectiles launched horizontally.**
- **find the maximum height and range of projectiles launched at an arbitrary angle if initial velocity and angle are given.**

7.1 PROJECTILE MOTION

Objects launched like the water drops are **projectiles.** The path they follow is called a **trajectory.** The motion of a projectile is described in terms of its position, velocity, and acceleration. These are all vector quantities, and we have seen that the perpendicular components of vector quantities are independent. How does this fact let us analyze the motion?

The path of a projectile is its trajectory.

Independence of Motion in Two Dimensions

Let's start with a simple trajectory. Figure 7–1 shows a photograph of two falling golf balls, taken with a strobe light that flashed 30 times each second. One ball was launched horizontally at 2.0 m/s, the other ball was simply dropped. Notice that the thrown ball moves the same distance to the right during each time interval. That is, its horizontal velocity is constant. The dropped ball also has a constant horizontal velocity, equal to zero. In each case, the force acting on the ball has no horizontal component, so there is no horizontal acceleration.

The horizontal and vertical velocities of a projectile are independent.

The golf ball photograph shows a remarkable property of motion. Look carefully at the height of the balls. At each flash, the vertical position of the dropped ball is the same as that of the thrown ball. This means that the vertical motion of the thrown ball and the dropped ball are the same. In addition, the change in vertical position between two successive flashes is the same for the two balls. This means that their average vertical velocities during these intervals also must be equal. The spaces between images grow larger because both balls are accelerated downward by the force of gravity. The photograph shows that the horizontal motion of the thrown ball does not affect its vertical motion at all.

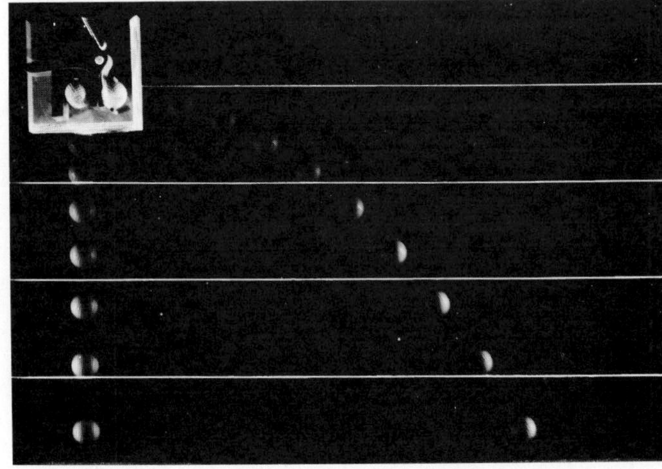

FIGURE 7–1. A flash photograph of two golf balls released simultaneously. Both balls were allowed to fall freely, but one was projected horizontally with an initial velocity of 2.00 m/s. The light flashes are 1/30 s apart.

FIGURE 7–2. To the passenger, the apple falls straight down. To the observer on the sidewalk, the path of the apple is a parabola.

Suppose that a car slowly passes as you stand by the side of a road, Figure 7–2. A passenger in the car accidentally drops an apple out the window. Imagine that you can watch the apple only. What path will you see it take? Remember that the apple has the same horizontal velocity as the car. From your frame of reference, or point of view, the path will be curved like that of the launched golf ball. Will the passenger see the same path? The passenger and the apple both move with the same horizontal velocity. Thus, the passenger will see a straight vertical path like that of the dropped golf ball. The trajectory as seen by the two observers will be different, but both observers will agree that it takes the same time for the apple to hit the ground. Thus, the shape of the trajectory and the horizontal motion depend on the viewpoint, or frame of reference, of the observer. The vertical motion does not.

The shape of a trajectory depends on the viewpoint of the observer.

The independence of vertical and horizontal motion and our motion equations can be used to determine the position of thrown objects. If we call the horizontal displacement x and the initial horizontal velocity v_x then, at time t,

$$x = v_x t$$
$$\text{and } v_{xf} = v_i.$$

The equations for an object falling with constant acceleration, g, describe the vertical motion. If y is the vertical displacement, the initial vertical velocity of the object is v_y. At time t, the vertical displacement is

$$y = v_y t + \tfrac{1}{2}gt^2$$
$$\text{also, } v_{yf} = v_y + gt.$$

Using these equations, we can analyze the motion of projectiles. The simplicity of these calculations is due, in part, to the fact that for the golf ball, the force due to air resistance is negligible. For an object such as a feather, it could be a very important factor.

POCKET LAB

WHERE THE BALL BOUNCES

Place a golf ball in your hand and extend your arm sideways so the ball is at shoulder height. Drop the ball and have a lab partner start a stopwatch when the ball strikes the floor and stop it the next time the ball strikes the floor. Where would you expect the ball to hit when you walk at a steady speed and drop the ball? Would the ball take the same time to bounce? Try it. Where does it hit? Does it take more time?

CONCEPT DEVELOPMENT

Emphasize again that horizontal motion is constant in the absence of friction. The gravitational force makes the projectile slow down on the way up and accelerate on the way down.

Study Guide Master. To reinforce the concepts in this section, have the students complete the Study Guide Master for Section 7.1 from the Teacher Resource Package.

ACTIVITY

Discovery: This activity will allow students to find the horizontal velocity of a dart shot from a toy dart gun by measuring the vertical height of the dart in the gun and the horizontal distance it travels. Have students working in groups shoot the dart gun several times horizontally from the same height above the floor. Have them measure the horizontal distance traveled each time and compute an average. Using the height of the dart, they can calculate the time it takes to reach the floor. Using this time of travel and the horizontal distance, students can compute the horizontal velocity. This activity will help initiate a discussion about error in measurements.

Transparency Package. Use Transparency 8, Projectile Motion, to review the horizontal and vertical components of motion.

Laboratory Manual. Give students additional experience with projectile motion by doing Lab 7.1, Projectile Motion.

POCKET LAB

WHERE THE BALL BOUNCES

Purpose: to allow students to explore the motion of a bouncing ball.
Materials: golf ball; stopwatch.
Outcome: The ball continues forward with the student. The ball has the same forward velocity as the student. The ball takes the same amount of time to bounce as before. The time to bounce does not depend on the horizontal motion.

STUDY GUIDE MASTER

Use the Study Guide master for section 7.1.

LABORATORY MANUAL

Use Lab 7.1 with this section.

TRANSPARENCY

Use Transparency 8 with this section.

Answers To
PRACTICE PROBLEMS

Have students refer to Appendix A of the Solutions Appendix for complete solutions to Practice Problems.

1. **a.** 4.00 s; **b.** 20 m; **c.** $v_x = 5.0$ m/s; $v_y = -39.2$ m/s
2. **a.** (a) no change (b) distance doubles (c) v_x doubles; no change in v_y
   b. (a) increases by the $\sqrt{2}$ (b) increases by the $\sqrt{2}$ (c) no change in v_x; v_y increases by $\sqrt{2}$
3. 0.800 m/s

Assessment

Portfolio

Have students submit copies of problem solutions in the following classifications:

1) horizontal initial velocity.
2) launched at some angle above the horizontal
   a) where the range is calculated.
   b) where the maximum height is found.
   c) where range is known and one of the initial conditions is found.

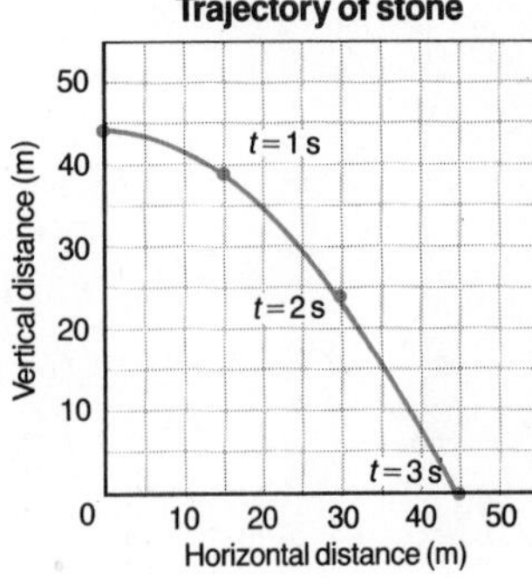

FIGURE 7–3. The path of a projectile thrown horizontally.

The horizontal velocity is constant. The vertical velocity is constantly changing because of gravity.

Objects Launched Horizontally

We'll first look at the motion of objects that have an initial vertical velocity of zero.

Example Problem

Projectile Launched Horizontally

A stone is thrown horizontally at +15 m/s from the top of a cliff 44 m high, Figure 7–3. **a.** How long does the stone take to reach the bottom of the cliff? **b.** How far from the base of the cliff does the stone strike the ground? **c.** Sketch the trajectory of the stone.

Given: horizontal velocity, $v_x = +15$ m/s; initial vertical velocity, $v_y = 0$ m/s; vertical acceleration, $g = -9.80$ m/s^2; initial height, 44 m

Unknowns: **a.** time of flight, t; **b.** horizontal displacement, x

Basic equations: $x = v_x t$; $y = v_y t + \frac{1}{2}gt^2$

Solution:

The cliff height is 44 m, so if we assign the initial position $y = 0$, then at the end of the flight (time t) the position is $y = -44$ m.

a. We know all quantities in the equation $y = v_y t + \frac{1}{2}gt^2$ except the unknown, the time t. Since $v_y = 0$, $y = \frac{1}{2}gt^2$, or $t^2 = 2\frac{y}{g}$.

$$t^2 = \frac{2(-44\text{ m})}{-9.80\text{ m/s}^2} = 9.0\text{ s}^2$$

$$t = \sqrt{9.0\text{ s}^2} = 3.0\text{ s}$$

b. To find the horizontal displacement use

$$x = v_x t = (+15\text{ m/s})(3.0\text{ s}) = +45\text{ m}$$

c. See Figure 7–3.

Practice Problems

1. A stone is thrown horizontally at a speed of +5.0 m/s from the top of a cliff 78.4 m high.
   a. How long does it take the stone to reach the bottom of the cliff?
   b. How far from the base of the cliff does the stone strike the ground?
   c. What are the horizontal and vertical components of the velocity of the stone just before it hits the ground?
2. How would the three answers to Practice Problem 1 change if
   a. the stone were thrown with twice the horizontal speed?
   b. the stone were thrown with the same speed but the cliff was twice as high?
3. A steel ball rolls with constant velocity across a tabletop 0.950 m high. It rolls off and hits the ground +0.352 m horizontally from the edge of the table. How fast was the ball rolling?

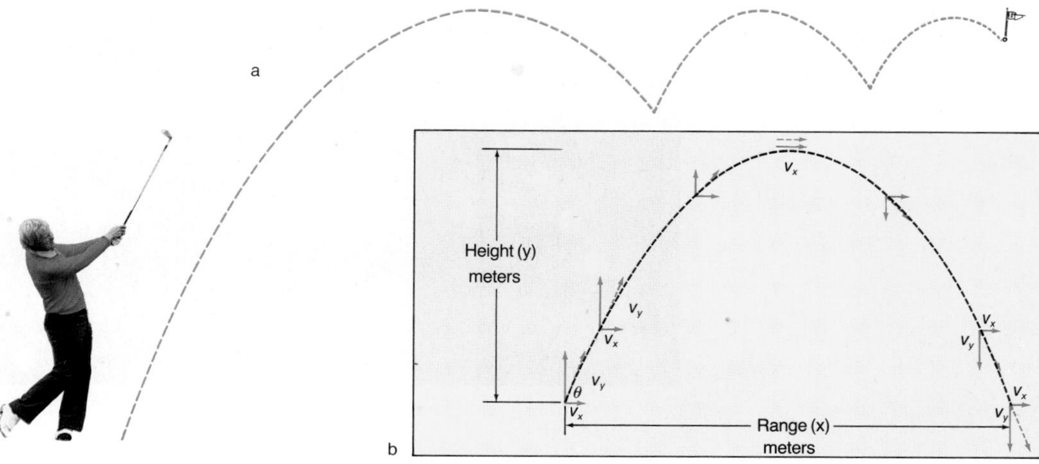

FIGURE 7–4. The flight of a golf ball can be described in terms of horizontal and vertical components.

4. An auto, moving too fast on a horizontal stretch of mountain road, slides off the road, falling into deep snow 43.9 m below the road and 87.7 m beyond the edge of the road.
   a. How long did the auto take to fall?
   b. How fast was it going when it left the road? (in m/s and km/h)
   c. What was its acceleration 10 m below the edge of the road?

Objects Launched at an Angle

Figure 7–4a shows what happens when a golf ball bounces off a hard surface. The vertical and horizontal velocity components during one of the bounces are shown in Figure 7–4b. The horizontal component, v_x, is constant because very little force is exerted in the horizontal direction. Gravity, however, acts on the ball, giving it a downward acceleration. Thus, the vertical velocity component is large and positive at the beginning, decreases to zero at the top of the path, then increases in the negative direction as the projectile falls. When the object returns to its launch position, the vertical speed is the same as it was at launch, but its direction is reversed. The **range,** *R*, is the horizontal distance from the point of bounce until the projectile returns to the surface height.

$V_x + V_y$

PROBLEM SOLVING STRATEGY

When solving a projectile motion problem, first determine the horizontal and vertical components of the initial velocity. Then the parts of the problem involving either component can be solved separately. The symmetry of the trajectory can be used when the launching and landing locations are at equal height. Rising and falling times are equal, as are the horizontal distances moved in each half of the trajectory. We will ignore air resistance in projectile motion problems.

4. a. 2.99 s; **b.** 29.3 m/s, 105 km/h; **c.** -9.80 m/s^2

ACTIVITY

Cooperative Learning: This activity will allow students to observe projectile paths. Have teams of students attach pieces of string at equal intervals along a meter stick. The intervals represent equal time intervals. The string lengths should have a ratio of 1:4:9:16. The lengths of string represent distances traveled and are proportional to the square of the distance from the pivot point. Have student teams attach small washers to the end of each string. By holding their sticks at various angles, students can observe the trajectories of projectiles with different initial velocities.

TEACHER F.Y.I.

It is possible to derive an equation to give the horizontal distance (range) of a projectile from the velocity given at an angle with the horizontal. The equation is

$$R = \frac{v_0^2 \sin 2\theta}{g}.$$

Using this equation, you can show that the maximum range occurs when θ equals 45°. You can also show that the range will be the same for pairs of angles, 75° and 15°, 60° and 30°, 10° and 80°. A sketch of the paths would look like the diagram shown here. Encourage students to appreciate the symmetry of the motion.

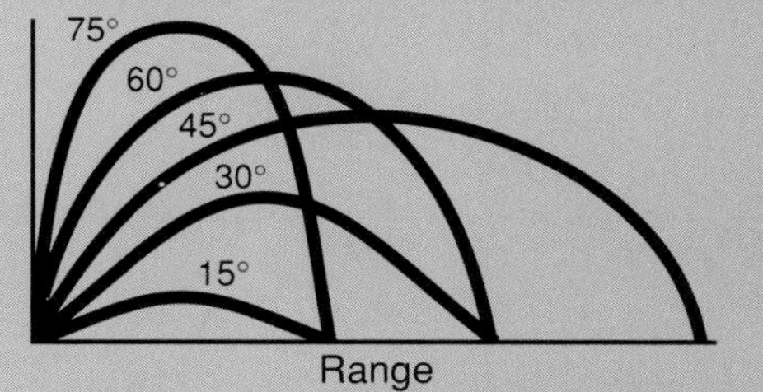

CHECKING FOR UNDERSTANDING

Give the horizontal and vertical components of the initial motion of a projectile, then ask students to figure the components at later times. You may want to have them use $g = 10\ m/s^2$ to make quick calculation easier. Stress that the vertical component changes and the horizontal component stays constant.

RETEACHING

Reteaching Master. Teacher Resource Package. Use the Reteaching Master for Chapter 7, Horizontal and Vertical Components of Motion.

EXTENSION

Ask students to describe the motion of a ball they throw straight up into the air. Then ask how this motion changes if they now walk at constant speed and throw the ball straight up. Allow students to demonstrate this. How does it look to the person walking? How about to an observer?

Laboratory Manual. Give students additional experience with the range of a projectile by doing Lab 7.2 from the Laboratory Manual.

FIGURE 7–5. The time interval between each position of the ball is 1/30 of a second.

The trajectory of a projectile is a parabola.

Example Problem

Flight of a Ball

In the strobe photo of the flight of the ball in Figure 7–5, the initial velocity of the ball was 4.47 m/s at an angle of 66° above the horizontal. Find **a.** how long it took the ball to land, **b.** how high the ball flew, **c.** what its range was.

Given: initial velocity, $v_i = +4.47$ m/s at 66°; initial angle, $\theta = 66°$

Unknowns: **a.** time in flight, t; **b.** maximum vertical displacement (height), y; **c.** range, R

Basic equations: $x = v_x t$; $y = v_y t + \frac{1}{2}gt^2$

Solution: Find the components of initial velocity.

$$v_x = v_i \cos\theta = (+4.47\ \text{m/s})(\cos 66°) = (4.47\ \text{m/s})(0.407) = +1.82\ \text{m/s}$$

$$v_y = v_i \sin\theta = (+4.47\ \text{m/s})(\sin 66°) = (4.47\ \text{m/s})(0.914) = +4.08\ \text{m/s}$$

a. When it lands, the height is zero: $y = 0$, but $y = v_y t + \frac{1}{2}gt^2 = 0$. Therefore, $t = \frac{-2v_y}{g}$.

$$t = \frac{-2(+4.08\ \text{m/s})}{-9.80\ \text{m/s}^2} = 0.833\ \text{s}$$

b. From the symmetry of the trajectory, the maximum height occurred at half the flight time, or 0.417 s after launch. At this time,

$$y = v_y t + \frac{1}{2}gt^2$$
$$= (+4.08\ \text{m/s})(0.417\ \text{s}) + \frac{1}{2}(-9.80\ \text{m/s}^2)(0.417\ \text{s})^2$$
$$y = 1.70\ \text{m} - 0.852\ \text{m} = +0.85\ \text{m}$$

F.Y.I.

In baseball and most other games, the player does not throw a ball so that it goes farthest, but so that it goes a certain distance in the least time. Consider a throw from third to first base. If thrown at 38 m/s, the smallest angle it could be thrown to go the 37 m is 7° above the horizontal. It would take 0.97 s without air resistance. The drag caused by the air means the thrower must increase the angle to 9°, and makes the ball take about 1.1 s.

RETEACHING MASTER

Use the Reteaching master for Chapter 7 with this section.

LABORATORY MANUAL

Use Lab 7.2 with this section.

c. The range is the horizontal distance traveled during the entire flight time, $t = 0.833$ s, or
$R = v_x t = (+1.82 \text{ m/s})(0.833 \text{ s}) = +1.52 \text{ m}$

PROBLEM SOLVING STRATEGY

Always check a problem to see if your answers are reasonable. In this case, you can use the photo and the knowledge that there were 30 flashes per second. The flight time was calculated to be 0.833 s. At 30 flashes/second this would be 25 flashes. You can count 25 flash intervals during this bounce, so the answer is fine. We don't know the photo scale, but the calculated maximum height is 0.85 m and the range is 1.5 m. The ratio of these two is 0.57/1. On the photo, the ratio of height to range is 57 mm/100 mm = 0.57/1, also in very good agreement.

Practice Problems

5. A player kicks a football from ground level with a velocity of magnitude 27.0 m/s at an angle of 30.0° above the horizontal, Figure 7–6. Find
  a. its "hang time," that is, the time the ball is in the air.
  b. the distance the ball travels before it hits the ground.
  c. its maximum height.

6. The kicker now kicks the ball with the same speed, but at 60.0° from the horizontal, or 30.0° from the vertical. Find
  a. its "hang time," that is, the time the ball is in the air.
  b. the distance the ball travels before it hits the ground.
  c. its maximum height.

7. Using the results for Practice Problems 5 and 6, compare qualitatively the flight times, ranges, and maximum heights for projectiles launched with high and low trajectories, when the high angle is the complement of the low angle. (The complement of angle θ is $(90° - \theta)$.)

▶ **8.** A rude tourist throws a peach pit horizontally with a 7.0 m/s velocity out of an elevator cage.
  a. If the elevator is not moving, how long will the pit take to reach the ground, 17.0 m below?
  b. How far (horizontally) from the elevator will the pit land?
  c. He throws the next pit when the elevator is at the same height but moving upward at a constant 8.5 m/s velocity. How long will it take this pit to land?
  d. How far away will this pit land?

BIOLOGY CONNECTION

Have you ever watched a frog? The launch angle of a frog's jump is approximately 45°. This innate behavior at this angle helps the frog cover maximum distance on flat ground.

The velocity of a projectile can be resolved into horizontal and vertical components.

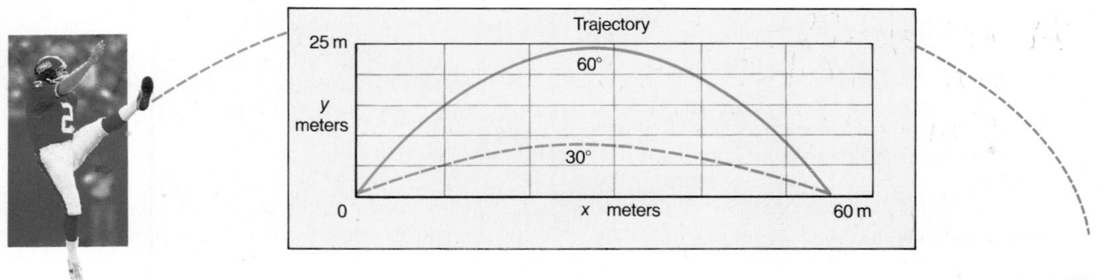

FIGURE 7–6. Use with Practice Problems 5, 6, and 7.

Guided Practice: After going over the Example Problem on p. 138, have students try the first Practice Problem on this page.

Independent Practice: Assign the remaining Practice Problems for homework and take time discussing them the next day.

Critical Thinking: How can it be possible that, at the top of its flight where its vertical velocity is zero, a projectile is still accelerating vertically? [Refer students to Concept Review 1.2, page 69.]

Enrichment: How would the motion of a projectile change if you add in the effects of air resistance? [One effect is that its range is shorter; another is that the trajectory is no longer symmetric.]

Answers To
PRACTICE PROBLEMS

Have students refer to Appendix A of the Solutions Appendix for complete solutions to Practice Problems.

5. **a.** 2.76 s; **b.** 64.6 m; **c.** 9.3 m
6. **a.** 4.78 s; **b.** 64.5 m; **c.** 27.9 m
7. Higher trajectory has the longest flight time and the greatest maximum height. The ranges are the same.
8. The solution requires the use of the quadratic equation:

$$x = \frac{-b \pm \sqrt{b^2 - 4ac}}{2a}.$$

a. 1.86 s; **b.** 13 m; **c.** 2.92 s; **d.** 20 m

3 Close

CONVERGENT QUESTION

List the previously learned concepts and ideas which come into play in the analysis of projectile motion. Such a list might include velocity, acceleration, motion of falling objects, resolution of vectors, and independence of vector quantities.

PHYSICS LAB

Process Skills: observing, cooperating, controlling variables, inferring, measuring, using numbers, interpreting data, hypothesizing.

MISCONCEPTIONS

Most students believe that projectile motion is complex. The motion is actually quite simple when the effects of friction are small.

Troubleshooting: The path of the softball is really quite simple. The horizontal velocity is constant. The vertical velocity always changes by 9.8 m/s every 1.0 s.

Teaching Suggestions: Only *one* ball should be used for the entire class.

- Students who are not measuring the range *must be away from the flight path.*
- A typical student throw might travel 60 m and be in the air for 4.0 s.

Calculations: Using the above data, v_x is 15 m/s, v_y is 19.6 m/s.

$$v_i = \sqrt{15^2 + 19.6^2} = 25 \text{ m/s}$$

Lab Worksheet, Teacher Resource Package. If desired, use the lab worksheet master for this chapter for students to record their data.

OBSERVATIONS

1. Students will throw at a wide variety of ranges.
2. Students will throw at a wide variety of speeds.

ANALYSIS

Neglecting friction, the largest range will be reached for angles near 45°. In practice, due to the starting height above the ground, friction, and the physiology of the shoulder, the angle will be less than 45°.

APPLICATION

The most important factor in the kickoff is distance. On punts, the time in the air is often as important as the distance. Punts are purposely kicked at a large angle.

PHYSICS LAB: The Softball Throw

Purpose

To discover how fast you can throw a softball by measuring range and time.

Materials

- *one* each—softball, stopwatch, paper, pencil, and calculator

Procedure

1. Take all of your materials out to the football field (or a large open area with premeasured distances).
2. Select a thrower, a timer, and a marker from each group.
3. All throwers should toss the ball around to loosen up the arm muscles.
4. Set up a data table to record the distance the ball flies in the air and the time of flight.
5. The thrower should stand at the goal line. The marker should move downfield and stand at a place where she feels the ball might land.
6. Measure the time and use the lines on the field to estimate the range for two throws.
7. As soon as your group has estimated the range, give the softball to another group and *leave the area!*

Calculations

1. Determine the initial values of v_x for each throw. **Hint:** Since

   $R = v_x t$, then $v_x = \frac{R}{t}$.

   Sample calculation:

   $R = 60 \text{ m}, t = 4.0 \text{ s}; v_x = \frac{60 \text{ m}}{4.0 \text{ s}} = 15 \text{ m/s}$

2. Determine the initial value of v_y. **Hint:** The ball spent an equal time moving up and down. Divide the time by 2 and then multiply by 9.8 m/s^2 to find the value of v_y.
   Sample calculation: $t = 4.0$ s indicates that the ball was at the top in 2.0 s. The initial value of v_y:

   $v_y = 9.8 \text{ m/s}^2 \times 2.0 \text{ s} = 19.6 \text{ m/s}$

3. Draw a triangle as shown here. Record *your values* of v_x and v_y.
4. Use the Pythagorean Theorem to find the value of v_i.

Observations and Data

1. Did each person throw at about the same range?
2. Did each person throw at about the same speed, v_i?

Analysis

1. Should the thrower try to throw with a larger v_x or v_y? Explain.

Applications

1. Why might a kickoff in a football game be made at a different angle than a punt?

ASSESSMENT

Critical Thinking: To further assess students' understanding of the relationship between range and horizontal velocity, ask the following questions.

1. Would the equations used in step 1 of Calculations also apply to a batted ball? Why or why not? [Yes. After the ball leaves the bat, it is only subject to friction and gravity.]

2. List some factors that would affect the motion of the ball that were not included in the calculations. Explain your ideas. [The equations of motion do not include provisions for the wind or for friction. Friction reduces the speed of the ball and the wind affects the flight path. Friction with the air is the reason a pitcher can throw a breaking ball.]

CONCEPT REVIEW

1.1 Two baseballs are pitched horizontally from the same height but at different speeds. The faster ball crosses home plate within the strike zone, but the slower one is below the batter's knees. Why does the faster ball not fall as far as the slower one? After all, they travel the same distance and accelerate down at the same rate.

1.2 A teflon hockey puck slides without friction across a table at constant velocity. When it reaches the end of the table, it flies off and lands on the ground.

a. Draw the situation above, drawing vectors showing the force on the puck at two positions while it is on the table and at two more when it is in the air. Draw all vectors to scale.

b. On a separate diagram, draw vectors showing the acceleration of the puck in the four locations.

1.3 For the puck in question 1.2,

a. draw vectors showing the horizontal and vertical components of the puck's velocity at the four points.

b. using a different colored pen or pencil, draw the total velocity vector at the four points.

1.4 Critical Thinking: Suppose an object is thrown with the same initial velocity and direction on the moon, where g is 1/6 as large as on Earth. Will the following quantities change? If so, will they become larger or smaller?

a. v_x **c.** maximum height
b. time of flight **d.** range

7.2 PERIODIC MOTION

Projectile motion is two dimensional, but the motion does not repeat. Projectiles move along their trajectories only once. On the other hand, if you swing a toy on a string, such as a yo-yo, horizontally around your head, its motion repeats itself at regular intervals. That is, its motion is periodic. An object bouncing on a spring or the pendulum of a clock is also periodic. Although different terms are used to describe this type of motion, Newton's laws can still be used to understand it.

Objectives

- **show an understanding of the centripetal acceleration of objects in circular motion and be able to apply Newton's laws to such motion.**
- **be able to characterize simple harmonic motion and apply Newton's laws to such motion.**
- **recognize resonance as a phenomenon often seen in daily life.**

FIGURE 7–7. The regular up-and-down motion of a yo-yo is an example of periodic motion.

CONCEPT REVIEW ANSWERS

1.1 The faster ball is in the air a shorter time, and thus gains a smaller vertical velocity.

1.2 a. and **b.**

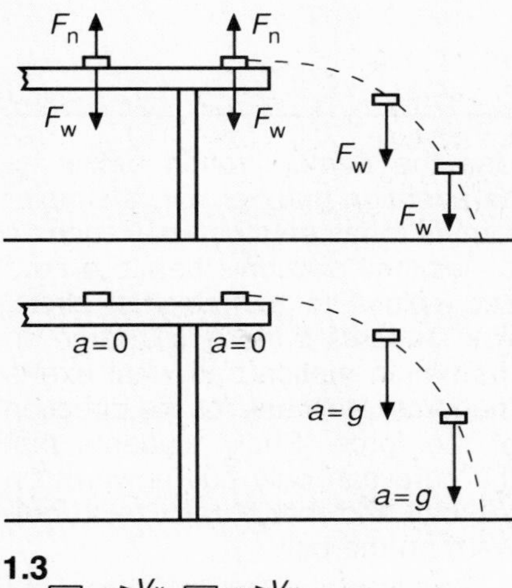

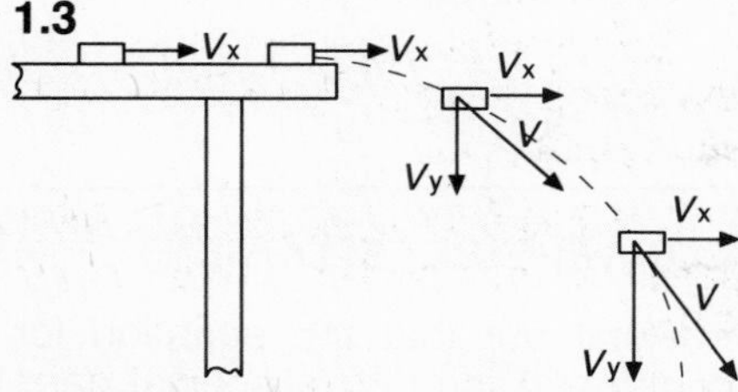

1.3

1.4 Critical Thinking:
a. no; **b.** yes; larger; $t = \frac{-2v_y}{g}$; **c.** yes; larger; **d.** yes; larger

INDEPENDENT PRACTICE/ EXTENSION

Refer to the Assignment Guide below for additional questions and problems for independent practice.

7.2 PERIODIC MOTION

Preparation

OBJECTIVES

The objectives are listed on the student page. Remind students to preview these objectives as a study guide to this major section.

OVERVIEW

The concepts of centripetal acceleration, centripetal force, as well as the behavior of objects in circular motion, are introduced in this section.

7:1 ASSIGNMENT GUIDE

	PRACTICE	EXTENSION
CHAPTER REVIEW pp. 150–153		
· Reviewing Concepts	1–3	
· Applying Concepts		1–5
· Problems*	2–4	1, 5–12
APPENDIX B PROBLEMS*		
· Chapter 7, p. 693	1, 3–6, 9	2, 7–8

* Complete solutions to all Chapter Review and Appendix problems appear in the Problems and Solutions Manual.

LAB WORKSHEET

Use the Lab Worksheet for Chapter 7 with this Physics Lab.

BRIDGING

The topics which may need review are vectors; especially the importance of direction, instantaneous velocity, acceleration, and Newton's second law.

1 Focus

Use the demonstration below as an attention grabber. Or, a simpler form is to fasten a soft ball such as a Nerf ball or tennis ball to a cord and spin it in a horizontal circle. Ask students if there is a force on the ball in motion and what exerts the force. Now ask for the direction of the force. Show students that the cord can only pull (inward) on the ball and that it can't push outward on the ball.

2 Teach

CONCEPT DEVELOPMENT

- Point out that the equation for centripetal force is a special case of Newton's second law.
- When you swing an object in a circle, the speed may be constant, but since the direction is always changing, it is accelerating.

Study Guide Master. To reinforce the concepts in this section, have the students complete the Study Guide Master for Section 7.2 from the Teacher Resource Package.

FIGURE 7–8. Friction is the force that holds people up. Centripetal force keeps them from flying out.

Circular Motion

Your body can't sense constant velocity, but it is a sensitive accelerometer. Your stomach can detect the acceleration of an elevator or of an airplane in rough weather. It can also feel acceleration in an amusement park ride similar to the one in Figure 7–8. Except when the ride is starting or stopping, the speed is constant, but the velocity is changing because its direction is changing. The riders are moving with uniform circular motion.

A vector diagram like Figure 7–9a can help you find the acceleration of an object moving in a circle at constant speed. Points **A** and **B** are two successive positions of an object moving with uniform circular motion. The radius of the circle is r. The radius and speed are constant, so the velocity is always perpendicular to the radius. That is, the velocity is tangent to the circle. The vector v_1 represents the instantaneous velocity of the object at **A.** The vector v_2 represents the instantaneous velocity of the object at **B.** Note that the two vectors have the same length, but their directions are different.

Acceleration is the change in velocity, Δv, divided by the time interval, Δt. The difference between the two vectors, v_1 and v_2, is Δv. That is, $\Delta v = v_2 - v_1$. You know how to find a vector sum, but not a difference. We can convert the equation into a sum by adding v_1 to both sides of this equation to get $v_2 = v_1 + \Delta v$. In Chapter 6, you found a vector sum by placing two vectors head to tail. Consider Figure 7–9b. The size of Δv can be found by using a ratio of the sides of similar triangles ABC and DEF. The distance traveled by the object between point **A** and point **B** is the arc AB. If we choose **A** and **B** so they are close together, then arc AB is approximately equal to chord AB. Thus,

$$\frac{\Delta v}{v} = \text{chord } \frac{AB}{r}.$$

a

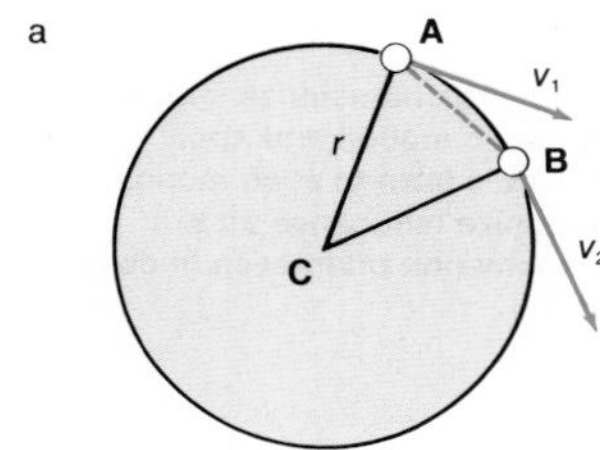

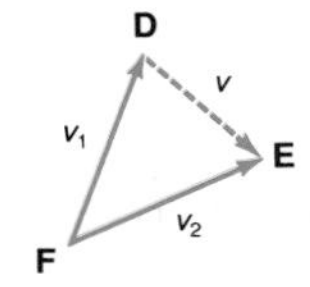

FIGURE 7–9. Vector diagrams can be used to analyze uniform circular motion.

DEMONSTRATION

Purpose: to demonstrate the centripetal acceleration of objects in circular motion.

Equipment: large jar; plastic fishing bob; string; water; tape

Procedure: 1. Tape the bob to the lid of the jar so that the bob hangs inside the jar about 2 cm from the bottom. Fill the jar with water and screw the lid on with attached bob. **2.** Holding the jar upside down and away from your body, sit on a stool and spin around. Encourage students to notice what happens to the bob.

Results: The bob will move in toward you (toward the center of the circle), showing the direction of the acceleration.

Teaching Suggestion: Liquid accelerometers may also be used for this demonstration, but the liquid will flow in the opposite direction to the acceleration. If, however, you hold the liquid accelero-

But the distance traveled in the time interval Δt is just $v\Delta t$. Thus, we obtain

$$\frac{\Delta v}{v} = \frac{v\Delta t}{r}.$$

Since acceleration is given by $a = \Delta v/\Delta t$, we find

$$a = \frac{\Delta v}{\Delta t} = \frac{v^2}{r}.$$

The direction of Δv can be seen in Figure 7–9b. As positions **A** and **B** become very close together, Δv becomes perpendicular to the two velocity vectors. That is, it is in the direction of the radius, pointing toward the center of the circle. Newton originated the word *centripetal* (sen ***TRIP*** uht uhl) for a quantity that always points toward the center of the circle. Centripetal means "center seeking." For this reason, we call the acceleration just defined **centripetal acceleration** and write

$$a_c = \frac{\Delta v}{\Delta t} = \frac{v^2}{r}.$$

Centripetal acceleration always points toward the center of the circle. It is directly proportional to the square of the speed and inversely proportional to the radius of the circle.

Centripetal acceleration is always toward the center of a circle.

It is often difficult to measure the speed of an object, but easier to measure the time needed to make a complete revolution, or the **period,** T. During this time, an object travels a distance equal to the circumference of the circle, $2\pi r$. The speed of the object is then

$$v = \frac{2\pi r}{T}.$$

F. Y. I.

A stone that is stuck in a tire of an automobile moving at highway speeds experiences a centripetal acceleration of about 2500 m/s² or 250 g.

FIGURE 7–10. In this projected rotating colony, "gravity" would actually be the centripetal force provided by the outer wall of the wheel. "Down" would be toward the outer circumference of the wheel.

CONCEPT DEVELOPMENT

Enrichment: Many amusement park rides rely on circular motion for their excitement (see facing page). Have students research these rides. Which use centripetal force as a safety factor? (For an excellent reference on the topic, see "Amusement Park Physics," by Carole Escobar, in the October, 1990 issue of *The Physics Teacher.*)

Demonstration: To demonstrate centripetal force, use 4 pieces of heavy cord 1½ m each; 30-cm × 30-cm piece of stiff cardboard; and 2–4 plastic drinking glasses. Make a hole in each corner of the cardboard. Insert a piece of cord through each hole and secure the cord to the bottom of the cardboard by knotting each end. Lay the cardboard flat on a table, bringing the cords together above the cardboard and knotting them. Tie another knot at the end of the bundle of cords. Fill the glasses about three-quarters full of water and place them on the corners of the cardboard. Carefully lift the cardboard tray up by the cords and swing until you can make a full circle. Be careful to keep the tension in the cords. The filled glasses will remain on the cardboard without spilling or falling.

Ask: What force keeps the glasses on the cardboard tray? [The tension on the cords supplies a centripetal force to keep the tray moving in a circle. The tray pushes on the bottoms of the glasses.] Why doesn't the water fall out of the glasses at the top of the swing? [When a glass is at the top of the swing, the water would fly off horizontally if there were no glass.] If the cords lose their tension, what will happen? [You will have a lot of water to clean up.]

meter tangent to the circle as you spin, it will stay level, showing there is no acceleration in that direction.

STUDY GUIDE MASTER

Use the Study Guide master for section 7.2.

CHECKING FOR UNDERSTANDING

Ask students how speed, velocity, and acceleration behave in uniform circular motion. Review the equation for centripetal force and acceleration.

RETEACHING

If centripetal force acts toward the center, why do you slide toward the outside when making a turn in a vehicle? Before you enter the turn, you travel in a straight line. Your inertia tends to keep you moving in that same fashion. However, as the car turns beneath you, if the force of friction between you and the seat is not great enough, you continue in a straight line until you encounter a resistance (the door) great enough to allow you to follow the car.

EXTENSION

Enrichment Master. Use the Enrichment Master, Gyroscope, from the Teacher Resource Package.

Critical Thinking: Think about a compact disc spinning around as it plays. Does every point on the disc have exactly the same circular motion? If not, how does the motion of different points compare? Note: The farther from the center of the disc the greater linear speed it has.

Multicultural Connections

Although throwing and killing sticks have been discovered around the world, only the Australian aborigines developed one that returned. The boomerang does not fly straight out and straight back, but flies in a loop because of torque. The torque is created because the arms of the boomerang are shaped to cause air pressure to push it to the left. The force of the air pressure creates a centripetal acceleration that causes the stick to fly in a circle.

This expression for v can be substituted into the equation for centripetal acceleration to yield

$$a_c = \frac{\left(\frac{2\pi r}{T}\right)^2}{r} = \frac{4\pi^2 r}{T^2}.$$

In circular motion, centripetal acceleration is at right angles to the instantaneous velocity.

Newton's second law tells us that an object does not accelerate unless a net force acts on it. The acceleration is in the same direction as the force. What exerts the force that gives a body its centripetal acceleration? In the case of the amusement park ride, the drum exerts a force against the backs of the riders. The force that causes the centripetal acceleration of a model plane flying in a circle is the force of the string on the plane. The moon orbits Earth with nearly uniform circular motion. Earth's gravity is the force that causes this acceleration. Because the force, as well as the acceleration, is toward the center of the circle, these forces are often called **centripetal forces.** To understand centripetal acceleration, it is very important to identify the source of the force. For a body in uniform circular motion, Newton's second law can be written in the form

$$F_{net} = F_c = ma_c = \frac{mv^2}{r} = m\left(\frac{4\pi^2 r}{T^2}\right).$$

In what direction does an object fly if the force giving it centripetal acceleration suddenly disappears? Remember that with no net force, an object moves in a straight line at constant speed. Consider an Olympic hammer thrower. The "hammer" is a heavy ball on a chain that the thrower whirls in a circle. As he whirls it at greater and greater speeds, his arms and the chain supply the force that gives it centripetal acceleration. At the correct time, he lets go of the chain. The hammer flies off in a straight line tangent to the circle. After its release, only the gravitational force acts on it.

FIGURE 7–11. The force on the hammer is exerted toward the center of the circle. When the thrower lets go, the hammer moves away in a straight line tangent to the point of release.

ENRICHMENT MASTER

Use the Enrichment master for Chapter 7 with this section.

Example Problem

Uniform Circular Motion

A 0.013-kg rubber stopper is attached to a 0.93 m length of string. The stopper is swung in a horizontal circle, making one revolution in 1.18 s. **a.** Find the speed of the stopper. **b.** Find its centripetal acceleration. **c.** Find the force the string exerts on it.

Given: mass, $m = 0.013$ kg
circle radius, $r = 0.93$ m
period, $T = 1.18$ s

Unknowns: **a.** speed, v
b. acceleration, a_c
c. force, F_c

Basic equations: **a.** $v = \frac{2\pi r}{T}$
b. $a_c = \frac{v^2}{r}$
c. $F_c = ma_c$

Solution:

a. From the period of the revolution, find the velocity.

$$\text{velocity} = \frac{\text{distance}}{\text{time}} = \frac{2\pi r}{T}$$
$$= \frac{2(3.14)(0.93\text{ m})}{1.18\text{ s}}$$
$$= \frac{5.8\text{ m}}{1.18\text{ s}} = 5.0\text{ m/s}$$

b. acceleration, $a_c = \frac{v^2}{r} = \frac{(5.0\text{ m/s})^2}{0.93\text{ m}} = 27\text{ m/s}^2$ (radially inward)

c. force, $F_c = ma_c = (0.013\text{ kg})(27\text{ m/s}^2)$
$= 0.35$ N (radially inward)

Practice Problems

9. a. Suppose the mass of the rubber stopper in the Example Problem above is doubled, but all other given quantities remain the same. How would the velocity, acceleration, and force change?

b. If the radius in the Example Problem were twice as large, but all other given quantities remained the same, how would velocity, acceleration, and force change?

c. If the stopper were swung in the same circle so it had a period half as large as in the example, how would the answers change?

10. A runner moving at a speed of 8.8 m/s rounds a bend with a radius of 25 m.

a. Find the centripetal acceleration of the runner.

b. What supplies the force needed to give this acceleration to the runner?

11. Racing on a flat track, a car going 32 m/s rounds a curve 56 m in radius.

a. What is the car's centripetal acceleration?

b. What would be the minimum coefficient of static friction between tires and road that would be needed for the car to round the curve without skidding?

POCKET LAB

TARGET PRACTICE

Tie a 1.0 m length of a string onto a one-hole rubber stopper. Note: Everyone in the classroom should be wearing goggles before anyone proceeds with the experiment. Swing the stopper around your head in a horizontal circle. Release the string from your hand when the string is lined up with a spot on the wall. Did the stopper travel toward the spot on the wall? What does this indicate about the direction of the velocity compared to the orientation of the string? Repeat the experiment until the stopper flies toward the spot on the wall.

POCKET LAB

Purpose: to allow students to investigate the circular motion of a rubber stopper.
Materials: 1.0-m string; rubber stopper with hole.
Outcome: The stopper always moves in a direction that is perpendicular to the string. Since the string is always a radius to the circle, the velocity is always tangent to the circle.

Enrichment: Have students list five examples of circular motion. Ask them which cases are uniform circular motion. Which are not?

Guided Practice: Review the Example Problem on this page with the class. Then have them try the first two Practice Problems with your guidance.

Independent Practice: Assign the remaining Practice Problems to work on at home. Go over student solutions in class the next day.

Answers To
PRACTICE PROBLEMS

Have students refer to Appendix A of the Solutions Appendix for complete solutions to Practice Problems.

9. a. v and a remain the same; F is doubled; **b.** v is doubled; a is doubled; f is doubled; **c.** v is doubled; a is four times original; f is four times original
10. a. 3.1 m/s^2; **b.** the track
11. a. 18 m/s^2; **b.** 1.8

TEACHER F.Y.I.

Newton's laws work only in inertial reference frames. An object in circular motion is always accelerating because its velocity is constantly changing direction. As a result, Newton's laws don't work in a rotating reference frame. It is possible, however, to invent "fictitious forces" to allow observers to use Newton's laws in an accelerating frame of reference. For example, the riders in Figure 7–8 feel a force pushing them outward. This force permits them to think in terms of Newton's laws. No matter how real the force seems to the riders, it is fictitious, and is the result of trying to apply Newton's laws in an accelerating reference frame. The supplementary lessons on rotational motion in the Teacher Resource Package describe this and other fictitious forces in more detail.

Answers To
PRACTICE PROBLEMS (cont.)

12. a. Refer to Solutions Appendix for diagram. **b.** horizontal component of the normal force and the horizontal component of the friction force

CONCEPT DEVELOPMENT

Mechanically inclined students, especially those who work on auto engines, may have used a tool called a torque wrench. Ask them about it. (The wrench has an indicator on it that shows the amount of torque applied to the wrench. It's used to tighten something down evenly, such as the head of an auto engine.)

Supplemental Lesson Master, Teacher Resource Package. For further investigation into torque, assign Supplemental Lesson 1, Rotational Fundamentals, and Supplemental Lesson 2, Rotational Motion.

Connect to BIOLOGY

The concept of torque is important in understanding the motion of arms and legs. If, for example, you bend your arm at the elbow, your forearm rotates about the elbow. The biceps produce the torque. Muscles exert forces when they shorten; tendons carry these forces to the required location. The elbow is the axis of rotation.

Suppose you bend your arm and hold a metal block in your hand. The force of gravity on the block would tend to straighten your arm. To keep your arm bent, your biceps must produce a torque in the opposite direction. Would the force exerted by the biceps be larger, the same size, or smaller than the force of gravity on the block? Explain using the principles shown in Figure 7–12. [The force must be larger. Figure 7–12 c and d show that if the same force is exerted far from the hinge, the torque is greater. We require that the torque produced by the force exerted by the biceps equal the torque produced by the force on your hand. Therefore, the force exerted closer to the hinge (elbow) must be greater than that exerted far away.]

▶**12.** A racing car rounds a curve that is banked.

a. Sketch the auto tire on the incline, drawing vectors representing all the forces on the tire.

b. Components of what two forces provide the centripetal acceleration for the auto tire, and therefore, the auto?

FIGURE 7–12. Not only the magnitude and direction of the applied force, but also its point of application affects the amount of torque produced.

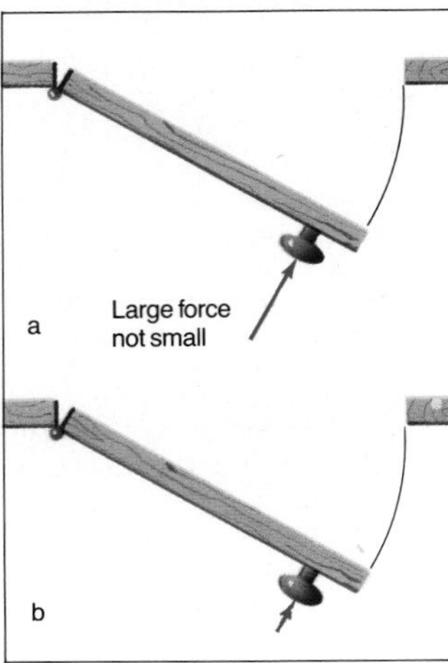

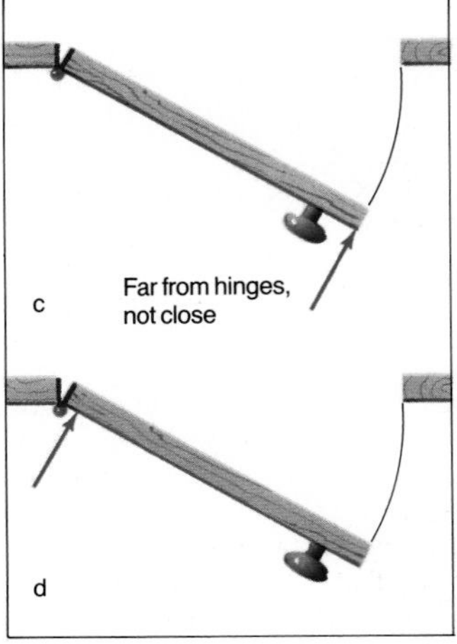

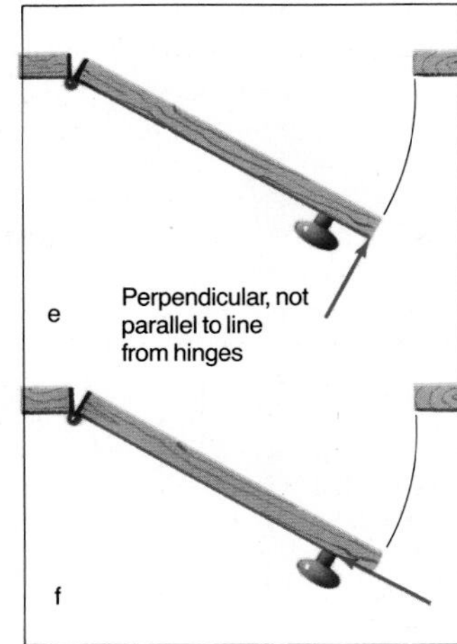

Changing Circular Motion: Torque

As we have seen, if an object moves with constant circular motion its acceleration is always perpendicular to its velocity. In this case, the acceleration can change only the direction of the velocity, not its magnitude. How then can you start or stop circular motion? You have to apply another force on the object, one that has a component parallel to its velocity. But, changing the speed of circular motion is slightly more complicated.

Consider how you close a door, Figure 7–12. How do you make the door rotate rapidly about its axis of rotation, its hinges? First, you exert a large force. Second, you must exert the force as far from the hinges as possible. Pushing on the hinges does not start it rotating. Pushing half-way to the edge does some good, but pushing on the knob or the far edge gets the door rotating most rapidly. Third, you push perpendicular to the door, not toward the hinges. We combine the information about distance and direction into one concept, the lever arm. The lever arm, *d*, Figure 7–13, is defined as the perpendicular distance from the axis of rotation to a line along which the force acts. The product of the force and the lever arm is called **torque.** The greater the torque, the greater the change in rotational motion. Thus, torque plays the role of force for rotational motion.

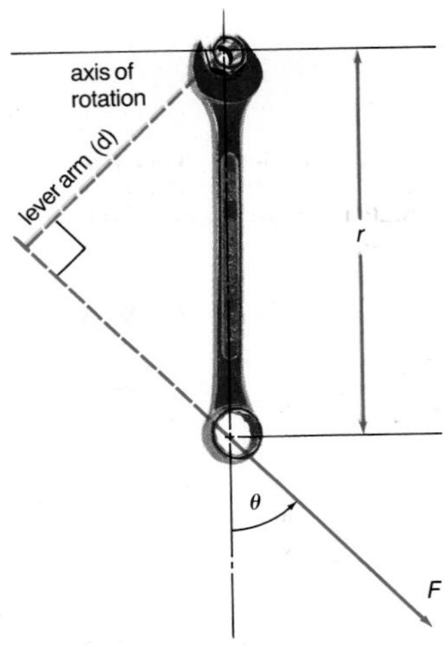

FIGURE 7–13. Torque is the product of the lever arm and the applied force.

Torques can either stop, start, or change the direction of rotation. To stop the door from closing, or to open it, you exert a force in the opposite direction. Another example of torque is the seesaw. If a seesaw is balanced there is no net torque. If it is not rotating, it remains non-

DEMONSTRATION

Purpose: to demonstrate the relationship between torque and the lever arm.

Equipment: croquet mallet; several screw eyes or hooks; mass

Procedure: 1. Put 3 or 4 screw eyes along the handle of the mallet. Hold the head of the mallet with both hands, one hand on each side of the head with the handle pointing out in front of you. **2.** Hook a mass on the screw eye closest to the head. Move the mass to each eye screw and compare the difference in difficulty you experience trying to hold up the mallet.

Results: As you move the mass farther away from the head, you'll find it much harder to keep the mallet from rotating because the mass now exerts a much larger torque (longer lever arm). Let students hold the mallet so they feel the difference in torque.

rotating. How do two children, one light, the other heavy, balance? Each child exerts a torque of the same magnitude, but in the opposite direction. The heavier one sits closer to the axis of rotation, the pivot. Each torque is the product of the force, the child's weight, *mg,* and the lever arm, *d,* the distance to the pivot. That is, the seesaw is balanced if $m_1gd_1 = m_2gd_2$.

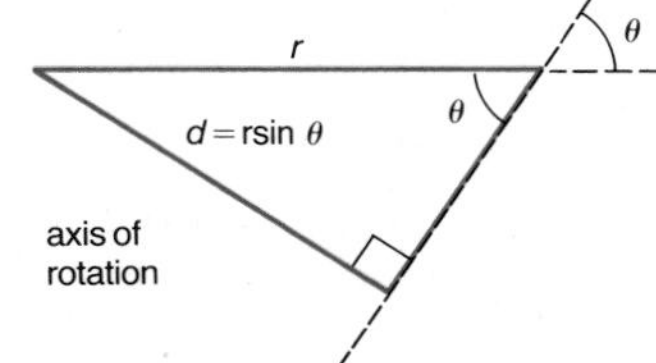

FIGURE 7–14. The lever arm is the perpendicular distance from a line along which the force acts and the axis of rotation.

Simple Harmonic Motion

A playground swing moves back and forth over the same path. A vibrating guitar string, a pendulum, and a metal block on a spring are other examples of back and forth or vibrational motion.

In each case, the object has an equilibrium position. Whenever the object is pulled away from its equilibrium position, a force in the system pulls it back toward equilibrium. The force might be gravity, as in the case of the swing or pendulum. It could be the stretch of a guitar string or a spring. *If the restoring force varies linearly with the displacement, the motion that results is called* ***simple harmonic motion.***

In simple harmonic motion, the restoring force varies linearly with displacement.

The motion of objects with SHM can be described by two quantities, period and amplitude. The **period,** *T,* is the time needed to repeat one complete cycle of motion. The **amplitude** of the motion is the maximum distance the object moves from its equilibrium position.

The period is the time required to complete a full complete cycle.

Let's look more closely at the motion of a metal block on a spring. The spring exerts a restoring force, a force that acts to oppose the force that stretched or compressed it. The force increases linearly with the amount the spring is stretched or compressed. An object that exerts a force in this way obeys a relationship called Hooke's law. Because the force dependence is linear, the movement of an object suspended on a spring is an example of simple harmonic motion.

When the block is at the equilibrium point, as shown in Figure 7–15a, the weight of the block is balanced by the force of the spring, F_1. Suppose you start the motion as shown in Figure 7–15b by pulling the block down just a few centimeters and letting go. At first, the restoring force of the spring is more than the weight. There is a net upward force, so the block is accelerated upward. As the block rises, the spring is stretched less and less and the force it exerts gradually decreases. Thus, the net force decreases and the acceleration is less.

FIGURE 7–15. Simple harmonic motion can be shown by the vibration of a metal cylinder on a spring.

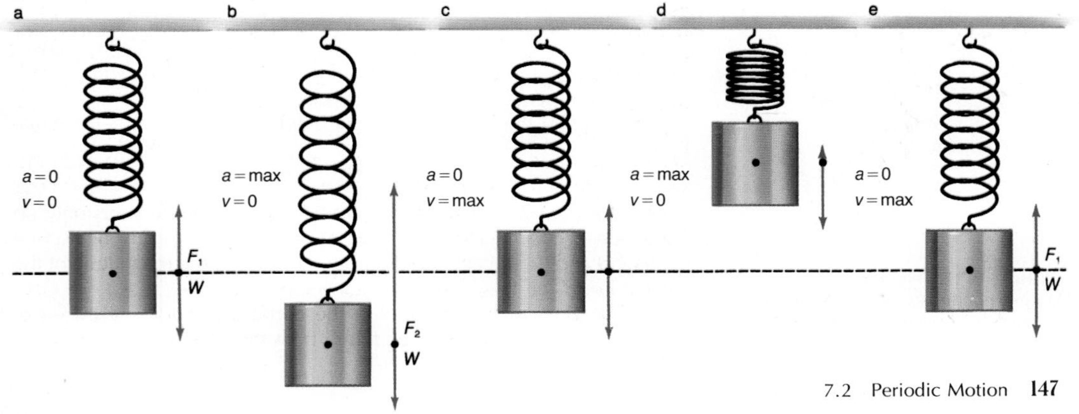

CONCEPT DEVELOPMENT

- This section introduces the concepts of simple harmonic motion (SHM), torque, period, and mechanical resonance.
- The ideas of force, displacement (position), velocity, and acceleration are all used in the analysis of SHM.
- SHM is difficult to understand because everything—position, velocity, and acceleration—is always changing. Use a diagram or an actual pendulum to show how position and velocity change. You might want to refer to Figure 7–17 on p. 148 for details, although for a pendulum the motion is basically a horizontal one.
- An object as simple as a mass suspended on a vertical spring can be intriguing to students. Let its motion start a discussion on why SHM occurs. Especially try to get them to analyze what forces cause the motion.
- A hacksaw blade or reasonably stiff strip of metal clamped at one end and plucked at the free end also makes a good example of SHM. One can even darken the room and illuminate the motion with a strobe light to show considerable detail.

Enrichment: Remind students of their experiences at a laser light show. Ask them to recall that anytime the moving laser beam reverses or abruptly changes its direction, the extreme position seems to have a brighter spot there. This is because at the extreme of its motion, it must stop and reverse so the beam is there longer and therefore looks brighter. At this extreme position, the laser beam is showing an aspect of SHM.

SUPPLEMENT

Use Supplemental Lesson Masters 1 and 2.

CONCEPT DEVELOPMENT

Have students consider how objects in SHM would behave on the moon. Have them specifically consider a pendulum and a mass on a spring.

One common example of mechanical resonance is a shopping cart with a bad wheel. If you push the cart so that the frequency of vibration caused by the bad wheel equals the natural frequency of some part of the cart, the cart will vibrate with a large amplitude. Change the speed of the cart and the resonant vibration lessens or increases.

RETEACHING

Ask students if there are amusement park rides that make them move with approximate SHM. Remind them that they feel most queasy during acceleration and, in particular, changing acceleration. Can they relate the way their stomachs feel to the characteristics of SHM?

EXTENSION

- Ask students to explain the meaning of each word in the phrase *simple harmonic motion.* What is responsible for making SHM a repetitive kind of motion?
- Explore the link between circular motion and SHM. An introductory college textbook would be a good source.

Critical Thinking Master, Teacher Resource Package. Students may further investigate concepts in this section by completing the Critical Thinking Master, Mechanical Resonance.

FIGURE 7–16. The graph in (a) shows the displacement, *d*, with respect to time, *t*. The velocity, *v*, and acceleration, *a*, with respect to time are shown in (b) and (c), respectively. Note how the amplitudes and the relative phases of the three curves are related.

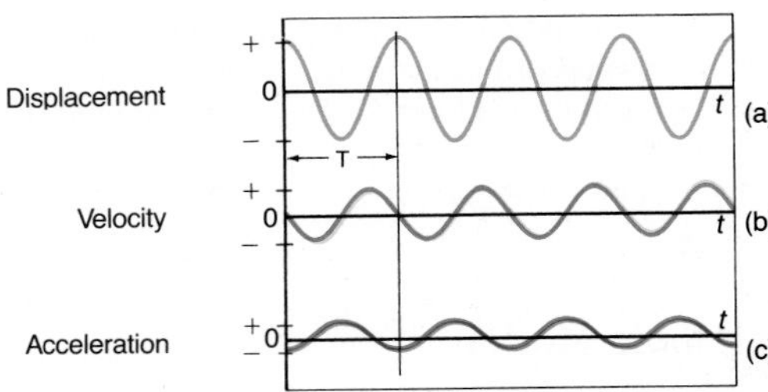

When the block returns to its equilibrium position, the net force is again zero. Why doesn't the block stop? According to Newton's laws, a force is needed to change velocity. With no net force, the block continues with its upward motion. When the block is above the equilibrium position, the weight is larger than the force exerted by the spring. There is a net downward force and resulting downward acceleration. The speed of the block decreases. When the speed is zero, the block is as high as it will go. Even though the speed is zero, there is a net downward force, and the block accelerates down. When it again reaches the equilibrium position, there is no force, but the downward motion continues. When the block returns to its lowest location, one period, *T*, has elapsed, and the cycle of motion starts over. For a small displacement, the period depends on the mass of the block and stiffness of the spring. It does not depend on the amplitude of the motion.

A pendulum making small swings undergoes simple harmonic motion.

Figure 7–16 shows graphs of the position, velocity, and acceleration of the block. At the vertical line, the block is at its largest distance from equilibrium. Its velocity is zero; it is momentarily at rest. Its acceleration is most negative, and thus the force pulling it back down to equilibrium is largest. Notice also that the speed is largest when the acceleration is zero, which occurs when the block is at the equilibrium position.

The swing of a pendulum also demonstrates SHM. A simple **pendulum** consists of an object (the bob) suspended by a string of length, *l*. The bob swings back and forth, as shown in Figure 7–17. The force on the bob when it is pulled away from the vertical is also shown. The gravitational force, the weight, *W*, is resolved into two components. $F_{\parallel}$ is along the direction of the string. The component $F_{\perp}$ is at right angles to the direction of the string. When the bob is pulled to the right, $F_{\perp}$ is to the left, and vice versa. That is, the component of the weight, $F_{\perp}$, is a restoring force. Further, for small angles (θ less than 15°) the magnitude of $F_{\perp}$ is proportional to the displacement of the bob. Thus, small-displacement pendulum motion is an example of SHM.

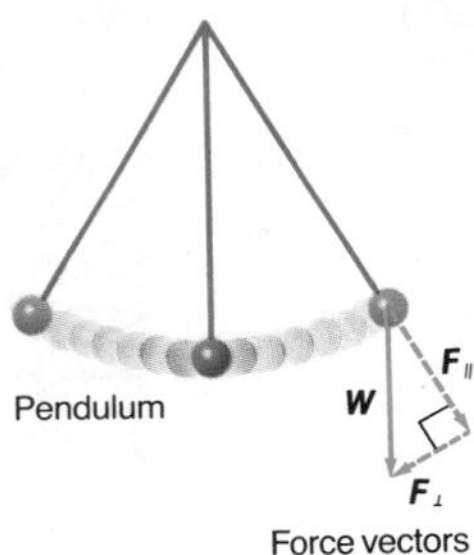

FIGURE 7–17. The motion of a simple pendulum. The gravitational force on a pendulum can be resolved into two components.

The period of the simple pendulum of length, *l*, is given by the equation

$$T = 2\pi\sqrt{l/|g|}.$$

Notice that for small-angle displacements, the period depends only on the length of the pendulum, not its mass or amplitude. By measuring the length and period of a pendulum, you can find the magnitude of the local value of the gravitational acceleration, $|g|$.

The frequency of a pendulum is the number of complete cycles of motion in one second. It can be found from the period using $f = 1/T$.

7:2 ASSIGNMENT GUIDE

	PRACTICE	EXTENSION
CHAPTER REVIEW pp. 150–153		
· Reviewing Concepts	4–12	
· Applying Concepts		6–11
· Problems*	13–17, 21	18–20, 22
APPENDIX B PROBLEMS*		
· Chapter 7, pp. 693–694	13–15	10–12, 16

* Complete solutions to all Chapter Review and Appendix problems appear in the Problems and Solutions Manual.

CRITICAL THINKING

Use the Critical Thinking master for Chapter 7 with this section.

Example Problem

The Pendulum

On top of a mountain a pendulum 1.55 m long has a period of 2.51 s. What is the acceleration due to gravity at this location?

Given: period of pendulum, $T = 2.51$ s
length of pendulum, $l = 1.55$ m

Unknown: $|g|$

Basic equation: $T = 2\pi\sqrt{\frac{l}{|g|}}$

Solution:

$$g = \frac{4\pi^2}{T^2}l = \frac{4(3.14)^2}{(2.51\ \text{s})^2}1.55\ \text{m} = 9.71\ \text{m/s}^2$$

POCKET LAB

TICK-TOCK

Use the pendulum equation to predict the length needed for a period of 1.00 s. Use a piece of string and a steel nut to build your pendulum. Test your pendulum for 30 complete swings. Note: The equation is accurate only for small displacements.

Practice Problems

13. What is the length of a simple pendulum whose period is 1.00 s? Assume normal g.

▶ **14.** A future astronaut lands on a planet with an unknown value of g. She finds that the period of a pendulum 0.65 m long is 2.8 s. What is g for the surface of this planet?

Physics and technology

CENTRIFUGES

Have you ever watched the spin cycle on a washing machine? The wet clothes are spun in a circle at high speed. Most of the water flies out through the holes in the drum, and the clothes come out almost dry. From your point of view, the drum exerts an inward, or centripetal force on the clothes, but not on the water escaping through the holes. From the point of view of the clothes, there is a new, strong force that pushes everything outward toward the drum.

Centrifuges are widely used outside the home. In dairies, they are used to separate cream from milk. In industry, they are used to reclaim used motor oil or refine vegetable oil. In scientific research laboratories, they are used to measure the molecular weights of large molecules. Centripetal accelerations are usually measured in units of "g", 9.80 m/s^2. Values as high as 300 000 g are not uncommon.

The centrifuge is now being used to grow pure crystals for the semiconductor industry. Crystals grown in a centrifuge are better than those grown under normal conditions or even at 0 g in space.

Centrifuges have also been used to separate the isotopes of uranium for use in nuclear reactors or weapons. Separation of the slightly lighter uranium-235 is usually done by gaseous diffusion in plants the size of small cities.

How can peaceful applications of centrifuges be developed while weapons uses be stopped?

Guided Practice: After going over the Example Problem on this page, have students work on the first Practice Problem.

Independent Practice: Assign the remaining Practice Problem on this page for homework and go over it in class the next day.

Answers To
PRACTICE PROBLEMS

Have students refer to Appendix A of the Solutions Appendix for complete solutions to Practice Problems.

13. 0.248 m
14. 3.3 m/s^2

POCKET LAB

TICK-TOCK

Purpose: to allow students to investigate the motion of a swinging pendulum.
Materials: 1.0-m string; steel nut.
Outcome: The length of the pendulum should be 0.248 m. Most students will find that their pendulum is accurate to within 1.0 s per minute. Students should be reminded that the length is measured from the center of the mass of the nut.

Assessment

Performance

After students have found the length of a pendulum with a 1.00-s period, ask them to predict the length needed for a 2.00-s period pendulum. Have them check their results. Challenge them to plan the construction of a pendulum with a period of 10.0 s. [A pendulum about 1 m long will have a period of 2 s. A 10-s pendulum would have to be 25 m long!]

Physics and technology

Answer to student question: There are no easy methods. A country determined to use a centrifuge for weapon production can usually find ways to obtain the highly specialized materials needed even if laws exist to prevent their export.

Teacher Resources: Davis, Jay C. and David A. Kay. "Iraq's Secret Nuclear Weapon Program." *Physics Today,* July 1992, page 21.
Yam, Philip. "High on Gravity: Increasing the G's Grows Crystals with Few Defects." *Scientific American,* March 1993, page 138.

3 Close

CONVERGENT QUESTION

Compare SHM and projectile motion.

CONCEPT REVIEW ANSWERS

2.1 To move you in a circular path, there is an added upward force on you. Since you react to external forces, this makes you feel heavier.
2.2 Earth's gravity
2.3 Either keep the same amplitude and decrease the period (and length), or hold the period constant and increase the amplitude.
2.4 Critical Thinking: Yes, if the amplitude (measured by the noise it makes) depends on the speed (and thus frequency of driving oscillation).

CLOSING CHAPTER 7

Review Summary statements and Key Terms with your students.

ASSESSMENT

Vocabulary Review Master, Teacher Resource Package. Use this master to check students' understanding of Key Terms.

Evaluation Masters. Use the A and B Evaluation Masters from the Teacher Resource Package to test qualitative chapter objectives and parts C and D to test quantitative chapter objectives.

F. Y. I.

Audiences who sit in balconies at concerts and jump up and down in time with the music have caused damage to the balcony when the jumping frequency matched the natural vibration frequency of the balcony.

The amplitude of a vibrating object can be increased by the application of small forces at specific intervals.

The amplitude of any vibrating object can be greatly increased by applying small external forces at specific regular intervals of time. This effect is called **mechanical resonance.** You were probably first introduced to resonance when you learned to "pump" a playground swing. You found that you could increase the amplitude of the swing if your friend applied forces to it at just the right times. The time interval between the applied forces had to equal the period of the swing. Other familiar examples of mechanical resonance include rocking a car to free it from a snow bank and jumping up and down on a trampoline or diving board. Resonances can also cause damage. To avoid resonance, soldiers do not march across bridges in cadence. The rhythm of their steps could otherwise create large oscillations caused by their steps resonating with the natural period of the bridge. Audiences in theater balconies who jump up and down in time with the music have caused damage to the balcony when the jumping frequency matched the natural vibration frequency of the balcony.

CONCEPT REVIEW

2.1 When you drive rapidly on a hilly road or ride in a roller coaster, you feel lighter as you go over the top of a hill, and heavier when you go through a valley. Sketch the situation, showing the forces that explain this sensation.
2.2 Thanks to Earth's rotation, you move with uniform circular motion. What supplies the force that keeps you moving in this circle?
2.3 The speed of a pendulum bob is largest when it is directly below the support. Give two ways you could increase this speed.
2.4 Critical Thinking: Is the rattle in a car ever an example of resonance? If so, how could you tell?

CHAPTER 7 REVIEW

SUMMARY

7.1 Projectile Motion

- The horizontal and vertical motions of a projectile are independent of one another, in the absence of air resistance.
- Ignoring air resistance, a projectile moves with constant velocity in the horizontal direction and constant acceleration in the vertical direction.
- The trajectory of a projectile depends on the horizontal and vertical components of its initial velocity.

7.2 Periodic Motion

- A body moving in uniform circular motion has a constant speed and is accelerated toward the center of the circle.
- Torque is the product of the force and the lever arm. Torque can either stop, start, or change the direction of rotation.
- An object moving with simple harmonic motion moves back and forth with a constant period.
- Mechanical resonance can greatly increase the amplitude of SHM when a small, periodic net force acts on an oscillating object at its natural frequency.

REVIEW MASTER

Use the Vocabulary Review master for Chapter 7 with this section.

EVALUATION MASTER

Use the Chapter Evaluation master for Chapter 7 with this section.

KEY TERMS

projectiles
trajectory
range
centripetal acceleration
period
centripetal forces
torque
simple harmonic motion
amplitude
pendulum
mechanical resonance

REVIEWING CONCEPTS

1. Consider the ball's trajectory in Figure 7–18.
   a. Where is the vertical velocity the greatest?
   b. Where is the greatest horizontal velocity?
   c. Where is the vertical velocity least?
   d. Name the curve traveled by the ball.

FIGURE 7–18. Use with Reviewing Concepts 1.

2. A student is playing with a radio-controlled race car on a balcony of a 6th-floor condominium. An accidental turn sends the car through the railing and off the edge of the balcony. Does the vertical distance the car falls depend on the velocity with which it speeds off the edge?
3. An airplane pilot flying at constant velocity and altitude drops a flare. Ignoring air resistance, where will the plane be relative to the flare when the flare hits the ground?
4. Can you go around a curve
   a. with zero acceleration? Explain.
   b. with constant acceleration? Explain.
5. What relationship must exist between an applied force and the velocity of a moving object if uniform circular motion is to result?
6. Sue whirls a yo-yo horizontally above her head. What is the direction of the force that acts on the yo-yo?
7. What is the direction of the force that acts on clothes in the spin cycle of a washing machine?
8. In general, a long-handled wrench is better to remove a stuck bolt than a short-handled wrench. Explain.
9. What is the difference between the period and the amplitude of a pendulum?
10. Describe a method of using a simple pendulum to find the value of g at a given location.
11. Sue is swinging her yo-yo as if it was a pendulum. At what point in the swing does the yo-yo have the greatest force acting on it?
12. When an object is vibrating on a spring and passes through the equilibrium position, there is no net force on it. Why is the velocity not zero at this point? What quantity is zero?

APPLYING CONCEPTS

1. A batter hits a pop-up straight up over home plate at an initial velocity of 20 m/s. The ball is caught by the catcher at the same height that it was hit. At what velocity will the ball land in the catcher's mitt?
2. Sam throws a baseball horizontally from the top of a cliff. If Sam throws the baseball with higher speed,
   a. how will the time it takes to hit the ground be affected?
   b. how will the horizontal distance be affected?
3. A zoologist standing on a cliff aims a tranquilizer gun at a monkey hanging from a distant tree branch. The barrel of the gun is horizontal. Just as the zoologist pulls the trigger, the monkey lets go of the branch and begins to fall. Will the dart hit the monkey?
4. Bernie throws a football at a 45° angle. How long is the football in the air if it took 3.0 s to reach the top of its path?
5. A friend who is competing in the long jump asks you to explain the physics of this event. Does the height of the jump make any difference? What influences the length of the jump?
6. Sue is swinging a yo-yo around her head. What happens to the size of the centripetal acceleration if the mass of the yo-yo is doubled without changing the period or length of the string?
7. Imagine you are sitting in a car tossing a ball straight up into the air.
   a. If the car is moving with constant velocity, will the ball land in front of, behind, or in your hand?
   b. If the car rounds a curve at constant speed, where will the ball land?
8. Which is easier for turning a stuck screw, a screwdriver with a thick handle or one with a long handle?

Answers To

REVIEWING CONCEPTS

1. Up is positive and down is negative. **a.** The greatest vertical velocity occurs at point **A.** **b.** The horizontal velocity at all points is the same. Horizontal velocity is constant and independent of vertical velocity. **c.** The least vertical velocity occurs at point **E.** **d.** The curve is a parabola.

2. No. The horizontal component of motion does not affect the vertical component.

3. The plane will be directly over the flare when the flare hits the ground. Both have the same horizontal velocity.

4. a. No. Going around a curve causes a change in direction of velocity. Thus, the acceleration cannot be zero. **b.** No. The magnitude of the acceleration may be constant, but the direction of the acceleration changes.

5. Circular motion results when the direction of the force is constantly perpendicular to the instantaneous velocity of the object.

6. along the string toward the center of the circle that the yo-yo follows

7. The walls of the tub push the clothes toward the center of the tub. Some of the water in the clothes is not pushed toward the center of the tub, and goes out through the holes in the wall of the tub. Check out the pattern in the clothes next to the wall right after the spin cycle stops.

8. A specific torque is necessary to unstick a bolt. By increasing the length of the handle (torque arm) of the wrench, a smaller force is necessary for the same torque.

9. The period of a pendulum, and any vibrating object, is the time required for one vibration. The amplitude is the distance from rest position to the point of greatest displacement.

10. Use the equation

$$T = 2\pi\sqrt{\frac{l}{|g|}},\ g = \frac{4\pi^2 l}{T^2}.$$

Measure the length of the pendulum and its period, and calculate g.

11. at the bottom of the swing

Answers continue on page 152.

Answers To
REVIEWING CONCEPTS (cont)

12. According to Newton's laws, net force = zero means acceleration is zero. Passing through the equilibrium position, the acceleration has become zero and the velocity is maximum.

Answers To
APPLYING CONCEPTS

1. −20 m/s, where the negative sign indicates down

2. a. No change in time—the time it takes to hit the ground depends only on vertical velocities and acceleration. **b.** higher horizontal speed, longer horizontal distance

3. Yes. In fact the monkey would be safe if it did not let go of the branch. The vertical acceleration of the dart will be the same as that of the monkey. Therefore, the dart will be at the same vertical height when it reaches the monkey.

4. 6.0 s; 3.0 s up, and 3.0 s down

5. Both speed and angle of launch matter, so height does make a difference. Maximum range is achieved when the resultant velocity has equal vertical and horizontal components; in other words, a launch angle of 45°. For this reason, height as well as speed affect the range.

6. Nothing—the size of the centripetal acceleration is independent of the mass.

7. a. The ball will land in your hand since you, the ball, and the car are all moving forward with the same speed. **b.** The ball will land beside you, toward the outside of the curve. A top view would show the ball moving straight while you and the car moved out from under the ball.

8. long handle—a longer lever arm, smaller force

9. The European door has a shorter lever arm and requires more force.

10. Since $T = 2\pi\sqrt{\frac{l}{|g|}}$, slide the bob down to lengthen the pendulum and increase the time interval.

11. $T = 2\pi\sqrt{\frac{l}{|g|}}$, so with g smaller, T would be longer.

9. Some doors in Europe have door knobs in the center of the door rather than at the edge. Which door requires more force to produce the same torque to close the door?

10. If you find a pendulum clock running slightly fast, how can you adjust it to keep better time? Explain.

11. Suppose an astronaut carries a pendulum to the moon. Would the period of the pendulum be shorter, longer, or the same on the moon as on Earth?

PROBLEMS

▶ **1.** Assuming that the two baseballs in Figure 7–19 have the same velocity, 25 m/s, draw two separate graphs of y as a function of t and x as a function of t for each ball.

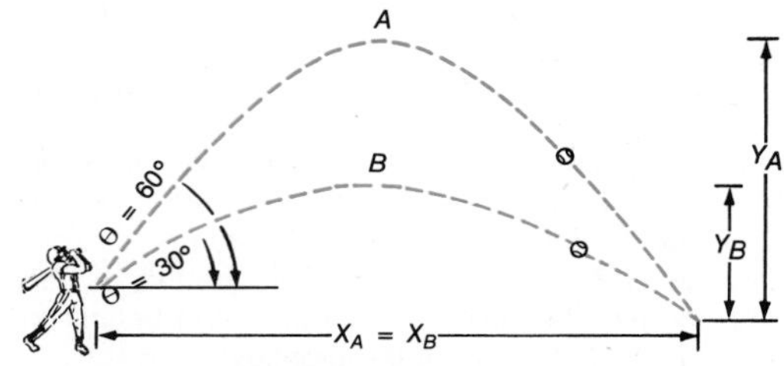

FIGURE 7–19. Use with Problem 1.

2. A stone is thrown horizontally at 8.0 m/s from a cliff 78.4 m high. How far from the base of the cliff does the stone strike the ground?

3. A toy car runs off the edge of a table that is 1.225 m high. If the car lands 0.400 m from the base of the table,
a. how long does it take for the car to fall?
b. what is the horizontal velocity of the car?

4. Janet jumps off a high-diving platform with a horizontal velocity of 2.8 m/s and lands in the water 2.6 s later. How high is the platform, and how far from the base of the platform does she land?

▶ **5.** An airplane traveling 1001 m above the ocean at 125 km/h is to drop a box of supplies to shipwrecked victims below.
a. How many seconds before being directly overhead should the box be dropped?
b. What is the horizontal distance between the plane and the victims when the box is dropped?

▶ **6.** Divers at Acapulco dive from a cliff that is 61 m high. If the rocks below the cliff extend outward for 23 m, what is the minimum horizontal velocity a diver must have to clear the rocks safely?

▶ **7.** A dart player throws a dart horizontally at a speed of +12.4 m/s. The dart hits the board 0.32 m below the height from which it was thrown. How far away is the player from the board?

▶ **8.** An arrow is shot at a 30.0° angle with the horizontal. It has a velocity of 49 m/s.
a. How high will the arrow go?
b. What horizontal distance will it travel?

▶ **9.** A pitched ball is hit by a batter at a 45° angle. It just clears the outfield fence, 98 m away. Find the velocity of the ball when it left the bat. Assume the fence is the same height as the pitch.

▶ **10.** Trailing by two points, and with only 2.0 s remaining in a basketball game, a player makes a jump-shot at an angle of 60° with the horizontal, giving the ball a velocity of 10 m/s. The ball is released at the height of the basket, 3.05 m above the floor. Yes! It's a score.
a. How much time is left in the game when the basket is made?
b. Shots made outside a semicircle of 6.02-m radius from a spot directly beneath the basket are awarded 3 points, while those inside score 2 points. Did the player tie the game or put the team ahead?

▶ **11.** A basketball player tries to make a half-court jump-shot, releasing the ball at the height of the basket. Assuming the ball is launched at 51.0°, 14.0 m from the basket, what velocity must the player give the ball?

▶ **12.** A baseball is hit at 30.0 m/s at an angle of 53.0° with the horizontal. Immediately an outfielder runs 4.00 m/s toward the infield and catches the ball at the same height it was hit. What was the original distance between the batter and the outfielder?

7.2 Periodic Motion

13. It takes a 615-kg racing car 14.3 s to travel at a uniform speed around a circular racetrack of 50.0 m radius.
a. What is the acceleration of the car?
b. What average force must the track exert on the tires to produce this acceleration?

Answers To
PROBLEMS

Complete solutions for all Chapter Review Problems can be found in the Problems and Solutions Manual accompanying this text.

1. Refer to Problems and Solutions Manual.
2. 32 m
3. a. 0.500 s; **b.** 0.800 m/s
4. 33 m; 7.3 m
5. a. 14.3 s; **b.** 496 m
6. 6.6 m/s
7. 3.2 m
8. a. 32 m; **b.** 2.1×10^2 m
9. 31 m/s, 45°
10. a. 0.2 s; **b.** ahead
11. 11.8 m/s, 51.0°
12. 108.3 m
13. a. 9.65 m/s^2; **b.** 5.94×10^3 N
14. a. 51 m/s^2; **b.** 3.6×10^2 N
15. a. 6.3 N; **b.** 25 N; **c.** 4:1

14. An athlete whirls a 7.00-kg hammer tied to the end of a 1.3-m chain in a horizontal circle. The hammer moves at the rate of 1.0 rev/s.
   a. What is the centripetal acceleration of the hammer?
   b. What is the tension in the chain?
15. Sue whirls a yo-yo in a horizontal circle. The yo-yo has a mass of 0.20 kg and is attached to a string 0.80 m long.
   a. If the yo-yo makes 1.0 complete revolution each second, what force does the string exert on it?
   b. If Sue increases the speed of the yo-yo to 2.0 revolutions per second, what force does the string now exert?
   c. What is the ratio of answer **b** to **a?** Why?
16. A coin is placed on a stereo record revolving at 33 1/3 revolutions per minute.
   a. In what direction is the acceleration of the coin, if any?
   b. Find the acceleration of the coin when it is placed 5.0, 10, and 15 cm from the center of the record.
   c. What force accelerates the coin?
   d. At which of the three radii listed in **b** would the coin be most likely to fly off? Why?
17. According to the *Guinness Book of World Records,* (1990 edition, p. 169) the highest rotary speed ever attained was 2010 m/s (4500 mph). The rotating rod was 15.3 cm (6 in) long. Assume the speed quoted is that of the end of the rod.
   a. What is the centripetal acceleration of the end of the rod?
   b. If you were to attach a 1.00-g object to the end of the rod, what force would be needed to hold it on the rod?
   c. What is the period of rotation of the rod?
▶ 18. Refer to Figure 7–8. The carnival ride has a 2.0-m radius and rotates 1.1 times per second.
   a. Find the speed of a rider.
   b. Find the centripetal acceleration of a rider.
   c. What produces this acceleration?
   d. When the floor drops down, riders are held up by friction. What coefficient of friction is needed to keep the riders from slipping?
▶ 19. An early major objection to the idea that Earth is spinning on its axis was that Earth would turn so fast at the equator that people would be thrown off into space. Show the error in this logic by calculating
   a. the speed of a 97-kg person at the equator. The radius of Earth is about 6400 km.
   b. the centripetal force on the person.
   c. the weight of the person.
▶ 20. Friction provides the centripetal force necessary for a car to travel around a flat circular race track. What is the maximum speed at which a car can safely travel around a circular track of radius 80.0 m if the coefficient of friction between the tire and road is 0.30?
21. A pendulum has a length of 0.67 m.
   a. Find its period.
   b. How long would the pendulum have to be to double the period?
   c. Why is your answer to part **b** not just double the length?
▶ 22. Find the length of a pendulum oscillating on the moon that would have the same period as a 1.0-m pendulum oscillating on Earth. The moon's gravity is one-sixth of Earth's gravity.

USING LAB SKILLS

1. After doing the Pocket Lab on page 135, estimate the absolute and percent uncertainty in your measurements of the time of fall for the golf ball. How could you increase the accuracy of the measurement?

USING A GRAPHING CALCULATOR

Ken Griffey Jr. hits a belt-high (1.0m) fastball down the left field line in Fenway Park. The ball has an initial velocity of 42.0 m/s at an initial angle of 26 degrees. The left field wall in Fenway Park is 96.0 meters away from home plate at the foul pole and is 14 meters high. Use a graphing calculator to plot the path of the ball. Trace along the path to find how high above the ground the ball is at 96.0 meters. Does the ball clear the wall?

THINKING PHYSIC-LY

Two small, heavy objects are dropped simultaneously into a very deep and narrow canyon from opposite sides. One of them is given a shove in the horizontal direction toward the other object at the same instant they are dropped. Explain why they will eventually collide if the canyon is deep enough.

16. a. toward center; **b.** 0.61 m/s^2; 1.2 m/s^2; 1.8 m/s^2; **c.** friction; **d.** 15 cm
17. a. 2.64×10^7 m/s^2; **b.** 2.64×10^4 N; **c.** 4.78×10^{-4} s
18. a. 14 m/s; **b.** 98 m/s^2; **c.** drum wall; **d.** 0.10
19. a. 465 m/s; **b.** 3.3 N; **c.** 9.5×10^2 N
20. 15 m/s
21. a. 1.6 s; **b.** 2.7 m; **c.** $T \propto \sqrt{l}$
22. 0.16 m

Answer To
USING LAB SKILLS

1. The uncertainty of the measurement is about 0.1 s out of a measurement of about 0.6 s, so that the % uncertainty is

$$\text{uncertainty} = \frac{0.10\text{ s}}{0.60\text{ s}} \times 100 = 17\%$$

To increase their accuracy, students might suggest a videotape of the event with a timer superimposed on the screen.

Answer To
THINKING PHYSIC-LY

Both objects fall at exactly the same rate. Since one object has a horizontal velocity, the two objects get closer to each other and, if the canyon is deep enough, they hit.

Answers To
USING YOUR GRAPHING CALCULATOR

1. Set the range values (RANGE 0 100 10 0 20 2)
2. Clear the graph (Cls EXE)
3. Graph the equation of the path of the ball:
4. Trace along the graph to $x = 96$ and find y. (TRACE –> X <–> Y)

Answer: The ball is 2.7 m above the ground. It clears the wall.

$$y = 1.0 + x \tan 26° - 4.9\left(\frac{x}{42 \cos 26°}\right)^2$$
$$= 1.0 + 0.49\,x - 3.4 \times 10^{-3}\,x^2 \text{ (GRAPH 1 + .49xX – .0034xXxX)}$$

CHAPTER

8 Universal Gravitation

PLANNING GUIDE (6 class sessions)

CONTENTS	TEXT FEATURES	TEACHER RESOURCE PACKAGE	OTHER COMPONENTS
8.1 Motion in the Heavens and on Earth, pp. 156–163 (3 Class Sessions) • Kepler's Laws of Planetary Motion • Universal Gravitation • Newton's Use of His Law of Universal Gravitation • Weighing Earth	**Physics Lab:** The Orbit, p. 158 **Pocket Lab:** Weight in Free Fall, p. 157 **Problem Solving Strategy:** Extracting Square and Cube Roots, p. 157 **Concept Review**, p. 163	**Study Guide:** Motion in the Heavens and on Earth **Physics Lab Data Sheet:** The Orbit **Critical Thinking Master:** Acceleration Due to Gravity **Enrichment Master:** Variations in Acceleration on Earth **Transparency Worksheet:** Kepler's Second Law **Transparency Worksheet:** Gravitation	**Laboratory Manual:** Lab 8.1 Kepler's Laws **Transparency 9:** Kepler's Second Law **Transparency 10:** Gravitation
8.2 Using the Law of Universal Gravitation, pp. 164–170 (3 Class Sessions) • Motion of Planets and Satellites • Weight and Weightlessness • The Gravitational Field • Einstein's Theory of Gravity	**Physics and Technology:** Effects of Weightlessness, p. 167 **Pocket Lab:** Water, Water, Everywhere, p. 166 **Concept Review,** p. 170	**Study Guide:** Using the Law of Universal Gravitation **Reteaching Master:** Testing Einstein's Theory	
Chapter Review, pp. 170–173	Summary Key Terms Reviewing Concepts Applying Concepts Problems Using a Graphing Calculator Thinking Physic-ly	**Vocabulary Review** **Chapter Test**	**Test Bank**

SUPPLEMENTARY MATERIALS

SOFTWARE	AUDIOVISUAL	BOOKS/MAGAZINES
Planetary Motion, Queue, Inc. (Apple II). *Gravitational Fields,* Queue, Inc. (Apple II). *Investigating Gravitational Force,* IBM Corp. (IBM PC).	Filmstrips: *Gravity: The Universal Force,* Science and Mankind. *General Relativity: A Theory of Gravity,* AVNA Media. Video: *Galileo: The Challenge of Reason,* Learning Corporation of America.	Leyden, Michael B. "The Elliptical Johannes Kepler." *The Science Teacher,* November 1984, pp. 52–56. Okun, L.B. "The Concept of Mass." *Physics Today,* June 1989, p. 31. Peterson, I. "Stronger Support for Equivalence Principle." *Science News,* September 22, 1990, p. 183. Whitman, John C. "Are Your Students Proportionality Literate?" *The Science Teacher,* November 1987, pp. 37–39.

PROBLEM CORRELATION

CONCEPTS	CHAPTER REVIEW			PROBLEMS APPENDIX
	Reviewing Concepts	Applying Concepts	Problems	
8.1 Motion in the Heavens and on Earth				
Kepler's Laws of Planetary Motion	1,2,3	1	1,**2**,**3**,4,**5**	1,2,**3**
Universal Gravitation	4,5	2,3	6,7,8,9,10,11,12, **13**,14,**15**,**16**	4,5,6,7,8,9,**10**,11
Newton's Use of His Law of Universal Gravitation	6,7,8	4,5	17,**18**,**19**	12
Weighing Earth				
8.2 Using the Law of Universal Gravitation				
Motion of Planets and Satellites	9,10,11	6,7,8	20,**21**	13
Weight and Weightlessness	12,13	9,10,11	22,23,**24**,**25**	14
The Gravitational Field	14	12,13	26,27,28	15,16
Einstein's Theory of Gravity	15			

ACTIVITY AND DEMONSTRATION MATERIALS

PHYSICS LAB	POCKET LAB	DEMONSTRATIONS
Page 158 2 thumbtacks 21 cm x 28 cm piece of cardboard or corkboard sheet of paper 30 cm of string or thread pencil	Pages 157, 166 string spring scale 1-kg mass pencil Styrofoam or paper cup colored water	Page 157 2 suction-cup darts chalkboard chalk 30-cm string

EXTENSION PROJECTS

LIBRARY RESEARCH

1. Space Travel
Through library research, find out how astronauts train for space travel and how changes in gravity affect them. What are the effects of long-term weightlessness?

HANDS-ON

2. Reaction Time
Compute your reaction time by having a partner drop a meter stick between your forefinger and thumb. Use $t \approx \sqrt{2s/g}$, where t is reaction time, and s is the distance the meter stick falls before you stop it.

STUDENT READINGS

Adney, Kenneth J. "Applying Kepler's Third Law." *The Physics Teacher,* November 1987.

Eckroth, Charles A. "Earth and Moon Motions Around Their Common Center of Mass." *The Physics Teacher,* September 1990.

Oppenheimer, Steve. "The Search for Gravity Waves." *Science Digest,* March 1984.

"Overcoming the Human Factor [cosmonauts deal with problems living in space]." *U.S. News and World Report,* May 16, 1988.

Rees, Martin J. "Black Holes in Galactic Centers." *Scientific American,* November 1990.

"Space Gyroscopes for Testing Relativity." *Science News,* March 3, 1990.

Chapter 8

Universal Gravitation

CHAPTER OVERVIEW

Theme Development: The chapter introduces the theme of patterns of change, particularly cycles of motion. Also discussed is the approach to scientific inquiry exemplified in the work of both Newton and Kepler; the enormous scale over which the force of gravitation acts; and an essential aspect of Newton's world view.

MISCONCEPTIONS

Perhaps the most difficult idea here is the inverse square nature of the law of universal gravitation, since it is the first time that students have met with it in this course. Also hard to internalize is that the law of universal gravitation gives the *interaction* force of A on B and B on A. The concept of weightlessness gives students trouble as well.

KEY TERMS

gravitational force
inverse square laws
Kepler's laws of planetary motion
satellite
weightlessness

Laboratory Options

STUDENT EDITION

Physics Lab

The Orbit	158

Pocket Labs

Weight in Free Fall	157
Water, Water, Everywhere	166

TEACHER EDITION

Activities

Demonstration	157
Cooperative Learning	162, 169

LABORATORY MANUAL

Kepler's Laws	Lab 8.1

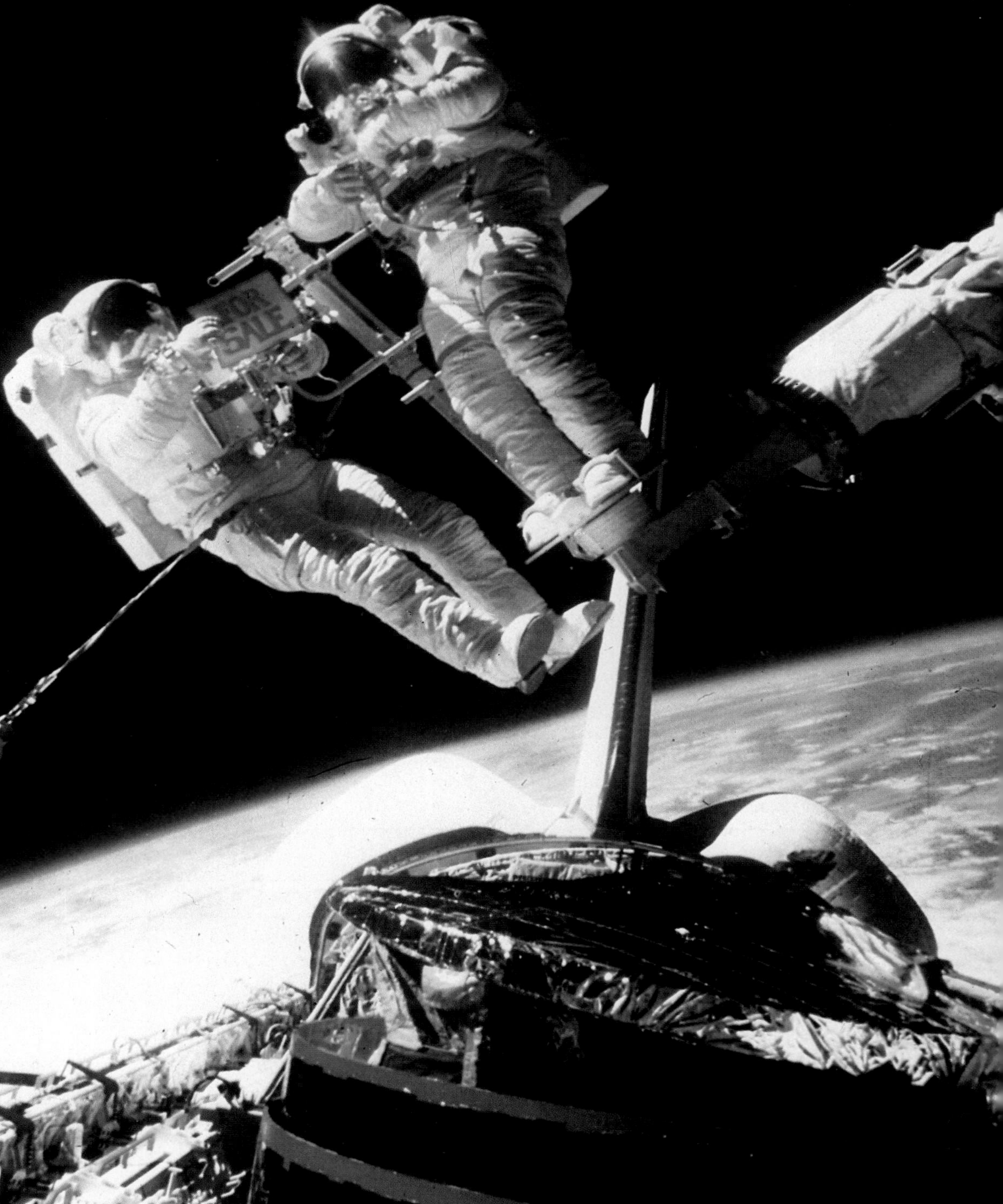

CHAPTER 8 Universal Gravitation

Floating Freely

Two astronauts, a satellite, and the space shuttle are seen in orbit about Earth. They appear to be floating weightless in space. Does Earth's gravitational force reach into space? Is this force the same strength as it is on Earth?

Why do objects fall toward Earth? To ancient Greek scientists, certain things, like hot air or smoke, rose; others, like rocks and shoes, fell simply because they had some built-in desire to rise or fall. The Greeks gave the names "levity" and "gravity" to these properties. If you ask a child today why things fall, he or she will probably say "because of gravity." But, giving something a name does not explain it. Galileo and Newton gave the name *gravity* to the force that exists between Earth and objects. Newton showed that the same force exists between all bodies. In this century, Einstein gave a much different and deeper description of the gravitational attraction. But, we still know only how things fall, not why.

As Galileo wrote almost four hundred years ago in response to a statement that "gravity" is why stones fall downward,

> *What I am asking you for is not the name of the thing, but its essence, of which essence you know not a bit more than you know about the essence of whatever moves the stars around. ...we do not really understand what principle or what force it is that moves stones downward.*

The question of why objects attract each other is still not answered.

Chapter Outline

Concept Check

The following terms or concepts from earlier chapters are important for a good understanding of this chapter. If you are not familiar with them, you should review them before studying this chapter.
- velocity, Chapter 3
- acceleration, Chapter 4
- Newton's second law, Chapter 5
- circular motion, Chapter 7
- centripetal acceleration, Chapter 7

155

Introducing The Chapter

Floating Freely

Using The Photo: The motion of things in orbit is different in many ways from motions that we usually see. The speed of orbital motion is an important key to understanding such motion. To answer the chapter opener question, refer students to page 166.

Concept Check

Make sure students have a clear understanding of the concepts taught in Chapters 3, 4, 5 and 7 that are listed in the Concept Check. Students with a good grasp of the nature of physical motion and Newton's second law will have a useful context for understanding the principles of universal gravitation introduced in this chapter.

Assessment Options

Portfolio Assessment
Extension 1, TWE, p. 154b
Portfolio Assessment, p. 159
Discrepant Event, p. 164
Critical Thinking Assessment, p. 166
Portfolio Assessment, p. 166

Performance Assessment
Extension 2, TWE, p. 154b
Pocket Labs, pp. 157, 166
Physics Lab, p. 158
Using Lab Skills 1, p. 173

Content
Self Assessment: Practice Problems, pp. 160, 166
Assessment, Critical Thinking, p. 158
Pocket Lab Assessment, p. 166
Concept Reviews, pp. 163, 170
Chapter Review, pp. 170–173
Supplemental Problems, p. 694

Group Assessment
Activities for group assessment occur with Cooperative Learning and lab activities.

8.1 MOTION IN THE HEAVENS AND ON EARTH

Preparation

OBJECTIVES

The objectives are listed on the student page. Remind students to preview these objectives as a study guide to this major section.

OVERVIEW

The most important new concepts introduced here are Kepler's laws of planetary motion and the law of universal gravitation.

BRIDGING

Students will be asked to recall the ideas of period, mass, force, and weight as they study this section.

1 Focus

Hold a discussion on the all-pervasive nature of gravitation. For example, what's probably the first force you noticed and adjusted to when you were a baby learning to get around? As we grow up and learn to do things like sports, we're always having to allow for gravitation and its effects. What would the world be like if the force of gravitation were one-tenth (or ten times) as strong as at present? How has the force of gravitation influenced the course of evolution?

2 Teach

CONCEPT DEVELOPMENT

• Use this chapter to examine how a theory is developed and how many people contribute to new theories.

• Kepler originally conceived the paths of the planets as perfect circles. However, when he compared his predictions with Tycho's measurements, he found the predictions incorrect by eight minutes of an arc (one-fourth the apparent width of the moon). By using Tycho's careful measurements as a guideline, Kepler eventually discovered ellipses to be the true paths of the planets.

• Explain that Kepler's laws can now be derived from the principles of conservation of energy and angular momentum. Further, these laws are applicable to motion in any conic section (ellipse, parabola, and hyperbola, as well as a circle).

Objectives

- **gain an understanding of need for precision and hard work in gathering data needed to understand how the universe works; list Kepler's laws and understand them.**
- **recognize how Kepler's laws resulted in Newton's law of gravitation; be able to calculate periods and velocities of orbiting objects.**
- **understand that gravitational force is proportional to both masses and the inverse square of the distance between the centers of spherical bodies.**
- **state the method used by Cavendish to measure *G* and understand the results of knowing *G*.**

8.1 MOTION IN THE HEAVENS AND ON EARTH

We know how objects move on Earth. We can describe and even calculate projectile motion. Early humans could not do that, but they did notice that the motion of stars and other bodies in the heavens was quite different. Stars moved in regular paths. Planets, or wanderers, moved through the sky in much more complicated paths. Astrologers claimed that the motions of these bodies were able to control events in human lives. Comets were even more erratic. These mysterious bodies appeared without warning, spouting bright tails, and were considered bearers of evil omens. Because of the works of Galileo, Kepler, Newton, and others, we now know that all of these objects follow the same laws that govern the motion of golf balls and other objects on Earth.

Kepler's Laws of Planetary Motion

As a boy of fourteen in Denmark, Tycho Brahe (1546–1601) observed an eclipse of the sun on August 21, 1560, and vowed to become an astronomer. In 1563, he observed two planets in conjunction, that is, located at the same point in the sky. The date of the event, predicted by all the books of that period, was off by two days, so Brahe decided to dedicate his life to making accurate predictions of astronomical events.

Brahe studied astronomy as he traveled throughout Europe for five years. In 1576, he persuaded King Frederick II of Denmark to give him the island of Hven as the site for the finest observatory of its time. Using huge instruments like those in Figure 8–1, he spent the next 20 years carefully recording the exact positions of the planets and stars.

Brahe was not known for his sunny disposition, so in 1597, out of favor with the new Danish king, Brahe moved to Prague. He became the astronomer to the court of Emperor Rudolph of Bohemia where, in 1600, a nineteen-year-old German Johannes Kepler (1571–1630) became one of his assistants. Although Brahe still believed strongly that Earth was the center of the universe, Kepler wanted to use a sun-centered system to explain Brahe's precise data. He was convinced that geometry and mathematics could be used to explain the number, dis-

FIGURE 8–1. Some of the huge astronomical instruments Tycho Brahe had constructed to use at Hven: an astrolabe (a); a sextant (b); and a quadrant (c).

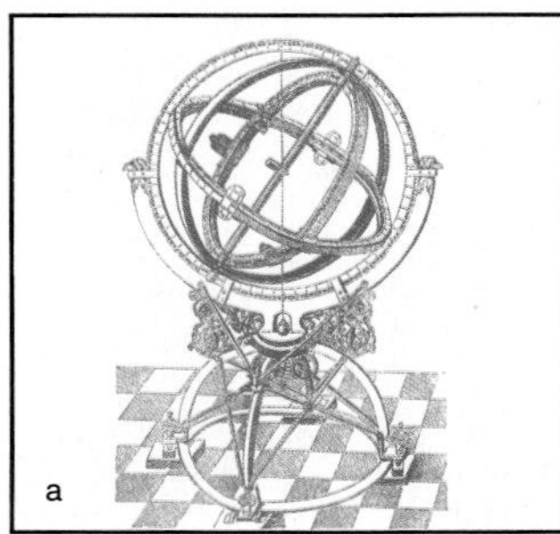

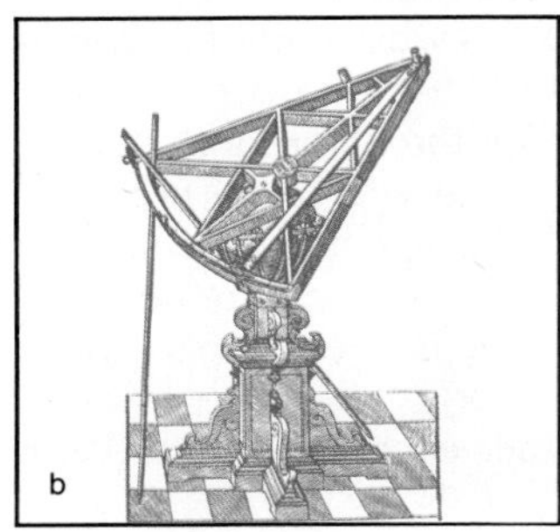

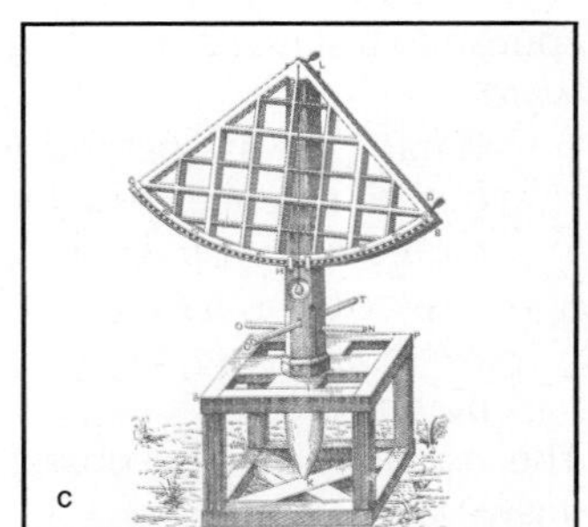

tance, and motion of the planets. By doing a careful mathematical analysis of Brahe's data, Kepler discovered three laws that still describe the behavior of every planet and satellite. The theories he developed to explain his laws, however, are no longer considered correct. The three laws can be stated as follows.

1. The paths of the planets are ellipses with the center of the sun at one focus.
2. An imaginary line from the sun to a planet sweeps out equal areas in equal time intervals. Thus, planets move fastest when closest to the sun, slowest when farthest away, Figure 8–2.
3. The ratio of the squares of the periods of any two planets revolving about the sun is equal to the ratio of the cubes of their average distances from the sun. Thus, if T_a and T_b are their periods and r_a and r_b their average distances, $\left(\frac{T_a}{T_b}\right)^2 = \left(\frac{r_a}{r_b}\right)^3$.

Notice that the first two laws apply to each planet, moon, or satellite individually. The third law relates the motion of several satellites about a single body. For example, it can be used to compare the distances and periods of the planets about the sun. It can also be used to compare distances and periods of the moon and artificial satellites around Earth.

FIGURE 8–2. An imaginary line from Earth to the sun sweeps out equal areas each second whether Earth is close to or far from the sun.

PROBLEM SOLVING STRATEGY

When working with equations that involve squares and square roots, or cubes and cube roots, your solution is more precise if you keep at least one extra digit in your calculations until you reach the end.

When you use Kepler's third law to find the radius of the orbit of a planet or satellite, first solve for the cube of the radius, then take the cube root. This is easier to do if your calculator has a cube-root key, $\sqrt[3]{x}$. If your calculator has a key y^x or x^y, you can also find the cube root. Check the instructions of your calculator, but you usually enter the cube of the radius, press the y^x key, then enter 0.3333333 and press $=$.

POCKET LAB

WEIGHT IN FREE FALL

Tie a string to the top of a spring scale. Hang a 1.0-kg mass on the bottom of it. Hold the scale in your hand. Observe the weight of the mass. What will the reading be when the string is released (as the mass and spring scale are falling)? Why? Try it.

Tycho Brahe made very accurate measurements of the positions of planets and stars that Kepler used to formulate his laws.

F.Y.I.

Kepler calculated that the first voyages to the moon would take four hours. He felt that the passengers should take narcotics to endure the trip.

Multicultural Connections

There is evidence that the science of astronomy was part of many ancient cultures such as the Chinese, Egyptian, and Arabic. Since the beginning of human civilization, people have passed to succeeding generations the history of comets, eclipses, and planets through art, myths, and written form. The astrolabe, a piece of equipment for mathematically determining the position of the stars and planets, is one of the oldest scientific devices. Astrolabes are thought to have originated in the eastern Mediterranean more than 1500 years ago.

POCKET LAB

WEIGHT IN FREE FALL

Materials: string; spring scale; 1-kg mass.

Outcome: Student answers will vary. Many students will predict that the readings will go down. Some may suggest that the reading will approach zero. It is best to let everyone have a chance to discuss this thoroughly before actually doing the activity. The reading on the falling spring scale will be zero. Students should indicate that the force went to zero very quickly. The mass is accelerating downward. The mass is in apparent weightlessness.

Demonstration: To review the construction of ellipses, use 2 suction-cup darts, chalkboard, chalk, and 30 cm string. Stick two darts to the chalkboard several inches apart. Tie the ends of the string together, making a large loop. Fit the loop around the two darts, leaving several inches of slack. Pulling the string taut with the chalk inside the loop, draw an ellipse. (Refer to the figure in the Chapter 8 Physics Lab for clarification.) The eccentricity of the ellipse, or its deviation from a circular path, is dependent on how far away the foci are from one another. Kepler found that the orbits of the planets are ellipses but they are not very eccentric, that is, they are very close to being circles.

Study Guide Master. To reinforce the concepts in this section, have the students complete the Study Guide Master for Section 8.1 from the Teacher Resource Package.

PHYSICS LAB

Process Skills: using numbers, modeling, observing, classifying, communicating, interpreting, measuring, questioning, controlling variables.

Troubleshooting: Most students have difficulty with the concept of ellipses.

Teaching Suggestions: Students will likely make a wide variety of elliptical shapes. This makes it almost impossible for you to monitor them closely. Ask students to help each other after each step in the procedure. The increased student interaction will also tend to reinforce learning.

Lab Worksheet, Teacher Resource Package. If desired, use the lab worksheet master for this chapter for students to record their responses.

OBSERVATIONS

1. Student graph
2. Measurements will vary.
3. Student drawing

APPLICATIONS

1. The velocity vectors should be tangent to the ellipse.
2. At the closest and farthest positions, the force is perpendicular to velocity. The force changes the direction but not the speed of the planet. See the sample drawing for other position examples.

PHYSICS LAB: The Orbit

Purpose

To draw an ellipse and demonstrate how the force varies.

Materials

- 2 thumbtacks
- 21 cm × 28 cm piece of cardboard or corkboard
- sheet of paper
- 30 cm of string or thread
- pencil

Procedure

1. Push the thumbtacks into the paper and cardboard so that they are between 7 and 10 cm apart.
2. Make a loop with the string. Place the loop over the two thumbtacks. Keep the loop tight as you draw the ellipse. (See sketch.)
3. Remove the tacks and string. Draw a small star centered at one of the tack holes.

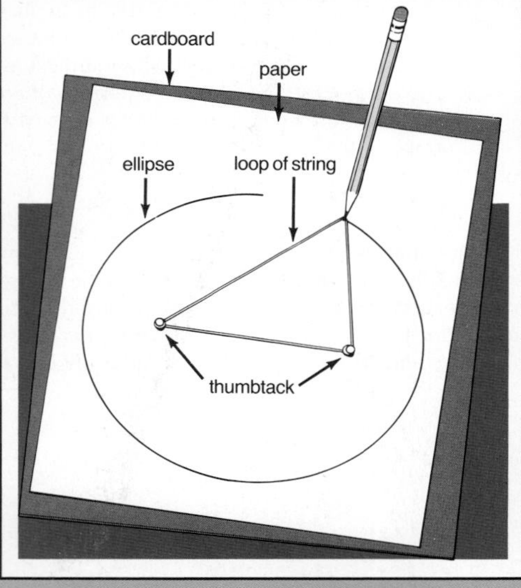

Observations and Data

1. Draw the position of a planet in the orbit where it is farthest from the star.
2. Measure the distance from this position to the center of the star.
3. Draw a 1 cm long force vector from the planet directly toward the star. Label this vector 1.0 F.
4. Draw the position of the planet when it is nearest the star.
5. Measure the distance from this position to the star's center.

Analysis

1. Calculate the amount of force on the planet at the closest distance. Gravity is an inverse square force. If the planet is 0.45 as far, the force is $1/(0.45)^2$ as much or 4.9 F. **Hint:** The force will be more than 1.0 F.
2. Draw the force vector (correct length and direction) for this position. Use the scale of 1.0 F : 1.0 cm.
3. Draw the planet at two other positions in the orbit and draw the force vectors.

Applications

1. Assume the planet moves in a clockwise pattern on the ellipse. Draw a velocity vector at each planet position to show the direction of motion. Remember that the planet moves faster when it is closer.
2. Look at the direction of velocity vectors and the direction of the force vectors. Identify the positions where the planet is gaining speed and also where it is losing speed.

ASSESSMENT

Critical Thinking: To further assess your students' understanding of elliptical orbits, have them answer the following questions.

1. As the planet moves in its orbit, does the kinetic energy change? Does the potential energy change? Explain your reasoning. [Yes, both the kinetic and potential energy change. The kinetic energy is greatest when the planet has the most speed (at the closest approach). The potential energy is the greatest at the farthest point in the orbit (the slowest speed). The total energy is a constant value.]

2. Locate any places in the orbit where the planet is not accelerating. [The planet is always being pulled by the star, therefore there is always a net force toward the star. A net force always causes an acceleration, so even when the planet is moving away, it is accelerating toward the star. Remind students that acceleration is always in the same direction as the net force.]

Table 8–1

Planetary Data			
Name	Average radius (m)	Mass (kg)	Mean distance from sun (m)
Sun	696.0×10^6	1.991×10^{30}	———
Mercury	2.43×10^6	3.2×10^{23}	5.80×10^{10}
Venus	6.073×10^6	4.88×10^{24}	1.081×10^{11}
Earth	6.3713×10^6	5.979×10^{24}	1.4957×10^{11}
Mars	3.38×10^6	6.42×10^{23}	2.278×10^{11}
Jupiter	69.8×10^6	1.901×10^{27}	7.781×10^{11}
Saturn	58.2×10^6	5.68×10^{26}	1.427×10^{12}
Uranus	23.5×10^6	8.68×10^{25}	2.870×10^{12}
Neptune	22.7×10^6	1.03×10^{26}	4.500×10^{12}
Pluto	1.15×10^6	1.2×10^{22}	5.9×10^{12}

Example Problem

Using Kepler's Third Law to Find an Orbital Period

Galileo discovered four moons of Jupiter. Io, which he measured to be 4.2 units from the center of Jupiter, has a period of 1.8 days. He measured the radius of Ganymede's orbit as 10.7 units. Use Kepler's third law to find the period of Ganymede.

Given: for Io
period, $T_b = 1.8$ days
radius, $r_b = 4.2$ units
for Ganymede
radius, $r_a = 10.7$ units

Unknown: Ganymede's period, T_a

Basic equation: $\left(\frac{T_a}{T_b}\right)^2 = \left(\frac{r_a}{r_b}\right)^3$

Solution:

$$T_a^2 = T_b^2\left(\frac{r_a}{r_b}\right)^3$$
$$= (1.8 \text{ days})^2\left(\frac{10.7 \text{ units}}{4.2 \text{ units}}\right)^3$$
$$= (3.2 \text{ days}^2)(16.5) = 52.8 \text{ days}^2$$
$$T_a = 7.3 \text{ days}$$

The observed period is 7.16 days.

Kepler's laws can be used to calculate planetary orbits or periods.

Notice that when working problems that involve ratios, you do not need to convert all units to meters and seconds. You must, however, use the same units throughout the problem.

FIGURE 8–3. Io, one of Jupiter's moons, appears yellow because of sulfur deposits.

CONCEPT DEVELOPMENT

The equality of this form of Kepler's third law is valid only for two objects which are orbiting the same central body, such as the sun.

Laboratory Manual. Give students additional experience with Kepler's laws by doing Lab 8.1 from the Laboratory Manual.

Assessment

Portfolio

Students interested in astronomy should be encouraged to do additional problems involving Kepler's laws and Newton's universal gravitation law applied to planets and satellites. These problems should be added to the portfolio.

TEACHER 

• "If thou, dear reader, art bored with this wearisome method of calculation, take pity on me who had to go through at least seventy repetitions of it...."
—Kepler

• Tycho Brahe was an unconventional sort. At age 20, he was resigned to wearing a gold alloy replacement after losing a piece of his nose in a duel with a student over who was the better mathematician.

Guided Practice: After going over the Example Problems on pages 159 and 160, have students try the first Practice Problem on page 160.

Independent Practice: Assign the remaining Practice Problems (2–4) on this page for homework and review them in class the next day.

Transparency Package. Review Kepler's second law using Transparency 9 and the accompanying worksheet.

Answers To
PRACTICE PROBLEMS

Have students refer to Appendix A of the Solutions Appendix for complete solutions to Practice Problems.

1. 2.8 yr
2. 684 days
3. 88.5 min
4. 4.30×10^4 km

CONCEPT DEVELOPMENT

- The cause or underlying reason for the existence of gravitational forces has continued to be a fascinating scientific problem. Currently there are serious attempts to try to unify gravitational forces with the other known forces. So far these attempts have not been successful.

- Note that d is the distance between the centers of mass of the objects. It took Newton 20 years to prove that this law is valid for large bodies as well as point particles.

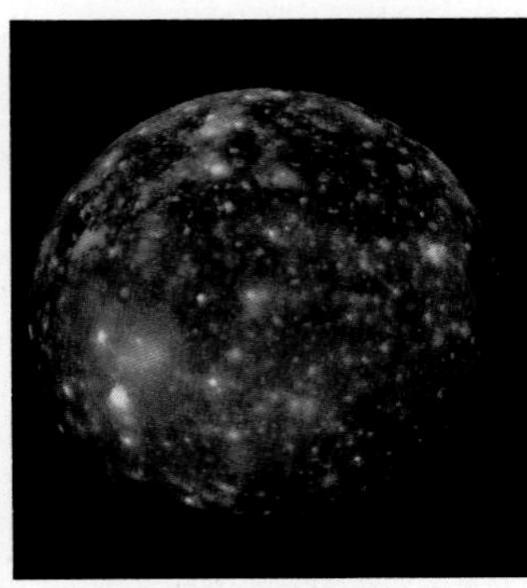

FIGURE 8–4. Callisto, the fourth moon of Jupiter, is covered with ice.

Example Problem

Using Kepler's Third Law to Find an Orbital Radius

The fourth moon of Jupiter, Callisto, has a period of 16.7 days. Find its distance from Jupiter using the same units Galileo used.

Given: for Io
period, $T_b = 1.8$ days
radius, $r_b = 4.2$ units
for Callisto
period, $T_a = 16.7$ days

Unknown: Callisto's radius, r_a

Basic equation: $\left(\frac{T_a}{T_b}\right)^2 = \left(\frac{r_a}{r_b}\right)^3$

Solution:
$$r_a^3 = r_b^3\left(\frac{T_a}{T_b}\right)^2$$
$$= (4.2\text{ units})^3\left(\frac{16.7\text{ days}}{1.8\text{ days}}\right)^2$$
$$= (74.1\text{ units}^3)(86.1)$$
$$= 6.38 \times 10^3\text{ units}^3$$
$$r_a = 18.5\text{ units}$$

LITERATURE CONNECTION

Jules Verne (1828–1905) was a French novelist who wrote science fiction. He wrote about airplanes, submarines, guided missiles, and space satellites years before their invention; he accurately predicted their uses. His use of detail and knowledge of geography added realism to his stories. His readers travel over, under, and around the Earth. Perhaps you have read some of his exciting works, *Twenty Thousand Leagues Under the Sea, Around the World in Eighty Days, A Journey to the Center of the Earth, From the Earth to the Moon,* and *Around the Moon.* Check out Verne's perspective on adventure and science. Why do you think his books remain popular today?

Practice Problems

1. An asteroid revolves around the sun with a mean (average) orbital radius twice that of Earth's. Predict the period of the asteroid in earth years.
2. From Table 8–1, you can calculate that, on the average, Mars is 1.52 times as far from the sun as is Earth. Predict the time required for Mars to circle the sun in earth days.
3. The moon has a period of 27.3 days and has a mean distance of 3.90×10^5 km from the center of Earth. Find the period of an artificial satellite that is 6.70×10^3 km from the center of Earth.
4. ▶ From the data on the period and radius of revolution of the moon in Practice Problem 3, find the mean distance from Earth's center to an artificial satellite that has a period of 1.00 day.

Universal Gravitation

In 1666, some 45 years after Kepler's work, young Isaac Newton was living at home in rural England because the plague had closed all schools. Newton had used mathematical arguments to show that if the path of a planet were an ellipse, in agreement with Kepler's first law, then the net force, F, on the planet must vary inversely with the square of the distance between the planet and the sun. That is, he could write an equation,

$$F \propto \frac{1}{d^2},$$

where the symbol $\propto$ means "is proportional to," and d is the average distance between the centers of the two bodies. He also showed that the force acted in the direction of a line connecting the centers. But, at

STUDY GUIDE MASTER
Use the Study Guide master for section 8.1.

LABORATORY MANUAL
Use Lab 8.1 with this section.

LAB WORKSHEET
Use the Lab Worksheet for Chapter 8 with this Physics Lab.

TRANSPARENCY
Use Transparency 9 with this section.

this time, Newton could go no further because he could not measure the magnitude of the force, F.

Newton later wrote that the sight of a falling apple made him think of the problem of the motion of the planets. Newton recognized that the apple fell straight down because Earth attracted it. Might not this force extend beyond the trees, to the clouds, to the moon, and even beyond? Gravity could even be the force that attracts the planets to the sun. Newton recognized that the force on the apple must be proportional to its mass. Further, according to his own third law of motion, the apple would also attract Earth, so the force of attraction must be proportional to the mass of Earth as well. He was so confident the laws that governed motion on Earth would work anywhere that he assumed the same force of attraction acted between any two masses, m_1 and m_2. He proposed

$$F = G\frac{m_1 m_2}{d^2}$$

where d is the distance between the centers of the spherical masses, and G is a universal constant, one that is the same everywhere. According to Newton's equation, if the mass of a planet were doubled, the force of attraction would be doubled. Similarly, if the planet were attracted toward a star with twice the mass of the sun, the force would be twice as great. And, if the planet were twice the distance from the sun, the force would be only one-quarter as strong. Figure 8–5 illustrates these relationships. Because the force depends on $1/d^2$, it is called an **inverse square law.**

FIGURE 8–5. The gravitational force between any two bodies varies directly as the product of their masses and inversely as the square of the distance between them.

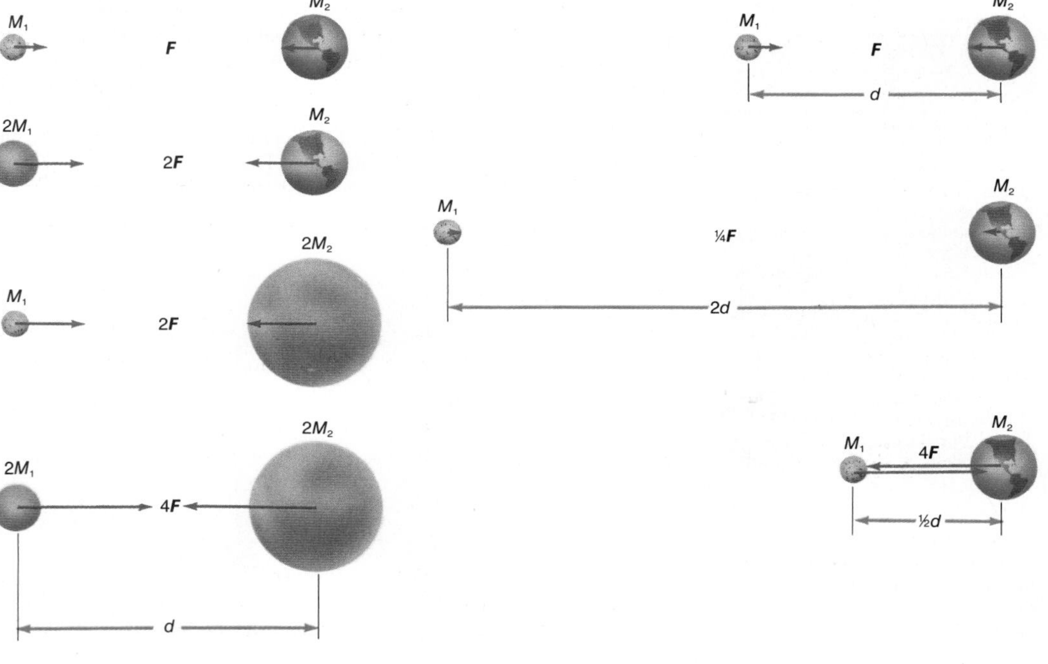

CONCEPT DEVELOPMENT

Point out that Newton couldn't determine the proportionality constant, G, because the mass of the Earth was unknown.

Enrichment: What do the planets of the solar system tell a physicist about the mass of the sun?

The mass of the sun is measured by the velocity of the satellites orbiting it. The greater the velocity, the greater the weight of the gravitating center. The orbiting object thus "weighs" the matter that is pulling it because its own mass does not affect the velocity of size of the described path. The weight of the Earth is determined by the velocities of its satellites.

TEACHER F.Y.I.

For an object to escape Earth's gravitational pull, the sum of the potential and kinetic energies must be zero. You can show that a projectile needs to attain a horizontal speed of 11.2 km/s to escape from Earth's gravitational pull.

If $PE = -\frac{Gm_e m_o}{r_e}$ and a long way from Earth $KE + PE = 0$, then on Earth's surface $1/2\ m_o v^2 - \frac{Gm_e m_o}{r_e} = 0$ and

$$v^2 = \frac{2Gm_e}{r_e}, \text{ so } \quad v = \sqrt{\frac{2(6.67 \times 10^{-11}\ \text{N}\cdot\text{m}^2/\text{kg}^2)(5.98 \times 10^{24}\ \text{kg})}{6.38 \times 10^6\ \text{m}}}$$

$$v = 1.12 \times 10^4\ \text{m/s because } 1\ \text{N·m/kg} = 1\ \text{m/s}^2.$$

CHECKING FOR UNDERSTANDING

How are Kepler's laws and the law of universal gravitation connected? Draw a picture of the Earth, moon, and an artificial Earth satellite. Ask students to identify the gravitational forces acting on all three objects and then have them arrange these forces by size.

RETEACHING

Transparency Package. Reteach the concepts presented in this section by using Transparency 10, Gravitation, and the accompanying worksheet.

EXTENSION

Critical Thinking Master. Teacher Resource Package. You may wish to have students complete the Critical Thinking Master, Acceleration Due to Gravity, with this section.

Enrichment Master. With this section, use the Enrichment Master, Variations in Acceleration on Earth, from the Teacher Resource Package.

CONCEPT DEVELOPMENT

Because the law of gravitation is universal, G is the same for any two bodies. Knowing G, Cavendish could determine the mass of the Earth.

ACTIVITY

Cooperative Learning: For years, people have considered whether it might be possible to build a shield against the force of gravity. One of the assumptions behind such a plan is that gravitational forces exist as some form of current, like an electric field. Have students discuss possible antigravity inventions in groups, then come together to share their ideas.

Critical Thinking: Have students list five devices which would work better without gravitational force. Then have them list five devices which wouldn't work without gravitational forces. Ask them to explain their choices.

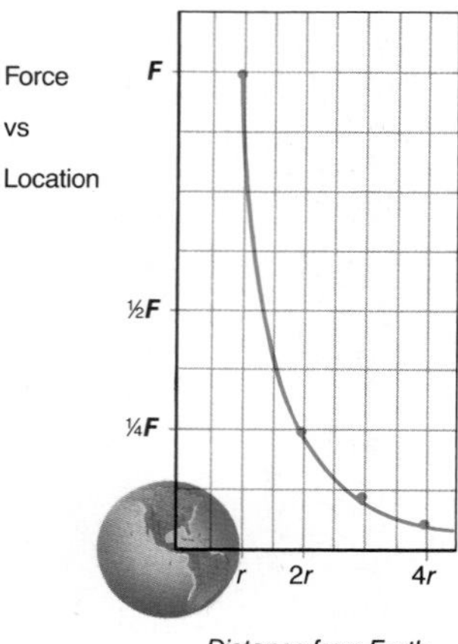

FIGURE 8–6. The change in gravitational force with distance follows the inverse square law.

HELP WANTED

PILOT

We need "safety-first" individuals who can make quick but correct decisions, even under occasional adverse conditions.

A current FAA commercial license with instrument rating and the ability to continue to pass strict physical, vision, hearing, flying, and rules exams are a must. Graduates of accredited flying schools/colleges or those with military flying experience will be considered equally. For information contact:

Air Pilots Association, 1625 Massachusetts Avenue, N.W., Washington, DC 20036

Newton's Use of His Law of Universal Gravitation

Newton applied his inverse square law to the motion of the planets about the sun. He used the symbol M_p for the mass of the planet, M_s for the mass of the sun, and r_{ps} for the radius of the planet's orbit. He then used his second law of motion, $F = ma$, with F the gravitational force and a the centripetal acceleration. That is, $F = M_p a$. For the sake of simplicity, we assume circular orbits.

$$G\frac{M_s M_p}{{r_{ps}}^2} = M_p\frac{4\pi^2 r_{ps}}{{T_p}^2},$$

where T_p is the time required for the planet to make one complete revolution about the sun. He rearranged the equation in the form

$${T_p}^2 = \left(\frac{4\pi^2}{GM_s}\right){r_{ps}}^3.$$

This equation is Kepler's third law—the square of the period is proportional to the cube of the distance. The proportionality constant, $4\pi^2/GM_s$, depends only on the mass of the sun and Newton's universal gravitational constant G. It does not depend on any property of the planet. Thus, Newton's law of gravitation not only leads to Kepler's third law, but it also predicts the value of the constant. In our derivation of this equation, we have assumed the orbits of the planets are circles. Newton found the same result for elliptical orbits.

Weighing Earth

As you know, the force of gravitational attraction between two objects on Earth is very small. You cannot feel the slightest attraction even between two massive bowling balls. In fact, it took 100 years after Newton's work to develop an apparatus that was sensitive enough to measure the force. In 1798, the Englishman Henry Cavendish (1731–1810) used equipment like that sketched in Figure 8–7. A rod about 20 cm long had two small lead balls attached. The rod was suspended by a thin wire so it could rotate. Cavendish measured the force on the

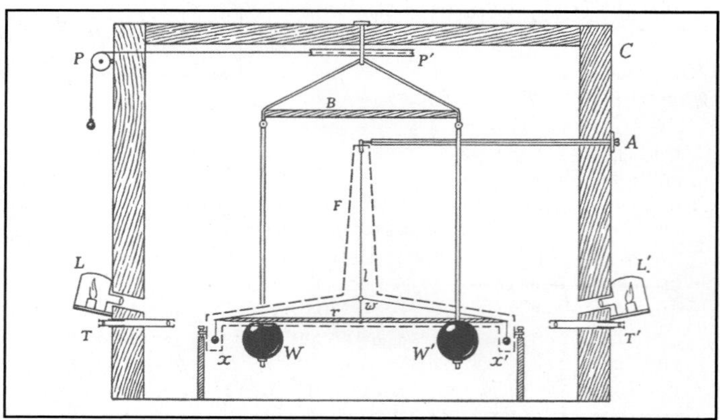

FIGURE 8–7. Cavendish verified the existence of gravitational forces between masses by using the apparatus shown.

TEACHER F.Y.I.

To show the steps involved in Newton's application a little more clearly:

$$F = G\frac{M_p M_s}{r_{ps}^2} \text{ and } F = M_p a \text{ thus,}$$

$$F = M_p a = M_p\left(\frac{4\pi^2 r_{ps}}{T_p^2}\right).$$

But the force that causes this acceleration is the gravitational force, so

$$G\frac{\cancel{M_p} M_s}{r_{ps}^2} = \cancel{M_p}\frac{4\pi^2 r_{ps}}{T_p^2}$$

$$T_p^2 = 4\pi^2 r_{ps}\frac{r_{ps}^2}{GM_s}$$

$$T_p^2 = \frac{4\pi^2}{GM_s}r_{ps}^3.$$

spheres needed to rotate the rod through given angles. Then, he placed two large lead balls close to the small ones. The force of attraction between the balls caused the rod to rotate. By measuring the angle through which it turned, Cavendish was able to calculate the attractive force between the masses. He found that the force agreed with Newton's law of gravitation.

Cavendish measured the masses of the balls and the distance between their centers. Substituting these values for force, mass, and distance into Newton's law, he found the value of G.

Newton's law of universal gravitation says

$$F = G\frac{m_1 m_2}{d^2}.$$

When m_1 and m_2 are measured in kilograms, d in meters, and F in newtons, then $G = 6.67 \times 10^{-11}\ \text{N·m}^2/\text{kg}^2$. For example, the attractive gravitational force between two bowling balls, each of mass 7.26 kg, with their centers separated by 0.30 m is

$$F_g = \frac{(6.67 \times 10^{-11}\ \text{N·m}^2/\text{kg}^2)(7.26\ \text{kg})(7.26\ \text{kg})}{(0.30\ \text{m})^2} = 3.91 \times 10^{-8}\ \text{N}.$$

Cavendish's experiment is often called "weighing the earth." You know that on Earth's surface the weight of an object is a measure of Earth's gravitational attraction: $F = W = mg$. According to Newton, however,

$$F = \frac{GM_e m}{r^2}, \text{ so, } g = \frac{GM_e}{r^2}.$$

Because Cavendish measured the constant G, we can rearrange this equation as

$$M_e = \frac{gr_e^2}{G}.$$

Using modern values of the constants, we find

$$M_e = \frac{(9.80\ \text{m/s}^2)(6.37 \times 10^6\ \text{m})^2}{6.67 \times 10^{-11}\ \text{N·m}^2/\text{kg}^2} = 5.98 \times 10^{24}\ \text{kg}.$$

Comparing the mass of Earth to that of a bowling ball, you can see why the gravitational attraction of everyday objects is not easily sensed.

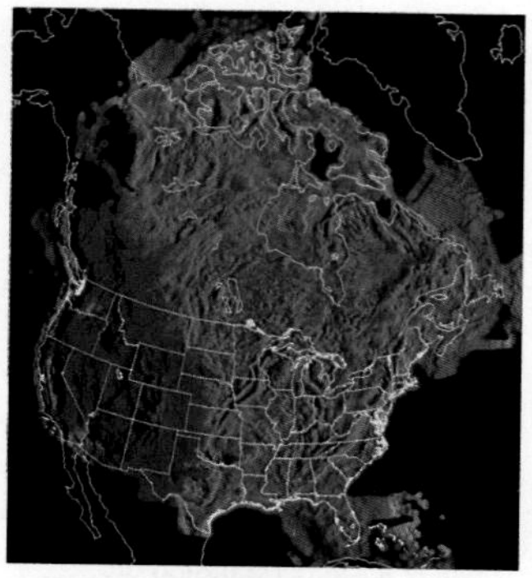

FIGURE 8–8. The map shows the variations in the acceleration due to gravity over North America. The force is weaker in the regions shown in blue and violet. It is stronger in those shown in yellow, orange, and brown. The largest difference is about 5 mm/s².

Cavendish tested the law of universal gravitation between small masses on Earth.

Cavendish was able to measure, experimentally, the constant, G, in Newton's law of universal gravitation.

CONCEPT REVIEW

1.1 Earth is attracted to the sun by the force of gravity. Why doesn't Earth fall into the sun? Explain.

1.2 If Earth began to shrink but its mass remained the same, predict what would happen to the value of g on shrinking Earth's surface.

1.3 Cavendish did his experiment using lead spheres. Suppose he had used equal masses of copper instead. Would his value of G be the same or different? Explain.

Critical Thinking: In a space colony on the moon, an astronaut can pick up a rock with less effort than on Earth. Is this also true when she throws the rock horizontally? If the rock drops on her toe, will it hurt more or less than on Earth? Explain your answers.

3 Close

CONVERGENT QUESTION

How does the law of gravitation help to explain why larger planets are all roughly spherical in shape?

CONCEPT REVIEW ANSWERS

1.1 It does fall *toward* the sun in the same sense that a stone on a string falls toward the center when swung in circular motion. This falling results as the centripetal force provided by gravity pulls the Earth out of a straight-line path into a near-circular orbit.

1.2 The value of g would increase because $g = \frac{G M_e}{R_e^2}$ indicates that g is inversely proportional to the square of the radius of Earth.

1.3 The same, because the same value of G has been used successfully to describe the attraction of bodies having diverse chemical compositions: the sun (a star), the planets, and satellites, both natural and man-made.

1.4 Critical Thinking: Horizontal throwing requires the same effort since the inertial character, $F = ma$, of the rock is involved. The mass of the rock depends only on the amount of matter in the rock, not on its location in the universe. The rock will be kinder to the toe since the smaller value of g on the moon means that the rock strikes the toe with a smaller velocity than on Earth.

INDEPENDENT PRACTICE/ EXTENSION

Refer to the Assignment Guide on this page for additional questions and problems for independent practice.

8:1 ASSIGNMENT GUIDE

	PRACTICE	EXTENSION
CHAPTER REVIEW pp. 170–173		
· Reviewing Concepts	1–8	
· Applying Concepts		1–5
· Problems*	1, 4, 6–12, 14, 17	2, 3, 5, 13, 15, 16, 18, 19
PROBLEM APPENDIX*		
· Chapter 8, p. 694	1, 2, 4–9, 11, 12	3, 10

* Complete solutions to all Chapter Review and Appendix problems appear in the Problems and Solutions Manual.

TRANSPARENCY

Use Transparency 10 with this section.

CRITICAL THINKING

Use the Critical Thinking master for Chapter 8 with this section.

ENRICHMENT MASTER

Use the Enrichment master for Chapter 8 with this section.

8.2 USING THE LAW OF UNIVERSAL GRAVITATION

Preparation

OBJECTIVES

The objectives are listed on the student page. Remind students to preview these objectives as a study guide to this major section.

OVERVIEW

The new concepts in this section include satellite motion, weightlessness, gravitational field, and the principle of equivalence.

BRIDGING

Terms and concepts from previous chapters include parabolic trajectory, air resistance, circular motion, centripetal acceleration, newton (the force unit), and vectors.

1 Focus

DISCREPANT EVENT

You will need a plastic or paper cup, two large heavy washers, two thin rubber bands, and a toothpick or paper clip. Loop the rubber bands around the washers. Punch a small hole through the bottom of the cup. Push the rubber bands through the hole from the inside to the out. Pass the toothpick or paper clip through the loops of the rubber bands protruding through the bottom of the cup. Extend the rubber bands so that the washers hang over the edge of the cup. The washers should stretch the rubber bands. You may have to experiment with different sizes of rubber bands and washers until the weight of the washers is enough to keep them hanging over the outside of the cup.

Hold the cup high and drop it. When the cup lands, the washers will be inside the cup. Explain, noting that during free fall the washers are weightless. The force of the rubber band is no longer balanced by gravity, and so the rubber band pulls the washers into the cup.

Objectives

- recognize that the motion of satellites in circular orbits about Earth can be understood using equations of uniform circular motion; solve problems involving orbital velocity and period.
- understand the use of the term "weightlessness" in describing objects in freefall near Earth and in orbit.
- describe gravitational fields and that the field concept does not explain the origin of gravity.
- display an understanding of Einstein's concept of gravity.

8.2 USING THE LAW OF UNIVERSAL GRAVITATION

The planet Uranus was discovered in 1741. By 1830, it appeared that Newton's law of gravitation didn't correctly predict its orbit. Some astronomers thought gravitational attraction from an undiscovered planet might be changing its path. In 1845, the location of such a planet was calculated, and astronomers at the Berlin Observatory searched for it. During the first evening, they found the giant planet now called Neptune.

Motion of Planets and Satellites

Newton used a drawing similar to Figure 8–9 to illustrate a "thought experiment." Imagine a cannon, perched atop a high mountain, shooting a cannonball horizontally. The cannonball is a projectile and its motion has vertical and horizontal components. It follows a parabolic trajectory. During the first second the ball is in flight, it falls 4.9 m. If its speed increases, it will travel farther across the surface of Earth, but it will still fall 4.9 m in the first second of flight. Meanwhile, the surface of Earth is curved. If the ball goes just fast enough, after one second, it will reach a point where Earth has curved 4.9 m away from the horizontal. That is, the curvature of Earth will just match the curvature of the trajectory, and the ball will orbit Earth.

Figure 8–9 shows that Earth curves away from a line tangent to its surface at a rate of 4.9 m for every 8 km. That is, the altitude of the line tangent to Earth at **A** will be 4.9 m above Earth at **B.** If the cannonball in Figure 8–9 were given just enough horizontal velocity to travel from **A** to **B** in one second, it would also fall 4.9 m and arrive at **C.** The altitude of the ball in relation to Earth's surface would not have changed. The cannonball would fall toward Earth at the same rate that Earth's surface curves away. An object with a horizontal speed of 8 km/s will keep the same altitude and circle Earth as an artificial satellite.

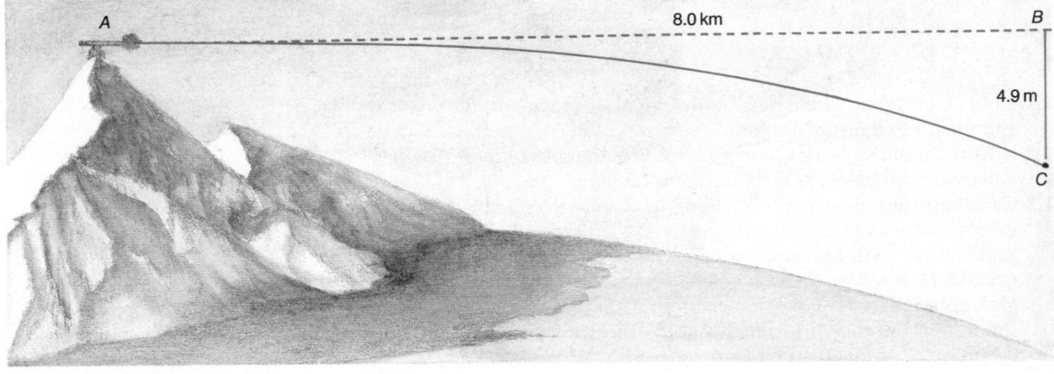

FIGURE 8–9. If the cannonball travels 8 km horizontally in 1 s, it will fall the same distance toward Earth as Earth curves away from the cannonball.

Enrichment/Critical Thinking: Gravitational collapse is now believed to be the final stage of stellar evolution. Stars that undergo gravitational collapse become neutron stars, white dwarves, etc. A star must be at least three solar masses to experience gravitational collapse to a black hole. Karl Schwarzschild developed an equation for the "radius" of a black hole: $R = 2GM/c^2$ where M is the object's mass. Ask your students to compute the diameter of Earth if it could collapse into a neutron star (about 9 mm). Figure 8–5 gives an idea of the incredible density of a black hole. For further class discussion, make copies of a recent article on this subject from *Scientific American.* Another reference: Maggs, William Ward. "Scientists Continue to Search for the Elusive Fifth Force—Does It Exist?" *Earth in Space.* March 1990, pages 11–12.

Newton's thought experiment ignored air resistance. The mountain would have to be more than 150 km above Earth's surface to be above most of the atmosphere. A satellite at this altitude encounters little air resistance and can orbit Earth for a long time.

A satellite in an orbit that is always the same height above Earth moves with uniform circular motion. Its centripetal acceleration is $a_c = v^2/r$. Using Newton's second law, $F = ma$, with the gravitational force between Earth and the satellite, we obtain

$$\frac{GM_Em}{r^2} = \frac{mv^2}{r}.$$

Solving this for the velocity, v, we find

$$v = \sqrt{\frac{GM_E}{r}}.$$

By using Newton's law of universal gravitation, we have shown that the time for a satellite to circle Earth, its period, is given by

$$T = 2\pi\sqrt{\frac{r^3}{GM_E}}.$$

Note that the orbital velocity and period are independent of the mass of the satellite. Satellites are accelerated to the speeds needed to achieve orbit by large rockets, such as the shuttle booster rocket. The acceleration of any mass must follow Newton's law, $F = ma$, so a more massive satellite requires more force to put it into orbit. Thus, the mass of a satellite is limited by the capability of the rocket used to launch it.

Note that these equations for the velocity and period of a satellite can be used for any body in orbit about another. The mass of the central body, like the sun, would replace M_E in the equations, and r is the distance from the sun to the orbiting body.

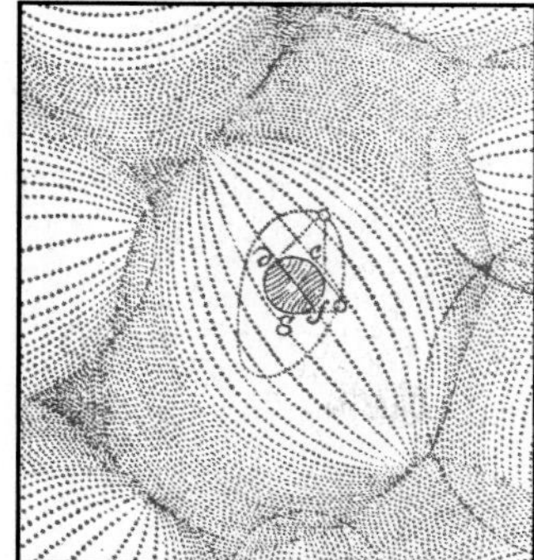

FIGURE 8–10. This drawing by Rene Descartes illustrated his theory that space was filled with whirlpools of matter that moved the planets in their orbits.

The velocity of a satellite is independent of its mass.

Example Problem

Finding the Velocity of a Satellite

A satellite in low Earth orbit is 225 km above the surface. What is its orbital velocity?

Given: height above Earth, 225 km

needed constants,

radius of Earth, $R_E = 6.37 \times 10^6$ m

mass of Earth, $M_E = 5.98 \times 10^{24}$ kg

$G = 6.67 \times 10^{-11}$ N·m²/kg²

Unknown: velocity, v

Basic equation: $v = \sqrt{\frac{GM_E}{r}}$

Solution:

$$r = R_E + 225 \text{ km} = 6.60 \times 10^6 \text{ m}$$

$$v = \sqrt{\frac{(6.67 \times 10^{-11}\ \text{N·m}^2/\text{kg}^2)(5.98 \times 10^{24}\ \text{kg})}{6.60 \times 10^6\ \text{m}}}$$

$$= 7.78 \times 10^3 \text{ m/s} = 7.78 \text{ km/s}$$

2 Teach

CONCEPT DEVELOPMENT

Have students calculate their weights at the height of a satellite and on the moon. Discuss the question of weightlessness in satellites. Point out that objects are weightless in satellites because everything, including the weighing device, is in free fall.

CONCEPT DEVELOPMENT

Critical Thinking: Ask students to think of evidence from common experience that Newton probably used in formulating the law of gravitation.

Enrichment: Have interested students investigate how Newton's development of the law of gravitation was connected to his development of calculus. You might want to suggest consulting a college physics text or a book on the history of mathematics.

Guided Practice: Go over the Example Problem on this page. Then have students work on the first Practice Problem on page 166, offering assistance when needed.

Independent Practice: Assign Practice Problems 6–8 on page 166 for homework. Review student answers in class the next day.

Study Guide Master. To reinforce the concepts in this section, have the students complete the Study Guide Master for Section 8.2 from the Teacher Resource Package.

TEACHER F.Y.I.

Hundreds of satellites and space probes orbit the Earth today. They collect and transmit data on agriculture, minerals, solar radiation, environmental effects, weather, land and ocean surveillance, and astronomy, as well as provide global communications facilities.

A geosynchronous, or geostationary, satellite maintains a fixed position over a designated latitude and longitude by remaining at such a distance that its orbital period is synchronized with the rotational period of the Earth. Global communication satellites are geosynchronous.

Answers To
PRACTICE PROBLEMS

Have students refer to Appendix A of the Solutions Appendix for complete solutions to Practice Problems.

5. a. 7.82×10^3 m/s; **b.** 87.3 min
6. a. 2.8×10^3 m/s; **b.** 1.0×10^2 min
7. a. 4.79×10^4 m/s; **b.** 9.65×10^3 m/s, about 1/5 as fast as Mercury
8. a. 1.0×10^{41} kg; **b.** 5.0×10^{10}; **c.** 6.1 km/h

CONCEPT DEVELOPMENT

G has been called by some a "Force shaper." The value of *G* determines the size of gravitational forces.

POCKET LAB

WATER, WATER, EVERYWHERE

Purpose: to observe the effects of weightlessness in free fall.
Materials: pencil; Styrofoam or paper cup; colored water.
Outcome: Most students will predict that the water will run out of the bottom opening. Some students will believe that the water will only run out of the bottom but not the side opening. Ask all students to think and talk this through before they do it. When the cup is dropped, the water stays in the cup. There is no pressure between the falling cup and the water inside it. Both the cup and the water are being accelerated the same amount by gravity. The water is in apparent weightlessness.

POCKET LAB

WATER, WATER, EVERYWHERE

This activity is best done outdoors. Use a pencil to poke a hole in the bottom and side of a cup. Hold your fingers over the two openings as you fill the cup 2/3 full of colored water. Predict what will happen as the cup is allowed to fall. Drop the cup and watch closely. What happened? Why?

Gravitational force diminishes as you go away from Earth, but it is never zero.

Practice Problems

Assume a near-circular orbit for all calculations.

5. a. Calculate the velocity that a satellite shot from Newton's cannon must have in order to orbit Earth, 150 km above its surface.
b. How long would it take for the satellite to return to the cannon in seconds and minutes?

6. Use the data in Table 8–1 for Mercury to find
a. the speed of a satellite in orbit 265 km above the surface.
b. the period of the satellite.

7. a. Find the velocity with which Mercury moves around the sun.
b. Also, find the velocity of Saturn. Now, comment on whether or not it makes sense that Mercury is named after a speedy messenger of the gods, while Saturn is named after the father of Jupiter.

▶ **8.** We can consider the sun to be a satellite of our galaxy, the Milky Way. The sun revolves around the center of the galaxy with a radius of 2.2×10^{20} m. The period of one rotation is 2.5×10^8 years.
a. Find the mass of the galaxy.
b. Assuming the average star in the galaxy has the mass of the sun, find the number of stars.
c. Find the speed with which the sun moves around the center of the galaxy.

Weight and Weightlessness

The acceleration of objects due to Earth's gravitation can be found by using the inverse square law and Newton's second law. Since

$$F = \frac{GM_Em}{d^2} = ma, \text{ so } a = \frac{GM_E}{d^2},$$

but on Earth's surface, the equation can be written as

$$g = \frac{GM_E}{{R_E}^2}. \text{ Thus, } a = g\left(\frac{R_E}{d}\right)^2.$$

As we move farther from Earth's center, the acceleration due to gravity is reduced according to this inverse square relationship.

Floating Freely ▶

You have probably seen astronauts on a space shuttle working and relaxing in "zero-g", or "weightlessness." The shuttle orbits Earth about 400 km above its surface. At that distance, $g = 8.7$ m/s^2, only slightly less than on Earth's surface. Thus, Earth's gravitational force is certainly not zero in the shuttle. In fact, gravity causes the shuttle to circle Earth. Why, then, do the astronauts appear to have no weight? Just as with Newton's cannonball, the shuttle and everything in it are falling freely toward Earth as they orbit around it.

How do you measure weight? You either stand on a spring scale or hang an object from a scale. Weight is found by measuring the force the scale exerts in opposing the force of gravity. As we saw in Chapter 5, if you stand on a scale in an elevator that is accelerating downward, your weight is reduced. If the elevator is in freefall, that is, accelerating downward at 9.80 m/s^2, then the scale exerts no force on you. With no

Assessment

Critical Thinking

In order to further assess students' understanding of free fall, ask them to cite examples of near weightlessness. Besides space shuttle photos and videos, they should mention the highest point in a trampoline jump, the discrepant event on page 164, and the change in weight when an elevator accelerates.

Assessment

Portfolio

Have interested students research and report on Einstein's theory that gravity and acceleration are equivalent. That is, from inside a spaceship you could not tell whether you were on Earth or accelerating upward at 9.8 m/s^2 in a region with no gravity.

Physics and technology

EFFECTS OF WEIGHTLESSNESS

When you watch astronauts working or playing in the space shuttle, do you think that the laws of physics have been suspended? They haven't been of course, but with both the people and the ship falling toward Earth with an acceleration of almost 9 m/s^2, some of Newton's laws become more important.

Suppose, for example, you want to walk to the wall across the room. By Newton's third law, the floor pushes you forward, accelerating you toward the other wall. But, when you are weightless there is no frictional force between the floor and your shoe. The floor can't push you forward. If you are at rest, you will remain at rest until someone or something provides an external force.

If you want to turn a knob you have to exert a torque on it. You grab the knob and twist it with your wrist. But, in space, with no force between your shoes and the floor, your body rotates instead of the knob. Astronauts must learn to hold on to a part of the shuttle to keep themselves from rotating.

The effects of weightlessness were also evident when astronauts rescued a satellite in the wrong orbit. They had to fasten themselves to the shuttle. The slightest wrong push, pull, or twist could accelerate the huge satellite, giving it an incorrect or even dangerous velocity.

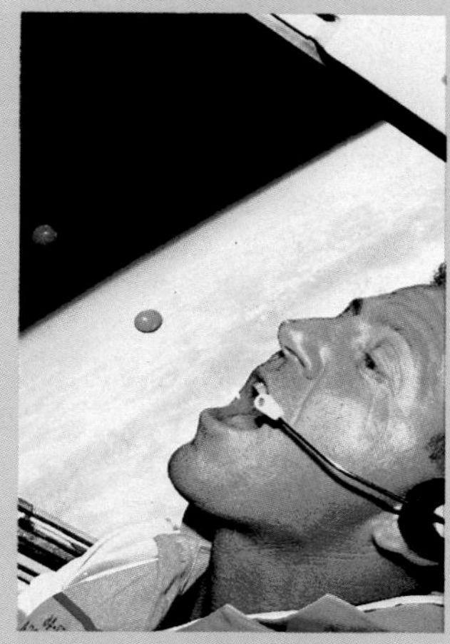

· Gravity causes heavier objects to fall. Water, for example, stays in the bottom of the glass. How would weightlessness affect the way you eat?

force on your feet, you feel weightless. So it is in an orbiting satellite. The satellite, the scale, you, and everything else in it are accelerating toward Earth.

Objects in freefall experience weightlessness.

FIGURE 8–11. Astronauts in training experience a moment of weightlessness in a diving aircraft.

Physics and technology

Answer to student question: Solid foods stick together and aren't much affected by weightlessness. Liquids, however, don't spread out if spilled; they form spherical drops. They are drunk through straws, and the straws must be closed off when not in use to keep the liquids from climbing out of the straws.

Teacher Resource: "Physics in Weightlessness" by Sally Ride, in *Fundamentals of Physics* by Halliday, Resnick, and Walker, 4th Ed. 1992. p. E3-1–4.

Assessment

Portfolio

Have interested students research how food is processed and packaged for space travel and some of the eating problems encountered under weightless conditions.

STUDY GUIDE MASTER

Use the Study Guide master for section 8.2.

CONCEPT DEVELOPMENT

- This is the student's first exposure to the field concept. Go over the idea carefully since you will use it later in Chapter 21 on electric fields.
- An extension of problem 20, page 173, on geosynchronous satellites is to make a model. Get a globe, measure its radius, then cut a piece of stiff wire 5.5 times the globe's radius. The satellite must be that distance from the surface of the Earth. Put a bead on one end of the wire to represent the satellite.

Enrichment: Perhaps students who are familiar with "The Little Prince" could make some estimates of the gravitational forces which acted on him on his small world.

Connect to BIOLOGY

Weightlessness can cause medical problems for astronauts in space for long periods. For the same reason you are longer when lying down (Pocket Lab, page 25), astronauts "grow" about 2 cm while they are in a weightless environment. When the weight of your upper body is taken off the discs in your spine, the discs expand making you longer. The hearts of astronauts who have spent weeks or more in space are weakened. Because blood isn't pulled downward, the heart doesn't have to pump as hard to push the blood into the upper body. Astronauts who have been in orbit 7–10 days can recover from this weakness quickly. But, if we are to send humans to Mars, we must do additional research on ways to keep the cardiovascular system in shape.

- The faces of astronauts appear puffy from excess fluid. Why would this be the case? [In a weightless environment, fluids are not pulled downward, and thus redistribute themselves.]

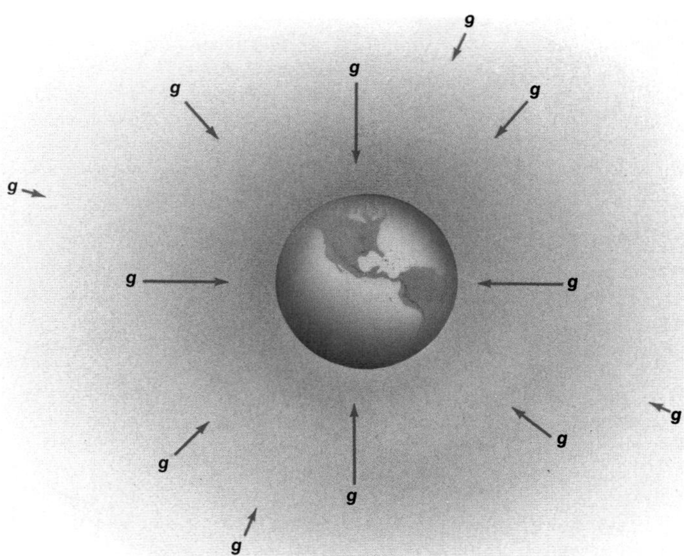

FIGURE 8–12. Vectors can be used to show Earth's gravitational field.

Einstein's concept of gravity agrees with every experimental test.

The Gravitational Field

Many common forces are contact forces. Friction is exerted where two objects touch; the floor and your chair or desk push on you. Gravity is different. It acts on an apple falling from a tree and on the moon in orbit; it even acts on you in midair. In other words, gravity acts over a distance. Newton himself was uneasy with such an idea. How can the sun exert a force on Earth 150 million kilometers away?

In the nineteenth century, Michael Faraday invented the concept of the field to explain how a magnet attracts objects. Later, the field concept was applied to gravity. Anything that has mass is surrounded by a gravitational field. It is the field that acts on a second body, resulting in a force of attraction. The field acts on the second body at the location of that body. In general, the field concept makes the idea of a force acting across great distances unnecessary.

To find the strength of the gravitational field, place a small body of mass m in the field and measure the force. We define the field strength, g, to be the force divided by a unit mass, F/m. It is measured in newtons per kilogram. The direction of g is in the direction of the force. Thus,

$$g = \frac{F}{m}.$$

Note that the field is numerically equal to the acceleration of gravity at the location of the mass. On Earth's surface, the strength of the gravitational field is 9.8 N/kg. It is independent of the size of the test mass. The field can be represented by a vector of length g and pointing toward the object producing the field. We can picture the gravitational field of Earth as a collection of vectors surrounding Earth and pointing toward it, Figure 8–12. The strength of the field varies inversely with the square of the distance from the center of Earth. To get a feeling for the field,

F. Y. I.

Little Miss Muffet
Sits on her tuffet
in a nonchalant sort of a way.
With her force field around her
The spider, the bounder,
is not in the picture today.
—Frederick Winsor
The Space Child's
Mother Goose

8:2 ASSIGNMENT GUIDE

	PRACTICE	EXTENSION
CHAPTER REVIEW pp. 170–173		
· Reviewing Concepts	9–15	
· Applying Concepts		6–13
· Problems*	20, 22, 23, 26–28	21, 24, 25
APPENDIX B PROBLEMS		
· Chapter 8 p. 694	13–16	

* Complete solutions to all Chapter Review and Appendix problems appear in the Problems and Solutions Manual.

hold a heavy book in your hands and close your eyes. Imagine a spring pulling the book back toward the center of Earth. As you lift the book, the spring stretches. Both the spring and gravitational field are invisible.

FIGURE 8–13. Matter causes space to curve just as a mass on a rubber sheet curves the sheet around it. Moving bodies, near the mass, follow the curvature of space.

Einstein's Theory of Gravity

Newton's law of universal gravitation allows us to calculate the force that exists between two bodies because of their masses. The concept of a gravitational field allows us to picture the way gravity acts on bodies far away. Neither *explains* the origin of gravity.

Albert Einstein (1879–1955) proposed that gravity is not a force, but an effect of space itself. According to Einstein, a mass changes the space about it. Mass causes space to be curved, and other bodies are accelerated because they move in this curved space.

One way to picture how space is affected by mass is to compare it to a large two-dimensional rubber sheet, Figure 8–13. The yellow ball on the sheet represents a massive object. It forms an indentation. A marble rolling across the sheet simulates the motion of an object in space. If the marble moves near the sagging region of the sheet, its path will be curved. In the same way, Earth orbits the sun because space is distorted by the two bodies.

Einstein's theory, called the general theory of relativity, makes predictions that differ slightly from the predictions of Newton's laws. In every test, Einstein's theory has been shown to give the correct results.

Perhaps the most interesting prediction is the deflection of light by massive objects. In 1919, during an eclipse of the sun, astronomers found that light from distant stars that passed near the sun was deflected in agreement with Einstein's predictions. Astronomers have seen light from a distant, bright galaxy bent as it passed by a closer, dark galaxy.

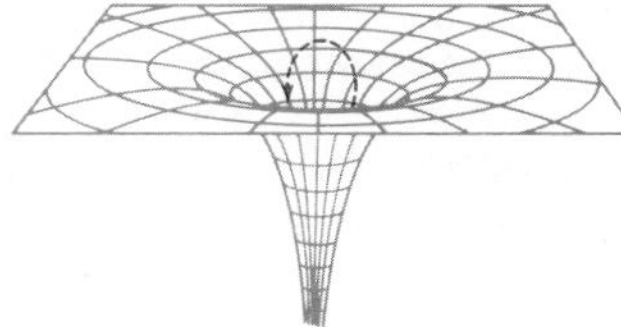

FIGURE 8–14. A black hole is so massive and of such unimaginable density, that light leaving it will be bent back to the black hole.

CONCEPT DEVELOPMENT

This spring analogy, used to help explain the Earth's gravitational field, can't be pushed too far. Spring forces and gravitational forces don't behave the same way. Spring forces get larger as the distance increases, while gravitational forces get smaller as the distance increases.

Cooperative Learning: Assign small groups of students each a Chapter Review problem, then have them present their solutions in front of the class.

CHECKING FOR UNDERSTANDING

Have students summarize the material in this section and show the connections between topics.

RETEACHING

Reteaching Master, Teacher Resource Package. Use the Reteaching Master for Chapter 8, Testing Einstein's Theory.

INDEPENDENT PRACTICE/ EXTENSION

Refer to the Assignment Guide on page 168 for additional questions and problems for independent practice.

3 Close

CONVERGENT QUESTION

Describe Newton's own conception of gravitation. What more recent ideas have been grafted onto his original ideas?

TEACHER F.Y.I.

The book *Flatland* by Edwin A. Abbott could be used to illustrate the difficulty of visualizing three-dimensional space that is "curved" in a fourth dimension.

CONCEPT REVIEW ANSWERS

2.1 It is about one-sixth that on Earth. 1.6 N/kg

2.2 The one at 160 km has the larger period. The one at 150 km has the larger velocity.

2.3 *g* is either the acceleration (9.8 m/s^2) an object experiences when it is acted on by the gravitational force, or it is the strength of the gravitational field (in N/kg).

2.4 Critical Thinking: Earth rotates toward the east, and this velocity adds to the velocity given the satellite by the rocket, reducing the velocity the rocket must supply.

CLOSING CHAPTER 8

Review Summary statements and Key Terms with your students.

ASSESSMENT

Vocabulary Review Master, Teacher Resource Package. Use this master to check students' understanding of Key Terms.

Evaluation Masters. Use Parts A and B of the Chapter Evaluation Masters from the Teacher Resource Package to test qualitative chapter objectives. Use Parts C and D to test quantitative chapter objectives.

F.Y.I.

Einstein refused the offer of the presidency of Israel. He said that he had no head for human problems.
—Asimov's Book of Facts

The result is two or more images of the bright galaxy. Another result of general relativity is the effect on light of very massive objects. If the object is massive enough, light leaving it will be totally bent back to the object, Figure 8–14. No light ever escapes. Such an object, called a black hole, has been identified as a result of its effect on nearby stars.

Einstein's theory is not yet complete. It does not explain how masses curve space. Physicists are still working to understand the true nature of gravity.

CONCEPT REVIEW

2.1 What is the gravitational field strength on the surface of the moon?

2.2 Two satellites are in circular orbits about Earth, one 150 km above the surface, the other 160 km.

a. Which satellite has the larger orbital period?

b. Which one has the larger velocity?

2.3 What is *g*? Explain in your own words two different meanings for *g*. Be sure to use the correct units.

2.4 **Critical Thinking:** It is easier to launch an Earth satellite into an orbit that circles eastward than one that circles westward. Explain.

CHAPTER 8 REVIEW

SUMMARY

8.1 Motion in the Heavens and on Earth

- Kepler's laws of planetary motion state that planets move in elliptical orbits, that they sweep out equal areas in equal times, and that the ratio of the square of the periods of any two planets is equal to the ratio of the cube of their distances to the sun.
- Newton's law of universal gravitation states that the force between two bodies depends on the product of their masses divided by the square of the distance between their centers. It is along a line connecting their centers.
- The mass of the sun can be found from the period and radius of a planet's orbit. The mass of the planet can be found only if it has a satellite orbiting it.
- Cavendish was the first to measure the gravitational attraction between two bodies on Earth.

8.2 Using the Law of Universal Gravitation

- A satellite in a circular orbit accelerates toward Earth at a rate equal to the acceleration of gravity at its orbital radius.
- All bodies have gravitational fields surrounding them that can be represented by a collection of vectors representing the force per unit mass at all locations.
- Einstein's theory of gravity describes gravitational attraction as a property of space itself.

KEY TERMS

gravitational force
inverse square laws
Kepler's laws of planetary motion
satellite
weightlessness

RETEACHING MASTER

Use the Reteaching master for Chapter 8 with this section.

EVALUATION MASTER

Use the Chapter Evaluation master for Chapter 8 with this section.

REVIEW MASTER

Use the Vocabulary Review master for Chapter 8 with this section.

REVIEWING CONCEPTS

1. In 1609, Galileo looked through his telescope at Jupiter and saw four moons. The name of one of the moons is Io. Restate Kepler's first law for Io and Jupiter.
2. Earth moves more slowly in its orbit during summer than during winter. Is it closer to the sun in summer or in winter?
3. Is the area swept out per unit time by Earth moving around the sun equal to the area swept out per unit time by Mars moving around the sun?
4. Why did Newton think that a force must act on the moon?
5. The force of gravity acting on an object near Earth's surface is proportional to the mass of the object. Why does a heavy object not fall faster than a light object?
6. What information do you need to find the mass of Jupiter using Newton's version of Kepler's third law?
7. The mass of Pluto was not known until a satellite of the planet was discovered. Why?
8. How did Cavendish demonstrate that a gravitational force of attraction exists between two small bodies?
9. What provides the centripetal force that keeps a satellite in orbit?
10. How do you answer the question, "What keeps a satellite up?"
11. A satellite is going around Earth. On which of the following does the speed depend?
    a. mass of the satellite
    b. distance from Earth
    c. mass of Earth
12. Chairs in an orbiting spacecraft are weightless. If you were on board and barefoot, would you stub your toe if you kicked one? Explain.
13. During space flight, astronauts often refer to forces as multiples of the force of gravity on Earth's surface. What does a force of 5 g mean to an astronaut?
14. Show that the dimensions of g in the equation $g = F/m$ are m/s^2.
15. Newton assumed that the gravitational force acts directly between Earth and the moon. How does Einstein's view of the attraction between the two bodies differ from the view of Newton?

APPLYING CONCEPTS

1. For each of the orbits shown in Figure 8–15, tell whether or not it is a possible orbit for a planet.

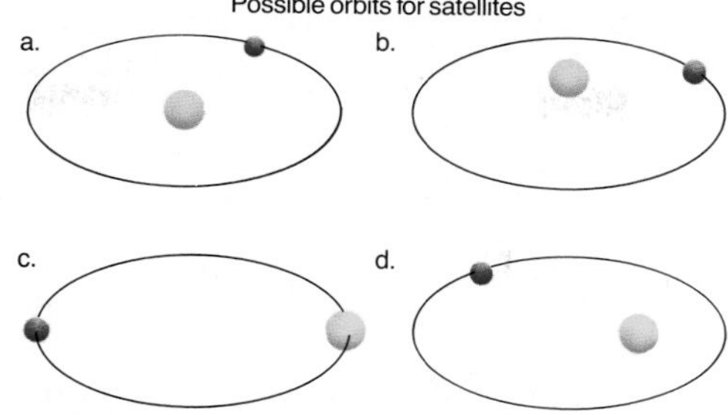

FIGURE 8–15. Use with Applying Concepts 1.

2. What happens to the gravitational force between two masses when the distance between the masses is doubled?
3. The moon and Earth are attracted to each other by gravitational force. Does the more massive Earth attract the moon with a greater force than the moon attracts Earth? Explain.
4. According to Newton's version of Kepler's third law, how does the ratio $\left(\frac{T^2}{r^3}\right)$ change if the mass of the sun is doubled?
5. If Earth were twice as massive but remained the same size, what would happen to the value of G?
6. Examine the equation relating the speed of an orbiting satellite and the distance from the center of Earth.
    a. Does a satellite with a large or small orbital radius have the greater velocity?
    b. When a satellite is too close to Earth, it can get into the atmosphere where there is air drag. As a result, its orbit gets smaller. Does its speed increase or decrease?
7. If a space shuttle goes into a higher orbit, what happens to the shuttle's period?
8. Mars has about half the mass of Earth. Satellite **M** orbits Mars with the same orbital radius as satellite **E** that orbits Earth. Which satellite has a smaller period?
9. A satellite is one earth radius above the surface of Earth. How does the acceleration due

Answers To
REVIEWING CONCEPTS

1. The path of Io is an ellipse with Jupiter at one focus.

2. Since Earth moves more slowly in its orbit during summer, by Kepler's second law it must be farther from the sun. Therefore, Earth is closer to the sun in the winter months.

3. No. The equality of area swept out per unit time applies to each planet individually.

4. Newton knew that the moon followed a curved path, therefore it was accelerated, and that a force is required for an acceleration.

5.

$F = G\frac{m_1 m_2}{d^2}$, m_1 = Earth's mass

$a = \frac{F}{m_2}$, m_2 = object's mass

$a = G\frac{m_1}{d^2}$

The acceleration is independent of the object's mass. This is because heavier objects require more force to accelerate at the same rate.

6. period and orbital radius of at least one satellite

7. Orbital motion of a planet does not depend on its mass, and cannot be used to find the mass. A satellite orbiting the planet is necessary to find its mass.

8. He very carefully measured the masses, the distance between the masses, and the force of attraction. He then calculated G using Newton's universal law of gravitation.

9. gravity

10. its speed: It is falling all the time.

11. only on the distance from Earth and the mass of Earth

12. Yes; the chairs are weightless but not massless. They still have inertia.

13. A force of 5 g means that an astronaut's weight is 5 times heavier than it is on Earth. The force exerted on an astronaut is 5 times the force of Earth's gravitational force.

14. The units of $\frac{F}{m}$ are

$$\frac{\text{N}}{\text{kg}} = \frac{\text{kg m/s}^2}{\text{kg}} = \text{m/s}^2$$

Answers continue on page 172.

Answers To

REVIEWING CONCEPTS (cont)

15. Einstein's view is that gravity is an effect of the curvature of space as a result of the presence of mass, while Newton's view of gravity is a force acting directly between objects. Thus, according to Einstein, the attraction between Earth and the moon is the effect of the curvature of space caused by their combined masses.

Answers To

APPLYING CONCEPTS

1. See Figure 8–15. Only d is possible. a and b do not have sun at a focus; c does not have planet in plane of ellipse.

2. According to Newton, $F \propto \frac{1}{d^2}$. If the distance is doubled, the force is one-quarter.

3. No. The forces constitute an action-reaction pair, so under Newton's third law, they are equal and opposite.

4. Since $\frac{T^2}{R^3} = \frac{4\pi^2}{GM_s}$, if the mass of the sun, M_s, is doubled, the ratio will be halved.

5. Nothing. G is a universal constant and it is independent of Earth's mass.

6. a. $v = R_e\sqrt{g/r}$, so, small.
b. decrease: The drag will slow it down causing its orbit to decay, so, $v = R_e\sqrt{g/r}$ does not apply.

7. Since $T = 2\pi\sqrt{r^3/Gm}$, if the orbital radius increases, so will the period.

8. Since $T = 2\pi\sqrt{r^3/Gm}$, as the mass of the planet increases, the period of a satellite will decrease, and since Earth has a larger mass, Earth's satellite will have the smaller period.

9. $d = R_E + R_E = 2R_E$, so,

$$a = g\left(\frac{R_E}{2R_E}\right)^2 = \frac{1}{4}g.$$

10. The value of g would double.

11. $g \propto \frac{m}{d^2}$ 300 times the mass and 10 times the radius;

$$g \propto \frac{300}{(10)^2} = 3 \text{ times}$$

Earth's acceleration due to gravity.

12. It will also double.

13. a. Her mass increased. **b.** The ratio remained constant because it is equal to the gravitational field at that location.

to gravity at that location compare to the surface of Earth?

10. If Earth were twice as massive but remained the same size, what would happen to the value of g.

11. Jupiter has about 300 times the mass of Earth and about 10 times earth's radius. Estimate the size of g on the surface of Jupiter.

12. If the mass in Earth's gravitational field is doubled, what will happen to the force exerted by the field upon it?

13. Yesterday, Sally had a mass of 50.0 kg. This morning she stepped on a scale and found that she gained weight.
- **a.** What happened, if anything, to Sally's mass?
- **b.** What happened, if anything, to the ratio of Sally's weight to her mass?

PROBLEMS

8.1 Motion in the Heavens and on Earth

Use $G = 6.670 \times 10^{-11}$ Nm²/kg².

1. Jupiter is 5.2 times farther than Earth is from the sun. Find Jupiter's orbital period in earth years.

▶ **2.** Uranus requires 84 years to circle the sun. Find Uranus' orbital radius as a multiple of Earth's orbital radius.

▶ **3.** Venus has a period of revolution of 225 earth days. Find the distance between the sun and Venus, as a multiple of Earth's orbital radius.

4. If a small planet were located 8.0 times as far from the sun as Earth, how many years would it take the planet to orbit the sun?

▶ **5.** A satellite is placed in an orbit with a radius that is half the radius of the moon's orbit. Find its period in units of the period of the moon.

6. An apparatus like the one Cavendish used to find G has a large lead ball that is 5.9 kg in mass and a small one that is 0.047 kg. Their centers are separated by 0.055 m. Find the force of attraction between them.

7. Use the data in Table 8–1 to compute the gravitational force the sun exerts on Jupiter.

8. Tom has a mass of 70.0 kg and Sally has a mass of 50.0 kg. Tom and Sally are standing 20.0 m apart on the dance floor. Sally looks up and she sees Him. She feels an attraction. If the attraction is gravitation, find its size. Assume both can be replaced by spherical masses.

9. Two balls have their centers 2.0 m apart. One has a mass of 8.0 kg. The other has a mass of 6.0 kg. What is the gravitational force between them?

10. Two bowling balls each have a mass of 6.8 kg. They are located next to one another with their centers 21.8 cm apart. What gravitational force do they exert on each other?

11. Sally has a mass of 50.0 kg and Earth has a mass of 5.98×10^{24} kg. The radius of Earth is 6.371×10^6 m.
- **a.** What is the force of gravitational attraction between Sally and Earth?
- **b.** What is Sally's weight?

12. The gravitational force between two electrons 1.00 m apart is 5.42×10^{-71} N. Find the mass of an electron.

▶ **13.** Two spherical balls are placed so their centers are 2.6 m apart. The force between the two balls is 2.75×10^{-12} N. What is the mass of each ball if one ball is twice the mass of the other ball?

14. Using the fact that a 1.0-kg mass weighs 9.8 N on the surface of Earth and the radius of Earth is roughly 6.4×10^6 m,
- **a.** calculate the mass of Earth.
- **b.** calculate the average density of Earth.

▶ **15.** The moon is 3.9×10^5 km from Earth's center and 1.5×10^8 km from the sun's center. If the masses of the moon, Earth, and sun are 7.3×10^{22} kg, 6.0×10^{24} kg, and 2.0×10^{30} kg, respectively, find the ratio of the gravitational forces exerted by Earth and the sun on the moon.

▶ **16.** A force of 40.0 N is required to pull a 10.0-kg wooden block at a constant velocity across a smooth glass surface on Earth. What force would be required to pull the same wooden block across the same glass surface on the planet Jupiter?

17. Use the information for Earth from Table 8–1 to calculate the mass of the sun using Newton's variations of Kepler's third law.

▶ **18.** Mimas, a moon of Saturn, has an orbital radius of 1.87×10^8 m and an orbital period of about 23 h. Use Newton's version of Kepler's third law and these data to find the mass of Saturn.

▶ **19.** Use Newton's version of Kepler's third law to find the mass of Earth. The moon is 3.9×10^8 m away from Earth and the moon has a

Answers To

PROBLEMS

Complete solutions for all Chapter Review Problems can be found in the Problems and Solutions Manual accompanying this text.

1. 12 yrs
2. 19 r_E
3. 0.724 r_E
4. 23 yrs
5. 0.35 T_m
6. 6.1×10^{-9} N
7. 4.17×10^{23} N
8. 5.84×10^{-10} N
9. 8.0×10^{-10} N
10. 6.5×10^{-8} N
11. a. 491 N
b. 490 N
12. 9.01×10^{-31} kg
13. $m_1 = 0.37$ kg
$m_2 = 0.75$ kg
14. a. 6.0×10^{24} kg
b. 5.5×10^3 kg/m³
15. 1.0 to 2.3
16. 100 N
17. 1.989×10^{30} kg
18. 5.6×10^{26} kg
19. 6.3×10^{24} kg
very close

period of 27.33 days. Compare this mass to the mass found in Problem 14.

8.2 Using the Law of Universal Gravitation

20. A geosynchronous satellite appears to remain over one spot on Earth. A geosynchronous satellite has an orbital radius of 4.23×10^7 m.
  a. Calculate its speed in orbit.
  b. Calculate its period.

▶ **21.** On July 19, 1969, Apollo II's orbit around the moon was adjusted to an average orbit of 111 km. The radius of the moon is 1785 km and the mass of the moon is 7.3×10^{22} kg.
  a. How many minutes did it take to orbit once?
  b. At what velocity did it orbit the moon?

22. The asteroid Ceres has a mass 7×10^{20} kg and a radius of 500 km.
  a. What is g on the surface?
  b. How much would a 85-kg astronaut weigh on Ceres?

23. The radius of Earth is about 6.40×10^3 km. A 7.20×10^3-N spacecraft travels away from Earth. What is the weight of the spacecraft at the following distances from Earth's surface?
  a. 6.40×10^3 km **b.** 1.28×10^4 km

▶ **24.** How high does a rocket have to go above Earth's surface until its weight is half what it would be on Earth?

▶ **25.** The formula for the period of a pendulum, T, is $T = 2\pi\sqrt{l/g}$.
  a. What would be the period of a 2.0 m long pendulum on the moon's surface? The moon's mass is 7.34×10^{22} kg and its radius is 1.74×10^6 m.
  b. What is the period of this pendulum on Earth?

26. A 1.25-kg book in space has a weight of 8.35 N. What is the value of the gravitational field at that location?

27. The moon's mass is 7.34×10^{22} kg and it is 3.8×10^8 m away from Earth. Earth's mass can be found in Table 8–1.
  a. Calculate the gravitational force of attraction between the two.
  b. Find Earth's gravitational field at the moon.

28. Earth's gravitational field is 7.83 N/kg at the altitude of the space shuttle. What is the size of the force of attraction between a student, mass of 45.0 kg, and Earth?

USING LAB SKILLS

1. Kepler's second law says that a planet sweeps out equal areas in equal time intervals. What does this suggest about the speed of the planet when it is farthest away from the sun? Draw an elliptical orbit as directed in the Physics Lab on p. 158. Label a planet's closest point to the sun point **A** and the farthest point **C.** Use a centimeter scale to measure a point of the orbit that is 4.0 cm from point **A.** Mark this point and label it point **B.** Label the sun **S.** Shade the area of the triangle **ABS** and calculate its area. Find a point **D** on the orbit near **C** so that the area of **CDS** equals that of **ABS.** What does this diagram indicate about the speed of the planet through the two portions of the orbit?

USING A GRAPHING CALCULATOR

Use Newton's universal gravitational equation and constant and the radius of Earth to find an equation where x is equal to an object's distance from Earth's center, and y is equal to that object's acceleration due to gravity. The equation should be of the form $y = c(1/x^2)$. Use a graphing calculator to graph this equation, using 6400 – 6600 km as the range for x and 9 m/s^2 – 10 m/s^2 as the range for y. Trace along this graph and find a: at sea level, 6400 km; on top of Mt. Everest, 6410 km; in a typical satellite orbit, 6500 km; and in a much higher orbit, 6600 km.

THINKING PHYSIC-LY

1. As an astronaut in an orbiting space shuttle, how would you go about "dropping" an object down to Earth?

2. The weather pictures you see every day on TV come from a spacecraft in a stationary position 35 700 km above Earth's equator. Explain how it can stay exactly in position day after day. What would happen if it were closer in? farther out? **Hint:** A sketch may help.

20. **a.** 3.07×10^3 m/s; **b.** 24.0 h
21. **a.** 1.2×10^2 min; **b.** 1.6×10^3 m/s
22. **a.** 0.2 m/s^2; **b.** 2×10^1 N
23. **a.** 1.80×10^3 N; **b.** 800 N
24. 2.65×10^3 km
25. **a.** 7.0 s; **b.** 2.8 s
26. 6.68 N/kg
27. **a.** 2.0×10^{20} N; **b.** 0.0028 N/kg
28. 352 N

Answer To
USING LAB SKILLS

1. Although the areas are equal, the drawings will dramatically demonstrate that the planet moves much slower when it is farther away from the sun.

Answers To
USING A GRAPHING CALCULATOR

1. Set the range values (RANGE 6400 6600 50 9 10 .5).
2. Clear the graph (Cls EXE).
3. Graph the equation (GRAPH 4.0 EXP 8/x^2 EXE).
4. Trace along the graph to the three x's and find the y's (TRACE –> x <–> y).
Answers: 9.77 m/s^2, 9.73 m/s^2, 9.46 m/s^2, 9.18 m/s^2

Answers To
THINKING PHYSIC-LY

1. In order to "drop" an object down to Earth, you would have to launch it backward at the same speed that you are traveling in your orbit. With respect to Earth, its speed perpendicular to Earth's gravity would be zero, and it could then "drop" down to Earth below. However, the object is likely to burn up as a result of friction with Earth's atmosphere on the way down.

2. The satellite is positioned as close to the equator as possible so it doesn't appear to have much north-south movement. Because it is placed at that distance, the satellite has a period of 24.0 h. Any closer, its period would be less than 24.0 h and it would appear to move toward the east. Any farther, the period would be longer than 24.0 h.

CHAPTER

9 Momentum and Its Conservation

PLANNING GUIDE (6 class sessions)

CONTENTS	TEXT FEATURES	TEACHER RESOURCE PACKAGE	OTHER COMPONENTS
9.1 Impulse and Change in Momentum, pp. 176–180 (1 Class Session) • Momentum and Impulse • Angular Momentum	**Pocket Lab:** Cart Momentum, p. 176 **Concept Review,** p. 180	**Study Guide:** Impulse and Change in Momentum **Reteaching Master:** Momentum and Football **Transparency Worksheet:** Impulse and Change in Momentum	**Laboratory Manual:** Lab 9.2 Angular Momentum **Transparency 11:** Impulse and Change in Momentum
9.2 The Conservation of Momentum, pp. 180–191 (5 Class Sessions) • Newton's Third Law and Momentum • Law of Conservation of Momentum • Internal and External Forces • Conservation of Momentum in Two Dimensions	**Physics Lab:** The Explosion, p. 182 **Physics and Technology:** Running Shoe Design, p. 187 **Pocket Lab:** Skateboard Fun, p. 181 **Using Your Calculator:** Using Memory, p. 185 **Concept Review,** p. 191	**Study Guide:** The Conservation of Momentum **Physics Lab Data Sheet:** The Explosion **Critical Thinking Master:** Highway Barriers **Enrichment Master:** Conservation of Momentum	**Laboratory Manual:** Lab 9.1 Conservation of Momentum
Chapter Review, pp. 192–195	Summary Key Terms Reviewing Concepts Applying Concepts Problems Thinking Physic-ly	**Vocabulary Review** **Chapter Test**	**Test Bank**

SUPPLEMENTARY MATERIALS

SOFTWARE	AUDIOVISUAL	BOOKS/MAGAZINES
ALB Momentum, Queue, Inc. (Apple II). *Collisions,* Queue, Inc. (Apple II). *Conservation Laws,* Cross (Apple II, IBM PC).	Videos: *Kinetic Karnival,* Jearl Walker, WVIZ-TV. *The Mechanical Universe-High School Adaptation, Conservation of Momentum,* Annenberg Project, 1985. Interactive Videodisc: *Physics and Automobile Collisions,* John Wiley and Sons, Inc.	Escobar, Carole. "Amusement Park Physics." *The Physics Teacher,* October 1990, p. 446. Ficken, George W., Jr. "Home Experiment Using a Garden Hose." *The Physics Teacher,* April 1987, p. 218. Irwin, Jack, and Swinson, Derek. "A Demonstration of Car Braking Instabilities." *The Physics Teacher,* November 1990, p. 522.

PROBLEM CORRELATION

CONCEPTS	CHAPTER REVIEW: Reviewing Concepts	Applying Concepts	Problems	PROBLEMS APPENDIX
9.1 Impulse and Change in Momentum				
Momentum and Impulse	1,2,4	1,2,3,4	1,2,3,4,5,6,7,8, 9,**10**,11,**12**,**13**, **14**,**15**	1,2,3,**4**,5,6
Angular Momentum				
9.2 The Conservation of Momentum				
Newton's Third Law and Momentum	3,5			7
Law of Conservation of Momentum	6,8	6,8,9,10,11	16,17,18,19,20,21, 22,23,24,**25**,**26**,27 **28**,**33**	8,9,10,**11**,12,**13**
Internal and External Forces	7,9,10	5,7		
Conservation of Momentum in Two Dimensions			**29**,**30**,**31**,**32**	**14**,**15**

ACTIVITY AND DEMONSTRATION MATERIALS

PHYSICS LAB	POCKET LAB	DEMONSTRATIONS
Page 182 2 laboratory carts 2 C-clamps 2 blocks of wood 20-N spring balance 0.50-kg mass stopwatch masking tape	Pages 176, 181 2 laboratory carts stopwatch spring scale 2 skateboards 5-m length of rope	Page 184 cardbard box packing material softball meter stick spring scale platform balance

EXTENSION PROJECTS

LIBRARY RESEARCH

1. Forensic Physics
Through library research, investigate the field of forensic physics. How does a knowledge of momentum allow the determination of events?

DISPLAY MODEL

2. Billiard Balls
Videotape billiard balls in motion. Using freeze-frame and an overhead transparency, sketch the force and velocity diagrams of the colliding balls.

STUDENT READINGS

Bernardo, Stephanie. "The Physics of the Sweet Spot." *Science Digest,* May 1984.

Boudreau, William. "Cheap and Simple Yo-Yos." *The Physics Teacher,* February 1990.

Dewhurst, David. "Torque vs. Horsepower: You Can't Have One Without the Other." *Cycle Guide,* April 1985.

Chapter 9

Momentum and Its Conservation

CHAPTER OVERVIEW

Theme Development: Important to the study of momentum is the definition of a closed system. The constancy theme is present in the form of a conservation principle for momentum.

MISCONCEPTIONS

Students will continue to have trouble understanding action-reaction forces. Momentum is an abstract concept difficult to understand—particularly its vector nature. The distinction between internal and external forces is not obvious.

KEY TERMS

angular momentum
closed, isolated system
external force
impulse
impulse-momentum theorem
internal force
law of conservation of momentum
momentum
system

Laboratory Options

STUDENT EDITION

Physics Lab

The Explosion	182

Pocket Labs

Cart Momentum	176
Skateboard Fun	181

TEACHER EDITION

Demonstration	184

LABORATORY MANUAL

Conservation of Momentum	Lab 9.1
Angular Momentum	Lab 9.2

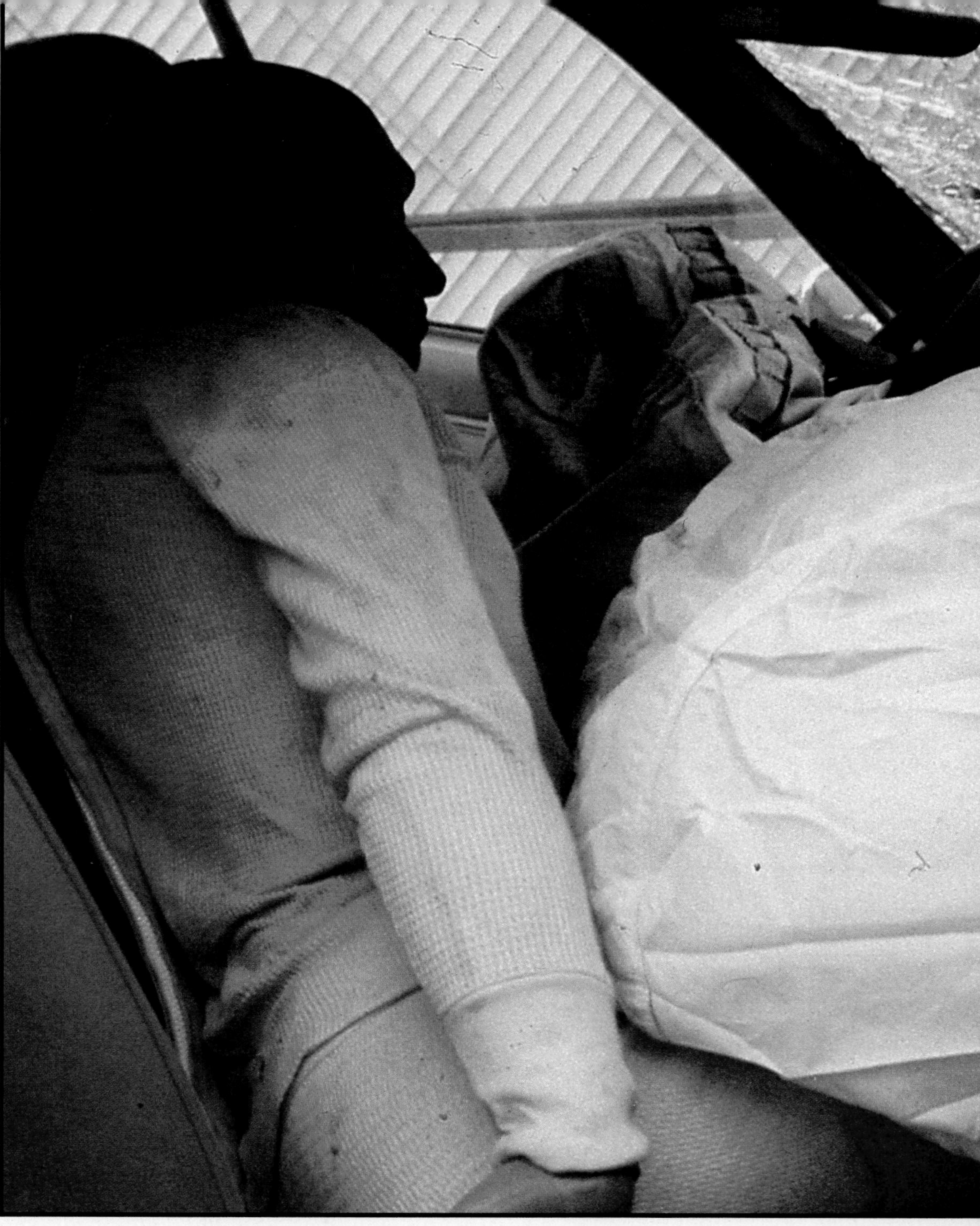

CHAPTER 9

Momentum and Its Conservation

◀ Air Force

Some cars already have air bags. In a head-on crash of two air bag-equipped cars, both drivers walked away uninjured. How does an air bag help to reduce the injury to a person in a car crash?

Chapter Outline

In the crash of a car moving at high speed, the passengers are brought to a stop very quickly. You have learned that force is needed to produce the acceleration of the passengers. We will now take a slightly different point of view. Rather than studying forces acting on an object, and the acceleration that results, we will look at a clearly defined collection of objects before and after an interaction takes place. We will look for properties that remain constant. Such properties are said to be conserved.

✓ Concept Check

The following terms or concepts from earlier chapters are important for a good understanding of this chapter. If you are not familiar with them, you should review them before studying this chapter.
- velocity, Chapter 3
- mass, force, Newton's second and third laws, Chapter 5
- vectors, Chapter 6

Introducing The Chapter

Air Force

Using The Photo: The amount of stopping force experienced in a car crash is critical to survival. Air bags serve to decrease the force involved by increasing the time over which it is applied.

Other automobile safety devices such as padded dashboards and collapsible steering wheels use the same operating principles as air bags. That is, they all seek to lessen the force exerted on passengers in a crash by increasing the time during which the force acts.

Students will find the information they need to answer the chapter opener question by referring to page 179.

✓ Concept Check

Make sure students have a clear understanding of the concepts taught in Chapters 3, 5, and 6 that are listed in the Concept Check. Students with a good grasp of the nature of physical motion, Newton's second and third laws, and vectors will more easily understand the principles of momentum and its conservation introduced in this chapter.

Assessment

Portfolio

Collect examples of problems and questions involving conservation of momentum in both one and two dimensions.

Assessment Options

Portfolio Assessment
Portfolio Assessment, TWE, p. 175
Enrichment, TWE, p. 177
Cooperative Learning, TWE, p. 178
Thinking Physic-ly, p. 195

Performance
Pocket Labs, pp. 176, 181
Pocket Lab Assessment, TWE, p. 181
Physics Lab, p. 182

Content
Self Assessment: Practice Problems, pp. 178, 185, 188, 191
Pocket Lab Assessment, TWE, p. 176
Assessment, Critical Thinking, TWE, p. 182
Concept Reviews, pp. 180, 191
Chapter Review, pp. 192–195
Supplemental Problems, p. 695

Group Assessment
Activities for group assessment occur with Cooperative Learning and lab activities.

9.1 IMPULSE AND CHANGE IN MOMENTUM

Preparation

OBJECTIVES

The objectives are listed on the student page. Remind students to preview these objectives as a study guide to this major section.

OVERVIEW

Introduced here are momentum, impulse, the impulse-momentum theorem, and the concept of a system.

BRIDGING

Previously introduced concepts that are developed further in this chapter include mass, velocity, force, and Newton's first and second laws.

POCKET LAB

CART MOMENTUM

Purpose: to allow students to investigate which variable, force or the time over which it is applied, causes the greater change in a cart's velocity.
Materials: laboratory cart; stopwatch; spring scale.
Outcome: Trial 1 will produce more acceleration because the force is larger ($a = F/m$). Both trials will produce the same change in velocity. Students will find that both trials resulted in the same velocity. The F and the Δt are equally important.

Objectives

- define momentum and impulse and use the momentum-impulse theorem to calculate changes in momentum; understand the relation between average force and time interval for a fixed impulse.
- recognize the connection between the third law and conservation of momentum; use the definition of a closed, isolated system.

9.1 IMPULSE AND CHANGE IN MOMENTUM

The word momentum is often used in everyday speech. A winning sports team is said to have the "big mo," momentum—as is a politician who rates high in opinion polls. In physics, however, momentum has a very special definition. Newton actually wrote his three laws of motion in terms of momentum, which he called the *quantity of motion*.

Momentum and Impulse

Momentum is the product of the mass and the velocity of a body. It is a vector quantity.

Suppose a heavy truck and a compact car move down the road at the same velocity. If the two stop in the same time interval, it takes more force to stop the more massive truck. Now consider two cars of equal mass. If one car is moving faster than the other, a larger force is needed to stop the faster car in the same time interval. Obviously both the velocity and the mass of a moving object help determine what is needed to change its motion. The product of the mass and velocity of a body is called **momentum.** Momentum is a vector quantity that has the same direction as the velocity of the object.

Momentum is represented by p. The equation for momentum is

$$p = mv.$$

The unit for momentum is kilogram·meter/second (kg·m/s).

According to Newton's first law, if no net force acts on a body, its velocity is constant. If we consider only a single isolated object, then its mass cannot change. If its velocity is also constant, then so is its momentum, the product of its mass and velocity. In other words, if a single body has no net force acting on it, its momentum is constant. Its momentum is conserved.

Newton's second law describes how the velocity of a body is changed by a force acting on it, Figure 9–1. Let's rewrite Newton's second law using the definition of acceleration as the change in velocity divided by the time interval,

$$F = ma = \frac{m\Delta v}{\Delta t}.$$

POCKET LAB

CART MOMENTUM

Attach a spring scale to a laboratory cart. First, pull the cart for 1.0 s exerting 1.0 N of force. Second, pull the cart for 2.0 s exerting about 0.50 N of force. Predict which trial will give the cart more acceleration. Explain. Predict which trial will give the cart more velocity. Explain. Try it. What happened? Which factor, F or Δt, seems to be more important in changing the velocity of the cart?

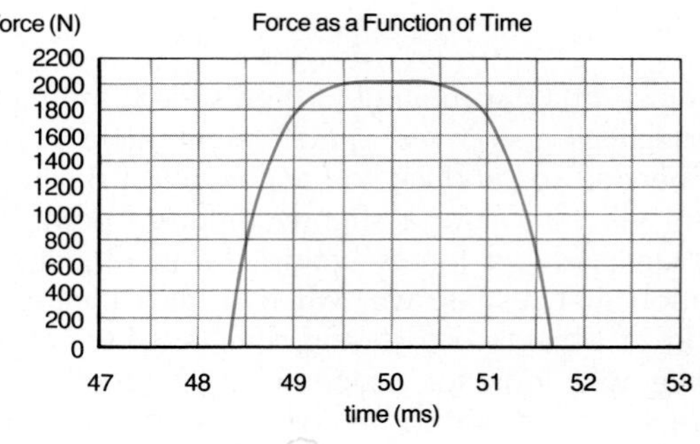

FIGURE 9–1. The graph shows the force exerted by a moving ball colliding with a ball at rest.

Assessment

Critical Thinking

To further assess students' understanding of momentum, ask students to explain why, although theoretically the cart should have a steady acceleration as you pull on it, realistically it does not. [First, you are not practiced enough to keep a steady force on the cart—as the cart speeds up you are not able to move quickly enough. Additionally, as the cart speeds up, the friction increases. More friction causes less net force and less acceleration.]

Multiplying both sides of the equation by Δt, we have the equation

$$F\Delta t = m\Delta v.$$

The left side of this equation, the product of the net force and the time interval over which it acts, is called the **impulse.** Impulse is a vector in the direction of the force. Impulse is measured in units of newton·second (N·s).

If the mass of an object is constant, then a change in its velocity results in a change in its momentum. Under these conditions,

$$\Delta p = m\Delta v.$$

Thus, we see that the impulse given to an object is equal to the change in its momentum,

$$F\Delta t = \Delta p.$$

This equation is called the **impulse-momentum theorem.** The equality of impulse and change in momentum is another way of writing Newton's second law. Often the force is not constant during the time it is exerted. In that case, the average force is used in the impulse-momentum theorem.

Impulse is the product of the average force and the time interval during which the force is exerted. A large change in momentum occurs only when there is a large impulse. A large impulse, however, can result from either a large force acting over a short time, or a smaller force acting over a longer time. What happens to the driver when a crash suddenly stops a car? An impulse is needed to bring the driver's momentum to zero. The steering wheel can exert a large force during a short length of time. An air bag reduces the force exerted on the driver by greatly increasing the length of time the force is exerted. The product of the average force and time interval of the crash would be the same.

FIGURE 9–2. With an equal amount of force, it will take longer to stop a truck than a compact car.

◀ Air Force

Impulse is the product of a force and the time interval over which it acts.

Example Problem

Calculating Momentum

A baseball of mass 0.14 kg is moving at +35 m/s. **a.** Find the momentum of the baseball. **b.** Find the velocity at which a bowling ball, mass 7.26 kg, would have the same momentum as the baseball.

a. Given: mass, $m = 0.14$ kg; velocity, $v = +35$ m/s

Unknown: momentum, p

Basic equation: $p = mv$

Solution: $p = mv = (0.14\text{ kg})(+35\text{ m/s}) = +4.9\text{ kg·m/s}$

Note that the momentum is in the same direction (+) as the velocity.

b. Given: momentum, $p = +4.9$ kg·m/s; mass, $m = 7.26$ kg

Unknown: velocity, v

Basic equation: $p = mv$

Solution: $p = mv \quad v = \dfrac{p}{m} = \dfrac{+4.9\text{ kg·m/s}}{7.26\text{ kg}} = +0.67\text{ m/s}$

Note that the velocity is in the same (+) direction as the momentum.

1 Focus

Have some students help you with a sheet or other large piece of cloth. Hold the sheet up vertically with the bottom edge folded up to make a trough. Now stand back and throw a raw egg at the sheet, being careful to have your assistants catch the egg in the folded up edge of the sheet. Regardless of how hard you throw the egg at the sheet, it won't break because the sheet slows the egg down gradually, hence the force on the egg is small. Practice this before attempting it the first time in class! At the end you might want to crack the egg just to show that it's raw.

2 Teach

CONCEPT DEVELOPMENT

Study Guide Master. To reinforce the concepts in this section, have the students complete the Study Guide Master for Section 9.1 from the Teacher Resource Package.

- Point out that when a truck and car collide, the force of the car on the truck is equal to the force of the truck on the car—this will bear repeating.
- Differentiate between momentum, *mv*, and change in momentum, *m*Δ*v*. Emphasize that momentum is a vector.
- One way of remembering the impulse-momentum theorem is to think of it as a type of cause-and-effect relationship. The impulse is the cause and the change of momentum is the effect produced.
- A fan cart demonstration is a good way to help clarify Newton's third law.

Enrichment: Have students prepare a report on how the impulse-momentum theorem can be illustrated with examples from sports. Be sure they include a discussion of the importance of follow through. You are trying to make the impulse time as long as possible so that the momentum change will be large.

TEACHER

Why do people bend their knees when they land from a jump? When you bend your knees as you land, you greatly increase the impact time, thus reducing the impact force. Why do baseball players catch a ball by allowing it to land in the mitt as they move their arm in the same direction the ball is moving? Same reason!

Why do baseball players and golfers "follow through" with a swing? The bat or club remains in contact with the ball for a longer period of time, thus increasing the impulse and making the ball travel farther.

CONCEPT DEVELOPMENT

Show students that the impulse-momentum theorem is nothing new, as it is contained in Newton's second law. $F = ma$ or $F = m\Delta v$ over Δt from which follows $F\Delta t = m\Delta v$.

CHECKING FOR UNDERSTANDING

Blow up a simple balloon, release it, then ask students about how the propulsion works.

RETEACHING

Reteaching Master. Use the Reteaching Worksheet from the Teacher Resource Package with this section.

EXTENSION

Ask students if they would land stiff-legged if they jumped from the lecture table to the floor. Most will probably say that they would bend their knees. Ask them why they do this. The change in momentum will be the same regardless of whether they bend their knees or not, but the size of F and t can be controlled. Since mv is constant, F can be made smaller if t is made longer. When the legs are bent, the time it takes to stop is increased and the force is decreased.

Cooperative Learning: Have a student or students who are interested in model rocketry explain to the class how impulse and momentum are involved in the operation of rockets. A good article on rocketry is "Measuring Model Rocket Acceleration" by R. A. Jenkins on page 10 of the January, 1993 *Physics Teacher.*

Guided Practice: After reviewing the Example Problem on this page, have students try the first Practice Problem in class.

Independent Practice: Assign Practice Problems 2–4 on page 179 for homework. Go over solutions with students the next day.

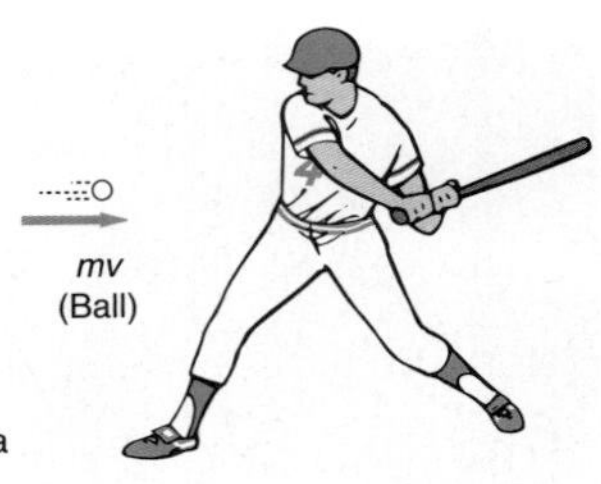

FIGURE 9–3. The ball moves in the direction of the batter with momentum mv. The bat provides impulse $F_{\text{bat on ball}}t$ to the ball. The ball moves off with a change in momentum mv' equal to the impulse from the bat.

Example Problem

Impulse and Momentum Change

A 0.144-kg baseball is pitched horizontally at +38 m/s. After it is hit by a bat, it moves horizontally at −38 m/s.

a. What impulse did the bat deliver to the ball?

b. If the bat and ball were in contact 0.80 ms, what was the average force the bat exerted on the ball?

c. Find the average acceleration of the ball during its contact with the bat.

Indicate the direction of the impulse, force, and acceleration.

a. Given: $m = 0.144$ kg; initial velocity, $v_i = +38$ m/s; final velocity, $v_f = -38$ m/s

Unknown: impulse, $F\Delta t$
Basic equation: $F\Delta t = \Delta p$

Solution:
$$F\Delta t = \Delta p = mv_f - mv_i = m(v_f - v_i)$$
$$= (0.144\text{ kg})(-38\text{ m/s} - (+38\text{ m/s}))$$
$$= (0.144\text{ kg})(-76\text{ m/s})$$
$$= -11\text{ kg·m/s (in the direction of the batted ball)}$$

b. Given: momentum change, $\Delta p = -11$ kg·m/s; time interval, $\Delta t = 0.80\text{ ms} = 8.0 \times 10^{-4}$ s

Unknown: average force, F
Basic equation: $F\Delta t = \Delta p$

Solution: $F\Delta t = \Delta p$, so
$$F = \frac{\Delta p}{\Delta t} = \frac{-11\text{kg·m/s}}{0.80\text{ ms}} = \frac{-11\text{kg·m/s}}{8.0 \times 10^{-4}\text{ s}}$$
$$= -1.4 \times 10^4\text{ N (in the direction of the batted ball)}$$

c. Given: average force, $F = -1.4 \times 10^4$ N; mass, $m = 0.144$ kg

Unknown: average acceleration, a
Basic equation: $F = ma$

Solution: $F = ma$, so
$$a = \frac{F}{m} = \frac{-1.4 \times 10^4\text{ N}}{0.144\text{ kg}} = -9.7 \times 10^4\text{ m/s}^2,$$
about 10 000 gs in the direction of the batted ball.

Practice Problems

1. A compact car, mass 725 kg, is moving at +100 km/h.

a. Find its momentum.

b. At what velocity is the momentum of a larger car, mass 2175 kg, equal to that of the smaller car?

Answers To
PRACTICE PROBLEMS

Have students refer to Appendix A of the Solutions Appendix for complete solutions to Practice Problems.

1. a. 2.02×10^4 kg · m/s
b. 33.4 km/h

9:1 ASSIGNMENT GUIDE

	PRACTICE	EXTENSION
CHAPTER REVIEW pp. 192–195		
· Reviewing Concepts	1, 2, 4	
· Applying Concepts		1–4
· Problems*	1–9, 11	10, 12–15
APPENDIX B PROBLEMS*		
· Chapter 9 p. 695	1–3, 5, 6	4

* Complete solutions to all Chapter Review and Appendix problems appear in the Problems and Solutions Manual.

2. A snowmobile has a mass of 2.50×10^2 kg. A constant force is exerted on it for 60.0 s. The snowmobile's initial velocity is 6.00 m/s and its final velocity 28.0 m/s.
   a. What is its change in momentum?
   b. What is the magnitude of the force exerted on it?
3. The brakes exert a 6.40×10^2 N force on a car weighing 15 680 N and moving at 20.0 m/s. The car finally stops.
   a. What is the car's mass?
   b. What is its initial momentum?
   c. What is the change in the car's momentum?
   d. How long does the braking force act on the car to bring it to a halt?
4. ▶ Figure 9–1 shows, as a function of time, the force exerted by a ball that collided with a box at rest. The impulse, $F\Delta t$, is the area under the curve.
   a. Find the impulse given to the box by the ball.
   b. If the box has a mass of 2.4 kg, what velocity did it have after the collision.

FINE ARTS CONNECTION

You often see mobiles at a museum or mall. Mobiles are made of different shaped objects that depend on the equilibrium of forces and torques to balance and move with air currents. The shape of mobiles and the shadows they make are part of their artistic value. However, the aesthetic value of a mobile depends on its movement as the swinging parts cut shapes in the air. American sculptor, Alexander Calder was the first artist to make a mobile in which movement was the basic purpose. The next time you see a mobile, look for the relationship of space shapes to each other and to the mobile.

Angular Momentum

As we have seen, the speed of an object moving in a circle changes only if a torque is applied to it. The quantity of angular motion that is similar to linear momentum is called **angular momentum.** Thus, if there is no torque on an object, its angular momentum is constant.

Momentum is the product of the object's mass and velocity. Angular momentum is the product of its mass, velocity, and distance from the center of rotation, and the component of velocity perpendicular to that distance. For example, the angular momentum of planets around the sun is constant. Therefore, when a planet's distance from the sun is larger, its velocity must be smaller. This is another statement of Kepler's second law.

Angular momentum is the product of an object's mass, velocity, and distance from center of rotation.

FIGURE 9–4. This hurricane was photographed from space. The huge rotating mass of air possesses a large angular momentum.

TEACHER F.Y.I.

Angular momentum is conserved if the external torque on the system is zero. When a body rotates about a fixed axis, $I_i\omega_i = I_f\omega_f$, where I is the moment of inertia and ω is the angular velocity. A skater is able to spin faster by bringing his or her legs together close to the body, decreasing the moment of inertia. Because angular momentum is conserved, angular velocity is increased. For further discussion, see Supplemental Lesson 2, Rotational Motion: Applications in the Teacher Resource Package.

2. **a.** 5.50×10^3 kg · m/s
   b. 91.7 N
3. **a.** 1.60×10^3 kg
   b. 3.20×10^4 kg · m/s
   c. -3.20×10^4 kg · m/s
   d. 50.0 s
4. **a.** 5.25 N · s
   b. 2.2 m/s

CONCEPT DEVELOPMENT

Which strikes a surface with more force, an object that comes to a dead halt or one that bounces? An object that stops on contact has a change in momentum of $p = m(v_i - v_f)$, where $v_f = 0$. Assuming that an object that bounces leaves the surface at the same velocity at which it struck, but in a different direction, and that it had the same impact time, you come up with the equation: $p = m(v_i - v_f)$ where $v_f = -v_i$. This means that the change in momentum is twice as great as it is for an object that stops; therefore, impact force is twice as great.

Supplemental Lesson Master. For more details on angular momentum, use the Supplemental Lesson Master in the Teacher Resource Package.

Critical Thinking: Suppose your class has a graph prepared by an engineering department that gives the force versus time for a particular rocket motor. Ask students what other information they could extract from such a graph.

Enrichment: When NASA fires a rocket, how is their use of the impulse-momentum theorem more complex than the examples you've considered in class so far?

INDEPENDENT PRACTICE/ EXTENSION

Refer to the Assignment Guide on page 178 for additional questions and problems for independent practice.

3 Close

CONVERGENT QUESTION

Assuming that the theory of the expanding universe is true, ask students what the total momentum of the universe was before the "Big Bang." What should the total momentum of the universe be now?

CONCEPT REVIEW ANSWERS

1.1 Yes. Momentum is a vector quantity, and the momenta of the two cars are in opposite directions.
1.2 You reduce the force by increasing the length of time it takes to stop the motion of your body.
1.3 The raindrop, because a supertanker at rest has zero momentum.
1.4 Critical Thinking: The ones that bounce off give more impulse because they end up with some momentum in the reverse direction, meaning they have a larger change in momentum.

9.2 THE CONSERVATION OF MOMENTUM

Preparation

OBJECTIVES

The objectives are listed on the student page. Remind students to preview these objectives as a study guide to this major section.

OVERVIEW

The major new concept here is the conservation of momentum, which involves external and internal forces.

BRIDGING

Newton's third law is central to a good understanding of the conservation of momentum.

1 Focus

For a simple, easily seen, and controlled illustration of the conservation of momentum, use the commercially available apparatus with six or seven steel balls suspended from two parallel bars. These collisions are fascinating. A much less effective version is a grooved board on which marbles are rolled.

Vector Conventions

- *Velocity vectors are red.*
- *Displacement vectors are green.*
- *Acceleration vectors are purple.*
- *Force vectors are blue.*
- ▶ ***Momentum vectors are orange.***
- *Vector resultants are dashed lines.*

Objectives

- **state the law of conservation of momentum and use it, especially in collision problems.**
- **distinguish between external and internal forces and use this distinction.**
- **explain the extension of the law of conservation of momentum to two dimensions; solve collision problems using vectors.**

CONCEPT REVIEW

1.1 Is the momentum of a car traveling south different from that of the same car moving north at the same speed? Explain.
1.2 If you jump off a table, as your feet hit the floor you let your legs bend at the knees. Explain why.
1.3 Which has more momentum, a supertanker tied at the dock or a falling raindrop?
1.4 **Critical Thinking:** An archer shoots arrows at a target. Some arrows stick in the target while others bounce off. Assuming the mass and velocity are the same, which arrows give a bigger impulse to the target? **Hint:** Consider the change in momentum of the arrow.

9.2 THE CONSERVATION OF MOMENTUM

Suppose you place several sugar cubes in a box and close it. We can call the box and the sugar in it a **system,** a defined collection of objects. Shake the box hard for several minutes. When you open it, you find that the shapes of the cubes have changed. In addition, there are sugar grains in the box that were not there before. It would be almost impossible to apply Newton's laws to each of the forces that were acting while the box was being shaken. Instead, we can look for a property of the system that has remained constant. A balance would show that the mass of the sugar and the box remains the same. The mass is conserved. Over the past century, physicists have found that studying conserved properties has produced great success in solving problems and understanding the principles of the physical world.

Newton's Third Law and Momentum

The impulse-momentum theorem is another way of stating Newton's third law.

The example of a batted ball involved a type of collision. The baseball collided with the bat. In the collision, the momentum of the baseball changed as a result of the impulse given it by the bat. But, what happened to the bat? The bat exerted a force on the ball. By Newton's third law, the ball must have exerted a force on the bat of equal magnitude, but in the opposite direction. Thus, the bat also received an impulse. The direction of force on the bat is opposite the force on the ball, so the impulse given to the bat must also be in the opposite direction. By the impulse-momentum theorem, we know that the momentum of the bat must have changed. Its forward momentum was reduced as a result of its collision with the ball.

A system is isolated if no net external force acts on it.

The momentum change of the bat may not be obvious because the bat is massive and is held by a batter who stands with his feet firmly planted on the ground, usually wearing spiked shoes for a firmer grip. In the ball and bat collision, as with almost all natural processes, many forces are exerted. We need to look at a much simpler system to really understand the impulses and changes in momentum.

To study momentum changes in collisions, we must use a **closed, isolated system.** Remember, a system can be any specified collection of

TEACHER F.Y.I.

Collisions can be: elastic—both kinetic energy and momentum are conserved; perfectly inelastic—objects stick together or couple after the collision, and momentum, but not kinetic energy, is conserved; inelastic—momentum, but not kinetic energy, is conserved. In the real world, the collision of gas molecules with the walls of a container at reasonable temperatures is highly elastic.

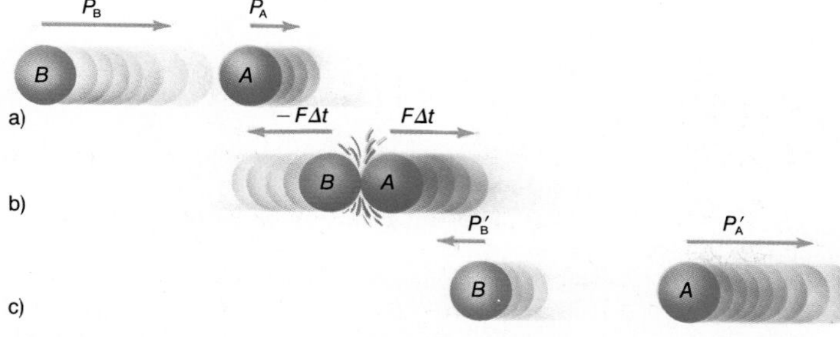

FIGURE 9–5. Ball A is moving with momentum p_A while ball B is moving with momentum p_B (a). When they collide, the impulses provided to the balls are equal in magnitude, but opposite in direction (b). After the collision, ball A moves with new momentum p'_A, while ball B moves with new momentum p'_B (c).

objects. A system is closed if objects neither enter nor leave it. It is isolated if no net external force is exerted on it. Two balls on a billiard table are an isolated system as long as friction is small enough to be ignored, and as long as neither ball hits the bumper at the edge of the table.

In Figure 9–5, ball A is moving with momentum p_A and ball B with momentum p_B. They collide, and ball B exerts force $+F$ on ball A. The balls are in contact for a time Δt, so the impulse given ball A is $+F\Delta t$. The momentum of ball A is changed by an amount equal to the impulse, $\Delta p = +F\Delta t$. The new momentum of ball A is

$$p'_A = p_A + \Delta p.$$

During the collision, ball A also exerts a force on ball B. According to Newton's third law, the force ball A exerts on ball B is equal in magnitude but opposite in direction to the force B exerts on A. The time interval of the collision is the same, so the impulse given ball B is $-F\Delta t$. The momentum of B is changed by an amount $-\Delta p$ that is equal in size but opposite in direction to the momentum change of ball A; $-\Delta p = -F\Delta t$. Thus the new momentum of ball B is

$$p'_B = p_B + (-\Delta p).$$

The momentum of ball B decreases while the momentum of ball A increases. The momentum lost by B equals the momentum gained by A. For the whole system consisting of the two balls, *the net change in momentum is zero*. That is, the final momentum of the system equals the initial momentum of the system; $p_A + p_B = p'_A + p'_B$. The total momentum before the collision is the same as the total momentum after the collision. That is, the momentum of the system is not changed; it is conserved. In summary:

Table 9–1

Object	Ball A	Ball B	System
Initial momentum	p_A	p_B	$p_A + p_B$
Impulse	$+F\Delta t$	$-F\Delta t$	0
Momentum change	$+\Delta p$	$-\Delta p$	0
Final momentum	p'_A	p'_B	$p'_A + p'_B$

POCKET LAB

SKATEBOARD FUN

Have two students sit facing each other on skateboards or laboratory carts, approximately three to five meters apart. Place a rope in their hands. Predict what will happen when one student pulls on the rope while the other just holds his end. Explain your prediction. Which person is exerting more force on the rope? Compare the amount of time that the force is acting on each person. Which person will have a greater change in momentum? Explain. Do it. Describe what really happened. Can you devise a method to pull only one student to the other?

POCKET LAB

SKATEBOARD FUN

Purpose: to help students increase their understanding of conservation of momentum.

Materials: 2 skateboards or laboratory carts; 5-m length of rope.

Outcome: Students should realize that one cannot pull without the other pulling. To make this easy to see, attach the ends of the rope to a large spring balance and repeat the activity. Both students will accelerate toward each other. Equal (but opposite) forces act for equal times. The students will have equal (but opposite) changes in momentum. There should be no way to pull one student to the other—unless one student is fixed to the Earth.

Assessment

Performance

To further assess your students' understanding of conservation of momentum, have the students on the skateboards move so they are touching. Have the students push on each other's hands. Ask what the momentum of the system was (two people plus two carts) before and after they pushed apart. [Zero in both cases] Try repeating the experiment using one light and one heavy student. Contrast the momenta of the two students [equal] and velocities [unequal].

STUDY GUIDE MASTER

Use the Study Guide master for section 9.1.

SUPPLEMENTS

Use Supplemental Lessons 1 and 2 with this section.

RETEACHING MASTER

Use the Reteaching master for Chapter 9 with this section.

PHYSICS LAB

Process Skills: using numbers, observing, classifying, communicating, measuring, predicting, questioning, controlling variables.

MISCONCEPTIONS

Most students will have difficulty accepting that forces always come in pairs.

Teaching Suggestions: Have students stand back once the mechanism that releases the spring has been depressed.

Lab Worksheet, Teacher Resource Package. If desired, have students record their data on the lab worksheet for this chapter.

OBSERVATIONS

1. The less massive cart will travel more distance.
2. The less massive cart will have more speed.

ANALYSIS

1. Assuming a typical laboratory cart has a mass of about 1.0 kg, the 1.0-kg cart will travel about 1.5 times the speed of the 1.5-kg cart.
2. Each cart will have equal (but opposite) changes in momentum.
3. The times of interaction must be equal.
4. The average force on the carts depends on the individual spring. Typical values may be in the range of 10 to 25 N. The forces on the carts must be equal (but opposite).

APPLICATIONS

Target shooters know that a more massive gun will "kick" less than a less massive gun. For a given change of momentum, the change of velocity will be less for a greater mass gun.

LAB WORKSHEET

Use the Lab Worksheet for Chapter 9 with this Physics Lab

PHYSICS LAB: The Explosion

Purpose

To investigate and compare the forces and change in momentum acting on different masses during an explosion.

Materials

- 2 laboratory carts (one with a spring mechanism)
- 2 C-clamps
- 2 blocks of wood
- 20-N spring scale
- 0.50-kg mass
- stopwatch
- masking tape

Procedure

1. Securely tape the 0.50-kg mass to cart 2 and then use the scale to determine the mass of each cart.
2. Arrange the equipment as shown in the diagram.
3. Predict the starting position so that the carts will hit the blocks at the same instant when the spring mechanism is released.
4. Place pieces of tape on the table at the front of the carts. (See sketch.)
5. Depress the mechanism to release the spring mechanism and explode the carts.
6. Notice which cart hits the block first.
7. Adjust the starting position until the carts hit at the same instant. (Remember to move the tapes.)

Observations and Data

1. Which cart moved farther?
2. Which cart moved faster? Explain.

Analysis

1. Estimate the velocity of each cart. Which was greater?
2. Compare the change in momentum of each cart.
3. Suppose that the spring pushed on cart 1 for 0.05 s. How long did cart 2 push on the spring? Explain.
4. Using $F\Delta t = m\Delta v$, which cart had the greater force?

Applications

1. Explain why a target shooter might prefer to shoot a more massive gun.

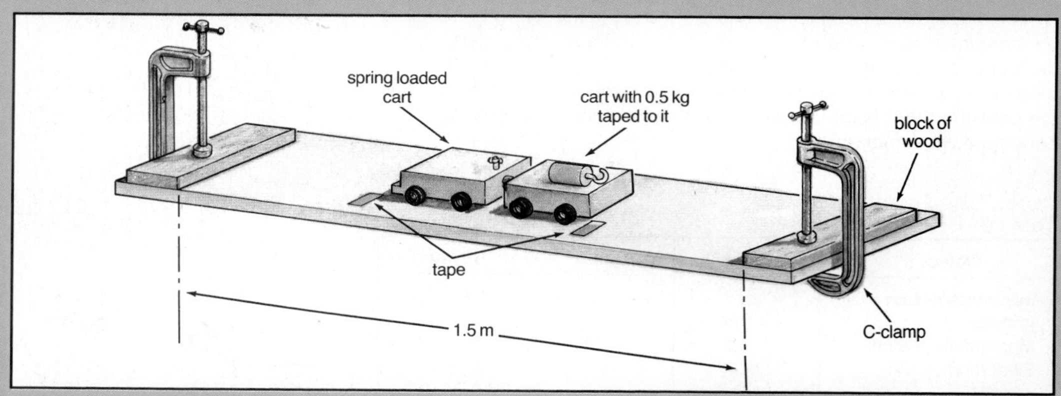

ASSESSMENT

Critical Thinking: To further assess your students' understanding of the roles of force and mass in momentum change, ask the following questions.

1. Suppose that you used the same carts but replaced the spring with a stronger spring. How would the new, stronger spring effect the following: the time to hit, the velocity of each cart, and the ratio of change in momentum of the carts? [A stronger spring would put more force on each cart. The carts would take less time to hit. Although each cart would have a greater velocity, the ratio of change in momentums would still be the same as before.]

2. How can you use your results to predict the ratio of the masses? Predict the masses? Use the spring scale to mass the carts and then check your prediction. [The ratio of the masses is inversely proportional to the ratio of their distances. For example, if $d_1 = 0.60$ and $d_2 = 0.40$, then m_1/m_2 should be 40/60 of 0.67. Predictions should be within 10%.]

Law of Conservation of Momentum

The **law of conservation of momentum** states: *The momentum of any closed, isolated system does not change.* It doesn't matter how many objects are in the system. It is only necessary that no objects enter or leave the system and that there is no net external force on the system. Because all interactions can be classified as collisions in one form or another, the law of conservation of momentum is a very powerful tool.

As an example, imagine two freight cars, A and B, each with a mass of 3.0×10^5 kg, as seen in Figure 9–6. Car B is moving at +2.2 m/s while car A is at rest. The system is composed of the cars A and B. Assume that the cars roll without friction so there is no net external force. Thus, the two cars make up a closed, isolated system, and the momentum of the system is conserved. When the two cars collide, they couple and move away together. We can use conservation of momentum to find the velocity of the coupled cars.

The masses of the cars are equal, so we can write $m_A = m_B = m$. The initial velocity of A is zero, so $v_A = 0$ and $p_A = 0$. The initial velocity of B is v_B. The initial momentum of B is mv_B or p_B. Thus, the initial momentum of the system is

$$p_A + p_B = p_B = mv_B.$$

After the collision, the two coupled cars of course have the same velocity, $v'_A = v'_B = v'$. Because their masses are also equal, $p'_A = p'_B = mv'$. Therefore, the final momentum of the system is

$$p'_A + p'_B = 2mv'.$$

By the law of conservation of momentum,

$$p_A + p_B = p'_A + p'_B$$
$$mv_B = 2mv'$$
$$v_B = 2v'$$
$$\text{or } v' = {}^1\!/_2 v_B.$$

Since $v_B = +2.2$ m/s, $v' = ½(+2.2 \text{ m/s}) = +1.1$ m/s.

After the collision, the two cars move together with half the velocity of the moving car B before the collision.

F. Y. I.

It takes a fully loaded supertanker, traveling at a normal speed of 16 knots, at least 20 minutes to stop. If an immobile object appeared suddenly as much as 3 miles away, a collision would occur.

The total momentum of an isolated system always remains constant.

FIGURE 9–6. The total momentum of the freight car system after collision is the same as the total momentum of the system before collision.

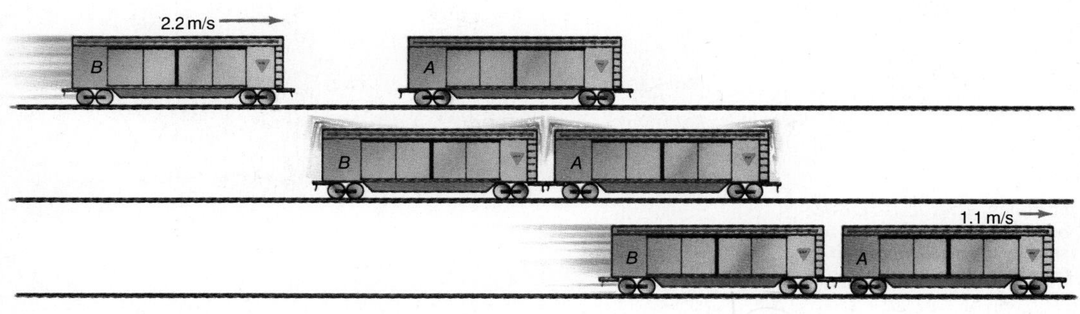

2 Teach

CONCEPT DEVELOPMENT

Study Guide Master. To reinforce the concepts in this section, have the students complete the Study Guide Master for Section 9.2 from the Teacher Resource Package.

- There are basically two types of collisions in a straight line. The objects either collide and go off separately:
$m_Av_A + m_Bv_B = m_Av_A' + m_Bv_B'$;
or collide and stick together:
$m_Av_A + m_Bv_B = (m_A + m_B)v'$.
Emphasize that whenever v_A and v_B have opposite directions, one must have a negative sign.
- Demonstrate some of these collisions. To make two objects stick together, use clay or Velcro.

Multicultural Connections

Christiaan Huygens was a Dutch physicist and astronomer who lived from 1629 to 1695. He conducted experiments which demonstrated that momentum *(mv)* is conserved in physical interactions. In addition, he showed that mv^2, a quantity equal to twice the kinetic energy of a moving object, was conserved. These conservation laws served as a foundation for many later discoveries in physics, such as neutrinos and antimatter.

TEACHER F.Y.I.

The ballistic pendulum is a system used to measure the velocity of a fast-moving projectile (like a bullet). A large block of wood is suspended from wires to act as a pendulum. The projectile, usually a bullet or dart, is fired from a gun and becomes imbedded in the block, resulting in a completely inelastic collision, with the two objects coupled so that momentum is conserved. The velocity of the system immediately after the collision is approximately the impulse. Mathematical analysis is as follows: $v_{pi} = (1 + m_w / m_p)\sqrt{2gh}$ where m_p is the mass of the projectile, m_w is the mass of the block of wood, v_{pi} is the velocity of the projectile initially, and h is the height to which the projectile/block couple rises.

CONCEPT DEVELOPMENT

Remember that we have been using positive and negative numbers to indicate directions in the right-left sense; or, east as positive and west as negative. So negative numbers here represent the direction opposite to whatever the positive direction is.

Connect to BIOLOGY

A bicycle helmet protects the head by applying two physical principles. The foam liner increases the time over which the impulse is applied, reducing the force. The rigid helmet also spreads the force, applying it over a wider area. The pressure exerted (force per unit area) is thus reduced. Applied pressure, rather than force, breaks skin and bones.

What are the three physical things that can reduce the chances of injury while catching a fast ball? [Moving your hand in the direction of the ball to reduce change in momentum and increase time of contact, wearing a soft glove to increase time of contact, and wearing a glove to spread out force, reducing pressure.]

FIGURE 9–7. The horns of two elk fighting often become entangled, producing an inelastic collision.

The momentum of the two cars before the collision is given by

$$\begin{aligned} p_A + p_B &= m_A v_A + m_B v_B \\ &= (3.0 \times 10^5 \text{ kg})(0 \text{ m/s}) + (3.0 \times 10^5 \text{ kg})(+2.2 \text{ m/s}) \\ &= +6.6 \times 10^5 \text{ kg·m/s}. \end{aligned}$$

The final momentum of the system is given by

$$\begin{aligned} p'_A + p'_B &= m_A v'_A + m_B v'_B \\ &= (3.0 \times 10^5 \text{ kg})(+1.1 \text{ m/s}) + (3.0 \times 10^5 \text{ kg})(+1.1 \text{ m/s}) \\ &= +6.6 \times 10^5 \text{ kg·m/s in the direction of car B's original motion.} \end{aligned}$$

We can also look at the changes in momentum of individual parts of the system. The change in momentum of car A is

$$\begin{aligned} \Delta p_A &= p'_A - p_A \\ &= m_A v'_A - m_A v_A \\ &= (3.0 \times 10^5 \text{ kg})(1.1 \text{ m/s}) - (3.0 \times 10^5 \text{ kg})(0 \text{ m/s}) \\ &= +3.3 \times 10^5 \text{ kg·m/s}. \end{aligned}$$

The change in momentum of car B is

$$\begin{aligned} \Delta p_B &= p'_B - p_B \\ &= m_B v'_B - m_B v_B \\ &= (3.0 \times 10^5 \text{ kg})(1.1 \text{ m/s}) - (3.0 \times 10^5 \text{ kg})(+2.2 \text{ m/s}) \\ &= -3.3 \times 10^5 \text{ kg·m/s}. \end{aligned}$$

The magnitude of the momentum lost by car B (-3.3×10^5 kg·m/s) is equal to the magnitude of the momentum gained by car A ($+3.3 \times 10^5$ kg·m/s).

The freight cars illustrate two important features of any collision. First, for the closed, isolated system as a whole, the total momentum is the same before and after the collision.

$$p_A + p_B = p'_A + p'_B$$

Second, the momentum gained by one part of the system is lost by the other part. Momentum is transferred,

$$\Delta p_A = -\Delta p_B.$$

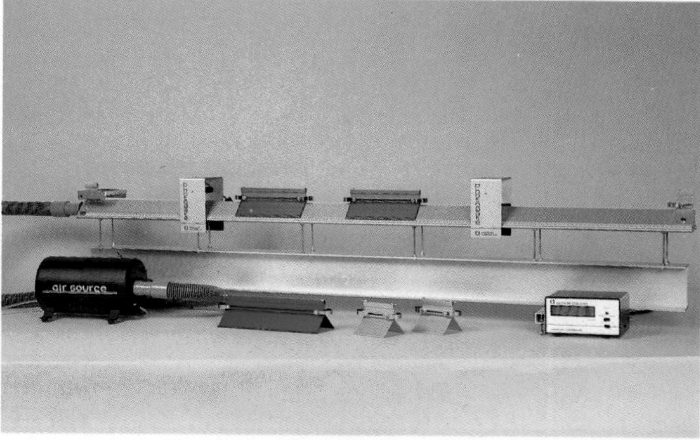

FIGURE 9–8. Air tracks provide nearly frictionless surfaces to simplify the measurement of the change in momentum during collisions.

DEMONSTRATION

Purpose: to determine the velocity of a softball using the law of conservation of momentum.

Equipment: cardboard box, packing material, softball, meter stick, spring scale, platform balance.

Procedure:

1. Pack a cardboard box loosely with packing material so that a softball thrown into the box will remain there. Measure and record the mass of the box and packing material. Place the box on a smooth surface and mark the position.
2. Throw (do not roll) the ball into the box. Measure and record the distance the box and ball moved.
3. Measure the force of friction by pulling the box and ball over the surface with a constant velocity. Record.
4. Measure and record the mass of the box, packing, and ball

Example Problem

Conservation of Momentum—1

Glider A of mass 0.355 kg moves along a frictionless air track with a velocity of 0.095 m/s. It collides with glider B of mass 0.710 kg moving in the same direction at a speed of 0.045 m/s. After the collision, glider A continues in the same direction with a velocity of 0.035 m/s. What is the velocity of glider B after the collision?

Given: $m_A = 0.355$ kg
$v_A = +0.095$ m/s
$m_B = 0.710$ kg
$v_B = +0.045$ m/s
$v'_A = +0.035$ m/s

Unknown: v'_B

Basic equation: $p_A + p_B = p'_A + p'_B$

Solution: $p_A + p_B = p'_A + p'_B$, so
$p'_B = p_B + p_A - p'_A$
$m_B v'_B = m_B v_B + m_A v_A - m_A v'_A$

or

$$v'_B = \frac{m_B v_B + m_A v_A - m_A v'_A}{m_B}$$
$$= \frac{(0.710 \text{ kg})(+0.045 \text{ m/s}) + (0.355 \text{ kg})(+0.095 \text{ m/s})}{0.710 \text{ kg}}$$
$$- \frac{(0.355 \text{ kg})(+0.035 \text{ m/s})}{0.710 \text{ kg}}$$
$$= +0.075 \text{ m/s}$$

Practice Problems

5. A 0.105-kg hockey puck moving at 48 m/s is caught by a 75-kg goalie at rest. With what speed does the goalie slide on the ice?
6. A 35.0-g bullet strikes a 5.0-kg stationary wooden block and embeds itself in the block. The block and bullet fly off together at 8.6 m/s. What was the original velocity of the bullet?
7. A 35.0-g bullet moving at 475 m/s strikes a 2.5-kg wooden block. The bullet passes through the block, leaving at 275 m/s. The block was at rest when it was hit. How fast is it moving when the bullet leaves?
8. ▶ A 0.50-kg ball traveling at 6.0 m/s collides head-on with a 1.00-kg ball moving in the opposite direction at a velocity of −12.0 m/s. The 0.50-kg ball moves away at −14 m/s after the collision. Find the velocity of the second ball.

HELP WANTED

PODIATRIST

Do you have a strong need to help people? Do you communicate well? Are you a graduate of one of the seven U.S. Colleges of Podiatric Medicine? If your answer to the above questions is yes, perhaps you should consider joining our flourishing group practice. In addition to our private practices, our members are affiliated with hospitals and nursing homes, teach, and serve as consultants to shoe manufacturers. For information contact:
American Podiatric Medical Association, 9312 Old Georgetown Road, Bethesda, MD 20814

Using Your CALCULATOR

Using the memory function of your calculator can simplify the evaluation of complex expressions. Note that, since the third term in the numerator is subtracted, the +/− key is used to make the term negative before the subtotal is recalled from memory and added.

$$v'_B = \frac{m_B v_B + m_A v_A - m_A v'_A}{m_B}$$

Keys	Display
.710 × .045 = M_in	0. 03195
AC .355 × .095 =	0. 033725
+ MR = M_in AC	0. 065675
.355 × .035 = +/−	−0. 012425
+ MR =	0. 05325
÷ .710 =	0. 075

$v'_B = 0.075$ m/s

The momentum gained by one object in an interaction is equal to the momentum lost by the other object.

CONCEPT DEVELOPMENT

In other words, the change of momentum in one part of the system is equal in size and opposite in direction to the change of momentum occurring in the rest of the system.

Guided Practice: Go over the Example Problem in class, then have students work on the first two Practice Problems on this page.

Independent Practice: Assign the remaining Practice Problems on this page for homework. Review student work in class the next day.

Answers To
PRACTICE PROBLEMS

Have students refer to Appendix A of the Solutions Appendix for complete solutions to Practice Problems.

5. 0.067 m/s
6. 1.2×10^3 m/s
7. 2.8 m/s
8. −2.0 m/s

Data:
Mass of box + packing ______ kg
Mass of box + packing + ball ______ kg
Distance box moves ______ m
Force of friction ______ N
Mass of softball ______ kg

Results: Use the law of conservation of momentum with your data to calculate the softball's velocity.

STUDY GUIDE MASTER

Use the Study Guide master for section 9.2.

LABORATORY MANUAL

Use Lab 9.1 with this section.

LABORATORY MANUAL

Use Lab 9.2 with this section.

CONCEPT DEVELOPMENT

- Relate $m_A v_A' = -m_B v_B'$ to the recoil of a rifle and the way a rocket works. When a bullet is fired, the small bullet goes off at a high speed in one direction and the massive rifle moves at a small velocity in the opposite direction. This is analogous to a rocket that fires out exhaust gas in one direction and moves in the opposite direction. The rocket continues to accelerate until there is no more exhaust.
- Ask students how they could get off the ice if they were stranded in the middle of a frozen lake with perfectly frictionless ice. [Since the ice is frictionless, they could toss a shoe and move across the ice until they were able to get off the lake.]

Laboratory Manual. Give students additional experience with conservation of momentum by doing Lab 9.1 from the Laboratory Manual.

Laboratory Manual. Give students additional experience with angular momentum by doing Lab 9.2 from the Laboratory Manual.

Internal and External Forces

An internal force cannot change the total momentum of a system.

In the example of the collision of two railroad cars, the cars exerted forces on each other. The forces between objects within a system are called **internal forces.** The total momentum of a system is conserved, or stays the same, only when it is closed and isolated from external forces. What if we define the system as car A only? When car A collides with car B, a force is exerted by an object outside the system. An **external force** acts. Our system is no longer isolated, and the momentum of the system is not conserved. You see, it is very important to define the system carefully.

It is important to define a system carefully. A force may be either internal or external depending on the system definition.

Consider the two roller bladers shown in Figure 9–9 as an isolated, closed system. That is, we will assume no external forces because the surface is so smooth that there is very little frictional force. Blader A has a mass of 60.0 kg; blader B has a mass of 45.0 kg. At first the bladers are standing still. The initial momentum of the system is zero. Blader A gives blader B a push. Now both bladers are moving. Only an internal force has been exerted, so the momentum of the system is conserved. We can find the relative velocities of the two bladers using conservation of momentum.

$$p_A + p_B = p'_A + p'_B$$
$$0 = p'_A + p'_B$$

or

$$p'_A = -p'_B$$
$$m_A v'_A = -m_B v'_B$$

Since the initial momentum of the system is zero, the vector sum of the momenta after the collision must also be zero. Therefore, the mo-

FIGURE 9–9. The internal forces exerted by these bladers cannot change the total momentum of the system.

TEACHER F.Y.I.

Forensic investigations frequently involve the study of momentum. Careful analysis of skid marks, bullet tracks, fragment patterns, wounds, and cracks in fragile materials can indicate the initial velocity of moving objects and provide important evidence about crimes.

Physics and technology

RUNNING SHOE DESIGN

About $3 million a year are spent on athletic shoes in the United States. Not only are athletic shoes big business, they are also "high-tech". Athletic shoes are now engineered to give the best performance for a specific use. Because running shoes take the most beating during use, they are the testing ground for other kinds of athletic shoes.

Each time an average runner's foot strikes the ground, the runner's body must absorb the force of two to four times its own weight. A goal of athletic shoe engineering is to reduce the stress of this load on the leg and foot. The vertical component of momentum goes to zero when the runner's foot hits the ground, requiring a large impulse. By using materials that lengthen the time of impact on the runner's foot, shoe engineers can reduce the force on the foot.

Therefore, the midsole, sandwiched between the insole and the outsole, becomes the most important part of the shoe. The midsole, which cushions the foot and absorbs part of the force on the runner's body, can be made of a wide variety of materials. One manufacturer uses a three-dimensional, woven-coil fabric developed by NASA for moonboots. Another uses an encapsulated silicone-based gel. Some midsoles consist of polyurethane that contains trapped bubbles of air or a freon-type gas. A recent design provides the runner with two sets of air cylinders that can be placed beneath the insole.

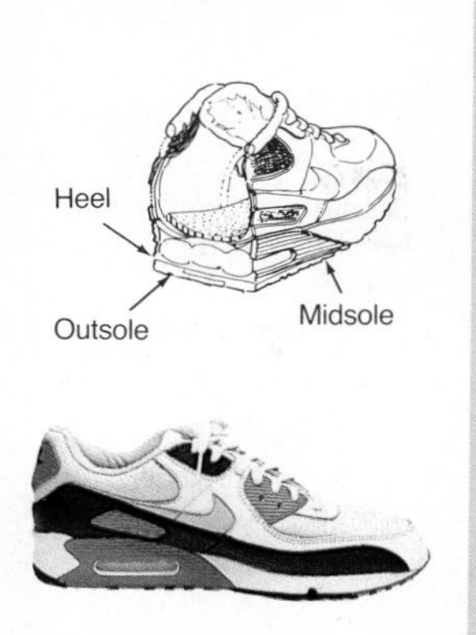

· What is the value of a design feature such as this?

menta of the two bladers are equal in magnitude and opposite in direction. Their velocities, however, are not equal. The more massive blader moves more slowly than the smaller one.

The system we defined included both bladers. Therefore, when one blader pushed on the other, the force was an internal force. The total momentum of the system remained the same. On the other hand, if we had defined the system as only blader B, there would have been an external force, and the total momentum of the system would have changed.

A system can contain more than two objects. For example, a stoppered flask filled with gas, Figure 9–10, is a system consisting of many particles. The gas particles are constantly colliding with each other and the walls of the flask. Their momenta are changing with every collision. In these collisions, the momentum gained by one particle is equal to the momentum lost by the other particle. Thus, the total momentum of the system does not change. The total momentum of any closed, isolated system is constant.

How does a rocket accelerate in space? This is another example of conservation of momentum. Fuel and oxidizer chemically combine, and the hot gases that result are expelled from the rocket's exhaust nozzle at high speed. Before combustion, the rocket with its unburned fuel

FIGURE 9–10. The total momentum of an isolated system is constant.

Physics and technology

Answer to student question: to provide more shock absorption where the individual runner needs it most. Each person's foot is different and each person runs in a different way.

Athletic shoes have four parts: the upper section, the insole, the midsole, and the outsole. For running, uppers are usually made of lightweight materials that "breathe." Better-quality uppers have stabilizing strips. Ethyl vinyl acetate (EVA) and polyurethane (PU) are the most-used high-quality midsole materials. PU is more durable, but is stiffer than EVA and therefore lacks energy return. Energy return has recently become a widely used marketing term. If a shoe has good energy return, it will have superior rebound characteristics. Interestingly, the shoe with good energy return is supposed to simulate the bounce of a bare foot.

There are also many kinds of athletic socks which claim a large cushioning effect due to their resilient construction.

Teacher Resources: Hamill, Joe. "Fancy Footwork." *Popular Mechanics.* September 1986, pages 71–73, 108–109.
Wolkomir, Richard. "The Race to Make a 'Perfect' Shoe Starts in the Laboratory." *Smithsonian.* September 1989, pages 95–104.

TEACHER 

New running tracks usually have a rubber coating. When the foot makes contact with asphalt, there is very little "give," thus the impact time is short and the impact force is relatively high. The rubber track has a bit of "give" to it, that is, it allows the foot to sink into it, increasing the impact time and reducing the impact force. Just for the record, shin splints are not caused by running on a hard surface, but by muscle imbalance. Runners frequently overdevelop the gastrocnemius (calf) by repetitive contraction, but fail to adequately work the muscle that runs down the front of the lower leg, the tibialis anterior. The gastrocnemius becomes much stronger and tighter than the tibialis and effectively begins to bend the bones, causing the condition know as shin splints. The way to avoid this is to work the tibialis anterior by pointing and flexing the feet.

CONCEPT DEVELOPMENT

This is a fine place for diagrams. Making quick sketches—including directions—of the objects in a momentum problem is an excellent way of keeping everything straight.

Critical Thinking: In order for astronauts to maneuver in space, their momentum must be determined. They effectively act as a closed system and operate in a frictionless environment. In order to move forward, they must throw an object or fire exhaust gases in the reverse direction. Their velocity is a recoil velocity as the projectile moves away from them. Ask students why an astronaut would need to launch a projectile at a large speed in order to obtain any speed herself. [The projectile would have a low mass in comparison to that of the astronaut. Since momentum is conserved, the projectile would have to have a high velocity to effect a reasonable change in that of the astronaut.]

Guided Practice: Review the Example Problem on this page, then have students work on Practice Problem 9.

Independent Practice: Assign the remaining Practice Problems on pages 188 and 189 for homework. Allow time in class the next day to review student work and answer questions.

Answers To
PRACTICE PROBLEMS

Have students refer to Appendix A of the Solutions Appendix for complete solutions to Practice Problems.

9. 7.91 m/s
10. 9.0 cm/s to the right

FIGURE 9–11. A rocket increases its forward momentum by expelling part of its mass at high speed in the opposite direction.

moves forward at some constant speed. It has a momentum mv. After the firing, the mass of the combustion gases moves backward with high relative velocity. In order to conserve momentum, the rocket, with its mass reduced by the burned fuel, must move with increased speed in the forward direction.

Example Problem

Conservation of Momentum—2

An astronaut at rest in space with mass 84 kg fires a thruster that expels 35 g of hot gas at 875 m/s. What is the velocity of the astronaut after firing the shot?

Given: before firing: $m_A = 84$ kg, $v_A = 0$ m/s, $m_B = 0.035$ kg, $v_B = 0$ m/s; after firing: $v'_B = 875$ m/s

Unknown: v'_A

Basic equation: $p_A + p_B = p'_A + p'_B$

Solution: $p_A + p_B = p'_A + p'_B$

But $v_A = v_B = 0$, so $p_A = p_B = 0$, and $p'_A = -p'_B$

$$m_Av'_A = -m_Bv'_B \qquad v'_A = -\frac{m_Bv'_B}{m_A}$$

$$v'_A = -\frac{(0.035\text{ kg})(+875\text{ m/s})}{84\text{ kg}} = -0.36\text{ m/s}$$

The astronaut recoils in a direction opposite that of the moving gas.

Practice Problems

9. A 4.00-kg model rocket is launched, shooting 50.0 g of burned fuel from its exhaust at an average velocity of 625 m/s. What is the velocity of the rocket after the fuel has burned? (Ignore effects of gravity and air resistance.)

10. A thread holds two carts together on a frictionless surface as in Figure 9–12. A compressed spring acts upon the carts. After the thread is burned, the 1.5-kg cart moves with a velocity of 27 cm/s to the left. What is the velocity of the 4.5-kg cart?

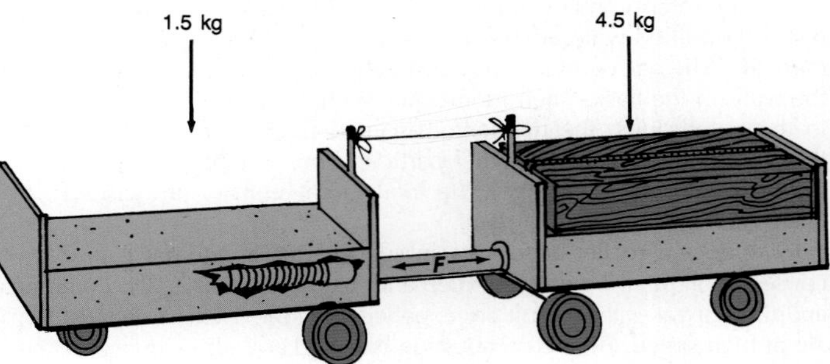

FIGURE 9–12. Use with Practice Problem 10.

11. Two campers dock a canoe. One camper steps onto the dock. This camper has a mass of 80.0 kg and moves forward at 4.0 m/s. With what speed and direction do the canoe and the other camper move if their combined mass is 110 kg?

▶ 12. A colonial gunner sets up his 225-kg cannon at the edge of the flat top of a high tower. It shoots a 4.5-kg cannon ball horizontally. The ball hits the ground 215 m from the base of the tower. The cannon also moves, on frictionless wheels, and falls off the back of the tower, landing on the ground.

a. What is the horizontal distance of the cannon's landing, measured from the base of the back of the tower?

b. Why do you not need to know the width of the tower?

Conservation of Momentum in Two Dimensions

Until now we have looked at momentum in one dimension only. The law of conservation of momentum, however, holds for all isolated, closed systems. It is true regardless of the directions of the particles before and after they collide.

The total momentum of a system is the vector sum of the momenta of all the parts of the system.

Figure 9–13a shows the result of billiard ball A striking stationary ball B. The momentum of the moving ball is represented by the vector p_A. The momentum of the ball at rest is zero. Therefore, the total momentum of the system is the vector p_A going toward the right. After the collision, the momenta of the two balls are represented by the vectors p'_A and p'_B. Figure 9–13b shows that the vector sum of p'_A and p'_B equals the original momentum, p_A. The vertical and horizontal components of the vectors can also be added. The initial momentum has no vertical or y component, so the vector sum of the final vertical components of the two balls, p'_{Ay} and p'_{By}, must be zero. They are equal in magnitude but opposite in direction. The sum of the final horizontal components, p'_{Ax} and p'_{Bx}, must equal the original momentum, which is totally horizontal.

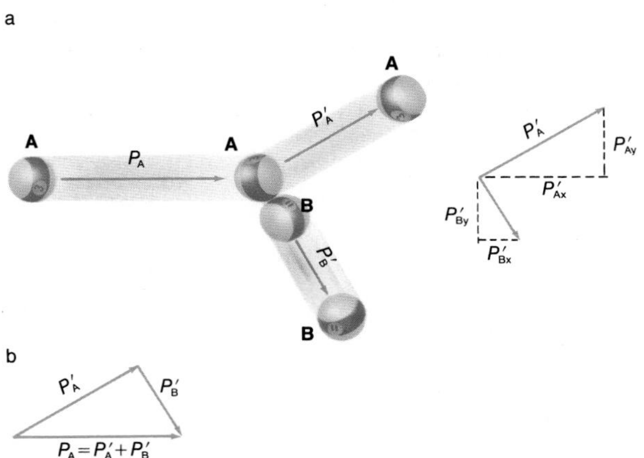

FIGURE 9–13. The law of conservation of momentum holds for all isolated, closed systems, regardless of the directions of objects before and after they collide (a). The vector sum of the momenta is constant (b).

TEACHER F.Y.I.

The structure of a rocket is such that it carries as much fuel as possible. Why? In the derivation of an equation using momentum, the increase in velocity of a rocket is proportional to its exhaust velocity, so its exhaust velocity should be as high as possible. In addition, the increase in velocity is proportional to the logarithm of the $m_{\text{prior to takeoff}}/m_{\text{after takeoff}}$, so this ratio must be high. The father of modern rocketry was an American physicist, Robert Goddard, who worked in rocketry for most of his life. He demonstrated that rockets could move through space without air to push against, something that was considered impossible by other scientists. He offered his assistance to the armed forces in WWII, but did not contribute due to lack of interest on the part of the military.

11. 2.9 m/s in the opposite direction
12. a. 4.3 m b. Speed does not change as it crosses the tower.

CONCEPT DEVELOPMENT

- Remind students about how the two perpendicular components of a vector can be used to replace that vector. After getting the components, the x and y situations can be worked out independently.
- Summarize the steps used in solving a two-dimensional momentum problem as outlined in the Example Problem on page 190, then go over a two-dimensional momentum problem, encouraging class involvement.

Critical Thinking: Sports balls are tested for what is know as the "coefficient of restitution." The balls are dropped onto surfaces from some height and their rebound height is measured. Racquetballs, tennis balls, and golf balls have a high coefficient of restitution. Balls which do not meet standards are discarded. Disney made a movie about a substance called "Flubber" which could bounce to a height greater than that from which it had been dropped. Ask students why this is impossible.

CHECKING FOR UNDERSTANDING

Choose a Chapter Review Problem to go over with the class, working it out on the blackboard or overhead.

RETEACHING

Transparency Package. Use Transparency 13 and accompanying worksheet, Impulse and Change in Momentum, to reteach this section.

EXTENSION

Have interested students do some research to find out how the concept of momentum changes when very high (relativistic) speeds are involved.

CONCEPT DEVELOPMENT

- Suppose a moving projectile explodes. Ask students what the total momentum of the pieces would be right after the explosion. What kind of forces caused the explosion?
- When an explosion takes place and pieces of objects fly off in several different directions, momentum is observed. Since the momentum before the explosion was zero, the momentum after the explosion also must be zero. Therefore, the vectors representing momentum after the explosion must all be added heat-to-tail to give a closed figure.

Critical Thinking: Assume an explosion occurs and a 1-kg piece goes north at 16 m/s and a 3-kg piece goes east at 4 m/s. The last piece has a mass of 2 kg. What is the magnitude and direction of the velocity of the piece? Have students first draw the vector diagram, putting in the known quantities. Remind them that the vectors represent momentum. The unknown momentum is 20 kg m/s. Therefore, the unknown velocity for the 2-kg mass is 10 m/s. From the diagram, they will find that the angle is 233°.

- Emphasize to students the importance of identifying objects A and B and keeping all quantities carefully labeled.
- Other kinds of internal forces are explosions and releasing compressed springs.
- Emphasize that the same principles are used here as in Section 9.1, but since angles are involved, triangles must be used. Therefore, arithmetic addition will not work here and trigonometry must be used.

Enrichment: The technical information sheet from some toy rocket motors (Estes) contains a lot of detail about the impulse provided by the motor. Some of your students might be talked into following up on this and giving a presentation.

FIGURE 9–14. Use with the following Example Problem.

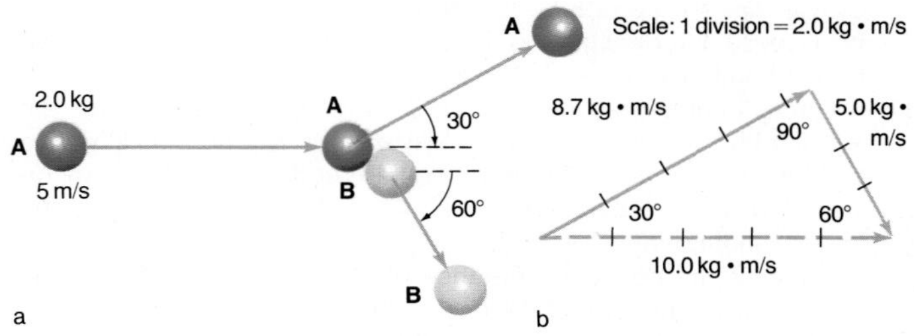

Example Problem

Conservation of Momentum in Two Dimensions

A 2.00-kg ball, A, is moving at a velocity of 5.00 m/s. It collides with a stationary ball, B, also of mass 2.00 kg, Figure 9–14. After the collision, ball A moves off in a direction 30.0° to the left of its original direction. Ball B moves off in a direction 90.0° to the right of ball A's final direction. **a.** Draw a vector diagram to find the momentum of ball A and of ball B after the collision. **b.** Find the velocities of the balls after the collision.

Given: $m_A = 2.00$ kg
$v_A = +5.00$ m/s
$m_B = 2.00$ kg
$v_B = 0.00$ m/s

Unknowns: $p_A, p'_A, p'_B, v'_A, v'_B$
Basic equation: $p = p'$, so $p_A + p_B = p'_A + p'_B$

Solution: Find the initial momenta.

$p_A = m_A v_A = +10.0$ kg·m/s $p_B = 0$

Therefore, $p = p_A + p_B = +10.0$ kg·m/s

The vector representing the initial momentum is an arrow to the right. The initial and final momenta are equal, $p = p'$, so $p_A + p_B = p'_A + p'_B$. Because the angle between the final directions of ball A and ball B is 90°, the vector triangle is a right triangle with the initial momentum as the hypotenuse. The vector p'_A is at 30.0°. We can use trigonometry to find the magnitudes of the vectors.

Ball A

$$\cos 30° = \frac{p'_A}{p'}$$

$$p'_A = p' \cos 30° = (1.0 \times 10^1 \text{ kg·m/s})(0.87) = 8.7 \text{ kg·m/s}$$

Ball B

$$\sin 30° = \frac{p'_B}{p'}$$

$$p_B = p' \sin 30° = (1.0 \times 10^1 \text{ kg·m/s})(0.50) = 5.0 \text{ kg·m/s}$$

9:2 ASSIGNMENT GUIDE

	PRACTICE	EXTENSION
CHAPTER REVIEW pp. 192–195		
· Reviewing Concepts	3, 5–10	5–11
· Applying Concepts		
· Problems*	16–24, 27	25, 26 28–33
APPENDIX B PROBLEMS*		
· Chapter 9 p. 695	7–10, 12	11, 13–15

* Complete solutions to all Chapter Review and Appendix problems appear in the Problems and Solutions Manual.

Now use the definition of momentum, $p = mv$, to find the magnitudes of the velocities.

$$p'_A = m_A v'_A \qquad p'_B = m_B v'_B$$

$$v'_A = \frac{p'_A}{m_A} \qquad v'_B = \frac{p'_B}{m_B}$$

$$= \frac{8.7\ \text{kg}\cdot\text{m/s}}{2.0\ \text{kg}} = 4.4\ \text{m/s} \qquad = \frac{5.0\ \text{kg}\cdot\text{m/s}}{2.0\ \text{kg}} = 2.5\ \text{m/s}$$

Practice Problems

13. A 1325-kg car moving north at 27.0 m/s collides with a 2165-kg car moving east at 17.0 m/s. They stick together. Draw a vector diagram of the collision. In what direction and with what speed do they move after the collision?

14. A 6.0-kg object, A, moving at velocity 3.0 m/s, collides with a 6.0-kg object, B, at rest. After the collision, A moves off in a direction 40.0° to the left of its original direction. B moves off in a direction 50.0° to the right of A's original direction.

a. Draw a vector diagram and determine the momenta of object A and object B after the collision.

b. What is the velocity of each object after the collision?

▶**15.** A stationary billiard ball, mass 0.17 kg, is struck by an identical ball moving at 4.0 m/s. After the collision, the second ball moves off at 60° to the left of its original direction. The stationary ball moves off at 30° to the right of the second ball's original direction. What is the velocity of each ball after the collision?

CONCEPT REVIEW

2.1 Two soccer players come from opposite directions. They leap in the air to try to hit the ball, but collide with each other instead, coming to rest in midair. What can you say about their original momenta?

2.2 During a tennis serve, momentum gained by the ball is lost by the racket. If momentum is conserved, why doesn't the racket's speed change much?

2.3 Someone throws a heavy ball to you when you are standing on a skateboard. You catch it and roll backward with the skateboard. If you were standing on the ground, however, you would be able to avoid moving. Explain both using momentum conservation.

2.4 A pole vaulter runs toward the launch point with horizontal momentum. Where does the vertical momentum come from as the athlete vaults over the crossbar?

2.5 **Critical Thinking:** A hockey player deflects a fast-moving puck through an angle of 90°. The puck's speed is not changed. By considering the two components of the impulse given the puck by the stick, tell in what direction the stick must have been moving when it deflected the puck.

FIGURE 9–15. An inelastic collision.

CONCEPT DEVELOPMENT

Cooperative Learning: Divide students into teams and assign each team a Chapter Review Problem. Go over team solutions in class.

Guided Practice: Go over the Example Problem on page 190, then have students try the first Practice Problem on this page.

Independent Practice: Assign the remaining Practice Problems on this page for homework. Review the Problems in class the next day.

INDENDEPENT PRACTICE/ EXTENSION

Refer to the Assignment Guide on page 190 for additional questions and problems for independent practice.

3 Close

CONVERGENT QUESTION

Using the conservation of momentum principle, have students estimate the amount of momentum that the Earth acquires when they jump up into the air. How fast would the Earth be going?

Answers To
PRACTICE PROBLEMS

Have students refer to Appendix A of the Solutions Appendix for complete solutions to Practice Problems.

13. Refer to Appendix A
$\theta = 44.2°$ north of east
$v' = 14.7$ m/s

14. Refer to Appendix A
a. $p_A' = 14$ kg · m/s
$p_B' = 12$ kg · m/s
b. $v_A' = 2.3$ m/s, 40° to left
$v_B' = 2.0$ m/s, 50° to right

15. Refer to Appendix A
$v_1' = 3.5$ m/s, 30° to right
$v_2' = 2.0$ m/s, 60° to left

CONCEPT REVIEW ANSWERS

2.1 Since the initial total momentum must be zero, their initial momenta were equal and opposite.

2.2 Since the mass of the racket is much larger than that of the ball, only a small change in its velocity is required. In addition, it is being held by a massive, moving arm.

2.3 In the case of the skateboard, the ball, the skateboard, and you are an isolated system, and the momentum of the ball is shared. In the second case, unless Earth is included, there is an external force, so momentum is not conserved. If Earth's large mass is included in the system, the change in its velocity is negligible.

2.4 From the impulsive force of Earth against the pole. Earth acquires an equal and opposite vertical momentum.

2.5 Critical Thinking: The puck's forward momentum changed to zero, and its perpendicular momentum went from zero to the original momentum. Thus the stick must have had one component opposite the direction of the incoming puck, the other in the direction of the outgoing puck. These two components are equal. Thus the stick was moving along the line that bisects the puck's 90° deflection angle.

CLOSING CHAPTER 9

Review Summary statements and Key Terms with your students.

ASSESSMENT

Vocabulary Review Master, Teacher Resource Package. Use this master to check students' understanding of Key Terms.

Evaluation Masters. Use Parts A and B of the Chapter Evaluation Masters from the Teacher Resource Package to test qualitative chapter objectives. Use Parts C and D to test quantitative chapter objectives.

Answers To
REVIEWING CONCEPTS

1. Yes. In order for a bullet to have the same momentum as a truck, it must have a higher velocity such that $mv_{\text{bullet}} = mv_{\text{truck}}$.
2. a. The pitcher and catcher exert the same impulse on the ball, but the two impulses are opposite in direction. **b.** The catcher exerts the larger force on the ball, because the time interval over which the force is exerted is smaller.
3. No net force on the system means no net impulse on the system and no net change in momentum. However, individual parts of the system may have a change in momentum as long as the net change in momentum is zero.
4. Cars are made with bumpers that retract during a crash in order to increase the time of a collision, reducing the force.
5. An isolated system has no external forces acting on it.
6. A conservation law states that a quantity is the same before and after an interaction.
7. Momentum is conserved. The change in momentum of gases in one direction must be balanced by an equal change in momentum of the spacecraft in the opposite direction.
8. The eight ball must be moving with the same velocity that the cue ball had just before the collision.
9. a. The momentum of a falling ball is not conserved because there is a net external force, gravity, acting on it. **b.** One such system in which total momentum is conserved includes the ball plus Earth.
10. The internal force of a car's brakes can bring the car to a stop by stopping the wheels and allowing the external frictional force of the road against the tires to stop the car. If there is no friction, for example, if the road is icy, then there is no external force and the car does not stop.

CHAPTER 9 REVIEW

SUMMARY

9.1 Impulse and Change in Momentum

- The momentum of an object is the product of its mass and velocity.
- The change in momentum of an object is equal to the impulse that acts on it.
- Impulse is the product of the average force and the time interval over which the force acts.

9.2 The Conservation of Momentum

- Newton's third law is another statement of the law of conservation of momentum.
- The law of conservation of momentum states: *In a closed, isolated system, the total momentum of the system does not change.*
- The momentum of a system changes when it is not isolated, that is, when a net external force acts on it.

KEY WORDS

momentum
impulse
impulse-momentum theorem
angular momentum
system
closed, isolated system
law of conservation of momentum
internal forces
external force

REVIEWING CONCEPTS

1. Can a bullet have the same momentum as a truck? Explain.
2. A pitcher throws a fastball to the catcher. Assuming the speed of the ball does not change appreciably in flight,
   a. which player exerts the larger impulse on the ball?
   b. which player exerts the larger force on the ball?
3. Newton's second law says that if there is no net force exerted on a system, no acceleration is possible. Does it follow that no change in momentum can occur?
4. Why are cars made with bumpers that can be pushed in during a crash?
5. What is meant by an isolated system?
6. What is a conservation law?
7. A spacecraft in outer space increases velocity by firing its rockets. How can hot gases escaping from its rockets change the velocity of the craft when there is nothing in space for the gases to push against?
8. The white cue ball travels across a pool table and collides with the stationary eight-ball. The two balls have equal mass. After the collision the cue ball is at rest. What must be true of the speed of the 8-ball?
9. Consider a falling ball.
   a. Why is the momentum not conserved?
   b. Define a system including the falling ball in which the total momentum is conserved.
10. If only an external force can change the momentum of an object, how can the internal force of a car's brakes bring the car to a stop?

APPLYING CONCEPTS

1. Is it possible for an object to obtain a larger impulse from a smaller force than it does from a larger force? How?
2. You are sitting at a baseball game when a foul ball comes in your direction. You prepare to catch it barehanded. In order to catch it safely, should you move your hands toward the ball, hold them still, or move them in the same direction as the moving ball? Why?
3. A 0.11-g bullet leaves a pistol at 323 m/s, while a similar bullet leaves a rifle at 396 m/s. Explain the difference in exit speeds of the bullets.
4. Jim Walewander slides into second base. What happens to his momentum?
5. During a "space walk", the tether connecting an astronaut to the space capsule breaks. Using a gas pistol, the astronaut manages to get back to the capsule. Explain.
6. A tennis ball bounces off a wall and its momentum is reversed. Explain this in view of the law of conservation of momentum.

TRANSPARENCY

Use Transparency 11 with this section.

REVIEW MASTER

Use the Vocabulary Review master for Chapter 9 with this section.

EVALUATION MASTER

Use the Chapter Evaluation master for Chapter 9 with this section.

7. You command Spaceship Zero, which is moving at high speed through interplanetary space. Using the law of conservation of momentum, explain how you would slow down your ship.

FIGURE 9–16.

8. Two trucks that look the same collide. One was originally at rest. The trucks stick together and move off at more than half the original speed of the moving truck. What can you say about the contents of the two trucks?
9. When you shoot a rifle for the first time, you quickly learn to place the butt of the rifle firmly against your shoulder. In terms of momentum, why is this good advice?
10. Two bullets of equal mass are shot at equal speeds at blocks of wood on a smooth ice rink. One bullet, made of rubber, bounces off the wood. The other bullet, made of aluminum, burrows into the wood. Which bullet makes the wood move faster? Why?
11. Which collision presents the greater possibility of danger to the passengers involved: (1) two cars colliding and remaining entangled, or (2) the same two cars colliding and rebounding off each other? Explain.

PROBLEMS

9.1 Impulse and Change in Momentum

1. Jenny has a mass of 35.6 kg and her skateboard has a mass of 1.3 kg. What is the momentum of Jenny and her skateboard together if they are going 9.50 m/s?
2. A hockey player makes a slap shot, exerting a force of 30.0 N on the hockey puck for 0.16 s. What impulse is given to the puck?
3. The hockey puck shot in Problem 2 has a mass of 0.115 kg and was at rest before the shot. With what speed does it head toward the goal?
4. A force of 6.00 N acts on a 3.00-kg object for 10.0 s.
   a. What is the object's change in momentum?
   b. What is its change in velocity?
5. The velocity of a 600-kg auto is changed from +10.0 m/s to +44.0 m/s in 68.0 s by an applied, constant force.
   a. What change in momentum does the force produce?
   b. What is the magnitude of the force?
6. A 845-kg drag race car accelerates from rest to 100 km/h in 0.90 seconds.
   a. What is the change in momentum of the car?
   b. What average force is exerted on the car?
7. A sprinter with a mass of 76 kg accelerates from 0 to 9.4 m/s in 2.8 s. Find the average force acting on the runner.
8. A 0.25-kg soccer ball is rolling at 6.0 m/s toward a player. The player kicks the ball back in the opposite direction and gives it a velocity of −14 m/s. What is the average force during the interaction between the player's foot and the ball if the interaction lasts 2.0×10^{-2} s.
9. A force of 1.21×10^3 N is needed to bring a car moving at +22.0 m/s to a halt in 20.0 s? What is the mass of the car?
10. ▶ Small rockets are used to make small adjustments in the speed of satellites. One such rocket has a thrust of 35 N. If it is fired to change the velocity of a 72 000-kg spacecraft by 63 cm/s, how long should it be fired?
11. A 10 000-kg freight car is rolling along a track at 3.00 m/s. Calculate the time needed for a force of 1000 N to stop the car.
12. ▶ A car moving at 10 m/s crashes into a barrier and stops in 0.25 m.
   a. Find the time required to stop the car.
   b. If a 20-kg child were to be stopped in the same time as the car, what average force must be exerted?
   c. Approximately what is the mass of an object whose weight equals the force from part **b?** Could you lift such a mass with your arm?
   d. What does your answer to part **c** say about holding an infant on your lap instead of using a separate infant restraint?

Answers To
APPLYING CONCEPTS

1. Yes. If the smaller force acts for a long enough time, it can provide a larger impulse.
2. You should move your hands in the same direction the ball is traveling to increase the time of the collision, reducing the force.
3. The bullet is in the rifle a longer time, so the momentum it gains is larger.
4. His momentum is transferred to Earth. Both Jim and Earth together must be considered as a system in order to use conservation of momentum.
5. When the gas pistol is fired in the opposite direction, it provides the impulse needed to move the astronaut toward the capsule.
6. Consider the system to be the ball and wall (and Earth). The wall and Earth gain some momentum in the collision.
7. By shooting mass, exhaust gas, at high velocity in the same direction in which you are moving, its momentum would cause your ship's momentum to be decreased.
8. If the two trucks had equal masses, they would have moved off at half the speed. Thus the moving truck must have had a more massive load.
9. Held loosely, the recoil momentum of the rifle works against only the mass of the rifle, producing a larger velocity and striking your shoulder smartly. When held firmly against your shoulder, the recoil momentum must work against the mass of the rifle and yourself, resulting in a smaller velocity.
10. Momentum is conserved, so the momentum of the block and bullet after the collision equals the momentum of the bullet before. The rubber bullet has a negative momentum after impact with respect to the block, so the block's momentum must be greater in this case. Bouncing beats sticking.
11. Rebounding presents the greater danger because it requires a greater change in momentum and, therefore, a greater impulse.

Answers To
PROBLEMS

Complete solutions to all Chapter Review Problems can be found in the Problems and Solutions Manual accompanying this text.

1. 351 kg·m/s
2. 4.8 kg·m/s
3. 42 m/s
4. a. 60.0 N·s
   b. 20.0 m/s
5. a. 2.04×10^4 N·s
   b. 300 N
6. a. 2.35×10^4 kg·m/s
   b. 2.6×10^4 N
7. 2.6×10^2 N
8. -2.5×10^2 N
9. 1.10×10^3 kg
10. 1.3×10^3 s
11. 30.0 s
12. a. 5.0×10^{-2}s
    b. -4.0×10^3 N
    c. 4.1×10^2 kg: no
    d. Holding a child is dangerous to the child.
13. 888 kg·m/s at 43.6° below horizontal
14. a. 63 kg·m/s
    b. 63 N·s
    c. 2.0×10^4 N
    d. 4.0×10^3 N
15. a. 1.5×10^2 kg·m/s
    b. 1.5×10^2 N·s
    c. 3.0×10^3 N
    d. Force is about 5 times the weight.
16. a. 7.8×10^2 kg·m/s
    b. -7.8×10^2 kg·m/s
    c. 7.8×10^2 kg·m/s
    d. -7.8×10^2 kg·m/s
    e. 6.1 m/s
17. a. 1.0×10^{-3} kg·m/s
    b. -6.0×10^{-4} kg·m/s
    c. 6.0×10^{-4} kg·m/s
    d. 1.6×10^{-3} kg·m/s
    e. 16 cm/s

▶ **13.** An animal-rescue plane flying due east at 36.0 m/s drops a bale of hay from an altitude of 60.0 m. If the bale of hay weighs 175 N, what is the momentum of the bale the moment it strikes the ground?

▶ **14.** A 10-kg lead brick falls from a height of 2.0 m.
- **a.** Find its momentum as it reaches the ground.
- **b.** What impulse is needed to bring the brick to rest?
- **c.** The brick falls onto a carpet, 1.0 cm thick. Assuming the force stopping it is constant, find the average force the carpet exerts on the brick.
- **d.** If the brick falls onto a 5.0-cm foam rubber pad, what constant force is needed to bring it to rest?

▶ **15.** A 60-kg dancer leaps 0.32 m high.
- **a.** With what momentum does the dancer reach the ground?
- **b.** What impulse is needed to make a stop?
- **c.** As the dancer lands, the knees bend, lengthening the stopping time to 0.050 s. Find the average force exerted on the body.
- **d.** Compare the stopping force to the performer's weight.

9.2 The Conservation of Momentum

16. A 95-kg fullback, running at 8.2 m/s, collides in midair with a 128-kg defensive tackle moving in the opposite direction. Both players end up with zero speed.
- **a.** What was the fullback's momentum before the collision?
- **b.** What was the change in the fullback's momentum?
- **c.** What was the change in the tackle's momentum?
- **d.** What was the tackle's original momentum?
- **e.** How fast was the tackle moving originally?

17. A glass ball, ball A, of mass 5.0 g, moves at a velocity of 20.0 cm/s. It collides with a second glass ball, ball B, of mass 10.0 g, moving along the same line with a velocity of 10.0 cm/s. After the collision, ball A is still moving, but with a velocity of 8.0 cm/s.
- **a.** What was ball A's original momentum?
- **b.** What is ball A's change in momentum?
- **c.** What is ball B's change in momentum?
- **d.** What is the momentum of ball B after the collision?
- **e.** What is ball B's speed after the collision?

18. Before a collision, a 25-kg object is moving at +12 m/s. Find the impulse that acted on this object if after the collision it moves at
a. +8 m/s. **b.** −8 m/s.

19. A 2575-kg van runs into the back of a 825-kg compact car at rest. They move off together at 8.5 m/s. Assuming no friction with the ground, find the initial speed of the van.

20. A 15-g bullet is shot into a 5085-g wooden block standing on a frictionless surface. The block, with the bullet in it, acquires a velocity of 1.0 m/s. Calculate the velocity of the bullet before striking the block.

21. A hockey puck, mass 0.115 kg, moving at 35.0 m/s, strikes an octopus thrown on the ice by a fan. The octopus has a mass of 0.265 kg. The puck and octopus slide off together. Find their velocity.

FIGURE 9–17.

22. A 50-kg woman, riding on a 10-kg cart, is moving east at 5.0 m/s. The woman jumps off the cart and hits the ground at 7.0 m/s eastward, relative to the ground. Calculate the velocity of the cart after she jumps off.

23. Two students on roller skates stand face-to-face, then push each other away. One student has a mass of 90 kg, the other 60 kg. Find the ratio of their velocities just after their hands lose contact. Which student has the greater speed?

24. A car with mass 1245 kg, moving at 29 m/s, strikes a 2175-kg car at rest. If the two cars stick together, with what speed do they move?

▶ **25.** A 92-kg fullback, running at 5.0 m/s, attempts to dive across the goal line for a touchdown. Just as he reaches the goal line, he is met head-on in midair by two 75-kg linebackers, one moving at 2.0 m/s and the other at 4.0 m/s. If they all become entangled as one mass, with what velocity do they travel? Does the fullback score?

▶ **26.** A 5.00-g bullet is fired with a velocity of 100 m/s toward a 10.00-kg stationary solid block resting on a frictionless surface.

a. What is the change in momentum of the bullet if it is embedded in the block?

b. What is the change in momentum of the bullet if it ricochets in the opposite direction with a speed of 99 m/s–almost the same speed as it had originally?

27. A 0.200-kg plastic ball moves with a velocity of 0.30 m/s. It collides with a second plastic ball of mass 0.100 kg, moving along the same line at a velocity of 0.10 m/s. After the collision, the velocity of the 0.100-kg ball is 0.26 m/s. What is the new velocity of the first ball?

▶ **28.** Figure 9–18 shows a brick weighing 24.5 N being released from rest on a 1.00-m frictionless plane, inclined at an angle of 30.0°. The brick slides down the incline and strikes a second brick weighing 36.8 N.

a. Calculate the speed of the brick at the bottom of the incline.

b. If the two bricks stick together, with what initial speed will they move along?

c. If the force of friction acting on the two bricks is 5.0 N, how much time will elapse before the bricks come to rest?

d. How far will the two bricks slide before coming to rest?

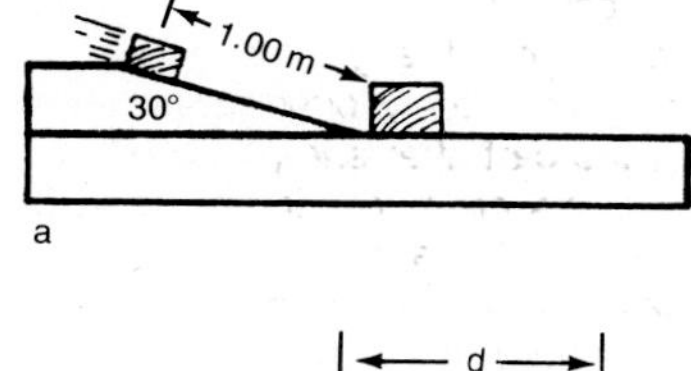

FIGURE 9–18. Use with Problem 28.

▶ **29.** Ball A, rolling west at 3.0 m/s, has a mass of 1.0 kg. Ball B has a mass of 2.0 kg and is stationary. After colliding with ball B, ball A moves south at 2.0 m/s. Calculate the momentum and velocity of ball B after the collision.

▶ **30.** A cue ball, moving with 7.0 N·s of momentum strikes the nine-ball at rest. The nine-ball moves off with 2.0 N·s in the original direction of the cue ball and 2.0 N·s perpendicular to that direction. What is the momentum of the cue ball after the collision?

▶ **31.** A 7600-kg space probe is traveling through space at 120 m/s. Mission control determines that a change in course of 30.0° is necessary and, by electronic communication, instructs the probe to fire rockets perpendicular to its present direction of motion. If the escaping gas leaves the craft's rockets at an average speed of 3200 m/s, what mass of gas should be expelled?

▶ **32.** Figure 9–19, which is drawn to scale, shows two balls during an elastic collision. The balls enter from the left of the page, collide, and bounce away. The heavier ball at the bottom of the diagram has a mass of 600 g, while the ball on the top has a mass of 400 g. Using a vector diagram, determine if momentum is conserved in this collision. **Hint:** *Remember that the two masses are not equal.* Try to account for any discrepancy found in the total momentum before and after the collision.

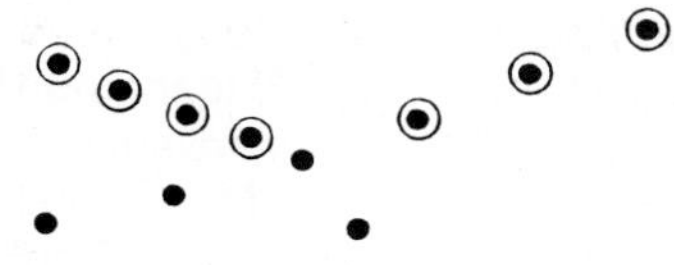

FIGURE 9–19. Use with Problem 32.

▶ **33.** The head of a 1.0-kg hammer, moving at 3.6 m/s, strikes a nail and drives it into hardwood.

a. The head stays in contact 2.0 ms and rebounds with neglibible velocity. What is the average force exerted on the nail?

b. When the same hammer hits a springy nail, it rebounds with its initial speed, 3.6 m/s. The contact time is the same. What force is exerted this time?

THINKING PHYSIC-LY

You cannot throw a raw egg against a brick wall without breaking the egg, but you can throw it with the same speed into a sagging sheet without breaking the egg. Explain.

18. **a.** -1.0×10^2 kg·m/s
b. -5.0×10^2 kg·m/s
19. 11 m/s
20. 3.4×10^2 m/s
21. 10.6 m/s
22. 5.0 m/s, west
23. 1:-1.5, the student with the smaller mass
24. 10 m/s
25. 0.041 m/s, yes
26. **a.** -0.500 kg·m/s
b. -0.995 kg·m/s
27. 0.22 m/s, original direction
28. **a.** 3.1 m/s
b. 1.24 m/s
c. 1.6 s
d. 0.99 m
29. 3.6 kg·m/s at 34°N of W: 1.8 m/s at 34°N of W
30. 5.4 N·s at 22° from original direction
31. 170 kg
32. Refer to Problems and Solutions Manual.
33. **a.** 1.8×10^3 N
b. 3.6×10^3 N

Answers To
THINKING PHYSIC-LY

Initially, the egg will have the same momentum and will require the same impulse to bring the egg to rest. The sagging sheet will increase the impulse action time and will thus decrease the average force, saving the egg.

CHAPTER

10 Work, Energy, and Simple Machines

PLANNING GUIDE (5 class sessions)

CONTENTS	TEXT FEATURES	TEACHER RESOURCE PACKAGE	OTHER COMPONENTS
10.1 Work and Energy, pp. 198-203 (3 Class Sessions) • Work • Work and Direction of Force • Power	**Physics Lab:** Your Power, p. 204 **Pocket Lab:** An Inclined Mass, p. 198 **Pocket Lab:** Working Out, p. 200 **Problem Solving Strategy:** Doing Work Problems, p. 201 **Concept Review,** p. 203	**Study Guide:** Work and Energy **Physics Lab Data Sheet:** Your Power	**Transparency 12:** Simple Machines
10.2 Machines, pp. 205–211 (2 Class Sessions) • Simple and Complex Machines • Energy Conservation and Mechanical Advantage • Compound Machines • The Human Walking Machine	**Physics and Technology:** Artificial Joints, p. 211 **Concept Review,** p. 210–211	**Study Guide:** Machines **Reteaching Master:** The Advantage of a Low Mechanical Advantage **Critical Thinking Master:** Bicycle Gears **Enrichment Master:** The Efficiency of a Pulley System **Transparency Worksheet:** Simple Machines	**Laboratory Manual:** Lab 10.1 Pulleys Lab 10.2 Torques **Transparency 12:** Simple Machines
Chapter Review, pp. 212–215	Summary Key Terms Reviewing Concepts Applying Concepts Problems Thinking Physic-ly	**Vocabulary Review** **Chapter Test**	**Test Bank**

SUPPLEMENTARY MATERIALS

SOFTWARE	AUDIOVISUAL	BOOKS/MAGAZINES
Work and Machines, Queue, Inc. (Apple II, IBM PC, Macintosh). *Introduction to General Physics, Disk II: Momentum and Work,* COMPress/Queue, Inc. (Apple II, IBM PC, Macintosh). *Work and Energy,* J&S (Apple II).	Video: *Simple and Compound Machines: How They Work,* Queue, Inc.	Chiapetta, Eugene, L. "Body Levers." *The Science Teacher,* January 1987, pp. 39–41. Engel, C., and Girard, B. "Motorcycle Physics." *The Science Teacher,* January 1983, p. 40. Hayn, Carl H., "Pedagogical Interlude." *The Physics Teacher,* March 1990, p. 166. Leff, Harvey S. "Conveyor-Belt Work, Displacement, and Dissipation." *The Physics Teacher,* February 1990, p. 172.

PROBLEM CORRELATION

CONCEPTS	CHAPTER REVIEW			PROBLEMS APPENDIX
	Reviewing Concepts	Applying Concepts	Problems	
10.1 Work and Energy				
Work	1,2,3	1,2	1,2,3,**4**,5,**6**,**7**	1,2,3,4
Work and Direction of Force		3,4,5	8,9,10,11,12,13, **14**,**15**,**16**	**5**,**6**,7,**8**
Power	4,5	6	17,18,19,**20**,**21**,22, 23,24,25,26,27, 28	9,10,**11**,**12**
10.2 Machines				
Simple and Complex Machines	6			
Energy Conservation and Mechanical Advantage	7	7,8,9	29,30,31,**32**,33,34	13,**14**
Compound Machines			**35**,**36**,37	**15**

ACTIVITY AND DEMONSTRATION MATERIALS

PHYSICS LAB	POCKET LAB	DEMONSTRATIONS
Page 204 meter stick stopwatch student climber (for stairs)	Pages 198, 200 spring scale 1.0-kg mass string	

EXTENSION PROJECTS

LIBRARY RESEARCH

1. Physics in Ancient Egypt
Investigate in the library how ancient Egyptians raised water from the Nile to irrigate their fields. What basic principles of physics did they utilize?

DISPLAY MODEL

2. The Worm Screw
Find a device that uses a worm screw and explain its function to the class.

STUDENT READINGS

Bartlett, Albert A. "Physics and a Skiing Record." *The Physics Teacher,* February 1990.

Britton, Peter. "How Canada Is Tapping the Tides for Power." *Popular Science,* January 1985.

Kaeck, Jack A. "Power Transfer in Physical Systems." *The Physics Teacher,* April 1990.

Kyle, Chester. "The Aerodynamics of Human Powered Land Vehicles." *Scientific American,* December 1983.

Chapter 10

Work, Energy, and Simple Machines

CHAPTER OVERVIEW

Theme Development: The mathematical modeling of machines is presented here.

MISCONCEPTIONS

Since work involves two vector quantities, force and displacement, students often assume work should be a vector quantity, which it is not. The concepts of work and power get confused; power as a rate of doing work seems to be difficult to understand. Students often think that machines do more work than is put into them.

KEY TERMS

compound machine
efficiency
effort force
energy
ideal mechanical advantage (IMA)
joule
machine
mechanical advantage (MA)
power
resistance force
watt
work

Laboratory Options

STUDENT EDITION

Physics Lab

Your Power	204

Pocket Labs

An Inclined Mass	198
Working Out	200

TEACHER EDITION

Activities

Cooperative Learning	210

LABORATORY MANUAL

Pulleys	Lab 10.1
Torques	Lab 10.2

CHAPTER 10

Work, Energy, and Simple Machines

A-Not-So-Simple Machine

How does a multispeed bicycle let a rider ride over any kind of terrain with the least effort?

Chapter Outline

What is energy? When you have a lot of energy you can run farther or faster; you can jump higher. Objects, as well as people, can have energy. A stone falling off a high ledge has enough energy to damage a car roof. One way to summarize the examples of energy above is to say that an object has energy if it can produce a change in itself or in its surroundings. This may not seem very exact, but there is no more precise definition.

In this chapter, we will concentrate on ways of producing changes in objects or their environment. The human race has developed many tools and machines that make it easier to produce such changes. A 10-speed bicycle is a machine that allows the rider to select the speed that makes the bike easiest to ride whether it is going uphill or along a level path. You will discover the physical principles that make this kind of machine work.

Concept Check

The following terms or concepts from earlier chapters are important for a good understanding of this chapter. If you are not familiar with them, you should review them before studying this chapter.

- finding area under graph, Chapters 2, 3, 4
- force and force components, Chapter 5
- Newton's second and third laws, Chapter 5
- friction, Chapter 5
- cosine of an angle, Chapter 6

Introducing The Chapter

A Not-So-Simple Machine

Using The Photo: Bicycles are the most efficient form of human transportation in terms of distance traveled per amount of energy expended. Efforts continue to make them even more efficient by using solid wheels and elliptical sprockets. In his recent book, *The Ring of Truth,* Philip Morrison has a fascinating chapter on the Tour de France bicycle race.

Students will find the method for solving the chapter opener question on page 208.

Concept Check

Make sure students have a clear understanding of the concepts taught in Chapters 2–6 that are listed in the Concept Check. Students with a good grasp of forces, Newton's second and third laws, friction, angle cosines, and finding area under a graph will more easily understand the principles of work, energy, and simple machines presented in this chapter.

Assessment

Portfolio

Have students submit solutions of both simple, one-step problems and problems that require two or more steps or use graphical calculation of work from area under a force-displacement graph.

Assessment Options

Portfolio Assessment
Portfolio Assessment, TWE, p. 197
Enrichment, TWE, p. 206
Critical Thinking, TWE, p. 210
Connect to Biology, TWE, p. 210
Thinking Physic-ly, p. 215

Performance
Pocket Labs, pp. 198, 200
Physics Lab, p. 204

Content
Self assessment: Practice Problems, pp. 199, 202, 203, 210
Pocket Lab Assessment, TWE, p. 200
Critical Thinking, TWE, p. 203
Assessment, Critical Thinking, TWE, p. 204
Concept Reviews, pp. 203, 210
Chapter Review, pp. 212–215
Supplemental Problems, pp. 695–696

Group Assessment
Activities for group assessment occur with Cooperative Learning and lab activities.

10.1 WORK AND ENERGY

Preparation

OBJECTIVES

The objectives are listed on the student page. Remind students to preview these objectives as a study guide to this major section.

OVERVIEW

The concepts of work and power, with their SI units, are introduced in this section.

BRIDGING

The ideas of force, displacement, vector components, friction, and time reappear here.

POCKET LAB

Purpose: to observe the effect of horizontal and vertical components of force exerted on an object.
Materials: spring scale; 1.0-kg mass; string.
Outcome: The reading on the scale is a measure of the sliding friction between the table and the mass. The smoothness of the table and the hardness of each surface affect the frictional force. The work done is the average force times the displacement. The force and the work should be approximately two times the original value.

Objectives

- display an ability to calculate work done by a force.
- identify the force that does the work.
- understand the relationship between work done and energy transferred.
- differentiate between work and power and correctly calculate power used.

10.1 WORK AND ENERGY

If you spend the morning lifting crates from the floor of a warehouse up onto a truck, you will get tired and hungry. You will need to eat food to "get more energy." Somehow, the energy in the food will be transferred into the energy in the raised crates. We use the word *work* to indicate the amount of energy that was transferred from food to you to the crates. The word work has both an everyday and a scientific meaning. In the case of lifting crates, everyone will agree that work was done. In everyday life, however, we use the word when talking about other activities. For example, everyone says that learning physics is hard work! But in physics, we reserve the term work to mean a very special form of physical activity.

FIGURE 10–1. In physics, work is done only when a force causes an object to move a certain distance. Work is a product of a force and the displacement of an object in the direction of the force.

POCKET LAB

AN INCLINED MASS

Attach a spring scale to a 1.0-kg mass with a string. Keep the string parallel to the table and measure the force needed to pull the mass at a steady speed. Increase the angle between the string and the table top, for example, to 30°. Try to keep the angle constant as you pull the 1.0-kg mass along the table at a slow, steady speed. Notice the reading on the scale. How much force is in the direction of motion? How much work is done when the 1.0 kg moves 1.0 m? How does the work compare to the previous value?

Work

When lifting crates, or any other object, we do more work when the crate is heavier. The task is even harder if the crate must be lifted higher. It seems reasonable to use the quantity force times distance to measure the amount of energy transferred when lifting. For cases where the force is constant, we define **work** as the product of the force exerted on an object and the distance the object moves in the direction of the force. In equation form,

$$W = Fd,$$

where W is the work, F is the magnitude of force, and d is the magnitude of displacement in the direction of the force. Note that work is a scalar quantity; it has no direction. The SI unit of work is the **joule** [JOOL]. The joule is named after James Prescott Joule, a nineteenth century English physicist and brewer. If a force of one newton moves an object one meter, one joule of work is done.

$$1 \text{ joule (J)} = 1 \text{ newton} \cdot \text{meter (N} \cdot \text{m)}$$

Work is done on an object only if the object moves. If you hold a heavy banner at the same height in the same place for an hour, you may get tired, but you do no work on the banner. Even if you carry the banner at constant velocity and at a constant height, you do no work on it. The force you exert is upward while the motion is sideways, so the banner gains no energy. Work is only done when the force and displacement are in the same direction.

TEACHER 

Hunger is not an indication of work done. One may spend many hours doing anything, including resting, and experience the sensation of hunger. Hunger may be an indication of the need for more fuel, but the work done by the body is not necessarily defined by that term in physics.

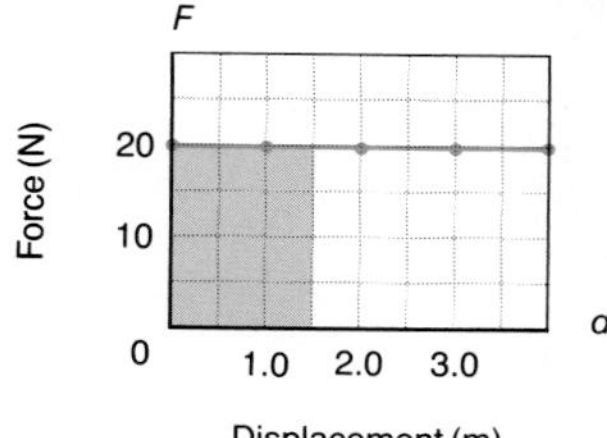

FIGURE 10–2. A force-displacement graph of a rock being pushed horizontally.

A force-displacement graph can give you a picture of the work done. Figure 10–2 shows the force-displacement graph of a rock being pushed horizontally. A net force of 20 N is needed to push the rock 1.5 m with constant velocity. The work done on the rock is the product of the force and the displacement, $W = Fd = (20 \text{ N})(1.5 \text{ m}) = 30 \text{ J}$. The shaded area under the curve of Figure 10–2 is equal to $20 \text{ N} \times 1.5 \text{ m}$, or 30 J. The area under the curve of a force-displacement graph represents the work done. If you increase either the width of the rectangle (displacement) or the height (force), you increase the work done.

Work is done on an object only if it moves in the direction of the force.

Example Problem

Calculating Work

A student lifts a box of books that weighs 185 N. The box is lifted 0.800 m. How much work does the student do?

Given: $mg = 185$ N, $d = 0.800$ m

Unknown: work, W

Basic equation: $W = Fd$

Solution: The student exerted enough force to lift the box, that is, enough to balance the weight of the box. Thus,

$$W = Fd = (185 \text{ N})(0.800 \text{ m}) = 148 \text{ N} \cdot \text{m} = 148 \text{ J}$$

Practice Problems

1. A force of 825 N is needed to push a car across a lot. Two students push the car 35 m.
   a. How much work is done?
   b. After a rainstorm, the force needed to push the car doubled because the ground became soft. By what amount does the work done by the students change?
2. A delivery clerk carries a 34-N package from the ground to the fifth floor of an office building, a total height of 15 m. How much work is done by the clerk?
3. What work is done by a forklift raising a 583-kg box 1.2 m?
4. ▶ You and a friend each carry identical boxes to a room one floor above you and down the hall. You choose to carry it first up the stairs, then down the hall. Your friend carries it down the hall, then up another stairwell. Who does more work?

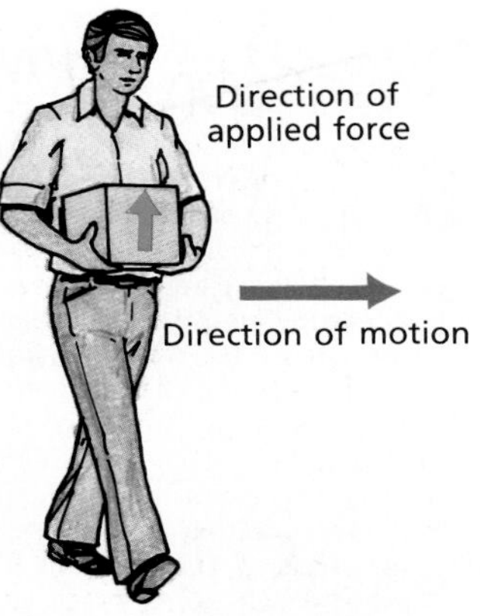

FIGURE 10–3. Work is done on the box only when it moves in the direction of the applied force.

1 Focus

Because of the relationship developed here, note that the unit for work and energy is the same, the joule. Students should know this useful fact.

2 Teach

CONCEPT DEVELOPMENT

• Your students may be familiar with the Calorie as a unit of work and energy from their chemistry class. 1 Calorie = 4.18 joules

• In the equations for work and power, stress that W stands for work and not weight. This often leads to student confusion.

Study Guide Master. To reinforce the concepts in this section, have the students complete the Study Guide Master for Section 10.1 from the Teacher Resource Package.

Answers To
PRACTICE PROBLEMS

Have students refer to Appendix A of the Solutions Appendix for complete solutions to Practice Problems.

1. a. 2.9×10^4 J
   b. The work doubles.
2. 510 J
3. 6.9×10^3 J
4. Both do the same amount of work.

TEACHER F.Y.I.

Many important forces are not constant, but vary with position, as shown in the diagram.

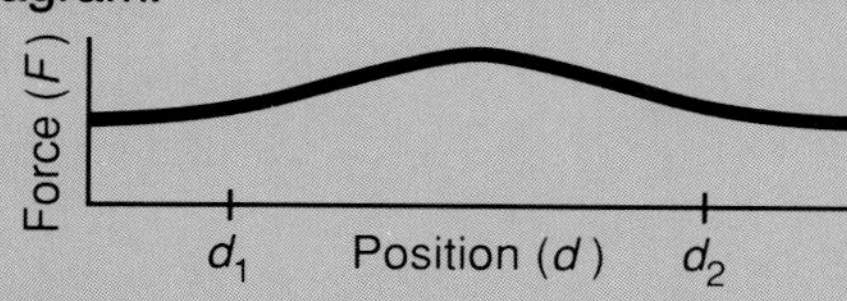

You cannot say that the work done is $F(d_2 - d_1)$, because there is no single value of F. The region can be divided into small rectangles of width Δd and the

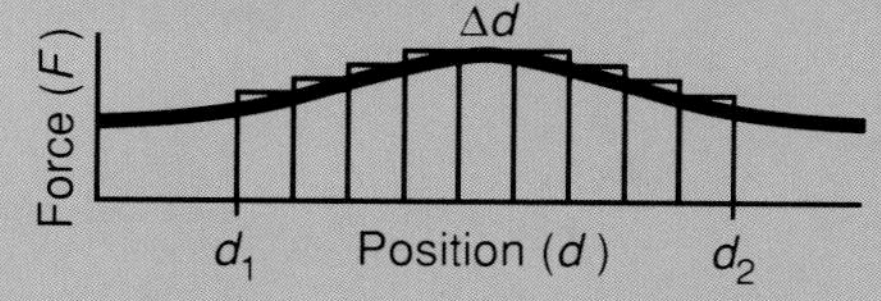

areas of the rectangles added to determine total work done.

CONCEPT DEVELOPMENT

It's worth emphasizing that as the angle between the force and the direction of motion changes from zero to 90°, the amount of work done goes from maximum to zero. All students will surely realize that pushing in the same direction as the desired motion is the most effective way of doing work.

POCKET LAB

WORKING OUT

Purpose: to demonstrate the relationship between work and the direction of force.

Materials: spring balance; 1.0-kg mass; string.

Outcome: The reading on the balance is greater than when the 1.0-kg mass was pulled with a horizontal force. The force in the direction of motion is almost the same as before. The work equals the horizontal part of the force times 1.0 m. The work is close to the previous value.

Assessment

Critical Thinking

To further assess students' understanding of work, ask the following question. The definition of work is the transfer of energy by mechanical means. When the block in the Pocket Lab was pulled, what was the source of the energy, and where did it go? [The energy came from the person who pulled the block. If the block were pulled long enough, the person would become tired and hungry. Food would replace the energy used. When the block is moving, it has energy. A fast-moving block can damage anything it hits; it can change its surroundings. In addition, there is a frictional force on the block. Work is done against friction, and the block and table will become warmer.]

a

$F = 125$ N

F_v

$\theta = 25.0°$

F_h

$F_h = F \cos 25.0°$
$= (125 \text{ N})(0.906)$
$F_h = 113$ N

b

FIGURE 10–4. If a force is applied to the mower at an angle, the net force doing the work is the component that acts in the direction of the motion.

Only the component in the direction of the motion does work.

Work and Direction of Force

Work is done only if a force is exerted in the direction of motion. The person or object that exerts the force does the work. If a force is exerted perpendicular to the motion, no work is done. What if a force is exerted at some other angle to the motion? For example, if you push the lawn mower in Figure 10–4a, what work do you do? You know that any force can be replaced by its components. The 125-N force (F) you exert in the direction of the handle has two components, Figure 10–4b. The horizontal component (F_h) is 113 N; the vertical component (F_v) is −53 N (downward). The vertical component is perpendicular to the motion. It does no work. Only the horizontal component does work. The work you do when you exert a force at an angle to a motion is equal to the component of the force in the direction of the motion times the distance moved.

The magnitude of the component of the force F acting in the direction of motion is found by multiplying the force F by the cosine of the angle between F and the direction of motion.

$$W = F(\cos\theta)d$$
$$= Fd\cos\theta$$

Other objects exert forces on the lawn mower. Which of these objects do work? Earth's gravity acts downward, and the ground exerts the normal force upward. Both are perpendicular to the direction of motion. That is, the angle between the force and direction of motion is 90°. Since $\cos 90° = 0$, no work is done.

The lawn exerts a force, friction, in the direction opposite the motion. In fact, if the lawn mower moves at a constant speed, the horizontal component of the applied force is balanced by the force of friction, $F_{friction}$. The angle between the force of friction and the direction of motion is 180°. Since $\cos 180° = -1$, the work done by the grass is $W = -F_{friction}d$. The work done by the friction of the grass is negative. The force is exerted in one direction, while the motion was in the opposite direction. Negative work indicates that work is being done on the grass by the mower. The positive sign of the work done by you exerting the force on the handle means you are doing work.

POCKET LAB

WORKING OUT

Attach a spring balance to a 1.0-kg mass with a string. Pull the mass along the table at a slow, steady speed keeping the balance parallel to the table top. Notice the reading on the spring balance. What are the physical factors that determine the amount of force? How much work is done in moving the mass 1.0 m? Predict the force and the work when a 2.0-kg mass is pulled along the table. Try it. Was your prediction accurate?

STUDY GUIDE MASTER

Use the Study Guide master for section 10.1.

What is the effect of doing work? When you lift a box of books onto a shelf, you give the box a certain property. If the box falls, it can do work; it might exert forces that crush another object. If the box is on a cart and you push on it, you will start it moving. Again, the box could exert forces that crush another object. In this case too, you have given the box **energy**—the ability to produce a change in itself or its surroundings.

By doing work on the box, you have transferred energy from your body to the box. Thus, we say that *work is the transfer of energy by mechanical means*. You can think of work as energy transferred as the result of motion. When you lift a box, the work you do is positive. Energy is transferred from you to the box. When you lower the box, work is negative. The energy is transferred from the box to you.

F.Y.I.

In physics, *work* and *energy* have precise meanings, which must not be confused with their everyday meanings. Robert Oppenheimer wrote, "Often the very fact that the words of science are the same as those of our common life and tongue can be more misleading than enlightening."

PROBLEM SOLVING STRATEGY

When doing work problems, you should:

1. Carefully check the forces acting on the object. Draw a diagram indicating all the force vectors.
2. Ask, "What is the displacement? What is the angle between force and displacement?"
3. Check the sign of the work by determining the direction energy is transferred. If the energy of the object increases, the work done on it is positive.

Example Problem

Work—Force and Displacement at an Angle

A sailor pulls a boat along a dock using a rope at an angle of 60.0° with the horizontal, Figure 10–5. How much work is done by the sailor if he exerts a force of 255 N on the rope and pulls the boat 30.0 m?

Given: $\theta = 60.0°$
$F = 255$ N
$d = 30.0$ m

Unknown: work, W
Basic equation: $W = Fd\cos\theta$

Solution: The work done by the sailor,

$$W = Fd\cos\theta = (255\text{ N})(30.0\text{ m})(\cos 60.0°)$$
$$= (255\text{ N})(30.0\text{ m})(0.500) = 3.83 \times 10^3\text{ J}$$

FIGURE 10–5. The force exerted by the sailor must exceed the force needed to move the boat because only the horizontal force changes the velocity.

CONCEPT DEVELOPMENT

Since work and power get used almost synonymously in ordinary language, students tend to confuse the two. Remind them that power is the time rate of doing work. Two students completing identical tasks accomplish the same amount of work regardless of the time it takes to do it. The one who completes the task in the shortest time demonstrates the most power.

Guided Practice: Go over the Example Problem on pages 201 and 202, then have students try the first Practice Problem on page 202.

Independent Practice: Assign the remaining Practice Problems on page 202 for homework and spend time reviewing them in class the next day.

CONCEPT DEVELOPMENT

- Is the unit of power, the watt, conveniently sized from the point of view of a person? In other words, can most of what a person does be measured in a small number of watts?
- Point out that $F \cos \theta$ is just the component of force in the direction of motion. Review the material about components of vectors from Chapter 6.

CHECKING FOR UNDERSTANDING

Ask students to give examples of work and power, being careful about the distinction between the two.

RETEACHING

Transparency Package. Use Transparency 12, Simple Machines, and accompanying worksheet to reteach this section.

EXTENSION

Compare the time rates in motion (velocity and acceleration) to the time rate of work in power. Stress that time rates are very important and give us valuable information. Emphasize the point that the work done is the same. Ask your students what is different in both events. The way to describe these two situations is power—the rate of work done.

Answers To
PRACTICE PROBLEMS

Have students refer to Appendix A of the Solutions Appendix for complete solutions to Practice Problems.

5. 88 J
6. **a.** 903 J
b. −903 J
7. 6.54×10^3 J
8. **a.** 340 J
b. −279 J
c. -1.3×10^2 J

Practice Problems

5. How much work does the force of gravity do when a 25-N object falls a distance of 3.5 m?

6. An airplane passenger carries a 215-N suitcase up stairs, a displacement of 4.20 m vertically and 4.60 m horizontally.
  a. How much work does the passenger do?
  b. The same passenger carries the same suitcase back down the same stairs. How much work does the passenger do now?

7. A rope is used to pull a metal box 15.0 m across the floor. The rope is held at an angle of 46.0° with the floor and a force of 628 N is used. How much work does the force on the rope do?

▶ **8.** A worker pushes a crate weighing 93 N up an inclined plane, pushing horizontally, parallel to the ground, Figure 10–6.
  a. The worker exerts a force of 85 N. How much work does he do?
  b. How much work is done by gravity? (Be careful of signs.)
  c. The coefficient of friction is $\mu = 0.20$. How much work is done by friction? (Be careful of signs.)

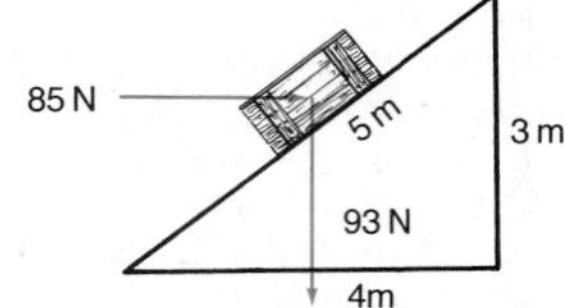

FIGURE 10–6. Use with Practice Problem 8.

Power

Power is the rate at which work is done.

Until now, none of the discussions of work have mentioned the time it takes to move an object. The work done lifting a box of books is the same whether the box is lifted in 2 seconds or if each book is lifted separately, so that it takes 20 minutes to put them all on the shelf. The work done is the same, but the power is different. **Power** is the rate of doing work. That is, *power is the rate at which energy is transferred.* Power is work done divided by the time it takes. Power can be calculated using

$$P = \frac{W}{t}.$$

Power is measured in watts (W). One **watt** is one joule of energy transferred in one second. A machine that does work at a rate of one joule per second has a power of one watt. A watt is a relatively small unit of power. For example, a glass of water weighs about 2 N. If you lift it 0.5 meter to your mouth, you do 1 joule of work. If you do it in one second, you are doing work at the rate of one watt. Because a watt is such a small unit, power is often measured in kilowatts (kW). A kilowatt is 1000 watts.

FIGURE 10–7. The same amount of work is being done as in Figure 10–4, but the power is greater here.

Example Problem

Power

An electric motor lifts an elevator that weighs 1.20×10^4 N a distance of 9.00 m in 15.0 s, Figure 10–8, **a.** What is the power of the motor in watts? **b.** What is the power in kilowatts?

Given: $F = 1.20 \times 10^4$ N
$d = 9.00$ m
$t = 15.0$ s

Unknown: power, P

Basic equation: $P = \frac{W}{t}$

TRANSPARENCY

Use Transparency 12 with this section.

Solution:

a. power of a motor,

$$P = \frac{W}{t} = \frac{Fd}{t} = \frac{(1.20 \times 10^4\ \text{N})(9.00\ \text{m})}{15.0\ \text{s}}$$
$$= 7.20 \times 10^3\ \text{N} \cdot \text{m/s} = 7.20 \times 10^3\ \text{J/s} = 7.20 \times 10^3\ \text{W}$$

b. $P = 7.20 \times 10^3\ \text{W}\left(\frac{1\ \text{kW}}{1000\ \text{W}}\right) = 7.20\ \text{kW}$

Practice Problems

9. A box that weighs 575 N is lifted a distance of 20.0 m straight up by a rope. The job is done in 10.0 s. What power is developed in watts and kilowatts?

10. A rock climber wears a 7.50-kg knapsack while scaling a cliff. After 30.0 min, the climber is 8.2 m above the starting point.
- **a.** How much work does the climber do on the knapsack?
- **b.** If the climber weighs 645 N, how much work does she do lifting herself and the knapsack?
- **c.** What is the average power developed by the climber?

11. An electric motor develops 65 kW of power as it lifts a loaded elevator 17.5 m in 35.0 s. How much force does the motor exert?

▶ **12.** Two cars travel the same speed, so that they move 105 km in 1 h. One car, a sleek sports car, has a motor that delivers only 35 kW of power at this speed. The other car needs its motor to produce 65 kW to move the car this fast. Forces exerted by friction from the air resistance cause the difference.
- **a.** For each car, list the external horizontal forces exerted on it, and give the cause of each force. Compare their magnitudes.
- **b.** By Newton's third law, the car exerts forces. What are their directions?
- **c.** Calculate the magnitude of the forward frictional force exerted by each car.
- **d.** The car engines did work. Where did the energy they transferred come from?

FIGURE 10–8. If the elevator took 20.0 s instead of 15.0 s, would the work change? Would the power change?

A watt, one joule/second, is a relatively small unit. A kilowatt, 1000 watts, is commonly used.

CONCEPT REVIEW

1.1 Explain in words, without the use of a formula, what work is.

1.2 When a bowling ball rolls down a level alley, does Earth's gravity do any work on the ball? Explain.

1.3 As you walk, there is a static frictional force between your shoes and the ground. Is any work done?

1.4 **Critical Thinking:** If three objects exert forces on a body, can they all do work at the same time? Explain.

CONCEPT DEVELOPMENT

Have interested students investigate how the English unit of power, horsepower, got the word "horse" in it.

Critical Thinking: Assume a boat moves along at constant velocity. Its motor is exerting a constant force, F, to maintain it at constant velocity against the water's drag forces. Ask students to develop an argument to show that the motor's power output is given by $P = Fv$. $[P = \frac{W}{t} = \frac{Fd}{t} = Fv]$

3 Close

CONVERGENT QUESTION

Is the concept of power restricted just to mechanical situations or can it be used in other areas as well? (No, power can be used wherever energy of any kind is being transferred. For example, we might say an intense light source is delivering power to a surface. The electrical use of power is another common example.)

INDEPENDENT PRACTICE/ EXTENSION

Refer to the Assignment Guide below for additional questions and problems for independent practice.

Answers To
PRACTICE PROBLEMS

Have students refer to Appendix A of the Solutions Appendix for complete solutions to Practice Problems.

9. 1.15×10^3 W = 1.15 kW

10. **a.** 6.0×10^2 J
b. 5.9×10^3 J
c. 3.3 W

11. 1.3×10^5 N

12. **a.** forward: force of road on car
rearward: force of air on car
These forces are equal in magnitude when the car moves with constant speed.
b. Car exerts a rearward force on road and a forward force on air.
c. 1.2×10^3 N
2.2×10^3 N
d. from the chemical energy in the gasoline

10:1 ASSIGNMENT GUIDE

	PRACTICE	EXTENSION
CHAPTER REVIEW pp. 212–215		
· Reviewing Concepts	1–5	
· Applying Concepts		1–6
· Problems*	1, 3, 5, 8–13, 17–19, 22–24, 28	4, 6–7, 14–16, 20–21, 25–27
APPENDIX B PROBLEMS*		
· Chapter 10 pp. 695–696	1–4, 7, 9, 10	5, 6, 8, 11, 12

* Complete solutions to all Chapter Review and Appendix problems appear in the Problems and Solutions Manual.

CONCEPT REVIEW ANSWERS

1.1 Work is the amount of energy transferred by mechanical means.

1.2 No. The ball has not moved in the direction of the gravitational force. (If mass of ball missing from finger holes is disregarded.)

1.3 No. Unless your shoes slip, there is no movement between shoes and ground; no work is done.

1.4 **Critical Thinking:** Yes. We could add them to find the net force and then the total work done, or we could find the work done by each separately.

PHYSICS LAB

Process Skills: observing, using numbers, measuring, communicating, controlling variables.

MISCONCEPTIONS

Many students will have difficulty distinguishing between the concepts of work and power.

Lab Worksheet, Teacher Resource Package. If desired, use the lab worksheet master for this chapter for students to record their data.

OBSERVATIONS

1. A 70.0-kg student climbing 5.0 m in 8.0 s will do 3.5×10^3 J of work (W = mgh) and have a power rating of 4.4×10^2 W of power.

ANALYSIS

1. Most students should have a power rating between 250 and 500 watts.
2. More massive students must exert more force to lift themselves. More massive students do more work.
3. Both mass and time determine the power. For example, a 90.0-kg person climbing the 5.0-m stairs in 10.0 s would have a power rating of 4.5×10^2 W. To increase power output, the time to climb stairs could be reduced, the mass increased, or the height increased (keeping mass and time constant).

APPLICATIONS

Most students would be doing work worth $0.03 or $0.04 for an hour.

PHYSICS LAB: Your Power

Purpose

To determine the work and power as you climb stairs.

Materials

- Each lab group will need a meter stick, a stopwatch, and a climber.

Procedure

1. Estimate the mass of the climber in kg. (**Hint:** 100 kg weighs approximately 220 lbs.)
2. Measure the height (vertical distance) of the stairs.
3. The climber should approach the stairs with a steady speed.

   NOTE - Do NOT run. Do NOT skip stairs. Do NOT trip.

4. The timer will start the watch as the climber hits the first stair and stop the clock when the climber reaches the top.
5. Climbers and timers should rotate until all students have had the opportunity to climb.

Observations and Data

1. Calculate the work and the power for yourself.
2. Compare your work and power calculations to others.

Analysis

1. Which students did the most work? Explain.
2. Which students had the most power? Explain with examples.
3. Calculate your power in kilowatts.

Applications

1. Your local electric company supplies you 1 kW of power for 1 h for 8¢. Assume that you could climb stairs continuously for 1 h. How much money would this climb be worth?

ASSESSMENT

Critical Thinking: To further assess students' understanding of work and power, ask the following questions.

1. Estimate the uncertainty and percent uncertainty in each measurement: mass, time, and height. What is the percent uncertainty of your calculated power? [Typical student values might be: mass, 70 kg ± 2 kg, 3%; time, 4.5 s ± 0.3 s, 7%; height, 5.0 m ± 0.2 m, 4%. Since the power calculation involves multiplication and division of each measurement, the total percent uncertainty of the power is the sum of the three uncertainties (3% + 7% + 4% = 14%).]

2. Do you think that your calculated power rating would be accurate for climbing the stairs up to a fifth floor apartment? Explain. [It is unlikely that you could maintain your climbing speed for five floors. As you tire and slow down, your power will decrease.]

10.2 MACHINES

Everyone uses some machines every day. Some are simple tools like bottle openers and screwdrivers; others are complex objects such as bicycles and automobiles. Machines, whether powered by engines or people, make our tasks easier. A **machine** eases the load either by changing the magnitude or the direction of a force, but does not change the amount of work done.

Objectives

- demonstrate knowledge of why simple machines are useful.
- understand the concept of mechanical advantage in ideal and real machines and use it correctly in solving problems.
- recognize that complex machines are simple machines linked together; show an ability to calculate mechanical advantage for some complex machines.

Simple and Complex Machines

Consider the bottle opener in Figure 10–9. When you use the opener, you lift the handle, doing work on the opener. The opener lifts the cap, doing work on it. The work you do is called the input work, W_i. The work the machine does is called the output work, W_o.

Work, you remember, is the transfer of energy by mechanical means. You put work into the machine. That is, you transfer energy to the bottle opener. The machine does work on another object. The opener, in turn, transfers energy to the cap. The opener is not a source of energy, so the cap cannot receive more energy than you put into the opener. Thus, the output work can never be larger than the input work. The machine simply aids in the transfer of energy from you to the bottle cap.

Energy Conservation and Mechanical Advantage

The force you exert on a machine is called the **effort force**, F_e. The force exerted by the machine is called the **resistance force**, F_r. The ratio of resistance force to effort force, F_r/F_e, is called the **mechanical advantage** (MA) of the machine. That is,

$$MA = \frac{F_r}{F_e}.$$

Many machines, like the bottle opener, have a mechanical advantage greater than one. When the mechanical advantage is greater than one, the machine increases the force you apply.

We can calculate the mechanical advantage of a machine using the definition of work. The input work is the product of the effort force you exert, F_e, and the displacement of your hand, d_e. In the same way, the output work is the product of the resistance force, F_r, and the displacement caused by the machine, d_r. A machine can increase force, but it cannot increase energy. An ideal machine transfers all the energy, so the output work equals the input work,

$$W_o = W_i \text{, or}$$
$$F_r d_r = F_e d_e .$$

This equation can be rewritten $\frac{F_r}{F_e} = \frac{d_e}{d_r}$. We know that the mechanical advantage is given by $MA = F_r/F_e$. For an ideal machine, we also have $MA = d_e/d_r$. Because this equation is characteristic of an ideal machine,

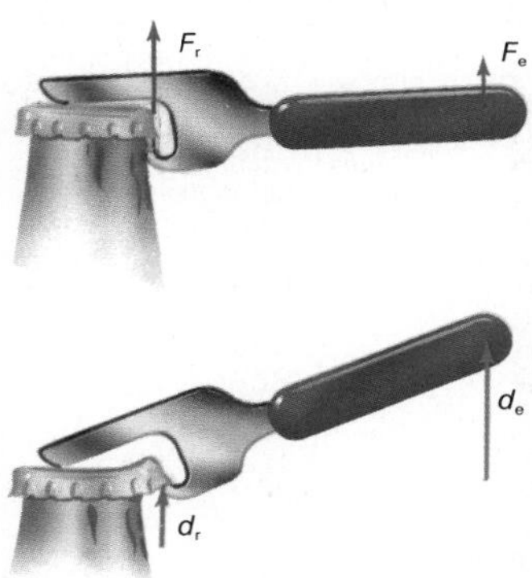

FIGURE 10–9. A bottle opener is an example of a simple machine. It makes opening a bottle easier, but not less work.

10.2 MACHINES

Preparation

OBJECTIVES

The objectives are listed on the student page. Remind students to preview these objectives as a study guide to this major section.

OVERVIEW

The concepts of machine, mechanical advantage, ideal mechanical advantage, effort force, resistance force, and efficiency are introduced here.

BRIDGING

The nature of forces and motion, as well as force and work, are both extended in this section on machines.

1 Focus

DISCREPANT EVENT

Have several tools available for students to look at such as a bottle opener, a car jack, a wrench, a nutcracker, and pliers. Discuss where the effort and resistance forces are when each machine is used.

Students can see that a screw, for example, is a modified inclined plane by cutting a piece of paper on the diagonal to make a triangle. Hold a pencil along the short side of the triangle and roll the paper around the pencil to get a spiral effect.

LAB WORKSHEET

Use the Lab Worksheet for Chapter 10 with this Physics Lab.

STUDY GUIDE MASTER

Use the Study Guide master for section 10.2.

TRANSPARENCY

Use Transparency 12 with this section.

ENRICHMENT MASTER

Use the Enrichment master for Chapter 10 with this section.

2 Teach

CONCEPT DEVELOPMENT

Study Guide Master, To reinforce the concepts in this section, have the students complete the Study Guide Master for Section 10.2 from the Teacher Resource Package.

Enrichment: Have students report on the body's use of levers. One reference to this is "Body Levers" by Eugene L. Chiapetta in the January, 1987 issue of *Science Teacher.* Other information can be found in Chapter 3 of *Sport Science* by Peter J. Brancazio.

- You may also wish to do the exercise on the mechanical advantage of the forearm as described in "Body Levers." The forearm is a third-class lever; force exerted by its muscle is many times the weight being lifted.

- When explaining efficiency, be sure you show what happens when you hook two machines together. Students often think that a 40% efficient machine hooked to a 60% efficient machine will produce 100% efficiency. In fact, it produces 24% efficiency overall:

$$40\% \times 60\% = 24\%.$$

- Lower efficiency means a greater effort force for levers, but not for inclined planes. In fact, the most efficient plane is straight up, but then the $F_e = F_r$. When the ramp angle is small (measured from the horizontal), F_e is low. This is useful, but the efficiency is low.

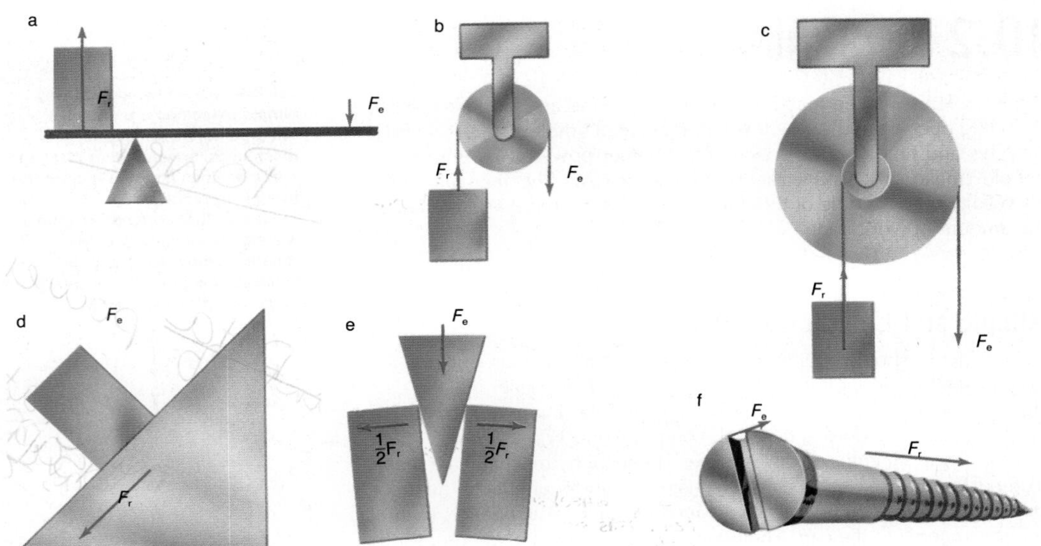

FIGURE 10–10. The simple machines pictured are the lever (a); pulley (b); wheel-and-axle (c); inclined plane (d); wedge (e); and screw (f).

the mechanical advantage is called the **ideal mechanical advantage,** *IMA,*

$$IMA = \frac{d_e}{d_r}.$$

Note that you measure distances moved to calculate the ideal mechanical advantage, *IMA,* but you measure the forces exerted to find the actual mechanical advantage, *MA.*

The mechanical advantage of a machine is the ratio of the force exerted by the machine to the force applied to the machine.

In a real machine, not all of the input work is available as output work. The **efficiency** of a machine is defined as the ratio of output work to input work. That is,

$$efficiency = \frac{W_o}{W_i} \times 100\%.$$

Efficiency is the ratio of the work done by the machine to the work put into the machine.

An ideal machine has equal output and input work, $W_o/W_i = 1$, and the efficiency is 100%. All real machines have efficiencies less than 100%. We can express the efficiency in terms of the mechanical advantage and ideal mechanical advantage.

$$efficiency = \frac{F_r/F_e}{d_e/d_r} \times 100\%$$

$$efficiency = \frac{MA}{IMA} \times 100\%$$

The *IMA* of most machines is fixed by the machine's design. An efficient machine has an *MA* almost equal to its *IMA*. A less efficient machine has a smaller *MA*. Lower efficiency means that a greater effort force is needed to exert the same resistance force.

Multicultural Connections

The wheelbarrow was created in Europe to help move heavy loads. A similar machine was invented in China, but it was called a wooden ox. Both devices use a lever in combination with a wheel and axle to create a mechanical advantage. The main difference is that a wheelbarrow puts the container for the load between the worker and the wheel. A wooden ox puts the container directly over the wheel.

All machines, no matter how complex, are combinations of up to six simple machines shown in Figure 10–10. They are the lever, pulley, wheel-and-axle, inclined plane, wedge, and screw. Gears, one of the simple machines used in a bicycle, are really a form of the wheel-and-axle. The *IMA* of all machines is the ratio of distances moved. Figure 10–11 shows that for levers and wheel-and-axles this ratio can be replaced by the ratio of the distances between the places where the forces are applied and the pivot point. A common version of the wheel-and-axle is a pair of gears on a rotating shaft. The *IMA* is the ratio of the radii of the two gears.

Compound Machines

A **compound machine** consists of two or more simple machines linked so that the resistance force of one machine becomes the effort force of the second. For example, in the bicycle, the pedal and sprocket (or gear) act like a wheel-and-axle. The effort force is the force you exert on the pedal, $F_{\text{on pedal}}$. The resistance is the force the sprocket exerts on the chain, $F_{\text{on chain}}$.

The chain exerts an effort force on the rear wheel sprocket, $F_{\text{by chain}}$, equal to the force exerted on the chain. This sprocket and the rear wheel act like another wheel-and-axle. The resistance force is the force the wheel exerts on the road, $F_{\text{on road}}$. By Newton's third law, the ground exerts an equal forward force on the wheel. This force accelerates the bicycle forward.

The mechanical advantage of a complex machine is the product of the mechanical advantages of the simple machines it is made up of. For example, in the case of the bicycle,

$$MA = \frac{F_{\text{on chain}}}{F_{\text{on pedal}}} \cdot \frac{F_{\text{on road}}}{F_{\text{by chain}}}$$

$$= \frac{F_{\text{on road}}}{F_{\text{on pedal}}}.$$

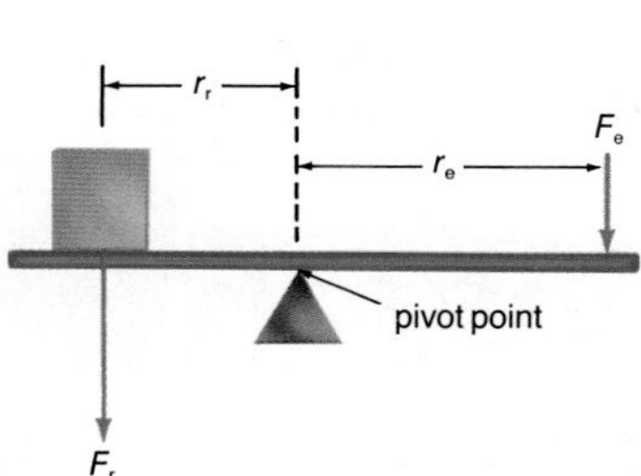

a

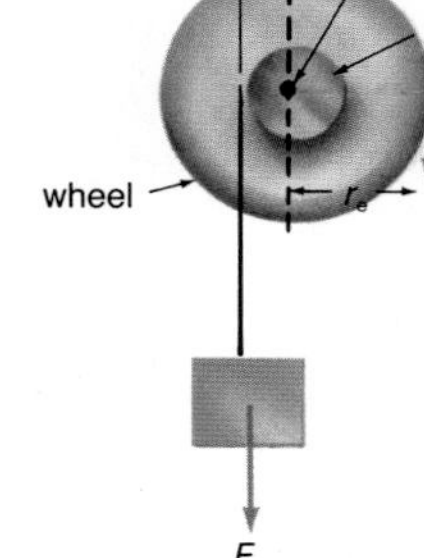

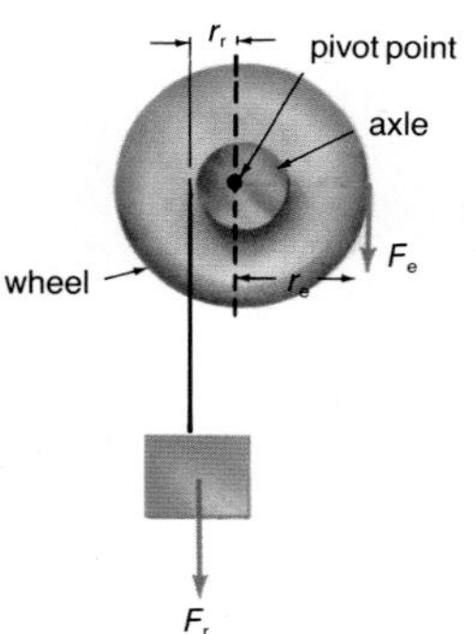

Figure 10–11. For levers and wheel and axles, the IMA is $\frac{r_e}{r_r}$

> **HELP WANTED**
>
> **CHIROPRACTOR**
>
> Do you like to work on "the human machine?" A group practice in a small city desires a new partner to expand services. A belief in the holistic (non-drug, non-surgical) approach to medicine and a positive, professional demeanor are required for one to be a successful chiropractor. Completion of an accredited, 6-year Chiropractic College program with a Doctor of Chiropractic (D.C.) degree and a state license are required. For information contact:
> International Chiropractors Association, 1901 L Street, N.W. Suite 800, Washington, DC 20036

CONCEPT DEVELOPMENT

Summarize the types of machines and their similarities. For example, a wedge can be two inclined planes back to back, or a single inclined plane. (When a box is pushed up an incline, the box and the Earth are "wedged apart.") A screw is an inclined plane wrapped around a cylinder. Pulleys and the wheel and axle are also quite similar.

CHECKING FOR UNDERSTANDING

Ask students the purpose of a machine, that is, exactly what does a machine do for us? What does a machine *not* do for us?

(A machine can change the direction of the force required. It can increase the amount of force required or the velocity, but not both at once. A machine does not put out more energy than we put into it. In fact, the amount of energy put out is always less than the amount of energy put in.)

RETEACHING

Transparency Package. Use the transparency, Simple Machines, and accompanying worksheet, to reteach this section.

EXTENSION

Enrichment Master. With this section, use the Enrichment Master, The Efficiency of a Pulley System, from the Teacher Resource Package.

TEACHER F.Y.I.

Not all machines make work "easier," although most do. This occurs when F_e and F_r are confused with W_o and W_i. The work is "easier" because the force of effort is reduced. This is paid for by requiring a larger displacement for the force. In many machines, speed is more important than that $F_e < F_r$. Consider the bodybuilder doing dumbbell curls; this is a class three lever, so $F_e > F_r$.

CONCEPT DEVELOPMENT

- Note that both the actual mechanical advantage and the ideal mechanical advantage are pure numbers, that is, they have no units.
- In summary, actual mechanical advantage refers to a real machine that has friction in its parts. Ideal mechanical advantage refers to an idealized machine (which doesn't exist) that has no friction.
- A bicycle is a distance multiplier, not a force multiplier. Changing gears to the smaller rear sprocket decreases the IMA, but makes the rear wheel turn farther for each pedal turn.

F.Y.I.

A bicyclist in a road race like the *Tour de France* rides at about 20 mi/h (9 m/s) for over six hours a day. The power output of the racer is about one kilowatt. One-quarter of that power goes into moving the bike against the resistance of the air, gears, and tires. Three-quarters of the power is used to cool the racer's body. To generate this power, the racer eats 7000-8000 food calories each day of the 23-day race.

The *IMA* of each wheel-and-axle machine is the ratio of the distances moved. For the pedal sprocket,

$$IMA = \frac{\textit{pedal radius}}{\textit{front sprocket radius}}.$$

For the rear wheel, we have

$$IMA = \frac{\textit{rear sprocket radius}}{\textit{wheel radius}}.$$

For the bicycle, then

$$IMA = \frac{\textit{pedal radius}}{\textit{front sprocket radius}} \cdot \frac{\textit{rear sprocket radius}}{\textit{wheel radius}}$$

$$= \frac{\textit{rear sprocket radius}}{\textit{front sprocket radius}} \cdot \frac{\textit{pedal radius}}{\textit{wheel radius}}.$$

Since both sprockets use the same chain and have teeth of the same size, you can simply count the number of teeth on the gears and find that

$$IMA = \frac{\textit{teeth on rear sprocket}}{\textit{teeth on front sprocket}} \cdot \frac{\textit{pedal arm length}}{\textit{wheel radius}}.$$

A-Not-So-Simple Machine

On a multi-gear bike, the rider can change the mechanical advantage of the machine by choosing the size of one or both sprockets. When accelerating or climbing a hill, the rider increases the mechanical advantage to increase the force the wheel exerts on the road. On the other hand, when going at high speed on a level road, less force is needed, and the rider decreases the mechanical advantage to reduce the distance the pedals must move for each revolution of the wheel.

You know that if the pedal is at the top or bottom of its circle, no matter how much force downward you exert, the pedals will not turn. The force of your foot is most effective when the force is exerted perpendicular to the arm of the pedal. Whenever a force on a pedal is specified, you should assume that it is applied perpendicular to the arm.

FIGURE 10–12. Some of the most ingenious compound machines ever conceived came from the imagination of cartoonist Rube Goldberg, who was famous for devising complex ways for doing simple tasks.

TEACHER 

Rube Goldberg (1883–1970) was an American cartoonist known for the crazy inventions he sketched in his published work, in which an incredibly elaborate device, usually with many moving parts, performed very simple operations. Any device that is complicated and impractical is often now referred to as a "Rube Goldberg" device (*Encyclopedia Americana*).

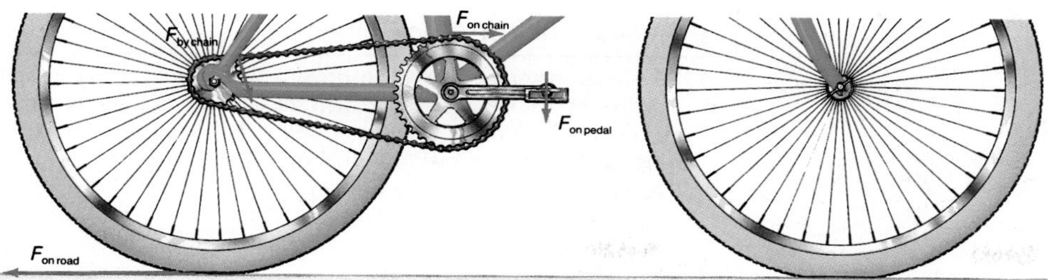

FIGURE 10–13. A series of simple machines combine to transmit the force the rider exerts on the pedal to the rear wheel of the bike.

Example Problem

The Bicycle Wheel

A student uses the bicycle wheel with gear radius 4.00 cm and wheel radius 35.6 cm. When a force of 155 N is exerted on the chain, the wheel rim moves 14.0 cm. Due to friction, its efficiency is 95.0%. **a.** What is the *IMA* of the wheel and gear? **b.** What is the *MA* of the wheel and gear? **c.** What force does the scale attached to the wheel read? **d.** How far did the student pull the chain?

Given: effort force, F_e = 155 N
gear radius = 4.00 cm
wheel radius = 35.6 cm
efficiency = 95.0%
resistance displacement, d_r = 14.0 cm

Unknowns: **a.** *IMA*
b. *MA*
c. resistance force, F_r
d. effort displacement, d_e

Solution:

a. $$IMA = \frac{d_e}{d_r} = \frac{\text{gear radius}}{\text{wheel radius}} = \frac{4.00\text{ cm}}{35.6\text{ cm}} = 0.112$$

b. Since $$efficiency = \frac{MA}{IMA} \times 100\%$$

$$MA = eff \cdot \frac{IMA}{100\%} = \frac{(95.0\%)(0.112)}{100\%} = 0.107$$

c. $$MA = \frac{F_r}{F_e}$$

$$F_r = (MA)(F_e) = (0.107)(155\text{ N}) = 16.6\text{ N}$$

d. $$IMA = \frac{d_e}{d_r}$$

$$d_e = (IMA)(d_r) = (0.112)(14.0\text{ cm}) = 1.57\text{ cm}$$

CONCEPT DEVELOPMENT

Critical Thinking Master, Teacher Resource Package. Assign the Critical Thinking Master, Bicycle Gears, to provide further investigation into compound machines and work.

Laboratory Manual. Give students additional experience with pulleys by doing Lab 10.1 from the Laboratory Manual.

Laboratory Manual. Give students additional experience with torques by doing Lab. 10.2 from the Laboratory Manual.

TEACHER F.Y.I.

The human powered land speed record is 105.37 km/h (65.48 mph).

CONCEPT DEVELOPMENT

Critical Thinking: Ask students to discuss what part machines (or tools) and their use play in the efforts of anthropologists to understand the early development of human beings.

ACTIVITY

Cooperative Learning: Construct a wall chart of power and efficiencies for various devices. Have students make entries on it throughout the year as they read and hear about various devices.

Guided Practice: Go over the Example Problem on page 209, then have students work on the first Practice Problem on this page.

Independent Practice: Assign the remaining Practice Problems on this page and spend time going over them during the next class period.

3 Close

CONVERGENT QUESTION

In the long history of the human animal, which machine do you think was invented first? Rank the six kinds of machines in order of discovery and defend your choices. Of course, the real ranking will probably never be known.

Answers To
PRACTICE PROBLEMS

Have students refer to Appendix A of the Solutions Appendix for complete solutions to Practice Problems.

13. **a.** 4.0
b. 1.9
c. 48%
14. **a.** 1.74
b. 87%
15. 0.81 m
16. The MA, wheel force, and chain displacement each double.

CONCEPT REVIEW ANSWERS

2.1 **a.** wheel-and-axle **b.** lever **c.** wedge **d.** lever **e.** wheel-and-axle

Practice Problems

13. A sledge hammer is used to drive a wedge into a log to split it. When the wedge is driven 20 cm into the log, the log is separated a distance of 5.0 cm. A force of 1.9×10^4 N is needed to split the log, and the sledge exerts a force of 9.8×10^3 N.
  a. What is the *IMA* of the wedge?
  b. Find the *MA* of the wedge.
  c. Calculate the efficiency of the wedge as a machine.

14. A worker uses a pulley system to raise a 225-N carton 16.5 m. A force of 129 N is exerted and the rope is pulled 33.0 m.
  a. What is the mechanical advantage of the pulley system?
  b. What is the efficiency of the system?

15. A boy exerts a force of 225 N on a lever to raise a 1.25×10^3-N rock a distance of 0.13 m. If the efficiency of the lever is 88.7%, how far did the boy move his end of the lever?

▶ **16.** If the gear radius is doubled in the example above, while the force exerted on the chain and the distance the wheel rim moves remain the same, what quantities change, and by how much?

BIOLOGY CONNECTION

The Human Walking Machine

Movement of the human body is explained by the same principles of force and work that describe all motion. Simple machines, in the form of levers, give us the ability to walk and run. Lever systems of the body are complex, but each system has four basic parts: 1) a rigid bar (bone), 2) a source of force (muscle contraction), 3) a fulcrum or pivot (movable joints between bones), and 4) a resistance (the weight of the body or an object being lifted or moved), Figure 10–14. Lever systems of the body are not very efficient, and mechanical advantages are low. This is why walking and jogging require energy (burn calories) and help individuals lose weight.

When a person walks, the hip acts as a fulcrum and moves through the arc of a circle centered on the foot. The center of mass of the body moves as a resistance around the fulcrum in the same arc. The length of the radius of the circle is the length of the lever formed by the bones of the leg. Athletes in walking races increase their velocity by swinging their hips upward to increase this radius.

A tall person has a lever with a lower *MA* than a short person. Although tall people can usually walk faster than short people, a tall person must apply a greater force to move the longer lever formed by the leg bones. Walking races are usually 20 or 50 km long. Because of the inefficiency of their lever systems and the length of a walking race, very tall people rarely have the stamina to win.

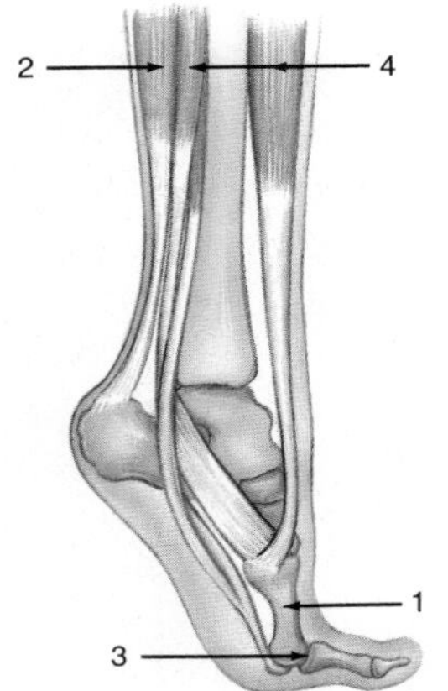

FIGURE 10–14. The human walking machine.

CONCEPT REVIEW

2.1 Many hand tools are simple machines. Classify the tools below as levers, wheel-and-axles, inclined planes, wedges, or pulleys.
  a. screwdriver, **b.** pliers, **c.** chisel, **d.** nail puller, **e.** wrench

Connect to BIOLOGY

The professional football/baseball player, Bo Jackson, underwent hip replacement surgery. His hip joint was injured while playing football. An artificial joint was installed, and he was soon able to walk. Against the advice of his doctors, he resumed playing baseball in 1993. The doctors argued that the artificial joint was designed for the stresses that occur during walking. It was unlikely, they said, that the joint could long survive the increased stresses caused by running and the quick stops and starts of a baseball player. After a short time, they said, the hip might be damaged in such a way that the joint could never be repaired.

How would you balance a short time of active participation in a high-paying, high-risk job against a possibility that you would have a lifetime of limited mobility? Should the government support research and development of medical devices for this use? [There are no correct or wrong answers.]

Physics and technology

ARTIFICIAL JOINTS

Great progress has been made in designing and substituting artificial joints for damaged or missing joints. Because of the tremendous stresses in the bones and joints of the arms and legs, the materials from which artificial parts are made and the means of attachment must be extremely strong.

Titanium is a common material used to make artificial joints. However, lightweight plastics and materials similar to bone are being developed and tested for strength.

Permanent attachment of artificial joints is usually done by using special cement, by biologic fixation, or with "press-fit" systems. In biologic fixation, a porous material is used that allows bone growth into the artificial part. "Press-fit" bones are made so precisely that they snap into place around natural bones. Whatever method is used, the artificial joint must be able to withstand fairly normal stress loads.

The hip and elbow joints are the most stressed areas. The ball and socket joint in the hip carries most of the body weight and is essential for walking. Though the elbow is not a weight-bearing joint, it is the fulcrum of the forearm lever and must endure significant stress. For example, holding a 10-N weight in the palm of the hand with the elbow at 90° places a force of about 90 N on the elbow.

· What is another major consideration in the design and use of artificial limb and joint materials?

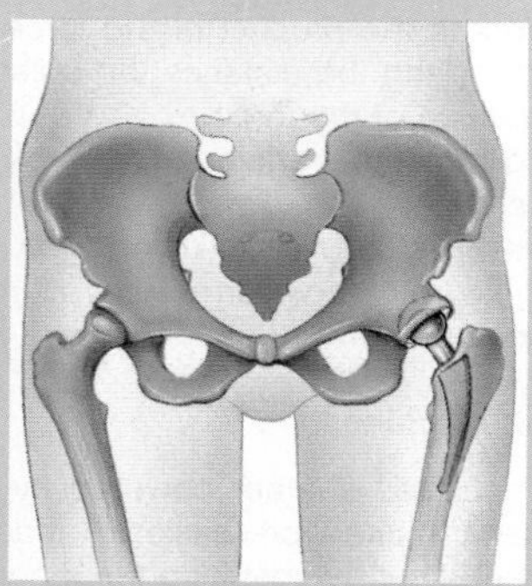

2.2 If you increase the efficiency of a simple machine, does the
  a. *MA* increase, decrease, or remain the same?
  b. *IMA* increase, decrease, or remain the same?

2.3 A worker exerts a force of 20 N on a machine with *IMA* = 2.0, moving it 10 cm.
  a. Draw a graph of the force as a function of distance. Shade in the area representing the work done by this force and calculate the amount of work.
  b. On the same graph, draw the force supplied by the machine as a function of resistance distance. Shade in the area representing the work done by the machine. Calculate this work and compare to your answer above.

2.4 **Critical Thinking:** The mechanical advantage of a multi-gear bike is changed by moving the chain so that it moves to the correct back sprocket.
  a. To start out, you must accelerate the bike, so you want to have the bike exert the largest possible force. Do you choose a small or large sprocket?
  b. As you reach your traveling speed, you want to rotate the pedals as few times as possible. Do you choose a small or large sprocket?
  c. Many bikes also let you choose the size of the front sprocket. If you want even more force to accelerate while climbing a hill, would you move to a larger or smaller front sprocket?

2.2 a. increases **b.** remains the same

2.3 $W = (20\ N)(0.10\ m) = 2\ J$

2.4 Critical Thinking: a. large, to make $IMA = v_{sprocket}/v_{wheel}$ **b.** small, since less chain travel, hence fewer pedal revolutions, will be required per wheel revolution **c.** smaller, to increase pedal-front sprocket IMA ($IMA = v_{pedal}/v_{front\ sprocket}$)

Physics and technology

Answer to student question: A major consideration for the design and use of materials for artificial limbs and joints is their biocompatibility. Many systems fail after a while because the body rejects the cement used to interface the artificial and real body parts.

Teacher Resources: Hankers, Jacob S. and Beverly L. Giammara. "Biomaterials and Biomedical Devices." *Science*. November 11, 1988, pages 885–891.
Kluger, Jeffrey. "Rebuilding the Body, Part by Part." *Discover.* November 1988, pages 46–51.
Volz, Robert G. "Recent Strides in Total Joint Replacement." *Drug Therapy*. November 1984, pages 117–126.
Walker, Peter S. "Joints to Spare." *Science*. November 1985, pages 56–57.

INDEPENDENT PRACTICE/EXTENSION

Refer to the Assignment Guide below for additional questions and problems for independent practice.

10:2 ASSIGNMENT GUIDE

	PRACTICE	EXTENSION
CHAPTER REVIEW pp. 212–215		
· Reviewing Concepts	6–7	
· Applying Concepts		7–9
· Problems*	29–31, 33, 34	32, 35–36
APPENDIX B PROBLEMS*		
· Chapter 10 p. 696	13	14, 15

* Complete solutions to all Chapter Review and Appendix problems appear in the Problems and Solutions Manual.

CRITICAL THINKING
Use the Critical Thinking master for Chapter 10 with this section.

LABORATORY MANUAL
Use Lab 10.2 with this section.

LABORATORY MANUAL
Use Lab 10.1 with this section.

CLOSING CHAPTER 10

Review Summary statements and Key Terms with your students.

ASSESSMENT

Vocabulary Review Master, Teacher Resource Package. Use this master to check students' understanding of Key Terms.

Evaluation Masters. Use Parts A and B of the Chapter Evaluation Masters from the Teacher Resource Package to test qualitative chapter objectives. Use Parts C and D to test quantitative chapter objectives.

Answers To
REVIEWING CONCEPTS

1. joules
2. No. The force of gravity is directed toward Earth and is perpendicular to the direction of motion of the satellite.
3. Gravity and upward, normal force only. No work is done because the motion is perpendicular to these forces. There is no force in the direction of motion because the object is sliding at a constant speed.
4. Work is the product of force and the distance an object is moved in the direction of the force. Power is the time rate at which work is done.
5. $W = \frac{J}{s} = \frac{N \cdot m}{s} = \frac{\left(\frac{kg \cdot m}{s^2}\right) \cdot m}{s} = \frac{kg \cdot m^2}{s^3}$
6. No
7. Pedals of a bike transfer force from the rider to the machine through a distance.

Answers To
APPLYING CONCEPTS

1. Each requires the same amount of work because force times distance is the same.
2. You do positive work on the box because the force and motion are in the same direction. Gravity does negative work on the box because the force of gravity is opposite to the direction of motion. The work done by you and by gravity are separate and do not cancel each other.
3. Either ramp: only the vertical distance is important. If Guy used the shorter ramp, he would have to apply more force; the longer ramp would require less force. The work done would be the same.
4. Net work is zero. Carrying the carton upstairs requires positive work; carrying it back down is negative work. The work done in both cases is equal and opposite because the distances are equal and opposite. The student might arrange payments on the basis of the time it takes to carry paper, whether up or down, not on the basis of net work done.

REVIEW MASTER

Use the Vocabulary Review master for Chapter 10 with this section.

EVALUATION MASTER

Use the Chapter Evaluation master for Chapter 10 with this section.

CHAPTER 10 REVIEW

SUMMARY

10.1 Work and Energy

- Work is the product of the force exerted on an object and the distance the object moves in the direction of the force.
- Work is the transfer of energy by mechanical means.
- Power is the rate of doing work. That is, power is the rate at which energy is transferred. It is measured in watts.

10.2 Machines

- Machines, whether powered by engines or humans, make work easier. A machine eases the load either by changing the magnitude or the direction of the force exerted to do work.
- The mechanical advantage, *MA*, is the ratio of resistance force to effort force.
- The ideal mechanical advantage, *IMA*, is the ratio of the displacements. In all real machines, *MA* is less than *IMA*.

KEY TERMS

work	effort force
joule	resistance force
energy	mechanical advantage
power	ideal mechanical advantage
watt	efficiency
machine	compound machine

REVIEWING CONCEPTS

1. In what units is work measured?
2. A satellite orbits Earth in a circular orbit. Does Earth's gravity do any work on the satellite?
3. An object slides at constant speed on a frictionless surface. What forces act on the object? What work is done?
4. Define work and power.
5. What is a watt equivalent to in terms of kg, m, and s?
6. Is it possible to get more work out of a machine than you put in?
7. How are the pedals of a bicycle a simple machine?

APPLYING CONCEPTS

1. Which requires more work, carrying a 420-N knapsack up a 200 m high hill or carrying a 210-N knapsack up a 400 m high hill? Why?
2. You slowly lift a box of books from the floor and put it on a table. Earth's gravity exerts a force, magnitude *mg*, downward, and you exert a force, magnitude *mg*, upward. The two forces have equal magnitude and opposite direction. It appears no work is done, but you know you did work. Explain what work is done.
3. Guy has to get a piano onto a 2.0 m high platform. He can use a 3.0 m long, frictionless ramp or a 4.0 m long, frictionless ramp. Which ramp will Guy use if he wants to do the least amount of work?
4. Grace has an after-school job carrying cartons of new copy paper up a flight of stairs, and then carrying used paper back down the stairs. The mass of the paper does not change. Grace's physics teacher suggests that Grace does no work all day, so she should not be paid. In what sense is the physics teacher correct? What arrangement of payments might Grace make to ensure compensation?

FIGURE 10–15.

5. Grace now carries the copy paper boxes down a level, 15.0 m long hall. Is Grace working now? Explain.
6. Two people of the same mass climb the same flight of stairs. The first person climbs the stairs in 25 s; the second person takes 35 s.
   a. Which person does more work? Explain your answer.
   b. Which person produces more power? Explain your answer.
7. How can one increase the ideal mechanical advantage of a machine?
8. A claw hammer is used to pull a nail from a piece of wood. How can you place your hand on the handle and locate the nail in the claw to make the effort force as small as possible?
9. How could you increase the mechanical advantage of a wedge without changing the ideal mechanical advantage?

PROBLEMS

10.1 Work and Energy

1. Lee pushes horizontally with a 80-N force on a 20-kg mass 10 m across a floor. Calculate the amount of work Lee did.
2. The third floor of a house is 8.0 m above street level. How much work is needed to move a 150-kg refrigerator to the third floor?
3. Stan does 176 J of work lifting himself 0.300 m. What is Stan's mass?
4. ▶ A crane lifts a 2.25×10^3-N bucket containing 1.15 m^3 of soil (density = 2.00×10^3 kg/m^3) to a height of 7.50 m. Calculate the work the crane performs.
5. The graph in Figure 10–16 shows the force needed to stretch a spring. Find the work needed to stretch it from 0.12 m to 0.28 m.

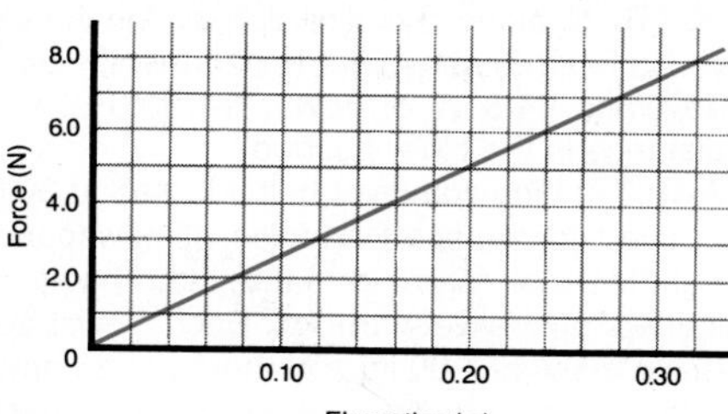

FIGURE 10–16. Use with Problems 5 and 6.

6. ▶ In Figure 10–16, the magnitude of the force necessary to stretch a spring is plotted against the distance the spring is stretched.
   a. Calculate the slope of the graph and show that
   $$F = kd,$$
   where k = 25 N/m.
   b. Find the amount of work done in stretching the spring from 0.00 m to 0.20 m by calculating the area under the curve from 0.00 m to 0.20 m in Figure 10–16.
   c. Show that the answer to part **b** can be calculated using the formula
   $$W = \tfrac{1}{2}kd^2,$$
   where W is the work, k = 25 N/m (the slope of the graph), and d is the distance the spring is stretched (0.20 m).
7. ▶ John pushes a crate across the floor of a factory with a horizontal force. The roughness of the floor changes, and John must exert a force of 20 N for 5 m, then 35 N for 12 m, then 10 N for 8 m.
   a. Draw a graph of force as a function of distance.
   b. Find the work John does pushing the crate.
8. Sally applies a horizontal force of 462 N with a rope to drag a wooden crate across a floor with a constant speed. The rope tied to the crate is pulled at an angle of 56.0°.
   a. How much force is exerted by the rope on the crate?
   b. What work is done by Sally if the crate is moved 24.5 m?
   c. What work is done by the floor through force of friction between the floor and the crate?
9. Mike pulls a sled across level snow with a force of 225 N along a rope that is 35.0° above the horizontal. If the sled moved a distance of 65.3 m, how much work did Mike do?
10. An 845-N sled is pulled a distance of 185 m. The task requires 1.20×10^4 J of work and is done by pulling on a rope with a force of 125 N. At what angle is the rope held?
11. Karen has a mass of 57.0 kg and she rides the up escalator at Woodley Park Station of the Washington D.C. Metro. Karen rode a distance of 65 m, the longest escalator in the free world. How much work did the escalator do on Karen if it has an inclination of 30°?

5. No. The force on the box is up and the displacement is down the hall. They are perpendicular and no work is done.
6. a. Both people are doing the same amount of work because they are both climbing the same flight of stairs.
b. The person who climbs the stairs in 25 seconds expends more power, as less time is needed to cover the distance.
7. Increase the ratio of $\frac{d_e}{d_r}$ to increase the ideal mechanical advantage of a machine.
8. Your hand should be as far from the head as possible to make d_e as large as possible. The nail should be as close to the head as possible to make d_r as small as possible.
9. Reduce friction as much as possible to reduce the resistance force.

Answers To
PROBLEMS

Complete solutions to all Chapter Review Problems can be found in the Problems and Solutions Manual accompanying this text.

1. 8.0×10^2 J
2. 1.2×10^4 J
3. 59.9 kg
4. 1.86×10^5 J
5. 0.80 J
6. Refer to Problems and Solutions Manual.
   a. 25 N/m
   b. 0.50 J
   c. Refer to Problems and Solutions Manual.
7. a. Refer to Problems and Solutions Manual.
   b. 600 J
8. a. 826 N
   b. 1.13×10^4 J
   c. -1.13×10^4 J
9. 1.20×10^4 J
10. 58.7°
11. 1.8×10^4 J

Answers To
PROBLEMS (cont)

12. no work
13. 7.7 J
14. 518 J
15. 7.4×10^3 J
16. a. 800 J
    b. 600 J
17. a. -5.53×10^3 J
    b. no work
    c. 5.53×10^3 J
    d. no
    e. 2.2 kW
18. a. 9.00×10^3 J
    b. 3.00 kW
19. a. 348 W
    b. 696 W
20. Refer to Problems and Solutions Manual.
    a. 2.2×10^2 J
    b. 1.1×10^2 W
21. a. 110 kJ
    b. 3.14 kW
22. a. 949 N
    b. 1.8×10^4 J
    c. 2.3 kW
23. 1.6×10^2 W
24. 54.7 m
25. 3.68×10^2 W

12. Chris carried a carton of milk, weight 10.0 N, along a level hall to the kitchen, a distance of 3.50 m. How much work did Chris do?

13. A student librarian picks up a 22-N book from the floor to a height of 1.25 m. He carries the book 8.0 m to the stacks and places the book on a shelf that is 0.35 m high. How much work does he do on the book?

▶ **14.** Pete slides a crate up a ramp at an angle of 30.0° by exerting a 225-N force parallel to the ramp. The crate moves at constant speed. The coefficient of friction is 0.28. How much work has been done when the crate is raised a vertical distance of 1.15 m?

▶ **15.** A 4200-N piano is to be slid up a 3.5-m frictionless plank that makes an angle of 30.0° with the horizontal. Calculate the work done in sliding the piano up the plank.

▶ **16.** A 60-kg crate is slid up an inclined ramp 2.0 m long onto a platform 1.0 m above floor level. A 400-N force, parallel to the ramp, is needed to slide the crate up the ramp at a constant speed.
   a. How much work is done in sliding the crate up the ramp?
   b. How much work would be done if the crate were simply lifted straight up from the floor to the platform?

17. Brutus, a champion weightlifter, raises 240 kg a distance of 2.35 m.
   a. How much work is done by Brutus lifting the weights?
   b. How much work is done holding the weights above his head?
   c. How much work is done lowering them back to the ground?
   d. Does Brutus do work if the weights are let go and fall back to the ground?
   e. If Brutus completes the lift in 2.5 s, how much power is developed?

18. A force of 300 N is used to push a 145-kg mass 30.0 m horizontally in 3.00 s.
   a. Calculate the work done on the mass.
   b. Calculate the power.

19. Robin pushes a wheelbarrow by exerting a 145-N force horizontally. Robin moves it 60.0 m at a constant speed for 25.0 s.
   a. What power does Robin develop?
   b. If Robin moves the wheelbarrow twice as fast, how much power is developed?

▶ **20.** Use the graph in Figure 10–17.
   a. Calculate the work done to pull the object 7.0 m.
   b. Calculate the power if the work were done in 2.0 s.

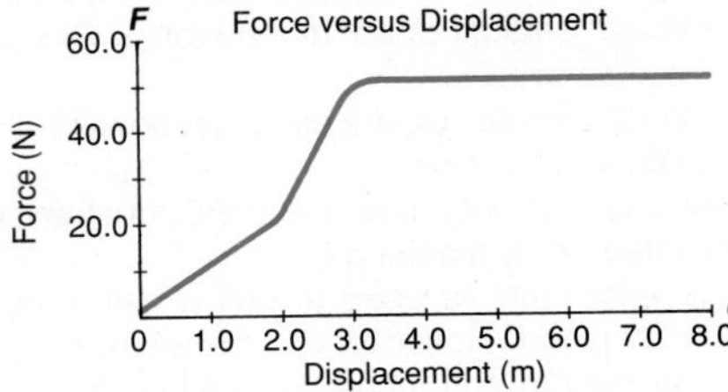

FIGURE 10–17. Use with Problem 20.

▶ **21.** In 35.0 s, a pump delivers 0.550 dm^3 of oil into barrels on a platform 25.0 m above the pump intake pipe. The density of the oil is 0.820 g/cm^3.
   a. Calculate the work done by the pump.
   b. Calculate the power produced by the pump.

22. A horizontal force of 805 N is needed to drag a crate across a horizontal floor with a constant speed. Pete drags the crate using a rope held at an angle of 32°.
   a. What force does Pete exert on the rope?
   b. How much work does Pete do on the crate when moving it 22 m?
   c. If Pete completes the job in 8.0 s, what power is developed?

23. Wayne pulls a 305-N sled along a snowy path using a rope that makes a 45.0° angle with the ground. Wayne pulls with a force of 42.3 N. The sled moves 16 m in 3.0 s. What is Wayne's power?

24. A lawn roller is rolled across a lawn by a force of 115 N along the direction of the handle, which is 22.5° above the horizontal. If George develops 64.6 W of power for 90.0 s, what distance is the roller pushed?

▶ **25.** A 12.0 m long conveyor belt, inclined at 30.0°, is used to transport bundles of newspapers from the mail room up to the cargo bay to be loaded on delivery trucks. Each newspaper has a mass of 1.00 kg and there are 25 newspapers per bundle. Determine the useful power of the conveyor if it delivers 15 bundles per minute.

▶ **26.** An engine moves a boat through the water at a constant speed of 15 m/s. The engine must exert a force of 6.0×10^3 N to balance the force that water exerts against the hull. What power does the engine develop?

▶ **27.** A 188-W motor will lift a load at the rate (speed) of 6.50 cm/s. How great a load can the motor lift at this speed?

28. A car is driven at a constant speed of 21 m/s (76 km/h) down a road. The car's engine delivers 48 kW of power. Calculate the average force of friction that is resisting the motion of the car.

10.2 Machines

29. Stan raises a 1000-N piano a distance of 5.00 m using a set of pulleys. Stan pulls in 20.0 m of rope.
- **a.** How much effort force did Stan apply if this was an ideal machine?
- **b.** What force is used to overcome friction if the actual effort is 300 N?
- **c.** What is the work output?
- **d.** What is the work input?
- **e.** What is the mechanical advantage?

30. A mover's dolly is used to deliver a refrigerator up a ramp into a house. The refrigerator has a mass of 115 kg. The ramp is 2.10 m long and rises 0.850 m. The mover pulls the dolly with a force of 496 N up the ramp. The dolly and ramp constitute a machine.
- **a.** What work does the mover do?
- **b.** What is the work done on the refrigerator by the machine?
- **c.** What is the efficiency of the machine?

31. A pulley system lifts a 1345-N weight a distance of 0.975 m. Paul pulls the rope a distance of 3.90 m, exerting a force of 375 N.
- **a.** What is the ideal mechanical advantage of the system?
- **b.** What is the mechanical advantage?
- **c.** How efficient is the system?

▶ **32.** The ramp in Figure 10–18 is 18 m long and 4.5 m high.
- **a.** What force parallel to the ramp ($F_{\parallel}$) is required to slide a 25-kg box to the top of the ramp if friction is neglected?
- **b.** What is the *IMA* of the ramp?
- **c.** What are the real *MA* and the efficiency of the ramp if a parallel force of 75 N is actually required?

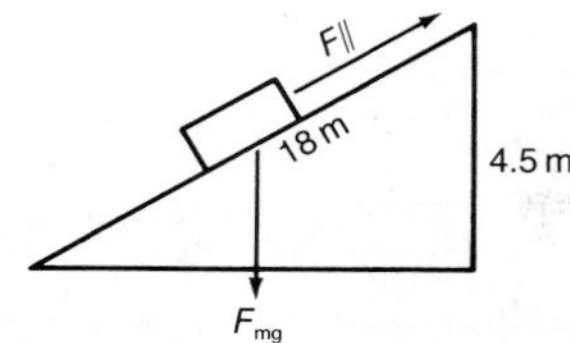

FIGURE 10–18. Use with Problem 32.

33. Because there is very little friction, the lever is an extremely efficient simple machine. Using a 90.0% efficient lever, what input work is required to lift an 18.0-kg mass through a distance of 0.50 m?

34. What work is required to lift a 215-kg mass a distance of 5.65 m using a machine that is 72.5% efficient?

▶ **35.** A motor having an efficiency of 88% operates a crane having an efficiency of 42%. With what constant speed does the crane lift a 410-kg crate of machine parts if the power supplied to the motor is 5.5 kW?

▶ **36.** A complex machine is constructed by attaching the lever to the pulley system. Consider an ideal complex machine consisting of a lever with an *IMA* of 3.0 and a pulley system with an *IMA* of 2.0.
- **a.** Show that the *IMA* of this complex machine is 6.0.
- **b.** If the complex machine is 60.0% efficient, how much effort must be applied to the lever to lift a 540-N box?
- **c.** If you move the effort side of the lever 12.0 cm, how far is the box lifted?

THINKING PHYSIC-LY

A powerful rifle is one that propels a bullet with a high muzzle velocity. Does this use of the word "powerful" agree with the physics definition of power? Support your answers.

26. 90 kW
27. 2.89×10^3 N
28. 2.3×10^3 N
29. **a.** 250 N
b. 50 N
c. 5.00×10^3 J
d. 6.00×10^3 J
e. 4.00
30. **a.** 1.04×10^3 J
b. 958 J
c. 92.1%
31. **a.** 4.00
b. 3.59
c. 89.8%
32. **a.** 61 N
b. 4.0
c. 83%
33. 98 J
34. 1.64×10^4 J
35. 0.50 m/s
36. **a.** 6.0
b. 150 N
c. 2.0 cm

Answer To
THINKING PHYSIC-LY

Yes. The higher the muzzle velocity, the larger the kinetic energy and the greater the power for a given time interval. In this case, the time interval is really smaller because of the higher velocity of the bullet, and the smaller time interval requiring more power.

CHAPTER

11 Energy

PLANNING GUIDE (6 class sessions)

CONTENTS	TEXT FEATURES	TEACHER RESOURCE PACKAGE	OTHER COMPONENTS
11.1 Energy In Its Many Forms, pp. 218–226 (3 Class Sessions) • Forms of Energy • Doing Work to Change Kinetic Energy • Potential Energy	**Physics Lab:** Down the Hill, p. 225 **Pocket Lab:** Energy in Coins, p. 221 **Concept Review,** p. 226	**Study Guide:** Energy In Its Many Forms **Physics Lab Data Sheet:** Down the Hill **Transparency Worksheet:** Energy Transfer	**Transparency 13:** Energy Transfer
11.2 Conservation of Energy, pp. 227–235 (3 Class Sessions) • Systems • Analyzing Collisions	**Physics and Society:** Tidal Energy: Too Costly?, p. 232 **Problem Solving Strategy:** Solving Conservation of Energy Problems, p. 229 **Pocket Lab:** Energy Exchange, p. 233 **Concept Review,** p. 235	**Study Guide:** Conservation of Energy **Enrichment Master:** The Energy of a Projectile **Critical Thinking Master:** Endless Energy? **Reteaching Master:** Toying Around with Energy	**Laboratory Manual:** Lab 11.1 Conservation of Energy
Chapter Review, pp. 236–239	Summary Key Terms Reviewing Concepts Applying Concepts Problems Thinking Physic-ly	**Vocabulary Review** **Chapter Test**	**Test Bank**

SUPPLEMENTARY MATERIALS

SOFTWARE	AUDIOVISUAL	BOOKS/MAGAZINES
Collisions, Queue, Inc. (Apple II). *Conservation Laws,* Cross (Apple II, IBM PC). *Energy Conversions,* Queue, Inc. (Apple II). *Work and Energy,* J&S (Apple II).	Video: *The Mechanical Universe-High School Adaptation, The Conservation of Energy,* Annenberg Project, 1985. *The Forms of Energy,* Focus Media (still frame). Filmstrip: *Matter and Energy,* United Learning.	Crane, H. Richard. "The Foucault Pendulum As a Murder Weapon and a Physicist's Delight." *The Physics Teacher,* May 1990, p. 264. Mammock, Frank M. "If Only Newton Had a Rocket." *The Science Teacher,* April 1988, pp. 42–45. Priest, Joseph, and Potts, Larry. "Computer Analysis of a Physical Pendulum." *The Physics Teacher,* September 1990, p. 413. Roueché, B., and C. "Tin Can Rally." *The Science Teacher*, September 1988, pp. 78-79.

PROBLEM CORRELATION

CONCEPTS	CHAPTER REVIEW			PROBLEMS APPENDIX
	Reviewing Concepts	Applying Concepts	Problems	
11.2 Energy In Its Many Forms				
Forms of Energy	1,2,3			
Doing Work to Change Kinetic Energy	4,5,6	1,2,3,4,5,6	1,2,3,4,**5,6,**7, 8,9,10,**11**	1,2,3,4,**5**
Potential Energy	7,8,9,10,11, 12,13	7,8	12,13,14,15,16, 17,18,**19**	6,7,8,9,**10**
11.2 Conservation of Energy				
Systems	14,15,16,	9,10,11,12,13, 15,16	20,21,22,23,**24,25, 26,**27,28	11,12,**13,14**
Analyzing Collisions	17,18,19	14	29,30,**31,**32,33	**15**

ACTIVITY AND DEMONSTRATION MATERIALS

PHYSICS LAB	POCKET LAB	DEMONSTRATIONS
Page 225 20-N spring scale meter stick stopwatch cart 0.5 to 1.0-m ramp (board, cardboard, and so on) several textbooks	Pages 221, 233 2 quarters ruler a third coin tape goggles 3 steel balls of various masses laboratory cart with spring mechanism meter stick	

EXTENSION PROJECTS

LIBRARY RESEARCH

1. Foot Physics
Investigate the latest designs in athletic shoes. What principles of physics are involved in the construction of the better-quality shoes? Can a shoe return energy? Explain.

DISPLAY MODEL

2. Joule's Apparatus
Build a working model of Joule's apparatus for determining the mechanical equivalent of heat. Explain how it works to the class.

STUDENT READINGS

Ayres, Thomas. "Thermodynamics and Economics." *Physics Today,* November 1984.

Denardo, Bruce, and Masada, Richard. "A Not-So-Obvious Pendulum Experiment." *The Physics Teacher,* January 1990.

Keefer, Robert K. F. "So What Else Can You Do with a Ballistic Pendulum?" *The Physics Teacher,* October 1990.

Scott, David. "Gigantic Dutch Project: Sea Storage for Wind Energy." *Popular Science,* April 1983.

Southworth, Tom. "Potential Energy Analysis of a Bow." *The Physics Teacher,* January 1990.

Chapter 11

Energy

CHAPTER OVERVIEW

Theme Development: Energy is understood within the context of a system, in which energy is a conserved or constant quantity. Both conceptual and mathematical models extend the definition so that students are able to analyze conservation of energy problems.

MISCONCEPTIONS

The dependence of kinetic energy on velocity squared is a troublesome idea for students. Students also are reluctant to use the general and somewhat abstract conservation of energy principle as a quantitative problem-solving tool.

KEY TERMS

elastic collision
inelastic collision
kinetic energy
law of conservation of energy
mechanical energy
potential energy
reference level
work-energy theorem

Laboratory Options

STUDENT EDITION
Physics Lab
Down the Hill 225
Pocket Labs
Energy in Coins 221
Energy Exchange 233

TEACHER EDITION
Activities
Discovery 220
Cooperative Learning 223

LABORATORY MANUAL
Conservation of Energy 233

CHAPTER

11 Energy

◀ Who-o-o-o-sh

Must the first hill of the roller coaster be the highest one?

Chapter Outline

In everyday speech, we use the term "energy" in many ways. A child who runs and plays long after adults are tired is said to be full of energy. We call the depletion of our oil and natural gas resources an "energy crisis."

In this chapter, you will investigate various forms of energy and ways of converting energy from one form to another.

✓ Concept Check

The following terms or concepts from earlier chapters are important for a good understanding of this chapter. If you are not familiar with them, you should review them before studying this chapter.
- Newton's laws of motion, Chapter 5
- conservation of momentum, Chapter 9
- work and energy, Chapter 10

Introducing The Chapter

Who-o-o-o-sh

Using The Photo: Changes of energy from one form to another occur continually all around us. One of the more dramatic examples is on amusement park rides such as the roller coaster in the photograph.

To answer the chapter opener question, students will find the information they need on page 228.

✓ Concept Check

Make sure students have a clear understanding of the concepts taught in Chapters 5, 9, and 10 that are listed in the Concept Check. Students with a good grasp of the principles of work and energy, conservation of momentum, and Newton's laws of motion will more easily understand the concept of energy presented in this chapter.

Assessment

Portfolio

Include reports from laboratory exercises that involve conservation of energy.

Assessment Options

Portfolio Assessment
Portfolio Assessment, TWE, p. 217
Portfolio Assessment, TWE, p. 219
Convergent Question, TWE, p. 226
Physics and Society, Developing a Viewpoint, p. 232
Convergent Question, TWE, p. 235

Performance Assessment
Pocket Labs, pp. 221, 233
Physics Lab, p. 225
Pocket Lab Assessment, TWE, p. 221

Content Assessment
Self Assessment: Practice Problems, pp. 221, 224, 230, 234
Assessment, Critical Thinking, TWE, p. 225
Extension, TWE, p. 226
Concept Reviews, pp. 226, 235
Chapter Review, pp. 236–239
Supplemental Problems, pp. 696–697

Group Assessment
Activities for group assessment occur with Cooperative Learning and Lab Activities.

11.1 ENERGY IN ITS MANY FORMS

Preparation

OBJECTIVES

The objectives are listed on the student page. Remind students to preview these objectives as a study guide to this major section.

OVERVIEW

The concepts of kinetic and potential energy are introduced here.

BRIDGING

The subject matter of this section is closely related to previous topics in mechanics, such as force, work, weight, speed, mass, conservation laws, and Newton's second law. In many ways, it is a synthesis of mechanics topics.

1 Focus

Have a student who pitches for the baseball or softball team come in for a short talk about how he or she increases the speed of the ball. The pitcher may be able to tell the class a bit about curve balls as well as why "roughing up" a ball is considered such a sin by professional batters.

Objectives

- be able to define kinetic and potential energy.
- be able to calculate kinetic energy and apply the work-energy theorem.
- demonstrate an ability to solve problems involving gravitational potential energy.

11.1 ENERGY IN ITS MANY FORMS

In Chapter 10, we defined energy as the ability to change an object or its environment. Change can occur in several ways. A speeding automobile can change itself, people, and objects in its path. The energy that causes the car's motion is normally stored in the chemical bonds of gasoline. Energy is stored in many other forms. A heavy object placed high on a shelf has a potential to change almost anything on which it might fall. A stretched spring or rubber band has the ability to give an object a high velocity.

Forms of Energy

Kinetic energy is energy due to the motion of an object.

Anything moving, from a roller coaster car to a falling leaf, is capable of causing some kind of change in an object it touches. Moving objects have a form of energy called **kinetic energy**.

Potential energy is energy stored in an object because of its state or position.

Where did the roller coaster car get its kinetic energy? The work done by the electric motor was saved or stored by raising the cars to the top of the hill. The cars were said to have **potential energy**. In the roller coaster example, potential energy is stored in the cars as a result of their height, because work was done on the cars against gravity. When they go downhill, the potential energy is changed into kinetic energy.

Figure 11–1 shows another means of storing energy. The photo shows a football just as it is kicked. The kicker's foot has done work compressing the ball. Energy is transferred from the kicker into the ball in the form of potential energy. In an instant, that potential energy will be converted into kinetic energy, and the ball will move with great velocity off the foot and into the air.

Work is the transfer of energy by mechanical means. In the examples above, work was done, transferring energy into potential energy of an object. From where did this energy come? In the case of the place-kicker, the body obtains energy from food and stores it in certain chemical compounds until needed. The compounds can produce motion in

FIGURE 11–1. The work done on the football by the kicker's foot is temporarily stored as potential energy.

TEACHER F.Y.I.

Energy is measured in a number of different units. In the *mks* (meters, kilograms, seconds) system, the unit is the joule. In the *cgs* (centimeters, grams, seconds) system, the unit is the erg. 1 joule = 10^7 ergs. Students may be familiar with the calorie from previous science classes. 1 calorie = 4.184 joules. A food calorie is 1000 calories. In home heating and cooling, energy is measured using the BTU (British Thermal Unit). 1 BTU = 1055 Joules. Later in this text the eV (electron volt) will be introduced. Kilowatt-hours are also used, but an explanation requires the student to understand the physical definition of *power.*

FIGURE 11–2. There are a great number of energy transfers in this photograph. See how many you can identify.

muscles, transferring their stored energy to kinetic energy. Energy in both food and the body is stored in chemical bonds, and so is called chemical energy. In the case of the roller coaster, the energy came from electricity, which was probably generated by burning coal. Coal and gasoline also store chemical energy, which is released when they burn.

There are many forms of potential energy. No matter what the form, the amount of potential energy depends on the position, shape, or form of an object. Potential energy can be converted into kinetic energy, the energy of motion, Figure 11–2.

Kinetic energy depends on an object's mass and velocity.

Doing Work to Change Kinetic Energy

A pitcher winds up and throws the baseball. During the throw, a force is exerted on the ball. As a result, the ball leaves the pitcher's hand with a high velocity and considerable kinetic energy. How can you find the amount of energy? How is the kinetic energy related to the work done on the ball?

As is shown on page 220, the kinetic energy of an object is given by

$$KE = \tfrac{1}{2}mv^2,$$

where m is the mass of the object and v is its velocity. The kinetic energy is proportional to the mass of the object. Thus a 7.26-kg shot has much more kinetic energy than a 148-g baseball with the same velocity. Kinetic energy is also proportional to the square of the velocity. A car speeding at 30 m/s has four times the kinetic energy of the same car traveling at 15 m/s. Kinetic energy, like any form of energy, is measured in joules.

Imagine you are the pitcher. How can you give the ball more kinetic energy? You can either pitch the ball with greater force or exert that force over a larger distance. In other words, you can do more work on the ball. Newton's second law shows the connection between work and kinetic energy. According to Newton's second law, $F = ma$, an object

FIGURE 11–3. This device is used to determine the horizontal velocity of such objects as a tennis ball or baseball.

2 Teach

CONCEPT DEVELOPMENT

Study Guide Master. To reinforce the concepts in this section, have the students complete the Study Guide Master for Section 11.1 from the Teacher Resource Package.

- Use toys freely to teach concepts of energy. Some students may have their own favorites they want to show.
- Give examples of kinetic energy changing to thermal energy, such as rubbing two sticks together to start a fire or rubbing hands together to warm them.
- Keep reminding students when W means weight and when it means work. Tell them that context and units will usually help them make the distinction.
- Point out that potential energy can be stored in a rubber band or spring, as it is in many toys.

Assessment

Portfolio

Have students gather a collection of toys—some using energy from batteries, some spring energy, and some gravitational energy—that show energy transformations. A particularly good type of toy is the "pop-up," a plastic figure that has a spring suction cup that jumps into the air when it is compressed and stuck down on a flat surface. Have students sketch or photograph each toy and attach a description of the action of the toy and the energy transformations.

CONCEPT DEVELOPMENT

ACTIVITY

Discovery: Students who are drivers or in a Driver's Education class will be interested in determining the stopping distance for a vehicle traveling at various speeds. From a driving manual, you can find this distance for a given vehicle and determine the force needed to stop. Assuming that this is the maximum force the brakes can apply, have students determine the stopping distance at different velocities. Why do conditions such as worn brakes or the car's mass make a difference? What does the phrase "stopping on a dime" mean, and why is it difficult for all but the most experienced drivers? A discussion of reaction time may also prove thought-provoking.

Transparency Package. Use Transparency 13 and accompanying worksheet to quiz students on energy transformations.

F.Y.I.

The matter in one pound of anything, when it is completely converted into energy according to $E_0 = mc^2$, will produce 11 400 million kilowatt-hours of energy.

is accelerated with a constant acceleration if a constant net force is exerted on it. The work done on an object is given by $W = Fd$. Thus the work done is $W = (ma)d$. Assume the object was originally at rest, $v_i = 0$. As it accelerates,

$$v^2 = 2ad, \text{ or } d = \frac{v^2}{2a}, \text{ since a is a constant.}$$

Therefore,
$$\begin{aligned} W &= mad \\ &= ma\left(\frac{v^2}{2a}\right) \\ &= 1/2\, mv^2. \end{aligned}$$

That is, $W = KE$; the work done equals the kinetic energy gained by the ball.

Doing work on an object can increase its kinetic energy.

Not all objects start at rest. They may already have kinetic energy when additional work is done on them. If we define initial kinetic energy, KE_i, and final kinetic energy, KE_f, as the energies the object has before and after the work is done, we can write

$$W_{net} = KE_f - KE_i = \Delta KE.$$

The work-energy theorem states that the change in the kinetic energy of an object is equal to the net work done on it.

That is, the change in the kinetic energy of an object is equal to the net work done on it, Figure 11–4. This equation represents the **work-energy theorem**. It can be stated: *The net work done on an object is equal to its change in kinetic energy*. Note that the work in the work-energy theorem is the work done on an object by a net force. It is the algebraic sum of work done by all forces.

The work-energy theorem indicates that if the net work is positive, the kinetic energy increases. Net work is positive when the net force acts in the same direction as the motion. For example, consider a ball pitched in a baseball game. The net force on the pitched ball is in the same direction as the motion of the ball. The net work is positive and the kinetic energy of the ball increases.

If the net work is negative, the kinetic energy decreases. When the catcher catches the ball, the net force acting on it is in the direction opposite its motion. The kinetic energy decreases to zero as the ball stops in the catcher's mitt. The catcher does negative work on the ball.

The kinetic energy of several common moving objects is shown in Table 11–1.

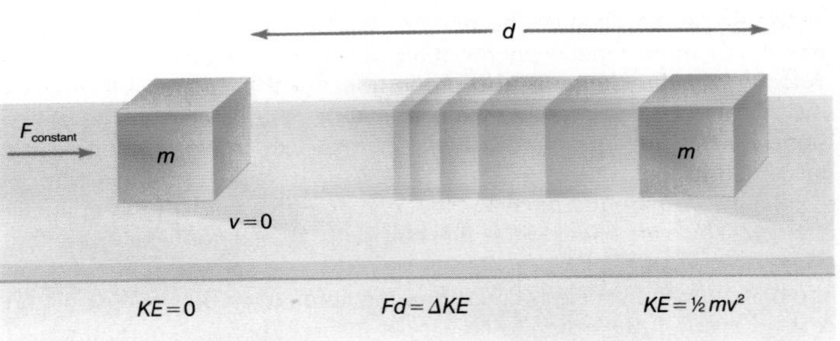

FIGURE 11–4. The increase in kinetic energy of an object is equal to the work done on it.

STUDY GUIDE MASTER

Use the Study Guide master for section 11.1.

TRANSPARENCY

Use Transparency 13 with this section.

Table 11-1

Typical Kinetic Energies		
Item	Remarks	Kinetic Energy (J)
Aircraft carrier	91 400 tons at 30 knots	9.9×10^9
Orbiting satellite	100 kg at 7.8 km/s	3.0×10^9
Trailer truck	5700 kg at 100 km/h	2.2×10^6
Compact car	750 kg at 100 km/h	2.9×10^5
Football linebacker	110 kg at 9.0 m/s	4.5×10^3
Pitched baseball	148 g at 45 m/s	1.5×10^2
Falling nickel	5 g from 50-m height	2.5
Bumblebee	2 g at 2 m/s	4×10^{-3}
Snail	5 g at 0.05 km/h	4.5×10^{-7}

Example Problem

Kinetic Energy and Work

A shotputter heaves a 7.26-kg shot with a final velocity of 7.50 m/s. **a.** What is the kinetic energy of the shot? **b.** The shot was initially at rest. How much work was done on it to give it this kinetic energy?

Given: $m = 7.26$ kg
$v_i = 0$ m/s
$v_f = 7.50$ m/s

Unknowns: a. kinetic energy, KE
b. work, W

Basic equations: a. $KE = ½mv^2$
b. $W = \Delta KE$

Solution: a. $KE = 1/2\ mv^2 = 1/2(7.26\text{ kg})(7.50\text{ m/s})^2$
$= 204\text{ kg}\cdot\text{m}^2/\text{s}^2$
$KE = 204$ J

b. Work done is equal to change in kinetic energy.
$W = \Delta KE = KE_f - KE_i$
$= 204\text{ J} - 0\text{ J}$
$W = 204$ J

Practice Problems

1. **a.** Using the data in Table 11–1, calculate the kinetic energy of a compact car moving at 50 km/h.
   b. How much work must be done on the car to slow it from 100 km/h to 50 km/h?
   c. How much work must be done on the car to bring it to rest?
   d. The force that does the work slowing the car is constant. Find the ratio of the distance needed to slow the car from 100 km/h to 50 km/h to the distance needed to slow it from 50 km/h to rest. State your conclusion in a sentence.

POCKET LAB

ENERGY IN COINS

A large car and a compact car are going the same speed when they start to slide on an ice-covered road. The wheels on both cars are locked (they aren't turning). Which car travels farther before stopping? Explain. A short activity will aid in answering the question. Lay a ruler on a smooth table. Place two quarters against the edge of the ruler. Momentarily push the two quarters at the same speed across the table and then stop the ruler. Choose two quarters that slide the same distance before stopping. Now tape another coin on top of one quarter to increase its mass. Again push the coins with the ruler. Does the stopping distance depend upon the mass? Explain why?

The total energy of an object is the sum of its potential and kinetic energies.

F.Y.I.

Try bending a paper clip back and forth rapidly. Then quickly put the clip against your forehead. You will notice the clip is warm. This energy came from the work you did bending the clip.

POCKET LAB

ENERGY IN COINS

Purpose: to determine if heavier objects require a greater stopping distance.

Materials: 2 quarters; ruler; a third coin; tape.

Outcome: The coins will take about the same distance to stop. The heavier coin has more kinetic energy, but because the normal force between the coin and the table is larger, the frictional force is larger. Therefore, more work is done for the same distance traveled. The same is true in the case of the cars. The heavier car has more kinetic energy, but the frictional force between its tires and the ice is also larger, so more work is done in the same distance. The coins will take about the same distance to stop. The heavier coin has more energy, but the force on it (friction) is proportionally greater.

Answers To
PRACTICE PROBLEMS

Have students refer to Appendix A of the Solutions Appendix for complete solutions to Practice Problems.

1. Student answers may vary depending on rounding.
   a. 7.4×10^4 J
   b. -2.20×10^5 J
   c. -7.4×10^4 J
   d. It takes 3 times the distance to slow the car to half its speed than it does to slow it to a complete stop.

To further assess your students' understanding of energy, ask them if the results of the Pocket Lab depend on the surface of the table. Have them try covering the table with a piece of either rough or smooth paper. Make sure that both coins slide on the paper. You might also have them try using smooth metal disks rather than coins. Ask if the heavier and lighter objects will stop in the same distance. [As long as the frictional force depends only on the normal force between the two surfaces, the two objects will continue to stop in approximately the same distance.]

Answers To
PRACTICE PROBLEMS (cont)

2. a. 1.96×10^3 J
   b. 1.96×10^3 J
   c. 2.6×10^3 N
   d. -1.3×10^5 N, direction opposite its motion
3. a. 2.5×10^{20} J
   b. The work is that of 60 000 100-megaton bombs.
4. a. 71 km/h
   b. 140 km/h

2. A rifle can shoot a 4.20-g bullet at a speed of 965 m/s.
   a. Find the kinetic energy of the bullet.
   b. What work is done on the bullet if it starts from rest?
   c. If the work is done over a distance of 0.75 m, what is the average force on the bullet?
   d. If the bullet comes to rest by pushing 1.5 cm into metal, what is the magnitude and direction of the average force it exerts?
3. A comet with mass 7.85×10^{11} kg strikes Earth at a speed, relative to Earth, of 25 km/s.
   a. Find the kinetic energy of the comet in joules.
   b. Compare the work done on Earth with the energy released in exploding the largest nuclear weapon ever built, equivalent to 100 million tons of TNT, or 4.2×10^{15} J of energy. Such a comet collision has been suggested as having caused the extinction of the dinosaurs.
4. ▶ Table 11–1 shows that 2.2×10^6 J of work are needed to accelerate a 5700-kg trailer truck to 100 km/h.
   a. How fast would it go if just 1/2 as much work were done on it?
   b. What if twice as much work was done?

FIGURE 11–5. Kinetic and potential energy are constantly being interchanged in a juggling act.

Potential Energy

If you throw a ball up into the air, Figure 11–5, you do work on it. As it leaves your hand, it has kinetic energy. As the ball rises, its speed is reduced because of the downward force of Earth's gravity. The ball moves up, but the force is down, so the work done on the ball is negative, and the kinetic energy of the ball becomes smaller. At the top of its flight, its speed is instantaneously zero and it has no kinetic energy. By the time it returns to your hand, however, gravity has done an equal amount of positive work, and the ball has regained its original speed. Thus its kinetic energy is the same as it was when it left your hand.

The kinetic energy you give the ball is transferred to potential energy and then back into kinetic energy. It makes sense, then, to describe the total energy, E, as the sum of the kinetic energy and potential energy.

$$E = KE + PE$$

During the flight of the ball, the sum of kinetic and potential energy is constant. At the start and end of the flight, the energy is totally kinetic. Potential energy is zero. At the top, the energy is fully potential, and the kinetic energy is zero. In between, the energy is partially kinetic and partially potential.

How does potential energy depend on height? As long as the ball is close to Earth, the gravitational acceleration, g, is constant, where $g = 9.80\ \text{m/s}^2$. Using the equation for motion with constant acceleration, we find the velocity of the ball at any height, v_f, is given by

$$v_f^2 = v_i^2 + 2gh.$$

TEACHER 

One way to find the speed of a bullet is to use a ballistic pendulum. The calculation requires the use of both conservation of momentum and energy. Assume that a 15-g bullet is shot into a 3.000-kg block of wood hanging at the end of a string. The block of wood with the bullet in it rises a height of 17 cm. First use conservation of energy to find the velocity of the block and bullet just after the bullet hits, and then use conservation of momentum to find the original velocity of the bullet.

Conservation of Energy

$$PE_{top} = KE_{bottom} \qquad mgh = \frac{1}{2}mv'^2$$

$$v' = \sqrt{2gh} = \sqrt{2(9.8\ \text{m/s}^2)(.17\ \text{m})}$$

$v' = 1.8$ m/s for bullet and block

Conservation of Momentum

$$m_A v_A + m_B v_B = (m_A + m_B)v'$$

$$0.015\ \text{kg}\ (v_A) + 0 = (3.015\ \text{kg})(1.8\ \text{m/s})$$

$v_A = 362$ m/s for bullet

In this equation, h is the vertical distance measured from the launching height of the ball. Multiplying each term in this equation by $\frac{1}{2}m$ gives the kinetic energy, $\frac{1}{2}mv_f^2$, at any height, h,

$$\frac{1}{2}mv_f^2 = \frac{1}{2}mv_i^2 + mgh.$$

At the start of the flight, $h = 0$. The energy is all kinetic, $E = \frac{1}{2}mv_i^2$. Because the total energy of the ball does not change,

$$E = \frac{1}{2}mv_i^2$$
$$= \frac{1}{2}mv_f^2 + mgh.$$

But $E = KE + PE$, so the gravitational potential energy is given by

$$\boxed{PE = mgh.}$$

Gravitational potential energy depends on an object's position above Earth's surface.

Only changes in energy can be measured.

Only changes in potential energy can be measured; thus the total amount of energy cannot be determined. This means that gravitational potential energy can be set equal to zero at any height you choose. Often potential energy is conveniently measured from the surface of Earth or from the floor of a room. That is, h is set equal to zero at the ground or floor level. In fact, any height, called the **reference level**, can be used. It is important, however, that the reference level not be changed in the middle of a problem.

The formula for gravitational potential energy, $PE = mgh$, is valid only if the gravitational force, and thus the acceleration, is constant. When the distance is far above Earth, the gravitational force, mg, is reduced, and the potential energy no longer increases linearly with the height.

Energy can be stored by bending, stretching, or deforming an object.

Energy also can be stored in the bending or stretching of an object. The stretching, squeezing, or bending of objects such as metal springs, slingshots, and trampolines stores potential energy. The modern fiberglass pole used in the pole vault has led to greatly increased records in

a

b

FIGURE 11–6. The kinetic energy of a pole vaulter is first stored in the bending of the pole (a). As the pole straightens, it is converted into gravitational potential energy as the vaulter is lifted above the ground (b).

TEACHER F.Y.I.

James Prescott Joule (1819–1889) suspected that energy could be conserved. Through experimental research, he determined the mechanical equivalent of heat. He submerged a paddle into a wooden bucket filled with water at a given temperature. He then attached a known mass to a thin rope and tied it to the handle so that the paddle would turn in the water as the mass fell. Repetitive release of the mass produced a change in the temperature of the water. His work indicated that 41 800 000 ergs of energy equals one calorie of heat. The joule is named in his honor.

CONCEPT DEVELOPMENT

Ask students where chemical energy goes when batteries are drained in a device such as a toy.

Guided Practice: After going over the Example Problem on this page, have students try the first Practice Problem.

Independent Practice: Assign the remaining Practice Problems on this page for homework and spend time reviewing them during your next class period.

Answers To
PRACTICE PROBLEMS

Have students refer to Appendix A of the Solutions Appendix for complete solutions to Practice Problems.

5. at edge, $+4.0 \times 10^4$ J
at bottom, -3.5×10^4 J

6. a. 1.96×10^5 J
b. -9.80×10^4 J

7. a. 3200 J
b. 3200 J
c. directly from the work done by the person; indirectly from the chemical energy stored in the person's body

8. a. 52 J
b. the height of the ball when the rope was vertical

competition. The pole vaulter runs with the pole, then plants the end of it into a socket in the ground. The kinetic energy of the runner is first stored in the bending of the pole. Then, as the pole straightens, the stored energy is converted into gravitational potential energy and kinetic energy as the vaulter is lifted up to 6 m above the ground.

Example Problem

Gravitational Potential Energy

A 2.00-kg textbook is lifted from the floor to a shelf 2.10 m above the floor. **a.** What is its gravitational potential energy relative to the floor? **b.** What is its gravitational potential energy relative to the head of a 1.65 m tall person?

Given: $m = 2.00$ kg
change in heights
a. $h = 2.10\text{ m} - 0\text{ m} = 2.10\text{ m}$
b. $h = 2.10\text{ m} - 1.65\text{ m} = 0.45\text{ m}$

Unknown: potential energy, PE
Basic equation: $PE = mgh$

Solution:
a. $PE = mgh = (2.00\text{ kg})(9.80\text{ m/s}^2)(2.10\text{ m}) = 41.2\text{ J}$
b. $PE = mgh = (2.00\text{ kg})(9.80\text{ m/s}^2)(0.45\text{ m}) = 8.8\text{ J}$

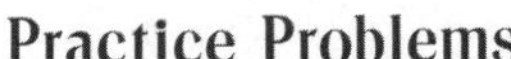

Practice Problems

5. A 90-kg rock climber first climbs 45 m upward to the top edge of a quarry, then, from the top, descends 85 m to the bottom. Find the potential energy of the climber at the edge and at the bottom, using the initial height as the reference level.
6. A 50.0-kg shell is shot from a cannon at Earth's surface to a height of 4.00×10^2 m.
   a. What is the gravitational potential energy with respect to Earth's surface of the Earth-shell system when the shell is at this height?
   b. What is the change in potential energy of the system when the shell falls to a height of 2.00×10^2 m?
7. A person weighing 630 N climbs up a ladder to a height of 5.0 m.
   a. What work does the person do?
   b. What is the increase in the gravitational potential energy of the person from the ground to this height?
   c. Where does the energy come from to cause this increase in the gravitational potential energy?
8. ▶ A pendulum is constructed from a 7.26-kg bowling ball hanging on a 2.5-m long rope. The ball is pulled back until the rope makes a 45° angle with the vertical.
   a. What is the potential energy of the ball?
   b. What reference level did you use in your calculation?

FIGURE 11–7.

Multicultural Connections

Benjamin Banneker was an African American inventor who lived from 1731 to 1806. His abilities in mathematics and surveying prompted George Washington to appoint him to the commission that laid out Washington, D.C. Another of his accomplishments was to construct a clock made entirely of carved wood. He powered his clock using the potential energy of weights. The weights were attached to ropes that turned a series of gears that eventually moved the hands of the clock. By pulling the weights up, potential energy was stored. As the weights lowered, the potential energy was transformed into the kinetic energy of the gears. The hammer which struck the chimes at 6 and 12 o'clock was driven by a separate set of weights.

PHYSICS LAB: Down the Hill

Purpose

To compare the starting potential energy of a cart on top of a ramp to the kinetic energy of the cart as it rolls along the floor.

Materials

- 20-N spring scale
- meter stick
- stopwatch
- cart
- 0.5-m to 1.0-m ramp (board, cardboard, and so on)
- several textbooks

Procedure

1. Make a sketch of the cart on the ramp.
2. Describe the measurements that are needed to determine the starting potential energy of the cart.
3. Make those measurements for your set-up and show your data and a calculation.
4. Describe the measurements that would allow you to calculate the kinetic energy as the cart rolls along the floor.
5. Make the measurements on the moving cart. Show your data for several trials and show a calculation.

Observations and Data

1. Observe the moving cart and write a sentence describing the motion of the cart on the ramp.
2. Write a sentence describing the motion of the cart along the floor.

Analysis

1. Compare the starting potential energy to the kinetic energy at the bottom of the hill. Should the values be equal? Explain any differences.
2. Could the starting potential energy be less than the measured kinetic energy? Explain.
3. Does the angle of the ramp affect the potential energy? Explain your reasoning.

Applications

1. The soap box derby is a race between two carts as they roll down a hill. Does the weight of the cart make much difference?

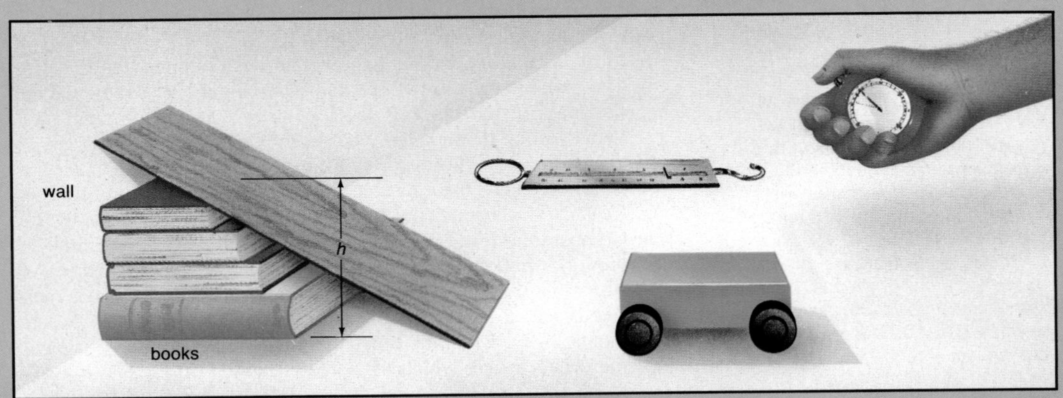

PHYSICS LAB

Process Skills: using numbers, observing, communicating, measuring, questioning, defining operations, predicting.

MISCONCEPTIONS

Many students have difficulty understanding the change of potential energy to kinetic energy. Many will have trouble remembering that *KE* depends on speed squared.

TEACHER NOTES

1. To determine the *PE,* students will need to measure the mass and the starting height of the cart.
2. A typical calculation for *PE:* $PE = mgh = (0.96\text{ kg})(9.8\text{ m/s})(0.21\text{ m}) = 2.0\text{ J}$.
3. To calculate the *KE,* students must determine the speed of the cart. Students should measure the time needed for the cart to travel a short distance from the bottom of the ramp.
4. A typical calculation of *KE:* $KE = 1/2\ mv^2 = 1/2(0.96\text{ kg})(1.8\text{ m/s})^2 = 1.6\text{ J}$.

OBSERVATIONS

1. The cart accelerates on the ramp.
2. The cart moves at a steady (almost) speed on the floor.

ANALYSIS

1. The starting *PE* should be larger than the *KE* by 20% to 30%. Some of the energy will go into friction and rotational energy of the wheels.
2. The starting *PE* should not be less than the measured *KE* at the bottom. The possible reasons for this happening are errors in measured values, errors in calculations, and giving the cart a push.
3. As long as the starting height is measured accurately, the angle is not too important. If the angle is too steep, the cart will "hit" the floor, losing energy and speed.

APPLICATIONS

Soap box cars are built to be close to their maximum allowed weight. A heavier car will have a slight advantage because the effect of air resistance will be slightly less. The winner of the soap box derby is the car with the lowest friction.

ASSESSMENT

Critical Thinking: To further assess your students' understanding of mechanical energy exchange, ask the following questions.

1. Exactly which part of the cart should be measured to determine the starting height of the cart? [Measure halfway between where the two sets of wheels start on the ramp. By holding the cart on the ramp, you can show that when the front wheel touches the floor, most of the cart is still higher than it will be on the floor. The cart still has some potential energy.]

2. When measuring the speed of the cart at the bottom of the ramp, should you use a short distance such as 0.5 m or a larger distance such as 2.5 m? Explain. [If the distance is very short (0.5 m), then it will be very difficult to measure the time accurately. If the distance is large (2.5 m), then the cart will be slowing down and the average speed will be much less than the speed at the bottom of the ramp.]

CONCEPT DEVELOPMENT

You can introduce students to energy calculations by referring them to Table 11–1 on page 221, which gives typical values for kinetic energy in terms of joules.

CHECKING FOR UNDERSTANDING

Ask students to identify forms of energy. Have each of them give an example of one type of energy transformed into another.

RETEACHING

Reteaching Master. Use Teacher Resource Package. Use the Reteaching Master for Chapter 11, Toying Around with Energy, with this section.

EXTENSION

Have students compute other entries for Table 11–1 on page 221. For example, a thundering dinosaur, a bowling ball, a speeding bullet, etc.

Enrichment Master. With this section, use the Enrichment Master, The Energy of a Projectile, from the Teacher Resource Package.

INDEPENDENT PRACTICE/ EXTENSION

Refer to the Assignment Guide on the next page for additional questions and problems for independent practice.

3 Close

CONVERGENT QUESTION

Ask students to give examples from news or their own experiences in which the concept of energy extends to most areas of life. Ask them what is meant by an energy crisis or shortage, given that energy is always conserved according to the law of conservation.

FIGURE 11–8. The potential energy of the water above the wheel is converted to kinetic energy as the water falls.

CONCEPT REVIEW

1.1 Describe the work done and the energy changes taking place when
- **a.** you climb a rope.
- **b.** you throw a ball horizontally.
- **c.** a horizontally thrown ball is caught in a mitt.
- **d.** a horizontally thrown ball falls, gaining vertical velocity.

1.2 A student is doing a problem involving a ball falling down a well. If the top of the well is chosen as the reference level for potential energy, then what is the sign of the potential energy at the bottom of the well?

1.3 Describe the work done and energy changes taking place when, using a toy dart gun,
- **a.** you push the dart into the gun barrel, squeezing a spring.
- **b.** after you pull the trigger, the spring expands and the dart leaves the gun.
- **c.** the dart sticks on a wall.

1.4 In an experiment, a student uses an air hose to exert a constant horizontal force on a block on a frictionless table. The student is told to keep the air aimed at the block during the time the block moves a fixed distance.
- **a.** In terms of work and energy, explain what happens.
- **b.** The experiment is now repeated. Everything is the same except the mass of the block is less. What results will be the same? What will be different? in what way?

1.5 **Critical Thinking:** The experiment above is modified slightly. The student now exerts the constant force for a fixed amount of time.
- **a.** Explain what happens in terms of impulse and momentum.
- **b.** Compare the results of the new experiment on the two blocks.
- **c.** How do the kinetic energies of the blocks compare? (**Hint:** Assume that during the time the force is exerted on the more massive block, it moves the distance used in the first set of experiments. Now, when the times the force is exerted are equal, will the distance over which the force is exerted on the less massive block be larger or smaller?)

F.Y.I.

Some of the most powerful laws of physics are the conservation laws. For example, the gravitational potential energy stored in a block of stone when it was lifted to the top of a pyramid 2500 years ago is still there undiminished. Making allowances for erosion, dropping the stone today could do as much work as when the stone was first put in place.

CONCEPT REVIEW ANSWERS

1.1 a. You do work against gravity, converting it into potential energy. **b.** You do work on the ball and it gains kinetic energy. **c.** The ball loses kinetic energy, doing work on the mitt (or the catcher does negative work on the ball). **d.** Gravity does work on the ball, and the ball gains kinetic energy.

1.2 It is negative.

1.3 a. You do work on the spring, and the spring gains potential energy. **b.** The potential energy of the spring is converted into the kinetic energy of the dart. **c.** The dart does work on the wall, and its kinetic energy is reduced to zero.

1.4 a. Work is done on the block by the force of the air, and the block gains kinetic energy. **b.** The same work is done and the new block gains the same kinetic energy. Because the mass is less, the velocity will be larger.

1.5 Critical Thinking: a. An impulse is given to the blocks and they gain momentum. **b.** The impulse and change in momentum is the same, so the more massive block has a lower velocity. **c.** The less massive block accelerates faster, covering the same distance in less time. Thus the force will be exerted on it over a larger distance. More work will be done, and its kinetic energy will be larger.

11.2 CONSERVATION OF ENERGY

We found the equation for gravitational potential energy by assuming that the total energy of a ball in flight was constant. Although the energy changed from kinetic to potential and back again, the total amount of energy stayed the same. Unlike the conservation of momentum, the constancy of energy is not predicted by Newton's laws. It is a separate fact of nature. The total amount of this thing we call energy does not change.

Objectives

- state the law of conservation of energy.
- demonstrate the ability to solve problems using the law of conservation of energy.
- understand the difference between elastic and inelastic collisions including which quantities are conserved in each kind.

Systems

In your experience, you have probably seen few examples of energy remaining constant. The kinetic energy of a ball rolling on the grass is soon lost. Even on smooth ice, a hockey puck eventually stops. The key to understanding and using the constancy of energy is in selecting the system, the collection of objects we want to study. Just as in the case of conservation of momentum, we need a special kind of a system, a closed, isolated one.

Objects do not enter or leave a closed, isolated system. It is isolated from external forces, and so no work can be done on it. The **law of conservation of energy** states that *within a closed, isolated system, energy can change form, but the total amount of energy is constant.* That is, energy can be neither created nor destroyed.

In a closed, isolated system, the total amount of energy does not change.

A ball alone, acted on by gravity, is not an isolated system. A ball and Earth, however, is an example of a closed, isolated system, Figure 11–9. The kinetic energy of the ball can change, but the sum of gravitational potential and kinetic energy is constant. The sum of potential and kinetic energy is often called the **mechanical energy**. Suppose the ball has a weight of 10.0 N. If it is at rest on a shelf 2.00 m above Earth's surface, it has no kinetic energy, but a potential energy related to Earth's surface given by

$$\begin{aligned} PE &= mgh \\ &= (10.0\ \text{N})(2.00\ \text{m}) = 20.0\ \text{J}. \end{aligned}$$

If the ball rolls from the shelf, there are no forces on the ball other than the gravitational force of Earth, so the ball falls. When it is 1.00 m above Earth's surface, its potential energy is

$$\begin{aligned} PE &= mgh \\ &= (10.0\ \text{N})(1.00\ \text{m}) = 10.0\ \text{J}. \end{aligned}$$

The ball has lost half its potential energy falling 1.00 m. The ball is moving, however, and has gained kinetic energy. The change in kinetic energy can be found from the work-energy theorem:

$$\begin{aligned} W &= \Delta KE \\ &= KE_f - KE_i \\ &= KE_f. \end{aligned}$$

The work done on the falling ball by the gravitational force, mg, is given by

$$\begin{aligned} W &= Fd \\ &= (10.0\ \text{N})(1.00\ \text{m}) = 10.0\ \text{J}. \end{aligned}$$

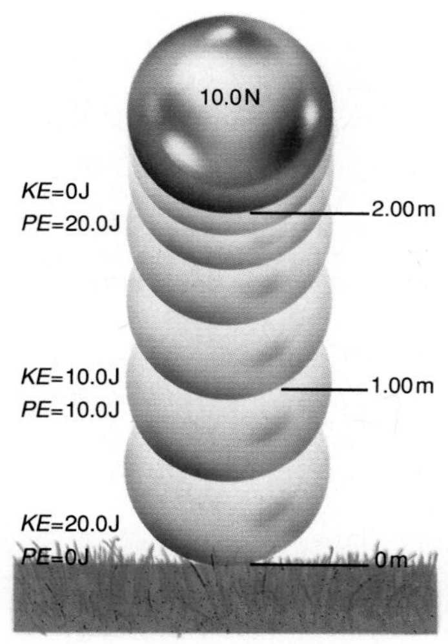

FIGURE 11–9. The decrease in potential energy is equal to the increase in kinetic energy.

11.2 CONSERVATION OF ENERGY

Preparation

OBJECTIVES

The objectives are listed on the student page. Remind students to preview these objectives as a study guide to this major section.

OVERVIEW

New concepts introduced here are conservation of energy and elastic and inelastic collisions.

BRIDGING

Simple harmonic motion, closed systems, equilibrium position, strong nuclear force, and momentum and its conservation are all concepts revisited in this section to help explain energy conservation and collisions.

1 Focus

DISCREPANT EVENT

Get out the swinging balls apparatus that you used in the study of momentum to illustrate how the conservation of momentum *and* conservation of energy limit the possible motions of the ball(s) on the far end. For example, one ball *lifted* at one end could not conserve momentum and simultaneously make another ball fly off at the other end with the same velocity. But the second of these possibilities won't conserve energy as well as momentum. Conservation of energy adds just one more constraint to how things can behave in the world. You can also add a bit of clay between the balls to study collisions that are inelastic.

11:1 ASSIGNMENT GUIDE

	PRACTICE	EXTENSION
CHAPTER REVIEW pp. 236–239		
· Reviewing Concepts	1–13	
· Applying Concepts		1–8
· Problems*	1–4, 7–10, 12–18	5, 6, 11, 19
APPENDIX B PROBLEMS		
· Chapter 11 p. 696	1–4, 6–9	5, 10

* Complete solutions to all Chapter Review and Appendix problems appear in the Problems and Solutions Manual.

RETEACHING MASTER

Use the Reteaching master for Chapter 11 with this section.

ENRICHMENT MASTER

Use the Enrichment master for Chapter 11 with this section.

2 Teach

CONCEPT DEVELOPMENT

Study Guide Master. To reinforce the concepts in this section, have the students complete the Study Guide Master for Section 11.2 from the Teacher Resource Package.

- Remind students that usually when an object slides down a plane its temperature increases due to friction, so final *KE* and velocity are not as high as predicted.
- Explain to students that when we say kinetic energy is lost we mean it is transformed into another form of energy.
- Sometimes students think that energy is not conserved in an inelastic collision. Energy is conserved but some of the kinetic energy is transformed into other forms, such as heat, light, or sound.

Critical Thinking: Ask students what happens to kinetic energy when speed is doubled. [It is quadrupled.]

FIGURE 11–10. Disregarding friction, no matter what downward path the ball follows, the total amount of work it can do will be the same.

The work is positive because the force and motion are in the same direction. Thus the kinetic energy of the ball is

$$KE_f = 10.0 \text{ J}.$$

A decrease in potential energy is accompanied by an increase in kinetic energy.

The decrease in the potential energy of the ball is equal to the increase in its kinetic energy. Thus the sum of potential and kinetic energies is not changed. The mechanical energy is constant. When the ball reaches Earth's surface, its potential energy will be zero. All its energy will be kinetic. The final kinetic energy will equal the initial potential energy. The equation describing the conservation of energy is

$$KE_i + PE_i = KE_f + PE_f.$$

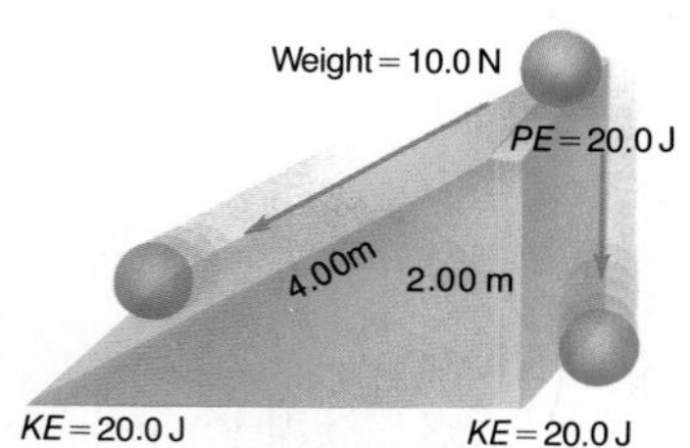

FIGURE 11–11. The path an object follows in reaching the ground does not affect the final kinetic energy.

Changing the path an object follows as it falls does not change its potential energy. As shown in Figure 11–11, the 10.00-N ball might be on a frictionless inclined plane. As it slides down the plane, it moves horizontally as well as vertically, but its change in height above Earth is still 2.00 m. Its potential energy depends only on its height above Earth's surface. The kinetic energy of the ball at the bottom of the plane is the same whether the ball falls vertically or slides down without friction.

Who-o-o-o-sh

Thus, in the case of a roller coaster that is almost at rest at the top of the first hill, if any hill were higher than the first, the potential energy needed to reach the top of that hill would be larger than the mechanical energy stored in the car at the top of the first hill.

The simple harmonic motion of a pendulum also demonstrates the conservation of energy. Usually the gravitational potential energy is chosen to be zero at the equilibrium position of the bob. The initial gravitational potential energy of a raised pendulum bob is transferred to kinetic energy as the bob moves along its path. At the equilibrium point, the gravitational potential energy is at a minimum (zero) and kinetic energy is at a maximum. Figure 11–12 is a graph of the changing potential and kinetic energy of a pendulum bob during one-half period of its oscillation. The sum of potential and kinetic energies is constant.

STUDY GUIDE MASTER

Use the Study Guide master for section 11.2.

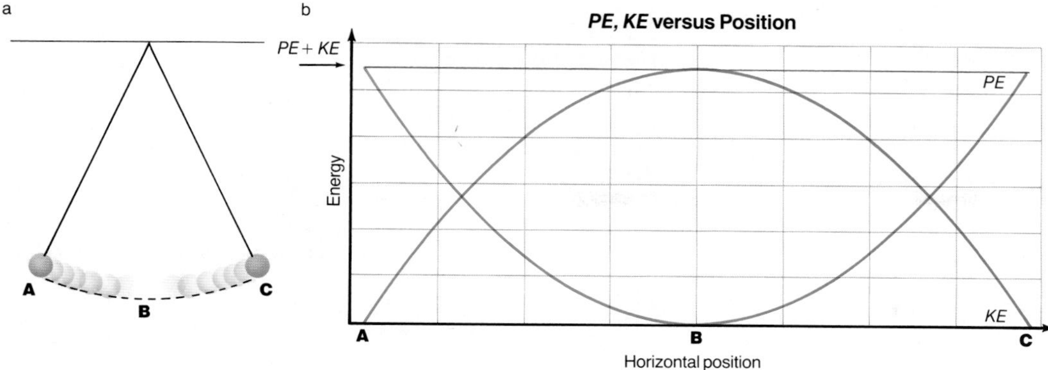

FIGURE 11–12. For the simple harmonic motion of a pendulum bob (a), the sum of the potential and kinetic energies is a constant (b).

As you know, the oscillations of a pendulum bob eventually die away, and a bouncing ball finally comes to rest. Where did the mechanical energy go? Work was done against friction, and in the case of the ball, to change its shape when it bounces. The system was not isolated so its mechanical energy was not conserved.

If total energy is conserved, the potential and kinetic energies must have changed into other forms. When a heavy crate is dropped on the floor, you feel the floor tremble. Some energy has changed into the motion of the floor. If you measure the temperature of the dropped crate or of the stopped pendulum bob very accurately, you will find that they are slightly warmer. The energy has changed into a different form, the increased motion of the particles that make up the object. This form of energy, thermal energy, will be discussed in Chapter 12.

Albert Einstein recognized another form of potential energy, mass itself. This equivalence is expressed in his famous equation $E_0 = mc^2$. Mass, by its very nature, has energy, E_0, called its rest energy. Further, energy has mass. Stretching a spring or bending a bow causes them to gain mass. In these cases, the mass change is too small to be easily detected. When the strong nuclear forces are involved, however, the energy released by changes in mass can be very large indeed.

PROBLEM SOLVING STRATEGY

When solving conservation of energy problems:

1. Carefully identify the system. Make sure it is closed; no objects can leave or enter it. It must also be isolated; no external forces can act on any object in the system. Thus, no work can be done on or by objects outside the system.
2. Is friction present? If it is, then the sum of kinetic and potential energies will not be constant. But, the sum of the kinetic energy, potential energy, and the work done against friction will be constant.
3. Finally, if there is no friction, find the initial and final total energies and set them equal.

HELP WANTED

RECREATIONAL THERAPIST

A big heart is a fine quality to have, but knowledge of a patient's physiological and emotional abilities and limitations, and of the best treatment to meet the needs is also important.

You must be able to relate well to all types of people while maintaining a professional perspective. Thorough knowledge of the arts, athletics, and other activities plus a bachelor's degree (or associate's degree with extensive experience) and appropriate certification are required. For information contact:
National Therapeutic Recreation Society, 3101 Park Center Drive, Alexandria, VA 22302

Enrichment: There are other forms of energy not discussed in this chapter. Discuss with students that sometimes when energy appears to disappear, it is just being changed into a form not familiar to us. Have students investigate other forms of energy such as rotational kinetic energy.

TEACHER F.Y.I.

When an object moves at a speed approaching that of light, the formula $KE = 1/2mv^2$ no longer holds true. The situation is more accurately described by the formula

$$KE = \left(\frac{1}{\sqrt{1 - \frac{v^2}{c^2}}} - 1\right) mc^2.$$

CONCEPT DEVELOPMENT

Check with other local physics teachers to find out if your region has an annual "Physics Day" at a nearby theme park. It's an excellent way for your students to learn about energy, velocity, acceleration, etc., in an interesting, real-world setting.

Answers To
PRACTICE PROBLEMS

Have students refer to Appendix A of the Solutions Appendix for complete solutions to Practice Problems.

9. a. 3.1×10^3 J
b. 3.7 m
c. No, both PE and KE are proportional to mass. The *m*'s cancel.

10. a. 8.9 m/s
b. no
c. no

11. a. 30 m/s
b. 10 m/s

12. a. The system of Earth, bike, and rider remains the same, but now the energy involved is not mechanical energy alone.
b. Energy came from chemical potential energy stored in the rider's body.

Connect to
CHEMISTRY

How does a car reach high speeds? How does a person scale high cliffs? That is, what are the sources of this kinetic or potential energy? In the case of the car, the energy source is gasoline and the oxygen in the air. For the human, it is food and oxygen. In both cases the fuel and the oxygen are chemically combined in a process called combustion or burning. The result of the process is energy and different chemical compounds. One can describe the combustion process as removing some of the energy stored in the bonds between the atoms. Energy stored in bonds is called chemical energy. It is a form of potential energy because the energy depends on the positions of the atoms. What are the transformations of energy when a boy pulls the starting rope in order to start a gasoline-powered lawn mower? [Chemical energy (from food) is changed into kinetic energy of the rope and motion of the piston in the engine. When the engine starts, the chemical energy in the gasoline is now converted into the kinetic energy of the piston and other moving parts of the engine.]

The change in the gravitational potential energy of an object does not depend on the path it takes.

Example Problem

Conservation of Energy

A large chunk of ice with mass 15.0 kg falls from a roof 8.00 m above the ground. **a.** Find the kinetic energy of the ice when it reaches the ground. **b.** What is the speed of the ice when it reaches the ground? **c.** Is the answer the same as you would determine by solving as a constant acceleration problem?

Given: $m = 15.0$ kg, $g = 9.80$ m/s^2, $h = 8.00$ m, $KE_i = 0$, $PE_f = 0$

Unknowns: a. KE_f **b.** v_f

Basic equation: $KE_i + PE_i = KE_f + PE_f$

Solution:

a. $KE_i + PE_i = KE_f + PE_f$

$0 + mgh = KE_f + 0$

$KE_f = mgh = (15.0 \text{ kg})(9.80 \text{ m/s}^2)(8.00 \text{ m}) = 1.18 \times 10^3 \text{ J}$

b. $KE_f = \frac{1}{2}mv_f^2$

$$v_f^2 = 2\frac{KE_f}{m} = \frac{2(1.18 \times 10^3 \text{ J})}{15.0 \text{ kg}} = 157 \text{ m}^2/\text{s}^2$$

$v_f = 12.5$ m/s

c. yes

Practice Problems

9. A bike rider approaches a hill with a speed of 8.5 m/s. The total mass of the bike and rider is 85 kg.
a. Find the kinetic energy of the bike and rider.
b. The rider coasts up the hill. Assuming there is no friction, at what height will the bike come to a stop?
c. Does your answer depend on the mass of the bike and rider? Explain.

10. Tarzan, mass 85 kg, swings down from a tree limb on the end of a 20-m vine. His feet touch the ground 4.0 m below the limb.
a. How fast is Tarzan moving when he reaches the ground?
b. Does your answer depend on Tarzan's mass?
c. Does your answer depend on the length of the vine?

11. A skier starts from rest at the top of a 45-m hill, skis down a 30° incline into a valley, and continues up a 40-m hill. Both hill heights are measured from the valley floor. Assume you can neglect friction and the effect of ski poles.
a. How fast is the skier moving at the bottom of the valley?
b. What is the skier's speed at the top of the next hill?

▶ **12.** Suppose, in the case of Practice Problem 9, the bike rider pedaled up the hill and never came to a stop.
a. How could you define a system in which energy is conserved?
b. From what form of energy did the bike gain kinetic energy?

F.Y.I.

James Prescott Joule was one of the early advocates of the theory of conservation of energy. Because he was a brewer and not a professional scientist, he could not publish his paper in a professional journal. He presented his ideas in a public lecture and in a public newspaper.

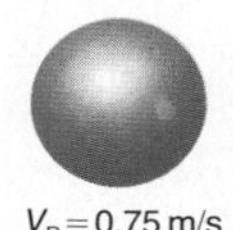

FIGURE 11–13. In an elastic collision between two billiard balls, kinetic energy, as well as momentum, is conserved.

Analyzing Collisions

During a collision between two objects, forces act that slightly change the shape of the colliding bodies. The kinetic energy of motion is changed into potential energy. If the potential energy is completely converted back into kinetic energy after the collision, the collision is called an **elastic collision**. For this special case, the kinetic energy of the bodies before the collision is equal to their kinetic energy after the collision. The collision between two billiard balls or glass marbles is very nearly elastic.

Kinetic energy is conserved in elastic collisions.

What conservation laws can be used to analyze collisions? Momentum is conserved whenever bodies collide with no external forces present. Suppose a red billiard ball of mass m = 95 g moves with a speed v = +0.75 m/s. It collides head-on with a white billiard ball of equal mass that is at rest. The total momentum before the collision is mv = (0.095 kg)(+0.75 m/s) = +0.071 kg · m/s. What are the speeds of the two balls after the collision? Using only the momentum equation, the two speeds cannot be determined—with two unknowns, two equations are needed. If kinetic energy is also conserved, we have a second equation and can solve the two equations simultaneously to find the final speeds. The results show that the moving red ball must come to rest and the white ball must move with the final speed v_f = +0.75 m/s, the initial speed of the red ball.

Momentum is conserved in all collisions that occur in closed, isolated systems.

If, during a collision, some kinetic energy is changed into other forms, the collision is called an **inelastic collision**. In the case of real billiard balls, some energy is usually needed to do work against the surface of the table. The red ball will not stop, and the white ball will have a smaller final speed. If, instead of billiard balls, two balls of soft

CONCEPT DEVELOPMENT

The son of a brewer, James Joule observed heat being released in the brewing process. These early observations led him to eventually develop the conservation of energy principle.

Critical Thinking Master, Teacher Resource Package. You may wish to have students complete the Critical Thinking Master, Endless Energy, with this section.

TEACHER 

The search for a perpetual motion machine has kept inventors occupied for centuries. Theoretically, there are generally three types of perpetual motion machines. The first type of mechanism would have an efficiency exceeding 100%. This violates the first law of thermodynamics (to be covered in Chapter 12). The second type is a device that would extract heat from a source and convert it *completely* into other forms of energy. A dramatic idea put forth was an ocean liner that uses heat from the ocean in propulsion. This is precluded by the second law of thermodynamics. The third type could work if all mechanisms by which energy is dissipated could be eliminated. Superconductors provide a genuine case for the third type. When a current is introduced into a superconductor, the energy loss is zero and it should continue to flow undiminished. But the current can do no work.

Physics and society

Answers To DEVELOPING A VIEWPOINT

1. *Advantages:* Utility companies in the U.S. could postpone construction and thus the cost of building new power-generating facilities. The United States could reduce the pollution caused by burning oil and coal to produce electricity. Because hydropower is the least expensive way to generate electricity, U.S. utility companies would save money. For example, in 1985, New England imported 7.3% of its electricity from Canada at a cost of $254.7 million, resulting in a savings of about $45 million. *Disadvantages:* Construction of transmission lines from Canada through the New England region would cause damage to the environment. If Canada-U.S. relations were to become unfriendly, the supply of U.S. electricity might be cut off.

2, 3. Student answers will vary, depending on their knowledge and bias.

Teacher Resource: Dodson, James. "Fundy's Thundering Tide: Can We Harness Its Power?", *International Wildlife* 14, November/December 1984, pp. 34–39.

Physics and society

Tidal Energy: Too Costly?

The Bay of Fundy is in eastern Canada, on the western side of Nova Scotia. Twice each day the Atlantic Ocean pours into this bay, producing the highest tides in the world, ranging from 12 meters to an extreme of 17 meters. Because of the huge amount of kinetic energy available in these tides,—each tidal flow through the bay could generate the electrical energy output of 250 large nuclear power plants—the Canadian government has studied the possibility of building a dam and a hydroelectric power plant at the entrance to the bay.

Such a dam would obstruct the natural movement of the tides to capture their energy. Every twelve hours, the incoming tide would rush through the open floodgates in the dam and be impounded behind the dam. As the tide recedes, the water would exit through turbines, generating electricity.

A dam would be an attractive prospect for several reasons. It would make huge amounts of electricity available to eastern Canada and to the northeastern part of the United States. At present, New England has little reserve electrical-generating capability. Such a project could save this area some 23 million barrels of oil a year. The construction of a dam would also create jobs and promote general economic development in the area during the ten years required to construct a dam. Finally, hydropower is generally the least expensive way to generate electricity, and it does not create the pollution problems of coal and oil-fired power plants.

Opponents of a dam have pointed out several disadvantages. It has been estimated that the difference between high and low tides in the Gulf of Maine to the south would increase by 10%, raising the high tide level by 10 to 20 cm. This could flood coastal roads and bridges and waterfront homes along the Maine coast. Tidal currents would be altered, resulting in a change of surface water temperature and recreational use of the area. Millions of fish—shad, salmon, and others—could be killed by passage through the turbines. This could affect sport and commercial fishing as far away as Florida. Numerous migrating birds stop to feed in the mudflats of the Bay of Fundy on their way from South America to the Arctic Circle. They would have to find new feeding grounds because the mudflats behind the dam would be flooded.

DEVELOPING A VIEWPOINT

Find and read references concerning the potential positive and negative effects of building a dam to harness tidal energy. Come to class prepared to discuss the following questions.

1. What are some advantages and disadvantages if the United States were to depend on a source of electricity outside its borders?
2. Consider all the factors involved and be prepared to discuss why you would or would not vote for the construction of such a dam.
3. Consider such a project from the viewpoint of a Canadian citizen. Would you be willing to share the electrical power with the United States? Why or why not?

SUGGESTED READINGS

Greenberg, David A. "Modeling Tidal Power." *Scientific American* 257(5), November 1987, pp. 128–131.

Lennox, Frank H. and Donnamarie McCarthy, Mark P. Mills, Ruth Deloli. "Importing Electricity from Canada." *Science Concepts,* Inc. Perspective. U.S. Council for Energy Awareness, Washington, DC, October 1987.

Ross, David. "The Potential of Tidal Power...Still All at Sea." *New Scientist* 126(1717), May 19, 1990, p. 52.

CRITICAL THINKING

Use the Critical Thinking master for Chapter 11 with this section.

clay, each with a mass of 0.095 kg, collide and stick together, the collision is said to be completely inelastic. The two clay balls will have the same final speed. As was shown in Chapter 9, because of conservation of momentum, the final speed is half the initial speed. The momentum of the balls is not changed.

$$2m(v/2) = (0.190 \text{ kg})((0.75 \text{ m/s})/2) = 0.07125 \text{ kg} \cdot \text{m/s}$$

The energy after the collision is

$$\tfrac{1}{2}(2m)(v/2)^2 = \tfrac{1}{2}(0.190 \text{ kg})(0.375 \text{ m/s})^2 = 0.01336 \text{ J}.$$

This result indicates that half the initial kinetic energy has changed into other forms of energy.

Many collisions are neither completely elastic nor completely inelastic. The velocities can then be calculated only if the amount of energy loss is known.

Many collisions are neither completely elastic nor completely inelastic.

Example Problem

Elastic Collision

Block A with mass 12 kg moving at +2.4 m/s makes a perfectly elastic head-on collision with a block B, mass 36 kg, at rest. Find the velocities of the two blocks after the collision. Assume all motion is in one dimension.

Given: before collision,
block A, $m = 12$ kg
$v = +2.4$ m/s
block B, $M = 36$ kg
$V = 0$ m/s

Unknowns: after collision,
block A, v'
block B, V'

Basic equations:
conservation of momentum, $mv + MV = mv' + MV'$
conservation of energy, $\tfrac{1}{2}mv^2 + \tfrac{1}{2}MV^2 = \tfrac{1}{2}mv'^2 + \tfrac{1}{2}MV'^2$

Solution:

Use the fact that $V = 0$ to simplify the basic equations $mv = mv' + MV'$ and $\tfrac{1}{2}mv^2 = \tfrac{1}{2}mv'^2 + \tfrac{1}{2}MV'^2$. Now solve the momentum equation for

$V' = m\left(\dfrac{v - v'}{M}\right)$ and substitute into the energy equation

$$\tfrac{1}{2}mv^2 = \tfrac{1}{2}mv'^2 + \tfrac{1}{2}M\left(\frac{m(v - v')}{M}\right)^2.$$

By solving this quadratic equation for v', we obtain

$$v' = \frac{m - M}{m + M}v \text{ and } V' = \frac{2\,mv}{m + M}$$

In this particular case,

$$v' = \frac{(12 \text{ kg} - 36 \text{ kg})(+2.4 \text{ m/s})}{12 \text{ kg} + 36 \text{ kg}}$$

$= -1.2$ m/s (backward), and

$$V' = \frac{2(12 \text{ kg})(+2.4 \text{ m/s})}{12 \text{ kg} + 36 \text{ kg}} = +1.2 \text{ m/s (forward)}$$

POCKET LAB

ENERGY EXCHANGE

Wear goggles for this activity. Select several different size steel balls and mass them. Stand a spring-loaded laboratory cart on end with the spring mechanism pointing upward. Place a ball on top of the spring mechanism. Press down on the ball to compress the spring until the ball is touching the cart. Quickly release the ball so that the spring shoots it upward. Repeat several times and measure the average height. Predict how high the other sizes of steel balls should go. Try it. Record the values in a data table. Classify the balls in order of height attained.

POCKET LAB

ENERGY EXCHANGE

Purpose: to allow students to investigate mechanical energy transfer.

Materials: goggles; 3 steel balls of various masses; laboratory cart with spring mechanism; meter stick.

Outcome: A sample set of data is:

diameter	mass
small 16 mm	0.028 kg
medium 25 mm	0.066 kg
large 32 mm	0.13 kg

The distance that the medium ball will travel will depend on the individual spring. A typical value is 0.8 m. Students will predict that the small ball will go about twice as high and the large ball will go half as high. Students will find that the small ball does not quite go twice as high and the large ball goes a little more than half as high. Some of the energy goes into moving the spring and the metal rod attached to the spring.

Laboratory Manual. Give students additional experience with the conservation of energy by doing Lab 11.1 from the Laboratory Manual.

LABORATORY MANUAL

Use Lab 11.1 with this section.

CHECKING FOR UNDERSTANDING

Develop a chart of elastic vs. inelastic collisions with the class. Include columns for conservation of energy, momentum, and typical types of material involved.

RETEACHING

Pick a suitable Chapter Review problem and work it out in detail on the board, pointing out all the assumptions that you make to reach your solution. You might use the problem-solving strategy on page 229 as a framework for your discussion.

EXTENSION

Have students refer to a consumer magazine (*Consumer Reports*) or a government publication to find out how so-called EER (Energy Efficiency Rating) numbers are arrived at for appliances. Ask them if this is the same kind of efficiency they learned about in Chapter 10 on machines.

Guided Practice: After going over the Example Problems on pages 233 and 234, have students work on the first Practice Problem on page 234.

Independent Practice: Assign the remaining Practice Problems on page 235 for homework and review them with students during the next class period.

Answers To
PRACTICE PROBLEMS

Have students refer to Appendix A of the Solutions Appendix for complete solutions to Practice Problems.

13. a. 4.27 m/s
b. 289 J
c. 2.30 J
d. 287 J
e. 99.3%

FIGURE 11–14. The conservation of momentum sometimes becomes very obvious on a slippery road.

Example Problem

Energy Loss in a Collision

In an accident due to slippery roads, a compact car, mass 575 kg, moving at +15 m/s, smashes head-on into the rear end of a car with a mass of 1575 kg, originally moving at +5.0 m/s. They lock together and slide forward.

a. What is the final velocity of the wrecked cars?
b. How much kinetic energy was lost in the collision?
c. What fraction of the original energy was lost?
d. Into what forms did this energy most likely go?

Given: $m_A = 575$ kg
$v_A = +15$ m/s
$m_B = 1575$ kg
$v_B = +5.0$ m/s

Unknowns: final velocity, V
lost kinetic energy, $\Delta KE = KE_{final} - KE_{initial}$

Basic equations: conservation of momentum, $m_Av_A + m_Bv_B = (m_A + m_B)V$
kinetic energy, $KE = ½mv^2$

Solution:

a. From conservation of momentum,

$$V = \frac{m_Av_A + m_Bv_B}{m_A + m_B} = \frac{(575\text{ kg})(+15\text{ m/s}) + (1575\text{ kg})(+5.0\text{ m/s})}{575\text{ kg} + 1575\text{ kg}} = +7.7\text{ m/s}$$

b. $$\Delta KE = KE_{final} - KE_{initial} = ½(m_A + m_B)V^2 - ½m_Av_A^2 - ½m_Bv_B^2$$
$$= ½(2150\text{ kg})(7.7\text{ m/s})^2 - ½(575\text{ kg})(15\text{ m/s})^2 - ½(1575\text{ kg})(5.0\text{ m/s})^2 = -2.1 \times 10^4\text{ J}$$

c. Fraction lost is $\Delta KE/KE_{initial}$ =

$$\frac{\Delta KE}{KE_{initial}} = \frac{-2.1 \times 10^4\text{ J}}{8.4 \times 10^4\text{ J}} = -\frac{1}{4}\text{ (25\% lost)}$$

d. Energy went into bent metal, warmed car parts, and so on.

BIOLOGY CONNECTION

In the process of photosynthesis, chlorophyll in green plants captures energy from sunlight. The process converts light energy to stored chemical energy as the plant synthesizes carbohydrates. This stored energy is converted to other forms of energy as plants are used as food by animals.

Practice Problems

13. A 2.00-g bullet, moving at 538 m/s, strikes a 0.250-kg piece of wood at rest on a frictionless table. The bullet sticks in the wood, and the combined mass moves slowly down the table.
a. Find the speed of the combination after the collision.
b. Find the kinetic energy of the bullet before the collision.
c. Find the kinetic energy of the combination after the collision.
d. How much kinetic energy did the bullet lose?
e. What percent of the bullet's original kinetic energy is lost?

14. An 8.00-g bullet is fired horizontally into a 9.00-kg block of wood on an air table and is embedded in it. After the collision, the block and the bullet slide along a frictionless surface together with a speed of 10 cm/s. What was the initial speed of the bullet?

15. As everyone knows, bullets bounce from Superman's chest. Suppose Superman, mass 104 kg, while not moving, is struck by a 4.2-g bullet moving with a speed of 835 m/s. If the collision is elastic, find the speed that Superman had after the collision. (Assume the bottoms of his superfeet are frictionless.)

▶ 16. A 0.73-kg magnetic target is suspended on a string. A 0.025-kg magnetic dart, shot horizontally, strikes it head on. The dart and the target together swing up 12 cm above the initial level. What was the initial velocity of the dart? (**Hint:** Since your equation will have two unknowns, you will need an additional equation to solve for v_i. Consider the fact that the target had zero potential energy before the collision, but the dart and target no longer had zero potential energy after the collision.)

CONCEPT REVIEW

2.1 Is "spaceship Earth" a closed, isolated system? Give examples to support your answer.

2.2 A surfboarder crouches down and moves high up into the "curl" of a wave. How does this person use conservation of energy?

2.3 A child jumps on a trampoline. What are the forms of energy when
- **a.** the child is as high as he goes in the air?
- **b.** the child's feet are just touching the trampoline?
- **c.** the child is momentarily at rest as low as he goes into the trampoline?

2.4 Critical Thinking: A ball drops 20 m. When it has fallen half the distance, 10 m, half of its energy is potential, half kinetic. When it has fallen instead for half the amount of time it takes to fall, will more, less, or exactly half of its energy be potential energy?

FIGURE 11–15.

14. 1.1×10^2 m/s
15. 6.7×10^{-2} m/s
16. 46 m/s

CONCEPT DEVELOPMENT

Ask students to list factors that would enter into making a decision about whether electric hand dryers or paper towels are more energy-efficient in restrooms.

3 Close

CONVERGENT QUESTION

In terms of energy use per person, Americans are at the top of the list for the world. If they could make the decision, ask students what energy intensive activities they would forbid, tax, or curtail. Have them defend their choices.

CONCEPT REVIEW ANSWERS

2.1 No. Objects enter (meteorites, solar wind) and leave (space probes). Energy enters (solar energy) and leaves (radiation of Earth). Forces due to sun, moon, and planets act on Earth.
2.2 By moving up, the person converts kinetic into potential energy. When coming out of the curl, potential energy is returned into kinetic.
2.3 a. gravitational potential energy **b.** mostly kinetic, some gravitational potential **c.** totally potential energy of the stretched trampoline
2.4 Critical Thinking: Since its velocity increases as it falls, in half the time it falls less than half the distance. Thus more than half of its energy will still be potential energy.

INDEPENDENT PRACTICE/ EXTENSION

Refer to the Assignment Guide below for additional questions and problems for independent practice.

11:2 ASSIGNMENT GUIDE

	PRACTICE	EXTENSION
CHAPTER REVIEW pp. 236–239		
· Reviewing Concepts	14–19	
· Applying Concepts		9–16
· Problems*	20–23, 27–30, 32, 33	24, 25, 26, 31
APPENDIX B PROBLEMS*		
· Chapter 11 p. 696–697	11, 12	13–15

* Complete solutions to all Chapter Review and Appendix problems appear in the Problems and Solutions Manual.

CHAPTER 11 REVIEW

SUMMARY

11.1 Energy in Its Many Forms

- Kinetic energy is the energy an object has because of its motion.
- Potential energy is the energy an object has because of its position, shape, or form.
- According to the work-energy theorem, the work done on an object by the net force acting on it is equal to the change in kinetic energy of the body.
- Gravitational potential energy depends on the weight of the body and its separation from Earth: $PE = mgh$.

11.2 Conservation of Energy

- The sum of kinetic and potential energies of a system is called the mechanical energy.
- According to the law of conservation of energy, the total energy of a closed, isolated system is constant. Within the system, energy can change form, but the total energy does not change.
- In an elastic collision, the total momentum and kinetic energy of the system is the same before and after the collision.
- In an inelastic collision, momentum is conserved; total kinetic energy is decreased.

KEY TERMS

kinetic energy
potential energy
work-energy theorem
reference level
law of conservation of energy
mechanical energy
elastic collision
inelastic collision

REVIEWING CONCEPTS

1. Explain how energy and work are related.
2. What type of energy does a wound watch spring have? What form of energy does a running mechanical watch use? When a watch runs down, what has happened to the energy?
3. Name the types of mechanical energy in the Earth-sun system.
4. Explain how energy and force are related.
5. Can the kinetic energy of a baseball ever have a negative value? Explain.
6. Does the work-energy theorem apply when a speeding car puts on its brakes and comes to a stop? Explain.
7. Can a baseball have potential energy and kinetic energy at the same time?
8. Describe the energy transformations that occur when an athlete is pole vaulting.
9. Pole vaulting was transformed when the wooden pole was replaced by the fiberglass pole. Explain why.
10. Can the gravitational potential energy of a baseball ever have a negative value? Explain.
11. An earthquake can release energy to devastate a city. Where does this energy reside an instant before the earthquake takes place?
12. Work is required to lift a barbell. How many times as much work is required to lift the barbell three times as high?
13. A ball is dropped by Sam from the top of a building, while Sue at the bottom of the building observes the motion. Will these two people agree on the value of the ball's potential energy for reference level? on the change in potential energy of the ball? on the kinetic energy of the ball?
14. A rubber ball is dropped from a height of 8 m. After striking the floor, the ball bounces to a height of 5 m.
    a. If the ball had bounced to a height of 8 m, how would you describe the collision between the ball and the floor?
    b. If the ball had not bounced at all, how would you describe the collision between the ball and the floor?
    c. What happened to the energy lost by the ball during the collision?
15. Does the work–energy theorem hold if friction acts on an object? Explain your answer.
16. Air bags greatly reduce the chance of injury in a car accident. Explain how they do so, in terms of energy transfers.
17. The cue ball hits the eight ball.

CLOSING CHAPTER 11

Review Summary statements and Key Terms with your students.

ASSESSMENT

Vocabulary Review Master, Teacher Resource Package. Use this master to check students' understanding of Key Terms.

Evaluation Masters. Use Parts A and B of the Chapter Evaluation Masters from the Teacher Resource Package to test qualitative chapter objectives. Use Parts C and D to test quantitative chapter objectives.

Answers To

REVIEWING CONCEPTS

1. Work is the transfer of the energy.

2. A wound-up watch spring has potential energy. Work was done to wind the spring. When running, a watch converts the potential energy of the spring into kinetic energy of the gears. When a watch runs down, its energy has been converted to heat and sound.

3. The Earth-sun system possesses both kinetic and potential energy. As a matter of fact, the two are constantly interchanging. This is the reason Earth moves faster along its orbit when closer to the sun, in accordance with Kepler's law.

4. Forces applied through a distance do work and transfer energy between points and between objects.

5. No. Mass is positive and the square of any velocity, positive or negative, is positive. The change in kinetic energy may be negative or positive.

6. Yes. The net force acting on a car, the force exerted backwards by the road, does negative work on the car, reducing its kinetic energy.

7. Yes. A baseball can have a height (potential energy) and a velocity (kinetic energy).

8. Work done by vaulter: kinetic energy of running, potential energy of bent pole, kinetic energy of rising vaulter, potential energy of vaulter at top of trajectory, kinetic energy of vaulter falling.

9. The fiberglass pole can bend more, can store more potential energy, and can transfer that energy into gravitational potential energy.

10. Yes, if the baseball is below the reference level.

11. In the potential energy of the rock that makes up the Earth: The rock is slowly compressed like a spring and suddenly releases that potential energy.

12. three times as much work

13. No, since they have different reference levels; yes, since the change in distance is the same for both of them; yes, they measure the same velocity.

14. a. If the ball had bounced 8 m, the collision would have been perfectly elastic. **b.** If the ball had not bounced at all, the collision would have been perfectly inelastic. **c.** Some of the ball's kinetic energy is converted to heat and sound as it collides with Earth.

15. No, some of the work goes into overcoming friction.

a. What is an elastic collision?
b. What quantities are conserved in an elastic collision?
c. Which of the laws does not apply to inelastic collision?

18. A child throws a ball of clay against a wall and it sticks. Has energy been conserved?

APPLYING CONCEPTS

1. A compact car and a semi-truck are both traveling at the same velocity. Which has more kinetic energy?
2. Sally and Lisa have identical compact cars. Sally drives on the freeway with a greater speed than Lisa. Which car has more kinetic energy?
3. Sally and Lisa have identical compact cars. Sally is northbound on the freeway and Lisa is southbound with the same speed. Which car has more kinetic energy?
4. Is it possible to exert a force and yet not cause a change in kinetic energy?
5. Two bodies of unequal mass each have the same kinetic energy and are moving in the same direction. If the same retarding force is applied to each, how will the stopping distances of the bodies compare?
6. If you drop a tennis ball onto a concrete floor, it will bounce back farther than if you drop it on a rug. Where does the lost energy go when it strikes the rug?
7. Most earth satellites follow an elliptical path rather than a circular path around Earth. The *PE* increases when the satellite moves farther from Earth. According to energy conservation, does a satellite have its greatest speed when it is closest to or farthest from Earth?
8. In mountainous areas, road designers build escape ramps to help trucks with failed brakes stop. These escape ramps are usually roads made of loose gravel that go uphill. Describe changes in forms of energy when a fast-moving truck uses one of these escape ramps.
9. If two identical bowling balls are raised to the same height, one on Earth and the other on the moon, which has the larger potential energy relative to the surface of the bodies?
10. Roads seldom go straight up a mountain but wind around and go up gradually. Explain.
11. What will be the kinetic energy of an arrow shot from a bow having a potential energy of 50 J?
12. Two pendulums are swinging side by side. At the bottom of the swing, the speed of one pendulum bob is twice the speed of the other. Compare the heights to which the two bobs rise at the ends of their swings.
13. In a baseball game, two pop-ups are hit in succession. The second rises twice as high as the first. Compare the speeds of the two balls when they leave the bat.
14. Two identical balls are thrown from the top of a cliff, each with the same speed. One is thrown straight down, the other straight up. How do the speeds and the kinetic energies of the balls compare as they strike the ground?
15. A ball is dropped from the top of a tall building and reaches terminal velocity as it falls. Will the potential energy of the ball upon release equal the kinetic energy it has when striking the ground? Explain.
16. According to Einstein's equation $E_o = mc^2$, does the rock-Earth system have more or less mass when the rock is lifted high above Earth than when the same rock is on Earth's surface?

PROBLEMS

11.1 Energy in Its Many Forms

Unless otherwise directed, assume air resistance is negligible.

1. A 1600-kg car travels at a speed of 12.5 m/s. What is its kinetic energy?
2. A racing car has a mass of 1500 kg. What is its kinetic energy if it has a speed of 108 km/h?
3. Sally has a mass of 45 kg and is moving with a speed of 10.0 m/s.
   a. Find Sally's kinetic energy.
   b. Sally's speed changes to 5.0 m/s. Now what is her kinetic energy?
   c. What is the ratio of the kinetic energies in **a** and **b**? Explain the ratio.
4. Shawn and his bike have a total mass of 45.0 kg. Shawn rides his bike 1.80 km in 10.0 min at a constant velocity. What is Shawn's kinetic energy?

REVIEW MASTER

Use the Vocabulary Review master for Chapter 11 with this section.

EVALUATION MASTER

Use the Chapter Evaluation master for Chapter 11 with this section.

16. The collision causes a change in momentum. The air bags increase the time over which the force of the collision acts on your body, decreasing the force. $Ft = m\Delta v$

17. a. The kinetic energy of the colliding bodies before the collision equals the kinetic energy of the bodies after the collision. **b.** conservation of momentum and energy **c.** conservation of momentum—some energy changed to thermal energy

18. Yes. The kinetic energy turns into heat and sound energy.

Answers To
APPLYING CONCEPTS

1. The semi-truck has more kinetic energy because kinetic energy is directly proportional to the mass of an object.

2. Sally's car; the greater the speed, the greater the kinetic energy.

3. Direction is not important to kinetic energy. The cars have the same kinetic energy.

4. Yes. If the force is not applied through a distance, no work is done and there is no change in kinetic energy.

5. They will be equal.

6. Most of the energy goes into heating up the rug.

7. The greatest kinetic energy occurs when the satellite is closest to Earth.

8. The kinetic energy of the truck is converted to potential energy as the truck goes up the escape ramp. The loose gravel releases energy in the form of sound and heat, and additional energy is used to compact the gravel.

9. The bowling ball on Earth will have the larger potential energy because potential energy is directly proportional to gravitational acceleration, *g*.

10. Work is needed to change the potential energy of a car. By increasing the distance, *d*, the force, *F*, is reduced.

11. 50 J

12. The faster pendulum rises four times as high because the kinetic energy at the bottom becomes potential energy at the top, and kinetic energy is proportional to the square of the speed, while potential energy is proportional to the height.

Answers To
APPLYING CONCEPTS (cont)

13. Potential energy is doubled at the top, so kinetic energy is doubled at the bottom of the trajectory. Thus the square of speed is doubled, so speed is larger by a ratio of $\sqrt{2}/1 = 1.414$.
14. Even though the balls do not hit the ground at the same time, they have identical velocities and kinetic energies when they hit.
15. No. Since the ball does not maintain a constant acceleration throughout its entire fall, some of its energy is transformed as it works against air resistance.
16. Potential energy is greater, so E is greater. Thus m is larger.

Answers To
PROBLEMS

Complete solutions to all Chapter Review Problems can be found in the Problems and Solutions Manual accompanying this text.

1. 1.25×10^5 J
2. 6.75×10^5 J
3. a. 2.3×10^3 J
b. 5.6×10^2 J
c. $\frac{4}{1}$
4. 203 J
5. 1.7×10^2 J
6. a. 3.50×10^3 N
b. 7.69×10^4 J
7. a. 4.5×10^3 J
b. $\frac{2}{1}$
c. $\frac{2}{1}$
8. a. 2.50×10^8 J
b. 2.50×10^8 J
c. 2.50×10^8 J
d. 141 m/s
9. 66 m
10. a. -345 J
b. -345 J
c. 34.5 m
11. a. -1.44×10^5 J
b. -1.44×10^5 J
c. -2.88×10^5 N
12. 2.1×10^3 J

▶ **5.** It is not uncommon during the service of a professional tennis player for the racquet to exert an average force of 150.0 N on the ball. If the ball has a mass of 0.060 kg and is in contact with the strings of the racquet for 0.030 s, what is the kinetic energy of the ball as it leaves the racquet? Assume the ball starts from rest.

▶ **6.** Pam, wearing a rocket pack, stands on frictionless ice. She has a mass of 40 kg. The rocket supplies a constant force for 22.0 m and Pam acquires a speed of 62.0 m/s.
a. What is the magnitude of the force?
b. What is Pam's final kinetic energy?

7. Sally and Lisa have a mass of 45 kg and they are moving together with a speed of 10.0 m/s.
a. What is their combined kinetic energy?
b. What is the ratio of their combined mass to Sally's mass?
c. What is the ratio of their combined kinetic energy to Sally's kinetic energy. Explain.

8. In the 1950s, an experimental train that had a mass of 2.50×10^4 kg was powered across level track by a jet engine that produced a thrust of 5.00×10^5 N for a distance of 500 m.
a. Find the work done on the train.
b. Find the change in kinetic energy.
c. Find the final kinetic energy of the train if it started from rest.
d. Find the final speed of the train if there was no friction.

9. A 14 700-N car is traveling at 25 m/s. The brakes are suddenly applied and the car slides to a stop. The average braking force between the tires and the road is 7100 N. How far will the car slide once the brakes are applied?

10. A 15.0-kg cart is moving with a velocity of 7.50 m/s down a level hallway. A constant force of -10.0 N acts on the cart and its velocity becomes 3.20 m/s.
a. What is the change in kinetic energy of the cart?
b. How much work was done on the cart?
c. How far did the cart move while the force acted?

▶ **11.** A 2.00×10^3-kg car has a speed of 12.0 m/s. The car then hits a tree. The tree doesn't move and the car comes to rest.
a. Find the change in kinetic energy of the car.
b. Find the amount of work done in pushing in the front of the car.
c. Find the size of the force that pushed the front of the car in 50.0 cm.

12. How much potential energy does Tim, mass 60.0 kg, gain when he climbs a gymnasium rope a distance of 3.5 m?

13. A 6.4-kg bowling ball is lifted 2.1 m into a storage rack. Calculate the increase in the ball's potential energy.

14. Mary weighs 500 N and she walks down a flight of stairs to a level 5.50 m below her starting point. What is the change in Mary's potential energy?

15. A weightlifter raises a 180-kg barbell to a height of 1.95 m. What is the increase in the barbell's potential energy?

16. A 10.0-kg test rocket is fired vertically from Cape Canaveral. Its fuel gives it a kinetic energy of 1960 J by the time the rocket motor burns all of the fuel. What additional height will the rocket rise?

17. Ace raised a 12.0-N physics book from a table 75 cm above the floor to a shelf, 2.15 m above the floor. What was the change in potential energy?

18. A hallway display of energy is constructed. People are told that to do 1.00 J of work, they should pull on a rope that lifts a block 1.00 m. What should be the mass of the block?

▶ **19.** A constant net force of 410 N, up, is applied to a stone that weighs 32 N. The upward force is applied through a distance of 2.0 m, and the stone is then released. To what height, from the point of release, will the stone rise?

11.2 Conservation of Energy

20. A 98-N sack of grain is hoisted to a storage room 50 m above the ground floor of a grain elevator.
a. How much work was required?
b. What is the potential energy of the sack of grain at this height?
c. The rope being used to lift the sack of grain breaks just as the sack reaches the storage room. What kinetic energy does the sack have just before it strikes the ground floor?

21. A 20-kg rock is on the edge of a 100-m cliff.
   a. What potential energy does the rock possess relative to the base of the cliff?
   b. The rock falls from the cliff. What is its kinetic energy just before it strikes the ground?
   c. What speed does the rock have as it strikes the ground?
22. An archer puts a 0.30-kg arrow to the bowstring. An average force of 201 N is exerted to draw the string back 1.3 m.
   a. Assuming no frictional loss, with what speed does the arrow leave the bow?
   b. If the arrow is shot straight up, how high does it rise?
23. A 2.0-kg rock initially at rest loses 400 J of potential energy while falling to the ground.
   a. Calculate the kinetic energy that the rock gains while falling.
   b. What is the rock's speed just before it strikes the ground?
24. ▶ Betty weighs 420 N and she is sitting on a playground swing seat that hangs 0.40 m above the ground. Tom pulls the swing back and releases it when the seat is 1.00 m above the ground.
   a. How fast is Betty moving when the swing passes through its lowest position?
   b. If Betty moves through the lowest point at 2.0 m/s, how much work was done on the swing by friction?
25. ▶ Bill throws a 10.0-g ball straight down from a height of 2.0 m. The ball strikes the floor at a speed of 7.5 m/s. What was the initial speed of the ball?
26. ▶ Magen's mass is 28 kg. She climbs the 4.8-m ladder of a slide, and reaches a velocity of 3.2 m/s at the bottom of the slide. How much work was done by friction on Magen?
27. A physics book, mass unknown, is dropped 4.50 m. What speed does the book have just before it hits the ground?
28. A 30.0-kg gun is standing on a frictionless surface. The gun fires a 50.0-g bullet with a muzzle velocity of 310 m/s.
   a. Calculate the momenta of the bullet and the gun after the gun was fired.
   b. Calculate the kinetic energy of both the bullet and the gun just after firing.
29. A railroad car with a mass of 5.0×10^5 kg collides with a stationary railroad car of equal mass. After the collision, the two cars lock together and move off at 4.0 m/s.
   a. Before the collision, the first railroad car was moving at 8.0 m/s. What was its momentum?
   b. What is the total momentum of the two cars after the collision?
   c. Find the kinetic energies of the two cars before and after the collision.
   d. Account for the loss of kinetic energy.
30. From what height would a compact car have to be dropped to have the same kinetic energy that it has when being driven at 100 km/h?
31. ▶ A golf ball, mass 0.046 kg, rests on a tee. It is struck by a golf club with an effective mass of 0.220 kg and a speed of 44 m/s. Assuming the collision is elastic, find the speed of the ball when it leaves the tee.
32. A steel ball has a mass of 4.0 kg and rolls along a smooth, level surface at 62 m/s.
   a. Find its kinetic energy.
   b. At first, the ball was at rest on the surface. A constant force acted on it through a distance of 22 m to give it the speed of 62 m/s. What was the magnitude of the force?
33. Show that $W = KE_f - KE_i$ if an object is not originally at rest. Use the equation relating initial and final velocity with constant acceleration and distance.

USING LAB SKILLS

1. After doing the Pocket Lab on page 233, describe the exchanges of mechanical energy from the time the spring is compressed until the metal ball finally hits the table.

THINKING PHYSIC-LY

One of the important concepts in golf, tennis, baseball, and other sports is follow-through! How can applying a force to a ball for the longest possible time affect the speed of the ball?

13. 1.3×10^2 J
14. -2.75×10^3 J
15. 3.44×10^3 J
16. 20.0 m
17. 16.8 J
18. 0.102 kg
19. 26 m
20. a. 4.9×10^3 J
    b. 4.9×10^3 J
    c. 4.9×10^3 J
21. a. 2.0×10^4 J
    b. 2.0×10^4 J
    c. 45 m/s
22. a. 42 m/s
    b. 90 m
23. a. 400 J
    b. 20 m/s
24. a. 3.4 m/s
    b. 1.6×10^2 J
25. 4.1 m/s
26. 1.2×10^3 J
27. 9.39 m/s
28. a. $P_b = 15.5 \frac{\text{kg·m}}{\text{s}}$; $P_g = -15.5 \frac{\text{kg·m}}{\text{s}}$
    b. $KE_b = 2.40 \times 10^3$ J
    $KE_g = 4.00$ J
29. a. 4.0×10^6 kg·m/s
    b. 4.0×10^6 kg·m/s
    c. before: $KE_1 = 1.6 \times 10^7$ J; $KE_2 = 0$
    after: $KE = 8.0 \times 10^6$ J
    d. heat and sound
30. 39.4 m
31. 73 m/s
32. a. 7.7×10^3 J
    b. 3.5×10^2 N
33. Refer to Problems and Solutions Manual.

Answer To
USING LAB SKILLS

1. You do work on the spring to give it elastic potential energy. This is changed into kinetic energy in the spring, rod, and ball. As the ball rises, its kinetic energy is changed into gravitational potential energy; as it descends, potential energy is changed back into gravitational energy, plus some energy lost to friction with the air. When the ball hits the table, the kinetic energy changes into thermal energy, sound energy, and elastic potential energy as it slightly compressed the table.

Answer To
THINKING PHYSIC-LY

The longer the displacement for the same force, the greater the work done on the ball, the greater the kinetic energy of the ball, and the higher the speed.

CHAPTER 12 Thermal Energy

PLANNING GUIDE (6 class sessions)

CONTENTS	TEXT FEATURES	TEACHER RESOURCE PACKAGE	OTHER COMPONENTS
12.1 Temperature and Thermal Energy, pp. 242–252 (3 Class Sessions) • What Makes a Hot Body Hot? • Thermal Energy Transfer • Thermal Energy and Temperature • Equilibrium and Thermometry • Temperature Scales: Celsius and Kelvin • Heat and Thermal Energy • Calorimetry: Measuring Specific Heat	**Physics Lab:** Heating Up, p. 249 **Pocket Lab:** Cool Times, p. 251 **Using Your Calculator:** Using Parens, p. 251 **Concept Review,** p. 252	**Study Guide:** Temperature and Thermal Energy **Physics Lab Data Sheet:** Heating Up **Reteaching Master:** The Transfer of Thermal Energy **Enrichment Master:** Calorimetry **Transparency Worksheet:** Temperature Scale	**Laboratory Manual:** Lab 12.1 Specific Heat **Transparency 14:** Temperature Scale
12.2 Change of State and Laws of Thermodynamics, pp. 252–260 (3 Class Sessions) • Change of State • The First Law of Thermodynamics • The Second Law of Thermodynamics	**Physics and Technology:** Range-Top Cooking, p. 260 **Pocket Lab:** Melting, p. 253 **Pocket Lab:** Drip, Drip, Drip, p. 258 **Concept Review,** p. 260	**Study Guide:** Change of State and Laws of Thermodynamics **Critical Thinking Master:** Comparing Heat Engines **Transparency Worksheet:** A Heat Pump **Transparency Worksheet:** Change of State Graph	**Transparency 15:** A Heat Pump **Transparency 16:** Change of State Graph
Chapter Review, pp. 261–263	Summary Key Terms Reviewing Concepts Applying Concepts Problems Thinking Physic-ly	**Vocabulary Review** **Chapter Test**	**Test Bank**

SUPPLEMENTARY MATERIALS

SOFTWARE	AUDIOVISUAL	BOOKS/MAGAZINES
Heat, Queue, Inc. (Apple II, IBM PC, Macintosh). *Heat and Temperature: A Microcomputer-Based Lab,* HRM (Apple II). *Introduction to General Physics, Disk III: Heat,* COMPress/Queue, Inc. (Apple II, IBM PC, Macintosh). *Thermodynamics,* Cross (Apple II, IBM PC).	Videos: *The Flow of Heat Energy,* Focus Media (still frame). *Kinetic Karnival, Cooking,* WVIZ-TV. Filmstrip: *Heat and Temperature,* Clearvue.	Baierlein, Ralph. "The Meaning of Temperature." *The Physics Teacher,* February 1990, p. 94. Crane, H. Richard. "The Stirling Engine—173 Years Old and Running." *The Physics Teacher,* April 1990, p. 252. Switzer, Terry G. "Cheap Heat." *The Science Teacher,* April 1986, pp. 32–34. Wagner, William S. "Measuring the Heat Produced by a Single Candle." *The Physics Teacher,* September 1990, p. 420.

PROBLEM CORRELATION

CONCEPTS	CHAPTER REVIEW			PROBLEMS APPENDIX
	Reviewing Concepts	Applying Concepts	Problems	
12.1 Temperature and Thermal Energy				
What Makes a Hot Body Hot?	1			
Thermal Energy Transfer				
Thermal Energy and Temperature	2,3,4	1		
Equilibrium and Thermometry	6			
Temperature Scales: Celsius and Kelvin	5	2	1,2,3	1,2
Heat and Thermal Energy	7,8,9,10	3,4,5	4,5,6,7,8,11	3,4,5,6,7
Calorimetry: Measuring Specific Heat		6	9,10,13,**14**,15	**8,9,10**
12.2 Change of State and Laws of Thermodynamics				
Change of State	11,12	7,8	16,17,18,**19,21,22**	11,**12,13**
The First Law of Thermodynamics	13	9	20,23,24,25	**14,15**
The Second Law of Thermodynamics	14			

ACTIVITY AND DEMONSTRATION MATERIALS

PHYSICS LAB	POCKET LAB	DEMONSTRATIONS
Page 249 hot plate or bunsen burner 250-ml pyrex beaker water thermometer stopwatch goggles	Pages 251, 253, 258 100-mL beaker 250-mL beaker hot water room temperature water stopwatch 2 thermometers 2 foam cups ice water ice cube 2 glasses (or beakers) food coloring dropper	Pages 243, 250, 254 heater 3 beakers thermometer pan water large glass marble lead sheet 2 polystyrene cups

EXTENSION PROJECTS

LIBRARY RESEARCH

1. Thermal Pollution
Do some library research on thermal pollution. Read about the Cook nuclear plant. What did researchers discover about the source of thermal pollution in that area?

DISPLAY MODEL

2. The Thermocouple
Build a thermocouple. Explain to the class how such a device gauges temperature change.

STUDENT READINGS

Fritz, Ron. "Calibration and Efficiency of Microwave Ovens." *The Physics Teacher,* November 1990.

Holt, Floyd, and Amann, George. "Cryogenics." *The Physics Teacher,* May 1990.

Peterson, Ivars. "Demons, Engines and Information." *Science News,* June 16,1990.

Smay, Elaine. "Heat-Pipe Furnace." *Popular Science*, February 1984.

Warren, David. "Solar Systems and Heat Pumps Combine to Cut Energy Bills." *Discover,* Jan. 1983.

Weinberg, Carl J., and Williams, Robert H. "Energy From the Sun." *Scientific American,* Sept. 1990.

Chapter 12

Thermal Energy

CHAPTER OVERVIEW

Theme Development: Energy within a system is further defined to give an understanding of inputs and outputs. The kinetic-molecular theory's conceptual picture of matter provides a bridge to the study of states of matter.

MISCONCEPTIONS

The fact that materials do not undergo a change of temperature while undergoing a change of state is counterintuitive to students. Emphasize the distinctions between thermal energy, temperature, and heat. Make sure students understand that heat is not something "contained" in an object, but energy that flows between objects due to a difference in temperatures.

KEY TERMS

absolute zero
boiling point
calorimeter
conduction
convection
entropy
first law of thermodynamics
heat
heat engine
heat of fusion
heat of vaporization
Kelvin
kinetic-molecular theory
melting point
radiation
second law of thermodynamics
specific heat
temperature
thermal energy
thermal equilibrium
thermodydamics
thermometer

Laboratory Options

STUDENT EDITION

Physics Lab

Heating Up	249

Pocket Labs

Cool Times	251
Melting	253
Drip, Drip, Drip	258

TEACHER EDITION

Activities

Demonstration	243, 250, 254
Cooperative Learning	244, 246

LABORATORY MANUAL

Specific Heat	Lab 12.1

CHAPTER

12 Thermal Energy

◀ **Perpetual Motion?**

The engine converts the chemical energy stored in the fuel and oxygen into kinetic energy. Could we ever invent an engine that converts all the energy into useful energy of motion?

What invention has changed our lives more than the internal combustion engine? In the 1700s, the steam engine changed our society from a nation of farms to one of factories. The steam engine burned fuel to change water to steam in a boiler outside the engine. The gasoline engine, invented in Germany by Otto in 1876, burns the fuel inside the engine, and thus is an internal combustion engine. These engines and their descendants, the diesel engines and the turbines used in jet aircraft, change the chemical energy in fuel to thermal energy in hot gases. The thermal energy, in turn, is converted into kinetic energy of motion. Internal combustion engines vary in size from the small engines in lawnmowers and motorbikes, to larger ones in cars, buses, and airplanes, to the giant engines that produce electricity for millions of people. Consider how often we make use of this invention in our everyday lives.

Chapter Outline

✓ Concept Check

The following terms or concepts from earlier chapters are important for a good understanding of this chapter. If you are not familiar with them, you should review them before studying this chapter.

- work and energy, Chapter 10
- energy conservation, Chapter 11

Introducing The Chapter

Perpetual Motion?

Using The Photo: Rapid volume and pressure changes such as those shown in the photograph can make interesting effects. An auto engine converts thermal energy into a more useful form called mechanical energy.

To answer the chapter opener question, students will find the information they need on page 258.

Concept Check

Make sure students have a clear understanding of the concepts taught in Chapters 10 and 11 that are listed in the Concept Check. Understanding energy conservation, and work and energy will prepare students to work with the principles of thermal energy introduced in this chapter.

Assessment Options

Portfolio Assessment
Portfolio Assessment, TWE, p. 244
Extension, TWE, p. 245
Portfolio Assessment, TWE, p. 247
Enrichment, TWE, p. 248
Extension, TWE, p. 259

Performance Assessment
Pocket Labs, pp. 251, 253, 258
Physics Lab, p. 249
Activity, TWE, p. 246
Pocket Lab Assessment, TWE, p. 251

Content Assessment
Self Assessment: Practice Problems, pp. 247, 248, 252, 255
Critical Thinking, TWE, p. 246
Assessment, Critical Thinking, TWE, p. 249
Concept Reviews, pp. 252, 260
Chapter Review, pp. 261–263
Supplemental Problems, p. 697

Group Assessment
Activities for group assessment occur with Cooperative Learning and lab activities.

12.1 TEMPERATURE AND THERMAL ENERGY

Preparation

OBJECTIVES

The objectives are listed on the student page. Remind students to preview these objectives as a study guide to this major section.

OVERVIEW

The concepts introduced in this section are thermal equilibrium, temperature, thermal energy, temperature scales, the extension of conservation of energy to include thermal energy, and specific heat.

BRIDGING

Kinetic energy, potential energy, and the conservation of energy are used here to introduce the idea of heat and temperature, and the principles of calorimetry.

1 Focus

Show students the devices you have in the laboratory that measure temperature, and briefly explain how they are used. The devices might include mercury or alcohol in glass thermometers, liquid crystal strips that change colors, and various kinds of resistance thermometers or thermocouples.

Objectives

- understand the nature of thermal energy as explained by the kinetic theory.
- define temperature and distinguish it from thermal energy.
- understand the process of reaching equilibrium and its application to the measurement of temperature.
- describe and use the Celsius and Kelvin temperature scales; demonstrate the ability to convert between Celsius and Kelvin.
- distinguish heat from thermal energy.
- define and display an understanding of specific heat; be able to calculate heat transfer.
- display an understanding of the application of conservation of energy to heat transfers; be able to calculate temperature changes due to heat transfer.

12.1 TEMPERATURE AND THERMAL ENERGY

In the 1600s and 1700s, Europe went through a "Little Ice Age" when temperatures were lower than any other period in the last one thousand years. Keeping warm was vitally important. As a result, many people devoted themselves to the study of heat. One result was the invention of machines that used the energy produced by burning fuel to produce useful work. Although not as convenient as the internal combustion engine, these machines freed society from its dependence on the energy of people and animals. As inventors tried to make these machines more powerful and more efficient, they developed the science of thermodynamics, the study of heat.

What Makes a Hot Body Hot?

To operate, internal combustion engines require very high temperatures—usually produced by burning fuel. Although the effects of fire have been known since ancient times, only in the eighteenth century did scientists begin to understand how a hot body differs from a cold body. They proposed that when a body was heated, an invisible fluid called "caloric" was added to the body. Hot bodies contained more caloric than cold bodies. The caloric theory could explain observations such as the expansion of objects when heated, but it could not easily explain why hands get warm when they are rubbed together.

In the mid-nineteenth century, scientists developed a new theory to replace caloric theory. This theory is based on the assumption that matter is made up of many tiny particles that are always in motion. In a hot body, the particles move faster, and thus have a higher energy than particles in a cooler body. The theory is called the **kinetic-molecular theory**.

The kinetic theory is difficult to visualize because the individual particles are too tiny to be seen. A thrown baseball, Figure 12–1, has a kinetic energy that depends on its velocity and a potential energy that is proportional to its height above the ground. These external properties can be seen. The tiny particles that make up the baseball, however, are

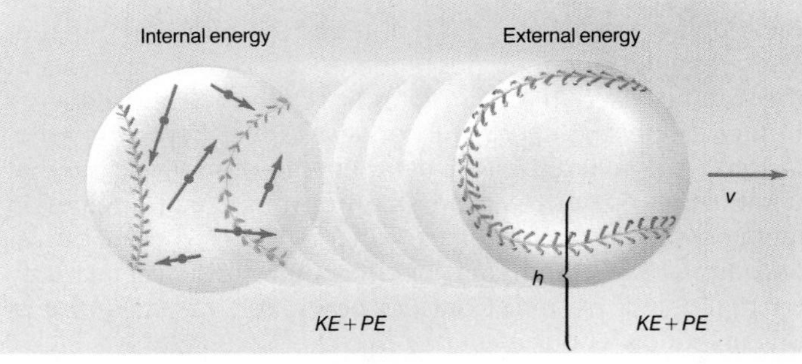

FIGURE 12–1. A baseball in flight has both internal and external energy. The internal energy is the result of the kinetic and potential energies of its particles. The external energy is the result of the position and motion of the baseball in flight.

TEACHER F.Y.I.

Gabriel Daniel Fahrenheit (1686–1736) developed the mercury thermometer in 1714 because the water and alcohol thermometers of the day had so many problems. Water didn't expand or contract evenly and did not allow good precision. Alcohol boiled at too low a temperature. The mercury thermometer is the ideal liquid thermometer because it produces little vapor, expands and contracts evenly, and stays liquid at low temperatures. Newton originally suggested a scale based on 0 for the freezing point of water and 12 for normal body temperature. Fahrenheit introduced a temperature scale based on 96 as normal body temperature and zero as the freezing point of a water and ammonium chloride mixture. He later adjusted his scale so that there were exactly 180.0 points between the boiling and freezing points of water.

in constant motion within the ball. This internal motion is invisible under most circumstances.

The model of a solid, Figure 12–2, can help you understand the kinetic theory. This model pictures a solid made up of tiny spherical particles held together by massless springs. The springs represent the electromagnetic forces that bind the solid together. The particles vibrate back and forth and thus have kinetic energy. The vibrations compress and extend the springs, so the solid has potential energy as well. The sum of the kinetic and potential energies of the internal motion of particles that make up an object is called the internal energy or **thermal energy** of that object.

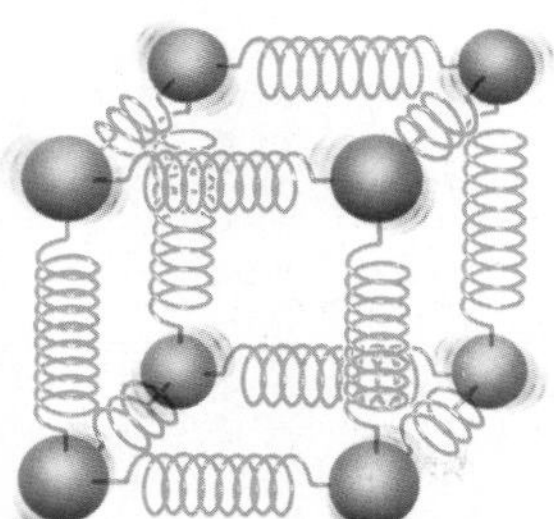

FIGURE 12–2. Molecules of a solid behave in some ways as if they were held together by springs.

Thermal Energy Transfer

Thermal energy is transferred in three ways. **Conduction,** most common in solids, involves transfer of kinetic energy when the particles of an object collide. It is the principle on which the common household thermometer operates. The movement of fluids caused by their different densities at different temperatures transfers heat by **convection.** Convection currents in the atmosphere are responsible for much of Earth's weather. Both conduction and convection depend on the presence of matter. The third method of transfer, **radiation,** does not. Thermal energy can be transferred through space in the form of electromagnetic waves. Solar energy is transmitted to Earth by radiation.

Thermal Energy and Temperature

According to the kinetic-molecular theory, a hot body has more thermal energy than a similar cold body, Figure 12–3. This means that, as a whole, the particles in a hot body have larger kinetic and potential energies than the particles in a cold body. It does not mean that all the particles in a body have exactly the same energy. The particles have a range of energies, some high, others low. It is the *average* energy of particles in a hot body that is higher than that of particles in a cold body. To help you understand this, consider the heights of students in a sixth-grade class. The heights vary, but you can calculate the average height. This average is likely to be larger than the average height of students in a fourth-grade class, even though some fourth-graders might be taller than some sixth-graders.

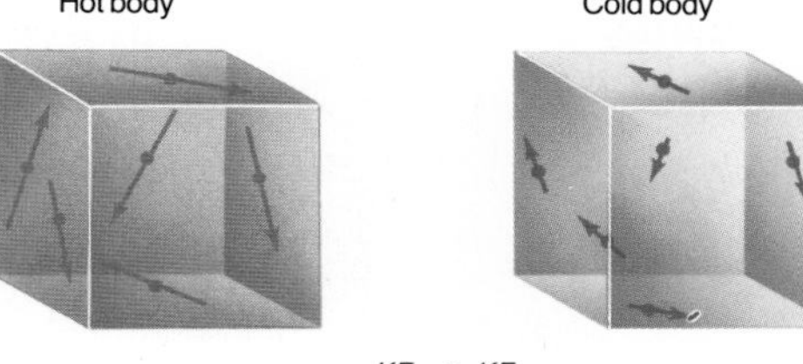

FIGURE 12–3. Particles in a hot body have larger kinetic and potential energies than particles in a cold body.

2 Teach

CONCEPT DEVELOPMENT

Study Guide Master. To reinforce the concepts in this section, have the students complete the Study Guide Master for Section 12.1 from the Teacher Resource Package.

It is important that students think of heat as the internal energy of a substance or object. It is not "something" that is contained by the body, but a transfer of energy. Hot and cold are descriptive terms, but only to compare the internal energies of substances. That is, something may be "hot" in comparison to one substance, but "cold" in comparison to another which may actually have a high temperature.

ACTIVITY

Demonstration: Line up three beakers of water on your desk: one near 0°C, one near 20°C, and one near 50°C. Have a student put one hand in the coldest beaker of water and the other hand in the hottest beaker of water. After a minute or two, have the student put both hands in the beaker with the middle temperature. Ask the student to describe how the water feels on each hand. The student will notice that it feels hot to one hand and cold to the other. This demonstration stresses the importance of using accurate measuring devices for measuring temperature.

STUDY GUIDE MASTER

Use the Study Guide master for section 12.1.

TRANSPARENCY

Use Transparency 14 with this section.

CONCEPT DEVELOPMENT

When measuring temperatures, it's important to choose a thermometer suitable to the job at hand. One would not use a fever thermometer to attempt to measure the temperature of a flea! In general, the active part of the thermometer should be smaller than the object to be measured.

ACTIVITY

Cooperative Learning: Organize students into groups of 3 or 4. Students should wear safety goggles. Have one member of each group (wearing gloves) pound a number 10 common nail into a 2 × 4 board. Have them turn the board over and pound the nail back through, then use the claw to remove the nail. Tell sudents to feel the nail and the head of the hammer. Ask them to explain the result in terms of energy flow. [The nail and hammer heat up. The kinetic energy of the hammer is transformed into thermal energy.]

Assessment

Portfolio

Have an interested student build a thermocouple (see Teacher F.Y.I.) and demonstrate it for the class. The portfolio should include a labeled sketch and a description of how the thermocouple works.

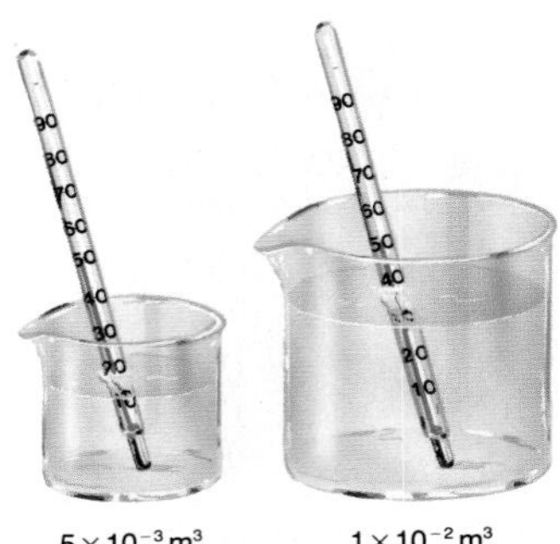

FIGURE 12–4. Temperature does not depend on the number of particles in a body.

How can we measure the "hotness" of an object? Hotness, measured on some definite scale, is a property of an object called its **temperature.** In a hotter object, the particles are moving faster; they have a larger average kinetic energy. For gases, the temperature is proportional to the average kinetic energy of the particles. For solids and liquids, this is only approximately true. For any form of matter, the temperature does not depend on the number of particles in the body. If a one-kilogram mass of steel is at the same temperature as a two-kilogram mass, the average kinetic energy of the particles in both masses is the same. The total amount of kinetic energy of particles in the two-kilogram mass, however, is twice the amount in the one-kilogram mass. The thermal energy in an object is proportional to the number of particles in it, but its temperature is not, Figure 12–4.

Temperature is hotness measured on some definite scale.

Equilibrium and Thermometry

You are familiar with the idea of measuring temperature. If you suspect that you have a fever, you may place a thermometer in your mouth and wait two or three minutes. The thermometer then provides a measure of the temperature of your body.

You are probably less familiar with the microscopic process involved in measuring temperature. Your body is hot compared to the thermometer, which means the particles in your body have higher thermal energy. The thermometer is made of a glass tube. When the cold glass touches your hotter body, the particles in your body hit the particles in the glass. These collisions transfer energy to the glass particles by conduction. The thermal energy of the particles that make up the thermometer increases. As the particles in the glass become more energetic, they begin to transfer energy back to the particles in your body. At some point, the rate of transfer of energy back and forth between the glass and your body is equal. Your body and the thermometer are in **thermal equilibrium**. That is, the rate at which energy that flows from your body to the glass is equal to the rate of flow from the glass to your body. The thermometer and your body are at the same temperature. Objects that are in thermal equilibrium are at the same temperature, Figure 12–5. Note, however, that if the masses of the objects are different, they may not have the same thermal energy.

The temperature of a gas is proportional to the average kinetic energy of the particles.

Temperature does not depend on the mass of the object; thermal energy does.

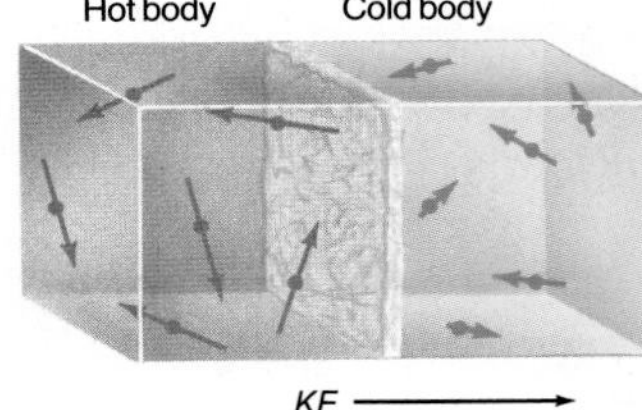

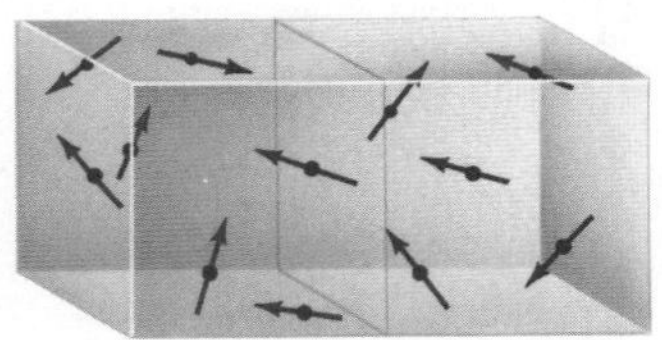

FIGURE 12–5. Thermal energy is transferred from a hot body to a cold body. When thermal equilibrium is reached, the transfer of energy between bodies is equal.

TEACHER F.Y.I.

A thermocouple is a device composed of two wires made of different metals (often copper and iron). Both ends of the wires are twisted together to form two junctions. The copper wire is cut and a voltmeter is connected between the cut ends. One of the copper-iron junctions is placed where the temperature will be measured. The other is kept at a constant temperature, usually in an ice-water mixture. The difference in temperatures between the two junctions produces a voltage across the meter that is approximatley proportional to the temperature difference. Thermocouples are often used for measuring temperatures of furnaces and other devices too hot for liquid-in-glass thermometers.

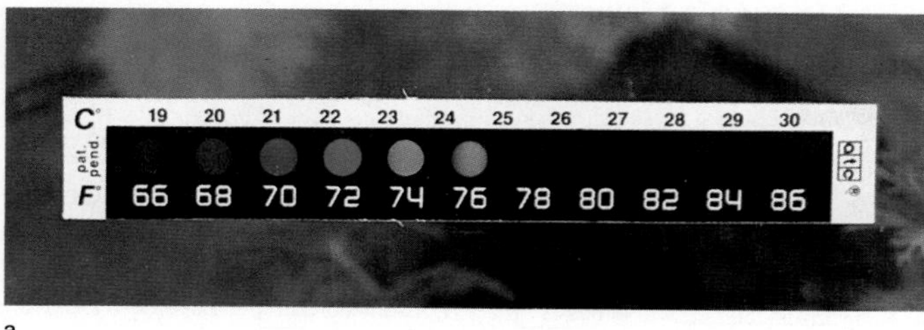

a

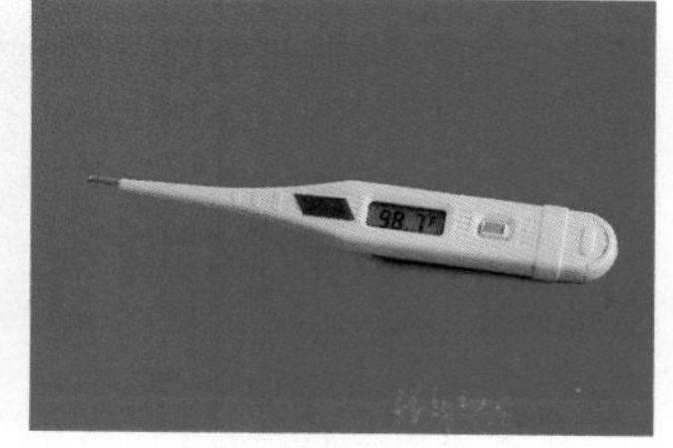

b

FIGURE 12–6. Thermometers use a change in physical properties to measure temperature. A liquid crystal thermometer changes color with temperature change (a). Some modern thermometers determine temperature electronically (b).

A **thermometer** is a device to measure temperature. It is placed in contact with an object and allowed to come to thermal equilibrium with that object. The operation of a thermometer depends on some property, such as volume, that changes with temperature. Many household thermometers contain colored alcohol that expands when heated and rises in a narrow tube. The hotter the thermometer, the larger the volume of the alcohol in it and the higher it rises. Mercury is another liquid commonly used in thermometers.

Other properties of materials change with temperature, allowing them to be used as thermometers. In liquid crystal thermometers, Figure 12–6, the arrangement of the molecules changes at a specific temperature, changing the color of the crystal. As a result, the color depends on temperature. A set of different kinds of liquid crystals is used. Each changes color at a different temperature, creating an instrument that can indicate the temperature by color.

Temperature Scales: Celsius and Kelvin

A thermometer measures the temperature of an object with which it is in thermal equilibrium.

Temperature scales were developed by scientists to allow them to compare their temperature measurements with those of other scientists. A scale based on the properties of water was devised in 1741 by the Swedish astronomer and physicist Anders Celsius (1704–1744). On this scale, now called the Celsius scale, Figure 12–7, the freezing point of pure water is 0 degrees (0°C). The boiling point of pure water at sea level is 100 degrees (100°C). On the Celsius scale, the temperature of the human body is 37°C. Figure 12–7 shows representative temperatures on the three most common scales.

Three Temperature Scales

Celsius to Kelvin °C + 273

Celsius to Fahrenheit (°C × 1.8) + 32

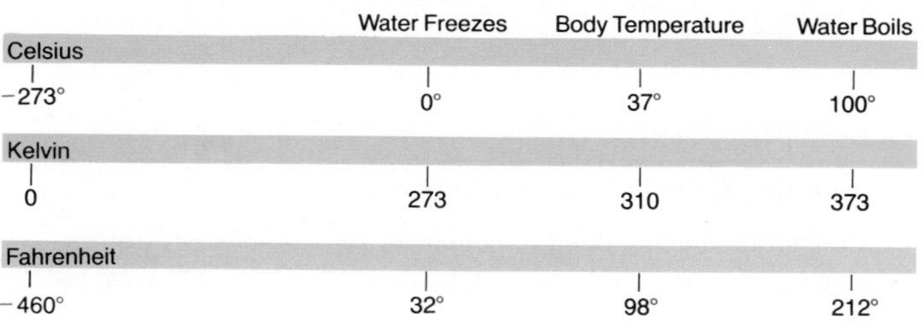

FIGURE 12–7. Some familiar reference temperatures on three temperature scales.

CHECKING FOR UNDERSTANDING

Have students answer the first three questions from the Chapter Review which deal with temperature and thermal energy.

RETEACHING

Transparency Package. Use Transparency 14 as an aid to discussing thermometers and temperature scales.

EXTENSION

Have interested students find out if there are or have ever been other temperature scales in use in addition to those already mentioned in this section.

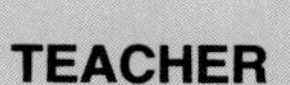

TEACHER F.Y.I.

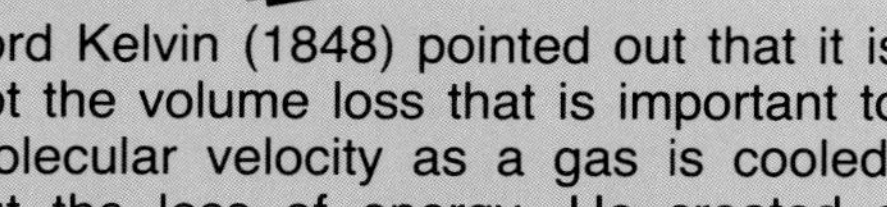

Lord Kelvin (1848) pointed out that it is not the volume loss that is important to molecular velocity as a gas is cooled, but the loss of energy. He created a temperature scale based on absolute zero that eliminates negative temperatures.

CONCEPT DEVELOPMENT

Remind students that at absolute zero, no more energy can be extracted from a substance. Also point out that there are no negative values on the Kelvin scale.

Critical Thinking: Ask students if two different gases with the same temperature have the same molecular speed. Have them explain their answers.

ACTIVITY

Cooperative Learning: Have several students prepare a demonstration involving four or five small metal samples (they're usually called specific heat samples and have masses of 70–100 grams) that are heated by lowering them into boiling water using strings. The usual sample set is copper, aluminum, lead, zinc, and tin. Prepare a block of ice by removing the divider from an ice cube tray. The students should put the ice block with its smooth side down on some paper towels to prevent it from sliding and quickly remove the samples by their strings, putting them on the ice side by side a couple of centimeters apart. Have the students hold the samples as they melt into the ice. Ask the rest of the class to predict the relative depth of ice melted for each sample. Then relate the results to the concept of specific heat.

Guided Practice: After going over the Example Problem on this page, have students try the first Practice Problem on page 247.

Independent Practice: Assign the remaining Practice Problems on page 247 for homework and spend time reviewing them during the next class period.

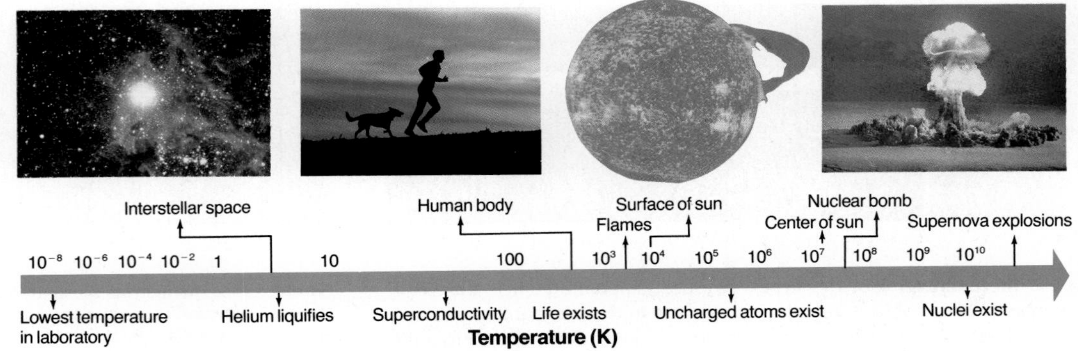

FIGURE 12–8. There is an extremely wide range of temperatures throughout the universe. Note that the scale has been expanded in areas of particular interest.

No temperature can be colder than absolute zero, −273.15°C or 0 K.

The wide range of temperatures in the universe is shown in Figure 12–8. Temperatures do not appear to have an upper limit. The interior of the sun is at least 1.5×10^7°C. Other stars are even hotter. Temperatures do, however, have a lower limit. Generally, materials contract as they cool. If you cooled an "ideal" gas, one in which the particles have no volume and don't interact, it would contract in such a way that it would have zero volume at −273.15°C. At this temperature, all the thermal energy would be removed from the gas. It would be impossible to reduce the thermal energy any further. Therefore, there can be no lower temperature than −273.15°C. This is called **absolute zero**.

The Kelvin temperature scale is based on absolute zero. Absolute zero is the zero point of the Kelvin scale. On the Kelvin scale, the freezing point of water (0°C) is 273.15 K and the boiling point of water is 373.15 K. Each interval on this scale, called a **kelvin**, is equal to one Celsius degree. Thus, °C + 273.15 = K.

Very cold temperatures are reached by liquefying gases. Helium liquefies at 4.2 K, or −269.0°C. Even colder temperatures can be reached by using the properties of special substances placed in the fields of large magnets. By using these techniques, physicists have reached temperatures of only 2.0×10^{-9} K.

F.Y.I.

For many years, thermal energy was measured in calories. One calorie is equal to 4.18 J. The calorie is not used in the SI system.

Example Problem

Converting Celsius to Kelvin Temperature

Convert 25°C to kelvins.

Solution: K = °C + 273.15 = 25° + 273.15 = 298 K

Example Problem

Converting Kelvin to Celsius Temperature

Convert the boiling point of helium, 4.22 K, to degrees Celsius.

Solution: °C = K − 273.15 = 4.22 − 273.15 = −268.93°C

TEACHER F.Y.I.

The centigrade scale—0° assigned to ice water (ice point) and 100° assigned to the boiling point of water at 1 ATM of pressure (steam point)—has been succeeded by the Celsius scale, in which the ice and steam points vary by a few hundredths of a degree from the centigrade scale. Because the difference between the two scales is so minimal, they are considered to be essentially the same today.

Practice Problems

1. Make the following conversions.
   a. 0°C to kelvins   c. 273°C to kelvins
   b. 0 K to degrees Celsius   d. 273 K to degrees Celsius
2. Convert these Celsius temperatures to Kelvin temperatures.
   a. 27°C   b. 560°C   c. −184°C   d. −300°C
3. Convert these Kelvin temperatures to Celsius temperatures.
   a. 110 K   b. 22 K   c. 402 K   d. 323 K
4. ► Find the Celsius and Kelvin temperatures for the following.
   a. room temperature   c. typical hot summer day
   b. refrigerator temperature   d. typical winter night

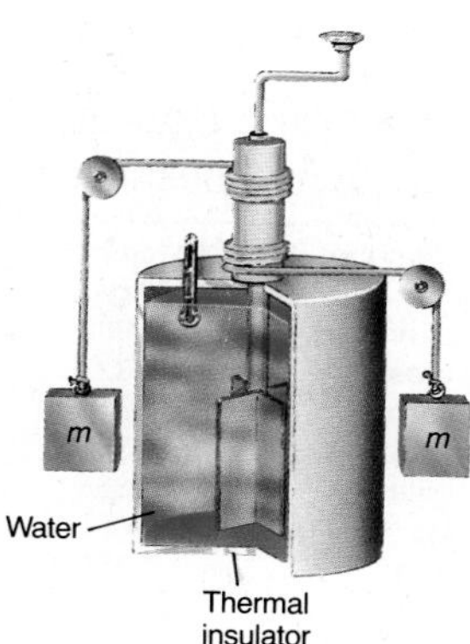

FIGURE 12–9. James Joule's experiment for measuring the mechanical equivalent of heat. The falling weights rotate the paddles, causing the temperature of the water to rise.

Heat and Thermal Energy

One way to increase the temperature of an object is to place it in contact with a hotter object. The thermal energy of the hotter object is decreased, and the thermal energy of the cooler object is increased. Energy flows from the hotter object to the cooler object. **Heat** *is the energy that flows as a result of a difference in temperature.* We will use the symbol Q for heat. Heat, like any other form of energy, is measured in joules.

Heat is thermal energy transferred because of a difference in temperature. Heat flows spontaneously from a warmer to a cooler body.

Note that this definition of heat is different from the one in everyday use. We commonly speak of a body containing "heat". This description is left over from the caloric theory. As we now know, a hot body contains a larger amount of thermal energy than a colder body of the same size. Heat is the energy transferred because of a difference in temperature.

When heat flows into an object, its thermal energy increases, and so does its temperature. The amount of increase depends on the size of the object. It also depends on the material from which the object is made. The **specific heat** of a material is the amount of energy that must be added to raise the temperature of a unit mass one temperature unit. In SI units, specific heat, C, is measured in J/kg · K. For example, 903 J must be added to one kilogram of aluminum to raise the temperature one kelvin. The specific heat of aluminum is 903 J/kg · K.

Specific heat is the increase in thermal energy that raises one kilogram of a substance one kelvin.

Note that water has a high specific heat compared to other substances, even ice and steam. One kilogram of water requires the addition of 4180 J of energy to increase its temperature one kelvin. By comparison, the same mass of copper requires only 385 J. The energy needed to raise the temperature of one kilogram of water 1 K would increase the temperature of the same mass of copper 11 K. The high specific heat of water is the reason water is used in car radiators to remove waste heat.

Specific heat can be used to find the amount of heat that must be transferred to change the temperature of a given mass by any amount. The specific heat of water is 4180 J/kg · K. When the temperature of one kilogram of water is increased by one kelvin, the heat absorbed by the water is 4180 J. When the temperature of 10 kilograms of water is increased by 5.0 K, the heat absorbed, Q, is

$$Q = (10\text{ kg})(4180\text{ J/kg}\cdot\text{K})(5.0\text{ K}) = 2.1 \times 10^5\text{ J}.$$

LABORATORY MANUAL

Use Lab 12.1 with this section.

Answers To
PRACTICE PROBLEMS

Have students refer to Appendix A of the Solutions Appendix for complete solutions to Practice Problems.

1. a. 273 K
   b. −273°C
   c. 546 K
   d. 0°C
2. a. 300 K
   b. 833 K
   c. 89 K
   d. impossible temperature
3. a. −163°C
   b. −251°C
   c. 129°C
   d. 50°C
4. a. answers will vary 20 to 22°C, 293–295 K
   b. about 4°C, 277 K
   c. about 30°C, 303 K
   d. about −18°C, 255 K

Laboratory Manual. Give students additional experience with specific heat by doing Lab 12.1 in the Laboratory Manual.

CONCEPT DEVELOPMENT

Have students list various ways of warming things (microwave, oven cooking, heating over a flame, and so on). Help them classify each as heat or work. This concept is discussed in greater detail on page 256.

Assessment

Portfolio

The word "heat" can be a source of great confusion. When used as a verb, it causes little trouble because it is usually used in an everyday way. For example, you might heat your food in a microwave oven or on a range. When used as a noun, however, "heat" is used in such a way as to suggest that heat is a substance that, when added to matter, increases its temperature. Have students collect sentences from newspapers, magazines, and books that use the word both correctly and incorrectly.

CONCEPT DEVELOPMENT

- It should be noted that the specific heats given in Table 12–1 are valid for temperatures near room temperature. For most practical purposes, specific heats can be considered to be constant over a reasonable temperature range.
- Emphasize to students the unusually high specific heat of water. This makes water an excellent coolant. Large bodies of water have a moderating effect on climate because they are so difficult to warm up or cool off.
- Stress to students that temperature change terms can be either positive or negative. The change is calculated by subtracting the initial temperature from the final temperature. This formula, used carefully, will always give the correct result.

Answers To
PRACTICE PROBLEMS

Have students refer to Appendix A of the Solutions Appendix for complete solutions to Practice Problems.

5. 1.39×10^3 J
6. 1.0×10^6 J
7. a. 10.0°C
b. 21°C
c. water
8. a. 2.0×10^4 J
b. 0.24 kg

Enrichment: Have interested students research and report on how the climate and weather of land areas is affected by adjacent bodies of water.

Table 12–1

Specific Heat of Common Substances

Material	Specific heat J/kg · K
aluminum	903
brass	376
carbon	710
copper	385
glass	664
ice	2060
iron	450
lead	130
methanol	2450
silver	235
steam	2020
water	4180
zinc	388

The heat gained or lost by an object as its temperature changes depends on the mass, change in temperature, and specific heat of the substance. The relationship can be written

$$Q = mC\Delta T,$$

where Q is the heat gained or lost, m is the mass of the object, C is the specific heat of the substance, and ΔT is the change in temperature. Since one Celsius degree is equal to one kelvin, temperature changes can be measured in either kelvins or Celsius degrees.

Example Problem

Heat Transfer

A 0.400-kg block of iron is heated from 295 K to 325 K. How much heat is absorbed by the iron?

Given: mass, $m = 0.400$ kg
specific heat, $C = 450$ J/kg · K
$T_i = 295$ K
$T_f = 325$ K

Unknown: Q

Basic equations: $\Delta T = T_f - T_i$
$Q = mC\Delta T$

Solution: $Q = mC\Delta T$
$= (0.400\text{ kg})(450\text{ J/kg}\cdot\text{K})(325\text{ K} - 295\text{ K})$
$= 5.4 \times 10^3$ J

FIGURE 12–10. Brine solutions are evaporated in solar ponds to obtain potassium compounds. The blue dye added to the brine solutions absorbs solar radiation faster and speeds up evaporation.

Practice Problems

5. How much heat is absorbed by 60.0 g of copper when it is heated from 20.0°C to 80.0°C?

6. A 38-kg block of lead is heated from −26°C to 180°C. How much heat does it absorb during the heating?

7. The cooling system of a car engine contains 20.0 L of water. (1 L of water has a mass of 1 kg.)
 a. What is the change in the temperature of the water if the engine operates until 836.0 kJ of heat are added?
 b. Suppose it is winter and the system is filled with methanol. The density of methanol is 0.80 g/cm³. What would be the increase in temperature of the methanol if it absorbed 836.0 kJ of heat?
 c. Which is the better coolant, water or methanol? Explain.

▶ **8.** A 565-g cube of iron is cooled from the temperature of boiling water to room temperature (20°C).
 a. How much heat must be absorbed from the cube?
 b. If the iron is cooled by dunking it into water at 0°C that rises in temperature to 20°C, how much water is needed?

TEACHER F.Y.I.

In 1819, Dulong and Petit demonstrated that the specific heat of an element is approximately inversely proportional to its atomic weight. This means that if the specific heat of a new element is determined, one can get an idea of its atomic weight quickly. This discovery was very beneficial to the work of Berzelius in improving his table of atomic weights, the precursor to the periodic table.

PHYSICS LAB : Heating Up

Purpose

To discover how the temperature increases with a constant supply of thermal energy.

Materials

- hot plate (or bunsen burner)
- 250-mL pyrex beaker
- water
- thermometer
- stopwatch
- goggles

Procedure

1. Turn your hot plate to a medium setting (or as recommended by your teacher). Allow a few minutes for the plate to heat up. While heating water wear goggles.
2. Pour 150 ml of room temperature water into the 250-mL beaker.
3. Measure the initial temperature of the water. Keep the thermometer in the water.
4. Place the beaker on the hot plate and record the temperature every 1.0 minute. Carefully stir the water before taking a temperature reading.
5. Record the time when the water starts to boil. Continue recording the temperature for an additional 4.0 minutes.
6. Carefully remove the beaker from the hot plate. Record the remaining water.

Observations and Data

1. Make a graph of temperature (vertical axis) vs time (horizontal axis).
2. Make a generalization about the graph during the first few minutes of the experiment.

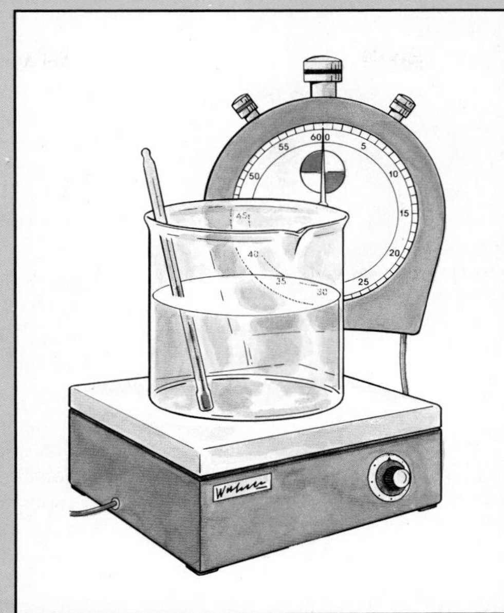

Analysis

1. What is the slope of the graph for the first 3.0 minutes? Be sure to include units.
2. What is the thermal energy given to the water in the first 3.0 minutes? **Hint:** $Q = mC\Delta T$.
3. Use a dotted line on the same graph to predict what the graph would look like if the same procedure was made with only half as much water.

Applications

1. Would you expect that the hot plate transferred energy to the water at a steady rate? Explain.
2. Where is the energy going when the water is boiling?

PHYSICS LAB

Process Skills: observing, communicating, interpreting data, measuring, predicting, questioning, defining operationally, using numbers.

MISCONCEPTION

Many students simply do not realize the great amount of energy required for a change of state.

Lab Worksheet, Teacher Resource Package. If desired, use the lab worksheet master for this chapter for students to record their data.

OBSERVATIONS

1. Sample graph:

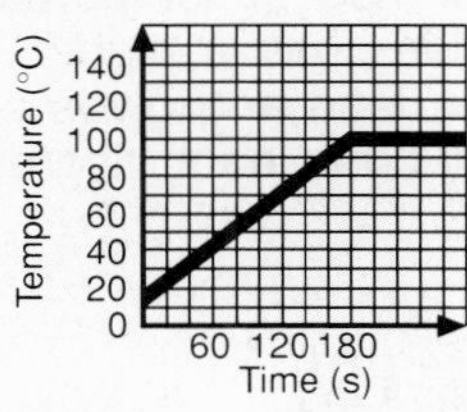

2. The slope is fairly constant for the first few minutes.

ANALYSIS

1. The slope of the graph depends on the amount of water and the setting of the hot plate.

2. Sample calculation:

$$Q = mc\Delta T$$
$$= (0.15 \text{ kg})(4180 \text{ J/kg °C})(45\text{°C})$$
$$= 2.8 \times 10^4 \text{ J}$$

3. With only half the amount of water, the graph should have twice the slope.

Teaching Suggestion: The time needed to boil all the water can be calculated by using the following ratio:

$$\frac{4.0 \text{ min}}{\textit{water boiled}} = \frac{t \text{ min}}{\textit{total water}}.$$

APPLICATIONS

1. The setting on the hot plate was constant. The rate of energy into the water was probably constant.

2. After the water reached 100°C, all of the energy went into changing the water from a liquid into a gas.

LAB WORKSHEET

Use the Lab Worksheet for Chapter 12 with this Physics Lab.

ASSESSMENT

Critical Thinking: To further assess students' understanding of the relationship of energy to change of state, ask the following questions.

1. List several factors that would change the slope of the graph. Explain with specific examples. [With a lower heat setting on the hot plate, the slope of the graph would be less. With less water in the beaker, the slope would be greater.]

2. Can you predict how much thermal energy was given off by the hot plate during the experiment? Explain your answer. [The thermal energy transferred to the water can be calculated, but the beaker, the hot plate, and the water also transfer energy into the air. It would be very difficult to measure this energy.]

ACTIVITY

Demonstration: Find and note the mass of a large glass marble. Cut a piece of lead sheet to the same mass. Heat the marble and the lead sheet in boiling water for a few minutes. While they are heating, measure out equal amounts of cold water into two polystyrene cups. Record the water temperature. Ask the students to predict whether both materials will heat up the water the same amount since they are at the same temperature, or if one of the materials will heat up the water more. Quickly transfer the marble to one cup and the lead to the other. Gently stir the water in each cup. When the temperatures level off, record them. [The glass will cause a greater rise in temperature because glass has a higher specific heat than lead and gives off more heat as it cools each degree.]

Connect to CHEMISTRY

Many chemical reactions convert chemical energy to thermal energy. These reactions are called exothermic. Some, like the combination of hydrogen and oxygen to form water, release so much energy so quickly that an explosion results. Chemical reactions in which the final state has more energy stored in the chemical bonds than the initial state absorb thermal energy from their surroundings. Such reactions are called endothermic. A commercial product uses an endothermic reaction to create a cold compress to be applied to athletic injuries. Some chemical reactions do not occur spontaneously. For example, a kitchen match must be rubbed against a rough surface to raise its temperature before it ignites. Thus thermal energy is first added, then released. How could you find out if such a reaction is exothermic or endothermic? [Measure the net thermal energy change. If the amount released is greater than that added, the reaction is exothermic.]

FIGURE 12–11. A calorimeter provides a closed, isolated system in which to measure energy transfer.

Calorimetry: Measuring Specific Heat

A **calorimeter,** Figure 12–11, is a device used to measure changes in thermal energy. A measured mass of a substance is heated to a known temperature and placed in the calorimeter. The calorimeter contains a known mass of cold water at a measured temperature. From the resulting increase in water temperature, the change in thermal energy of the substance is calculated.

The total energy of an isolated, closed system is constant. Energy lost by one part is gained by another.

The calorimeter depends on the conservation of energy in isolated, closed systems. Energy can neither enter nor leave an isolated system. A calorimeter is carefully insulated so that heat transfer in or out is very small. Often a covered Styrofoam cup is used. As a result of the isolation, if the energy of one part of the system increases, the energy of another part must decrease by the same amount. Consider a system composed of two blocks of metal, block A and block B, Figure 12–12. The total energy of the system is constant;

$$E_A + E_B = \text{constant}.$$

Suppose that the two blocks are initially separated but can be placed in contact. If the thermal energy of block A changes by an amount ΔE_A, then the change in thermal energy of block B, ΔE_B, must be related by the equation

$$\Delta E_A + \Delta E_B = 0.$$

The change in energy of one block is positive, while the change in energy of the other block is negative. If the thermal energy change is positive, the temperature of that block rises. If the change is negative, the temperature falls.

Heat flows until all parts of the system are at the same temperature.

Assume that the initial temperatures of the two blocks are different. When the blocks are brought together, heat flows from the hotter to the colder block, Figure 12–12. The flow continues until the blocks are in thermal equilibrium. The blocks then have the same temperature.

The change in thermal energy is equal to the heat transferred:

$$\Delta E = Q = mC\Delta T.$$

The increase in thermal energy of block A is equal to the decrease in thermal energy of block B. Thus,

$$m_A C_A \Delta T_A + m_B C_B \Delta T_B = 0.$$

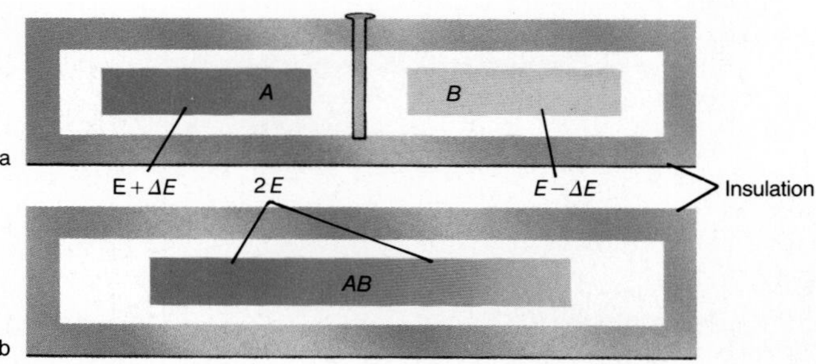

FIGURE 12–12. The total energy for this system is constant.

RETEACHING MASTER

Use the Reteaching master for Chapter 12 with this section.

ENRICHMENT MASTER

Use the Enrichment master for Chapter 12 with this section.

The change in temperature is the difference between the final and initial temperatures, $\Delta T = T_f - T_i$. If the temperature of a block increases, $T_f > T_i$, and ΔT is positive. If the temperature of the block decreases, $T_f < T_i$, and ΔT is negative.

The final temperatures of the two blocks are equal. The equation for the transfer of energy is

$$m_A C_A(T_f - T_{A,i}) + m_B C_B(T_f - T_{B,i}) = 0.$$

To solve for T_f, expand the equation:

$$m_A C_A T_f - m_A C_A T_{A,i} + m_B C_B T_f - m_B C_B T_{B,i} = 0.$$

Isolate T_f and solve,

$$T_f(m_A C_A + m_B C_B) = m_A C_A T_{A,i} + m_B C_B T_{B,i}.$$

$$T_f = \frac{m_A C_A T_{A,i} + m_B C_B T_{B,i}}{m_A C_A + m_B C_B}$$

Note that either the Celsius or Kelvin temperature scale may be used with this equation.

POCKET LAB

COOL TIMES

Place a 100-mL beaker in a 250-mL beaker. Put a thermometer into each beaker. Fill the small beaker with hot, colored water. Determine the temperature of the colored water. Slowly pour tap water into the large beaker until the water is at the same height in both beakers. Record the temperature in the large beaker. Record the temperature in both beakers every minute for 5 minutes. Plot your data for both beakers on the same graph of temperature vs time. Measure and record the mass of water in each beaker. Predict the final temperature. Describe each curve.

Example Problem

Conservation in Energy Transfer

A 0.500-kg sample of water is at 15.0°C in a calorimeter. A 0.0400-kg block of zinc at 115°C is placed in the water. Find the final temperature of the system? The specific heat of zinc is 388 J/kg · K.

Given: zinc

$m_A = 0.0400$ kg

$T_{A,i} = 115°C$

$C_A = 388$ J/kg · K

water

$m_B = 0.500$ kg

$T_{B,i} = 15.0°C$

$C_B = 4180$ J/kg · K

1 J/kg · K = 1 J/kg · °C

Unknown: T_f

Basic equations: $\Delta E_A + \Delta E_B = 0$

$m_A C_A \Delta T_A + m_B C_B \Delta T_B = 0$

Solution: $m_A C_A(T_f - T_{A,i}) + m_B C_B(T_f - T_{B,i}) = 0$

$$T_f = \frac{m_A C_A T_{A,i} + m_B C_B T_{B,i}}{m_A C_A + m_B C_B} =$$

$$\frac{(0.0400 \text{ kg})(388 \text{ J/kg}\cdot°C)(115°C) + (0.500 \text{ kg})(4180 \text{ J/kg}\cdot°C)(15.0°C)}{(0.0400 \text{ kg})(388 \text{ J/kg}\cdot°C) + (0.500 \text{ kg})(4180 \text{ J/kg}\cdot°C)}$$

$$T_f = \frac{(1.78 \times 10^3 \text{ J}) + (3.14 \times 10^4 \text{ J})}{15.5 \text{ J/°C} + 2.09 \times 10^3 \text{ J/°C}}$$

$$T_f = \frac{3.32 \times 10^4 \text{ J}}{2.11 \times 10^3 \text{ J/°C}}$$

$$= 15.7 \text{ °C}$$

Using Your CALCULATOR

Use the parentheses ( ) function on your calculator to evaluate complex equations. Note the use of two levels of parentheses in the denominator.

$$T_f = \frac{m_A C_A T_{A,i} + m_B C_B T_{B,i}}{m_A C_A + m_B C_B}$$

Keys	Display
(.0400 × 388 × 115)	1784. 8
+ (.500 × 4180 × 15)	31350
= ÷	33134. 8
((.0400 × 388) +	15. 52
(.500 × 4180)	2090
)	2105. 52
=	15. 73711

T_f = 15.7°C

Assessment

Performance

To further assess your students' understanding of thermal energy transfer, have them experiment with methods of reducing the loss of heat in this experiment. They might surround the large beaker with insulations such as polystyrene foam or even newspapers, cut cardboard disks to cover the two beakers, gently stir the water in the two beakers, or use water from the refrigerator rather than tap water. They should experiment to determine which ones work and explain why. Any method that makes the system more isolated will improve the experiment. Stirring makes the water temperatures more uniform. Using colder water balances the energy lost by the hot water to the room with energy gained from the room by the cold water.

POCKET LAB

COOL TIMES

Purpose: to investigate thermal energy transfer.

Materials: 100-mL beaker; 250-mL beaker; hot and room temperature water; stopwatch; 2 thermometers.

Outcome: Students should predict that the final temperature will be between the hot and cold temperatures. Since the specific heat of hot and cold water is the same, the equation used in calorimetry can be simplified to $T_f = (m_A T_{A,i} + m_B T_{B,i})/(m_A + m_B)$. They may find the measured temperature lower than predicted by the equation because of energy lost by the hot water to the beakers and the air. The curves should have a greater slope at the beginning when the temperatures are farthest apart. Later, the changes in temperature will become smaller as the two temperatures gradually approach each other.

CHECKING FOR UNDERSTANDING

Go over the Example Problem on this page, then analyze a heat problem from the Practice Problems on page 252.

Reteaching Master. Use the Reteaching Master for Chapter 12, The Transfer of Thermal Energy, from the Teacher Resource Package.

EXTENSION

In the colder parts of the United States, a common roadside sign reads, "CAUTION: Bridge freezes before road surface." Ask students why this is true. [The underside of the bridge is exposed to the air, which can cool it. Earth under the road both insulates it and provides additional mass that must be cooled to the freezing point.]

Enrichment Master. With this section, use the Enrichment Master, Calorimetry, from the Teacher Resource Package.

Answers To
PRACTICE PROBLEMS

Have students refer to Appendix A of the Solutions Appendix for complete solutions to Practice Problems.

9. 45.0°C
10. 59.5°C
11. 23.0°C
12. 8.4×10^2 J/kg · K

INDEPENDENT PRACTICE/ EXTENSION

Refer to the Assignment Guide below for additional questions and problems for independent practice.

3 Close

CONVERGENT QUESTION

Ask students to name several jobs or places in the everyday world where having a good knowledge of the temperature of things is important.

CONCEPT REVIEW ANSWERS

1.1 Yes, if the bowl that contains hot water is smaller than the bowl that contains cold water.
1.2 The high specific heat of water means the same mass at the same temperature contains more thermal energy.
1.3 The specific heat of water is much higher than that of any metal. Thus, water affects the temperature of your tongue much more.
1.4 Critical Thinking: As the water is warmed by the hot sample, heat leaks out, and the final temperature is reduced. Thus you would think the thermal energy of the sample is smaller than it really is, and the measure of its specific heat would be too low.

F.Y.I.

Laws of Thermodynamics:
1. You cannot win.
2. You cannot break even.
3. You cannot get out of the game.

Anon

Practice Problems

9. A 2.00×10^2-g sample of water at 80.0°C is mixed with 2.00×10^2 g of water at 10.0°C. Assume no heat loss to the surroundings. What is the final temperature of the mixture?
10. A 4.00×10^2-g sample of methanol at 16.0°C is mixed with 4.00×10^2 g of water at 85.0°C. Assume no heat loss to the surroundings. What is the final temperature of the mixture?
11. A 1.00×10^2-g brass block at 90.0°C is placed in a styrofoam cup containing 2.00×10^2 g of water at 20.0°C. No heat is lost to the cup or the surroundings. Find the final temperature of the mixture.
▶ **12.** A 1.0×10^2-g aluminum block at 100.0°C is placed in 1.00×10^2 g of water at 10.0°C. The final temperature of the mixture is 25°C. What is the specific heat of the aluminum?

CONCEPT REVIEW

1.1 Could the thermal energy of a bowl of hot water equal that of a bowl of cold water? Explain.
1.2 On cold winter nights before central heating, people often placed hot water bottles in their beds. Why would this be better than, say warmed bricks?
1.3 If you take a spoon out of a cup of hot coffee and put it in your mouth, you won't burn your tongue. But, you could very easily burn your tongue if you put the liquid in your mouth. Why?
1.4 Critical Thinking: You use an aluminum cup instead of a styrofoam cup as a calorimeter, allowing heat to flow between the water and the environment. You measure the specific heat of a sample by putting the hot object into room-temperature water. How might your experiment be affected? Would your result be too large or too small?

Thermodynamics is the study of the properties of thermal energy and its changes.

Objectives

- **define heats of fusion and vaporization; understand the microscopic basis of changes of state; calculate heat transfers needed to effect changes of state.**
- **distinguish heat from work.**
- **state the first law of thermodynamics.**
- **define a heat engine, refrigerator, and heat pump.**
- **state the second law of thermodynamics; define entropy.**

12.2 CHANGE OF STATE AND LAWS OF THERMODYNAMICS

If you rub your hands together, you exert a force and move your hands over a distance. You do work against friction. Your hands start and end at rest, so there is no net change in kinetic energy. They remain the same distance above Earth so there is no change in potential energy. Yet, if conservation of energy is true, then the energy transferred by the work you did must have gone somewhere. You notice that your hands feel warm; their temperature is increased. The energy is now in the form of thermal energy. The branch of physics called **thermodynamics** explores the properties of thermal energy.

Change of State

The three most common states of matter are solids, liquids, and gases, Figure 12–13. As the temperature of a solid is raised, it first changes to a liquid. At even higher temperatures, it will become a gas. How can we explain these changes? Our simplified model of a solid consists of

12:1 ASSIGNMENT GUIDE

	PRACTICE	EXTENSION
CHAPTER REVIEW pp. 261–263		
· Reviewing Concepts	1–10	
· Applying Concepts		1–6
· Problems*	1–13, 15	14
APPENDIX B PROBLEMS*		
· Chapter 12, p. 697	1–7	8, 9, 10

* Complete solutions to all Chapter Review and Appendix problems appear in the Problems and Solutions Manual.

FIGURE 12–13. The three states of water are represented in this photograph. The gaseous state, water vapor, is dispersed in the air and is invisible until it condenses.

tiny particles bonded together by springs. The springs represent the electromagnetic forces between the particles. When the thermal energy of a solid is increased, both the potential and kinetic energies of the particles increase.

At sufficiently high temperatures, the forces between the particles are no longer strong enough to hold them in fixed locations. The particles are still touching, but they have more freedom of movement. Eventually, the particles become free enough to slide past each other. At this point, the substance has changed from a solid to a liquid. The temperature at which this change occurs is called the **melting point.**

While a substance is melting, added energy does not increase the temperature.

When a substance is melting, added thermal energy increases the potential energy of particles, breaking the bonds holding them together. The added thermal energy does not increase the temperature.

The heat of fusion is the energy needed to melt one kilogram of a substance.

The amount of energy needed to melt one kilogram of a substance is called the **heat of fusion** of that substance. For example, the heat of fusion of ice is 3.34×10^5 J/kg. If 1 kg of ice at its melting point, 273 K, absorbs 3.34×10^5 J, the ice becomes 1 kg of water at the same temperature, 273 K. The added energy causes a change in state but not in temperature.

The heat of vaporization is the energy needed to vaporize one kilogram of a substance.

After the substance is totally melted, a further increase in thermal energy once again increases the temperature. Added thermal energy increases the kinetic and potential energies. As the temperature increases, some particles in the liquid acquire enough energy to break free from other particles. At a specific temperature, known as the **boiling point,** further addition of energy causes another change of state. It does not raise the temperature; it converts particles in the liquid state to particles in the vapor or gaseous state. At normal atmospheric pressure, water boils at 373 K. The amount of thermal energy needed to vaporize one kilogram of a liquid is called the **heat of vaporization.** For water, the heat of vaporization is 2.26×10^6 J/kg. Each substance has a characteristic heat of vaporization.

The heat, Q, required to melt a solid of mass m is given by

$$Q = mH_f.$$

The value of some heats of fusion, H_f, can be found in Table 12–2.

POCKET LAB

MELTING

Label two foam cups A and B. Measure 75 ml of room temperature water into the two cups. Add an ice cube to cup A. Add ice water to cup B until the water levels are equal. Measure the temperature of each cup at 1 minute intervals until the ice has melted. Do the samples reach the same final temperature? Why?

12.2 CHANGE OF STATE AND LAWS OF THERMODYNAMICS

Preparation

OVERVIEW

The first and second laws of thermodynamics, heat, heat engines, melting and boiling points, heat of fusion and heat of vaporization, and entropy are introduced in this major section.

BRIDGING

Friction and temperature are reintroduced in this section.

1 Focus

DISCREPANT EVENT

Steam burns are worse than boiling water burns because more thermal energy is transferred to your skin when steam condenses than when water cools.

POCKET LAB

MELTING

Purpose: to observe heat transfer during a change of state.

Materials: 2 foam cups; water; ice water; ice cube; 2 thermometers.

Outcome: Many students will not believe the results. Even though the ice cube and the ice water are both at approximately 0°C, the ice will cool the water much more than the ice water. The ice cube takes energy to change from a solid to a liquid.

2 Teach

CONCEPT DEVELOPMENT

Study Guide Master. To reinforce the concepts in this section, have the students complete the Study Guide Master for Section 12.2 from the Teacher Resource Package.

Critical Thinking: Have students look at Table 12–2, heats of fusion and vaporization. Ask them what the range is of these quantities. Ask them what the range is for specific heats in Table 12–1 on page 248. Ask students by how large a factor each of these differ.

Enrichment: Along with heats of fusion and vaporization, some students may have heard of heat of sublimation. Have interested students investigate and explain this type of heat.

Demonstration: As an aid to remembering how materials undergoing a change of state behave, boil water and record its temperature every 30 seconds or so. The temperature will level off at the boiling point and not increase any more. If you have a temperature probe interfacing device and the ability to display the readings on a video monitor, you can display the temperature continuously. Otherwise, a graph on the blackboard will do as well. Be sure to ask students where all the energy being supplied to the boiling water goes after the temperature stabilizes.

Table 12–2

Heats of Fusion and Vaporization of Common Substances

Material	Heat of fusion H_f (J/kg)	Heat of vaporization H_v (J/kg)	Material	Heat of fusion H_f (J/kg)	Heat of vaporization H_v (J/kg)
copper	2.05×10^5	5.07×10^6	mercury	1.15×10^4	2.72×10^5
gold	6.30×10^4	1.64×10^6	methanol	1.09×10^5	8.78×10^5
iron	2.66×10^5	6.29×10^6	silver	1.04×10^4	2.36×10^6
lead	2.04×10^4	8.64×10^5	water (ice)	3.34×10^5	2.26×10^6

Similarly, the heat, Q, required to vaporize a mass, m, of liquid is given by

$$Q = mH_v.$$

Heats of vaporization, H_v, can also be found in Table 12–2.

When a liquid freezes, an amount of heat $Q = -mH_f$ must be removed from the liquid to turn it into a solid. The negative sign indicates the heat is transferred from the sample to the environment. In the same way, when a vapor condenses to a liquid, an amount of heat, $Q = -mH_v$, must be removed.

Example Problem

Heat of Fusion—1

If 5.00×10^3 J is added to ice at 273 K, how much ice is melted?

Given: heat added, $Q = 5.00 \times 10^3$ J
heat of fusion, $H_f = 3.34 \times 10^5$ J/kg

Unknown: mass, m
Basic equation: $Q = mH_f$

Solution: $m = \dfrac{5.00 \times 10^3 \text{ J}}{3.34 \times 10^5 \text{ J/kg}} = 0.0150$ kg

Figure 12–14 shows the changes in temperature as thermal energy is added to 1.0 g of H_2O at 243 K. Between points **A** and **B,** the ice is warmed to 273 K. Between points **B** and **C,** the added thermal energy melts the ice at a constant 273 K. The horizontal distance from point **B** to point **C** represents the heat of fusion. Between points **C** and **D,** the

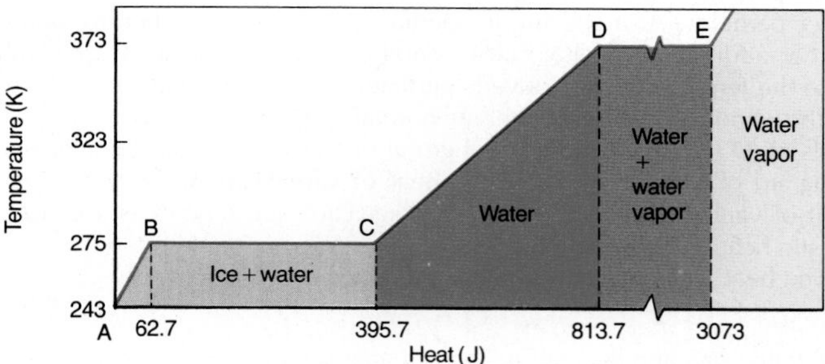

FIGURE 12–14. A plot of temperature versus heat added when 1 g of ice is initially converted to steam.

STUDY GUIDE MASTER

Use the Study Guide master for section 12.2

water temperature rises. The slope is smaller here than between points **A** and **B,** showing that the specific heat of water is higher than that of ice. Between points **D** and **E,** the water boils, becoming water vapor. The distance from point **D** to point **E** represents the heat of vaporization. Between points **E** and **F,** the steam is heated to 473 K. The slope is larger than that from point **C** to point **D,** indicating that the specific heat of steam is less than that of water.

Example Problem

Heat of Fusion—2

How much heat must be transferred to 100.0 g of ice at 0.0°C until the ice melts and the temperature of the resulting water rises to 20.0°C?

Given: $m = 100.0$ g
$T_i = 0.0°C$
$T_f = 20.0°C$
$H_f = 3.34 \times 10^5$ J/kg
$C = 4180$ J/kg · °C

Unknown: Q_{total}
Basic equations: $Q = mH_f$
$Q = mC\Delta T$

Solution:
First, find the amount of heat the ice absorbs as it changes from solid to liquid.

$$Q = mH_f = (0.100 \text{ kg})(3.34 \times 10^5 \text{ J/kg}) = 33\,400 \text{ J}$$

Second, calculate the amount of heat the water absorbs as its temperature rises from 0.0°C to 20.0°C.

$$Q = mC\Delta T = (0.100 \text{ kg})(4180 \text{ J/kg} \cdot °\text{C})(20.0°\text{C} - 0.0°\text{C}) = 8360 \text{ J}$$

Finally, add the two quantities of heat.

$$Q_{total} = 33\,400 \text{ J} + 8360 \text{ J} = 41\,760 \text{ J}$$

Thus, 41.8 kJ of heat is transferred from the water to the ice.

Practice Problems

13. How much heat is absorbed by 1.00×10^2 g of ice at −20.0°C to become water at 0.0°C?

14. A 2.00×10^2-g sample of water at 60.0°C is heated to steam at 140.0°C. How much heat is absorbed?

15. How much heat is needed to change 3.00×10^2 g of ice at −30.0°C to steam at 130.0°C?

▶ **16.** A 175-g lump of molten lead at its melting point, 327°C, is dropped into 55 g of water at 20.0°C.

a. What is the temperature of the water when the lead becomes solid?

b. When the lead and water are in thermal equilibrium, what is the temperature?

HELP WANTED

HVAC TECHNICIAN

Knowledge of thermodynamics; ability to read blueprints, specifications and manuals; familiarity with current products, procedures, tools, and test equipment; and ability to work hard in sometimes physically demanding conditions make you an ideal candidate for this position.

Knowledge of all kinds of heating, ventilation, and air conditioning systems is required. This organization offers excellent opportunity to work your way up into other positions based on your work performance and completion of further training.

For information contact:
Association Builders and Contractors, 729 15th Street, N.W., Washington, DC 20005

F.Y.I.

Evaporation of perspiration from the skin is an effective way of cooling your body. Over two million joules of thermal energy are carried away for each liter of liquid lost. If the perspiration runs down your face, however, its ability to cool is almost all lost.

Answers To
PRACTICE PROBLEMS

Have students refer to Appendix A of the Solutions Appendix for complete solutions to Practice Problems.

13. 3.75×10^4 J
14. 5.02×10^5 J
15. 9.40×10^5 J
16. a. 36°C
b. 62°C

CONCEPT DEVELOPMENT

Many other things can be deduced from the laws of thermodynamics, such as the efficiency of various thermal processes. There are also many different ways of expressing the laws, which your students might enjoy looking up in college-level books or encyclopedias.

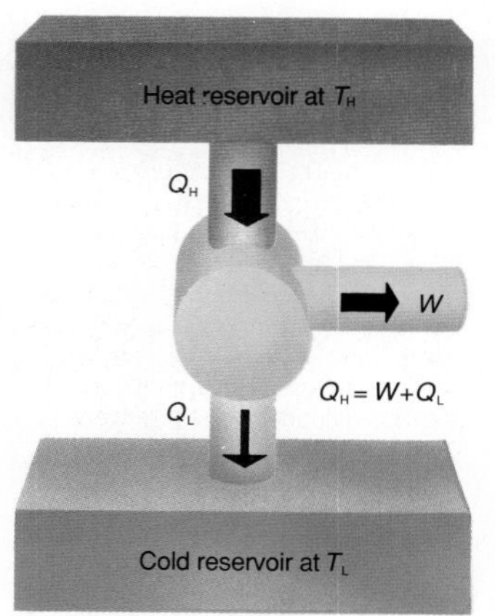

FIGURE 12–15. The flow chart diagram represents heat at high temperature transformed into mechanical energy and low temperature waste heat.

The First Law of Thermodynamics

You don't have to transfer heat to increase the thermal energy of a body. If you rub your hands together, they are warmed, yet they were not brought into contact with a hotter body. Instead, work was done on your hands by means of friction. The mechanical energy of your moving hands was changed into thermal energy.

There are other means of converting mechanical energy into thermal energy. If you use a hand pump to inflate a bicycle tire, the air and pump become warm. The mechanical energy in the moving piston is converted into thermal energy of the gas. Other forms of energy—light, sound, electrical, as well as mechanical—can be changed into thermal energy.

Thermal energy is increased by both work done and heat added to a system.

Thermal energy can be increased either by adding heat or by doing work on a system. Thus, *the total increase in the thermal energy of a system is the sum of the work done on it and the heat added to it.* This fact is called the **first law of thermodynamics.** Thermodynamics is the study of the changes in thermal properties of matter. The first law is merely a restatement of the law of conservation of energy.

All forms of energy are measured in joules. Work, energy transferred by mechanical means, and heat, energy transferred because of a difference in temperature, are also measured in joules.

The conversion of mechanical energy to thermal energy, as when you rub your hands together, is easy. The reverse process, conversion of thermal to mechanical energy, is more difficult. A device able to convert thermal energy to mechanical energy continuously is called a **heat engine.**

A heat engine accepts heat from a high temperature source, performs work, and transfers heat out at a low temperature.

Heat engines require a high temperature source from which thermal energy can be removed, and a low temperature sink into which thermal energy can be delivered, Figure 12–15. An automobile engine is an example of a heat engine, Figure 12–16. A mixture of air and gasoline vapor is ignited, producing a very high temperature flame. Heat flows from the flame to the air in the cylinder. The hot air expands and pushes on a piston, changing thermal energy into mechanical energy. In order to obtain continuous mechanical energy, the engine must be returned to its starting condition. The heated air is expelled and replaced by new

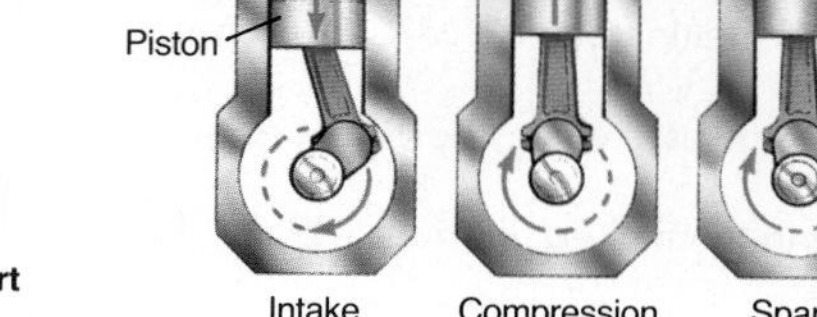

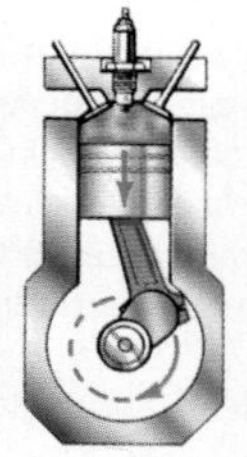
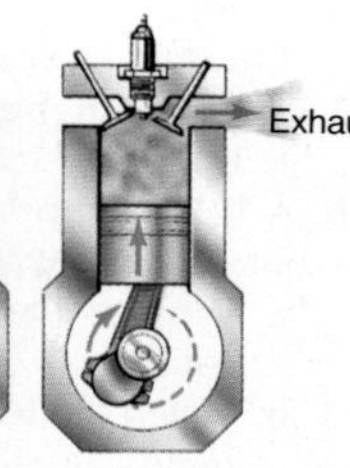

FIGURE 12–16. The heat produced by burning gasoline causes the gases produced to expand and exert force on the cylinder.

Multicultural Connections

The Chinese were the first to use central heating for their homes. Instead of building fires inside the house, they would build one outside and heat air to create a convection current that would move into the house. The Inuits reverse the concept in their igloos. By digging the entrance way lower than the inside of the igloo, they create a natural pressure barrier to keep cold air out. Since cold air sinks to the lowest point, the entrance way fills with cold air from the outside and then the flow stops. The warmer air inside the igloo stays in because it would have to go down through colder air to escape.

air, and the piston is returned to the top of the cylinder. The entire cycle is repeated many times each minute. The heat from the burning gasoline is converted into mechanical energy that eventually results in the movement of the car.

Not all the thermal energy from the very high temperature flame is converted into mechanical energy. The exhaust gases and the engine parts become hot. The exhaust comes in contact with outside air, transferring heat to it. Heat from the hot engine is transferred to a radiator. Outside air passes through the radiator and the air temperature is raised. This heat transferred out of the engine is called waste heat, heat that cannot be converted into work. All heat engines generate waste heat. In a car engine, the waste heat is at a lower temperature than the heat of the gasoline flame. The overall change in total energy of the car-air system is zero. Thus, according to the first law of thermodynamics, the thermal energy in the flame is equal to the sum of the mechanical energy produced and the waste heat expelled.

Heat flows spontaneously from a warm body to a cold body. It is possible to remove thermal energy from a colder body and add it to a warmer body. An external source of energy, usually mechanical energy, however, is required to accomplish this transfer. A refrigerator is a common example of a device that accomplishes this transfer. Electrical energy runs a motor that does work on a gas such as Freon. Heat is transferred from the contents of the refrigerator to the Freon. Food is cooled, usually to 4.0°C, and the Freon is warmed. Outside the refrigerator, heat is transferred from the Freon to room air, cooling the Freon again. The overall change in the thermal energy of the Freon is zero. Thus, according to the first law of thermodynamics, the sum of the heat removed from the food and the work done by the motor is equal to the heat expelled to the outside at a higher temperature, Figure 12–17.

A heat pump is a refrigerator that can be run in two directions. In summer, heat is removed from the house, cooling the house. The heat is expelled into the warmer air outside. In winter, heat is removed from the cold outside air and transferred into the warmer house, Figure 12–18. In either case, mechanical energy is required to transfer heat from a cold object to a warmer one.

Perpetual Motion?

FIGURE 12–17. Diagram for a refrigerator. It absorbs heat Q_L from the cold reservoir and gives off heat Q_H to the hot reservoir. Work, W, is done *on* the refrigerator.

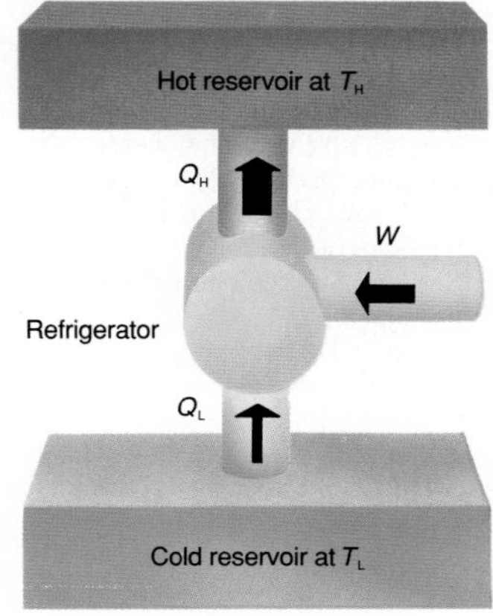

FIGURE 12–18. A heat pump runs in either direction depending on whether it is used in heating or cooling. In cooling, heat is extracted from the air in the house and pumped outside (a). In heating, heat is extracted from the outside and pumped inside (b).

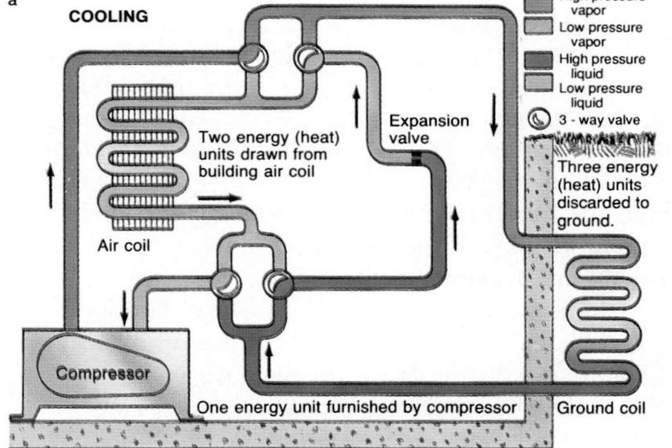

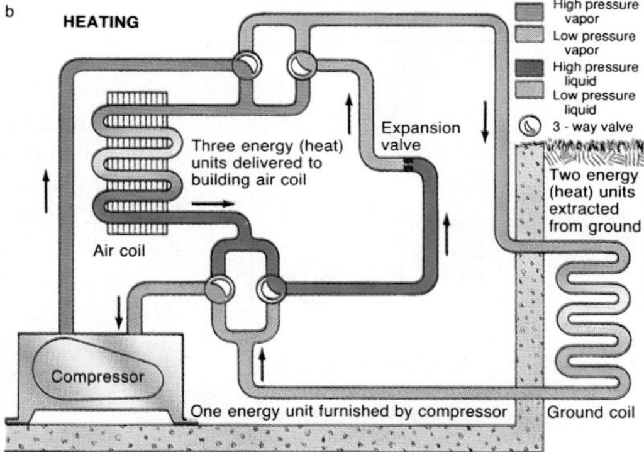

CONCEPT DEVELOPMENT

- The following is an outline of the refrigerator cycle. Low pressure gas enters the compressor where it becomes high-pressure, hot gas. The gas goes into the condenser coil (ground coil for cooling, air coil for heating) where the thermal energy is removed and cold liquid comes out, still at high pressure. The liquid goes into the expansion valve where the pressure drops. The low-pressure liquid goes into the evaporator coil (air coil for cooling, ground coil for heating) where the liquid evaporates into gas, absorbing thermal energy in the process. The gas goes back into the compressor, repeating the process.

Critical Thinking Master, Teacher Resource Package. You may wish to have students complete the Critical Thinking Master, Comparing Heat Engines, with this section.

Transparency Package. Use Transparency 15 to demonstrate the transfer of energy in a heat pump.

CRITICAL THINKING

Use the Critical Thinking master for Chapter 12 with this section.

TRANSPARENCY

Use Transparency 15 with this section.

POCKET LAB

DRIP, DRIP, DRIP

Purpose: to observe the disorder associated with temperature in liquids.

Materials: 2 glasses (or beakers); hot and cold water; food coloring; dropper.

Outcome: Many students will predict that the rate of mixing will be different. Students will be surprised to see how quickly the coloring mixes in the hot water. The mixing is faster in the hot water because the molecules have a higher average speed. The mixing is not symmetric due to the random motion of the molecules.

CONCEPT DEVELOPMENT

- Entropy is all around us: cars rust out, abandonded houses crumble, people age, and our rooms get messy. Have students give other examples of the tendency toward greater entropy in the world.
- *Project Physics* has a great deal of additional material on the laws of thermodynamics and their development.

Critical Thinking: Ask students why a portable air conditioner has to be mounted in a window. Have them explain what happens to the thermal energy removed from the room.

EARTH SCIENCE CONNECTION

Freon is the name of a family of chemical compounds invented for use in refrigerators and air conditioners. Each Freon compound was designed by chemists to have a specific boiling point. They were also designed to be very stable, and not to react with materials used in refrigerators. They work very well in a variety of important applications. Unfortunately, these properties also mean that when these gases escape into the atmosphere, they also do not decompose at low altitudes. In the past few years, however, scientists have found that these chemicals do react when they move into the upper atmosphere, miles above Earth. The products of the reaction can destroy Earth's protective ozone layer, increasing ultraviolet radiation that reaches Earth, and increasing incidence of skin cancer. They may also increase the "greenhouse effect" and raise Earth's temperature. Scientists are now trying to create new molecules to replace the Freons that are safe for the ozone and are not greenhouse gases.

POCKET LAB

DRIP, DRIP, DRIP

Measure equal amounts of very hot and very cold water into 2 clear glasses (or beakers). Predict what will happen if you simultaneously put 1 drop of food coloring into each glass. Try it. What happened? Why? Was the mixing symmetric?

The Second Law of Thermodynamics

Many processes that do not violate the first law of thermodynamics have never been observed to occur spontaneously. For example, the first law does not prohibit heat flowing from a cold body to a hot body, Figure 12–19a. Still, when a hot body is placed in contact with a cold body, the hot body has never been observed to become hotter and the cold body colder. Heat flows spontaneously from hot to cold bodies. As another example, heat engines could convert thermal energy completely into mechanical energy with no waste heat and still obey the first law, Figure 12–19b. Yet waste heat is always generated.

In the nineteenth century, the French engineer Sadi Carnot (1796–1832) studied the ability of engines to convert heat into mechanical energy. He developed a logical proof that even an ideal engine would generate some waste heat. Real engines generate even more waste heat. Carnot's result is best described in terms of a quantity called **entropy** (EN truh pee). Entropy, like thermal energy, is contained in an object. If heat is added to a body, entropy is increased. If heat is removed from a body, entropy is decreased. If an object does work with no change in temperature, however, the entropy does not change, as long as friction is ignored.

On a microscopic level, entropy is described as the disorder in a system. When heat is added to an object, the particles move in a random way. Some move very quickly, others move slowly, many move at intermediate speeds. The greater the range of speeds exhibited by the particles, the greater the disorder. The greater the disorder, the larger the entropy. While it is theoretically possible that all the particles could have the same speed, the random collisions and energy exchanges of the particles make the probability of this extremely unlikely.

The **second law of thermodynamics** states: *natural processes go in a direction that increases the total entropy of the universe.* Entropy and the second law can be thought of as statements of the probability of events happening. Figure 12–20 illustrates an increase in entropy as food color molecules. originally separate from clear water, are thoroughly mixed with the water molecules after a time.

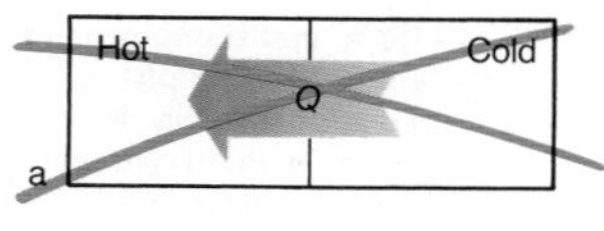

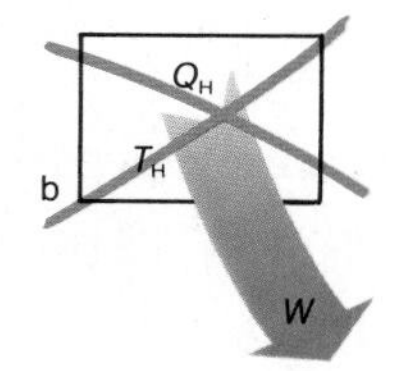

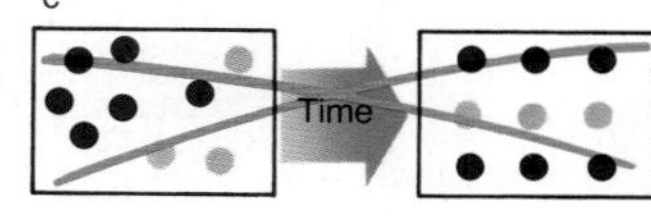

FIGURE 12–19. A representation of three processes forbidden by the second law of thermodynamics, but not the first law.

TEACHER 

Clausius (1822–1888) found that in any energy conversion, some energy is lost in the form of heat which cannot be recovered as useful energy. In effect, the energy supply of the universe is decreasing! Clausius proposed that the ratio of the energy content in a system to its absolute temperature always increases as a process proceeds. The term *entropy* has been credited to Clausius, though its true origin remains unknown.

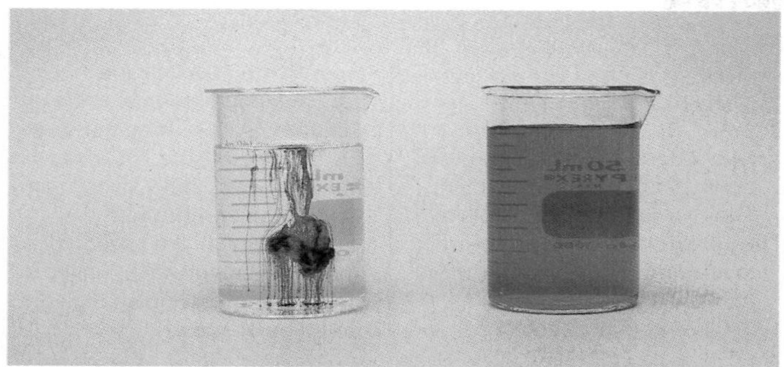

FIGURE 12–20. An example of the second law of thermodynamics.

The second law predicts that heat flows spontaneously only from a hot body to a cold body. Consider a hot iron bar and a cold cup of water. On the average, the particles in the iron will be moving very fast, whereas the particles in the water move more slowly. The bar is plunged into the water. When thermal equilibrium is reached, the average kinetic energy of the particles in the iron and the water will be the same. This final state is less ordered than the first situation. No longer are the fast particles confined mainly in the iron and the slow particles in the water. All speeds are evenly distributed. The entropy of the final state is larger than that of the initial state.

When fuel is burned, energy is not lost; entropy is increased.

We take for granted many daily events that occur spontaneously, or naturally, in one direction, but that would really shock us if they happened in reverse. You are not surprised when a metal spoon, heated at one end, soon becomes uniformly hot, or when smoke from a too-hot frying pan diffuses throughout the kitchen. Consider your reaction, however, if a spoon lying on a table suddenly, on its own, became red hot at one end and icy cold at the other, or if all the smoke from the skillet collected in a 9-cm^3 cube in the exact center of the kitchen. Neither of the reverse processes violates the first law of thermodynamics. The events are simply examples of the countless events that are not spontaneously reversible because the reverse process would violate the second law of thermodynamics.

The second law and entropy also give new meaning to what is commonly called the "energy crisis." When you use a resource such as natural gas to heat your home, you do not use up the energy in the gas. The potential energy contained in the molecules of the gas is converted into thermal energy of the flame, which is then transferred to thermal energy in the air of your home. Even if this warm air leaks to the outside, the energy is not lost. Energy has not been used up. The entropy, however, has been increased. The chemical structure of natural gas is very ordered. In contrast, the thermal motion of the warmed air is very disordered. While it is mathematically possible for the original order to be reestablished, the probability of this occurring is essentially zero. For this reason, entropy is often used as a measure of the unavailability of energy. The energy in the warmed air in a house is not as available to do mechanical work or to transfer heat to other bodies as the original gas molecules. The lack of usable energy is really a surplus of entropy.

a

b

FIGURE 12–21. A familiar example of the second law of thermodynamics. If no work is done on a system, entropy spontaneously reaches a maximum.

CHECKING FOR UNDERSTANDING

The second law of thermodynamics dictates which processes are reversible and which are nonreversible.

How does this idea apply to the following joke:

Q: How can you unscramble an egg?

A: Feed it to a chicken.

Ask students if this process violates the second law of thermodynamics.

RETEACHING

Have students translate the laws of thermodynamics into their own words.

Transparency Package. Use Transparency 16, Change of State Graph, and accompanying worksheet to quiz students on this section.

EXTENSION

Have students look up the zeroth law of thermodynamics. Have them explain why it is logically necessary to have this law. [The zeroth law is logically needed to explain how a single thermometer could be used to show that two bodies have the same temperature.]

INDEPENDENT PRACTICE/ EXTENSION

Refer to the Assignment Guide for additional questions and problems for independent practice.

3 Close

CONVERGENT QUESTION

Ask students how the second law of thermodynamics could be used to give a direction to the concept of time. This law is sometimes said to define the "arrow of time." [Since entropy either remains the same or increases in time, if the entropy of a closed system is larger, the time is later.]

TEACHER F.Y.I.

The zeroth law, proposed by James Clerk Maxwell (of electromagnetic fame), states that two bodies equal in temperature to a third body will be equal in temperature to each other.

Nernst's law (also known as the third law or the Nernst heat theorem, 1906) states that absolute zero is a limit that, like the speed of light, can be approached but not reached by massive particles.

Physics and technology

Answer to the student question: The solid disks contain more mass than the electric coils. They can therefore carry or hold more thermal energy than the coils.

Teacher Resources: Arnott, Ann. "Hot New Cooktop Technologies," *Home Mechanix*. April 1989, pages 60–63.
"Electric and Gas Ranges," *Consumer Reports*. February 1989, pages 80–83.
"Electric Ranges: Coil or Disk?" *Consumer Reports*. March 1990, pages 144–149.

CONCEPT DEVELOPMENT

Demonstration: Order a deck of playing cards (Aces, Kings, etc.). Shuffle the deck three or four times. Ask students what the chances are that the cards are in original order (Aces, Kings, etc.). Ask them if it is possible that enough shuffling will restore the original order. Ask if it is probable. [The chances that the deck has been "restored" to the original order are very small. There is a mathematical possibility that the order has been restored, but the probability is very, very small.]

CONCEPT REVIEW ANSWERS

2.1 It takes an amount of heat, $Q = mH_v$, to vaporize water to steam, so the same amount of heat is released when the steam is condensed to water.
2.2 The potential energy of the water at the top of the fall would be converted into thermal energy.
2.3 The kinetic energy of the moving hammer was converted into thermal energy in the lead.
2.4 Critical Thinking: No. It is an example of the increase of entropy, the second law of thermodynamics.

Physics and technology

RANGE-TOP COOKING

Top-of-the-range cooking is bringing new technology into the kitchen. In addition to the electric coil and gas burner, consumers can select solid disk heating elements, glass-ceramic cooktops, and sealed gas burners, among others.

The familiar electric coil cooks food with radiant heat and conduction. It heats up and cools down quickly. A disadvantage is that the heating elements and drip bowls can be hard to clean.

Solid disk heating elements were introduced in the United States in the 1980s and have grown in popularity. The disks consist of cast iron which has electric heating wires embedded in the underside. Solid disks are easier to clean but take longer to heat up and cool down than coil-type elements. They also require cookware with extra-flat bottoms in order to maximize heat transfer from the disk to the utensil.

Glass-ceramic cooktops, or smoothtops, contain their heating elements under a sheet of ceramic glass. They may use electric resistance heating, a halogen gas "bulb", or magnetic induction heating.

· Why would the solid disk heating elements take longer to heat up and cool down than the coil-type elements?

CONCEPT REVIEW

2.1 Old-fashioned heating systems sent steam into radiators in each room. In the radiator, the steam condensed back to water. How did this heat the room?

2.2 James Joule carefully measured the difference in temperature of water at the top and bottom of a waterfall. Why would he have expected a difference?

2.3 In 1861, the French scientist Hirn used a 320-kg hammer moving at 5 m/s to smash a 3-kg block of lead against a 450-kg rock. He found that the temperature of the lead increased 5°C. Explain.

2.4 Critical Thinking: A new deck of cards has all the suits (clubs, diamonds, hearts, and spades) in order, and the cards ordered by number within the suits. If you shuffle the cards many times, are you likely to return the cards to the original order? Of what physical law is this an example?

TRANSPARENCY

Use Transparency 16 with this section.

12:2 ASSIGNMENT GUIDE

	PRACTICE	EXTENSION
CHAPTER REVIEW pp. 261–263		
· Reviewing Concepts	11–14	
· Applying Concepts		7–9
· Problems*	16–18, 20 23–25	19, 21, 22
APPENDIX B PROBLEMS*		
· Chapter 12, p. 697	11	12–15

* Complete solutions to all Chapter Review and Appendix problems appear in the Problems and Solutions Manual.

CHAPTER 12 REVIEW

SUMMARY

12.1 Temperature and Thermal Energy

- The thermal energy of an object is the sum of the kinetic and potential energies of the internal motion of the particles.
- The temperature of a gas is proportional to the average kinetic energy of the particles.
- Thermometers use some property of a substance, such as thermal expansion, that depends on temperature.
- Thermometers reach thermal equilibrium with the objects they contact, and then some temperature-dependent property of the thermometer is measured.
- The Celsius and Kelvin temperature scales are widely used in scientific work. One kelvin is equal to one degree Celsius.
- At absolute zero, 0 K or −273.15°C, matter has no thermal energy.
- Heat is the energy transferred because of a difference in temperature. Heat flows naturally from a hot to a cold body.
- Specific heat is the quantity of heat required to raise the temperature of one kilogram of a substance one kelvin.
- In an isolated system, the thermal energy of one part may change but the total energy of the system is constant.

12.2 Change of State and Laws of Thermodynamics

- The heat of fusion is the quantity of heat required to change one kilogram of a substance from its solid state to its liquid state at its melting point.
- The heat of vaporization is the quantity of heat required to change one kilogram of a substance from the liquid state to the vapor state at its boiling point.
- The heat transferred during a change of state does not produce a change in temperature.
- The first law of thermodynamics states that the total increase in thermal energy of a system is equal to the sum of the heat added to it and the work done on it.
- A heat engine continuously converts thermal energy to mechanical energy.
- A heat pump or refrigerator uses mechanical energy to transfer heat from an area of lower temperature to an area of higher temperature.
- Entropy, a measure of disorder, never decreases in natural processes.

KEY TERMS

kinetic-molecular theory
thermal energy
conduction
convection
radiation
temperature
thermal equilibrium
thermometer
absolute zero
kelvin
heat
specific heat
calorimeter
thermodynamics
melting point
heat of fusion
boiling point
heat of vaporization
first law of thermodynamics
heat engine
entropy
second law of thermodynamics

REVIEWING CONCEPTS

1. Explain the difference between a ball's external energy and its thermal energy. Give an example.
2. Explain the difference between a ball's thermal energy and temperature.
3. Can temperature be assigned to a vacuum? Explain.
4. Do all of the molecules or atoms in a liquid have about the same speed?
5. Your teacher just told your class that the temperature of the sun is 1.5×10^7 degrees.
   a. Sally asks whether this is the Kelvin or Celsius scale. What is the teacher's answer?
   b. Would it matter, between the Celsius and Fahrenheit scales, which one you use?
6. Is your body a good judge of temperature? On a cold winter day, a metal door knob feels

CLOSING CHAPTER 12

Review Summary statements and Key Terms with your students.

ASSESSMENT

Vocabulary Review Master, Teacher Resource Package. Use this master to check students' understanding of Key Terms.

Evaluation Masters. Use Parts A and B of the Chapter Evaluation Masters from the Teacher Resource Package to test qualitative chapter objectives. Use Parts C and D to test quantitative chapter objectives.

Answers To
REVIEWING CONCEPTS

1. The external energy of a ball is the sum of all energy outside of the ball. The external energy of a baseball in flight is the result of its motion and position above Earth. Its thermal energy is the total kinetic and potential energy of all particles that compose the ball. The baseball will have thermal energy even if it has an external energy of zero.
2. Thermal energy is the sum of the kinetic and potential energies of the particles that make up a ball. Temperature is the measure of the average kinetic energy of the particles of a ball.
3. Since temperature is defined as the average kinetic energy of particles, by classical physics, temperature in a true vacuum is undefined because there are no particles.
4. No. The particles in a liquid have a very wide distribution of speeds. However, as the temperature increases, the average speed increases.
5. a. Either scale is correct. The difference between the scales at any temperature is 273, which is insignificant compared to 1.5×10^7 degrees. **b.** Yes. The scale is important. Fahrenheit would be almost double.
6. No. The metal knob and the wood are at the same temperature. However, the metal knob conducts the thermal energy of your fingers away from the point of contact much more rapidly than does the wood. Therefore, your fingers feel colder touching the metal than the wood.
7. Heat is the thermal energy that flows from the hot steel ball into the cool water. The transfer of heat causes the thermal energy of the ball to decrease, while the thermal energy of the water increases.
8. No. We measure temperature changes and infer heat transfer from these measurements.
9. No. Heat, not temperature, flows from the warmer to the colder object. The temperature changes are equal only if the product of the mass and specific heat of the two are the same.

REVIEW MASTER

Use the Vocabulary Review master for Chapter 12 with this section.

EVALUATION MASTER

Use the Chapter Evaluation master for Chapter 12 with this section.

Answers To
REVIEWING CONCEPTS (cont)

10. Yes. If the object is at its melting point or its boiling point, the added energy will go into the energy of the particles, causing a change of state, not temperature.
11. Energy is released by the wax when it freezes.
12. Water will vaporize from the wet canvas cover, which requires energy. Some of the energy will come from the water in the canteen, which will lower its temperature. The rest of the energy will come from the outside air which will not be able to "warm" the water in the canteen.
13. Vaporization. Changing liquid Freon to vapor requires energy. Heat is drawn from the air in the house for this, so the air becomes cooler.
14. The scrambled egg is more disordered than the unbroken egg, so the scrambled egg has more entropy.

Answers To
APPLYING CONCEPTS

1. No. The water is at the same temperature in either case, therefore the pasta cooks at the same rate.
2. a. $T_c = T_f$, so $T_c = 9/5\ T_c + 32$, or $-4/5\ T_c = 32$, or $T_c = -40$. Therefore, $-40°C = -40°F$.
b. $T_k = T_f$ and $T_k = T_c + 273$.
By substitution,
$T_k = 9/5(T_k - 273) + 32 = 9/5\ T_k - 491 + 32$, or
$-4/5\ T_k = -459$, or $T_k = +574$.
Therefore, 574 K = 574°F.
c. Celsius and Kelvin temperatures can never be the same.
3. If the same amount of heat is removed by the ice from equal masses of methanol and water, the methanol will have a greater drop in temperature since it has a lower specific heat.
4. It takes less water than other liquids to transfer a given amount of heat to the air.
5. Aluminum. The specific heat of aluminum is higher than the specific heat of lead and it can release more heat through the same temperature change.
6. No. The more massive Block A has a larger thermal energy and can heat the water to a higher temperature.
7. Vaporization requires energy, which comes from your skin. The more easily a liquid vaporizes, the faster the energy is drawn from your skin and the cooler it feels.
8. The freezing of the water releases thermal energy that slightly warms the air and reduces the amount of heat extracted from the fruit. Also, a layer of ice over the fruit slightly insulates the fruit from the cold.
9. No. Cool air would go into the room, but the refrigerator would turn on to replace the lost cool air. The heat removed from the refrigerator is pumped back into the room through the back of the refrigerator along with waste heat. So the room warms up.

much colder to your hand than the wooden door. Is this true? Explain.

7. A hot steel ball is dropped into a cup of cool water. Explain the difference between heat and the ball's thermal energy.
8. Do we ever measure heat transfer directly? Explain.
9. When a warmer object is in contact with a colder object, does temperature flow from one to the other? Do the two have the same temperature changes?
10. Can you add thermal energy to an object without increasing its temperature? Explain.
11. When wax freezes, is energy absorbed or released by the wax?
12. Why does water in a canteen stay cooler if it has a canvas cover that is kept wet?
13. Are the coils of an air conditioner that are inside the house the location of vaporization or condensation of the Freon? Explain.
14. Which situation has more entropy, an unbroken egg or a scrambled egg?

APPLYING CONCEPTS

1. Sally is cooking pasta in a pot of boiling water. Will the pasta cook faster if the water is boiling vigorously than if it is boiling gently?
2. What temperatures on the following pairs of scales are the same? ($T_F = 9/5\ T_C + 32$)
   a. Celsius and Fahrenheit
   b. Kelvin and Fahrenheit
   c. Celsius and Kelvin
3. Which liquid would an ice cube cool faster, water or methanol? Explain.
4. Explain why the high specific heat of water makes it desirable for use in hot water heating systems.
5. Equal masses of aluminum and lead are heated to the same temperature. The pieces of metal are placed on a block of ice. Which metal melts more ice? Explain.
6. Two blocks of lead are heated to the same temperature. Block A has twice the mass of block B. They are dropped into identical cups of water, and both systems come to thermal equilibrium. If the cups started with water at the same temperature, will the water have the same temperature after the blocks are added? Explain.
7. Why do easily vaporized liquids, such as acetone or methanol, feel cool to the skin?
8. Explain why fruit growers spray their trees with water, when frost is expected, to protect the fruit from freezing.
9. Would opening the refrigerator door on a warm day help cool the kitchen? Explain.

PROBLEMS

12.1 Temperature and Thermal Energy

1. Liquid nitrogen boils at 77 K. Find this temperature in degrees Celsius.
2. The melting point of hydrogen is −259.14°C. Find this temperature in kelvin.
3. Sadi Carnot showed that no real heat engine can have an efficiency greater than

$$efficiency = \frac{work\ output}{heat\ input} = \frac{T_{hot} - T_{cold}}{T_{hot}}$$

   where T_{hot} and T_{cold} are the temperatures of the input and waste thermal energy reservoirs. Note: Kelvin temperatures must be used in this equation.
   a. What is the efficiency of an ideal steam engine that uses superheated steam at 685 K to drive the engine and ejects waste steam at 298 K?
   b. If the steam generator produces 1.00×10^8 J each second, how much work can the ideal engine do each second?
4. How much heat is needed to raise the temperature of 50.0 g of water from 4.5°C to 83.0°C?
5. How much heat must be added to 50.0 g of aluminum at 25°C to raise its temperature to 125°C?
6. A 5.00×10^2-g block of metal absorbs 5016 J of heat when its temperature changes from 20.0°C to 30.0°C. Calculate the specific heat of the metal.
7. A 4.00×10^2-g glass coffee cup is at room temperature, 20.0°C. It is then plunged into hot dishwater, 80.0°C. If the temperature of the cup reaches that of the dishwater, how much heat does the cup absorb? Assume the mass of the dishwater is large enough so its temperature doesn't change appreciably.
8. A copper wire has a mass of 165 g. An electric current runs through the wire for a short

time and its temperature rises from 21°C to 39°C. What minimum quantity of energy is converted by the electric current?

9. A 1.00 $\times$ 10^2-g mass of tungsten at 100.0°C is placed in 2.00 $\times$ 10^2 g of water at 20.0°C. The mixture reaches equilibrium at 21.6°C. Calculate the specific heat of tungsten.

10. A 6.0 $\times$ 10^2-g sample of water at 90.0°C is mixed with 4.00 $\times$ 10^2 g of water at 22°C. Assume no heat loss to the surroundings. What is the final temperature of the mixture?

11. To get a feeling for the amount of energy needed to heat water, recall from Table 11–1 that the kinetic energy of a compact car moving at 100 km/h is 2.9 $\times$ 10^5 J. What volume of water (in liters) would 2.9 $\times$ 10^5 J of energy warm from room temperature (20°C) to boiling (100°C)?

12. A 10.0-kg piece of zinc at 71°C is placed in a container of water. The water has a mass of 20.0 kg and has a temperature of 10.0°C before the zinc is added. What is the final temperature of the water and zinc?

13. A 2.00 $\times$ 10^2-g sample of brass at 100.0°C is placed in a calorimeter cup that contains 261 g of water at 20.0°C. Disregard the absorption of heat by the cup and calculate the final temperature of the brass and water.

▶ 14. A 3.00 $\times$ 10^2-W electric immersion heater is used to heat a cup of water. The cup is made of glass and its mass is 3.00 $\times$ 10^2 g. It contains 250 g of water at 15° C. How much time is needed for the heater to bring the water to the boiling point? Assume the temperature of the cup to be the same as the temperature of the water at all times and no heat is lost to the air.

15. A 2.50 $\times$ 10^2-kg cast-iron car engine contains water as a coolant. Suppose the engine's temperature is 35°C when it is shut off. The air temperature is 10°C. The heat given off by the engine and water in it as they cool to air temperature is 4.4 $\times$ 10^6 J. What mass of water is used to cool the engine?

12.2 Change of State and Laws of Thermodynamics

16. Years ago, a block of ice with a mass of about 20.0 kg was used daily in a home icebox. The temperature of the ice was 0.0°C when delivered. As it melted, how much heat did a block of ice that size absorb?

17. A person who eats 2400 food calories each day consumes 1.0 $\times$ 10^7 J of energy in a day. How much water at 100°C could that much energy vaporize?

18. A 40.0-g sample of chloroform is condensed from a vapor at 61.6°C to a liquid at 61.6°C. It liberates 9870 J of heat. What is the heat of vaporization of chloroform?

▶ 19. How much heat is removed from 60.0 g of steam at 100.0°C to change it to 60.0 g of water at 20.0°C?

20. A 750-kg car moving at 23 m/s brakes to a stop. The brakes contain about 15 kg of iron that absorb the energy. What is the increase in temperature of the brakes?

▶ 21. How much heat is added to 10.0 g of ice at −20.0°C to convert it to steam at 120.0°C?

▶ 22. A 50.0-g sample of ice at 0.00°C is placed in a glass beaker containing 4.00 $\times$ 10^2 g of water at 50.0°C. All the ice melts. What is the final temperature of the mixture? Disregard any heat loss to the glass.

23. A 4.2-g lead bullet moving at 275 m/s strikes a steel plate and stops. If all its kinetic energy is converted to thermal energy and none leaves the bullet, what is its temperature change?

24. A soft drink from Australia is labeled "Low Joule Cola." The label says "100 mL yields 1.7 kJ." The can contains 375 mL. Sally drinks the cola and then offsets this input of food energy by climbing stairs. How high would she have to climb if Sally has a mass of 65.0 kg?

25. When air is compressed in a bicycle pump, an average force of 45 N is exerted as the pump handle moves 0.24 m. During this time, 2.0 J of heat leave the cylinder through the walls. What is the net change in thermal energy of the air in the cylinder?

THINKING PHYSIC-LY

1. Picture a cup of hot tea and an iceberg.
   a. Which has a greater amount of internal energy?
   b. Which has a higher temperature?
2. Why can't you tell if you have a fever by touching your own forehead?

Answers To
PROBLEMS

Have students refer to Solutions Manual for complete solutions.

1. −196°C
2. 14.01 K
3. **a.** 0.565
   b. 5.65 $\times$ 10^7 J/s
4. 1.6 $\times$ 10^4 J
5. 4.5 $\times$ 10^3 J
6. 1.00 $\times$ 10^3 J/kg·K
7. 1.59 $\times$ 10^4 J
8. 1.1 $\times$ 10^3 J
9. 171 J/kg·K
10. 63°C
11. 0.87 L
12. 12.7°C
13. 25.1°C
14. 3.7 $\times$ 10^2 s
15. 15 kg
16. 6.68 $\times$ 10^6 J
17. 4.4 kg
18. 2.47 $\times$ 10^5 J/kg
19. 1.56 $\times$ 10^5 J
20. 29°C
21. 3.09 $\times$ 10^4 J
22. 35.6°C
23. 291°C
24. 10 m
25. 8.8 J

Answers To
THINKING PHYSIC-LY

1. **a.** The iceberg. It has a larger mass.
   b. The hot cup of coffee. The particles are moving faster, on average.
2. There is no temperature difference between your own hand and your head.

CHAPTER 13 States of Matter

PLANNING GUIDE (6 class sessions)

CONTENTS	TEXT FEATURES	TEACHER RESOURCE PACKAGE	OTHER COMPONENTS
13.1 The Fluid States, pp. 266–277 (3 Class Sessions) • Pressure • Fluids at Rest—Hydrostatics • Fluids in Motion—Hydrodynamics • Liquids vs Gases • Surface Tension • Evaporation and Condensation • Plasma	**Physics Lab:** Float or Sink, p. 271 **Pocket Lab:** Foot Pressure, p. 267 **Pocket Lab:** Floating?, p. 274 **Physics and Technology:** Aerodynamic Helmets, p. 277 **Concept Review,** p. 277	**Study Guide:** The Fluid State **Physics Lab Data Sheet:** Float or Sink? **Reteaching Master:** Surface Tension **Enrichment Master:** Bernoulli's Equation **Transparency Worksheet:** Pascal's, Archimedes', and Bernoulli's Principles	**Laboratory Manual:** Lab 13.1 Archimedes' Principle **Transparency 17:** Pascal's, Archimedes' and Bernoulli's Principles **Physics Skill Master 15**
13.2 The Solid State, pp. 278–282 (3 Class Sessions) • Solid Bodies • Elasticity of Solids • Thermal Expansion of Matter	**Pocket Lab:** Jumpers, p. 279 **Concept Review,** p. 282	**Study Guide:** The Solid State **Critical Thinking Master:** The Effect of Thermal Expansion on Lakes	
Chapter Review, pp. 283–285	Summary Key Terms Reviewing Concepts Applying Concepts Problems Thinking Physic-ly	**Vocabulary Review** **Chapter Test**	**Test Bank**

SUPPLEMENTARY MATERIALS

SOFTWARE	AUDIOVISUAL	BOOKS/MAGAZINES
Gas Laws, J&S (Apple II). *Gaseous Diffusion,* Queue, Inc.(Apple II). *Moving Molecules,* HRM (Apple II).	Video: *All About Matter,* Focus Media (still frame). Filmstrip: *The Structure of Matter,* United Learning.	Badeer, Henry S.,and Hicks, James W. "Role of Viscous Resistance in Siphon Flow." *The Physics Teacher,* November 1990, p. 558. Bauman, Robert P. "Archimedes' Bath." *The Physics Teacher,* March 1987, pp. 150–151. Edge, R.D. "Surface Tension." *The Physics Teacher,* December 1988, pp. 586–587. Taylor, Tim. "The Imploding Beer Can." *The Physics Teacher,* October 1982, p. 458.

PROBLEM CORRELATION

CONCEPTS	CHAPTER REVIEW			PROBLEMS APPENDIX
	Reviewing Concepts	Applying Concepts	Problems	
13.1 The Fluid States				
Pressure	1	1,2	3,4,5	1,2,3,**4**,**5**
Fluids at Rest—Hydrostatics	2,3,4	3,4	**1**,**2**,6,7,8,9,10, 11,12,13,**14**,15	6,7,8,**9**,**10**
Fluids in Motion—Hydrodynamics	5			
Liquids vs Gases	6			
Surface Tension	7,8	5		
Evaporation and Condensation	9,10,11	6,7		
Plasma	12,13			
13.2 The Solid State				
Solid Bodies		8		
Elasticity of Solids				
Thermal Expansion of Matter		9,10,11,12	16, 17, **18**, **19**, **20**	11,12,13,**14**,**15**

ACTIVITY AND DEMONSTRATION MATERIALS

PHYSICS LAB	POCKET LAB	DEMONSTRATIONS
Page 271 beaker water film can with top 25 pennies 250-g spring balance pan balance	Pages 267, 274, 279 metric ruler paper beaker water needle paper clip staple safety goggles jumping disks	Pages 267, 268, 273 pine stick (0.5 cm x 3 cm x 60 cm) newspaper test tube plastic soda bottle piece of balloon rubber band horizontal and vertical supports 2 burned out light bulbs thread

EXTENSION PROJECTS

LIBRARY RESEARCH

1. Maneuvering in the Depths
Investigate how submarines move from one depth to another. How does this compare to the methods used by scuba divers or fish?

DISPLAY MODEL

2. Water Clock
Build a water clock and explain how it works to the class.

STUDENT READINGS

Amato, I. "Stretching Liquid to Its Physical Limit." *Science News,* August 11,1990.

Beeker, Daniel E. "Depth Dependence of Pressure." *The Physics Teacher,* October 1990.

Gosline, John. "Jet-Propelled Swimming in Liquids." *Scientific American,* January 1985.

Peterson, I. "Computing Liquid Water as a Transient Gel." *Science News,* April 14, 1990.

Weltner, Klaus. "Bernoulli's Law and Aerodynamic Lifting Force." *The Physics Teacher,* February 1990.

Winter, Rolf G. "On the Difference between Fluids and Dried Beans." *The Physics Teacher,* February 1990.

Chapter 13

States of Matter

CHAPTER OVERVIEW

Theme Development: Pascal's principle demonstrates symmetry of forces as pressure is transmitted through fluids. The main theme of the chapter, however, is scale: the small scale over which capillary action acts, and scales of order within crystalline substances.

MISCONCEPTIONS

Archimedes' principle is the most difficult concept to understand in this chapter. Confusion arises over the difference between force and pressure. Some students tend to believe that it is the atoms themselves that become larger rather than the interatomic spacing that increases when materials expand.

KEY TERMS

adhesion
amorphous solids
Archimedes' principle
Bernoulli's principle
buoyant force
capillary action
coefficient of linear expansion
cohesive forces
condensation
crystal lattice
elasticity
evaporation
fluid
pascal
Pascal's principle
plasma
pressure
surface tension
thermal expansion
volatile

Laboratory Options

STUDENT EDITION

Physics Lab

Float or Sink	271

Pocket Labs

Foot Pressure	267
Floating?	274
Jumpers	279

TEACHER EDITION

Activities

Demonstration	267, 268, 273
Cooperative Learning	268
Discovery	274, 274, 279

LABORATORY MANUAL

Archimedes' Principle	Lab 13.1

CHAPTER

13 States of Matter

Bottled Cloud

Janet was helping her parents prepare for a dinner party. As she popped the cork on a bottle of sparkling grape juice, a small cloud formed around the bottle's mouth. The cloud surprised Janet's mother. What explanation did Janet give her mother?

Chapter Outline

✓ Concept Check

The following terms or concepts from earlier chapters are important for a good understanding of this chapter. If you are not familiar with them, you should review them before studying this chapter.

- force, Chapter 5
- work, kinetic energy, potential energy, Chapter 11
- temperature, thermal energy, heat, Chapter 12

You have lived with the three common states of matter all your life. You breathe air, drink and swim in water, and build with solid objects. In general, you are familiar with most of their properties. Yet, there can be some surprises. The photo shows a bottle that contained cold, sparkling grape juice. Carbon dioxide gas is dissolved in the liquid. When the cork is removed, the pressure in the bottle suddenly drops. The result is a beautiful display of the states of matter.

Introducing The Chapter

Bottled Cloud

Using The Photo: Students are probably familiar with the "cloud" that forms when a soft drink bottle is opened, especially in hot, humid weather. Increase interest by demonstrating the phenomenon. Use this photograph again when discussing the first law of thermodynamics and change of state.

✓ Concept Check

Make sure students have a clear understanding of the concepts taught in Chapters 5, 11, and 12 that are listed in the Concept Check. Understanding force, work, kinetic and potential energy, temperature, thermal energy, and heat will prepare students to work with the principles of states of matter introduced in this chapter.

Assessment

Portfolio

Students should collect questions and problems involving thermal expansion to place in their portfolios.

Assessment Options

Portfolio Assessment
Portfolio Assessment, TWE, p. 265
Enrichment, TWE, p. 270
Concept Development, TWE, p. 275
Portfolio Assessment, TWE, p. 280

Performance Assessment
Pocket Labs, pp. 267, 279
Physics Lab, p. 271
Activity, TWE, p. 268
Pocket Lab Assessment, p. 274

Content Assessment
Self Assessment: Practice Problems, pp. 268, 272, 282
Assessment, Critical Thinking, TWE, p. 271
Reteaching, TWE, p. 275
Convergent Question, TWE, p. 282
Concept Reviews, pp. 277, 282
Chapter Review, pp. 283–285
Supplemental Problems, p. 698

Group Assessment
Activities for group assessment occur with Cooperative Learning and lab activities.

13.1 THE FLUID STATES

Preparation

OBJECTIVES

The objectives are listed on the student page. Remind students to preview these objectives as a study guide to this major section.

OVERVIEW

This major section includes all the definitions and concepts listed in Key Terms, except *elasticity* and *coefficient of linear expansion.*

BRIDGING

Friction, surface area, cross-sectional area, weight, density, force, kinetic energy, potential energy, and velocity are all brought up again in this section. Mechanics terms continue to reappear because they are fundamental to the study of physics.

1 Focus

DISCREPANT EVENT

Blow up a balloon about a third full. Hold the mouths of two small plastic cups against the sides of the balloon and continue to blow it up until it is about twice the size. The cups will now stick to the balloon by themselves. Ask students to explain why the cups don't fall. [The curvature of the balloon decreases and actually flattens out, increasing the volume of the air trapped in the cup and thus decreasing its pressure. The pressure outside the cups is now greater and pushes the cups against the balloon.]

Objectives

- **demonstrate an understanding of the concept of pressure, the definition of the pascal, and the ability to calculate pressure and total force.**
- **understand the origin of Pascal's and Archimedes' principles and their applications.**
- **explain Bernoulli's principle and its applications in producing lift.**
- **compare and contrast liquids and gases.**
- **describe how cohesive and adhesive forces cause surface tension and capillary action, respectively.**
- **understand the origin of evaporation and condensation from the viewpoint of kinetic energy.**
- **define a plasma and give examples of plasmas in nature.**

13.1 THE FLUID STATES

What is a fluid? A **fluid** is any material that flows and offers little resistance to a change in its shape when under pressure. Both liquids and gases are fluids.

Much of our life is spent in these two fluid states of matter. We live and breathe in the gaseous atmosphere. The large amounts of liquid water on Earth makes it unique in the solar system and is probably the reason Earth supports life. The properties of fluids allow airplanes to fly, boats to float, and submarines either to float or submerge. They also allow paper towels to absorb spilled milk, and insects to walk on the surface of water. The final fluid state, plasma, provides us with the beautiful northern lights.

Pressure

The kinetic-molecular theory that we discussed in the last chapter helps to explain the properties of gases. The theory is based on three simplified assumptions.

- Gases are made up of a large number of very small particles.
- The particles are in constant, random motion. They are widely separated and make only elastic collisions with one another.
- The particles make perfectly elastic collisions with the walls of the container that holds them.

Pressure is the force on each unit area of a surface.

The kinetic theory is a microscopic theory. It pictures a volume of gas as a box filled with a large number of very small moving particles. According to the theory, the pressure exerted on the walls of the box is the result of the collisions of the particles with the walls of the box.

What do we mean by the pressure exerted by a gas? **Pressure** is defined as the force on a unit surface area. That is,

$$p = \frac{F}{A}.$$

FIGURE 13–1. Pressure measuring instruments: a tire gauge (a); an aircraft altimeter (b); a sphygmomanometer (c).

a

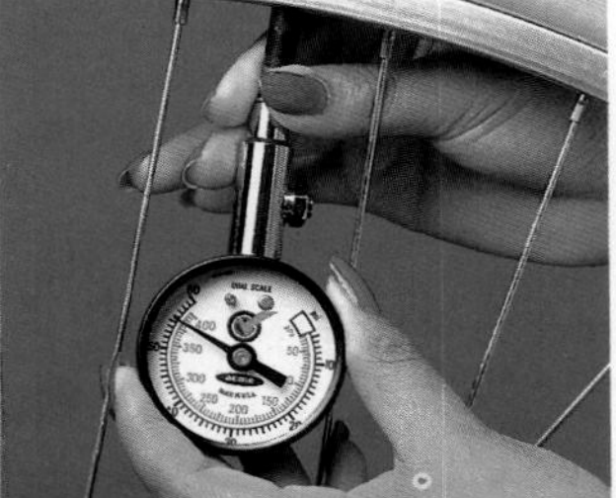

b

c

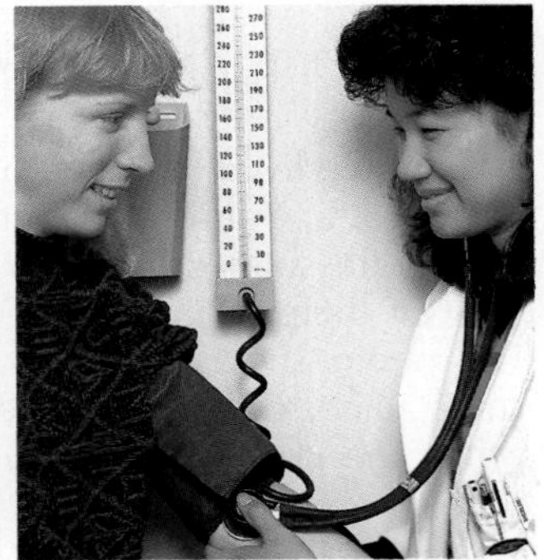

STUDY GUIDE MASTER

Use the Study Guide master for section 13.1.

Table 13–1

Some Typical Pressures

Location	Pressure (Pa)
Center of sun	2×10^{16}
Center of Earth	4×10^{11}
Deepest ocean trench	1.1×10^{8}
High heels on floor	1×10^{6}
Auto tire	2×10^{5}
Standard atmosphere	1×10^{5}
Blood pressure	1.6×10^{4}
Loudest sound	30
Faintest sound	3×10^{-5}
Best vacuum	1×10^{-12}

In the SI system, the unit of pressure is the **pascal,** Pa, one newton per square meter. Because the pascal is a small unit of pressure, the kilopascal, kPa, equal to 1000 Pa, is more commonly used. Earth's atmosphere at sea level is about 100 000 Pa.

The pressure of Earth's gaseous atmosphere is so well balanced by our bodies that we hardly ever notice it. You become aware of the pressure only when your ears "pop" as a result of pressure changes. This might occur when riding the elevator in a tall building, driving on a high mountain road, or flying in an airplane. Yet, on every square centimeter of Earth's surface at sea level, the atmosphere exerts a force of approximately 10 N, about the weight of a 1-kg object. This is equal to about 1.0×10^5 Pa or 100 kPa.

POCKET LAB

FOOT PRESSURE

How much pressure do you exert when standing on the ground with one foot? Is it more or less than air pressure? Estimate your weight in newtons. **Hint:** 500 N = 110 lb. Stand on a piece of paper and have a lab partner trace the outline of your foot. Draw a rectangle that has about the same area as the outline. Calculate the area in square meters. Use the definition of pressure to estimate your pressure. $P = F/A$

The unit of pressure is the pascal, Pa.

Example Problem

Calculating Pressure

A typical high school student weighs 725 N and wears shoes that touch the ground over an area of 412 cm². **a.** What is the average pressure his shoes exert on the ground? **b.** How does the answer change when he stands on only one foot?

Given: force, $F = 725$ N
area, $A = 412\text{ cm}^2 = 0.0412\text{ m}^2$

Unknown: pressure, p
Basic equation: $p = F/A$

Solution:

a. $p = \dfrac{F}{A} = \dfrac{725\text{ N}}{0.0412\text{ m}^2} = 1.76 \times 10^4\text{ N/m}^2 = 17.6\text{ kPa}$

b. $p = \dfrac{F}{A} = \dfrac{725\text{ N}}{0.0206\text{ m}^2} = 3.52 \times 10^4\text{ N/m}^2 = 35.2\text{ kPa}$

The same amount of force can create even larger pressures. If a woman puts her whole weight on the heel of one high-heeled shoe, Figure 13–2, the pressure can exceed a million pascals.

FIGURE 13–2. Pressure is the force exerted on a unit area of a surface. Similar forces may produce vastly different pressures—the pressure on the ground under a woman's high heel is far greater than that under an elephant's foot.

POCKET LAB

FOOT PRESSURE

Purpose: to determine what pressure one's foot exerts.
Materials: metric ruler, paper.
Outcome: The student's pressure is much less than atmospheric pressure. Here is a sample calculation:

$P = F/A$
$= 600\text{ N}/0.03\text{ m}^2$
$= 2.0 \times 10^4\text{ N/m}^2$

2 Teach

CONCEPT DEVELOPMENT

Since this section is largely qualitative, demonstrations should be used generously to add concreteness to concepts.

Study Guide Master. To reinforce the concepts in this section, have the students complete the Study Guide Master for Section 13.1 from the Teacher Resource Package.

ACTIVITY

Demonstration: Lay a pine stick (0.5 cm × 3 cm × 60 cm) on a table with about 15 cm of the stick extending over the edge. Give the stick a sharp blow on the end and let it go flying into the air. Put the stick back on the table with 15 cm extending over the edge. Cover the stick with an unfolded newspaper so the paper is flat and even with the edge of the table. Again give the stick a sharp blow. It will break at the edge of the table because the pressure of the atmosphere on the paper held down the other end of the stick. CAUTION: *Do not have anyone sitting close when you do this demonstration.*

TEACHER F.Y.I.

The manometer is a U-shaped tube containing a liquid (usually mercury because of its low vapor pressure and great density) with one end open to the atmosphere and the other end connected to a system of unknown pressure.

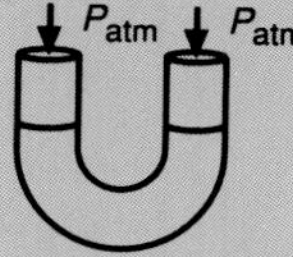

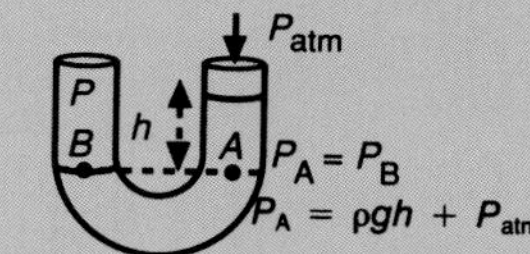

If both ends are open, then the level of the liquid on both sides will be equal because the pressure on both sides will be equal.

If one end is attached to a system of unknown pressure, then

$P_a = P_b$ and $P_a = \rho gh + P_{atm}$.

The unknown pressure is easily determined. Note that the vapor pressure of the liquid must be taken into account.

Answers To
PRACTICE PROBLEMS

Have students refer to Appendix A of the Solutions Appendix for complete solutions to Practice Problems.

1. 1.2×10^5 N
2. 1.0×10^5 Pa
3. 23 kPa
4. -2.5×10^4 N, toward the outside

CONCEPT DEVELOPMENT

ACTIVITY

Demonstration: Demonstrate the properties of a fluid with a Cartesian diver. Use a toy diver or construct one with a test tube and a plastic bottle. Partially fill with water a small test tube. Cover the open end with a piece cut from a balloon, fastening the piece securely with a rubber band. Place the test tube in a clear plastic soda bottle that is completely filled with water. Wait for the test tube to float in the water, glass end up. Cap the pop bottle securely and squeeze it. The test tube should sink. You may have to experiment with the amount of water needed in the test tube to produce the dramatic effect. Explain how this demonstrates that fluids transmit pressure equally, and that liquids are much less compressible than gases.

Cooperative Learning: As a class exercise, have students estimate their own bodies' surface area. [somewhere between one and two square meters] Then have them compute the force of air pressure on the surface of their bodies. Follow up with this question: Why don't you collapse under such a large force? [There is an equally large outward force acting inside your body.]

FIGURE 13–3. The deeper the swimmers go, the greater is the pressure exerted by the water.

Practice Problems

1. The atmospheric pressure at sea level is about 1.0×10^5 Pa. What is the force exerted on the top of a typical office desk, 152 cm long and 76 cm wide?
2. A car's tire makes contact with the ground on a rectangular "footprint" 12 cm by 18 cm. The car's mass is 925 kg. What pressure does the car exert on the ground?
3. A lead brick, $5.0 \times 10 \times 20$ cm, rests on the ground on its smallest face. What pressure does it exert? (Lead has a density 11.8 gm/cm^3.)
4. ▶ In a tornado, the pressure can be 15% below normal atmospheric pressure. Further, a tornado can move so quickly that this pressure drop can occur in one second. Suppose a tornado suddenly occurred outside your front door (182 cm high, 91 cm wide). What force would be exerted on the door? in what direction?

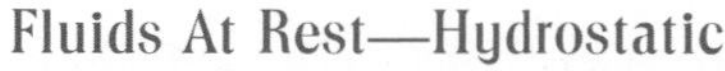

Fluids At Rest—Hydrostatics

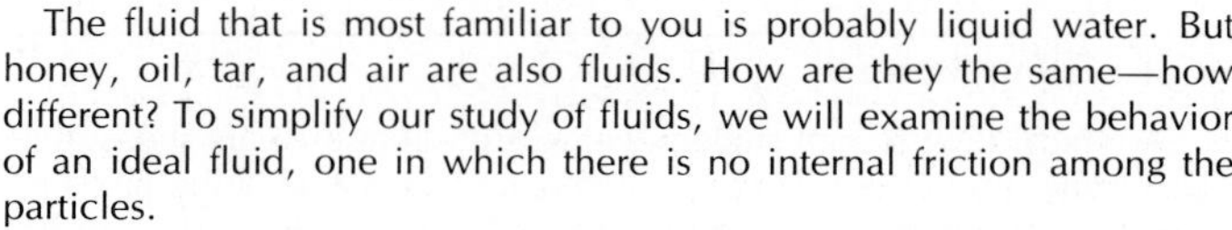

The fluid that is most familiar to you is probably liquid water. But honey, oil, tar, and air are also fluids. How are they the same—how different? To simplify our study of fluids, we will examine the behavior of an ideal fluid, one in which there is no internal friction among the particles.

If you have ever dived deep into a swimming pool or lake, you know that fluids exert pressure. Your body is sensitive to water pressure. You probably noticed that the pressure you felt on your ears did not depend on whether your head was upright or tilted. If your body is horizontal, the pressure is nearly the same on all parts of your body.

Blaise Pascal (1623–1662), a French physician, noted that the shape of a container had no affect on the pressure at any given depth. He was the first to discover that any change in pressure applied to a confined fluid at any point is transmitted undiminished throughout the fluid. This discovery became known as **Pascal's principle**. Every time you squeeze a tube of toothpaste, you use Pascal's principle.

Pascal's principle is applied in the operation of machines that use fluids to multiply forces, as in hydraulic lifts. In a hydraulic system, a fluid is confined in two connecting chambers, Figure 13–4. Each cham-

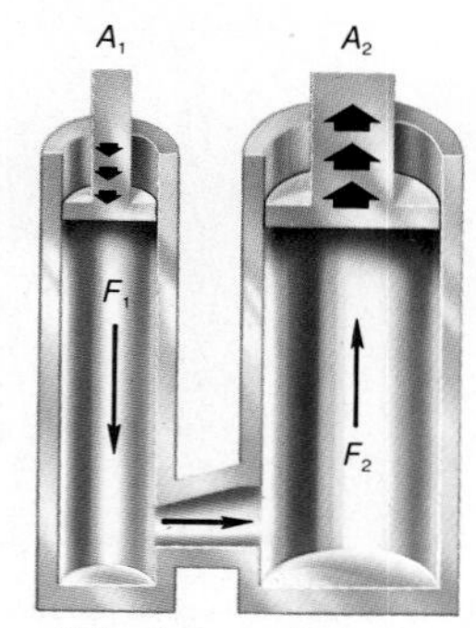

FIGURE 13–4. Pascal's principle is the basis of a hydraulic lift and other machines that use fluids to multiply forces.

TEACHER F.Y.I.

The barometer was invented by Torricelli, an assistant of Galileo. A tube is filled with mercury and inverted in a container of mercury. The closed end is nearly a vacuum, so its pressure can be assumed to be zero.

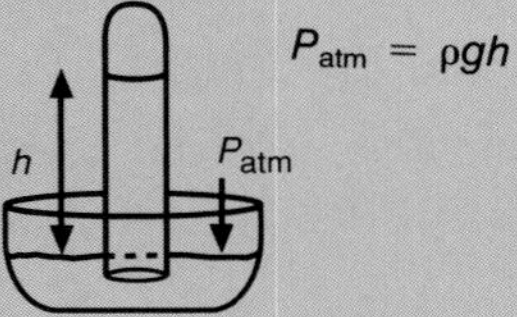

Pressure is measured in pascals (Pa), Torr or mm of mercury, pounds/in^2, and atmospheres (atm).

1.013×10^5 Pa $=$ 1 atm $=$ 14.7 lbs/in^2 $=$ 760 Torr or 760 mm of Hg

ber has a piston that is free to move. A force, F_1, is exerted on piston 1 with surface area A_1. The pressure exerted on the fluid is

$$p_1 = \frac{F_1}{A_1}.$$

By Pascal's principle, pressure is transmitted throughout the fluid without change. The pressure exerted by the fluid on piston 2, with surface area A_2, is given by

$$p_2 = \frac{F_2}{A_2}.$$

Thus, p_2 is the same as p_1. Therefore,

$$F_1/A_1 = F_2/A_2.$$

The force that piston 2 can exert is given by

$$F_2 = F_1A_2/A_1.$$

Example Problem

Hydraulic System

A 20.0-N force is exerted on the small piston of a hydraulic system. The cross-sectional area of the small piston is 0.0500 m^2. What is the magnitude of the weight that can be lifted by the large piston, which has a surface area of 0.100 m^2?

Given: $F_1 = 20.0$ N, $A_1 = 0.0500\ m^2$, $A_2 = 0.100\ m^2$

Unknown: F_2

Basic equation: $\frac{F_1}{A_1} = \frac{F_2}{A_2}$

Solution: $\frac{F_1}{A_1} = \frac{F_2}{A_2}$ $\quad F_2 = \frac{F_1A_2}{A_1}$

$$F_2 = \frac{(20.0\ \text{N})(0.100\ \text{m}^2)}{0.0500\ \text{m}^2} = 40.0\ \text{N}$$

You can observe another characteristic of fluids while swimming. The deeper you swim, the greater the pressure you feel. The pressure of a fluid on a horizontal surface is the weight per unit area, A, of the fluid above the surface. The weight, W, of the water above you is

$$W = mg.$$

Recall that ρ (density) $= m/V$ and $V = Ah$. Therefore, $W = \rho Vg = \rho Ahg$. Substituting this value for W will give

$$P = \frac{W}{A} = \rho\frac{Ahg}{A} \qquad P = \rho hg.$$

Therefore, the pressure is proportional only to the depth of the fluid and its density. The shape of the container has no effect, as shown in Figure 13–5.

When an object of height l is placed in a fluid, force is exerted on all sides, Figure 13–6a. The forces on the four sides are balanced. The forces on the top and bottom, however, are given by

$$F_{top} = p_{top}A = \rho hAg$$
$$F_{bottom} = p_{bottom}A = \rho(h + l)Ag.$$

F.Y.I.

The Heimlich maneuver is a sharp pressure applied to the abdomen of a person to dislodge a foreign object caught in the throat. It is an application of Pascal's principle.

A hydraulic machine can increase force exerted, but cannot increase the work done.

Pressure depends on the weight of the fluid above you.

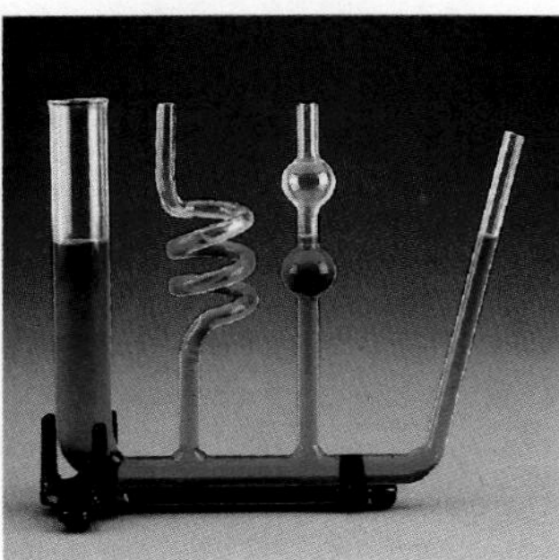

FIGURE 13–5. Pascal's vases show that a container's shape has no effect on pressure.

CONCEPT DEVELOPMENT

- The ideas of surface area and cross-sectional area are introduced here. The surface area of a round balloon, for example, would be the surface area of a sphere. [$A = 4\pi r^2$.] Cross-sectional area is just the area of a circle.
- Force and pressure should be clearly differentiated. Describing the purpose of skis and snowshoes should help to do this. In both cases your weight force is spread out over a larger area, reducing the pressure you exert on the snow, thus allowing you to walk on the surface.
- When swimming, the pressure you feel on your eardrums depends on the depth, not the size, of the swimming pool.

CONCEPT DEVELOPMENT

Critical Thinking: Think about the extremes of pressure. The smallest value one can imagine is zero, but the largest seems undefined. What would a zero pressure correspond to? [a perfect vacuum] What would limit maximum pressures? [our ability to produce and concentrate forces.]

Enrichment: One of the most fascinating uses of ultrahigh pressure is in the creation of artificial diamonds. Interested students may wish to investigate how such pressures are produced and applied.

Suggested References: "Diamond Fever" by Ivan Amato, *Science News*, August 4, 1990, pages 72–74; "The Diamond-Anvil High Pressure Cell" by A. Jayaraman, *Scientific American*, April 1984, pages 54–62; "A Gem of an Idea" in Science Newsfront by Arthur Fisher, *Popular Science*, October 1990.

Laboratory Manual. Give students additional experience with Archimedes' principle by doing Lab 13.1 from the Laboratory Manual.

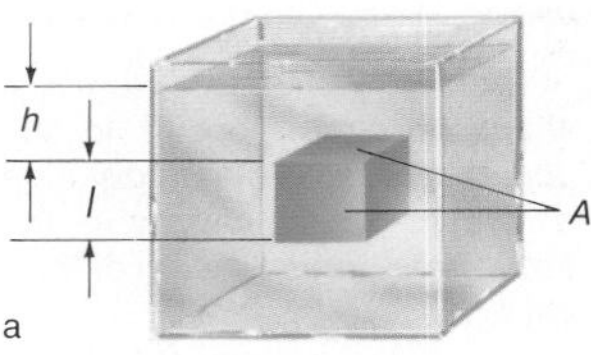

FIGURE 13–6. Archimedes' principle can be derived from considering a volume of fluid as shown (a). If the density of an object is less than that of the fluid, the object will sink only until it displaces a volume of water with a weight equal to the weight of the object (b).

The force on the bottom is larger than that on the top. The difference is

$$F_{bottom} - F_{top} = \rho(h + l)Ag - \rho Ahg$$
$$= \rho Alg = \rho Vg.$$

The buoyant force is equal to the weight of the fluid displaced.

Thus, there is an upward force of the fluid on the object. This force is called the **buoyant force.** Note that the volume of the immersed object is the same as the volume of the fluid displaced. Therefore, the buoyant force, ρVg, has a magnitude equal to the weight of the fluid displaced by the immersed object. This relationship was discovered by the Greek scientist Archimedes in 212 B.C. and is called **Archimedes' principle.** *An object immersed in a fluid is buoyed up by a force equal to the weight of the fluid displaced by the object.* It is important to note that the buoyant force *does not* depend on the weight of the submerged object, only the weight of the displaced fluid. A solid cube of aluminum, a solid cube of iron, and a hollow cube of iron, all of the same volume, would experience the same buoyant force.

Archimedes' principle applies to objects of all densities. If the density of the object is greater than that of the fluid, the upward buoyant force will be less than the weight of the object, W_{object}, and the object will sink. If the density of the object is equal to the density of the fluid, the buoyant force and W_{object} will be equal. The net force will be zero and the object will neither sink nor float. If the density of the object is less than that of the fluid, the object will float. The portion of the object submerged will just displace a volume of fluid with a weight equal to the weight of the object. Wearing a life jacket filled with material of very low density has the effect of decreasing the body's average density.

Shipbuilders can build ships of steel (density 9.0×10^3 kg/m^3) by designing them with large hollow hulls so that the average density of the ship is less than that of water. You will notice that a ship loaded with cargo rides much lower in the water than a ship with an empty cargo hold. Submarines take advantage of Archimedes' principle by pumping water into or out of special chambers to regulate the vertical force, causing the sub to rise or sink. Fish have air sacs that allow them to adjust their density so they can rise or sink.

FIGURE 13–7. FLIP is a research vessel used to study waves in deep water. It is towed into position floating horizontally. Then water is pumped into its stern tanks and it flips to a vertical position, as shown.

TEACHER F.Y.I.

Archimedes (287–212 B.C.) was asked by King Hiero to determine if a crown Hiero had an artisan make contained the actual quantity of gold given him or if it had been adulterated with silver. As he lowered himself into water while bathing, Archimedes is said to have realized that water was displaced and his body seemed to weigh less. Legend has it that he lept from his bath and ran through the streets of Syracuse shouting, "Eureka!" (I have found it). Archimedes realized that by submerging weights of gold and silver equal to that of the crown, different volumes of water would be displaced. This discovery allowed him to demonstrate that the crown was indeed not pure.

From: *The Little Brown Book of Anecdotes,* Clifton Fadiman, 1985, Little, Brown and Co.

PHYSICS LAB Float or Sink

Purpose

To investigate the buoyancy of objects.

Materials

- beaker
- water
- film can with top
- 25 pennies
- 250-g spring balance
- pan balance

Procedure

1. Measure and calculate the volume of a film can. Record the volume in your data table.
2. Fill the can with water. Carefully find the mass of the filled can on the pan balance. Record the value in your data table.
3. Empty the can of water.
4. Place a few pennies in the can and put the top on tightly. Find its mass and record the value in your data table.
5. Put the capped film can into the water to see if it floats.
6. If it floats, estimate the percentage that it is underwater. Record this amount in the data table.
7. If it sinks, use the spring balance to measure the mass while it is underwater (but not touching the bottom). Record this value in the data table.
8. Calculate the density of each trial in g/cm^3.

Observations and Data

Set up a data table similar to the following:
volume of can = _____ cm^3
mass of can with water = _____ g

FLOATERS		
mass with pennies	% below water	density

SINKERS		
mass with pennies	apparent mass	density

Analysis

1. Look closely at the mass of the floaters and the percentages below the water. What seems to be the rule?
2. Look closely at the sinkers. How much lighter are the cans when massed underwater?

Applications

1. Explain why a steel-hulled boat can float, even though it is quite massive.

PHYSICS LAB

Process Skills: observing, classifying, communicating, interpreting data, measuring, hypothesizing, using numbers, defining operationally, questioning.

MISCONCEPTIONS

Many students have difficulty with the concept of buoyancy. They know from experience that objects are easier to lift underwater, but are not sure why.

Teaching Suggestion: Some students may wish to experiment with Archimedes' procedure for identifying metals by measuring overflow.

Lab Worksheet, Teacher Resource Package. If desired, use the lab worksheet master for this chapter for students to record their data.

OBSERVATIONS AND DATA

Objects with a density less than 1.0 g/cm^3 will float in water.

ANALYSIS

1. The density is approximately the same as the percentage of the object underwater.
2. Objects that sink seem to weigh less. The apparent difference in mass is the same as the volume of the object.

APPLICATIONS

A steel-hulled boat can easily float if its overall density is less than 1.0 g/cm^3. It will sink into the water until the water that is displaced is equal to the weight of the boat.

ASSESSMENT

Critical Thinking: To further test your students' understanding of density and buoyancy, ask the following questions.

1. Estimate the percent uncertainty in your calculation of density of the floaters. Which measurement probably caused the largest error? [Typical uncertainties will be between 10% and 15%. The radius measurement will cause the most error, particularly because this value is squared in the calculation of the volume.]

2. Could the same experimental design be used to estimate the density of a person considering the way a person floats in a swimming pool? Give a reasonable estimate of a person's density. [Yes. The same design should work. Most people float, but just barely. A reasonable estimate for a person's density would be 0.95 g/cm^3.]

LABORATORY MANUAL

Use Lab 13.1 with this section.

LAB WORKSHEET

Use the Lab Worksheet for Chapter 13 with this Physics lab

Answers To
PRACTICE PROBLEMS

Have students refer to Appendix A of the Solutions Appendix for complete solutions to Practice Problems.

5. 160 N
6. 80 N
7. 0.06 m^3
8. 4.4×10^2 N

Example Problem

Archimedes' Principle

A cubic decimeter (10^{-3} m^3) of steel is submerged in water. **a.** What is the magnitude of the buoyant force acting on the steel? **b.** What is the apparent weight of the body? (The density of steel is 9.0×10^3 kg/m^3.)

Given: $V = 1.00 \times 10^{-3}$ m^3
$\rho_{steel} = 9.0 \times 10^3$ kg/m^3
$\rho_{water} = 1.00 \times 10^3$ kg/m^3

Unknowns: **a.** $F_{buoyant}$
b. $W_{apparent}$

Basic equations:
a. $F_{buoyant} = \rho_{water}Vg$
b. $W_{apparent} = mg - F_{buoyant}$

Solution:

a. $F_{buoyant} = \rho_{water}Vg$
$= (1.00 \times 10^3 \text{ kg/m}^3)(1.00 \times 10^{-1} \text{ m})^3(9.8 \text{ m/s}^2)$
$= 9.8$ N

b. $W_{apparent} = mg - F_{buoyant}$
$= [(1.00 \times 10^{-1} \text{ m})^3(9.0 \times 10^3 \text{ kg/m}^3)(9.8 \text{ m/s}^2)] - 9.8$ N
$= 88.2 \text{ N} - 9.8 \text{ N} = 78.4$ N

Practice Problems

5. If the diameter of the larger piston in Figure 13–4 were doubled, what force would be lifted if 20.0 N were applied to the smaller piston?

6. Dentists' chairs are examples of hydraulic lift systems. If the chair weighs 1600 N and rests on a piston with a cross-sectional area of 1440 cm^2, what force must be applied to the small piston with a cross-sectional area of 72 cm^2 to lift the chair?

7. A teenager is floating in a freshwater lake with her head just above the water. If she weighs 600 N, what is the volume of the submerged part of her body?

▶ **8.** What is the tension in a wire supporting a 1250-N camera submerged in water? The volume of the camera is 8.3×10^{-2} m^3.

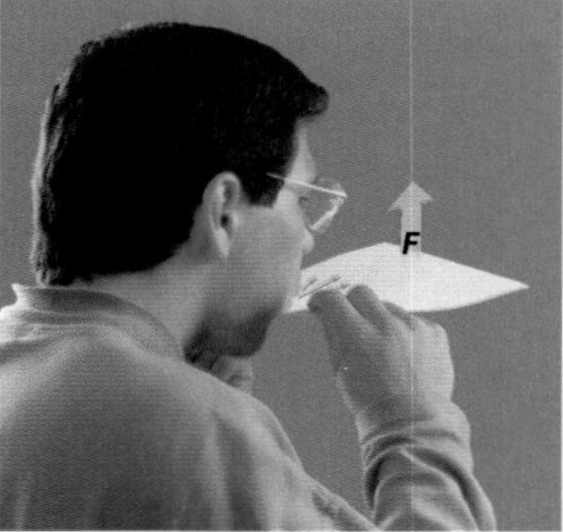

FIGURE 13–8. Blowing across the surface of a sheet of paper demonstrates Bernoulli's principle.

Fluids in Motion–Hydrodynamics

To see the effect of moving fluids, try the experiment in Figure 13–8. Hold a strip of notebook paper just under your lower lip. Now blow hard across the top surface. The strip will rise. The pressure on top of the paper where air is flowing fast is lower than the pressure beneath where air is not in motion. This is an example of Bernoulli's principle, named for the Swiss scientist Daniel Bernoulli (1700–1782).

Imagine a horizontal pipe completely filled with a smoothly flowing ideal fluid. If a certain mass of the fluid enters one end of the pipe, then an equal mass must come out the other end. Now consider a section of pipe where the cross section becomes narrower, as shown in Figure 13–9. To keep the same mass of fluid moving through the narrow section in a fixed amount of time, the velocity of the fluid must increase. If the

TEACHER

The Venturi tube is a constricted pipe, placed horizontally, which is used to measure the low velocity of an incompressible fluid, such as water.

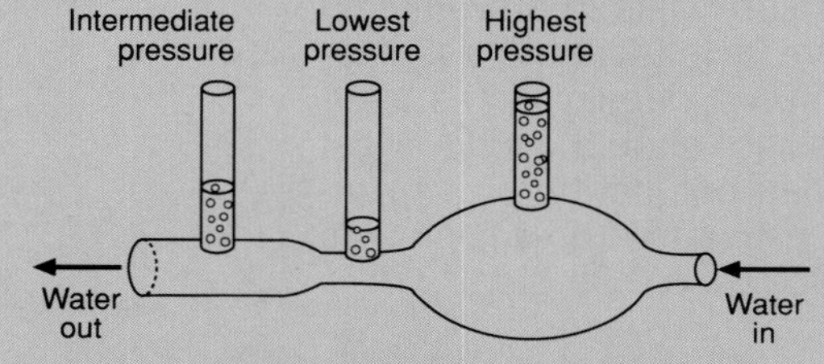

The level in the three lower tubes indicates the pressure as water passes through the upper tube. Velocity is high where the tube is constricted, so the pressure is low.

velocity increases, then so must the kinetic energy. This means that net work must be done on the fluid. The net work is the difference between the work done *on* the mass of fluid to move it into the pipe and the work done *by* the fluid pushing the same mass out of the pipe. The work is proportional to the force on the fluid, which, in turn, depends on the pressure. If the net work is positive, the pressure at the input end of the section, where the velocity is lower, must be larger than the pressure at the output end, where the velocity is higher. The relationship between the velocity and pressure exerted by a moving fluid is described by **Bernoulli's principle**: *As the velocity of a fluid increases, the pressure exerted by that fluid decreases.*

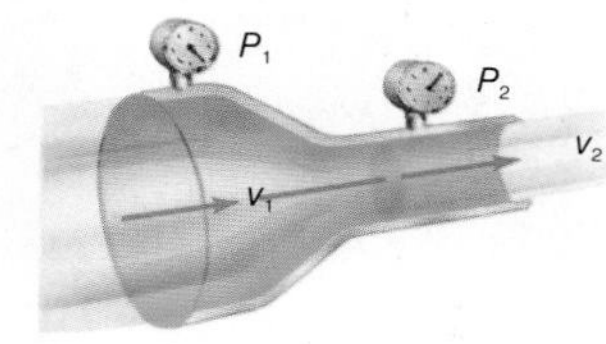

FIGURE 13–9. The pressure, P_1, is greater than P_2 because v_1 is less than v_2.

Most aircraft get part of their lift by taking advantage of Bernoulli's principle. Airplane wings are airfoils, devices designed to produce lift when moving through a fluid. The curvature of the top surface of a wing is greater than that of the bottom. As the wing travels through the air, the air moving over the top surface travels farther, and therefore must go faster than air moving past the bottom surface. The decreased air pressure created on the top surface results in a net upward pressure producing an upward force on the wings, or lift, that helps to hold the airplane aloft. Race cars use airfoils with a greater curvature on the bottom surface. The airfoils, called spoilers, produce a net downward pressure that helps to hold the rear wheels of the cars on the road at high speeds.

Did you ever notice that boat docks are designed so that water can flow freely through them? Consider what would happen at a solid-walled pier as a boat approached. As the space between the boat and the pier narrowed, the velocity of the water flowing through the space would increase, and the pressure exerted by the water on the pier side of the boat would decrease. The boat could be pushed against the pier by the greater pressure of the water against the other side.

Figure 13–10 shows that the flow of a fluid can be represented by streamlines. Streamlines can best be illustrated by a simple demonstration. Imagine carefully dropping tiny drops of food coloring into a smoothly flowing fluid. If the colored lines that form stay thin and well

FIGURE 13–10. Smooth streamlines in a computer simulation of airflow around a space shuttle indicate smooth air flow (a). A turbulent air flow appears around a rotating blade heated in a flame (b).

a

b

CONCEPT DEVELOPMENT

Perform some demonstrations of Bernoulli's principle. Blow through a straw so the air comes out next to a candle flame. The flame moves toward the straw.

DEMONSTRATION

Purpose: to demonstrate Bernoulli's principle.

Equipment: horizontal and vertical supports, two burned-out light bulbs, thread or fishing line

Procedure:

1. Suspend the bulbs from the horizontal support so they are about 2.5 cm apart. Ask students what will happen when you blow between them.
2. Blow strongly between the bulbs.

Results: The bulbs can be seen to move together and a "ping" is heard when they touch.

Question: What caused the bulbs to behave as they did? *The rapidly moving air between the bulbs created an area of lower pressure. The air pressure on the other sides of the bulbs pushed them together.*

CONCEPT DEVELOPMENT

ACTIVITY

Discovery: Fill a balloon with air. Gently squeeze the balloon. Does the volume of the balloon change? Can the volume of the air be decreased? Fill a balloon with water (no air). Place the balloon in a sink or large beaker. Gently squeeze the balloon. Does the volume of the balloon change? Can the volume of the water be compressed? Why? (The balloon with air can be easily compressed. Students may be surprised to find that the balloon with water seems to maintain a constant volume.)

POCKET LAB

FLOATING?

Purpose: to investigate what can be floated on the surface of water.
Materials: beaker; water; needle; paper clip; staple.
Outcome: It is possible to float needles, staples, paper clips, etc., on the surface of water. The small forces exerted by these objects on the water are not great enough to overcome the intermolecular forces at the surface of the water.

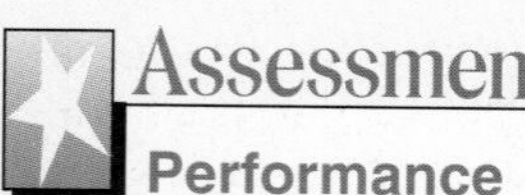

Assessment

Performance

To further assess students' understanding of surface tension, have them explore the effect of additives on the surface tension of water. Try adding salt, alcohol, or detergent to the water before you try floating a needle on its surface. If the surface tension supports the needle, which substances decreased the surface tension? [Detergent has the greatest effect, although dishwashing detergents containing hand lotion have a much smaller effect.]

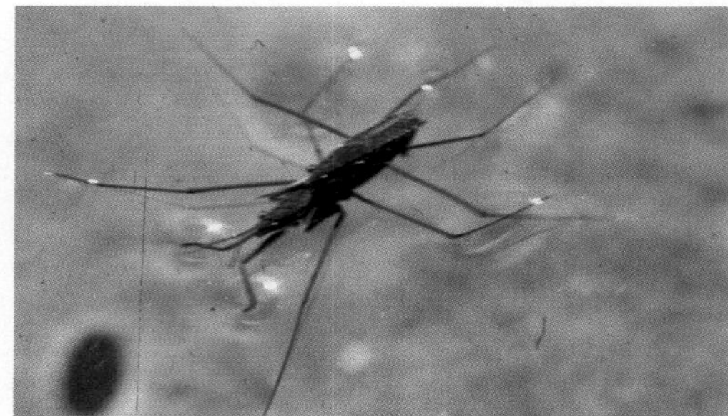

a

b

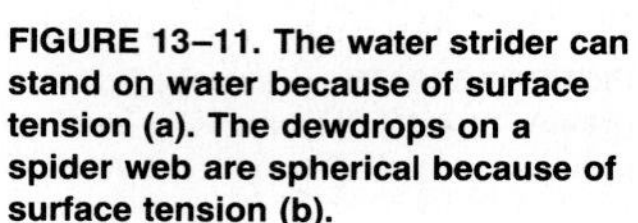

FIGURE 13–11. The water strider can stand on water because of surface tension (a). The dewdrops on a spider web are spherical because of surface tension (b).

defined, the flow is said to be streamlined. Notice that if the flow narrows, the streamlines move closer together. Closely-spaced streamlines indicate greater velocity, and therefore reduced pressure.

If streamlines swirl and become diffused, the flow of a fluid is said to be turbulent. Bernoulli's principle does not apply to turbulent flow. Since objects require less energy to move through a streamline flow, automobile and aircraft manufacturers spend a great deal of time and money testing new designs in wind tunnels to ensure a streamlined flow of air around vehicles.

Liquids vs Gases

Although liquids and gases are grouped together as fluids, liquids are different from gases in several ways.

- A liquid has a definite volume; a gas takes the volume of any container that holds it.
- A liquid is practically incompressible; a gas is easily compressed.
- The particles of a liquid are very close together—the volume of the particles makes up almost all the volume of a liquid; the particles of a gas take up relatively little space—a container of gas is mostly empty space.

Furthermore, although the particles of an ideal liquid are totally free to slide over and around one another, in real liquids the particles do exert electromagnetic forces of attraction on each other. These forces are called **cohesive forces**, and they directly affect the behavior of the liquid.

Surface tension makes liquids form spherical drops. It results from cohesive forces.

POCKET LAB

FLOATING?

Fill a glass or small beaker 3/4 full of water. Gently place a needle on the surface of the water. Try to float it. Try to float a paper clip, a metal staple, or other small items. Explain the results.

Surface Tension

Have you ever noticed that dewdrops on spiderwebs and falling drops of milk or oil are nearly spherical? What happens when it rains just after you have washed and waxed your car? The water drops bead up into rounded shapes. But a drop of alcohol on the same surface will flatten out. All of these phenomena are examples of surface tension. **Surface tension** is a result of the cohesive forces among the particles of a liquid. It is the tendency of the surface of a liquid to contract to the smallest area.

Multicultural Connections

Page 144 explains that boomerangs fly in a loop due to differences in air pressure on the surfaces of the arms. Bernoulli's principle explains how this happens. Think of a boomerang as a large "L" shape. The Australian aborigines discovered that by changing the curvature of the outside edge of the upper arm and the inside edge of the lower arm in the same way, their throwing sticks would return. The shape they discovered was the airfoil. The result is that as the boomerang spins through the air, the air moves across one side of the arms faster than the other. Bernoulli's principle explains that this means there is a difference in air pressure on the arms. Since the two curved edges follow one another as the boomerang spins, the difference in air pressure is always on one side of the boomerang, so it is pushed into a looped path.

Beneath the surface of the liquid in Figure 13–12, each particle of the liquid is attracted equally in all directions by neighboring particles. As a result, there is no net force acting on any of the particles beneath the surface. At the surface, however, the particles are attracted to the sides and downward, but not upward. Thus, there is a net downward force acting on the top layers. This net force causes the surface layer to be slightly compressed. The layer acts like a tightly stretched rubber sheet or a film. The film is strong enough to support the weight of light objects. Water bugs can stand on the surface of quiet pools of water because of surface tension. The surface tension of water also supports an object such as a steel razor blade, even though the density of steel is nine times greater than that of water.

Why does surface tension produce the spherical drops? The force pulling the surface particles into the liquid causes the surface to become as small as possible. The shape that has the least surface for a given volume is a sphere. Liquid mercury has a much stronger cohesive force among its particles than water. This allows small amounts of mercury to form spherical drops, even when placed on a smooth surface. On the other hand, liquids such as alcohol or ether have weaker cohesive forces between their particles. A drop of either of these liquids flattens out when placed on a smooth surface.

A force similar to cohesion is adhesion. **Adhesion** is the attractive force that acts between particles of different substances. Like cohesive forces, adhesive forces are electromagnetic in nature.

If a piece of glass tubing with a small inside diameter is placed in water, the water rises inside the tube. The water rises because the adhesive force between glass and water molecules is stronger than the cohesive force between water molecules. This phenomenon is called **capillary action.** The water continues to rise until the weight of the water lifted balances the adhesive force between the glass and water molecules. If the radius of the tube increases, the volume, and therefore the weight, of the water increases proportionally faster than the surface area of the tube. For this reason, water is lifted higher in a narrow tube than in one that is wider.

As shown in Figure 13–13a, the surface of the water dips in the center of the tube. This is because the adhesive force between the glass molecules and water molecules is greater than the cohesive force between the water molecules. If the liquid in the tube were mercury, it

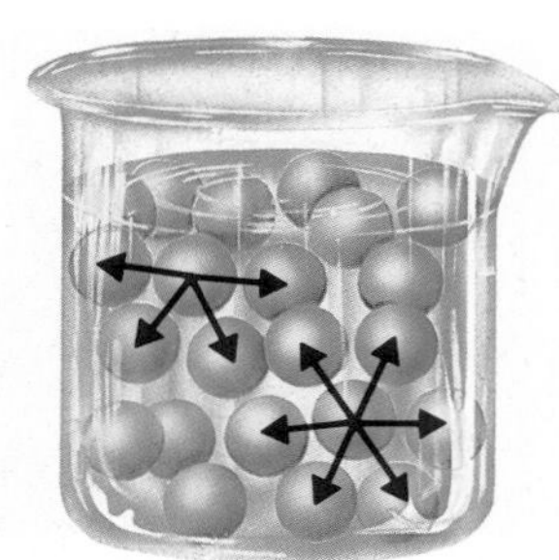

FIGURE 13–12. Molecules in the interior of a liquid are attracted in all directions. Molecules at the surface have a net inward attraction that results in surface tension.

BIOLOGY CONNECTION

Botanists use paper chromatography to identify the chemical make-up of plants. Leaves from a plant are ground up and mixed with a solvent to make a mobile phase. Capillary action causes the liquid to move through the piece of paper. Different chemical substances move at different speeds, and so can be separated. Medical technologists use paper chromatography to test the urine of diabetic patients to determine if a patient's pancreas is functioning properly.

a

b

FIGURE 13–13. Water climbs the wall of this capillary tube (a), while the mercury is depressed in the tube (b). The force of attraction between mercury atoms is stronger than any adhesive force between the mercury and the glass.

CONCEPT DEVELOPMENT

An interesting problem in biology has been to figure out how water gets to the top of a very tall tree. Capillary action and surface tension play a part but don't seem to be the total answer. A student might be interested in following this up.

CHECKING FOR UNDERSTANDING

Why does a sharp knife cut better than a dull one? [A dull knife's edge has a greater surface area so the pressure for a given force on the edge is less, hence it doesn't cut as well.]

RETEACHING

Use the following questions to help reteach: What's the best thing to do if you are ice skating on a sheet of ice on a pond and the ice starts to crack? [Lie down.] Why is this effective? [It spreads your weight out over a larger area and thus reduces the pressure you exert on the ice.] Would the same advice apply if you were trapped in quicksand? [Yes, but it might be difficult to get into a horizontal position.]

How is Bernoulli's principle used to make a perfume sprayer work? [Squeezing the bulb forces a high-speed jet of air over the top of a tube thus reducing the pressure there, so the higher air pressure within the bottle forces liquid up the tube where it is broken into fine droplets.]

Reteaching Master, Teacher Resource Package. Use the Reteaching Master for Chapter 13, Surface Tension.

EXTENSION

Enrichment Master. With this section, use the Enrichment Master, Bernoulli's Equation, from the Teacher Resource Package.

Guided Practice: Use the Practice Problems in this block.

Independent Practice: Use the material at the end of the chapter.

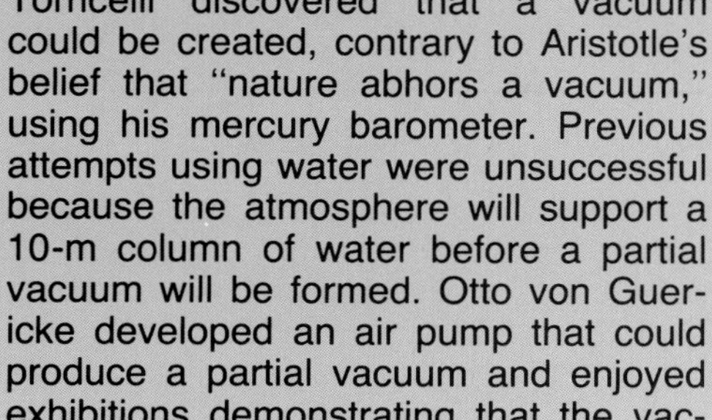

TEACHER F.Y.I.

Torricelli discovered that a vacuum could be created, contrary to Aristotle's belief that "nature abhors a vacuum," using his mercury barometer. Previous attempts using water were unsuccessful because the atmosphere will support a 10-m column of water before a partial vacuum will be formed. Otto von Guericke developed an air pump that could produce a partial vacuum and enjoyed exhibitions demonstrating that the vacuum it produced was stronger than two teams of horses (Magdeburg spheres). Boyle further improved on this pump and the production in 1854 of a method of producing a better vacuum led to the discovery of X rays, the electron, and indirectly, radioactivity—the birth of modern physics!

From: *Timetables of Science*, Hellemans and Bunch, Simon & Schuster, 1988.

Transparency Package. Use Transparency 17, Pascal/Archimedes/Bernoulli, and accompanying worksheet with this section.

3 Close

CONVERGENT QUESTION

What is it about the properties of liquids (as compared to gases) that causes these evaporation- and condensation-related phenomena? [Basically they're all due to appreciable forces between liquid molecules, whereas in ideal gases, intermolecular forces are negligible.]

FIGURE 13–14. Convection currents carry warm surface air aloft until it reaches the temperature layer at which the water vapor condenses.

would not rise in the tube. Furthermore, the center of the surface would bulge upward, as shown in Figure 13–13b. Both of these phenomena occur because the cohesive forces between the mercury molecules are greater than the adhesive forces between the mercury and glass.

Molten wax rises in the wick of a candle because of capillary action. Paint moves up through the bristles of a brush for the same reason. It is also capillary action that causes water to move up through the soil to the roots of plants.

Evaporation and Condensation

What happens to a puddle of water on a hot, dry day? After a few hours the water is gone. Why? The particles in a liquid move at random speeds. Some are moving rapidly; others are moving slowly. The temperature of a liquid is dependent on the average *KE* of its particles. Suppose a fast-moving particle is near the surface of the liquid. If it can break through the surface layers, it will escape from the liquid. Since there is a net downward cohesive force at the surface, only the more energetic particles escape. The escape of particles is called **evaporation.**

Evaporation cools the remaining liquid.

Evaporation cools the remaining liquid. Why? Each time a particle with higher than average kinetic energy escapes from the liquid, the average kinetic energy of the remaining particles decreases. A decrease in kinetic energy is a decrease in temperature. The cooling can be demonstrated by pouring some rubbing alcohol into the palm of your hand. Alcohol molecules have weak cohesive forces (low surface tension). Alcohol molecules, therefore, evaporate easily. The cooling effect is quite noticeable. Liquids such as alcohol and ether evaporate quickly because the forces between their molecules are weak. A liquid that evaporates quickly is called a **volatile** (VAHL uht uhl) liquid.

F.Y.I.

If all the water vapor in Earth's atmosphere were condensed to liquid water at the same time, there would be enough water to cover the United States with a layer of water twenty-five feet deep.

The opposite process also exists. What happens if you bring a cold glass into a hot, humid area? The outside of the glass soon becomes coated with water. Water molecules moving randomly in the air surrounding the glass may strike the cold surface. If a molecule loses enough energy, the cohesive force will be strong enough to prevent the particle's escape. This process is called **condensation**.

The air above water contains evaporated water vapor, water in the form of a gas. If the temperature is reduced, the water vapor condenses around tiny dust particles in the air, producing droplets only 0.01 mm in diameter. A cloud of these droplets is called a fog. Fogs often form when moist air is chilled by cold ground. Fogs can also be formed in your home. When a carbonated drink is opened, the sudden decrease in pressure causes the temperature to drop, condensing the water vapor and forming the fog seen when Janet opened the bottle of sparkling grape juice.

Bottled Cloud ▶

Plasma

If you heat a solid, it melts to form a liquid. Further heating results in a gas. What happens if you increase the temperature still further? Collisions between the particles become violent enough to tear the particles

RETEACHING MASTER

Use the Reteaching master for Chapter 13 with this section.

TRANSPARENCY

Use Transparency 17 with this section.

ENRICHMENT MASTER

Use the Enrichment master for Chapter 13 with this section.

apart. Electrons are pulled off the atoms, producing positively-charged ions. The gaslike state of negatively-charged electrons and positively-charged ions is called a **plasma**. Plasma is another fluid state of matter.

A lightning bolt is in the plasma state. So is most of the sun and other stars. In addition, much of the matter between the stars is in the form of plasma. The primary difference between a gas and a plasma is that a plasma can conduct electricity, and gas cannot. Neon signs and mercury and sodium vapor street lights contain glowing plasmas.

FIGURE 13–15. The spectacular lighting effects in "neon" signs are caused by luminous plasmas formed in the glass tubing.

A plasma is a gas of charged particles.

CONCEPT REVIEW

1.1 You have two boxes. One is 20 cm by 20 cm by 20 cm. The other is 20 cm by 20 cm by 40 cm. **a.** How does the pressure of the air on the outside of the boxes compare on the two boxes? **b.** How does the total force of the air compare on the two boxes?

1.2 Does a full, soft-drink can float or sink in water? Try it. Does it matter whether the drink is diet or not? All drink cans contain the same volume of liquid, 354 ml, and displace the same volume. What is the difference between a can that sinks and one that floats?

1.3 When a baby has a high fever, doctors may suggest gently sponging off the baby with "rubbing alcohol." Why would this help?

1.4 **Critical Thinking:** It was a hot, humid day. Nicole had a glass of cold water on her desk. The outside of the glass was coated with water. Dan said that the water had leaked through the glass from the inside to the outside. Suggest an experiment Nicole could do to show Dan where the water came from.

Physics and technology

AERODYNAMIC HELMETS

In the 74th Indy 500, Arie Luyendyk drove an average speed of 185.984 mph (297.5 km/h) to win. His maximum speed was greater than 220 mph (352 km/h). At these speeds, drivers complain that their heads are buffeted severely; their helmets lift up, impairing their vision.

Airflow over the curved top of a racing helmet produces lift in the same way as over an airplane wing. The air speeds up as it passes over the helmet, creating an area of low pressure; the higher pressure below the helmet pushes it upward. Simpson Race Products Company found a way to break up the airflow over the helmet through the use of pressure-relief ducts and stall strips. The Simpson helmet has two gill-like outlet ducts and two ripple strips on each side of the top of the helmet. The ducts allow low-energy airflow out of the helmet to mix with the faster moving air over the top, thus reducing the lift. The ripple-strips enhance the mixing process.

Twenty-one of the thirty-three drivers in the 74th Indy 500, including the winner, wore a Simpson helmet. The helmet won the 1990 Schwitzer Award given by the Society of Automotive Engineers for innovation and excellence in race car design. Besides its improved aerodynamic qualities, the helmet has a new liner that provides better protection and it improves airflow to cool the driver's head.

· What other applications might this improved helmet have?

CONCEPT REVIEW ANSWERS

1.1 a. Pressures are both the same (pressure doesn't depend on size or shape). **b.** Force is proportional to surface area. The surface area of the first box is 6(20 cm)(20 cm) = 2400 cm^2. The surface area of the second box is 2(20 cm)(20 cm) + 4(20 cm)(40 cm) = 4000 cm^2, so force is (4000 cm^2)/(2400 cm^2) = 1.67 times as much on the second.

1.2 The mass is less for a floater. A floating can is less dense than water. A sinker is more dense than water. Since the can volumes are the same, the masses of the cans must be different. (Artificial sweetener has less mass than corn syrup!)

1.3 Alcohol is a volatile liquid. It will quickly evaporate, cooling the baby's skin.

1.4 Critical Thinking: Add food coloring to water inside a glass. Does water on the outside become colored? If the glass is in the refrigerator, does it get coated? If not, why wouldn't water "leak" through there? Put the glass out on a hot, dry day. Does this make any difference? Set a cold metal object out into the air and it will become coated with water too.

Physics and technology

When fast-moving air flows over a curved surface, there is a line of separation when the airflow becomes separated from the surface. Prior to the separation, the airflow is essentially attached to the surface. According to Bernoulli's principle, this attached high-speed airflow will produce a pressure differential that results in lift. When this lifting force is undesirable, a way must be found to counteract or prevent it. Since lift occurs during the stage when the airflow is attached to the object's surface, it can be prevented or reduced by forcing earlier separation of the airflow. Ducts and rippled "stall" strips are two devices which can be used to induce separation by changing the airflow.

13:1 ASSIGNMENT GUIDE

	PRACTICE	EXTENSION
CHAPTER REVIEW pp. 283–285		
· Reviewing Concepts	1–13	
· Applying Concepts		1–7
· Problems*	3–13, 15	1, 2, 14
APPENDIX B PROBLEMS*		
· Chapter 13 p. 698	1–3, 6–8	4, 5, 9, 10

* Complete solutions to all Chapter Review and Appendix problems appear in the Problems and Solutions Manual.

13.2 THE SOLID STATE

Preparation

OBJECTIVES

The objectives are listed on the student page. Remind students to preview these objectives as a study guide to this major section.

OVERVIEW

Important new concepts here are elasticity and the coefficient of linear expansion.

BRIDGING

Temperature, length, and density reappear here.

1 Focus

DISCREPANT EVENT

Obtain a ball and ring set to demonstrate thermal expansion. The room-temperature ball slides through the ring. When the ball is heated, it won't fit through the ring. Ask students if the ball will fit through if both the ball and ring are heated. Most students will say no because they think the hole gets smaller as it is heated. Actually, the diameter of the hole gets larger and the hot ball fits through the hot ring. Point out to students that a metal lid on a jar can be loosened by running hot water on it.

2 Teach

CONCEPT DEVELOPMENT

Study Guide Master. To reinforce the concepts in this section, have the students complete the Study Guide Master for Section 13.2 from the Teacher Resource Package.

The solid state at a much smaller and more detailed level will be treated in Chapter 29, "Solid State Electronics." The characteristics treated there relate to the electrical properties of solids and are important in electronics.

Objectives

- display an understanding of the difference between solids and liquids on a microscopic level.
- discuss properties of solids such as elasticity.
- display an understanding of the origin of thermal expansion; be able to solve problems using linear thermal expansion; state some examples of applications and difficulties caused by thermal expansion.

13.2 THE SOLID STATE

What is the difference between a liquid and a solid? Solids are stiff. You can push them. Liquids are soft. Can you rest your finger on water? No, it goes right in. Of course, if you "bellyflop" into a swimming pool, you recognize that a liquid can seem rather solid. Scientists have recently found that, under certain laboratory conditions, solids and liquids are not so easily distinguished. The researchers have made clusters containing only a few dozen atoms. These clusters can be both liquid and solid at the same temperature. Study of this strange state of matter may help scientists to invent new, useful materials in the future.

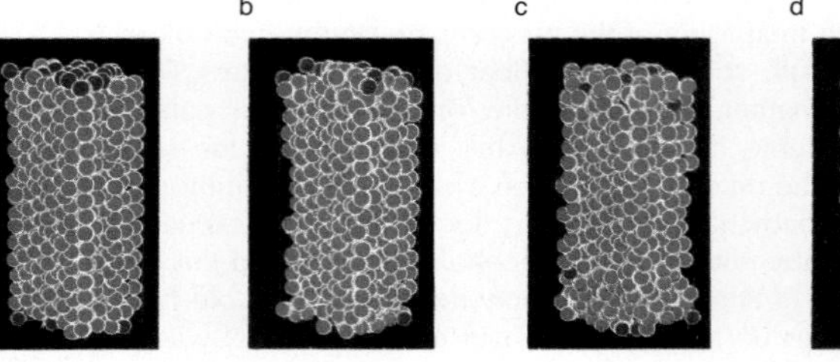

FIGURE 13–16. Computer models of the melting of a solid. The green and blue spheres represent the liquid phase, and the red spheres represent the solid phase. Notice how similar they are.

Solid Bodies

The particles in a true solid are fixed in a crystal lattice.

When the temperature of a liquid is lowered, the average kinetic energy of the particles is lowered. As the particles slow down, the cohesive forces become more effective, and the particles are no longer able to slide over one another. The particles become frozen into a fixed pattern called a **crystal lattice**, Figure 13–17. Despite the forces that hold the particles in place, the particles do not stop moving completely. Rather, they vibrate around their fixed positions in the crystal lattice. In some solid materials, the particles do not form a fixed crystalline pattern. Their positions are fixed, but the pattern is variable. These substances have no regular crystal structure but have definite volume and shape, so they are called **amorphous solids**. Butter, paraffin, and glass are examples. They are often classified as very viscous (slow-flowing) liquids.

FIGURE 13–17. The solid form of water, ice, has a larger volume than an equal mass of its liquid form (a). The crystalline structure of ice (b).

a

b

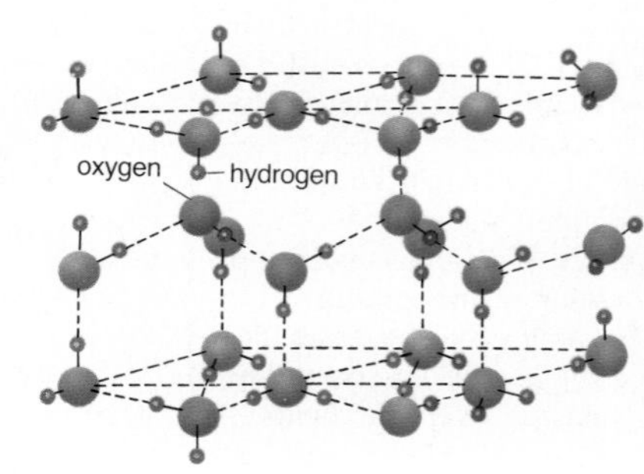

Connect to BIOLOGY

Because cells of living organisms are primarily composed of water, the expansion of water when it freezes can have disastrous results on the tissues of plants and animals. The increased volume can rupture cell walls and lead to death. Certain small fish that live in the arctic region are able to survive being frozen in ice during the winter. Their bodies have been found to contain a natural antifreeze. In what ways could such a substance prevent damage when the temperature drops? [Antifreeze can lower the freezing temperature of water by a few degrees. It can also reduce the size of the ice crystals that form, reducing the damage they cause.]

As a liquid freezes, its particles usually fit more closely together than in the liquid state. Solids usually are more dense than liquids. Water is an exception. Water is most dense at 4°C. Thus, water expands as it freezes, causing ice to have a lower density than liquid water at 0°C and to float on the surface.

An increase in the pressure on the surface of a liquid forces the particles closer together. The cohesive force becomes more important. For most liquids, the freezing point increases as the pressure on the liquid increases. Water is the exception. Since water expands as it freezes, an increase in pressure opposes this expansion. The freezing point of water is lowered as pressure on its surface is increased. For example, increased pressure from ice skate blades causes ice under the blades to melt. The thin film of water formed acts as a lubricant and allows the skates to move across the ice with almost no friction.

FIGURE 13–18. The pressure of the skate blade on the ice forms a thin film of water which acts as a lubricant to reduce friction.

Elasticity of Solids

External forces applied to a solid object may twist or bend it out of shape. The ability of an object to return to its original form when the external forces are removed is called the **elasticity** of the solid. If too much deformation occurs, the object will not return to its original shape—its elastic limit has been exceeded. Elasticity depends on the electromagnetic forces that hold the particles of a substance together. Malleability and ductility, the ability to be rolled into a thin sheet and drawn into a wire, respectively, are two properties that depend on the structure and elasticity of a substance. Gold is malleable; glass is not.

Elasticity is the ability of an object to return to its original form after external forces are removed.

Thermal Expansion of Matter

Most materials expand when heated and contract when cooled. This property, known as **thermal expansion,** has many useful applications. For example, when a gas such as air is heated, it becomes less dense. When the air near the floor of a room is warmed, gravity pulls the denser, colder ceiling air down, pushing the warmer air upward. This motion results in the circulation of air, called a convection current.

Table 13–2

Coefficients of Thermal Expansion at 20°C

Material	Coefficient of linear expansion, $\alpha(°C)^{-1}$	Coefficient of volume expansion, $\beta(°C)^{-1}$
Solids		
Aluminum	25×10^{-6}	75×10^{-6}
Iron, steel	12×10^{-6}	35×10^{-6}
Glass (soft)	9×10^{-6}	27×10^{-6}
Glass (Pyrex,	3×10^{-6}	9×10^{-6}
Concrete	12×10^{-6}	36×10^{-6}
Platinum	9×10^{-6}	
Copper	16×10^{-6}	48×10^{-6}
Liquids		
Methanol		1100×10^{-6}
Gasoline		950×10^{-6}
Mercury		180×10^{-6}
Water		210×10^{-6}
Gases		
Air (and most other gases)		3400×10^{-6}

POCKET LAB

JUMPERS

Put on a pair of safety goggles. Examine the jumping disk. Notice that it is slightly curved. Now rub the disk for several seconds until it becomes curved in the other direction. Place the disk on a flat level surface and stand back. Suggest a hypothesis that might explain the jumping. Suggest a method to test your hypothesis.

CONCEPT DEVELOPMENT

On older houses, usually historical ones, you may have noticed a heavy metal plate in the middle of a wall with the head of a metal rod protruding from it and a nut threaded onto the rod. A quick check of the opposite wall would show the other end of the rod with a metal plate and nut. These rods have been used to straighten buckling walls. The rod is heated in the middle, the nuts tightened on both ends, then the rod cools, contracting and pulling the walls together.

ACTIVITY

Discovery: Use a bimetallic strip to show how two metals expand by different amounts. When the strip is heated, it curls. This phenomenon is used in the construction of a thermostat. As the bimetallic strip is heated, it curves, breaking an electrical circuit that turns the furnace off.

POCKET LAB

JUMPERS

Purpose: to demonstrate different rates of expansion of metals.
Materials: safety goggles; jumping disks.
Outcome: After a short time, the disks will jump. The disks are wafers of two different metals and are called bimetallic. The bottom side expands more, due to heat from your hand, than the top side so that rubbing the disk causes it to curve in the opposite direction.

TEACHER F.Y.I.

The thermal expansion of matter can be extended to volume. The formula for change in volume is very similar to the change in length, $\Delta V = V_i\beta\Delta T$. The symbol β stands for the coefficient of volume expansion and is 3 times α. If you have water in a glass and want to find the expansion of the water, you use the relative coefficient of volume expansion, which is the difference in the coefficients for glass and water.

CONCEPT DEVELOPMENT

Critical Thinking Master, Teacher Resource Package. Use the worksheet, The Effect of Thermal Expansion on Lakes, for further investigation of the concepts presented in this section.

Assessment

Portfolio

Buildings, sidewalks, railroads, and highways contain expansion joints to prevent damage from thermal expansion. Have a group of interested students take photographs of expansion joints they find and write a caption for each photo explaining how the joint works to prevent damage.

FIGURE 13–19. The extreme heat of a July day caused these railroad tracks to buckle.

The expansion of liquids is useful in thermometers. Expansion also allows a liquid to be heated rapidly. When a container of liquid is heated from the bottom, convection currents form, just as in a gas. Cold, more dense liquid sinks to the bottom where it is warmed and then pushed up by the continuous flow of cooler liquid from the top. Thus, all the liquid is able to come in contact with the hot surface.

The expansion of concrete and steel in highway bridges means that the structures are longer in the summer than in the winter. Temperature extremes must be considered when bridges are designed. Gaps, called expansion joints, are built in to allow for seasonal changes in length.

Some materials have been specifically designed to have the smallest possible thermal expansion. Blocks used as standard lengths in machine shops are often made of Invar, a metal alloy. Pyrex glass is used for laboratory and cooking containers and in large telescope mirrors.

We can explain the expansion of heated solids in terms of the kinetic theory. Our model for a solid is a collection of particles connected by springs. The springs represent the forces that attract the particles to each other. When the particles get too close, the springs push them apart. If a solid did not have these forces of repulsion, it would collapse into a tiny sphere.

When a solid is heated, the kinetic energy of the particles increases; they vibrate more violently. The attractive force between particles in a solid is not exactly like the force exerted by a stretched spring. In the case of a solid, when the particles move farther apart, the force is weaker. As a result, when the particles vibrate more violently, their average separation increases. Thus, the solid expands when its temperature increases.

Most liquids also expand when heated. A good model for a liquid does not exist, but it is useful to think of a liquid as a ground-up solid. Groups of two, three, or more particles move together as if they were a tiny piece of a solid. When heated, particle motion causes these groups to expand just as a solid does. The spaces between groups also increase. As a result, the whole liquid expands. For an equal change in temperature, liquids expand considerably more than solids.

Liquid water expands only when its temperature is raised above 4°C. As water is heated from 0°C to 4°C, it contracts. The solid form of water, ice, has a larger volume than an equal mass of its liquid form. The forces between water molecules are strong. The crystals that make up

FIGURE 13–20. Computer-calculated paths of particles appear as bright lines on the face of a cathode-ray tube coupled to the computer. Motion of atoms in an atomic crystal (note that the atoms move only about fixed positions) (a). A crystal in the process of melting (note the breakdown of the ordered array but no great increase in distance) (b). A liquid and its vapor (the dark area represents a gas bubble surrounded by particles whose motions are characteristic of a liquid) (c).

a

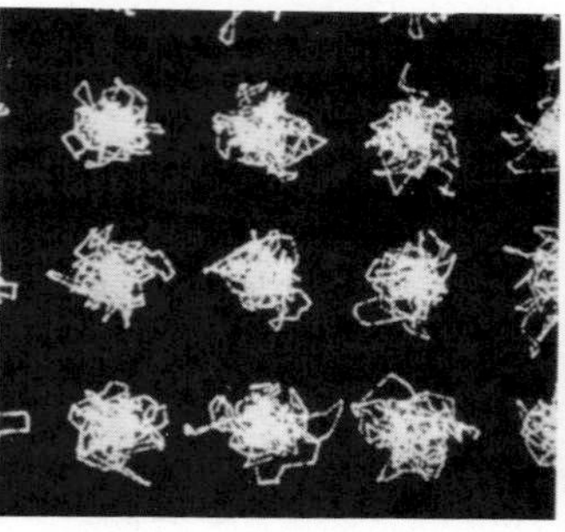

b

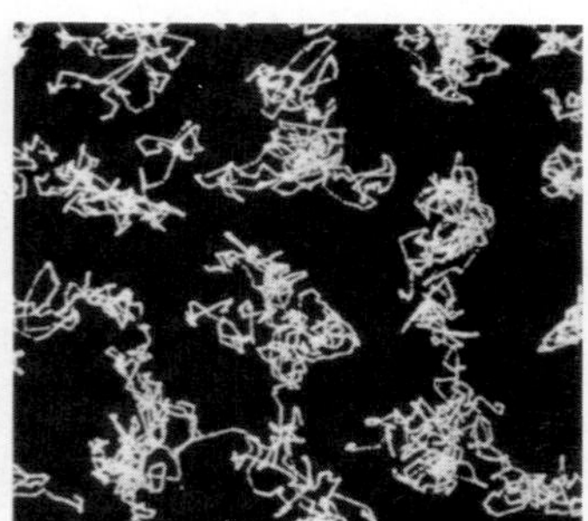

c

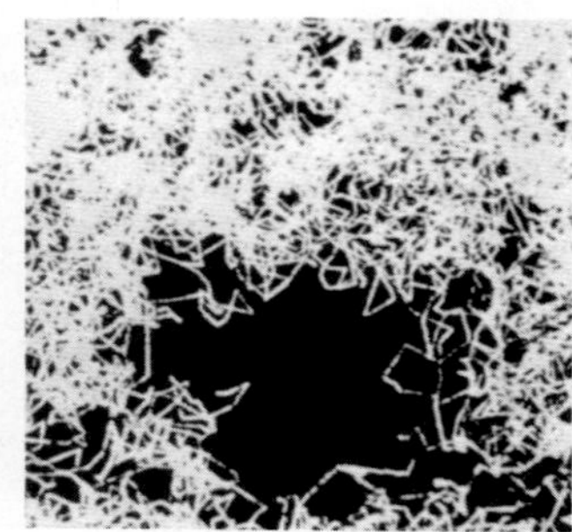

TEACHER 

The expansion of water as it is cooled below 4°C led to the development of the mercury thermometer by Fahrenheit. Mercury has the advantages of low vapor pressure, a rate of expansion that is independent of temperature, and a wide range for temperature measurement.

ice have a very open structure. Even when ice melts, tiny crystals remain. Between melting and 4°C, these remaining crystals melt, and the volume decreases. It is found that water is denser at 4°C than at any other temperature. The practical result is that ice floats, and that lakes, rivers, and other bodies of water freeze from the top down.

The change in length of a solid is proportional to the change in temperature. A solid will expand twice as much if the temperature is increased by 20°C than if it is increased by 10°C. The change is also proportional to its length. A two-meter bar will expand twice as much as a one-meter bar. Thus, the length, L, of a solid at temperature T is given by

$$L = L_i + \alpha L_i(T - T_i),$$

where L_i is the length at temperature T_i and the proportionality constant, α, is called the **coefficient of linear expansion**. The equation can also be written

$$L - L_i = \alpha L_i(T - T_i) \quad \text{or} \quad \Delta L = \alpha L_i \Delta T.$$

Then,

$$\frac{\Delta L}{L_i} = \alpha \Delta T \text{ and } \alpha = \frac{\Delta L}{L_i \Delta T}.$$

The dimensions of α are

$$\frac{\text{(length unit)}}{\text{(length unit)(temperature unit)}}.$$

Therefore, the unit for the coefficient of linear expansion is 1/°C or $(°C)^{-1}$. Volume expansion is three dimensional. Look at Table 13–2 on page 279. The coefficient of volume expansion is approximately three times the coefficient of linear expansion.

Different materials expand at different rates. The expansion rates of gases and liquids are larger than those of solids. Engineers must consider these different expansion rates when designing structures. Steel bars are often used to reinforce concrete. The steel and concrete must have the same expansion coefficient. Otherwise, the structure may crack on a hot day. For a similar reason, a dentist must use filling materials that expand and contract at the same rate as tooth enamel.

Sometimes different rates of expansion are useful. Engineers have taken advantage of these differences to construct a useful device called a bimetallic strip. A bimetallic strip consists of two strips of different metals. These two metals are either welded or riveted together. Usually one strip is brass and the other is iron. When heated, brass expands more than iron. Thus, when the bimetallic strip of brass and iron is heated, the brass strip becomes longer than the iron strip. The bimetallic strip bends with the brass on the outside of the curve. If the bimetallic strip is cooled, it bends in the opposite direction. The brass is now on the inside of the curve.

Thermostats used in homes usually contain a bimetallic strip. The bimetallic strip is installed so that it bends toward an electric contact as the room cools. When the room cools below the setting on the thermostat, the bimetallic strip bends enough to make electric contact with the switch, which turns on the heater. As the room warms, the bimetallic strip bends in the other direction. The electric circuit is broken, and the heater is switched off.

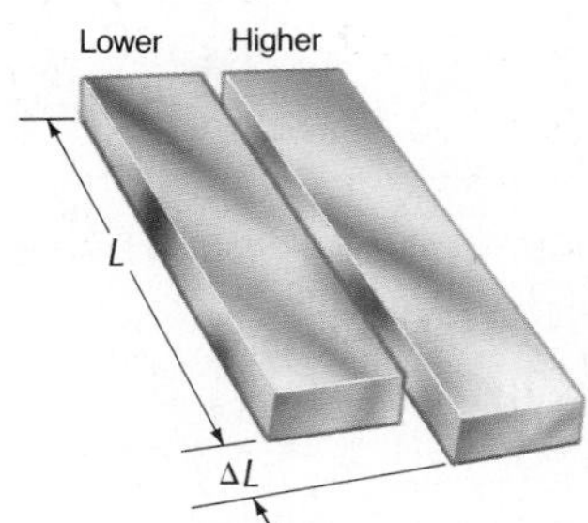

FIGURE 13–21. The change in length is proportional to the original length and the change in temperature.

a

b

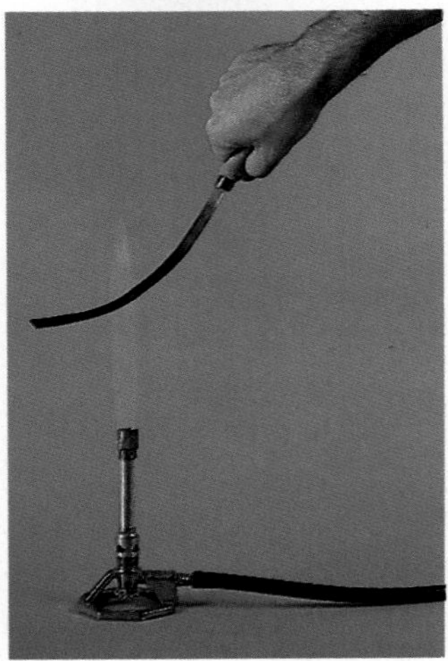

FIGURE 13–22. The properties of a bimetallic strip cause it to bend when heated (b). In this thermostat, a coiled bimetallic strip controls the flow of mercury for opening and closing electrical switches (a).

CHECKING FOR UNDERSTANDING

Ask students how high the temperature would have to go for a steel rod 1 meter long to double its length. [8.3 × 10^4°C.] Someone will probably point out that steel would have vaporized long before it reaches this temperature. The example also serves to show how small most lengths of expansion are.

RETEACHING

Review answers to quantitative problems about expansion. Compared to the original length, how much change (in percent) do expanding objects experience? [Fractions of 1%.] This is another way of pointing out the size of these expansion effects.

EXTENSION

Engineers face many problems in designing large buildings such as skyscrapers. One of them is the unequal heating of the building when the sun comes up in the morning and goes down at sunset. At these times, one side of the building gets heated much more than the other. Why does this cause a problem? [One side of the building will expand more than the other so it leans over slightly! Thus the stability of the building must take this leaning into account.]

Supplemental Lesson, Teacher Resource Package. With this chapter, refer students to the Supplemental Lesson Master concerning gas laws.

Guided Practice: Discuss the Example Problem on page 282. Have students try the first Practice Problem in class.

Independent Practice: Assign Practice Problems 10–12 for homework and discuss them in class the next day.

13:2 ASSIGNMENT GUIDE

	PRACTICE	EXTENSION
CHAPTER REVIEW pp. 283–285		
· Reviewing Concepts	14–16	
· Applying Concepts		8–12
· Problems*	16, 17	18–20
APPENDIX B PROBLEMS*		
· Chapter 13, p. 698	11–13	14, 15

* Complete solutions to all Chapter Review and Appendix problems appear in the Problems and Solutions Manual.

CRITICAL THINKING

Use the Critical Thinking master for Chapter 13 with this section.

SUPPLEMENT

Use Supplemental Lesson 3 with this section.

HELP WANTED

MATERIALS ENGINEER

A leading corporation that develops new materials or new uses for old ones seeks an engineer to join our research and development team. A creative, yet analytical mind; a bachelor's degree in materials, metallurgical or ceramics engineering; and the ability to work both independently and on teams are required.

Our professionals work with the finest resources in the industry. Your commitment to lifelong education and to outstanding performance will allow you to move into positions of increasing responsibility. For information contact:

ASU International, Metals Park, OH 44073 or National Institute of Ceramic Engineers, 757 Brooksedge Plaza Dr., Westerville, OH 43081

Example Problem

Linear Expansion

A metal bar is 2.60 m long at 21°C. The bar is heated uniformly to a temperature of 93°C and the change in length is measured to be 3.4 mm. What is the coefficient of linear expansion of this bar?

Given: $L_i = 2.60$ m
$\Delta L = 3.4 \times 10^{-3}$ m
$T_i = 21°C$
$T = 93°C$

Unknown: α

Basic equation: $\frac{\Delta L}{L_i} = \alpha \Delta T$, where $\Delta T = T - T_i$

Solution: $\Delta T = T - T_i = 72°C$

$$\alpha = \frac{\Delta L}{L_i \Delta T} = \frac{3.4 \times 10^{-3}\ \text{m}}{(2.60\ \text{m})(72\text{C}°)} = 1.8 \times 10^{-5}(°C)^{-1}$$

Practice Problems

9. A piece of aluminum house siding is 3.66 m long on a cold winter day (−28°C). How much longer is it on a very hot summer day (39°C)?

10. A piece of steel is 11.5 m long at 22°C. It is heated to 1221°C, close to its melting temperature. How long is it?

11. An aluminum soft-drink can, 354 ml, is filled to the brim with water in the refrigerator (4.4°C). **a.** What will be the volume of the liquid on a warm day (34.5°C)? **b.** What will be the volume of the can? (**Hint:** The can will expand as much as a block of metal the same size.) **c.** How much liquid will spill? ($\Delta V = \beta V \Delta T$)

▶ **12.** A tank truck takes on a load of 45 725 liters of gasoline in Houston at 32.0°C. The coefficient of volume expansion, β, for gasoline 950 × $10^{-6}(°C)^{-1}$. The truck delivers its load in Omaha a −18.0°C.

a. How many liters of gasoline does the truck deliver?

b. What happened to the gasoline?

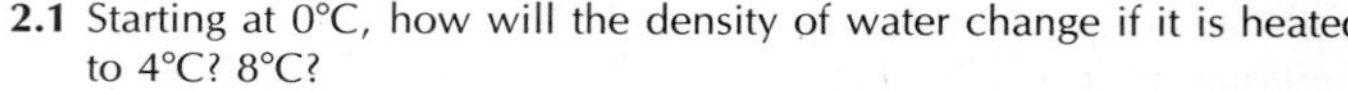

CONCEPT REVIEW

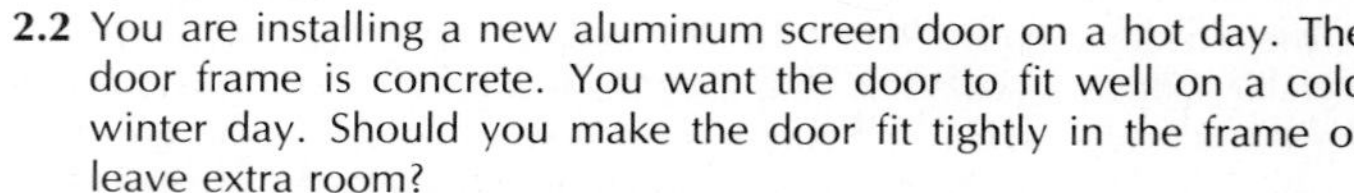

2.1 Starting at 0°C, how will the density of water change if it is heated to 4°C? 8°C?

2.2 You are installing a new aluminum screen door on a hot day. The door frame is concrete. You want the door to fit well on a cold winter day. Should you make the door fit tightly in the frame or leave extra room?

2.3 Why could candle wax be considered a solid? a viscous liquid?

2.4 **Critical Thinking:** If you heat an iron ring with a small gap in it, Figure 13–23, will the gap become wider or narrower?

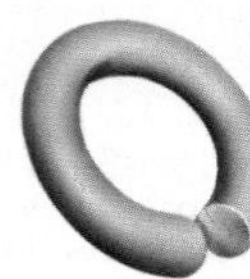

FIGURE 13–23. Use with Concept Review 2.4.

CONCEPT DEVELOPMENT

Critical Thinking: Would it be possible to get a negative answer for the change in length in an expansion problem? [yes] What would such a negative answer mean? [contraction, not expansion]

Enrichment: Would it be possible for a material to have a negative coefficient of expansion? What would this mean? Try to find some examples of such substances. [Yes. It would mean that the substance contracts when it is heated. Rubber is one such material.]

Answers To
PRACTICE PROBLEMS

Have students refer to Appendix A of the Solutions Appendix for complete solutions to Practice Problems.

9. 6.1 mm
10. 11.7 M
11. **a.** 356 mL
b. 355 mL
c. 1 mL or 1.44 mL
12. **a.** 43 560 L
b. volume has decreased

3 Close

CONVERGENT QUESTION

Surveyors use calibrated metal tape measures for the very careful measurements needed in their work. They need to know the temperature so they can correct for possible expansion (or contraction) of the tape. Assume a tape is calibrated for 20°C and is used on a hot day when the temperature is 30°C. What can you say about the correctness of the measurements made if this higher temperature is not taken into account? [The values the surveyors get for lengths will be too small.]

CONCEPT REVIEW ANSWERS

2.1 The density increases as the temperature increases from 0°C to 4°C. Above 4°C, the density decreases when the temperature increases.

2.2 Both will shrink in winter. ∝(Al) = 25 × 10^{-6} while ∝(concrete) = 12 × 10^{-6}, so aluminum will shrink more than concrete. To keep the door fitting well in winter, you should make it fit tightly in summer.

2.3 Candle wax, like a solid, will not change shape under applied forces provided they do not act for a long time. If forces are applied for long lengths of time, the wax tends to flow like a very viscous liquid.

2.4 Critical Thinking: Wider. Think about the ring as if the gap were still filled with metal. That particular wedge of metal would expand along with the rest of the ring; hence the gap expands, or becomes wider.

CHAPTER 13 REVIEW

SUMMARY

13.1 The Fluid States

- A gas fills any container in which it is placed. A liquid has a fixed volume but takes the shape of its container. A solid has a fixed volume and fixed shape. A plasma is like a gas but electrically charged.
- Pressure is the force exerted per unit of area. In SI, pressure is measured in pascals, Pa.
- According to Pascal's principle, a change in pressure is transmitted undiminished throughout a fluid.
- An object immersed in a fluid has an upward force exerted on it called the buoyant force.
- According to Archimedes' principle, the buoyant force on an object is equal to the weight of the fluid displaced by that object.
- Bernoulli's principle states that the pressure exerted by a fluid decreases as the velocity of the fluid increases.
- Cohesive forces are the attractive forces that like particles exert on one another.
- Adhesive forces are the attractive forces that particles of different substances exert on one another.
- Evaporation occurs when the most energetic particles in a liquid have enough energy to escape into the gas phase.
- Volatile liquids are those with weak cohesive forces that evaporate quickly.
- Plasma is an energetic state of matter made up of a mixture of positive and negative particles.

13.2 The Solid State

- As a liquid solidifies, its particles become frozen into a fixed pattern. If the pattern is regular, the solid is a crystalline solid. If the pattern is irregular, the solid is an amorphous solid.
- The ability of an object to return to its original form when stressed is elasticity.
- The increase of length of a material as the temperature increases varies directly with the temperature change and the original length. It also depends on the type of material.

KEY TERMS

fluid
pressure
pascal
Pascal's principle
buoyant force
Archimedes' principle
Bernoulli's principle
cohesive forces
surface tension
adhesion
capillary action
evaporation
volatile
condensation
plasma
crystal lattice
amorphous solids
elasticity
thermal expansion
coefficient of linear expansion

REVIEWING CONCEPTS

1. How are force and pressure different?
2. According to Pascal's principle, what happens to the pressure at the top of a container if the pressure at the bottom is increased?
3. How does the water pressure 1 m below the surface of a small pond compare to the water pressure the same distance below the surface of a lake?
4. Does Archimedes' principle apply inside a spaceship in orbit?
5. A river narrows as it enters a gorge. As the water speeds up, what happens to the water pressure?
6. A gas is placed in a sealed container and some liquid is placed in a same-sized container. They both have definite volume. How do the gas and the liquid differ?
7. A razor blade, which has a density greater than that of water, can be made to float on water. What procedures must you follow for this to happen? Explain.
8. In terms of adhesion and cohesion, explain why alcohol clings to a glass rod and mercury does not.
9. A frozen lake melts in the spring. What effect does it have on the temperature of the air above it?
10. Canteens are often covered with a canvas bag. If you wet the bag, the water in the canteen will be cooled. Explain.

REVIEW MASTER

Use the Vocabulary Review master for Chapter 13 with this section.

EVALUATION MASTER

Use the Chapter Evaluation master for Chapter 13 with this section.

CLOSING CHAPTER 13

Review Summary statements and Key Terms with your students.

ASSESSMENT

Vocabulary Review Master, Teacher Resource Package. Use this master to check students' understanding of Key Terms.

Evaluation Masters. Use Parts A and B of the Chapter Evaluation Masters from the Teacher Resource Package to test qualitative chapter objectives. Use Parts C and D to test quantitative chapter objectives.

Answers To
REVIEWING CONCEPTS

1. Force is a push or pull. Pressure is force per unit area.
2. The pressure at the top of the container also increases.
3. They are the same.
4. No. Archimedes' principle has no application under conditions of weightlessness.
5. The pressure will decrease according to Bernoulli's principle.
6. They differ in volume, compressibility, and density.
7. The razor blade should be placed carefully and flatly onto the surface of the water. This will reduce its weight per unit area of water surface on which it will rest. The surface tension of the water is then sufficient to support the reduced weight per unit area of the flat razor blade.
8. The adhesion between the alcohol and the glass is greater than between the alcohol molecules. The adhesion between the mercury and the glass is less than between the mercury molecules.
9. It cools the air above it by drawing heat from the air to melt the ice.
10. It takes energy to vaporize the water in the canvas bag. The energy comes from the water, thus cooling it.
11. The body is cooled by vaporizing water (perspiration). Vaporization is reduced when there is already a lot of water in the air.
12. Both fill any volume and consist of particles that are widely separated. The particles in plasmas are charged, while those in a gas are not.

Answers To
REVIEWING CONCEPTS (cont)

13. Those in the plasma state are charged, those in the gaseous state are neutral.
14. Crystalline solids have an organized geometric pattern. Amorphous solids lack a consistent pattern.
15. Yes. Elasticity is the ability of an object to return to its original form when the external forces are removed.
16. No. The coefficient of linear expansion is equal to the ratio $\frac{\Delta l}{l}$. As long as the units of length are the same, they divide out.

Answers To
APPLYING CONCEPTS

1. The pressure has increased since the constant force is now applied to a smaller area.
2. $Pa = \frac{N}{m^2} = \frac{kg\ m}{s^2\ m^2} = \frac{kg}{s^2\ m} = \frac{kg}{m \cdot s^2}$
3. The pitcher. The amount of water is not important. The water in the pitcher is deeper so it will have a larger pressure at the bottom.
4. Sink. The volume remains the same but mass has been added to the ship, so it sinks.
5. The cohesive forces are strongest in mercury and weakest in acetone. The stronger the cohesive force, the more spherical the drop will be.
6. Cohesive forces are greater in water than in alcohol and the boiling point of water is higher.
7. Alcohol for both, because weaker cohesive forces increase vaporization and decrease the boiling temperature.
8. The liter of water, because it has a higher density.
9. The size of the hole increases. The cut-out circle expands as well.
10. The soft glass of tube A expands three times as much as the Pyrex glass of tube B. The greater expansion of tube A gives it a wider opening or cross section than tube B. The equal volume of water fills the expanded cross section and thus will not rise as high in tube A. The lower coefficient of expansion of Pyrex glass prevents the glass from shattering with rapid increases and decreases in temperature.
11. The coefficients of expansion of platinum and glass are similar while the coefficients of expansion of copper and glass are different enough that different contraction rates break the seal.
12. Yes. Higher humidity means more vapor in the air, and less evaporation of water (perspiration) from the skin.

11. Why does high humidity make a hot day even more uncomfortable?
12. In what way are gases and plasmas similar? In what way are they different?
13. Some of the mercury atoms in a fluorescent lamp are in the gaseous form; others are in the form of plasma. How can you distinguish between the two?
14. How does the arrangement of atoms differ in a crystalline and an amorphous substance?
15. Can a spring be considered to be elastic?
16. Does the coefficient of linear expansion depend on the unit of length used? Explain.

APPLYING CONCEPTS

1. A rectangular box on a table is rotated so its smaller end is now on the table. Has the pressure on the table increased, decreased, or remained the same?
2. Show that a pascal is equivalent to $\frac{kg}{m \cdot s^2}$.
3. Is there more pressure at the bottom of a bathtub of water 30 cm deep or at the bottom of a pitcher of water 35 cm deep? Explain.
4. Compared to an identical empty ship, would a ship filled with ping pong balls sink deeper into the water or rise in the water? Explain.
5. Drops of mercury, water, and acetone are placed on a smooth, flat surface. The mercury drop is almost a perfect sphere. The water drop is a flattened sphere. The acetone, however, spreads out over the surface. What do these observations tell you about the cohesive forces in mercury, water, and acetone?
6. Alcohol evaporates more quickly than water at the same temperature. What does this observation allow you to conclude about the properties of the particles in the two liquids?

FIGURE 13–24.

7. Based on the observations in the previous question, which liquid would vaporize easier? Which would have the lower boiling point? Explain.
8. Which has a greater weight, a liter of ice or a liter of water?
9. Suppose you use a punch to make a circular hole in aluminum foil. If you heat the foil, will the size of the hole decrease or increase? Explain. (**Hint:** Pretend you put the circle you punched out back into the hole. What happens when you heat the foil now?)
10. Equal volumes of water were heated in two narrow almost identical tubes, identical except that tube A was made of soft glass and tube B was made of Pyrex glass. As the temperature increased, the water level rose higher in tube B than in tube A. Give a possible explanation for this observation. Why are many cooking utensils made from Pyrex glass?
11. A platinum wire can be easily sealed into a glass tube, but a copper wire does not form a tight seal with the glass. Explain.
12. Often, before a thunderstorm, when the humidity is high, someone will say, "The air is very heavy today." Is this statement correct? Describe a possible origin for the statement.

PROBLEMS

13.1 The Fluid States

▶ 1. A hydraulic jack used to lift cars is called a "three-ton jack." The large piston has a radius of 22 mm, the small one 6.3 mm. Assume that a force of three tons is 3.0×10^4 N.
 a. What force must be exerted on the small piston to lift the three-ton weight?
 b. Most jacks use a lever to reduce the force needed on the small piston. If the resistance arm is 3.0 cm, how long is the effort arm of an ideal lever to reduce the force to 100 N?

▶ 2. In a machine shop, a hydraulic lift is used to raise heavy equipment for repairs. The system has a small piston with a cross-sectional area of 7.0×10^{-2} m^2 and a large piston with a cross-sectional area of 2.1×10^{-1} m^2. An engine weighing 2.7×10^3 N rests on the large piston.

a. What force must be applied to the small piston in order to lift the engine?
b. If the engine rises 0.20 m, how far does the smaller piston move?

3. A 0.75-kg physics book with dimensions of 24 cm by 20 cm is on a table.
   a. What force does the book apply to the table?
   b. What pressure does the book apply?
4. The pressure exerted by the atmosphere is about 1.0×10^5 Pa. Convert this to kPa.
5. A 75-kg solid cylinder, 2.5 m long and with an end radius of 5.0 cm, stands on one end. How much pressure does it exert?
6. A reservoir behind a dam is 15 m deep. What is the pressure
   a. at the base of the dam?
   b. 5.0 m from the top of the dam?
7. A test tube standing vertically in a test tube rack contains 2.5 cm of oil (ρ = 0.81 g/cm^3) and 6.5 cm of water. What is the pressure on the bottom of the tube?
8. A metal object is suspended from a spring scale. The scale reads 920 N when the object is suspended in air, and 750 N when the object is completely submerged in water.
   a. Draw a diagram showing the three forces acting on the submerged object.
   b. Find the volume of the object.
   c. Find the density of the metal.
9. During an ecology experiment, an aquarium filled with water is placed on a scale. The scale reads 195 N.
   a. A rock weighing 8 N is added to the aquarium. If the rock sinks to the bottom of the aquarium, what will the scale read?
   b. The rock is removed from the aquarium, and the amount of water is adjusted until the scale again reads 195 N. A small fish weighing 2 N is added to the aquarium. What is the scale reading while the fish is swimming in the aquarium?
10. What is the size of the buoyant force that acts on a floating ball that normally weighs 5.0 N?
11. What is the apparent weight of a rock submerged in water if the rock weighs 54 N in air and has a volume of 2.3×10^{-3} m^3?
12. If the rock in the previous problem is submerged in a liquid with a density exactly twice that of water, what will be its new apparent weight reading in the liquid?
13. A 1.0-L container completely filled with mercury has a weight of 133.3 N. If the container is submerged in water, what is the buoyant force acting on it? Explain.
14. ▶ What is the acceleration of a small metal sphere as it falls through water? The sphere weighs 2.8×10^{-1} N in air and has a volume of 13 cm^3.
15. What is the maximum weight that a "massless" balloon filled with 1.00 m^3 of helium can lift in air? Assume the density of air is 1.20 kg/m^3 and that of helium is 0.177 kg/m^3.

13.2 The Solid State

16. What is the change in length of a 2.00-m length of copper pipe if its temperature is raised from 23°C to 978°C?
17. Bridge builders often use rivets that are larger than the rivet hole to make the joint tighter. The rivet is cooled before it is put into the hole. A builder drills a hole 1.2230 cm in diameter for a steel rivet 1.2250 cm in diameter. To what temperature must the rivet be cooled if it is to fit into the rivet hole that is at 20°C?
18. ▶ A steel tank is built to hold alcohol. The tank is 2.000 m in diameter and 5.000 m high. It is completely filled with alcohol at 10°C. If the temperature rises to 40°C, how much alcohol (in liters) will flow out of the tank? Remember that both the tank and the alcohol expand as the temperature rises.
19. ▶ An aluminum sphere is heated from 11°C to 580°C. If the volume of the sphere were 1.78 cm^3 at 11°C, what is the increase in volume of the sphere at 580°C?
20. ▶ The volume of a copper sphere is 2.56 cm^3 after being heated from 12°C to 984°C. What was the volume of the copper sphere at 12°C?

THINKING PHYSIC-LY

1. Why are sharp ice skates important to an ice skater?
2. Persons confined to bed are less likely to develop bedsores if they use a water bed rather than an ordinary mattress. Explain.

Answers To
PROBLEMS

Complete Solutions for all Chapter Review Problems can be found in the Problems and Solutions Manual accompanying this text.

1. a. 2.5×10^3 N
   b. 75 cm
2. a. 9.0×10^2 N
   b. 0.60 m
3. a. 7.4 N
   b. 1.5×10^2 Pa
4. 1.0×10^2 kPa
5. 94 kPa
6. a. 1.5×10^2 kPa
   b. 49 kPa
7. 8.4×10^2 Pa
8. a. Refer to Problems and Solutions Manual.
   b. 1.73×10^{-2} m^3
   c. 5.42×10^3 kg/m^3
9. a. 203 N
   b. 197 N
10. 5.0 N
11. 31 N
12. 8 N
13. 9.8 N
14. 5.3 m/s^2
15. 10.0 N
16. 3.17×10^{-2} m
17. −110°C
18. 5.0×10^2 L
19. 7.6×10^{-2} cm^3
20. 2.44 cm^3

Answers To
THINKING PHYSIC-LY

1. The area of the skate runner in contact with the ice is least when the skate is sharp. Therefore the pressure is greater, causing more water to melt and making more lubricant.
2. The person's body is supported more evenly and pressure is reduced from the areas supported by a normal bed.

CHAPTER

14 Waves and Energy Transfer

PLANNING GUIDE (5 class sessions)

CONTENTS	TEXT FEATURES	TEACHER RESOURCE PACKAGE	OTHER COMPONENTS
14.1 Wave Properties, pp. 288–294 (3 Class Sessions) • Types of Waves • The Measures of a Wave: Frequency, Wavelength, and Velocity • Amplitude of a Wave	**Physics Lab:** Waves on a Snakey, p. 292 **Pocket Lab:** The Snakey, p. 291 **Pocket Lab:** Feel the Pulse, p. 294 **Concept Review,** p. 294	**Study Guide:** Wave Properties **Physics Lab Data Sheet:** Waves on a Snakey **Reteaching Master:** Assembling a Wave Tape **Transparency Worksheet:** Wave Properties	**Laboratory Manual:** Lab 14.1 Ripple Tank Waves Lab 14.2 Velocity, Wavelength, and Frequency in Ripple Tanks **Transparency 18:** Wave Properties
14.2 Wave Interference, pp. 294–301 (3 Class Sessions) • Waves at Boundaries Between Media • Superposition of Waves • Standing Waves • Reflection of Waves • Refraction of Waves • Diffraction and Interference of Waves	**Physics and Technology:** Microwave-Powered Aircraft, p. 302 **Pocket Lab:** Wave Interaction, p. 300 **Concept Review,** p. 301	**Study Guide:** Wave Interference **Critical Thinking Master:** Wave Superposition **Enrichment Master:** Earthquake Wave Velocities	
Chapter Review, pp. 302–305	Summary Key Terms Reviewing Concepts Applying Concepts Problems Thinking Physic-ly	**Vocabulary Review** **Chapter Test**	**Test Bank**

SUPPLEMENTARY MATERIALS

SOFTWARE	AUDIOVISUAL	BOOKS/MAGAZINES
Introduction to General Physics, Disk IV: Waves and Sound, COMPress/Queue, Inc. (Apple II, IBM PC, Macintosh). *Longitudinal Waves,* Queue, Inc. (Apple II). *Standing Waves,* Queue, Inc. (Apple II). *Transverse Waves,* Queue, Inc. (Apple II).	Videos: *The Mechanical Universe: Resonance* and Waves, Films Inc. *What Is a Wave?,* Focus Media (still frame). Interactive Videodisc: *The Puzzle of the Tacoma Narrows Bridge Collapse,* John Wiley and Sons, Inc.	Fillmore, Keith. "Traveling Waves on a Rope." *The Physics Teacher,* May 1983, p. 314. Greenslade, Thomas B., Jr. "Transverse Wave Machine." *The Physics Teacher,* October 1990, p. 508. Wakeland, Ray Scott, and Brabson, Bennet. "Wave Speed on a String Revisited." *The Physics Teacher,* January 1990, p. 57. Williams, Warren. "Standing Waves on the Overhead Projector." *The Physics Teacher,* December 1980, pp. 674–675.

PROBLEM CORRELATION

CONCEPTS	CHAPTER REVIEW			PROBLEMS APPENDIX
	Reviewing Concepts	Applying Concepts	Problems	
14.1 Wave Properties				
Types of Waves	1,2,3,4,5	1		
The Measure of a Wave: Frequency, Wavelength, and Velocity	6,7,8,9	2,3,4	1,2,3,4,5,**6**,7,8, 9,10,**11**,**12**,13	1,2,3,4,5,**6**, **7**,8,9,10
Amplitude of a Wave	10,11,12	5		
14.2 Wave Interference				
Waves at Boundaries Between Media	13,14,15,16	6,7	**14**	
Superposition of Waves	17	8	15	
Standing Waves	18,19,20		16	
Reflection of Waves	21			11
Refraction of Waves				
Diffraction and Interference of Waves	22	9		

ACTIVITY AND DEMONSTRATION MATERIALS

PHYSICS LAB	POCKET LAB	DEMONSTRATIONS
Page 292 coil spring stopwatch meter stick	Pages 291, 294, 300 coil spring 2 meters of yarn	

EXTENSION PROJECTS

LIBRARY RESEARCH

1. Surf
Do some research into the phenomena of surf. Why do waves break? What is the purpose of a jetty?

DISPLAY MODEL

2. Seismograph
Construct a seismograph and simulate the motion of the P-waves and S-waves that occur during an earthquake. Demonstrate to the class how a seismograph records movement on Earth's surface caused by waves.

STUDENT READINGS

Berry, M. V. "The Geometric Phase." *Scientific American,* December 1988.

Gilbert, S. "How a Wave Works." *Science Digest,* August 1986.

Hicks, James, and Chiaverina, Chris. "Catch the Wave." *The Physics Teacher,* March 1990.

Johnston, Arch C., and Kanter, Lisa R. "Earthquakes in Stable Continental Crusts." *Scientific American,* March 1990.

Lapp, David R. "Wave Interference Pattern from the Wings of a Bee." *The Physics Teacher,* May 1990.

Monastersky, Richard. "Rattling the Northwest" *Science News,* February 17,1990.

Peterson, Ivars. "Rock and Roll Bridge." *Science News,* June 2, 1990.

Chapter 14

Waves and Energy Transfer

CHAPTER OVERVIEW

Theme Development: Because wave phenomena result from cyclic activity, the study of waves provides an excellent forum for the theme of patterns of change. Wave characteristics are extended into quantifiable features—amplitude, period, phase, and so on—thus introducing the tremendously useful mathematical wave model.

MISCONCEPTIONS

Students have difficulty understanding how a transverse wave can travel at right angles to the particles of the medium. The relationship between period and frequency is often troublesome.

KEY TERMS

amplitude
angle of incidence
angle of reflection
antinode
constructive interference
crests
destructive interference
diffraction
frequency
interference
law of reflection
longitudinal wave
node
normal
period
principle of superposition
refraction
standing wave
surface wave
transverse wave
traveling wave
troughs
wavelength
wave pulse

Laboratory Options

STUDENT EDITION

Physics Lab

Waves on a Snakey	292

Pocket Labs

The Snakey	291
Feel the Pulse	294
Wave Interaction	300

TEACHER EDITION

Discovery	290, 297, 298
Cooperative Learning	301

LABORATORY MANUAL

Ripple Tank Waves	Lab 14.1
Velocity, Frequency, and Wavelength	Lab 14.2

CHAPTER 14

Waves and Energy Transfer

◀ Surf's Up

Where does the surfer's kinetic energy come from? Try to trace the energy source back as far as you can.

Chapter Outline

Have you ever ridden a wave on a surf board, boogie board, or merely body surfed? Whether in ocean surf or in a wave pool, when you "catch the wave" you gain speed and stay just ahead of the breaking surf. Your body's kinetic energy increases. If you can, you do as this surfer does, and ride almost parallel to the wave at a very high speed. Surfing can be dangerous, however. Unless you are skilled, you can "wipe out" and be thrown down into the water or sand.

Does the water move with the wave? Leonardo da Vinci (1452–1519) answered this question five centuries ago.

> *The impetus is much quicker than the water, for it often happens that the wave flees the place of its creation, while the water does not...*

In other words, the wave moves on, the water does not. In this way, water waves are typical of the waves we will study in the next few chapters, those of sound and light.

✓ Concept Check

The following terms or concepts from earlier chapters are important for a good understanding of this chapter. If you are not familiar with them, you should review them before studying this chapter.
- velocity, Chapter 3
- period and frequency, Chapter 7
- potential energy and kinetic energy, Chapter 11

287

Introducing The Chapter

Surf's Up

Using The Photo: Of all sports, surfing uses waves and their properties most directly. Obviously, both timing and balance play a big part in successful surfing. Have students comment on how physics principles are demonstrated in surfing. To answer the chapter opener question, refer students to page 289.

✓ Concept Check

Make sure students have a clear understanding of the concepts listed in the Concept Check. The concepts of velocity, period, and frequency are a little more complex when applied to wave phenomena, compared to their application in previous chapters. The exchange of energy between potential and kinetic forms is important in understanding wave dynamics.

Assessment

Portfolio

Students should collect reports of experiments they did with coiled springs and create a listing of wave properties they have demonstrated.

Assessment Options

Portfolio Assessment
Portfolio Assessment, TWE, p. 287
Portfolio Assessment, TWE, p. 288
Extension, TWE, p. 294
Thinking Physic-ly, p. 305

Performance Assessment
Pocket Labs, pp. 291, 294, 300
Physics Lab, p. 292
Activity, TWE, p. 297
Pocket Lab Assessment, p. 300

Content Assessment
Self Assessment: Practice Problems, pp. 293, 296
Assessment, Critical Thinking, TWE, p. 292
Extension, TWE, p. 300
Concept Reviews, pp. 294, 301
Chapter Review, pp. 302–305
Supplemental Problems, p. 698

Group Assessment
Activities for group assessment occur with Cooperative Learning and lab activities.

14.1 WAVE PROPERTIES

Preparation

OBJECTIVES

The objectives are listed on the student page. Remind students to preview these objectives as a study guide to this major section.

OVERVIEW

Because of its introductory nature, this section introduces numerous new terms: *transverse wave, longitudinal wave, surface wave, wave pulse, traveling wave, crest, trough, period, frequency, wavelength,* and *amplitude.*

BRIDGING

Concepts previously introduced that students will need to recall here include speed, simple harmonic motion, time, distance, kinetic energy, and displacement.

Assessment

Portfolio

Pulses, traveling waves, and standing waves can be observed in many everyday occurrences. For example, waves occur in the oceans, lakes, rivers, pools, and water glasses. Standing waves appear in telephone or power wires. A longitudinal wave pulse can be seen when a long line of automobile traffic begins to move when a traffic light turns green. Collect descriptions of photographs of wave phenomena and indicate, where appropriate, wave parameters such as frequency, wavelength, velocity, or amplitude that can be identified or measured.

Objectives

- **recognize that waves transfer energy without transferring matter.**
- **distinguish between longitudinal and transverse waves; between a wave pulse and a continuous wave.**
- **define amplitude, wavelength, frequency, and period; state the relationship between speed, wavelength, and frequency; solve problems using these quantities.**

14.1 WAVE PROPERTIES

Both particles and waves transmit energy, but there is an important difference. If you throw a ball at a target, the target may gain some kinetic energy, but the ball will have moved from you to the target. If you tie a rope on the target and shake the rope, the target may also gain some kinetic energy. The rope, however, will remain in position, between you and the target. How do we describe waves, and how fast do they transmit the energy?

Types of Waves

Energy can be transferred by particles or by waves.

Water waves, sound waves, and the waves that travel along a spring or rope are mechanical waves. Mechanical wave motion requires a material medium. Water, air, and springs or ropes are the materials that carry the energy of these mechanical waves. Newton's laws govern the motion of mechanical waves.

Mechanical waves need a medium.

Light waves, radio waves, and X rays are examples of electromagnetic waves. No medium is needed for the motion of electromagnetic waves. They all travel through space at the speed of light, 299 792 458 m/s. The details of electromagnetic waves cannot be observed directly. Thus, we will use the easily observed mechanical waves as models for the behavior of electromagnetic waves that will be studied in later chapters.

There is a third type of wave, the matter wave. Electrons and other particles show wave-like behavior under certain conditions. Quantum mechanics is needed to describe the properties of matter waves. We will delay our study of matter waves until Chapter 27.

In a transverse wave, particles vibrate at right angles to the direction of the wave's velocity.

We can divide mechanical waves into three different types. Each type disturbs the medium in a different way. A **transverse wave** causes the particles of the medium to vibrate perpendicularly to the direction of motion of the wave. Figure 14–1a shows a transverse wave. The wave moves along the spring from left to right, but the spring is displaced up and down, at right angles to the motion of the wave. Waves in piano and guitar strings are examples of transverse waves.

A **longitudinal wave** causes the particles of a medium to move parallel to the direction of the wave. Figure 14–1b shows a longitudinal wave. The displacement of the spring is in the same direction as the motion of the wave. A sound wave is an example of a longitudinal

a

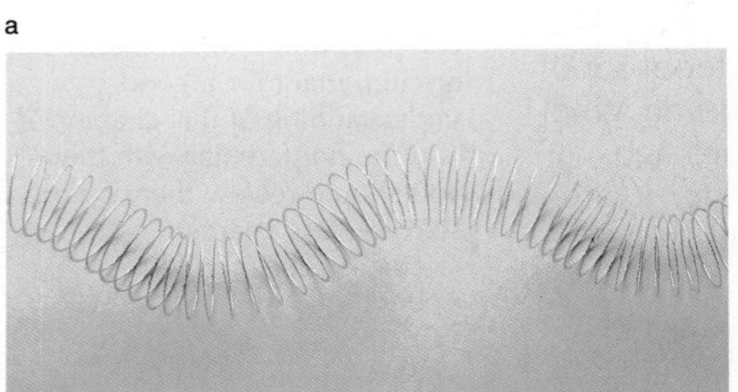

b

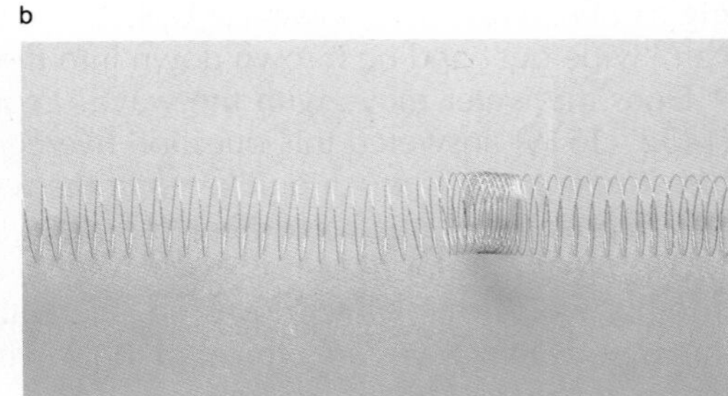

FIGURE 14–1. Two general types of waves are the transverse wave (a) and the longitudinal wave (b).

Multicultural Connections

Hertha Marks Ayrton was a British physicist who lived from 1854 to 1923. After inventing a tool needed by architects that could divide a line segment into as many equal parts as desired, she decided to pursue research and inventing as a career. One of her interests was her study of the formation of sand ripples as a result of the action of waves on a beach. She became the first woman to read a paper to the British Royal Society as a result of her work in this area. Although she could not become a fellow of the Society, she was later awarded the Hughes Medal for original research for her work on sand ripples and for her study of the electric arc.

a

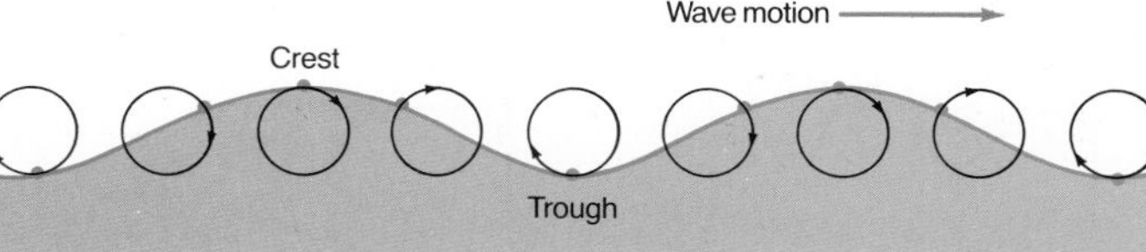

b

FIGURE 14–2. Surface waves show characteristics of both longitudinal and transverse waves. The paths of the particles are almost perfect circles.

A pulse is a single disturbance of a medium.

wave. Fluids, liquids, gases, or plasmas usually transmit only longitudinal waves.

Although waves deep in a lake or ocean are longitudinal, at the surface of the water, Figure 14–2, the particles move both parallel and perpendicular to the direction of the wave. These are **surface waves**, a mixture of transverse and longitudinal waves. The energy of water waves usually comes from storms far away. The energy of the storms initially came from the heating of Earth by solar energy. This energy, in turn, was carried to Earth by transverse electromagnetic waves.

Surf's Up

How are waves produced? Suppose you hold one end of a rope. If you suddenly jerk the rope to one side and quickly return it to the center, Figure 14–3, a wave pulse will travel down the rope. A **wave pulse** is a single disturbance that travels through a medium. A given point on the rope was at rest before the pulse reached it; it returned to rest after the pulse passed. If instead you move the rope from side to side in a regular manner, a **traveling wave** will move along the rope. A source that is vibrating with simple harmonic motion will produce a continuous traveling wave. Each point on the rope will vibrate regularly in response to the traveling wave.

A wave train, or traveling wave, is a series of pulses at regular intervals.

FIGURE 14–3. The two photographs were taken 1 s apart. During that time, the crest moved 0.8 m. The velocity of the wave is 0.8 m/s.

a

b

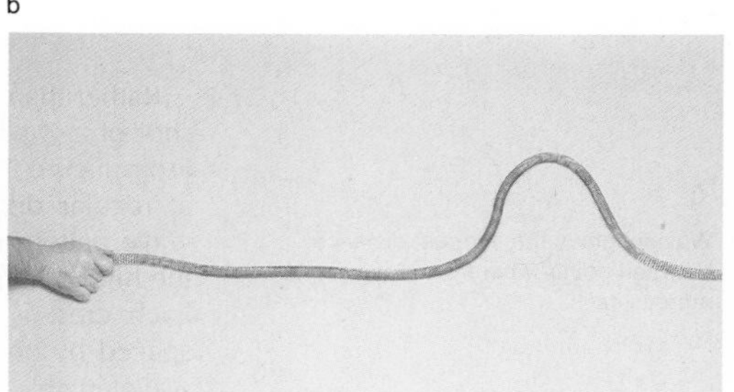

1 Focus

DISCREPANT EVENT

Go out into the hallway or other place where you have a smooth floor area of about two by five meters and room around the edges to stand. Stretch out a long coil spring on the floor to four or five meters in length, letting a student hold the other end.

1. Send a longitudinal pulse down the spring by pinching together several coils of the spring and then releasing them.

What kind of pulse is this? [longitudinal]

What happens to the shape of the pulse as it travels down the wire? [It does not change.]

2. Quickly pull the free end of the spring to one side and then return it to its original position.

What kind of pulse is this? [transverse]

What happens to the shape of the pulse as it travels down the spring? [It does not change—except for some loss of amplitude due to friction.]

3. Determine the time it takes a pulse to travel down the spring. Change the amplitude of the pulse and again determine the travel time.

How does changing the amplitude affect the speed of the wave? [no effect]

4. Alter the medium by stretching the spring to a different length. Determine the speed of a pulse in this new medium.

How does altering the medium affect the speed of the wave? [The speed changes.]

You may wish to produce pulses of different amplitudes in this new medium to reinforce the fact that amplitude does not affect speed. You might want to follow up this demonstration with some chalkboard drawings, with labels to summarize the phenomena seen. This beautifully visual demonstration will be a great help in getting wave terminology across—now supply words to describe what you saw!

TEACHER F.Y.I.

Earthquakes generate longitudinal, transverse, and surface waves with different periods, making their study a bit easier. Longitudinal waves have a period of 2–3 seconds, transverse of 10–15 seconds, and surface waves 10–60 seconds. Transverse waves will not pass through Earth's center, providing evidence that our planet has a fluid core. Refer students to Geology Connection on page 293.

2 Teach

CONCEPT DEVELOPMENT

Study Guide Master. To reinforce the concepts in this section, have students complete the Study Guide Master for Section 14.1 from the Teacher Resource Package.

- Note that we need to think about a wave in two different ways: 1. We stay at a fixed position and observe how the displacement changes over time. 2. We take a "snapshot" of the entire wave at one instant in time.
- Have students calculate the wavelength of their favorite radio station.
- The unit hertz is named after Heinrich Hertz, who demonstrated radio waves in 1887. More about his scientific work will be found in Chapter 27.
- An excellent account of some current research into waves is the article "Rogue Waves" by Joseph Brown, *Discover,* April 1989.

ACTIVITY

Discovery: This is a good place for a student experiment with the ripple tank. Students should get an opportunity to work with small water waves firsthand. Show that the medium does not move in the direction of wave travel for transverse waves by putting a small piece of cork in a ripple tank and making waves. The cork just bobs up and down as a fishing bobber does. Or you can carefully put a drop of food coloring in the tank, then make some waves showing that the drop doesn't spread out along the direction of wave travel.

Laboratory Manual. Give students additional experience with ripple tank waves by doing Lab 14.1 from the Laboratory Manual.

FIGURE 14–4. The left end of the string is attached to a vibrating blade. Note the change in position of the tape, P, over time.

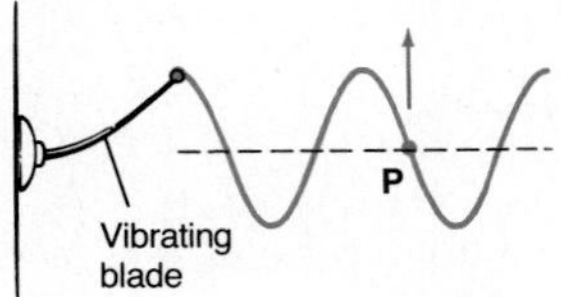

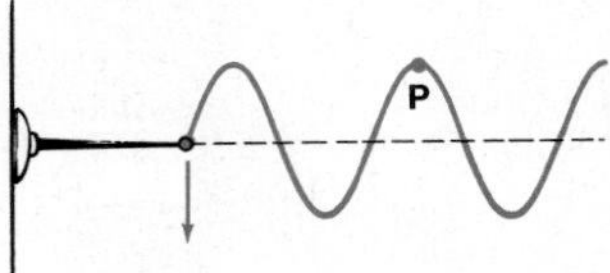

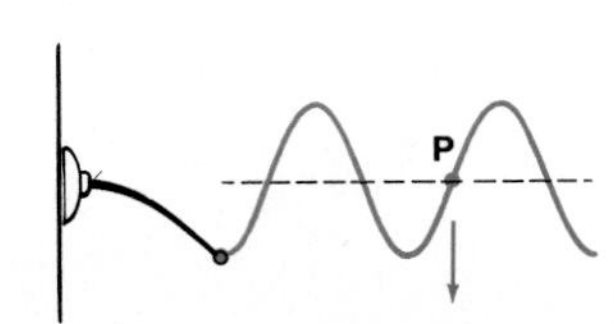

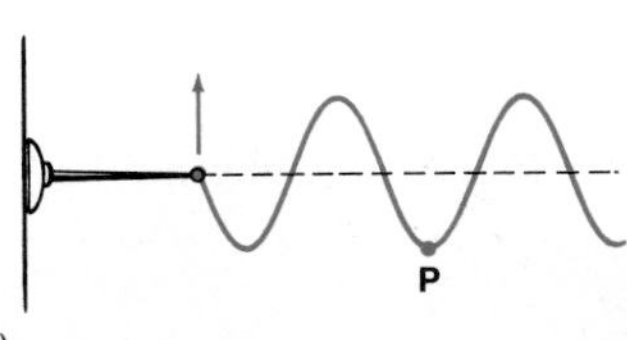

F.Y.I.

The letter "M" may have originated as a hieroglyphic symbol representing the crests of waves and meaning "water."

The Measures of a Wave: Frequency, Wavelength, and Velocity

The period of a wave is the time needed for the motion to repeat itself.

Imagine putting a piece of tape at point **P** on the rope. How does that piece of tape move in time? Figure 14–4 shows that the **P** moves back and forth. The shortest time interval during which the motion repeats itself is called the **period**, T.

The **frequency** of a wave, f, is the number of complete vibrations per second measured at a fixed location. Frequency is measured in hertz. One hertz (Hz) is one vibration per second. The frequency and period of a wave are related by the equation

$$f = \frac{1}{T}.$$

That is, they are reciprocals of each other.

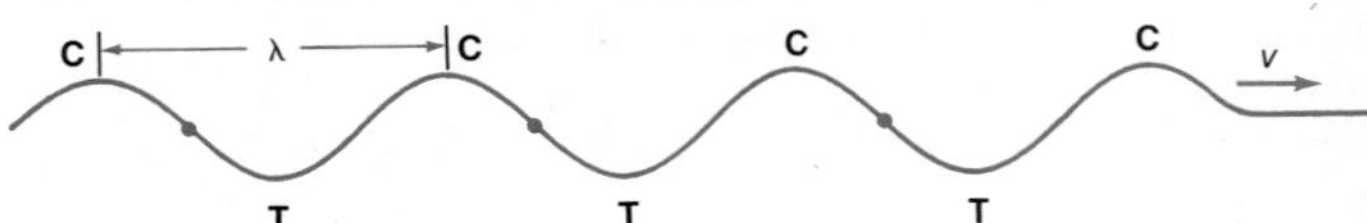

FIGURE 14–5. Points labeled C represent wave crests; points labeled T represent wave troughs.

Wavelength is the shortest distance between points where the wave pattern repeats itself.

Rather than focusing on one spot on the wave, think of taking a snapshot of a wave, so you can see the whole wave at one instant of time. From Figure 14–5, you can see that the form of the wave repeats itself at regular distances. The shortest distance between points where the wave pattern repeats itself is called the **wavelength**. The **crests**, C, are the high points of each wave motion; the **troughs,** T, are the low points. Each crest is one wavelength from the next crest. Troughs are also spaced by one wavelength. The Greek letter lambda, λ, represents the wavelength.

Connect to BIOLOGY

A nerve cell in an animal transmits information as impulses. The impulses move along the long, tubelike structure called the axon. It consists of positively charged sodium ions suddenly moving from the outside to inside the axon, followed by positive potassium ions rapidly moving out. This movement all happens within a thousandth of a second. Thereafter the sodium and potassium ions move back to their normal locations. The impulse moves along the axon because the motion of ions in one location causes the ions in the neighboring region to move.

Normally the inside of the axon is more negative than the outside, but the sudden inrush of sodium ions makes it positive. Speeds as high as 120 m/s have been measured.

Would you consider the impulse a transverse or longitudinal wave? [Motion of ions in one location causes motion in the neighboring region, just like the displacement of one coil of a spring produces displacement of its neighbor. Since the ions move perpendicularly to the direction of the impulse, it is a transverse wave.]

Example Problem

Period of a Wave

A sound wave has a frequency of 262 Hz. What is the time between successive wave crests?

Given: $f = 262$ Hz

Unknown: period, T

Basic equation: $f = \frac{1}{T}$

Solution: $f = \frac{1}{T}$, so $T = \frac{1}{f}$

$$T = \frac{1}{262 \text{ Hz}} = \frac{1}{262 \text{ s}^{-1}} = 3.82 \times 10^{-3} \text{ s}$$

How fast does a traveling wave move? You could run alongside the wave just fast enough so that the wave appears to stand still. An easier way is to take two photographs at a known time interval apart. Figure 14–6 shows a drawing of two waves made one second apart. During the one-second time interval, the crests moved 0.8 m to the right. The velocity of any object is the distance moved divided y the time interval. Thus, the wave velocity is 0.8 m/s to the right.

In the special case that the time interval is exactly one period, the wave would move a distance of one wavelength. Thus, the velocity can be calculated from the equation

$$v = \frac{\lambda}{T}.$$

This is more conveniently written as

$$\boxed{v = \lambda f.}$$

Wave velocity is the product of the frequency and the wavelength.

POCKET LAB

THE SNAKEY

Tie a piece of ribbon or yarn to the middle of a long coil spring (snakey). With a lab partner, stretch the snakey to twice its original length. Quickly shake your hand sideways to put a pulse of energy into the snakey. Closely watch the ribbon. This type of wave motion is a transverse wave. Describe the motion of the ribbon. Does the ribbon move in the direction parallel to the length of the snakey?

Tightly grasp the snakey so that your hands are about 30 cm apart. Move your hands together so that the snakey coils are closer together. This is a higher pressure (compression) region. This high pressure region will move along the length of the snakey. This is a pressure (longitudinal) wave. Describe the motion of the ribbon.

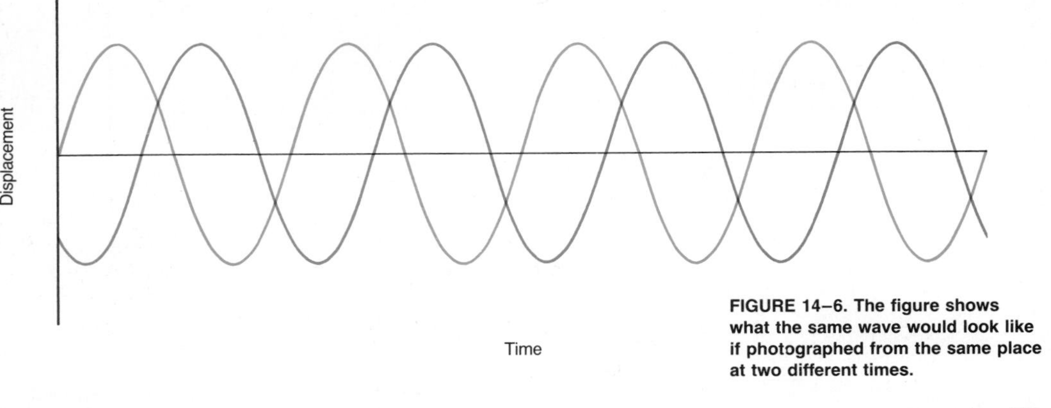

FIGURE 14–6. The figure shows what the same wave would look like if photographed from the same place at two different times.

POCKET LAB

THE SNAKEY

Purpose: to observe how energy is transferred in a coil spring.

Materials: coil spring; 2 meters of yarn (or ribbon).

Outcome: The ribbon moves in a perpendicular direction away from and back to its equilibrium position as the transverse pulse moves along the snakey. The ribbon does not move in the direction parallel to the snakey. In the case of the pressure (longitudinal) pulse, the ribbon moves parallel and perpendicular to the wave.

CONCEPT DEVELOPMENT

- In some materials the force that brings the particles displaced by the wave back to equilibrium is not proportional to the displacement—that is, the medium is not linear. In these media, the wave speed will depend on the frequency. Such a medium is called "dispersive." Examples are glass and diamond. Dispersion will be treated more fully in Chapter 17.
- This basic equation $v = \lambda f$ will also be used when you study optics and quantum theory.
- Of course, waves in an actual medium do not exhibit ideal wave behavior. In particular, waves die out, that is, they disappear after enough time has elapsed. The wave's energy gets used up in a frictional process, or its energy gets so spread out that it is no longer detectable.

STUDY GUIDE MASTER

Use the Study Guide master for section 14.1.

LABORATORY MANUAL

Use Lab 14.1, 14.2 with this section.

PHYSICS LAB

Process Skills: manipulating, observing, analyzing and evaluating, drawing inferences, applying terms.

MISCONCEPTIONS

Many students will believe that the wave must slow down as the amplitude decreases.

Lab Worksheet, Teacher Resource Package. If desired, use the lab worksheet master for this chapter for students to record their data.

OBSERVATIONS AND DATA

1. a. The amplitude (height) of the pulse decreases as it moves along the snakey. **b.** The pulse takes equal amounts of time to move back and forth along the snakey. The *speed* is *constant.*
2. The speed does *NOT* depend on the amplitude (see answers for 1 and 2).
3. The pulses stay the same distance apart. The wavelength does not change.
4. If there is less time between the pulses, the wavelength is smaller.
5. The pulses on the snakey travel through each other. This will not be obvious unless different sizes or types of pulses are made.

ANALYSIS

1. Students will not have enough experience to make an educated guess.
2. Students will find that their answers for pressure waves *are consistent* with their answers for transverse waves.
3. Students will not be able to determine whether the pressure waves go through or bounce off!

APPLICATIONS

1. Loud (high-amplitude) and quiet (low-amplitude) waves should travel at the same speed.
2. All frequencies should travel at the same speed (in non-dispersive media).
All of the properties of pulses on the snakey should be consistent with sound waves.

PHYSICS LAB: Waves on a Snakey

Purpose

To investigate properties of waves using a snakey as a model.

Materials

- a long coil spring (snakey)
- stopwatch
- meter stick

Procedure

1. You will need a clear path of about 6 meters for this activity.
2. Slowly stretch the snakey to the length suggested by your instructor.
3. Grip the snakey firmly with one hand for the entire activity.
4. It is easier to see the motion of the snakey if you are near one end. Don't watch from the side.
5. As the pulses die out, they can still be felt. Trust your feelings!
6. This activity is a sensory experience. Each student in the group should take some time on the end of the snakey.
7. Make a quick sideways snap with your wrist to produce a transverse pulse in the snakey.
8. Notice how many times the pulse will move back and forth on the snakey.
9. Look closely at the questions in the observation section. Try to design and conduct an experiment to answer each question.

Observations and Data

1. What happens to
   a. the amplitude of a wave as it travels?
   b. the speed of a wave as it travels?
2. Does the speed depend on the amplitude?
3. Put 2 quick pulses into the snakey. The distance between pulses is called λ. Does λ change as the pulses move?
4. What can you do to decrease the value of λ?
5. Do pulses bounce off each other or pass through?

Analysis

1. You probably used transverse waves for this activity. Should your answers be accurate for pressure (longitudinal) waves? Why?
2. Check your answers for steps 1-3 with *pressure* waves.
3. Use the snakey to find out if pressure waves go through each other. Describe your results.

Applications

Sound waves are pressure waves. Make your predictions consistent with your snakey results.

1. Does the speed of the sound depend on the loudness? (Do louder sounds travel *faster* than quiet sounds?)
2. Compare the speed of high frequency (short wavelength) sounds to low frequency (long wavelength) sounds.

* NOTE * Snakeys are *NOT SOCIAL.* Do not allow the snakeys to get tangled together! Each snakey should be stored in its own personal container!

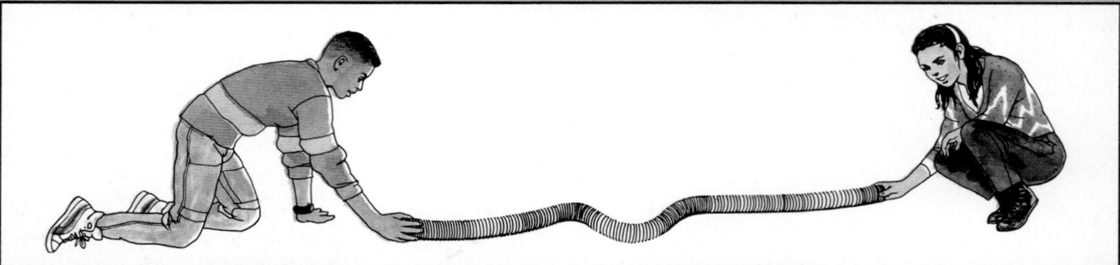

ASSESSMENT

Critical Thinking: To further assess students' understanding of wave interference, ask the following questions.

1. You discovered that transverse waves could pass through each other and longitudinal waves could pass through each other. Does this mean that transverse waves will pass through longitudinal waves? Try it. [Most students should correctly predict that the waves will pass through each other.]

2. What would you predict would happen to the speed when you stretched the snakey longer. Try it and describe your results. [The speed increases. It takes almost the same time, but the pulse travels a greater distance.]

Example Problem

Velocity of a Traveling Wave

A sound wave with frequency 262 Hz has a wavelength of 1.29 m. What is the velocity of the sound wave?

Given: frequency, $f = 262$ Hz; wavelength, $\lambda = 1.29$ m
Unknown: velocity, v
Basic equation: $v = \lambda f$

Solution: $v = \lambda f = (1.29 \text{ m})(262 \text{ Hz}) = 338 \text{ m/s}$

Practice Problems

1. A sound wave produced by a clock chime 515 m away is heard 1.50 s later.
   a. What is the speed of sound in air?
   b. The sound wave has a frequency of 436 Hz. What is its period?
   c. What is its wavelength?
2. A hiker shouts toward a vertical cliff 685 m away. The echo is heard 4.00 s later.
   a. What is the speed of sound in air?
   b. The wavelength of the sound is 0.750 m. What is its frequency?
   c. What is the period of the wave?
3. A radio wave, a form of electromagnetic wave, has a frequency of 99.5 MHz (99.5×10^6 Hz). What is its wavelength?
4. ▶ A typical light wave has a wavelength of 580 nm.
   a. What is the wavelength of the light in meters?
   b. What is the frequency of the wave?

GEOLOGY CONNECTION

Waves through a solid can be either transverse or longitudinal. An earthquake produces both transverse and longitudinal waves that travel through Earth. Geologists studying the waves with seismographs found that longitudinal waves could pass through Earth's core, transverse waves could not. From this evidence, they concluded that Earth's core is liquid. From its density, it is most likely molten iron.

When a wave passes through a medium, the particles move, but they are not carried along with the wave. For example, as a transverse wave passes through a spring, Figure 14–2a, each coil is in the same position as before the wave arrived. Even though huge waves may crash on a beach as the result of a distant storm, the water in the waves remains near the beach.

Amplitude of a Wave

Two waves with the same frequency can have different wavelengths. Waves can differ from one another in another way. A rope can be shaken violently or gently; a sound can be loud or soft. A water wave can be a giant tidal wave or a gentle ripple. The **amplitude** of a wave is its maximum displacement from the rest or equilibrium position. The two waves in Figure 14–7 have the same frequency, velocity, and wavelength, but their amplitudes differ.

In order to produce a wave with larger amplitude, more work has to be done. For example, strong winds produce larger water waves than

The speed of sound in air depends on temperature; it may not be the same in all problems.

The amplitude of a wave is its maximum displacement from the rest position.

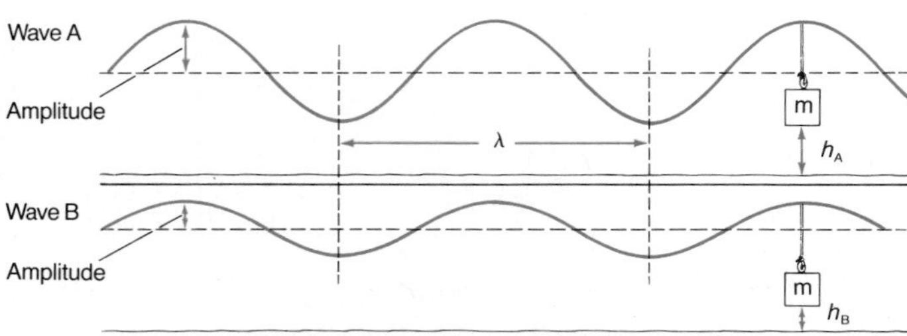

FIGURE 14–7. The relationship of the amplitude of a wave to the work it can perform is shown here. The greater the work done to create the wave, the greater the amplitude of the wave. The greater the amplitude of the wave, the more work it can do.

CHECKING FOR UNDERSTANDING

Ask students to think of their wave experiences around a lake or the ocean. See if they can use wave terminology correctly in describing what they have seen.

RETEACHING

Review basic wave terminology, then choose a type of wave, say small water waves, to concentrate on. Ask: Which wave properties are under your control if you are generating the waves? [Frequency, wavelength, amplitude, and speed if you change the depth of the water.] Specifically how would you change the wave's amplitude? Its frequency? How could you carry out a measurement of the wave's speed?

Laboratory Manual. Give students additional experience with velocity, wavelength, and frequency by doing Lab 14.2 from the Laboratory Manual.

Answers To
PRACTICE PROBLEMS

Have students refer to Appendix A of the Solutions Appendix for complete solutions to Practice Problems.

1. a. 343 m/s
   b. 2.29 ms
   c. 0.787 m
2. a. 343 m/s
   b. 457 Hz
   c. 2.19 ms
3. 3.02 m
4. a. 5.8×10^{-7} m
   b. 5.2×10^{14} Hz

CONCEPT DEVELOPMENT

Cooperative Learning: Challenge students to take pictures of interesting wave phenomena or to bring in pictures from other sources.

Guided Practice: Review the Example Problem in class on the board. Then have students work on the first two Practice Problems, offering individual assistance when needed.

Independent Practice: Assign Practice Problems 9 and 10 on page 116 for homework. Review the solutions in class the next day.

14:1 ASSIGNMENT GUIDE

	PRACTICE	EXTENSION
CHAPTER REVIEW pp. 302–305		
· Reviewing Concepts	1–12	
· Applying Concepts		1–5
· Problems*	1–5, 7–10, 13	6, 11,12
APPENDIX B PROBLEMS*		
· Chapter 14, p. 698	1–5, 8, 9, 10	6, 7

* Complete solutions to all Chapter Review and Appendix problems appear in the Problems and Solutions Manual.

LAB WORKSHEET

Use the Lab Worksheet for Chapter 14 with this Physics Lab.

CONCEPT DEVELOPMENT

A sound wave with a large amplitude is a loud sound.

POCKET LAB

FEEL THE PULSE

Purpose: to determine if wave speed is dependent upon amplitude.
Materials: coil spring.
Outcome: The speed of a pulse on the snakey does not depend on the amplitude. Students should observe that the same pulse takes the same time to go back and forth on the snakey (even though the amplitude is decreasing). If students send a large pulse followed quickly by a small pulse, they will observe that the distance between the pulses stays the same.

CHECKING FOR UNDERSTANDING

Have students respond in class to the Concept Review questions.

RETEACHING

Reteaching Master, Teacher Resource Package. Use the Reteaching Master, Assembling a Wave Tape, to give students practice building their own wave models.

Transparency Package. Use Transparency 18 to reteach wave properties.

EXTENSION

- Some class members may have studied trigonometry. Ask for a comparison of the mathematical treatment of the sine function to the waves we are studying here.
- Another possibility is to investigate the advanced wave concept known as a soliton, a kind of very persistent wave.

POCKET LAB

FEEL THE PULSE

Does the speed of a pulse depend on its amplitude? Without a stopwatch, design an experiment using a snakey to find out. Make a record of your procedures and observations.

The energy transferred by a wave depends on the square of its amplitude.

gentle breezes. A wave with larger amplitude transfers more energy. A small wave might move sand on a beach back and forth. When a giant wave crashes on a beach, however, it can uproot trees or move heavy boulders. The larger the amplitude, the greater the energy transferred. In fact, for waves that travel at the same velocity, the rate at which energy is carried is proportional to the square of the amplitude of the wave. Thus, if you double the amplitude of the wave, you increase the energy it transfers every second by a factor of four.

CONCEPT REVIEW

1.1 Suppose you and your lab partner were asked to measure the speed of a transverse wave in a giant Slinky. How could you do it? List the equipment you would need.

1.2 You are creating waves in a rope by shaking your hand back and forth. Without changing the distance your hand moves, you begin to shake it faster and faster. What happens to the amplitude, frequency, period, and velocity of the wave?

1.3 If you pull on one end of a Slinky, does the pulse reach the other end instantaneously? What if you pull on a rope? Hit the end of a metal rod? Discuss any differences.

1.4 Critical Thinking: If a rain drop falls into a pool, small-amplitude waves result. If a swimmer jumps into a pool, a very large-amplitude wave is produced. Why doesn't the heavy rain in a thunderstorm produce large waves?

Objectives

- understand that wave speed depends on the medium.
- understand what occurs when a wave crosses the boundary between two media with different wave speeds.
- be able to solve problems involving waves crossing boundaries.
- state the principle of superposition and understand how constructive and destructive interference result.
- state the law of reflection.
- describe refraction in terms of behavior of a transmitted wave.
- define diffraction of a wave around a barrier.

14.2 WAVE INTERFERENCE

Two particles cannot be in the same place at the same time. Matter, after all, takes up space. This is not true for waves. The properties that are characteristic of wave behavior are the result of two or more waves existing in the same area at the same time.

Waves at Boundaries Between Media

The speed of a mechanical wave does not depend on the amplitude or the frequency of the wave. It depends only on the properties of the

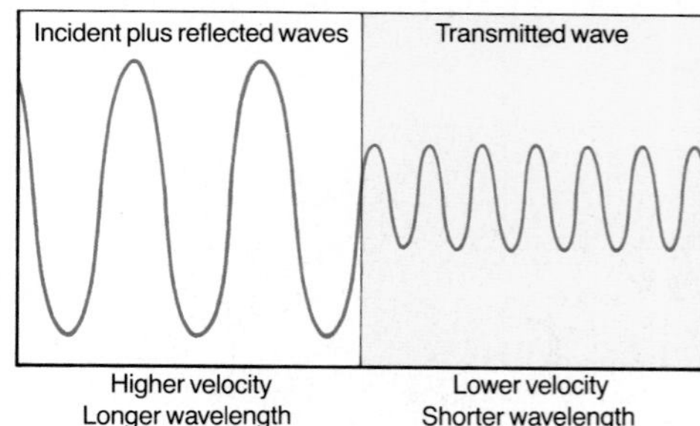

FIGURE 14–8. The speed and wavelength of a wave change when the wave enters a new medium. The left half of the figure shows the sum of the incident and reflected waves. The transmitted wave is on the right.

3 Close

CONVERGENT QUESTION

Compare the behavior and properties of gentle pond ripples, average ocean waves, and tidal waves.

CONCEPT REVIEW ANSWERS

1.1 You would need something to measure distance and a stopwatch timer. Extend the Slinky to a measured length. One of you starts a wave pulse at one end. The other person starts the timer, stopping it when the pulse reaches the other end. Divide distance by time.

1.2 Amplitude and velocity don't change. Frequency increases, period decreases.

1.3 No. The disturbance moves faster, but does take some time.

1.4 Critical Thinking: The waves are not large because small waves are formed at random times. For example, a drop might fall on the peak of one wave, reducing its amplitude.

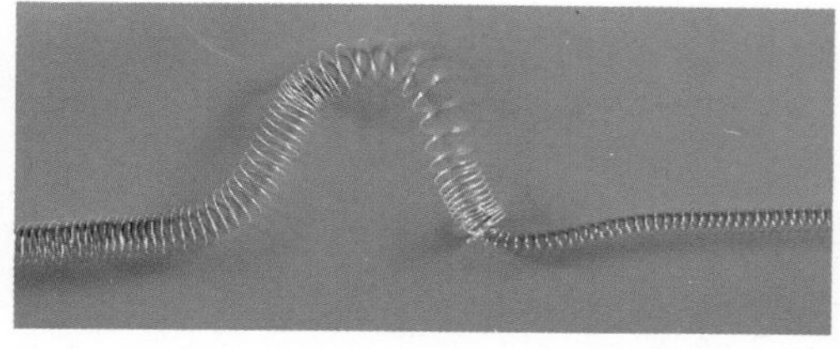

a

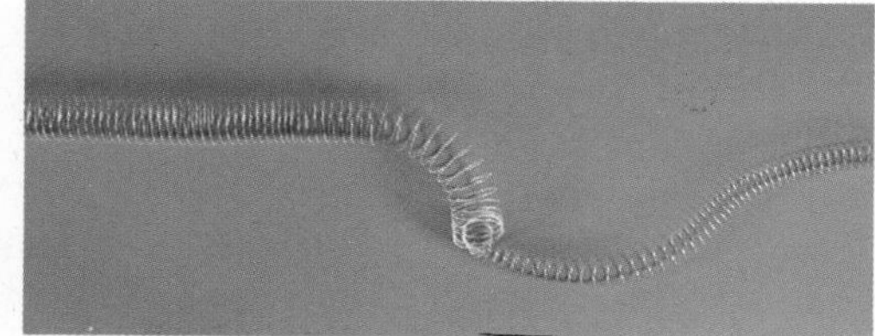

b

FIGURE 14–9. The junction of the two springs is a boundary between two media. A pulse reaching the boundary (a) is partially reflected and partially transmitted.

medium. The speed of water waves depends on the depth of the water. The speed of waves in a rope depends on the force exerted on the rope and its mass per unit length. The speed of sound in air depends on the temperature of the air. Although a wave with larger amplitude transfers more energy, it moves at the same speed as a smaller amplitude wave through a given medium. A wave with a higher frequency has a shorter wavelength, as given by the equation $v = \lambda f$. As long as the material is the same, the speed of high and low frequency waves is the same.

Often a wave moves from one medium to another. Light might move from air into water, Figure 14–8. In Figure 14–9, waves move from large to small springs. The spring can end by being fastened to a rigid wall, as in Figure 14–10, or by being allowed to move freely, Figure 14–11. What happens to a wave when the medium changes?

Suppose a wave, called the incident wave, reaches the boundary of a medium. Part of the energy carried by the incident wave continues on in the new medium as a wave with the same frequency. This wave is called the transmitted wave. In addition, part of the energy moves backward from the boundary as a wave in the old medium. This wave is called the reflected wave.

If the difference in the media is small, then the amplitude of the transmitted wave will be almost as large as that of the incident wave, and the amplitude of the reflected wave will be small. Most of the energy of the incident wave will be transmitted. If the two materials are very different, however, most of the wave energy will be reflected.

Figure 14–10 shows a wave on a spring approaching a rigid wall. The spring and wall are very different, so most of the wave energy is reflected. The figure also shows that the reflected wave is inverted. The incident wave pulse is in the upward direction, the reflected pulse is in the downward direction. Whenever a wave passes from a less dense to a more dense medium, the reflected wave is inverted.

F.Y.I.

Because radio waves travel at 3.0×10^8 m/s and sound waves are slower, 3.4×10^2 m/s, a broadcast voice can be heard sooner 13 000 miles away than it can be heard at the back of the room in which it originated.

FIGURE 14–10. A pulse is shown as it approaches a rigid wall (a) and as it is reflected from the wall (b). Notice that the amplitude of the reflected pulse is nearly equal to the amplitude of the incident pulse but that the reflected pulse is inverted.

a

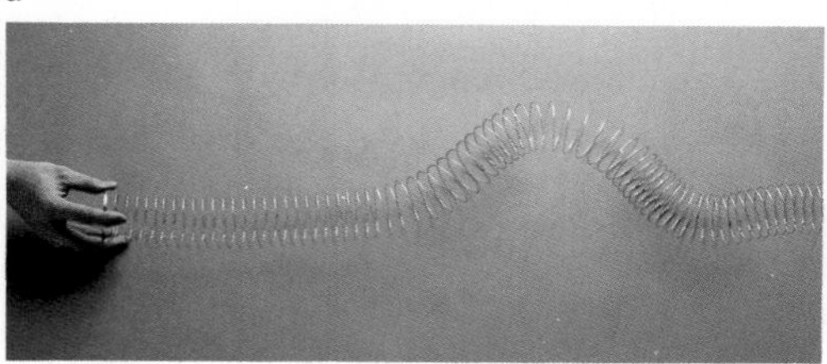

b

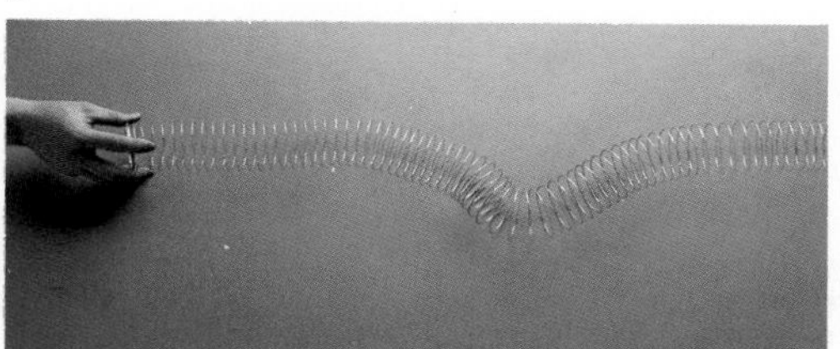

14.2 WAVE INTERFERENCE

Preparation

OBJECTIVES

The objectives are listed on the student page. Remind students to preview these objectives as a study guide to this major section.

OVERVIEW

New concepts introduced here concern the interactions of waves with themselves or with matter. Interference, principle of superposition, nodes, antinodes, standing waves, reflection, refraction, and diffraction are discussed.

BRIDGING

Topics reintroduced here are mass, temperature, resonance, and extensions of the concepts mentioned in the first teaching block.

1 Focus

DISCREPANT EVENT

Set up another hallway demonstration with the coiled spring, then follow these steps:

1. Tie a piece of string about one meter long to one end of the spring. With a student extending the string, send a pulse down the spring from the free end. What happens when the pulse arrives at the boundary between the two media? [Part of the pulse is transmitted and part is reflected.]

2. Remove the extra string and anchor the end of the Slinky, or have a student hold the end securely. Ask the students to observe the phases of original and reflected pulses. [Pulses reflected from a rigid barrier undergo a 180° phase change. Those reflected from a nonrigid barrier undergo no phase change.]

RETEACHING MASTER

Use the Reteaching master for Chapter 14 with this section.

TRANSPARENCY

Use Transparency 18 with this section.

2 Teach

CONCEPT DEVELOPMENT

Study Guide Master. To reinforce the concepts in this section, have students complete the Study Guide Master for Section 14.2 from the Teacher Resource Package.

- Inverted, reflected waves can be shown by rigidly attaching one end of a Slinky and making waves at the other end. Erect reflected waves can be shown by attaching a short length of rubber hose or other flexible material to a Slinky, rigidly attaching the non-Slinky, and then making waves at the other end.
- Wave machines made of rods mounted on a flexible spine are available, although expensive. If you have one, it will show wave behaviors at boundaries between media.
- To build your own wave machine, refer to the R. D. Edge book *String and Sticky Tape Experiments* for one you can build.
- Point out that individual waves do not change when they pass through one another.

Enrichment Master. With this section, use the Enrichment Master, Earthquake Wave Velocities, from the Teacher Resource Package.

Answers To
PRACTICE PROBLEMS

Have students refer to Appendix A of the Solutions Appendix for complete solutions to Practice Problems.

5. **a.** partially reflected, partially transmitted
b. erect
c. almost totally reflected
d. inverted

FIGURE 14–11. A pulse reflected from an open-ended boundary returns erect.

When the medium changes, wave energy is both reflected and transmitted.

In Figure 14–11, the spring is supported by light threads. When a pulse reaches the end of the spring, the pulse is transmitted into another medium, air. Because the two media are very different, most of the energy of the wave is reflected. In this case, however, the reflected wave is not inverted. When a wave passes from a more dense to a less dense medium, the reflected pulse is erect, not inverted.

Suppose a wave on a light spring is transmitted to a heavy spring. The wave in the light spring generated the wave in the heavy spring, so the frequencies of the two waves are the same. The speed of the wave in the heavier spring is slower. The speed, frequency, and wavelength of a wave are related by the equation $v = \lambda f$. Because the speed of the transmitted wave is different, but the frequency remains the same, the wavelength of the transmitted wave must also be different. The speed in the heavier spring is less, so the wavelength is smaller. On the other hand, if the speed of a wave increases when it passes into a new medium, then its wavelength also increases.

Waves passing from one medium to another have the same frequency. The wavelength change depends on velocity change so that $f = v/\lambda$ is constant.

Although the waves in the examples are transverse waves, longitudinal waves behave in exactly the same way. Whenever a wave reaches a boundary, some of the wave energy is transmitted, some is reflected. The amount of reflected energy is larger if the two media have vastly different properties.

Practice Problems

5. A pulse is sent along a spring. The spring is attached to a light thread that is tied to the wall, Figure 14–12.
   a. What happens when the pulse reaches point **A**?
   b. Is the pulse reflected from **A** erect or inverted?
   c. What happens when the transmitted pulse reaches **B**?
   d. Is the pulse reflected from **B** erect or inverted?

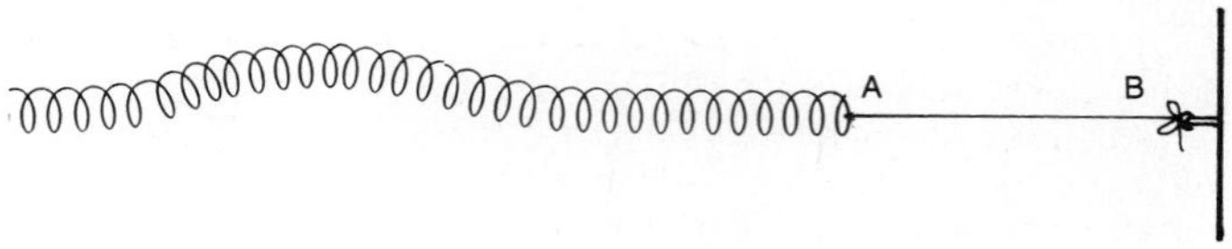

FIGURE 14–12. Use with Practice Problem 5.

STUDY GUIDE MASTER

Use the Study Guide master for section 14.2.

ENRICHMENT MASTER

Use the Enrichment master for Chapter 14 with this section.

6. A long spring runs across the floor of a room and out the door. A pulse is sent along the spring. After a few seconds, an inverted pulse returns. Is the spring attached to the wall in the next room or is it lying loose on the floor?
7. If you want to increase the wavelength of waves in a rope, should you shake it at a higher or lower frequency?

Constructive interference occurs when two waves combine to produce a wave with larger amplitude.

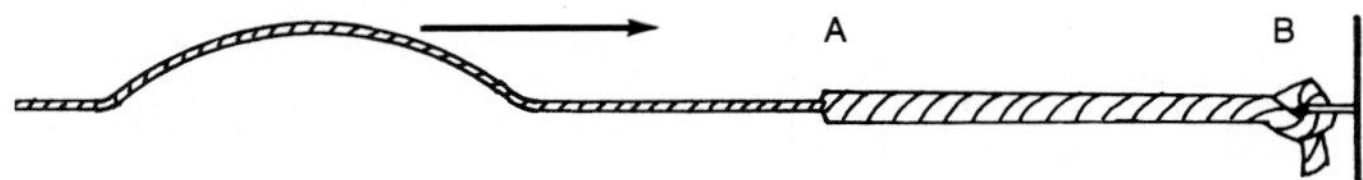

FIGURE 14–13. Use with Practice Problem 8.

▶ 8. A pulse is sent along a thin rope that is attached to a thick rope. The thick rope is itself tied to a wall, Figure 14–13.
   a. What happens when the pulse reaches point **A**?
   b. Is the pulse reflected from **A** erect or inverted?
   c. What happens when the transmitted pulse reaches **B**?
   d. Is the pulse reflected from **B** erect or inverted?

Destructive interference occurs when two waves combine to produce a wave with a smaller amplitude.

Superposition of Waves

What happens when two or more waves travel through a medium at the same time? Each wave affects the medium independently. As a result, we can analyze the effects of these waves using the principle of superposition. The **principle of superposition** states that *the displacement of a medium caused by two or more waves is the algebraic sum of the displacements caused by the individual waves.* The result of the superposition of two or more waves is called **interference.**

Interference can be either constructive or destructive. **Constructive interference** occurs when the wave displacements are in the same direction. The result is a wave with larger amplitude than any of the individual waves. Figure 14–14 shows the constructive interference of two equal pulses. When the two pulses meet, a larger pulse is formed. The amplitude of the larger pulse is the algebraic sum of the amplitudes of the two pulses. After the two pulses have passed through each other, they regain their original shape and size. The pulses are not changed by their interaction.

Figure 14–15 shows the **destructive interference** of two pulses with equal but opposite amplitudes. As the two pulses overlap, the displacement of the medium at each point in the overlap is reduced. When the pulses are at the same location, the displacement is zero. The pulses keep moving and resume their original form. An important characteristic of waves is the ability to pass through one another unchanged.

If the pulses have unequal amplitudes, the destructive interference is not complete. The pulse at overlap is the algebraic sum of the two pulses. Some wave amplitude always remains.

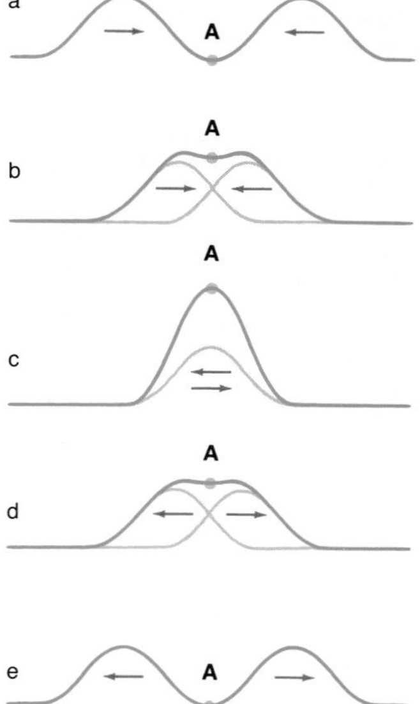

FIGURE 14–14. Constructive interference of two equal pulses. An antinode is a point of maximum displacement.

6. attached to wall
7. lower frequency
8. a. partially reflected, partially transmitted
   b. inverted
   c. almost totally reflected
   d. inverted

CONCEPT DEVELOPMENT

Critical Thinking Master, Teacher Resource Package. You may wish to have students complete the Critical Thinking Master, Wave Superposition, with this section.

ACTIVITY

Discovery: Using a hallway demonstration with a coiled spring, follow these steps:

1. Have two students send simultaneous pulses from opposite ends of the spring. Have the students experiment with pulses of the same and different sizes and pulses in phase and out of phase, with particular attention to pulses that are 180° out of phase. Ask: What happens to the pulses when they meet? [The pulses add.] What happens to the pulses after they have passed through one another? [The pulses continue unchanged.]

2. Produce a periodic wave by shaking the spring back and forth at a uniform rate. Have students determine the frequency of the wave and make an approximation of the wavelength. Repeat the procedure using a higher and then a lower frequency. Ask: How is the wavelength of a wave in a given medium related to its frequency? [The frequency is related inversely to the wavelength.]

CRITICAL THINKING

Use the Critical Thinking master for Chapter 14 with this section.

CONCEPT DEVELOPMENT

- A wave machine can show nodes. A Slinky or a rope can show a standing wave. Standing waves are formed in most musical instruments. They were also produced during the collapse of the Tacoma Narrows Bridge.
- Showing the film loop or video of the collapse of the Tacoma Narrows Bridge is a must. Depending on the explanatory material you have available with it you can tailor a presentation. However, students usually have many questions.
- Resonance will be treated more thoroughly in the next chapter, which is on sound. It was also discussed in the section on simple harmonic motion in Chapter 7.

ACTIVITY

Discovery: It is worth investing in a string vibrator to show standing waves. It is very easy to identify the nodes and antinodes. You can vary the tension in the string and get different numbers of nodes and antinodes and therefore different numbers of wavelengths. It is a very good visual tool.

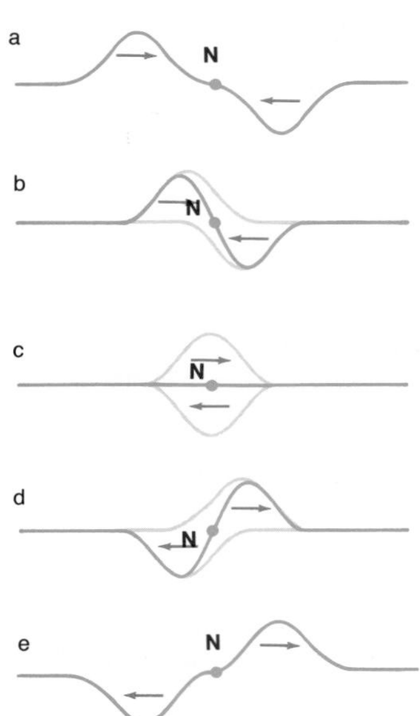

FIGURE 14–15. Destructive interference of two equal pulses. A node is a point of the medium that remains undisturbed.

Standing Waves

Look again at Figure 14–15. Two pulses with equal but opposite amplitudes meet. You can find one point in the medium that is completely undisturbed at all times. This point is called a **node**. At a node, the medium is never displaced. If you put your finger on the rope at the node, you will feel no motion. A node is produced by the destructive interference of waves.

In Figure 14–14, two pulses with equal amplitudes in the same direction meet. There is one point that undergoes the greatest displacement. Its maximum amplitude is equal to the sum of the amplitudes of the two pulses. This point of maximum displacement is called an **antinode.** Constructive interference of waves produces antinodes.

Imagine one end of a rope attached to a fixed point. You continuously vibrate the other end up and down. A traveling wave will leave your hand, move to the other end, be inverted and reflected, and return toward your hand. At your hand, the wave will be inverted and reflected again. At each reflection, the displacement direction will change. If the original displacement was upward, it will be downward when moving back to your hand, but be upward again after reflection from your hand.

Now, suppose you adjust the motion of your hand so that the period of the rope's vibration equals the time required for the wave to travel to the fixed point and back. The displacement your hand gives to the rope each time will add to the displacement of the reflected wave. The result is a very large amplitude oscillation in the rope, much larger than the motion of your hand. This large amplitude oscillation is an example of resonance. There are nodes at the ends of the rope and an antinode in the middle. The nodes and antinodes are stationary. The wave appears to be standing still. It is called a **standing wave**. If you double the frequency of vibration, you can produce additional nodes in the rope. It appears to vibrate in two segments. Further increases in frequency produce even more nodes, Figure 14–16.

At a node, the medium is not displaced as the waves pass through each other.

At an antinode, the displacement caused by interfering waves is largest.

A standing wave has stationary nodes and antinodes. It is the result of identical waves traveling in opposite directions.

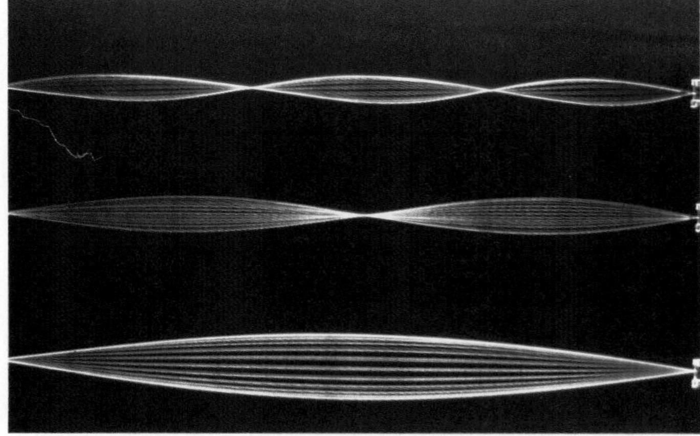

FIGURE 14–16. Interference produces standing waves in a rope.

TEACHER F.Y.I.

The following comments about the Tacoma Narrows Bridge collapse are summarized from Jearl Walker's book, *The Flying Circus of Physics.* The bridge oscillated even when it was being built. It often made the workmen seasick. After the bridge opened, motorists would come from miles away to be on the bridge when it was in motion. One day the bridge went into a torsional oscillation which destroyed it in about an hour. The question is why should a moderately strong steady wind cause such strong oscillations? It would appear that the large vertical plates on the bridge were probably responsible for the oscillations. Wind flowing around the plates caused pressure differences which ultimately made the bridge oscillate.

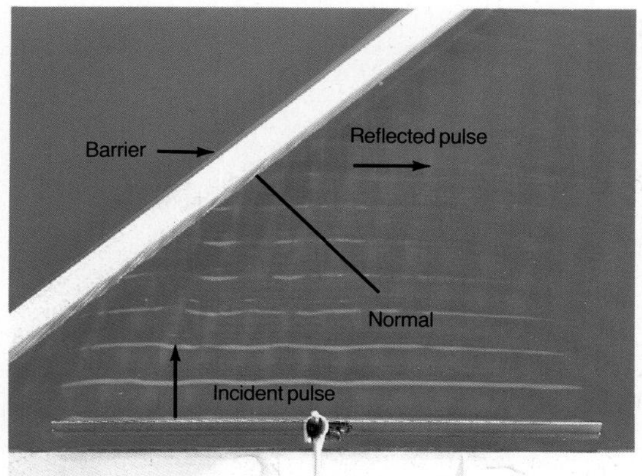

a

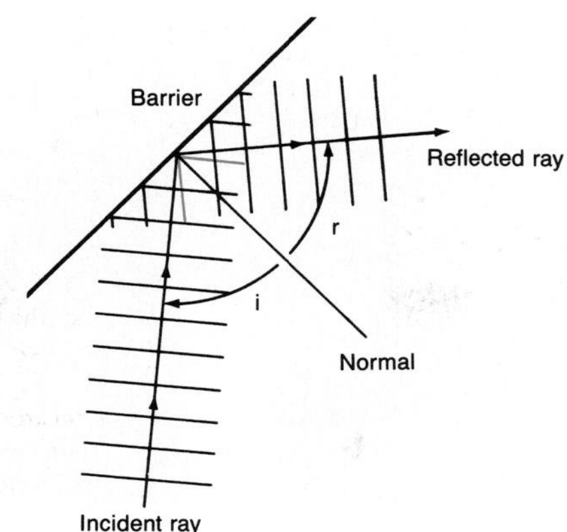

b

FIGURE 14–17. Reflection of a plane wave pulse by a barrier (a). In (b), part of the pulse front is shown in time sequence as it approaches, and then is reflected from the barrier.

Reflection of Waves

We have studied waves reflecting from a rigid support, where the amplitude of the wave was forced to be zero. These waves move in only one dimension. Waves on the surface of water move in two dimensions, while sound and electromagnetic waves move in three dimensions. A ripple tank can be used to show the properties of two-dimensional waves. A ripple tank contains a thin layer of water. Vibrating boards produce wave pulses or traveling waves with constant frequency. A lamp above the tank produces shadows below the tank that show the locations of the crests of the waves. Figure 14–17 shows a wave pulse traveling toward a straight rigid wall, a barrier that will reflect the wave. The incident pulse moves upward. The reflected pulse moves toward the right.

The direction of waves moving in two or three dimensions is often shown by ray diagrams. A ray is a line drawn at a right angle to the crest of the wave. A ray diagram shows only the direction of the waves, it does not show the actual waves. In Figure 14–17, the ray representing the incident ray is the arrow pointing upward. The ray representing the reflected ray points to the right.

The direction of the barrier is also shown by a line drawn at a right angle to it. This line is called the **normal**. The angle between the incident ray and the normal is called the **angle of incidence**. The angle between the normal and the reflected ray is called the **angle of reflection**. The **law of reflection** states that *the angle of incidence is equal to the angle of reflection.*

The angle at which a wave approaches a barrier is equal to the angle at which it is reflected.

Refraction of Waves

A ripple tank can also be used to study the behavior of waves as they move from one medium into another. Figure 14–18a shows a glass plate placed in a ripple tank. The water above the plate is shallower than in the rest of the tank. The velocity of water waves depends on the water depth, so the water above the plate acts like a different medium.

HELP WANTED

AUDIOLOGIST

A private practice seeks a certified audiologist to provide in-office services, as well as to deliver contract services to outside businesses and agencies.

Patience, compassion, excellent communicative skills, thorough knowledge of current equipment, strong concentration skills, and attention to detail are required for success in this career field. Only candidates with a master's degree need apply. For information contact:

American Speech-Language-Hearing Association, 10801 Rockville Pike, Rockville, MD 20852

CONCEPT DEVELOPMENT

- Call students' attention to the fact that light is reflected from mirrors and other shiny surfaces. Sound is reflected from hard surfaces to produce echoes.
- Refraction of water waves can be shown by placing a glass plate on the bottom of a ripple tank so that its edge is at an angle to the oncoming wave.
- Refraction of light produces rainbows, corrects our vision, and makes possible microscopes and binoculars.
- Point out to students that both reflection and refraction are ways of changing a wave's direction. Or, to put it another way, both are ways of controlling waves. So, for example, we use lenses and mirrors to form images.
- In discussing the term *normal,* it may help to add the fact that an infinite two-dimensional surface has no well-defined direction except that one which is perpendicular to it. Defining a normal is like defining a direction for angular momentum or angular velocity.

POCKET LAB

WAVE INTERACTION

Purpose: to investigate transverse wave interaction on a coil spring.
Materials: coil spring.
Outcome: Students will find it almost impossible to decide what happened unless they try different sizes, types, or orientations of waves. Students can observe that waves go through each other if: (1) they send different amplitude waves from different directions; (2) one student sends a pressure wave while another student sends a transverse wave; or (3) one student sends a pulse in a horizontal plane as the other student makes a pulse in a vertical plane.

CHECKING FOR UNDERSTANDING

Ask students about how many things a wave can do as it runs into various situations. Get them to describe and explain each one. [Reflect, refract, interfere, diffract, travel, and form standing waves are some possibilities.]

RETEACHING

Transparency Package. Use Transparency 18 to reteach wave behavior.

EXTENSION

Have students work through a pictorial representation of wave (or pulse) interference in the following way: Draw two pulses approaching each other on the top of a piece of graph paper so that the vertical lines of the graph paper divide the pulses up into, say, five or ten parts. Then ask students to draw successive pictures as the pulses travel along and just overlap. Next have students measure the displacements of each pulse (in each successive picture) and draw another pulse that is the sum of displacements of the two separate pulses.

a

b

FIGURE 14–18. Notice the change in wavelength, as the water waves enter a more shallow region (a). When waves enter at an angle they change direction, demonstrating refraction (b).

Refraction is the change of wave direction at the boundary between two media.

How does the velocity of waves depend on water depth? In Figure 14–18a, a wave train passes over a glass plate, changing the depth of the water. As the waves move from deep to shallow water, their wavelength decreases and the direction of the waves changes. Because the waves in the shallow water are generated by the waves in deep water, their frequency is not changed. From the equation $v = \lambda f$, the decrease in the wavelength of the waves means that the velocity is lower in the shallower water.

In Figure 14–18b, the waves approach the shore at an angle. The ray direction is not parallel to the normal. Not only does the wavelength decrease over the shallower bottom, but the direction of the waves changes. The change in the direction of waves at the boundary between two different media is known as **refraction**.

POCKET LAB

WAVE INTERACTION

What happens to the waves coming from different directions when they meet? Do they bounce off or go through each other? Do they slow down? Use the snakey to find out by devising a way to test these questions. Record your procedures and results.

Diffraction and Interference of Waves

If particles are thrown at a barrier with holes in it, the particles will either reflect off the barrier or pass straight through the holes. When waves encounter a small hole in a barrier, however, they do not pass straight through. Rather, they bend around the edges of the barrier, forming circular waves that spread out, Figure 14–19. The spreading of

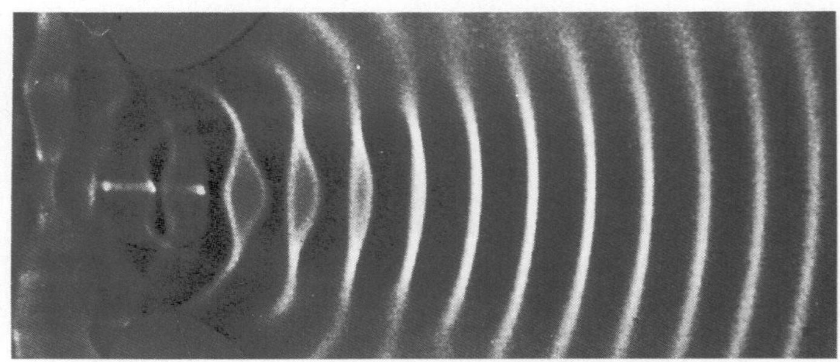

FIGURE 14–19. Waves bending around barriers demonstrate diffraction.

Assessment

Performance

To further assess students' understanding of wave properties, have two students, one at each end of a snakey, demonstrate reflection of an impulse off an imaginary rigid barrier in the center of the spring. How can they do this? [The two students send transverse pulses in opposite directions, *e.g.,* one up and one down. Then the pulse that appears to return to the sender will have the opposite phase.]

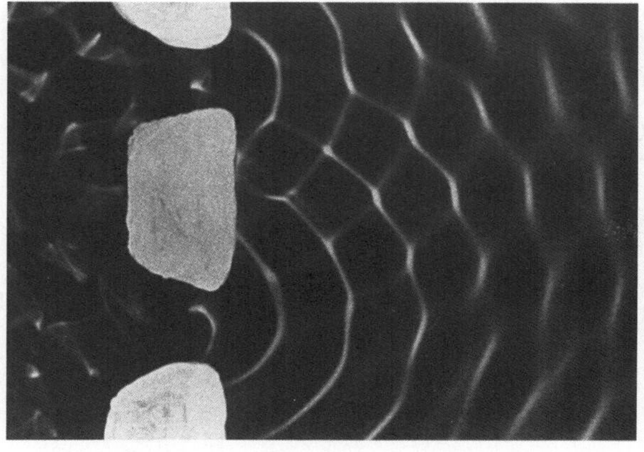

a

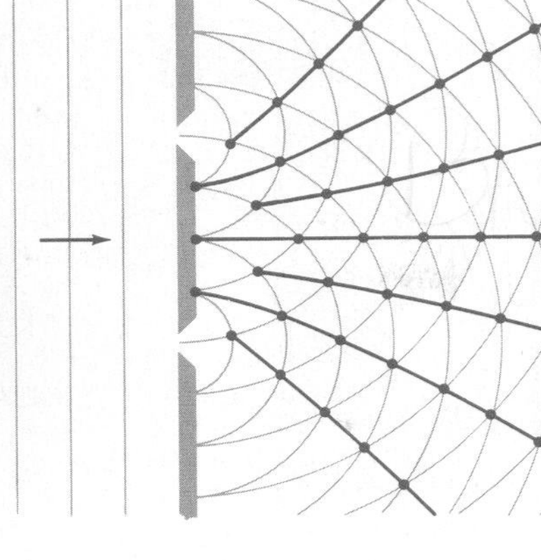

b

FIGURE 14–20. Waves are diffracted at two openings in the barrier. At each opening, circular waves are formed. The circular waves interfere with each other, with points of constructive interference appearing as bright spots in the photograph (a). Lines of constructive interference (antinodal lines) occur where crest meets crest (b).

waves around the edge of a barrier is called **diffraction**. Diffraction also occurs when waves meet a small obstacle. They can bend around the obstacle, producing waves behind it. The smaller the wavelength in comparison to the size of the obstacle, the less the diffraction.

Figure 14–20a shows the result of waves striking a barrier having two closely-spaced holes. The waves are diffracted by each hole, forming circular waves. But the circular waves interfere with each other. There are regions of constructive interference where the resulting waves are large, and bands of destructive interference where the water remains almost undisturbed. Constructive interference occurs where two crests or two troughs from the two circular waves meet. The antinodes lie on lines called antinodal lines. These lines radiate from the barrier, Figure 14–20b. Between the antinodal lines are areas where a crest from one circular wave and a trough from the other meet. Destructive interference produces nodes where the water is undisturbed. The lines of nodes, or nodal lines, lie between adjacent antinodal lines.

Diffraction is the spreading of waves around the edge of a barrier.

CONCEPT REVIEW

2.1 If a wave moves from a medium with a high wave velocity to one with a low wave velocity, which of the following CANNOT change: frequency, amplitude, wavelength, velocity, direction?

2.2 A rope vibrates with the two waves at once, Figure 14–21. Sketch the resulting wave.

2.3 Would you expect high frequency or low frequency sound waves to be more diffracted when they pass through an open door?

2.4 Critical Thinking: For another way to understand wave reflection, return to Figure 14–15. Cover the right-hand side of each drawing with a piece of paper. The edge of the paper should be at the point **N,** the node. Now, concentrate on the sum wave, shown in blue. Note that it acts like a wave reflected from a boundary. Is the boundary a rigid wall or open ended? Repeat for Figure 14–14.

FIGURE 14–21. Use with Concept Review 2.2.

CONCEPT DEVELOPMENT

ACTIVITY

Cooperative Learning: Have the class construct a table of all the types of waves with their individual properties. Much of the learning here will be in deciding how to structure the table to present the information most clearly.

Critical Thinking: One type of wave that has been predicted but not yet detected is the gravity wave. What kind of an event or process would you expect to generate a gravity wave? How would you detect such a gravity wave?

Enrichment: Does interference exist for sound waves? If you think so, what would such interference be like? Can you give any examples?

Guided Practice: Discuss the Concept Review questions in class.

INDEPENDENT PRACTICE/ EXTENSION

Refer to the Assignment Guide below for additional questions and problems for independent practice.

3 Close

CONVERGENT QUESTION

Suppose some waves move along encountering various media as they travel. What are some of the things that could happen to these waves?

CONCEPT REVIEW ANSWERS

2.1 frequency

2.2

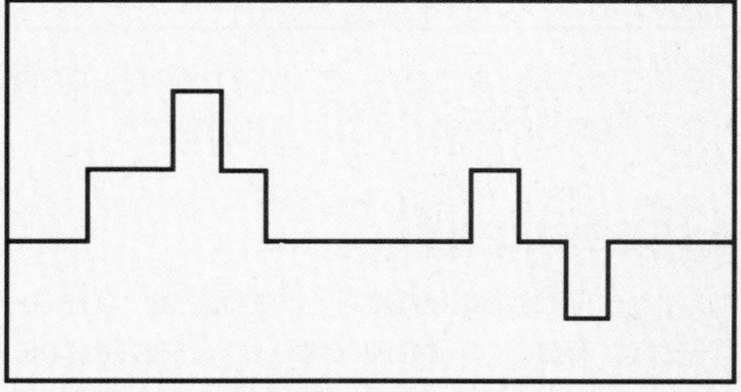

2.3 Low frequency (long wavelength), since the smaller the wavelength the less the diffraction.

2.4 Critical Thinking: For Figure 14–15, it is a rigid wall; for Figure 14–14, an open-ended boundary.

14:2 ASSIGNMENT GUIDE

	PRACTICE	EXTENSION
CHAPTER REVIEW pp. 302–305		
· Reviewing Concepts	13–22	
· Applying Concepts		6–9
· Problems*	15, 16	14
APPENDIX B PROBLEMS*		
· Chapter 14, pp. 698–699	11	

* Complete solutions to all Chapter Review and Appendix problems appear in the Problems and Solutions Manual.

TRANSPARENCY

Use Transparency 18 with this section.

Physics and technology

Answer to student question:

Answers could include less noise and air pollution, no risks from chemical explosions or nuclear radiation, ease of facility installation, and lower cost.

Applications for microwave power include small spacecraft that could carry several people into orbit; a new power source for the space shuttle, which would greatly increase its payload capacity; relay platforms for communications satellites; and new aircraft that could fly close to the edge of Earth's atmosphere.

A public concern that microwaves could be a health and environmental hazard will have to be addressed. Most scientists believe that the systems can be made safe because the operational power levels would be at acceptably low levels. More information is available from NASA's Lewis Research Center in Cleveland, Ohio.

Physics and technology

MICROWAVE-POWERED AIRCRAFT

Imagine an aircraft that does not carry on-board fuel and can stay in flight for half a year. Or imagine a spacecraft whose orbits could be adjusted using engines powered by microwave-energy beams transmitted from Earth. With less rocket fuel to carry, larger payloads could be lifted into space. Advances in microwave technology could bring both of these dreams to life.

Microwave-energy beaming is much like radio-wave transmission, except that it works with higher power levels. A transmitter sends out microwave energy, and a distant antenna and receiver pick it up and convert it to another form of energy, usually electricity. The waves transfer energy without moving matter.

Research on the potential of microwave power is underway at NASA's Lewis Research Center in Cleveland, Ohio. Scientists are working on a Mars mission in which a mother ship orbiting the planet would transmit microwave beams to power a remote-controlled drone. The drone would fly down, land, and unload a rover vehicle that would explore the planet's surface and collect samples. It is estimated that the drone could cover about 40% of Mars' surface without refueling.

· What advantages could microwave power have when compared to other power sources such as jet propulsion, chemical, rocket power, and nuclear power?

Teacher Resources: Rogers, Michael and Springen, Karen. "Can a Plane Fly Forever?" *Newsweek,* 110, September 28, 1987, pages 42, 47.

Broad, William. "New Kind of Aircraft Is on Horizon as Designers Try Microwave Power." *New York Times,* 136, July 21, 1987, page 17, national edition.

CHAPTER 14 REVIEW

SUMMARY

14.1 Wave Properties

- Waves transfer energy without the transfer of matter.
- Mechanical waves, such as sound waves and the waves on a rope, require a medium. Electromagnetic waves, such as light and radio waves, do not need a medium.
- In transverse waves, the particles of the medium move perpendicularly to the direction of the wave. In longitudinal waves, the particles move parallel to the wave direction. In surface waves, the particles move both perpendicularly and parallel to the direction of the wave's motion.
- The frequency of a wave, f, is the number of vibrations per second of any one point on a wave. The period of a wave is the time interval between successive wave crests or troughs.
- The shortest distance between points where the wave pattern repeats itself is called the wavelength, λ.
- The velocity of a wave, the distance a point on the wave moves in a unit time interval, can be calculated from the equation $v = \lambda f$.
- The amplitude of a wave is its maximum displacement from the rest or equilibrium position. Energy transferred by a wave is proportional to the square of the amplitude.

14.2 Wave Interference

- The speed of a wave depends on the properties of the medium through which the wave moves.
- When waves reach the boundary between two media, they are partially transmitted and partially reflected. The amount reflected depends on how much the two media differ.

CLOSING CHAPTER 14

Review Summary statements and Key Terms with your students.

ASSESSMENT

Vocabulary Review Master, Teacher Resource Package. Use this master to check students' understanding of Key Terms.

Evaluation Masters. Use Parts A and B of the Chapter Evaluation Masters from the Teacher Resource Package to test qualitative chapter objectives. Use Parts C and D to test quantitative chapter objectives.

REVIEW MASTER

Use the Vocabulary Review master for Chapter 14 with this section.

EVALUATION MASTER

Use the Chapter Evaluation master for Chapter 14 with this section.

- When a wave moves from a less dense to a more dense medium, the reflected wave is inverted. When it moves from a more dense to a less dense medium, the reflected wave is erect.
- The principle of superposition states that the displacement of a medium due to two or more waves is the algebraic sum of the displacements caused by the individual waves.
- The result of the superposition of two or more waves on a medium is called interference. Interference does not affect the individual waves.
- Maximum destructive interference produces a node where there is no displacement. Maximum constructive interference results in an antinode, a location of the largest displacement.
- The nodes and antinodes of a standing wave are stationary.
- The law of reflection states that the angle of incidence is equal to the angle of reflection. Waves are reflected from a barrier at the same angle at which they approach it.
- The change in the direction of waves at the boundary between two different media is known as refraction.
- The spreading of waves around the edge of a barrier is called diffraction.

KEY TERMS

transverse wave
longitudinal wave
surface waves
wave pulse
traveling wave
period
frequency
wavelength
crests
troughs
amplitude
principle of superposition
interference
constructive interference
destructive interference
node
antinode
standing wave
normal
angle of incidence
angle of reflection
law of reflection
refraction
diffraction

REVIEWING CONCEPTS

1. How many general methods of energy transfer are there? Give two examples of each.
2. What is the primary difference between a mechanical wave and an electromagnetic wave?
3. What is the difference among transverse, longitudinal, and surface waves?
4. Rhonda sends a pulse along a rope. How does the position of a point on the rope, before the pulse comes, compare to the position after the pulse has passed?
5. What is the difference between a pulse and a wave?
6. What is the difference between wave frequency and wave velocity?
7. Suppose you produce a transverse wave by shaking one end of a spring back and forth. How does the frequency of your hand compare with the frequency of the wave?
8. Waves are sent along a spring of fixed length.
   a. Can the speed of the waves in the spring be changed? Explain.
   b. Can the frequency of a wave in the spring be changed? Explain.
9. What is the difference between the speed of a transverse wave pulse down a spring and the motion of a point on the spring?
10. Sharon is lying on a raft in the wave pool. Describe to Sharon, in terms of the waves she is riding, each of the following: amplitude, period, wavelength, speed, frequency.
11. What is the amplitude of a wave and what does it represent?
12. What is the relationship between the amplitude of a wave and the energy carried?
13. When a wave reaches the boundary of a new medium, part of the wave is reflected and part is transmitted. What determines the amount of reflection?
14. A pulse reaches the boundary of a medium more dense than the one from which it came. Is the reflected pulse erect or inverted?
15. A pulse reaches the boundary of a medium less dense than the one from which it came. Is the reflected pulse erect or inverted?
16. When a wave crosses a boundary between thin and thick rope, its wavelength and velocity change, but its frequency does not. Explain why the frequency is constant.
17. When two waves interfere, is there a loss of energy in the system? Explain.
18. What happens to the spring at nodes of a standing wave?
19. A metal plate is held fixed in the center and sprinkled with sugar. Using a violin bow, the plate is stroked along one edge and made to vibrate. The sugar begins to collect in certain areas and move away from others. Describe these regions in terms of standing waves.

Answers To
REVIEWING CONCEPTS

1. Two. Energy is transferred by particle transfer and by waves. There are many examples that can be given of each, a baseball and a bullet for particle transfer; sound waves and light waves.
2. The primary difference is that mechanical waves require a medium to travel through and electromagnetic waves do not need a medium.
3. A transverse wave causes the particles of the medium to vibrate in a direction that is perpendicular to the direction in which the wave is moving. A longitudinal wave causes the particles of the medium to vibrate in a direction parallel with the direction of the wave. Surface waves have characteristics of both.
4. Once the pulse has passed, the point is exactly as it was prior to the advent of the pulse.
5. A pulse is a single disturbance in a medium, whereas a wave consists of several adjacent disturbances.
6. Frequency is the number of vibrations per second of a part of the medium. Velocity describes the motion of the wave, not the medium.
7. They are the same.
8. a. Speed of the waves cannot be changed; **b.** Frequency can be changed by changing the frequency at which the waves are generated.
9. The speed of the wave is uniform, along the direction of the spring. The coil has a vibratory motion perpendicular to the spring.
10. The amplitude is one-half the total up and down motion; the period is the amount of time it takes Sharon to go up and back down; the wavelength is the distance to the top of the next wave when she is on a wave top; the speed is how fast the waves are traveling; the frequency is how many times Sharon moves up in one minute.
11. Amplitude is the maximum displacement of a wave from the rest or equilibrium position.
12. The amplitude of the wave represents the amount of energy transferred.

Answers To
REVIEWING CONCEPTS (cont)

13. Amount of reflection is determined by the difference between the properties of the new medium and the properties of the old medium. The greater the difference, the greater the reflection.
14. The reflected pulse is inverted.
15. The reflected pulse is erect.
16. The frequency depends only on the rate the thin rope is shaken and the thin rope causes the vibrations in the thick rope.
17. No. Energy is not lost. The total energy of the system remains the same, but it is redistributed. The nodal areas have less energy and the antinodal areas have more energy.
18. Nothing. The spring doesn't move.
19. Bare areas are antinodal regions where there is maximum vibration. Sugar-covered areas are nodal regions where there is no vibration.
20. A standing wave exists and the string can be touched at any of its five nodal points.

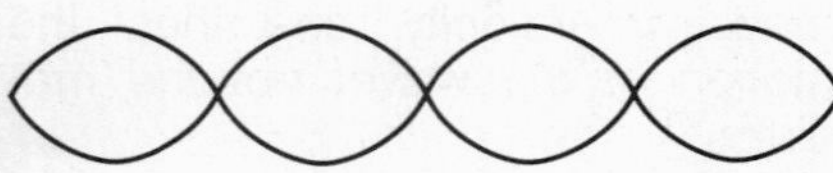

21. The pulse will be inverted.
22. All waves. It is a prime test for wave nature.

Answers To
APPLYING CONCEPTS

1. In the first case, longitudinal waves; in the second case, transverse waves.
2. The frequency of the waves will increase; the speed will remain the same; the wavelength will decrease.
3. As the frequency increases, the period decreases.
4. As the frequency increases, the wavelength decreases.
5. approximately four times the energy
6. Boundary A is more rigid; boundary B is less rigid; boundary C is less rigid; boundary D is more rigid.
7. The bottom, because the difference in media is greater in this case.
8. The period of the vibration must equal the time for the wave to go back and forth across the pan to create constructive interference.
9. AM wavelengths are longer, and therefore the diffraction is more. The waves are bent more.

20. If a string is vibrating in four parts, there are points it can be touched without disturbing its motion. Explain. How many points exist?
21. How does the pulse reflected from a rigid wall differ from the incident pulse?
22. Is interference a property of only some types of waves or all types of waves?

APPLYING CONCEPTS

1. George holds a 1-m metal bar in his hand and hits its end with a hammer; first, in a direction parallel to its length; second, in a direction at right angles to its length. Describe the waves George produces in the two cases.
2. You repeatedly dip your finger into a sink full of water to make circular waves. What happens to the wavelength as you move your finger faster?
3. What happens to the period of a wave as the frequency increases?
4. What happens to the wavelength of a wave as the frequency increases?
5. Joe makes a single pulse on a stretched spring. How much energy is required to make a pulse with twice the amplitude?
6. In each of the four waves in Figure 14–22, the pulse on the left is the original pulse moving toward the right. The center pulse is a reflected pulse; the pulse on the right is a transmitted pulse. Describe the boundaries at **A, B, C,** and **D.**

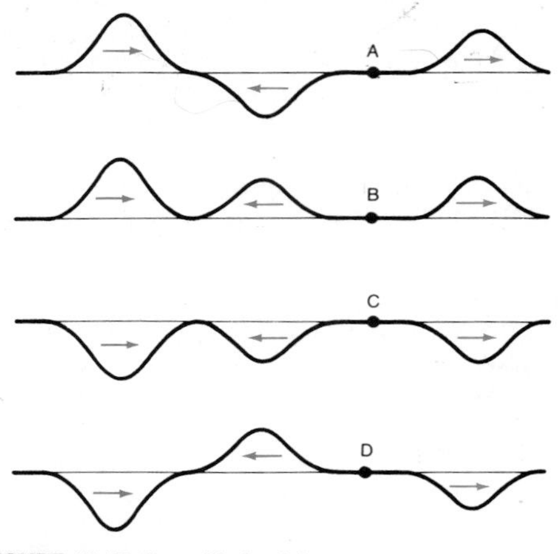

FIGURE 14-22. Use with Applying Concepts 6.

7. Sonar is the detection of sound waves reflected off boundaries in water. A region of warm water in a cold lake can produce a reflection, as can the bottom of the lake. Which would you expect to produce the stronger echo? Explain.
8. You can make water slosh back and forth in a shallow pan only if you shake the pan with the correct frequency. Explain.
9. AM radio signals have wavelengths between 600 m and 200 m, while FM signals have wavelengths about 3 m. Explain why AM signals can often be heard behind hills while FM signals cannot.

PROBLEMS

14.1 Wave Properties

1. The Sears Building in Chicago sways back and forth with a frequency of about 0.10 Hz. What is its period of vibration?
2. An ocean wave has a length of 10.0 m. A wave passes a fixed location every 2.0 s. What is the speed of the wave?
3. Water waves in a shallow dish are 6.0 cm long. At one point, the water oscillates up and down at a rate of 4.8 oscillations per second.
   a. What is the speed of the water waves?
   b. What is the period of the water waves?
4. Water waves in a lake travel 4.4 m in 1.8 s. The period of oscillation is 1.2 s.
   a. What is the speed of the water waves?
   b. What is their wavelength?
5. The frequency of yellow light is 5.0×10^{14} Hz. Find its wavelength.
6. ▶ A group of swimmers is resting in the sun on an off-shore raft. They estimate that 3.0 m separates a trough and an adjacent crest of surface waves on the lake. They count 14 crests that pass by the raft in 20 s. How fast are the waves moving?
7. AM radio signals are broadcast at frequencies between 550 kHz and 1600 kHz (kilohertz) and travel 3.0×10^8 m/s.
   a. What is the range of wavelengths for these signals?
   b. FM frequencies range between 88 MHz and 108 MHz (megahertz) and travel at the same speed. What is the range of FM wavelengths?

304 Waves and Energy Transfer

8. A sonar signal of frequency 1.00×10^6 Hz has a wavelength of 1.50 mm in water.
   a. What is the speed of the signal in water?
   b. What is its period in water?
   c. What is its period in air?

9. A sound wave of wavelength 0.70 m and velocity 330 m/s is produced for 0.50 s.
   a. What is the frequency of the wave?
   b. How many complete waves are emitted in this time interval?
   c. After 0.50 s, how far is the front wave from the source of the sound?

10. The speed of sound in water is 1498 m/s. A sonar signal is sent from a ship at a point just below the water surface and 1.80 s later the reflected signal is detected. How deep is the ocean beneath the ship?

► 11. The velocity of the transverse waves produced by an earthquake is 8.9 km/s, while that of the longitudinal waves is 5.1 km/s. A seismograph records the arrival of the transverse waves 73 s before that of the longitudinal waves. How far away was the earthquake?

► 12. The velocity of a wave on a string depends on how hard the string is stretched, and on the mass per unit length of the string. If T is the force exerted on the string, and μ is the mass/unit length, then the velocity, v, is

$$v = \sqrt{\frac{T}{\mu}}.$$

A piece of string 5.30 m long has a mass of 15.0 g. What must the force on the string be to make the wavelength of a 125 Hz wave 120.0 cm?

13. The time needed for a water wave to change from the equilibrium level to the crest is 0.18 s.
   a. What fraction of a wavelength is this?
   b. What is the period of the wave?
   c. What is the frequency of the wave?

14.2 Wave Interference

► 14. The wave speed in a guitar string is 265 m/s. The length of the string is 63 cm. You pluck the center of the string by pulling it up and letting go. Pulses move in both directions and are reflected off the ends of the string.
   a. How long does it take for the pulse to move to the string end and return to the center?
   b. When the pulses return, is the string above or below its resting location?
   c. If you plucked the string 15 cm from one end of the string, where would the two pulses meet?

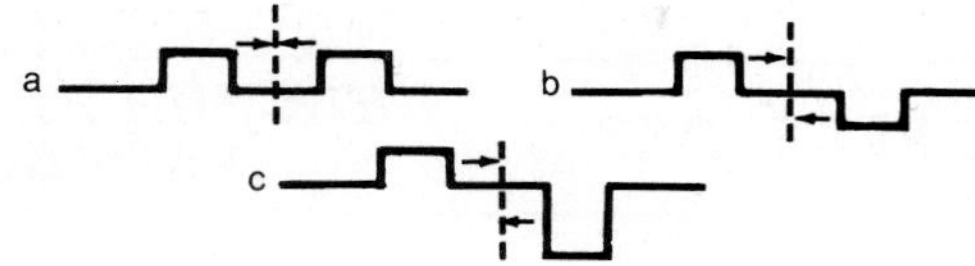

FIGURE 14-23. Use with Problem 15.

15. Sketch what happens, for each of the three cases shown in Figure 14–23, when centers of the two wave pulses lie on the dashed line so the pulses exactly overlap.

16. If you slosh the water back and forth in a bathtub at the correct frequency, the water rises first at one end and then at the other. Suppose you can make a standing wave in a 150-cm long tub with a frequency of 0.30 Hz. What is the velocity of the water wave?

USING LAB SKILLS

1. After doing the Pocket Lab on page 294, design an experiment using a stopwatch to show whether the amplitude of a wave pulse affects its speed.

THINKING PHYSIC-LY

1. Why can animals such as bats, that have tiny, light-weight ear parts, hear sounds with much higher frequencies than humans can hear?
2. If you put one ear under water in a bath tub, you can hear sounds from other parts of the house or apartment building where you live. Why is this true?

Answers To PROBLEMS

Complete Solutions for all Chapter Review Problems can be found in the Problems and Solutions Manual accompanying this text.

1. 10 s
2. 5.0 m/s
3. **a.** 29 cm/s
   b. 0.21 s
4. **a.** 2.4 m/s
   b. 2.9 m
5. 6.0×10^{-7} m
6. 4.2 m/s
7. **a.** 550 m, 190 m
   b. 3.4 m, 2.8 m
8. **a.** 1.50×10^3 m/s
   b. 1.00×10^{-6} s
   c. 1.00×10^{-6} s
9. **a.** 470 Hz
   b. 240 waves
   c. 170 m
10. 1350 m
11. 8.7×10^2 km
12. 63.7 N
13. **a.** 1/4
   b. 0.72 s
   c. 1.4 Hz
14. **a.** 2.4×10^{-3} s
   b. below
   c. 15 cm from the other end
15. **a.** amplitude doubled
   b. amplitudes cancel
   c. ½ of the second
16. 0.90 m/s

Answer To USING LAB SKILLS

1. Students can time the back and forth motion of a large and small amplitude wave pulse. They should find the times about the same.

Answers To THINKING PHYSIC-LY

1. The bat's small bones have less mass, therefore smaller inertia than human bones. The smaller bones can resonate with higher frequencies because they can change direction faster.
2. Sounds travel better through solids and liquids than through gases (air). Bathtubs and the accompanying plumbing are connected to the solid structure of the building; therefore, sounds from other parts of the building are transmitted more efficiently than through air.

CHAPTER 15 Sound

PLANNING GUIDE (5 class sessions)

CONTENTS	TEXT FEATURES	TEACHER RESOURCE PACKAGE	OTHER COMPONENTS
15.1 Properties of Sound, pp. 308–312 (3 Class Sessions) • Sound Waves • The Doppler Shift • Pitch and Loudness	**Physics Lab:** Speed of Sound, p. 313 **Pocket Lab:** Energy Transfer, p. 309 **Pocket Lab:** Sounds Like, p. 311 **Concept Review,** p. 312	**Study Guide:** Properties of Sound **Physics Lab Data Sheet:** Speed of Sound **Transparency Worksheet:** Decibel Scale	**Transparency 19:** Decibel Scale
15.2 The Sound of Music, pp. 314–324 (2 Class Sessions) • Sources of Sound • Resonance • Detection of Sound • The Quality of Sound	**Physics and Technology:** Synthetic Music, p. 323 **Pocket Lab:** Plunk, Plunk, p. 316 **Pocket Lab:** Sound Off, p. 321 **Concept Review,** p. 324	**Study Guide:** The Sound of Music **Critical Thinking Master:** Tuning a Guitar **Reteaching Master:** Making a Straw Oboe **Enrichment Master:** A Model of Sound Waves **Transparency Worksheet:** Standing Pressure Waves	**Laboratory Manual:** Lab 15.1 Intensity of Sound in Portable Tape Players Lab 15.2 Resonance in an Open Tube **Transparency 20:** Standing Pressure Waves
Chapter Review, pp. 324–327	Summary Key Terms Reviewing Concepts Applying Concepts Problems Using a Graphing Calculator Thinking Physic-ly	**Vocabulary Review** **Chapter Test**	**Test Bank**

SUPPLEMENTARY MATERIALS

SOFTWARE	AUDIOVISUAL	BOOKS/MAGAZINES
Introduction to General Physics, Disk IV: Waves and Sound, COMPress/Queue, Inc. (Apple II, IBM PC, Macintosh). *Sound,* J&S (Apple II). *Sound: A Microcomputer-Based Lab,* HRM (Apple II).	Videos: *The Music of Man, Volume IV: Sound or Unsound,* Home Vision. *The World of Sound Energy,* Focus Media (still frame).	Greenslade, Thomas B., Jr. "Harmonic Sliders." *The Physics Teacher,* November 1990, p. 568. Newburgh, R. G. "Lapping in Races as a Model for Beats." *The Physics Teacher,* November 1990, p. 557. Rossing, Thomas D. "Wine Glasses, Bell Modes, and Lord Rayleigh." *The Physics Teacher,* December 1990, p. 582. Zwicker, E. "Doing Physics, Pipe Music." *The Physics Teacher,* March 1987, pp. 172–174.

PROBLEM CORRELATION

CONCEPTS	CHAPTER REVIEW			PROBLEMS APPENDIX
	Reviewing Concepts	Applying Concepts	Problems	
15.1 Properties of Sound				
Sound Waves	1,2,3,4	1,2,3	1,2,3,4,5,**6**,7,8, 9,10	1,2,3,4,5,6,**7,8**
The Doppler Shift	5,6	4,5	11,12	**9,10**
Pitch and Loudness		6,7,8	13,14,15	11,12,14
15.2 The Sound of Music				
Sources of Sound				
Resonance	7,8,9,10	9	16,17,18	13
Detection of Sound			**19**	
The Quality of Sound	11	10,11	20,21,22,23,**24, 25,26**	15,16,17

ACTIVITY AND DEMONSTRATION MATERIALS

PHYSICS LAB	POCKET LAB	DEMONSTRATIONS
Page 313 tuning fork hollow glass tube 1000-ml graduated cylinder hot water ice water thermometer tuning fork hammer goggles	Pages 309, 311, 316, 321 10 dominoes ruler tape recorder car piano frequency generator meter stick musical instrument	Pages 309, 315, 316, 318, 320, 321 buzzer (sonalert) foam ball aluminum rod piano 2 tuning forks pith or Ping-Pong ball rubber mallet ring stand clamp clay 2 slide whistles

EXTENSION PROJECTS

LIBRARY RESEARCH

1. Noise Pollution
Research noise pollution. What effects does it have on people physically and psychologically? What are some ways it can be reduced?

HANDS-ON

2. Sounds in Solids
Using a ticking clock and a vibrating tuning fork, conduct an experiment to determine how sound travels through various solids. For example, press the clock against a piece of wood or a metal rod and listen. Which is a better carrier of sound? Does sound travel better through a solid or air? Make a chart of your results.

STUDENT READINGS

Dabrowski, Jan Paul. "Speed of Sound in a Parking Lot." *The Physics Teacher,* September 1990.

Fletcher, Neville. "The Physics of Organ Pipes." *Scientific American,* January 1983.

"Infants tune in to the sounds of music." *Science News,* July 21, 1990.

Kruglak, Haym, Hiltbrand, Robert, and Kangas, Don. "Shattering Glass with Sound Simplified." *The Physics Teacher,* September 1990.

McIntosh, Gordon C. "A Simple Resonance Demonstration." *The Physics Teacher,* Sept. 1990.

Suga, Nobuo. "Biosonar and Neural Computation in Bats." *Scientific American,* July 21,1990.

Chapter 15

Sound

CHAPTER OVERVIEW

Theme Development: The themes of scale and patterns of change are developed with a study of the nature of sound waves. Lessons include the range of sensitivity of the human ear, and the range over which the Doppler shift occurs. The cyclical behavior of sound, especially that of musical sounds, is central to the content.

MISCONCEPTIONS

It is difficult to grasp that our ears can detect the tiny pressure changes in sound waves. The logarithmic decibel scale is also confusing.

KEY TERMS

beat
closed-pipe resonator
consonance
decibel
dissonance
Doppler shift
fundamental
harmonics
loudness
octave
open-pipe resonator
pitch
sound level
standing wave
timbre

STUDENT EDITION

Physics Lab

Speed of Sound 313

Pocket Labs

Energy Transfer 309
Sounds Like 311
Plunk, Plunk 316
Sound Off 321

TEACHER EDITION

Activities

Demonstration 309, 315, 316, 316, 318, 320, 321
Cooperative Learning 319, 322

LABORATORY MANUAL

Resonance in an Open Tube Lab 15.1
Intensity of Sound in Portable Tape Players Lab 15.2

CHAPTER
15 Sound

Bat Music

How can a bat determine how far away this insect is? How can it tell whether it is getting closer to the insect?

Chapter Outline

Sound and music are important components of the human experience. Primitive people made sounds not only with their voices, but also with drums, rattles, and whistles. Stringed instruments are at least 3000 years old. Some animals use for survival sound with frequencies too high for humans to hear. Bats, in particular, hunt flying insects by emitting pulses of very high-frequency sound. They learn how far away the insect is, how large it is, where it is, and what its relative velocity is. Further, bats that hunt in forests must distinguish the insect from the vegetation. In addition, since bats live in large colonies, they must separate the echoes of their sounds from the sounds of hundreds of other bats. The methods they use are truly amazing, and are based on a few physical principles of sound.

Concept Check

The following terms or concepts from earlier chapters are important for a good understanding of this chapter. If you are not familiar with them, you should review them before studying this chapter.
- velocity, Chapter 3
- pressure, Chapter 13
- frequency, wavelength, amplitude, superposition, diffraction, interference, resonance, Chapter 14

Introducing The Chapter

Bat Music

Using The Photo: In the long course of Earth's evolution, diverse living creatures have exploited almost all aspects of sound for purposes of communication and survival. The navigational sounds emitted by bats are in the ultrasound region, above the range of normal human hearing. To answer the chapter opener question, students will find the information they need on page 310.

Concept Check

Make sure students have a clear understanding of the concepts taught in Chapters 13 and 14 that are listed in the Concept Check. Students familiar with the concepts of velocity, pressure, frequency, wavelength, amplitude, superposition, diffraction, interference, and resonance will be better equipped to understand the principles of sound introduced in this chapter.

Assessment

Portfolio

Collect solutions of problems and answers to questions that involve the concept of resonance.

Assessment Options

Portfolio Assessment
Extension Project 1, TWE, p. 306b,
Portfolio Assessment, TWE, p. 307
Enrichment, TWE, p. 311
Portfolio Assessment, TWE, p. 316
Thinking Physic-ly, p. 327

Performance Assessment
Extension Project 2, p. 306b
Pocket Labs, pp. 309, 311, 316, 321
Physics Lab, p. 313
Activity, TWE, p. 319

Content Assessment
Self Assessment: Practice Problems, pp. 309, 318, 321
Critical Thinking, TWE, p. 311
Assessment, Critical Thinking, TWE, p. 313
Concept Reviews, pp. 312, 324
Chapter Review, pp. 324–327
Supplemental Problems, p. 699

Group Assessment
Activities for group assessment occur with Cooperative Learning and lab activities.

15.1 PROPERTIES OF SOUND

Preparation

OBJECTIVES

The objectives are listed on the student page. Remind students to preview these objectives as a study guide to this major section.

OVERVIEW

The Doppler shift is the major new concept introduced in this section. Loudness, sound level, and intensity are among the concepts in this section that involve the mechanical energy in a sound wave.

BRIDGING

Previously introduced concepts of frequency, wavelength, velocity, amplitude, longitudinal wave, pressure, temperature, reflection, refraction, diffraction, and interference are developed further in this section.

1 Focus

DISCREPANT EVENT

To emphasize that a sound wave is produced by a mechanical vibration, strike a tuning fork and put the very tip in water. Water will splash out as a result of the tuning fork's movement. You could also show a vibrating string on a stringed instrument, which blurs visibly.

2 Teach

CONCEPT DEVELOPMENT

Study Guide Master. To reinforce the concepts in this section, have the students complete the Study Guide Master for Section 15.1 from the Teacher Resource Package.

• Have students compare the speed of sound with that of radio waves. In the time it takes light to travel around Earth, sound waves travel only about 44 m.

• Sound travels about four times faster in water than in air; about eleven times as fast in steel. Emphasize that elasticity, not density, affects its speed.

• Oceanographers study the behavior of sound waves in water to learn about Earth's oceans. The speed of sound in water depends on temperature, pressure (or depth), and salinity.

STUDY GUIDE MASTER

Use the Study Guide master for section 15.1.

Objectives

- demonstrate knowledge of the nature of sound waves and the properties sound shares with other waves.
- solve problems relating the frequency, wavelength, and velocity of sound.
- define the Doppler shift and identify some applications.
- relate physical properties of sound waves to perceived pitch and loudness; describe the meaning of the octave; use the decibel scale.

15.1 PROPERTIES OF SOUND

Sound is a longitudinal wave. A longitudinal wave consists of alternate areas of high pressure, compressions, and low pressure, rarefactions. It can be characterized by velocity, frequency, wavelength, and amplitude just as any other periodic wave. It shares with other waves the properties of reflection, refraction, and interference. Living things use sound to obtain information about the surroundings and to communicate with others by means of speech and music.

Sound Waves

Sound waves are longitudinal waves.

Sound is produced by the compression and rarefaction of matter. Sound waves move through air because a vibrating source produces regular variations in air pressure. The air molecules collide, transmitting the pressure oscillations away from the source of the sound. The pressure of the air varies or oscillates about an average value, the mean air pressure, Figure 15–1. The frequency of the wave is the number of oscillations in pressure each second. Sound is a longitudinal wave because the motion of the air molecules is parallel to the direction of motion of the wave.

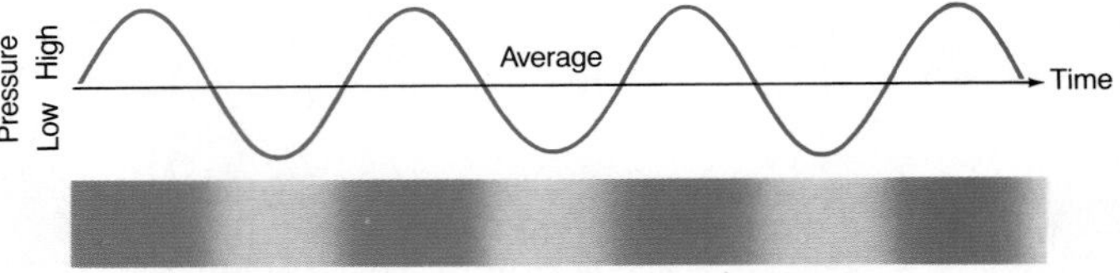

FIGURE 15–1. Graphic representation of the change in pressure over time in a sound wave. Dark areas indicate high pressure, light areas, low pressure.

The speed in air increases 0.6 m/s for each °C increase.

The velocity of the sound wave in air depends on the temperature of the air. Sound waves move through air at sea level at a velocity of 343 m/s at room temperature (20°C). Sound can also travel through liquids and solids. In general, the velocity of sound is greater in solids and liquids than in gases. Sound cannot travel through a vacuum because there are no particles to move and collide.

FIGURE 15–2. In an anechoic chamber, used for acoustical research, sound is almost completely absorbed by the soft materials covering all the surfaces.

Sound waves share the general properties of other waves. They can be reflected by hard objects, such as the walls of a room. Reflected sound waves are called echoes. The time required for an echo to return to the source of the sound can be used to find the distance between the source and reflector. This principle is used by bats, by some cameras, and by ships employing *sonar*. Sound waves can also be diffracted, spreading outward after passing through narrow openings. Two sound waves can interfere, causing "dead spots" at nodes where little sound can be heard.

The wavelength of a sound wave is the distance between adjacent regions of maximum pressure. The frequency and wavelength of a wave are related to the velocity of the wave by the equation

$$v = \lambda f.$$

Example Problem

Determining the Wavelength of Sound

A sound wave has a frequency of 261.6 Hz. What is the wavelength of this sound traveling in air at 343 m/s?

Given: frequency, $f = 261.6$ Hz; velocity, $v = 343$ m/s

Unknown: wavelength, λ

Basic equation: $v = \lambda f$

Solution: $v = \lambda f$, so $\lambda = v/f = \frac{(343 \text{ m/s})}{(261.6 \text{ Hz})} = 1.31$ m

POCKET LAB

ENERGY TRANSFER

Use dominoes to represent the molecules in a liquid. Set up 10 dominoes on the table so that they are 1.0 cm apart. Push on the end domino to start the chain reaction. The vibration moved through all of them. How far did each domino move? Use the domino model to demonstrate a pressure wave moving through a solid. How are the results similar? How are they different?

The speed of sound is higher in liquids and solids than it is in gases.

Practice Problems

1. Sound with a frequency of 261.6 Hz travels through water at a speed of 1435 m/s. Find its wavelength in water.
2. Find the frequency of a sound wave moving in air at room temperature with a wavelength of 0.667 m.
3. The human ear can detect sounds with frequencies between 20 Hz and 16 kHz. Find the largest and smallest wavelengths the ear can detect, assuming the sound travels through air with a speed of 343 m/s at 20°C.
4. ▶ What is the frequency of sound in air at 20°C having a wavelength equal to the diameter of a 15-in. (38 cm) "woofer" loudspeaker? of a 3.0-in. (7.6 cm) diameter "tweeter"?

Sound has properties of all other waves: reflection, refraction, interference, diffraction.

The Doppler Shift

Have you ever noticed the pitch of an ambulance, fire, or police siren as the vehicle sped past you? The frequency is higher when the vehicle is moving toward you, then suddenly drops to a lower pitch as the source moves away. This effect is called the **Doppler shift**, and is shown in Figure 15–3. The sound source is moving to the right with velocity v_s. The waves it emits spread in circles centered on the location of the source at the time it produced the wave. The frequency of the

When a sound source moves toward the observer, the detected frequency is higher.

POCKET LAB

ENERGY TRANSFER

Purpose: to investigate energy transfer by waves.
Materials: 10 dominoes; ruler.
Outcome: Each domino only moved a small distance, although the wave traveled the entire length. To simulate the spacing in a solid, students should have placed the dominoes closer together. This time the dominoes moved a smaller distance. Because the time between collisions was shorter, the speed of the wave was greater.

Answers To
PRACTICE PROBLEMS

Have students refer to Appendix A of the Solutions Appendix for complete solutions to Practice Problems.

1. 5.485 m
2. 514 Hz
3. largest, 17 m
   smallest, 0.021 m
4. woofer, 0.90 kHz
   tweeter, 4.5 kHz

CONCEPT DEVELOPMENT

There are various small, lightweight buzzers (one type is called the Sonalert) that operate on 1.5-V DC current available from electronic stores. They are ideal for showing the Doppler shift, as in the following demonstration.

ACTIVITY

Demonstration: Install a buzzer in a foam ball. Start the buzzer and ask your students to predict what they will hear when the ball is thrown back and forth. Have two students throw the ball back and forth. Students should observe a sudden change in pitch when the ball changes direction. The pitch drops sharply to a lower pitch when it goes away from them. Explain to students that this is an example of the Doppler shift.

TEACHER F.Y.I.

The ratio of the speed of a fast-moving object to the speed of sound is sometimes expressed as a Mach number:

$$\frac{v_{object}}{v_{sound}} = \text{Mach number}.$$

When $v_{obj} > v_{sound}$ (supersonic speeds), a conical wave front called a shock wave is produced. The energy of the shock wave is concentrated at the surface of the cone and is the cause of a jet plane's "sonic boom." Because this type of shock wave can cause damage to buildings, aircraft are not permitted to fly at supersonic speeds at low altitudes. The crack of a whip is a sonic boom on a very small scale because the tip moves faster than the speed of sound. Paul Langevin invented sonar in 1915. It was used initially on ships to detect icebergs. Oceanography became a science only after sonar was used in World War II.

CONCEPT DEVELOPMENT

- Emphasize that the Doppler shift can be used to measure velocity over a very wide range of scale—from atoms, to autos, to galaxies.
- If you have a loudspeaker and signal generator available, hook the speaker up to the signal generator and slowly modulate the frequency range of the generator. You might make it into a mini-hearing test by asking students if they can hear the higher frequencies (around 10 000 Hz). If an oscilloscope is available, hook that up to the signal generator so students can see how the waves change as the sound frequency changes. (Point out that the oscilloscope shows sound waves as transverse waves although they are actually longitudinal.)

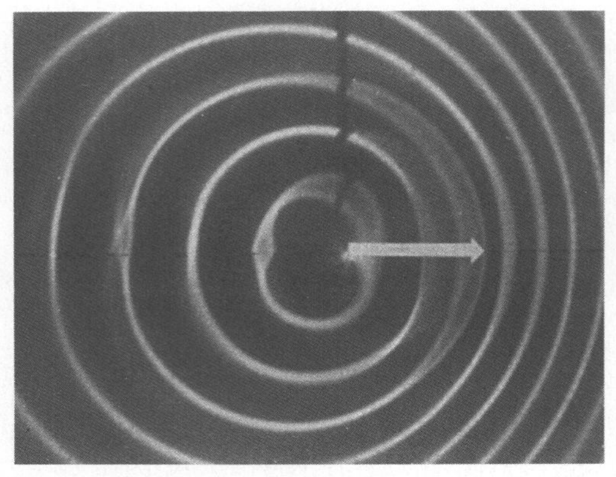

a b

FIGURE 15–3. A point source moving across a ripple tank (a) can be used to show the Doppler shift (b).

sound source does not change, but when the source is moving toward the sound detector, O_1 on Figure 15–3b, more waves are crowded into the space between them. The wavelength is shortened to λ_1. Because the velocity is not changed, the frequency of the detected sound is greater.

When the source is moving away from the detector, O_2 on Figure 15–3b, the wavelength is lengthened to λ_2 and the detected frequency is lower. A Doppler shift also occurs if the detector is moving and the source is stationary.

The Doppler shift occurs in all waves.

The Doppler shift occurs in all wave motion, both mechanical and electromagnetic. It has many applications. Radar detectors use the Doppler shift to measure the speed of baseballs and automobiles. Astronomers use the Doppler shift of light from distant galaxies to measure their speed and infer their distance. Physicians can detect the velocity of the moving heart wall in a fetus by means of the Doppler shift in ultrasound. A bat uses the Doppler shift to detect and catch flying insects. When an insect is flying faster than the bat, the reflected frequency is lower, but when the bat is catching up to the insect, the reflected frequency is higher.

Bat Music ▶

Pitch and Loudness

The physical characteristics of sound waves are measured by frequency, wavelength, and amplitude. In humans, sound is detected by the ear and interpreted by the brain. Sound characteristics are defined in terms describing what we perceive. **Pitch** is essentially the frequency of the wave. **Loudness** depends on the amplitude of the pressure variation wave.

Marin Mersenne (1588–1648) and Robert Hooke (1635–1703) first connected pitch with the frequency of vibration. Pitch can also be given the name of a note on a musical scale. Musical scales are based on the work of Pythagoras, a Greek mathematician who lived in the sixth century B.C. He noted that when two strings had lengths in the ratio of small whole numbers, for example 2:1, 3:2, or 4:3, pleasing sounds resulted

F.Y.I.

The thermal energy equivalent of the sound emitted over a 90 minute period by a crowd of 50 000 at a football game is only enough to heat one cup of coffee.

TEACHER 

Christian Johann Doppler (1803–1853) did experiments in 1842 with trumpeters sounding a single note as they sat on a flat car pulled back and forth by a locomotive. When the source of sound is moving and the observer is stationary, the equation for the apparent (perceived) frequency is

$$f' = \frac{f}{1 \pm \frac{v}{v_w}}$$

where v is the velocity of the source, v_w is the velocity of the sound, and f is the stationary frequency of the sound. Use the (−) if the motion of the source of the sound is toward the observer and the (+) if the source is moving away.

If the observer is moving, then

$$f' = f\left(1 \pm \frac{v}{v_w}\right).$$

Use the (+) when the observer is moving toward the source.

when the strings were plucked together. Two notes with frequencies related by the ratio 2:1 are said to differ by an **octave.** For example, if a note has a frequency of 440 Hz, a note an octave higher has a frequency of 880 Hz. A note one octave lower has a frequency of 220 Hz. It is important to recognize that it is the ratio of two frequencies, not the size of the interval between them, that determines the musical interval.

In other common musical intervals, the frequencies have ratios of small whole numbers. For example, the notes in an interval called a "major third" have a ratio of frequencies of 5:4. A typical major third is the notes C and E. The note C has a frequency of 262 Hz, so E has a frequency (5/4)(262 Hz) = 327 Hz. In the same way, notes in a "fourth" (C and F) have a frequency ratio of 4:3 and those in a "fifth" (C and G) have a ratio of 3:2.

The human ear is extremely sensitive to the variations in air pressure in sound. It can detect wave amplitudes of less than one billionth of an atmosphere (or 2×10^{-5} N/m^2). At the other end of the audible range, the pressure variations that cause pain are one million times greater, (20 N/m^2). Notice that this is still less than one one-thousandths of an atmosphere.

Because of this wide range in pressure variation, sound pressures are measured by a quantity called sound level. **Sound level** is measured in **decibels** (dB). The level depends on the ratio of the pressure of a given sound wave to the pressure in the most faintly heard sound, 2×10^{-5} N/m^2. Such an amplitude has a sound level of zero decibels (0 dB). A sound with 10 times larger pressure amplitude (2×10^{-4} N/m^2) is 20 dB. A pressure amplitude 10 times larger than this is 40 dB. Figure 15–5 shows the sound level in decibels for a variety of sounds.

Loudness, as perceived by the human ear, is not directly proportional to the pressure variations in a sound wave. Further, the ear's sensitivity depends on both sound frequency and sound level. Perception is also different for pure tones than it is for mixtures of tones. Most people find that a 10-dB increase in sound level is heard as being about twice as loud.

POCKET LAB

SOUNDS LIKE

This is a home lab. Use a tape recorder to make a 5.0 s recording of your car horn. Leave 5 to 10 s of blank tape between each trial. Let someone stand at the curb and make a recording of the car horn as you drive by at a steady speed while sounding the horn. Repeat horn sounding and recording as you drive by at a different speed. Listen to the recordings and describe how the loudness changes and when pitch changes.

A note one octave above another has twice the frequency.

The ear can detect very tiny pressure variations.

FIGURE 15–4. The loudness heard at a concert depends on the sensitivity of our ears to sound in different frequency ranges.

POCKET LAB

SOUNDS LIKE

Purpose: to investigate the Doppler shift of sound waves.

Materials: tape recorder; car.

Outcome: The tape recordings will clearly show that the moving horn has pitches that vary distinctly. Compared to a stationary horn, a higher pitch is heard when the car is moving toward the recorder. A lower pitch is heard when the car is moving away. A faster-moving car will cause more shift in the frequency. Emphasize that the Doppler shift varies with speed, not with distance.

CONCEPT DEVELOPMENT

Critical Thinking: Ask students to sketch a representation of a 500-Hz sound in the manner of the top drawing in Figure 15–1. Label the *x*-axis in milliseconds. Using a different color, sketch a sound that is louder but has the same pitch. [The period of the wave is 2 ms, and the louder sound has a larger amplitude but the same period.]

Enrichment: Weather reports sometimes refer to data from Doppler radar. Suggest that interested students find out how such data is collected and how it depends on the Doppler shift.

Guided Practice: Have students work on the first Concept Review problem on page 312, then go over answers as a group.

Independent Practice: Assign the remaining Concept Review problems on page 312 for homework and discuss them during the next class period.

TEACHER F.Y.I.

One atmosphere of pressure (air pressure) = 1.01×10^5 N/m^2.

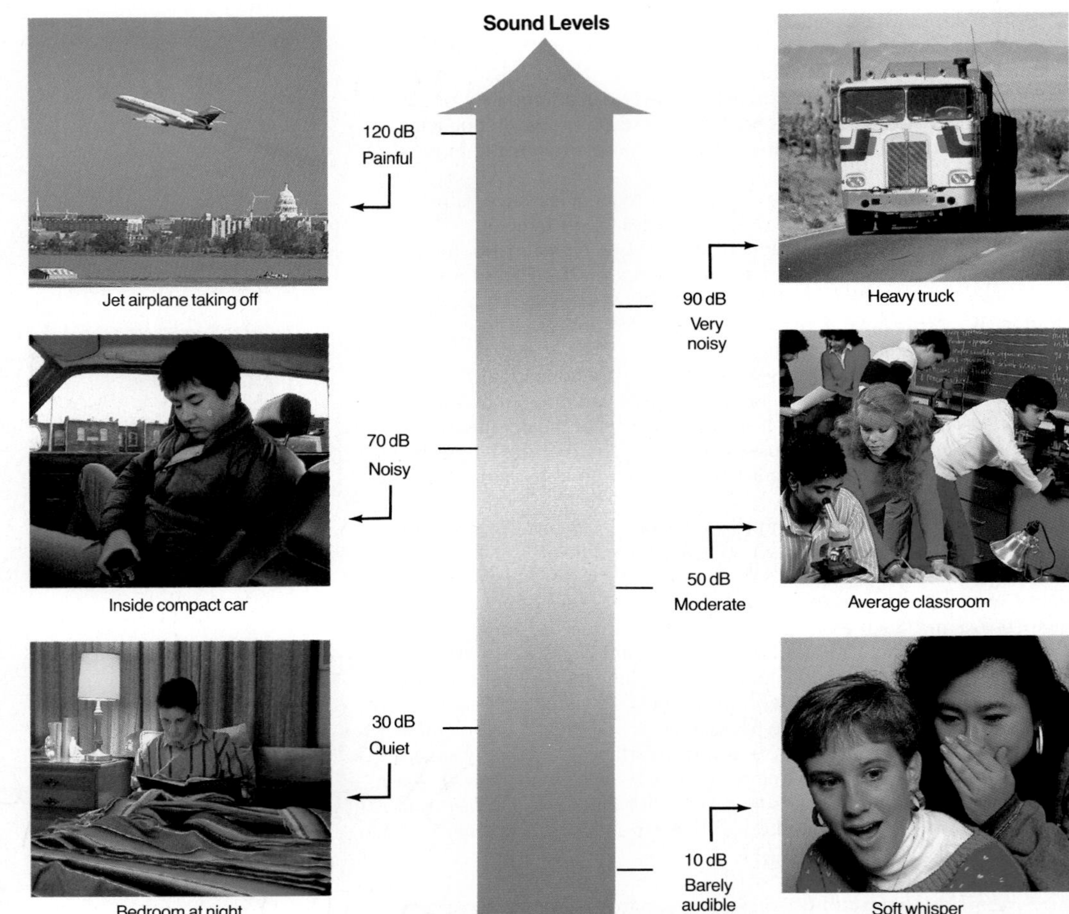

FIGURE 15–5. Decibel scale showing the sound level of some familiar sounds.

CONCEPT REVIEW

1.1 The eardrum moves back and forth in response to the pressure variations of a sound wave. Sketch the displacement of the eardrum versus time for a 1-kHz tone and for a 2-kHz tone.

1.2 If you hear a train whistle pitch drop as the train passes you, can you tell from which direction the train was coming?

1.3 What physical characteristic of a wave would you change to increase the loudness of a sound? to change the pitch?

1.4 **Critical Thinking:** To a person who is hard of hearing, normal conversation sounds like a soft whisper. What increase in sound levels (in dB) must a hearing aid provide? How many times must the sound wave pressure be increased? (Use Figure 15–5.)

CHECKING FOR UNDERSTANDING

Ask students to list ways in which we rely on sound in our daily lives. Try to get them to use their imaginations to think of some of the less obvious examples.

RETEACHING

Ask students for examples of the Doppler shift that they've experienced. Be careful that they do not confuse changes in loudness relating to distance with changes in apparent pitch that are due to the Doppler shift. Help students with explanations of their examples.

Transparency Package. Use Transparency 19 to go over sound levels. Stress that this is not a linear scale, that is, 80 dB is not twice as loud as 40 dB.

INDEPENDENT PRACTICE/ EXTENSION

Refer to the Assignment Guide below for additional questions and problems for independent practice.

3 Close

CONVERGENT QUESTION

Ask students why we explain the Doppler shift in terms of frequency (pitch) changes rather than wavelength changes. [Because frequency changes are much easier to observe.]

CONCEPT REVIEW ANSWERS

1.1

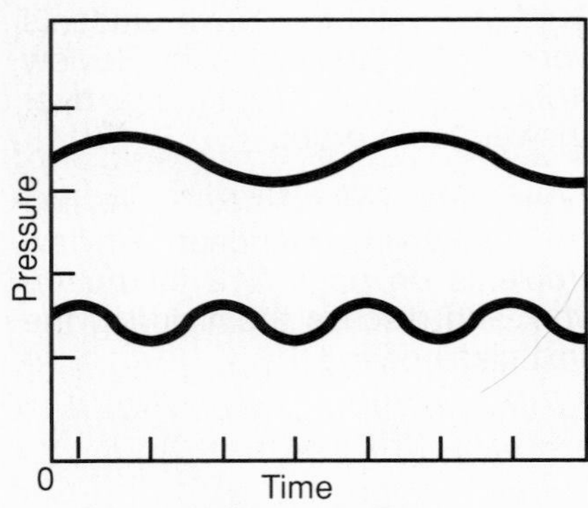

1.2 No. The Doppler shift depends only on whether or not source and receiver are approaching or separating, not on direction.

1.3 Increase the amplitude to increase the loudness; increase the frequency to increase the pitch.

1.4 Critical Thinking: The sound level must increase from 10 dB to 60 dB, or 50 dB. The pressure must increase from 6×10^{-5} N/m^2 to 0.02 N/m^2, a factor of about 300.

TRANSPARENCY

Use Transparency 19 with this section.

15:1 ASSIGNMENT GUIDE

	PRACTICE	EXTENSION
CHAPTER REVIEW pp. 224–227		
· Reviewing Concepts	1–6	
· Applying Concepts		1–8
· Problems*	1–5, 7–15	6
APPENDIX B PROBLEMS*		
· Chapter 15, p. 699	1–6, 11, 12, 14	7–10

* Complete solutions to all Chapter Review and Appendix problems appear in the Problems and Solutions Manual.

PHYSICS LAB: Speed of Sound

Purpose

To measure the speed of sound.

Materials

- tuning fork
- hollow glass tube
- 1000-ml graduated cylinder
- hot water
- ice water
- thermometer
- tuning fork hammer
- goggles

Procedure

1. Place cylinders with hot water on one side of the classroom and ice water on the other side of the classroom.
2. Record the value of the frequency that is stamped on the tuning fork.
3. Wear goggles while using tuning forks next to the glass tubes. Strike the tuning fork with the rubber hammer.
4. Hold the tuning fork above the glass tube while you slowly raise the tube until the sound is amplified, and is loudest by the tube.
5. Measure l, the distance from the water to the top of the tube, to the nearest 0.01 m.
6. Repeat steps 3-5 with the same fork but struck so that the tuning fork sound is quiet.
7. Hold a thermometer in the middle of the glass tube and measure the air temperature.
8. Trade places with another group on the other side of the room and repeat steps 3-7 using the same tuning fork.

Observations and Data

1. Set up a data table like the one below:
   Ice Water $f =$ __ Hz; Temperature = __ °C
   Loud Sound: $l =$ __ m; $\lambda =$ __ m
   $v =$ __ m/s
   Quiet Sound: $l =$ __ m; $\lambda =$ __ m
   $v =$ __ m/s

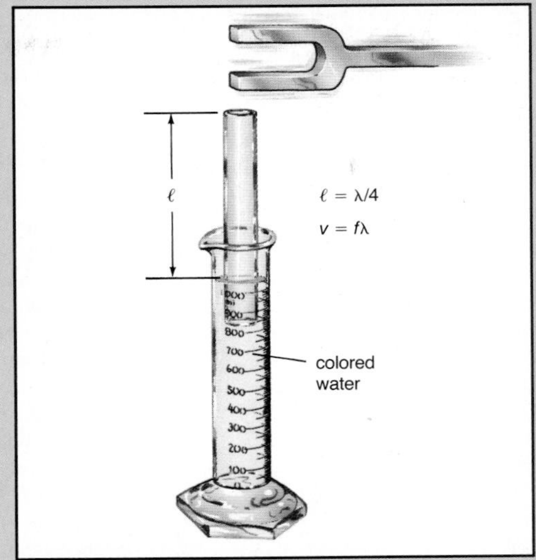

   Hot Water $f =$ __ Hz; Temperature = __ °C
   Loud Sound: $l =$ __ m; $\lambda =$ __ m
   $v =$ __ m/s
   Quiet Sound: $l =$ __ m; $\lambda =$ __ m
   $v =$ __ m/s
2. Were the values of "l" different for loud and soft sounds?
3. Were the values of "l" different for cold and hot air?

Analysis

1. Calculate the values for λ and v.
2. Write a general statement describing how the speed of sound depends on loudness.
3. Does the speed seem to depend on the air temperature?

Applications

1. What would an orchestra sound like if the higher frequencies traveled faster than the lower frequencies?

ASSESSMENT

Critical Thinking: To further assess students' understanding of the speed of sound, ask the following questions.

1. The speed of sound through a medium depends on the physical properties of the medium. Would you expect sound to travel faster through a sample of hydrogen gas or oxygen gas at equal temperatures and pressures? Hydrogen molecules are lighter than oxygen molecules. [The less massive hydrogen atoms will be moving faster than the oxygen atoms so it will take less time between collisions. Since the vibration depends on the interaction between the molecules, sound will travel much faster in the hydrogen.]

2. Why was coloring added to the water? What effect did it have on the results? [The coloring was used to make it easier to see the surface of the water; it did not affect the speed of the sound waves.]

PHYSICS LAB

Process Skills: using numbers, observing, communicating, measuring, hypothesizing, questioning, controlling variables.

MISCONCEPTION:

Many students believe that sound slows down as it decreases in amplitude.

Teaching Suggestions: **1.** Remind students to be careful when handling the cylinder of hot water.
2. Put a few drops of red food coloring in the hot water.
3. Put a few drops of blue food coloring in the cold water.
4. The diameter of the tube affects the resonance in the tube. Correcting for the diameter, wavelength $= 4(l + 0.4d)$.

Lab Worksheet, Teacher Resource Package. If desired, use the lab worksheet master for this chapter for students to record their data.

OBSERVATIONS

1. student data table
2. The value of l is the same for loud and quiet sounds. Wavelength varies with the frequency of the tuning fork.
3. The value is slightly different when the air is at a different temperature.

ANALYSIS

1. The velocity should be in the range of 320 m/s to 340 m/s.
2. Loud and quiet sounds (at the same frequency) traveled at the same speed. The speed of sound is independent of amplitude.
3. Sound seems to travel slightly faster in hot air. The speed of sound increases 0.6 m/s/°C where $v = 331.45$ m/s at 0°C.

APPLICATIONS

A person in the back of the auditorium would hear the high notes before the low notes.

LAB WORKSHEET

Use the Lab Worksheet for Chapter 15 with this Physics Lab.

15.2 THE SOUND OF MUSIC

Preparation

OBJECTIVES

The objectives are listed on the student page. Remind students to preview these objectives as a study guide to this major section.

OVERVIEW

Several terms that describe characteristics of musical sounds are introduced: *pitch, timbre, beats, consonance, dissonance, fundamental, harmonics,* and *resonance.*

BRIDGING

The concepts of frequency, reflection, nodes, antinodes, wavelength, energy, and amplitude as they relate specifically to sound are developed further in this section.

1 Focus

DISCREPANT EVENT

Duplicate Edison's phonograph. Make a paper cone about the size of a small megaphone. Put a regular straight pin in the small end of the cone perpendicular to the axis of the cone. Using a record you don't mind abusing, support the cone as lightly as possible and put the point of the pin into the groove of the spinning record. You should be able to hear the recorded sounds. Adjust the design to make it play more loudly. For example, a dissecting pin may provide a better sound than the straight pin.

Objectives

- **describe the origin of sound in general and in various musical instruments in particular.**
- **show an understanding of resonance, especially applied to an air column; describe or sketch a standing wave; solve problems involving standing waves in resonating air columns.**
- **identify the parts of the ear and the function of each in detecting sound.**
- **define timbre; recognize the origin of and solve problems involving beats; define harmonics and their origins.**

15.2 THE SOUND OF MUSIC

In the middle of the nineteenth century, a German physicist and an English physicist, Hermann Helmholtz and Lord Rayleigh, studied how the human voice as well as musical instruments produce sounds, and how the human ear detects these sounds. In the twentieth century, scientists and engineers have developed electronics that permit not only detailed study of sound, but the creation of electronic musical instruments and recording devices that allow us to have music whenever and wherever we wish.

Sources of Sound

Sound is produced by vibrating objects.

Sound is produced by a vibrating object. The vibrations of the object create molecular motions and pressure oscillations in the air. A loudspeaker has a diaphragm, or cone, that is made to vibrate by electrical currents. The cone creates the sound waves. Musical instruments such as gongs or cymbals and the surface of a drum are other examples of vibrating sources of sound.

Vibrating vocal cords produce the human voice.

The human voice is the result of vibrations of the vocal cords, two membranes located in the throat. Air from the lungs rushing through the throat starts the vocal cords vibrating. The frequency of vibration is controlled by the muscular tension placed on the cords.

In brass instruments, such as the trumpet, trombone, and tuba, the lips of the performer vibrate, Figure 15–6a. Reed instruments, like the clarinet, saxophone, and oboe, have a thin wooden strip, or reed, that vibrates as a result of air blown across it, Figure 15–6b. In a flute, recorder, organ pipe, or whistle, air is blown across an opening in a pipe. Air moving past the mouthpiece edge sets the column of air in the instrument into vibration.

In stringed instruments, such as the piano, guitar, and violin, a wire or string is set into vibration. In the piano, the wire is struck; in the guitar, it is plucked. In the violin, the friction of the bow pulls the string

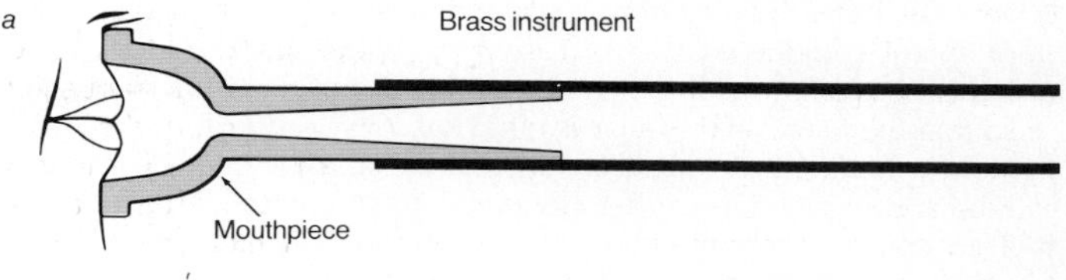

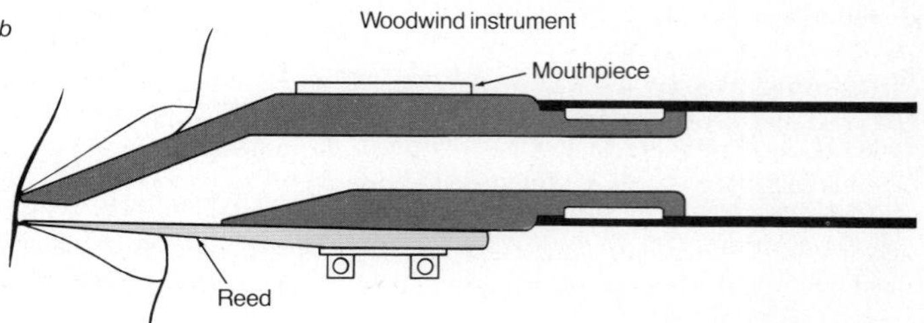

FIGURE 15–6. The shapes of the mouthpieces of a brass instrument (a) and a reed instrument (b) help determine the characteristics of the sound each instrument produces.

STUDY GUIDE MASTER

Use the Study Guide master for section 15.2.

FIGURE 15–7. In all the instruments illustrated, changes in pitch are brought about by changing the length of the resonating column of air.

aside. The string is attached to a sounding board that vibrates with the string. The vibrations of the sounding board cause the pressure oscillations in the air that we hear as sound. Electric guitars use electronic devices to detect and amplify the vibrations of the strings.

Vibrating air columns determine the sound produced by wind instruments.

Resonance

If you have ever used just the mouthpiece of a brass or reed instrument, you know that the vibration of your lips or the reed alone does not make a sound with any particular pitch. The long tube that makes up the instrument must be attached if music is to result. When the instrument is played, the air within this tube vibrates at the same frequency, or in resonance, with a particular vibration of the lips or reed. Remember that resonance increases the amplitude of a vibration by repeatedly applying a small external force at the same natural frequency. The pitch of an instrument is varied by changing the length of the resonating column of vibrating air. The length of the air column determines the resonant frequencies of the vibrating air. The mouthpiece creates a mixture of different frequencies. The resonating air column acting on the vibrating lips or reed amplifies a single note.

A tuning fork above a hollow tube, Figure 15–8, can provide resonance in an air column. The tube is placed in water so that the bottom end of the tube is below the water surface. A resonating tube with one end closed is called a **closed-pipe resonator.** The length of the air column is adjusted by changing the height of the tube above the water. The tuning fork is struck with a rubber hammer. When the length of the air column is varied, the sound heard will alternately become louder and softer. The sound is loud when the air column is in resonance with the tuning fork. The air column has intensified the sound of the tuning fork.

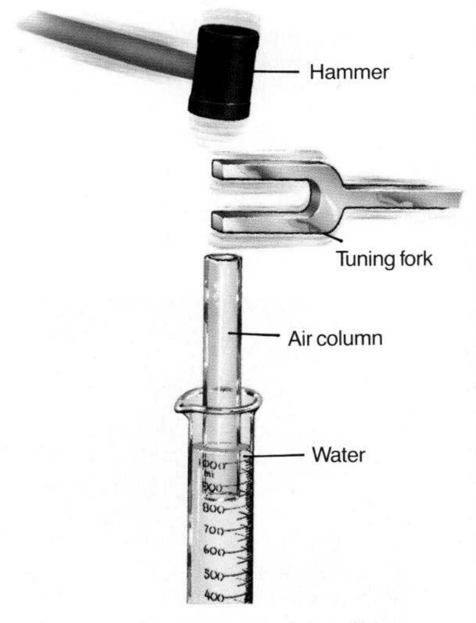

FIGURE 15–8. Resonance of an air column.

2 Teach

CONCEPT DEVELOPMENT

Study Guide Master. To reinforce the concepts in this section, have the students complete the Study Guide Master for Section 15.2 from the Teacher Resource Package.

• Encourage students who like popular music to help you illustrate sound and its properties. For example, class musicians (or technicians) may be able to explain the gadgets used to make today's variety of musical effects.

• Consider taking the class to the band hall for a demonstration of percussion equipment. Allow students to examine the tubes (open and closed) of the chimes, xylophone, and vibraphone. Have students examine the various kinds of drums and determine how pitch is adjusted. Other instruments to examine are the cymbals, blocks, slide whistle, and gong.

• Show a graphic representation of sound waves by connecting a microphone to an oscilloscope. Depending on the type of microphone, you may need to amplify its output before it goes into the oscilloscope. Remember to point out that the transverse waves on the screen actually represent longitudinal waves.

Critical Thinking: Students who have played a wind instrument alone in the band hall or orchestra room may have noticed that the snares (metal chain-like attachments on a snare drum) begin to hum when a particular note is played. Ask students if they can explain why this happens. [When a tone is the natural frequency of the drumhead, the snares vibrate in resonance.]

ACTIVITY

Demonstration: Here's an excellent resonance demonstration: Obtain an aluminum rod, 10–25 mm in diameter and anywhere from 50–200 cm in length. Aluminum rods from ring stands work well. Holding the rod by the middle (node), stroke it with your thumb and index finger until it starts to vibrate. You will probably need to use some rosin or golfer's Firmgrip on your fingers. Don't grip the rod too tightly. Adjust your grip until the rod starts to resonate loudly. Many more demonstrations and tricks are possible with the "singing" rods. Refer to a book on demonstrations for further suggestions.

CONCEPT DEVELOPMENT

Demonstration: Moisten your finger and rub it around the top of the rim of a wine glass until the glass starts to hum. You are making the glass vibrate at its resonant frequency.

Demonstration: Hold the sustaining pedal of a piano down to lift the damper off the strings, then whistle near the strings. Stop whistling and listen. You will hear a ghostly rendition of the whistle as the piano strings that have the same frequencies as the whistle begin to resonate.

POCKET LAB

PLUNK, PLUNK

Purpose: to compare the pitches of different strings on a piano.
Materials: piano; tape recorder; frequency generator.
Outcome: the lower-pitched notes will have strings that are longer, less taut, and wrapped to slow them down.

Assessment

Portfolio

Resonance occurs frequently in everyday life. For example, a plate on the wall may rattle when the stereo plays a certain musical note, or the car radio antenna may vibrate strongly when the car travels on a rough road at a certain speed. Have students identify one or more examples of resonance. They should describe it carefully, noting the object that is moving and the vibration or oscillation that causes it and explain what changes the frequency of the vibration. For example, in the case of the radio antenna, the faster the car moves, the higher the frequency of the vibration.

FIGURE 15–9. Reflections of pressure waves in pipes.

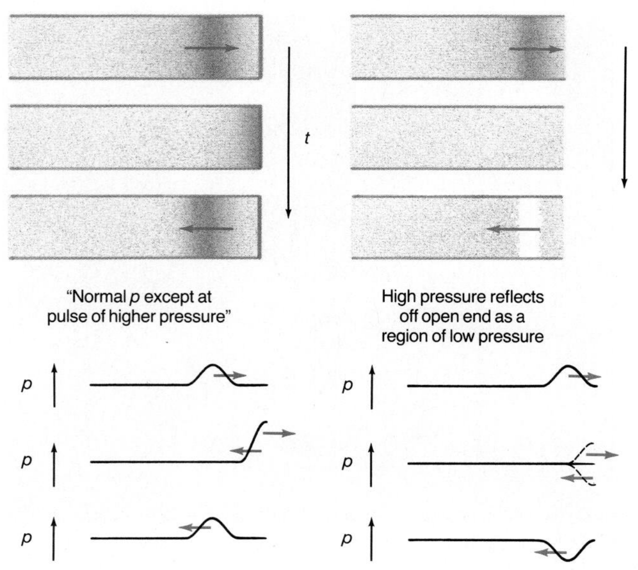

The vibrating tuning fork produces alternate high and low pressure variations. This sound wave moves down the air column. When the wave hits the water surface, it is reflected back up to the tuning fork, Figure 15–9. If the high pressure reflected wave reaches the tuning fork when the fork has produced high pressure, then the leaving and returning waves reinforce each other. A **standing wave** is produced.

A closed pipe resonates when its length is an odd number of quarter wavelengths.

A standing wave has pressure nodes and antinodes, Figure 15–10. At the nodes, the pressure is the mean atmospheric pressure. At the antinodes, the pressure is at its maximum or minimum value. Two antinodes (or two nodes) are separated by one-half wavelength. A pressure wave is reflected from a hard surface without inversion, like a rope wave is reflected from an open end. Thus, there is a pressure antinode at the water surface. A pressure wave is reflected inverted from the open end. That is, if a region of high pressure reaches the open end, a region of low pressure will be reflected. This is similar to the reflection of a rope wave off a fixed end. Thus, the open end of the pipe has a pressure node.

The shortest column of air that can have an antinode at the bottom and a node at the top is one-fourth wavelength long. As the air column is lengthened, additional resonances are found. Thus columns $\lambda/4$, $3\lambda/4$, $5\lambda/4$, $7\lambda/4$, and so on, will all be in resonance with the tuning fork.

In practice, the first resonance length is slightly longer than one-fourth wavelength. This is because the pressure variations do not drop to zero exactly at the end of the pipe. Actually, the node is approximately 1.2 pipe diameters beyond the end. Each additional resonance length, how-

POCKET LAB

PLUNK, PLUNK

Take a walk down to the music room. Look closely at the grand piano. Describe the differences in the strings. Gently push on the different strings. Do the strings seem to have the same tightness?

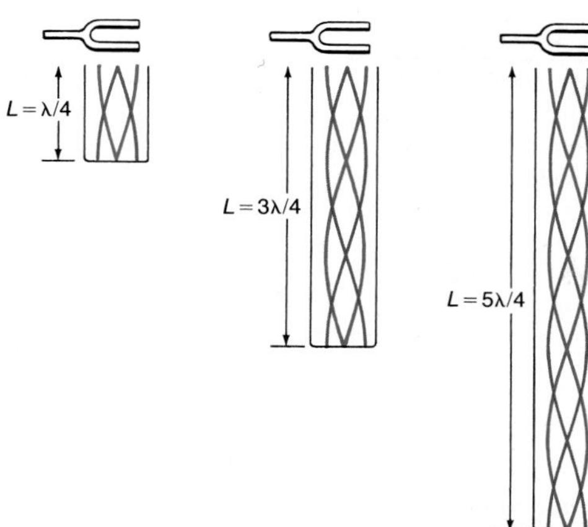

FIGURE 15–10. Standing waves in closed pipes. Purple lines show pressure variations; green lines show displacement of air molecules. Pressure antinodes are at the same locations as displacement nodes. Three pipe lengths that have resonances at the same frequency are shown.

ever, is spaced by exactly one-half wavelength. Measurement of the spacings between resonances can be used to find the velocity of sound in air.

Have you ever put your ear to a large seashell and heard a low frequency sound? The shell acts like a closed-pipe resonator. The source of the sound is the soft background noise that occurs almost everywhere. This sound contains almost all frequencies the ear can hear. The shell increases the intensity of sounds with frequency equal to the resonant frequency of the shell. The result is the almost pure tone you hear.

The small size of the vibrating string of a guitar or other stringed instrument cannot cause much vibration in the air. The instrument uses resonance to increase the sound wave amplitude. Vibration of the string causes the sounding box to vibrate. The large size of the box produces a sound of greater intensity in the air around it.

BIOLOGY CONNECTION

The human auditory canal acts as a closed-pipe resonator that increases the ear's sensitivity for frequencies between 2000 and 5000 Hz. In the middle ear, the three bones, or ossicles, act as a lever, a simple machine with a mechanical advantage of 1.5. By a feedback mechanism, the bones also help to protect the inner ear from loud sounds. Muscles, triggered by a loud noise, pull the third bone away from the oval window. The pressure variations of sound are also increased by Pascal's principle.

Example Problem

Measuring Sound Velocity

A tuning fork with a frequency of 392 Hz is found to cause resonances in an air column at 21.0 cm and 65.3 cm. The air temperature is 27°C. Find the velocity of sound in air at that temperature.

Given: $f = 392$ Hz, $l_2 = 65.3$ cm, $l_1 = 21.0$ cm

Unknown: v

Basic equation: $v = \lambda f$

Solution: Spacing of resonances, $\Delta l = l_2 - l_1 = (65.3 - 21.0)$ cm $= 44.3$ cm.

Thus, $\frac{1}{2}\lambda = \Delta l$, or $\lambda = 2\Delta l = 2(44.3 \text{ cm}) = 88.6$ cm.

Now, $v = \lambda f = (0.886 \text{ m})(392 \text{ Hz}) = 347$ m/s.

Guided Practice: After reviewing the Example Problem on this page, have students try the first two Practice Problems on page 318 in class.

Independent Practice: Assign the remaining Practice Problems on page 318 for homework. Spend time discussing them during the following class period.

CONCEPT DEVELOPMENT

- Pieces of plastic water pipe and golf club tubes can both be used to demonstrate closed and open pipes. A string vibrator will demonstrate nodes and antinodes nicely.
- Figures 15–10 and 15–11 show how both pressure and molecular displacement vary in a resonant pipe. Students may find it helpful to make the connection between the transverse displacement of a wave in a rope and the longitudinal displacement of the air molecules in a sound wave. Both have a node at the closed end of a pipe and an antinode at the source of the vibration. These figures show how a source with a single frequency and wavelength can resonate with several lengths of pipe. The timbre, or quality of the sound (pages 320–323) depends on the fact that a pipe of a single length can resonate with sources of several different frequencies. A closed pipe resonates with $f_0 = v/4l$ and $3f_{0'}$, $5f_{0'}$, $7f_{0'}$, and so forth, while an open pipe resonates with the frequencies $2f_{0'}$, $4f_{0'}$, $6f_{0'}$, and so forth. A tuning fork vibrates at only one frequency. If a source is used that produces many frequencies, like a woodwind reed or a brass mouthpiece, then the pipe will resonate with many frequencies at once, giving the sound richness and "color." The sound of closed pipes contains the odd harmonics. The sound of open pipes have the even harmonics. Thus, their timbres will be different.

Critical Thinking: As temperature increases, woodwinds tend to go "sharp" (the frequency increases), but a stringed instrument goes "flat." Ask students if they can explain why. [As the strings warm up, they get a bit longer, producing a lower frequency. As the air temperature increases for a woodwind, the velocity of sound increases. Since the length of the tube, which determines the wavelength, does not change, the frequency increases.]

Answers To
PRACTICE PROBLEMS

Have students refer to Appendix A of the Solutions Appendix for complete solutions to Practice Problems.

5. 0.390 m
6. 968 m/s
7. 443 Hz
8. 2.9 kHz

Transparency Package. Use Transparency 20 to illustrate standing pressure waves.

Laboratory Manual. Give students additional experience with resonance by doing Lab 15.1 from the Laboratory Manual.

Answers To
PRACTICE PROBLEMS

Have students refer to Appendix A of the Solutions Appendix for complete solutions to Practice Problems.

9. a. 64.7 Hz
b. 129 Hz
194 Hz
10. 260 Hz

Multicultural Connections

The Chinese used pottery jars to detect the sounds of an advancing enemy. Leather membranes were stretched over the mouths of empty, 80-liter pottery jars. The jars were lowered into deep shafts that were dug a few paces apart around the city, and men with good hearing were stationed near these shafts. Not only could they hear the sounds of an approaching army, but by listening to the different sounds from the shafts, the watchmen could judge from what direction the enemy was coming and how far away they were.

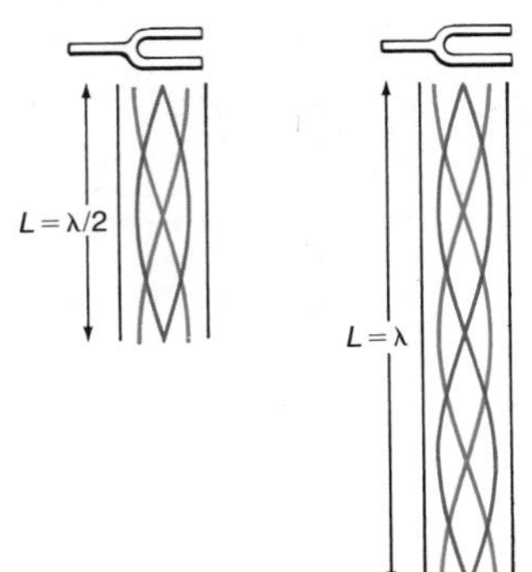

FIGURE 15–11. Standing waves in open pipes. Purple lines show pressure variations; green lines show displacement of air molecules. Pressure antinodes are at the same locations as displacement nodes. Two pipe lengths that have resonances at the same frequency are shown.

An open pipe resonates when its length is an even number of quarter wavelengths.

Practice Problems

5. A 440-Hz tuning fork is held above a closed pipe. Find the spacings between the resonances when the air temperature is 20°C.

6. The 440-Hz tuning fork is used with a resonating column to determine the velocity of sound in helium gas. If the spacings between resonances are 110 cm, what is the velocity of sound in He?

7. The frequency of a tuning fork is unknown. A student uses an air column at 27°C and finds resonances spaced by 39.2 cm. What is the frequency of the tuning fork?

▶ **8.** The auditory canal, leading to the eardrum, is a closed pipe 3.0 cm long. Find the approximate value (ignoring end correction) of the lowest resonant frequency.

An **open-pipe resonator,** a resonating tube with both ends open, Figure 15–11, will also resonate with a sound source. There are pressure nodes near each of the ends, and at least one antinode between. There is also some sound transmission at the open ends of the tube. We hear the transmitted sound. The remainder is reflected to form a standing wave. The minimum length of a resonating open pipe is one-half wavelength. If open and closed pipes of the same length are used as resonators, the wavelength of the resonant sound for the open pipe will be half as long. Therefore, the frequency will be twice as high for the open pipe as for the closed pipe. The resonances in the open pipe are spaced by half wavelengths just as in closed pipes. Have you ever shouted into a long tunnel or underpass? The booming sound you hear is the tube acting as a resonator. Many musical instruments are also open-pipe resonators. Some examples are the saxophone and the flute.

Practice Problems

9. A bugle can be thought of as an open pipe. If a bugle were straightened out, it would be 2.65 m long.
a. If the speed of sound is 343 m/s, find the lowest frequency that is resonant in a bugle (ignoring end corrections).
b. Find the next two higher resonant frequencies in the bugle.

▶ **10.** A soprano saxophone is an open pipe. If all keys are closed, it is approximately 65 cm long. Using 343 m/s as the speed of sound, find the lowest frequency that can be played on this instrument (ignoring end corrections).

Detection of Sound

Sound detectors convert sound energy—kinetic energy of the air molecules—into another form of energy. In a sound detector, a diaphragm vibrates at the frequency of the sound wave. The vibration of the diaphragm is then converted into another form of energy. A microphone is an electronic device that converts sound energy into electrical energy. It is discussed in Chapter 25.

DEMONSTRATION

Purpose: to demonstrate resonance.

Equipment: 2 tuning forks of the same frequency mounted on resonance boxes, pith ball or Ping-Pong ball mounted on a string, rubber mallet or rubber stopper on a stick, ring stand, clamp

Procedure: 1. Line up the resonance boxes so that the open ends of the boxes are about 40 cm apart and facing each other. **2.** Suspend the pith ball from the ring stand and position it so that the ball rests against the first tuning fork. **3.** Strike the second tuning fork with the rubber mallet. After a few seconds, stop the vibrations of the second fork with your hand.

Results: The first tuning fork was heard and the pith ball bounced, indicating that the first tuning fork vibrated.

Questions 1. What kind of wave was produced? *Longitudinal or compres-*

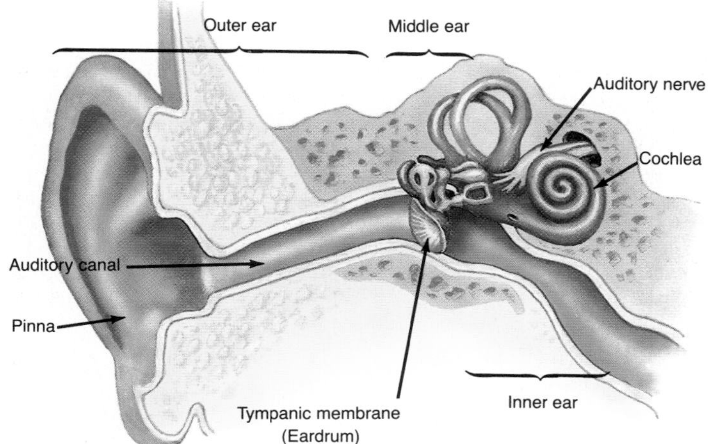

FIGURE 15–12. The human ear is a complex sense organ that translates sound vibrations into nerve impulses that are then sent to the brain for interpretation.

The ear is an amazing sound detector. Not only can it detect sound waves over a very wide range of frequencies, it is also sensitive to an enormous range of wave amplitudes. In addition, human hearing can distinguish many different qualities of sound. The ear is a complex detector that requires knowledge of both physics and biology to understand. The interpretation of sounds by the brain is even more complex and not totally understood.

The ear is most sensitive to sounds with frequencies between 1000 and 5000 Hz.

The ear, Figure 15–12, is divided into three parts: the outer, middle, and inner ear. The outer ear consists of the fleshy, visible part of the ear called the pinna, which collects sound; the auditory canal; and the eardrum. Sound waves cause vibrations in the eardrum. The middle ear consists of three tiny bones in an air-filled space in the skull. The bones transmit the vibrations of the eardrum to the oval window on the inner ear. The inner ear is filled with a watery liquid. Sound vibrations are transmitted through the liquid into sensitive portions of the spiral-shaped cochlea. In the cochlea, tiny hair cells are vibrated by the waves. Vibrations of these cells stimulate nerve cells that lead to the brain, producing the sensation of sound.

Loud sounds can permanently damage the ears.

The ear is not equally sensitive to all frequencies. Most people cannot hear sounds with frequencies below 20 Hz or above 16 000 Hz. In general, people are most sensitive to sounds with frequencies between 1000 Hz and 5000 Hz. Older people are less sensitive to frequencies above 10 000 Hz than are young people. By age 70, most people can hear nothing above 8000 Hz. This loss affects the ability to understand speech.

Exposure to loud sounds, either noise or music, has been shown to cause the ear to lose its sensitivity, especially to high frequencies. The longer a person is exposed to loud sounds, the greater the effect. A person can recover from a short-term exposure in a period of hours, but the effects of long-term exposure can last for days or weeks. Long exposure to 100 dB or greater sound levels can produce permanent damage. Many rock performers have suffered serious hearing loss, some as

FIGURE 15–13. Continuous exposure to loud sounds can cause serious hearing loss. In many occupations, workers such as aircraft line personnel and rock musicians wear ear protection.

CONCEPT DEVELOPMENT

The pressure of sound at the threshold of hearing is nearly the same as the pressure of bright sunlight on Earth's surface!

ACTIVITY

Cooperative Learning: For each pair of students, provide a metal coat hanger twisted into a rectangular U. Attach string about 1 m long to the ends of the metal. Have students drape the string over their heads, making sure the hangers swing freely. Have them hold the strings snugly in each ear while a partner taps the coat hanger. Then have someone tap the hanger when the string is not in their ears. Ask students to compare the intensity of the sound under both circumstances.

Enrichment: When the human ear is exposed to sound, vibrations on the eardrum are converted into pressure changes in the inner ear by the much smaller oval window. The area of the oval window is 1/20 the area of the eardrum. Thus the pressure is increased by a factor of 20 by this simple machine. From the oval window, a pressure pulse travels down a membrane in the cochlea. Near the oval window, the membrane is stiff, and resonates with high-frequency sounds. Deep within the cochlea, the membrane is more flexible, and responds to low frequencies. Thus different parts of the cochlea respond to different frequencies.

sional wave **2.** Describe the motion of the particles. *The particles vibrated in the direction of the motion* **3.** Why did the first tuning fork vibrate? *The compression wave in the air set up by the second tuning fork started the vibration. Because both forks were the same frequency, resonance reinforced the vibrations.*

TRANSPARENCY

Use Transparency 20 with this section.

LABORATORY MANUAL

Use Lab 15.1 with this section.

LABORATORY MANUAL

Use Lab 15.2 with this section.

CONCEPT DEVELOPMENT

- Try to obtain a model of the human ear if students seem to have an interest in the mechanics of hearing.
- Point out that the kind of beat defined here is *not* the same as counting out the time for a piece of music.

ACTIVITY

Demonstration: Obtain two slide whistles. Demonstrate beats by playing both whistles at the same time and adjust them so the pitch is just slightly different. You can also play combinations of notes that are consonant and dissonant.

Laboratory Manual. Give students additional experience with sound intensity by doing Lab 15.2 from the Laboratory Manual.

Connect to BIOLOGY

Sound waves are converted to electrical impulses by nerves in the hair cells of the cochlea. The cochlea is a coiled, tapered tube. The tube is divided by membranes into three parallel liquid-filled tubes. The sensitive cells are on the membrane that separates two of the tubes. The vibrations of the eardrums are transmitted via the three small bones in the middle ear to the oval window on the cochlea. The vibrations of the oval window, in turn, send pressure pulses down one of the tubes. These pulses produce ripples in the membrane that stimulate the hair cells to produce neural impulses.

A sound can be heard if the eardrum vibrates with an amplitude of 10^{-11} m or more. The ripples in the membrane of the inner ear are about 1/100 as large. Compare the size of these vibration amplitudes to the diameter of an atom. [The diameter of an atom is about 10^{-10} m, so the eardrum vibration amplitude is about 1/10 the diameter of an atom, and that of the membrane is 1/1000 the diameter.]

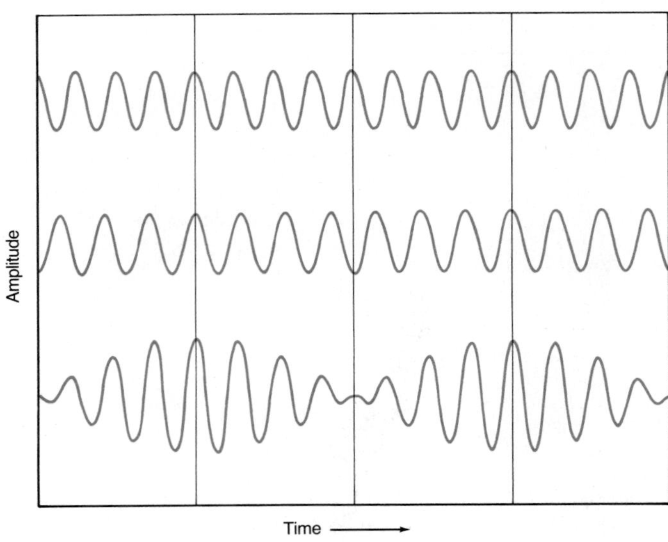

FIGURE 15–14. Beats occur as a result of the superposition of two sound waves of slightly different frequencies.

much as 40%. Cotton ear plugs reduce the sound level only by about 10 dB. Special ear inserts can provide a 25-dB reduction. Specifically designed ear muffs and inserts can reduce the level by up to 45 dB. Another source of hearing loss is the result of loud music from stereo headphones on personal radios and tape players. The wearer may be unaware just how high the sound level is. Some doctors have said that an earphone is "like the nozzle of a fire hose stuck down the ear canal."

Complex sounds are composed of many frequencies.

The Quality of Sound

Musical instruments sound very different from one another, even when playing the same note. This is true because most sounds are made up of a number of frequencies. The quality of a sound depends on the relative intensities of these frequencies. In physical terms, it depends on the spectrum of the sound. In musical terms, sound quality is called **timbre** (TOM bur) or sometimes "tone color."

When two waves of the same frequency arrive at the ear or another sound detector, the detector senses the sum of the amplitudes of the waves. If the waves are of slightly different frequencies, the sum of the two waves has an amplitude that oscillates in intensity. A listener hears a pulsing variation in loudness. This oscillation of wave amplitude is called a **beat**, Figure 15–14. The frequency of the beat is the difference in the frequencies of the two waves. Musical instruments in an orchestra are often tuned by sounding them against a standard note, and then adjusting them until the beat disappears. This technique is also used by piano tuners.

F.Y.I.

The Hungarian communications engineer Georg von Békésy, while studying ways to improve the telephone, learned most of what we know about the human ear. He removed the cochleas of fresh cadavers and worked under a microscope using micro-sized tools he had built himself. He won the Nobel prize in 1961 for his work.

TEACHER 

- Sound waves produced by musical instruments are not pure tones, but complex wave forms caused by the superposition of the harmonics and the fundamental. These wave forms can be made discrete using Fourier's theorem, or Fourier analysis.
- The hearing aid was the first commercial product to use transistors instead of vacuum tubes. It was introduced in 1952.
- There are few places in the world where one can find absolute silence. Even an empty church usually has a decibel rating of about 30.

Example Problem

Beats

A 442-Hz tuning fork and a 444-Hz tuning fork are struck simultaneously. What beat frequency will be produced?

Given: $f_1 = 442$ Hz
$f_2 = 444$ Hz

Unknown: beat frequency
Basic equation: beat frequency, $\Delta f = |f_2 - f_1|$

Solution: $\Delta f = |f_2 - f_1| = |444 \text{ Hz} - 442 \text{ Hz}| = 2$ Hz

Practice Problems

11. A 330-Hz and a 333-Hz tuning fork are struck simultaneously. What will the beat frequency be?

▶ **12.** A student has two tuning forks, one with a frequency of 349 Hz and the other with frequency unknown. When struck together, the tuning forks produce 3 beats per second. What are possible frequencies of the unknown tuning fork?

The human ear can detect beat frequencies as high as 7 Hz. When two waves differ by more than 7 Hz, the ear detects a complex wave. If the resulting sound is unpleasant, the result is called a **dissonance**. If the sound is pleasant, the result is a **consonance**, or a chord. As discovered by Pythagoras, consonances occur when the wave frequencies have ratios that are small whole numbers. Figure 15–15 shows the waves that result when sound waves have frequencies with ratios of 2:1 (octave), 3:2 (fifth), 4:3 (fourth), and 5:4 (major third).

As discussed earlier, open and closed pipes resonate at more than one frequency. As a result, musical instruments using pipe resonators produce sounds that contain more than one resonant frequency. The lowest frequency making up the sound is called the **fundamental**. Waves of frequencies that are whole-number multiples of the fundamental are called **harmonics**. The fundamental is also called the first harmonic. Usually the intensity of the higher harmonics is less than the intensity of the fundamental.

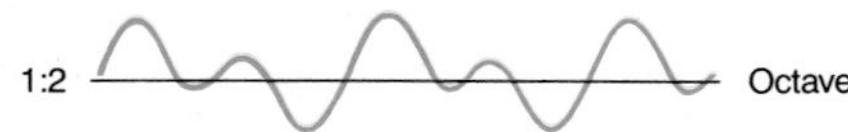

3:4 Perfect fourth

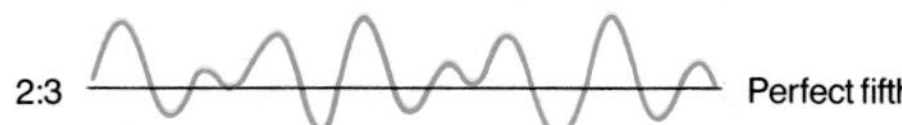

4:5 Major third

FIGURE 15–15. Time graphs showing the superposition of two waves having the ratios of 2:1, 3:2, 4:3, and 5:4.

POCKET LAB

SOUND OFF

Take a meter stick and tape recorder to the band room. Measure the entire length of a wind instrument. Ask a musician to play the lowest note possible on her instrument. Make a recording of the lowest note. Return to the physics room. For the lowest note, $l = \lambda/2$, what is the wavelength played by the instrument? Use this estimate of the wavelength and the wave equation to predict the frequency. **Hint:** $f = v/\lambda$. Use a frequency generator to try to match the recorded note. Read the value on the frequency generator. Is this reading close to your prediction?

Two sound waves of slightly different frequencies produce beat notes.

POCKET LAB

SOUND OFF

Purpose: to predict the frequency of a note played by a musical instrument.
Materials: meter stick; musical instrument; tape recorder; frequency generator.
Outcome: Students should notice that longer instruments can play lower notes. The lowest notes on the valve instruments are played when all valves are closed. This forces air to pass through all the tubes. Student comparison of calculated frequencies to values on the frequency generator should be within 25%.

Assessment

Critical Thinking

To further assess students' understanding of predicting frequency, have them compare the lowest notes of open-pipe and closed-pipe instruments. For an open-pipe instrument, choose a member of the saxophone family, a flute, or an oboe. For a closed-pipe instrument, choose a clarinet. Brass instruments will be harder to study, but you probably can measure the length of a trombone or sousaphone. Ask if these instruments are open- or closed-pipe. [both are open pipe]

DEMONSTRATION

Purpose: to demonstrate beat.

Equipment: 2 tuning forks of the same frequency on resonance boxes, small piece of clay, rubber mallet

Procedure: **1.** Stick a small piece of clay on one prong of one tuning fork. **2.** Strike the tuning forks so that they both sound at the same time.

Results: Beats are produced.

Question: Why do you hear beats? *The clay slightly changes the frequency of one tuning fork. Therefore, the amplitude of the sum of the two waves that reaches your ears changes in a regular pattern, and you hear a sound that varies from loud to soft.*

Critical Thinking Master, Teacher Resource Package. You may wish to have students complete the Critical Thinking Master, Tuning a Guitar, with this section.

Answers To
PRACTICE PROBLEMS

Have students refer to Appendix A of the Solutions Appendix for complete solutions to Practice Problems.

11. 3 Hz
12. either 352 Hz or 346 Hz

CONCEPT DEVELOPMENT

ACTIVITY

Cooperative Learning: Ask your student musicians to organize a demonstration of the properties of sound with their musical instruments or other sound sources.

Critical Thinking: An area of active research is in voice recognition devices. For example, you give your name or a short phrase to a device that admits you to a restricted area. Have students imagine how such systems would work and some of the difficulties that must be overcome.

CHECKING FOR UNDERSTANDING

Use musical instruments to illustrate the harmonic structure of musical notes. For the fundamental, try to use instruments that employ an obvious change of length of the vibrating air column or string. (Some student musicians may be quite knowledgeable in this area.)

RETEACHING

Reteaching Master, Teacher Resource Package. Use the Reteaching Master, Making a Straw Oboe, for Chapter 15 with this section.

EXTENSION

Medical ultrasound diagnosis is rapidly becoming more sophisticated. Have students find out how the wave principles they've just studied provide a mechanism for ultrasound sensors.

Enrichment Master. With this section, use the Enrichment Master, A Model of Sound Waves, from the Teacher Resource Package.

INDEPENDENT PRACTICE/ EXTENSION

Refer to the Assignment Guide on page 324 for additional questions and problems for independent practice.

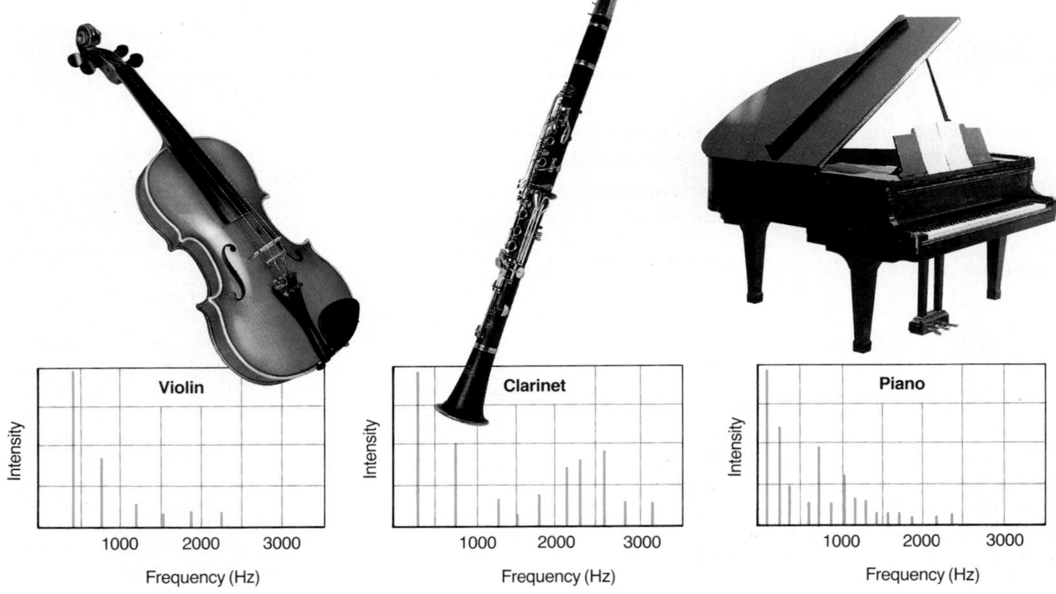

FIGURE 15–16. A violin, clarinet, and piano produce characteristic sound spectra.

An open pipe resonates when the length is an integral number of half wavelengths, $\lambda/2$, $2\lambda/2$, $3\lambda/2$,.... Thus, the frequencies produced by an open-pipe instrument with fundamental frequency f are f, $2f$, $3f$, ... The second harmonic, $2f$, is one octave above the fundamental. The third harmonic, $3f$, is an octave and a fifth (a musical twelfth) above the fundamental. Many familiar musical instruments are open-pipe resonators. Brass instruments, flutes, oboes, and saxophones are some examples. Closed-pipe resonators, like the clarinet, have only the odd harmonics. Notice that in Figure 15–16 the second harmonic in the clarinet spectrum is missing.

Sound can be transmitted through the air or changed into electrical energy and back into sound by a public address system. The air transmits different frequencies with varying efficiencies that can lead to distortion of the original sound. An electrical system can also distort the sound quality. A high-fidelity system is carefully designed to transmit all frequencies with equal efficiency. A system that has a response within 3 dB between 20 and 20 000 Hz is considered to be very good.

On the other hand, it is sometimes useful to transmit only certain frequencies. Telephone systems transmit only frequencies between 300 and 3000 Hz, where most information in spoken language exists. Words can be understood even when the high and low frequencies are missing. The distortion of musical sounds can also produce effects that are interesting and even desired by musicians.

Noise consists of a large number of frequencies with no particular relationship. If all frequencies are present in equal amplitudes, the result is white noise. White noise has been found to have a relaxing effect, and as a result has been used by dentists to help their patients relax.

HELP WANTED

BROADCAST TECHNICIAN

An electronics and computer whiz is needed as the technical expert of a large TV station to monitor and adjust equipment, as well as troubleshoot and repair it in high-pressure situations. An associate degree or a vocational/technical school background, with knowledge of current FCC rules and appropriate licensure certification is necessary. For information on careers and schools offering preparation in this field contact:
National Association of Broadcasters, 1771 N. Street, N.W., Washington, DC 20036

322 Sound

TEACHER F.Y.I.

The clarinet acts like a pipe closed at the reed end. The oboe acts like an open pipe because of its conical bore. Excellent material on the mechanics of music can be found in "The Physics of Woodwinds" and "The Physics of Brasses" in the October 1960 and the July 1973 issues of *Scientific American*.

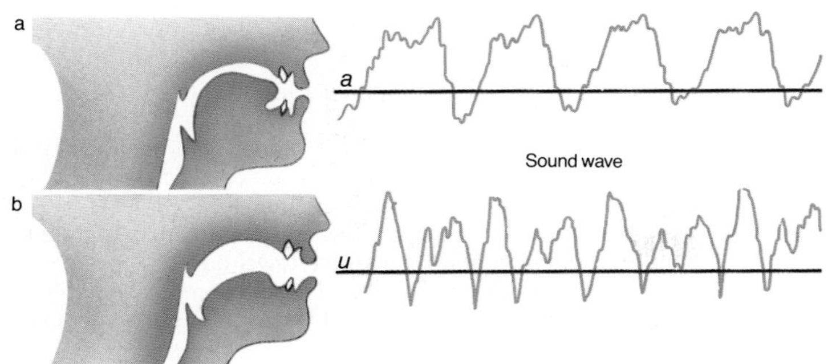

FIGURE 15–17. The shape of the vocal tract determines the resonant wave forms for *a* as in sat (a) and *u* as in suit (b).

The human voice uses the throat and mouth cavity as a resonator. The number of harmonics present, and thus the quality of the tone, depends on the shape of the resonator. Closing the throat, moving the tongue, and closing the teeth change the shape of the resonant cavity. Even nasal cavities, or sinuses, can affect the sound quality. The complex sound waves produced when the vowels *a* (as in sat) and *u* (as in suit) are spoken are shown in Figure 15–17.

Physics and technology

SYNTHETIC MUSIC

The first electronic musical instrument was invented by Thaddeus Cahill in 1897. This 200-ton monster was heard only a few times. In the 1950s, many electronic organs were sold for churches, theaters, and homes. These instruments imitated pipe organs with some success.

In 1964, Robert Moog developed a low cost synthesizer that not only imitated sounds of existing instruments, but created sounds never heard before. As a result, composers and performers were given the freedom to be creative in new ways. The Moog synthesizer used the analog electronics of its day. Just as the hands of an analog clock represent time, in a Moog synthesizer, an electrical voltage was an analog of the pressure of a sound wave. This voltage drives a loudspeaker that produces the sound.

Today, most synthesizers use digital electronics. Numbers, stored in the computer memory, are converted into the electrical voltage that drives the loudspeaker. The composer-musician can use a keyboard, like that on a piano, to select the pitch of the musical note. Then the computer is used to create a waveform to produce the desired sound quality. Once the result is stored in the computer's memory, the musician can add the voices of other instruments to create an entire band.

· What are some possible effects of synthesizers on the music industry?

Physics and technology

Answer to student question: The development of the electronic synthesizer has led to the creation of totally new sounds and musical effects, more people doing their own composing, and the loss of many musicians' jobs.

A synthesizer does not produce waves in the normal sense. Instead, it produces a number that represents the amplitude of a wave at any instant. Any waveform can be represented by a series of these numbers. To combine various harmonics, the synthesizer sums the numbers representing each of the desired waveforms. The synthesizer must provide a large number of sums each second; the human ear can detect frequencies as high as 16 000 Hz. The synthesizer must provide at least twice this many—32 000 numbers—each second. The computer then converts these numbers into electrical signals that produce the sounds in a speaker system.

The sampler synthesizer takes this process one step further. This instrument records any sound, such as a dog barking or door slamming, then converts the sound into a sequence of numbers. The numbers can then be replayed at a speed determined by the pitch desired. The entire musical scale can be produced with nothing but the sounds of door slams at different pitches.

TEACHER F.Y.I.

A transducer is a device that converts one form of energy into another. A microphone is a type of transducer that converts sound energy into electrical energy that can then be amplified and reemitted as sound. Some microphones do this by piezoelectricity. They have a crystal that produces a voltage when even small pressure changes (like the compression of a sound wave in air) occur. The voltage is then amplified and converted back into sound by a speaker.

3 Close

CONVERGENT QUESTION

Ask students how an electronically generated trumpet sound fools the ear. What does the artificial sound have to duplicate? [It must generate fundamental and harmonic structures very similar to those of a real trumpet, and it must reproduce the correct loudness and frequency for the various components of a trumpet's sound; also, how the intensity varies with time—the "attack" and "decay" of the sound.]

CONCEPT REVIEW ANSWERS

2.1 a. vocal cords; **b.** reed; **c.** player's lips

2.2 a. It comes from vibrations in the desk top. **b.** You hear less because vibrations of the ruler do not cause vibrations in the desk. **c.** In the guitar string, vibration is coupled with vibrations of the sounding board.

2.3 Resonance in nasal passages changes the tone quality. Those passages are often blocked by a cold.

2.4 Critical Thinking: a. Yes. $f = \frac{v}{\lambda} = \frac{nv}{4l}$, where $n = 1, 3, 5. . . .$ Increasing l by the same amount decreases each frequency, but their ratios are still 1:3:5. **b.** Yes. l now depends on n, so the frequencies would vary slightly.

CLOSING CHAPTER 15

Review Summary statements and Key Terms with your students.

ASSESSMENT

Vocabulary Review Master, Teacher Resource Package. Use this master to check students' understanding of Key Terms.

Evaluation Masters. Use Parts A and B of the Chapter Evaluation Masters from the Teacher Resource Package to test qualitative chapter objectives. Use Parts C and D to test quantitative chapter objectives.

CONCEPT REVIEW

2.1 What is the vibrating object that produces sounds in
a. the human voice? **b.** a clarinet? **c.** a tuba?

2.2 Hold one end of a ruler against your desk top, with one-quarter of it extending over the desk. Pluck the extended end of the ruler.
- **a.** Where does the noise you hear come from?
- **b.** Test your answer by placing a towel between the ruler and desk. What do you hear and what does the towel do?
- **c.** How does part **a** demonstrate sound production by a guitar?

2.3 The speech of a person with a head cold often sounds different from that person's normal speech. Explain.

2.4 **Critical Thinking:** The end correction to a closed organ pipe increases the effective length by about 1.2 pipe diameters.
- **a.** Are the frequencies of the fundamental and higher harmonics still related by the numbers 1, 3, 5, and so on?
- **b.** Actually, the end correction depends slightly on wavelength. Does that change your answer to part **a**? Explain.

CHAPTER 15 REVIEW

SUMMARY

15.1 Properties of Sound

- Sound is a longitudinal wave transmitted through a gas, liquid, or solid.
- A sound wave is an oscillation in the pressure of the medium.
- The velocity of sound in air at sea level at room temperature (20°C) is 343 m/s.
- The Doppler shift is the change in frequency of sound caused by the motion of either the source or detector.
- The frequency of a sound wave is called its pitch.
- Two notes that differ by one octave have pitches in the ratio of two to one.
- The amplitude of a sound pressure wave is measured on a scale of decibels (dB). The ear and brain perceive the amplitude as loudness.

15.2 The Sound of Music

- Sound is produced by vibrating objects.
- An air column can resonate with a sound source, increasing the loudness of the source.
- A closed pipe resonates when its length is $\lambda/4$, $3\lambda/4$, $5\lambda/4$, and so on.
- An open pipe resonates when its length is $\lambda/2$, $2\lambda/2$, $3\lambda/2$, and so on.
- Sound detectors convert sound energy into a different form of energy.
- Two waves with almost the same frequency interfere to produce a beat note.
- Most sounds consist of waves with more than one frequency. The quality of the wave is called its timbre.
- The timbre of a musical instrument depends on the number and intensity of the harmonics it produces.
- The shape of the throat and mouth cavity determine the vowel sounds produced by the human voice.

KEY TERMS

Doppler shift	open-pipe resonator
pitch	timbre
loudness	beat
octave	dissonance
sound level	consonance
decibel	fundamental
closed-pipe resonator	harmonics
standing wave	

REVIEW MASTER

Use the Vocabulary Review master for Chapter 15 with this section.

EVALUATION MASTER

Use the Chapter Evaluation master for Chapter 15 with this section.

15:2 ASSIGNMENT GUIDE

	PRACTICE	EXTENSION
CHAPTER REVIEW pp. 224–227		
· Reviewing Concepts	7–11	
· Applying Concepts		9–11
· Problems*	16–18, 20–23	19, 24–26
APPENDIX B PROBLEMS*		
· Chapter 15, p. 699	13, 15–17	

* Complete solutions to all Chapter Review and Appendix problems appear in the Problems and Solutions Manual.

REVIEWING CONCEPTS

1. A firecracker is set off at the same level as a set of hanging ribbons. Describe how they might vibrate.
2. When a ringing bell is placed inside a jar connected to a vacuum pump and the air is removed, no sound is heard. Explain.
3. In the last century, people put their ears to a railroad track to get an early warning of an approaching train. Why did this work?
4. When timing the 100-m run, officials at the finish line are instructed to start their stopwatches at the sight of smoke from the starter's pistol and not on the sound of its firing. Explain. What would happen to the times for the runners if the timing started when sound was heard?
5. Does the Doppler shift occur for only some types of waves or all types of waves?
6. Sound waves with frequencies higher than can be heard by humans, called ultrasound, can be transmitted through the human body. How could ultrasound be used to measure the speed of blood flowing in veins or arteries?
7. How can a certain note sung by an opera singer cause a crystal glass to shatter?
8. In the military, as marching soldiers approach a bridge, the command "route step" is given. The soldiers then walk out-of-step with each other as they cross the bridge. Explain.
9. How must the length of an open tube compare to the wavelength of the sound to produce the strongest resonance?
10. Explain how the slide of a trombone changes the pitch of the sound using the idea of a trombone as a resonance tube.
11. What property distinguishes notes played on both a trumpet and a clarinet if they have the same pitch and loudness?

APPLYING CONCEPTS

1. A common method of estimating how far a lightning flash is from you is to count the seconds between the flash and the thunder, and divide by three. The result is the distance in kilometers. Explain how this rule works.
2. The speed of sound increases when the air temperature increases. For a given sound, as the temperature rises, what happens to
   a. the frequency?
   b. the wavelength?
3. In a science fiction movie, when a spaceship explodes, the vibrations from the sound nearly destroy a nearby spaceship. If you were the science consultant for the movie, what would your advice be for the producer?
4. Suppose the horns of all cars emitted sound to the same pitch or frequency. What would be the change in the frequency of the horn of a car moving
   a. toward you?
   b. away from you?
5. A bat emits short pulses of high-frequency sound and detects the echoes.
   a. In what way would the echoes from large and small insects compare if they were the same distance from the bat?
   b. In what way would the echo from an insect flying toward the bat differ from that of an insect flying away from the bat?
6. If the pitch of sound is increased, what are the changes in
   a. the frequency?
   b. the wavelength?
   c. the wave velocity?
   d. the amplitude of the wave?
7. Does a sound of 40 dB have a factor of 100 (10^2) times greater pressure variations than the threshold of hearing, or a factor of 40 times greater?
8. Simon lit a firecracker, and the firecracker produced a sound level of 90 dB. How many identical firecrackers would have to be exploded simultaneously at the same location to produce a 100-dB sound level?
9. The speed of sound increases with temperature. Would the pitch of a closed pipe increase or decrease when the temperature rises? Assume the length of the pipe does not change.
10. Two flutes are tuning up. If the conductor hears the beat frequency increasing, are the two flute frequencies getting closer together or farther apart?
11. A covered organ pipe plays a certain note. If the cover is removed to make it an open pipe, is the pitch increased or decreased?

Answers To
REVIEWING CONCEPTS

1. Sound waves in air consist of a series of compressions (maximum pressure) and rarefactions (minimum pressure) of air. As each compression of air reaches the ribbons, they move in the direction of the wave motion, then back with each rarefaction.

2. Sound is a mechanical wave and requires a medium (air) for transmission.

3. The velocity of sound is greater in solids than in gases. Therefore, sound travels faster in steel rails than in air, and the rails help focus the sound so it does not die out as quickly as in air.

4. Light travels at 3.0×10^8 m/s while sound travels at 343 m/s. Officials would see the smoke before they would hear the pistol fire. The times would be less than actual, if sound were used.

5. all types of waves

6. by measuring the Doppler shift from sound reflected by the moving blood cells

7. The frequency of the note is the same as the natural resonance of the crystal, causing its molecules to increase their amplitude of vibration as energy from the sound is accepted.

8. While marching in-step, a certain frequency is established that could resonate the bridge into destructive oscillation. No single frequency is maintained under "route step."

9. The length of the tube should be one-half the wavelength.

10. The slide of a trombone varies pitch by changing the length of the resonating column of vibrating air.

11. the sound quality or timbre

Answers To
APPLYING CONCEPTS

1. The speed of sound = 343 m/s = 0.343 km/s = (1/2.92) km/s = 1/3 km/s; or, sound travels approximately 1 km in 3 s. Therefore, divide the number of seconds by three.

2. a. There is no change in frequency. **b.** The wavelength increases.

3. Rewrite the script—sound waves cannot travel through a vacuum.

4. As a result of the Doppler shift, **a.** the pitch of the horn of a car moving toward you would be higher; **b.** the pitch of the horn of a car moving away from you would be lower.

CRITICAL THINKING

Use the Critical Thinking master for Chapter 15 with this section.

RETEACHING MASTER

Use the Reteaching master for Chapter 15 with this section.

ENRICHMENT MASTER

Use the Enrichment master for Chapter 15 with this section.

Answers to

APPLYING CONCEPTS (cont)

5. a. They would differ in intensity. Larger insects would reflect more of the sound energy back to the bat. **b.** An insect flying toward the bat would return an echo of higher frequency (Doppler shift). An insect flying away from the bat would return an echo of lower frequency.

6. a. Frequency will increase. **b.** Wavelength will decrease. **c.** Wave velocity will remain the same. **d.** Amplitude will remain the same.

7. A 40 dB sound has sound pressures 100 times greater.

8. Ten firecrackers would have to explode together because 100 dB is ten times as loud as 90 dB.

9. $\lambda = 2l$ and $v = f\lambda$ so $v = 2fl$. If v increases and l remains unchanged, f increases.

10. The frequencies are getting farther apart.

11. The pitch is increased; the frequency is twice as high for an open pipe as for a closed pipe.

Answers To

PROBLEMS

Complete solutions for all Chapter Review Problems can be found in the Problems and Solutions Manual accompanying this text.

1. 2.06×10^3 m
2. 1.02×10^3 m
3. 34 m
4. 686 m
5. 0.0175 s
6. 5.36 s
7. 1.45×10^3 m/s
8. 5.15×10^3 m/s
9. 9.8×10^4 Hz
10. 3.53×10^{-4} m
11. a. 340 Hz
b. 360 Hz
12. a. 280 Hz
b. 260 Hz
13. 9 cm
14. a. 40 dB reduction
b. 50 dB
15. a. 10
b. 100
16. 540 Hz
17. 2.6 kHz
18. a. 10.5 m
b. 8.20 Hz
19. a. 1.0×10^{-6} N
b. 1.5×10^{-6} N
c. 0.58 N/m^2

PROBLEMS

15.1 Properties of Sound

1. Andrew hears the sound of the firing of a distant cannon 6.00 s after seeing the flash. How far is Andrew from the cannon?

2. A rifle is fired in a valley with parallel vertical walls. The echo from one wall is heard 2.0 s after the rifle was fired. The echo from the other wall is heard 2.0 s after the first echo. How wide is the valley?

3. If Karen claps her hands and hears the echo from a distant wall 0.20 s later, how far away is the wall?

4. If Karen shouts across a canyon and hears an echo 4.00 s later, how wide is the canyon?

5. A certain instant camera determines the distance to the subject by sending out a sound wave and measuring the time needed for the echo to return to the camera. How long would it take the sound wave to return to the camera if the subject were 3.00 m away?

▶ **6.** Carol drops a stone into a mine shaft 122.5 m deep. How soon after she drops the stone does she hear it hit the bottom of the shaft?

7. If the wavelength of a 4.40×10^2 Hz sound in fresh water is 3.30 m, what is the speed of sound in water?

8. Sound with a frequency of 442 Hz travels through steel. A wavelength of 11.66 m is measured. Find the speed of the sound in steel.

9. The sound emitted by bats has a wavelength of 3.5 mm. What is its frequency in air?

10. Ultrasound with a frequency of 4.25 MHz can be used to produce images of the human body. If the speed of sound in the body is the same as in salt water, 1.50 km/s, what is the wavelength in the body?

11. The equation for the Doppler shift of a sound wave of speed v, reaching a moving detector, is

$$f' = f\left(\frac{v + v_d}{v - v_s}\right),$$

where v_d is the speed of the detector; v_s is the speed of the source; f is the frequency of the source; f' is the frequency at the detector. If the detector moves toward the source, v_d is positive; if the source moves toward the detector, v_s is positive. A train moving toward a detector at 31 m/s blows a 305-Hz horn. What frequency is detected by a
a. stationary train?
b. train moving toward the first train at a speed of 21 m/s?

12. The train in the previous problem is moving away from the detector. Now what frequency is detected by a
a. stationary train?
b. train moving away from the first train at a speed of 21 m/s?

13. A slide whistle has a length of 27 cm. If you want to play a note one octave higher, the whistle should be how long?

14. Adam, an airport worker, working near a jet plane taking off, experiences a sound level of 150 dB.
a. If Adam wore ear protectors that reduce the sound level to that of a chain saw (110 dB), what decrease in dB would be required?
b. If Adam now heard something that sounds like a whisper, what would a person not wearing the protectors hear?

15. A rock band plays at a 80-dB sound level. How many times greater is the sound pressure from another rock band playing at
a. 100 dB?
b. 120 dB?

15.2 The Sound of Music

16. An open vertical tube is filled with water and a tuning fork vibrates over its mouth. As the water level is lowered in the tube, resonance is heard when the water level has dropped 17 cm, and again after 49 cm of distance exists from the water to the top of the tube. What is the frequency of the tuning fork?

17. If you hold a 1.0-m metal rod in the center and hit one end with a hammer, it will oscillate like an open pipe. Antinodes of air pressure correspond to nodes of molecular motion, so there is a pressure antinode in the center of the bar. The speed of sound in aluminum is 5150 m/s. What would be the lowest frequency of oscillation?

18. The lowest note on an organ is 16.4 Hz.
a. What is the shortest open organ pipe that will resonate at this frequency?
b. What would be the pitch if the same organ pipe were closed?

▶ **19.** During normal conversation, the amplitude of the pressure wave is 0.020 N/m^2.
   a. If the area of the eardrum is 0.52 cm^2, what is the force on the eardrum?
   b. The mechanical advantage of the bones in the inner ear is 1.5. What force is exerted on the oval window?
   c. The area of the oval window is 0.026 cm^2. What is the pressure increase transmitted to the liquid in the cochlea?

20. One tuning fork has a 445-Hz pitch. When a second fork is struck, beat notes occur with a frequency of 3 Hz. What are the two possible frequencies of the second fork?

21. A flute acts like an open pipe and sounds a note with a 370-Hz pitch. What are the frequencies of the second, third, and fourth harmonics of this pitch?

22. A clarinet sounds the same note as in the previous problem, 370 Hz. It, however, produces harmonics that are only odd multiples of the fundamental frequency. What are the frequencies of the lowest three harmonics produced by the clarinet?

23. One closed organ pipe has a length of 2.40 m.
   a. What is the frequency of the note played by this pipe?
   b. When a second pipe is played at the same time, a 1.40 Hz beat note is heard. By how much is the second pipe too long?

▶ **24.** One organ pipe has a length of 836 mm. A second pipe should have a pitch one major third higher. The pipe should be how long?

▶ **25.** The Doppler shift was first tested in 1845 by the French scientist B. Ballot. He had a trumpet player sound an A, 440 Hz, while riding on a flatcar pulled by a locomotive. At the same time, a stationary trumpeter played the same note. Ballot heard 3.0 beats per second. How fast was the train moving toward him?

▶ **26.** A student wants to repeat Ballot's experiment. She plans to have a trumpet played in a rapidly moving car. Rather than listening for beat notes, she wants to have the car move fast enough so the moving trumpet sounds a major third above a stationary trumpet.
   a. How fast would the car have to move?
   b. Should she try the experiment?

USING LAB SKILLS

1. In the Pocket Lab on p. 311, suppose that the frequency of the car horn (when not moving) was 300 hz. What would the graph of the frequency vs. time look like as the car approached then moved past you. Complete a rough sketch.

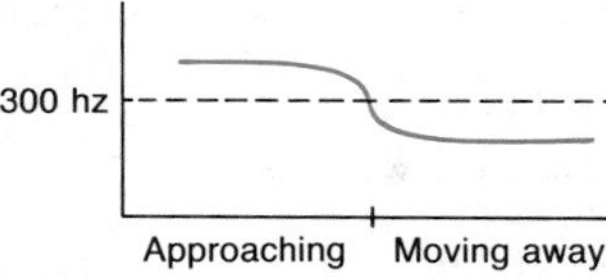

2. Describe how you could use a stopwatch to estimate the speed of sound if you were near the green on a 200-meter golf hole as another group of golfers were hitting their tee shots. Would your estimates of velocity be too large or too small? Explain.

USING A GRAPHING CALCULATOR

Graph the equation $y = \sin x$ on a graphing calculator, using -360 to 360 as the range for x and 2 to -2 as the range for y. Now graph $y = 2 \sin x$ and notice if the wavelength or amplitude changed. Also graph $y = \sin 2x$ and notice how the wave changes. Next clear the graphics area and graph $y = \sin x$. Next graph $y = \cos x$. Finally graph $y = \sin x + \cos x$. What is the amplitude of this wave? the wavelength? Trace along the graph to find out.

THINKING PHYSIC-LY

1. Light coming from a point on the left edge of the sun is found by astronomers to have a slightly higher frequency than light from the right side. What do these measurements tell you about the sun's motion?

20. 442 Hz and 448 Hz
21. 740 Hz, 1100 Hz, 1500 Hz
22. 1100 Hz, 1900 Hz, 2600 Hz
23. **a.** 35.7 Hz
   b. 0.10 m
24. 670 mm
25. 2.3 m/s
26. **a.** 250 km/h
   b. no

Answers To
USING LAB SKILLS

1. The graph should show a fairly steady frequency above 300 Hz as it approaches and a fairly steady frequency below 300 Hz as it moves away.

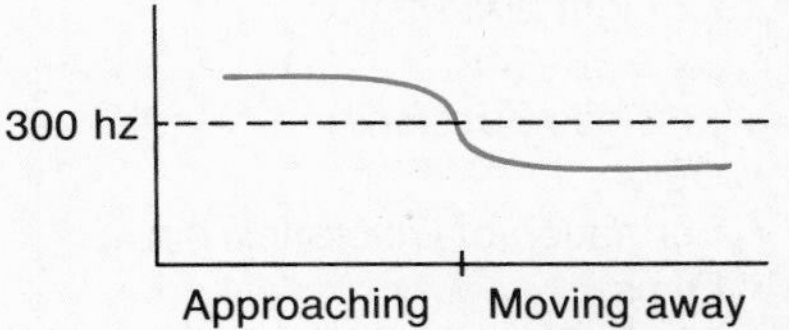

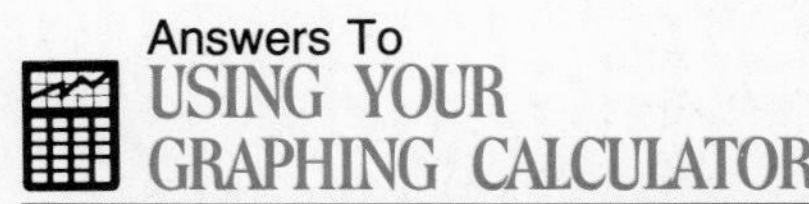

2. You could start the watch when you saw the hit and stop the watch when the sound reached you. The speed would be calculated by dividing the distance, 200 m, by the time. The time estimate would be too large because you could anticipate the impact by sight, but you could not anticipate the sound. The calculated velocity would be too small.

Answers To
THINKING PHYSIC-LY

1. The sun must be rotating on its axis in the same manner as Earth. The Doppler shift indicates that the left side of the sun is coming toward us, while the right side is moving away.

Answers To
USING YOUR GRAPHING CALCULATOR

1. Set the range values (RANGE −360 360 90 −2 2 1)
2. Clear the graph (Cls EXE)
3. Graph the first three equations (GRAPH sin X EXE) (GRAPH 2*sin X EXE)
4. Clear the graph (Cls EXE)
5. Graph the next three equations (GRAPH sin X EXE) (GRAPH cos X EXE) (GRAPH sin X + cos X EXE)
6. Trace along the graph to find the amplitude and wavelength of the last graph
(TRACE −> X <−> Y)

Answers: The amplitude of the last wave is 1.41, and the wavelength is 360.

CHAPTER 16 Light

PLANNING GUIDE (5 class sessions)			
CONTENTS	**TEXT FEATURES**	**TEACHER RESOURCE PACKAGE**	**OTHER COMPONENTS**
16.1 Light Fundamentals, pp. 330–336 (2 Class Sessions) • The Facts of Light • The Speed of Light • Sources of Light	**Physics Lab:** Pinhole Camera, p. 334 **Pocket Lab:** A Matter of Perception, p. 333 **Pocket Lab:** An Illuminating Matter, p. 335 **Concept Review,** p. 336	**Study Guide:** Light Fundamentals **Physics Lab Data Sheet:** Pinhole Camera **Critical Thinking Master:** Using Light to Estimate Distance **Enrichment Master:** Timing a Comet	**Laboratory Manual:** Lab 16.1 Light Days
16.2 Light and Matter, pp. 336–342 (3 Class Sessions) • Color • Formation of Colors in Thin Films • Polarization of Light	**Physics and Technology:** Compact Discs, p. 337 **Pocket Lab:** Soap Solutions, p. 340 **Pocket Lab:** Light Polarization, p. 342 **Concept Review,** p. 342	**Study Guide:** Light and Matter **Reteaching Master:** Adding Colors **Transparency Worksheet:** 4-Color Process **Transparency Worksheet:** Electromagnetic Spectrum	**Laboratory Manual:** Lab 16.2 Polarized Light **Transparency 21:** 4-Color Process **Transparency 22:** Electromagnetic Spectrum
Chapter Review, pp. 343–345	Summary Key Terms Reviewing Concepts Applying Concepts Problems Thinking Physic-ly	**Vocabulary Review** **Chapter Test**	**Test Bank**

SUPPLEMENTARY MATERIALS		
SOFTWARE	**AUDIOVISUAL**	**BOOKS/MAGAZINES**
Sound and Light, Queue, Inc. (Apple II, IBM PC, Macintosh). *Wave Superposition,* Conduit (Apple II).	Videos: *Color: Light Fantastic,* National Geographic. *The World of Light Energy,* Focus Media (still frame). Filmstrip: *Heat and Temperature,* Clearvue.	Connolly, Walter. "Color Mixing Using a Single Projector." *The Physics Teacher,* May 1988, pp. 296–297. Davies, G.R. "Polarized Light Corridor Demonstrations." *The Physics Teacher,* October 1990, p. 464. Leff, Harvey S. "Illuminating Physics with Light Bulbs." *The Physics Teacher,* January 1990, p. 30. Schroeder, M.C., and Smith, C.W. "Estimating the Speed of Light with a TV Set." *The Physics Teacher,* September 1985, p. 360.

PROBLEM CORRELATION

CONCEPTS	CHAPTER REVIEW			PROBLEMS APPENDIX
	Reviewing Concepts	Applying Concepts	Problems	
16.1 Light Fundamentals				
The Facts of Light	1,2,3		1	1
The Speed of Light	4	1	2,3,4,5,**6**,7	2,3,4,5,6,7,8
Sources of Light	5,6,7,8,9	2,3,4	8,9,10,**11**,12,13, 14,**15**	9,**10**,**11**
16.2 Light and Matter				
Color	10,11,12,13,14	5,6,7,10,11,13, 14,15		12,13,14,15,16
Formation of Colors in Thin Films		8,12,16		
Polarization of Light	15,16	9		

ACTIVITY AND DEMONSTRATION MATERIALS

PHYSICS LAB	POCKET LAB	DEMONSTRATIONS
Page 334 large coffee can with translucent cover 5-cm masking tape 40-watt light bulb (non-frosted) in fixture small nail (#2 finishing) large nail (#8 common)	Pages 333, 335, 340, 342 sponge ball meter stick light bulbs (of different wattages) and boxes soap solution soap bubble wand red filter polarizing filter	Pages 330, 340 flashlight peg board Plexiglass tube ring stand soap solution

EXTENSION PROJECTS

LIBRARY RESEARCH

1. **Edison's Incandescent Light**
   Research Edison's work on incandescent lights.

HANDS-ON

2. **Measuring Light Intensity**
   Investigate the intensity of bulbs of various wattages using a light meter. Is the illumination on a surface uniform?

STUDENT READINGS

Crane, H. Richard. "How Does the Honeybee Sense Polarization?" *The Physics Teacher,* October 1990.

Edelson, Edward. "Faster Than Light." *Popular Science*, April 1984.

Greenslade, Thomas B., Jr. "Photography in the Classroom." *The Physics Teacher,* March 1990.

Keeports, David. "Looking for Ghosts to Measure the Speed of Light." *The Physics Teacher,* September 1990.

Peterson, I. "Putting a Far Finer Point on Visible Light." *Science News,* January 6, 1990.

Shapiro, Alan. "Experiment and Mathematics in Newton's Theory of Color." *Physics Today,* September 1984.

Chapter 16

Light

CHAPTER OVERVIEW

Theme Development: The behavior and properties of light waves are taught in relation to light's place within the range of the electromagnetic spectrum. An inquiry into the mechanics of light is centered around mathematical modeling of light as rays and makes use of Newton's definitions as derived through his research into light and color.

MISCONCEPTIONS

Luminous flux and illuminance are troublesome when presented as units. Students may also tend to confuse pigments with colors of light.

KEY TERMS

candela
complementary color
dye
illuminance
illuminated
light
lumen
luminous
luminous flux
opaque
pigment
polarized
primary colors
primary pigment
ray
ray model
ray optics
secondary light colors
secondary pigment
spectrum
translucent
transparent

Laboratory Options

STUDENT EDITION

Physics Lab

Pinhole Camera	334

Pocket Labs

A Matter of Perception	333
An Illuminating Matter	335
Soap Solutions	340
Light Polarization	342

TEACHER EDITION

Activities

Demonstration	330, 340
Discovery	332, 339
Cooperative Learning	339

LABORATORY MANUAL

Light Days	Lab 16.1
Polarization of Light	Lab 16.2

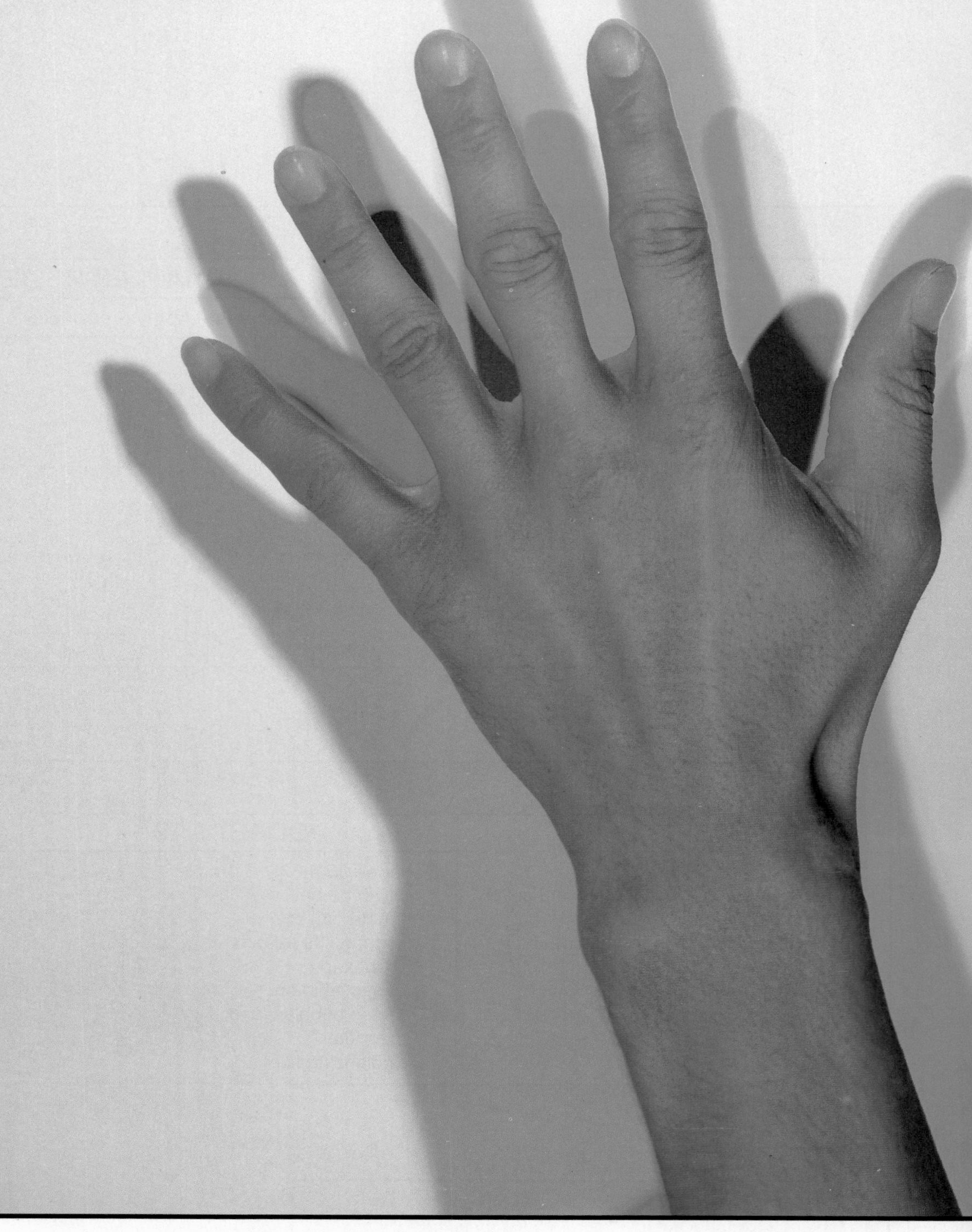

CHAPTER 16 Light

Colors to Mix and Match

Explain how each of the colors in the shadows are formed.

Chapter Outline

Light and sound are the two major ways that we receive information about the world. Of the two, light provides the greater variety of information. The eye can detect tiny changes in the size, brightness, and color of an object. Examine, for example, the photo of the hand illuminated by adjacent red, blue, and green lights. Notice the variety of colors, both on the hand and in the multicolored shadows on the wall.

Concept Check

The following terms or concepts from earlier chapters are important for a good understanding of this chapter. If you are not familiar with them, you should review them before studying this chapter.
- $v = d/t$ for constant velocity, Chapter 3
- wave characteristics, Chapter 14
- $v = \lambda f$, Chapter 14

329

Introducing The Chapter

Colors to Mix and Match

Using The Photo: Colored shadows are easy to produce with colored filters affixed to three sources of light. Adjust the placement of the light sources and the objects casting the shadows to achieve the best results.

To answer the chapter opener question, refer students to page 339.

Concept Check

Make sure students have a clear understanding of the concepts covered in Chapters 3 and 14 that are listed in the Concept Check. Students who are familiar with the characteristics of waves and the formulas $v = \lambda f$ and $v = d/t$ will find it easier to understand the principles of light presented in this chapter.

Assessment Options

Portfolio Assessment
Extension Project 1, TWE, p. 328b
Enrichment, TWE, p. 332
Critical Thinking, TWE, p. 335
Portfolio Assessment, TWE, pp. 333, 338
Enrichment, TWE, p. 341

Performance Assessment
Extension Project 2, TWE, p. 328b
Pocket Labs, pp. 333, 335, 340, 342
Physics Lab, p. 334
Pocket Lab Assessment, TWE, p. 342

Content Assessment
Self Assessment: Practice Problems, pp. 332, 336
Assessment, Critical Thinking, TWE, p. 334
Convergent Question, TWE, p. 342
Concept Reviews, pp. 336, 342
Chapter Review, pp. 343–345
Supplemental Problems, pp. 699–700

Group Assessment
Activities for group assessment occur with Cooperative Learning and lab activities.

16.1 LIGHT FUNDAMENTALS

Preparation

OBJECTIVES

The objectives are listed on the student page. Remind students to preview these objectives as a study guide to this major section.

OVERVIEW

Major concepts introduced in this section include the ray model of light, the speed of light, and other quantitative measurements of light, such as luminous flux and illuminance.

BRIDGING

Topics from previous chapters that are important to this section include wavelength, speed, distance, frequency, reflection, energy, and power.

1 Focus

Demonstration: A Mini-Mag Lite (flashlight) and a piece of pegboard are ideal for demonstrating the inverse square law of light. A Mini-Mag Lite may be ordered through a scientific equipment company or found in sporting goods stores. This flashlight bulb acts as a good point source of light—it can be used without the flashlight. Darken the room and have two students hold the piece of pegboard in front of a chalkboard. Standing 75 cm from the chalkboard, shine the flashlight onto the chalkboard through the pegboard. Have a student draw a square around the area of transmitted light by connecting four dots. Then shine the flashlight from a distance of 1.5 m and have the same student draw a square around this area of light. Students should observe that the area of the second square is four times larger than the first, though the distance was only doubled.

Objectives

- recognize that light is an electromagnetic wave, and know its wavelength range.
- define a ray and give examples of evidence that light in a uniform medium travels in straight lines.
- state the speed of light to 1 or 3 significant digits; solve problems involving the speed of light.
- define luminous intensity, luminous flux, and illuminance; solve illumination problems.

16.1 LIGHT FUNDAMENTALS

We see objects because light is either reflected or emitted by them. Light is emitted by incandescent and fluorescent lamps, by television screens and tiny LEDs (light-emitting diodes), by flames, sparks, and even fireflies. Our major source of emitted light is the sun. Light is reflected not only by mirrors and white paper, but by the moon, trees, and even dark, black cloth. In fact, it is very difficult to find an object that does not reflect some light. Although light is only a small portion of the entire range of electromagnetic waves, the study of light is, in many ways, a study of all electromagnetic radiation.

The Facts of Light

Light is an electromagnetic wave that the human eye can detect.

Light is the range of frequencies of electromagnetic waves that stimulates the retina of the eye. Light waves have wavelengths from about 400 nm (4.00×10^{-7} m) to 700 nm (7.00×10^{-7} m). The shortest wavelengths are seen as violet light. As the wavelength increases, the colors change to blue, green, yellow, orange, and finally, red, Figure 16–1.

Different light wavelengths are seen as different colors.

Light travels in a straight line in a vacuum or uniform medium. When your body blocks sunlight, you see a sharp shadow. If light from the sun or a flashlight is made visible by dust particles in the air, the path of the light is seen to be a straight line. We locate objects by assuming that light travels from them to our eyes in straight lines.

A ray is a straight line that represents the path of a light beam.

The straight-line path of light has led to the **ray model** of light. A **ray** is a straight line that represents the path of a very narrow beam of light. Using ray diagrams to study the travel of light is called **ray optics**. Even though ray optics ignores the wave nature of light, it is very useful in describing how light is reflected and refracted.

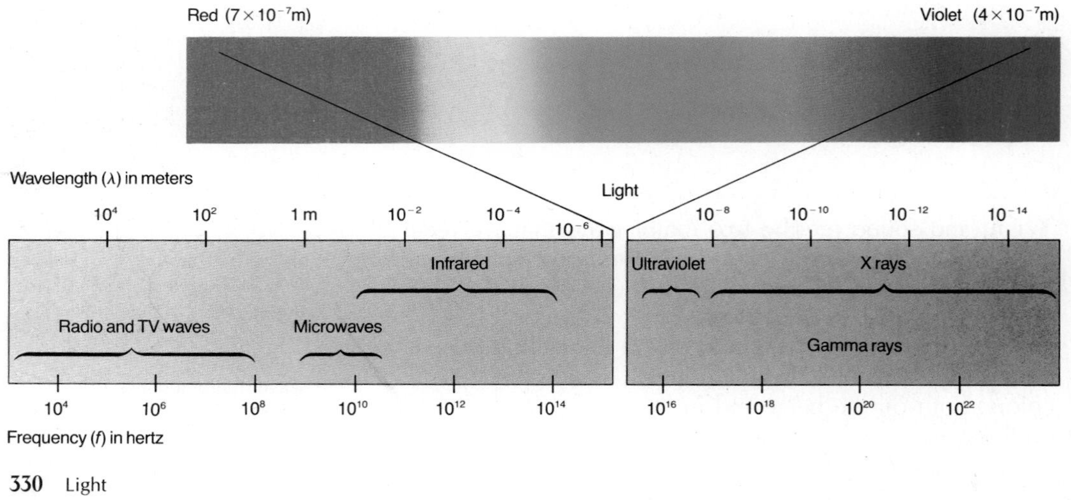

FIGURE 16–1. The visible spectrum is only a very small portion of the whole electromagnetic spectrum.

STUDY GUIDE MASTER

Use the Study Guide master for section 16.1.

CRITICAL THINKING

Use the Critical Thinking master for Chapter 16 with this section.

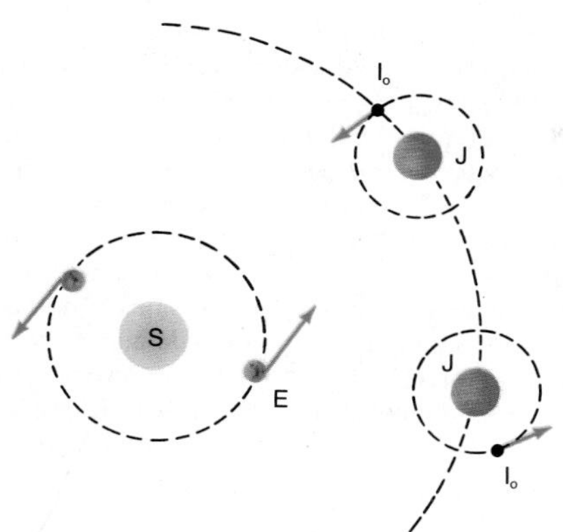

FIGURE 16–2. Roemer measured the time differences of an eclipse of one of Jupiter's moons, Io. During successive eclipses, Jupiter's position changes much less than shown here.

The Speed of Light

Before the seventeenth century, most people believed that light traveled instantaneously. Galileo was the first to hypothesize that light had a finite speed and to suggest a method of determining it. His method, however, was not sensitive enough, and he was forced to conclude that the speed of light was too fast to be measured at all over a distance of a few kilometers. The Danish astronomer Ole Roemer (1644–1710) was the first to determine that light did travel with a measurable speed. Between 1668 and 1674, Roemer made 70 careful measurements of the 42.5-hour orbital period of Io, one of the moons of Jupiter, Figure 16–2. He recorded the times when Io emerged from behind Jupiter and found that the period varied slightly. The variation was as much as 14 seconds longer when Earth was moving away from Jupiter and 14 seconds shorter when Earth was approaching Jupiter. He concluded that as Earth moved away from Jupiter, the light from each new appearance of Io took longer to travel the increasing distance to Earth. Thus the measured period was increased. Based on these data, in 1676 Roemer calculated that light took 22 minutes to cross a diameter of Earth's orbit. The speed of light was finite, but so fast that light took less than one second to cross the entire Earth!

Ole Roemer was the first to take data from which the speed of light could be measured.

Roemer was more interested in proving that light did move at a finite speed than calculating exactly what that speed was. If we use the correct value of the diameter of Earth's orbit, 3.0×10^{11} m, Roemer's value of 22 minutes gives a speed of 2.2×10^{8} m/s. Today we know that light takes 16 minutes, not 22, to cross Earth's orbit.

A. A. Michelson won the Nobel prize for his measurements of the speed of light.

Although many laboratory measurements have been made, the most notable was a series performed by the American physicist Albert A. Michelson (1852–1931), Figure 16–3. Between 1880 and the 1920s, he developed Earth-based techniques of measuring the speed of light. In 1926, Michelson measured the time light required to make a round trip between two California mountains 35 km apart. Michelson's best result was $2.997996 \pm 0.00004 \times 10^{8}$ m/s. For this work, he became the first American to receive the Nobel prize.

FIGURE 16–3. For his investigations of the speed of light, Albert A. Michelson became the first American to win the Nobel prize.

2 Teach

CONCEPT DEVELOPMENT

Study Guide Master. To reinforce the concepts in this section, have the students complete the Study Guide Master for Section 16.1 from the Teacher Resource Package.

The experiments on the speed of light by Albert A. Michelson are classics in the history of science for their beautiful design and precise measurement. At the turn of the century, Michelson's work brought worldwide recognition to American scientific research at a time when western Europe was preeminent in the realm of pure science.

TEACHER F.Y.I.

Although Michelson's interferometer did not measure the absolute velocity of Earth, it has offered astronomers new and better ways to observe space. For example, astronomers discovered in the 1960's that groups of radiotelescopes give better resolution than a single telescope. Today, computers linked to satellites provide us with as much information about our universe as a telescope with an objective whose diameter equals Earth's. Interferometry is precise enough to detect a variance as slight as 1 centimeter over the course of hundreds of years. Furthermore, lasers are now able to detect the tiny movements in Earth's crust that precede an earthquake. Refer interested students to the selections and books listed under *Student Readings* on the Planning Guide pages that begin this chapter.

CONCEPT DEVELOPMENT

Michelson's daughter, Dorothy Michelson Livingston, wrote an interesting study of her father, called *The Master of Light—A Biography of Albert A. Michelson.* She includes many details about his speed of light experiments and numerous amusing anecdotes.

Enrichment: Have interested students research Michelson's speed of light measurements and present reports to the class.

ACTIVITY

Discovery: The fact that light travels in straight lines can be shown with a simple pinhole camera demonstration. (The principles behind the pinhole camera are further investigated in the Physics Lab on page 334.) Use a thumbtack to punch a hole in the bottom of a polystyrene cup. Put a piece of waxed paper over the top of the cup and fasten it with a rubber band. Darken the room and light a candle. Hold the cup sideways with the pinhole toward the nearby candlelight. Students will see an image of an upside-down candle flame on the waxed paper, formed by the rays coming through the pinhole. Draw a ray diagram to illustrate to students how the image is formed.

Critical Thinking Master, Teacher Resource Package. You may wish to have students complete the Critical Thinking Master, Using Light to Estimate Distance, with this section.

Answers To
PRACTICE PROBLEMS

Have students refer to Appendix A of the Solutions Appendix for complete solutions to Practice Problems.

1. 5.40×10^{14} Hz
2. 0.30 m
3. a. 1.8×10^{-6} m
   b. 4.5
4. 3.840×10^{8} m
5. 3.1×10^{8} m/s

F.Y.I.

Ole Roemer made his measurements in Paris as part of a project to improve maps by calculating the longitude of locations on Earth. The method required simultaneous observations of Io's eclipses, so it was important to compile accurate tables of Io's motion. This is an early example of the needs of technology resulting in scientific advances.

The development of the laser in the 1960s provided new methods of measuring the speed of light. As with other electromagnetic waves, the speed of light is equal to the product of its frequency and wavelength. The speed of light in a vacuum is such an important and universal value that it has its own special symbol, c. Thus $c = \lambda f$. The frequency of light can be counted with extreme precision using the time standard provided by atomic clocks. Measurements of its wavelength, however, are much less precise. As a result, in 1983 the International Committee on Weights and Measurements decided to make the speed of light a defined quantity. In principle, an object's length is now measured in terms of the time required by light to travel from one end of the object to the other. The committee defined the speed of light in a vacuum to be exactly $c = 299\ 792\ 458$ m/s. For most calculations you should use $c = 3.00 \times 10^{8}$ m/s.

The speed of light is now a defined quantity.

Officially, one meter is the distance light travels in 1/(299 792 458) seconds.

Practice Problems

1. What is the frequency of yellow light, $\lambda = 556$ nm?
2. One nanosecond (ns) is 10^{-9} s. Laboratory workers often estimate the distance light travels in a certain time by remembering the approximation "light goes one foot in one nanosecond." How far, in meters, does light actually travel in 1.0 ns?
3. Modern lasers can create a pulse of light that lasts only a few femtoseconds (1 fs = 1×10^{-15} s).
   a. What is the length of a pulse of light that lasts 6.0 fs?
   b. How many wavelengths of violet light ($\lambda = 400$ nm) are included in such a pulse?
4. The distance to the moon can be found with the help of mirrors left on the moon by astronauts. A pulse of light is sent to the moon and returns to Earth in 2.562 s. Using the defined velocity of light, calculate the distance to the moon.
5. ▶ Use the correct time taken for light to cross Earth's orbit, 16 minutes, and the diameter of the orbit, 3.0×10^{11} m, to calculate the velocity of light using Roemer's method.

a

b

FIGURE 16–4. Objects that emit light waves are luminous (a). Objects that reflect light waves are illuminated (b).

Multicultural Connections

One of the greatest early physicists was an Arabian scientist named Abu 'Ali al-Hassan ibn al-Hagthan, better known in the West as al-Hazen. Born in Basra, he lived from 965 to 1038, and his book, *The Optical Thesaurus,* was unsurpassed until Johannes Kepler's work 600 years later. Among the contributions 'Ali al-Hassan made was the theory that vision is based on light coming from a source, striking an object, and being reflected to the eye. His Greek contemporaries, primarily Hero and Ptolemy, maintained that rays were emitted by the eye and reflected back to it from an object. Another achievement was the development of the *camera obscura,* which we know as a pinhole camera. Although he was very knowledgeable in science, he was not necessarily wise with people. At one point, 'Ali al-Hassan made a promise to control the flooding of the Nile to the mad Caliph of Egypt, al-Hakim. When he failed, 'Ali al-Hassan had to pretend he was mad, as well, to escape death. The pretense had to go on for many years until the Caliph died.

Sources of Light

A **luminous** body emits light waves; an **illuminated** body reflects light waves. The sun is a luminous body and the moon is an illuminated body. An incandescent lamp, such as a common light bulb, is luminous because electrical energy heats a thin tungsten wire in the bulb and causes it to glow. An incandescent object emits light as a result of its being extremely hot.

We register the sensation of light when rays from either a luminous or an illuminated body reach our eyes. Our eyes have different sensitivities for different wavelengths. For that reason, measurements of light are made in units based on comparisons with standard luminous bodies.

The rate at which light is emitted from a source is called the **luminous flux**, P. The unit of luminous flux is the **lumen,** lm. A typical 100-W incandescent light bulb emits 1750 lm. A bulb emits light in almost all directions. Imagine placing the bulb at the center of a sphere one meter in radius. The 1750 lm of luminous flux refers to all of the light that strikes the surface of the sphere.

Often we are not interested in the total amount of light emitted. We are more interested in the amount of illumination the bulb provides on a book, sheet of paper, or highway. The illumination of a surface is called the **illuminance**, E. Illuminance is measured in lumens per square meter, lm/m^2, or lux, lx.

Suppose a bulb is in the middle of a sphere. What is the illumination of the sphere's surface? The area of the surface of a sphere is $4\pi r^2$. Thus the area of a sphere of 1-meter radius is $4\pi\ \text{m}^2$. Figure 16–5 shows that the luminous flux striking each square meter of the sphere is

$$\frac{1750}{4\pi}\ \text{lm/m}^2.$$

That is, the illumination provided by the bulb on the surface of the 1-m radius sphere is $1750/4\pi$ lux.

What happens if the sphere surrounding the lamp is larger? If the sphere had a radius of two meters, the luminous flux would still total 1750 lm, but the area of the sphere would now be $4\pi(2\ \text{m})^2 = 16\pi\ \text{m}^2$, four times larger. The illumination on the surface would be reduced by a factor of four to $1750/16\pi$ lx. Thus, if the distance from a point source of light is doubled, the illumination provided by the source is one fourth as great. In the same way, if the distance is increased to three meters, the illumination would be $(\frac{1}{3})^2$ or one ninth as large as it was when the light source was 1 m away.

POCKET LAB

A MATTER OF PERCEPTION

Your depth perception occurs because you have two eyes. Close one eye and toss a sponge ball back and forth with your lab partner.

Have your lab partner extend a pencil pointing horizontally about one-half meter from your face. Close one eye and then put your hand about one-half meter away from the pencil, but along the line that the pencil is pointing. Point your index finger and slowly bring it toward the pencil. Were you too close or too far? Repeat the experiment using the other eye. Let your partner try the activity.

An object that emits light is luminous; one that reflects light is illuminated.

Measurements of light depend on the sensitivity of the human eye.

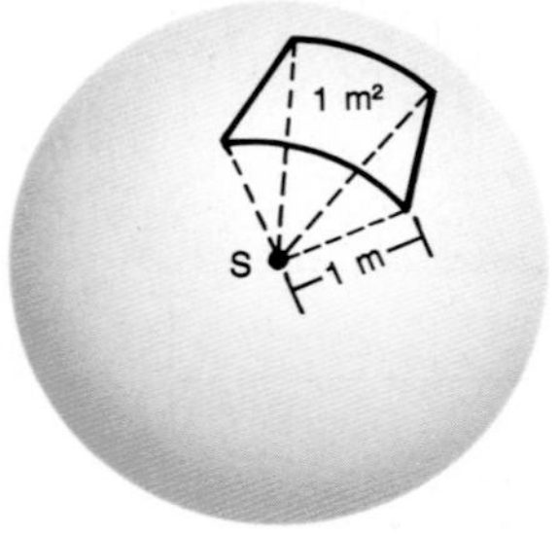

FIGURE 16–5. The lumen is the unit of luminous flux and is a measure of the rate of flow of light energy from a source.

POCKET LAB

A MATTER OF PERCEPTION

Purpose: to investigate depth perception.

Materials: sponge ball; meter stick.

Outcome: Do not use a hard ball for this activity because some students will have difficulty catching with the use of only one eye. Make sure students understand that they are to point straight ahead at the pencil point. Again, many students will be surprised to find out how difficult this is.

CONCEPT DEVELOPMENT

- The luminous flux of a light bulb is printed on the box it comes in. Have students note the difference in luminous flux for incandescent and fluorescent bulbs of the same wattage. You may want to have them calculate the cost per lumen for various bulbs and fluorescent tubes.
- *Illuminance* is the illumination on a surface. A candela is a measure of light *intensity.*

Assessment

Portfolio

Have students do research at a local store to find the cost, light output in lumens, electrical power in watts, and expected life in hours for several of the newer compact fluorescent and incandescent lamps. Calculate the cost/hr to own plus cost/hr to operate ((power)(cost of electricity)/(lifetime)(1000)) to find out which lamp is cheaper.

TEACHER

Illuminance can be measured fairly accurately with a photoelectric cell that generates an electric current when light is incident on its surface. Here are some examples of everyday illuminance:

maximum sunlight (bright, clear day)—100 000 lux
overcast day—10 000 lux
minimum for close work with artificial lighting—100 lux
full moonlight—0.2 lux

PHYSICS LAB

Process Skills: observing, interpreting data, measuring, hypothesizing, questioning, controlling variables.

MISCONCEPTION

Many students have difficulty with the idea that light travels in straight lines.

Teaching Suggestion: Ask all groups to check that the masking tape is covering the larger hole before turning off the room lights.

Lab Worksheet, Teacher Resource Package. If desired, use the lab worksheet master for this chapter for students to record their data.

OBSERVATIONS

1. The image is reversed left to right. Many students will write on the bulb or cover part of the bulb, watching how the image changes.
2. When d_o increases, the value of h_i will decrease.
3. Measurements will vary.

ANALYSIS

1. The drawing should show a light ray from the top of the light bulb passing through the pinhole and striking the cover. A second ray should go from the bottom of the bulb through the pinhole and strike the cover above the first ray.
2. Most students will predict that the image will become larger; some will predict that the image will become brighter; few will predict that the image will turn right side up.
3. The image becomes brighter; it does not become larger or turn right side up.
4. Students should find that:

$$\frac{d_i}{d_o} = \frac{h_i}{h_o}.$$

APPLICATIONS

The images on the back of your eyes are upside down, but this is difficult to prove because the brain interprets images as right side up.

Laboratory Manual. Give students further experience with the properties of light by doing Lab 16.1, Light Days, from the Laboratory Manual.

PHYSICS LAB: Pinhole Camera

Purpose

To discover how light rays travel.

Materials

- large coffee can with translucent cover
- 5 cm masking tape
- 40-watt light bulb (non-frosted) in fixture
- small nail (#2 finishing)
- large nail (#8 common)

Procedure

1. Select a coffee can and punch two holes in the bottom—one with the small nail and one with the large nail.
2. Place the masking tape over the larger hole.
3. Place the translucent top on the coffee can.
4. Turn on the 40-watt light bulb. Turn off the room lights.
5. Point the hole at the light and notice the pattern (image) formed on the cover of the can. (See sketch below.)
6. Draw the path of the light to show the orientation of the image.

Observations and Data

1. Is the image reversed right to left? Design an activity to find out. Record your results.
2. Move the can farther away from the bulb. Notice how the image changes. Record your observations.
3. Measure for three values of d_o, d_i, h_o, and h_i.

Analysis

1. Make a drawing to show why the image gets smaller as the can is moved away from the light.
2. Predict how the image formed by the nail hole would compare to the image formed by the pinhole. List the similarities and differences.
3. Check your predictions. Record your results.
4. Try to determine a mathematical rule between h_i, h_o, d_i, and d_o. Show your results.

Applications

1. Your eye is a form of pinhole camera. Would you expect the images to be upside down? Explain.

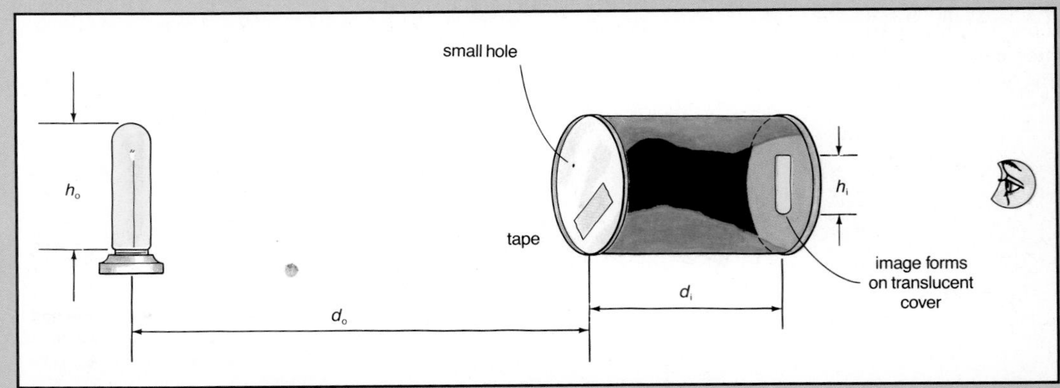

ASSESSMENT

Critical Thinking: To further assess students' understanding of the way light travels, ask the following questions.

1. The image on the screen of the can was always upside down compared to the object. Would this be true if the distance between the screen and the pinhole was made smaller? larger? Explain your reasoning. [The images formed by a pinhole are always upside down. All light from the object must pass through the opening to reach the screen. Since light travels in straight lines, the image will be reversed at the pinhole.]
2. How would your vision be affected if you received light through a very small opening? Would the images be upside down? [The only difference will be that the images would be less bright. The images formed on the retina are always upside down. We see them right side up because the brain automatically flips the images.]

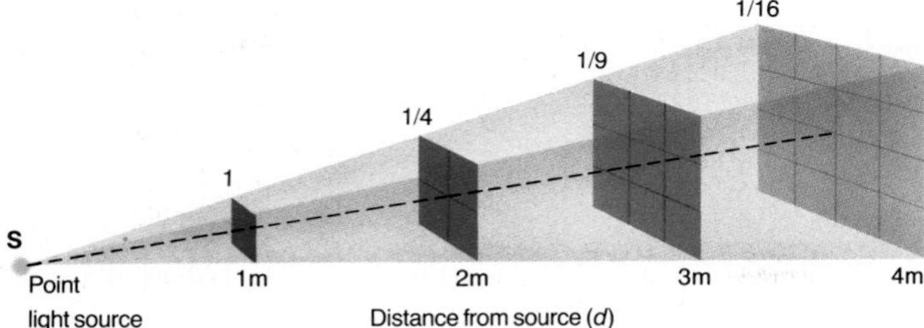

FIGURE 16–6. The illuminance on a surface varies inversely as the square of its distance from a light source.

Some light sources are specified in candela, cd, or candle power. A **candela** is not a measure of luminous flux, but of luminous intensity. The luminous intensity of a point source is the luminous flux that falls on one square meter of a sphere one meter in radius. Thus luminous intensity is luminous flux divided by 4π. A bulb with 1750 lm flux has an intensity (1750 lm)/4π = 139 cd. A flashlight bulb labeled 1.5 cd emits a flux of 4π (1.5 cd) = 19 lm. The candela is the official SI unit from which all light intensity units are calculated.

There are two ways to increase the illumination on a surface. The luminous flux of a light source can be increased, or the distance between the source and surface can be decreased. Thus illuminance varies directly with the flux of the light source and inversely with the square of the distance from the source, Figure 16–6. The illuminance, E, directly under a small light source, is given by

$$E = \frac{P}{4\pi d^2},$$

where P represents the luminous flux of the source and d its distance from the surface. This equation is valid only if a line perpendicular to the surface points toward the bulb. It is also valid only for sources that are small enough or far enough away to be considered point sources. Thus the equation does not give accurate values with long fluorescent lamps, or with incandescent bulbs in large reflectors that are close to the illuminated surface.

LITERATURE CONNECTION

"No light, but rather darkness visible."

John Milton
Paradise Lost, I

Example Problem

Illumination of a Surface

A student's desktop is 2.5 m below a 1750-lm incandescent lamp. What is the illumination on the desktop?

Given: luminous flux, $P = 1750$ lm; distance, $d = 2.5$ m

Unknown: illuminance, E

Basic equation: $E = \frac{P}{4\pi d^2}$

Solution:

$$E = \frac{P}{4\pi d^2} = \frac{1750 \text{ lm}}{4\pi\,(2.5 \text{ m})^2} = 22.3 \text{ lm/m}^2 = 22.3 \text{ lx}$$

POCKET LAB

AN ILLUMINATING MATTER

This is an at-home lab. Which is more efficient, or has the highest lm/W, a lower or higher power light bulb? Look through your light bulbs and record the power (W) and lumens for at least three different bulbs. Make a graph of power (horizontal axis) vs. lumens (vertical axis). Summarize your results.

CONCEPT DEVELOPMENT

Critical Thinking: Have students imagine that light travels in a curve instead of a straight line. Ask them how this would affect the way we see.

CHECKING FOR UNDERSTANDING

Ask students what characteristic of the behavior of light makes it possible for us to model light as rays. [the fact that light travels in straight lines.]

RETEACHING

Go over the Concept Review questions for this section in class.

EXTENSION

Enrichment Master. With this section, use the Enrichment Master, Timing a Comet, from the Teacher Resource Package.

INDEPENDENT PRACTICE/ EXTENSION

Refer to the Assignment Guide below for additional questions and problems for independent practice.

POCKET LAB

AN ILLUMINATING MATTER

Purpose: to investigate the light output from light bulbs.
Materials: a variety of light bulbs with boxes.
Outcome: The graph is not a straight line. Higher wattage bulbs are more efficient.

Guided Practice: After going over the Example Problem on this page, have students work on the first two Practice Problems on page 336.

Independent Practice: Assign the remaining Practice Problems for homework and spend time reviewing them with students the next class period.

16:1 ASSIGNMENT GUIDE

	PRACTICE	EXTENSION
CHAPTER REVIEW pp. 343–345		
· Reviewing Concepts	1–9	
· Applying Concepts		1–4
· Problems*	1–5, 7–10, 12–14	6, 11–15
APPENDIX B PROBLEMS*		
· Chapter 16 pp. 699–700	1–9	10, 11

* Complete solutions to all Chapter Review and Appendix problems appear in the Problems and Solutions Manual.

ENRICHMENT MASTER

Use the Enrichment master for Chapter 16 with this section.

Answers To
PRACTICE PROBLEMS

Have students refer to Appendix A of the Solutions Appendix for complete solutions to Practice Problems.

6. $\frac{E_{after}}{E_{before}} = \frac{1}{9}$
7. 20 lx
8. Refer to Appendix A.
9. 7.1 lx
10. 320 cd

3 Close

CONVERGENT QUESTION

Have students imagine that the speed of light is the same as the speed of sound. Ask them to describe how this would change our visual perception of the world.

CONCEPT REVIEW ANSWERS

1.1 Sound velocity is 343 m/s, so sound takes 3×10^{-5} s to travel 1 cm. In that time, light travels 9 km.

1.2 Yes. Since $v = \lambda f$ and $\lambda = v/f$ when v decreases, so does λ.

1.3 Bringing it closer. If its distance is half as much, the illuminance will be four times larger. A second bulb only doubles the illuminance.

1.4 Critical Thinking: Illumination depends on $\frac{1}{d^2}$, so

$$\frac{E_2}{E_1} = \frac{{d_1}^2}{{d_2}^2}.$$

If the illumination is to be doubled, then $\frac{{d_1}^2}{{d_2}^2} = 2$ or

$$d_2 = \sqrt{0.5}\, d_1 = \sqrt{0.5}\,(1.0 \text{ m}) = 0.71 \text{ m}.$$

Practice Problems

6. A lamp is moved from 30 cm to 90 cm above the pages of a book. Compare the illumination before and after the lamp is moved.
7. What is the illumination on a surface 3.0 m below a 150-watt incandescent lamp that emits a luminous flux of 2275 lm?
8. Draw a graph of the illuminance from a 150-watt incandescent lamp between 0.50 m and 5.0 m.
9. A 64-cd point source of light is 3.0 m above the surface of a desk. What is the illumination on the desk's surface in lux?
10. ▶ The illumination on a tabletop is 2.0×10^1 lx. The lamp providing the illumination is 4.0 m above the table. What is the intensity of the lamp?

CONCEPT REVIEW

1.1 How far does light travel in the time it takes sound to go 1 cm (at 20°C)?

1.2 The speed of light is slower in air or water than in a vacuum. The frequency does not change when light enters water. Does the wavelength change? in which direction?

1.3 What provides greater illumination of a surface, putting in two equal bulbs instead of one or bringing the bulb twice as close?

1.4 Critical Thinking: A bulb illuminating your desk provides only half the illumination it should. If it is 1.0 m away, how far should it be to provide the correct illumination?

Objectives

- **define transparent, translucent, and opaque.**
- **understand the formation of color by addition of light and by subtraction by pigments or dyes.**
- **explain the cause and give examples of interference in thin films.**
- **describe methods of producing polarized light.**

16.2 LIGHT AND MATTER

Objects can be seen clearly through air, glass, some plastics, and other materials. These materials transmit light waves and are called **transparent** materials. Other materials, such as frosted glass, transmit light but do not permit objects to be seen clearly through them. These materials are called **translucent**. Lampshades and frosted light bulbs are translucent. Materials such as brick transmit no light. They absorb or reflect all the light waves that fall on them. These materials are called **opaque**. All three types are illustrated in Figure 16–7.

FIGURE 16–7. The figurine and its stand illustrate transparent, translucent, and opaque objects.

16.2 LIGHT AND MATTER

Preparation

OBJECTIVES

The objectives are listed on the student page. Remind students to preview these objectives as a study guide to this major section.

OVERVIEW

This section explores some of the ways in which light interacts with matter such as pigments, glass, and filters. In addition, the related concept of polarization is discussed in detail.

BRIDGING

This section asks students to use the previously introduced concepts of constructive and destructive interference, phase, and transverse waves.

LAB WORKSHEET

Use the Lab Worksheet for Chapter 16 with this Physics Lab.

FIGURE 16–8. White light, when passed through a prism, is separated into a spectrum of colors.

Color

One of the most beautiful phenomena in nature is a rainbow. People have long wondered about the source of the colors. Artificial rainbows can be produced by prisms. In 1666, the 24-year-old Isaac Newton did his first scientific experiments on the colors produced when a narrow beam of sunlight passed through a prism. Newton called the ordered arrangement of colors from violet to red a **spectrum**, Figure 16–8. He thought that some unevenness in the glass might be producing the spectrum. To test this assumption, he allowed the spectrum from one prism to fall on a second, reversed prism. If the spectrum were caused by irregularities in the glass, the second prism should have increased the

Colors of the spectrum are associated with specific light wavelengths.

Physics and technology

COMPACT DISCS

The audio compact disc (CD) represents a technology that is made for no other purpose than to enhance listening pleasure. The invention of many new industrial processes involved in mass producing CDs has been a major accomplishment. Music can now be reproduced with a clarity and accuracy never before possible.

The CD is essentially a sandwich of three layers of different materials: the plastic substrate, the reflective coating, and the sealing layer. The musical information in a digital recording consists of binary numbers, strings of 1s or 0s. These digits are represented by approximately five billion tiny pits in the substrate. The reflective coating covers the surface of these tiny pits. The laser beam from the CD player reflects off these coated pits and is translated into a digital code. This code is converted into an analog signal (continuously changing voltage) that is amplified to make music.

Since the microscopic pits are smaller than most dirt particles, the manufacturing process must take place under strict clean-room conditions. The "dirty" areas of a CD plant are usually cleaner than the "clean" areas of other factories.

• Why won't a compact disc wear out the way a phonograph record does?

1 Focus

Transparency Package. Begin the section by using Transparency 21, 4-Color Process, to introduce the idea of mixing colors.

Physics and technology

Answer to student question: There is no stylus to inflict wear or damage. In fact, nothing actually touches the surface of the disc. Only light is reflected off the inscribed pits.

The article listed below describes new video-game technology that provides a much higher level of realism. The technology relies on compact discs that hold computer programs and video, audio, text, and graphics data. The games utilize the new compact disc interactive (CD-I) format and should be on the market beginning in 1991.

Teacher Resources: Free, John. "Interactive CD's." *Popular Science.* November 1989, pages 92–94.

TEACHER F.Y.I.

Light sources are typically classified in one of the three categories below.

Incandescent lamp—a tungsten filament is heated by an electric current. Most of the energy is wasted as heat. A 100-W lamp has a rating of 16 lm/W.

Vapor lamp—a vapor or gas radiates visible light produced by an electric current. Street lamps and mercury lamps are types of vapor lamps. A 100-W mercury lamp has a rating of 36 lm/W. The higher rating means that a higher percentage of the lamp's energy goes into visible light.

Fluorescent lamp—a glass tube is filled with mercury and an inert gas. An electric current is passed through the tube, and ultraviolet radiation is emitted. A phosphor coating on the inside of the tube emits visible light when excited by the UV radiation. Fluorescent lamps are much more efficient than the other two types. A 100-W tube produces 55 lm/W.

2 Teach

CONCEPT DEVELOPMENT

Study Guide Master. To reinforce the concepts in this section, have the students complete the Study Guide Master for Section 16.2 from the Teacher Resource Package.

- Newspaper printing shops use transparencies to make color pictures. See if you can obtain some of these transparencies to illustrate color mixing on the overhead projector.
- Color illusion, graphics, psychological color puzzles, and color blindness testing material (available from scientific supply houses) are effective for sparking student interest.

Transparency Package. Use Transparency 22, "Electromagnetic Spectrum," to show the broad range of waves the spectrum encompasses. Remind students that sound waves are mechanical waves and are not a part of this spectrum.

Assessment

Portfolio

To help students recognize the difference between additive and subtractive primary colors, they should create separate lists of sources of color—one list of additive sources, the other list of subtractive color. To these separate lists, they should append collections of answers to questions and problems involving the two ways of creating color.

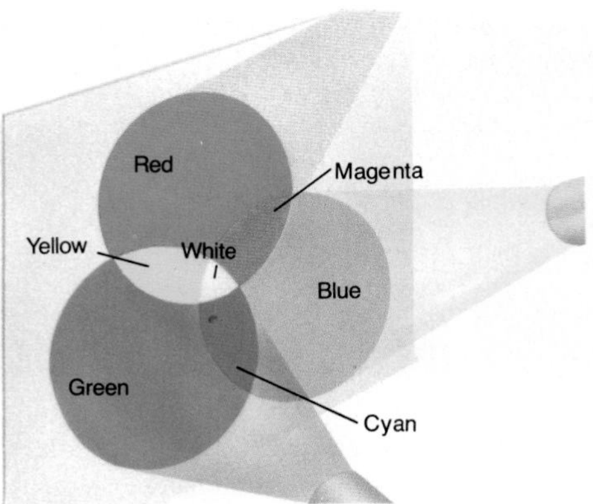

FIGURE 16–9. The additive mixture of blue, green, and red light produces white light.

spread in colors. Instead, a spot of white light was formed. After more experiments, Newton convinced himself that white light is composed of colors. We now know that each color in the spectrum is associated with a specific wavelength of light, Figure 16–1.

Red, green, and blue are the primary light colors.

White light can be formed from colored light in a variety of ways. For example, if correct intensities of red, green, and blue light are projected onto a white screen, as in Figure 16–9, the screen will appear white. Thus red, green, and blue light added together form white light. This is called the additive color process. A color television tube uses the additive process. It has tiny dot-like sources of red, blue, and green light. When all have the correct intensities, the screen appears white. For this reason red light, green light, and blue light are called the **primary colors** of light. The primary colors can be mixed by pairs to form three different colors. Red and green light together produce yellow light. Blue and green light produce cyan, and red and blue light produce magenta. These three colors, yellow, cyan, and magenta, are called the **secondary light colors**.

FIGURE 16–10. A tomato absorbs the blue and green wavelengths of white light and reflects red light (a). In red light, the tomato still appears red (b). In blue light, the tomato appears black since the blue light is absorbed (c).

a

b

c

338 Light

LABORATORY MANUAL

Use Lab 16.1 with this section.

TRANSPARENCY

Use Transparency 22 with this section.

STUDY GUIDE MASTER

Use the Study Guide master for section 16.2.

TRANSPARENCY

Use Transparency 21 with this section.

In the chapter-opening photograph, each shadow occurs when the hand blocks one color of light, leaving the secondary colors. Thus, in order from the left, the yellow shadow is illuminated by red and green lights, the cyan shadow by blue and green, and the magenta shadow by red and blue. Smaller shadows showing the primary light colors appear where two lights are blocked. In the central, black shadow, all three are blocked.

Colors to Mix and Match

Yellow light consists of red light and green light. If yellow light and blue light are projected onto a white screen with the correct intensities, the surface will appear white. Thus yellow and blue light add to form white light. Yellow light is called the **complementary color** to blue light. Yellow light is made up of the two other primary colors. In the same way, cyan and red are complementary colors, as are magenta and green.

Light of a color and its complementary color add to produce white light.

CHEMISTRY CONNECTION

A **dye** is a molecule that absorbs certain wavelengths of light and transmits or reflects others. A tomato is red because it reflects red light to our eyes. When white light falls on the tomato, dye molecules in the tomato skin absorb the blue and green light and reflect the red. When only blue light falls on the tomato, no light is reflected. The tomato appears black, Figure 16–10. Black is the absence of reflected light.

Like a dye, a **pigment** is a colored material that absorbs certain colors and transmits or reflects others. A pigment particle is larger than a molecule and can be seen with a microscope. Often a pigment is a finely ground inorganic compound such as titanium(IV) oxide (white), chromium(III) oxide (green), or cadmium sulfide (yellow). Pigments mix to form suspensions rather than solutions.

The absorption of light forms colors by the subtractive process. Molecules in pigments and dyes absorb certain colors from white light. A pigment that absorbs only one color from white light is called a **primary pigment**. Yellow pigment absorbs blue light and reflects red and green light. Yellow, cyan, and magenta are the primary pigments. A pigment that absorbs two primary colors and reflects one is a **secondary pigment**. The secondary pigments are red (absorbs green and blue light), green (absorbs red and blue light), and blue (absorbs red and green light). Note that the primary pigment colors are the secondary light colors. In the same way, the secondary pigment colors are the primary light colors.

F.Y.I.

People often use the name "Roy G. Biv" to memorize the colors produced by a prism. Why are there seven? After all, it is very hard to detect the differences among blue, indigo, and violet. Newton, who was the first to separate white light using a prism, was interested in connecting light and sound. So, knowing that there are seven notes in the musical scale, he identified seven colors in the rainbow.

FIGURE 16–11. The primary pigment colors are yellow, cyan, and magenta. In each case the pigment absorbs one of the primary light colors and reflects the other two.

CONCEPT DEVELOPMENT

Cooperative Learning: Have student artists demonstrate to the class how to produce colors by mixing paints.

ACTIVITY

Discovery: Arrange to take your students to a darkroom. Have them bring an assortment of colored objects (books with color photographs, combs, apples, etc.). Bring three flashlights and transparent filters of various colors. Close the door and turn on the red light. Have students observe their clothing and the changes in apparent color. Cover a flashlight with a filter and make the same observations for the various colors of light (with the red light off). Mix colors of light to show the secondary colors by covering each flashlight with a blue, red, or green filter and shining the mix onto a color photograph. Students are hesitant to believe that red and green make yellow because of experience with pigments. This demonstration should settle any doubts.

Connect to BIOLOGY

How does the eye detect colors? Light is converted to neural impulses in the retina, some 125 million cells that cover the back of each eye. There are two kinds of cells, rods and cones. When a flash of light strikes a cell, it causes a chemical reaction that produces a nerve pulse. Some 95% of the cells are rods, responsible for night vision, and thus sensitive to very faint light. The cones are concentrated in a small region in the center of the retina. There are three kinds of cones: one sensitive primarily to blue light (λ = 400–480 nm), a second to green (λ = 450–600 nm), and the third to red (λ = 500–700 nm). As you can see from the wavelengths listed, the cells are sensitive to a range of colors. The rods and cones do not send nerve pulses directly to the brain. Rather, the nerves in the retina combine the information from several rods or cones and do some "data processing" before passing the signal to the brain where the image is created.

About 8% of men are color-blind because one of the three types of cones is missing. Suppose a person has no blue-sensitive cones. How would such a person see colors? [The person could not distinguish the differences among blue, blue-green, and green. Green, yellow, orange, and red could still be distinguished.]

CONCEPT DEVELOPMENT

- Blow a large bubble with a bubble solution and put it on a clear transparency on the overhead projector. Students will observe colors on the screen as well as through the bubble.
- Explain to students that thin film interference creates the colors that are often seen when oil or gasoline lies on the surface of a puddle of water.
- Soap film demonstrations are interesting as well as beautiful. A soap solution that will make lasting films can be made by combining 71 g of Joy detergent, 184 g of glycerine, and 227 g of distilled water a few days in advance.

Demonstration: The following arrangement will project a soap film on a screen. A plexiglass tube about 15 cm long and 7 cm in diameter is ideal for holding the film. A soup can will suffice if the tube is not available. Set up a ring stand to hold the tube horizontally after you have dipped it in the soap solution and withdrawn it with a film on the end. Reflect light from the film and focus it on a screen with a long focal length lens. The film will be wedge-shaped, and multi-colored interference fringes will form. A dark spot on the bottom of the image of the film will appear where it has gotten too thin or has broken. If you place a radio speaker at the far end of the tube from the soap film and play some music, you will produce some very interesting wave patterns in the film.

POCKET LAB

SOAP SOLUTIONS

Purpose: to examine reflection of light from a soap film.
Materials: soap solution; soap bubble wand; red filter.
Outcome: The colors form in horizontal lines. Each line is the same thickness. The lines move downward because the soap is thinning at the top. Students looking through a red filter will see alternating red and dark bands.

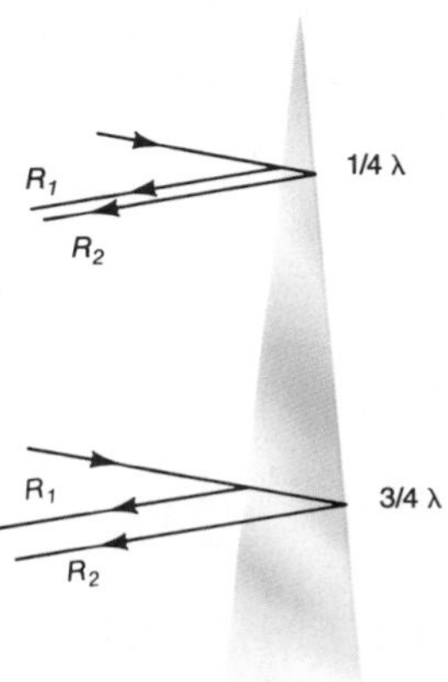

FIGURE 16–12. Each color is reinforced where the soap film is 1/4, 3/4, 5/4,... of the wavelength for that color. Since each color has a different wavelength, a series of color bands is seen reflected from the soap films.

The primary pigment yellow absorbs blue light. If it is mixed with the secondary pigment blue that absorbs green and red light, all light will be absorbed. No light will be reflected, so the result will be black. Yellow and blue are called complementary pigments. Cyan and red, as well as magenta and green, are also complementary pigments.

Light Conventions

► ***Light rays are red.***

The colors of thin films are the result of interference of light reflected from the front and back surfaces of the film.

Formation of Colors in Thin Films

Have you ever seen a spectrum of colors produced by a soap bubble or by the oil film on a water puddle in a parking lot? These colors are not the result of separation of white light by a prism or absorption of colors in a pigment. They are a result of the constructive and destructive interference of light waves or thin-film interference.

If a soap film is held vertically, Figure 16–12, its weight makes it thicker at the bottom than at the top. The thickness varies gradually from top to bottom. When a light wave strikes the film, part of it is reflected, as shown by R_1, and part is transmitted. The transmitted wave travels through the film to the back surface where again part is reflected, R_2. If the thickness of the film is one-quarter of the wavelength of the wave in the film ($\lambda/4$), the "round trip" path length in the film is $\lambda/2$. It would appear that the wave returning from the back surface would reach the front surface one-half wavelength behind the first reflected wave and the two waves would cancel. But, as we learned in Chapter 14, when a wave is reflected from a more optically dense medium, it is inverted. As a result, the first reflected wave, R_1, is inverted on reflection. The second reflected wave, R_2, is reflected from a less dense medium and is not inverted. Thus, when the film has a thickness of $\lambda/4$, the wave reflected from the back surface returns to the front surface in step with the first reflected wave. The two waves reinforce each other as they leave the film. Light with other wavelengths suffers partial or complete destructive interference. At any point on the film, the light most strongly reflected has a wavelength satisfying the requirement that the film thickness equals $\lambda/4$.

POCKET LAB

SOAP SOLUTIONS

Dip the ring into the soap solution and hold it at a 45° angle to the horizontal. Look for color bands to form in horizontal stripes. Why do the bands move? Why are the bands horizontal? What type of pattern would you see if you looked through the soap with a red filter? Try it. Describe and explain your results.

FIGURE 16–13. Waves are polarized with respect to the vertical plane (a). Vertically polarized waves can't pass through a horizontal polarizer (b).

Different colors of light have different wavelengths. As the thickness of the film changes, the $\lambda/4$ requirement will be met at different locations for different colors. As the thickness increases, first light with the shortest wavelength, blue, will be most strongly reflected, then green, yellow, orange, and finally red, which has the longest wavelength. A rainbow of color results. Notice in Figure 16–12 that the spectrum repeats. When the thickness is $3\lambda/4$, the round trip distance is $3\lambda/2$, and constructive interference occurs again. Any thickness equal to an odd multiple of quarter wavelengths, $\lambda/4$, $3\lambda/4$, $5\lambda/4$, $7\lambda/4$, and so on satisfies the conditions for reinforcement for a given color. Look at the film on the right in Figure 16–12. The bottom half appears black because of the way it was photographed. If you watch the film for long enough, you will find that all color leaves the top of the film. The film will appear black because it is too thin to produce constructive interference for any color. Shortly after the top of the film becomes thin enough to appear black, it breaks.

Light, being a transverse wave, can be polarized.

Polarization of Light

Have you ever looked at light reflected off a road through Polaroid sunglasses? As you rotate the glasses, the road first appears dark, then light, then dark again. Light from a lamp, however, changes very little as the glasses are rotated. The light reflected from the road is partially polarized. Only transverse waves can be polarized.

Polarization can be understood by considering the rope model of light waves, Figure 16–13. The transverse mechanical waves in the rope represent the transverse electromagnetic waves of light. The slots represent the polarizing axis of the Polaroid material. When the rope waves are parallel to the slots, they pass through. When they are perpendicular to the slots, the waves are blocked. Polaroid material contains long molecules that allow electromagnetic waves of one direction to pass while absorbing the waves vibrating in the other direction. One direction of the Polaroid material is called the polarizing axis. Only waves vibrating parallel to that axis can pass through.

Ordinary light contains electromagnetic waves vibrating in every direction perpendicular to its direction of travel. Each wave can be resolved into two perpendicular components. On the average, therefore, half the waves vibrate in one plane, the other half in a plane perpendic-

HELP WANTED

PHOTOGRAPHER

A large advertising agency is looking for a talented staff photographer. Technological knowledge of cameras, lenses, sources of light, various films and the processes for developing them can be the result of formal or on-the-job training.

Because of the variety of our accounts, your "subjects" will range from products to people to places. Proof of your qualifications is in your portfolio, so send yours for our review. For information contact:

Professional Photographers of America, Inc., 1090 Executive Way, Des Plaines, IL 60018

CONCEPT DEVELOPMENT

Critical Thinking: In what way would thin film interference be changed if the film wedge had its thick side up instead of down? [The order of colors would be reversed.]

Enrichment: Have interested students investigate Edwin Land's efforts to produce full-color images with two black-and-white negatives and light of one color. An excellent reference is Edwin H. Land's, "Experiments in Color Vision." *Scientific American*, May 1959, pages 84–99.

CHECKING FOR UNDERSTANDING

Ask students to explain color formation by both additive and subtractive processes. Also ask them to describe polarization.

RETEACHING

Reteaching Master, Teacher Resource Package. Use the Reteaching Master for Chapter 16, Adding Colors, with this section.

INDEPENDENT PRACTICE/ EXTENSION

Refer to the Assignment Guide on page 341 for additional questions and problems for independent practice.

Laboratory Manual. Give students additional experience with light polarization by doing Lab 16.2 from the Laboratory Manual.

Guided Practice: Discuss the first three Concept Review Problems on page 342. Encourage students to explain their answers.

Independent Practice: Assign the last Concept Review Problem on page 342 for homework and review it with students during the next class period.

16:2 ASSIGNMENT GUIDE

	PRACTICE	EXTENSION
CHAPTER REVIEW pp. 343–345		
· Reviewing Concepts	10–16	
· Applying Concepts · Problems*		5–16
APPENDIX B PROBLEMS*		
· Chapter 16, p. 700	12–16	

* Complete solutions to all Chapter Review and Appendix problems appear in the Problems and Solutions Manual.

LABORATORY MANUAL

Use Lab 16.2 with this section.

POCKET LAB

LIGHT POLARIZATION

Purpose: to observe objects through a polarizing filter.
Materials: polarizing filter.
Outcome: Students will find that the filter does not change the color of objects. Most objects will not change their appearance as the filter is rotated. Students should notice the contrast between clouds and sky is greatly changed as the polarizer is rotated. Smooth reflecting surfaces such as windows and car windshields will have changed noticeably.

Assessment

Performance

Some objects will polarize reflected light. In other words, if unpolarized light strikes these objects, the reflected light will be polarized.

To further assess students' understanding of the polarization of light, have them explore the results of shining polarized light on such surfaces. For example, suppose in the Pocket Lab they found that holding the filter horizontally made the surface look brighter. Now hold the filter between the lamp and the surface. Does the surface appear brighter now when the filter is held horizontally or vertically? Make drawings similar to Figure 16–14a to explain your results. [Reflection of light from the surfaces will depend on its polarization. Thus, if unpolarized light strikes a surface and the reflected light is polarized parallel to the surface, then light that is polarized parallel to the surface will be reflected more strongly than light polarized perpendicular to the surface.]

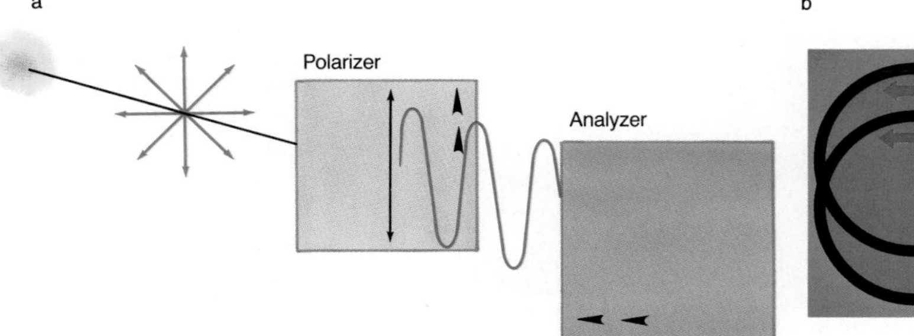

FIGURE 16–14. The arrows show that unpolarized light vibrates in many planes (a). Plane polarized light vibrates in only one plane. Polarized light from the first polarizer (b) is absorbed by the analyzer (c).

A polarizer produces polarized light.

A polarizer will permit only light of one polarization to be transmitted.

Light can be polarized by reflection and by scattering.

ular to the first. If polarizing material is placed in a beam of ordinary light, only those waves vibrating in one plane pass through. Half the light passes through and the intensity of the light is reduced by half. The polarizing material produces light that is **polarized** in a particular plane of vibration. The material is said to be a "polarizer" of light and is called a polarizing filter.

Suppose a second polarizing filter is placed in the path of the polarized light. If the direction of the plane of vibration that passes through the filter is perpendicular to the plane of the polarized light, no light will pass through, Figure 16–14c. If it is parallel, most light will be transmitted, Figure 16–14b. Thus a polarizing filter can also analyze the polarization of light, and is often called an "analyzer."

Light can also be polarized by reflection. If you look through a polarizing filter at the light reflected by a sheet of glass and rotate the filter, you will see the light brighten and dim. The light was partially polarized when it was reflected. The polarization of light reflected by roads is the reason polarizing sunglasses reduce glare. The fact that the intensity of light reflected off a road varies as Polaroid sunglasses are rotated suggests that the reflected light must contain a great deal of light vibrating in only one direction. Light is also polarized when it is scattered by molecules in the air. If you look through Polaroid glasses along the horizon when the sun is overhead and rotate the glasses, you will see the brightness change, showing the light is polarized.

POCKET LAB

LIGHT POLARIZATION

This is an at-home lab. Check out a polarizing filter to take home. Look through the filter at various objects as you rotate the filter. Make a record of those objects that seem to change in brightness as the filter is rotated. What seems to be the pattern?

CONCEPT REVIEW

2.1 Why might you choose a window shade that is translucent? opaque?
2.2 What light color do you add to blue light to obtain white?
2.3 What primary pigment colors must be mixed to get red?
2.4 **Critical Thinking:** Colors in butterfly wings are caused by the constructive interference of light reflected from closely-spaced spine-like structures. Assume that the light wave is inverted when reflected from all these structures. At what fraction of a wavelength are they spaced?

3 Close

CONVERGENT QUESTION

Ask students to summarize how white light is modified so that we can see colors, both with pigments and with direct mixing of light.

CONCEPT REVIEW ANSWERS

2.1 Translucent to keep people from looking in or out, but allowing light to pass; opaque to make the room dark.
2.2 Yellow (a mixture of the other two primaries, red and green)
2.3 Yellow and magenta (Yellow reflects red and green, magenta reflects red and blue, so together they reflect red.)
2.4 Critical Thinking: For constructive interference, the round-trip distance must be λ. Thus the spacing is $\lambda/2$. It is not $\lambda/4$ because there is inversion on reflection from all surfaces.

CHAPTER 16 REVIEW

SUMMARY

16.1 Light Fundamentals

- Light is electromagnetic radiation capable of stimulating the retina of the eye.
- Light in a uniform medium travels in a straight line at a speed of 3.00×10^8 m/s in a vacuum.
- The rate at which light energy is emitted by a source is called luminous flux. The unit of luminous flux is the lumen.
- The rate at which light energy falls on a unit area is illuminance, measured in lux.

16.2 Light and Matter

- Materials may be characterized as either transparent, translucent, or opaque depending on the amount of light they reflect, transmit, or absorb.
- White light is a combination of the spectrum of colors, each having a different wavelength.
- White light can be formed by adding together the primary light colors, red, blue, and green.
- The subtractive primary colors, cyan, magenta, and yellow, are used in pigments and dyes to produce a wide variety of colors.
- Colors in soap and oil films are caused by the interference of specific colors of light reflected from the front and back surfaces of the thin film.
- Light is polarized if only waves vibrating in a particular plane are present.

KEY TERMS

light
ray model
ray
ray optics
luminous
illuminated
luminous flux
lumen
illuminance
candela
transparent
translucent
opaque
spectrum
primary colors
secondary light colors
complementary color
dye
pigment
primary pigment
secondary pigment
polarized

REVIEWING CONCEPT

1. Sound doesn't travel through a vacuum; how do we know light does?
2. What is the range of wavelength, from shortest to longest, the human eye can detect?
3. What color of visible light has the shortest wavelength?
4. What was changed in the equation $v = \lambda f$ in this chapter?
5. Distinguish between a luminous body and an illuminated body.
6. Look carefully at an ordinary frosted incandescent bulb. Is it a luminous or an illuminated body?
7. Explain how we can see ordinary nonluminous classroom objects.
8. State the units for each of the following.
   a. luminous intensity
   b. illuminance
   c. luminous flux
9. State the symbol that represents each of the following.
   a. luminous intensity
   b. illuminance
   c. luminous flux
10. Distinguish among transparent, translucent, and opaque objects.
11. Of what colors does white light consist?
12. Is black a color? Why does an object appear black?
13. Name each primary color and its secondary light color.
14. Name each primary pigment and its secondary pigment.
15. Why can sound waves not be polarized?
16. Why would a perfect polarizing filter transmit half the nonpolarized light incident on it?

APPLYING CONCEPTS

1. What happens to the wavelength of light as the frequency increases?
2. To what is the illumination of a surface by a light source directly proportional? To what is it inversely proportional?

CLOSING CHAPTER 16

Review Summary statements and Key Terms with your students.

ASSESSMENT

Vocabulary Review Master, Teacher Resource Package. Use this master to check students' understanding of Key Terms.

Evaluation Masters. Use Parts A and B of the Chapter Evaluation Masters from the Teacher Resource Package to test qualitative chapter objectives. Use Parts C and D to test quantitative chapter objectives.

Answers To
REVIEWING CONCEPTS

1. Light comes through the vacuum of space from the sun.
2. 400 nm to 700 nm
3. Violet light has the shortest wavelength.
4. The speed of the wave, v, was changed to the speed of light, c.
5. A luminous body emits light. An illuminated body is one on which light falls and is reflected.
6. It is mainly illuminated. The filament is luminous, the frosted glass is illuminated. You can barely see the hot filament through the frosted glass.
7. Ordinary nonluminous objects are illuminated by reflected light, allowing them to be seen.
8. **a.** candela, cd **b.** lux, lx **c.** lumen, lm
9. **a.** I **b.** E **c.** P
10. A transparent object is a material through which light can pass without distortion. A translucent object allows light to pass but distorts the light to the point where images are not discernable. An opaque object does not allow light to pass through.
11. White light is a combination of all the colors, or at least the primary colors.

RETEACHING MASTER

Use the Reteaching master for Chapter 16 with this section.

EVALUATION MASTER

Use the Chapter Evaluation master for Chapter 16 with this section.

REVIEW MASTER

Use the Vocabulary Review master for Chapter 16 with this section.

Answers To
REVIEWING CONCEPTS (cont)

12. Black is not a color but is the absence of all color. An object appears to be black because little, if any, light is being reflected from it.
13. Red, cyan; green, magenta; blue, yellow
14. yellow, blue; cyan, red; magenta, green
15. Sound waves are longitudinal, not transverse, waves. The particles of the medium move parallel to the motion of the wave rather than perpendicular, as required for polarization.
16. Nonpolarized light can be analyzed as half parallel to the filter, half perpendicular. Only the parallel half passes through.

Answers To
APPLYING CONCEPTS

1. As the frequency increases, the wavelength decreases.
2. The illumination on a surface is directly proportional to the intensity of the source and inversely proportional to the square of the distance of the surface from the source.
3. Illumination $E \propto I/d^2$; therefore, the illumination at screen B will be 1/4 of that at screen A since it is twice as far from the source.
4. No. Distance is doubled, so the illumination of the page is 1/4 as great.
5. The insides are painted black because black does not reflect any light, and thus there is no interference while observing or photographing objects.
6. Fire trucks should be painted yellow-green, 550 nm, because less light has to be reflected to the eye for the fire truck to be seen.
7. Blue pigment of a police car will absorb the red and yellow light. Dark blue police cars would not be very visible. If a community wants its police cars to be visible, they should select yellow cars.

3. A point source of light is 2.0 m from screen A and 4.0 from screen B. How does the illumination of screen B compare with the illumination of screen A?

4. You have a small reading lamp 35 cm from the pages of a book. You decide to double the distance. Is the illumination on the book the same? If not, how much more or less is it?

5. Why are the insides of binoculars and cameras painted black?

6. The eye is most sensitive to 550-nm wavelength light. Its sensitivity to red and blue light is less than 10% as great. Based on this knowledge, what color would you recommend fire trucks and ambulances be painted? Why?

7. Some very efficient streetlights contain sodium vapor under high pressure. They produce light that is mainly yellow with some red. Should a community having these lights buy dark blue police cars? Why or why not?

8. Suppose astronauts made a soap film in the space shuttle. Would you expect an orderly set of colored lines, such as in Figure 16–12? Explain.

9. Photographers often put polarizing filters over the camera lens to make clouds more visible in the sky. The clouds remain white while the sky looks darker. Explain this based on your knowledge of polarized light.

10. An apple is red because it reflects red light and either absorbs or transmits blue and green. Follow these steps to decide if a piece of transparent red cellophane absorbs or transmits blue and green.
- **a.** Explain why it looks red in reflected light.
- **b.** When you hold it between your eye and a white light, it looks red. Explain.
- **c.** Now, what happens to the blue and green?

11. What color will a yellow banana appear when illuminated by
- **a.** white light?
- **b.** green plus red light?
- **c.** blue light?

12. A soap film is too thin to absorb any color. If such a film reflects blue light, what kind of light does it transmit?

13. You put a piece of red cellophane over one flashlight and a piece of green cellophane over another. You shine the light beams on a white wall. What color will you see where the two flashlight beams overlap?

14. You now put both the red and green cellophane pieces over one of the flashlights in the previous problem. If you shine the flashlight beam on a white wall, what color will you see? Explain.

15. If you have yellow, cyan, and magenta pigments, how can you make a blue pigment? Explain.

16. Consider a thin film of gasoline floating on water. The speed of light is slower in gasoline than in air, and slower in water than in gasoline. Would you expect the $\lambda/4$ rule to hold in this case? Explain.

PROBLEMS

16.1 Light Fundamentals

1. Convert 700 nm, the wavelength of red light, to meters.

2. Light takes 1.28 s to travel from the moon to Earth. What is the distance between them?

3. The sun is 1.5×10^8 km from Earth. How long does it take for its light to reach us?

4. Ole Roemer found that the maximum increased delay in the appearance of Io from one orbit to the next was 14 s.
- **a.** How far does light travel in 14 s?
- **b.** Each orbit of Io is 42.5 h. Earth traveled the distance calculated above in 42.5 h. Find the speed of Earth in km/s.
- **c.** See if your answer for part **b** is reasonable. Calculate Earth's speed in orbit using the orbital radius, 1.5×10^8 km, and the period, one year.

5. Radio stations are usually identified by their frequency. One radio station in the middle of the FM band has a frequency of 99.0 MHz. What is its wavelength?

▶ **6.** Suppose you wanted to measure the speed of light by putting a mirror on a distant mountain, setting off a camera flash, and measuring the time it takes the flash to reflect off the mirror and return to you. Without instruments, a person can detect a time interval of about 0.1 s. How many kilometers away would the mirror have to be? Compare this size with that of some known objects.

7. What is the frequency of a microwave that has a wavelength of 3.0 cm?
8. Find the illumination 4.0 m below a 405-lm lamp.
9. A public school law requires a minimum illumination of 160 lx on the surface of each student's desk. An architect's specifications call for classroom lights to be located 2.0 m above the desks. What is the minimum luminous flux the lights must deliver?
10. A 3-way bulb uses 50-100-150 W of electrical power to deliver 665, 1620, or 2285 lm in its three settings. The bulb is placed 80 cm above a sheet of paper. If an illumination of at least 175 lx is needed on the paper, what is the minimum setting that should be used?
11. ▶ A streetlight contains two identical bulbs 3.3 m above the ground. If the community wants to save electrical energy by removing one bulb, how far from the ground should the streetlight be positioned to have the same illumination on the ground under the lamp?

12. A student wants to compare the luminous flux from a bulb with that of a 1750-lm lamp. The two bulbs illuminate a sheet of paper equally. The 1750-lm lamp is 1.25 m away; the unknown bulb is 1.08 m away. What is its luminous flux?
13. A screen is placed between two lamps so that they illuminate the screen equally. The first lamp emits a luminous flux of 1445 lm and is 2.5 m from the screen. What is the distance of the second lamp from the screen if the luminous flux is 2375 lm?
14. Two lamps illuminate a screen equally. The first lamp has an intensity of 101 cd and is 5.0 m from the screen. The second lamp is 3.0 m from the screen. What is the intensity of the second lamp?
15. ▶ A 10-cd point source lamp and a 60-cd point source lamp cast equal intensities on a wall. If the 10-cd lamp is 6.0 m from the wall, how far is the 60-cd lamp?

USING LAB SKILLS

1. After doing the Physics Lab on page 334, use the small opening on the pinhole camera to form an image of the sun on the screen. Given that the diameter of the sun is approximately 1.4×10^6, use the relationship developed in Analysis question 4 to estimate the distance to the sun.
2. After completing the Pocket Lab on page 335, consider the following. Would you expect the values of lumens and watts for a fluorescent lamp to fit near the data for the incandescent lamps? Why? Find the data for fluorescent lamps. Use a different symbol and include this data on the graph. What does it show?

THINKING PHYSIC-LY

In a dress shop that has only fluorescent lighting, Jill insists on taking a sweater and scarf to the front door to check them together in daylight. Is she being reasonable?

8. No. In a weightless environment, the soap film would not be thicker at the bottom.
9. Light scattered from the atmosphere is polarized, but light scattered from the clouds is not. By rotating the filter, the photographer can reduce the amount of polarized light reaching the film.
10. a. Cellophane reflects red light, and either absorbs or transmits blue and green light. **b.** Cellophane transmits red light. **c.** Blue and green light are absorbed.
11. a. yellow **b.** yellow **c.** black
12. green and red
13. yellow
14. Black. Almost no light would get through.
15. Mix cyan and magenta.
16. No. Reflections off the top and bottom surfaces are inverted.

Answers To PROBLEMS

Complete solutions for all Chapter Review Problems can be found in the Problems and Solutions Manual accompanying this text.

1. 7.00×10^{-7} m
2. 3.84×10^{8} m
3. 5.0×10^{2} s
4. **a.** 4.2×10^{9} m
   b. 28 km/s
   c. 30 km/s
5. 3.03 m
6. 1.5×10^{4} km, 3/8 of the way around Earth
7. 1.0×10^{10} Hz
8. 2.0 lx
9. 8.0×10^{3} lm
10. 100-W (1620 lm) setting
11. 2.3 m
12. 1.31×10^{3} lm
13. 3.2 m
14. 36 cd
15. 15 m

Answers To USING LAB SKILLS

1. Students should use the relationship $d_i/d_o = h_i/h_o$. Typical values are $d_i = 16$ cm and $h_i = 0.15$ cm, so a typical estimate for d_o (the distance to the sun) is 1.5×10^8 km.
2. The data for the fluorescent lamps is quite different from the incandescent lamps. The data points for fluorescent lamps is much higher than the incandescent lamp curve. The graph shows that fluorescent lamps are more efficient.

Answer To THINKING PHYSIC-LY

Yes. Sunlight has different colors in its spectrum and will cause the colors to appear different than they appear in fluorescent light. In daylight, the sweater and scarf might not match at all.

CHAPTER 17 Reflection and Refraction

PLANNING GUIDE (5 class sessions)

CONTENTS	TEXT FEATURES	TEACHER RESOURCE PACKAGE	OTHER COMPONENTS
17.1 How Light Behaves at a Boundary, pp. 348–356 (4 Class Sessions) • The Law of Reflection • Refraction of Light • Snell's Law • Index of Refraction and the Speed of Light	**Physics Lab:** Bending of Light, p. 352 **Pocket Lab:** Reflections, p. 348 **Pocket Lab:** Refraction, p. 354 **Problem Solving Strategy:** Drawing Ray Diagrams, p. 353 **Concept Review,** p. 356	**Study Guide:** How Light Behaves at a Boundary **Physics Lab Data Sheet:** Bending of Light **Reteaching Master:** Demonstrating the Law of Reflection **Transparency Worksheet:** Index of Refraction	**Laboratory Manual:** Lab 17.1 Reflection of Light Lab 17.2 Snell's Law **Transparency 23:** Index of Refraction
17.2 Applications of Reflected and Refracted Light, pp. 356–361 (2 Class Sessions) • Total Internal Reflection • Effects of Refraction • Dispersion of Light	**Physics and Technology:** Fiber Optics in Medicine, p. 362 **Pocket Lab:** Now You See It..., p. 356 **Pocket Lab:** Just a Mirage, p. 358 **Concept Review,** p. 361	**Study Guide:** Applications of Reflected and Refracted Light **Critical Thinking Master:** The Shape of a Diamond **Enrichment Master:** Refraction	
Chapter Review, pp. 362–365	Summary Key Terms Reviewing Concepts Applying Concepts Problems Thinking Physic-ly	**Vocabulary Review** **Chapter Test**	**Test Bank**

SUPPLEMENTARY MATERIALS

SOFTWARE	AUDIOVISUAL	BOOKS/MAGAZINES
Introduction to General Physics, Disk VII: Reflection and Refraction, COMPress/Queue, Inc. (Apple II, IBM PC, Macintosh). *Ray Tracer,* Vernier (Apple II). *Sound and Light,* Queue, Inc. (Apple II, IBM PC, Macintosh).	Video: *The World of Light Energy,* Focus Media (still frame). Filmstrip: *Light,* Clearvue.	Easton, D. "On Reflections in Ponds." *The Physics Teacher,* March 1987, pp. 150–151. Edgar, Dale. "Simulating Optical Fibers." *The Physics Teacher,* November 1988, pp. 504–506. Hewitt, Paul G. "On Teaching Why a Rainbow Is Bowshaped." *The Physics Teacher,* October 1990, p. 509. Olson, Donald. "Monte Carlo Computer Simulation of a Rainbow." *The Physics Teacher,* April 1990, p. 226.

PROBLEM CORRELATION

CONCEPTS	CHAPTER REVIEW			PROBLEMS APPENDIX
	Reviewing Concepts	Applying Concepts	Problems	
17.1 How Light Behaves at a Boundary				
The Law of Reflection	1,2,3	1,2	1,2	1
Refraction of Light	4,5,6	3,4		
Snell's Law	7,8,9	5,6,7	3,4,5,6,7,8,9,10, 11,**12,13,14,15**	2,3,4,5,6,**7**,8,12
Index of Refraction and the Speed of Light		8,9	16,17,**18,19**	9,10,11
17.2 Applications of Reflected and Refracted Light				
Total Internal Reflection	10,11	10,11,12,13	20,21,22,**23**,24	13,14,15,**16**
Effects of Refraction	12	14		
Dispersion of Light	13,14	15,16,17	25,**26**,27,28	17,18

ACTIVITY AND DEMONSTRATION MATERIALS

PHYSICS LAB	POCKET LAB	DEMONSTRATIONS
Page 352 graph paper felt-tip pen ruler semicircular plastic dish water (or glycerine)	Pages 348, 354, 356, 358 tennis ball 1000-mL beaker nut golf ball aquarium calculator spoon wall facing the sun	Pages 348, 350, 351, 357, 359, 361 coin polystyrene cup dropping bottle microscope immersion oil fish tank laser fluorescent dye or milk mirror right angle prism chalk dust plastic 1 L cola bottle clear plastic box overhead projector

EXTENSION PROJECTS

LIBRARY RESEARCH

1. Newton's Rings
Investigate in the library to find out the significance of Newton's rings.

DISPLAY MODEL

2. Simulated Sunset
Demonstrate an artificial sunset using a bright incandescent light and an aquarium full of clean water. Add milk, drop by drop, and observe the results. What causes this effect? What is the purpose of the milk?

STUDENT READINGS

Mandolini, Dina. "Fiber Optics in Plants." *Scientific American,* August 1984.

Olivastro, D. "About the Looking Glass." *Science,* June 1988.

Peterson, I. "Shaking Raindrops Wash Out Rainbows." *Science News,* January 6, 1990.

Shellenberger, George. "Using a Standard Force to Verify Snell's Law." *The Physics Teacher,* September 1990, p. 422.

Tan, A., and King, Tom. "Solar Zenith and Local Time from a Rainbow." *The Physics Teacher,* April 1990.

Weiss, Peter L. "Reflections of Refraction." *Science News,* October 13, 1990.

Chapter 17

Reflection and Refraction

CHAPTER OVERVIEW

Theme Development: The mathematical ray model for light is shown to behave like a system by the application of the laws of reflection and refraction, and Snell's law. Content is built up from definitions of concepts and phenomena related to the symmetrical behavior of the model.

MISCONCEPTIONS

The changes of direction associated with refraction seem difficult for students to sort out. In Snell's law and the definition of the index of refraction, students may tend to neglect the trigonometric functions and calculate using the angles by themselves.

KEY TERMS

critical angle
diffuse reflection
dispersion
index of refraction
optically dense
refraction
regular reflection
Snell's law
total internal reflection

Laboratory Options

STUDENT EDITION

Physics Lab

Bending of Light	352

Pocket Labs

Reflections	348
Refraction	354
Now You See It . . .	356
Just a Mirage	358

TEACHER EDITION

Activities

Demonstration	348, 350, 351, 357, 359, 361
Discovery	353, 359

LABORATORY MANUAL

Reflection of Light	Lab 17.1
Snell's Law	Lab 17.2

CHAPTER 17

Reflection and Refraction

A Smile in the Sky

Rainbows are created by a combination of refraction and reflection in raindrops. As the rainbow is viewed, violet always appears on the bottom and red on the top. Explain the origin of the rainbow in this photograph.

Chapter Outline

A rainbow! Has anything seen in the sky captured the human imagination more than a rainbow? All you need to produce a rainbow is simultaneous sunshine and rain. Even the drops from a hose or lawn sprinkler will do. Stand with the sun low and behind you and look into the water drops. Each drop of water separates sunlight into a spectrum. Violet at the inside of the arc, then blue, green, yellow, and, at the outside, red. Look carefully at the photo, and you will see more. The sky is brighter inside the bow than outside. There is also a secondary rainbow, with the order of colors reversed. The fact that we can use our knowledge of the behavior of light to explain the rainbow makes it no less beautiful.

✓ Concept Check

The following terms or concepts from earlier chapters are important for a good understanding of this chapter. If you are not familiar with them, you should review them before studying this chapter.
- wave properties, behavior at boundaries, reflection, Chapter 14
- light wavelengths, Chapter 16

Introducing The Chapter

A Smile in the Sky

Using The Photo: Rainbows have been a source of wonderment to people since the beginning of recorded history. The principles behind the formation of a rainbow are so complex that some are still not fully understood. Scientists do know that refraction, total internal reflection, and dispersion all play a part in the rainbow effect. To answer the chapter opener question, refer students to page 361.

✓ Concept Check

Make sure students have a clear understanding of the concepts taught in Chapters 14 and 16 that are listed in the Concept Check. Students with a knowledge of wave properties, behavior at boundaries, reflection, and light wavelengths will more successfully assimilate the concepts of light reflection and refraction explored in detail in this chapter.

Assessment Options

Portfolio Assessment
Extension Project 1, TWE, p. 346b
Critical Thinking, TWE, p. 350
Portfolio Assessment, TWE, p. 357
Enrichment, TWE, p. 358
Applying Concepts 13, p. 364

Performance Assessment
Extension Project 2, TWE, p. 346b
Pocket Labs, pp. 348, 354, 356, 358
Physics Lab, p. 352

Content Assessment
Self Assessment: Practice Problems, pp. 354, 355
Assessment, Critical Thinking, TWE, p. 352
Pocket Lab Assessment, p. 354
Concept Reviews, pp. 356, 361
Chapter Review, pp. 362–365
Supplemental Problems, pp. 700–701

Group Assessment
Activities for group assessment occur with Cooperative Learning and lab activities.

17.1 HOW LIGHT BEHAVES AT A BOUNDARY

Preparation

OBJECTIVES

The objectives are listed on the student page. Remind students to preview these objectives as a study guide to this major section.

OVERVIEW

This section sets out the behavior of the light model according to the law of reflection. The lesson introduces index of refraction and explains how it is derived from Snell's law.

BRIDGING

Previously introduced terms that students will be using in this section include *medium, angles of incidence* and *reflection, normal, ray, sine,* and *transparent.*

POCKET LAB

REFLECTIONS

Purpose: to observe the law of reflection.
Materials: tennis ball or handball.
Outcome: The ball will bounce off the wall in a very predictable way: The angle of incidence will equal the angle of reflection (disregard the vertical component of the ball's path). This rule can be applied to light as long as the reflecting surface is very smooth.

1 Focus

Demonstration: Place a coin in the bottom of a polystyrene cup. Have students gather around the cup and move back until the coin just disappears from view. Have students remain standing at a distance while you pour water into the cup until it is full or the coin reappears. Ask students if they can explain what is happening. [With only air in the cup, light traveled in a straight line. As the water is added, light is refracted from the water/air boundary and more of the cup's bottom is visible.]

Objectives

- state the law of reflection.
- distinguish between diffuse and regular reflection and give examples.
- define refraction; predict whether a ray will be bent toward or away from normal when light moves from one medium to another.
- state Snell's law; be able to solve refraction problems.
- relate index of refraction to speed of light in medium; solve problems relating these two quantities.

17.1 HOW LIGHT BEHAVES AT A BOUNDARY

Light, as we know, travels in straight lines and at a very high velocity. But, its velocity depends on the medium through which it moves. So, it acts just like any other wave moving from one medium to another. What happens to light striking such a surface?

POCKET LAB

REFLECTIONS

Toss a tennis ball or a handball against a wall so that it will bounce to a lab partner. Can you predict where the ball must hit on the wall to bounce in the right direction? If your partner is closer (or farther) from the wall, does your rule still work? Write a general rule that seems to work. Does your rule for the bouncing ball work for predicting the path of light? How is it similar?

The Law of Reflection

When a light ray strikes a reflecting surface, the angle of reflection is equal to the angle of incidence. Both of these angles are measured from a normal (perpendicular) to the surface at the point of incidence. The incident ray, the reflected ray, and the normal all lie in the same plane, Figure 17–1.

When a beam of light strikes most surfaces, it reflects in many directions. A painted wall or a page in a book may appear to be very smooth. On the scale of the wavelength of light, these surfaces are rough and have many small projections. Rays of light strike different parts of these projections. Each ray reflects according to the law of reflection. The rays are reflected in many different directions, producing a **diffuse reflection,** in Figure 17–2b, d.

If a beam of light falls on a very smooth surface, the rays undergo **regular reflection**. Figure 17–2a and c shows a beam of parallel rays reflecting from a smooth, flat surface. Since each ray follows the law of reflection, the reflected rays are also parallel. The rays are arranged in the same order after they leave a smooth surface as they were before they approached the surface.

Refraction of Light

Light travels at different speeds in different media. When the speed of light in one medium is slower than that in another, the medium is said to be more **optically dense**. Light also changes direction, or bends, as it moves from one medium to another if the angle of incidence is not zero. The change in direction or bending of light at the boundary between two media is called **refraction**.

FIGURE 17–1. A light ray reflecting from a mirror shows that the angle of incidence equals the angle of reflection.

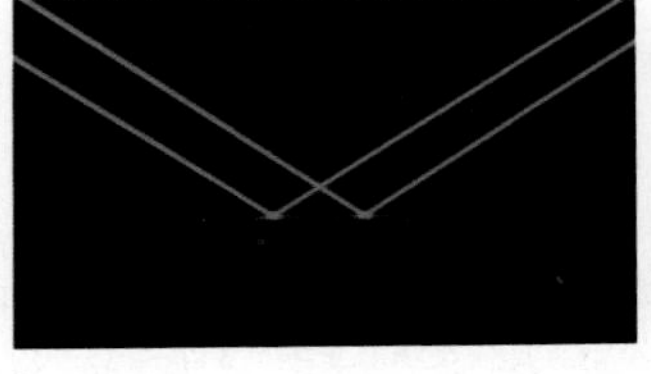
a

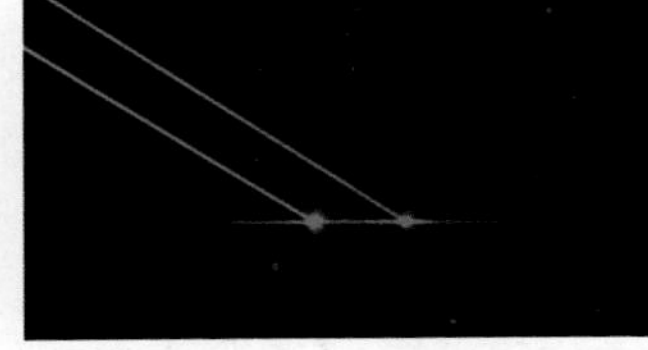
b

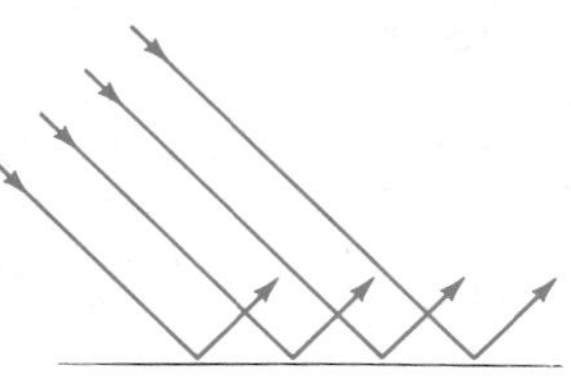
c

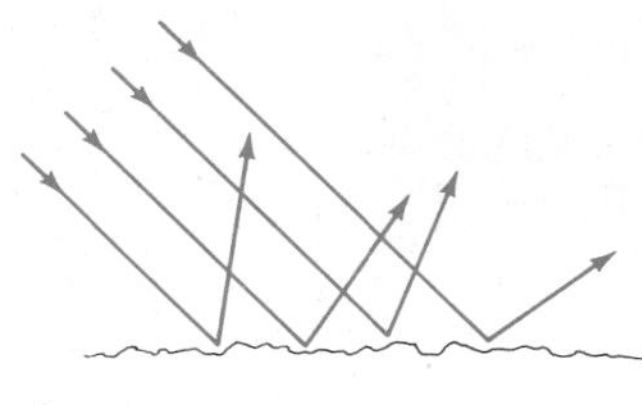
d

FIGURE 17–2. When parallel light rays strike a mirror surface, they reflect as parallel rays (a) (c). When parallel light rays strike a rough surface, they are randomly reflected (b) (d).

Consider an incident ray that falls on the boundary between two media. Once the ray enters a new medium, it is a refracted ray. The angle between the incident ray and a normal to the surface at the point of incidence is the angle of incidence, *i*. The angle between the refracted ray and the same normal is the angle of refraction, *r*. The incident ray, the refracted ray, and the normal lie in the same plane. Refraction occurs only when the incident ray strikes the boundary between the two media at a non-zero angle. When the angle of incidence is zero (the ray is perpendicular to the surface), the angle of refraction is also zero. The ray changes speed but passes straight into the new medium.

Refraction is the change in angle of light when moving from one medium into another.

Figure 17–3 shows two rays of light as they pass from air into glass. Part of the rays are reflected and part are transmitted (refracted). Note that as the rays enter a more optically dense medium where they travel more slowly, the refracted rays bend toward the normal. The angle of refraction is smaller than the angle of incidence.

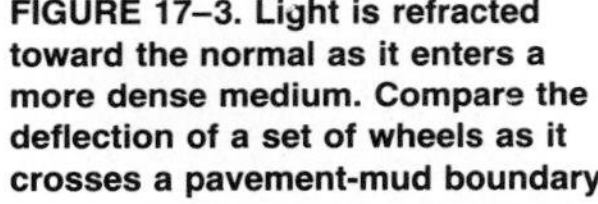
FIGURE 17–3. Light is refracted toward the normal as it enters a more dense medium. Compare the deflection of a set of wheels as it crosses a pavement-mud boundary.

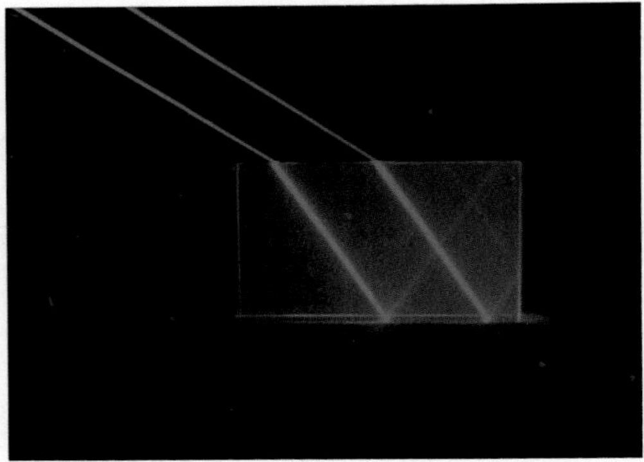

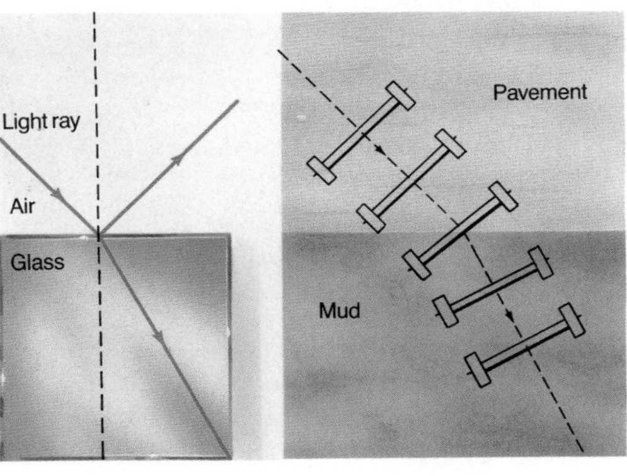

2 Teach

CONCEPT DEVELOPMENT

- There are three types of apparatus available from scientific supply houses that are equally useful in demonstrating reflection and refraction phenomena: the ray box, the optical disk, and the blackboard optics set. Instructions with these devices will provide many ideas for activities and demonstrations.
- The small, magnet-backed mirrors that students use in their lockers make fine reflecting surfaces in class on steel blackboards.

Connect to CHEMISTRY

The method of coating mirrors still used today was developed by Justus von Liebig in 1835. A compound of silver and ammonia is poured on the glass surface. Then a reducing agent such as formaldehyde is added to reduce the compound to metallic silver.

Telescope mirrors are coated without using a chemical reaction. The mirror is placed in a sealed chamber and all the air is removed. An aluminum rod is heated until it evaporates. The aluminum vapor slowly covers the mirror. Mirrors can also be covered with silver this way. Household mirrors are coated on the back in order to protect the coating. If you look carefully in a mirror, you can see two reflections—the bright one from the back surface and a weak one from the front. Telescope mirrors are coated on the front so that light will reflect from only one surface.

An aluminum coating reflects about 92% of blue light striking it and 90% of the green and red. Silver reflects 97% of the blue, but 99% of the green and red. How would the colors of objects seen in reflections in these two mirrors differ? [Blue is a little more strongly reflected by aluminum than the other colors, while it is a little less strongly reflected by silver. Therefore, reflections in aluminum are tinted slightly bluish, while those in silver are slightly reddish.]

Study Guide Master. Have students complete the Study Guide Master for Section 17.2.

Laboratory Manual. Give students additional experience with reflection of light by doing Lab 17.1 from the Laboratory Manual.

STUDY GUIDE MASTER

Use the Study Guide master for section 17.1.

LABORATORY MANUAL

Use Lab 17.1 with this section.

CONCEPT DEVELOPMENT

Show students the symmetrical form of Snell's law. Written in this form, the law should be much easier for students to remember.

Emphasize that the equation $n = \sin\theta_i/\sin\theta_r$ represents rays passing from a vacuum or air into a given medium. The general form of Snell's law works for all situations.

Critical Thinking: Here's a good challenge problem for students. Draw two flat mirrors facing each other at a 90° angle. Have students use the law of reflection and geometry to show that an incoming ray of light that strikes both mirrors will be reflected back opposite to the way it came in.

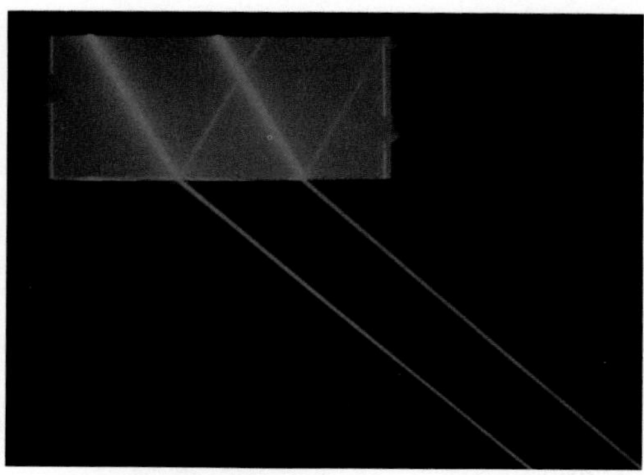

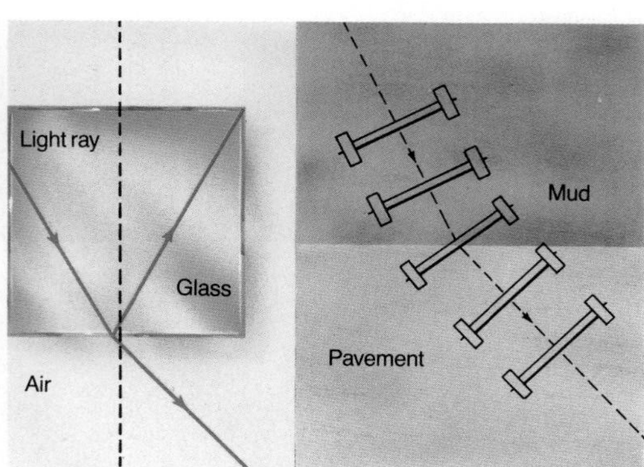

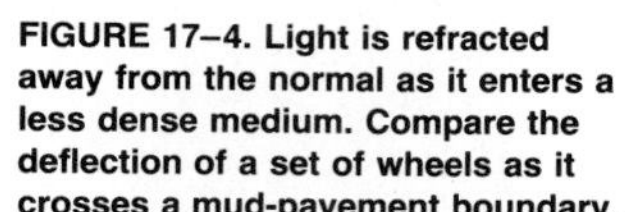

FIGURE 17–4. Light is refracted away from the normal as it enters a less dense medium. Compare the deflection of a set of wheels as it crosses a mud-pavement boundary.

In Figure 17–4, a light ray passes from glass into air. Rays that strike the surface at an angle are refracted away from the normal. When a light ray passes into a medium in which it travels faster, the light ray bends or refracts away from the normal. In other words, the angle of refraction is larger than the angle of incidence.

Figures 17–3 and 17–4 compare the refraction of light to a car entering or leaving a patch of mud. When the wheels enter the mud at an angle, Figure 17–3, the right wheel enters the mud before the left wheel. The right wheel slows before the left wheel. As a result, the car swings to the right or toward the normal. Figure 17–4 shows the car as it leaves the mud at an angle. The right wheel leaves the mud first and speeds up. The left wheel is still held back. Therefore, the car swings to the left or away from the normal. Keep this car analogy in mind until the behavior of light at various surfaces becomes more familiar to you.

Snell's Law

Rays of light that travel from air into glass, or any other medium more optically dense than air, are refracted toward the normal. As the angle of incidence increases, the angle of refraction increases, Figure 17–5. The relationship between the angle of incidence and the angle of refraction was discovered by the Dutch scientist Willebrord Snell (1591–1626) and is called **Snell's law**. This law states: *a ray of light bends in such a way that the ratio of the sine of the angle of incidence to the sine of the angle of refraction is a constant.* For a light ray passing from a vacuum into a given medium, this constant (the ratio of the sines) is called the **index of refraction**, n, for that medium. Snell's law can be written

$$n = \frac{\sin\theta_i}{\sin\theta_r}.$$

In this equation, θ_i is the angle of incidence, θ_r is the angle of refraction, and n is the index of refraction of the medium. Note that this equation applies *only* to a ray traveling from a vacuum into another medium.

F.Y.I.

Although Snell made his discovery in 1621, it was not well publicized until 1638. Descartes published the discovery without giving proper credit to Snell. Another of Snell's accomplishments is the development of a method for determining distances by trigonometric triangulation. This led to modern map making.

DEMONSTRATION

Purpose: to demonstrate index of refraction.

Equipment: dropping bottle, microscope, immersion oil

Procedure: 1. Fill the bottle almost to the top with immersion oil. Put the dropper in place. **2.** Show the bottle to the students. **3.** Squeeze the dropper top and release.

Results: the dropper becomes invisible in the oil.

Questions: Why does the dropper disappear after the top is squeezed? *The glass of the dropper has the same index of refraction as the immersion oil and therefore is invisible in the oil. When the top is squeezed, air, with a different index of refraction is forced out and replaced by the oil.*

Note: This demonstration will not work with Pyrex glass.

FIGURE 17–5. When light passes from one medium to another, the angle of refraction depends upon the angle of incidence. This is shown very clearly by the pencils of light leaving the glass prism.

In general, for a ray traveling from one medium into another medium, Snell's law can be written

$$n_i \sin \theta_i = n_r \sin \theta_r.$$

In this equation, n_i is the index of refraction of the incident medium, and n_r is the index of refraction of the second medium. Angles θ_i and θ_r are the angles of incidence and refraction, respectively. Figure 17–6 shows the path of light rays into and out of glass and water.

A ray diagram is very useful in solving problems involving the reflection and refraction of light. Some problems can be solved, at least approximately, using a diagram. You should sketch a ray diagram for all problems involving reflection or refraction to check the answer you get using a calculator.

The index of refraction of many transparent substances, such as water or glass, can be found by measurement. Direct a ray of light on the substance at a measured angle of incidence and measure the angle of refraction. The sine of the angle of incidence divided by the sine of the angle of refraction gives the index of refraction of the substance.

The refractive index can be determined by measuring angles of incidence and refraction.

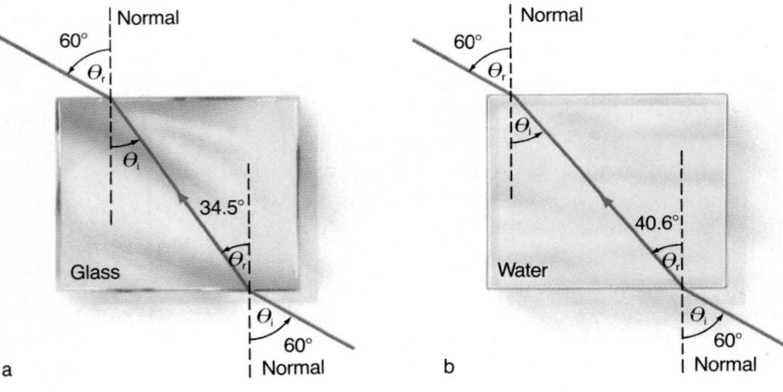

FIGURE 17–6. The index of refraction for glass is greater than that for water. If light enters both media at the same angle, the angle of refraction is greater for water. This result agrees with Snell's law.

CONCEPT DEVELOPMENT

- Use extreme care in doing any laser demonstration. Avoid looking into the direct beam or into reflected beams. Viewing diffuse reflections (such as the red spot made on a wall and a light beam scattered by dusty air) is safe.

Demonstrations: Many demonstrations can be done with a tank of water (an old fish tank could be used). By adding some fluorescent dye or a little milk, you can see a laser beam when you shine it into the tank.

- Place a mirror on the bottom of a tank. Shine a laser light on the mirror to see a ray of reflected light. Move the beam to show different angles of incidence and reflection.
- Shine a laser beam on a mirror on the bottom of a tank of water. The beam will emerge and make a spot on the ceiling. Have students note that the spot is not directly in line with the beam being reflected from the mirror. The beam is bent away from the normal as it leaves the water because it is refracted.

TEACHER F.Y.I.

In 1916–1917, Einstein demonstrated that molecules that were energized appropriately would emit monochromatic light. This principle led to the development of masers and lasers. The MASER (microwave amplification by stimulated emission of radiation) was conceived in 1951. The first visible light laser was produced in 1960. Lasers have the ability to transfer energy (and thus information) to a specific location with great accuracy because their light does not diverge as rapidly as ordinary light. Lasers are now in use in grocery stores to read price and product codes, in CD players to read discs, in medical facilities for cauterizing and cutting, in industry for welding and cutting, and in telephone systems in the form of fiber optics. They are also used in earthquake detectors and leveling devices, and are being developed as the ignition source for fusion reactions, which hold the promise of future energy production.

PHYSICS LAB

Process Skills: observing, questioning, defining operationally, hypothesizing, interpreting data, measuring.

Misconceptions: Many students will assume that light bends whenever it passes from one medium to another, including along the normal.

Teaching Suggestions: Give some groups glycerine instead of water. Ask all groups to check the accuracy of the sight lines. Ask students to measure the angles to the nearest 1/2 degree.

Lab Worksheet, Teacher Resource Package. Use the lab worksheet master provided for this chapter for students to record their data.

OBSERVATIONS

1. The sight lines point directly at the object. The light did not bend when passing from water into air.
2. The sight lines do not point directly toward the object.

ANALYSIS

1. In Part 1, the light passed directly along the normal. Whenever light passes along the normal, it does not bend.
2. Drawing these lines emphasizes that light bends at the boundary.
3. The angles must always be measured from the normal.
4. The angles in air will be larger than angles in water.
5. Student values should be in the range of 1.2 to 1.45 (10% error).
6. The class average for water should be close to 1.33.

APPLICATIONS

A flat piece of material would not focus light. All the light rays refract in the same direction when passing through it.

PHYSICS LAB: Bending of Light

Purpose

To observe when light bends and determine the index of refraction of water (or glycerine).

Materials

- graph paper
- felt-tip pen
- ruler
- semicircular plastic dish
- water (or glycerine)

Procedure

Part 1

1. Draw a line on the graph paper dividing the paper in half.
2. Use the felt-tip pen to draw a vertical line at the center of the straight edge of the plastic dish. This line will be your object.
3. Place the edge of the dish along the straight line so that the dish is on the bottom half of the paper and trace the outline of the dish on the paper.
4. Mark the position of the object on your paper.
5. Fill the dish 3/4 full of water (or glycerine) as your teacher indicates.
6. Lay a ruler on the bottom half of the paper. Adjust the position until the edge of the ruler seems to point at the object when you look through the water.
7. Have a lab partner look to verify that the ruler position is accurate.
8. Draw the line along the ruler edge to the edge of the dish.
9. Repeat steps 5-7 for a different position of the ruler.

Part 2

1. Wipe the vertical line from the dish and draw a vertical line at the center of the curved edge. This is your new object.

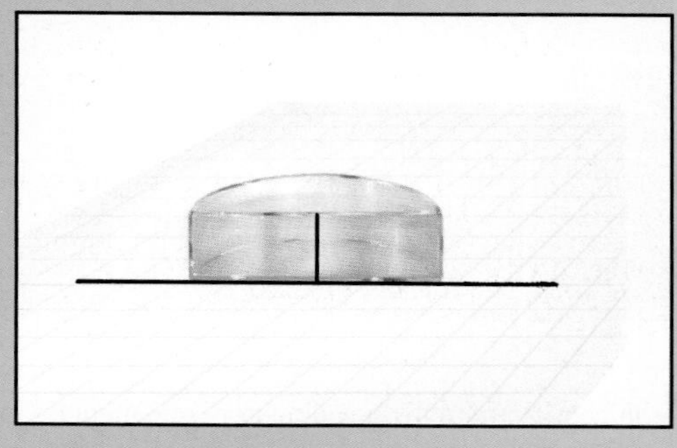

2. Repeat all steps above except this time the sighting of the ruler will be placed on the top half of the paper.
3. Carefully remove the dish from the graph paper.

Observations and Data

1. Look at the sight lines drawn in Part 1. Did the light bend when moving from water to air?
2. For Part 2, do the sight lines point directly toward the object?

Analysis

1. Explain why the light did not bend in Part 1. **Hint:** Draw the normal to the surface.
2. For Part 2, draw a line from the object position to where each sight line touched the dish.
3. Draw the normal at each point where the sight line touched the dish.
4. Measure the angles from the normal for the angles in air and water.
5. Calculate n, using Snell's law.
6. Write the values of the angles and the ratio of the sines on the chalkboard.

Applications

1. Could a flat piece of material be used for focusing light? Make a drawing to support your answer.

ASSESSMENT

Critical Thinking: To further assess students' understanding of the determination of refraction, ask the following questions.

1. Estimate the uncertainty and percent uncertainty in your angle measurements. [All angles should be within 2°. Using 2° as the uncertainty, the percent uncertainty of a 20° angle would be (2/20) x 100 = 10%. Note that the percentage will be larger for smaller angles.]

2. Identify the major sources of error in the experimental design and equipment. [The major sources of error were: lining up the flat edge of the dish with the reference line on the paper; difficulty in aligning the ruler toward the object; drawing the sight line without moving the ruler; accurately measuring the angles.]

Table 17–1

Indices of Refraction			
Medium	***n***	**Medium**	***n***
vacuum	1.00	crown glass	1.52
air	1.0003	quartz	1.54
water	1.33	flint glass	1.61
ethanol	1.36	diamond	2.42

PROBLEM SOLVING STRATEGY

1. Draw a diagram showing the two media. Label them, indicating the two indices of refraction, n_1 and n_2.
2. Draw the incoming ray to the point where it hits the surface. Draw a normal to the surface at that point.
3. Use a protractor to measure the angle of incidence.
4. Use Snell's law to calculate the angle of refraction.
5. Draw the refracted ray, using a protractor to find the correct angle.
6. Always make sure your answer obeys the qualitative statement of Snell's law: "Light moving from smaller n to larger n is bent toward the normal. Light moving from larger n to smaller n is bent away from the normal."

LITERATURE CONNECTION

It was the Rainbow gave thee birth
And left thee all her lovely hues.
W.H. Davies, 'The Kingfisher'

My heart leaps up when I behold
A rainbow in the sky.
Wordsworth

Example Problem

Snell's Law

A ray of light traveling through air is incident upon a sheet of crown glass at an angle of 30.0°. What is the angle of refraction?

Given: incident medium (air)
second medium (crown glass)
incident angle, $\theta_i = 30.0°$

Unknown: refracted angle, θ_r
Basic equation: $n_i \sin \theta_i = n_r \sin \theta_r$

Solution:
From Table 17–1, the index of refraction of air is 1.00 and that of crown glass is 1.52.

$$n_i \sin \theta_i = n_r \sin \theta_r$$

$$\text{so,} \quad \sin \theta_r = \frac{n_i \sin \theta_i}{n_r} = \frac{1.00 \sin 30.0°}{1.52} = \frac{0.500}{1.52} = 0.329$$

$$\text{or} \quad \theta_r = 19.2°$$

CONCEPT DEVELOPMENT

ACTIVITY

Discovery: Obtain test tubes large enough for students to put a finger in with room to spare. Have them fill the test tubes with water and observe how refraction makes their fingers appear "fat."

Laboratory Manual. Give students additional experience with Snell's law by doing Lab 17.2 from the Laboratory Manual.

CHECKING FOR UNDERSTANDING

We study reflection and refraction separately, although they usually occur together. Draw a simple sketch of a light ray incident on the boundary of a second medium and ask students to help you complete the total picture.

RETEACHING

Reteaching Master, Teacher Resource Package. Use the Reteaching Master for Chapter 17, Demonstrating the Law of Reflection.

Transparency Package. Reteach the concept of index of refraction using Transparency 23 and the accompanying worksheet.

EXTENSION

Earlier conceptions of the index of refraction referred to it as the ratio of the semichords. Draw a sketch of an interface between two media and show a ray of light incident on that interface. Draw a circle of a reasonable size with the center at the point of incidence. Label the angles of incidence and refraction. Draw the semichord (half the chord) of each angle from the normal over to where the incident or refracted ray hits the circle. Ask interested students if they can show that the ratio of the semichords is equivalent to our modern definition.

LAB WORKSHEET
Use the Lab Worksheet for Chapter 17 with this Physics Lab.

RETEACHING MASTER
Use the Reteaching master for Chapter 17 with this section.

LABORATORY MANUAL
Use Lab 17.2 with this section.

TRANSPARENCY
Use Transparency 23 with this section.

Answers To
PRACTICE PROBLEMS

Have students refer to Appendix A of the Solutions Appendix for complete solutions to Practice Problems.

1. 27.7°
2. 22.1°
3. **a.** 17.0°
   b. diamond
4. 1.5

POCKET LAB

REFRACTION

Purpose: to observe light refraction.

Materials: 1000-mL beaker; nut; golf ball.

Outcome: The nut will appear slightly larger than actual size. Students may be surprised to find that the edge of the ruler points to the center of the nut. The light that moves along the center of curvature does not bend. This light moves perpendicular to the curved surface. The golf ball appears wider, but not taller. The light bends because it does not hit perpendicular to the surface.

Assessment

Performance

Some beverage glasses are made with very thick glass walls so that it looks as if there is more beverage in the glass than there really is. Make a drawing to show the origin of this optical effect.

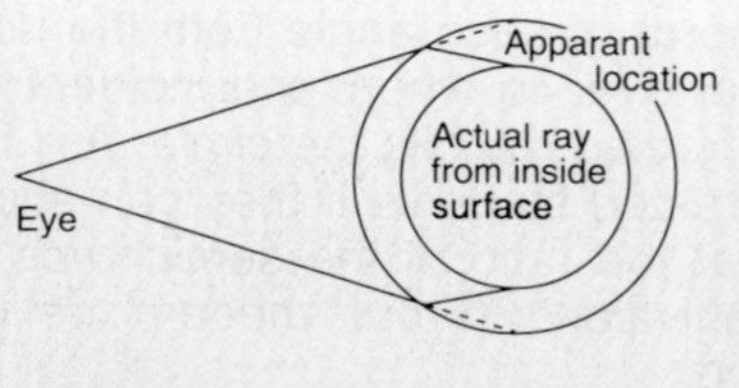

POCKET LAB

REFRACTION

Place a small hexagonal nut in the center of the bottom of a 1000-ml beaker. Fill the beaker one-half full of water. Look through the sides of the beaker at the nut while placing a ruler along the tabletop so that the edge of the ruler appears to point to the center of the nut. Do you think that the ruler really points to the nut? Look from the top to see where the ruler points. Place a golf ball on the nut. Look through the sides of the beaker at the ball. Describe your observations. Look through the sides of the beaker as you adjust the edge of the ruler to point to the edge of the golf ball. Look from the top. Make a drawing to show why the ball appears wide.

Practice Problems

1. Light in air is incident upon a piece of crown glass at an angle of 45.0°. What is the angle of refraction?
2. A ray of light passes from air into water at an angle of 30.0°. Find the angle of refraction.
3. A ray of light is incident upon a diamond at 45.0°.
   a. What is the angle of refraction?
   b. Compare your answer for **a** to your answer for Practice Problem 1. Does glass or diamond bend light more?
4. ▶ A block of unknown material is submerged in water. Light in the water is incident on the block at an angle of 31°. The angle of refraction in the block is 27°. What is the index of refraction of the unknown material?

Index of Refraction and the Speed of Light

Refraction occurs because the speed of light depends on the medium through which it travels. The index of refraction is a measure of the amount that light bends when passing into the medium from a vacuum.

Figure 17–7 shows the behavior of two parallel rays of light that are incident upon a glass plate from air. The rays are refracted toward the normal. Consider the wave front *CB* as it approaches the glass plate. After a time interval, the wave front reaches position *DA*. Since the speed of the wave is slower in the glass, point **C** on ray *y* travels only distance *CD*. Point **B** on ray *x* travels distance *BA*. This difference causes the wave front to turn.

During a time interval *t*, point **B** on ray *x* travels to **A** and point **C** on ray *y* travels to **D.** Therefore, the ratio of *BA* to *CD* is the same as the ratio of the speed of light in vacuum, *c*, to the speed of light in glass, v_g.

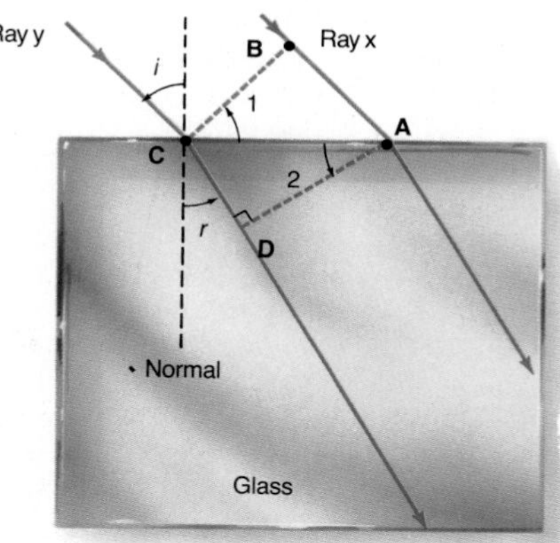

FIGURE 17–7. A diagram for refraction of two parallel light rays incident on a piece of glass. Dashed red lines represent wave fronts.

$$\frac{\frac{BA}{t}}{\frac{CD}{t}} = \frac{BA}{CD} = \frac{c}{v_g}$$

Angle θ_i in Figure 17–7 is equal to the angle of incidence of the ray. Angle θ_r is equal to the angle of refraction of the ray (corresponding sides mutually perpendicular). The sine of angle θ_i is BA/CA. The sine of angle θ_r is CD/CA. Since $n_{vacuum} = 1$, using Snell's law, the index of refraction is

$$n_g = \frac{\sin i}{\sin r} = \frac{\sin \theta_i}{\sin \theta_r} = \frac{BA/CA}{CD/CA} = \frac{BA}{CD} = \frac{c}{v_g}.$$

The index of refraction for any substance is then

$$\boxed{n_s = \frac{c}{v_s},}$$

where v_s represents the speed of light in the substance. The speed of light in a vacuum, 3.00×10^8 m/s, is known. Therefore, it is possible to calculate the speed of light in many substances by using the equation $v_s = c/n_s$.

Example Problem

Speed of Light in a Medium

The index of refraction of water is 1.33. Calculate the speed of light in water.

Given: $n_{water} = 1.33$, $c = 3.00 \times 10^8$ m/s

Unknown: v_{water}

Basic equation: $n_s = \frac{c}{v_s}$

Solution: $n_{water} = \frac{c}{v_{water}}$

so, $v_{water} = \frac{c}{n_{water}} = \frac{3.00 \times 10^8 \text{ m/s}}{1.33} = 2.26 \times 10^8$ m/s

The index of refraction is the ratio of the speed of light in a vacuum to the speed in the medium.

Practice Problems

5. Use Table 17–1 to find the speed of light in
   a. ethanol. **b.** quartz. **c.** flint glass.
6. The speed of light in a plastic is 2.00×10^8 m/s. What is the index of refraction of the plastic?
7. What is the speed of light for the substance of Practice Problem 4?
8. ▶ Suppose you had two pulses of light "racing" each other, one in air, the other in a vacuum. You could tell the winner if the time difference is 10 ns (10×10^{-9} s). How long would the race have to be to determine the winner?

CONCEPT DEVELOPMENT

Check to make sure that students can draw simple ray diagrams. Students may have difficulty translating the words of a problem into a suitable drawing.

Critical Thinking: Ask students why it is so difficult to see at night when the highway is wet. [The layer of water on the road changes it from a diffuse reflector to a regular one, so only a little light is in the correct direction to be reflected back to your eyes. Some light is scattered by rain droplets, too.]

Guided Practice: Go over the Example Problem on this page, then have students work in class on the first two Practice Problems that follow.

Independent Practice: Assign the remaining Practice Problems for homework and spend time reviewing them with students during the next class period.

INDEPENDENT PRACTICE/ EXTENSION

Refer to the Assignment Guide on page 362 for additional questions and problems for independent practice.

Answers To
PRACTICE PROBLEMS

Have students refer to Appendix A of the Solutions Appendix for complete solutions to Practice Problems.

5. **a.** 2.21×10^8 m/s
   b. 1.95×10^8 m/s
   c. 1.86×10^8 m/s
6. 1.50
7. 2.0×10^8 m/s
8. 10 km

3 Close

CONVERGENT QUESTION

Have students explain why knowing the speed of light in a material is equivalent to knowing the material's index of refraction.

17:1 ASSIGNMENT GUIDE

	PRACTICE	EXTENSION
CHAPTER REVIEW pp. 362–365		
· Reviewing Concepts	1–9	
· Applying Concepts		1–9
· Problems*	1–11, 16–17	12–15, 18–19
APPENDIX B PROBLEMS*		
· Chapter 17, p. 700	1–6, 8–12	7

* Complete solutions to all Chapter Review and Appendix problems appear in the Problems and Solutions Manual.

CONCEPT REVIEW ANSWERS

1.1 Diffuse: paper, rough metal, ground glass, milk-jug plastic. Regular: glass, smooth water, polished metal.

1.2 No. If the sine of the incident angle doubles, the sine of the angle of refraction doubles. The sine of an angle is not proportional to the angle.

1.3 $n_{water} < n_{liquid} < n_{crown\ glass}$ therefore, n_{liquid} must be between 1.33 and 1.52.

1.4 Critical Thinking: No. It would mean the velocity of light in the medium is faster than it is in a vacuum.

17.2 APPLICATIONS OF REFLECTED AND REFRACTED LIGHT

Preparation

OBJECTIVES

The objectives are listed on the student page. Remind students to preview these objectives as a study guide to this major section.

OVERVIEW

New concepts in this teaching block include total internal reflection, critical angle, and dispersion.

BRIDGING

Students will apply their definitions for amplitude, wavelength, and spectrum to the topic of refractive indices in this section.

POCKET LAB

NOW YOU SEE IT . . .

Purpose: to observe effects of total internal reflection.

Materials: aquarium; calculator.

Outcome: The calculator is easily seen through the front surface of the aquarium. The calculator cannot be seen through either side. This is an example of total internal reflection.

CONCEPT REVIEW

1.1 Give examples of diffuse and regular reflectors.

1.2 If you double the angle of incidence, the angle of reflection also doubles. Does the angle of refraction?

1.3 You notice that when a light ray enters a certain liquid from water, it is bent toward the normal, but when it enters the same liquid from crown glass, it is bent away from the normal. What can you conclude about its index of refraction?

1.4 **Critical Thinking:** Could an index of refraction ever be less than 1? What would that imply about the velocity of light in that medium?

Objectives

- **explain total internal reflection; define the critical angle.**
- **explain effects caused by the refraction of light in a medium with varying refractive indices.**
- **explain dispersion of light in terms of index of refraction.**

17.2 APPLICATIONS OF REFLECTED AND REFRACTED LIGHT

Modern societies depend on communication systems. The telephone has become necessary for both homes and businesses. But, in many cities, the underground pipes containing telephone wires are so full that no new customers can be added. Now the old wires can be replaced by a bundle of optical fibers that can carry thousands of telephone conservations at once. Moreover, illegal tapping of optical fibers is almost impossible. This application of the reflection of light is revolutionizing our communication systems.

POCKET LAB

NOW YOU SEE IT...

Fill an aquarium with water. Place a hand-held calculator against the back side (outside) of the aquarium. Look at the calculator through the front side of the aquarium. Look at the calculator through the left side and right side of the aquarium. Explain your observations.

Total Internal Reflection

When a ray of light passes from a more optically dense medium into air, the light is bent away from the normal. In other words, the angle of refraction is larger than the angle of incidence. The fact that the angle of refraction is larger than the angle of incidence leads to an interesting phenomenon known as total internal reflection. **Total internal reflection** occurs when light passes from a more optically dense medium to a less optically dense medium at an angle so great that there is no refracted ray. Figure 17–8 shows such an occurrence. Ray 1 is incident upon the surface of the water at angle θ_i. Ray 1 produces the angle of refraction, θ_r. Ray 2 is incident at such a large angle, θ_i, that the refracted ray lies along the surface of the water. The angle of refraction is 90°.

For light traveling from one medium into another, Snell's law is

$$n_i \sin \theta_i = n_r \sin \theta_r$$
$$(n_{water})(\sin \theta_i) = (n_{air})(\sin \theta_r)$$
$$(1.33)(\sin \theta_i) = (1.00)(\sin 90°).$$

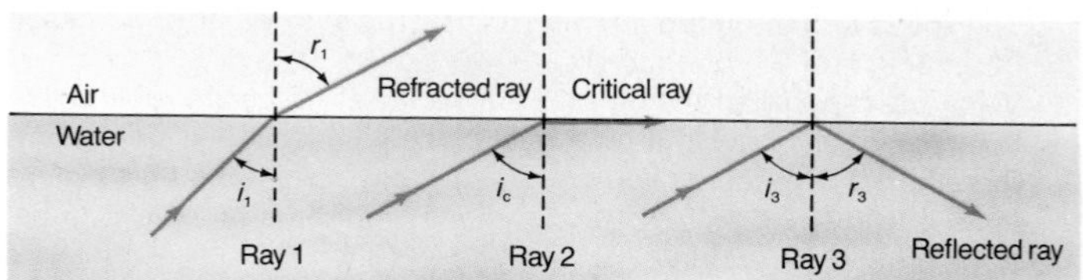

FIGURE 17–8. Ray 1 is refracted. Ray 2 is refracted along the boundary of the medium showing the critical angle. An angle of incidence greater than the critical angle results in the total internal reflection of ray 3.

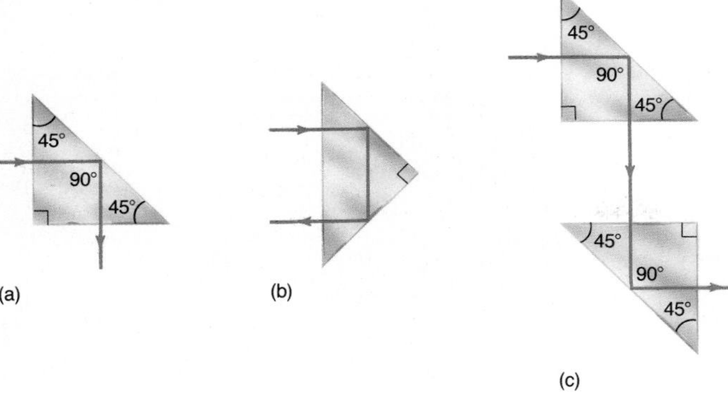

FIGURE 17–9. Internal reflection in a prism.

Solving the equation for $\sin \theta_i$,

$$\sin \theta_i = \frac{(1.00)(\sin 90°)}{1.33} = 0.752$$

$$\text{so, } \theta_i = 48.8°.$$

When an incident ray of light passing from water to air makes an angle of 48.8°, the angle of refraction is 90°.

The incident angle that causes the refracted ray to lie right along the boundary of the substance, angle θ_c, is unique to the substance. It is known as the **critical angle** of the substance. The critical angle, θ_c, of any substance may be calculated as follows.

$$n_i \sin \theta_i = n_r \sin \theta_r$$

In this situation, $\theta_i = \theta_c$; $n_r = 1.000$; and $\theta_r = 90.0°$.

$$\sin \theta_c = \frac{(1.00)(\sin 90.0°)}{n_i} = \frac{1}{n_i}$$

For crown glass, the critical angle can be calculated as follows.

$$\sin \theta_c = \frac{1}{1.52} = 0.658$$

$$\theta_c = 41.1°$$

Any ray that reaches the surface of water at an angle greater than the critical angle, Figure 17–8, ray 3 cannot leave the water. All of the light is reflected. Total internal reflection has occurred.

Total internal reflection causes some curious effects. Suppose you look at the surface of a tank from underwater, Figure 17–10. A doll with its legs submerged may appear to be inverted. Likewise, if a swimmer is near the surface of a quiet pool, the swimmer may not be visible to an observer standing near the side of the pool. Total internal reflection has also given rise to the field of fiber optics.

FIGURE 17–10. This underwater photograph of a partly submerged doll shows both the direct and transmitted images of its hands and legs

1 Focus

Total internal reflection is easily misunderstood. The series of pictures in Figure 17–8 on page 356 is helpful in illustrating the progression from refraction to reflection. Do as many demonstrations with total internal reflection as your time and ingenuity will allow.

2 Teach

CONCEPT DEVELOPMENT

- Point out that optical fibers are used in communication because many thousands of signals can be transmitted simultaneously through a thin cable over long distances by total internal reflection.

Demonstration: Shine a laser through a right-angle prism as in Figure 17–9. Put some chalk dust in the air so students can see the rays going in and coming out. Also shine the laser through a Plexiglass rod curled at one end so students can see that the light is "trapped" inside the rod and comes out the end.

- Because there is no light refracting into the outer medium with total internal reflection, totally reflecting prisms are used instead of mirrors in such instruments as binoculars and periscopes.

Study Guide Master. Have students complete the Study Guide Master for Section 17.2.

Assessment

Portfolio

Collect newspaper and magazine stories on present and future uses of optical fibers. Write a summary paragraph for each article explaining how the fiber is used. What are the advantages of optical fibers in the selected applications?

TEACHER F.Y.I.

Most binoculars contain two prisms mounted at right angles to each other, redirecting light from the objective to the eyepiece by total internal reflection.

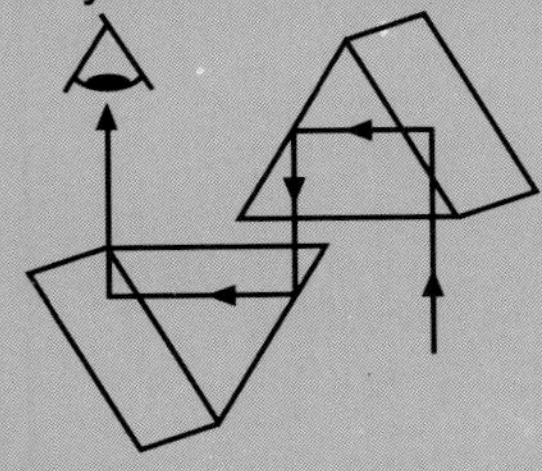

The point is to "fold" the light path to make the binoculars shorter and more compact than they would otherwise have to be. Some very high-quality binoculars, which are long and straight, do not use prisms because they degrade the image slightly.

CONCEPT DEVELOPMENT

- The three optical demonstration devices mentioned earlier (optical disk, ray box, and blackboard optics) can all be used to demonstrate total internal reflection.
- Total internal reflection can also be shown with a light source and the coiled plastic rods available from science supply houses.

Enrichment: Optical fibers are a mainstay of modern technology whether they are used as phone lines, in automobiles, carrying signals in computers, or as novelties. Some of your students may want to investigate the very interesting process by which optical fibers are manufactured.

- A popular toy, often available at souvenir shops, is a small flashlight with a bundle of attached optical fibers. When the light is on, you can see the light coming out of the ends of the fibers.

POCKET LAB

JUST A MIRAGE

Purpose: to observe bending of light producing a mirage.

Materials: spoon; wall facing the sun.

Outcome: A close look along the surface of the wall will reveal the wavy "heat lines" that are often seen on highways. As the spoon is brought near the wall, a mirror image will be seen.

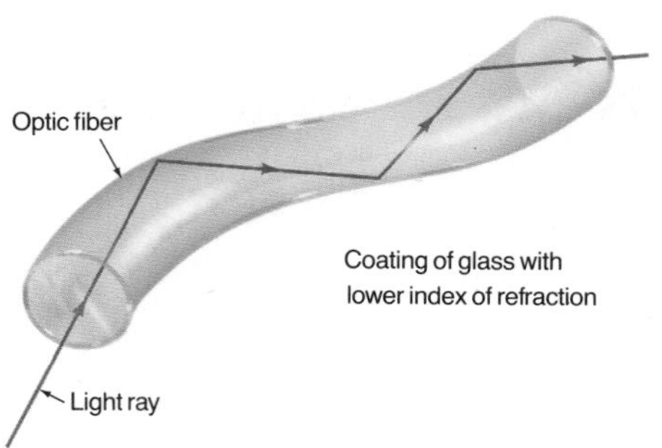

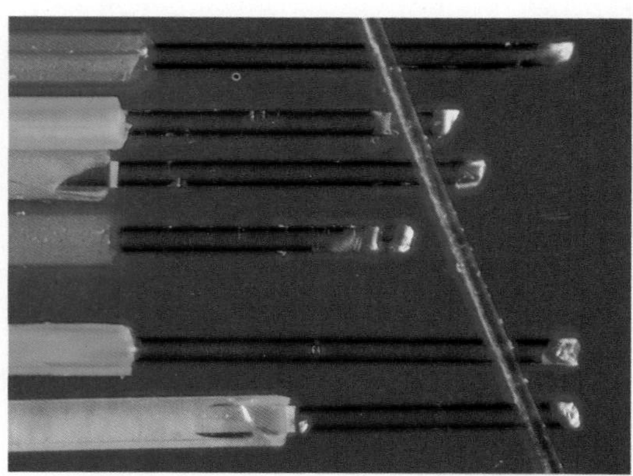

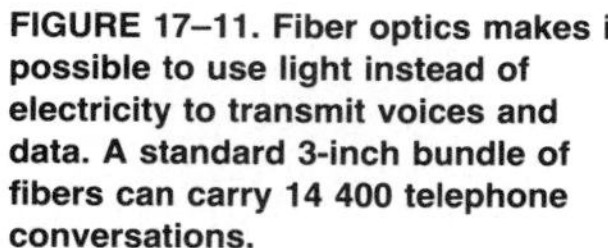

FIGURE 17–11. Fiber optics makes it possible to use light instead of electricity to transmit voices and data. A standard 3-inch bundle of fibers can carry 14 400 telephone conversations.

What happens to light that enters a long, thin glass rod? Figure 17–11 shows the path of one ray. Each surface reflection is at an angle larger than the critical angle. The reflection is total, keeping the light within the rod. Light acts the same way in a thin glass fiber coated with a layer of glass with a lower index of refraction. Such a thin, flexible optical fiber can be easily bent around corners or combined with many other fibers into a cable.

Optical fibers are used to transmit light signals.

Light passing through optical fibers can be used to transmit information. Normally telephone, radio, and television information is transmitted by varying the amplitude of the signal. In fiber optics technology, the amplitude of the electromagnetic signal can be converted into a digital signal, a series of binary bits, "0"s and "1"s. For example, a signal with amplitude 13 would be 1,1,0,1, while 3 would be 0,0,1,1. A light that is turned on (for a 1) and off (for a 0) produces a signal made up of a series of light pulses that can be transmitted by a fiber. A solid-state laser at one end of an optical fiber is turned on and off very rapidly. The series of pulses is detected at the other end of the fiber and is converted back into a signal of varying amplitude. Information equivalent to 25 000 telephone conversations can be carried by a fiber the thickness of a human hair. For this reason, optical fibers are being used to transmit telephone, computer, and video signals within buildings, from city to city, and even across oceans.

Optical fibers are used for more than communication. Two bundles of fibers are used to explore the inside of the human body. One bundle transmits light, while the other carries the reflected light back to the doctor. Plants have also been shown to use total internal reflection to "pipe" light to cells that utilize light energy.

POCKET LAB

JUST A MIRAGE

Have you ever seen a mirage? Have you ever seen a mirage produced by a vertical surface? Find a wall at least 10 m long that is facing the sun. Place the side of your head against one end of the wall and watch closely as your lab partner brings a spoon or other shiny object near the opposite end of the wall. Describe your observations. Explain the results.

Effects of Refraction

Many interesting effects are caused by the refraction of light. Mirages, the apparent shift in the position of objects immersed in liquids, and the lingering daylight after the sun is below the horizon are a few examples.

TEACHER F.Y.I.

Due to a peculiarity in the way the speed of sound changes with depth in the ocean, there is a layer in the ocean called the SOFAR channel that acts like an optical fiber for sound, and can allow sound to travel for great distances—tens of thousands of kilometers. This channel is used by ships in distress for sending signals and probably has military applications as well. A textbook on oceanography will describe this phenomenon further.

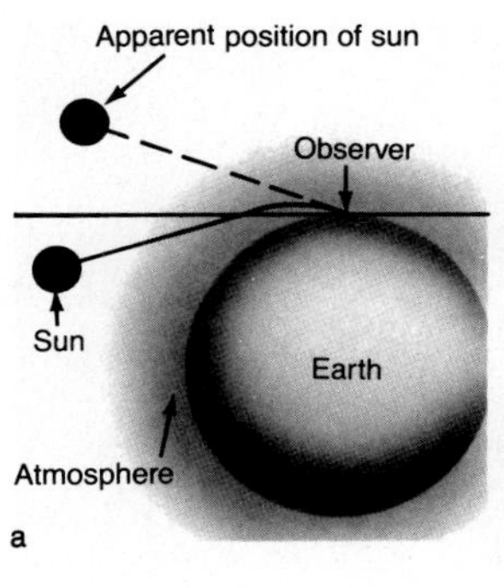

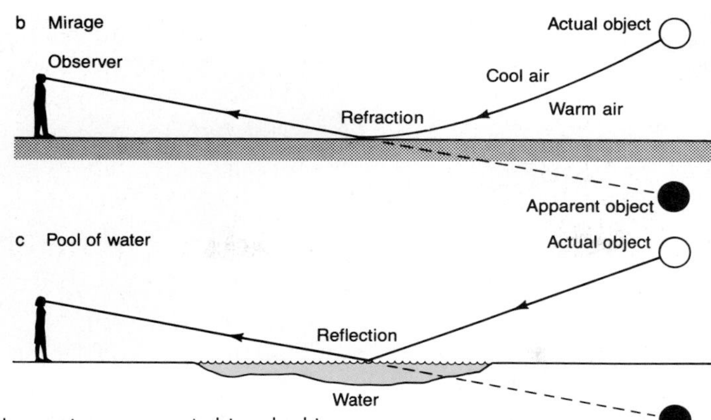

FIGURE 17–12. After the sun has actually set, it is still visible due to refraction of light over the horizon through the atmosphere (a). Refraction of light in air of different densities (b) produces an effect similar to the reflection of light off a pool of water (c).

Mirages can be observed along highways in summer. A driver looking almost parallel to the road sees what looks like a puddle of water. The puddle, however, disappears as the car approaches. The mirage is the result of the sun heating the road. The hot road, in turn, heats the air above it, while the air farther above the road remains cool. The index of refraction of air at 30°C, for example, is 1.00026, while that of air at 15°C is 1.00028. Thus, there is a continuous change in the index of refraction of the air. A ray of light aimed toward the road encounters the smaller index of refraction and is bent away from the normal, that is, more parallel to the road. The ray bends, in Figure 17–12b. The motorist actually sees light from the sky, which looks like light reflected from a puddle.

An object submerged in a liquid is not where it appears to be. As a result of refraction, an object may appear to be much closer to the surface of the liquid than it really is. Refraction also makes a spoon placed in a glass of water appear bent.

Light travels at a slightly slower speed in Earth's atmosphere than it does in outer space. As a result, sunlight is refracted by the atmosphere. In the morning, this refraction causes sunlight to reach us before the sun is actually above the horizon, Figure 17–12a. In the evening, the sunlight is bent above the horizon after the sun has actually set. Thus, daylight is extended in the morning and evening because of the refraction of light.

F. Y. I.

In 1880, a few years after he invented the telephone, Alexander Graham Bell created a device, called the photophone, that transmitted sound using a beam of light. The device was not useful because there were no sources of intense light beams and no sensitive detectors. Today, fiber optics make an adaptation of the photophone a reality.

FIGURE 17–13. Mirages are caused by the refracting properties of a nonuniform atmosphere. Scientists are unable to explain exactly some complex mirage.

CONCEPT DEVELOPMENT

As an aid in remembering which color of light bends the most going through a prism, use this mnemonic: "blue bends best."

Critical Thinking Master, Teacher Resource Package. You may wish to have students complete the Critical Thinking Master for Chapter 17, The Shape of a Diamond.

ACTIVITY

Discovery: Pass around some ordinary three-sided prisms. Have students put a finger below the bottom face and move their eyes around the prism until the finger disappears. Explain that this is due to total internal reflection.

Demonstration: Total internal reflection can be shown in a stream of water. Punch a small hole in a plastic 1-L soft drink bottle near the bottom on the side. Fill the bottle with water, darken the room, and shine a laser through the bottle from the side opposite the hole so that the laser light exits the hole with the water. The laser will make the stream of water appear red. (Place the bottle at the edge of the table so you can catch the water as it flows out.) For a touch of humor, catch the water in a cup to which you have secretly added a few drops of red food coloring. When you turn on the lights, the students will be surprised that the water still appears red.

STUDY GUIDE MASTER

Use the Study Guide master for section 17.2.

CRITICAL THINKING

Use the Critical Thinking master for Chapter 17 with this section.

CONCEPT DEVELOPMENT

CHECKING FOR UNDERSTANDING

Select a problem on total internal reflection at the end of the chapter. Begin by asking students to diagram the situation and then solve it. The drawing is a critical aid to understanding.

RETEACHING

Review the phenomenon of refraction. If possible, demonstrate how refraction works, proceeding into total internal reflection as the angle of incidence increases beyond the critical angle. Take time to use a prism to disperse light. Stress how the main phenomenon is refraction, the behavior of light at an interface, and that total internal reflection and dispersion are examples of refraction under special circumstances.

EXTENSION

Enrichment Master. With this section, use the Enrichment Master, Refraction in Minerals, from the Teacher Resource Package.

INDEPENDENT PRACTICE/ EXTENSION

Refer to the Assignment Guide for additional questions and problems for independent practice.

Guided Practice: Go over the Concept Review Questions on page 361 in class to help review the concepts of this section.

Critical Thinking: Suppose that the phenomenon of dispersion did not occur. Ask students what optical effects would be missing from our visual experience. [Rainbows, colored rings around the moon or sun, colored fringes around many brightly illuminated objects, spectra from prisms, chromatic aberration in lenses, colors in sparkling gems, etc.]

FIGURE 17–14. White light directed through a prism is dispersed into bands of different colors.

Dispersion of Light

In most materials, the index of refraction depends on the wavelength.

Light of all wavelengths travels through the vacuum of space at 3.00×10^8 m/s. In other media, however, light waves travel more slowly. In addition, waves of different wavelengths travel at different speeds. This fact means that the index of refraction of a material depends on the wavelength of the incident light.

If the angle of refraction depends on wavelength, the light is dispersed.

In glass and most other materials, red light travels fastest; it has the smallest index of refraction. Violet light, on the other hand, is slowed the most; it has the largest index of refraction. As a result, when white light falls on a prism, red light is bent the least and violet light the most, Figure 17–14. The wavelengths (colors) are separated. The light leaving the prism is dispersed to form a spectrum. **Dispersion** is the separation of light into a spectrum by refraction. Newton investigated dispersion as shown in Figure 17–15. The first prism, *ABC*, spread the colors into the spectrum *p, q, r, s, t*. Newton then used a lens to direct all colors on to the second prism, *EDG*. White light came out of this prism. In this way Newton demonstrated that the prisms did not somehow add the colors to the light.

Glass is not the only substance that disperses light. A diamond not only has one of the highest refractive indices of any material, it also has one of the largest variations in the index. Thus, it disperses light more than most other materials. The intense colors seen when light is dispersed in a diamond is the reason these gems are said to have "fire."

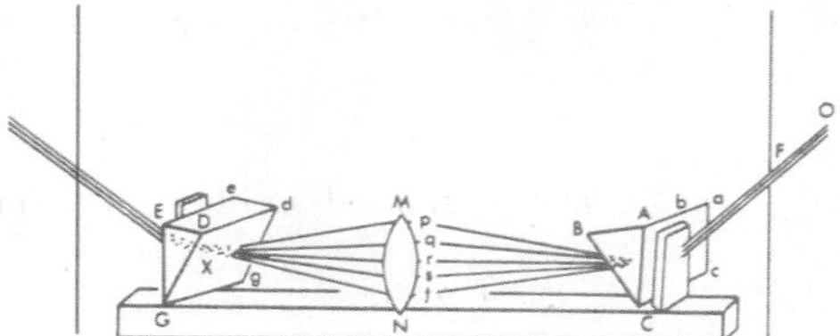

FIGURE 17–15. This figure is an old sketch showing Newton's demonstration using prisms. Prism *ABC* separates white light into colors; prism *EDG* combines the colors back into white light.

Multicultural Connections

Many civilizations have used astronomical information about Sirius A, the brightest star visible in the northern hemisphere, to construct calendars. The Dogon tribe of Mali, in Africa, not only used Sirius A, but also Sirius B, a white dwarf. Their 700-year-old knowledge about such things as the period of Sirius B is interesting because Sirius B is not visible to the naked eye. There have been several attempts to explain how the Dogon obtained their knowledge. One theory holds that a traveling Jesuit priest gave them the information. Another suggests that traders from North Africa brought lenses that the Dogon fashioned into a simple telescope. Whatever the true story is, there is no evidence among present-day Dogons as to the validity of either of these theories.

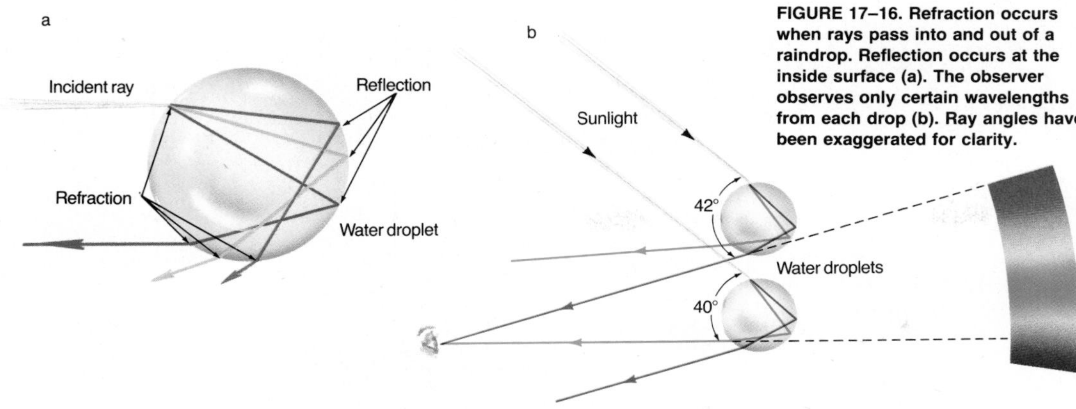

FIGURE 17–16. Refraction occurs when rays pass into and out of a raindrop. Reflection occurs at the inside surface (a). The observer observes only certain wavelengths from each drop (b). Ray angles have been exaggerated for clarity.

Different light sources have different spectra. A prism can be used to determine the spectrum of a source. Light from an incandescent lamp, for example, contains all visible wavelengths of light. When this light passes through a prism, a continuous band of color is seen. Light from a fluorescent lamp has both a continuous spectrum and light emitted at four individual wavelengths. Thus, its spectrum contains both a continuous band and bright lines at specific colors.

Dispersion in a prism is used to analyze the spectrum of light source.

A rainbow is a spectrum formed when sunlight is dispersed by water droplets in the atmosphere. Sunlight that is incident on a water droplet is refracted. Because of dispersion, each color is refracted at a slightly different angle, Figure 17–16a. At the back surface of the droplet, the light undergoes total internal reflection. On the way out of the droplet, the light is once more refracted and dispersed. Although each droplet produces a complete spectrum, an observer will see only a certain wavelength of light from each droplet. The wavelength depends on the relative positions of sun, droplet, and observer. Because there are millions of droplets in the sky, a complete spectrum is seen. Red light is most intense from droplets that make an angle of 42° with respect to the direction of the sun's rays. Blue light is most intense from those drops making a 40° angle.

The separation of colors in a rainbow is the result of dispersion in a raindrop.

◀ A Smile in the Sky

CONCEPT REVIEW

2.1 If you were to use quartz and crown glass to make an optical fiber, which would you use for the coating layer? Why?

2.2 Is there a critical angle for light going from glass to water? How about water to glass?

2.3 Why can you see the sun just above the horizon when it has already set?

2.4 **Critical Thinking:** In what direction can you see a rainbow on a rainy late afternoon?

CONCEPT DEVELOPMENT

Remind students that a rainbow can be produced outside by standing with the sun at your back, then spraying water into the air in front of you. If there are enough droplets, you'll get a lovely rainbow. It works best in the morning or late afternoon when the sun angle is fairly low.

Demonstration: You can make a rainbow using a clear plastic box and an overhead projector. Position the projector as if you were going to project an image on the front wall of the room. Tape a piece of paper over the upper mirror unit of the projector. Place a clear plastic box 3/4 full of water on the stage of the overhead. Turn off the lights, turn on the overhead projector, and observe rainbows on each side wall.

Critical Thinking: Ask students to consider their experiences viewing a spectrum through a prism. Ask them to try to estimate by how much (by what angle) the refraction is different for red and blue light. Have them check their estimates by looking in the problems for this section at the end of the chapter.

3 Close

CONVERGENT QUESTION

Have students imagine how sound would behave if air showed dispersive behavior. Suggest a situation where three or four notes are played simultaneously and they are listening to them from a distance. [Since dispersion means different frequencies travel at different speeds, the notes would be heard at slightly different times instead of all at once.]

CONCEPT REVIEW ANSWERS

2.1 Crown glass, because it has a lower index of refraction.

2.2 Yes, since $n_{glass} > n_{water}$. No, there is a critical angle only when light goes from glass to water.

2.3 Because of bending of light rays in the atmosphere; refraction.

2.4 **Critical Thinking:** In the east (the sun must always be at your back).

TEACHER F.Y.I.

In the chapter opening photograph, you can see a faint second-order rainbow. Descartes was probably the first person to explain the formation of the primary and secondary rainbow in a treatise published in 1637. The second-order rainbow occurs because the light rays are reflected twice inside the drop before emerging, Figure 17–16.

Newton derived a formula for the angular size of the rainbow after multiple (N) reflections of the light inside the raindrops. For $N = 1$ the angle would be about 42°, and for $N = 2$, about 51°. These are indeed the angles for the first two rainbows.

Edmund Halley worked on the problem and found that for $N = 3$ and $N = 4$, the rainbows would appear around the sun. These would be difficult to see because of the brightness of the sun.

Physics and technology

A fiber material should be strong, flexible, and easy to manufacture. It should be immune to chemical attack, have low optical attenuation (light loss), and have a relatively high index of refraction.

The first reference describes the development of new glass and crystalline fibers that can transmit infrared light and promise higher transparencies than silica and silica-based glasses. It includes communications, medical, and laser applications. The other two references concentrate on medical applications.

Physics and technology

FIBER OPTICS IN MEDICINE

Optical fibers are providing physicians with revolutionary tools for medical imaging, diagnosis, and treatment. The small, flexible fibers can be inserted into many areas of the body that are inaccessible by other means.

By directing a light source through the fibers, physicians can examine light reflected from internal organs and blood vessels in minute detail. Using a variety of sensing techniques, optical fibers can analyze blood chemistry, measure blood flow, compute various body pressures, and monitor levels of toxins, hormones, and therapeutic drugs.

Some of the most important applications of optical fibers are in laser surgery. Laser light transmitted through optical fibers is used to cauterize blood vessels and incisions to stop bleeding, vaporize blockages in coronary arteries, and destroy localized tumors.

Many fiber-optic procedures do not require anesthesia or hospitalization. They thus have the potential to reduce the cost and risk of many types of medical care.

· What would be the desirable characteristics of materials used as optical fibers?

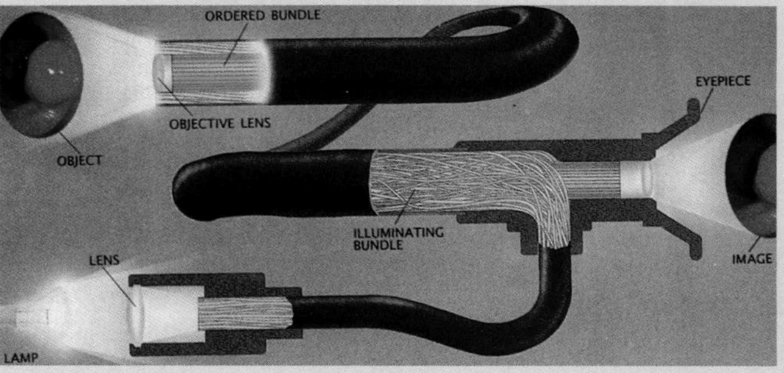

Teacher Resources: Drexhage, Martin G. and Moynihan, Cornelius T. "Infrared Optical Fibers," *Scientific American.* November 1988, pages 110–114, 116.
Katzir, Abraham. "Optical Fibers in Medicine," *Scientific American.* May 1989, pages 120–125.
"Shedding Light on Tumors," *Discover.* September 1990, pages 12, 14.

CHAPTER 17 REVIEW

SUMMARY

17.1 How Light Behaves at a Boundary

- The law of reflection states that the angle of reflection is equal to the angle of incidence.
- Refraction is the bending of light rays at the boundary between two media. Refraction occurs only when the incident ray strikes the boundary at an angle.
- Snell's law states that when light goes from a medium with small n to one with large n, it is bent toward the normal. Light going from materials with a large n to those with a small n is bent away from the normal.

17.2 Applications of Reflected and Refracted Light

- Total internal reflection occurs if light is incident on a boundary from the medium with the larger index of refraction. If the angle of incidence is greater than the critical angle, no light leaves; it is all reflected.
- Light waves of different wavelengths have slightly different refractive indices. Thus they are refracted at different angles. Light falling on a prism is dispersed into a spectrum of colors.

KEY TERMS

diffuse reflection
regular reflection
optically dense
refraction
Snell's law
index of refraction
total internal reflection
critical angle
dispersion

CLOSING CHAPTER 17

Review Summary statements and Key Terms with your students.

ASSESSMENT

Vocabulary Review Master, Teacher Resource Package. Use this master to check students' understanding of Key Terms.

Evaluation Masters. Use Parts A and B of the Chapter Evaluation Masters from the Teacher Resource Package to test qualitative chapter objectives. Use Parts C and D to test quantitative chapter objectives.

ENRICHMENT MASTER

Use the Enrichment master for Chapter 17 with this section.

REVIEW MASTER

Use the Vocabulary Review master for Chapter 17 with this section.

EVALUATION MASTER

Use the Chapter Evaluation master for Chapter 17 with this section.

17:2 ASSIGNMENT GUIDE

	PRACTICE	EXTENSION
CHAPTER REVIEW pp. 362–365		
· Reviewing Concepts	10–14	
· Applying Concepts		10–17
· Problems*	20–22, 24–25, 27–28	23, 26
APPENDIX B PROBLEMS*		
· Chapter 17, pp. 700–701	13–15, 17–18	16

* Complete solutions to all Chapter Review and Appendix problems appear in the Problems and Solutions Manual.

REVIEWING CONCEPTS

1. What is meant by the normal to a surface?
2. How does regular reflection differ from diffuse reflection?
3. Does the law of reflection hold for diffuse reflection? Explain.
4. Copy Figure 17–17 onto your paper. Draw a normal and label the angle of incidence and the angle of refraction if the light went from substance A to substance B.

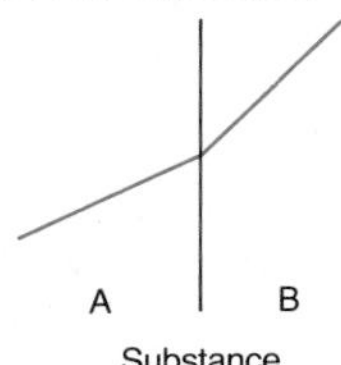

FIGURE 17–17. Use with Reviewing Concepts 4 and Applying Concepts 7.

5. Compare the angle of incidence with the angle of refraction when a light ray passes from air into glass at a non-zero angle.
6. Compare the angle of incidence with the angle of refraction when a light ray leaves glass and enters air at a non-zero angle.
7. What are the units of the index of refraction?
8. State Snell's law in your own words.
9. Derive $n = \frac{\sin \theta_i}{\sin \theta_r}$ from the general form of Snell's law, $n_1 \sin \theta_1 = n_2 \sin \theta_2$. State any assumptions and restrictions.
10. What is the "critical angle" of incidence?
11. What happens to a ray of light with an angle of incidence greater than the critical angle?
12. Explain mirages.
13. List the different colors of light in the order of increasing
    a. wavelength. **b.** frequency.
14. What evidence is there that diamond has a slightly different index of refraction for each color of light?

APPLYING CONCEPTS

1. A dry road is a diffuse reflector, while a wet road is not. Sketch a car with headlights illuminating the road ahead. Show why the wet road would appear darker to the driver than the dry road.
2. Why is it desirable that the pages of a book be rough rather than smooth and glossy?
3. Is it necessary to measure the volume of a glass block to find its optical density? Explain.
4. A light ray strikes the boundary between two transparent media. What is the angle of incidence for which there is no refraction?
5. In the Example Problem on Snell's law, a ray of light is incident upon crown glass at 30.0°. The angle of refraction is 19.2°. Assume the glass is rectangular in shape. Construct a diagram to show the incident ray, the refracted ray, and the normal. Continue the ray through the glass until it reaches the opposite edge.
   a. Construct a normal at this point. What is the angle at which the refracted ray is incident upon the opposite edge of the glass?
   b. Assume the material outside the opposite edge is air. What is the angle at which the ray leaves the glass?
   c. As the ray leaves the glass, is it refracted away from or toward the normal?
   d. How is the orientation of the ray leaving the glass related to the ray entering the glass?
6. Assume the angle of incidence remains the same. What happens to the angle of refraction as the index of refraction increases?
7. Which substance, A or B, in Figure 17–17 has a larger index of refraction? Explain.
8. How does the speed of light change as the index of refraction increases?
9. How does the size of the critical angle change as the index of refraction increases?
10. Which two pairs of media, air and water or air and glass, have the smaller critical angle?
11. Examine Figure 17–5. Why do the two left-hand bottom rays that enter the prism exit vertically while the two top rays exit horizontally? **Hint:** If you look carefully, you will find that the middle ray has both vertical and horizontal intensity and that there is a trace of the other ray moving vertically.
12. If you crack the windshield in your car, you will see a silvery line along the crack. The two pieces of glass have separated at the crack, and there is air between them. The silvery line indicates light is reflecting off the crack. Draw a ray diagram to explain why this occurs. What phenomenon does this illustrate?

Answers To
REVIEWING CONCEPTS

1. any line that is perpendicular to the surface at any point
2. When parallel light is reflected from a smooth surface, the rays are reflected parallel to each other. The result is an image of the origin of the rays. When light is reflected from a rough surface, it is reflected in many different directions. The rays are diffused or scattered. No image of the source results.
3. Yes. Each individual ray follows the law of reflection. Because the surface is rough, the normals at individual locations are typically not parallel to each other. Therefore, the reflected rays are not parallel to each other.
4.

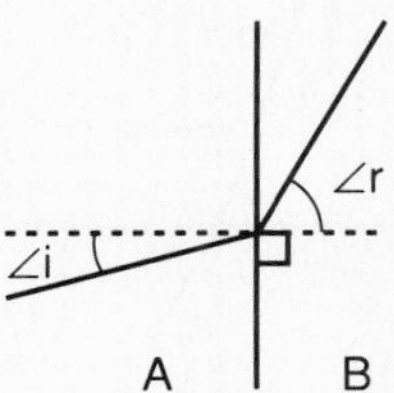

5. The angle of incidence is larger than the angle of refraction, since air has a smaller index of refraction.
6. The angle of incidence is smaller than the angle of refraction, since glass has a larger index of refraction.
7. The index of refraction has no units.
8. Whenever a ray of light passes from one medium into another at some angle, the ray is refracted in such a way that the ratio of the sine of the angle of incidence to the sine of the angle of refraction is a constant for all angles of incidence.
9. The angle of incidence must be in air. If we let substance 1 be air, then $n_1 = 1.000$, $\theta_1 = \theta_i$, and $\theta_2 = \theta_r$. Therefore,

$$n_1 \sin \theta_1 = n_2 \sin \theta_2$$
$$\sin \theta_i = n \sin \theta_r$$
$$\frac{\sin \theta_i}{\sin \theta_r} = n$$

10. The term "critical angle" refers to the incident angle that causes the refracted ray to lie right along the boundary of the substance when a ray is passing from a dense to less dense medium. It may also be termed the "incident angle," which, if exceeded, will cause total internal reflection.

Answers To
REVIEWING CONCEPTS (cont.)

11. The ray is totally reflected and none of the light is refracted.
12. Mirages are caused by a phenomenon of light refraction that is detailed in the chapter.
13. a. violet, indigo, blue, green, yellow, orange, red **b.** red, orange, yellow, green, blue, indigo, violet
14. White light travels through a diamond and is dispersed, which means that each color of light has a different index of refraction.

Answers To
APPLYING CONCEPTS

1. Less light is reflected back to the car from a wet road.

2. The smoother and glossier the pages are, the less diffuse reflection the light will have and the greater the glare from the page.
3. No. Optical density is related to the speed of light in the block and has nothing to do with the block's volume.
4. An angle of incidence of 0° allows the light to go through unchanged.
5. a. 19.2° **b.** 30.0° **c.** It is refracted away from the normal. **d.** The ray leaving the glass is parallel to the ray entering the glass, but it is at a different location.

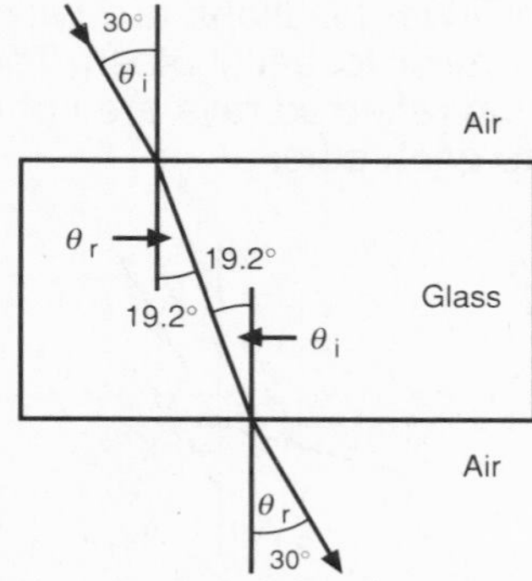

6. The angle of refraction will decrease as the index of refraction increases.
7. Refer to Figure 17–17. The angle in substance A is smaller, so it has the larger index of refraction.
8. As the index of refraction of a material increases, the speed of light in that material decreases.
9. The critical angle decreases as the index of refraction increases.
10. Air and glass have the smaller critical angle. The critical angle for air and water is 48.6°. The critical angle for air and glass is 41°.
11. The incident angles with which the two bottom rays strike the surface of the glass are greater than the critical angle for glass, and, therefore, total internal reflection occurs.
12.

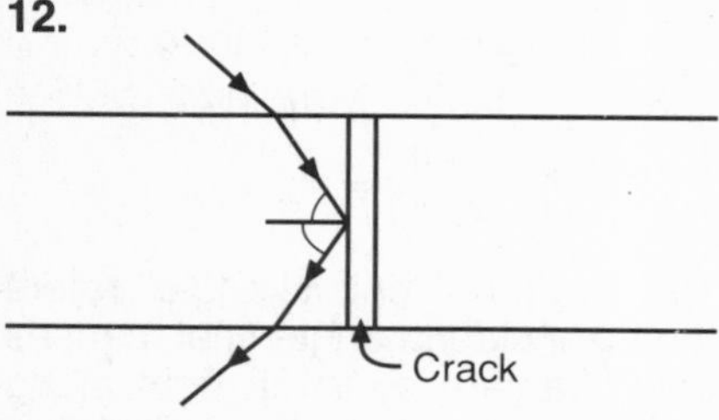

This illustrates light reflected at angles larger than the critical angle.

13. According to legend, Erik the Red sailed from Iceland and discovered Greenland after he had seen the land in a mirage. Draw a sketch of Iceland and Greenland and explain how the mirage might have occurred.

FIGURE 17–18.

14. A prism bends violet light more than red light. Explain.
15. Which color of light travels fastest in glass: red, green, or blue?
16. Why would you never see a rainbow in the southern sky if you were in the northern hemisphere?

PROBLEMS

17.1 How Light Behaves at a Boundary

1. A ray of light strikes a mirror at an angle of 53° to the normal.
   a. What is the angle of reflection?
   b. What is the angle between the incident ray and the reflected ray?
2. A ray of light incident upon a mirror makes an angle of 36.0° with the mirror. What is the angle between the incident ray and the reflected ray?
3. A ray of light has an angle of incidence of 30.0° on a block of quartz and an angle of refraction of 20.0°. What is the index of refraction for this block of quartz?
4. A ray of light travels from air into a liquid. The ray is incident upon the liquid at an angle of 30.0°. The angle of refraction is 22.0°.
   a. What is the index of refraction of the liquid?
   b. Refer to Table 17–1. What might the liquid be?
5. A ray of light is incident at an angle of 60.0° upon the surface of a piece of crown glass. What is the angle of refraction?
6. A light ray strikes the surface of a pond at an angle of incidence of 36.0°. At what angle is the ray refracted?
7. Light is incident at an angle of 60.0° on the surface of a diamond. Find the angle of refraction.
8. A ray of light has an angle of incidence of 33.0° in crown glass. What is the angle of refraction?
9. A ray of light passes from water into crown glass at an angle of 23.2°. Find the angle of refraction.
10. Light goes from flint glass into ethanol. The angle of refraction in the ethanol is 25°. What is the angle of incidence in the glass?
11. A beam of light strikes the flat, glass side of a water-filled aquarium at an angle of 40° to the normal. For glass, $n = 1.50$. At what angle does the beam
    a. enter the glass?
    b. enter the water?
12. ▶ A thick sheet of plastic, $n = 1.500$, is used as the side of an aquarium tank. Light reflected from a fish in the water has an angle of incidence of 35.0°. At what angle does the light enter the air?
13. ▶ A light source, *S*, is located 2.0 m below the surface of a swimming pool and 1.5 m from one edge of the pool. The pool is filled to the top with water.
    a. At what angle does the light reaching the edge of the pool leave the water?
    b. Does this cause the light viewed from this angle to appear deeper or shallower than it actually is?
14. ▶ A ray of light is incident upon a 60-60-60-degree glass prism, $n = 1.5$, Figure 17–19.
    a. Using Snell's law, determine the angle θ_r to the nearest degree.
    b. Using elementary geometry, determine the values of angles *A, B,* and *C*.
    c. Determine angle *D*.

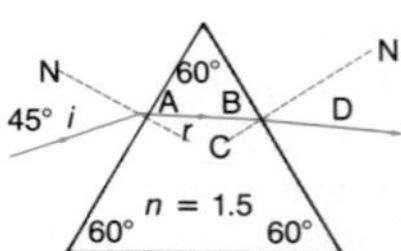

FIGURE 17–19. Use with Problem 14.

13.

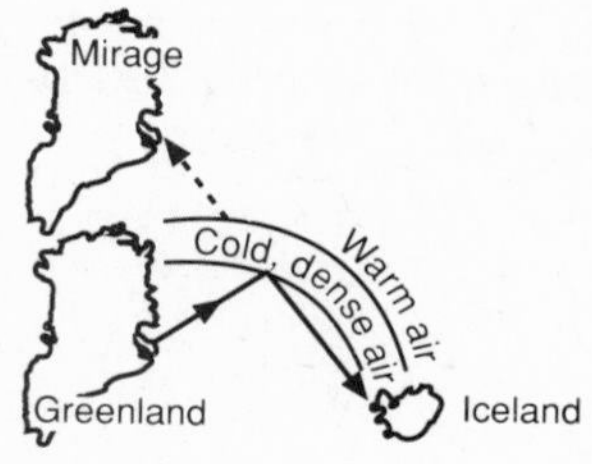

Even though Greenland is below the horizon, it is visible as a mirage due to the refraction of light.
14. Violet light travels slower in a prism than red light.

▶ **15.** A sheet of plastic, $n = 1.500$, 25 mm thick is used in a bank teller's window. A ray of light strikes the sheet at an angle of 45°. The ray leaves the sheet at 45° but at a different location. Use a ray diagram to find the distance between the ray that leaves and the one that would have left if the plastic were not there.

16. What is the speed of light in diamond?

17. The speed of light in chloroform is 1.99×10^8 m/s. What is its index of refraction?

▶ **18.** The speed of light in a clear plastic is 1.90×10^8 m/s. A ray of light enters the plastic at an angle of 22°. At what angle is the ray refracted?

▶ **19.** How many more minutes would it take light from the sun to reach Earth if the space between them were filled with water rather than a vacuum? The sun is 1.5×10^8 km from Earth.

17.2 Applications of Reflected and Refracted Light

20. Find the critical angle for diamond.

21. A block of glass has a critical angle of 45.0°. What is its index of refraction?

22. A ray of light in a tank of water has an angle of incidence of 55°. What is the angle of refraction in air?

▶ **23.** A light ray enters a rectangle of crown glass, Figure 17–20. Use a ray diagram to trace the path of the ray until it leaves the glass.

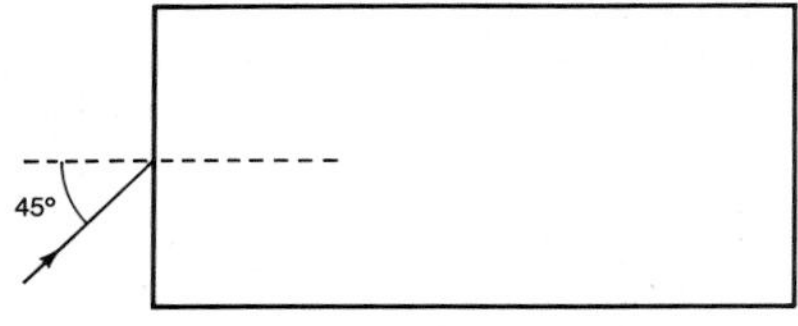

FIGURE 17–20. Use with Problem 23.

24. The critical angle for special glass in air is 41°. What is the critical angle if the glass is immersed in water?

25. The index of refraction for a diamond for red light, 656 nm, is 2.410, while that for blue light, 434 nm, is 2.450. Suppose white light is incident on the diamond at 30.0°. Find the angles of refraction for these two colors.

▶ **26.** The index of refraction for crown glass for red light is 1.514, while that for blue light is 1.528. White light is incident on the glass at 30.0°.
- **a.** Find the angles of refraction for these two colors.
- **b.** Compare the difference in angles to that for diamond found in Problem 25.
- **c.** Use the results to explain why diamonds are said to have "fire."

27. The index of refraction of crown glass for violet light is 1.53, while for red light it is 1.51.
- **a.** What is the speed of violet light in crown glass?
- **b.** What is the speed of red light in crown glass?

28. Just before sunset, you see a rainbow in the water from a lawn sprinkler. Carefully draw your location and the locations of the sun and the water from the sprinkler that show the rainbow.

USING LAB SKILLS

1. Would the reflection rule you devised in the Pocket Lab on page 348 work for a brick wall? Why? Would the rule work for a smaller object such as a golf ball or a small steel ball? Explain.
2. In the Pocket Lab on page 356, apparently the light reflected from the calculator does not travel through the back of the aquarium and through the side toward your eye. What do you predict should happen to a laser light that is pointed through the back wall toward the side wall? Would it go through the side wall? Try it? Describe and explain your results.

THINKING PHYSIC-LY

Although the light coming from the sun is refracted while passing through Earth's atmosphere, the light is not separated into its spectrum. What does this tell us about the speeds of different colors of light traveling through air?

15. Red light because it is refracted the least by glass.

16. You can see a rainbow only when the sun's rays come from behind you at an angle not greater than 42° with the horizon. When you are facing south in the northern hemisphere, the sun is never behind you at an angle of 42° or less.

Answers To
PROBLEMS

Complete solutions for all Chapter Review problems can be found in the Problems and Solutions Manual accompanying this text.

1. **a.** 53°
b. 106°
2. 108°
3. 1.46
4. **a.** 1.34
b. water
5. 34.7°
6. 26.2°
7. 21.0°
8. 55.9°
9. 20.2°
10. 20.9°
11. **a.** 25°
b. 29°
12. 49.8°
13. **a.** 53°
b. shallower
14. **a.** 28°
b. *A,* 62°; *B,* 58°; *C,* 32°
c. 53°
15. 8 mm
16. 1.24×10^8 m/s
17. 1.51
18. 14°
19. 2.7 min
20. 24.4°
21. 1.41
22. no angle
23. Refer to Problems and Solutions Manual.
24. 61°
25. red, 12.0°; blue, 11.8°
26. **a.** red, 19.3°; blue, 19.1°
b. diamond difference: red, 18.0°; blue, 18.2°; crown glass difference: red, 10.7°; blue, 10.9°
c. more red light emerges than blue light
27. **a.** 1.96×10^8 m/s
b. 1.99×10^8 m/s
28. Refer to Problems and Solutions Manual.

Answers To
USING LAB SKILLS

1. The reflection rule would work as long as the wall was fairly smooth. For a smaller object or a rougher wall, the rule still works, but the angle of reflection would be less predictable. The phenomena would be like diffuse reflection instead of regular reflection.

2. The laser beam could not be seen. The laser light bends when it enters the back wall of the aquarium and reflects at the side wall. Most students will be surprised at this result, but it is easy to predict and explain. The laser light is more concentrated but obeys the same laws as other light. The laser light shows an internal reflection.

Answer To
THINKING PHYSIC-LY

The fact that the light is not separated into its spectrum shows that different colors of light travel through air at almost exactly the same speed.

CHAPTER

18 Mirrors and Lenses

PLANNING GUIDE (6 class sessions)

CONTENTS	TEXT FEATURES	TEACHER RESOURCE PACKAGE	OTHER COMPONENTS
18.1 Mirrors, pp. 368–378 (3 Class Sessions) • Objects and Their Images in Plane Mirrors • Concave Mirrors • Spherical Aberration and Parabolic Mirrors • Real vs Virtual Images • Real Images Formed by Concave Mirrors • Virtual Images Formed by Concave Mirrors • Virtual Images Formed by Convex Mirrors	**Pocket Lab:** Where's the Image?, p. 371 **Pocket Lab:** Reflections, p. 372 **Pocket Lab:** Real or Virtual, p. 373 **Pocket Lab:** Makeup, p. 376 **Problem Solving Strategy:** Finding Images and Constructing a Ray Diagram, p. 372 **Concept Review,** p. 378	**Study Guide:** Mirrors **Transparency Worksheet:** Image Formation by Mirrors and Lenses	**Laboratory Manual:** Lab 18.1 Concave and Convex Mirrors **Transparency 24:** Image Formation by Mirrors and Lenses
18.2 Lenses, p. 378–386 (3 Class Sessions) • Types of Lenses • Real Images Formed by Convex Lenses • Virtual Images Formed by Convex Lenses • Virtual Images Formed by Concave Lenses • Chromatic Aberration • Optical Instruments	**Physics Lab:** Seeing Is Believing, p. 379 **Physics and Technology:** Stargazing, p. 386 **Pocket Lab:** Burned Lab, p. 381 **Pocket Lab:** Bright Ideas, p. 382 **Concept Review,** p. 386	**Study Guide:** Lenses **Physics Lab Data Sheet:** Seeing Is Believing **Reteaching Master:** Correcting Vision **Enrichment Master:** The Telescope **Critical Thinking Master:** Reflecting Telescopes	**Laboratory Manual:** Lab 18.2 Convex and Concave Lenses
Chapter Review, pp. 387–389	Summary Key Terms Reviewing Concepts Applying Concepts Problems Using a Graphing Calculator Thinking Physic-ly	**Vocabulary Review** **Chapter Test**	**Test Bank**

SUPPLEMENTARY MATERIALS

SOFTWARE	AUDIOVISUAL	BOOKS/MAGAZINES
Interactive Optics, EduTech (Apple II). *Lenses,* Queue, Inc. (Apple II). *Optics,* Cross (Apple II, IBM PC). *Optics: Mirrors & Beams,* HRM (Apple II).	Video: *The Mechanical Universe and Beyond: Maxwell's Equations* and *Optics,* Films Inc.	Berg, Richard E. "Heat-Wave Focusing by Concave Reflectors." *The Physics Teacher,* January 1990, p. 56. Derman, Samuel. "Ray Tracing with Spherical and Parabolic Reflectors." *The Physics Teacher,* December 1990, p. 590. Linas, C.F. "Building a Telescope." *The Science Teacher,* December 1988, pp. 33–34. Ouseph, P. J. "How Many Fish Are in the Tank?" *The Physics Teacher,* October 1987, p. 440.

PROBLEM CORRELATION

CONCEPTS	CHAPTER REVIEW			PROBLEMS APPENDIX
	Reviewing Concepts	Applying Concepts	Problems	
18.1 Mirrors				
Objects and Their Images in Plane Mirrors	1,2		1,2,**3**	1
Concave Mirror			4	2
Spherical Aberrations and Parabolic Mirrors	3	2		
Real vs Virtual Images	4,5,6,7			
Real Images Formed by Concave Mirrors	8	3,4,5	5,**6**,7	3,4,5,6,7,**8**
Virtual Images Formed by Concave Mirrors	9	1	8,9,10	9
Virtual Images Formed by Convex Mirrors	11	6,7,8,10	11	10,11
18.2 Lenses				
Types of Lenses		9		
Real Images Formed by Convex Lenses	10,12,13	12	12,13,14,15,16,**17**,18	12,13,14,15,16
Virtual Images Formed by Convex Lenses		11		18
Virtual Images Formed by Concave Lenses				
Chromatic Aberration		13		
Optical Instruments			**17**,18	17

ACTIVITY AND DEMONSTRATION MATERIALS

PHYSICS LAB	POCKET LAB	DEMONSTRATIONS
Page 379 3 converging lenses 1 diverging lens meter stick ball of clay 40-watt lamp ruler small screen	Pages 371, 372, 373, 376, 381, 382 camera assorted mirrors makeup mirror piece of clay several pairs of eyeglasses converging lens small light bulb with power supply	Pages 368, 370, 372 plate glass (30 cm × 60 cm) 2 identical candles or identical burners supports for glass plates light source concave mirror lighted candle or straight filament lamp converging mirror

EXTENSION PROJECTS

LIBRARY RESEARCH

1. **Fresnel Lenses**
   Investigate fresnel lenses. How do they work? Where are they used?

DISPLAY MODEL

2. **Telescope**
   Build a telescope from cardboard tubes and lenses or mirrors.

STUDENT READINGS

Khandelwal, Govind S., and Harries, Wynford L. "The Mirror Equation." *The Physics Teacher,* May 1990.

"Leaf Lenses: A Finer Focus." *Science News,* August 11, 1990.

"NASA Identifies What Hobbled Hubble." *Science News,* October 6, 1990.

O'Dell, C. R. "The Hubble Space Telescope Observatory." *Physics Today,* April 1990.

Read, Albert J. "Sawblade Optics." *The Physics Teacher,* October 1990.

Yulsman, T. "The Ultimate Zoom: A Revolution in Glassmaking Design Could Lead to Lighter, Smaller Lenses." *Discover,* August 1988.

Chapter 18

Mirrors and Lenses

CHAPTER OVERVIEW

Theme Development: Principles of optics are investigated by extending the ray model of light. Symmetry in ray optics diagrams is important to definitions of lenses and images.

MISCONCEPTIONS

Students have trouble drawing ray diagrams to actually locate image positions. It is important for students to understand that we "locate" objects by mentally tracing light rays our eyes intercept back to the place from which the light rays appear to diverge.

KEY TERMS

achromatic lens
chromatic aberration
concave lens
concave mirror
converging mirror
convex lens
convex mirror
focal length
focal point
image
lens
lens equation
magnification
mirror equation
object
plane mirror
principle axis
real image
spherical aberration
virtual image

Laboratory Options

STUDENT EDITION

Physics Lab

Seeing Is Believing 379

Pocket Labs

Where's the Image? 371
Reflections 372
Real or Virtual 373
Makeup 376
Burned Up 381
Bright Ideas 382

TEACHER EDITION

Activities

Demonstration 368, 370, 372
Discovery 369, 375, 380, 381

LABORATORY MANUAL

Concave and Convex Mirrors Lab 18.1
Concave and Convex Lenses Lab 18.2

CHAPTER 18

Mirrors and Lenses

Butterfly ylfrettuB

Wing-Yui produced this image of a butterfly on the screen. Wesley said, "That must be a concave lens since the butterfly image is spread out and larger than the real butterfly. Wing-Yui replied, "Maybe, but I'm not so sure." Who is correct, and what is the source of the two small images that seem to float in the lens?

Chapter Outline

We are so accustomed to using mirrors and lenses that we give them little thought. Eyeglasses, magnifying glasses, microscopes, and camcorders use the laws of refraction and reflection. Notice the four butterflies in the photo. Only one is the real butterfly. The other three, small, large, upright or turned upside down, are the result of reflection and refraction in a single piece of glass. Moreover, our entire view of the world is the result of the optical images formed on our retinas by the lenses in our eyes.

✓ Concept Check

The following terms or concepts from earlier chapters are important for a good understanding of this chapter. If you are not familiar with them, you should review them before studying this chapter.

- law of reflection, Snell's law, law of refraction, Chapter 17

367

Introducing The Chapter

Butterfly ylfrettuB

Using The Photo: *Image* is a word with many popular usages today. Students may be surprised to find that physics has a specific definition for the term. You might ask students to identify the cause of each of the three images in the photo. Refer students to page 377 for the answer to the question in the caption.

✓ Concept Check

Make sure students have a clear understanding of the concepts taught in Chapter 17 that are listed in the Concept Check. Ray diagrams are developed from Snell's law and the law of reflection. Students will use indices of refraction to study lenses in Section 18.2.

Assessment

Portfolio

Collect examples of ray drawings that locate images in mirrors (plane, convex, and concave) and lenses (convex and concave). Include drawings of both real and virtual images.

Assessment Options

Portfolio Assessment
Extension 1, TWE, p. 366b
Portfolio Assessment, TWE, p. 367
Enrichment, TWE, pp. 372, 385

Performance Assessment
Extension 2, TWE, p. 366b
Pocket Labs, pp. 371, 372, 373, 376, 381, 382
Physics Lab, p. 379
Activity, TWE, p. 381
Pocket Lab Assessment, TWE, p. 382

Content Assessment
Self Assessment: Practice Problems, pp. 374, 376, 377, 381, 383
Checking for Understanding, TWE, p. 374
Assessment, Critical Thinking, p. 379
Concept Reviews, pp. 378, 386
Chapter Review, pp. 387–389
Supplemental Problems, p. 701

Group Assessment
Activities for group assessment occur with Cooperative Learning and lab activities.

18.1 MIRRORS

Preparation

OBJECTIVES

The objectives are listed on the student page. Remind students to preview these objectives as a study guide to this major section.

OVERVIEW

Mirror terminology, such as *plane mirror, concave* (converging) *mirror, object, focal length,* and *principal axis,* are introduced, as well as the phenomena of real and virtual images.

Major new concepts in this section are real image and magnification. In addition, the mirror equation is presented here for the first time.

BRIDGING

In this section, students will be working again with ray diagrams and will see a number of terms from previous lessons: *reflection, refraction, luminosity, angle of incidence.* Previously introduced concepts include ray convergence and divergence.

2 Focus

DISCREPANT EVENT

Set up two 20-cm mirrors 10 cm apart and facing each other. Scrape a little hole in the paint on the back of one of the mirrors about 1/3 of the way down from the top. Place a soft drink can between the mirrors. Have students look through the hole and describe the images they see.

Objectives

- **describe the image produced by a plane mirror.**
- **define the focal point; explain the origin of parallel rays.**
- **explain the rules of ray tracing in concave mirrors.**
- **define spherical aberration and describe uses of parabolic mirrors.**
- **distinguish between real and virtual images.**
- **explain how concave mirrors form real and virtual images; locate the image with ray diagrams; use the mirror equation to calculate location and magnification.**
- **explain how convex mirrors form virtual images using ray diagrams; locate image; calculate location and magnification with mirror equation.**

18.1 MIRRORS

Mirrors are probably the oldest optical instrument. Polished metal was used to reflect the faces of inhabitants of ancient Egypt almost four thousand years ago. It wasn't until 1857, however, that the bright images we see today became possible. In that year, Jean Foucault developed a method of coating glass with silver.

Objects and Their Images in Plane Mirrors

When you look at yourself in a bathroom mirror, you are seeing your image in a plane mirror. A **plane mirror** is a flat, smooth surface that reflects light in a regular way. You are the object. An **object** is a source of diverging light rays. An object may be luminous, like a candle or lamp. More often an object is illuminated, like the moon or the page you are reading. An illuminated object diffusely reflects light in all directions.

Light rays spread from each point on an object.

Figure 18–1a shows how some of the rays from point **P** strike the mirror and are reflected with equal angles of incidence and reflection. After reflection, the rays continue to spread. If we extend the rays backward, behind the mirror, as done with the dashed lines in Figure 18–1, we find that they intersect at a point **P′**. Point **P′**, where the extended rays apparently intersect, is called the **image.** Although, to an observer, the rays appear to come from point **P′**, you can see that no source is really there. For that reason, this kind of image is called a **virtual image.**

There is one image for each point on the object.

Where is the image located? Figure 18–2 shows two rays from object **P.** One strikes the mirror at **B,** the other at **M.** Both rays are reflected with equal angles of incidence and reflection. Thus the triangles **BPM**

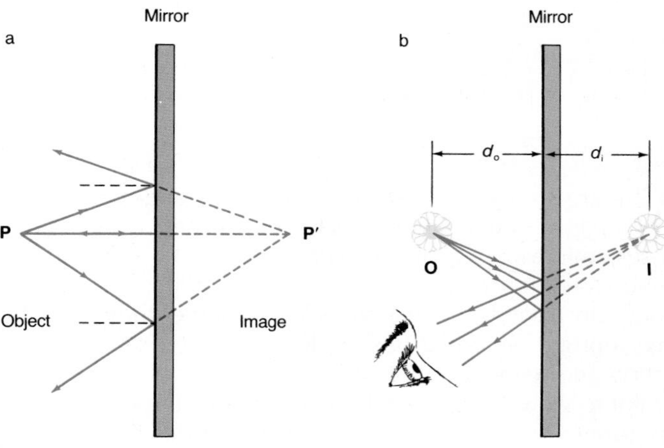

FIGURE 18–1. The image formed by a plane mirror appears to be a distance d_i, behind the mirror, equal to the object distance, d_o.

DEMONSTRATION

Purpose: to demonstrate the law of reflection.

Equipment: glass plate about 30 cm × 60 cm, 2 identical candles or 2 identical burners, supports for glass plate

Note: This demonstration takes some practice to be convincing.

Procedure: 1. Mount the glass plate vertically on your lecture table, facing the students. **2.** Set one candle in front of the glass. Place the other candle behind the glass at exactly the same distance from the glass and in line with the first candle. **3.** Light only the front candle, but pretend to light both. (You might hold a book in front of the candles, pretending to protect them from the draft, then remove the book.) **4.** Generate student curiosity by holding your hand for several seconds above the second candle where the tip of the flame should be.

Results: Although only one candle is lit, both will appear lit to the onlooking stu-

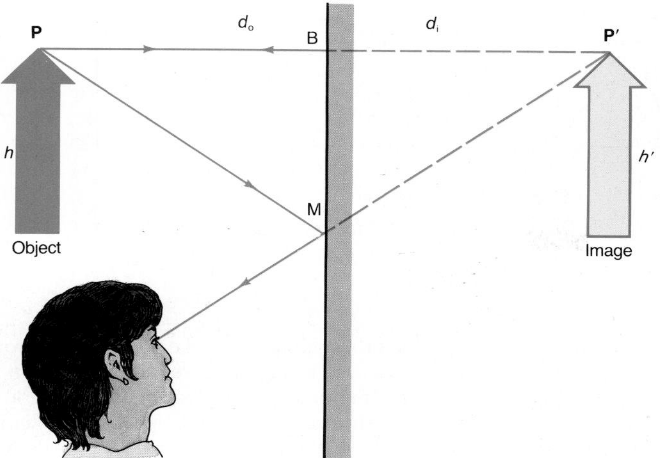

FIGURE 18–2. Ray diagram for locating an image in a plane mirror. Light rays (two are shown) leave a point on the object. Some strike the mirror and are reflected into the eye. Sight lines (drawn as dashed lines) extend from the location on the mirror where the reflections occurred back to where they converge. The image is located where the sight lines converge. By geometry, $d_i = d_o$.

and **BP′M** are congruent. From **P** to **B,** the distance between the object and the mirror, is d_o. From **P′** to **B,** the distance between the image and the mirror, is d_i; $d_o = d_i$. The image is thus the same distance behind the mirror that the object is in front of it. In a similar way, you can show that the image is the same size as the object and is erect, Figure 18–3a.

In Figure 18–3b, the right and left hands of an image appear to be reversed. You might ask why the top and bottom are not also reversed. If you look at the figure carefully, you will see that the direction that is really reversed is the one perpendicular to the surface of mirror. Left and right are interchanged, in the same manner that a right-hand glove can be worn on the left hand by turning it inside out. Thus, it is more correct to say that the front and back of an image are reversed.

Light Conventions

- *Light rays are red.*
- *Lenses and mirrors are light blue.*
- *Objects are dark blue.*
- ***Images are yellow.***

FIGURE 18–3. The image formed in a plane mirror is the same size as the object and is the same distance behind the mirror as the object is in front (a). A mirror seems to reverse right and left (b).

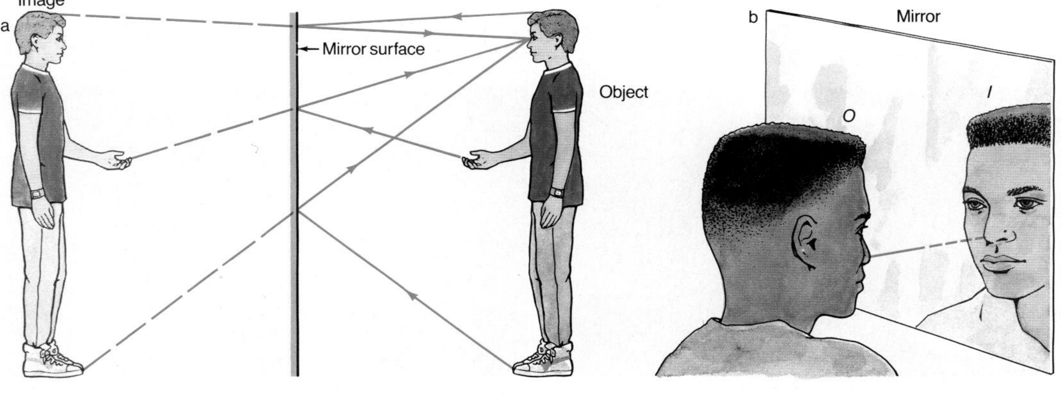

dents. Students will eventually conclude that the candle beneath your hand is not lit.

Questions: 1. What property of light created the illusion that the second candle was lit? *The law of reflection.*
2. Where must the second candle be placed with respect to the first? *The second candle must be as far behind the mirror as the first candle is in front of it. This will locate the image flame as far behind the glass (mirror) as the real flame is in front of it.*

STUDY GUIDE MASTER

Use the Study Guide master for section 18.1.

2 Teach

CONCEPT DEVELOPMENT

- Give students hands-on experience with mirrors right away. Pass around some plane mirrors and let students experiment with them for a few minutes.

- Refer to Figure 18–3a and ask students how long a mirror has to be so you can see your reflection from head to toe. At what height must you hang the mirror on the wall? Show how to answer these questions, using either a full-length mirror or a long glass cabinet door. On the glass, mark locations of the reflections of a student volunteer's head and feet, comparing different d_o's. For a smaller mirror, use a half-meter stick held next to the face.

Study Guide Master. To reinforce the concepts in this section, have the students complete the Study Guide Master for Section 18.1 from the Teacher Resource Package.

- Work through the proof described on these pages in detail with students.

ACTIVITY

Discovery: Give students two plane mirrors and have them set these upright to look like one plane mirror. Have students observe their reflections. Now, keeping the two adjoining edges of the mirrors in contact, ask students to turn the mirrors toward each other as if on a hinge and observe what happens as the angle between the mirrors is reduced. This is the principle on which a kaleidoscope works. A kaleidoscope is an optical instrument containing two or more mirrors set at angles to one another. Most kaleidoscopes are rotating tubes containing a triangular configuration of mirrors that produces multiple reflections of material, such as beads or colored bits of glass, held loosely at one end. Some tubes contain a lens at one end instead, and produce multiple reflections of objects in line with the tube.

Take apart an inexpensive paper kaleidoscope so that students can see how it is made. Allow students to build their own from household materials if time allows!

CONCEPT DEVELOPMENT

Have students help you draw a sketch of a TV satellite dish. Show the path of incoming electromagnetic waves.

Demonstration: Hold a light source in one hand and a concave mirror in the other. First cast a large image on a wall and point out that the object is between **C** and **F**, but close to the focal point. Then hold the object far from the mirror and form a small image. Now hold the object between **F** and the mirror, and demonstrate that no real image is found. Only by looking into the mirror is a virtual image seen. Also show that no image is formed when the object is at the focal point.

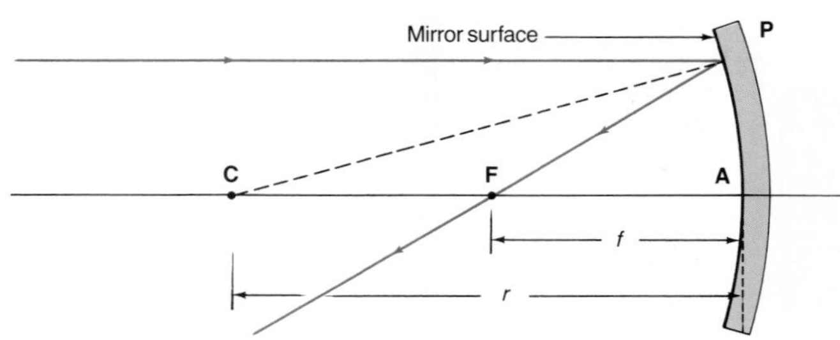

FIGURE 18–4. The focus of a concave spherical mirror is located halfway between the center of curvature and the mirror surface. Rays entering parallel to the principal axis are reflected to converge at the focal point.

Concave Mirrors

A concave mirror is caved in.

Incident rays parallel to the principal axis are reflected to converge at the focal point.

Examine the inside surface of a spoon. It acts like a concave mirror. A **concave mirror** reflects light from its inner ("caved in") surface. In a spherical concave mirror, the mirror is part of the inner surface of a hollow sphere, Figure 18–4. The sphere of radius *r* has a geometric center, **C.** Point **A** is the center of the mirror, and the line **CA** is the **principal axis,** the straight line perpendicular to the surface of the mirror at its center.

How does light reflect from a concave mirror? Think of a concave mirror as a large number of small plane mirrors arranged around the surface of a sphere, Figure 18–5. Each mirror is perpendicular to a radius of the sphere. When a ray strikes a mirror, it is reflected with equal angles of incidence and reflection. A ray parallel to the principal axis is reflected at **P** and crosses the principal axis at some point **F,** as in Figure 18–4. A parallel ray an equal distance below the principal axis would, by symmetry, also cross the principal axis at **F.** These parallel rays would meet, or converge, at the **focal point** of the mirror. The two sides **FC** and **FP** of the triangle **CFP** are equal in length. Thus, for very small angles, the focal point, **F,** is half the distance between the mirror and the center of curvature, **C.**

How can you find the location of the focal point of a concave mirror? A source of nearly parallel rays is the sun. Therefore, if you point the principal axis of a concave mirror at the sun, all the rays will be reflected through a point near the focal point. Hold a piece of paper near the mirror and move the paper toward and away from the mirror until

F.Y.I.

A parabolic mirror can also be used for cooking in areas where fuel is scarce. If a cooking pot is placed at the focal point of a large concave mirror, the energy of the sunlight can be concentrated at one point, producing high temperatures.

a

b

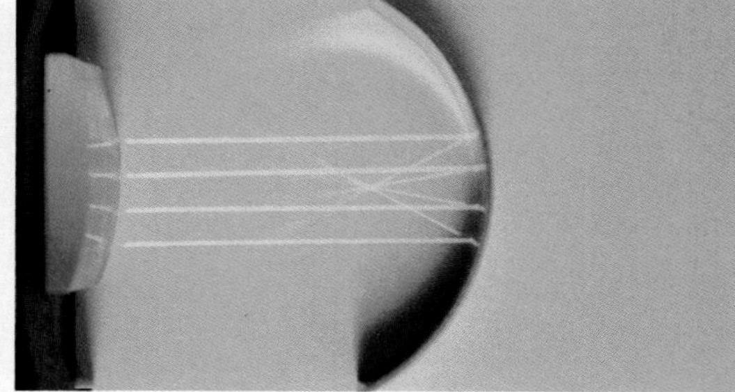

FIGURE 18–5. The surface of a concave mirror reflects light to a given point (b), much like a group of plane mirrors arranged in a curve (a).

TEACHER F.Y.I.

The principal axis is the axis of symmetry of the mirror drawn from the center of the spherical segment of the mirror to the center of curvature.

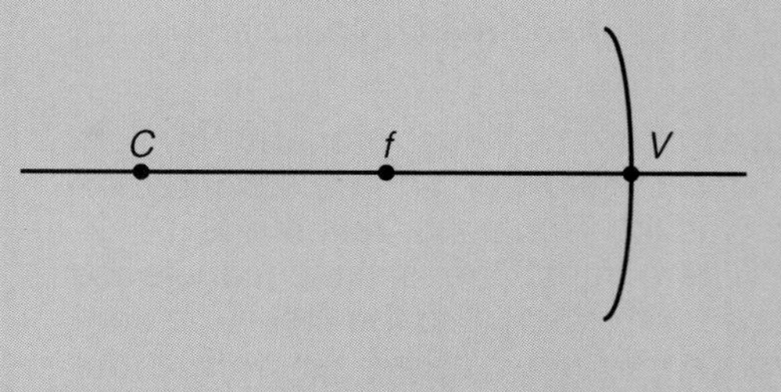

the smallest and sharpest spot is formed. The spot must be at the focal point because, as discussed above, the rays striking the mirror were, for all practical purposes, parallel. The distance from the focal point to the mirror along the principal axis is the **focal length,** *f*, of the mirror. The focal length is half the radius of curvature of the mirror.

Spherical Aberration and Parabolic Mirrors

Parallel rays converge at the focal point of a spherical mirror only if they are close to the principal axis. As seen in Figure 18–6, the two rays farthest from the principal axis converge at a point slightly closer to the mirror than the others. The image formed by parallel rays in a large spherical mirror is a disk, not a point. This effect is called **spherical aberration** (ab uh RAY shuhn).

Parabolic mirrors have no spherical aberration. They are used to focus parallel rays from distant stars to a sharp focus in telescopes. Perfectly parabolic mirrors are very difficult to make. Makers of the mirror in the Hubble Space Telescope made an error in grinding the glass of 2μm, about the thickness of a human hair, resulting in spherical aberration in the mirror. It focuses only 15% of the light into a tiny spot, not the 70% it was designed to.

Parabolic mirrors can also produce the parallel beams of light needed in flashlights, car headlights, and searchlights. The light source is placed at **F** and the reflected rays leave in a parallel beam. This illustrates an important principle of ray optics, the object and the image can be interchanged. Light rays can go in either direction.

Real vs Virtual Images

Parallel rays of the sun or other distant objects reflected from a concave mirror converge at the focal point of the mirror. The converging rays form a bright spot on a piece of paper at the focal point. An image is a **real image** if rays actually converge and pass through the image. A real image can be seen on a piece of paper or screen.

In contrast, the image produced by a plane mirror is behind the mirror. The rays reflected from a plane mirror never actually converge but appear to diverge from a point behind the mirror. A virtual image cannot be projected on a screen or captured on a piece of paper because light rays do not converge at a virtual image.

POCKET LAB

WHERE'S THE IMAGE?

Suppose that you are standing directly in front of a mirror and see your image. Exactly where is the image? Here is a simple activity to find out. Find a camera with a focusing ring that has distances marked on it. Stand 1.0 m from a mirror and focus on the edge of the mirror. Check the reading on the focusing ring. It should be 1.0 m. Now focus on your image. What is the reading on the ring now? What does this tell you?

The focal length is the distance between the focal point and the mirror.

Because of spherical aberration, parallel rays are not reflected to a point.

Perfectly parabolic mirrors have no spherical aberration.

A real image can be projected on a screen.

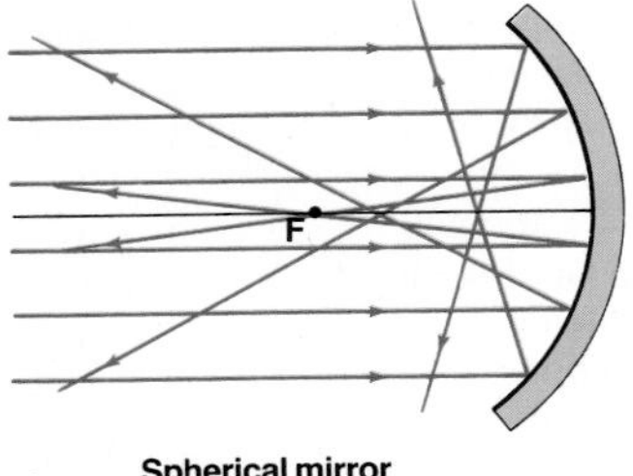

a Spherical mirror

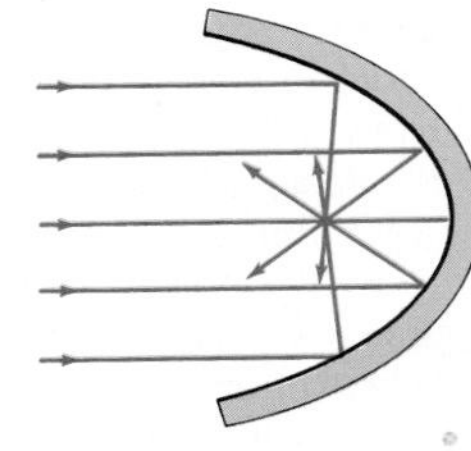
b Parabolic mirror

FIGURE 18–6. In a concave spherical mirror, some rays converge at points other than the focus (a). A parabolic mirror focuses all parallel rays at a point (b).

POCKET LAB

WHERE'S THE IMAGE?

Purpose: to estimate the distance of an image from a plane mirror.

Materials: camera; plane mirror.

Outcome: When the image is in focus, the reading on the ring will be 2.0 m. Many students will find that the image is an equal distance behind the mirror.

CONCEPT DEVELOPMENT

- For a regular mirror, most of the reflection is from the silver coating on the back side. A little light does reflect from the front surface, which sometimes produces a faintly visible image if you look carefully. "Front-silvered" or "front-surfaced" mirrors give a sharper image because light reflects directly off the silver coating without passing through glass. The silver coating also eliminates refraction of the light by the glass.
- A major difficulty of the Hubble Space Telescope was spherical aberration in its concave mirror system. This defect caused images to lose their sharpness.

TEACHER F.Y.I.

It is interesting to consider the structure of other types of telescopes in addition to the Space Telescope. All modern large telescopes use a concave mirror instead of an objective lens to form the real image. The concave mirror has the advantage of being much lighter than a lens and being free of chromatic aberration. Spherical aberration in the mirror is avoided by making the mirror parabolic rather than spherical. The larger telescopes have the advantage of having less fuzziness due to diffraction, and they can gather more light for a brighter image.

Radio telescopes use electromagnetic radiation of 1 mm or longer wavelength. The incoming radiation is focused on a receiving antenna at the focal point of a parabolic mirror.

CONCEPT DEVELOPMENT

- Point out the difference between **F,** the focal point, and *f,* the distance between the focal point and the mirror or lens.
- The vertical line at the location of the mirror's reflecting surface is called the *principal plane.*
- Take some time to clarify the idea that objects (whether illuminated or luminous) can be seen from any angle. This explains why, when drawing ray diagrams, we can take light going any direction from the object and send it into the mirror (or lens).
- Be sure to point out that ray drawing techniques serve as a check on algebraic methods and vice versa. The two methods should agree.

Demonstration: Darken the classroom. Hold a lighted candle or a straight filament lamp in one hand and a converging mirror in the other. Project inverted images on a screen. Show that as the object comes very close to the mirror, you no longer produce an image on the screen even though you still see an image in the mirror.

Enrichment: There has been some interesting psychological research done on self-awareness in animals, particularly with primates, where mirror images play an important role. Have interested students investigate the details.

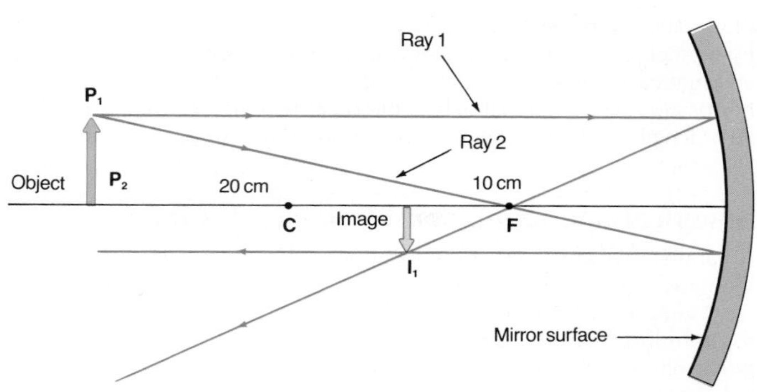

FIGURE 18–7. Finding the real image formed by a concave spherical mirror when the object is located beyond the center of curvature, *C*, of the mirror.

A virtual image cannot be projected on a screen.

Ray diagrams can be used to find the location and size of images.

Real Images Formed by Concave Mirrors

Concave mirrors can form both real and virtual images. We will use ray diagrams to show how concave mirrors form real images and how to locate these images. Figure 18–7 shows a concave mirror with an object farther from the mirror than C, the center of curvature of the mirror. Such an object is said to be "beyond C." Rays leave the object in all directions. A few of these rays fall on the mirror. We will now find the image formed by those rays.

PROBLEM SOLVING STRATEGIES

Two rules are used to find the images formed by mirrors.

1. Incident light rays parallel to the principal axis of a mirror are reflected through the focal point.
2. Incident rays that pass through the focal point are reflected parallel to the principal axis.

To construct a ray diagram follow these steps:

1. Choose a scale. Your goal is to make the drawing close to the width of your paper, about 20 cm. You will find that if the object is beyond **F,** the image is real and on the object side of the mirror. If the object is beyond **2F,** we will see that the object distance is larger than the image distance. If not, the image distance is equal or larger. Choose the scale such that the larger distance, object or image, is 15 to 20 cm on your paper. To make calculating simpler, let 1 cm on the paper equal 1, 2, 4, 5, or 10 cm.
2. Draw the principal axis and put the mirror at the right-hand side of the paper. Draw a vertical line at the location of the mirror. Place a dot on the axis at the location of the focal point.
3. Draw the object. Usually the object and image height have to be drawn to a larger scale than used in Step 1 to be visible.
4. Select a point, $\mathbf{P_1}$, to be the top of the object. Draw Ray 1 parallel to the principal axis. As shown above, Ray 1, called the parallel ray, reflects through the focal point, **F.** Draw Ray 2 so it passes through **F**

POCKET LAB

REFLECTIONS

Take a concave mirror into an area of direct sunlight. Use a piece of clay to hold the mirror steady so that the concave mirror directly faces the sun. Move your finger toward or away from the mirror in the area of reflected light to find the brightest spot (focal point). Turn the mirror so that the convex side faces the sun and repeat the experiment. Record and explain your results.

POCKET LAB

REFLECTIONS

Purpose: to observe focal distance of curved mirrors.
Materials: convex and concave mirror; piece of clay.
Outcome: This simple activity gives students direct experience seeing and feeling the focal point. Many students will be surprised to find there is no focal point using the convex side. It is important that they understand why. (The reflected light is diverging.)

Multicultural Connections

Many of the fundamental principles about spherical and parabolic mirrors and lenses were discovered by al-Hazen. He measured the reflection and refraction of light by mirrors and lenses, and he determined it was the curvature of the lens or mirror that accounted for focusing. This resulted in his developing the geometric equations for image formation for spherical and parabolic mirrors. Using his knowledge of refraction, he was able to measure the refraction of the atmosphere. This led to two conclusions—first, that when twilight ended, the sun was really 19° below the horizon and, second, that the depth of the atmosphere is about 16 km (in current measurements), which is the first recorded, accurate estimate.

on its way to the mirror. Ray 2 is called the focus ray. This ray reflects parallel to the principal axis. The two rays drawn from $\mathbf{P}_1$ converge at $\mathbf{I}_1$.

5. Draw the image as a vertical line between $\mathbf{I}_1$ and the principal axis.

The image formed by an object beyond **C** is found to be between **C** and **F.** It is a real image because the rays actually come together at this point. The image is inverted. That is, point $\mathbf{I}_1$, the image of the top of the object, is below the principal axis. The image is also smaller than the object.

As an object is moved inward toward **C,** the image position moves outward toward **C.** When the object is at **C,** the image is also located there. The image is real, inverted, and, in this case, the same size as the object. If the object is moved from **C** toward **F,** the image moves out beyond **C.** This can be seen by reversing the direction of the light rays in Figure 18–7. The roles of image and object are reversed.

An equation can also be used to locate the image and find its size. The focal length, f, the distance of the object from the mirror, d_o, and the distance of the image from the mirror, d_i, are related by the **mirror equation.**

$$\frac{1}{f} = \frac{1}{d_i} + \frac{1}{d_o}$$

The ratio of the size of the image, h_i, to the size of the object, h_o, is called the **magnification,** m. The magnification is related to the distances to the mirror by the equation

$$m = \frac{h_i}{h_o} = \frac{-d_i}{d_o}.$$

If d_i and d_o are both positive, then both m and h_i are negative. This means the image is inverted.

POCKET LAB

REAL OR VIRTUAL

Hold a small concave mirror at arm's length and look at your image. What do you see? Is the image in front or behind the mirror? What happens to the image as you slowly bring the mirror toward your face?

For objects beyond F, as the object is moved closer to a concave mirror, the image moves farther away and grows in size.

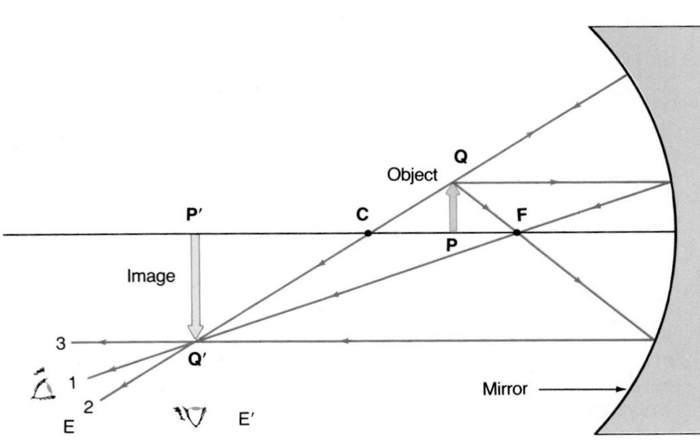

FIGURE 18–8. To the eye, E, it appears that there is an object at Q′ blocking the view of the mirror behind. However, if the eye moves to E′ and looks toward Q′, the "object" disappears because there is then no light reflected from Q′ to E′.

POCKET LAB

REAL OR VIRTUAL

Purpose: to observe the images produced by a concave mirror.
Materials: concave mirror.
Outcome: Students will see a small upside-down image that is in front of the mirror. As the mirror is brought closer to the face, the image will increase in size and also get further from the mirror. When the mirror is very close to the face, the image will be right side up and behind the mirror.

CONCEPT DEVELOPMENT

Enrichment: As students work with individual concave mirrors, challenge them to estimate their mirrors' focal lengths.

- Pass a curved rearview mirror around in class. Point out that for any object, near or far, you always get a smaller, right-side-up image.
- Students who aren't strong in mathematical techniques may like the artwork involved with ray diagrams. Here's a chance to praise their nice artwork.

TEACHER F.Y.I.

In the 1930's, Karl Jansky discovered the source of a mysterious interference that disturbed shortwave communication. He determined that this interference originated from the center of our galaxy. After World War II, astronomers developed radio telescopes after they found that all sorts of astronomical bodies emit radio waves. While the first radio telescopes could not pinpoint the exact location of an object (because the wavelength of radiowaves is very long compared to that of visible light), current models have a resolution much greater than that of any optical telescope.

CONCEPT DEVELOPMENT

Discuss what happens when an object is *at f* (the image goes to infinity).

It is worth the effort to have students derive the equation:

$$h_i = \frac{-d_i h_o}{d_o}.$$

(A derivation of the lens equation appears in the Solutions Appendix as a solution to Chapter Review Problem 9.)

CHECKING FOR UNDERSTANDING

- What light phenomena allow us to locate images produced by mirrors? [straight line travel and the law of reflection]
- Ask students to summarize the procedure for doing ray drawing diagrams for mirrors.

RETEACHING

With the aid of students, complete a diagram locating an image in a plane mirror by the use of ray drawing and the law of reflection.

Transparency Package. Reteach the concepts of lenses and mirrors using Transparency 24 and accompanying worksheet.

EXTENSION

Ask students if they would expect a difference in brightness between magnified and reduced images. Have interested students investigate the principles of image brightness.

Critical Thinking: Ask students why some antique mirrors give a very dim image. [Often the reflective coating on the back of the mirror has deteriorated and no longer reflects light evenly.]

Answers To
PRACTICE PROBLEMS

Have students refer to Appendix A of the Solutions Appendix for complete solutions to Practice Problems.

1. Refer to Solutions Appendix for diagram.
2. Refer to Solutions Appendix for diagram.
   b. 15 cm
   c. −1.5
   d. −4.5 mm
3. 15.0 cm
4. 25 cm

TRANSPARENCY

Use Transparency 24 with this section.

Mirror Equation Conventions

d_o is *positive for real objects. negative for virtual objects.*

d_i is *positive for real images. negative for virtual images.*

f is *positive for concave mirrors. negative for convex mirrors.*

Example Problem

Real Image from a Concave Mirror

An object 2.0 cm high is 30.0 cm from a concave mirror. The radius of curvature of the mirror is 20.0 cm. **a.** What is the location of the image? **b.** What is the size of the image?

Given: object height, $h_o = 2.0$ cm; object location, $d_o = 30.0$ cm; radius of curvature, $r = 20.0$ cm; focal length, $f = ½r$

Unknowns: **a.** image location, d_i **b.** image height, h_i

Basic equations: $\frac{1}{f} = \frac{1}{d_i} + \frac{1}{d_o}$, $m = \frac{h_i}{h_o} = \frac{-d_i}{d_o}$

Solution: a. $f = ½r = \frac{20.0\text{ cm}}{2} = 10.0\text{ cm}$

$$\frac{1}{f} = \frac{1}{d_o} + \frac{1}{d_i}$$

$$\text{so } \frac{1}{d_i} = \frac{1}{f} - \frac{1}{d_o}$$

$$\text{or } d_i = \frac{fd_o}{d_o - f} = \frac{(10.0\text{ cm})(30.0\text{ cm})}{(30.0\text{ cm} - 10.0\text{ cm})} = 15.0\text{ cm}$$

b. $m = \frac{h_i}{h_o} = \frac{-d_i}{d_o}$,

$$\text{so } h_i = \frac{-d_i h_o}{d_o} = \frac{-(15.0\text{ cm})(2.0\text{ cm})}{30.0\text{ cm}} = -1.0\text{ cm}$$

The image size is negative, meaning it is inverted.

Practice Problems

1. Solve the Example Problem above using a ray diagram.
2. An object 3.0 mm high is 10.0 cm in front of a concave mirror having a 6.0-cm focal length. Find the image by means of
   a. a ray diagram.
   b. the mirror equation.
   c. Find the magnification of the mirror.
   d. What is the height of the image?
3. The image of an object is 30.0 cm from a concave mirror with a 20.0-cm radius of curvature. Locate the object.
4. An old "magic trick" used a concave mirror to project an image the same size as the object and at the same distance from the mirror. If the object is 25 cm from the mirror, what should be the radius of curvature of the mirror?

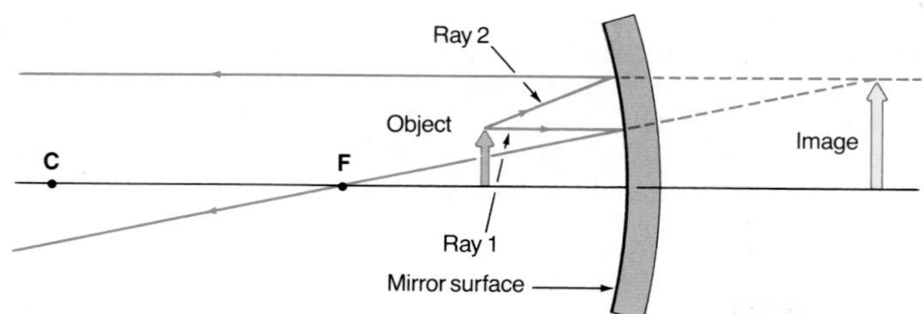

FIGURE 18–9. Find the virtual image formed by a concave spherical mirror when the object is located between the mirror and F.

Virtual Images Formed by Concave Mirrors

We have seen that as the object approaches the focal point, **F,** of a mirror, the image moves farther out. If the object is at the focal point, all reflected rays are parallel. The image is said to be at infinity. What happens if the object is closer to the mirror than **F**? Figure 18–9 shows an object 5.0 cm in front of a mirror of 10.0 cm focal length. The two rays have been drawn to locate the image. Ray 1 approaches the mirror parallel to the principal axis and is reflected through the focal point. Ray 2 moves away from the object as if it has come from the focal point. It is reflected parallel to the principal axis. The two reflected rays spread apart and will never converge. No real image exists. The dashed lines show the rays coming from their apparent origin behind the mirror. This virtual image is located behind the mirror.

An object closer to a concave mirror than the focal point forms a virtual image.

Example Problem

Virtual Image from a Concave Mirror

Find the location of the image in Figure 18–9 if an object 2.0 cm in height is 5.0 cm in front of a concave mirror of focal length 10.0 cm. How large is the image?

Given: $d_o = 5.0$ cm, $h_o = 2.0$ cm, $f = 10.0$ cm

Unknowns: image distance, d_i; image height, h_i

Basic equations: $\frac{1}{f} = \frac{1}{d_i} + \frac{1}{d_o}$

$$m = \frac{h_i}{h_o} = \frac{-d_i}{d_o}$$

Solution: $\frac{1}{f} = \frac{1}{d_o} + \frac{1}{d_i}$, so $d_i = \frac{fd_o}{d_o - f} = \frac{(10.0 \text{ cm})(5.0 \text{ cm})}{5.0 \text{ cm} - 10.0 \text{ cm}}$

$$= \frac{5.0 \times 10^1 \text{ cm}^2}{-5.0 \text{ cm}} = -1.0 \times 10^1 \text{ cm}$$

A negative image distance indicates a virtual image, located behind the mirror.

$m = \frac{h_i}{h_o} = \frac{-d_i}{d_o}$, so $h_i = \frac{-h_o d_i}{d_o}$

$$= \frac{-(2.0 \text{ cm})(-10.0 \text{ cm})}{5.0 \text{ cm}} = +4.0 \text{ cm}$$

FIGURE 18–10. Objects placed between the focal point and the surface of a concave mirror form enlarged virtual images.

CONCEPT DEVELOPMENT

Check to see if students can draw simple ray diagrams. This important skill, used throughout this chapter, helps greatly in visualizing optical situations.

Critical Thinking: Ask students if they think a mirror is a perfect reflector. Choose a figure for a mirror's amount of reflection, say 90%. Imagine light bouncing off three such mirrors one after the other. Ask students what percentage of the original light would bounce off the third mirror. [Since 90% of the incoming light reflects from each mirror surface, the total amount after three reflections is 0.90 × 0.90 × 0.90 = 0.73 or 73%.]

ACTIVITY

Discovery: Obtain a car side-view mirror and discuss the printing on the mirror that says, "Objects are closer than they appear." Pass around a convex mirror and have students hold it close to their faces and then move it away. Have them observe that the image is always right side up and smaller than the actual size of their face. Have them compare this to the same exercise they did with the concave mirror.

POCKET LAB

MAKEUP

Purpose: to observe images of a makeup mirror (concave).

Materials: makeup mirror.

Outcome: Makeup mirrors are designed to produce virtual images that are magnified. This implies that they are concave. It is difficult, but possible, to feel the curvature on most mirrors. Students might use sunlight to find the focal point of these mirrors, but they will not be able to produce high-quality images.

Answers To

PRACTICE PROBLEMS

Have students refer to Appendix A of the Solutions Appendix for complete solutions to Practice Problems.

5. -12 cm

6. a. -18 cm

b. 45 mm

7. a. -27 cm

b. 11 cm

8. (f = 37.5 cm); r = 75 cm

POCKET LAB

MAKEUP

Do you have a makeup mirror in your house? Does this mirror produce images that are larger or smaller than your face? What does this tell you about the curvature? Feel the surface of the mirror. Does this confirm your prediction about the curvature? Try to discover the focal length of this mirror. Record your procedure and your results.

A positive height indicates an upright image. Notice that the image height is larger than the object height; the image is enlarged.

If an object is located between the focal point and a concave mirror, its image will be virtual, erect, and enlarged. Shaving and makeup mirrors are concave. If you hold the mirror close to your face, the image will be virtual, erect, and enlarged.

Practice Problems

5. An object is 4.0 cm in front of a concave mirror having a 12.0-cm radius. Locate the image using the mirror equation and a ray diagram.

6. A concave mirror has a focal length of 9.0 cm. A 15-mm high object is placed 6.0 cm from the mirror.

a. Find the image using the mirror equation.

b. How large is the image?

7. A 4.0-cm high candle is placed 10.0 cm from a concave mirror having a focal length of 16.0 cm.

a. Where is the image located?

b. What is the height of the candle's image?

▶ **8.** What should be the radius of curvature of a concave mirror that magnifies an object placed 25 cm from the mirror by a factor of +3.0?

Virtual Images Formed by Convex Mirrors

Images formed by convex mirrors are virtual, erect, and reduced in size.

A **convex mirror** is a spherical mirror that reflects light from its outer surface. The outside bottom of a spoon is a convex mirror. Rays reflected from a convex mirror always diverge. Thus, convex mirrors do not form real images. When doing ray diagrams, the focal point, **F,** is placed behind the mirror, half the distance to the center of curvature. When using the mirror equation, the focal length, f, of a convex mirror is a negative number.

The ray diagram, Figure 18–11, shows how an image is formed in a convex mirror. Ray 1 approaches the mirror parallel to the principal

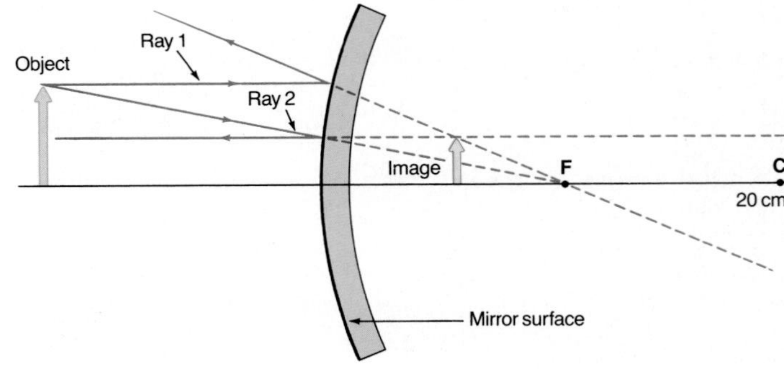

FIGURE 18–11. Convex spherical mirrors cause reflected light rays to diverge.

axis. To draw the reflected ray, draw a dashed line from the focal point, **F,** to the point where Ray 1 strikes the mirror. The reflected ray is in the same direction on the dashed line. Ray 2 approaches the mirror on a path that, if extended behind the mirror, would pass through **F.** The reflected part of Ray 2 is parallel to the principal axis. The two reflected rays diverge, as if coming from a point behind the mirror. The image, located at the apparent intersection of the extended rays behind the mirror, is virtual, erect, and reduced in size.

The mirror equation can be used to predict the location and size of images formed by convex mirrors. The value of f is negative, and d_i will be negative if the image is behind the mirror.

Convex mirrors are called diverging mirrors because the reflected rays spread apart. Convex mirrors form images reduced in size, but they also reflect an enlarged field of view. Rearview mirrors used in cars are often convex mirrors, as are mirrors used in stores to observe shoppers.

Glass that has not been silvered also reflects light. If that glass is curved outward it will act like a convex mirror. You can frequently see reduced images of yourself if you look into someone's eyeglasses. The photo at the beginning of this chapter has a glass lens that reflects some light off both its front (convex) and rear (concave) surfaces. Both are reduced in size; one is inverted. The upright one comes from the convex surface, the inverted one from the concave surface.

A convex lens is thicker in the center than at the edges.

A concave lens is thicker at the edges than in the center.

◀ Butterfly ylfrettuB

Example Problem

Image from a Convex Mirror

Calculate the position of the image in Figure 18–11. Use the mirror equation.

Given: $d_o = 15$ cm
$f = -10.0$ cm

Unknown: d_i

Basic equation: $\frac{1}{f} = \frac{1}{d_i} + \frac{1}{d_o}$

Solution: $\frac{1}{f} = \frac{1}{d_o} + \frac{1}{d_i}$,

$$\text{so } d_i = \frac{fd_o}{d_o - f} = \frac{(-10.0\text{ cm})(15\text{ cm})}{15\text{ cm} - (-10.0\text{ cm})} = -6.0\text{ cm}$$

Since d_i is negative, the image is virtual, located 6.0 cm behind the mirror.

Practice Problems

9. An object is 20.0 cm in front of a convex mirror with a −15.0-cm focal length. Find the location of the image using
  a. a ray diagram.
  b. the mirror equation.

FIGURE 18–12. Convex mirrors form smaller, virtual images. For this reason they are often used as wide-angle mirrors for safety and security.

CONCEPT DEVELOPMENT

Guided Practice: Go over the Example Problem on this page, then have students work on the first two Practice Problems.

Independent Practice: Assign the remaining Practice Problems on page 378 for homework and spend time reviewing them during the next class period.

Laboratory Manual. Give students additional experience with concave and convex mirrors by doing Lab 18.1 from the Laboratory Manual.

3 Close

CONVERGENT QUESTION

Ask students what common experiences probably gave people the idea to invent mirrors. [Most likely reflections from still water.]

Answers To
PRACTICE PROBLEMS

Have students refer to Appendix A of the Solutions Appendix for complete solutions to Practice Problems.

9. a. Refer to Problems and Solutions Manual.
b. −8.57 cm

18:1 ASSIGNMENT GUIDE

	PRACTICE	EXTENSION
CHAPTER REVIEW pp. 387–389		
· Reviewing Concepts	1–9, 11	
· Applying Concepts		1–8, 10
· Problems*	1–2, 4–5, 7–10	3, 6, 11
APPENDIX B PROBLEMS*		
· Chapter 18, p. 701	1–7, 9–11	8

* Complete solutions to all Chapter Review and Appendix problems appear in the Problems and Solutions Manual.

LABORATORY MANUAL

Use Lab 18.1 with this section.

Answers To

PRACTICE PROBLEMS (cont)

10. **a.** -10 cm

b. 1.0 cm

11. -0.38 m, erect, smaller

12. -96 cm

CONCEPT REVIEW ANSWERS

1.1

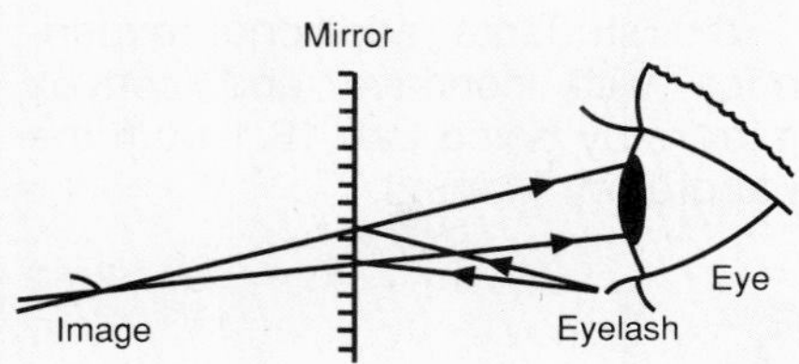

1.2 No. This defect is called spherical aberration.

1.3 No. It could also be a convex mirror or a concave mirror with the object closer to the mirror than the focal point.

1.4 **Critical Thinking:**

a.

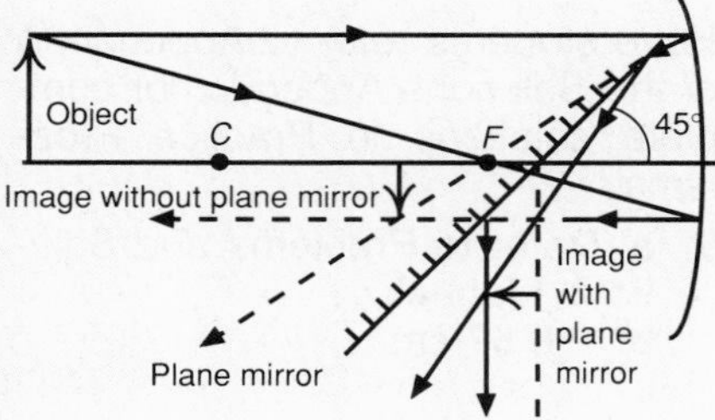

b. In both cases, the final image is real. The rays actually intersect in front of the new mirror. The object distance for the inserted mirror is negative (the object is said to be virtual), so the image distance is positive and the image is real. This arrangement is used in most reflecting telescopes.

10. A convex mirror has a focal length of -12 cm. A light bulb with a diameter of 6.0 cm is placed 60.0 cm in front of the mirror.

a. Where is the image of the light bulb? Use the mirror equation.

b. What is the diameter of the image?

11. In a department store, a mirror used to watch for shoplifters has a focal length of -40.0 cm. A person stands in an aisle 6.0 m from the mirror. Locate the person's image using the mirror equation. Is it erect or inverted? larger or smaller than the object?

▶ **12.** A convex mirror is needed to produce an image located 24 cm behind the mirror that is 3/4 the size of the object. What focal length should be specified?

CONCEPT REVIEW

1.1 Draw a ray diagram showing your eye placed 12 cm from a plane mirror. Two rays leave a point on an eyelash and enter opposite sides of the pupil of your eye, 1 cm apart. Locate the image of the eyelash.

1.2 If a beam of parallel light rays is sent into a spherical concave mirror, do all the rays converge at the focal point?

1.3 If a mirror produces an erect, virtual image, can you immediately say it is a plane mirror? Explain.

1.4 **Critical Thinking:** A concave mirror is used to produce a real image of a distant object. A small plane mirror is put between the mirror and the image. The mirror is put at a 45° angle to the principal axis of the concave mirror. **a.** Make a ray diagram. Is the image of the plane mirror real or virtual? Explain. **b.** If the small mirror were a convex mirror, would the image be real or virtual? Explain.

Objectives

- **differentiate between concave and convex lenses.**
- **describe formation of real and virtual images by convex lenses; locate image with ray diagram; calculate image location and size using lens equation.**
- **describe formation of virtual images by concave lenses; locate image with ray diagram; calculate image location and size using lens equation.**
- **define chromatic aberration and understand how it can be greatly reduced.**
- **explain the operation of optical instruments such as the microscope and the telescope.**

18.2 LENSES

Eyeglasses were made from lenses as early as the thirteenth century. Around 1610, Galileo combined two lenses into a telescope. With this instrument he discovered the moons of Jupiter. Lenses have since been used in optical instruments such as microscopes and cameras. Lenses are probably the most useful and important of all optical devices.

Types of Lenses

A **lens** is made of transparent material, such as glass or plastic, with a refractive index larger than that of air. Each of a lens's two faces is part of a sphere and can be convex or concave. One face may also be plane, or flat. A lens is called a **convex lens** if it is thicker at the center than at the edges, Figure 18–14a. Convex lenses are converging lenses because they refract parallel light rays so that they meet. A **concave lens** is thinner in the middle than at the edges and is called a diverging lens, Figure 18–14b. Rays passing through concave lenses spread out.

18.2 LENSES

Preparation

OBJECTIVES

The objectives are listed on the student page. Remind students to preview these objectives as a study guide to this major section.

OVERVIEW

Optics is extended into the study of lenses. Both convex and concave lenses are treated along with the lens equation. The lesson includes chromatic aberration.

BRIDGING

In this section, students will use the definition of wavelength, an understanding of the refractive index, and their knowledge of colored light.

1 Focus

It is essential that students are given an opportunity to observe the formation of a real image with a convex lens. Pass around several convex lenses and have students form images on a white piece of paper. Imaging things through the classroom windows works very well. Many will be surprised to find that the image is in color!

PHYSICS LAB: Seeing Is Believing

Purpose

To discover how the property of a lens depends on its shape.

Materials

- 3 converging lenses
- 1 diverging lens
- meter stick
- ball of clay
- 40-watt lamp
- ruler
- small screen

Procedure

1. Make a sketch of each lens. Label the sketches A, B, C, D.
2. Use the sun to form a bright spot for each lens. The distance from the spot to the lens is the focal length, f. Measure and record f for each lens.
3. Try using each lens as a magnifying glass. Record your observations.
4. Place the lamp and the screen 100 cm apart. Stand the lens in the ball of clay and place it near the lamp.
5. Slowly move the lens toward the screen and record d_o, d_i, and h_i when the image becomes clear on the screen.
6. Continue to move the lens toward the screen. If you find another position of sharp image, again record the three values.

Observations and Data

1. Repeat Procedure steps 3–6 for the other lenses.
2. How is the image oriented top to bottom with respect to the object?
3. How is the image oriented left to right? How do you know?
4. Could you produce a hot spot by holding two of the converging lenses together? Try it and record your results.
5. What happens to the magnifying power of a lens if it is reversed? Try it and record your results.

Analysis

1. Write a statement that describes how the value of f depends on the shape of the lens.
2. Write a statement that describes how the magnifying power depends on the shape.
3. What happens when two lenses are placed together? Can you make a general statement that describes the results?

Applications

1. What type of lens do you expect to find in a film projector or overhead projector? Explain.

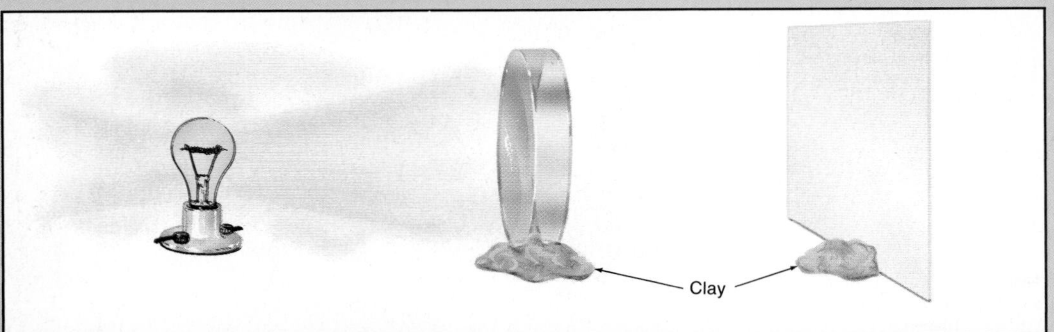

ASSESSMENT

Critical Thinking: To further assess students' understanding of lenses, ask the following questions.

1. What do you predict will happen to an image if you block the top half of the lens? Why? Try it and record what happens. [Most students will believe that the bottom half of the image will disappear. Actually a full image is still on the screen, it is just dimmer.]

2. How much of a lens is needed to produce a complete image? Predict what will happen to the image as more and more of the lens is blocked. Try it and explain the results. [Students will be surprised that only a very small fraction of the lens is needed to produce a full image. Every single point on the lens will produce a full and complete image. Having more lens area will brighten the image because more light is focused on the screen.]

PHYSICS LAB

Process Skills: observing, questioning, formulating models, classifying, communicating, interpreting data.

MISCONCEPTIONS

Most students will not realize that there are two different places where the lens can be placed to produce a sharp image on the screen.

Teaching Suggestions: For the selection of lenses provide a large diameter and a small diameter converging lens, a plano-converging lens, and a diverging lens.

- If your converging lenses have focal lengths greater than 25 cm, increase the distance in Procedure step 4.

OBSERVATIONS

1. Lenses with different focal lengths have different values for d_o, d_i, and h_i. Students will not be able to project images for the diverging lens.
2. The image is upside down.
3. The image is reversed left to right. Some groups may mark on the lamp or cover part of it.
4. The bright spot gets closer to the lenses when more than one is used. Both lenses bend the light toward the center.
5. Reversing the lens has no effect on the light.

ANALYSIS

1. For the converging lens, the greater the curvature the shorter the focal length. The focal length of the diverging lens cannot be directly measured.
2. Converging lenses with more curvature have more magnifying power. Diverging lenses produce smaller images.
3. Two converging lenses placed together will bend the light more than either one alone. A converging lens placed with a diverging lens tend to cancel each other out.

APPLICATIONS

1. Only converging lenses produce images on a screen, so that the lenses in projectors must be converging.

2 Teach

CONCEPT DEVELOPMENT

ACTIVITY

Discovery: Have students hold concave lenses close to some printing and then move them away from the page. In contrast to the convex lens effects, they'll see upright and reduced images.

Point out to students that we are discussing refraction in lenses, so light rays go through the lens. Check students' ray diagrams to make sure rays are drawn through the lens.

Critical Thinking: Ask students why it is necessary to put slides into a slide projector upside down.

Enrichment: One of the characters in William Golding's *Lord of the Flies* uses an eyeglass lens to start a fire. Have interested students check out the passage and see if it is an optically accurate description. (Later on in the book the character is said to be nearsighted.)

FIGURE 18–14. Light is refracted as it passes through a lens. In (a) the rays converge while in (b) they diverge.

a

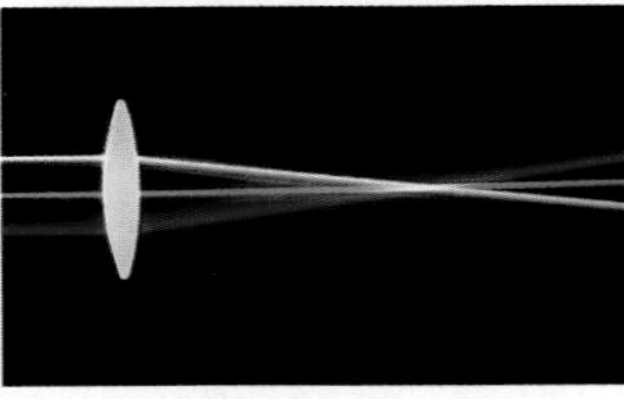

b

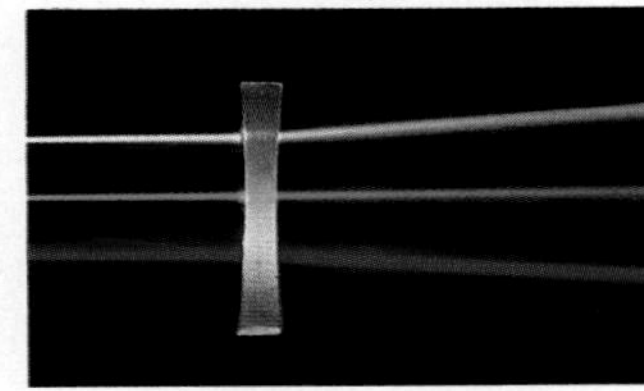

Real Images Formed by Convex Lenses

A convex lens can form an image that can be projected on a screen. In Figure 18–15, a convex lens is used to form an image of the sun on a leaf. As in the case of a mirror, the principal axis of a lens is a line perpendicular to the plane of the lens that passes through its midpoint. The rays of the sun are examples of light rays that approach a convex lens parallel to the principal axis. After being refracted, these rays will converge to a tiny spot at a point called the focal point, **F,** of the lens. The distance from the lens to the focal point is the focal length, *f*. The focal length of a lens depends on its shape and on the refractive index of the lens material.

As discussed in Chapter 17, refraction occurs at the two lens surfaces. Snell's law and geometry can be used to predict the paths of rays passing through a lens. To simplify our drawings and calculations, we use the approximation that all refraction occurs on a plane, called the principal plane, passing through the middle of the lens. This approximation is good for the thin lenses we will be discussing.

Let's trace rays from an object far from a convex lens, Figure 18–16. Problem Solving Strategies used for mirrors can also be used for lenses. Ray 1 is parallel to the principal axis. It refracts and passes through **F** on the other side of the lens. Ray 2 passes through **F** on its way to the lens. After refraction, its path is parallel to the principal axis. The two rays intersect at a point beyond **F,** locating the image. Rays selected from other points on the object would converge at corresponding points on the image. Note that the image is real, inverted, and smaller than the object.

The image of an object that is beyond the focal point of a convex lens is real and inverted.

To find the image of an object that is closer to the focal point, reverse the path of light through the lens in Figure 18–16. The image and object are reversed. The image is again real and inverted, but it is now larger than the object.

If the object were placed at a distance twice the focal length from the lens, the point **2F** on Figure 18–16, then the image is also found to be at **2F.** By symmetry, the two have the same size. Thus we see that if an object is more than twice the focal length from the lens, the image is reduced in size. If the object is between **F** and **2F,** then the image is enlarged.

As the object comes closer to the focal point of the lens, the image moves farther away and increases in size.

FIGURE 18–15. This camper is using a converging lens to start a fire in this pile of leaves.

TEACHER F.Y.I.

The telescope was invented by Hans Lippershey in 1608. In 1609, Galileo built one from information he had received on Lippershey's work. Galileo was able to produce a magnification of 30x by careful modifications on the device. He used this telescope to study Saturn and its rings, and sent out regular newsletters on his observations.

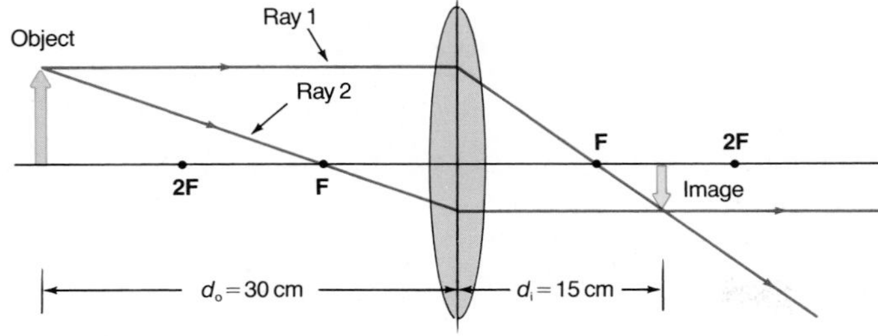

FIGURE 18–16. Finding the real image formed by a convex lens when the object is located beyond the principal focus, F, of the lens. Rays through the lens are drawn using the thin lens approximation.

The lens equation can also be used to find the location of the image and the magnification equation can be used to find its size.

$$\frac{1}{f} = \frac{1}{d_i} + \frac{1}{d_o}$$

$$m = \frac{h_i}{h_o} = \frac{-d_i}{d_o}$$

The **lens equation,** as well as the equation for magnification, is the same as that used for mirrors.

Lens Equation Conventions

d_o is *positive for real objects. negative for virtual objects.*

d_i is *positive for real images. negative for virtual images.*

f is *positive for convex lenses. negative for concave lenses.*

Example Problem

Real Image from a Convex Lens

An object is 32.0 cm to the left of a convex lens of +8.0-cm focal length. Use the lens equation to locate the image.

Given: $d_o = 32.0$ cm, $f = +8.0$ cm

Unknown: image distance, d_i

Basic equation: $\frac{1}{f} = \frac{1}{d_i} + \frac{1}{d_o}$

Solution: $\frac{1}{f} = \frac{1}{d_o} + \frac{1}{d_i}$, so $d_i = \frac{fd_o}{d_o - f}$

$$= \frac{(+8.0 \text{ cm})(32.0 \text{ cm})}{32.0 \text{ cm} - 8.0 \text{ cm}} = +11 \text{ cm}$$

The positive sign indicates the image is on the right side of the lens. It is real.

Practice Problems

13. Use a ray diagram to find the image position of an object 30 cm to the left of a convex lens with a +10-cm focal length. (Let 1 cm on the drawing represent 20 cm.)

14. An object 2.25 mm high is 8.5 cm to the left of a convex lens of 5.5-cm focal length. Find the image location and height.

15. An object is placed to the left of a 25-mm focal length convex lens so that its image is the same size as the object. What are the image and object locations?

▶ **16.** A lens is needed to create an inverted image twice as large as the object when the object is 7.0 cm from the lens. What focal length lens is needed?

POCKET LAB

BURNED UP

Convex (converging) lenses can be used as magnifying glasses. Borrow someone's eyeglasses and see if they magnify. Are the glasses converging? Can the lenses be used in sunlight to start a fire? Why?

CONCEPT DEVELOPMENT

ACTIVITY

Discovery: Have students place a penny heads-up in the bottom of a test tube. Fill half of the test tube with water and look down into it. The penny looks small and far away because the meniscus behaves like a concave lens. Now fill the test tube to the top and add water until there is a convex surface. The penny appears much larger and closer.

POCKET LAB

BURNED UP

Purpose: to observe the magnification power of eyeglasses.

Materials: several pairs of eyeglasses.

Outcome: Even if the lenses magnify, they will not start a fire. The surface area of the lenses cannot gather enough energy to start a fire.

Answers To

PRACTICE PROBLEMS

Have students refer to Appendix A of the Solutions Appendix for complete solutions to Practice Problems.

13. Refer to Solutions Appendix for diagram.

14. 16 cm; −4.2 mm

15. 50 mm

16. 4.7 cm

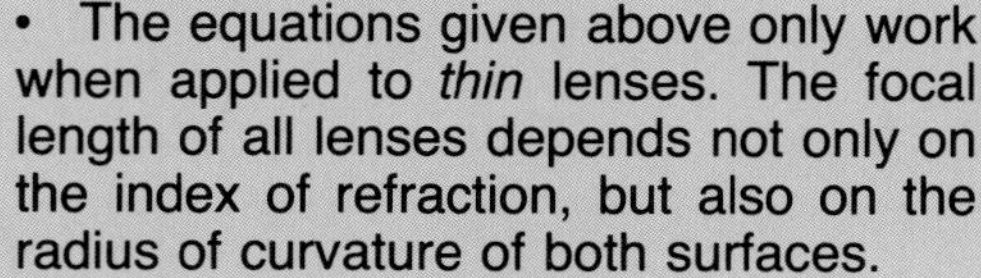

• The equations given above only work when applied to *thin* lenses. The focal length of all lenses depends not only on the index of refraction, but also on the radius of curvature of both surfaces.

• The focal length is positive for convex lenses and negative for concave lenses. For a real image, the image distance is positive if the image is on the side of the lens opposite the object.

CONCEPT DEVELOPMENT

- Ask students if they've seen the colored fringe around the outside of the circle of light produced by a spotlight or overhead projector. What causes this?

POCKET LAB

BRIGHT IDEAS

Purpose: to investigate the image produced by a converging lens.

Materials: converging lens; clay; small light bulb with power supply.

Outcome: One of the most important (and least emphasized) ideas about lenses is that each part of the lens forms a complete image. Students need to see this and talk about it. It might be useful to refer to the pinhole camera lab from Chapter 17 that proved that a single opening produces a complete image.

Assessment

Performance

To further assess students' understanding of image formation by lenses, have them block part of the lens and observe the brightness of the image. To further study this effect, form an image of a distant object (a light bulb) so that the image covers the sensitive surface of a light meter. In pieces of heavy paper, cut a series of round holes from 5 mm to the size of the lens. Place a hole over the lens and record the reading on the light meter. Repeat with the other holes. Make a graph of brightness versus hole diameter. How does brightness depend on hole size? [The brightness will depend on the square of the hole diameter. A plot of brightness versus hole diameter squared should give a straight line. Brightness depends on the area of the uncovered part of the lens.]

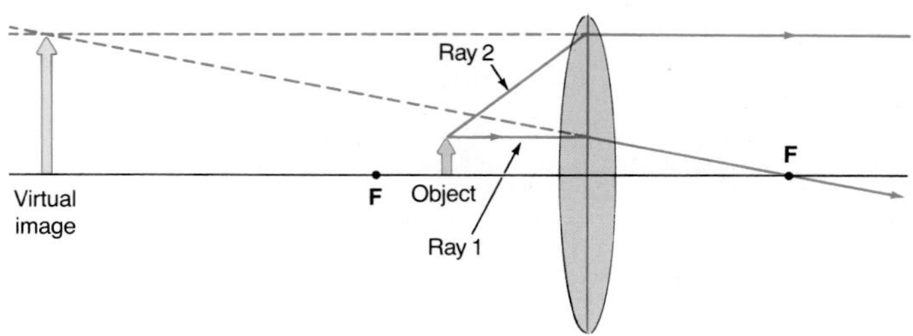

FIGURE 18–17. Finding the virtual image formed by a convex lens when the object is placed between the lens and principal focus, F.

Virtual Images Formed by Convex Lenses

The image of an object closer than the focal point of a convex lens is virtual, upright, and enlarged.

If an object is placed at the focal point of a convex lens, the refracted rays will emerge in a parallel beam. If the object is brought closer to the lens, the rays do not converge on the opposite side of the lens. We will find that the image appears on the same side of the lens as the object. This image is virtual, erect, and enlarged.

Figure 18–17 shows how a convex lens forms a virtual image. The object is between **F** and the lens. Ray 1, as usual, approaches the lens parallel to the principal axis and is refracted through the focal point, **F.** Ray 2 starts at the tip of the object, in the direction it would have if it had started at **F** on the object side of the lens. It leaves the lens parallel to the principal axis. Rays 1 and 2 diverge as they leave the lens. Thus no real image is possible. Tracing the two rays back to their apparent intersection locates the virtual image. It is on the same side as the object, erect, and larger than the object. A magnifying glass is a convex lens used to produce an enlarged, virtual image.

POCKET LAB

BRIGHT IDEAS

Stick the edge of a converging lens into a ball of clay and place the lens on a tabletop. Use a small light bulb on one side and a screen on the other side to get a sharp image of the bulb. Predict what will happen to the image if you place your hand over the top half of the lens. Try it. What really happened? How much of the lens is needed for a complete image?

Example Problem

Virtual Image from a Convex Lens

An object is 4.0 cm to the left of a convex lens of 6.0-cm focal length. **a.** Locate its image. **b.** What kind of image is formed?

Given: $d_o = 4.0$ cm, $f = 6.0$ cm

Unknown: image distance, d_i

Basic equation: $\frac{1}{f} = \frac{1}{d_i} + \frac{1}{d_o}$

Solution:

a. $\frac{1}{f} = \frac{1}{d_i} + \frac{1}{d_o}$,

so $d_i = \frac{fd_o}{d_o - f} = \frac{(6.0\text{ cm})(4.0\text{ cm})}{4.0\text{ cm} - 6.0\text{ cm}} = -12$ cm

b. Since the image distance is negative, the image is virtual. It is on the same side, the left side, of the lens as the object and is erect.

TEACHER 

When two thin lenses are brought into contact, the combination will have a focal length of $1/f = 1/f_1 + 1/f_2$. When the lenses are separated, the image distance for the first lens may be calculated as if the second lens did not exist. The equation is

$$1/d_o + 1/d_{if} = 1/f_1 + 1/f_2$$

where d_o is the original object distance, d_{if} is the final image distance, and f_1 and f_2 are the focal lengths of the two lenses, respectively. In the diagram,

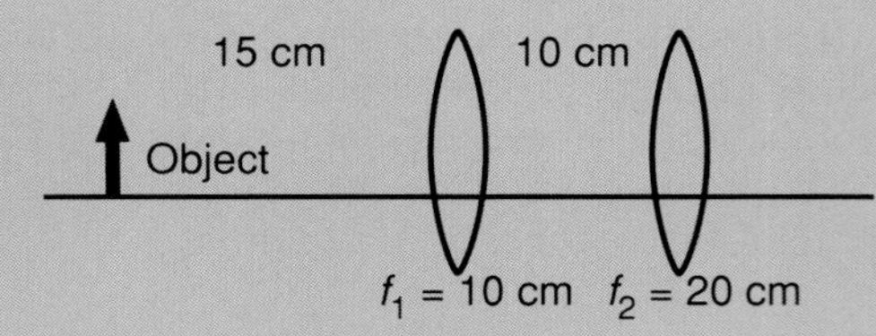

$\frac{1}{d_o} + \frac{1}{d_i} = \frac{1}{f}$, and $\frac{1}{d_i} = \frac{1}{10} - \frac{1}{15}$, so $d_i = 30$ cm, which is 20 cm to the right of the second lens.

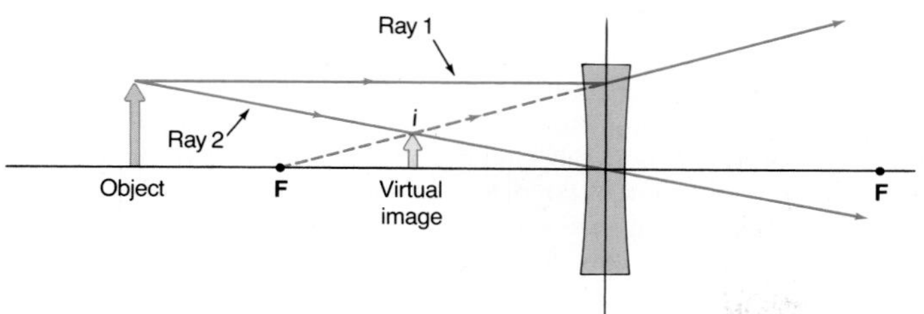

FIGURE 18–18. Formation of a virtual image by a concave lens.

Practice Problems

17. A newspaper is held 6.0 cm from a convex lens of 20.0-cm focal length. Find the image distance of the newsprint image.

18. A magnifying glass has a focal length of 12.0 cm. A coin, 2.0 cm in diameter, is placed 3.4 cm from the lens.
   a. Locate the image of the coin.
   b. What is the diameter of the image?

19. A stamp collector wants to magnify images by 4.0 when the object is 3.5 cm from the lens. What focal length lens is needed?

▶ **20.** Suppose you are looking at a stamp through a magnifying glass and want to increase the size of the image. Should you move the glass closer to the stamp or farther away? Explain and indicate the maximum distance you should move it.

Virtual Images Formed by Concave Lenses

Image formation by a concave lens is shown in Figure 18–18. A concave lens causes all rays to diverge. Ray 1 approaches the lens parallel to the principal axis. It leaves the lens in the direction it would have if it had passed through the focal point. Ray 2 passes directly through the center of the lens. Such a ray is not bent at all. Rays 1 and 2 diverge after passing through the lens. Their apparent intersection is *i*, on the same side of the lens as the object. The image is virtual, erect, and reduced in size. This is true no matter how far from the lens the object is located. The focal length of a concave lens is negative. Concave lenses are used in eyeglasses to correct nearsightedness and in combination with convex lenses in cameras and telescopes.

Concave lenses produce virtual images from real objects.

Chromatic Aberration

The edges of a lens resemble a prism, and different wavelengths of light are bent at slightly different angles, Figure 18–19a. Thus, the light that passes through a lens, especially near the edges, is slightly dispersed. An object viewed through a lens appears ringed with color. This effect is called **chromatic aberration.** The term chromatic comes from the Greek *chromo,* related to color.

The dispersion of light in lenses causes different colors to be focused different distances from the lenses.

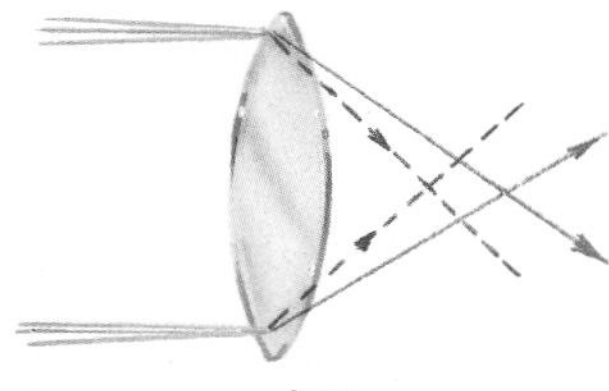

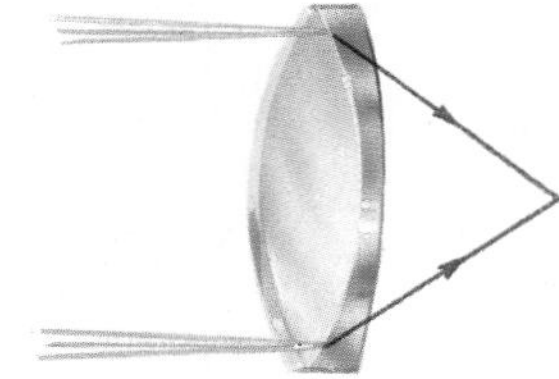

FIGURE 18–19. In chromatic aberration, rays of different wavelengths focus at different points, causing an object to appear ringed with color (a). An achromatic lens reduces chromatic aberration (b).

Answers To
PRACTICE PROBLEMS

Have students refer to Appendix A of the Solutions Appendix for complete solutions to Practice Problems.

17. −8.6 cm
18. a. −4.7 cm
b. 2.8 cm
19. 4.7 cm
20. From Figure 18–17, you can increase image size by making $(d_o - f)$ as small as possible. Thus, increase d_o until it is almost f, which is the limit.

CONCEPT DEVELOPMENT

- Look up the use of lens systems in solar energy applications.
- Use an optical bench set (or a meter stick with lens holders) to set up a simple telescope and a simple microscope.

TEACHER F.Y.I.

The construction of images produced by concave lenses uses a different principle ray than is used in the construction of images produced by convex lenses. This ray goes through the center of the lens without refraction. It is also possible to use this ray in the construction of convex lens images.

CHECKING FOR UNDERSTANDING

Choose a suitable problem from the end of the chapter and have various students contribute a step at a time, either verbally or by coming up to the board.

RETEACHING

Reteaching Master, Teacher Resource Package. Use the Reteaching Master for Chapter 18, Correcting Vision, to reinforce the concepts in this section.

EXTENSION

Enrichment Master. With this section, use the Enrichment Master, The Telescope, from the Teacher Resource Package.

Guided Practice: Do the first three Concept Review problems on page 386 as a classroom exercise.

Independent Practice: Assign the last Concept Review Problem for homework, then spend some time discussing it during the next class period.

Laboratory Manual. Give students additional experience with concave and convex lenses by doing Lab 18.2 from the Laboratory Manual.

F.Y.I.

Chester Moor Hall discovered the principle of the achromatic lens. Attempting to keep it a secret, he hired one lens maker to construct the crown glass lens and another to make the one of flint glass. Unfortunately, both lens makers had so much work to do that they subcontracted the job out to the same person, John Dollond. Dollond recognized the purpose of the two lenses and applied for a patent. The court assigned the patent to Dollond, even though the achromatic lens was Hall's idea. The judge said that the person who made the invention public for the good of all deserved the patent.

BIOLOGY CONNECTION

Chromatic aberration is always present when a single lens is used. By joining a convex lens with a concave lens that has a different index of refraction, chromatic aberration can be greatly reduced, Figure 18–19b. Both lenses disperse the light. The dispersion caused by the converging lens, however, is almost canceled by that caused by the diverging lens. The index of refraction of the diverging lens is chosen so that the combination lens still converges the light. A lens constructed in this way is called an **achromatic lens.** All precision optical instruments use achromatic lenses.

Optical Instruments

Although the eye itself is a remarkable optical device, its abilities can be greatly extended by a wide variety of instruments based on lenses and mirrors. The eye is a fluid-filled, almost spherical object that focuses the image of an object on the retina, Figure 18–20. Most of the refraction occurs at the curved surface of the cornea. The eye lens is made of flexible material with a refractive index different from that of the fluid. Muscles can change the shape of the lens, thereby changing its focal length. When the muscles are relaxed, the image of distant objects is focused on the retina. When the muscles contract, the focal length is shortened, permitting images of objects 25 cm or closer to be focused on the retina.

The eyes of many people do not focus sharp images on the retina. External lenses, eyeglasses or contact lenses, are needed to adjust the focal length and move the image to the retina, Figure 18–21. The nearsighted, or myopic, eye has too short a focal length. Images of distant

The eye lens changes shape to allow the eye to focus at objects different distances away.

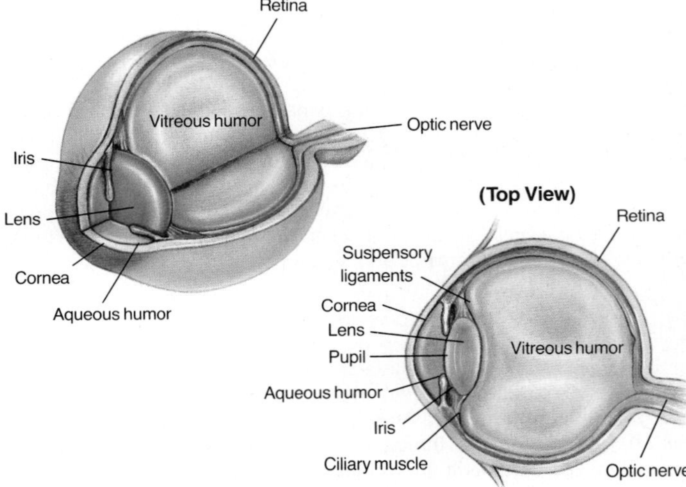

FIGURE 18–20. Structure of the eye.

TEACHER F.Y.I.

- The near point is the closest distance for which the lens of the eye will produce a sharp image on the retina and has an average value of 25 cm. Have your students determine their near point by finding the closest distance to their eyes to which they can bring a printed page before the letters are no longer distinct. This value will be off a bit because the distance from the front of the eye to the retina is not included.

To get the magnification of a hand lens, the near point (25 cm) is divided by the focal length. So, a 5-cm-focal-length lens has a magnification of 5x, and one with a focal length of 10 cm, 2.5x.

- Occulists measure lenses in diopters. The number of diopters is $1/f$ where the focal length is in meters. Thus, a 0.5 diopter lens has a focal length of +2 m (convex), and a −2.0 diopter lens has a focal length of −50 cm (concave).

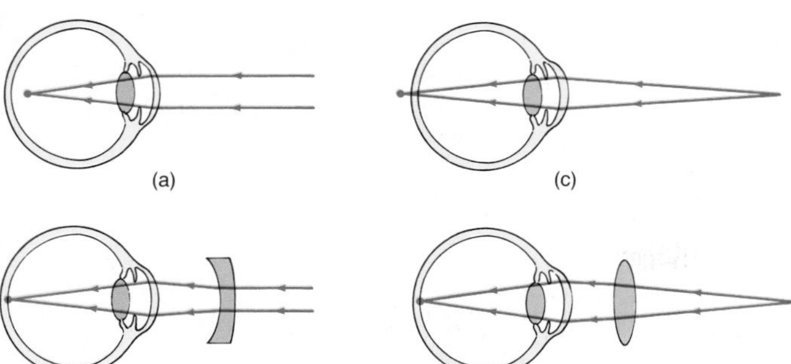

FIGURE 18–21. A nearsighted person cannot see distant objects. The image is focused in front of the retina (a). A concave lens will correct this defect (b). A person with farsightedness cannot see close objects. The image is focused behind the retina (c). A convex lens will correct the problem by refracting light to focus the image on the retina (d).

objects are formed in front of the retina. Concave lenses correct this defect by diverging the light rays, increasing the image distance, and placing the image on the retina. Farsightedness, or hyperopia, is the result of too long a focal length, resulting in the image falling behind the retina. A similar result is caused by the increasing rigidity of the lens in people more than about 45 years old. Their muscles cannot shorten the focal length enough to focus images of close objects on the retina. For either defect, convex lenses produce a virtual image farther from the eye than the object. This image then becomes the object for the eye lens and can be focused on the retina, correcting the defect. Some people have lenses or eye shapes that are not spherical. This defect is called astigmatism, and the result is that vertical lines of images can be in focus while horizontal lines are not. Eyeglasses having a non-spherical shape can correct astigmatism.

A microscope produces a very enlarged virtual image by means of at least two lenses.

A telescope collects more light and separates the images of stars.

Contact lenses have the same result, Figure 18–22. They are very thin lenses placed directly on the cornea. A thin layer of tears between the cornea and lens keeps the lens in place. Most of the refraction occurs at the air-lens surface where the change in refractive index is greatest.

Microscopes allow the eye to see extremely small objects. They use at least two convex lenses. An object is placed very close to a lens with a very short focal length, the objective lens. This lens produces a real image located between the second lens, the eyepiece lens, and its focal point. The eyepiece produces a greatly magnified virtual image of the image formed by the objective lens.

An astronomical refracting telescope uses two convex lenses. The objective lens of a telescope has a long focal length. The parallel rays from a star or other distant object come to focus in a plane at the focal point of this lens. The eyepiece lens, with a short focal length, then refracts the rays into another parallel beam. The viewer sees a virtual, enlarged, inverted image. The primary purpose of a telescope is not to magnify the image. It is to increase the angle between the rays from two different stars and to collect more light than would strike the unaided eye.

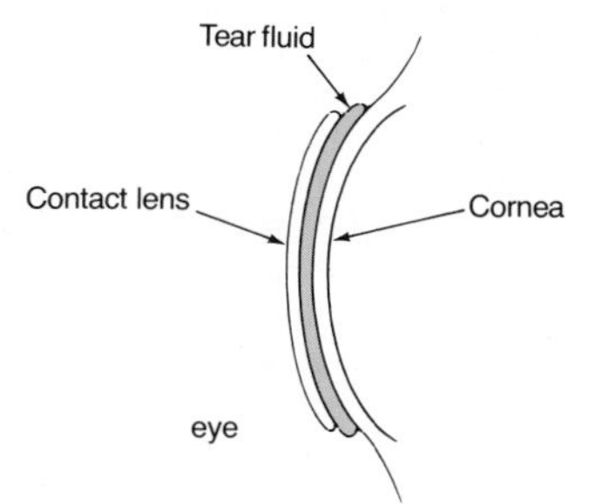

FIGURE 18–22. A contact lens rests on a layer of tears between it and the surface of the cornea.

RETEACHING MASTER

Use the Reteaching master for Chapter 18 with this section.

LABORATORY MANUAL

Use Lab 18.2 with this section.

ENRICHMENT MASTER

Use the Enrichment master for Chapter 18 with this section.

CRITICAL THINKING

Use the Critical Thinking master for Chapter 18 with this section.

CONCEPT DEVELOPMENT

Critical Thinking Master, Teacher Resource Package. Use the Critical Thinking Master, Reflecting Telescopes, with this section.

Enrichment: If you've done some photography, you probably know that most lenses are coated (note the bluish tint). Have interested students investigate these.

INDEPENDENT PRACTICE/ EXTENSION.

Refer to the Assignment Guide on page 386 for additional questions and problems for independent practice.

3 Close

CONVERGENT QUESTION

Ask students what optical phenomena occur in lenses. Which are the most important to the basic operation of the lens?

Connect to MEDICINE

Several methods of correcting myopia (nearsightedness) are being developed that do not require corrective lenses. Since most myopia is caused by the cornea being too bulged, these methods are designed to flatten the cornea. In radial kerotomy (RK), a surgeon makes small slits in a pattern like the spokes of a wheel. In another technique the top layer of the cornea is removed, as is a thin slice below it. The top layer is then sewn back on. Finally, high-power lasers have been used to vaporize the cells in the center of the cornea. A low-power laser first produces a map of the shape of the cornea, then a computer decides how much should be removed. The high-power laser then sculpts the cornea to its corrected shape. What do you think are the strengths and weakness of any of these methods. [Because of the side slits, RK may make side vision less clear than straight-ahead vision. The double slice technique demands a highly skilled surgeon to sew the top piece on again. The laser may leave the cornea too rough for good vision.]

CONCEPT REVIEW ANSWERS

2.1 Lenses a and c are converging; b and d are diverging.
2.2 Closer. Real images are always farther from the lens than the focal point. The farther away the object is, the closer the image is to the focal point.
2.3 Closer to the lens.
2.4

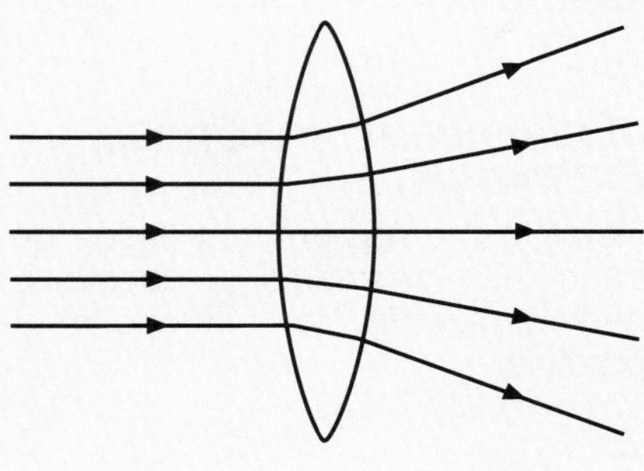

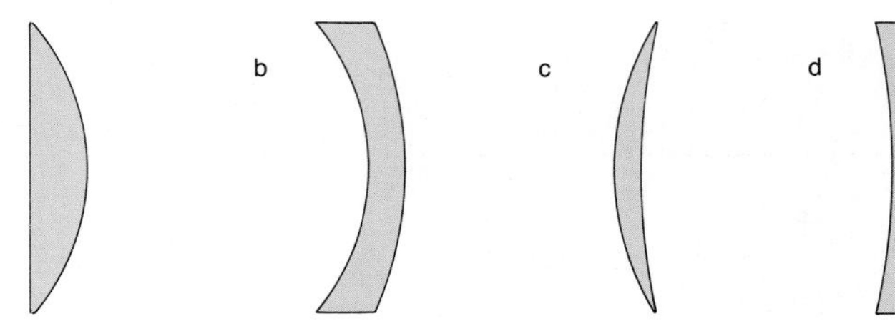

FIGURE 18–23. Use with Concept Review 2.1.

CONCEPT REVIEW

2.1 Which of the lenses whose cross-sections are shown in Figure 18–23 are convex or converging lenses? Which are concave or diverging lenses?
2.2 Suppose your camera has focused the image of a person 2 m away on the film. You now want it to focus the image of a tree farther away. Should the lens be moved closer to the film or farther away? Explain.
2.3 You first focus white light through a single lens so that red is focused to the smallest point on a sheet of paper. Which direction should you move the paper to best focus the blue?
2.4 **Critical Thinking:** An "air lens" constructed of two watch glasses, Figure 18–24, is placed in a tank of water. Draw the effect of this lens on parallel light rays incident on the lens.

Water
Light
Rays
Air
Water

FIGURE 18–24. Use with Concept Review 2.4.

Physics and technology

One large mirror would be easier to focus and control. But it would also be thicker and much heavier than the segmented mirror. This requires more substantial mountings to move the greater weight. If the large mirror was ever cracked or damaged, the loss could be catastrophic. The thinner segmented mirror would use less glass and be much lighter. If one of the segments were to become damaged or dysfunctional, that segment could be removed and replaced by a substitute segment. One of the major concerns about a segmented design such as that being used in the Keck telescope is whether all the segments can be precisely controlled and focused. The required alignment accuracy is one-millionth of an inch.

The mirror of the Keck telescope will be about twice as large as the mirror in the telescope at Mount Palomar in California. The Keck telescope is the only large optical telescope in the world with a mosaic primary mirror. The last reference below provides a good description of the Keck technology and project.

Physics and technology

STARGAZING

Astronomers have known for decades that to push the observational horizon farther back in space and time would require radically different telescopes. To see farther, more light must be collected, and this requires larger mirrors. But massive mirrors bend under their own weight, distorting the images being observed. Atmospheric distortions, temperature effects, and light pollution from nearby cities also limit the performance of existing telescopes.

Scientists are using two approaches to overcome these limitations—active optics and the space telescope. Earth-bound telescopes using active optics have flexible mirrors whose shape is changed under computer control to keep a sharp focus despite the effects of gravity and temperature changes. The giant Keck telescope now under construction in Hawaii will use active optics to control a mosaic-type mirror made of 36 separate hexagonal glass segments. It will be the largest optical telescope in the world when completed.

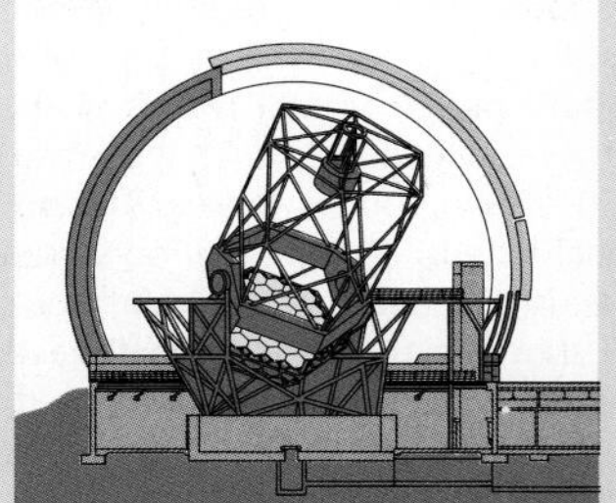

A second approach is to put a telescope into Earth orbit. The Hubble Space Telescope was launched into orbit by the U.S. in 1990. Spherical aberration in one of the telescope's mirrors, however, has reduced its capabilities.

· What do you see as the advantages and disadvantages of the solid-mirror vs. segmented-mirror telescope technology?

Teacher Resources: Crawford, David L. and Hunter, Tim B. "The Battle Against Light Pollution." *Sky and Telescope* 80 (No. 1), July 1990, pages 23–29.
Fienberg, Richard T. "The Hobbled Space Telescope." *Sky and Telescope* 80 (No. 3), September 1990, page 245.
Lemonick, Michael D. "Who Needs the Hubble?" *Time* 136 (No. 17), October 22, 1990, page 90.
Sinnott, R. W. "The Keck Telescope's Giant Eye." *Sky and Telescope* 80 (No. 1), July 1990, pages 15–22.

18:2 ASSIGNMENT GUIDE

	PRACTICE	EXTENSION
CHAPTER REVIEW pp. 387–389		
· Reviewing Concepts	10, 12, 13	
· Applying Concepts		9, 11–13
· Problems*	12–16, 18	17
APPENDIX B PROBLEMS*		
· Chapter 18, p. 701	12–15	16–18

* Complete solutions to all Chapter Review and Appendix problems appear in the Problems and Solutions Manual.

CHAPTER

18 REVIEW

SUMMARY

18.1 Mirrors

- The image in a plane mirror is the same size as the object. It is as far behind the mirror as the object is in front of the mirror. The image is virtual and erect.
- The focal point of a spherical mirror, concave or convex, is halfway between the center of curvature of the mirror and the mirror.
- The distance from the focal point to the center of the mirror is the focal length of the mirror.
- An imaginary line that passes from the center of the mirror through the center of curvature and beyond is called the principal axis of the mirror.
- Parallel light rays that fall far from the center of a spherical mirror do not pass through its focal point. This defect is called spherical aberration.
- A real image is located where light rays actually converge and can be displayed on a screen. Light rays only appear to converge at a virtual image. A virtual image thus cannot be displayed on a screen.
- Concave mirrors produce real, inverted images if the object is farther from the mirror than the focal point and virtual, upright images if the object is between the mirror and the focal point.
- Convex mirrors always produce virtual, upright, reduced images.

18.2 Lenses

- Lenses that are thinner at their outer edges than at their centers are called converging or convex lenses. Lenses that are thicker at their outer edges are diverging or concave lenses.
- The location of an image can be found either by ray tracing or by using the lens or mirror equation, as fits the situation.
- Convex lenses produce real, inverted images if the object is farther from the lens than the focal point. A virtual image is formed if the object is closer than the focal point.
- Concave lenses are seldom used alone. When they are, they produce virtual, upright, reduced images.
- Chromatic aberration is a lens defect caused by the dispersion of different wavelengths of light as they pass through the lens.

KEY TERMS

plane mirror	mirror equation
object	magnification
image	convex mirror
virtual image	lens
concave mirror	convex lens
principal axis	concave lens
focal point	lens equation
focal length	chromatic aberration
spherical aberration	achromatic lens
real image	

REVIEWING CONCEPTS

1. Describe the physical properties of the image of a person seen in a plane mirror.
2. Where is the image of an object in a plane mirror?
3. What causes the defect that all concave spherical mirrors have?
4. Describe the physical properties of a virtual image.
5. How does a virtual image differ from a real image?
6. A student believes that very sensitive photographic film can detect a virtual image. The student puts photographic film at the location of the image. Does this attempt succeed? Explain.
7. How can you prove to someone that an image is a real image?
8. Consider a plane mirror.
   a. What is its focal length?
   b. Does the mirror equation work for plane mirrors? Explain.
9. An object produces a virtual image in a concave mirror. Where is the object located?
10. Locate and describe the physical properties of the image produced by a convex lens if an object is placed some distance beyond $2F$.

REVIEW MASTER

Use the Vocabulary Review master for Chapter 18 with this section.

EVALUATION MASTER

Use the Chapter Evaluation master for Chapter 18 with this section.

CLOSING CHAPTER 18

Review Summary statements and Key Terms with your students.

ASSESSMENT

Vocabulary Review Master, Teacher Resource Package. Use this master to check students' understanding of Key Terms.

Evaluation Masters. Use Parts A and B of the Chapter Evaluation Masters from the Teacher Resource Package to test qualitative chapter objectives, Parts C and D to test quantitative chapter objectives.

Answers To

REVIEWING CONCEPTS

1. Image is erect, virtual, as far in back of the mirror as the object is in front of the mirror and the same size as the object.
2. The image is on a line that is perpendicular to the mirror, and the same distance behind the mirror as the object is in front of the mirror.
3. Rays parallel to the axis that strike the edges of a concave spherical mirror are not reflected through the focal point. This effect is called spherical aberration.
4. All virtual images are erect and are the result of divergent rays.
5. A virtual image cannot be cast upon a screen; a real image can. The rays that form a virtual image only *appear* to originate at the location of the image. They actually originate elsewhere. The rays that form a real image *really do* originate at the position of the image.
6. No. The rays do not converge at a virtual image. No image forms and the student would not get a picture. Some virtual images are behind the mirror. Could you put a camera behind your bathroom mirror to take a picture of your image?
7. Place a sheet of plain paper or photographic film at the image location and you should be able to find the image.

Answers To
REVIEWING CONCEPTS (cont)

8. a. The focal length of a plane mirror is infinite.
b. Yes.

$$\frac{1}{f} = \frac{1}{d_i} + \frac{1}{d_o}, \text{ so}$$

$$\frac{1}{\infty} = 0 = \frac{1}{d_i} + \frac{1}{d_o},$$

and $d_i = d_o$.

9. Object must be located between F and the mirror.

10. The image will be between F and $2F$, inverted, real, and smaller than the object.

11. Convex mirrors are used as rearview mirrors because they allow for a wide range of view, allowing the driver to see a much larger area about the bus than is afforded by ordinary mirrors.

12. The index of refraction of the material from which the lens is made also determines the focus.

13. The film is run through the projector with the actors upside down on the film. When they are inverted on the screen, they appear right side up.

Answers To
APPLYING CONCEPTS

1. No. Focal length depends only on the law of reflection, which is independent of the index of refraction.

2. You should order a parabolic mirror to eliminate spherical aberrations.

3. The image will be at C, the center of curvature, inverted, real, and the same size as the object.

4. The image will be between C and F, will be inverted, real, and smaller than the object.

5. The image will be beyond C, inverted, real, and larger than the object.

6. The image in a convex mirror is always virtual, erect, smaller than the object, and located closer to the mirror than the object.

7. You can use only a concave mirror with the object beyond the focal point. A convex mirror will never form a real image.

8. You may use a concave mirror with the object beyond the center of curvature, or a convex mirror with the object anywhere.

9. In general, a converging lens is convex, thicker in the middle; a diverging lens is concave, thicker at the edge.

10. a. a convex mirror **b.** It provides a wider field of view.

11. Convex mirrors are used as rearview mirrors on school buses. Why are convex mirrors used?

12. What factor, other than the curvature of the surfaces of a lens, determines the location of the focal point of a lens?

13. To project an image from a movie projector onto a screen, the film is placed between F and $2F$ of a converging lens. This arrangement produces an inverted image. Why do the actors appear to be erect when the film is viewed?

APPLYING CONCEPTS

1. If you use a shaving or makeup mirror underwater in a swimming pool, will its focal length change? Explain.

2. You have to order a large concave mirror for a piece of high quality equipment. Should you order a spherical mirror or a parabolic mirror? Explain.

3. Locate and describe the physical properties of the image produced by a concave mirror when the object is located at the center of curvature.

4. An object is located beyond the center of curvature of a spherical concave mirror. Locate and describe the physical properties of the image of the object.

5. An object is located between the center of curvature and the focus of a concave mirror. Locate and describe the physical properties of the image of the object.

6. Describe the physical properties of the image seen in a convex mirror.

7. List all the possible arrangements in which you can use a spherical mirror, either concave or convex, to form a real image.

8. List all the possible arrangements in which you can use a spherical mirror, either concave or convex, to form an image reduced in size.

9. What physical characteristic of a lens distinguishes a converging lens from a diverging lens?

10. The outside rearview mirrors of cars often carry the warning "Objects in the mirror are closer than they appear."

a. What kind of mirror would have such a warning?

b. What advantage does this type of mirror have?

11. If you try to use a magnifying glass underwater, will its properties change? Explain.

12. Suppose Figure 18–16 was redrawn with a lens of the same focal length but a larger diameter. How would the location of the image change?

13. Why is there chromatic aberration for light that goes through a lens but there is no chromatic aberration for light that reflects from a mirror?

PROBLEMS

18.1 Mirrors

1. Find the image of the object in Figure 18–25.

FIGURE 18–25. Use with Problem 1.

2. Penny wishes to take a picture of her image in a plane mirror. If the camera is 1.2 m in front of the mirror, at what distance should the camera lens be focused?

▶ **3.** Draw a ray diagram of a plane mirror to show that if you want to see yourself from your feet to the top of your head, the mirror must be at least half your height.

4. A concave mirror has a focal length of 10.0 cm. What is its radius of curvature?

5. Light from a distant star is collected by a concave mirror. How far from the mirror is the image of the star if the radius of curvature is 150 cm?

▶ **6.** The sun falls on a concave mirror and forms an image 3.0 cm from the mirror. If an object 24 mm high is placed 12.0 cm from the mirror, where will its image be formed?

a. Use a ray diagram.
b. Use the mirror equation.
c. How high is the image?

7. An object is 30.0 cm from a concave mirror of 15-cm focal length. The object is 1.8 cm high.
a. Find the image with the mirror equation.
b. How high is the image?

8. A jeweler inspects a watch with a diameter of 3.0 cm by placing it 8.0 cm in front of a concave mirror of 12.0 cm focal length.
a. Where will the image of the watch appear?
b. What will be the diameter of the image?

9. A dentist uses a small mirror of radius 40 mm to locate a cavity in a patient's tooth. If the mirror is concave and is held 16 mm from the tooth, what is the magnification of the resulting image?

10. A production line inspector wants a mirror that produces an upright image with magnification of 7.5 when it is located 14.0 mm from a machine part.
a. What kind of mirror would do this job?
b. What is its radius of curvature?

▶ **11.** Shiny lawn spheres placed on pedestals are convex mirrors. One such sphere has a diameter of 40 cm. A 12 cm robin sits in a tree 1.5 m from the sphere.
a. Where is the image of the robin?
b. How long is the robin's image?

18.2 Lenses

12. The focal length of a convex lens is 17 cm. A candle is placed 34 cm in front of the lens. Make a ray diagram to find the location of the image.

13. The convex lens of a copy machine has a focal length of 25.0 cm. A letter to be copied is placed 40.0 cm from the lens.
a. How far from the lens is the copy paper located?
b. The machine was adjusted to give an enlarged copy of the letter. How much larger will the copy be?

14. Camera lenses are described in terms of their focal length. A 50.0-mm lens has a focal length of 50.0 mm.
a. A camera is focused on an object 3.0 m away using a 50.0 mm lens. Locate the position of the image.
b. A 1.00×10^3 mm lens is focused on an object 125 m away. Locate the position of the image.

15. Solve Problem 10 using a lens rather than a mirror.

16. A convex lens is needed to produce an image located 24 cm behind the lens that is 0.75 the size of the object. What focal length should be specified?

▶ **17.** A slide of an onion cell is placed 12 mm from the objective lens of a microscope. The focal length of the objective lens is 10.0 mm.
a. How far from the lens is the image formed?
b. What is the magnification of this image?
c. The real image formed is located 10.0 mm beneath the eyepiece lens. If the focal length of the eyepiece is 20.0 mm, where does the final image appear?
d. What is the final magnification of this compound system?

18. In order to clearly read a book at 25 cm away, a farsighted person needs an image distance of −45 cm. What focal length lens is needed?

USING A GRAPHING CALCULATOR

Mary has just captured a beautiful butterfly and is proudly examining it under a magnifying glass. The focal length of the magnifying glass is 15cm and the butterfly is 5cm across. As you have learned, the equation for calculating how large the butterfly appears is $h_1 = |(-h_o f)/(d - f)|$. Graph this equation on a graphing calculator with h_1 on the y axis (with a range of −50cm to 50cm) and d on the x axis (with a range of 0cm to 50cm). How large does the butterfly appear at 5cm? At 10cm? 13cm? 17cm? 20cm? 30cm? 50cm? For what distances is the image upright?

THINKING PHYSIC-LY

1. What is responsible for the rainbow-colored fringe commonly seen at the edges of a spot of white light from a slide projector or overhead projector?

2. Maps of the moon are actually upside down. Explain.

11. Yes. Refraction depends on the difference in refractive indices at the interface; therefore the focal length will be increased.
12. The location of the image would not change.
13. Chromatic aberration for lenses is due to the dispersion of light (different wavelengths of light have different speeds in the lens and refract with slightly different angles). Mirrors reflect, and reflection is wavelength-independent.

Answers To
PROBLEMS

Complete solutions for all Chapter Review Problems can be found in the Problems and Solutions Manual accompanying this text.

1. Refer to Problems and Solutions Manual.
2. 2.4 m
3. Refer to Problems and Solutions Manual.
4. 20.0 cm
5. 75.0 cm
6. **a.** Refer to Problems and Solutions Manual.
b. 4.0 cm
c. −8.0 mm
7. **a.** 30 cm
b. −1.8 cm
8. **a.** −24 cm
b. + 9.0 cm
9. 5.0
10. **a.** concave mirror
b. 32.4 mm
11. **a.** −9.4 cm
b. 0.75 cm
12. Refer to Problems and Solutions Manual.
13. **a.** 66.7 cm
b. 1.67 h_o
14. **a.** 51 mm
b. 1.01×10^3 mm
15. **a.** convex lens
b. 16.2 mm
16. 14 cm
17. **a.** 60.0 mm
b. −5.0
c. −20.0 mm
d. −10.0
18. 56 cm

Answers To
THINKING PHYSIC-LY

1. chromatic aberration
2. To match the inverted image seen through the telescope.

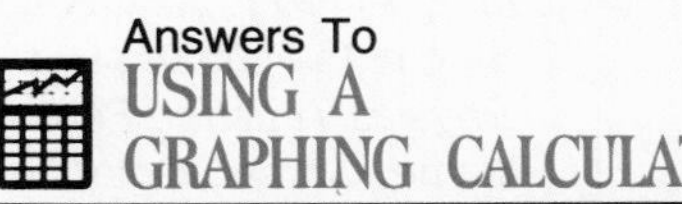

Answers To
USING A GRAPHING CALCULATOR

1. Set the range values (RANGE 0 50 10 −50 50 10)
2. Clear the graph (Cls EXE)
3. Graph the equation (GRAPH −75/(X − 15) EXE)
4. Trace along the graph to the x's and find the y's (TRACE −> X < −> Y)

Answers: at 5cm, 7.5 cm; at 10 cm, 15.2 cm; at 13 cm, 38 cm; at 17 cm, 37 cm; at 20 cm, 14.4 cm; at 30 cm, 5.0 cm; at 50 cm, 2.1 cm. The image is upright for all distances less than 15 cm.

CHAPTER

19 Diffraction and Interference of Light

PLANNING GUIDE (4 class sessions)

CONTENTS	TEXT FEATURES	TEACHER RESOURCE PACKAGE	OTHER COMPONENTS
19.1 When Light Waves Interfere, pp. 392–398 (3 Class Sessions) • The Two-Slit Interference Pattern • Measuring the Wavelength of Light • Single-Slit Diffraction	**Physics Lab:** Wavelengths of Colors, p. 399 **Pocket Lab:** Laser Spots, p. 395 **Concept Review,** p. 398	**Study Guide:** When Light Waves Interfere **Physics Lab Data Sheet:** Wavelengths of Colors **Reteaching Master:** Resolving Power **Critical Thinking Master:** Diffraction **Enrichment Master:** Determining the Wavelength of Light **Transparency Worksheet:** Wave Interference **Transparency Worksheet:** Double Slit/Single Slit	**Laboratory Manual:** Lab 19.1 Double Slit Interference **Transparency 25:** Wave Interference **Transparency 26:** Double Slit/Single Slit
19.2 Applications of Diffraction, pp. 400–402 (1 Class Session) • Diffraction Gratings • Resolving Power of Lenses	**Physics and Technology:** Holograms, p. 402 **Pocket Lab:** Hot Lights, p. 400 **Concept Review,** p. 402	**Study Guide:** Applications of Diffraction	**Laboratory Manual:** Lab 19.2 White Light Holograms
Chapter Review, pp. 403–405	Summary Key Terms Reviewing Concepts Applying Concepts Problems Thinking Physic-ly	**Vocabulary Review** **Chapter Test**	**Test Bank**

SUPPLEMENTARY MATERIALS

SOFTWARE	AUDIOVISUAL	BOOKS/MAGAZINES
Slit Interference And Diffraction, COMPress/Queue, Inc. (Apple II). *Young's Slits,* Queue, Inc. (Apple II).	Filmstrip: *Light,* Clearvue. Various: Integraf Holography Supplies (send self-addressed, stamped envelope) 745 N. Waukegan Road Lake Forest, IL 60045	Heideman, Edwin Paul. "Film-Canister Spectroscope." *The Physics Teacher,* May 1990, p. 343. Hewitt, Paul G. "Openings between Leaves." *The Physics Teacher,* November 1990, p. 574. Leung, Alfred F., and George, Simon. "Which Side of the Grating Has the Grooves." *The Physics Teacher,* February 1990, p. 98. Rämme, Göran. "Colors on Soap Films—An Interference Phenomenon." *The Physics Teacher,* October 1990, p. 479.

PROBLEM CORRELATION

CONCEPTS	CHAPTER REVIEW			PROBLEMS APPENDIX
	Reviewing Concepts	Applying Concepts	Problems	
19.1 When Light Waves Interfere				
The Two-Slit Interference Pattern	1			
Measuring the Wavelength of a Light Wave	2,3	1,2	1,2,3,4,**5**	1,2,3,4,**5**
Single-Slit Diffraction	5	3,4,5	6,7,8,**9**	6,7,8,**9**
19.2 Applications of Diffraction				
Diffraction Gratings	6,7,8,9	7,8,9	10,11,12,**13,14**	10,11,12,13
Resolving Power of Lenses	4,10	6	15,16,17,18,**19**	14

ACTIVITY AND DEMONSTRATION MATERIALS

PHYSICS LAB	POCKET LAB	DEMONSTRATIONS
Page 399 meter stick index card 40-W straight filament light ball of clay tape diffraction grating	Pages 395, 400 laser movie screen piece of screen variable power supply (variac) 100-W clear lamp with socket diffraction grating	Pages 392, 393, 394, 395, 396, 401 laser glass brick (or some other kind of irregular glass) record overhead projector 2 transparent sheets black marker ripple tank ruler

EXTENSION PROJECTS

LIBRARY RESEARCH

1. Colored Holograms
Investigate how colored holograms are produced.

DISPLAY MODEL

2. Diffraction and Interference
Collect photographic examples of diffraction and interference. Explain the occurrence of these phenomena in each photograph.

STUDENT READINGS

Altman, T.C. "Pre-Newtonian Holograms or How to Make Holograms Without All the Bother of Inertia and Vibrations." *The Physics Teacher,* April 1988.

Kruglak, Haym. "Another Legend Debunked." *The Physics Teacher,* October 1990.

Nöldeke, Christian. "Compact Disc Diffraction." *The Physics Teacher,* October 1990.

Ronada, David. "Compact Disc Digital Audio Systems." *Computers and Electronics,* August 1983.

Tonomura, A. "Electron Holography: A New View of the Microscope." *Physics Today,* April 1990.

Chapter 19

Diffraction and Interference of Light

CHAPTER OVERVIEW

Theme Development: Interference fringes and patterns show strong symmetry. Mathematical modeling of light phenomena is extended by geometrical interpretations of single-slit and double-slit diffraction effects.

MISCONCEPTIONS

Overall, this material will seem very abstract to students because the phenomena are less common than other aspects of optics. Students should be reminded that diffraction and interference patterns are most easily observed when produced by a coherent light source.

KEY TERMS

coherent
diffraction
diffraction grating
interference fringes
monochromatic
Rayleigh criterion

Laboratory Options

STUDENT EDITION

Physics Lab

Wavelengths of Colors	399

Pocket Labs

Laser Spots	395
Hot Lights	400

TEACHER EDITION

Activities

Demonstration	392, 393, 394, 395, 396, 401
Discovery	393, 396, 396, 397

LABORATORY MANUAL

Double-Slit Interference	Lab 19.1
White Light Holograms	Lab 19.2

CHAPTER 19

Diffraction and Interference of Light

◀ In the Eyes of the Beholder

The South American Morpho butterfly has a unique and beautiful coloration. In daylight its wings appear a brilliant, metallic, iridescent blue. What characteristic of light could explain this unusual coloration?

Chapter Outline

You have seen that dyes and pigments produce colors when they absorb some wavelengths of light while transmitting or reflecting others. In prisms and raindrops, different wavelengths are bent through different angles. The colors in peacock tails, mother-of-pearl shells, and soap films are due to interference in thin films discussed in Chapter 16. None of these methods produces the colors in beetles and the wings of butterflies, which are some of the most beautiful in nature.

✓ Concept Check

The following terms or concepts from earlier chapters are important for a good understanding of this chapter. If you are not familiar with them, you should review them before studying this chapter.

- superposition of waves, wavelength, Chapters 14, 16

Introducing The Chapter

In the Eyes of the Beholder

Using The Photo: We observe the effects of diffraction as beautiful colors in jewelry, beetles, and butterflies. Ridges in the butterfly's wings act as a diffraction grating. For a more detailed explanation of the chapter opener question, refer students to page 400.

✓ Concept Check

Make sure students have a clear understanding of the concepts taught in Chapters 14 and 16 that are listed in the Concept Check. Students with a good understanding of superposition of waves will be prepared to learn why interference patterns occur. A familiarity with wavelengths is crucial to understanding the principles involved in diffraction and resolution effects.

Assessment

Portfolio

Students should collect photographs of natural or manufactured objects that obtain their colors from diffraction effects. Gemstones like opals, the wings of certain butterflies, and the bodies of some beetles are good examples. Some items sold as jewelry use diffraction gratings or holograms to produce colors.

Assessment Options

Portfolio Assessment
Extension 1, TWE, p. 390b
Portfolio Assessment, TWE, p. 391
Enrichment, TWE, p. 396
Enrichment, TWE, p. 398
Extension, TWE, p. 401

Performance Assessment
Pocket Labs, pp. 395, 400
Physics Lab, p. 399
Activity, TWE, p. 393
Activity 1, TWE, p. 396

Content Assessment
Self Assessment: Practice Problems, pp. 395, 398
Convergent Question, TWE, p. 398
Assessment, Critical Thinking, TWE, p. 399
Checking for Understanding, TWE, p. 401
Concept Reviews, pp. 398, 402
Chapter Review, pp. 403–405
Supplemental Problems, pp. 701–702

Group Assessment
Activities for group assessment occur with Cooperative Learning and lab activities.

19.1 WHEN LIGHT WAVES INTERFERE

Preparation

OBJECTIVES

The objectives are listed on the student page. Remind students to preview these objectives as a study guide to this major section.

OVERVIEW

This chapter introduces the student to Rayleigh criterion, diffraction gratings, diffraction patterns, coherence, monochromatic light, diffraction, and interference fringes.

BRIDGING

Waves, constructive and destructive interference, wavelength, crests and troughs, nodal and antinodal lines, spectrum, and ratio are previously taught terms and concepts that will help students understand the explanations of the optical effects presented in this section.

1 Focus

Demonstration: Darken the room and shine a laser beam through a glass brick, a piece of shower door glass, or some other irregular piece of glass. Interesting patterns will appear on the wall due to the diffraction and interference of the light rays.

Transparency Package. Use Transparency 25 to help illustrate wave interference.

Objectives

- **define diffraction of light.**
- **display an understanding of how light falling on two slits produces a pattern of dark and bright bands on a screen.**
- **understand the geometrical interpretation of two-slit interference.**
- **demonstrate an ability to calculate the wavelength of light from measurements of the two-slit interference pattern.**
- **explain geometrically how single-slit diffraction patterns occur; use the derived equation to relate the pattern width to slit width and light wavelength.**

19.1 WHEN LIGHT WAVES INTERFERE

An English physician, Thomas Young (1773–1829), became interested in optics when he studied the human eye. Young's early medical studies of the human voice led him to investigate waves. The insights he gained he applied to the understanding of wave interference in oceans and lakes. He read Newton's book on optics and became convinced that Newton's results could be explained if light were a wave of almost unimaginably small wavelength. In 1801, he developed an experiment that would allow him to make a precise measurement of that wavelength.

The Two-Slit Interference Pattern

The Italian, Francesco Maria Grimaldi (1618–1663) first noted that the edges of shadows are not perfectly sharp. He named the slight spreading of light waves diffraction. **Diffraction** is the bending of waves around the edges of barriers. The Dutch scientist Christiaan Huygens (1629–1695) proposed a model to explain diffraction. According to Huygens, you can replace the crest of any wave by series of equally-spaced wave sources, each producing new waves in step with one another. Figure 19–1 shows how Huygens' wavelets explain diffraction.

Diffraction is the bending of light around the edges of barriers.

Huygens' model may explain diffraction, but does that mean light has to be a wave? Young's experiment gave additional evidence of the wave nature of light. Young allowed light to fall on two closely-spaced narrow slits. The light passing through each slit was spread out, or diffracted. The spreading light from the two slits overlapped. When the light fell on an observing screen, the overlap did not produce extra light, but a pattern of bright and dark bands called **interference fringes.** Young explained that these bands were the result of constructive and destructive interference of the light waves from the two slits.

Young used a **monochromatic** (mahn uh croh MAT ik) light source, one that emits light of only one wavelength. He placed a narrow slit in front of the source. This slit allowed light from only a small part of the source to pass through. As a result, the waves were not only the same wavelength, but all were in step. That is, they were **coherent.** The

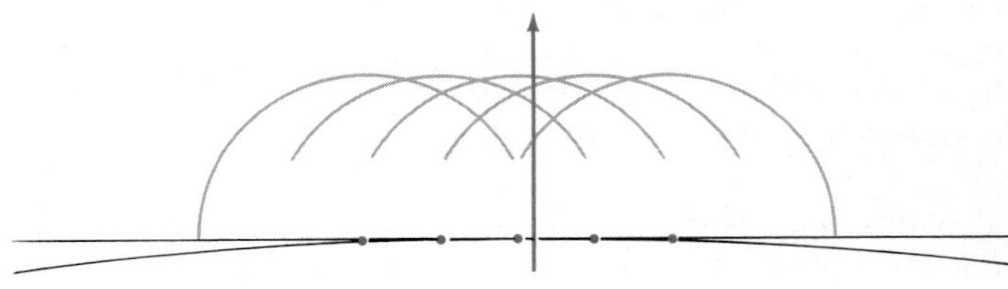

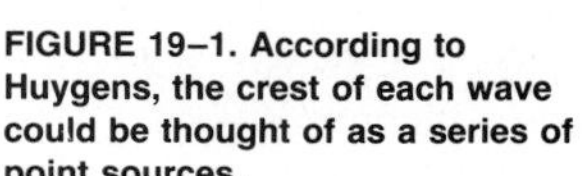

FIGURE 19–1. According to Huygens, the crest of each wave could be thought of as a series of point sources.

TEACHER F.Y.I.

Diffraction phenomena are usually classified as either Fraunhofer or Fresnel. Fraunhofer patterns are produced when either the screen is far from the slit or a converging lens is used to focus the parallel rays onto the screen. Where the angle is 0°, a bright band appears and is flanked by alternating bright and dark bands. A Fresnel pattern is produced when the screen is some finite distance from the slit and no lens is used. Because the Fresnel pattern is much more complex quantitatively, only Fraunhofer diffraction will be discussed here.

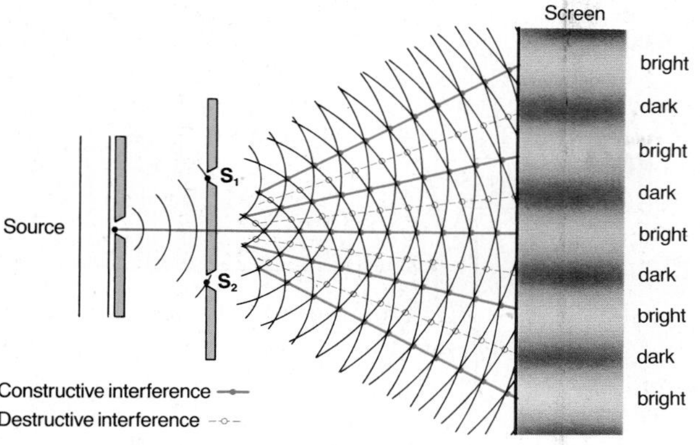

FIGURE 19–2. The diffraction of monochromatic light through a double slit produces bright and dark bands on a screen.

waves spread after passing through the single slit and fell on the double slit. The double slit acted as two sources of new circular waves. In Figure 19–2, the semicircles represent wave crests moving outward from the slits. Midway between the crests are the troughs. The waves from the two sources interfere constructively at points where two crests overlap. They interfere destructively where a crest and a trough meet.

When monochromatic light is used, Figure 19–3a, b, bright bands of light appear at points where the constructive interference occurs on the screen. One bright band appears at the center of the screen. On either side of the central band are bright bands corresponding to the other points of constructive interference. Between the bright bands are dark areas located where destructive interference occurs on the screen.

When white light is used in a double-slit experiment, Figure 19–3c, colored spectra are seen instead of bright and dark bands. The positions of the constructive and destructive interference bands depend on the wavelength of the light. All wavelengths interfere constructively in the central bright band, so that band is white. The positions of the other bands depend on the wavelength, so the light is separated by diffraction into a spectrum of color at each band.

FIGURE 19–3. The diffraction of a monochromatic light source produces an interference pattern on the screen resulting in a pattern, such as the one shown for blue light (a), and for red light (b). The diffraction of white light produces bands of colors (c).

2 Teach

CONCEPT DEVELOPMENT

Demonstration: Use a ripple tank (or film loops of ripple tank wave phenomena) to point out the close resemblance of light wave interference and interference patterns in water waves. Place the ripple tank apparatus on an overhead projector and demonstrate the interference pattern that results from two slits or two point sources. Light waves behave in the same manner as these water waves.

ACTIVITY

Discovery: Have students observe the interference patterns of light. Cut two slits as close together as possible in a 3″ × 5″ card or in exposed film. Pass around a double slit to each of your students. Darken the room and have students look through the slits at the filament of a showcase lamp. They can adjust the width of the slits by gently pulling on the edges of the card or film. Students will observe several images of the filament as fringes along the edge of the bulb. The spacing of the fringes depends on the width of the slits. Tape red, clear, and blue pieces of plastic together and place them in front of the filament so that the light shines through all three at the same time. Have students view the filament through the slits and observe the spacing between the fringes. Have them note how the spacing changes with the wavelength of light.

Laboratory Manual. Give students additional experience with double-slit interference by doing Lab 19.1 from the Laboratory Manual.

Study Guide Master. To reinforce the concepts in this section, have the students complete the Study Guide Master for Section 19.1 from the Teacher Resource Package.

TRANSPARENCY

Use Transparency 25 with this section.

CRITICAL THINKING

Use the Critical Thinking master for Chapter 19 with this section.

LABORATORY MANUAL

Use Lab 19.1 with this section.

ENRICHMENT MASTER

Use the Enrichment master for Chapter 19 with this section.

STUDY GUIDE MASTER

Use the Study Guide master for section 19.1.

CONCEPT DEVELOPMENT

- An interesting example of interference is produced when two periodic structures are overlapped. For example, two overlapping window screens or curtains will result in an image called a Moire pattern. Related phenomena are used in the type of artwork known as op art.

ACTIVITY

Demonstration: A laser can be used to find the spacing between the grooves on a 33-rpm record. Set a laser on a desk top and shine it on a record held vertically by a ring stand about 4 m from the laser. Put a piece of white paper on the wall as a screen for the reflected light pattern. Measure the distance from the record to the screen (L) and the spacing between the maxima on the white paper (Δx). Calculate the spacing between the grooves (d) using the equation $d = \lambda L/\Delta x$. Use the wavelength of the light laser for λ. The calculation can be checked by using the frequency of revolution ($33\frac{1}{3}$ rpm), the width of the band used, and the playing time given for the band, in the equation

$$d = \frac{\text{width of the band}}{\text{(frequency) (time for band)}}.$$

- Students sometimes have difficulty understanding the reason for the appearance of light and dark bands in a diffraction pattern. In positions of maximum constructive interference, the intensity is greatest. Note that the intensity is not sudden, but increases gradually over a distance. Both constructive interference and destructive interference are total at single points only.

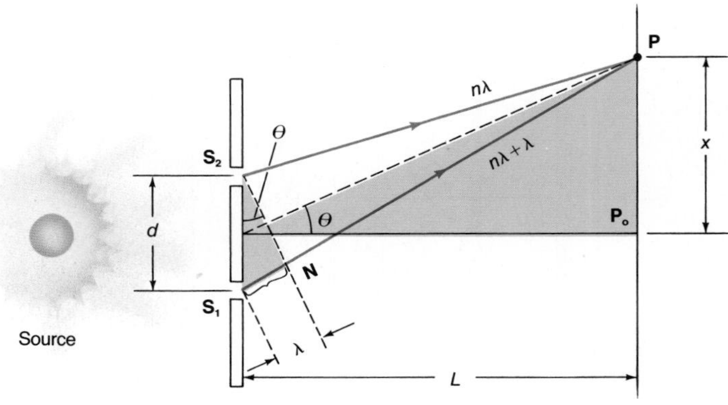

FIGURE 19–4. Schematic diagram for analysis of double-slit interference. The diagram is not to scale. Typically, L is about 10^5 times the slit separation, d.

When white light passes through a double slit, a continuous spectrum is formed.

HELP WANTED

COMPUTER AIDED DRAFTERS

Combine your artistic ability with technology and your skill at visualizing three dimensionally. Your training at a technical school in a CAD program prepares you for an important and exciting career by making you aware of the latest computer equipment and programs. Your ability to work with engineers, architects, and designers to put their ideas onto paper will determine your success in this field. For information contact:
National Assn. of Trade and Technical Schools, 2021 K Street, N.W., Washington, DC 20006

Measuring the Wavelength of a Light Wave

Young used the double-slit experiment to make the first precise measurement of the wavelength of light. The central bright band that falls on the screen at point $\mathbf{P_0}$ in Figure 19–4 does not depend on the wavelength, so another bright band is used. The first bright band on either side of the central band is called the first-order line. It falls on the screen at point **P**. The band is bright because light from the two slits interferes constructively. The two path lengths differ by one wavelength. That is, the distance $\mathbf{PS_1}$ is one wavelength longer than $\mathbf{PS_2}$.

To follow Young's experiment using Figure 19–4, you must understand that the drawing is not to scale. The length **PO** (L) is really very much greater than $\mathbf{S_1S_2}$ (d). It is necessary to distort the diagram so the details close to the slit can be shown. To measure the wavelength, Young first measured the distance between $\mathbf{P_0}$ and **P**, labeled x in the diagram. The distance between the screen and the slits is L, and the separation of the two slits is d. In the right triangle $\mathbf{NS_1S_2}$, the side $\mathbf{S_1N}$ is the length difference of the two paths. $\mathbf{S_1N}$ is one wavelength, λ, long. The lines from the slits to the screen are almost parallel because length L is so much larger than d. Thus the lines $\mathbf{NS_2}$ and **OP** are perpendicular. The triangle $\mathbf{NS_1S_2}$ is similar to triangle $\mathbf{PP_0O}$. Therefore, the ratio of the corresponding sides of these similar triangles is the same. That is,

$$\frac{x}{L} = \frac{\lambda}{d}.$$

Solving this equation for λ gives

$$\lambda = \frac{xd}{L}.$$

The wavelengths of light waves can be measured with considerable precision using double-slit interference patterns. It is not unusual for wavelength measurements to be precise to four digits.

Multicultural Connections

In 1926, Katharine Burr Blodgett became the first woman to receive a doctoral degree in physics from Cambridge University in England. She dramatically improved lenses for use in scientific instruments by combining her understanding of reflection, refraction, and interference of light with her original technique for depositing thin films on surfaces. The problem arose because light is both reflected and refracted when it travels into a more optically dense medium. This isn't serious when using a single lens, but when several lenses are combined, the reflected light can cause multiple images or haziness. Dr. Blodgett developed a method for producing films just fractions of a light wavelength thick. By depositing films $\lambda/4$ thick on lens surfaces, she produced interference that corrected the problem.

Example Problem

Wavelength of Light

Red light falls on two narrow slits 0.0190 mm apart. A first-order bright line is 21.1 mm from the central bright line on a screen 0.600 m from the slits. What is the wavelength of the red light?

Given: $d = 1.90 \times 10^{-5}$ m
$x = 21.1 \times 10^{-3}$ m
$L = 0.600$ m

Unknown: λ
Basic equation: $\lambda = xd/L$

Solution: $$\lambda = xd/L = \frac{(21.1 \times 10^{-3}\text{ m})(1.90 \times 10^{-5}\text{ m})}{(0.600\text{ m})} = 6.68 \times 10^{-7}\text{ m} = 668\text{ nm}$$

Practice Problems

1. Violet light falls on two slits separated by 1.90×10^{-5} m. A first-order line appears 13.2 mm from the central bright line on a screen 0.600 m from the slits. What is the wavelength of the violet light?
2. Yellow-orange light from a sodium lamp of wavelength 596 nm is used instead of the violet light of Problem 1. The slit separation and distance to the screen are not changed. What is the distance from the central line to the first-order yellow line?
3. A physics class uses a laser with a known wavelength of 632.8 nm in a double-slit experiment. The slit separation is unknown. A student places the screen 1.000 m from the slits and finds the first-order line 65.5 mm from the central line. What is the slit separation?
4. ▶ Using the double-slit apparatus of Problem 3, the student measures the wavelength of an unknown green light. The first-order line is 55.8 mm from the central line. What is the wavelength of the light?

Single-Slit Diffraction

As you are leaving school, you walk by the open door of the band rehearsal room. You hear the music, however, long before you can see the players through the door. Sound seems to have bent around the edge of the door, while light has traveled only in a straight line. They are both waves—why don't they act the same? Actually, they do. As Grimaldi first noted, the spreading, or diffraction, is there in both cases, but, because of light's much smaller wavelengths, the effect is tiny.

When light passes through a small single opening, a series of bright and dark interference bands appears. Instead of the equally-spaced, bright bands produced by two slits, the pattern from a single slit has a wide, bright central band with dimmer bright bands on either side.

To observe single-slit diffraction, fold a small piece of paper and cut a narrow slit along its folded edge. Unfold the paper and look through the slit at a light source. You will see an interference pattern. You can vary the width of the slit by pulling on the opposite edges of the paper. Observe the effect the change in slit width has on the pattern.

POCKET LAB

LASER SPOTS

Turn on the laser so that it makes a spot on the center of the movie screen. What do you expect should happen to the spot if you were to put a piece of screen door screen in the center of the beam? Explain your prediction. Try it. What really happened? Use the wave theory to explain your results.

Answers To
PRACTICE PROBLEMS

Have students refer to Appendix A of the Solutions Appendix for complete solutions to Practice Problems.

1. 418 nm
2. 18.8 mm
3. 9.66×10^{-6} m
4. 539 nm

CONCEPT DEVELOPMENT

Demonstration: Set up a two-point-source interference pattern in a ripple tank. Show what happens when the distance between the two sources is changed. Change the wave frequency to show its effect. Eliminate one of the sources to make the interference disappear. Set up and demonstrate single-slit diffraction in the ripple tank. If you have filmloops of these phenomena available, show them to the class.

Critical Thinking Master, Teacher Resource Package. You may wish to have students complete the Critical Thinking Master, Diffraction, with this section.

POCKET LAB

LASER SPOTS

Purpose: to show the wave nature of light.
Materials: laser; movie screen; piece of screen (screen door screen).
Outcome: A radiating starlike pattern with alternating dark and bright spots will appear. The light striking the edges of the screen will form an interference pattern when it combines on the movie screen. Light is behaving like a wave.

Assessment

Performance

To further assess students' understanding of interference patterns, have them explore how varying the spacing between the wires in the screen changes the pattern. They can change the effective spacing by rotating the screen. If it is rotated about a vertical axis, the effective horizontal spacing will be reduced. How does the pattern of dots change? If the screen is rotated about a horizontal axis, the effective vertical spacing will be reduced. What effects are observed? Explain in terms of the equation on page 394 for the quantity x/L. [From $x/L = \lambda/d$, reducing d increases the dot spacing, x. So, rotation about a vertical axis will increase the horizontal dot spacing, but will not affect the vertical dot spacing. Rotation about a horizontal axis will increase the vertical dot spacing, but will not affect the horizontal dot spacing.]

CONCEPT DEVELOPMENT

ACTIVITY

Discovery: For an at-home activity, suggest that your students look at streetlights at night through a handkerchief or other piece of fairly thin cloth to see the diffraction pattern. (A cloth umbrella works well.) Have them try to sketch the pattern.

Discovery: Have students hold up a sheet of paper to a window. They will see tiny light and dark fringes along the edge of the paper due to diffraction.

Enrichment: The smallest detail that can be seen with a microscope is about the same size as the wavelength of the light being used. For this reason, a microscope that can show atomic detail requires a wavelength in the range of several angstroms. Such a microscope was developed in 1980 and is known as the scanning tunneling microscope.

Enrichment Master. With this section, use the Enrichment Master, Determining the Wavelength of Light, from the Teacher Resource Package.

• More reproducible single-slit patterns can be obtained by using two ordinary lead pencils. The metal band at the eraser end is used to create a thin separation between the two pencils. This gap will function as a single slit. Place the two pencils parallel, but with the eraser end of one at the point end of the other. Use two rubber bands to hold the pair together. Rotate the pencils until the flats are facing one another. View a line light source through the slit. You should easily see the diffraction pattern. Squeeze the pencils together to make the slit narrower. Does the diffraction pattern get wider as predicted by the equation on page 397?

F.Y.I.

You can produce single-slit diffraction by holding the index and middle fingers of one hand together and looking at a bright light through the space between them. Then press the fingers together to change the opening size and observe how the diffraction pattern changes.

Light passing through a single slit produces a series of bright and dark bands equally spaced around a bright central band.

What causes the diffraction pattern? Figure 19–6 shows monochromatic light from a distant source falling on a slit of width w. Because the light is so far away, a crest in the wave strikes all points of the slit at the same time. Light coming through the slit falls on a screen placed a distance L from the slit. There is a wide central band, $\mathbf{P_0}$. What waves contribute to the central band? For this discussion we have divided the width of the slit into twelve parts. Because L is so much larger than w, all rays falling on the slit are, in effect, the same distance from $\mathbf{P_0}$. The distances $\mathbf{AP_0}$, $\mathbf{BP_0}$, $\mathbf{CP_0}$, and L are equal, and the crests of all waves arrive at $\mathbf{P_0}$ at the same time. Thus, the central band is bright. $\mathbf{P_p}$ is any point on the screen.

As you move away from the center, the distance **CP** becomes larger than **AP.** When you reach point $\mathbf{P_d}$, $\mathbf{CD} = \lambda$, so the distance $\mathbf{CP_d}$ is exactly one wavelength longer than $\mathbf{AP_d}$. Therefore, waves from point **1′** travel one-half wavelength longer than those from point **1.** They destructively interfere. The same is true for points **2′** and **2, 3′** and **3,** and so on down the slit. A wave from one point of the slit is canceled by a wave from another. The result is darkness.

If you go either closer to or farther away from the center, the distance **CP** is not exactly one wavelength longer and some waves no longer cancel. Thus the darkness is not complete. Consider going out far enough to make $\mathbf{CP_p}$ two wavelengths (2λ) larger than $\mathbf{AP_p}$. Then there is a second dark band. Third, fourth, and higher bands are reached when the difference in path length is 3λ, 4λ, and so forth.

What is the distance from $\mathbf{P_0}$ to the first dark band, $\mathbf{P_d}$? If angle θ is very small, triangles **CDA** and $\mathbf{BP_dP_0}$ are similar. From triangle **CDA,**

$$\sin\theta = \frac{\lambda}{w}.$$

In the same way, consider triangle $\mathbf{BP_dP_0}$. Because $\mathbf{BP_d}$ and L are nearly equal, we can say

$$\sin\theta = \frac{x}{BP_d} = \frac{x}{L}.$$

a

b

FIGURE 19–5. The beautiful colors of this opal (a) are produced by diffraction from ridges on the surface of the gem (b).

396 Diffraction and Interference of Light

DEMONSTRATION

Purpose: to observe interference patterns.

Equipment: overhead projector, transparent sheet, black marker

Procedure: 1. Prepare a second transparency of the wave pattern provided (Transparency 25). The solid lines represent crests and the dashed lines represent troughs. The centers of the circles are the sources. **2.** Place the transparencies on top of each other, aligned at the base. Slide the top sheet across the bottom sheet. Use a washable marker to draw nodal lines and antinodal lines, one color for the maxima and another color for the minima. You may wish to choose a student to draw the lines.

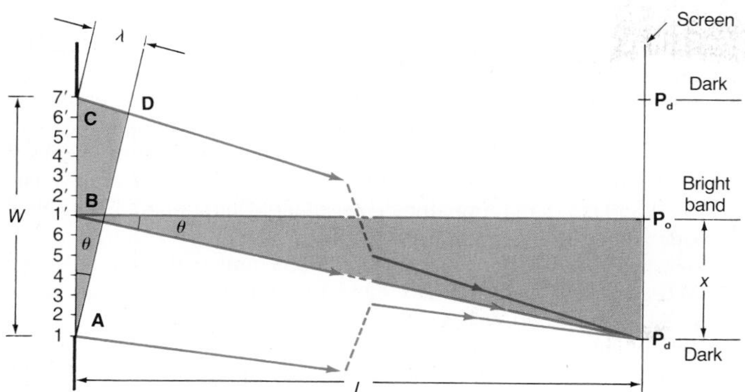

FIGURE 19–6. Schematic diagram for analysis of single-slit diffraction. The diagram is not to scale. Typically *L* is 10^5 times the slit width.

Therefore,

$$\frac{\lambda}{w} = \frac{x}{L}, \text{ or } x = \frac{\lambda L}{w}.$$

Notice that the smaller the slit width, *w*, the larger the distance, *x*. That is, the smaller the slit, the wider the central band. As a model, imagine a beam of light shining through an open door. The beam has sharp edges because the interference fringes are very close together and almost unnoticeable. As you close the door, the beam becomes smaller. If the opening is reduced to a few wavelengths wide, the edges of the beam become less well defined. The interference fringes become more widely spaced and more visible, making the edges appear fuzzy. Thus, sharp shadows are cast only by large openings. The pattern width also depends on wavelength. For a fixed slit width, the shorter the wavelength, the narrower the pattern, Figure 19–7.

Diffraction is at a maximum when the width of the opening is equal to the wavelength of light.

Example Problem

Single-Slit Diffraction

Monochromatic orange light of wavelength 605 nm falls on a single slit of width 0.095 mm. The slit is located 85 cm from a screen. How far from the center of the central band is the first dark band?

Given: slit width, $w = 0.095$ mm; distance to screen, $L = 85$ cm; light wavelength, $\lambda = 605 \text{ nm} = 6.05 \times 10^{-7}$ m

Unknown: separation between central band and dark band, *x*

Basic equation: $x = \frac{\lambda L}{w}$

Solution: $x = \frac{\lambda L}{w} = \frac{(6.05 \times 10^{-7} \text{ m})(0.85 \text{ m})}{9.5 \times 10^{-5} \text{ m}} = 5.4 \text{ mm}$

CONCEPT DEVELOPMENT

ACTIVITY

Discovery: A simple variable-width slit for studying single-slit diffraction can be made using two microscope slides, two single-edged razor blades, and black electrical tape. Position the two razor blades with their edges facing each other between the two microscope slides so the slit between the two razor edges is parallel to the long side of the microscope slide. Wind electrical tape around each end of the pair of glass slides to keep them tight and to protect students against the sharp edge of the slide. Students can vary the slit width and observe the change in the width of the central maximum while viewing the filament of a showcase light bulb.

CHECKING FOR UNDERSTANDING

With student help, construct a two-point-source interference pattern, explaining it as you go along.

RETEACHING

Transparency Package. Reteach double-slit and single-slit interference using Transparency 26 and accompanying worksheet.

INDEPENDENT PRACTICE/ EXTENSION

Refer to the Assignment Guide on page 397 for additional questions and problems for independent practice.

Guided Practice: After going over the Example Problem on this page, have students work on the first two Practice Problems on page 398 as a class activity.

Independent Practice: Assign the remaining Practice Problems on page 398 for homework, then spend time reviewing them with students during the next class period.

Questions: 1. If this were a diffraction made by light, what would you see? *You would see bright spots along the antinodal lines and dark spots along the nodal lines.* **2.** How are nodal and antinodal lines formed? *Nodal lines form where trough meets trough or crest meets crest. Antinodes form where crest meets trough.*

19:1 ASSIGNMENT GUIDE

	PRACTICE	EXTENSION
CHAPTER REVIEW pp. 403–405		
· Reviewing Concepts	1–3, 5	
· Applying Concepts		1–5
· Problems*	1–8	9
APPENDIX B PROBLEMS*		
· Chapter 19, pp. 701–702	1–4, 6–8	5, 9

* Complete solutions to all Chapter Review and Appendix problems appear in the Problems and Solutions Manual.

Answers To
PRACTICE PROBLEMS

Have students refer to Appendix A of the Solutions Appendix for complete solutions to Practice Problems.

5. 4.3 mm
6. 9.7×10^{-5} m
7. 590 nm
8. a. red
b. 18 mm, 25 mm

CONCEPT DEVELOPMENT

Critical Thinking: A two-point-source light interference pattern has alternating light and dark regions. Ask students what happens to the wave energy in the dark regions. [Dark regions show the effect of destructive interference.]

Enrichment: Notice the strong symmetry of a two-point-source interference pattern. This symmetry depends on having the two-point sources in phase. As the phase relationship is changed, the nodal and antinodal line pattern moves. Have interested students research the "phased array" radar system.

3 Close

CONVERGENT QUESTION

Ask students to compare two-point-source interference patterns due to water waves, sound waves, and light waves.

CONCEPT REVIEW ANSWERS

1.1 Light is diffracted by the slits. Light from one slit interferes with light from the other. If interference is constructive, there is a bright band; if destructive, the region is dark.

1.2 Pattern seen with red light.

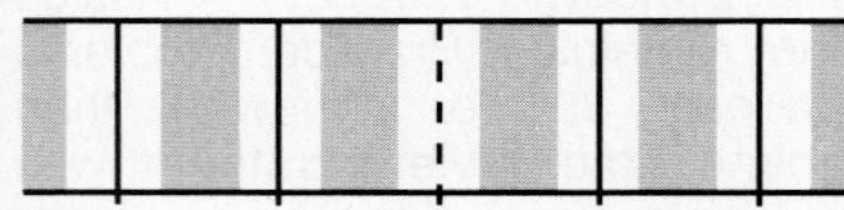

1.3 The light bands become more closely spaced (dotted line indicates center of pattern).

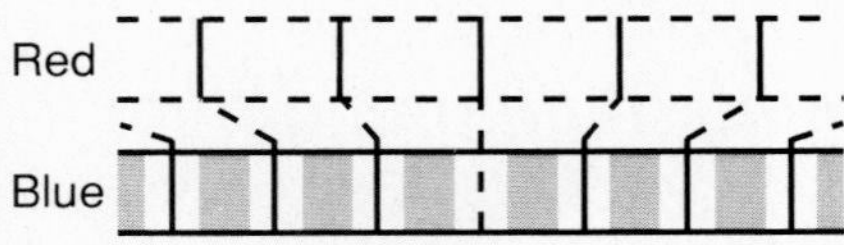

F.Y.I.

Thomas Young was a child prodigy. He could read at age two, and by age four, he had read the Bible twice. He studied many languages and played a variety of musical instruments. He also spent time deciphering Egyptian hieroglyphics.

Practice Problems

5. Monochromatic green light of wavelength 546 nm falls on a single slit of width 0.095 mm. The slit is located 75 cm from a screen. How far from the center of the central band is the first dark band?
6. Light from a He-Ne laser (λ = 632.8 nm) falls on a slit of unknown width. A pattern is formed on a screen 1.15 m away where the first dark band is 7.5 mm from the center of the central bright band. How wide is the slit?
7. Yellow light falls on a single slit 0.0295 mm wide. On a screen 60.0 cm away, there is a dark band 12.0 mm from the center of the bright central band. What is the wavelength of the light?
8. White light falls on a single slit 0.050 mm wide. A screen is placed 1.00 m away. A student first puts a blue-violet filter (λ = 441 nm) over the slit, then a red filter (λ = 622 nm). The student measures the width of the central peak, that is, the distance between the two dark bands.
   a. Will the band be wider with the blue-violet or the red filter?
   b. Find the width for the two filters.

CONCEPT REVIEW

1.1 Two very narrow slits are cut close to each other in a large piece of cardboard. They are illuminated by monochromatic red light. A sheet of white paper is placed far from the slits, and a pattern of bright and dark bands is seen on the paper. Explain why some regions are bright while others are dark.
1.2 Sketch a graph that shows the pattern seen.
1.3 Sketch what happens to the pattern if the red light is replaced by blue light.
1.4 Critical Thinking: One of the slits is covered so no light can get through. What happens to the pattern?

FIGURE 19–7. These diffraction patterns for red light (a), blue light (b), and white light (c) were produced with a slit of width 0.02 cm. Red light has a longer wavelength than blue light.

1.4 Critical Thinking: It becomes a single-slit pattern. Note that in a double-slit pattern all light bands have the same width, whereas in a single-slit pattern the central bright band is twice as wide as the remaining bright bands.

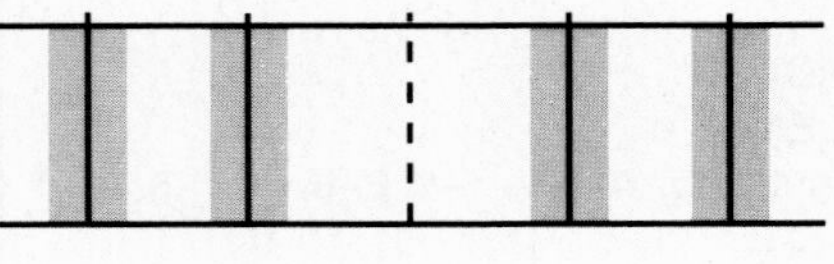

TRANSPARENCY

Use Transparency 26 with this section.

LAB WORKSHEET

Use the Lab Worksheet for Chapter 19 with this Physics Lab.

PHYSICS LAB: Wavelengths of Colors

Purpose

To measure accurately the wavelength of four colors of light.

Materials

- meter stick
- index card
- 40-W straight filament light
- ball of clay
- tape
- diffraction grating

Procedure

1. Cut the index card (lengthwise) into four equal strips.
2. Write the letters "O" (orange), "Y" (yellow), "G" (green), and "B" (blue) on the strips of index card.
3. Place the ball of clay 1.0 m in front of the lamp. Use the ball of clay to support the diffraction grating.
4. Plug in the lamp and turn off the room lights.
5. When you look through the diffraction grating, you should see the colors to the sides of the bulb. If you do not see the colors to the sides, then rotate the diffraction grating (90 °) until you do.
6. Have a lab partner move the "O" orange index card strip until it seems to be in the middle of its color. Tape the strip to the table.
7. Repeat for each of the other colored index card strips.

Observations and Data

1. What color is closest to the lamp? Suggest a reason.
2. List the order that colors occur, beginning from red.
3. Set up a data table to record *x*, *d*, and *L* for each of the four colors. Measure *x* for each index card strip (to the nearest 0.1 cm).
4. Record the value of *d* from the chalkboard.

Analysis

Use the following equation to estimate the wavelength for each color. Convert your answers for the wavelength to nm.

$$\lambda = xd/L$$

5. Record the value of *L*.

Applications

1. How could diffraction gratings be used in conjunction with telescopes?

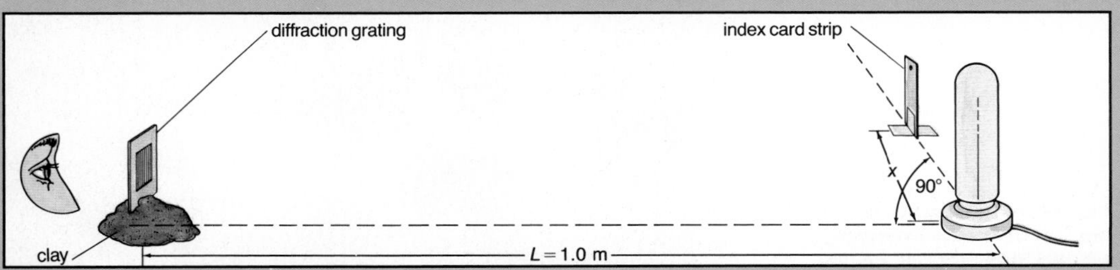

PHYSICS LAB

Process Skills: observing, interpreting data, measuring, questioning, controlling variables.

Misconception: Although students have heard the term *light-waves,* they lack any common experience indicating that light has wave properties.

Teaching Suggestions: Write the value of the distance, *d*, between the lines in the diffraction grating on the chalkboard. This value is the reciprocal of the number of lines per distance for your grating.

OBSERVATIONS

1. The violet light appears closest to the bulb. This occurs because violet has the shortest wavelength.
2. The order of colors is the same as in a rainbow: red, orange, yellow, green, blue, indigo, violet.
3. & 4. Student data table

ANALYSIS

Here are typical values from the lab: (Student values are usually within 5% of these).

Color	Wavelength
red	660 nm
orange	600 nm
yellow	580 nm
green	530 nm
blue	420 nm

APPLICATIONS

Astronomers measure wavelengths of light emitted from stars to identify the elements producing the light.

ASSESSMENT

Critical Thinking: To further assess students' understanding of wavelength measurement, ask the following questions.

1. Suppose your diffraction grating had more grooves/centimeter. How would this change the value of *d*? Explain. How would this change your value of *x*? Why? [More grooves/centimeter would cause the distance between grooves, *d*, to be less. This would cause the interference pattern to spread out more so that the new values of *x* would be larger.]

2. Estimate the uncertainty and percent uncertainty in your measurement of *x* and *L*.

[% uncertainty for L = 0.1 cm/100 cm × 100 = 0.1%

% uncertainty for x = 0.1 cm/30 cm × 100 = 0.3%]

19.2 APPLICATIONS OF DIFFRACTION

Preparation

OBJECTIVES

The objectives are listed on the student page. Remind students to preview these objectives as a study guide to this major section.

OVERVIEW

This short section introduces the operation of diffraction gratings and the Rayleigh criterion for the resolution of images.

BRIDGING

Students will need to recall the definition of an objective lens in studying this chapter.

1 Focus

DISCREPANT EVENT

Pass around diffraction gratings mounted in slide mounts (holograph gratings are ideal) so that students can look at the spectral lines from several different gas discharge tubes. Point out that these spectral line patterns are unique and serve to identify the gas.

POCKET LAB

HOT LIGHTS

Purpose: to observe the addition of colors with increasing temperature.
Materials: variable power supply (variac); 100-W clear lamp with socket; diffraction grating.
Outcome: Red and orange will occur at lower temperatures. Other colors will be added in the order of the spectrum. All colors will get brighter as the temperature of the lamp filament increases.

Objectives

- explain the interference pattern formed by the diffraction grating.
- understand the operation of a grating spectrometer.
- explain how diffraction effects limit the resolution of a lens.

19.2 APPLICATIONS OF DIFFRACTION

In the Eyes of the Beholder

Many beetles and butterflies, including the *morpho* butterfly shown in the chapter-opening photo, produce their iridescent colors by means of diffraction. The butterfly's wings are covered with tiny ridges only a few hundred nanometers apart. They each diffract the light hitting them, producing interference effects. Because of the orientation of the ridges, blue is the predominant color. Some dragonfly wings have dark veins spaced in such a way that sunlight is diffracted into spectra. Such a series of slits makes the interference pattern of two slits even stronger. It is called a **diffraction grating.**

Diffraction Gratings

Although single- or double-slit diffraction can be used to measure the wavelength of light, in practice a diffraction grating, Figure 19–8, is used. Diffraction gratings are made by scratching very fine lines with a diamond point on glass. The clear spaces between the lines serve as slits. Gratings can have as many as 10 000 lines per centimeter. That is, the spacing between the lines is 10^{-6} m, or 1000 nm. Inexpensive *replica gratings* are made by pressing a thin plastic sheet onto a glass grating. When the plastic is pulled away, it contains an accurate imprint of the scratches. Jewelry can be made from replica gratings.

Gratings form interference patterns in the same way a double slit does. The bright bands are in the same location, but they are narrower, and the dark regions are broader. As a result, individual colors are not smeared out and can be distinguished more easily. This means that wavelengths can be measured more precisely than with double slits.

In Section 19.1 the equation used to calculate the wavelength of light using double-slit interference was given as

$$\frac{x}{L} = \frac{\lambda}{d}.$$

The same equation holds for a diffraction grating where d is the distance between the lines. Instead of measuring the distance from the central band to the first bright band, x, most laboratory instruments mea-

POCKET LAB

HOT LIGHTS

Plug a 100-W clear lamp into a Variac (variable power supply). Turn off the room lights. Look through a diffraction grating at the lamp as you slowly increase the power. Describe what you see. Which color(s) appear first? What happens to the brightness of previous colors as new colors are seen? What is the order of the colors?

FIGURE 19–8. Diffraction gratings are used to create interference patterns to analyze light sources.

TEACHER F.Y.I.

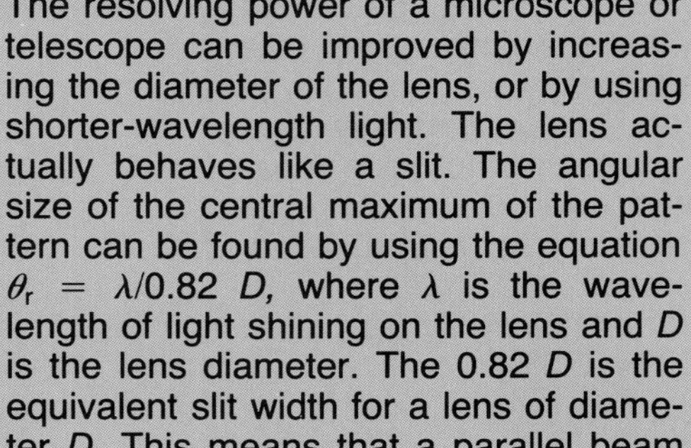

The resolving power of a microscope or telescope can be improved by increasing the diameter of the lens, or by using shorter-wavelength light. The lens actually behaves like a slit. The angular size of the central maximum of the pattern can be found by using the equation $\theta_r = \lambda/0.82\ D$, where λ is the wavelength of light shining on the lens and D is the lens diameter. The 0.82 D is the equivalent slit width for a lens of diameter D. This means that a parallel beam of light refracted by a lens does not produce a point image but gives a diffuse pattern whose angular radius is $\lambda/0.82\ D$. To reduce the angular radius, the wavelength can be made smaller by using UV light. However, glass does not transmit UV light, so expensive quartz lenses are required. The small value of λ for electrons makes the electron microscope magnify with 100 to 1000 times greater magnitude than a visible light microscope.

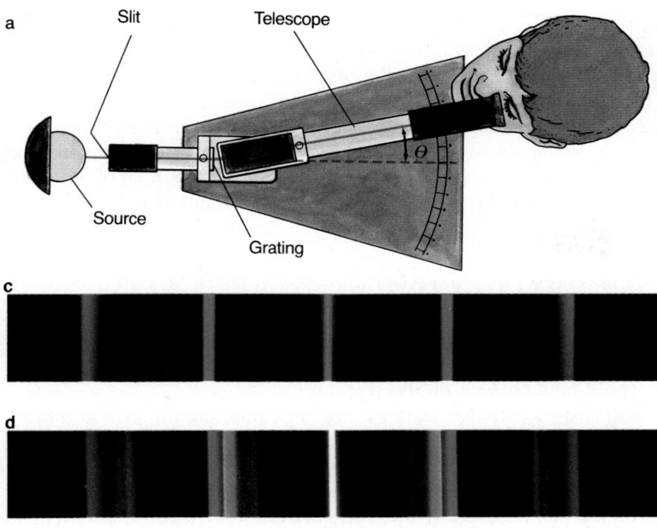

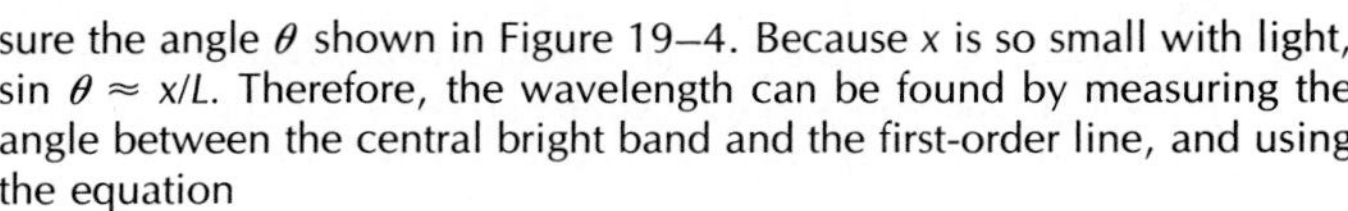

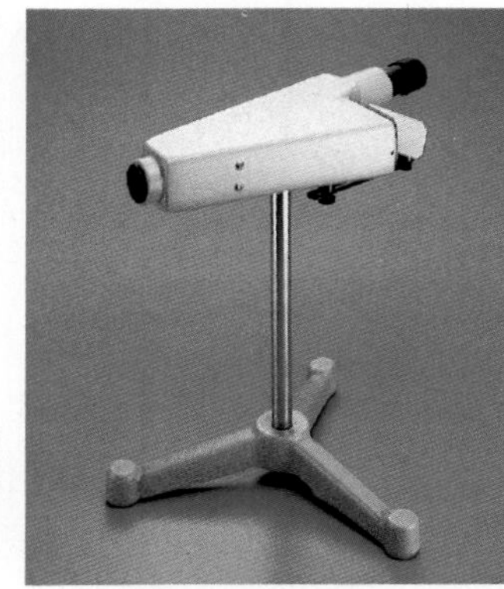

FIGURE 19–9. A spectrometer is used to measure the wavelengths of light emitted by a light source (a, b). A grating was used to produce interference patterns for red light (c) and white light (d).

sure the angle θ shown in Figure 19–4. Because x is so small with light, $\sin\theta \approx x/L$. Therefore, the wavelength can be found by measuring the angle between the central bright band and the first-order line, and using the equation

$$\lambda = \frac{xd}{L} = d\sin\theta.$$

The instrument used to measure light wavelengths with a diffraction grating is called a grating spectrometer, Figure 19–9. The source emits light that falls on a slit and then passes through a diffraction grating. When monochromatic red light is used, Figure 19–9c, a series of bright bands appears to the left and right of the central bright line. When white light falls on the instrument, each red band is replaced by a spectrum. The red band in the spectrum is at the same location as when monochromatic light is used. The telescope is moved until the desired line appears in the middle of the viewer. The angle θ is then read directly from the calibrated base of the spectrometer. Because d is known, λ can be calculated.

F.Y.I.

The Hubble Space Telescope was designed to resolve stars. It can resolve objects whose spacing is the equivalent to the spacing of car headlights 2500 miles away.

Resolving Power of Lenses

When light passes through the lens of a telescope, it passes through a circular hole. The lens diffracts the light just as a slit does. The smaller the lens, the wider the diffraction pattern. If the light comes from a star, the star will appear spread out. If two stars are close enough together, the images will be so blurred that a viewer cannot tell whether there are two stars or only one. The telescope can no longer resolve the images of the two stars. Lord Rayleigh set the **Rayleigh criterion** for resolution. If the central bright band of one star falls on the first dark band of the

2 Teach

CONCEPT DEVELOPMENT

Study Guide Master. To reinforce the concepts in this section, have students complete the Study Guide Master for Section 19.2 from the Teacher Resource Package.

Demonstration: Mount a finely marked ruler horizontally. Darken the room and aim the laser beam so it just grazes the ruler. Observe the diffraction pattern on a screen positioned about 2 meters away. Other objects that make interesting patterns are handkerchiefs, the eye of a needle, and wire gauze.

Critical Thinking: Ask students how diffraction is produced.

CHECKING FOR UNDERSTANDING

Have students explain how interference and diffraction are related.

RETEACHING

Reteaching Master, Teacher Resource Package. Use the Reteaching Master, Moire Patterns, for Chapter 19.

EXTENSION

In the nineteenth century, high-quality diffraction gratings were used to carefully measure the spectral lines of gases. An American physicist, Henry A. Rowland, made some of the very finest gratings. Have interested students investigate his methods.

Guided Practice: Go over the Concept Review questions on page 402 as a class activity.

INDEPENDENT PRACTICE/ EXTENSION

Refer to the Assignment Guide for additional questions and problems for independent practice.

3 Close

CONVERGENT QUESTION

Ask students to explain how resolving power is related to diffraction.

Connect to BIOLOGY

The pupil of the eye acts as a round "slit" that produces diffraction effects. As shown in problems 18 and 19 on page 405, the resolution of the human eye is matched to the size of the cells in the retina. That is, even if the eye had cone cells closer together, it couldn't see finer detail because of the diffraction of light.

Suppose that inhabitants of some other planet had eyes sensitive to infrared radiation with a wavelength, $\lambda = 10\ \mu m$. How should the eye of such a being be designed for maximum resolution? [A wavelength of 10 μm is about 20 times the wavelength of green light. The eye, including pupil and sensitive cells, should be about 20 times larger in diameter to keep diffraction effects from limiting eyesight.]

Laboratory Manual. Give students additional experience with holograms by doing Lab 19.2 from the Laboratory Manual.

CONCEPT REVIEW ANSWERS

2.1 Band spacing is exactly the same as the sketch for 1.2, but now light bands are much thinner, separated by wider dark bands.

2.2 $\lambda = xd/L$, so the greater the dot spacings, x, the narrower the slit spacing, d, and thus more lines per mm.

2.3 Blue. The shorter the wavelength, the smaller the diffraction pattern, so the easier it would be to distinguish the light coming from the individual stars.

2.4 Critical Thinking: Determine whether or not the violet or red end of the spectrum makes the largest angle with the direction of the beam of incident white light. A prism bends the violet end of the spectrum the most, while a grating diffracts red wavelengths the most.

Physics and technology

Light, sound, and electrons all have some wave characteristics. It is the wave aspects of interference phenomena that make holography possible.

Since sound can travel in places where light cannot, acoustical holography is finding applications in many areas of medicine. Acoustical holograms have been used to examine brain tumors and to generate images of fetuses in the womb. Electron holography is a new field that will permit scientists to examine materials and phenomena at an atomic scale.

A further development in optical holography is the creation of moving images. Scientists at the Media Laboratory at the Massachusetts Institute of Technology have produced computer-generated moving holograms.

The article by Jearl Walker gives a detailed description of how to construct a relatively simple apparatus that can produce holograms.

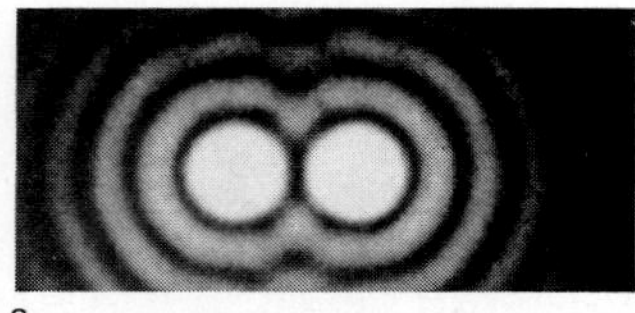
a

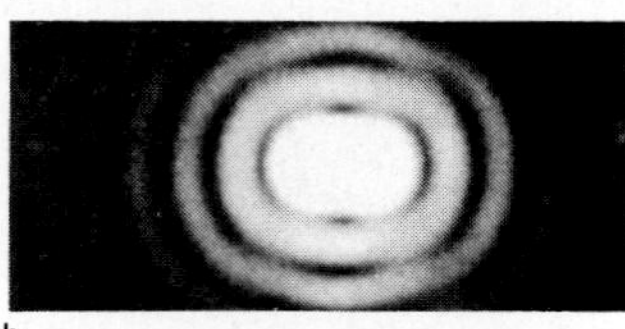
b

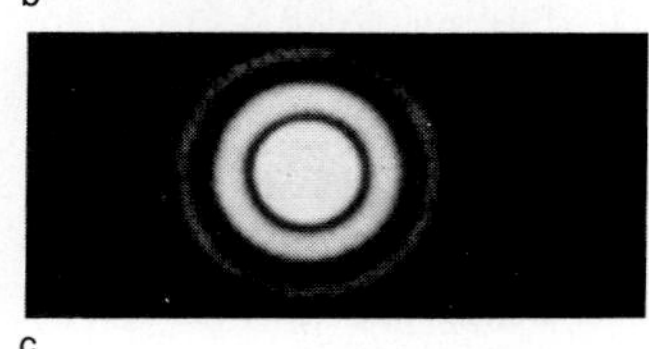
c

FIGURE 19–10. The diffraction patterns of two point sources (a). As the sources move closer together, the images become fuzzy (b) and eventually merge into one image (c).

second, the two stars are just resolved. That is, a viewer can tell that there are two stars and not just one.

The effects of diffraction on the resolving power of the telescope can be reduced by increasing the size of the lens. Diffraction also limits the resolving power of microscopes. The objective lens of a microscope cannot be enlarged, but the wavelength of light can be reduced. The diffraction pattern formed by blue light is narrower than that of red light. Thus biologists often use blue or violet light to illuminate microscopes.

CONCEPT REVIEW

2.1 The two slits of Concept Review Question 1.1 are replaced by very many narrow slits with the same spacing. Sketch the pattern that would now be seen on the screen.

2.2 You shine a red laser light through first one, then a second diffraction grating. Patterns of red dots are seen on a screen. The dots from one grating are spread more than those from the other. Which grating has more lines per mm?

2.3 A telescope is used to view a number of closely-spaced stars. Filters are used to select only certain colors from the starlight. In which color, red or blue, would the stars be more easily counted? Explain.

2.4 Critical Thinking: You are shown a spectrometer, but do not know whether it produces its spectrum with a prism or a grating. By looking at a white light spectrum, how could you tell?

Physics and technology

HOLOGRAMS

Interference properties of light are used to produce three-dimensional images called holograms. Developed by Dennis Gabor, who won the 1971 Nobel Prize in physics for his work, holograms record both the intensity and phase of light.

To make a hologram, laser light is split by a mirror into two parts. One part is directed to the object and then reflected off the object onto film. The other part goes directly to the film. The result is complex interference patterns. When the film is illuminated by laser light, the emerging light is an exact duplicate of the light reflected originally by the object. The image appears three-dimensional; you can observe it from all sides.

Because holograms are very difficult to counterfeit, holography is being used in security identification and credit cards. There is speculation that holograms may be used as part of a future United States currency. Research is being conducted to apply holograms in microscopic work, medicine, and information storage and display. Holograms may find uses in video games and displays, and motion pictures.

· What property of light, sound, and electrons enables them all to be used in making holograms?

Teacher Resources: Gross, N. "Drawing a Bead on the Atom—at Last." *Business Week Special Edition.* June 15, 1990, page 93.
Rennie, J. "Move Over, Mr. Spock." *Scientific American.* July 1990, pages 89, 92.
Walker, Jearl. "How to Stop Worrying about Vibration and Make Holograms Viewable in White Light." *Scientific American.* May 1989, pages 134–137.

19:2 ASSIGNMENT GUIDE

	PRACTICE	EXTENSION
CHAPTER REVIEW pp. 403–405		
· Reviewing Concepts	4, 6–10	
· Applying Concepts		6–9
· Problems*	10–12, 15–18	13, 14, 19
APPENDIX B PROBLEMS*		
· Chapter 19, p. 702	10–14	

* Complete solutions to all Chapter Review and Appendix problems appear in the Problems and Solutions Manual.

CHAPTER
19 REVIEW

SUMMARY

19.1 When Light Waves Interfere

- Light passing through a narrow hole or slit is diffracted, or bent from a straight-line path.
- Interference between light diffracted from two closely-spaced narrow slits causes an interference pattern to appear on a distant screen.
- The wavelength of light can be measured by analyzing the double-slit interference pattern.
- When light passes through a narrow opening, diffraction causes a pattern of light and dark bands to form.
- Single slits produce diffraction patterns that are less well defined than those formed by double slits.

19.2 Applications of Diffraction

- Diffraction gratings with large numbers of evenly-spaced slits produce interference patterns that are used to measure the wavelength of light precisely.
- Diffraction limits the resolving power of lenses.

KEY TERMS

diffraction	coherent
interference fringes	diffraction grating
monochromatic	Rayleigh criterion

REVIEWING CONCEPTS

1. Why is it important that monochromatic light be used to make the interference pattern in Young's interference experiment?
2. Explain why the central bright line produced when light is diffracted by a double slit cannot be used to measure the wavelength of the light waves.
3. Describe how you could use light of a known wavelength to find the distance between two slits.
4. Why is blue light used for illumination in an optical microscope?
5. Why is the diffraction of sound waves more familiar in everyday experience than the diffraction of light waves?
6. In each of the following examples, state whether the color is produced by diffraction, refraction, or the presence of pigments: (a) soap bubbles (b) peacock tails (c) rose petals (d) mother of pearl (e) oil films (f) blue jeans (g) the halo around the moon on a night when there is a high, thin cloud cover.
7. As monochromatic light passes through a diffraction grating, what is the difference in path length between two adjacent slits and a dark area on the screen?
8. When white light is passed through a grating, what is seen on the screen? Why are no dark areas seen?
9. Why do diffraction gratings have a large number of slits? Why are the slits so close together?
10. Why would a small diameter telescope not be able to resolve the images of two closely-spaced stars?

APPLYING CONCEPTS

1. Suppose you are using a double slit to measure light wavelength precisely. It is easier to measure a larger than a smaller distance precisely. How can the value of x be increased?
2. Two loudspeakers are placed 1.0 m apart on the edge of a stage. They emit sound of two wavelengths, 1.0 m long and 2.0 m long.
   a. If you are sitting 3.0 m from the stage, equidistant from the speakers, do you hear loud or quiet sounds for each of the wavelengths? Explain.
   b. If you sit 0.50 m from one speaker and 1.5 m from the other, what do you hear for each wavelength? Explain.
3. How can you tell whether an interference pattern is from a single slit or a double slit?
4. Describe the changes in a single-slit pattern as slit width is decreased.
5. Does interference aid or hinder radio reception? Explain.

RETEACHING MASTER

Use the Reteaching master for Chapter 19 with this section.

REVIEW MASTER

Use the Vocabulary Review master for Chapter 19 with this section.

STUDY GUIDE MASTER

Use the Study Guide master for section 19.2.

EVALUATION MASTER

Use the Chapter Evaluation master for Chapter 19 with this section.

LABORATORY MANUAL

Use Lab 19.2 with this section.

CLOSING CHAPTER 19

Review Summary statements and Key Terms with your students.

ASSESSMENT

Vocabulary Review Master, Teacher Resource Package. Use this master to check students' understanding of Key Terms.

Evaluation Masters. Use Parts A and B of the Chapter Evaluation Masters from the Teacher Resource Package to test qualitative chapter objectives. Use Parts C and D to test quantitative chapter objectives.

Answers To
REVIEWING CONCEPTS

1. When monochromatic light is used, you get a sharp interference pattern; if you use white light, you get sets of colored bands.
2. All wavelengths produce the line in the same place.
3. Let the light fall on the double slit, and let the interference pattern fall on a sheet of paper. Measure the spacings between the bright bands, x, and use the equation

$$d = \lambda L/x.$$

4. Less diffraction results from the short wavelength of blue light.
5. Diffraction is most pronounced around obstacles approximately the same size as the wavelength of the wave. We are more accustomed to obstacles of the size that diffract the much larger wavelength of sound.
6. a. refraction **b.** refraction **c.** pigments **d.** refraction **e.** refraction **f.** pigments **g.** refraction
7. The difference in wavelengths is one-half the wavelength of the color.
8. A full spectrum of color is seen. Because of the variety of wavelength, dark fringes of one wavelength would be filled by bright fringes of another color.
9. The large number of slits in diffraction gratings increases the intensity of the interference patterns. The slits are close together, producing sharper images of light.
10. Small apertures have large diffraction patterns that limit resolution.

Answers To
APPLYING CONCEPTS

1. Either increase *L,* the distance between the slits and the screen, or decrease *d,* the distance between the slits.
2. a. Loud. You are equidistant from the two speakers, so there is always reinforcement. **b.** The difference in distance from the two speakers is 1.0 m. The 1.0-m sound will be reinforced and will be loud; the 2.0-m wavelength sound will suffer destructive interference and be quiet.
3. A double-slit pattern consists of equally spaced lines of almost equal brightness. A single-slit pattern has a bright, broad central band and dimmer side bands.
4. The bands get wider and dimmer.
5. Interference between the direct transmission and waves reflected from buildings and cars hinders reception.
6. Diffraction hinders the viewing of images in a microscope. Blue light is often used to reduce diffraction.
7. Violet light, the color with the smallest wavelength.
8. The interference pattern will be spread farther apart for the 10^5-lines/cm grating.
9. Many diffraction gratings have a separation of about 2–4 times the wavelength they are being used with. A picket fence, having a separation of about 10 cm, could be used with wavelengths of about 30 cm or 0.3 m, which is a longer wavelength microwave.

Answers To
PROBLEMS

Complete solutions for all Chapter Review Problems can be found in the Problems and Solutions Manual accompanying this text.
1. Refer to Problems and Solutions Manual.
2. a. 500 m
b. Good. It is a multiple of the wavelength and constructive interference will take place.
3. 451 nm
4. 1.63×10^{-5} m
5. 1.2 m
6. 6.00×10^{-5} cm
7. 0.30 cm
8. 1.2×10^{-2} cm

6. Does diffraction aid or hinder the viewing of images in a microscope? Explain.
7. For a given grating, which color of light produces a bright line closest to the central bright line?
8. What changes occur in the characteristics of the interference patterns formed by a diffraction grating containing 10^4 lines/cm and one having 10^5 lines/cm?
9. Using Figure 16–1 or Figure 26–8, decide for which part of the electromagnetic spectrum a picket fence could possibly be used as a diffraction grating.

PROBLEMS

19.1 When Light Waves Interfere

1. Using a compass and ruler, construct a scale diagram of the interference pattern that results when waves 1 cm in length fall on two slits 2 cm apart. The slits may be represented by two dots spaced 2 cm apart and kept to one side of the paper. Draw a line through all points of reinforcement. Draw dotted lines through all nodal lines.
2. A radio station uses two antennas and broadcasts at 600 kHz. Radio waves travel at the speed of light. The waves from the two antennas are kept in step.
   a. What is the wavelength of the signals emitted by the station?
   b. The occupants of a home located 17 500 m from one antenna and 19 500 m from the other antenna have their receiver tuned to the station. Is the reception good or poor? Explain.
3. Light falls on a pair of slits 1.90×10^{-3} cm apart. The slits are 80.0 cm from the screen. The first-order bright line is 1.90 cm from the central bright line. What is the wavelength of the light?
4. Light of wavelength 542 nm falls on a double slit. First-order bright bands appear 4.00 cm from the central bright line. The screen is 1.20 m from the slits. How far apart are the slits?
5. A lecturer is demonstrating two-slit interference with sound waves. Two speakers are used, 4.0 m apart. The sound frequency is 325 Hz and the speed of sound is 343 m/s. Students sit in seats 4.5 m away. What is the spacing between the locations where no sound is heard because of destructive interference?
6. Monochromatic light passes through a single slit with a width of 0.010 cm and falls on a screen 100 cm away. If the distance from the center of the pattern to the first band is 0.60 cm, what is the wavelength of the light?
7. Light with a wavelength of 4.5×10^{-5} cm passes through a single slit and falls on a screen 100 cm away. If the slit is 0.015 cm wide, what is the distance from the center of the pattern to the first dark band?
8. Monochromatic light with a wavelength of 400 nm passes through a single slit and falls on a screen 90 cm away. If the distance of the first-order dark band is 0.30 cm from the center of the pattern, what is the width of the slit?
9. ▶ Sound waves of frequency 550 Hz enter a window 1.2 m wide. The window is in the exact center of one wall of a theater 24 m × 12 m. The window is 12 m from the opposite wall, along which is a row of seats occupied by people. The theater is acoustically prepared to prevent the reflection of sound waves, and the speed of sound is 330 m/s. Two people in the row along the wall hear no sound. Where are they sitting?

19.2 Applications of Diffraction

10. A good diffraction grating has 2.50×10^3 lines/cm. What is the distance between two lines in the grating?
11. Using grating with a spacing of 4.00×10^{-4} cm, a red line appears 16.5 cm from the central line on a screen. The screen is 1.00 m from the grating. What is the wavelength of the red light?
12. A spectrometer uses a grating with 12 000 lines/cm. Find the angles at which red light, 632 nm, and blue light, 421 nm, have the first-order bright bands.
13. ▶ The ridges in the *Morpho* butterfly wing in the chapter-opening photograph are spaced about 2.2×10^{-7} m apart. Explain how they could cause the wing to appear iridescent blue.
14. ▶ Janet uses a 33-1/3 rpm record as a diffraction grating. She shines a laser, $\lambda = 632.8$ nm, on the record. On a screen 4.0 m from the record, a series of red dots 21 mm apart are seen.

a. How many ridges are there in a centimeter along the radius of the record?

b. She checks her results by noting that the ridges came from a song that lasted 4.01 minutes and took up 16 mm on the record. How many ridges should there be in a centimeter?

15. A camera with a 50-mm lens set at $f/8$ aperture has an opening 6.25 mm in diameter. Suppose this lens acts like a slit 6.25 mm wide. For light with $\lambda = 550$ nm, what is the resolution of the lens, the distance from the middle of the central bright band to the first-order dark band? The film is 50 mm from the lens.

16. The owner of the camera in Problem 15 tries to decide which film to buy for it. The expensive one, called fine-grain film, has 200 grains/mm. The less costly, coarse-grain film has only 50 grains/mm. If the owner wants a grain to be no smaller than the width of the central bright band calculated above, which film should be purchased?

17. Suppose the Hubble Space Telescope, 2.4 m in diameter, is in orbit 100 km above Earth and is turned to look at Earth. If you ignore the effect of the atmosphere, what is the resolution of this telescope? Use $\lambda = 500$ nm.

FIGURE 19–11. Hubble Telescope

18. The image formed on the retina of the eye shows the effect of diffraction. The diameter of the iris opening in bright light is 3.0 mm. For green light, 545 nm wavelength, find the resolution of the eye. That is, find the distance from the center of the central band to the dark band. Assume the distance from iris to retina is 2.5 cm.

▶ **19.** Cone cells in the retina are about 1.5 μm apart. On how many cone cells does the image found in Problem 18 fall? Would the eye's resolution be better if the pupil were much larger, like the 10 mm diameter of an eagle's eye? Explain.

USING LAB SKILLS

1. In the Physics Lab on page 399, you estimated the wavelengths of several colors of light based on the interference effect. Take a new measurement of x when the L value is 2.0 m instead of 1.0 m. How does the relative error of your new calculated value compare with that for your original value.
2. Describe which colors are "cooler" and which colors correspond to higher temperatures. Would your choices of cool and warm colors agree with that of an artist?

THINKING PHYSIC-LY

When you look at light reflected in a compact disk you see one or more rainbow-like spectra. What is the cause of this beautiful display?

9. 6.0 m to either side of the center of the wall
10. 4.00×10^{-4} cm
11. 660 nm
12. red, $\theta = 49.4°$; blue, $\theta = 30.4°$
13. The ridges act as a diffraction grating. Any blue light of wavelength approximately 4.40×10^{-7} m is reflected strongly from this grating.
14. **a.** 83 ridges/cm
b. 84 ridges/cm
15. 4.4×10^{-3} mm
16. coarse grain
17. 2.1 cm
18. 4.5×10^{-4} cm
19. 3 cells. It would do no good to increase the resolution of the eye by using a larger pupil because resolution is limited by cone separation in the retina.

Answers To
USING LAB SKILLS

1. Assuming the same care in the measurement as before, the % error in the measurement should be half as much. The new calculated value should be closer to the accepted value than the previous calculation.

2. The red and orange occur first when the filament is relatively "cool." The green and blue only become bright when the filament is hot. This is exactly the opposite description used in the art world. Blue and green are called "cool" colors because they are more restful.

Answer To
THINKING PHYSIC-LY

Compact disks have rings of tiny pits in their surfaces. Light is diffracted when it reflects off the pits. Reflections from adjacent rings interfere with each wavelength having an interference maximum at a different angle. That is, the rings form a diffraction grating.

CHAPTER

20 Static Electricity

PLANNING GUIDE (6 class sessions)

CONTENTS	TEXT FEATURES	TEACHER RESOURCE PACKAGE	OTHER COMPONENTS
20.1 Electrical Charges, pp. 408–411 (2 Class Sessions) • Charged Objects • A Microscopic View of Charging • Conductors and Insulators	**Physics Lab:** What's the Charge?, p. 412 **Pocket Lab:** Charged Up, p. 409 **Pocket Lab:** Insulators and Conductors, p. 411 **Concept Review,** p. 411	**Study Guide:** Electrical Charges **Physics Lab Data Sheet:** What's the Charge? **Reteaching Master:** Forces Between Charged Objects	
20.2 Electrical Forces, pp. 413–420 (4 Class Sessions) • Forces on Charged Bodies • Separation of Charge and Charging by Induction • Coulomb's Law • The Unit of Charge: The Coulomb • Using Electrical Forces on Neutral Bodies	**Physics and Technology:** The Photocopier, p. 417 **Pocket Lab:** Reach Out, p. 416 **Concept Review,** p. 420	**Study Guide:** Electrical Forces **Critical Thinking Master:** Lightning **Enrichment Master:** Large Dimensionless Numbers **Transparency Worksheet:** Charging by Conduction and Induction **Transparency Worksheet:** Separation of Charge	**Laboratory Manual:** Lab 20.1 Investigating Static Electricity **Transparency 27:** Charging by Conduction and Induction **Transparency 28:** Separation of Charge
Chapter Review, pp. 421–423	Summary Key Terms Reviewing Concepts Applying Concepts Problems Thinking Physic-ly	**Vocabulary Review** **Chapter Test**	**Test Bank**

SUPPLEMENTARY MATERIALS

SOFTWARE	AUDIOVISUAL	BOOKS/MAGAZINES
MMV Electricity, Queue, Inc. (Apple II, IBM PC, Macintosh).	Filmstrip: *Electricity and Magnetism,* United Learning.	Berg, Richard E. "Van de Graaff Generators: Theory, Maintenance, and Belt Fabrication." *The Physics Teacher,* May 1990, p. 281. Deonarine, Samaroo. "Coulomb's Law after the Christmas Party." *The Physics Teacher,* December 1990, p. 607. Rheam, Harry. "Static Electricity and Mylar." *The Physics Teacher,* February 1990, p. 103. Zwicker, Earl. "Doing Physics." *The Physics Teacher,* October 1987, p. 469–470.

PROBLEM CORRELATION

CONCEPTS	CHAPTER REVIEW			PROBLEMS APPENDIX
	Reviewing Concepts	Applying Concepts	Problems	
20.1 Electrical Charges				
Charged Objects				
A Microscopic View of Charging	1,2,5,6	1,2		
Conductors and Insulators	3,4	3,4		
20.2 Electrical Forces				
Forces on Charged Bodies		5,8		
Separation of Charge and Charging by Induction	7,8	6,7,14,15		
Coulomb's Law		9,10,11,12	1	1,2,3,**4**
The Unit of Charge: The Coulomb		13	2,3,4,5,6,7,8,9, 10,11,12,13,**14, 15,16,17,18,19**	5,6,7,8,9,10, 11,12,**13,14**
Using Electric Forces on Neutral Bodies				

ACTIVITY AND DEMONSTRATION MATERIALS

PHYSICS LAB	POCKET LAB	DEMONSTRATIONS
Page 412 30 cm x 30 cm block of plastic foam insulation 22-cm aluminum pie pan plastic drinking glass drinking straw fur transparent tape thread pith ball (or small piece of plastic foam packing material) liquid graphite	Pages 409, 411, 416 balloon fur electroscope 1 nickel 1 dime 15 pennies	Pages 414, 418 Van de Graaff generator pith ball 6–8 ft. 2 x 4 charged rods watch glass ebonite rod fur water

EXTENSION PROJECTS

LIBRARY RESEARCH

1. Lightning Rods
Through library research, find out the structure and function of the lightning rod. Are lightning rods in use today? Why or why not?

DISPLAY MODEL

2. Faraday Cage
Construct a Faraday cage and demonstrate it to the class.

STUDENT READINGS

Eberhart, J. "Whistler's May Sing Neptune's Lightning Call." *Science News,* June 9, 1990.

Fincher, J. "Summer's Light and Sound Show: A Deadly Delight." *Smithsonian,* July 1988.

Kruglak, Haym. "A Simpler Soft-Drink-Can Electroscope." *The Physics Teacher,* December 1990.

Mellen, Walter Ray. "Inexpensive Electrostatic Halos." *The Physics Teacher,* December 1990.

Stern, Marc. "Zapping Static." *Popular Mechanics,* October 1985.

Chapter 20

Static Electricity

CHAPTER OVERVIEW

Theme Development: The basic properties of electrical interaction are taught according to a conceptual model of the atom. Coulomb's law is derived from a mathematical model of atomic forces in equilibrium.

MISCONCEPTIONS

Students have trouble building the conceptual framework for electrical phenomena. For example, in explaining charging effects, students often incorrectly say that an object runs out of electrons. Charging by induction is difficult because there is no direct transfer of charge. The inverse square nature of Coulomb's law causes trouble; students often want to add charges rather than to multiply them when using the law.

KEY TERMS

charging by conduction
charging by induction
conductors
coulomb (unit)
Coulomb's law
electroscope
electrostatics
elementary charge
insulators
neutral

Laboratory Options

STUDENT EDITION

Physics Lab

- What's the Charge? 412

Pocket Labs

- Charged Up 409
- Insulators and Conductors 411
- Reach Out 416

TEACHER EDITION

Activities

- Demonstration 414, 418, 418
- Discovery 415
- Cooperative Learning 415

LABORATORY MANUAL

- Investigating Static Electricity Lab 20.1

CHAPTER

20 Static Electricity

Sky Light

During a thunderstorm, Molly and Paresh were watching lightning bolts as they lit up the sky. Paresh was impressed by the patterns of the bolts. Molly asked Paresh, "Why do you suppose lightning jumps between a cloud and Earth?" What explanation might Paresh give?

Chapter Outline

Nature provides few more awesome displays than lightning. Benjamin Franklin was colonial America's foremost scientist. Starting in 1740, Franklin studied electricity produced by friction, charges that result from rubbing two surfaces together. Franklin proposed his famous kite experiment in 1750, and two years later showed that "electrical fire" could be drawn from a cloud. Franklin became famous as a scientist throughout Europe. This fame probably helped assure his diplomatic successes in France during the American Revolution.

✓ Concept Check

The following terms or concepts from earlier chapters are important for a good understanding of this chapter. If you are not familiar with them, you should review them before studying this chapter.
- forces and force addition, Chapter 5
- gravitation, Chapter 8

Introducing The Chapter

Sky Light

Using The Photo: Research into lightning is currently very active. Lightning emits a quite distinctive radio signal. Monitoring this signal has given us much of our lightning data. Put simply, lightning is like a giant spark! To answer the chapter opener question, refer students to page 414.

✓ Concept Check

Make sure students have a clear understanding of the concepts covered in Chapters 5 and 8 that are listed in the Concept Check. With a background knowledge of the nature of forces, force addition, and gravitation, students will find it easier to comprehend the principles of static electricity discussed in this chapter.

Assessment Options

Portfolio Assessment
Extension 1, TWE, p. 406b
Portfolio Assessment, TWE, p. 408
Critical Thinking, TWE, p. 409
Extension, TWE, p. 410
Cooperative Learning, p. 415

Performance Assessment
Extension 2, TWE, p. 406b
Pocket Labs, pp. 409, 411, 416
Physics Lab, p. 412
Pocket Lab Assessment, TWE, p. 409

Content Assessment
Self Assessment: Practice Problems, p. 420
Convergent Question, TWE, p. 411
Assessment, Critical Thinking, p. 412
Critical Thinking, p. 418
Concept Reviews, pp. 411, 420
Chapter Review, pp. 421–423
Supplemental Questions, pp. 702–703

Group Assessment
Activities for group assessment occur with Cooperative Learning and lab activities.

20.1 ELECTRICAL CHARGES

Preparation

OBJECTIVES

The objectives are listed on the student page. Remind students to preview these objectives as a study guide to this major section.

OVERVIEW

The central principle that atoms have charges sets up a conceptual framework in which substances are categorized as conductors, semiconductors, or insulators.

BRIDGING

Concepts introduced in previous chapters include force, energy, plasma, and light.

1 Focus

DISCREPANT EVENT

- Charge an electroscope with a negatively charged rod, such as a rubber rod rubbed with fur. To show that some things are conductors and others are insulators, touch the electroscope with a clean glass rod. Nothing will happen because glass is an insulator. Touch the electroscope with a metal rod and it will discharge. Ask students to explain this result.

Assessment

Portfolio

Using the Scotch tape strips, make lists of materials that are charged like the tape stuck to the desk and those materials charged like the tape stuck to the other tape. Have students compare their lists to see if all students who tested the same materials got the same results. If not, did they use different brands of tape? Did any objects repel both tapes? attract both?

Objectives

- recognize the basic properties of the electrical interaction.
- know how to charge an object.
- know that charging is the separation, not the creation, of charges.
- state the differences between conductors and insulators.

Charge and Field Conventions

- *Positive charges are red.*
- *Negative charges are blue.*

A charged object shows electrical effects.

20.1 ELECTRICAL CHARGES

You may have rubbed your shoes on the carpet hard enough to create a lightning-like spark when you touched someone. Franklin's kite experiment showed that lightning is similar to frictional electricity. We now call electrical effects produced this way static electricity. In this chapter we will investigate **electrostatics,** the study of electrical charges that can be collected and held in one place. Current electricity, produced by batteries and generators, will be explored in later chapters.

Charged Objects

Have you ever noticed the way your hair is attracted to the comb when you comb your hair on a dry day? Perhaps you have also found socks stuck together in a clothes dryer. Then you will recognize the attraction of bits of paper to a comb shown in Figure 20–1. If the weather is dry, you should try it now. Rub a plastic comb or ball-point pen on your clothing. Wool clothing is best. Then hold the pen or comb close to a pile of paper bits. Notice the way the paper pieces jump up toward the comb. There must be a new, relatively strong force causing this upward acceleration, because it is larger than the downward acceleration caused by the gravitational force of the entire Earth.

There are other differences between this new force and gravity. Paper is attracted to a comb only after the comb has been rubbed. If you wait awhile, the attractive property of the comb disappears. Gravity, on the other hand, does not require rubbing and does not leak away. The ancient Greeks noticed these effects when they rubbed amber. We now call the interaction "electrical" after the Greek word for amber, *elektron*. An object that exhibits this electrical interaction after rubbing is said to be "charged."

You can explore the electrical interaction with very simple equipment. You will need some Scotch Brand "Magic"™ tape. Fold over about 5 mm on the end of the tape for a handle and then stick an 8 to

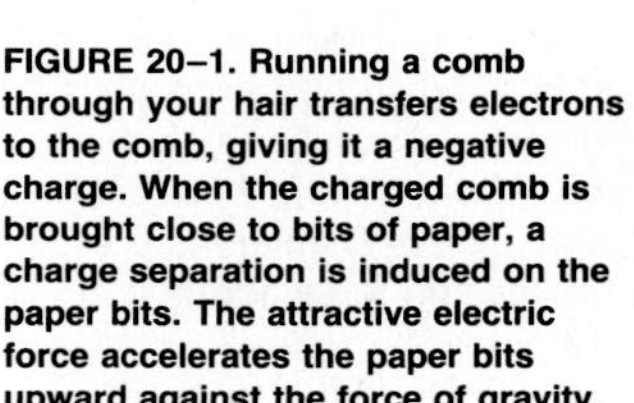

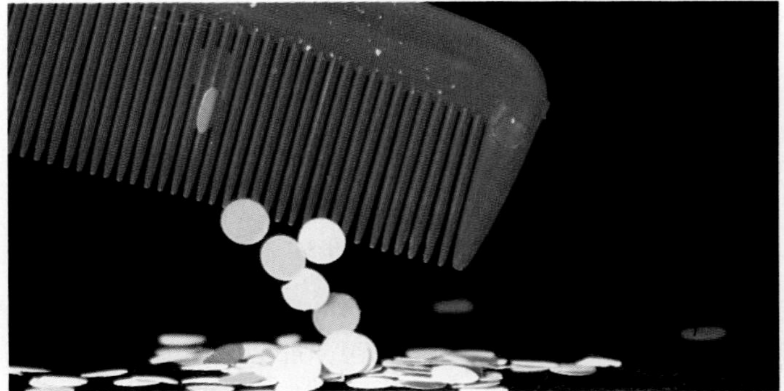

FIGURE 20–1. Running a comb through your hair transfers electrons to the comb, giving it a negative charge. When the charged comb is brought close to bits of paper, a charge separation is induced on the paper bits. The attractive electric force accelerates the paper bits upward against the force of gravity.

TEACHER

The atomic theory can be traced back to ancient history, long before scientists could actually see indications of atoms with electron microscopes. Students will study the evolution of the atomic model in Chapter 28, but you might mention here that in the atom, electrons surround a dense nucleus of protons and neutrons. Protons, moreover, have a charge that is equal and opposite to electrons, but they have nearly 2000 times the mass of electrons.

a

b

FIGURE 20–2. Strips of Scotch tape can be given the same charge (a), then used to demonstrate the interactions of like and opposite charges (b).

F.Y.I.

A single lightning bolt may transfer 3.75 million joules of electrical energy. It also generates temperatures five times hotter than the 6000°C found on the surface of the sun.

12-cm long piece on a dry, smooth surface like your desk top. Stick a second, similar, piece on top of the first, Figure 20–2a. Now quickly pull both pieces off together, then pull them apart. Finally stick one end of each piece to the edge of a table, bottom of a lamp shade, and so on. The two should hang down a short distance apart, Figure 20–2b. Now rub the comb or pen on your clothing and bring it near first one tape and then the other. You will find that one tape will be attracted to the comb, the other repelled from it. You can now explore the interactions of charged objects with the tapes.

Identical objects charged the same way repel each other.

Now charge two strips of tape by pressing the strips side by side on the desk and then pulling them off. Notice that these two tapes repel when they are suspended near each other. You will find that any tape pulled directly off the desk will repel another similarly prepared tape. On the other hand, two tapes attract when they are unlike in the way they were charged. A tape pulled off the back of another tape will attract a tape pulled off the desk. Try other objects like plates, glasses, or plastic bags. Rub them with different materials like silk, fur, wool, or plastic wrap. If the air is dry, scuff your shoes on the carpet and bring your finger near the tapes. You should find that most charged objects attract one tape and repel the other. To test silk, fur, or wool, you should slip a plastic bag over your hand before holding the cloth. After rubbing, take your hand out of the bag and bring both bag and cloth near the tapes.

Objects charged differently attract.

You will never find an object that repels both tapes, although you might find some that attract both tapes. Bring your finger near first one tape, then the other. You will find it attracts both tapes. We will explore this effect in Section 20.2.

From your experiments you can make a list of objects that are charged like the tape stuck on the desk and a list of other objects that are charged like the tape stuck on the back of the other tape. There are only two lists; thus there are only two states of charge. We could give these states the names "yellow" and "green." Benjamin Franklin called them *positive* and *negative*. The choice of which list to call positive and which negative was also made by Franklin. We still follow his convention and call the charge states for materials like vinyl and hard rubber negative, while materials like fur, glass, and wool we call positive.

POCKET LAB

CHARGED UP

Rub a balloon with fur. Touch the balloon to the knob of an electroscope and watch the leaves. Describe the result. Make a drawing to explain the result. Touch the knob of the electroscope to make the leaves fall. Would you expect that the fur could move the leaves? Why? Try it. Explain your results.

2 Teach

CONCEPT DEVELOPMENT

- Students have lots of experience with static electricity. Try to build on this experience when discussing the more abstract aspects of the lesson. Ask them how they have tried to explain these experiences.
- Lead students through this reasoning: Since the unlike charges are closer than the like charges, their attraction is greater than the repulsion of the like charges. This results in a net attractive force.
- Be consistent when explaining how an object acquires charge by saying it loses or gains electrons, not protons.
- Conductivity is a measure of how readily the free electrons in a material can move around.

Critical Thinking: Most people have observed static cling on freshly dried clothes. Various commercial products claim to eliminate the problem. On the other hand, plastic food wrap is an example of a product designed to enhance static cling! Have students research and report on these products.

Study Guide Master. To reinforce the concepts in this section, have the students complete the Study Guide Master for Section 20.1 from the Teacher Resource Package.

POCKET LAB

CHARGED UP

Purpose: to observe the effects of electron transfer.

Materials: balloon; fur; electroscope.

Outcome: The balloon becomes charged when it is rubbed, as does the fur. When both the balloon and the fur are touched to the electroscope, the leaves spread.

Assessment

Performance

To further assess students' understanding of the interaction between charges, have them do the following. Test a charged balloon with the Scotch tape electrometers. Which of the strips is charged like the balloon? How can you tell? Is the fur charged the same as the balloon or opposite? How can you tell? Students may find it necessary to put their hand in a plastic bag when they hold the fur to keep it from discharging through their hand. [The balloon will be charged like the tape stuck to the desk, because it repels this tape and attracts the other one. The fur will be charged the same as the top tape because it repels this tape and attracts the other one. Note: some brands of tape take the opposite charge and five opposite results.]

CONCEPT DEVELOPMENT

Critical Thinking: When we categorize substances as conductors, semiconductors, and insulators, we are actually ranking them according to the ease with which electrons move around in them (their conductivity). Ask students to explain, in terms of electrons, the two extreme limits of conductivity; that is, what would zero conductivity mean and what would the maximum possible conductivity mean. [Zero conductivity means that no charge carriers could move. Maximum conductivity means that all charge carriers were in motion.]

CHECKING FOR UNDERSTANDING

Have students explain what makes it possible to put a charge on an electroscope with a plastic strip even though someone is holding onto one end of the strip. [These materials are poor conductors and charge moves along them so slowly they aren't quickly discharged.]

RETEACHING

Reteaching Master, Teacher Resource Package. Use the Reteaching Master, Forces Between Charged Objects, for Chapter 20.

- Ask students for examples of conductors, semiconductors, and insulators.
- Review the simple charge structure of the atom, pointing out that static electricity is a result of the electrons present in all atoms.

Laboratory Manual. Give additional experience with static electricity by doing Lab 20.1 from the Laboratory Manual.

EXTENSION

The process of charging things by rubbing (electrification by friction) is poorly understood. This branch of science is called triboelectricity. With our increased ability to study surface layers of materials, triboelectricity has attracted new research efforts. Have interested students look into the latest developments in this field and report their findings to the class.

FIGURE 20–3.
A piece of plastic 0.02 mm wide was given a net positive charge. Areas of negative charge show as dark regions. Areas of positive charge show as yellow regions.

You were probably able to show that if you rubbed plastic with wool, the plastic was charged negatively, the wool positively. The two kinds of charges were not created alone, but in pairs. This experiment suggests that normal matter contains both charges, positive and negative. Rubbing in some way separates the two. To explore this further, we have to consider the microscopic picture of matter.

A Microscopic View of Charge

Electric charges exist in the atom itself. In 1890, J. J. Thomson discovered that all materials contain light, negatively-charged particles he called electrons. Between 1909 and 1911, Ernest Rutherford, a New Zealander, discovered that atoms have a massive, positively-charged nucleus, or center. The electrons surround the nucleus. The positive charge of the nucleus is exactly balanced by the negative charge of the electrons. That is, the atom is uncharged; it is **neutral**.

With the addition of energy, electrons can be removed from atoms. The positively-charged particle that results is called a positive ion. The freed electrons can remain unattached or become attached to other atoms, resulting in negatively-charged particles, or negative ions.

Charges are not created but separated.

If two objects are rubbed together, each can become charged. Scientists do not yet understand all the details of this process. They do know that when two different objects, like rubber and fur, are rubbed together, electrons from atoms on the fur are transferred to the rubber, Figure 20–4. Positive ions remain in the fur. Additional electrons give the atoms in the rubber a net negative charge. The total charge of the two objects remains the same, it is conserved. Individual charges are never created or destroyed. The separation of positive and negative charges means that electrons have been transferred.

Electrons can be removed from or added to atoms.

Friction between the tires of a moving car or truck and the road can cause the tires to become charged. Violent winds cause friction in thunderclouds that separate charges. Usually the tops of the clouds become positive, the bottoms negative.

FIGURE 20–4. A rubber object can be charged when rubbed with fur.

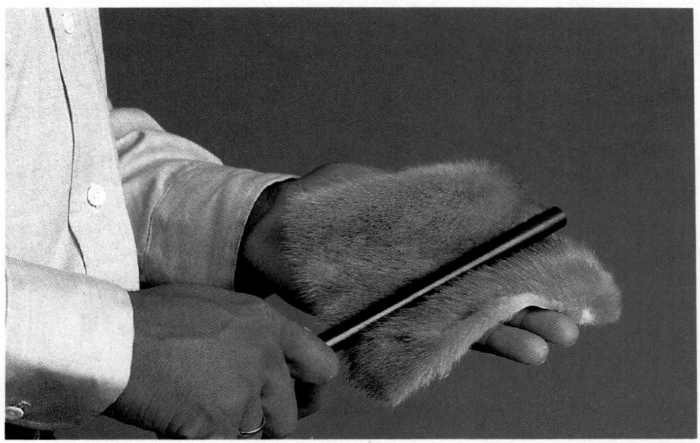

STUDY GUIDE MASTER
Use the Study Guide master for section 20.1.

RETEACHING MASTER
Use the Reteaching master for Chapter 20 with this section.

LAB WORKSHEET
Use the Lab Worksheet for Chapter 20 with this Physics Lab.

LABORATORY MANUAL
Use Lab 20.1 with this section.

Conductors and Insulators

Hold a plastic rod or comb in its middle and rub only one end. You will find that only the rubbed end becomes charged. The charges you added to the plastic stayed where they were put, they did not move. Materials through which charges will not move easily are called electrical **insulators.** Charges removed from one area on an insulator are not replaced by charges from another area. Glass, dry wood, most plastics, cloth, and dry air are good insulators.

Suppose you support a metal rod on an insulator so that it is isolated, or completely surrounded by insulators. If you now touch the charged comb to one end of the metal rod, you will find that the charge spreads very quickly over the entire piece. Materials such as metals that allow charges to move about easily are called electrical **conductors**. Electrons carry, or conduct, electric charge through the metal. Metals are good conductors because at least one electron on each atom can be removed easily. These electrons act as if they no longer belong to any one atom, but to the metal as a whole. They are free to move throughout the metal in the same way atoms in a gas move about a container. They are said to form an electron gas. Copper and aluminum are both excellent conductors and are used commercially to carry electricity. Graphite, the form of carbon used in pencils, also is a good conductor.

Air is an insulator, but under certain conditions sparks or lightning occurs, allowing charge to move as through a conductor. The spark that jumps between your finger and a doorknob after you have rubbed your feet on the carpet discharges you. That is, the charges separating during charging have recombined. Similarly, lightning discharges the charges in thunderclouds. How can air become a conductor? The forces exerted by the charges must have ripped electrons off of molecules in the air. The electrons and positively- or negatively-charged atoms, or ions, become free to move. They form a conductor called a plasma.

POCKET LAB

INSULATORS AND CONDUCTORS

Place a nickel on one half of a piece of paper and a dime on the other half. Place the appropriate number of pennies on each side to show neutral atoms. Make all pennies around the nickel "heads". The "heads" represent electrons that are tightly bound to the nucleus. The nickel side of the paper now represents an insulator. Adjust the number of heads and tails around the dime to represent a slightly different conductive material. What did you do?

Charges stay in one place on an insulator.

Charges move easily on a conductor.

CONCEPT REVIEW

1.1 How could you find out which strip of tape, the one pulled off the desk or the one pulled off the back of the other tape, is positively charged?

1.2 Suppose you attach a long metal rod to a plastic handle so the rod is isolated. You touch a charged glass rod to one end of the metal rod. Describe the charges on the metal rod.

1.3 In the 1730s, Stephan Gray tried to see how far electrical charge could be conducted by metal rods. He hung metal rods by thin silk cords from the ceiling. When the rods were longer than 293 feet, the silk broke. Gray replaced the silk with stronger wires made of brass, but now the experiments failed. The metal rod would no longer transmit charge from one end to the other. Why?

1.4 **Critical Thinking:** Suppose there was a third type of charge. What experiments could you suggest to explore its properties?

F.Y.I.

Benjamin Franklin was cautious while performing his famous kite experiment, in which he charged a Leyden jar with electricity drawn from the clouds. The first two men who tried to repeat the experiment were electrocuted.

—*Isaac Asimov's Book of Facts*

POCKET LAB

INSULATORS AND CONDUCTORS

Purpose: to build a model of an insulator and a conductor.

Materials: 1 nickel; 1 dime; 15 pennies.

Outcome: Insulators do not have electrons that are free to move. Conductors have one or more electrons in each atom that are free to move.

Guided Practice: Go over the Concept Review questions on this page as a class activity.

INDEPENDENT PRACTICE/ EXTENSION

Refer to the Assignment Guide below for additional questions and problems for independent practice.

3 Close

CONVERGENT QUESTION

Rub some balloons on cloth to charge them up. Stick them up on the walls, challenging students to explain what's going on. You might also show that there are substances to which the balloons won't stick.

CONCEPT REVIEW ANSWERS

1.1 Rub a piece of hard plastic with wool. The plastic is charged negatively. It will repel the negatively charged strip of tape and attract the positively charged one.

1.2 The glass rod was positively charged. This charge spreads over the entire metal rod, charging it positively.

1.3 Brass is a conductor. The electric charge flowed into the ceiling instead of along the metal rod.

1.4 **Critical Thinking:** If the new type is different from the other two types, then it should repel (or attract) both positively and negatively charged objects.

20:1 ASSIGNMENT GUIDE

	PRACTICE	EXTENSION
CHAPTER REVIEW pp. 421–423 · Reviewing Concepts · Applying Concepts · Problems*	1–6	1–4
APPENDIX B PROBLEMS* · Chapter 20, p. 702–703		

* Complete solutions to all Chapter Review and Appendix problems appear in the Problems and Solutions Manual.

PHYSICS LAB

Process Skills: observing, communicating, hypothesizing, questioning, defining operationally, designing experiments.

MISCONCEPTIONS

This material is difficult for many students because individual electric charges are too small to see. One common misconception is that positive charges move. Another misconception is that objects "run out of charges" as they are discharged.

Teaching Suggestions: **1.** Precut the insulating foam block into 30 cm × 30 cm squares. **2.** Paint the small pith balls with graphite or another type of conducting paint prior to class. **3.** Encourage lab groups that finish early to design and conduct their own investigations.

OBSERVATIONS

1. A definite pulling force was felt. The force increased as the distance decreased.
2. The small ball swung away from the edge of the plate, but as the plate was raised the ball returned to its former position.
3. This time the ball swung farther from the plate (almost horizontally). The ball stayed away from the edge even when the plate was lifted from the foam.

ANALYSIS

1. The negative charge on the plate pushes electrons on the plate so the bottom of the plate becomes slightly positive and the top of the plate slightly negative.
2. The pith ball is a sensitive indicator that shows when the edge of the plate is charged.
3. Each time the ball touches the pie pan it removes some electrons. These electrons are deposited on your finger. This process repeats.
4. A strong spark will be made several times. The spark does not seem to lessen in intensity. The foam does not "run out" of charges.

APPLICATIONS

The plastic wrap is a very good insulator. Excess charges on the wrap probably induce opposite charges on adjacent layers.

PHYSICS LAB: What's the Charge?

Purpose

To see and feel the effects of electrostatic charging.

Materials

- 30 cm x 30 cm block of plastic foam insulation material
- 22-cm aluminum pie pan
- plastic drinking glass
- drinking straw
- fur
- transparent tape
- thread
- pith ball (or small piece of plastic foam packing material)
- liquid graphite

Procedure

1. Paint the small pith (or plastic foam) ball with graphite and allow it to dry.
2. Securely tape the inverted glass to the center (inside) of the aluminum pie pan.
3. Tape the drinking straw to the top of the plastic glass as shown below. Use the thread to attach the ball as shown.
4. Rub the foam with the fur, then remove the fur.
5. Move the pie pan by holding onto the plastic glass.
6. Slowly lower the pie pan until it is about 3 cm above the charged plastic foam block and then slowly lift it away.
7. Place the pie pan directly on the charged foam block and lift it away.
8. Bring your finger near the ball until it touches.
9. Remove the straw, thread, and ball from the glass.
10. Place the pie pan on the foam block and touch the edge of the pie pan with your finger. Now remove the pie pan from the foam block and touch the ball again with your finger.
11. Repeat step 10 several times without recharging the foam block.

Observations and Data

1. As the pie pan was brought near the charged block, could you feel a force between the neutral pie pan and the charged foam? Describe it.
2. Describe what happened to the ball in step 6.
3. Describe what happened to the ball in step 7.

Analysis

1. Make a drawing to show the distribution of charges on the neutral pie pan as it is lowered toward the charged foam block.
2. What was the reason for using the ball on a thread?
3. State a hypothesis that explains the back and forth motion of the ball in step 8.
4. Does the plastic foam block seem to "run out of charges" in step 11?

Applications

1. Clear plastic wrap is sold to seal up containers of food. Suggest a reason why it clings to itself.

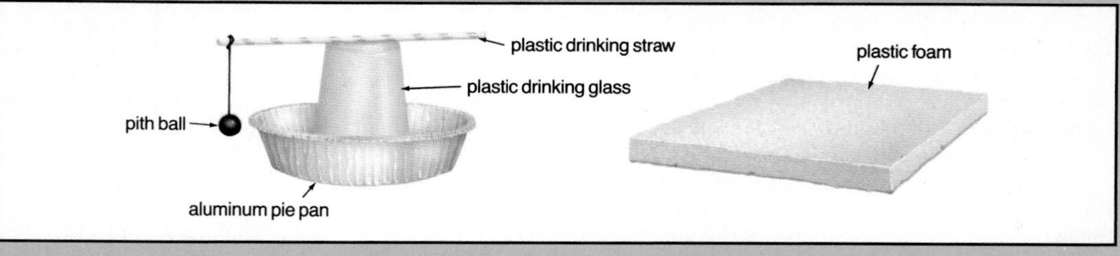

ASSESSMENT

Critical Thinking: To further assess students' understanding of the effects of electric charges, ask the following questions.

1. In Procedure steps 10 and 11, you found that the procedure could be repeated many times. What does this indicate about the amount of charge on the plastic foam? [The effect seems to be just as strong after 10 trials as when it was first noted. This indicates that the charge on the foam is either constant or only changing slightly.]

2. What are the major limitations in the experiment? [Students will probably say that they can't see whether the objects are charged or neutral. Students also can't see which way the charges are moving when they transfer.]

20.2 ELECTRICAL FORCES

Electrical forces must be strong, as they can easily produce accelerations larger than the acceleration caused by gravity. We have also seen that they can be either repulsive or attractive, while gravitational forces are always attractive. Many scientists made attempts to measure the electrical force. Daniel Bernoulli, otherwise known for his work on fluids, made some crude measurements in 1760. In 1770, Henry Cavendish showed electric forces must obey an inverse square force law, but, being extremely shy, he did not publish his work. His manuscripts were discovered over a century later, after all his work had been duplicated by others.

Objectives

- **be able to summarize the observed forces between charged objects; know how an electroscope detects the presence of charge and how an object is charged by conduction.**
- **explain separation of charge and charging by induction.**
- **state Coulomb's law and how the force depends on charges and their separation.**
- **state the SI unit of charge; understand the vector nature of the electric force; solve problems using Coulomb's law.**
- **understand the cause of the attractive force on neutral objects; list examples of this force.**

Forces on Charged Bodies

The forces you observed on tape strips can also be demonstrated by suspending a negatively-charged hard rubber rod so that it turns easily, Figure 20–5. If you bring another negatively-charged rod near the suspended rod, it will turn away. The negative charges on the rods repel each other. It is not necessary to bring the rods very close; the force, called the electric force, acts over a distance. If a positively-charged glass rod is suspended and a similarly-charged glass rod is brought close, the two positively-charged rods will also repel. If a negatively-charged rod is brought near the positively-charged rod, however, the two will attract each other, and the suspended rod will turn toward the oppositely-charged rod. The results of your tape experiments and these observations with charged rods can be summarized in this way:

- There are two kinds of electrical charges, positive and negative.
- Charges exert force on other charges over a distance.
- Like charges repel; opposite charges attract.

Like-charged objects repel. Unlike-charged objects attract.

An electroscope can measure the quantity of charge.

Neither a strip of tape nor a large rod hanging in open air is a very sensitive or convenient way of determining charge. Instead, a device

FIGURE 20–5. A charged rod, when brought close to another suspended rod, will attract or repel the suspended rod.

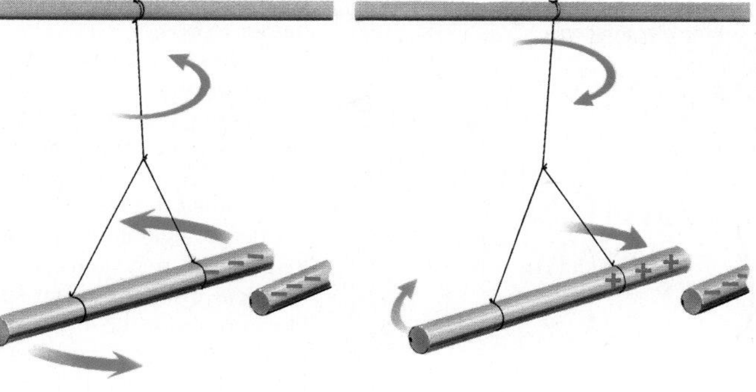

20.2 ELECTRICAL FORCES

Preparation

OBJECTIVES

The objectives are listed on the student page. Remind students to preview these objectives as a study guide to this major section.

OVERVIEW

Covered in this section are the concepts of Coulomb's law and the elementary charge, as well as the phenomena of charging by conduction and induction.

BRIDGING

Concepts from previous chapters include action-reaction forces, distance, newton (unit), vector, neutral, reflection, lens, and focus.

1 Focus

DISCREPANT EVENT

Hang two balloons from the ceiling and rub them each with fur. Students will observe that the balloons move away from one another and stay away. Point out that since you did the same thing to both balloons, you can assume the charge is similar and that the like charges will repel. Discuss students' observations and conclusions.

Connect to CHEMISTRY

Electric forces, acting on a microscopic scale, hold the atoms that make up solids and liquids together. In ionically bonded compounds like sodium chloride, the energy of the sodium and chlorine atoms is less if an electron from the sodium is transferred to the chlorine. As a result of the transfer, the two ions formed are oppositely charged and strongly attract each other. The hydrogen and oxygen atoms in water do not transfer electrons, but share them. The shared electrons move slightly toward the oxygen end of the molecule, giving that end a slight negative charge, while the end with the hydrogen has a small positive charge. Why would the force between a sodium and a water molecule be weaker than that between the same ion and a chloride ion the same distance away? [The negative charge of the water molecule is smaller than that of the chloride ion. Also, the positive end of the water molecule is not far away, and there is a repulsive force between it and the sodium ion.]

2 Teach

CONCEPT DEVELOPMENT

Study Guide Master. To reinforce the concepts in this section, have the students complete the Study Guide Master for Section 20.2 from the Teacher Resource Package.

Electrostatic demonstrations don't work well (or at all sometimes) in humid weather. For best results try to schedule them in dry weather. In an emergency you can try drying out your materials with outdoor floodlights, or the heat from an overhead projector, allowing you a few minutes to do the demonstrations. Be aware that the bright light can scorch cloth or paper.

Demonstration: There are many excellent demonstrations that can be done with the Van de Graaff generator. For example, take a pith ball and suspend it near the generator. The ball will be attracted, then repelled. Emphasize that neutral bodies are always attracted to charged bodies. Hold your hand a few inches from the generator and discharge the pith ball. Keep your hand near the generator so the pith ball bounces back and forth between your hand and the generator as it becomes charged and then discharged. Observe how quickly it moves.

Transparency Package. Use Transparency 27 to reinforce the concepts of conduction and induction.

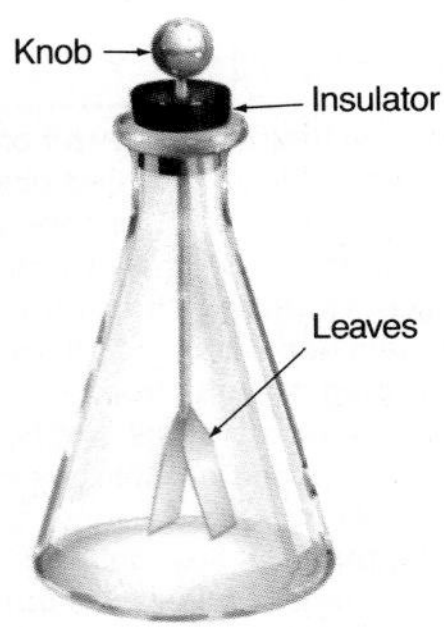

FIGURE 20–6. Electroscope.

Charges can be transferred directly by conduction.

called an **electroscope** is used. An electroscope consists of a metal knob connected by a metal stem to two thin, lightweight pieces of metal foil called leaves, Figure 20–6. Note that the leaves are enclosed to eliminate stray air currents.

When a negatively-charged rod is touched to the knob, negative charges (electrons) are added to the knob. The charges spread over all the metal surfaces. The two leaves are charged negatively and repel each other, causing them to spread apart. The electroscope has been given a net charge. Charging a neutral body this way, by touching it with a charged body, is called **charging by conduction**.

The leaves will also spread if the electroscope is charged positively. How then can you find out whether the electroscope is charged positively or negatively? The type of charge can be determined by observing what happens to the spread leaves if a rod of known charge is brought close to the knob. The leaves will spread farther apart if the electroscope has the same charge as that of the rod. The leaves will fall slightly if the electroscope has a charge opposite to that of the rod, Figure 20–7.

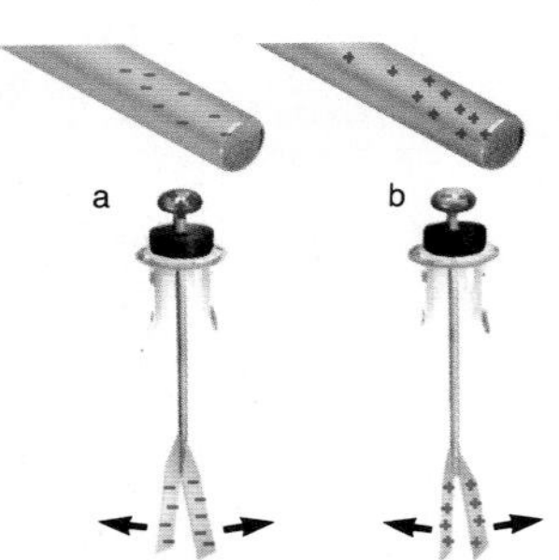

FIGURE 20–7. A negatively-charged rod repels electrons from the electroscope down to the leaves; a positively-charged rod attracts electrons from the leaves to the top of the electroscope.

Sky Light

EARTH SCIENCE CONNECTION

Separation of Charge and Charging by Induction

When you brought your finger near either charged tape, the tape was attracted toward your finger. Your finger was not charged; it was neutral and had equal amounts of positive and negative charge. We know that in materials that are conductors, charges can move easily; and that in the case of sparks, electric forces can change insulators into conductors. Given this information, we can suggest a plausible model for the force your finger exerted on the charged objects.

Suppose you move your finger, or any other uncharged object, close to a positively-charged object. The negative charges in your finger will be attracted to the positively-charged object, and the positive charges will be repelled. Your finger will remain neutral, but the positive and negative charges will be separated. The separation results in an attractive force between the neutral object and the charged object. The force of a charged comb on your hair or neutral pieces of paper can be seen easily. The equal and opposite force of your hair on the comb is much harder to observe.

The negative charges at the bottom of thunderclouds can also cause charge separation in Earth. Positive charges are attracted to Earth's surface under the cloud. The forces of the charges in the cloud and on Earth's surface on the neutral air molecules can rip the molecules apart. The charges from the cloud and Earth then pass through the conducting path, called the lightning bolt.

Charge separation can be used to charge an object without touching it. Suppose a negatively-charged rod is brought close to one of two identical insulated metal spheres that are touching, as in Figure 20–8. Electrons from the first sphere will be pushed onto the sphere farther from the rod making it negatively charged. The closer sphere is now positively charged. If the spheres are separated while the rod is nearby, each sphere will have a charge, and the charges will be equal but opposite. This process is called **charging by induction**.

An uncharged object can attract objects of either charge.

TEACHER F.Y.I.

Methods surprisingly like those of Benjamin Franklin are still used to study electricity. A team of researchers at the Kennedy Space Center study lightning by launching rockets attached to thin metal wires into lightning clouds. Positive and negative bursts of electron flow race up and down the wire between Earth and the charged cloud. These charged bursts, called leaders, behave much like natural lightning, allowing researchers to determine many surprising facts (a lightning stroke reaches its peak current in just 100 billionths of a second, for example). But many mysteries remain. We still do not know why lightning strikes a particular target.

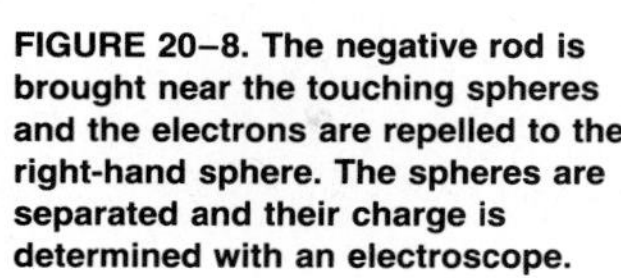

FIGURE 20–8. The negative rod is brought near the touching spheres and the electrons are repelled to the right-hand sphere. The spheres are separated and their charge is determined with an electroscope.

Coulomb's Law

How does the electric force depend on the size of the charges and their separation? Your tape experiments demonstrated some basic properties. You found that the force depends on distance. The closer you brought the charged rod to the tape, the stronger the force. You also found that the more you charged the rod, the stronger the force. But how can you vary the quantity of charge in a controlled way? This problem was solved in 1785 by a French physicist Charles Coulomb (1736–1806). The type of apparatus used by Coulomb is shown in Figure 20–9. An insulating rod with small conducting spheres, **A, A′** at each end was suspended by a thin wire. A similar sphere, **B,** was placed in contact with sphere **A.** When they were touched with a charged object, the charge spread evenly over the two spheres. Because they were the same size, they received equal amounts of charge.

Coulomb found how the force between the two charged spheres, **A** and **B,** depended on the distance. First, he carefully measured the amount of force needed to twist the suspending wire through a given angle. He then placed equal charges on spheres **A** and **B** and varied the distance, d, between them. The electric force moved **A** from its rest position, twisting the suspending wire. By measuring the deflection of **A,** Coulomb could calculate the force of repulsion. He made many

F.Y.I.

Henry Cavendish's measurements of the forces between charged objects were not as complete as Coulomb's because Cavendish had no way of varying the charge in a controlled way. He could measure charge only in terms of the pain produced when he touched the charged object.

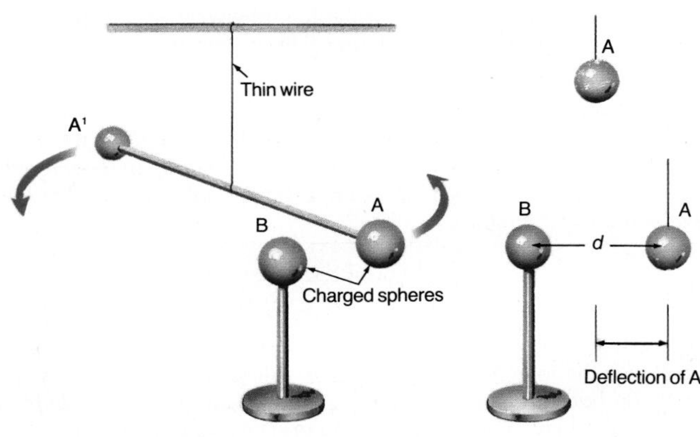

FIGURE 20–9. Coulomb used this type of apparatus to measure the force between two spheres, A and B. He observed the deflection of A while varying the distance between A and B.

CONCEPT DEVELOPMENT

ACTIVITY

Discovery: Place pieces of polystyrene in a polystyrene cup and in a metal cup. Ask students to predict what will happen when the cups are placed on top of the generator, then test to see what happens. [The pieces will remain in the metal cup and come bouncing out of the polystyrene cup.] Ask students to explain the difference in the properties of the two cups. [One cup is an insulator and the other a conductor. The charge is conducted to the outside of the metal cup, but is on both the inside and the outside of the polystyrene cup. Therefore, the pieces in the polystyrene cup develop like charges and repel each other and the cup.]

Cooperative Learning: Cartoonists often use physics in their creations. After all, physics—like humor—deals with the way the world works! Two principles often featured in cartoon gags are Newton's laws of motion and static electricity. Have students watch for physics-related cartoons. Make a bulletin board display of the best ones.

Enrichment Master. With this section, use the Enrichment Master, Large Dimensionless Numbers, from the Teacher Resource Package.

STUDY GUIDE MASTER

Use the Study Guide master for section 20.2.

ENRICHMENT MASTER

Use the Enrichment master for Chapter 20 with this section.

TRANSPARENCY

Use Transparency 28 with this section.

CONCEPT DEVELOPMENT

Coulomb's law holds only for point charges or spherically symmetric distributions of charge. The distance involved is the distance between the centers of such objects. In general, the law is a good approximation if the distance between the objects is much greater than the size of the objects—that is, if they look like point objects to each other.

POCKET LAB

REACH OUT

Purpose: to show that a nearby charged object can exert an influence on a neutral object.

Materials: balloon; fur; electroscope.

Outcome: As the balloon is brought near the electroscope, the leaves spread apart. This occurs because the charges in the balloon push some of the like charges away from the knob of the electroscope and into the leaves. Thus the leaves have a temporary charge.

FIGURE 20–10. Static electric precipitators are used to reduce the fly ash released into the environment. An electric field exerts a force on charged particles, deflecting them sideways. In (a) the device is off, in (b) it is on.

a

b

The electric force varies inversely with the square of the distance between the two charged objects.

measurements with spheres charged both positively and negatively. He showed that the force, F, varied inversely with the square of the distance between the centers of the spheres.

$$F \propto \frac{1}{d^2}$$

The electric force between two charged objects varies directly with the product of their charges.

To investigate the way the force depended on the amount of charge, Coulomb had to change the charges on the spheres in a measured way. Coulomb first charged spheres **A** and **B** equally as before. Then he selected an extra uncharged sphere, **C,** the same size as sphere **B.** When **C** was placed in contact with **B,** the spheres shared the charge that had been on **B** alone. Because the two were the same size, **B** now had only half its original charge. Therefore, the charge on **B** was only one half the charge on **A.** The extra sphere was then removed. After Coulomb adjusted the position of **B** so that the distance, d, between **A** and **B** was the same as before, he found that the force between **A** and **B** was half of its former value. That is, he found that the electric force varied directly with the charge of the bodies.

$$F \propto qq'$$

Coulomb's law describes the force between two charged objects.

After many similar measurements, Coulomb summarized the results in a law now known as **Coulomb's law.** *The magnitude of the force that a tiny sphere with charge q exerts on a second sphere with charge q′, separated a distance d, is*

$$\boxed{F = \frac{Kqq'}{d^2}.}$$

This equation gives the strength of the force that charge q exerts on q' and also the force that q' exerts on q. These two forces are equal in magnitude but opposite in direction. You can observe this example of Newton's third law in action when you bring two tapes with like charge

> **POCKET LAB**
>
> **REACH OUT**
>
> Start with the leaves of an electroscope down. Predict what should happen if you bring a charged balloon near (but not touching) the top of an electroscope. Explain your prediction. Try it. Describe and explain your results. **Hint:** Electrons move within the metal.

Multicultural Connections

One rare but interesting type of lightning is ball lightning. Ball lightning is usually seen as a bright sphere 10 to 20 centimeters in diameter. It may last for 5 seconds, although some lasts longer, and it moves horizontally a few centimeters above the ground. This effect was investigated by Russian physicist, Pyotr Kapitza, who hoped to use the principles involved to contain a nuclear fusion reaction. Kapitza's theory was that ball lightning was the result of naturally occurring electromagnetic standing waves that contain the plasma created by a bolt of lightning. Containment is a major problem in controlling fusion reactions. This theory might make available a new source of energy. Kapitza was committed to peaceful uses of nuclear energy to the point that he refused to work on nuclear weapons for Stalin. As a result, he was held under house arrest from 1946 until Stalin died in 1953. His theory about ball lightning remains unproven.

together. Each exerts forces on the other. If you bring a charged comb near the tape, the tape, with its small mass, moves readily. The acceleration of the comb and you is, of course, much less because of the much greater mass.

In the Coulomb's law equation, K is a constant that depends on the units used to measure charge, force, and distance. Experimental tests show that Coulomb's law works at all distances. It has even been found to be true for individual electrons separated by less than 10^{-18} m. This is a separation one ten-millionth as large as the size of the atom.

Each charged object exerts an equal but opposite force on the other charged object.

The Unit of Charge: The Coulomb

Coulomb showed that the quantity of charge could be related to force. Thus he could define a standard quantity of charge in terms of the amount of force it produces. The SI standard unit of charge is thus called the **coulomb**, C. One coulomb is the charge of 6.25×10^{18}

Physics and technology

THE PHOTOCOPIER

Forces on charged and uncharged bodies are important in photocopiers. A typical copier has a drum made of a conductor, aluminum, which is coated with a thin layer of the semiconductor selenium. In operation, the selenium layer is first charged by a spray of charged air molecules. In the dark, selenium is a poor conductor, and the charges remain in place. Light is reflected from the white parts of the page to be copied, passed through a lens, and focused on the drum. Where the light strikes the selenium, the semiconductor becomes a conductor, letting the charges flow away from the surface to the aluminum drum. However, where there was a dark area on the page, there will be a dark area on the drum, and the charge will remain on the selenium layer. The drum is then rotated through a container of toner. The toner consists of tiny charged plastic beads coated with carbon grains. The coated beads are attracted to the charged areas of the selenium layer on the drum but not to the areas where the charge has flowed away. A sheet of paper is then pressed against the drum and the coated beads are transferred to the paper. The paper is heated and the beads melt, attaching the carbon to the paper to form the image.

· Why does the photocopier drum need to be coated with a semiconductor rather than a conductor?

Physics and technology

If the drum were coated with a conducting material, the conducting layer would be unable to retain the applied charge. The charge would flow immediately to the conducting drum and would not be available at the surface to attract the carbon-coated plastic beads. In addition, a conductor would not be responsive to the light reflected from the original document.

Color copying is a relatively new technology that continues to improve. The basic methods of producing color copies are electrophotography, photography, and thermal transfer.

The conventional electrophotographic process uses the typical electrostatic technology with a drum, toner, and plain paper. It uses several different colors of toner. A digital version of this process is used in color laser copiers. It permits extensive editing and manipulation of colors.

Photographic copiers use a conventional photographic process. They use photographic paper or transparencies. Although this process costs less than electrophotography and produces very high quality images, it is also slower.

The thermal transfer technology is the least expensive but is also relatively slow. It also requires special paper. The CX 5000 model from Sharp uses a multicolored ribbon as the color source.

Teacher Resources: Santosus, Cathleen. "Color Copiers: Three Basic Technologies to Choose From." *The Office.* July 1988, pages 51–52, 70.
Vogel, Todd. "At Xerox, They're Shouting 'Once More into the Breach'." *Business Week.* July 23, 1990, pages 62–63.

CONCEPT DEVELOPMENT

Demonstration: Balance a long (6–8 ft) 2 × 4 on a good bearing, such as a watch glass. By holding charged rods near ends of the 2 × 4, you will attract the wood and make it rotate. This is caused by a temporary charge separation induced in the wood.

Critical Thinking: Ask students if they can develop a theory about why TV screens seem to get dusty much faster than most other surfaces. [When the TV is turned on, the inside surface of the screen is suddenly given a strong positive charge to attract electrons. This produces a charge on the outside surface of the screen that slowly becomes neutralized by dust and other attracted sources of negative charge.]

Critical Thinking Master, Teacher Resource Package. You may wish to have students complete the Critical Thinking Master, Lightning, with this section.

FIGURE 20–11. When the force is positive, the like charges are repelled; when the force is negative, the unlike charges are attracted.

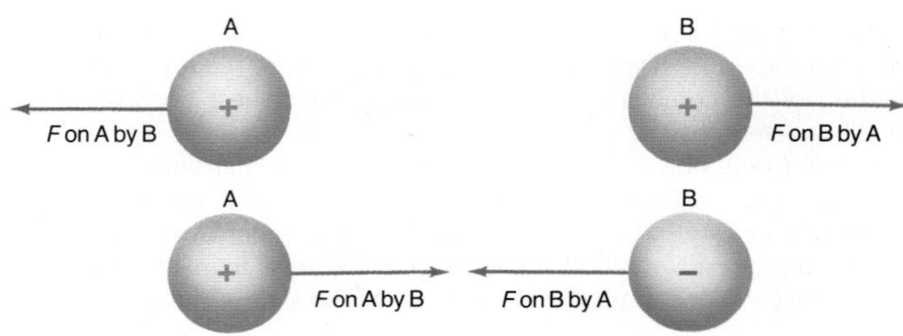

The coulomb is the SI unit charge.

electrons. The charge that produces a large lightning bolt is about 10 coulombs. The charge of an individual electron is only 1.60×10^{-19} C. The magnitude of the charge of an electron is called the **elementary charge**. Thus, as we will calculate in Problem 3 in the Chapter Review, even small pieces of matter, such as the coins in your pocket, contain up to one million coulombs of negative charge. This enormous amount of charge produces almost no external effects because it is balanced by an equal amount of positive charge. A charge even as small as 10^{-9} C can result in large forces.

A repulsive force has a positive sign.

According to Coulomb's law, the force on a body with charge q caused by a body with charge q' a distance d away can be written

$$F = \frac{Kqq'}{d^2}.$$

An attractive force has a negative sign.

When charges are measured in coulombs, the distance in meters, and the force in newtons, the constant K is $9.0 \times 10^9\ \mathrm{N \cdot m^2/C^2}$.

The electric force, like all other forces, is a vector quantity. Consider the direction of force on a positively-charged object called **A.** If another positively-charged object, **B,** is brought near, the force on **A** is repulsive. It is in the direction *from* **B** *to* **A,** Figure 20–11. The sign of the force is positive.

If, instead, **B** is negatively charged, the force on **A** is attractive. The force is in the opposite direction. The sign of the force is negative. Thus, it is important to include the positive or negative signs for q and q' when using Coulomb's law and to interpret the directions carefully.

HELP WANTED

TELECOMMUNICATIONS WORKER

Do you have vocational/technical school or military training with sophisticated, electronics/computer-based systems?

We want your ability to process numerous details from manuals and schematics, your mechanical skills, your ability to work with customers and co-workers, your knowledge of electronics and computers, and interest in on-going education. For information contact:

Communications Workers of America, 1925 K Street, NW, Washington, DC 20006

Example Problem

Coulomb's Law—Two Charges

Object **A** has a positive charge of 6.0×10^{-6} C. Object **B,** carrying a positive charge of 3.0×10^{-6} C, is 0.030 m away.

a. Calculate the force on **A.**

b. What would be the force if the charge on **B** were negative?

Given: $q = +6.0 \times 10^{-6}$ C
$q' = +3.0 \times 10^{-6}$ C
$d = 0.030$ m

Unknown: F_A

Basic equation: $F = \frac{Kqq'}{d^2}$

DEMONSTRATION

Purpose: to observe the attractive force between negatively and positively charged substances.

Equipment: ebonite rod, fur, running water

Procedure: 1. Adjust the water from the faucet so there is a fine steady stream. **2.** Charge the rod with fur and bring it close to the stream of water. Move the rod up and down.

Results: The stream of water bends toward the rod.

Questions: Why does the water bend? *The negative charge on the rod attracts the positive areas of the polar water molecules.*

Solution:

a. $F_A = \frac{Kqq'}{d^2}$

$= \frac{(9.0 \times 10^9 \text{ N} \cdot \text{m}^2/\text{C}^2)(+6.0 \times 10^{-6} \text{ C})(3.0 \times 10^{-6} \text{ C})}{(0.030 \text{ m})^2}$

$= \frac{(9.0 \times 10^9 \text{ N} \cdot \text{m}^2/\text{C}^2)(+18 \times 10^{-12} \text{ C}^2)}{9.0 \times 10^{-4} \text{ m}^2}$

$= +1.8 \times 10^2 \text{ N}$

The positive sign of the force indicates repulsion. The force on **A** is in the direction from **B** toward **A.**

b. If the second charge were negative, the sign of the force would be negative, in the opposite direction.

Example Problem

Coulomb's Law—Three Charges

An object, **A,** with $+6.0 \times 10^{-6}$ C charge, has two other charges nearby. Object **B,** -3.00×10^{-6} C, is 0.040 m to the right. Object **C,** $+1.5 \times 10^{-6}$ C, is 0.030 m below. What is the net force on **A?** Solve the problem graphically.

Solution:

Choose a coordinate system, with **A** at the origin, **B** on the positive x axis, **C** on the negative y axis. See Figure 20–12a. First the magnitude of the individual forces are calculated.

$F_B = \frac{Kqq'}{d^2}$

$= \frac{(9.0 \times 10^9 \text{ N} \cdot \text{m}^2/\text{C}^2)(+6.0 \times 10^{-6} \text{ C})(-3.0 \times 10^{-6} \text{ C})}{(4.0 \times 10^{-2} \text{ m})^2}$

$= -1.0 \times 10^2 \text{ N}$

Force F_B, is attractive, toward **B**, in the positive x direction.

$F_C = \frac{kqq'}{d^2}$

$= \frac{(9.0 \times 10^9 \text{ N} \cdot \text{m}^2/\text{C}^2)(+6.0 \times 10^{-6} \text{ C})(+1.5 \times 10^{-6} \text{ C})}{(3.0 \times 10^{-2} \text{ m})^2}$

$= +9.0 \times 10^1 \text{ N}$

Force F_C is repulsive, away from **C,** in the positive y direction.

Next, the forces are added vectorially to find the net force.
See the drawing.
We obtain

$F_{net} = 1.3 \times 10^2$ N at 42° above the x axis, Figure 20–12b.

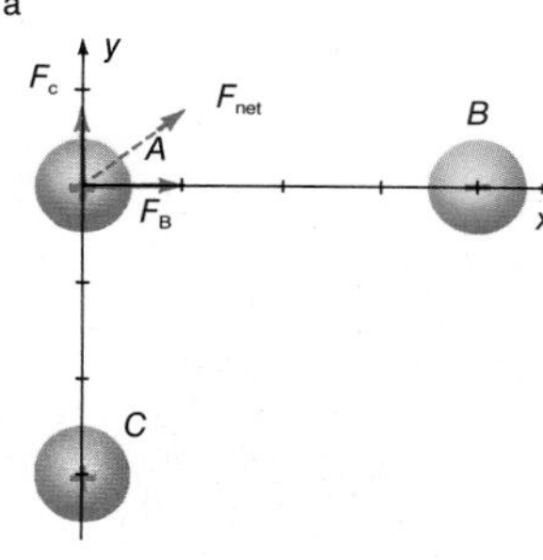

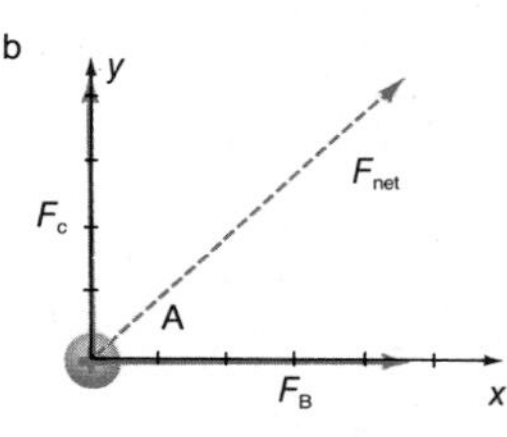

FIGURE 20–12. Example Problem set up is (a). graphical solution (b).

CONCEPT DEVELOPMENT

CHECKING FOR UNDERSTANDING

Ask students to describe the processes of charging by conduction and induction.

RETEACHING

Transparency Package. Reteach the concept of separation of charges using Transparency 28 and accompanying worksheet.

EXTENSION

Huge amounts of static electricity can be produced by Van de Graaff generators. Have interested students explore how these generators use static electricity to operate.

Guided Practice: Go over the Example Problems on page 418 and this page. Then have students work on the Practice Problems on page 420 and explain their answers in class.

INDEPENDENT PRACTICE/ EXTENSION

Refer to the Assignment Guide on page 420 for additional questions and problems for independent practice.

TEACHER F.Y.I.

Suppose you have three charges arranged as in the diagram. Find the net force on the 2.0×10^{-6}-C charge. Find each force individually and add them since they are both in the same direction.

+10.0 μC (q_1) — d_1 2.0 m — +2.0 μC (q_2) — d_2 4.0 m — −6.0 μC (q_3)

Force of repulsion between q_1 and q_2

$f_1 = \frac{Kq_1q_2}{d_1^2}$

$= \frac{(9.0 \times 10^9 \frac{\text{N}\cdot\text{m}^2}{\text{C}^2})(10.0 \times 10^{-6} \text{ C})(2.0 \times 10^{-6} \text{ C})}{(2.0 \text{ m})^2}$

$f_1 = 4.5 \times 10^{-2}$ N to the right

Force of attraction between q_2 and q_3

$F_2 = \frac{Kq_2q_3}{d_2^2}$

$= \frac{(9.0 \times 10^9 \frac{\text{N}\cdot\text{m}^2}{\text{C}^2})(2.0 \times 10^{-6} \text{ C})(6.0 \times 10^{-6} \text{ C})}{(4.0 \text{ m})^2}$

$F_2 = 6.8 \times 10^{-3}$ N to the right

Total force on q_2

$F_T = F_1 + F_2 = 5.2 \times 10^{-2}$ N to the right

Answers To
PRACTICE PROBLEMS

Have students refer to Appendix A of the Solutions Appendix for complete solutions to Practice Problems.

1. 1.3 N
2. -1.6×10^4 N
3. 3.0×10^{-6} C
4. Refer to Solutions Appendix.
5. Magnitudes of all forces remain the same. The direction changes to 42° above the $-x$-axis, or 138°.

3 Close

CONVERGENT QUESTION

Suppose the charges that move around easily in materials were positively charged. Ask students how this would change static electricity phenomena. [Virtually all static electricity phenomena would remain the same.]

CONCEPT REVIEW ANSWERS

2.1 The repulsive electrical force is balanced by the downward force of gravity on the leaves.

2.2 Drawings of each sphere must have a downward force (weight or force of gravity) and an upward force (normal force of surface) that are equal in length. Each must also have a horizontal force away from the other sphere. The two horizontal arrows are equal in length but opposite in direction. (Newton's third law)

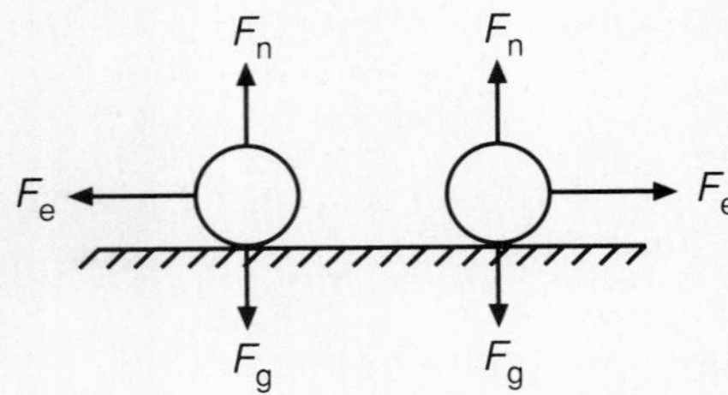

2.3 The balloon becomes charged by rubbing. It is attracted to the neutral wall because it separates the charges in the wall.

2.4 Critical Thinking: The charges on the large metal sphere are repelled and move away from the small sphere, reducing the force.

Practice Problems

1. Two positive charges of 6.0×10^{-6} C are separated by 0.50 m. What force exists between the charges?
2. A negative charge of -2.0×10^{-4} C and a positive charge of 8.0×10^{-4} C are separated by 0.30 m. What is the force between the two charges?
3. A negative charge of -6.0×10^{-6} C exerts an attractive force of 65 N on a second charge 0.050 m away. What is the magnitude of the second charge?
4. An object with charge $+7.5 \times 10^{-7}$ C is placed at the origin. The position of a second object, charge $+1.5 \times 10^{-7}$ C, is varied from 1.0 cm to 5.0 cm. Draw a graph of the force on the object at the origin.
5. ▶ The charge on **B** in the Example Problem is replaced by $+3.00 \times 10^{-6}$ C. Use graphical methods to find the net force on **A.**

Using Electric Forces on Neutral Bodies

As you have seen, a charged object may either attract or repel another charged object. A charged object, however, is always attracted by a neutral (uncharged) object. By Newton's third law, that neutral object must also be attracted toward the charged object. It doesn't matter whether the charge is positive or negative.

There are many applications of electric forces on neutral particles. These forces can collect soot in smokestacks, reducing air pollution, Figure 20–10. Tiny paint droplets, charged by induction, can be used to paint automobiles and other objects very uniformly.

CONCEPT REVIEW

2.1 When an electroscope is charged, the leaves rise to a certain angle and remain at that angle. Why don't they rise farther?

2.2 Two charged spheres are on a frictionless horizontal surface. One has $+3 \times 10^{-6}$ C charge, the other $+6 \times 10^{-6}$ C charge. Sketch the two spheres, showing all forces on them. Make the length of your force arrows proportional to the strength of the forces.

2.3 Explain why a balloon that has been rubbed on a wool shirt sticks to the wall.

2.4 **Critical Thinking:** Suppose you are testing Coulomb's law using a small, charged plastic sphere and a large, charged metal sphere. Both are charged positively. According to Coulomb's law, the force depends on $1/d^2$, where d is the distance between the centers of the spheres. As the two spheres get close together, the force is smaller than expected from Coulomb's law. Explain.

CRITICAL THINKING

Use the Critical Thinking master for Chapter 20 with this section.

TRANSPARENCY

Use Transparency 27 with this section.

20:2 ASSIGNMENT GUIDE

	PRACTICE	EXTENSION
CHAPTER REVIEW pp. 421–423		
· Reviewing Concepts	7–8	
· Applying Concepts		5–15
· Problems*	1–13	14–19
APPENDIX B PROBLEMS*		
· Chapter 20, pp. 702–703	1–3, 5–12	4, 13, 14

* Complete solutions to all Chapter Review and Appendix problems appear in the Problems and Solutions Manual.

CHAPTER 20 REVIEW

SUMMARY

20.1 Electrical Charges

- There are two kinds of electrical charges, positive and negative. Electrons are a negative.
- Electrical charge is conserved; it cannot be created or destroyed.
- Bodies can be charged negatively or positively by transferring electrons. An object is charged negatively by adding electrons to it. An object is charged positively by removing electrons from it.
- Charges added to one part of an insulator remain on that part.
- Charges added to a conductor very quickly spread over the surface of the body. This is called electrical conduction.
- Charges exert forces on other charges. Like charges repel; unlike charges attract.

20.2 Electrical Forces

- An electroscope indicates electrical charge. In an electroscope, forces on charges cause thin metal leaves to spread.
- A charged rod can charge an electroscope by induction by causing a separation of charges.
- Coulomb's law states that *the force between two charged point objects varies directly with the product of the two charges and inversely with the square of the distance between them.*
- The unit of charge is the coulomb. One coulomb, C, is the magnitude of the charge of 6.25×10^{18} electrons or protons. The elementary charge, the charge of the proton or electron, is 1.60×10^{-19} C.
- A charged body of either sign can produce separation of charge in a neutral body. Thus a charged body attracts a neutral body.

KEY TERMS

electrostatics
neutral
insulators
conductors
electroscope
charging by conduction
charging by induction
Coulomb's law
coulomb
elementary charge

REVIEWING CONCEPTS

1. If you comb your hair on a dry day, the comb can become positively charged. Can your hair remain neutral? Explain.
2. The combined charge of all electrons in a nickel coin is hundreds of thousands of coulombs, a unit of electrical charge. Does that imply anything about the net charge on the coin? Explain.
3. List some insulators and conductors.
4. What property makes a metal a good conductor and rubber a good insulator?
5. Why does a woolen sock taken from a clothes dryer sometimes cling to other clothes?
6. If you wipe a stereo record with a clean cloth, why does the record now attract dust?
7. Name three methods to charge an object.
8. Explain how to charge a conductor negatively if you have only a positively-charged rod.

APPLYING CONCEPTS

1. How does the charge of an electron differ from the charge of a proton?
2. If you scuff electrons from your feet while walking across a rug, are you now negatively charged or positively charged?
3. Using a charged rod and an electroscope, how can you find if an object is a conductor?
4. Explain why an insulator that is charged can be discharged by passing it above a flame.
5. A charged rod is brought near a pile of tiny plastic spheres. Some of the spheres are attracted to the rod, but as soon as they touch the rod, they fly away in different directions. Explain.
6. A rod-shaped insulator is suspended so it can rotate. A negatively-charged comb held nearby attracts the rod.
   a. Does this mean the rod is positively charged? Explain.
   b. If the comb repelled the rod, what could you conclude, if anything, about the charge on the rod?

REVIEW MASTER

Use the Vocabulary Review master for Chapter 20 with this section.

EVALUATION MASTER

Use the Chapter Evaluation master for Chapter 20 with this section.

CLOSING CHAPTER 20

Review Summary statements and Key Terms with your students.

ASSESSMENT

Vocabulary Review Master, Teacher Resource Package. Use this master to check students' understanding of Key Terms.

Evaluation Masters. Use Parts A and B of the Chapter Evaluation Masters from the Teacher Resource Package to test qualitative chapter objectives. Use Parts C and D to test quantitative chapter objectives.

Answers To
REVIEWING CONCEPTS

1. No. By conservation of charge, your hair must become negatively charged.
2. No. Net charge is the difference between positive and negative charges. It can still be zero.
3. Student answers will vary, but may include dry air, wood, plastic, glass, cloth, and deionized water as insulators; and metals, tap water, and your body as conductors.
4. Metals contain free electrons; rubber has bound electrons.
5. It has been charged by the tumbling of the clothes and is attracted to the other clothing.
6. Rubbing the record charges it. Neutral particles such as dust are attracted to a charged object.
7. conduction, friction, induction
8. Without touching the conductor, bring it close to, but not touching, the rod. Momentarily touch the side of the conductor farthest from the rod. The conductor will be charged by induction.

Answers To
APPLYING CONCEPTS

1. The charge of the proton is exactly the same size as the electron, but has the opposite sign.
2. When you lose electrons, you become positively charged.
3. Use a known insulator to hold 406 one end of the object against the electroscope. Touch the other end with the charged rod. If the electroscope indicates a charge, the object is a conductor.

Answers continue on page 422.

Answers To

APPLYING CONCEPTS (cont)

4. The hot gases above the flame are a plasma, which acts as a conductor and pulls excess charges away from the insulator.

5. The neutral spheres are initially attracted to the charged rod and all acquire the same charge as the rod when they touch it. Subsequently, they are repelled from each other and from the rod.

6. a. No. Neutral objects are attracted by either charge. **b.** It must be negative. Neutrals are never repelled.

7. The charge in the cloud repels electrons on Earth, causing a charge separation by induction. The side of Earth closest to the cloud is positive, resulting in an attractive force.

8. a. The leaves will move farther apart. **b.** The leaves will droop slightly.

9. Similar: inverse-square dependence on distance, force proportional to product of two masses or two charges. Different: only one sign of mass, so gravitational force is always attractive, while there are two signs of charge, so electrical force is either attractive or repulsive.

10. After charging spheres **A** and **B** equally, sphere **B** is touched to two other equally sized balls that are touching each other. The charge on **B** will be divided equally among all three balls, leaving 1/3 the total charge on it.

11. To have the same force with 1/3 the charge, the distance would have to be decreased such that $d^2 = 1/3$, or 0.58 times as far apart.

12. $F \propto \frac{1}{d^2}$ and $F \propto 1/(1/4)^2$, so $F = 16$ times the original force.

13. The electrical force is much larger than the gravitational force. Of course, the units are different.

14. a. yes **b.** The drops will be positive by induction.

15. The metal ball is neutral initially. It is attracted toward the charged bell. When it hits, it becomes charged. The ball is now repelled. It is now attracted to the uncharged bell. It hits this bell, becomes discharged, and starts up the process again.

7. Lightning usually occurs when a negative charge in a cloud is transported to Earth. If Earth is neutral, what provides the attractive force that pulls the electrons toward Earth?

8. Explain what happens to the leaves of a positively-charged electroscope when rods with the following charges are nearby but not touching the electroscope.
a. positive **b.** negative

9. Coulomb's law and Newton's law of universal gravitation appear similar. In what ways are the electrical and gravitational forces similar? How are they different?

10. The text describes Coulomb's method for obtaining two charged spheres, **A** and **B,** so that the charge on **B** was exactly half the charge on **A.** Suggest a way Coulomb could have placed a charge on sphere **B** that was exactly one third the charge on sphere **A.**

11. Coulomb measured the deflection of sphere **A** when **A** and **B** had equal charges and were a distance *d* apart. He then made the charge on **B** one third the charge on **A.** How far apart would the two spheres have to be now for **A** to have the same deflection it had before?

12. Two charged bodies exert a force of 0.145 N on each other. If they are now moved so they are one fourth as far apart, what force is exerted?

13. The constant *K* in Coulomb's equation is much larger than the constant *G* in the Universal Gravitation equation. Of what significance is this?

14. Salt water drips slowly from a narrow dropper inside a negatively-charged metal ring, as seen in Figure 20–13.
a. Will the drops be charged?
b. If they are charged, are they positive or negative?

FIGURE 20–13. Use with Applying Concepts 14.

15. Benjamin Franklin once wrote that he had "erected an iron rod to draw the lightning down into my house, in order to make some experiment on it, with two bells to give notice when the rod should be electrify'd...." The chime had two small bells mounted side by side. One bell was connected to the iron rod for a charge; the other bell was attached to Earth. Between the two bells, a small metal ball was suspended on a silk thread so it could swing back and forth, striking the two bells. Explain why, when the one bell was charged, the ball would keep swinging, hitting first one bell then the other.

PROBLEMS

20.2 Electrical Forces

1. Two charges, q_1 and q_2, are separated by a distance, *d,* and exert a force, *F,* on each other. What new force will exist if
a. q_1 is doubled?
b. q_1 and q_2 are cut in half?
c. *d* is tripled?
d. *d* is cut in half?
e. q_1 is tripled and *d* is doubled?

2. How many excess electrons are on a ball with a charge of -4.00×10^{-17} C?

3. How many coulombs of charge are on the electrons in a nickel coin? Follow this method to find the answer.
a. Find the number of atoms in a nickel coin. A nickel coin has a mass of about 5 g. Each mole (6.02×10^{23} atoms) has a mass of about 58 g.
b. Find the number of electrons in the coin. Each nickel atom has 28 electrons.
c. Find how many coulombs of charge are on the electrons.

4. A strong lightning bolt transfers about 25 C to Earth.
a. How many electrons are transferred?
b. If each water molecule donates one electron, what mass of water lost an electron to the lightning? One mole of water has a mass of 18 g.

5. What is the total charge on all of the electrons in one liter, 1.0 kg, of water? One mole of water has a mass of 18 g and each molecule of water contains 10 electrons.
6. Two electrons in an atom are separated by 1.5×10^{-10} m, the typical size of an atom. What is the force between them?
7. Object **A** has a charge $+1.8 \times 10^{-6}$ C. Object **B** has a charge -1.0×10^{-6} C. They are 0.014 m apart. What is the force on **A**? on **B**?
8. A positive and a negative charge, each of magnitude 1.5×10^{-5} C, are separated by a distance of 15 cm. Find the force on each of the particles.
9. Two negatively-charged bodies with -5.0×10^{-5} C are 0.20 m from each other. What force acts on each particle?
10. Two negative charges of -3.0×10^{-6} C exert a repulsive force of 2.0 N on each other. By what distance are they separated?
11. How far apart are two electrons if they exert a force of repulsion of 1.0 N on each other?
12. A force of -4.4×10^{3} N exists between a positive charge of 8.0×10^{-4} C and a negative charge of -3.0×10^{-4} C. What distance separates the charges?
13. Two identical positive charges exert a repulsive force of 6.4×10^{-9} N when separated by a distance of 3.8×10^{-10} m. Calculate the charge of each.
▶ 14. The hydrogen atom contains a proton, mass 1.67×10^{-27} kg, and an electron, mass 9.11×10^{-31} kg. The average distance between them is 5.3×10^{-11} m. The charge of the proton is the same size, opposite sign of an electron.
   a. What is the magnitude of the average electrostatic attraction between them?
   b. What is the magnitude of the average gravitational attraction between them?
   c. How do the magnitudes of the two forces compare?
▶ 15. A positive charge of 3.0×10^{-6} C is pulled on by two negative charges. One, -2.0×10^{-6} C, is 0.050 m to the north and the other, -4.0×10^{-6} C, is 0.030 m to the south. What total force is exerted on the positive charge?
▶ 16. Three particles are placed in a line. The left particle has a charge of -67×10^{-6} C, the middle, $+45 \times 10^{-6}$ C, and the right, -83×10^{-6} C. The middle particle is 72 cm from each of the others.
   a. Find the net force on the middle particle.
   b. Find the net force on the right particle.
▶ 17. Charges of 4.5×10^{-6} C exist on the three spheres in Figure 20–12. Find the magnitude of the total force on sphere B.
▶ 18. Two charges, q_1 and q_2, are at rest near a positive test charge, q, of 7.2×10^{-6} C. The first charge, q_1, is a positive charge of 3.6×10^{-6} C, located 0.025 m away from q at 35°; q_2 is a negative charge of -6.6×10^{-6} C, located 0.068 m away at 125°.
   a. Determine the magnitude of each of the forces acting on q.
   b. Sketch a force diagram.
   c. Graphically determine the resultant force acting on q.
▶ 19. The two pith balls in Figure 20–14 each have a mass of 1.0 g and equal charges. One pith ball is suspended by an insulating thread. The other is brought to 3.0 cm from the suspended ball. The suspended ball is now hanging with the thread forming an angle of 30.0° with the vertical. The ball is in equilibrium with F_E, mg, and T adding vectorially to yield zero. Calculate
   a. mg. **b.** F_E.
   c. the charge on the balls.

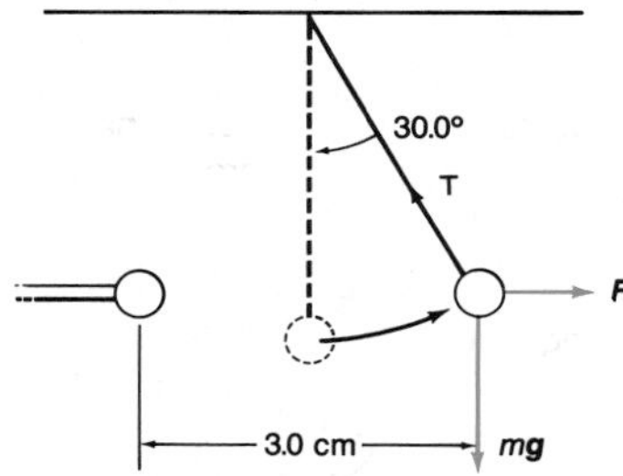

FIGURE 20–14. Use with Problem 19.

THINKING PHYSIC-LY

Electric forces between charges are enormous in comparison to gravitational forces. Yet, we normally do not sense electrical forces between us and our surroundings, while we do sense gravitational interreactions with Earth. Explain.

Answers To
PROBLEMS

Complete solutions for all Chapter Review Problems can be found in the Problems and Solutions Manual accompanying this text.

1. **a.** $2f$
   b. $\frac{1}{4}f$
   c. $\frac{1}{9}f$
   d. $4f$
   e. $\frac{3}{4}f$
2. 250 electrons
3. **a.** 5×10^{22} atoms
   b. 10^{24} electrons
   c. -2×10^{5} coulombs
4. **a.** 1.6×10^{20} electrons
   b. 4.8×10^{-3} g
5. -5.4×10^{7} C
6. 1.0×10^{-8} N
7. 83 N toward **B**; 83 N toward **A**
8. 90 N, toward the other charge
9. 5.6×10^{2} N
10. 0.20 m
11. 1.5×10^{-14} m
12. 0.70 m
13. 3.2×10^{-19} C
14. **a.** 8.2×10^{-8} N
    b. 3.6×10^{-47} N
    c. Gravitational force is weaker.
15. -98 N, south
16. **a.** 13 N, right
    b. 41 N, left
17. 1.8×10^{2} N at 76°, down from horizontal
18. **a.** 3.7×10^{2} N, away; 92 N, toward
    b., c. Refer to Problems and Solutions Manual for diagram.
19. **a.** 9.8×10^{-3} N
    b. 5.7×10^{-3} N
    c. 2.4×10^{-8} C

Answer To
THINKING PHYSIC-LY

Gravitational forces can only be attractive. Electrical forces can be either attractive or repulsive and we can only sense their vector sum, which is generally very small.

CHAPTER

21 Electric Fields

PLANNING GUIDE (6 class sessions)

CONTENTS	TEXT FEATURES	TEACHER RESOURCE PACKAGE	OTHER COMPONENTS
21.1 Creating and Measuring Electric Fields, pp. 426–431 (2 Class Sessions) • The Electric Field • Picturing the Electric Field	**Physics Lab:** Charges, Energy, Voltage, p. 430 **Pocket Lab:** Electric Fields, p. 426 **Concept Review,** p. 431	**Study Guide:** Creating and Measuring Electric Fields **Physics Lab Data Sheet:** Charges, Energy, Voltage **Reteaching Master:** Shielding an Electric Field	
21.2 Applications of the Electric Field, pp. 431–442 (4 Class Sessions) • Energy and the Electric Potential • The Electric Potential in a Uniform Field • Millikan's Oil Drop Experiment • Sharing of Charge • Electric Fields Near Conductors • Storing Electric Energy—The Capacitor	**Physics and Society:** Minimotors, p. 435 **Pocket Lab:** Unit Charge, p. 436 **Concept Review,** p. 442	**Study Guide:** Applications of the Electric Field **Enrichment Master:** The Capacitor **Critical Thinking Master:** A Jarful of Charge **Transparency Worksheet:** Millikan Apparatus **Transparency Worksheet:** Sharing Charges	**Laboratory Manual:** Lab 21.1 The Capacitor **Transparency 29:** Millikan Apparatus **Transparency 30:** Sharing Charges
Chapter Review, pp. 443–445	Summary Key Terms Reviewing Concepts Applying Concepts Problems Thinking Physic-ly	**Vocabulary Review** **Chapter Test**	**Test Bank**

SUPPLEMENTARY MATERIALS

SOFTWARE	AUDIOVISUAL	BOOKS/MAGAZINES
Introduction to General Physics, Disk V: Electrical Charge and Direct Current, COMPress/Queue, Inc. (Apple II, IBM PC, Macintosh). *Electricity,* Cross, (Apple II, IBM PC).	Videos: *The Mechanical Universe: Gravity, Electricity, Magnetism* and *The Millikan Experiment,* Films Inc. *The Mechanical Universe and Beyond: The Electric Field* and *Potential and Capacitance,* Films Inc. Filmstrip: *Exploring Electricity,* Clearvue.	Andereck, Barbara S. "Using Contour Maps to Teach Electric Field and Potential." *The Physics Teacher,* October 1990. p. 499. Huff, G. Bradley. "Dissectible Leyden Jar." *The Physics Teacher,* May 1986, p. 292. Payne, Mark M. "Electric Fields and Football Fields." *The Physics Teacher,* November 1990, p. 563.

PROBLEM CORRELATION

CONCEPTS	CHAPTER REVIEW			PROBLEMS APPENDIX
	Reviewing Concepts	Applying Concepts	Problems	
21.1 Creating and Measuring Electric Fields				
The Electric Field	2,3	1	1,2,3,4,**5**,**6**,9	1,2,3,4,5
Picturing the Electric Field	1,4,5	3	7,8	6
21.2 Applications of the Electric Field				
Energy and the Electric Potential	6,7	2,4	10,11,12,13,**14**	7,8,**9**
The Electric Potential in a Uniform Field	8,9	5	15,16	10,11,12
Millikan's Oil Drop Experiment		6,7	17,**18**	**13**
Sharing of Charge	10,11	8		
Electric Fields Near Conductors	12			
Storing Electric Energy—The Capacitor	13	9,10	19,20,21,**22**,**23**,**24**	14,15,16

ACTIVITY AND DEMONSTRATION MATERIALS

PHYSICS LAB	POCKET LAB	DEMONSTRATIONS
Page 430 ball of clay ruler cellophane tape 12 3-mm diameter steel balls	Pages 426, 436 25-cm square piece of plastic foam drinking straw thread pith ball 3-mm diameter steel balls balance	Page 434 electrostatic generator Leyden jar

EXTENSION PROJECTS

LIBRARY RESEARCH

1. St. Elmo's Fire
Research St. Elmo's Fire. What causes it? When does it occur?

HANDS-ON

2. Cathode-Ray Tube
Take an old TV apart to examine the cathode-ray tube. Demonstrate how it works to the class.

STUDENT READINGS

Conway, John. "Personal Robots." *Computers and Electronics,* December 1984.

Freedman, David H. "Bolts from the Blue." *Discover,* December 1990.

Noland, D. "Power Play." *Discover,* December 1989.

Patterson, David A. "Microprogramming." *Scientific American,* March 1984.

Stewart, Doug. "New Machines Are Smaller Than a Hair, and Do Real Work." *Smithsonian,* October 1990.

Chapter 21

Electric Field

CHAPTER OVERVIEW

Theme Development: Symmetry and constancy are themes underlying the field concept, a conceptual model that is central to contemporary physics. Chapter 21 examines the electric field by introducing the field line concept. Diagrams of field lines show strong symmetry and support a mathematical understanding of the relationship between field, force, and charge.

MISCONCEPTIONS

The electric field concept seems very abstract to students. They tend to forget that the direction of the field is based on the convention of a *positive* test charge. They also tend to think field lines describe *paths.* Students try to make potential difference something existing at a single point rather than a condition between two points. They have difficulty remembering that field strength describes a *position,* whereas the force depends on the particle *placed* at that position.

KEY TERMS

capacitance
capacitor
electric field
electric field lines
electric potential difference
grounding
potential difference
volt

Laboratory Options

STUDENT EDITION

Physics Lab

Charges, Energy, Voltage	430

Pocket Labs

Electric Fields	426
Unit Charge	436

TEACHER EDITION

Activities

Cooperative Learning	429, 440
Discovery	433, 436
Demonstration	434, 434

LABORATORY MANUAL

The Capacitor	Lab 21.1

CHAPTER 21

Electric Fields

High Energy Halo

Research into ultra-high-voltage—up to two million volts—transmission of electricity is essential for development of future power technology. At a special test facility, this ultra-high-voltage test line demonstrates a man-made corona effect. Why is the corona visible around this power line when the effect is not seen in the electric wires in our homes?

The blue glow around the wires in the photo is a modern version of "St. Elmo's Fire." Sailors in the time of Columbus saw these ghostly-colored streamers issuing from their high ships' masts. They recognized them as warning signs of an approaching lightning storm. The glow is indeed related to lightning. The man-made "fire" in the photo is called a corona discharge. Besides causing the eery glow, it causes radio interference and can start a spark jumping from the wire to another conductor, so designers of these experimental power lines try to reduce or eliminate it entirely.

Chapter Outline

Concept Check

The following terms or concepts from earlier chapters are important for a good understanding of this chapter. If you are not familiar with them, you should review them before studying this chapter.

- gravitational field, Chapter 8
- gravitational potential energy, Chapter 11
- electrical interactions, Coulomb's law, Chapter 20

Introducing The Chapter

High Energy Halo

Using The Photo: This corona effect can be observed in some natural atmospheric phenomena, such as ball lightning and St. Elmo's fire. The blue glow is caused by a very strong electric field ionizing air molecules. Ask students if they have seen sparks with a similar blue color. For a more detailed explanation of the chapter opener question, refer students to page 440.

Concept Check

Make sure students have a clear understanding of the concepts taught in Chapters 8, 11, and 20 that are listed in the Concept Check. Students who have a good knowledge of gravitational fields, potential energy, electrical interactions, and Coulomb's law will be prepared to study the principles of electric fields presented in this chapter.

Assessment Options

Portfolio Assessment
Extension 1, TWE, p. 424b
Enrichment, TWE, p. 427
Portfolio Assessment, TWE, p. 432
Developing a Viewpoint, p. 435
Enrichment, TWE, p. 438

Performance Assessment
Extension 2, TWE, p. 424b
Pocket Labs, pp. 426, 436
Physics Lab, p. 430
Pocket Lab Assessment, p. 426

Content Assessment
Self Assessment: Practice Problems, pp. 427, 434, 437
Critical Thinking, TWE, p. 428
Assessment, Critical Thinking, TWE, p. 430
Cooperative Learning, TWE, p. 440
Concept Reviews, pp. 431, 442
Chapter Review, pp. 443–445
Supplemental Problems, p. 703

Group Assessment
Activities for group assessment occur with Cooperative Learning and lab activities.

21.1 CREATING AND MEASURING ELECTRIC FIELDS

Preparation

OBJECTIVES

The objectives are listed on the student page. Remind students to preview these objectives.

OVERVIEW

The concept of the electric field is illustrated by electric field lines.

BRIDGING

Previously discussed concepts important to this section include gravitational force, charge, Coulomb's law, tangent line, and ratio.

1 Focus

DISCREPANT EVENT

Place an empty coffee can on an insulating platform and charge it. Touch a transfer disk to the inside of the can and then to an electroscope. The leaves will remain limp. Repeat, this time touching the outside of the can. The leaves will diverge, indicating that the charge is on the outside of the can.

POCKET LAB

ELECTRIC FIELDS

Purpose: to observe the effects of an electric field.
Materials: 25-cm square piece of plasticfoam; drinking straw; thread; pith ball.
Outcome: The pith ball will hang vertically with no electric field. As field strength increases, the ball will hang at an angle. The field is strongest near the center of the foam, and the field gets stronger as the distance separating the foam and the ball gets smaller.

Objectives

- define an electric field; explain how to measure it.
- distinguish between force and field.
- be able to solve problems relating field, force, and charge.
- distinguish between electric field and field lines.

21.1 CREATING AND MEASURING ELECTRIC FIELDS

The electric force, like the gravitational force, varies inversely as the square of the distance between two objects. Both forces can act at a great distance. How can a force be exerted across what seems to be empty space? In trying to understand the electric force, Michael Faraday (1791–1867) developed the concept of an electric field. According to Faraday, a charge creates an electric field about it in all directions. If a second charge is placed at some point in the field, the second charge interacts with the field at that point. The force it feels is the result of a local interaction. Interaction between particles separated by some distance is no longer required.

Charge and Field Conventions

- *Positive charges are red.*
- *Negative charges are blue.*
- ***Electric fields are red.***

The Electric Field

It is easy to state that a charge produces an electric field. But how can the field be detected and measured? We will describe a method that can be used to measure the field produced by an electric charge q.

You must measure the field at a specific location, for example, point **A.** An electrical field can be observed only because it produces forces on other charges, so a small positive test charge is placed at **A.** The force exerted on the test charge, q', at this location is measured. According to Coulomb's law, the force is proportional to the test charge. If the size of the charge is doubled, the force is doubled. Thus, the ratio of force to charge is independent of the size of the charge. If we divide the magnitude of the force, F, on the test charge, measured at point **A,** by the size of the test charge, q', we obtain a vector quantity, F/q'. This quantity does not depend on the test charge, only on the charge q and the location of point **A.** We call this vector quantity the magnitude of the **electric field**. The electric field at point **A,** the location of q', is

$$E = \frac{F_{\text{on } q'}}{q'}.$$

The direction of the electric field is the direction of the force on the positive test charge. The magnitude of the electric field intensity is measured in newtons per coulomb, N/C.

Notice that just as the electric field is the force per unit charge, the gravitational field is the force per unit mass, $g = F/m$.

We said that an electric field should be measured by a small test charge. Why? The test charge exerts a force on q. We want to make sure the force exerted by the test charge doesn't move q to another location, and thus change the force on q' and the electric field we are measuring.

So far we have found the field at a single point. The test charge is now moved to another location. The force on it is measured again and the electric field at that location calculated. This process is repeated again and again until every location in space has a measurement of the vector quantity, the electric field, on the test charge associated with it.

POCKET LAB

ELECTRIC FIELDS

Use a 5-cm long thread to hang a pith ball (or small plasticfoam ball) from the end of a dangling straw. Rub a 25-cm square piece of plasticfoam with fur to put a large negative charge on the foam. Stand the foam in a vertical orientation. Give the pith ball a positive test charge (use the fur). Notice that the pith ball hangs straight down until you bring it toward the charged foam. The pith ball is now in an electric field. How does the pith ball indicate the "strength" of the field? Move the test charge (pith ball) to investigate the electric field around the foam. Record your results.

Assessment

Performance

To further assess students' understanding of electric fields, have them use pith balls to explore the electric field around objects with different shapes. Hang a metal sphere on an insulating thread and touch it to the charged plasticfoam. When tested with a pith ball, students should find that the pith ball is repelled by the sphere equally in all directions. Then hang a metal rod from the thread and touch it to the charged plasticfoam. The pith ball should be repelled equally along its entire length, from both left and right, top and bottom.

Example Problem

Calculating the Magnitude of the Electric Field

A positive test charge of 4.0×10^{-5} C is placed in an electric field. The force on it is 0.60 N acting at 10°. What is the magnitude and direction of the electric field at the location of the test charge?

Given: size of test charge, $q' = 4.0 \times 10^{-5}$ C; force on test charge, $F = 0.60$ N at 10°

Unknown: electric field, E

Basic equation: $E = \frac{F}{q'}$

Solution:

Find the size of the field intensity.

$$E = \frac{F}{q'} = \frac{0.60\ \text{N}}{4.0 \times 10^{-5}\ \text{C}} = 1.5 \times 10^4\ \text{N/C}$$

The field direction is in the direction of the force since it is a positive test charge, so

$E = 1.5 \times 10^4$ N/C at 10°.

If the force were in the opposite direction, the field at the test charge would also be in the opposite direction, that is, $E = 1.5 \times 10^4$ N/C at 10° + 180° = 190°.

F.Y.I.

Robert Van de Graaff devised the high-voltage electrostatic generator in the 1930s. These generators can build up giant potentials that can accelerate particles to high energies.

Practice Problems

1. A negative charge of 2.0×10^{-8} C experiences a force of 0.060 N to the right in an electric field. What is the field magnitude and direction?
2. A positive test charge of 5.0×10^{-4} C is in an electric field that exerts a force of 2.5×10^{-4} N on it. What is the magnitude of the electric field at the location of the test charge?
3. Suppose the electric field in Practice Problem 2 were caused by a point charge. The test charge is moved to a distance twice as far from the charge. What is the magnitude of the force that the field exerts on the test charge now?
4. ▶ You are probing the field of a charge of unknown magnitude and sign. You first map the field with a 1.0×10^{-6} C test charge, then repeat your work with a 2.0×10^{-6} C charge.
   a. Would you measure the same forces with the two test charges? Explain.
   b. Would you find the same fields? Explain.

The collection of all the force vectors on the test charge is called an electric field. Any charge placed in an electric field experiences a force on it due to the electric field at that location. The strength of the force depends on the magnitude of the field, E, and the size of the charge, q. Thus $F = Eq$. The direction of the force depends on the direction of the field and the sign of the charge.

The total electric field is the vector sum of the fields of individual charges.

2 Teach

CONCEPT DEVELOPMENT

- Because the concept of electric fields is so abstract, use as many demonstrations as possible to help students internalize the concept.
- Emphasize the analogy between the electric field and the gravitational field. The gravitational field is the force per unit mass, $g = F/m$. The electric field intensity is the force per unit charge, $E = F/q$.
- Point out that electric field intensity does not depend on the particular value of the test charge. Rather, it is an intrinsic property like density and temperature.

Enrichment: It has been suggested recently by biological scientists that sharks are equipped with electrosensory organs that allow them to navigate and locate prey by sensing electric fields. Perhaps a student will want to investigate this subject.

Study Guide Master. To reinforce the concepts in this section, have the students complete the Study Guide Master for Section 21.1 from the Teacher Resource Package.

Guided Practice: Go over the Example Problem on this page, then have students work on the first two Practice Problems.

Independent Practice: Assign the remaining Practice Problems for homework and spend time reviewing them with students during the next class period.

Answers To
PRACTICE PROBLEMS

Have students refer to Appendix A of the Solutions Appendix for complete solutions to Practice Problems.

1. 3.0×10^6 N/C, directed to the left.
2. 0.50 N/C
3. 6.3×10^{-5} N
4. **a.** No. Force will double.
   b. Yes, since $E = \frac{F}{q'}$.

CONCEPT DEVELOPMENT

- Go over Table 21–1, pointing out the wide range of values for rather ordinary situations. Familiarity with these numbers will help students attach more meaning to the field concept.
- There is an electric field at the surface of Earth of about 150 N/C. Its direction is downward. Ask students what this means about how Earth is charged. [Earth must be charged negatively.]
- The concept of the electric field allows the derivation of a vector quantity that measures the electric force on objects. This measure is independent of the detecting device, that is, the size of the test charge. Body geometry refers to the size and shape of the object in question.
- Remember to point out that the definition of the direction of the electric field depends on always using a *positive* test charge.

Critical Thinking: Ask students if there is a limit to how strong an electric field could be. Suggest that they consider how a field is produced and its effects. [There is a limit because the production of a field depends on a collection of charges. After reaching a certain density, these charges would begin to repel each other to such an extent that sparks or corona discharge would occur, or air molecules in the electric field would rip apart.]

FIGURE 21–1. An electric field can be shown by using arrows to represent the direction of the field at various locations.

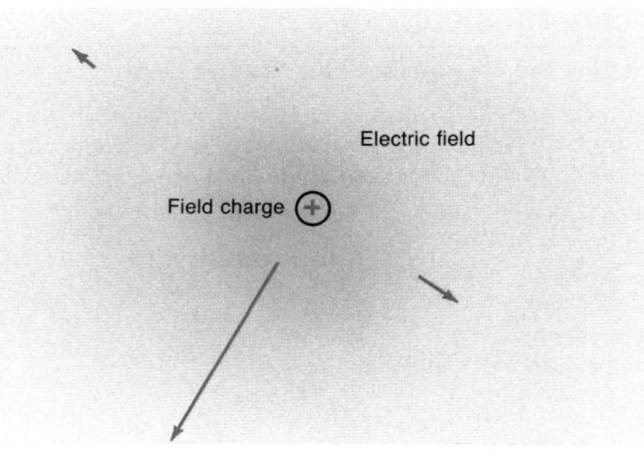

A picture of an electric field can be made by using arrows to represent the field vectors at various locations, Figure 21–1. The length of the arrow shows the magnitude of the field; the direction of the arrow shows its direction.

To find the field from two charges, the fields from the individual charges can be added vectorially. Or, a test charge can be used to map out the field due to any collection of charges. Typical electric fields produced by charge collections are shown in Table 21–1.

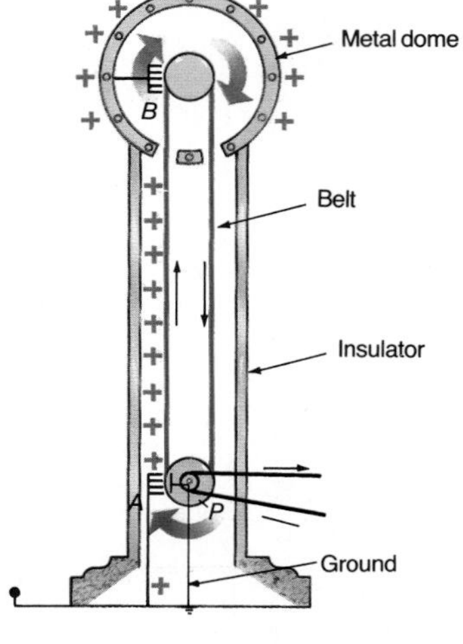

FIGURE 21–2. Charge is transferred onto a moving belt at A, and from the belt to the metal dome at B. An electric motor does the work needed to increase the electric potential energy.

Picturing the Electric Field

An alternative picture of an electric field is shown in Figure 21–3. The lines are called **electric field lines**. The direction of the field at any point is the tangent drawn to the field line at that point. The strength of the electric field is indicated by the spacing between the lines. The field is strong where the lines are close together. It is weaker where the lines are spaced farther apart. Remember that electric fields exist in three dimensions. Our drawings are only two-dimensional models.

The direction of the force on the positive test charge near a positive charge is away from the charge. Thus, the field lines extend radially outward like the spokes of a wheel, Figure 21–3a. Near a negative charge the direction of the force on the positive test charge is toward the charge, so the field lines point radially inward, Figure 21–3b.

Table 21–1

Approximate Values of Typical Electric Fields

Field	Value (N/C)
Near charged hard rubber rod	1×10^3
In television picture tube	1×10^5
Needed to create spark in air	3×10^6
At electron orbit in hydrogen atom	5×10^{11}

TEACHER F.Y.I.

Using K, the constant from Coulomb's law, it is possible to take the electric field for a point charge equation a step further:

$$E = \frac{F}{q'} = \frac{\frac{K \cdot q \cdot q'}{d^2}}{q'} = \frac{Kq}{d^2}.$$

a

b

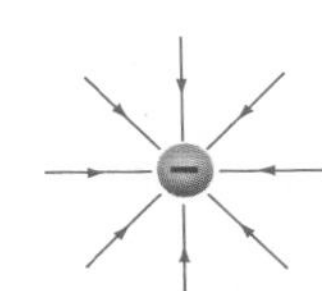

c

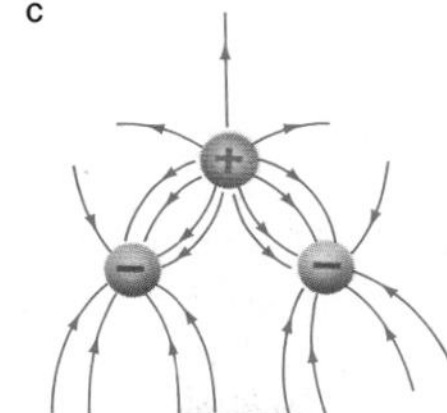

FIGURE 21–3. Lines of force are drawn perpendicularly away from the positive object (a) and perpendicularly into the negative object (b). Electric field lines between like- and oppositely-charged objects are shown in (c).

When there are two or more charges, the field is the vector sum of the fields due to the individual charges. The field lines become curved and the pattern complex, Figure 21–3c. Note that field lines always leave a positive charge and enter a negative charge.

An electric field points away from positive charges and toward negative charges.

The Van de Graaff machine is a device that transfers large amounts of charge from one part of the machine to the top metal terminal Figure 21–2. A person touching the terminal is charged electrically. The charges on the person's hairs repel each other, causing the hairs to follow the field lines. Another method of visualizing field lines is to use grass seed in an insulating liquid such as mineral oil. The electric forces cause a separation of charge in each long, thin grass seed. The seeds then turn so they line up along the direction of the electric field. Therefore, the seeds form a pattern of the electric field lines. The patterns in Figure 21–4 were made this way.

Field lines do not really exist. They are just a means of providing a model of an electric field. Electric fields, on the other hand, do exist. An electric field is produced by one or more charges and is independent of the existence of the test charge that is used to measure it. The field provides a method of calculating the force on a charged body. It does not explain, however, why charged bodies exert forces on each other. That question is still unanswered.

Electric fields are real. Electric field lines are imaginary, but help in making a picture of the field.

a

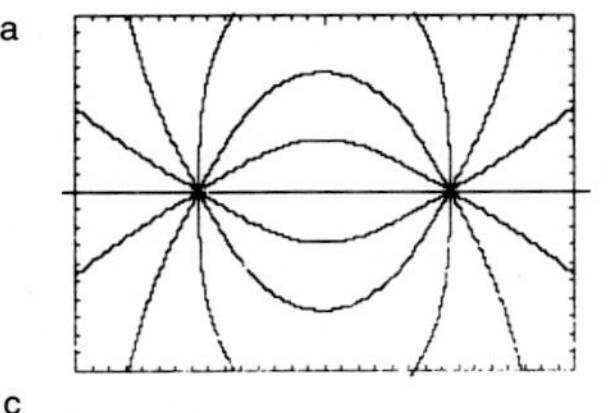

b

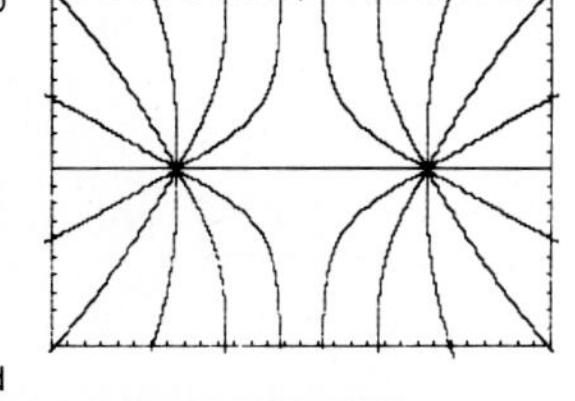

c

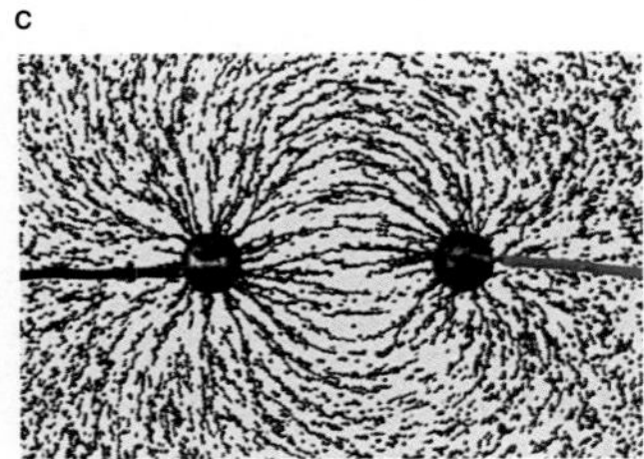

d

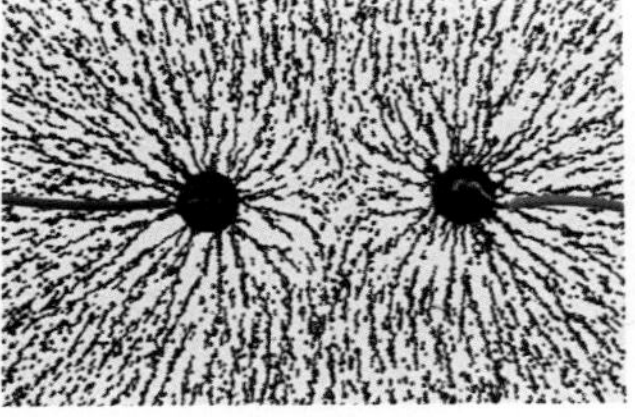

FIGURE 21–4. Lines of force between unlike charges (a, c) and between like charges (b, d) describe the behavior of a positively-charged object in a field. The top photographs are computer tracings of electric field lines.

CONCEPT DEVELOPMENT

The chapter's visual representations of electric fields are two-dimensional. Use toothpicks, modeling clay, and other suitable materials to model electric fields in three dimensions in order to help make the concept more concrete to students.

ACTIVITY

Cooperative Learning: Have students work together in groups to come up with the reason why the electric field between oppositely charged parallel plates is not uniform at the ends of the plates.

CHECKING FOR UNDERSTANDING

Suppose there are two oppositely charged, parallel metal plates. Have students use the idea of the test charge to figure out the electric field between plates.

RETEACHING

Review the concept of a gravitational field. Make sure that students can work with examples including details of energy at different places in the field. Building on this knowledge, reiterate the same point using an analogy between gravitational and electric fields.

Reteaching Master, Teacher Resource Package. Use the Reteaching Master, Shielding an Electric Field, for Chapter 21.

INDEPENDENT PRACTICE/ EXTENSION

Refer to the Assignment Guide below for additional questions and problems for independent practice.

21:1 ASSIGNMENT GUIDE

	PRACTICE	EXTENSION
CHAPTER REVIEW pp. 443–445		
· Reviewing Concepts	1–5	1, 3
· Applying Concepts		
· Problems*	1–4, 7–9	5, 6
APPENDIX B PROBLEMS*		
· Chapter 21, p. 703	1–6	

* Complete solutions to all Chapter Review and Appendix problems appear in the Problems and Solutions Manual.

STUDY GUIDE MASTER

Use the Study Guide master for section 21.1.

RETEACHING MASTER

Use the Reteaching master for Chapter 21 with this section.

PHYSICS LAB

Process Skills: observing, formulating models, questioning, communicating, hypothesizing, defining operationally.

MISCONCEPTIONS

Many students will confuse the abstract concepts of charge, energy, and voltage (potential difference). Students will tend to use the terms *energy* and *voltage* interchangeably.

Lab Worksheet, Teacher Resource Package. Use the lab worksheet master provided for this chapter for students to record their data.

OBSERVATIONS

1. The steel balls on the tabletop are at zero energy level. This is the 0″ on the ruler.
2. and 3. Data:

Charges (C)	Voltage (J/C)	Energy (J)
4	3	12
3	6	18
2	9	18
1	12	12

ANALYSIS

1. Each coulomb of charge requires 9 J to lift it to the 9-V level.
2. Each coulomb of charge has 9 J of potential energy. The total energy stored at the 9-V level is 2 × 9 J = 18 J.
3. The energy at the 6-V level is 3 C × 6 J/C = 18 J.
4. The change in energy would be 2 C × −3 J/C = −6 J.

APPLICATIONS

It takes energy to start the car. The energy is the voltage times the number of charges with stored energy. The amount of charge stored in one or even two 9-V batteries is too small. The 12-V car battery has considerably more charges and therefore a lot more stored energy.

LAB WORKSHEET

Use the Lab Worksheet for Chapter 21 with this Physics Lab.

PHYSICS LAB: Charges, Energy, Voltage

Purpose

To make a model that demonstrates the relationship of charge, energy, and voltage.

Materials

- ball of clay
- ruler
- cellophane tape
- 12 of 3-mm diameter steel balls

Procedure

1. Use the clay to support the ruler vertically on the tabletop. (The 0″ end should be at the table.)
2. Cut a 2 cm × 8 cm rectangular piece of paper and write on it "3 V = 3 J/C".
3. Cut three more rectangles and label them: 6 V = 6 J/C, 9 V = 9 J/C, 12 V = 12 J/C.
4. Tape the 3-V rectangle to the 3″ mark on the ruler, the 6-V to the 6″ mark, and so on.
5. Let each steel ball represent 1 C of charge.
6. Lift and tape 4 steel balls to the 3-V rectangle, 3 to the 6-V rectangle, and so on.

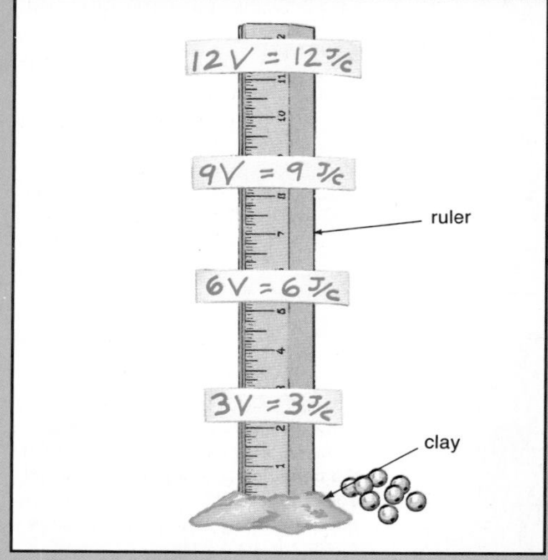

Observations and Data

1. The model shows different amounts of charges at different energy levels. Where should steel balls be placed to show a zero energy level? Explain.
2. Make a data table with the columns labeled "charge", "voltage", and "energy".
3. Fill in the data table for your model for each level of the model.

Analysis

1. How much energy is required to lift each coulomb of charge from the tabletop to the 9-V level?
2. What is the total potential energy stored in the 9-V level?
3. The total energy of the charges in the 6-V level is not 6 J. Explain this.
4. How much energy would be given off if the charges in the 9-V level fell to the 6-V level? Explain.

Applications

1. A 9-V battery is very small. A 12-V car battery is very big. Use your model to help explain why two 9-V batteries would not start your car.

ASSESSMENT

Critical Thinking: To further assess students' ability to distinguish among charge, voltage, and energy, ask the following questions.

1. Estimate the largest voltage and charge that you could use in this model. Explain your answer. [If students use the scale 1 in = 1 V, the highest voltage would be 12 V. If they use 1 cm = 1 V, then the highest voltage could be 30 V. The largest number of charges at any level would probably be about 10 coulombs (balls) before the tape came loose.]

2. Your model showed that charges were stored at various voltages. Is this similar to what happens in a 1.5 V dry cell? [No. The charges stored in the real 1.5 V cell are all at the same level (1.5 J/C).]

CONCEPT REVIEW

1.1 Suppose you are asked to measure the electric field in space. Answer the questions of this step-by-step procedure.
a. How do you detect the field at a point?
b. How do you determine the magnitude of the field?
c. How do you choose the size of the test charge?
d. What do you do next?

1.2 Suppose you are given an electric field, but the charges that produce the field are hidden. If all the field lines point into the hidden region, what can you say about the sign of the charge in that region?

1.3 How does the electric field, E, differ from the force, F, on the test charge?

1.4 Critical Thinking: Figure 21–4b shows the field from two like charges. The top positive charge in Figure 21–3c could be considered a test charge measuring the field due to the two negative charges. Is this positive charge small enough to produce an accurate measure of the field? Explain.

21.2 APPLICATIONS OF THE ELECTRIC FIELD

Objectives

- define the electric potential difference in terms of work done moving a unit test charge; distinguish potential from potential difference.
- know the units of potential; solve problems involving potential in uniform electric fields.
- understand how Millikan used electric fields to find the charge of the electron.
- understand how minimizing energy determines sharing of charge; define grounding and relate to charge sharing.
- know where charges reside on solid and hollow conductors; recognize the relationship between conductor shape and field strength.
- define capacitance; describe the principle of the capacitor; solve capacitor problems.

The concept of energy is extremely useful in mechanics. The law of conservation of energy allows us to solve problems without knowing the forces in detail. The same is true in our study of electrical interactions. The work done moving a charged particle in an electric field can result in the particle gaining either potential or kinetic energy, or both. In this chapter, since we are investigating charges at rest, we will discuss only changes in potential energy.

Energy and the Electric Potential

Recall the change in potential energy of a ball when you lift it, Figure 21–5. Both the gravitational force, F, and the gravitational field, $g = F/m$, point toward Earth. If you lift a ball against the force of gravity, you do work on it, and thus its potential energy is increased.

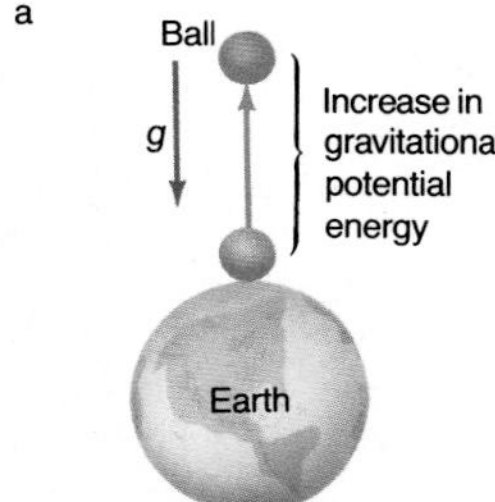

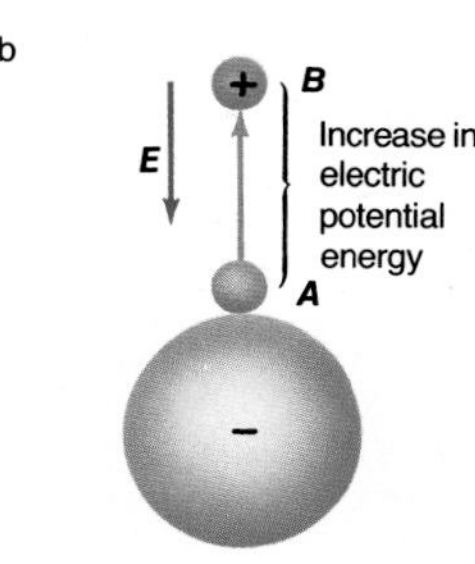

FIGURE 21–5. Work is needed to move an object against the force of gravity (a) and against the electric force (b). In both cases, the potential energy of the object is increased.

3 Close

CONVERGENT QUESTION

Bring a charged rod close to the face of an oscilloscope and watch for effects on the electron beam. By using some fur or wool cloth, put a charge on the face of the oscilloscope and you'll be able to make the electron beam distort or perhaps disappear altogether. Ask students to explain why this happens. [The excess charge you put on the scope face repels the electron beam.]

CONCEPT REVIEW ANSWERS

1.1 a. You place a test charge at a point and determine whether or not there is a force on it. **b.** You measure the force and divide by the size of the test charge. **c.** The size must be small enough not to disturb the charge distribution giving rise to the field you are measuring. **d.** You move the test charge to another point and repeat the measurements.
1.2 It is negative, because field lines go into a negative charge.
1.3 The field is the force on a unit charge; it is the magnitude of the force divided by the size of the charge on which it is measured.
1.4 Critical Thinking: No. Notice how the field lines in the top half are changed by the presence of the positive charge.

BRIDGING

Previously taught concepts include energy, work, joule, coulomb, weight, friction, terminal velocity, mass, and conductor.

21.2 APPLICATIONS OF THE ELECTRIC FIELD

Preparation

OBJECTIVES

The objectives are listed on the student page. Remind students to preview these objectives as a study guide to this major section.

OVERVIEW

Electric potential and potential difference are the major concepts of this section. In addition, capacitors are discussed, and the control of charges by electric fields is illustrated by Millikan's experiment.

1 Focus

DISCREPANT EVENT

To demonstrate that the field increases as you move toward the charge, attach a pith ball on a string to a stand about a meter away from the Van de Graaff generator. Slowly move the pith ball in so students can see that, as you get closer to the generator, the pith ball's attraction to it increases.

2 Teach

CONCEPT DEVELOPMENT

- Positive charges move toward regions of lower electrical potential the same way a boulder rolls down a hill toward lower gravitational potential.
- Fairly new technology makes it possible to construct very high capacitance capacitors, often called "supercaps," that can have capacitance values of 1 to 5 farads. The energy stored in these capacitors can light a flashlight bulb for a few seconds. Available from many supply houses, they make an effective demonstration. Be aware that extreme caution is necessary when using a capacitor. Make sure it is *completely* discharged at the end of all demonstrations.

Study Guide Master. To reinforce the concepts in this section, have the students complete the Study Guide Master for Section 21.2 from the Teacher Resource Package.

Assessment

Portfolio

Students should write a paragraph in which they carefully distinguish among the terms electric potential energy, electric potential, and electric potential difference. The units used to measure all three should be included.

F.Y.I.

"Even if I could be Shakespeare, I think I should still choose to be Faraday."
—Aldous Huxley (1925)

The situation is similar with two unlike charges. These two attract each other, and so you must do work to pull one away from the other. When you do the work, you store it as potential energy. The larger the test charge, the greater the increase in its potential energy, ΔPE.

The electric field at the location of the test charge does not depend on the size of the test charge. The field is the force per unit charge, or F/q'. In the same way, we will define a quantity that is the change in potential energy per unit charge. This quantity is called the **electric potential difference** and is defined by the equation $\Delta V = \Delta PE/q'$. The unit of electric potential, joule per coulomb, is called a **volt** (J/C = V).

Electric potential difference is change in potential energy divided by the charge.

Consider the situation shown in Figure 21–5. When you move the test charge from **A** to **B,** you do work on it. As a result, you increase its potential energy; you give it a positive change in potential energy. Because the test charge is positive, the electric potential difference between **A** and **B** is also positive. The electric potential at **B** is larger than the electric potential at **A.**

The volt is the unit of electric potential.

If you return the test charge from **B** back to **A,** the electric field does work on you. The potential energy of the charge is reduced. Therefore, the electric potential difference between **B** and **A** is negative. The work done on you returning the charge is equal and opposite to the work you do moving it away. Therefore, the electric potential difference between **A** and **B** is equal and opposite to the difference between **B** and **A.** The net change in potential going from **A** to **B** to **A** is zero. Thus, the potential of point **A,** or any other point, depends only on its position, not on the path taken to get there.

The reference point of zero level of potential is arbitrary.

As is the case for any kind of potential energy, only differences in electric potential energy can be measured. The same is true of electric potential. The reference, or zero, level is arbitrary. Thus, only differences in electric potential are important. We define the **potential difference** from point **A** to point **B** to be $V = V_B - V_A$. Potential differences are measured with a voltmeter. Sometimes the potential difference is simply called the *voltage*.

Only potential differences are meaningful.

As described in Chapter 11, the potential energy of a system can be defined to be zero at any convenient reference point. In the same way, the electric potential of any point, for example point **A,** can be defined to be zero. If $V_A = 0$, then $V_B = V$. If instead, $V_B = 0$, then $V_A = -V$. No matter what reference point is chosen, the value of the potential difference from point **A** to point **B** will always be the same.

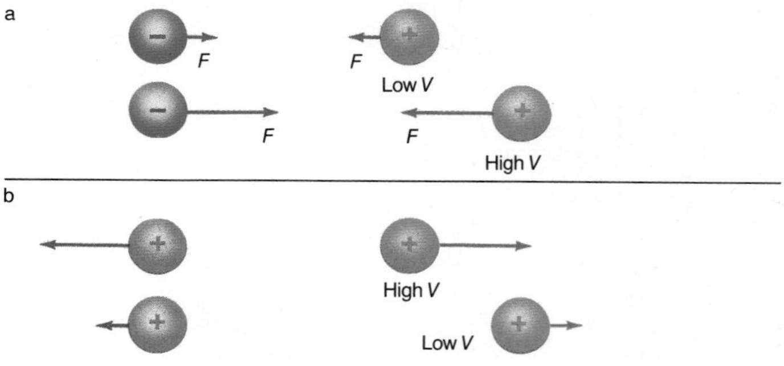

FIGURE 21–6. Electric potential energy is smaller when two unlike charges are closer together (a) and larger when two like charges are closer together (b).

STUDY GUIDE MASTER

Use the Study Guide master for section 21.2.

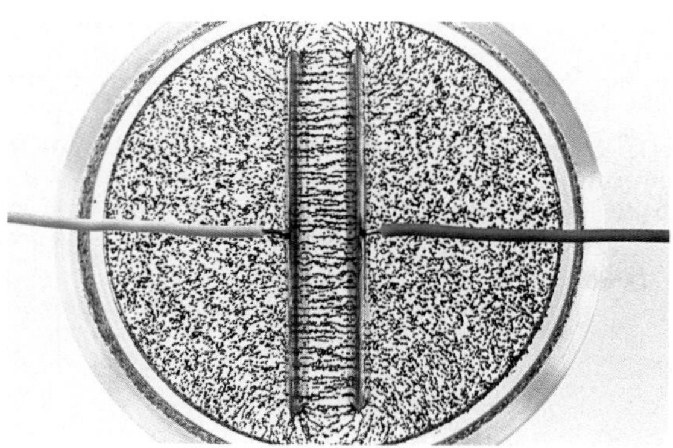

FIGURE 21–7. An electric field between parallel plates.

CONCEPT DEVELOPMENT

• Point out that the electric field between two parallel plates is uniform only if the length and width of the plates is much larger than their separation. The field is not uniform near the edges of the plates.

ACTIVITY

Discovery: Students have been introduced to the electric field and potential near a point charge or small charged sphere. They will now be shown a geometry that produces a uniform field that can be calculated easily. The parallel plate geometry is used to produce uniform fields in oscilloscope tubes, ink-jet printers, and other devices.

You can demonstrate oppositely charged parallel plates using a plasticfoam electrophorus, a metal pie plate, and a foam cup or plastic drinking glass. You will also need a pith ball to show the field. Use the cup as a handle for the plate as shown in the Physics Lab on page 412. Charge the plasticfoam by rubbing it with fur. Use the pith ball to demonstrate the field near the region of the foam you rubbed. Next, lay the plate on the foam and touch it with your finger. This gives it the opposite charge (charging by induction). Again use the pith ball to show that there is a field around it. Now hold the plate parallel to the foam to form parallel plates. The pith ball will show the field between the plates.

We have seen that electric potential increases as a positive test charge is separated from a negative charge. What happens when a positive test charge is separated from a positive charge? There is a repulsive force between these two charges. Potential energy decreases as the two charges are moved farther apart. Therefore, the electric potential is smaller at points farther from the positive charge, Figure 21–6.

The Electric Potential in a Uniform Field

How does the potential difference depend on the electric field? In the case of the gravitational field, near the surface of Earth the gravitational force and field are relatively constant. A constant electric force and field can be made by placing two large flat conducting plates parallel to each other. One is charged positively and the other negatively. The electric field between the plates is constant except at the edges of the plates. Its direction is from the positive to the negative plate. Figure 21–7 shows grass seeds representing the field between parallel plates.

The electric field between two parallel plates is uniform.

In a constant gravitational field, the change in potential energy when a body of mass m is raised a distance h is given by $\Delta PE = mgh$. Remember that g, the gravitational field intensity near Earth, is given by $g = F/m$. The gravitational potential, or potential energy per unit of mass, is $mgh/m = gh$.

What is the potential difference between two points in a uniform electric field? If a positive test charge is moved a distance d, in the direction opposite the electric field direction, the change in potential energy is given by $\Delta PE = +Fd$. Thus, the potential difference, the change in potential energy per unit charge, is $V = +Fd/q = +(F/q)d$. Now, the electric field intensity is the force per unit charge, $E = F/q$. Therefore, the potential difference, V, between two points a distance d apart in a uniform field, E, is given by

$$V = Ed.$$

The potential increases in the direction opposite the electric field direction. That is, the potential is higher near the positively-charged plate. By dimensional analysis, the product of the units of E and d is (N/C) · m. This is equivalent to a J/C, the definition of a volt.

Connect to BIOLOGY

Proteins are composed of sequences of amino acids. When placed in solution, the amino acids become charged ions. The amount of charge depends on the type of amino acid. If a charge is placed in an electric field, a force will be exerted on it that is proportional to the charge. Thus, proteins can be separated based on the types of amino acids from which they are made. The protein mixtures to be analyzed are placed at one end of a gelatin-like material and an electric field is turned on. Sometime later the gel shows dark bands at the places to which proteins have moved.

Suppose you extract a protein mixture from 15 different snails. You find bands from five mixtures at the same locations; the other ten have very different patterns. What might you conclude? [Five of the snails have similar protein mixtures and are likely to be closely related. The other ten are likely to be of different species.]

CONCEPT DEVELOPMENT

Demonstration: Charge a Leyden jar by touching a charged electrophorus to the knob. This gives the inside of the jar a charge. If you charge the inside positively, the outside will become negatively charged as electrons move onto it from the ground. Repeated chargings will build up a large charge difference between the inside and outside of the jar, separated by a glass insulator. If the outside and inside are connected, a spark will jump. Explain that this is the basic structure of a capacitor. Take apart a commercial capacitor to show its metal and plastic foils. Capacitors are used to tune radio receivers, as "condensers" in ignition systems of cars, and in camera flash attachment circuits. (Once again, use caution when demonstrating with capacitors. Don't connect the two plates with your hands.)

Demonstration: A metal point, such as the end of a paper clip, can be attached to a Van de Graaff generator to demonstrate point discharge. The charge leaking off this point is often enough to extinguish a lit match!

Answers To

PRACTICE PROBLEMS

Have students refer to Appendix A of the Solutions Appendix for complete solutions to Practice Problems.

5. 4×10^2 V
6. 2.5×10^4 N/C
7. 1.25×10^3 V
8. 7.5 J

HELP WANTED

VENDING MACHINE REPAIRERS

If you have a knack for fixing things, and can learn quickly from our in-house training on specific equipment, we would like to hear from you. You must be able to read electrical diagrams and manuals and use sophisticated test equipment. Vocational school training is a plus, but experience will be considered. We need reliable, bondable, productive people willing to work when needed and interested in advancement. For information contact:

National Automatic Merchandising Association, 20 North Wacker Drive, Chicago, IL 60606

Example Problem

Potential Difference Between Two Parallel Plates

Two large, charged parallel plates are 4.0 cm apart. The magnitude of the electric field between them is 625 N/C. **a.** What is the potential difference between the plates? **b.** What work is done moving a charge equal to that of one electron from one plate to another?

Given: $d = 0.040$ m, $E = 625$ N/C
Unknowns: V, W
Basic equations: $V = Ed$, $W = qV$

Solution: **a.**
$$V = Ed = (625\ \text{N/C})(0.040\ \text{m}) = 25\ \text{N}\cdot\text{m/C} = 25\ \text{J/C} = 25\ \text{V}$$

b.
$$W = qV = (1.6 \times 10^{-19}\ \text{C})(25\ \text{V}) = 4.0 \times 10^{-18}\ \text{CV} = 4.0 \times 10^{-18}\ \text{J}$$

Example Problem

Electric Field Between Two Parallel Plates

A voltmeter measures the potential difference between two large parallel plates to be 60.0 V. The plates are 3.0 cm apart. What is the magnitude of the electric field between them?

Given: $V = 60.0$ V, $d = 0.030$ m
Unknown: E
Basic equation: $V = Ed$

Solution: $V = Ed$, so $E = \frac{V}{d}$
$$= \frac{60.0\ \text{V}}{0.030\ \text{m}} = \frac{60.0\ \text{J/C}}{0.030\ \text{m}} = 2.0 \times 10^3\ \text{N/C}$$

Practice Problems

5. The electric field intensity between two large, charged, parallel metal plates is 8000 N/C. The plates are 0.05 m apart. What is the potential difference between them?
6. A voltmeter reads 500 V when placed across two charged, parallel plates. The plates are 0.020 m apart. What is the electric field between them?
7. What potential difference is applied to two metal plates 0.500 m apart if the electric field between them is 2.50×10^3 N/C?
▶ **8.** What work is done when 5.0 C is raised in potential by 1.5 V?

Physics and society

MINIMOTORS

What miracles could a doctor perform with a pump or motor small enough to fit into a blood vessel? Drugs, for example, could be administered precisely where needed in the exact amount required. Tiny rotating knives could remove plaque from arteries.

The parts for such machines could not be made by normal methods. The new techniques are often called nanotechnology methods. For more than ten years, scientists have adapted the methods used to make computer chips in order to produce electric motors and gears the diameter of a human hair. At this time, however, the most successful products are sensors. These sensors detect gas or liquid pressure and produce an electrical signal. They are already used to improve the efficiency of an auto engine and to monitor blood pressure inside a human. Other sensors can detect the presence of minuscule amounts of poisonous gases. Sensors still in development measure acceleration more sensitively than any existing device.

Nanotechnology can also produce actuators. An actuator converts an electrical signal into a mechanical force. One device, the size of a postage stamp, moves two million tiny mirros to project a computer display on the wall. One motor that was built uses electric fields to cause the rotor to spin. The magnetic forces that run ordinary motors have also been used to spin micromotors.

The rotors of early motors were as flat as pancakes and couldn't do any real work. Using a technique called LIGA, developed in Germany, scientists at the University of Wisconsin at Madison created metal gears one hundred times thicker than the rotors of the early motors. Electric charges were used to assemble these gears into six-gear transmissions.

DEVELOPING A VIEWPOINT

The development of nanotechnology is expensive and may not result in products that can be sold for decades, if ever. Who should finance the development? Read further and come to class prepared to discuss the following questions.

1. What applications do you foresee in some of the following fields: medicine, health and nutrition, transportation, and consumer electronics?
2. You are a scientist who wants to develop an application of nanotechnology in health, but you need money to support your project. You go to a government agency to ask for funds. What argument might you use to convince them to use tax money to support your work?

SUGGESTED READINGS

Heppenheimer, T. A. "Microbots." *Discover,* March 1989, pp. 78–84.

Gannon, Robert. "Micromachine Magic." *Popular Science,* March 1989, pp. 88–92.

Stewart, Doug. "New Machines Are Smaller Than a Hair, and Do Real Work." *Smithsonian,* October 1990, pp. 85–95.

Hapgood, Fred. "No Assembly Required." *Omni,* May 1990, pp. 66–70.

Physics and society

Background: Students may be curious about the manufacture of microscopic gears. A precise, enlarged drawing of the shape of the gears is made first. The drawing is then reduced until it is the size of the tiny gears and is photographically copied onto a metal sheet. Regions where the gears will be are chemically removed. The result is a stencil-like mask. A second metal sheet, or substrate, is coated with a layer of plastic 0.3 mm thick. The mask is placed above the plastic and exposed to X rays. The X rays pass through the regions removed from the mask and damage the plastic. The damaged plastic is removed chemically, leaving holes the shape and size of the gears. Nickel is then electroplated into the holes. Finally, the nickel gears are removed from the substrate. Thousands of gears can be made in a single exposure.

Answers To
DEVELOPING A VIEWPOINT

1. Students should be able to brainstorm many possibilities including the following: microscopic sensors could monitor conditions inside the body; micromachines could be directed by surgeons to perform operations; in cars, sensors could increase efficiency and reduce pollution.

2. The scientist might argue that the project could take longer to complete than most industries would be willing to wait, that Japan and Germany are supporting nanotechnology, and that potential applications could lead to improved lives for all citizens.

Teacher Resources: Stix, Gary. "Micron Machinations." *Scientific American,* November 1992, p. 106. Amato, Ivan. "Gearing Down." *Science News,* Vol 139, January 12, 1991, p. 26.

CONCEPT DEVELOPMENT

Most electrical quantities are abstract and students have little direct experience with them, so it's important to use all possible aids to understanding. Units are one such aid. Insist that students learn the units of each quantity carefully. Among other things, unit cancellation in quantitative problems helps you know if your answers are correct.

ACTIVITY

Discovery: Have students sketch the electric field of a single point charge, two points with both like and unlike charges, and oppositely charged parallel plates. Ask them to imagine how test charges would behave in these fields. Point out that the lines represent the direction of the force on the particle, not necessarily the path of the particle through the field.

POCKET LAB

UNIT CHARGE

Purpose: to have students use the logic used by Robert Millikan to find the unit charge.
Materials: 3-mm diameter steel balls or other small balls; balance.
Outcome: All the steel balls have the same mass. Students should recognize that each mass value represents a whole number of balls. Some students will recognize that each mass difference is a whole number of balls. Other students should recognize that the ratio of masses must be the same as the ratio of whole numbers. The unit mass suggested by the student might be too large. (The suggested mass might be 2 or 3, and so on, balls.) The unit mass cannot be too small because there were no 1/2 balls.

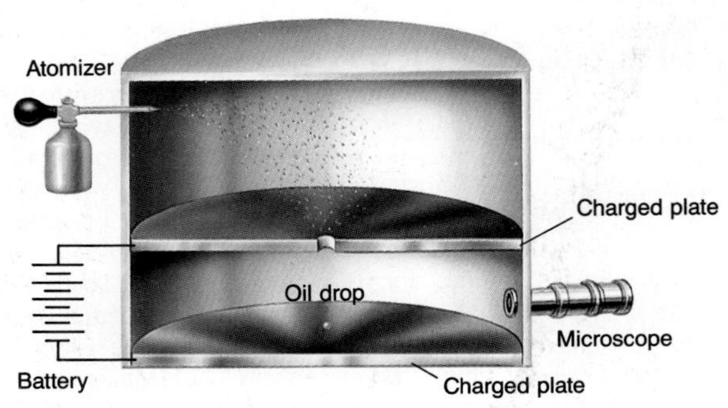

FIGURE 21–8. This illustration shows a cross-sectional view of Millikan's apparatus for determining the charge on an electron.

Millikan's Oil Drop Experiment

Millikan measured the charge of an electron.

One important application of the uniform electric field between two parallel plates was the measurement of the charge of an electron. This was made by American physicist Robert A. Millikan (1868–1953) in 1909.

A drop is suspended if the electric and gravitational forces are balanced.

Figure 21–8 shows the method used by Millikan to measure the charge carried by a single electron. Fine oil drops were sprayed from an atomizer into the air. These drops were often charged by friction with the atomizer as they were sprayed. Gravity acting on the drops caused them to fall. A few entered the hole in the top plate of the apparatus. A potential difference was placed across the two plates. The resulting electric field between the plates exerted a force on the charged drops. When the top plate was made positive enough, the electric force caused negatively-charged drops to rise. The potential difference between the plates was adjusted to suspend a charged drop between the plates. At this point, the downward force of the weight and the upward force of the electric field were equal in magnitude.

The magnitude of the electric field, E, was determined from the potential difference between the plates. A second measurement had to be made to find the weight of the drop, mg, which was too tiny to measure by ordinary methods. To make this measurement, a drop was first suspended. Then the electric field was turned off and the rate of the fall of the drop measured. Because of friction with the air molecules, the oil drop quickly reached terminal velocity. This velocity was related to the mass of the drop by a complex equation. Using the measured terminal velocity to calculate mg, and knowing E, the charge q could be calculated. Millikan found that the drops had a large variety of charges. When he used X rays to ionize the air and add or remove electrons from the drops, he noted, however, that the *changes* in the charge were always a multiple of -1.6×10^{-19} C. The changes were caused by one or more electrons being added to or removed from the drops. He concluded that the smallest change in charge that could occur was the amount of charge of one electron. Therefore, Millikan said that each electron always carried the same charge, -1.6×10^{-19} C. Millikan's

POCKET LAB

UNIT CHARGE

Place a small container on a balance and determine the mass of the empty container. (On an electronic balance, push the tare bar.) Place a small handful of 3-mm diameter steel balls in the container. Don't count them! Record the mass. Dump the balls out of the container and repeat the procedure with a different number of balls. Don't count! Record the mass. Repeat this loading and massing process a third time. Look closely at your mass values. Suggest a possible unit mass of each ball. Could your unit mass be too large? Could it be too small? Explain.

experiment showed that charge is quantized. This means that an object can have only a charge with a magnitude that is some integral multiple of the charge of the electron.

The presently accepted theory of matter says that protons are made up of fundamental particles called quarks. The charge on a quark is either $+1/3$ or $-2/3$ the charge on an electron. A theory of quarks that agrees with other experiments states that quarks can never be isolated. Many experimenters have used an updated Millikan apparatus to look for fractional charges on drops or tiny metal spheres. There have been no reproducible discoveries of fractional charges. Thus, no isolated quark has been discovered; the quark theory remains consistent with experiments.

Example Problem

Finding the Charge on an Oil Drop

An oil drop weighs 1.9×10^{-14} N. It is suspended in an electric field of intensity 4.0×10^{4} N/C. **a.** What is the charge on the oil drop? **b.** If the upper plate is positive, how many excess electrons does it have?

Given: $W = mg = 1.9 \times 10^{-14}$ N, $E = 4.0 \times 10^{4}$ N/C

Unknown: excess charge, q

Basic equation: $Eq = mg$

Solution: a. Electronic and gravitational forces balance, so $Eq = mg$.

$$\text{Thus, } q = \frac{mg}{E} = \frac{1.9 \times 10^{-14}\ \text{N}}{4.0 \times 10^{4}\ \text{N/C}} = 4.8 \times 10^{-19}\ \text{C}$$

b.
$$\text{number of electrons} = \frac{\text{(total charge on drop)}}{\text{(charge per electron)}} = \frac{4.8 \times 10^{-19}\ \text{C}}{1.6 \times 10^{-19}\ \text{C/e}} = 3\ \text{electrons}$$

There are three extra electrons because a negatively-charged drop is attracted toward a positively-charged plate.

Practice Problems

9. A drop is falling in a Millikan oil drop apparatus when the electric field is off.
   a. What are the forces on it, regardless of its acceleration?
   b. If it is falling at constant velocity, what can be said about the forces on it?

10. An oil drop weighs 1.9×10^{-15} N. It is suspended in an electric field of 6.0×10^{3} N/C.
   a. What is the charge on the drop?
   b. How many excess electrons does it carry?

BIOLOGY CONNECTION

The application of an electric stimulus causes a series of changes in the resting membrane potential (RMP) of nerve and muscle cells. A stimulus that is applied at one point on a cell causes a small region of the cell membrane to become depolarized. This is called a local potential. If large enough, the local potential can cause an action potential, which is a larger depolarization of the RMP. This spreads without changing its magnitude over the entire cell membrane.

The drop's mass was found from its terminal velocity.

The charge of an electron is -1.6×10^{-19} C.

CONCEPT DEVELOPMENT

- The direction of the field lines gives the direction of the force on a positive test charge in the field. Or, in the case of a curved field line, the tangent to the field line gives the direction of the force.
- If you have access to the "Mechanical Universe" videotapes, they contain an excellent lesson on the Millikan experiment and its historical background.
- Potential difference exists between two points. Students wil try to make PD into something existing at a point. Potential difference is measured by a voltmeter. The higher the potential difference, the more energy in a charge. Potential difference is often referred to as voltage.

Transparency Package. Use Transparency 29, Millikan Apparatus, to illustrate Millikan's experiment.

Answers To
PRACTICE PROBLEMS

Have students refer to Appendix A of the Solutions Appendix for complete solutions to Practice Problems.

9. a. weight, downward; frictional force of air, upward
b. The two are equal in magnitude.

10. a. 3.2×10^{-19} C
b. 2 electrons

TRANSPARENCY

Use Transparency 29 with this section.

Answers To

PRACTICE PROBLEMS (cont)

11. a. 1.6×10^{-19} C

b. 1 electron

12. 1.0×10^{6} N/C

CONCEPT DEVELOPMENT

- There are many details of lightning and other atmospheric phenomena in Volume II, Chapter 9, titled "Electricity in the Atmosphere," of the Feynman Lectures on Physics.
- The charge referred to in the definition of capacitance is the absolute value of the charge on either plate. As a complete device, a "charge" capacitor has zero total charge.

Enrichment: Have interested students investigate the details of the Millikan oil drop experiment. Have them pay special attention to the use of potential difference that produces the needed electric field. Ask them to explain how the electric field intensity is changed.

Enrichment Master. With this section, use the Enrichment Master, The Capacitor, from the Teacher Resource Package.

11. A positively-charged oil drop weighs 6.4×10^{-13} N. An electric field of 4.0×10^{6} N/C suspends the drop.

a. What is the charge on the drop?

b. How many electrons is the drop missing?

▶ **12.** If three more electrons were removed from the drop in Practice Problem 11, what field would be needed to balance the drop?

Sharing of Charge

All systems, mechanical and electrical, come to equilibrium when the energy of the system is at a minimum. For example, if a ball is put on a hill, it will finally come to rest in a valley where its gravitational potential energy is least. This same principle explains what happens when an insulated, negatively-charged metal sphere, Figure 21–9, touches a second, uncharged sphere.

Charges move until all parts of a conductor are at the same potential.

The excess negative charges on sphere A repel each other. Thus the potential of sphere A is high. We can choose the potential of the neutral sphere, B to be zero. When one charge is transferred from sphere A to sphere B, the potential of sphere A is reduced because it has fewer excess charges. The potential of sphere B does not change because no work is done adding the first extra charge to this neutral sphere. As more charges are transferred, however, work must be done on the charge to overcome the growing repulsive force between it and the other charges on sphere B. Therefore, the potential of sphere B increases as the potential of sphere A decreases. Negative charges continue to flow from sphere A to sphere B until the work done adding a charge to sphere B is equal to the work gained in removing a charge from sphere A. The potential of sphere A now equals the potential of sphere B. Thus charges flow until all parts of a conducting body, the two touching spheres in this case, are at the same potential.

If a large and a small sphere have the same charge, the large sphere will have a lower potential.

Consider a large sphere and a small sphere that have the same charge, Figure 21–10. The larger sphere has a larger surface area, so charges can spread farther apart than they can on the smaller sphere. With the charges farther apart, the repulsive force between them is reduced. Therefore, as long as the spheres have the same charge, the

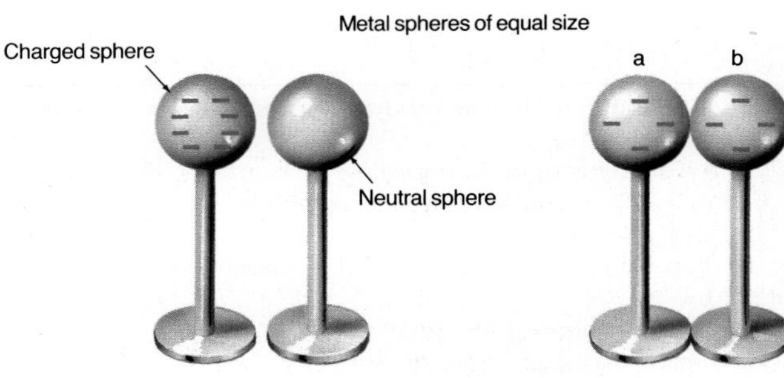

FIGURE 21–9. A charged sphere shares charge equally with a neutral sphere of equal size.

ENRICHMENT MASTER

Use the Enrichment master for Chapter 21 with this section.

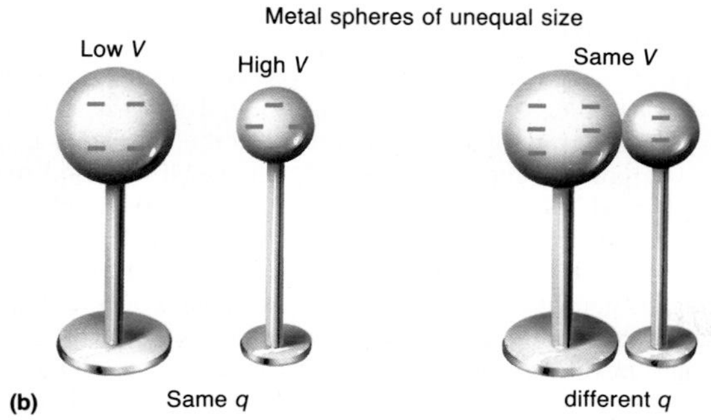

Metal spheres of unequal size

Low V High V Same V

(b) Same q different q

FIGURE 21–10. A charged sphere gives much of its charge to a larger sphere.

potential on the larger sphere is lower than the potential on the smaller sphere. If the two spheres are now touched together, charges will move to the sphere with the lower potential; that is, from the smaller to the larger sphere. The result is a greater charge on the larger sphere when two different-sized spheres are at the same potential.

The charges are closer together at sharp points of a conductor. Therefore, the field lines are closer together; the field is stronger, Figure 21–10.

Earth is a very large sphere. If a charged body is touched to Earth, almost any amount of charge can flow without changing Earth's potential. When all the excess charge on the body flows to Earth, the body becomes neutral. Touching an object to Earth to eliminate excess charge is called **grounding**. Moving gasoline trucks can become charged by friction. If that charge were to jump to Earth through gasoline vapor, it could cause an explosion. Instead, a metal wire safely conducts the charge to ground, Figure 21–11. If a computer or other sensitive instrument were not grounded, static charges could accumulate, raising the potential of the computer. A person touching the computer could suddenly lower the potential of the computer. The charges flowing through the computer to the person could damage the equipment or hurt the person.

If the two spheres are at the same potential, the large one will have greater charge.

FIGURE 21–11. Ground wire on a fuel truck.

CONCEPT DEVELOPMENT

Critical Thinking: Keeping in mind that Earth has an electric field, a lightning storm can be understood as a giant capacitor arrangement. Ask students to explain the parts of a capacitor. [Earth is one of the charged plates, the clouds are the other charged plate, and air is the insulator (or dielectric) in between.]

Critical Thinking Master, Teacher Resource Package. You may wish to have students complete the Critical Thinking Master, A Jarful of Charge, with this section.

Transparency Package. Use Transparency 30 to quiz students on the concept of sharing charges.

TEACHER F.Y.I.

- The tires now used on cars and trucks are slightly conductive. That is why fewer cars need static strips than in the past.
- Some computer manufacturers recommend keeping them plugged in to maintain the ground, even when not in use. It is also a good idea never to cut off the grounding pin on electrical equipment (a violation of the electrical code).

CONCEPT DEVELOPMENT

ACTIVITY

Cooperative Learning: Have students work in small groups to make a quick summary of the units of the major concepts of this chapter. Then pool their information to develop a class table.

CHECKING FOR UNDERSTANDING

Ask students to describe the process of measuring the magnitude of an electric field by using a positive test charge. Then ask what needs to be done to measure the potential difference between two points in this electric field. [Measure the work done in moving the charge between the two points.]

RETEACHING

Begin with a review of the idea of work. Go over charge attraction and repulsion, bringing in Coulomb's law. Draw a picture showing a test charge in the vicinity of a strongly charged object. Point out that when you move this test charge around, work is done and therefore there are energy changes. This will lead you into the idea of potential difference.

Transparency Package. Reteach the concept of separation of charges using Transparency 28 and accompanying worksheet.

INDEPENDENT PRACTICE/ EXTENSION

Refer to the Assignment Guide below for additional questions and problems for independent practice.

Electric Fields Near Conductors

All charges are on the outside of a conductor.

The charges on a conductor are spread as far apart as they can be to make the energy of the system as low as possible. The result is that all charges are on the surface of a solid conductor. If the conductor is hollow, excess charges will move to the outer surface. If a closed metal container is charged, there will be no charges on the inside surfaces of the container. In this way, a closed metal container shields the inside from electric fields. For example, people inside a car are protected from the electric fields generated by lightning. On an open coffee can there will be very few charges inside, and none near the bottom.

High Energy Halo ▶

Electric fields are largest near sharp points.

Even though the electric potential is the same at every point of a conductor, the electric field around the outside of it depends on the shape of the body as well as its potential. The charges are closer together at sharp points of a conductor. Therefore, the field lines are closer together; the field is stronger, Figure 21–12. The field there can become so strong that nearby air molecules are separated into electrons and positive ions. As the electrons and ions recombine, energy is released and light is produced. The result is the blue glow of a corona. The electrons and ions are accelerated by the field. If the field is strong enough, when the particles hit other molecules they will produce more ions and electrons. The stream of ions and electrons that results is a plasma, a conductor. The result is a spark, or, in extreme cases, lightning. To reduce corona and sparking, conductors that are highly charged or operate at high potentials are made smooth in shape to reduce the electric fields.

On the other hand, lightning rods, Figure 21–13, are pointed so that the electric field will be strong near the end of the rod. Air molecules are pulled apart near the rod, forming the start of a conducting path from the rod to the clouds. As a result of the sharply-pointed shape, charges in the clouds spark to the rod rather than to a chimney or other high point on a house. From the rod, a conductor takes the charges safely to the ground.

F.Y.I.

Even if the inner surface is pitted or bumpy, giving it a larger surface area than the outer surface, the charge will still be entirely on the outside.

Storing Electric Energy—The Capacitor

When you lift a book, you increase its potential energy. This can be interpreted as "storing" energy in a gravitational field. In a similar way, you can store energy in an electric field. In 1746, the Dutch physician and physicist Pieter Van Musschenbroek invented a device that could

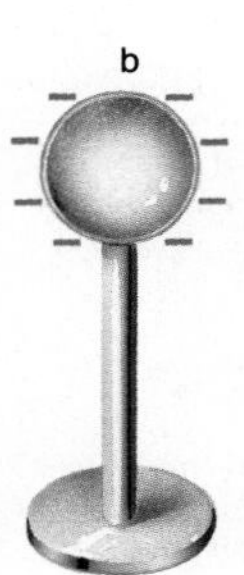

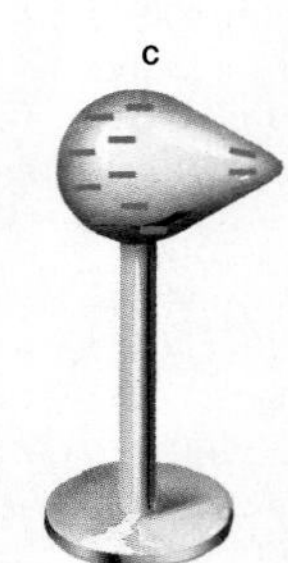

FIGURE 21–12. The electric field around a conducting body depends on the structure and shape (b is hollow) of the body.

(c)

CRITICAL THINKING

Use the Critical Thinking master for Chapter 21 with this section.

TRANSPARENCY

Use Transparency 30 with this section.

21:2 ASSIGNMENT GUIDE

	PRACTICE	EXTENSION
CHAPTER REVIEW pp. 443–445		
· Reviewing Concepts	6–13	
· Applying Concepts		2, 4–10
· Problems*	10–13, 15–17, 19–21	14, 18, 22–24
APPENDIX B PROBLEMS* · Chapter 21, p. 703	7, 8, 10–12, 14–16	9, 13

* Complete solutions to all Chapter Review and Appendix problems appear in the Problems and Solutions Manual.

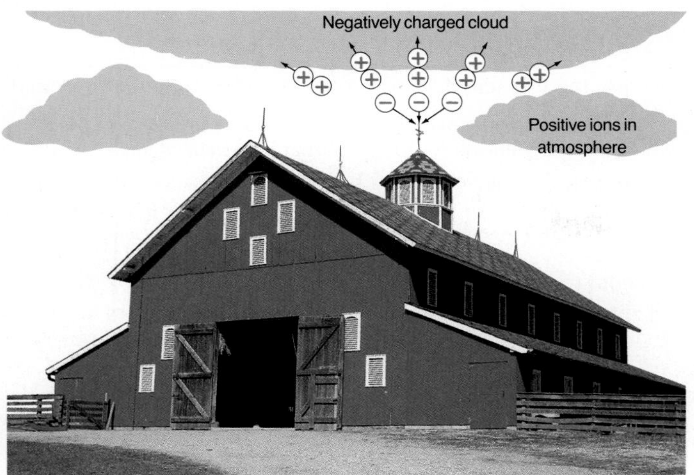

FIGURE 21–13. A lightning rod allows charges from the clouds to be grounded, rather than conducted through a barn.

store electric charge. In honor of the city in which he worked, it was called a Leyden jar. The Leyden jar was used by Benjamin Franklin to store the charge from lightning and in many other experiments.

As described previously, as charge is added to an object, the potential between that object and Earth increases. For a given shape and size of the object, the ratio of charge to potential difference, q/V, is a constant. The constant is called the **capacitance**, C, of the object. For a small sphere far from the ground, even a small amount of added charge will increase the potential difference. Thus, C is small. The larger the sphere, the greater the charge that can be added for the same increase in potential difference, thus the larger the capacitance. Van Musschenbroek found a way of producing a large capacitance in a small device. A device that is designed to have a specific capacitance is called a **capacitor**. All capacitors are made up of two conductors, separated by an insulator. The two conductors have equal and opposite charges. Capacitors are used in electrical circuits to store electric energy.

Capacitance is the ratio of charge stored to potential difference.

Capacitors store energy in the electric field between charged conductors.

Capacitors often are made of parallel conducting sheets, or plates, separated by air or another insulator. Commercial capacitors, Figure 21–14, contain strips of aluminum foil separated by thin plastic and are tightly rolled up to save room.

The capacitance is independent of the charge on it. Capacitance can be measured by placing charge q on one plate and $-q$ on the other, and measuring the potential difference, V, that results. The capacitance is then found by using the equation

$$C = \frac{q}{V}.$$

Capacitance is measured in farads, F, named after Michael Faraday. One farad is one coulomb per volt (C/V). Just as one coulomb is a large amount of charge, one farad is an enormous capacitance. Capacitors are usually between 10 picofarads (10×10^{-12} F) and 500 microfarads (500×10^{-6} F).

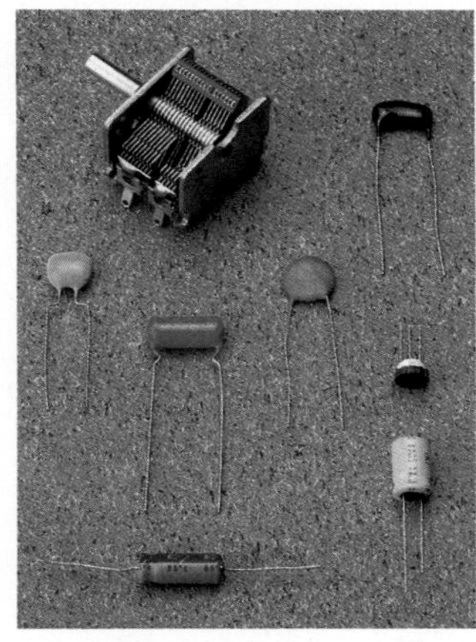

FIGURE 21–14. Various types of capacitors.

CONCEPT DEVELOPMENT

• The energy stored in a capacitor is given by $1/2qV$.

Laboratory Manual. Give students additional experience with capacitance by doing Lab 21.1, The Capacitor, from the Laboratory Manual.

Guided Practice: Go over the Example Problem on page 442, then have students work in class on the first two Practice Problems that follow.

Independent Practice: Assign the remaining Practice Problems for homework, then spend time going over them as a class during the next class period.

3 Close

CONVERGENT QUESTION

The only actual electrical quantities used in this chapter are charge, potential difference, and capacitance. Ask students to help you summarize how mechanical concepts such as work, force, and energy apply to the electrical concepts.

Multicultural Connections

During stormy weather, the potential difference between Earth and the atmosphere can be so great that a sudden, brilliant discharge (lightning) takes place. Or, the potential difference can be just high enough to cause electrons to escape a pointed object (like the mast of a ship or a steeple) more slowly, ionize the air around the object, and cause a glow. This glow, known today as St. Elmo's fire, was associated with the gods Castor and Pollux by Roman and Greek sailors. If they saw a double glow on a ship, then they were protected by both gods. However, if they saw only one glow, bad luck would overtake the ship. The current name is the result of a story about St. Erasmus. (The name was corrupted first to Sant' Ermo, then to St. Elmo.) According to this story, just before St. Elmo died in a storm at sea, he promised to return in some form to let sailors facing a shipwreck know they would survive. Modern observations indicate that most occurrences of St. Elmo's fire happen toward the end of a thunderstorm, so it does indeed mean good luck.

Answers To
PRACTICE PROBLEMS

Have students refer to Appendix A of the Solutions Appendix for complete solutions to Practice Problems.

13. 6.8×10^{-4} C
14. the larger capacitor, 1.0×10^{-4} C
15. the smaller capacitor, 76 V
16. 2.0×10^{-5} C

CONCEPT REVIEW ANSWERS

2.1 a. The field points up (force must be up and charge on drop is positive). **b.** Lower plate (field lines leave positive charges).
2.2 a. It is unchanged, fixed by geometry. **b.** It changes because by $q = CV$, it is directly proportional to q.
2.3 a. The potentials are equal. **b.** The charge on the smaller sphere is less than that on the larger one.
2.4 Critical Thinking: Zero. The charge on the inside of a conducting body is zero.

F.Y.I.

Michael Faraday, a self-educated man, was hired by chemist Sir Humphrey Davy as a bottle washer. As time went by, Faraday became an even greater scientist than Davy. Besides his brilliant discoveries in the fields of chemistry and physics, he was also a popular lecturer. A lecture for young people, *The Chemical History of a Candle,* was published in book form and became a classic.

Example Problem

Finding the Capacitance from Charge and Potential Difference

A sphere has a potential difference between it and Earth of 60.0 V when charged with 3.0×10^{-6} C. What is its capacitance?

Given: potential difference, $V = 60.0$ V
$q = 3.0 \times 10^{-6}$ C

Unknown: capacitance, C

Basic equation: $C = \frac{q}{V}$

Solution: $C = \frac{q}{V} = \frac{3.0 \times 10^{-6}\text{ C}}{60.0\text{ V}} = 5.0 \times 10^{-8}$ C/V
$= 5.0 \times 10^{-8}\text{ F} = 0.050\ \mu\text{F}$

Practice Problems

13. A 27-μF capacitor has a potential difference of 25 V across it. What is the charge on the capacitor?

14. Both a 3.3-μF and a 6.8-μF capacitor are connected across a 15-V potential difference. Which capacitor has a greater charge? What is it?

15. The same two capacitors are each charged to 2.5×10^{-4} C. Across which is the potential difference larger? What is it?

▶ **16.** A 2.2-μF capacitor is first charged so that the potential difference is 6.0 V. How much *additional* charge is needed to increase the potential difference to 15.0 V?

CONCEPT REVIEW

2.1 If an oil drop with too few electrons is motionless in a Millikan oil drop apparatus,
a. what is the direction of the electric field?
b. which plate, upper or lower, is positively charged?

2.2 If the charge on a capacitor is changed, what is the effect on
a. the capacitance, C?
b. the potential difference, V?

2.3 If a large, charged sphere is touched by a smaller, uncharged sphere, as in Figure 21–9, what can be said about
a. the potentials of the two spheres?
b. the charges on the two spheres?

2.4 **Critical Thinking:** Suppose we have a large, hollow sphere that has been charged. Through a small hole in the sphere, we insert a small, uncharged sphere into the hollow interior. The two touch. What is the charge on the small sphere?

TRANSPARENCY

Use Transparency 28 with this section.

LABORATORY MANUAL

Use Lab 21.1 with this section.

CHAPTER 21 REVIEW

SUMMARY

21.1 Creating and Measuring Electric Fields

- An electric field exists around any charged object. The field produces forces on other charged bodies.
- The electric field intensity is the force per unit charge. The direction of the electric field is the direction of the force on a tiny, positive test charge.
- Electric field lines provide a picture of the electric field. They are directed away from positive charges and toward negative charges.

21.2 Applications of Electric Fields

- Electric potential difference is the change in potential energy per unit charge in an electric field. Potential differences are measured in volts.
- The electric field between two parallel plates is uniform between the plates except near the edges.
- Robert Millikan's experiments showed that electric charge is quantized and that the charge carried by an electron is -1.6×10^{-19} C.
- Charges will move in conductors until the electric potential is the same everywhere on the conductor.
- A charged object can have its excess charge removed by touching it to Earth or to an object touching Earth. This is called grounding.
- Electric fields are strongest near sharply-pointed conductors.
- Capacitance is the ratio of the charge on a body to its potential. The capacitance of a body is independent of the charge on the body and the potential difference across it.

KEY TERMS

electric field	potential difference
electric field lines	grounding
electric potential difference	capacitance
volt	capacitor

REVIEWING CONCEPTS

1. Draw the electric field lines between
   a. two like charges.
   b. two unlike charges.
2. What are the two properties a test charge must have?
3. How is the direction of an electric field defined?
4. What are electric field lines?
5. How is the strength of an electric field indicated with electric field lines?
6. What SI unit is used to measure electrical potential energy? electric potential?
7. What will happen to the electric potential energy of a charged particle in an electric field when the particle is released and free to move?
8. Define the volt in terms of the change in potential energy of a charge moving in an electric field.
9. Draw the electric field lines between two parallel plates of opposite charge.
10. Why does a charged object lose its charge when it is touched to the ground?
11. A charged rubber rod placed on a table maintains its charge for some time. Why is the charged rod not grounded immediately?
12. A metal box is charged. Compare the concentration of charge at the corners of the box to the charge concentration on the sides.
13. In your own words, describe a capacitor.

APPLYING CONCEPTS

1. What happens to the size of the electric field if the charge on the test charge is halved?
2. Does it require more energy or less energy to move a fixed positive charge through an increased electric field?
3. Figure 21–15 shows three spheres with charges of equal magnitude, but with signs as shown. Spheres *y* and *z* are held in place but sphere *x* is free to move. Initially sphere *x* is equidistant from spheres *y* and *z*. Choose the

CLOSING CHAPTER 21

Review Summary statements and Key Terms with your students.

ASSESSMENT

Vocabulary Review Master, Teacher Resource Package. Use this master to check students' understanding of Key Terms.

Evaluation Masters. Use Parts A and B of the Chapter Evaluation Masters from the Teacher Resource Package to test qualitative chapter objectives. Use Parts C and D to test quantitative chapter objectives.

Answers To
REVIEWING CONCEPTS

1. a. b.

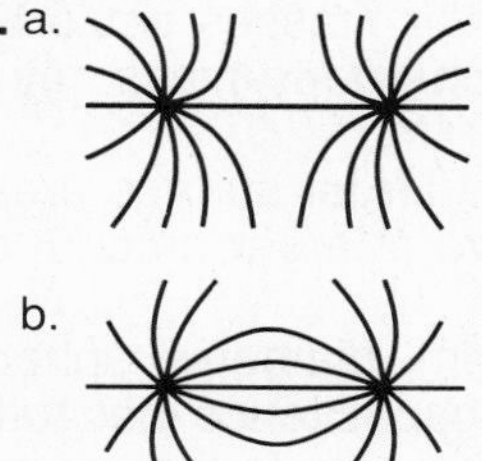

2. The test charge must be small in size and have a small positive charge.
3. The direction of an electric field is the direction of the force on a positive charge placed in the field. This would be away from a positive object and toward a negative object.
4. lines of force
5. The closer together the electric field lines are, the stronger the electric field.
6. electric potential energy-joule; electric potential-volt
7. The electric potential energy of the particle will be converted into kinetic energy of the particle.
8. The volt is related to the change in potential energy, *PE,* resulting from moving a test charge, *q,* a distance, *d,* in a uniform field of intensity, *E;* $V = \Delta PE/q = E \cdot d$.
9.

10. The charge is shared with the surface of Earth, which is an extremely large object.
11. The table is an insulator, or at least a very poor conductor.
12. The concentration of charge is greater at the corners.
13. A capacitor is a device that is made up of two conductors, or plates, isolated from each other by an insulator. As such, it stores charge. The larger the capacitance, the larger the charge that can be put on it for the same increase in the potential.

REVIEW MASTER

Use the Vocabulary Review master for Chapter 21 with this section.

EVALUATION MASTER

Use the Chapter Evaluation master for Chapter 21 with this section.

Answers To
APPLYING CONCEPTS

1. Nothing. Since the force on the test charge would also be halved, the ratio F/q' and the electric field would remain the same.
2. Energy is proportional to the force, and the force is proportional to the electric field. Therefore, it requires more energy.
3. Sphere x will follow path C. It will experience forces shown by D and B. The vector sum is C.
4. $V = \frac{J}{C} = \frac{N \cdot m}{C}$
$= \frac{kg\ m/s^2 \cdot m}{C} = \frac{kg\ m^2}{s^2\ C}$
5. They are parallel, equally spaced lines.
6. Slow. The larger the charge, the stronger the force, and thus the larger the (terminal) velocity.
7. a. No. Their masses could be different. **b.** charge-to-mass ratio, q/m (or m/q)
8. Tim has a larger surface area, so he will have a larger amount of charge.
9. The 10-cm diameter sphere has a larger capacitance because the charges can be farther apart, reducing potential rise as it is charged.
10. Change the voltage across the capacitor.

Answers To
PROBLEMS

Complete solutions for all Chapter Review Problems can be found in the Problems and Solutions Manual accompanying this text.

1. 2.0×10^4 N/C
2. 7.0×10^{-5} C
3. 4.4×10^{-7} C
4. a. downward
b. 2.4×10^{-17} N
c. one billion times smaller
5. a. -1.6×10^{-14} N, opposite the field
b. -1.8×10^{16} m/s^2
6. a. 1.2×10^{13} N/C, outward
b. -1.9×10^{-6} N, toward the nucleus
7. Refer to Problems and Solutions Manual.
8. Refer to Problems and Solutions Manual.
9. 4.0×10^{-3} N
10. 120 V
11. 1.4 J

path that sphere *x* will follow, assuming no other forces are acting.

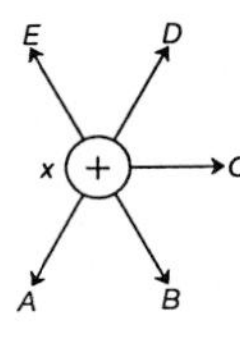

FIGURE 21–15. Use with Applying Concepts 3.

4. What is the unit of potential difference in terms of m, kg, s, and C?
5. What do the electric field lines look like when the electric field has the same strength at all points in a region?
6. When doing a Millikan oil drop experiment, it is best to work with drops that have small charges. Therefore, when the electric field is turned on, should you try to find drops that are moving fast or slow? Explain.
7. If two oil drops can be held motionless in a Millikan oil drop experiment,
a. can you be sure that the charges are the same?
b. the ratios of what two properties of the drops would have to be equal?
8. Tim and Sue are holding hands when they are given a charge while they are standing on an insulating platform. Tim is larger than Sue. Who has the larger amount of charge or do they both have the same amount?
9. Which has a larger capacitance, a 1-cm diameter or a 10-cm diameter aluminum sphere?
10. How can you store a different amount of charge in a capacitor?

PROBLEMS

21.1 Creating and Measuring Electric Fields

The charge on an electron is -1.60×10^{-19} C.

1. A positive charge of 1.0×10^{-5} C experiences a force of 0.20 N when located at a certain point. What is the electric field intensity at that point?
2. What charge exists on a test charge that experiences a force of 1.4×10^{-8} N at a point where the electric field intensity is 2.0×10^{-4} N/C?
3. A test charge has a force of 0.20 N on it when it is placed in an electric field intensity of 4.5×10^5 N/C. What is the magnitude of the charge?
4. The electric field in the atmosphere is about 150 N/C, downward.
a. What is the direction of the force on a positively-charged particle?
b. Find the electric force on a proton with charge $+1.6 \times 10^{-19}$ C.
c. Compare the force in **b** with the force of gravity on the same proton (mass 1.7×10^{-27} kg).

▶ **5.** Electrons are accelerated by the electric field in a television picture tube, Table 21–1.
a. Find the force on an electron.
b. If the field is constant, find the acceleration of the electron (mass $= 9.11 \times 10^{-31}$ kg).

▶ **6.** A lead nucleus has the charge of 82 protons.
a. What is the direction and magnitude of the electric field at 1.0×10^{-10} m from the nucleus?
b. Use Coulomb's law to find the direction and magnitude of the force exerted on an electron located at this distance.

7. Carefully sketch
a. the electric field produced by a $+1.0$ μC charge.
b. the electric field due to a $+2.0$ μC charge. Make the number of field lines proportional to the change in charge.
8. Charges X, Y, and Z are all equidistant from each other. X has a $+1.0$ μC charge, Y a $+2.0$ μC charge, and Z a small negative charge.
a. Draw an arrow showing the force on charge Z.
b. Charge Z now has a small positive charge on it. Draw an arrow showing the force on it.
9. A positive test charge of 8.0×10^{-5} C is placed in an electric field of 50.0-N/C intensity. What is the strength of the force exerted on the test charge?

21.2 Applications of Electric Fields

10. If 120 J of work are done to move one coulomb of charge from a positive plate to a negative plate, what voltage difference exists between the plates?

11. How much work is done to transfer 0.15 C of charge through a potential difference of 9.0 V?

12. An electron is moved through a potential difference of 500 V. How much work is done on the electron?

13. A 12-V battery does 1200 J of work transferring charge. How much charge is transferred?

▶ 14. A force 0.053 N is required to move a charge of 37 μC a distance of 25 cm in an electric field. What is the size of the potential difference between the two points?

15. The electric field intensity between two charged plates is 1.5×10^3 N/C. The plates are 0.080 m apart. What is the potential difference, in volts, between the plates?

16. A voltmeter indicates that the difference in potential between two plates is 50.0 V. The plates are 0.020 m apart. What electric field intensity exists between them?

17. A negatively-charged oil drop weighs 8.5×10^{-15} N. The drop is suspended in an electric field intensity of 5.3×10^3 N/C.
   a. What is the charge on the drop?
   b. How many electrons does it carry?

▶ 18. In an early set of experiments (1911), Millikan observed that the following measured charges, among others, appeared at different times on a single oil drop. What value of elementary charge can be deduced from these data?
   a. 6.563×10^{-19} C **f.** 18.08×10^{-19} C
   b. 8.204×10^{-19} C **g.** 19.71×10^{-19} C
   c. 11.50×10^{-19} C **h.** 22.89×10^{-19} C
   d. 13.13×10^{-19} C **i.** 26.13×10^{-19} C
   e. 16.48×10^{-19} C

19. A capacitor that is connected to a 45.0-V source contains 90.0 μC of charge. What is the capacitor's capacitance?

20. A 5.4-μF capacitor is charged with 2.7×10^{-3} C. What potential difference exists across it?

21. What is the charge in a 15.0-pf capacitor when it is connected across a 75.0-V source?

▶ 22. The energy stored in a capacitor with capacitance C, having a potential difference V, is given by $W = \frac{1}{2}CV^2$. One application is in the electronic photoflash or strobe light. In such a unit, a capacitor of 10.0 μF is charged to 3.00×10^2 V. Find the energy stored.

▶ 23. Suppose it took 30 s to charge the capacitor in the previous problem.
   a. Find the power required to charge it in this time.
   b. When this capacitor is discharged through the strobe lamp, it transfers all its energy in 1.0×10^{-4} s. Find the power delivered to the lamp.
   c. How is such a large amount of power possible?

▶ 24. Lasers are used to try to produce controlled fusion reactions that might supply large amounts of electrical energy. The lasers require brief pulses of energy that are stored in large rooms filled with capacitors. One such room has a capacitance of 61×10^{-3} F charged to a potential difference of 10 kV.
   a. Find the energy stored in the capacitors, given $W = \frac{1}{2}CV^2$.
   b. The capacitors are discharged in 10 ns (1.0×10^{-8} s). What power is produced?
   c. If the capacitors are charged by a generator with a power capacity of 1.0 kW, how many seconds will be required to charge the capacitors?

USING LAB SKILLS

1. In the Pocket Lab on page 426, does the angle of the thread show the direction of the electric field? Explain. Make a sketch as part of your answer.
2. In the Pocket Lab on page 436, you measured the mass of three groups of balls. Based on these measurements, predict what other values should occur if you continue to measure a random number of balls.

THINKING PHYSIC-LY

Why are many parts of stereo components covered with metal boxes or containers?

12. -8.00×10^{-17} J
13. 1.0×10^2 C
14. 3.6×10^2 V
15. 1.2×10^2 V
16. 2.5×10^3 N/C
17. **a.** 1.6×10^{-18} C
b. 10 electrons
18. 1.63×10^{-19} C
19. 2.00 μF
20. 5.0×10^2 V
21. 1.13×10^{-9} C
22. 0.450 J
23. **a.** 2×10^{-2} W
b. 4.5 kW
c. Power is inversely proportional to the time.
24. **a.** 3.1×10^6 J
b. 3.1×10^{14} W
c. 3.1×10^3 s

Answers To
USING LAB SKILLS

1. No. The angle of the thread may indicate the electric force on the ball compared to the force of gravity. The electric field near the center of the foam is horizontal, but near the surface of Earth, the thread will never be horizontal.

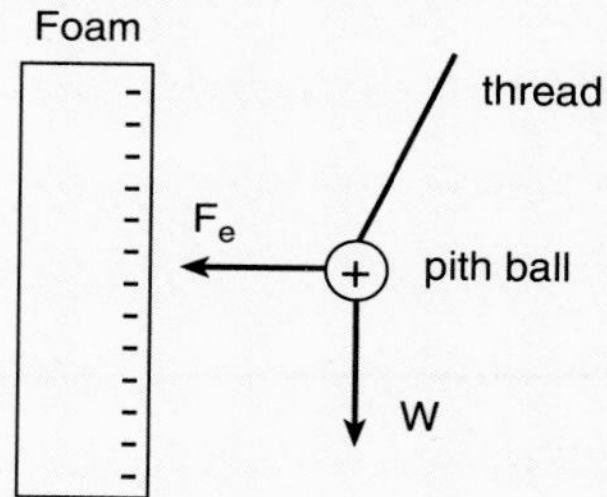

2. Since each measurement involves a whole number of balls, other masses can be predicted as sums and differences of the original measurements.

Answer To
THINKING PHYSIC-LY

Besides providing physical protection, the metal coverings (conductors) shield the components from unwanted external electric fields that would interfere with performance. (The charges remain on the surface of the boxes.)

CHAPTER
22 Current Electricity

PLANNING GUIDE (6 class sessions)

CONTENTS	TEXT FEATURES	TEACHER RESOURCE PACKAGE	OTHER COMPONENTS
22.1 Current and Circuits, pp. 448–457 (3 Class Sessions) • Producing Electric Current • Electric Circuits • Rates of Charge Flow and Energy Transfer • Resistance and Ohm's Law • Diagramming Circuits	**Physics Lab:** Mystery Cans, p. 456 **Pocket Lab:** Lighting Up, p. 451 **Pocket Lab:** Running Out, p. 455 **Problem Solving Strategy:** Drawing Schematic Diagrams, p. 455 **Concept Review,** p. 457	**Study Guide:** Current and Circuits **Physics Lab Data Sheet:** Mystery Cans **Enrichment Master:** Resistance **Transparency Worksheet:** Circuit Symbols **Transparency Worksheet:** Circuit and Circuit Diagram	**Laboratory Manual:** Lab 22.1 Ohm's Law **Transparency 31:** Circuit Symbols **Transparency 32:** Circuit and Circuit Diagram **Physics Skill Master 16**
22.2 Using Electrical Energy, pp. 457–463 (3 Class Sessions) • Energy Transfer in Electric Circuits • Transmission of Electric Energy • The Kilowatt Hour	**Physics and Technology:** Ultra-High Voltage Electric Power Transmission, p. 463 **Pocket Lab:** Heating Up, p. 458 **Pocket Lab:** Appliances, p. 462 **Concept Review,** p. 463	**Study Guide:** Using Electrical Energy **Reteaching Master:** Converting Energy **Critical Thinking Master:** Future Energy Uses	**Laboratory Manual:** Lab 22.2 Electric Equivalent of Heat
Chapter Review, pp. 464–467	Summary Key Terms Reviewing Concepts Applying Concepts Problems Thinking Physic-ly	**Vocabulary Review** **Chapter Test**	**Test Bank**

SUPPLEMENTARY MATERIALS

SOFTWARE	AUDIOVISUAL	BOOKS/MAGAZINES
Electric Bill, Queue, Inc. (Apple II). *MMV Electricity,* Queue, Inc. (Apple II, IBM PC, Macintosh). *Introduction to General Physics, Disk V: Electrical Charge and Direct Current,* COMPress/Queue, Inc. (Apple II, IBM PC, Macintosh).	Video: *The Mechanical Universe and Beyond: Electric Circuits* and *Magnets,* Films Inc. Filmstrip: *Exploring Electricity,* Clearvue.	Bauman, Robert P., and Adams, Saleh. "Misunderstandings of Electric Current." *The Physics Teacher,* May 1990, p. 334. Bransky, Judith. "Superconductivity—A New Demonstration." *The Physics Teacher,* September 1990, p. 392. Ihas, G.G., and Meisel, M.W. "Teaching Superconductivity via Analogy." *The Physics Teacher,* November 1990, p. 554. Leff, Harvey S. "Illuminating Physics with Light Bulbs." *The Physics Teacher,* January 1990, p. 30.

PROBLEM CORRELATION

CONCEPTS	CHAPTER REVIEW			PROBLEMS APPENDIX
	Reviewing Concepts	Applying Concepts	Problems	
22.1 Current and Circuits				
Producing Electric Current				
Electric Circuits	1	1		
Rates of Charge Flow and Energy Transfer	2,4		1,2,3,4,5,6,**7**	**1,2,3,4,5**
Resistance and Ohm's Law	3,5,6	2,3,4,5,6,7,8	8,9,10,11,12,13, 14,15,**16**,17,**18**	6,7,8,9,10,11
Diagramming Circuits	7,8	9	**19,20**	
22.2 Using Electrical Energy				
Energy Transfer in Electric Circuits	9,10	10	21,22,23,24,25,**26**	12,13,**14**
Transmission of Electric Energy	11			
The Kilowatt Hour			27,**28,29**	15,**16**

ACTIVITY AND DEMONSTRATION MATERIALS

PHYSICS LAB	POCKET LAB	DEMONSTRATIONS
Page 456 film cans (with a resistor inside) 0–6 V variable power supply wires ammeter voltmeter	Pages 451, 455, 458, 462 D cell 10 cm of wire (with bare ends) 0–6 V DC power supply wires 2 miniature lamps and sockets ammeter 3 different power resistors (1Ω, 5Ω, 15Ω and 10-W ratings) power supply ammeter	Pages 452, 460, 460 2 batteries (or other low-voltage power sources) flashlight bulb DC power supply voltmeter farad capacitor immersion heater water cup

EXTENSION PROJECTS

LIBRARY RESEARCH

1. Integrated Circuit
What is an integrated circuit? How and for what purpose is it used? When was it invented?

DISPLAY MODEL

2. Voltaic Pile
Build a working model of a voltaic pile. Demonstrate how it works to the class.

STUDENT READINGS

Cava, Robert J. "Superconductivity Beyond 1-2-3." *Scientific American,* August 1990.

Peterson, I. "Supercurrent Decay in High Magnetic Fields." *Science News,* April 1, 1990.

Raloff, J. "EPA Suggests ELF Fields Can Cause Cancer." *Science News,* June 30, 1990.

Triestly, Harry. "All About Thermistors." *Radio Electronics,* January 1985.

Yulsman, Tom. "Light at the End of the Tunnel." *Discover,* November 1988.

Chapter 22

Current Electricity

CHAPTER OVERVIEW

Theme Development: The conceptual flow model of electric current behavior is studied within the boundaries of an electric circuit, a closed system. Within this context the conservative relationship between current, potential difference, and power may be described mathematically and modeled pictorially.

MISCONCEPTIONS

Students may have trouble with the nature and function of resistors. Drawing electrical circuit schematics from abstract verbal descriptions causes problems.

KEY TERMS

ampere
battery
conventional current
electric circuit
electric current
kilowatt hour
parallel connection
photovoltaic cell
potentiometer
resistance
resistors
schematic
series connection

Laboratory Options

STUDENT EDITION

Physics Lab

Mystery Cans	456

Pocket Labs

Lighting Up	451
Running Out	455
Heating Up	458
Appliances	462

TEACHER EDITION

Activities

Demonstration	452, 460, 460
Cooperative Learning	454, 461, 462
Discovery	461

LABORATORY MANUAL

Ohm's Law	Lab 22.1
Electric Equivalent of Heat	Lab 22.2

CHAPTER 22 Current Electricity

◀ More for Less?

High-voltage power transmission lines, such as these 765-kV lines, crisscross our country. It would seem to be cheaper to eliminate all transformers and simply transmit electrical energy at the voltage used in the home. Why is this not true?

Chapter Outline

The most important aspects of electrical energy are its ability to be transferred efficiently over long distances and its ability to be changed into other forms of energy. The large amounts of natural potential and kinetic energy possessed by resources such as Niagara Falls are of little use to an industrial complex one hundred kilometers away unless that energy can be transferred efficiently. Electrical energy provides the means to transfer large quantities of energy great distances with little loss. This transfer is usually done at very high potentials, such as the 765 000 volts in the power line pictured.

✓ Concept Check

The following terms or concepts from earlier chapters are important for a good understanding of this chapter. If you are not familiar with them, you should review them before studying this chapter.
- power, forms of energy, Chapters 10,11
- electric charge and potentials, Chapters 20, 21

Introducing The Chapter

More for Less?

Using The Photo: High-voltage electrical power distribution lines dot our landscape. They're perhaps the most common reminder of our dependence on electricity. A great deal of engineering work has gone into making them so reliable.

The answer to the question asked in the caption can be found on page 461.

✓ Concept Check

Make sure students have a clear understanding of the concepts taught in Chapters 10, 11, 20, and 21 that are listed in the Concept Check. Students who understand the behavior of electricity as a fundamental energy form will be prepared to study electric circuits and devices, which are examined in this chapter.

Assessment Options

Portfolio Assessment
Extension 1, TWE, p. 446b
Activity, TWE, pp. 454, 461
Enrichment, TWE, p. 458
Portfolio Assessment, TWE, p. 462

Performance Assessment
Extension 2, TWE, p. 446b
Pocket Labs, pp. 451, 455, 458, 462
Physics Lab, p. 456
Pocket Lab Assessment, TWE, p. 451
Using Lab Skills, p. 467

Content Assessment
Self Assessment: Practice Problems, pp. 451, 454, 457, 459, 463
Checking for Understanding, TWE, p. 453
Assessment, Critical Thinking, TWE, p. 456
Convergent Question, TWE, p. 462
Concept Reviews, pp. 457, 463
Chapter Review, pp. 464–467
Supplemental Questions, pp. 703–704

Group Assessment
Activities for group assessment occur with Cooperative Learning and lab activities.

22.1 CURRENT AND CIRCUITS

Preparation

OBJECTIVES

The objectives are listed on the student page. Remind students to preview these objectives as a study guide to this major section.

OVERVIEW

This section covers the following basics: electric current, drawing schematic circuit diagrams, understanding energy and power in electric circuits, resistance and Ohm's law, and the use of ammeters and voltmeters.

BRIDGING

This section builds on several concepts from previous lessons, including power, forms of energy, electric charge, and electric potential.

1 Focus

DISCREPANT EVENT

Make a simple voltaic cell from a lemon, a bare copper wire or strip, and a zinc-coated nail. Use a galvanometer to show the flow of electricity and a voltmeter to show the potential difference. If possible, use the commercially available potato clock, which uses the same dissimilar metals in a potato to run a clock. You might also use a hand-cranked generator to light a light bulb, showing that work must be done to create electric energy.

Objectives

- **define an electric current and the ampere; describe conditions that permit current flow.**
- **be able to draw circuits; recognize they are closed loops; understand energy transfer in circuits.**
- **explain definition of power in electric circuits; solve problems involving current, potential difference, and power.**
- **define resistance; solve problems involving current, potential difference, and resistance.**
- **describe Ohm's law; be able to tell whether a device obeys Ohm's law.**
- **explain how current can be controlled in a circuit.**
- **diagram simple electric circuits; recognize the correct use of ammeters and voltmeters.**

22.1 CURRENT AND CIRCUITS

You have had many experiences with electric circuits. Every time you turn on a light, radio, or television, or turn the ignition key to start a car, or turn on a flashlight, you complete an electric circuit. Electric current flows and energy is transferred. In this section you will learn how these events came about.

Producing Electric Current

Charged particles flow around a closed loop called a circuit.

In Chapter 21 we discussed what happened when two conducting spheres at different potentials touched. When they touched, charges flowed from the object at a higher potential to the one at a lower potential. The flow continued until the potentials were equal.

A flow of charged particles is called an **electric current**. In some conductors, negatively-charged electrons move; in others, positively charged particles move. In this text, we will always assume that positive charges move as the result of a potential difference. In Figure 22–1a, two conductors, *A* and *B*, are at different potentials and connected by a wire conductor, *C*. Charges flow from *B* to *A* through *C*. The flow stops when the potentials of *A*, *B*, and *C* are equal. How could you keep the flow going? You would have to maintain a potential difference between *B* and *A*. This could be done by pumping charged particles from conductor *A* back to conductor *B*. The electrical potential energy of the charges would have to be increased by this pump, so it would require external energy to run. The electric energy could come from one of several other forms of energy. A familiar source, a voltaic or galvanic cell (a common dry cell) converts chemical energy to electric energy. Several cells connected together are called a **battery**. A **photovoltaic cell**, or solar cell, changes light energy into electric energy. A generator, driven by moving water, rushing steam, or the wind, converts kinetic energy into electric energy.

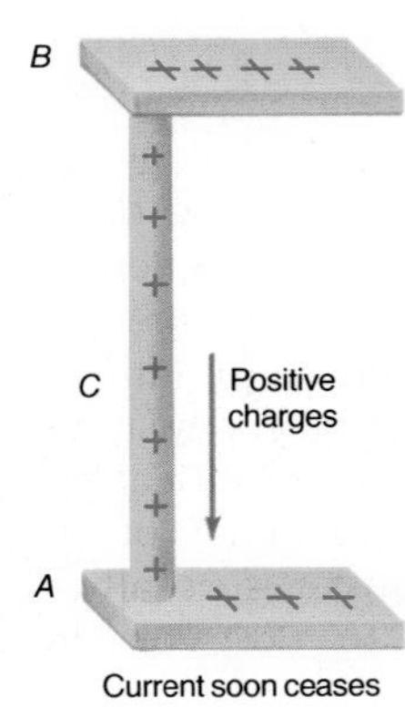

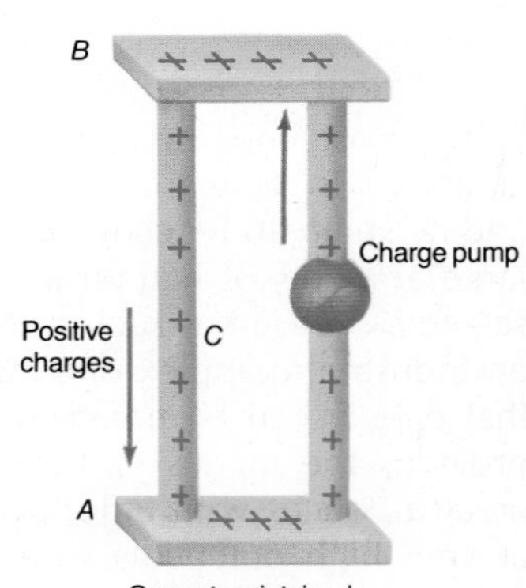

FIGURE 22–1. Positive charges flow from the positive to the negative plate (a). A generator (b) pumps the positive charges back to the positive plate, allowing current to continue to flow.

TEACHER 

It turns out that charges move down metal wires at average speeds under one millimeter per second. This can be derived easily for students:

Suppose 1 amp flows through a square wire, 1 mm across. In 1 s, 1 C of charge flows. One C = 6.25×10^{18} electrons. Each copper atom contributes one electron to the flow. What volume of copper contains 1 C of charge? How many moles are in 1 coulomb?

$$n = \frac{6.25 \times 10^{18} \text{ (atoms)}}{6.02 \times 10^{23} \text{ (atoms per mole)}} = 1.04 \times 10^{-5} \text{ mole.}$$

Copper is 63.5 g/mole with density 8.9 g/cm^3, so

$$V = \frac{(1.04 \times 10^{-5} \text{ mole})(63.5 \text{ g/mole})}{(8.9 \text{ g/cm}^3)} = 7.4 \times 10^{-5} \text{ cm}^3.$$

This is a 0.07-mm length of a 1-mm^2 wire. Thus the average speed of the electrons is less than 0.1 mm/s.

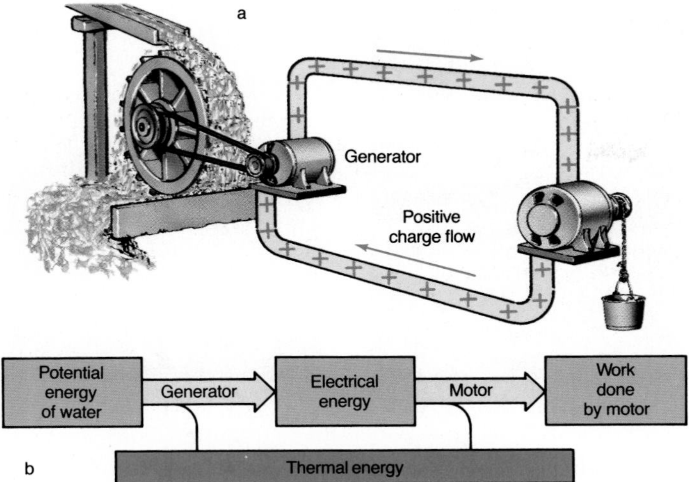

FIGURE 22–2. The potential energy of the waterfall is eventually converted into work done raising the bucket (a). The production and use of electric current is not 100% efficient. Some thermal energy is produced by the splashing water, friction, and electrical resistance.

Electric Circuits

The charges in Figure 22–1b move around a closed loop from the pump through *B* to *C* to *A*, and back to the pump. Such a closed loop is called an **electric circuit**. A circuit consists of a charge pump that increases the potential energy of the charges connected to a device that reduces the potential energy of the charges. The change in potential energy of the charge (qV) can be converted into some other form of energy. A motor converts electric energy to kinetic energy. A lamp changes electric energy into light. A heater converts electric energy into thermal energy.

A charge pump increases the potential energy of the charges. Batteries, generators, and photovoltaic cells are charge pumps.

Charged particles flowing through any of these energy conversion devices lose electric potential energy. Any device that reduces the potential energy of charges flowing through it is said to have resistance.

The charge pump creates the flow of charged particles, or current. Consider a generator driven by a waterwheel, Figure 22–2a. The water falls as it rotates the waterwheel and generator. Thus its potential energy is converted to electric energy by the generator. The generator increases the electric potential difference, V, between *B* and *A* as it removes charges from wire *B* and adds them to wire *A*. Energy in the amount qV is needed to increase the potential of the charges. This energy comes from the loss of potential energy of the water. No generator, however, is 100% efficient. Only 98% of the kinetic energy put into most generators is converted into electric energy. The remainder becomes thermal energy; the temperature of the generator increases, Figure 22–2b.

If wires *A* and *B* are connected to a motor, the charges in wire *A* flow through the wires in the motor. The flow continues through wire *B* back to the generator. A motor converts electric energy to kinetic energy. Like generators, motors are not 100% efficient. Typically, 90% of the electric energy is changed into kinetic energy.

Charge and Field Conventions

- *Positive charges are red.*
- *Negative charges are blue.*
- *Electric field lines are red.*
- ***Ammeters are blue.***
- ***Voltmeters are red.***

2 Teach

CONCEPT DEVELOPMENT

- Many students will see no connection between frictional, or static, electricity and voltaic, or current, electricity. Pose the question "How do we know they are the same?" The answer is that they have the same effects. The two effects you can mention at this point are the fact that they both produce sparks and they both hurt when they flow through you.
- The necessary characteristics of a circuit are not that obvious to a student. Draw separate drawings of batteries and bulbs and ask how to connect them into a complete circuit. In particular, the idea that a circuit must be a complete loop should be reinforced.
- Students may have trouble with schematic diagrams simply because the representations are so abstract. Make a small display of electrical devices such as wires, switches, resistors, ammeters, batteries, voltmeters, and so on, so that students can see in a hands-on way what they will be representing with symbols. Diagramming something you've never seen is tough!

Physics Skill Master, Teacher Resource Package. To familiarize students with handling actual electric circuits, assign the Physics Skill Master, Using Ammeters and Voltmeters.

RETEACHING

Transparency Package. Reteach the symbols for electrical devices using Transparency 31 and accompanying worksheet.

Study Guide Master. To reinforce the concepts in this section, have the students complete the Study Guide Master for Section 22.1 from the Teacher Resource Package.

SKILL MASTER

Use the Physics Skill master for Chapter 22 with this section.

STUDY GUIDE MASTER

Use the Study Guide master for section 22.1.

TRANSPARENCY

Use Transparency 31 with this section.

CONCEPT DEVELOPMENT

- There are inexpensive, commercially available plastic templates for drawing the standard circuit elements.
- Remember that the definition of electric potential *(V)* is the potential energy *(PE)* divided by the charge *(q)*. Therefore, solving for *PE,* we get $PE = qV$. (See Chapter 21.)
- To help prevent misunderstanding conventional current and electron flow, you might want to use the following idea. Start by drawing a collection of negative charges on the left and a similar collection of positive charges on the right. Then draw a wire connecting the two collections. If negative charge flows, what happens? Then draw the same setup again, only this time suppose that positive charge flows. Again, ask what happens. It can be seen that both situations produce identical effects. So electron flow of a certain rate in one direction is equivalent in its effects to conventional current of the same rate in the opposite direction.

a

b

c

FIGURE 22–3. Sources of electric energy include chemical, solar, hydrodynamic, wind, and nuclear energies.

You know that charges can't be created or destroyed, only separated. Thus, the total amount of charge (number of negative electrons and positive ions) in the circuit does not change. If one coulomb flows through the generator in one second, one coulomb will also flow through the motor in one second. Thus, charge is a conserved quantity. Energy is also conserved. The change in electric energy, E, equals qV. Since q is conserved, the net change in potential energy of the charges going completely around the circuit must be zero. The potential increase produced by the generator equals the potential drop across the motor.

If the difference in potential between the two wires is 120 V, the generator must do 120 J of work on each coulomb of positive charge that it transfers from the more negative wire to the more positive wire. Every coulomb of positive charge that moves from the more positive wire through the motor and back to the more negative wire delivers 120 J of energy to the motor. Thus electric energy serves as a way to transfer the initial potential energy of falling water to the kinetic energy of a turning motor.

F.Y.I.

In bright sunlight, the winner of the 1993 U.S. solar-powered automobile competition produced electrical energy at a rate of 1500 J/s (1.5 kW), about enough to power a hair dryer. By comparison, sub-compact car engines typically produce 50 kW.

Rates of Charge Flow and Energy Transfer

One watt of power is the transfer of one joule of energy each second.

Power measures the rate at which energy is transferred. If a generator transfers one joule of kinetic energy to electric energy each second, it is transferring energy at the rate of one joule per second, or one watt.

The energy carried by an electric current depends on the charge transferred and the potential difference across which it moves, $E = qV$. The unit used for quantity of electric charge is the coulomb. Thus the rate of flow of electric charge, or electric current, I, is measured in coulombs per second. A flow of one coulomb per second is called an **ampere**, A.

One ampere of current is the flow of a coulomb of charge each second.

$$1 \text{ C/s} = 1 \text{ A}$$

The ampere is named for the French scientist Andre Marie Ampere (1775–1836). A device that measures current is called an ammeter. The flow of positive charge is called **conventional current.**

TEACHER F.Y.I.

A word here on conventional current. Only in metals do electrons carry all the current, although no macroscopic observations can prove this. In electrolysis, conduction is mainly by positive ions; in plasmas, both types of ions carry the charge; and in many semiconductors, positive "holes" carry it. Further, in all technical and trade applications of electricity and electronics, conventional currents are used.

Suppose that the current through the motor shown in Figure 22–2 is 3.0 C/s (3.0 A). Since the potential difference is 120 V, each coulomb of charge supplies the motor with 120 J of energy. The power, or energy delivered to the motor per second, is

$$(120 \text{ J/C})(3.0 \text{ C/s}) = 360 \text{ J/s} = 360 \text{ W}.$$

The power of an electric device is found by multiplying the potential difference, V, by the current, I, or $P = VI$.

Power is the product of potential difference and current, $P = VI$.

Example Problem

Electric Power

A 6-V battery delivers a 0.5-A current to an electric motor that is connected across its terminals. **a.** What power is consumed by the motor? **b.** How much electric energy is delivered in 5.0 min?

Given: $V = 6$ V, $I = 0.5$ A, $t = 5.0$ min (300 s)

Unknowns: **a.** P **b.** E

Basic equations: **a.** $P = VI$ **b.** $P = E/t$

Solution:

a. $P = VI = (6 \text{ V})(0.5 \text{ A}) = (6 \text{ J/C})(0.5 \text{ C/s}) = 3 \text{ J/s} = 3 \text{ W}$

b. $P = E/t$, so $E = Pt = (3 \text{ W})(300 \text{ s}) = 900 \text{ J}$

Practice Problems

1. The current through a light bulb connected across the terminals of a 120-V outlet is 0.5 A. At what rate does the bulb convert electric energy to light?
2. A car battery causes a current of 2.0 A to flow through a lamp while 12 V is across it. What is the power used by the lamp?
3. What current flows through a 75-W light bulb connected to a 120-V outlet?
4. ▶ The current through the starter motor of a car is 210 A. If the battery keeps 12 V across the motor, what electric energy is delivered to the starter in 10.0 s?

Resistance and Ohm's Law

Suppose two conductors have a potential difference between them. If you connect them with a copper rod, a large current will flow. If, on the other hand, you put a glass rod between them, there will be almost no current. The property that determines how much current will flow is called the **resistance**. Resistance is measured by placing a potential difference across two points on a conductor and measuring the current that flows. The resistance, R, is defined to be the ratio of the potential difference, V, to the current, I,

$$R = \frac{V}{I}.$$

Resistance is the ratio of potential drop to current flow, $R = V/I$.

POCKET LAB

LIGHTING UP

Use a D cell and 10-cm length of wire to light a miniature lamp. Make a sketch of two ways that work and two ways that do not work. Can you light the lamp without having two connecting points on the lamp? Does a lamp connected in your house have two connecting points? Suggest a reason why two are needed.

CONCEPT DEVELOPMENT

Some teachers like to use a water analogy for teaching circuits. (Like all analogies, though, it has its limitations.) Electric current is compared to the flow of water in a pipe. Electric potential is similar to water pressure. A source of potential is like a water pump. Charge does not pile up anywhere in a circuit. If a certain amount of charge per time passes one point in a circuit consisting of a single loop, that same amount of charge per time must pass every other point in the circuit. Again, charge does not get lost or used up in a circuit.

Answers To
PRACTICE PROBLEMS

Have students refer to Appendix A of the Solutions Appendix for complete solutions to Practice Problems.

1. 60 W
2. 24 W
3. 0.63 A
4. 2.5×10^4 J

POCKET LAB

LIGHTING UP

Purpose: to construct a simple series circuit, demonstrating that a lamp must be part of a continuous loop.

Materials: D cell; 10 cm of wire (with bare ends); miniature lamp.

Outcome: A continuous path from cell to lamp to cell is needed for success. The cell must be connected on the bottom and top. The lamp must be connected on the side of the base and also at the tip of the base. Even in a household lamp, two connections are required. (The electrical cord contains two separate wires.)

Assessment

Performance

To further assess students' understanding of simple circuits, have them explore the construction of a light bulb. They should wear safety goggles and work with supervision. Wrap the glass with several layers of cloth, then hit it with a hammer. Carefully discard the cloth and broken glass. Using a pair of pliers, carefully remove all remaining pieces of glass from around the metal base. It is now possible to identify the filament, the thin wire between the two rigid supports. Trace the supports into the glass base. One is connected to the threaded part of the metal base, while the other goes to the central contact. Have students make a sketch showing the path and marking all insulating material.

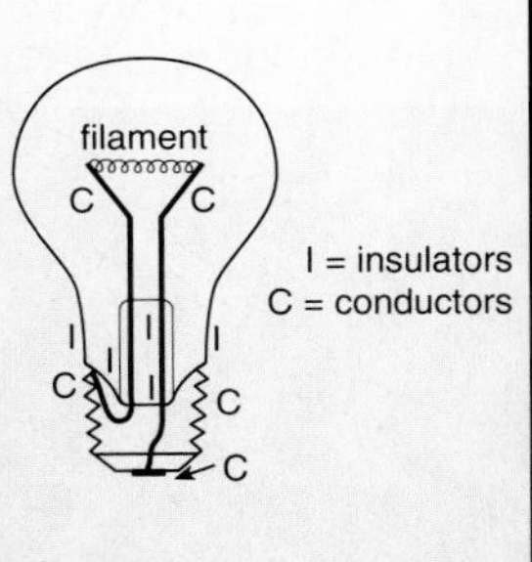

CONCEPT DEVELOPMENT

- The ampere is a convenient size. Currents in most household circuits are a few amperes and currents in most common electronic devices are from tens to hundreds of milliamperes. This means the ampere in ordinary usage need not be expressed in numbers small enough or large enough for scientific notation.
- The concept of controlling current is far from obvious for most students. Emphasize qualitative changes from the beginning; an ability to plug in numbers does not show understanding!

Demonstration: Begin with a battery (or other low-voltage power source) and a flashlight bulb. Have students observe the bulb's brightness. Then connect a second bulb in series. Brightness drops. Students can infer that current also drops. Suggest that they think of the bulb as an obstruction to current flow—a resistance. Put a second battery in series to restore the decreased brightness. Reverse the connections at one battery to show that the direction of the "charge pump" is important.

- Problem 14 of the Chapter Review lists some typical numbers giving the sizes of currents resulting in different levels of electric shock.

FIGURE 22–4. The current flow through a simple circuit (a) can be regulated by removing some of the dry cells (b) or increasing the resistance of the circuit (c).

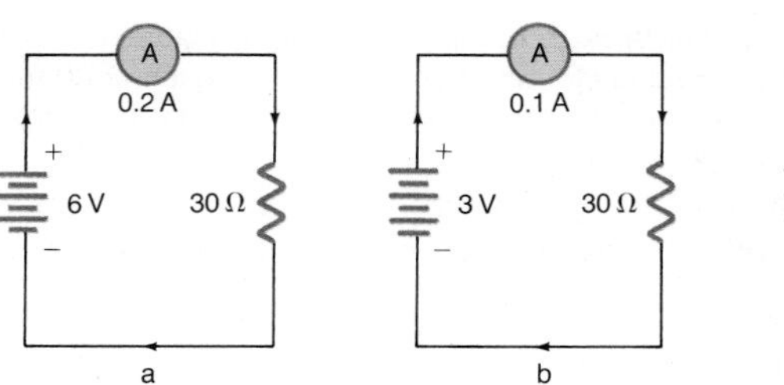

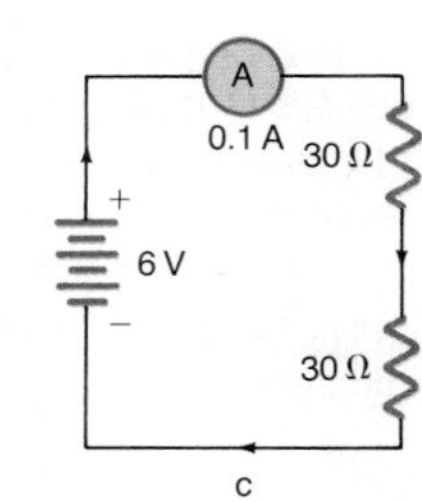

The electric current, I, is in amperes. The potential difference, V, is in volts. The resistance of the conductor, R, is measured in ohms. One ohm, 1 Ω, is the resistance that permits a current of 1 A to flow when a potential difference of 1 V is applied across the resistance.

The German scientist Georg Simon Ohm (1787–1854) measured the resistance of many conductors. He found that *the resistance for most conductors does not depend on size or direction of the potential difference across it.* A device that has a constant resistance that is independent of the potential difference is said to obey Ohm's law.

For a device that obeys Ohm's law, resistance is independent of voltage.

Most metallic conductors obey Ohm's law, at least over a limited range of voltages. Many important devices, however, do not. A transistor radio or pocket calculator contains many devices, such as transistors and diodes, that do not obey Ohm's law. Even a light bulb has a resistance that depends on the voltage and does not obey Ohm's law.

Wires used to connect electric devices have very small resistances. One meter of a typical wire used in physics labs has a resistance of about 0.03 Ω. Wires used in house wiring offer as little as 0.004 Ω resistance for each meter of length. **Resistors** are devices designed to have a specific resistance. They may be made of long, thin wires, graphite, or semiconductors.

Superconductors are materials that have zero resistance. There is no potential drop, V, across a superconductor. Since the power dissipated in a conductor is given by the product IV, a superconductor can conduct electricity without loss of energy. The development of superconductors that can be cooled by relatively inexpensive liquid nitrogen may lead to more efficient transfer of energy by electricity.

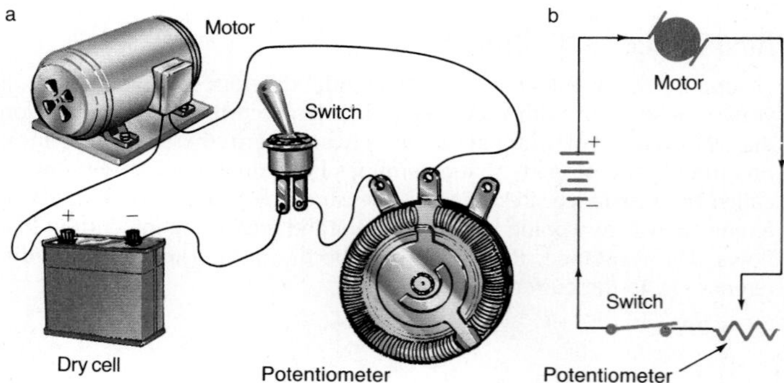

FIGURE 22–5. A potentiometer can be used to regulate current in an electric circuit.

TEACHER F.Y.I.

In Ohm's day it was not possible to go to the hardware store and buy wire, something we take for granted today. Fortunately, Georg learned how to make wire helping his father, who made his living as a locksmith.

There are two ways to control the current in a circuit. Since $I = V/R$, I can be changed by varying either V or R, or both. Figure 22–4a shows a simple circuit. When V is 6 V and R is 30 Ω, the current flow is 0.2 A. How could the current be reduced to 0.1 A?

The larger the potential difference, or voltage, placed across a resistor, the larger the current that passes through it. If the current through a resistor is to be cut in half, the drop in potential is cut in half. In Figure 22–4b, the voltage applied across the resistor has been reduced from 6 V to 3 V to reduce the current to 0.1 A. This may be an easy solution, since a 6-V battery is often made of two 3-V batteries connected in series.

A second way to reduce the current to 0.1 A is to increase the resistance to 60 Ω by adding a 30-Ω resistor to the circuit, Figure 22–4c. Both of these methods will reduce the current to 0.1 A. Resistors are often used to control the current in circuits or parts of circuits.

Sometimes a smooth, continuous variation of the current is desired. A lamp dimmer allows continuous rather than step-by-step change of light intensity. To achieve this kind of control, a potentiometer is used as a variable resistor, Figure 22–5. A **potentiometer** consists of a coil of resistance wire and a sliding contact point. By moving the contact point to various positions along the coil, the amount of wire added to the circuit is varied. As more wire is placed in the circuit, the resistance of the circuit increases; thus the current decreases in accordance with the equation $I = V/R$. In this way the light output of a lamp can be adjusted. This same type of device controls the speed of electric fans, electric mixers, and other appliances. To save space, the coil of wire is often bent into a circular shape and a sliding contact is moved by a knob, Figure 22–6.

Your body is a moderately good electrical conductor. If enough current flows through your body, your breathing or heart can be stopped. In addition, the power dissipated can burn you. If your skin is dry, its resistance is high enough to keep currents produced by small and moderate voltages low. If the skin becomes wet, however, its resistance is lower, and the currents can rise to dangerous levels, to tens of milliamps.

FIGURE 22–6. An inside view of a potentiometer.

Current can be changed by varying either voltage or resistance.

A variable resistor is called a potentiometer or rheostat.

Example Problem

Current Flow Through a Resistor

A 30-V battery maintains current through a 10-Ω resistance, Figure 22–7. What is the current?

Given: potential difference, $V = 30$ V; resistance, $R = 10\ \Omega$

Unknown: current, I

Basic equation: $R = V/I$

Solution: $R = \frac{V}{I}$, so $I = \frac{V}{R}$

$$= \frac{30\text{ V}}{10\ \Omega}$$

$$= 3.0\text{ A}$$

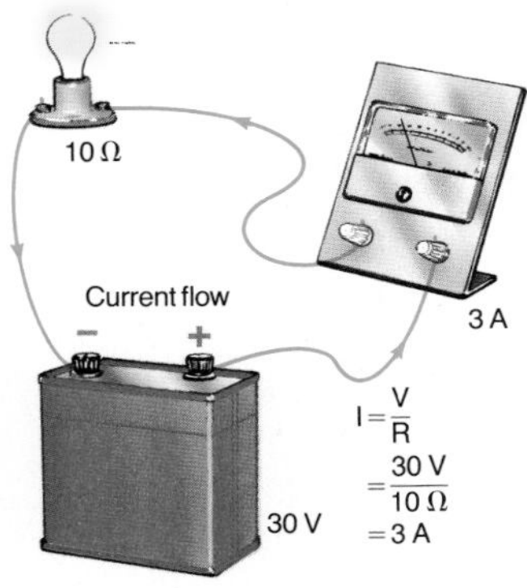

FIGURE 22–7. In a circuit having a 10-Ω resistance and 30-V battery, there is a 3-A current.

CHECKING FOR UNDERSTANDING

Choose one of the circuits drawn as a Practice Problem to put on the board. Ask questions such as what circuit device supplies energy, what circuit device uses energy, what device has resistance, through what device(s) does current flow, what is the direction of current flow, and so on. Students should rapidly answer such questions. Then, if needed, ask for numerical answers to quantitative questions.

RETEACHING

Take the students on a "charge's eye view" of an electric circuit. The journey starts with the energy of the positive charge being increased in the battery or power supply. The charge then moves down the connecting wires where relatively little happens until the charge meets a large resistance. Much of the charge's energy is given to the atoms of the resistor, causing thermal energy to flow out of the resistor and leaving the charge much less energetic.

Laboratory Manual. Give students additional experience with Ohm's law by doing Lab 22.1 from the Laboratory Manual.

EXTENSION

Many modern multimeters have a feature called continuity testing that indicates whether a circuit or a part of a circuit is a complete conducting path. Have interested students find out how such a testing circuit works. What is the circuit really measuring?

Enrichment Master. With this section, use the Enrichment Master for Chapter 22.

TEACHER F.Y.I.

The formula used to find the resistance of a piece of wire is $R = \rho L/A$. The letter ρ, rho, stands for resistivity; the value for ρ is found on a table of resistivity. The following metals and alloys are listed in order of increasing resistivity: silver, copper, gold, aluminum, and nichrome. Nichrome is often used in heating elements. Copper is usually used for connecting wires since its resistivity is low. The letter L is the length in m and A is the cross-sectional area in m^2.

The following equation finds the resistance of a piece of copper wire 2.0 m long and 2.0 mm in diameter. Its cross-sectional area will be πr^2. The resistivity of copper is $1.68 \times 10^{-8}\ \Omega$ m.

$$R = \frac{\rho L}{A} = \frac{\rho L}{\pi r^2}$$

$$= \frac{(1.68 \times 10^{-8}\Omega\text{ m})(2.0\text{ m})}{\pi(.001\text{ m})^2}$$

$$R = 1.1 \times 10^{-2}\Omega$$

Answers To
PRACTICE PROBLEMS

Have students refer to Appendix A of the Solutions Appendix for complete solutions to Practice Problems.

5. 0.40 A
6. 120 V
7. $2 \times 10^4\ \Omega$
8. a. 200 Ω
   b. 60 W
9. a. 0.63 A
   b. 190 Ω
10. a. 60 V
   b. 190 Ω
   c. 19 W

CONCEPT DEVELOPMENT

ACTIVITY

Cooperative Learning: Ask students to find examples of schematic drawings of circuits in their homes to share with the class. Ask them to identify some of the schematic symbols used. Ask them about the level of complexity in their examples.

Guided Practice: Go over the Example Problem on page 453, then have students work in class on the Practice Problems that follow. Offer assistance where needed.

INDEPENDENT PRACTICE/ EXTENSION

Refer to the Assignment Guide below for additional questions and problems for independent practice.

BIOLOGY CONNECTION

The resistance of the human body when the skin is dry is about $10^5\ \Omega$. It drops to about 1500 Ω for wet hands. Therefore, the current through the body from 120 V is about 1.2 mA for dry skin and 80 mA for wet skin. A person will feel a tingle at about 2 mA, at 10 to 20 mA there will be muscular effects, and by 20 mA a person will not be able to let go of a conducting wire. Respiratory paralysis occurs between 20 and 100 mA, and 100 mA to 3 A can be fatal.

Practice Problems

In all problems you should assume that the battery voltage is constant, no matter what current flows.

5. An automobile headlight with a resistance of 30 Ω is placed across a 12-V battery. What is the current through the circuit?

6. A motor with an operating resistance of 32 Ω is connected to a voltage source. The current in the circuit is 3.8 A. What is the voltage of the source?

7. A transistor radio uses 2×10^{-4} A of current when it is operated by a 3-V battery. What is the resistance of the radio circuit?

8. A lamp draws a current of 0.5 A when it is connected to a 120-V source.
   a. What is the resistance of the lamp?
   b. What is the power consumption of the lamp?

9. A 75-W lamp is connected to 120 V.
   a. How much current flows through the lamp?
   b. What is the resistance of the lamp?

▶ **10.** A resistor is now added in series with the lamp to reduce the current to half its original value.
   a. What is the potential difference across the lamp? Assume the lamp resistance is constant.
   b. How much resistance was added to the circuit?
   c. How much power is now dissipated in the lamp?

Diagramming Circuits

A schematic diagram uses symbols rather than pictures for components.

A simple circuit can be described in words. You can also use photographs or an artist's drawings of the parts. More frequently, a diagram of an electric circuit is drawn using standard symbols for the circuit elements. Such a diagram is called a circuit **schematic**. Some of the symbols are shown in Figure 22–8. Both an artist's drawing and a schematic of the same circuit are shown in Figure 22–9.

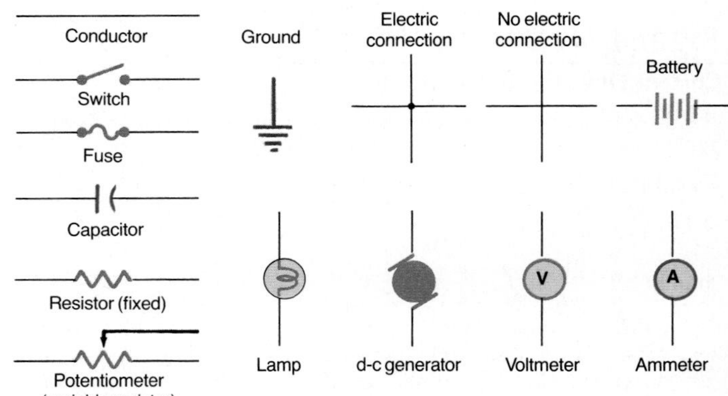

FIGURE 22–8. Electric circuit symbols.

LABORATORY MANUAL

Use Lab 22.1 with this section.

ENRICHMENT MASTER

Use the Enrichment master for Chapter 22 with this section.

TRANSPARENCY

Use Transparency 31 with this section.

22:1 ASSIGNMENT GUIDE

	PRACTICE	EXTENSION
CHAPTER REVIEW pp. 464–467		
· Reviewing Concepts	1–8	
· Applying Concepts		1–9
· Problems*	1–6, 8–15, 17	7, 16 18–20
APPENDIX B PROBLEMS*		
· Chapter 22, pp. 703–704	1–11	

* Complete solutions to all Chapter Review and Appendix problems appear in the Problems and Solutions Manual.

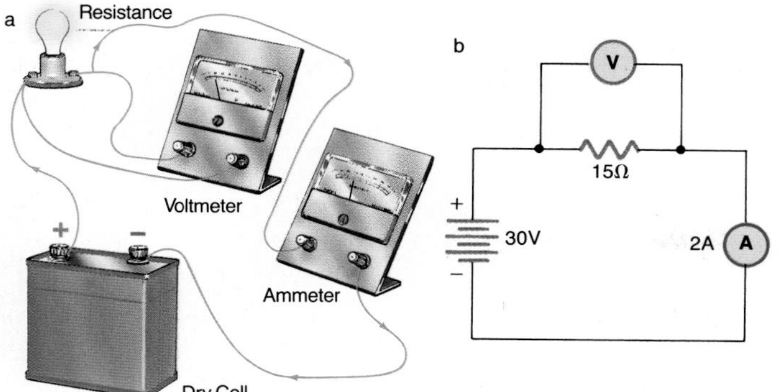

FIGURE 22–9. A simple electric circuit is represented both pictorially (a) and schematically (b).

Notice that in both the artist's drawing and the schematic, current is shown flowing out of the positive terminal of the battery. In metals, electrons are the mobile charged particles, but in other conductors the current can be carried by either positively- or negatively-charged particles. In diagramming electric circuits, we will draw current arrows in the direction that positive charge carriers would move. Often this is called a conventional current. The convention works because the effect of a negative charge moving from left to right is the same as that of a positive charge moving from right to left.

Ammeters measure current. They must be connected in series.

Voltmeters measure potential difference. They must be connected in parallel.

PROBLEM SOLVING STRATEGY

Drawing Schematic Diagrams

When drawing schematic diagrams, follow these steps.

1. Draw the symbol for the battery or other source of electric energy at the left side of the page. Put the positive terminal at the top.
2. Draw a wire following the conventional current out of the positive terminal. When you reach a resistor or other device, draw the symbol for it.
3. If you reach a point where there are two current paths, such as at a voltmeter, draw a + the diagram and follow one path until the two paths join again. Then draw the second path.
4. Follow the path until you reach the negative terminal of the battery.
5. Check your work to see that you have included all parts and that there are complete paths for current to follow.

Often instruments that measure current and voltage are connected into circuits. They must be connected in specific ways. An ammeter, which measures current, must be connected so there is only one current path. Such a connection is called a **series connection**, Figure 22–9. A voltmeter measures the potential difference across a circuit element. One voltmeter terminal is connected to one side of the element. The other terminal is connected to the other side. This connection is called a **parallel connection**. The potential difference across the element is equal to the potential difference across the voltmeter.

POCKET LAB

RUNNING OUT

Use the proper symbols and design a drawing that shows a power supply in a continuous circuit with two miniature lamps. Next draw the circuit with an ammeter included to measure the electrical flow between the power supply and the bulbs. Make a third drawing to show the ammeter at a position to measure the electrical flow between the bulbs. Would you predict the current between the lamps to be more or less than the current before the lamps? Why? Build the circuits to find out. Record your results.

CONCEPT DEVELOPMENT

Transparency Package. Use Transparency 31 to review circuit symbols.

Critical Thinking: In classroom discussion without referring back to the section just covered, develop the reasoning for using 220 V electrical power for running large appliances like electric stoves and air conditioners.

POCKET LAB

RUNNING OUT

Purpose: to draw and build simple circuits and to investigate current at different points in a series circuit.

Materials: 0–6 V DC power supply; wires; 2 miniature lamps and sockets; ammeter.

Outcome: The drawing can be used to help set up the actual equipment. The current is the same at different points in a series circuit.

3 Close

CONVERGENT QUESTION

The three quantities—potential difference, current, and resistance—are all used to describe an electrical circuit. Discuss which circuit element controls which quantity, and how charging one element will affect the others in a simple, one-loop (series) circuit.

Connect to CHEMISTRY

Standard dry cells have a zinc can that serves as the negative terminal (anode). Inside there is a cylindrical separator made of a paste of flour and starch filled with MnO_2, C, and NH_4Cl and $ZnCl_2$ electrolytes. Down the center of this mixture is a C rod that serves as the positive terminal (cathode). An "alkaline" cell has the anode, a powdered Zn and KOH electrolyte, in the center. Surrounding it is a MnO_2 and C cathode in a metallic can. Alkaline cells cost more but produce more electrical energy at moderate currents. A mercury cell, which is often used in cameras, calculators, and hearing aids, has an amalgamated Zn anode, HgO plus C cathode, and a NaOH electrolyte. These cells maintain a constant voltage (1.35 V) until they die, but are damaged if too much current is drawn from them. Their energy storage is very large for their volume. What type of cell would you recommend using in a radio that you intend to take on a week-long camping trip? Explain. [Alkaline cells would last longer and would be worth the extra cost.]

PHYSICS LAB

Process Skills: using numbers, predicting, hypothesizing, questioning, defining operationally, designing experiments, measuring, communicating, observing.

MISCONCEPTIONS

Voltage, current, and resistance are abstract concepts. Many students will have only a vague understanding of them and will be inexperienced in making electrical measurements.

Teaching Suggestions: 1. Many students are apprehensive about working with electricity. Emphasize that they are working with low voltages. Monitor the lab activity to ensure that everyone is involved.
2. The resistors need to be less than 50 ohms and should be rated at least 10 W if an ammeter is used. **Caution:** Low-resistance resistors can become very hot. Students should not touch the resistors while the power is on. Higher resistances, such as 100–500 ohms, can use a milliammeter and have one-half watt ratings.

OBSERVATIONS

1. Student data table
2. As the voltage increased, the current also increased through the resistor.
3. The calculator value of the resistors should be within 20% of the labeled values.

ANALYSIS

1. Student calculations
2. The ratio of voltage to current stays the same for the resistors. This means that they have constant resistance.

APPLICATION

When the bulb has been off for a long time, it is at room temperature. It has a low resistance. When the bulb is switched on, it has a large current called cold inrush current. As the filament quickly heats up, its resistance increases and the current decreases. The large current that occurs when the bulb is switched on damages the filament by causing it to burn through in thinner places.

PHYSICS LAB: Mystery Cans

Purpose

To design and construct a circuit to measure the resistance of mystery film cans.

Materials

- film cans (with a resistor inside)
- 0 - 6 V variable power supply
- wires
- ammeter
- voltmeter

Procedure

1. Use the proper symbols to make a drawing of the set-up that would allow you to calculate the resistance of each can.
2. Show your diagram to your teacher before proceeding to step 3. Turn the power supply all the way down usually by rotating the knob in a counterclockwise direction.
3. Build the circuit that you designed and slowly turn up the power supply as you watch the needles on the meters. Do not exceed one amp or the current limitation set by your teacher.
4. If the needle(s) move in a negative direction, reverse the connections of the positive and negative on that meter.
5. Record the voltage and current readings for two different settings on your power supply.
6. Repeat steps 4-5 with two more film cans.

Observations and Data

1. Set up a data table with space for two voltage and current readings for each of the three film cans to be tested.
2. Describe what happened to the current as you increased the setting on the power supply.
3. Look inside each film can to determine the actual value of each resistor. Record these values.

Analysis

1. Calculate the value of each film can resistance. Compare your value to the known values.
2. Look closely at your data table. Did the resistors change resistance as they heated up? Use your values to support your answer.

Applications

1. Most light bulbs "burn out" when they are first switched on. Write a hypothesis suggesting why this happens.

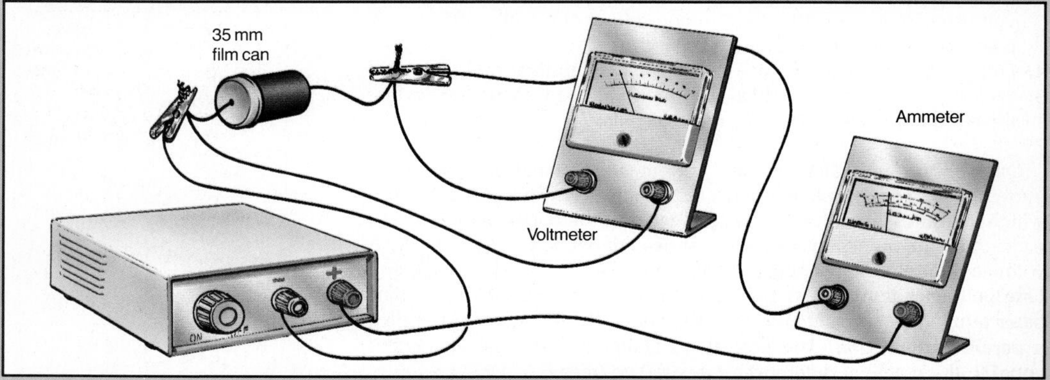

ASSESSMENT

Critical Thinking: To further assess students' understanding of circuits, ask the following questions.

1. Find the percent difference between your calculated values and the printed values for the carbon resistors. [The resistors are usually between 5% (gold band) and 10% (silver band), or within the limits printed directly on the resistors.]
2. What are the major sources of error in your calculations for the resistance values? How could they be minimized. [Students should realize that the calculated values can be only as accurate as their measurements of voltage and current. In general, larger meter readings will have lower percent uncertainty. Better meters would yield more accurate results. You might find this a good time to introduce students to the ohm scale if you are using multimeters.]

Practice Problems

11. Draw a circuit diagram to include a 60-V battery, an ammeter, and a resistance of 12.5 Ω in series. Indicate the ammeter reading and the direction of current flow.
12. Draw a series circuit diagram showing a 4.5-V battery, a resistor, and an ammeter reading 90 mA. Label the size of the resistor. Choose a direction for the conventional current and indicate the positive terminal of the battery.
13. ▶ Add a voltmeter that measures the potential difference across the resistors in each of the Practice Problems above.

F.Y.I.

$V = IR$ is often taken as a statement of Ohm's law, but this is not true. The equation simply defines resistance and applies to all resistances whether they obey Ohm's law or not.

CONCEPT REVIEW

1.1 Draw a schematic diagram of a circuit containing a battery and bulb that will make the bulb light.

1.2 Joe argues that, since $R = V/I$, if he increases the voltage, the resistance will increase. Is Joe correct? Explain.

1.3 You are asked to measure the resistance of a long piece of wire. Show how you would construct a circuit containing a battery, voltmeter, ammeter, and the wire to be tested to make the measurement. Specify what you would measure and how you would compute the resistance.

1.4 **Critical Thinking:** We have said that power is "dissipated" in a resistor. To dissipate is to use, or to waste, or to squander. What is "used" when charge flows through a resistor?

22.2 USING ELECTRICAL ENERGY

At an industrial site, electrical energy can be converted into other forms of energy, such as kinetic, sound, light, and thermal energy. Devices that make these conversions are very important in our everyday lives. Motors, loudspeakers, lamps, television sets, heaters, and air conditioners are examples of common devices that convert electric energy into other forms of energy.

Objectives

- explain how heaters convert electrical energy to thermal energy.
- describe the use of capacitors for energy storage in circuits.
- describe the reason for the use of high-voltage lines for transmitting electrical energy.
- define the kilowatt hour; solve problems involving the use and cost of electrical energy.

Energy Transfer in Electric Circuits

The motors, resistors, and lamps that we have discussed convert electrical energy into other forms. The capacitor, introduced in Chapter 21, stores electrical energy. If a capacitor is initially uncharged, then the voltage across it, $V = q/C$, will be zero. Suppose the capacitor is now

Answers To
PRACTICE PROBLEMS

Have students refer to Appendix A of the Solutions Appendix for complete solutions to Practice Problems.

11. Refer to Solutions Appendix A.
12. Refer to Solutions Appendix A.
13. Refer to Solutions Appendix A. Since the ammeter resistance is assumed to be zero, the voltmeter readings will be 60 V for Practice Problem 11 and 4.5 V for Practice Problem 12.

CONCEPT REVIEW ANSWERS

1.1

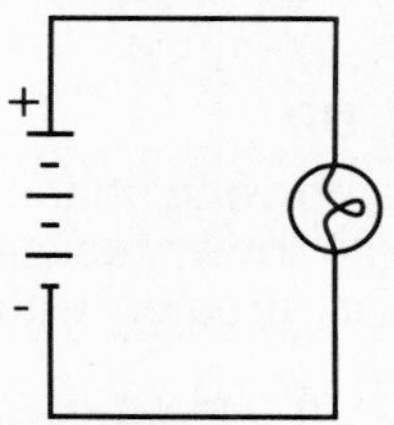

1.2 No. Resistance depends on the device. When V increases, so will I.

1.3 Measure the current through the wire and the potential difference across it. Divide the potential difference by the current to obtain the wire resistance.

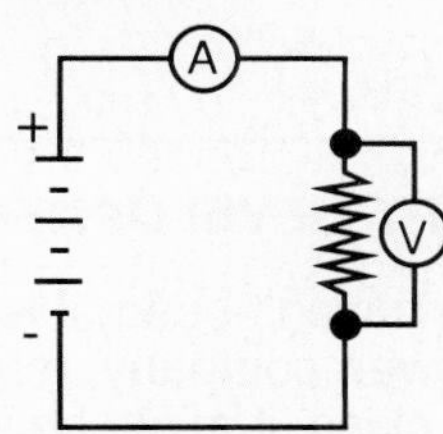

1.4 Critical Thinking: The potential energy of the charges decreases as they flow through the resistor. This decrease in potential energy is "used" to produce heat in the resistor.

LAB WORKSHEET

Use the Lab Worksheet for Chapter 22 with this Physics Lab.

OVERVIEW

Four major ideas are presented in this section: energy storage in capacitors, the thermal energy produced by an electric current, an efficient method for long-distance transmission of electrical energy, and the energy unit called the kilowatt hour.

BRIDGING

In studying this section, students will need to recall what they have learned about capacitors, thermal energy, and power (watts).

22.2 USING ELECTRICAL ENERGY

Preparation

OBJECTIVES

The objectives are listed on the student page. Remind students to preview these objectives as a study guide to this major section.

1 Focus

This would be the perfect time to have a representative of your local electrical power company speak to the class. Ask her or him to bring along some demonstration devices such as an electric watt-hour meter. Use this opportunity to discuss conservation measures as they apply to our use of electrical energy.

POCKET LAB

HEATING UP

Purpose: to verify that current increases with lower resistance and that heat is greater with greater current.

Materials: 3 different power resistors (1Ω, 5Ω, 15Ω with 10-W ratings); power supply; wires; ammeter.

Outcome: The lowest value resistor will allow the most current and heat up the fastest.

2 Teach

CONCEPT DEVELOPMENT

- If you haven't been able to get a local power company representative into class, it might be appropriate for class members to find out where the local supply of electricity is generated. We take electricity so much for granted that they probably have no idea.

Enrichment: An interesting project for a student who has a water bed is to find out the power rating of the heater for the bed. Then figure out what that means about the current in the heater and the rate at which thermal energy is supplied to the water. How long would it take to warm up the water in the bed? Does this figure agree with the student's experience?

Study Guide Master, To reinforce the concepts in this section, have the students complete the Study Guide Master for Section 22.2 from the Teacher Resource Package.

POCKET LAB

HEATING UP

Look at the markings on the three resistors. At the same setting on your power supply, predict which resistor would allow the most current flow through it. Explain your prediction. Predict which resistor will heat the most with equal settings on the power supply. Tape a thermometer bulb to the resistor. **CAUTION:** *Do not touch the resistors with power supplied. They may be extremely hot. Wait two minutes after turning off the power to remove the thermometer.* Turn the power on for one minute. Measure the temperature. Allow the resistor to cool off and then repeat the procedure with the remaining two resistors.

connected to a battery, voltage V_o, through a resistor, R, Figure 22–10a. Charges will flow from the battery through the resistor to the capacitor. Initially, with a large potential difference across the resistor, the current, I, will be large. The voltage across the capacitor will increase and current will become smaller until the voltage across the capacitor reaches the battery voltage. With no potential difference across the resistor, no more current will flow. The capacitor will be fully charged. Some energy from the battery is now stored in the electric field of the capacitor.

When a capacitor is charged or discharged through a resistor, the current is high initially and falls to zero.

The capacitor is discharged as in Figure 22–10b by connecting it across a resistor or other device. Because there is a potential difference, V, across the resistor, there will be current, I. As the charge in the capacitor decreases, so does the voltage across it. Thus the current, the rate at which the capacitor is discharging, also drops. Eventually the capacitor will be completely discharged; both q and V will be zero. All the energy will have been transferred to thermal energy at the resistor.

Electric power is the energy per unit time converted by an electric circuit into another form of energy. Power is equal to the voltage multiplied by the current, $P = VI$. For a resistor that obeys Ohm's law, by definition $V = IR$. Substituting this expression into the equation for electric power, we obtain

$$\boxed{P = I^2R.}$$

Power dissipated in a resistor is proportional to the resistance.

Power dissipated in a resistor is proportional to the square of the current.

The power dissipated in a resistor is thus proportional to the square of the current that passes through it and to the resistance. The energy is changed from electrical to thermal energy; the resistor gets hot.

The energy supplied to a circuit can be used in different ways. A motor converts electric energy into mechanical energy. An electric lamp changes electric energy into light. Unfortunately, not all of the electric energy delivered to a motor or to an electric light ends up in a useful form. Some energy is always converted into excess thermal energy. Certain devices, such as space heaters, are designed to convert most of the electric energy into thermal energy. Some electric energy is also converted into light.

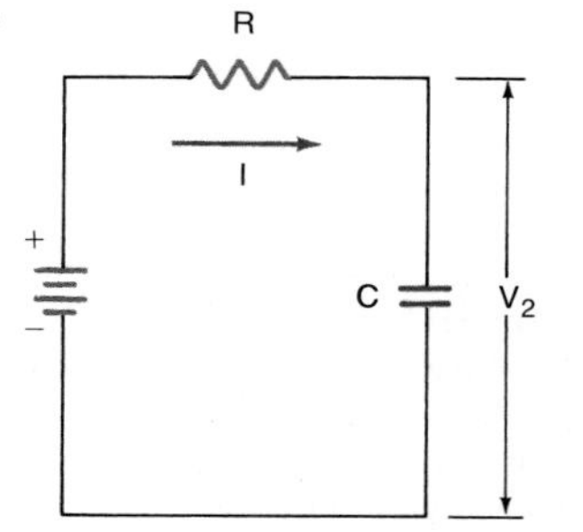

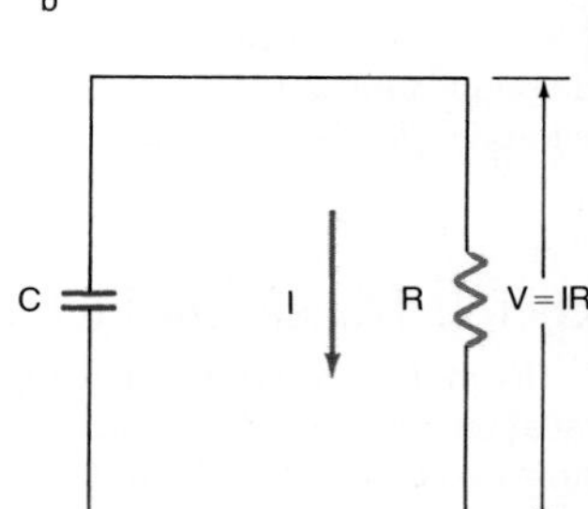

FIGURE 22–10. A capacitor is charged by connecting it to a battery (a). It is discharged by connecting it across some resistance (b).

Multicultural Connections

Would you choose to live without electric lights, television, radios, or video games? Some of the Amish people have chosen to do so. They have very strongly held beliefs about the value of family, church, and community. Machines that make it possible for one person to do a job that would otherwise take several people change the ways families and communities relate to each other. The same is true of entertainment technologies like television and radio, which take the place of doing things together as families or promote values to which the Amish object. So they are very careful about what new technology they allow into their lives. For example, they don't allow individual ownership of cars because owners are away from home too much, and cars make communities more scattered and less cohesive. They do, however, use public transportation. The basic question they ask about any change is, "What is the true cost to us to use this?" If the potential cost to the family and community is too high, they would rather do without it.

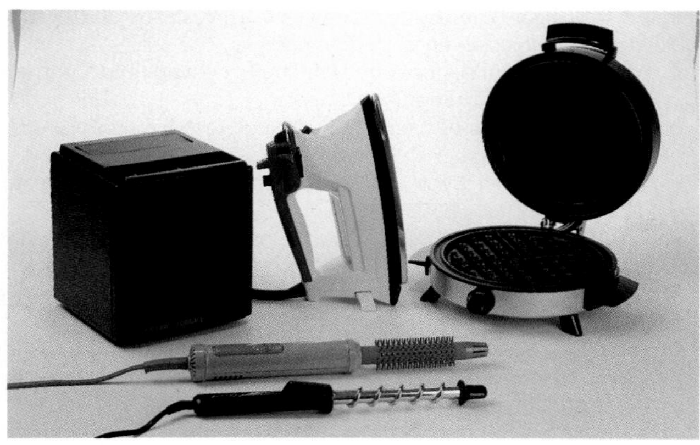

FIGURE 22–11. Some appliances are designed specifically to change electrical energy into thermal energy.

The electric energy transferred to a resistor in a time interval, t, is equal to I^2Rt. If all the electric energy is converted into thermal energy of the resistor, the increase in thermal energy is

$$E = I^2Rt.$$

The temperature of the resistor increases, allowing heat to flow into its colder surroundings. For example, in an immersion heater, a resistor placed in a cup of water can bring the water to the boiling point in a few minutes.

The energy transferred is the product of the power and the time.

Example Problem

Thermal Energy Produced by an Electric Current

A heater has a resistance of 10.0 Ω. It operates on 120.0 V. **a.** What is the current through the resistance? **b.** What thermal energy in joules is supplied by the heater in 10.0 s?

Given: resistance, $R = 10.0\ \Omega$; potential difference, $V = 120.0$ V; time, $t = 10.0$ s

Unknowns: **a.** I **b.** E

Basic equations: **a.** $R = V/I$ **b.** $E = I^2Rt$

Solution: **a.** $R = V/I$, so $I = V/R = (120.0\ \text{V})/(10.0\ \Omega) = 12.0$ A

b. $E = I^2Rt$

$= (12.0\ \text{A})^2(10.0\ \Omega)(10.0\ \text{s}) = 14\ 400$ J or 14.4 kJ

Practice Problems

14. A 15-Ω electric heater operates on a 120-V outlet.
    - **a.** What is the current through the heater?
    - **b.** How much energy is used by the heater in 30.0 s?
    - **c.** How much thermal energy is liberated by the heater in this time?
15. A 30-Ω resistor is connected across a 60-V battery.
    - **a.** What is the current in the circuit?
    - **b.** How much energy is used by the resistor in 5 min?

HELP WANTED

WELDER

Your technical knowledge of welding equipment and processes is important. A vocational/technical school or military training or extensive apprenticeship will be considered equally for this position with a major industrial employer. Excellent physical fitness, hand-eye coordination, and safety orientation are also important skills for a welder. Any additional skills (such as with laser or inertial welding techniques) might be useful in this diverse construction environment. For information contact: American Welding Society, 550 NW LeJeune Road, Miami, FL 33126

TEACHER F.Y.I.

At present, the Duracell company sells batteries in a package that includes a tester. This is a liquid crystal display whose color changes with temperature. The greater the current of the battery (the fresher the battery), the greater the heating effect on the crystals.

CONCEPT DEVELOPMENT

- Begin your study of thermal energy released from a current-carrying conductor by tying the idea into the everyday experience of students. Almost everyone has noticed the glowing, red hot wires inside a toaster. Many others will have seen the same thing in an electric space heater, and a few may have even seen the phenomenon in a hair dryer. Everyone has seen the glowing filament in a light bulb and knows that a bulb in use gets very hot. There's no mystery here, everyone has seen the effect!
- All these heating devices (and refrigerators, too) carry large currents, and are therefore large energy converters. This makes them prime targets for conservation efforts.

Guided Practice: After going over the Example Problem on this page, have students work on the first two Practice Problems that follow.

Independent Practice: Assign the remaining Practice Problems for homework and spend time going over them with students during the next class period.

Transparency Package. Use Transparency 32 to review circuits and circuit diagramming.

Laboratory Manual. Give students additional experience with energy conversion by doing Lab 22.2, Electric Equivalent of Heat, from the Laboratory Manual.

Answers To
PRACTICE PROBLEMS

Have students refer to Appendix A of the Solutions Appendix for complete solutions to Practice Problems.

14. **a.** 8.0 A
b. 2.9×10^4 J
c. 2.9×10^4 J

15. **a.** 2.0 A
b. 3.6×10^4 J

Answers To
PRACTICE PROBLEMS

Have students refer to Appendix A of the Solutions Appendix for complete solutions to Practice Problems.

16. a. 1.20×10^3 J
b. 4.80×10^3 J
17. a. 20 A
b. 1.3×10^5 J
c. 18°C

CONCEPT DEVELOPMENT

Demonstration: You can use a DC power supply, voltmeter, and a "supercap" or farad capacitor to show energy storage in a capacitor. Charge up the capacitor by connecting it to your power supply (being careful to connect the positive end of the capacitor to the red terminal of the power supply and the black terminal to the negative end of the capacitor). Use a capacitor that has a voltage rating similar to the maximum voltage of your power supply. The capacitor will become charged in about a minute. Then connect the charged capacitor to the voltmeter, again observing correct polarity of the connections. You'll see a large voltage reading that rapidly decreases as the energy stored inside is depleted. CAUTION: Be certain to completely discharge the capacitor before putting it away.

Demonstration: Use an immersion heater to warm up some water. Insulate a cup to reduce lost thermal energy. Put a known amount of water into the cup and measure the starting temperature. Turn on the heater and bring the water to a boil. Using the equation $Q = mC\Delta T$, compute the amount of thermal energy added. Time the interval from turning on the heater until the water boils. By dividing the amount of energy by the time, you can calculate a power for the heater. If you know the manufacturer's power rating you can check it against the value you calculated.

F.Y.I.

Eliha Thomson, an English-American inventor, devised a high frequency electrical generator among his 700 patented inventions. You are probably familiar with the company that he and Thomas Edison formed—General Electric.

16. A 100.0-W light bulb is 20.0% efficient. That means 20.0% of the electric energy is converted to light energy.
a. How many joules does the light bulb convert into light each minute it is in operation?
b. How many joules of thermal energy does the light bulb produce each minute?

▶ **17.** The resistance of an electric stove element at operating temperature is 11 Ω.
a. 220 V are applied across it. What is the current through the stove element?
b. How much energy does the element convert to thermal energy in 30.0 s?
c. The element is being used to heat a kettle containing 1.20 kg of water. Assume that 70% of the heat is absorbed by the water. What is its increase in temperature during the 30.0 s?

Transmission of Electric Energy

Niagara Falls and Hoover Dam can produce electric energy with little pollution. The energy, however, must often be transmitted long distances to reach homes and industries. How can the transmission take place with as little loss to thermal energy as possible? Thermal energy is produced at a rate given by $P = I^2R$. Electrical engineers call this unwanted thermal energy the "Joule heating" or "I^2R" loss. To reduce this loss, either the current, I, or the resistance, R, must be reduced.

All wires have some resistance, even though it is small. For example, one kilometer of the large wire used to carry electric current into a home has a resistance of 0.2 Ω. Suppose a farmhouse were connected directly to a power plant 3.5 km away, Figure 22–12. The resistance in the wires needed to carry a current to the home and back to the plant is

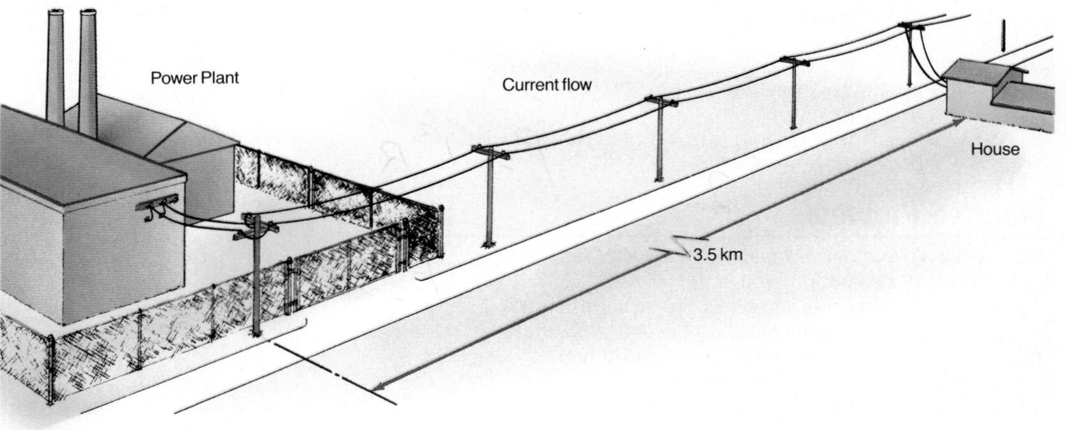

FIGURE 22–12. Electrical energy is transferred over long distances at high voltages to minimize I^2R losses.

STUDY GUIDE MASTER
Use the Study Guide master for section 22.2.

LABORATORY MANUAL
Use Lab 22.2 with this section.

TRANSPARENCY
Use Transparency 32 with this section.

FIGURE 22–13. The power-generating station converts the kinetic energy of the falling water into electrical energy without polluting the environment.

2(3.5 km) (0.2 Ω/km) = 1.4 Ω. An electric stove might cause a 41-A current through the wires. The power dissipated in the wires is given by $P = I^2R = (41\text{ A})^2 \times 1.4\ \Omega = 2400\text{ W}$. All this power is wasted.

High voltage transmission lines carry electrical energy over long distances with minimal loss.

This loss could be reduced by reducing the resistance. Cables of high conductivity and large diameter are used, but such cables are expensive and heavy. Since the loss is also proportional to the square of the current in the conductors, it is even more important to keep the current in the transmission lines low.

More for Less?

The electrical energy per second (power) transferred over a long-distance transmission line is determined by the relationship $P = VI$. The current can be reduced without reducing the power by increasing the voltage. Some long-distance lines use voltages over one-half million volts. The resulting lower current reduces the I^2R loss in the lines by keeping the I^2 factor low. Long-distance transmission lines always operate at high voltage to reduce I^2R loss.

FIGURE 22–14. Computerization of modern power grids makes it possible to draw electrical energy from distant sources in emergency situations.

22:2 ASSIGNMENT GUIDE

	PRACTICE	EXTENSION
CHAPTER REVIEW pp. 464–467		
· Reviewing Concepts	9–11	
· Applying Concepts		10
· Problems*	21–25, 27	26, 28, 29
APPENDIX B PROBLEMS*		
· Chapter 22, p. 704	12, 13, 15	14,16

* Complete solutions to all Chapter Review and Appendix problems appear in the Problems and Solutions Manual.

RETEACHING MASTER

Use the Reteaching master for Chapter 22 with this section.

CONCEPT DEVELOPMENT

ACTIVITY

Cooperative Learning: Have students do a survey to find out which devices in their homes use the most electricity. Have them read their electrical meters at the beginning of the week and then at the end of the week. If they can find the price per kilowatt hour, have them compute the cost of the week's electricity usage.

Discovery: Display different kinds of variable resistors for students. Hook one up in a circuit to show how it is used to dim a light. To make a variable resistor, carve the wood off the middle section of a pencil. Using leads from a battery, clip on a lead to the pencil point and touch the other lead along the graphite to change the length of graphite that is part of the circuit. Connect an ammeter to the circuit, noting the change in current as the length is varied.

CHECKING FOR UNDERSTANDING

Use a problem from the end of the chapter involving a simple circuit. Let students come up to the board and solve a portion of the problem until it has been completed. This will help you see where the students are having difficulty so you can help accordingly.

RETEACHING

Make an energy flow chart for an operating circuit. Energy *in* would come from the outlet, power supply, or battery. Energy could be stored in capacitors. Energy *out* would be heating of the wires and operating of circuit devices such as motors or bulbs. Stress that conservation of energy applies to electrical circuits as well as any other kind of system.

Reteaching Master, Teacher Resource Package. Use the Reteaching Master for Chapter 22, Converting Energy.

INDEPENDENT PRACTICE/ EXTENSION

Refer to the Assignment Guide for additional questions and problems for independent practice.

CONCEPT DEVELOPMENT

Cooperative Learning: The numerical value of resistors is indicated by colored bands painted onto the resistors, known as the resistor color code. Probably a few of your students have run into it while dabbling with electronics. Ask for volunteers to make a colored chart and explain the color code to the rest of the class.

Critical Thinking: Household fires often are caused by faulty electrical wiring. These fires sometimes start inside the walls. Based on what they know about the behavior of electricity in circuits, ask students to theorize about what happens to produce these fires. [A likely reason would be the heating effect of electrical currents. If currents are too large, they can produce enough thermal energy to ignite a fire.]

Critical Thinking Master, Teacher Resource Package. You may wish to have students complete the Critical Thinking Master, Future Energy Uses, with this section.

POCKET LAB

APPLIANCES

Purpose: to relate Ohm's law to common appliances.

Materials: various household appliances.

Outcome: Appliances with small resistances (such as toasters or hair dryers) have large power ratings.

3 Close

CONVERGENT QUESTION

This section describes an efficient method for long-distance transmission of electricity. Ask students how this method involves the heating effect of currents. [Long-distance transmission seeks to minimize thermal energy loss in wires by using lower currents.]

FIGURE 22–15. Watthour meters (a) measure the amount of electrical energy used by a consumer. The more current being used at a given time, the faster the horizontal disk in the center of the meter turns. Meter readings are then used in calculating the cost of energy (b).

a

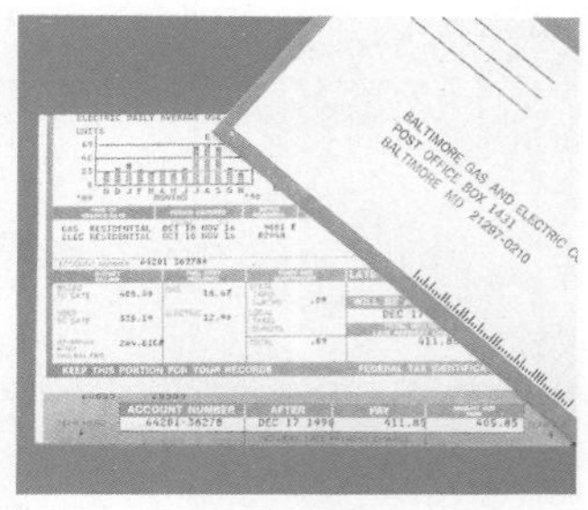

b

The Kilowatt Hour

The kilowatt hour (kWh) is a unit of energy, the product of power (kW) and time (h).

While electric companies often are called "power" companies, they really provide energy. When you pay your home electric bill, Figure 22–15, you pay for electric energy, not power.

The electric energy used by any device is its rate of energy consumption, in joules per second (watts), times the number of seconds it is operated. Joules per second times seconds, J/s · s, equals total joules of energy.

The joule, a watt-second, is a relatively small amount of energy. For that reason, electric companies measure their energy sales in a large number of joules called a kilowatt hour, kWh. A **kilowatt hour** is equal to 1000 watts delivered continuously for 3600 seconds (one hour). It is

$$1 \text{ kWh} = (1000 \text{ J/s})(3600 \text{ s}) = 3.6 \times 10^6 \text{ J}.$$

Not many devices in the home other than hot-water heaters, stoves, heaters, curling irons, and hair dryers require more than 1000 watts. Ten 100-watt light bulbs operating all at once would use one kilowatt hour of energy if left on for a full hour.

POCKET LAB

APPLIANCES

Look closely at three electrical appliances in your home. Record the power (watts) or the current (amps) of each appliance. Assume each appliance operates at 120 V. Determine the resistance of each appliance. Relate the power used in an appliance to its resistance.

Example Problem

The Cost of Operating an Electric Device

A modern color television set draws 2.0 A when operated on 120 V. **a.** How much power does the set use? **b.** If the set is operated for an average of 7.0 h/day, what energy in kWh does it consume per month (30 days)? **c.** At $0.11 per kWh, what is the cost of operating the set per month?

Given: $I = 2.0$ A
$V = 120$ V
$t = 7.0 \text{ h/d} \times 30 \text{ d} = 2.1 \times 10^2 \text{ h}$

Unknowns: a. P **b.** E

Basic equations: $P = VI$, $P = E/t$

Solution:

a. $P = VI = (120 \text{ V})(2.0 \text{ A}) = 2.4 \times 10^2 \text{ W}$

b. $E = Pt = (2.4 \times 10^2 \text{ W})(2.1 \times 10^2 \text{ h}) = 5.0 \times 10^4 \text{ Wh} = 5.0 \times 10^1 \text{ kWh}$

c. cost = $(5.0 \times 10^1 \text{ kWh})(\$0.11/\text{kWh}) = \$5.50$

Assessment

Portfolio

Have students construct charts of a variety of appliances in their homes, listing power dissipated (in watts), typical time used per month (in hours), and electrical energy used (in kilowatt hours).

Practice Problems

18. An electric space heater draws 15.0 A from a 120-V source. It is operated, on the average, for 5.0 h each day.
a. How much power does the heater use?
b. How much energy in kWh does it consume in 30 days?
c. At $0.11 per kWh, what does it cost to operate it for 30 days?

▶ **19.** A digital clock has an operating resistance of 12 000 Ω and is plugged into a 115-V outlet. Assume the clock obeys Ohm's law.
a. How much current does it draw?
b. How much power does it use?
c. If the owner of the clock pays $0.09 per kWh, what does it cost to operate the clock for 30 days?

CONCEPT REVIEW

2.1 A battery charges a capacitor. The capacitor is discharged through a photo flashlamp. List the forms of energy in these two operations.
2.2 A hair dryer operating from 120 V has two settings, hot and warm. In which setting is the resistance likely to be smaller? Why?
2.3 Why would a home using an electric range and hot water heater connect these appliances to 240 V rather than 120 V?
2.4 **Critical Thinking:** When demand for electrical power is high, power companies sometimes reduce the voltage, producing a "brown out." What is being saved?

F.Y.I.

Some electric companies still only charge for energy, but only for residential customers. Institutional customers, including schools, all commercial customers, and all industrial customers pay separate charges for power (kW) and energy (kWh). The directive of the 1978 Energy Act states that eventually all customers will be billed separately for power and energy.

Electric companies do, in fact, sell two separate products, power and energy, and charge for them separately.

Physics and technology

ULTRA-HIGH VOLTAGE ELECTRIC POWER TRANSMISSION

The electric utility industry in the United States has had to double its available capacity approximately every 10 years. Long-term projections continue to indicate a growing demand for electric energy. This means that electricity generation and transmission capacity must increase to keep pace with the need.

To deliver electric energy with less waste, transmission levels greater than the present extra-high voltage (EHV) levels of 345 and 765 kV will be needed in the years ahead. The new levels of transmission capacity being studied are called ultra-high voltage (UHV). UHV transmission levels of more than 2000 kV are being tested.

Research on environmental effects of high voltage electricity transmission is becoming increasingly important. Research generally falls into three areas: possible ozone emission by transmission lines, audible noise and radio- and television-frequency interference, and the biological effects of electrostatic and electromagnetic fields on organisms.

· If electric power lines could be shown to cause specific health problems, how might this affect electric utilities and homeowners?

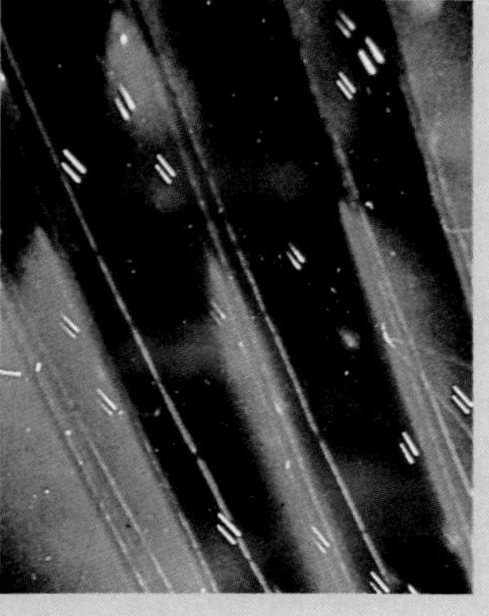

Answers To
PRACTICE PROBLEMS

Have students refer to Appendix A of the Solutions Appendix for complete solutions to Practice Problems.

18. a. 1.80 kW
b. 270 kWh
c. $29.70

19. a. 9.6×10^{-3} A
b. 1.10 W
c. $0.07

Physics and technology

Electric utilities could become subject to more strict government regulation that would likely result in higher costs. Plans for new projects might have to be changed or canceled. Many power lines already in place might have to be moved and rerouted. The companies could face many lawsuits from people claiming adverse health effects from power line exposure. Homeowners living near certain types of power lines may find the value of their properties diminished. If they are searching for a new home, the proximity of power lines in the area could influence their choice of which home to buy.

During the past decade, numerous studies have investigated the possible connection between electromagnetic fields and human cancer. In a draft report circulated in 1990, the U.S. Environmental Protection Agency (EPA) stated that, while studies indicate a possible link between low-frequency electromagnetic fields and cancer, there is not yet sufficient evidence to prove a cause-and-effect relationship. With more than 600 000 miles of overhead power lines already in place in the United States and with increasing environmental awareness, this issue is certain to receive increasing attention in the years ahead.

CRITICAL THINKING

Use the Critical Thinking master for Chapter 22 with this section.

CONCEPT REVIEW ANSWERS

2.1 chemical energy in the battery; electrical field energy in the capacitor; light and thermal energy in the flashlamp
2.2 Hot draws more power $P = VI$, so the fixed voltage current is larger. Since $I = V/R$, the resistance is smaller.
2.3 For the same power, at twice the voltage, the current would be halved. The I^2R loss is reduced.
2.4 **Critical Thinking:** Power, not energy; most devices will have to be run longer.

CLOSING CHAPTER 22

Review Summary statements and Key Terms with your students.

ASSESSMENT

Vocabulary Review Master, Teacher Resource Package. Use this master to check students' understanding of Key Terms.

Evaluation Masters. Use Parts A and B of the Chapter Evaluation Masters from the Teacher Resource Package to test qualitative chapter objectives. Use Parts C and D to test quantitative chapter objectives.

Answers To
REVIEWING CONCEPTS

1. a. Electrical energy to heat, and light. **b.** Electrical energy to heat, and kinetic energy. **c.** Electrical energy to light, and sound.

2. $1\text{A} = \dfrac{1\text{C}}{1\text{s}}$

3. A larger diameter wire has a smaller resistance because there are more electrons to carry the charge and more room for them to move.

4. $1\text{A} = \dfrac{1\text{C}}{1\text{s}}$, so 1C of charge passes the point each second and $1\text{C} = 6.25 \times 10^{18}$ electrons.

5. The low resistance of the cold filament allows a high current initially and a greater change in temperature, subjecting the filament to greater stress.

6. As the temperature increases, the average kinetic energy of the atoms in the wire increases, making it more difficult to pass electrons.

7.

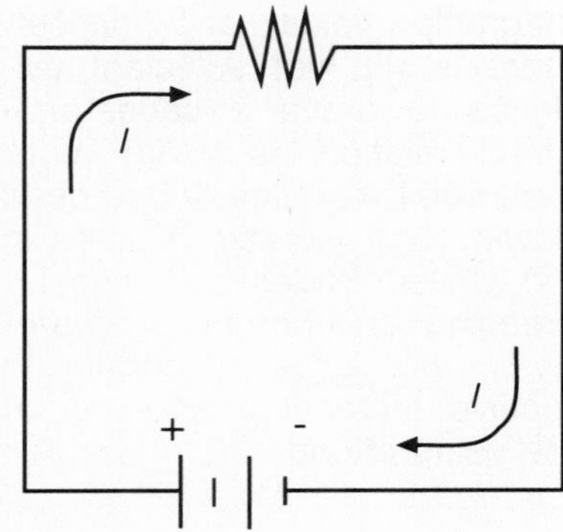

8.

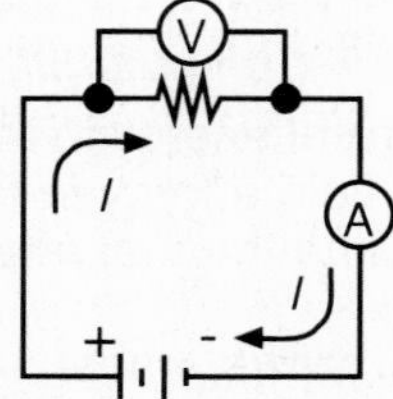

a. The ammeter must be connected in series. **b.** The voltmeter must be connected in parallel.

9. The short circuit produces a high current, which causes more electrons to collide with the atoms of the wire. This raises the atoms' kinetic energy and the temperature of the wire.

10. As electricity flows, electrons bump into the atoms of the wire, increasing their kinetic energy. This raises the temperature of the wire.

11. the resistance of the wire and the current in the wire

CHAPTER 22 REVIEW

SUMMARY

22.1 Current and Circuits

- Batteries, generators, and solar cells convert various forms of energy to electric energy.
- In an electric circuit, electric energy is transmitted from a device that produces electric energy to a resistor or other device that converts electric energy into the form needed.
- As a charge moves through resistors in a circuit, its potential energy is reduced. The energy released when the charge moves around the remainder of the circuit equals the work done to give the charge its initial potential energy.
- One ampere is one coulomb per second.
- Electric power is found by multiplying voltage by current.
- The resistance of a device is the ratio of the voltage across it divided by the current through it.
- In a device that obeys Ohm's law, the resistance does not depend on the current through it.
- The current in a circuit can be varied by changing either the voltage or the resistance, or both.
- In a circuit diagram we use conventional current, the direction in which a positive current carrier would move.

22.2 Using Electrical Energy

- A capacitor can store electrical energy.
- The thermal energy produced in a circuit from electric energy is equal to I^2Rt.
- In long-distance transmission, current is reduced without reducing power by increasing the voltage.
- A kilowatt hour, kWh, is an energy unit. It is equal to 3.6×10^6 J.

KEY TERMS

electric current	resistors
battery	potentiometer
photovoltaic cell	schematic
electric circuit	series connection
ampere	parallel connection
conventional current	kilowatt hour
resistance	

REVIEWING CONCEPTS

1. Describe the energy conversions that occur in each of these devices.
   a. incandescent light bulb
   b. clothes dryer
   c. digital clock radio
2. Define the unit of electric charge in terms of fundamental MKS units.
3. Which wire conducts electricity with the least resistance: one with a large cross-sectional diameter or one with a small cross-sectional diameter?

FIGURE 22–16.

4. How many electrons flow past a point in a wire each second if the wire has a current of 1 A?
5. Why do light bulbs burn out more frequently just as they are switched on rather than while the bulbs are operating?
6. Explain, in terms of the average kinetic energy of the atoms in the wire, why the resistance of a wire increases as the temperature of the wire increases.
7. A simple circuit consists of a battery, a resistor, and some connecting wires. Draw a circuit schematic of this simple circuit. Show the polarity of the battery and the direction of the current.
8. A simple circuit consists of a resistor, a battery, and connecting wires.
   a. How must an ammeter be connected in a circuit to correctly read the current?
   b. How must a voltmeter be connected to a resistor in order to read the potential difference across it?

9. If a battery is short-circuited by connecting a heavy copper wire from one terminal to the other, the temperature of the copper wire rises. Explain.
10. Why does a wire become warmer as current flows through it?
11. What electrical quantities must be kept small to transmit electric energy economically over long distances?

APPLYING CONCEPTS

1. When a battery is connected to a complete circuit, charges flow in the circuit almost instantaneously. Explain.
2. Explain why a cow that touches an electric fence experiences a mild shock.
3. Why can birds perch on high-voltage lines without being injured?
4. Describe two ways of increasing a circuit's current in a device that obeys Ohm's law.
5. You have two light bulbs that work on a 120-V circuit. One is 50 W, the other 100 W. Which bulb has a higher resistance? Explain.
6. If the voltage across a circuit is kept constant and the resistance is doubled, what effect does this have on the circuit's current?
7. What is the effect on the current in a circuit if both the voltage and the resistance are doubled? Explain.
8. Sue finds a device that looks like a resistor. When she connects it to a 1.5-V battery, only 45×10^{-6} A flows, but when a 3.0-V battery is used, 25×10^{-3} A flows. Does the device obey Ohm's law?
9. If the ammeter in Figure 22–4 were moved to the bottom of the diagram, would the ammeter have the same reading?
10. Two wires can be placed across the terminals of a 6.0-V battery. One has a high resistance, one low. Which wire will produce thermal energy at the faster rate? Explain.

PROBLEMS

22.1 Current and Circuits

1. The current through a toaster connected to a 120-V source is 8.0 A. What power is dissipated by the toaster?
2. A current of 1.2 A flows through a light bulb when it is connected across a 120-V source. What power is dissipated by the bulb?
3. A lamp draws 0.50 A from a 120-V generator.
   a. How much power does the generator deliver?
   b. How much energy does the lamp convert in 5.0 min?
4. A 12-V automobile battery is connected to an electric starter motor. The current through the motor is 210 A.
   a. How many joules of energy does the battery deliver to the motor each second?
   b. What power, in watts, does the motor use?
5. A 4000-W clothes dryer is connected to a 220-V circuit. How much current does the dryer draw?
6. A flashlight bulb is connected across a 3.0-V difference in potential. The current through the lamp is 1.5 A.
   a. What is the power rating of the lamp?
   b. How much electric energy does the lamp convert in 11 min?
7. ▶ How much energy does a 60.0-W light bulb use in half an hour? If the light bulb is 12% efficient, how much thermal energy does it generate during the half hour?
8. A resistance of 60 Ω has a current of 0.40 A through it when it is connected to the terminals of a battery. What is the voltage of the battery?
9. What voltage is applied to a 4.0-Ω resistor if the current is 1.5 A?
10. What voltage is placed across a motor of 15 Ω operating resistance if the current is 8.0 A of current?
11. A voltage of 75 V is placed across a 15-Ω resistor. What is the current through the resistor?
12. A 20.0-Ω resistor is connected to a 30.0-V battery. What is the current in the resistor?
13. A 12-V battery is connected to a device and 24 mA, 24×10^{-3} A, of current flows through it. If the device obeys Ohm's law, how much current will flow when a 24-V battery is used?
14. The damage caused by electric shock depends on the current flowing through the body—1 mA can be felt; 5 mA is painful. Above 15 mA, a person loses muscle control, and 70 mA can be fatal. A person with dry skin has a resistance from one arm to the other of about 1×10^5 Ω. When skin is wet,

Answers To
APPLYING CONCEPTS

1. A potential difference is felt over the entire circuit as soon as the battery is connected to the circuit. The potential difference causes the charges to begin to flow. Note: The charges flow very slowly compared to the change in potential difference.

2. By touching the fence and the ground, the cow encounters a difference in potential and conducts current, thus receiving a shock.

3. No potential difference exists across the wires, so no current flows.

4. Either increase the voltage or decrease the resistance.

5. 50 W. $P = IV$, so higher P has higher I. $R = V/I$, so with same V, larger I means lower R.

6. If the resistance is doubled, the current is halved.

7. No effect. $V = IR$, so $I = \frac{V}{R}$, and if the voltage and the current are both doubled, the current will not change.

8. No. $V = IR$, so $R = \frac{V}{I}$.

At 1.5 V, $R = \frac{1.5\text{ V}}{45 \times 10^{-6}\text{ A}}$
$= 3.3 \times 10^4\ \Omega$.

At 3.0 V, $R = \frac{3.0\text{ V}}{25 \times 10^{-3}\text{ A}}$
$= 120\Omega$.

If it obeyed Ohm's Law, the resistance should not change.

9. Yes, because the current is the same everywhere in this circuit.

10. The wire with the smaller resistance. $P = IV$, where V is the same. $V = IR$, and $I = V/R$, so larger R has lower I, and thus lower P.

REVIEW MASTER

Use the Vocabulary Review master for Chapter 22 with this section.

EVALUATION MASTER

Use the Chapter Evaluation master for Chapter 22 with this section.

Answers To
PROBLEMS

Complete solutions to Chapter Review Problems can be found in the Problems and Solutions Manual accompanying this text.

1. 9.6×10^2 W
2. 1.4×10^2 W
3. a. 60 W
   b. 1.8×10^4 J
4. a. 2.5×10^3 J/s
   b. 2.5×10^3 W
5. 18.2 A
6. a. 4.5 W
   b. 3.0×10^3 J
7. 1.08×10^5 J; 9.5×10^4 J
8. 24 V
9. 6.0 V
10. 1.2×10^2 V
11. 5.0 A
12. 1.50 A
13. 48 mA
14. a. 1×10^2 V
    b. 20 mA
    c. 5 V
15. a. No
    b. 0.40 W
    c. 0.68 W
16. a. R = 143 Ω, 148 Ω, 150 Ω, 154 Ω, 154 Ω, 143 Ω, 143 Ω, 154 Ω, 157 Ω, 156 Ω.
    b. Refer to Problems and Solutions Manual.
    c. Nichrome wire does not obey Ohm's law for all voltages. It obeys for voltages of +8.00 V to +10.00 V and in the −2.00 to −4.00 V range.
17. a. 3.0×10^2 Ω
    b. 60 Ω
    c. 2.0 A
18. a. 32 Ω
    b. 1.2×10^2 A
    c. No
19. 2.0 A: Refer to Problems and Solutions Manual.
20. 28 V: Refer to Problems and Solutions Manual.
21. 0.15 A
22. a. 34 W
    b. 2.0×10^4 J
23. 2.2×10^4 J
24. a. 2.5 A
    b. 2.3×10^4 J

the resistance drops to about 5×10^3 Ω.

a. What is the minimum voltage placed across the arms that would produce a current that could be felt by a person with dry skin?

b. What effect would the same voltage have if the person had wet skin?

c. What would be the minimum voltage that would produce a current that could be felt when the skin is wet?

15. A lamp draws a 66-mA current when connected to a 6.0-V battery. When a 9.0-V battery is used, the lamp draws 75 mA.
    a. Does the lamp obey Ohm's law?
    b. How much power does the lamp dissipate at 6.0 V?
    c. How much power does it dissipate at 9.0 V?

▸ 16. Table 22–1 shows data taken by students. They connected a length of nichrome wire to a variable power supply that could produce from 0 V to 10 V across the wire. They then measured the current through the wire for several voltages. The data table shows the voltages used and currents measured.
    a. For each measurement, calculate the resistance.
    b. Graph I versus V.
    c. Does the nichrome wire obey Ohm's law? If not for all the voltages, specify the voltage range for which Ohm's law holds.

Table 22–1

Voltage V (volts)	Current I (amps)	Resistance $R = V/I$ (ohms)
2.00	0.014	
4.00	0.027	
6.00	0.040	
8.00	0.052	
10.00	0.065	
−2.00	−0.014	
−4.00	−0.028	
−6.00	−0.039	
−8.00	−0.051	
−10.00	−0.064	

17. The current through a lamp connected across 120 V is 0.40 A when the lamp is on.
    a. What is its resistance when it is on?
    b. When the lamp is cold, its resistance is one fifth as large as when the lamp is hot. What is its cold resistance?
    c. What is the current through the lamp as it is turned on if it is connected to a potential difference of 120 V?

▸ 18. The graph in Figure 22–17 shows the current that flows through a device called a silicon diode.
    a. A potential difference of +0.70 V is placed across the diode. What resistance would be calculated?
    b. What resistance would be calculated if a +0.60-V potential difference was used?
    c. Does the diode obey Ohm's law?

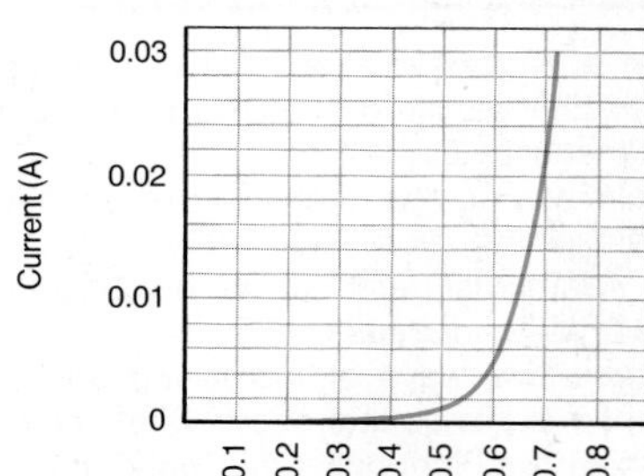

FIGURE 22–17. Use with Problem 18.

▸ 19. Draw a schematic diagram to show a circuit that includes a 90-V battery, an ammeter, and a resistance of 45 Ω connected in series. What is the ammeter reading? Draw arrows showing the direction of conventional current flow.

▸ 20. Draw a series circuit diagram to include a 16-Ω resistor, a battery, and an ammeter that reads 1.75 A. Current flows through the meter from left to right. Indicate the positive terminal and the voltage of the battery.

22.2 Using Electrical Energy

21. What is the maximum current that should be allowed in a 5.0-W, 220-Ω resistor?
22. The wire in a house circuit is rated at 15.0 A that has a resistance of 0.15 Ω.
    a. What is its power rating?
    b. How much heat does the wire give off in 10.0 min?
23. A current of 1.2 A flows through a 50-Ω resistor for 5.0 min. How much heat was generated by the resistor?
24. A 6.0-Ω resistor is connected to a 15 V battery.

a. What is the current in the circuit?
b. How much thermal energy is produced in 10 min?

25. A 110-V electric iron draws 3.0 A of current. How much heat is developed per hour?

▶ 26. An electric motor operates a pump that irrigates a farmer's crop by pumping 10 000 L of water a vertical distance of 8.0 m into a field each hour. The motor has an operating resistance of 22.0 Ω and is connected across a 110-V source.
a. What current does it draw?
b. How efficient is the motor?

27. A transistor radio operates by means of a 9.0-V battery that supplies it with a 50-mA current.
a. If the cost of the battery is $0.90 and it lasts for 300 h, what is the cost per kWh to operate the radio in this manner?
b. The same radio, by means of a converter, is plugged into a household circuit by a home owner who pays $0.08 per kWh. What does it now cost to operate the radio for 300 h?

FIGURE 22–18.

▶ 28. A heating coil has a resistance of 4.0 Ω and operates on 120 V.
a. What is the current in the coil while it is operating?
b. What energy is supplied to the coil in 5.0 min?
c. If the coil is immersed in an insulated container holding 20.0 kg of water, what will be the increase in the temperature of the water? Assume that 100% of the heat is absorbed by the water.
d. At $0.08 per kWh, what does it cost to operate the heating coil 30 min per day for 30 days?

▶ 29. An electric heater is rated at 500 W.
a. How much energy is delivered to the heater in half an hour?
b. The heater is being used to heat a room containing 50.0 kg of air. If the specific heat of air is 1.10 kJ/kg·°C, 1100 J/kg·°C, and 50% of the thermal energy heats the air in the room, what is the change in air temperature?
c. At $0.08 per kWh, what does it cost to run the heater 6.0 h per day for 30 days?

USING LAB SKILLS

1. After doing the Pocket Lab on page 451, predict whether you could light a 40-watt bulb with your D-cell. Why do you think so? Try it and record your results.
2. In the Pocket Lab on page 455, you found that the current between the lamps was the same as the current in front of the lamps. What do you predict to be the current after the lamps? Why? Try it and record your results.

THINKING PHYSIC-LY

1. What causes electric shock, current or voltage?
2. Some people say that an electrical appliance "uses up" electricity. What does the appliance "use up" and what becomes of it?

25. 1.2×10^6 J
26. a. 5.0 A
b. 39%
27. a. $6.70
b. 1 cent
28. a. 30 A
b. 1.1×10^6 J
c. 13°C
d. $4.40
29. a. 9.00×10^5 J
b. 8°C
c. $7.20

Answers To
USING LAB SKILLS

1. The 40-watt bulb is designed to operate at 120 V and will not operate at 1.5 V. The resistance of the lamp is so large that at 1.5 V the current will be too small for the lamp to light.
2. Many students will predict that the current will be less. This is not true. Students will find that the current is the same at every point in a series current.

Answers To
THINKING PHYSIC-LY

1. Electric shock occurs when current, caused by a voltage, is produced in the body.
2. The appliance "uses up" potential difference and converts it into energy to run the appliance.

CHAPTER

23 Series and Parallel Circuits

PLANNING GUIDE (6 class sessions)

CONTENTS	TEXT FEATURES	TEACHER RESOURCE PACKAGE	OTHER COMPONENTS
23.1 Simple Circuits, pp. 470–478 (3 Class Sessions) • Series Circuits • Voltage Drops in a Series Circuit • Parallel Circuits	**Physics Lab:** Circuits, p. 479 **Pocket Lab:** Series Resistance, p. 472 **Pocket Lab:** Parallel Resistance, p. 475 **Using Your Calculator:** Inverse Key, p. 474 **Concept Review,** p. 478	**Study Guide:** Simple Circuits **Physics Lab Data Sheet:** Circuits **Enrichment Master:** Analyzing Circuits **Transparency Worksheet:** Series Circuit/Parallel Circuit	**Laboratory Manual:** Lab 23.1 Series Resistance Lab 23.2 Parallel Resistance **Transparency 33:** Series Circuit/Parallel Circuit
23.2 Applications of Circuits, pp. 480–485 (3 Class Sessions) • Safety Devices • Combined Series-Parallel Circuits • Ammeters and Voltmeters	**Physics and Technology:** Robots and Ohm's Law, p. 486 **Pocket Lab:** Ammeter Resistance, p. 484 **Problem Solving Strategy:** Determining Resistors, p. 482 **Concept Review,** p. 485	**Study Guide:** Applications of Circuits **Reteaching Master:** Designing an Alarm System **Critical Thinking Master:** Breaking a Circuit **Transparency Worksheet:** Complex Circuit	**Transparency 34:** Complex Circuit
Chapter Review, pp. 486–489	Summary Key Terms Reviewing Concepts Applying Concepts Problems Thinking Physic-ly	**Vocabulary Review** **Chapter Test**	**Test Bank**

SUPPLEMENTARY MATERIALS

SOFTWARE	AUDIOVISUAL	BOOKS/MAGAZINES
Electricity, Cross (Apple II, IBM PC, Macintosh). *Making Circuits,* Queue, Inc. (Apple II). *MMV Electricity,* Queue, Inc. (Apple II, IBM PC, Macintosh).	Video: *The Mechanical Universe and Beyond: Electric Circuits* and *Magnets,* Films Inc.	Heald, Mark A. "Integer Solutions of $1/x + 1/y = 1/z$." *The Physics Teacher,* December 1990, p. 617. Keller, Clifton. "Mysterious Lights in Series and Parallel." *The Physics Teacher,* September 1980, p. 460. Leff, Harvey S. "Illuminating Physics with Light Bulbs." *The Physics Teacher,* January 1990, p. 30. Willis, Courtney W., and Nicholson, Lois. "The Lemon Screamer, the Lasagna Cell, and the Physics Teacher." *The Physics Teacher,* May 1990, p. 329.

PROBLEM CORRELATION

CONCEPTS	CHAPTER REVIEW			PROBLEMS APPENDIX
	Reviewing Concepts	Applying Concepts	Problems	
23.1 Simple Circuits				
Series Circuits	1	1	1,2,3,4,5,6,7,8,9	1,2,3,**4**
Voltage Drops in a Series Circuit		2	10,11	**5**
Parallel Circuits	2,3,4,6	3,4,5,6,7,8,9	**12,**13,14,15	6,7,**8,9**
23.2 Applications of Circuits				
Safety Devices	5,7,8	10	16	10
Combined Series-Parallel Circuits			17,18,19,**20**	11,12
Ammeters and Voltmeters	9,10			13,14,**15**

ACTIVITY AND DEMONSTRATION MATERIALS

PHYSICS LAB	POCKET LAB	DEMONSTRATIONS
Page 479 0–12 V power supply 4 small lamps with sockets and connecting wires	Pages 472, 475, 484 power supply ammeter and voltmeter wires 4 identical resistors—330 Ω or 470 Ω, 1/2 watt (Resistors of lower resistance may be used if they have higher power ratings such as 150 Ω or 220 Ω, 1 watt.) 5 Ω or 10 Ω, 1% or 0.1% precision resistor	Page 474 power supply three bulbs and sockets wire

EXTENSION PROJECTS

LIBRARY RESEARCH

1. Electric Shock
Describe varying degrees of electrical shock and the resulting biological damage.

DISPLAY MODEL

2. Flashlight
Build a flashlight from 2 batteries, 1 bulb, 1 piece of copper wire, and 1 8-cm^2 piece of aluminum foil. A sheet of paper can be used as the exterior covering.

STUDENT READINGS

Boyd, J. N. "Parallel Circuits and Probability." *The Physics Teacher,* February 1988.

Brodsky, Marc H. "Progress in Gallium Arsenide Semiconductors." *Scientific American,* February 1990.

Hughes, Thomas. "The Inventive Continuum." *Science,* November 1984.

Ong, P.P. "A Short-Circuit Method for Networks." *The Physics Teacher,* October 1983.

Rosenberg, Robert. "American Physics and the Origins of Electrical Engineering." *Physics Today,* October 1983.

Chapter 23

Series and Parallel Circuits

CHAPTER OVERVIEW

Theme Development: Students apply the conservation principle behind electrical quantities in the closed-system complete circuit in extending this mathematical model of electric forces. Phenomena associated with feedback from electrical devices within a circuit are observed in relation to a circuit's input and output.

MISCONCEPTIONS

Students think that current gets used up (decreases) in going around a series circuit and that the first circuit element gets all of the potential drop. They forget that current divides up in a parallel circuit. Students may continue to have difficulty with the abstractness of the circuit diagrams. The more hands-on experience your students can get with actual circuits, the better.

KEY TERMS

ammeter
equivalent resistance
fuse
ground-fault interrupter
parallel circuit
series circuit
short circuit
voltage divider
voltmeter

Laboratory Options

STUDENT EDITION

Physics Lab

Circuits	479

Pocket Labs

Series Resistance	472
Parallel Resistance	475
Ammeter Resistance	484

TEACHER EDITION

Activities

Demonstration	474
Cooperative Learning	476, 482
Discovery	481, 483

LABORATORY MANUAL

Series Resistance	Lab 23.1
Parallel Resistance	Lab 23.2

CHAPTER
23 Series and Parallel Circuits

Which Light Lights Lighter?

A 60-watt light bulb and a 100-watt light bulb are connected in series with a 120-volt source. If the circuit is closed, which bulb will glow brighter?

Chapter Outline

The electric circuits introduced in Chapter 22 had one source of electric energy and one device that used energy. Often many devices must be connected to one source. In this chapter, you will explore the ways in which devices can be connected in electric circuits. The photograph on the opposite page shows two light bulbs connected in series. Do you think the results would be the same if the two bulbs were connected in parallel?

If devices are connected in series, all the current travels through each device. A parallel connection allows the current to split and travel through several devices at once. A closer look will show how these connections work and how they can be used.

✓ Concept Check

The following terms or concepts from earlier chapters are important for a good understanding of this chapter. If you are not familiar with them, you should review them before studying this chapter.
- potential difference, Chapter 21
- electric circuits, resistance, Chapter 22

Introducing The Chapter

Which Light Lights Lighter?

Using The Photo: Even though students use electricity every day, they have many mistaken ideas about how it works. Student comments on the photo situation should reveal some of these misconceptions. The photo shows a series circuit and the way potential drops in a series work. For further explanation of the photo caption, refer students to page 478.

✓ Concept Check

Make sure students have a clear understanding of the concepts covered in Chapters 21 and 22 that are listed in the Concept Check. Students who have already applied the concepts of electric circuits, resistance, and potential difference in the lab will find it easier to master the material in this chapter on series and parallel circuits.

Assessment Options

Portfolio Assessment
Extension 1, TWE, p. 468b
Enrichment, TWE, pp. 476, 480
Portfolio, TWE, p. 481

Performance Assessment
Extension 2, TWE, p. 468b
Pocket Labs, pp. 472, 475, 484
Physics Lab, p. 479
Pocket Lab Assessment, TWE, p. 475
Activity, TWE, p. 482

Content Assessment
Self Assessment: Practice Problems, pp. 471, 474, 477, 484
Cooperative Learning, TWE, p. 476
Assessment, Critical Thinking, TWE, p. 479
Checking for Understanding, p. 483
Concept Reviews, pp. 478, 485
Chapter Review, pp. 486–489
Supplemental Problems, pp. 704–705

Group Assessment
Activities for group assessment occur with Cooperative Learning and lab activities.

23.1 SIMPLE CIRCUITS

Preparation

OBJECTIVES

The objectives are listed on the student page. Remind students to preview these objectives as a study guide to this major section.

OVERVIEW

The two ways of combining circuit elements, series and parallel, and the idea of voltage drops in a series circuit are discussed.

BRIDGING

Students will need to draw on their previous knowledge of resistance, current, and potential difference when studying this section.

1 Focus

DISCREPANT EVENT

Modify the electrical situation in the chapter opening photograph using two light bulbs. One light bulb should be 100 W and the other should have a small power rating (10 W or 15 W works best). Connect the bulbs in series, and then to an ordinary electrical outlet. CAUTION: This voltage is dangerous. When you connect the circuit, only the low-power light bulb will light. Ask students why. Many will say that the large bulb is burned out. Test this hypothesis by unscrewing the large bulb. This will make the small bulb go out, indicating that the large bulb is not burned out because it completes the series circuit. Since the combined resistance of the two bulbs is high, the current is fairly low. Because the low-power bulb has a higher resistance, it normally requires a lower current and thus lights up about as usual.

Objectives

- describe a series connection; state its important characteristics.
- calculate current, voltage drops, and equivalent resistance when devices are connected in series.
- describe a voltage divider and solve problems involving one.
- describe a parallel connection; state its important characteristics.
- calculate the voltage drop, currents, and equivalent resistance when devices are connected in parallel.

23.1 SIMPLE CIRCUITS

Have you ever driven along a single-lane road with no turn-offs? If there is an accident or if the road is being repaired, all traffic stops. There is only one path over which cars can move. This is like the path of electric charges in a series connection. In the case where there is a second road, however, cars can use either path and avoid road blocks. A parallel connection has the same characteristics as this second case.

Series Circuits

In a series circuit there is only one current path.

The current in a series circuit is the same in each element.

The total potential drop in a series circuit is the sum of the individual drops.

When resistors or other electrical devices are connected in a **series circuit**, all current travels through each resistor. It moves through one resistor after the other. Consider the flow of water in a river as a model of an electric current. At the river's source, the gravitational potential of the water is highest. Rapids are like resistors. A river having one rapid after another is like a series connection. All the water in the river passes through each of the rapids but loses some potential energy at each one. In Figure 23–1, current passes through the generator, the ammeter, and each lamp in succession. The current is the same in each device and in the generator. To find the current, we first find the potential drops around the circuit. If a charge is carried completely around the circuit, its potential returns to the original value. Thus the increase in potential across the generator is equal to the sum of the potential drops around the remainder of the circuit. The total distance the river drops is the sum of the vertical drops through each of the rapids. In the electrical circuit, there is almost no drop across the ammeter or the wires. The potential difference across the three lamps in series, V, is equal to the sum of the potential drops across the individual lamps,

$$V = V_1 + V_2 + V_3.$$

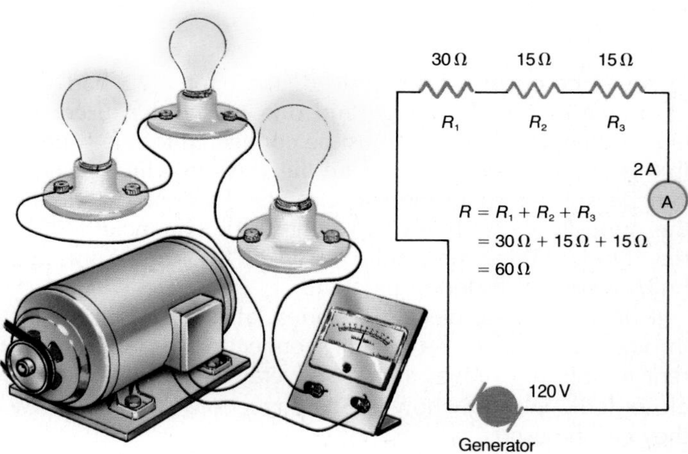

FIGURE 23–1. A series circuit can be represented both pictorially and schematically. The total resistance of a series circuit is equal to the sum of the individual resistances.

Multicultural Connections

In 1918, the Edison Pioneers was formed to honor some of the people who worked with Thomas Edison as the "creators of the electric industry." One member was the son of a freed slave. Lewis H. Latimer was born in 1848 in Massachusetts, taught himself how to be a draftsman when he was a teenager, and convinced a businessman to hire him. In 1876, Latimer prepared the drawings that Alexander Graham Bell needed to patent the telephone. In 1879, he was hired by the United States Electric Lighting Company where he invented and patented the first carbon filament electric lamp. He also invented a cheap way to produce the filaments, which made it possible for more people to afford electric lighting. In 1883, he joined Edison to help organize the patents coming from Edison's companies, and in 1890 he published the first textbook on electrical lighting in Edison's honor. Latimer died in 1928.

The resistance of each lamp is defined as $R = V/I$. Thus, the potential drop across the first lamp is $V_1 = IR_1$. Therefore,

$$V = IR_1 + IR_2 + IR_3, \text{ or } V = I(R_1 + R_2 + R_3).$$

The current is given by

$$I = \frac{V}{R_1 + R_2 + R_3}.$$

The same current would exist in a circuit with a single resistor, R, that has a resistance equal to the sum of the three lamp resistances. Such a resistance is called the **equivalent resistance** of the circuit. For resistors in series, the equivalent resistance is the sum of all the resistances,

$$\boxed{R = R_1 + R_2 + R_3.}$$

Notice that the equivalent resistance is larger than any single resistance.

The current through a series circuit is most easily found by first calculating the equivalent resistance, R, and then using the equation

$$I = \frac{V}{R}.$$

F. Y. I.

Henry Cavendish used the direct approach to measure the strength of an electric current. Lacking the appropriate instruments, he instead shocked himself with the current and then estimated the pain.

An equivalent resistance is the value of a single resistor that could replace all resistors in a circuit and not change the current. The equivalent resistance in a series circuit is the sum of the individual resistances.

Example Problem

Current in a Series Circuit

Four 15-Ω resistors are connected in series with a 45-V battery, Figure 23–2. What is the current in the circuit?

$$R = R_1 + R_2 + R_3 + R_4$$
$$= 15\ \Omega + 15\ \Omega + 15\ \Omega + 15\ \Omega = 60\ \Omega$$

Using the definition of resistance in the form $I = V/R$ gives

$$I = \frac{V}{R} = \frac{45\ \text{V}}{60\ \Omega} = 0.75\ \text{A}$$

Practice Problems

Assume batteries and generators provide the stated potential difference for any current that flows.

1. There are three 20-Ω resistors connected in series across a 120-V generator.
   a. What is the effective resistance of the circuit?
   b. What is the current in the circuit?
2. A 10-Ω resistor, a 15-Ω resistor, and a 5-Ω resistor are connected in series across a 90-V battery.
   a. What is the equivalent resistance of the circuit?
   b. What is the current in the circuit?

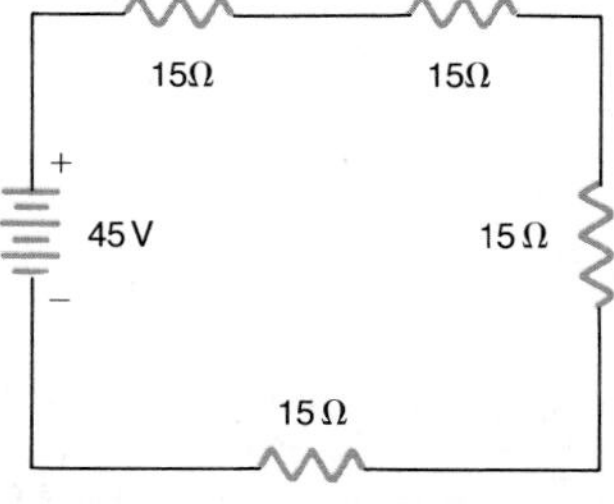

FIGURE 23–2. Use with the Example Problem.

2 Teach

CONCEPT DEVELOPMENT

- In terms of the water analogy mentioned in Chapter 22, a series circuit would be like a single closed loop of pipe that has only one path for the water to flow through. All water must pass all points in the pipe, and no water (or current) is lost.
- A helpful way of remembering what a series circuit is like (one device right after another) is to remind them of the World Series, one game right after another.
- The usual way of turning a circuit on or off is with a switch. Find out how many kinds of switches your students are familiar with. [Answers might include push buttons, rocker switches found on computers, toggle switches for the classroom lights, and pushthrough and twist switches on lamps.]
- There are various terms in use that all mean potential drop. *Voltage drop* and *IR drop* are two examples. Where does *IR drop* come from? Hint: Remember the definition of resistance.

Study Guide Master. To reinforce the concepts in this section, have the students complete the Study Guide Master for Section 23.1 from the Teacher Resource Package.

Answers To
PRACTICE PROBLEMS

Have students refer to Appendix A of the Solutions Appendix for complete solutions to Practice Problems.

1. **a.** 60 Ω
   b. 2.0 A
2. **a.** 30 Ω
   b. 3.0 A

STUDY GUIDE MASTER

Use the Study Guide master for section 23.1.

Answers To
PRACTICE PROBLEMS (cont.)

3. **a.** increase
   b. decrease
   c. no
4. **a.** 2000 Ω
   b. 200 Ω

POCKET LAB

SERIES RESISTANCE

Purpose: to construct a simple series circuit and monitor the effect of adding resistors by measuring the current.

Materials: power supply; ammeter; wires; 4 identical resistors (330 Ω or 470 Ω, 1/2 watt). Resistors of lower resistance, such as 150 Ω or 220 Ω, may be used if they have higher power ratings such as 1 watt.

Outcome: The current is inversely proportional to the number of resistors. For example, tripling the number of resistors reduces the current to 1/3 its original level.

POCKET LAB

SERIES RESISTANCE

Hook up a power supply, a resistor, and an ammeter in a series circuit. Predict what will happen to the current in the circuit when a second, identical resistor is added in series to the circuit. Predict the new currents when the circuit contains three and four resistors in series. Explain your prediction. Try it. Make a data table to show your results. Write a sentence that explains your results. (**Hint:** Include the idea of resistance.)

3. Consider a 9-V battery in a circuit with three resistors connected in series.
   a. If the resistance of one of the devices increases, how will the series resistance change?
   b. What will happen to the current?
   c. Will there be any change in the battery voltage?

▶ **4.** Ten Christmas tree bulbs connected in series have equal resistances. When connected to a 120-V outlet, the current through the bulbs is 0.06 A.
   a. What is the equivalent resistance of the circuit?
   b. What is the resistance of each bulb?

Voltage Drops in a Series Circuit

The total change in potential around a closed circuit is zero.

The net change in potential going around a circuit must be zero. A battery or generator raises the potential. While passing through the resistors, the potential drops an amount equal to the increase. The net change is zero.

The potential drop across each device in a series circuit can be calculated by rewriting the equation that defines resistance, $R = V/I$, as $V = IR$. First find the equivalent resistance, R, in the circuit. Then use the equivalent resistance to find the current. Find $I = V/R$, where V is the potential drop. Once the current in the circuit has been determined, multiply I by the resistance of the individual device to find the potential drop across that device.

A voltage divider is a simple series circuit.

An important application of series resistors is the **voltage divider**. Suppose you have a 9-V battery but need a 5-V potential source. A voltage divider can supply this voltage. Consider the circuit in Figure 23–3. Two resistors, R_1 and R_2, are connected in series across a battery of magnitude V. The equivalent resistance of the circuit is $R = R_1 + R_2$. The current I is given by $I = V/R = V/(R_1 + R_2)$. The desired voltage, 5 V, is the voltage drop, V_2, across resistor R_2.

$$V_2 = IR_2$$

Replacing I by the equation above gives

$$V_2 = IR_2 = \left(\frac{V}{R_1 + R_2}\right) \cdot R_2$$

$$= \frac{VR_2}{R_1 + R_2}.$$

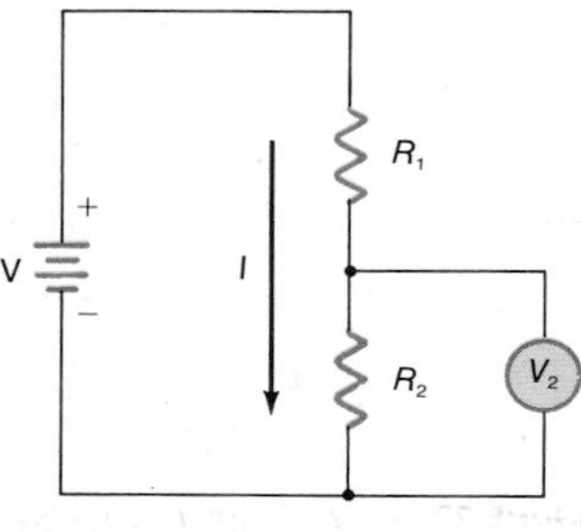

FIGURE 23–3.

Voltage dividers are often used with sensors like photoresistors. The resistance of a photoresistor depends on the amount of light that strikes it. Photoresistors are made of semiconductors like selenium or cadmium sulfide. A typical photoresistor can have a resistance of 400 Ω when light strikes it, but 400 000 Ω when in the dark. The output voltage of a voltage divider that uses a photoresistor depends on the amount

TEACHER 

The electrical diagram from an automobile owner's manual provides a convenient example of a fairly complex DC electrical system. Have students identify individual resistances and series circuits within the system.

a

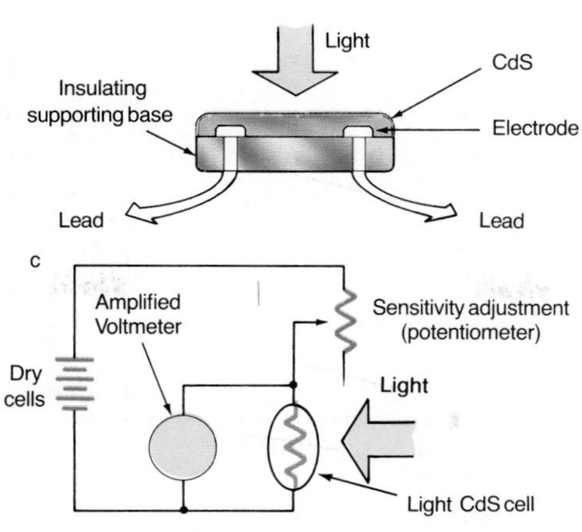

b

FIGURE 23–4. A light meter (a) and schematic diagram (b).

of light striking the photoresistor sensor. This circuit can be used as a light meter, Figure 23–4. In this device, an electronic circuit detects the potential difference and converts it to a measurement of illuminance that can be read on the digital display.

Example Problem

Voltage Drops in a Series Circuit

A 45.0-V potential difference is placed across a 5.0-Ω resistor and a 10.0-Ω resistor connected in series, Figure 23–5. **a.** What is the equivalent resistance of the circuit? **b.** What is the current through the circuit? **c.** What is the voltage drop across each resistor? **d.** What is the total voltage drop across the circuit?

Given: $R_1 = 5.0\ \Omega$
$R_2 = 10.0\ \Omega$
$V = 45.0\ \text{V}$

Unknowns: R, I, V_1, V_2
Basic equation: $V = IR$

Solution:

a. $R = R_1 + R_2$
$= 5.0\ \Omega + 10.0\ \Omega = 15.0\ \Omega$

b. $I = V/R = (45.0\ \text{V})/(15.0\ \Omega) = 3.00\ \text{A}$

c. The voltage drop across R_1 is
$V_1 = IR_1 = (3.00\ \text{A})(5.0\ \Omega) = 15\ \text{V}.$
The voltage drop across R_2 is
$V_2 = IR_2 = (3.00\ \text{A})(10.0\ \Omega) = 30.0\ \text{V}.$

d. $V = V_1 + V_2$
$= 15\ \text{V} + 30.0\ \text{V} = 45\ \text{V}$

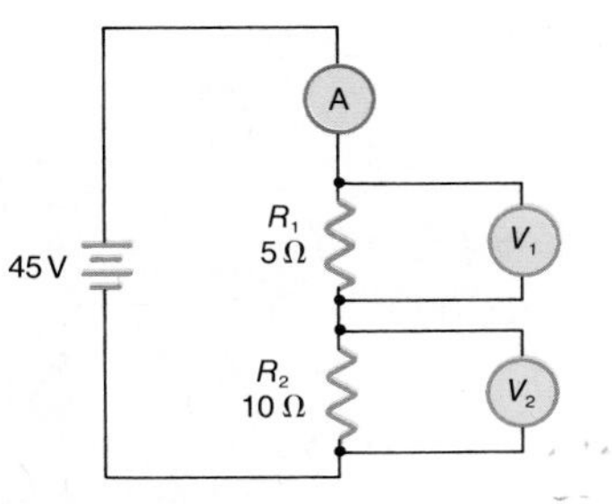

FIGURE 23–5. Use with the Example Problem.

CONCEPT DEVELOPMENT

Guided Practice: After going over the Example Problems on this page and page 473, have students work in class on the first two Practice Problems that follow.

Independent Practice: Assign the remaining Practice Problems for homework, then spend time reviewing them with students during the next class period.

Laboratory Manual. Give students additional experience with series resistance by doing Lab 23.1 from the Laboratory Manual.

LABORATORY MANUAL

Use Lab 23.1 with this section.

CONCEPT DEVELOPMENT

Doing calculations to compute the equivalent resistance of resistors in parallel, students are often confused by one of the last steps involving cross-multiplication. They have trouble getting the unknown out of the reciprocal form. Help with this step by reminding them that $\left(\frac{1}{a} + \frac{1}{b} \neq \frac{1}{a+b}\right)$. Emphasize that the equivalent resistance of several resistors in parallel is always less than the smallest resistor in the parallel combination. You might show this by calculating the equivalent resistance of 60 Ω, 60 Ω and 2 Ω in parallel.

Demonstration: Set up a power supply with three bulbs in a series so students can easily see that they are strung end-to-end and there is only a single path through which current may flow. Light the bulbs, observe the brightness, and unscrew one bulb so students can see that all the bulbs go out. Now set up the bulbs in parallel so the students can see that the pattern is like a series of stacked bridges. Observe the brightness and unscrew one bulb so students can observe that the rest of the bulbs stay lit. Compare the brightness of the bulbs in series to the brightness of those in parallel. Discuss *V* or *I* differences in the two types of circuits.

Answers To
PRACTICE PROBLEMS

Have students refer to Appendix A of the Solutions Appendix for complete solutions to Practice Problems.

5. a. 50.0 Ω
   b. 2.40 A
   c. 72.0 V
   d. 120 V
6. a. 12.0 kΩ
   b. 1.0×10^{-3} A
   c. 3.0 V, 5.0 V, and 4.0 V
   d. 12.0 V
7. 15 V

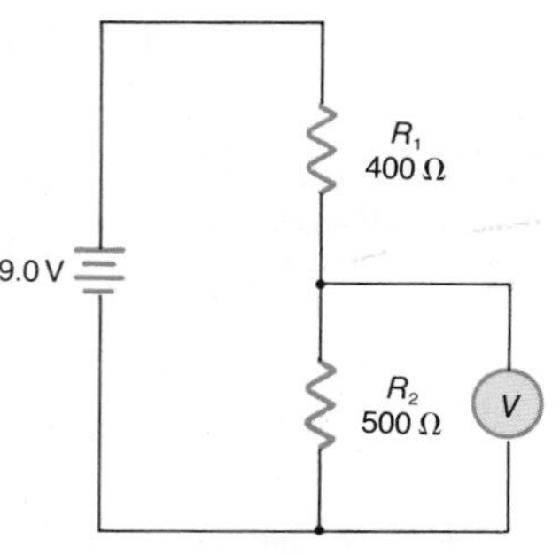

FIGURE 23–6. Use with the Example Problem.

Example Problem

Voltage Divider

A 9.0-V battery and two resistors, R_1 = 400 Ω and R_2 = 500 Ω, are connected as a voltage divider, Figure 23–6. What is the voltage across R_2?

Given: $V = 9.0$ V
$R_1 = 400\ \Omega$
$R_2 = 500\ \Omega$

Unknown: V_2

Basic equation: $V_2 = \frac{VR_2}{R_1 + R_2}$

Solution: $V_2 = \frac{VR_2}{R_1 + R_2} = \frac{(9.0\text{ V})(500\ \Omega)}{400\ \Omega + 500\ \Omega} = 5\text{ V}$

Using Your CALCULATOR

Since multiplication is the inverse of division, you can use the inverse key, 1/x, to perform calculation without having to reenter numbers.

$$\frac{(9\text{ V})(500\ \Omega)}{400\ \Omega + 500\ \Omega}$$

Keys	Answer
4 0 0 + 5 0 0 =	900
1/x =	1.11...-03
9 × 5 0 0 =	5

Practice Problems

5. A 20.0-Ω resistor and a 30.0-Ω resistor are connected in series and placed across a 120-V potential difference.
   a. What is the equivalent resistance of the circuit?
   b. What is the current in the circuit?
   c. What is the voltage drop across each resistor?
   d. What is the voltage drop across the two resistors together?
6. Three resistors of 3.0 kΩ (3.0×10^3 Ω), 5.0 kΩ, and 4.0 kΩ are connected in series across a 12-V battery.
   a. What is the equivalent resistance?
   b. What is the current through the resistors?
   c. What is the voltage drop across each resistor?
   d. Find the total voltage drop across the three resistors.
7. A student makes a voltage divider from a 45-V battery, a 475-kΩ (475×10^3 Ω) resistor, and a 235-kΩ resistor. The output voltage is measured across the smaller resistor. What is the voltage?

FIGURE 23–7. A typical parallel circuit is shown using both its pictorial and schematic representations. The total resistance of a parallel circuit is smaller than any of its individual resistances.

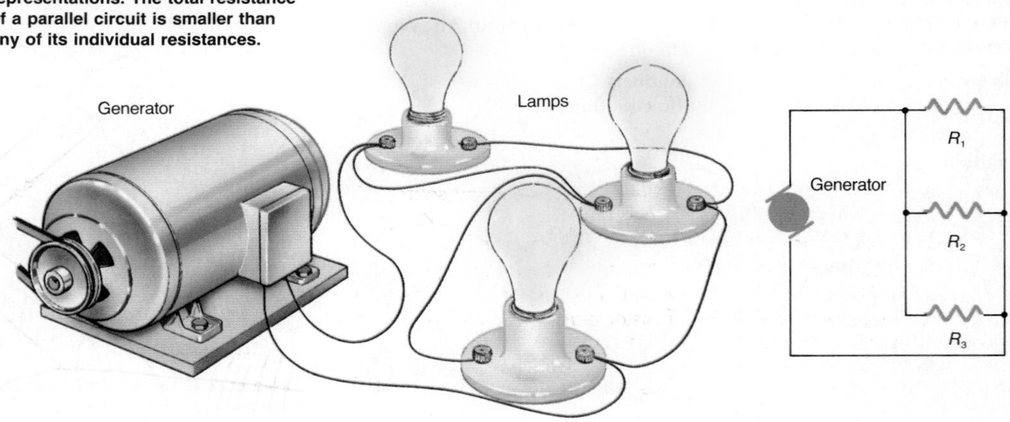

Connect to BIOLOGY

The electrical resistance across your skin is high, around 40 000 Ω. The resistance from one part of your body to another, however, is much smaller, closer to 100 Ω. If, for example, you torch the terminals of a 9-V battery with your two hands, the current encounters three resistances in series, skin, internal organs, and skin. The total resistance is over 80 000 Ω, and the current flow is small, less than 1/8 mA. Water lowers the resistance of your skin by about a factor of ten. If one hand is wet, the high resistance of the other hand keeps the current low. If, however, both hands are wet, the current can be high enough to be felt. Even low *EMFs* can be dangerous in hospitals where instrument probes are placed directly into the body, so the skin's resistance cannot keep currents low. Currents as high as 1 mA are to be avoided.

If the body's resistance between two probes is 50 Ω, what is the largest *EMF* that could be placed across the two probes? [(1 mA) (50 Ω) = 50 mV or 0.05 V]

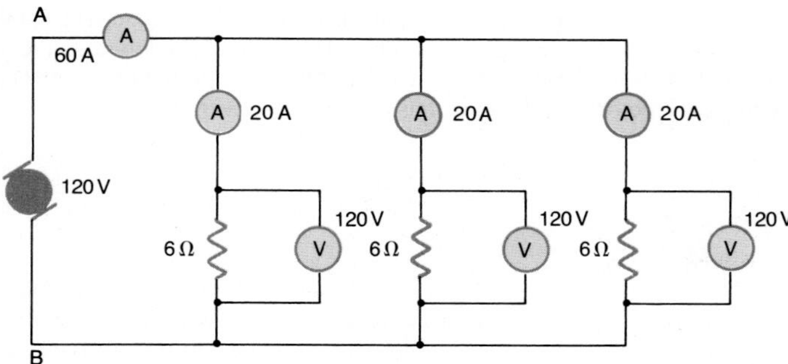

FIGURE 23–8. In a parallel circuit, the reciprocal of the total resistance is equal to the sum of the reciprocals of the individual resistances. Here you see three 60-Ω resistors connected in parallel. For each resistor, the voltage drop is 120 volts and the current is 2 amperes.

▶ **8.** A photoresistor is used in a voltage divider as R_2. $V = 9.0$ V and $R_1 = 500\ \Omega$.

a. What is the output voltage, V_2, across R_2, when a bright light strikes the photoresistor and $R_2 = 475\ \Omega$?

b. When the light is dim, $R_2 = 4.0\ \text{k}\Omega$. What is V_2?

c. When the photoresistor is in total darkness, $R_2 = 0.40\ \text{M}\Omega$ $(0.40 \times 10^6\ \Omega)$. What is V_2?

Parallel Circuits

In a **parallel circuit** there are several current paths. A typical parallel circuit is shown in Figure 23–7. The circuit contains a voltage source and three resistors. The three resistors are connected in parallel; their left-hand ends are connected together and their right-hand ends are connected together. The current flows through three paths in this parallel circuit. Rapids in a wide river can illustrate a parallel circuit. The water going through rapids often divides into several channels. Some channels may have a large flow of water, others a small flow. The sum of the flows, however, is equal to the total flow of water in the river. In addition, no matter which channel the water follows, the loss in gravitational potential will be the same. All the water starts at the same level and comes together again at the same level below the rapids. In the same way, in a parallel electrical circuit, the total current is the sum of the currents through each current path, and the potential difference across each path is the same.

A schematic diagram of three identical resistors connected in parallel is shown in Figure 23–8. The 120-V generator provides the source of potential difference for the circuit. Each current path from **A** to **B** is part of a closed circuit including the generator, resistors, and ammeters. Each path acts as if the other paths were not present. What is the current through one resistor? There is a 120-V potential difference across each resistor. The current through a 6-Ω resistor across a 120-V potential difference is

$$I = \frac{V}{R} = \frac{120\ \text{V}}{6\ \Omega} = 20\ \text{A}.$$

There is more than one current path in a parallel circuit.

POCKET LAB

PARALLEL RESISTANCE

Hook up a power supply, a resistor, and an ammeter in a series circuit. Predict what will happen to the current in the circuit when a second, identical resistor is added in parallel to the first. Predict the new currents when the circuit contains three and four resistors in parallel. Explain your prediction. Try it. Make a data table to show your results. Write a sentence that explains your results. (**Hint:** Include the idea of resistance.)

8. a. 4.4 V
b. 8.0 V
c. 9.0 V

POCKET LAB

PARALLEL RESISTANCE

Purpose: to construct a simple parallel circuit and monitor the effect of adding resistors by measuring the current.

Materials: power supply; ammeter; wires; 4 identical resistors (330 Ω or 470 Ω, 1/2 watt). Resistors of lower resistance may be used if they have higher power ratings.

Outcome: Students will be surprised to find that the current increases as more parallel branches are added. With three branches, the current will be three times the original value. The resistance decreases with the addition of more parallel branches.

Assessment

Performance

To further assess students' understanding of parallel circuits, ask if the current in the first resistor changes when you connect the second, third, and fourth resistors in parallel. Have them predict the answer and then devise a method of testing it. Have them explain how to connect an ammeter so it measures the current through just one resistor. [You must disconnect one lead from the first resistor from the point where the two, three, and four resistors join. Connect one lead of the ammeter to this point and the other lead to the resistor lead you disconnected. That is, it should be in the location of one of the meters reading 20 A in Figure 23–8, not in the location of the meter reading 60 A.]

CONCEPT DEVELOPMENT

ACTIVITY

Cooperative Learning: Have small groups of students make a summary chart of the properties of series and parallel circuits. The chart should include the behavior of voltage, resistance, and current; the dependence/independence of circuit devices; and the number of conducting paths. See who can make the clearest, best-organized chart.

Critical Thinking: Ask students why household circuits are parallel. [The two major reasons are that all appliances can easily run on the same voltage, making the engineering of appliances much simpler, and that appliances can be turned off and on independently of one another.]

Enrichment: The human body uses electricity in nerve impulses, muscle action, brain function, and bone growth. Have interested students investigate bioelectricity.

Laboratory Manual. Give students additional experience with parallel resistance by doing Lab 23.2 from the Laboratory Manual.

Transparency Package. Use Transparency 33 to help illustrate series and parallel circuits.

The equivalent resistance of parallel resistors is smaller than any resistor.

The current flow through each path from **A** to **B** is 20 A. The total current between the two points is 60 A. The potential difference across the two points is 120 V. A single resistor that would permit 60-A current with 120-V potential difference has a resistance given by

$$R = \frac{V}{I} = \frac{120\ \text{V}}{60\ \text{A}} = 2\ \Omega.$$

In a parallel circuit, the total current is the sum of the currents in each path.

The equivalent resistance can be replaced by this single resistor. Placing a resistor in parallel with an existing resistor always decreases the equivalent resistance of the circuit. The resistance decreases because each new resistor provides an additional path for current to flow between points **A** and **B.** Notice that the equivalent resistance of the circuit is less than the resistance of any resistor in the circuit.

In a parallel circuit, all the potential drops are the same.

To find the equivalent resistance of a parallel circuit, start by noting that the total current in the circuit is the sum of the currents through the branches of the circuit. Recall also that the potential across each is the same. If I is the total current, and I_1, I_2, and I_3 are the currents through each of the branches, then

$$I = I_1 + I_2 + I_3.$$

The current through each resistor, for example R_1, can be found from $I_1 = V/R_1$. The total current through the equivalent resistance, R, of the circuit is given by $I = V/R$, but all potential drops in a parallel circuit are the same.

$$\frac{V}{R} = \frac{V}{R_1} + \frac{V}{R_2} + \frac{V}{R_3}$$

Dividing both sides of the equation by V then gives an equation for the equivalent resistance of three parallel resistors,

$$\boxed{\frac{1}{R} = \frac{1}{R_1} + \frac{1}{R_2} + \frac{1}{R_3}.}$$

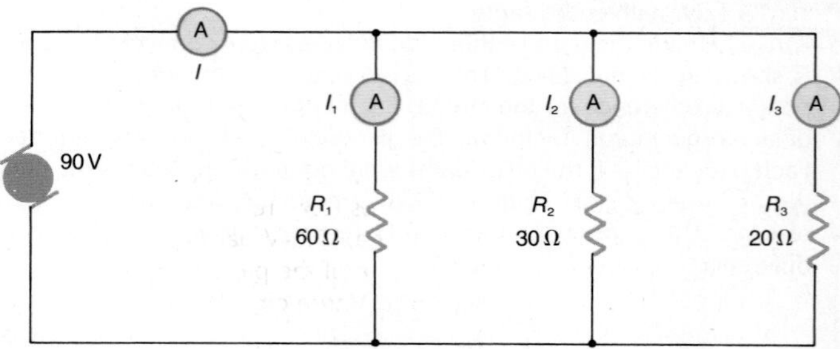

FIGURE 23–9. Use with the Example Problem.

Example Problem

Total Resistance and Current in a Parallel Circuit

Three resistors of 60.0 Ω, 30.0 Ω, and 20.0 Ω are connected in parallel across a 90.0-V difference in potential, Figure 23–9.
a. Find the equivalent resistance of the circuit.
b. Find the current in the entire circuit.
c. Find the current through each branch of the circuit.

Given: $R_1 = 60.0\ \Omega$, $R_2 = 30.0\ \Omega$, $R_3 = 20.0\ \Omega$, $V = 90.0$ V

Unknowns: R, I, I_1, I_2, I_3

Basic equations: $V = IR$

$$\frac{1}{R} = \frac{1}{R_1} + \frac{1}{R_2} + \frac{1}{R_3}$$

Solution:

a. $$\frac{1}{R} = \frac{1}{60.0\ \Omega} + \frac{1}{30.0\ \Omega} + \frac{1}{20.0\ \Omega}$$

$$\frac{1}{R} = \frac{6}{60.0\ \Omega}$$

$$R = 10.0\ \Omega$$

b. $$I = \frac{V}{R} = \frac{90.0\text{ V}}{10.0\ \Omega} = 9.00\text{ A}$$

c. The voltage drop across each resistor is 90.0 V. The currents are:

$$(\text{for } R_1)\ I_1 = \frac{V}{R_1} = \frac{90.0\text{ V}}{60.0\ \Omega} = 1.50\text{ A}$$

$$(\text{for } R_2)\ I_2 = \frac{V}{R_2} = \frac{90.0\text{ V}}{30.0\ \Omega} = 3.00\text{ A}$$

$$(\text{for } R_3)\ I_3 = \frac{V}{R_3} = \frac{90.0\text{ V}}{20.0\ \Omega} = 4.50\text{ A}$$

HELP WANTED

ELECTRIC POWER PLANT OPERATOR

A utility company needs high school graduates who have the interest and ability to learn detailed information about the production and distribution of electric power. Your high school record of reliability, effort, and cooperation are most important.

This entry-level position includes extensive training. Success in this career field is dependent on quality work, continued training, and the ability to contribute positively to the work environment. For information contact:

Utility Workers of America, 815 16th Street, N.W., Washington, DC 20006

Practice Problems

9. Three 15-Ω resistors are connected in parallel and placed across a 30-V potential difference.
 a. What is the equivalent resistance of the parallel circuit?
 b. What is the current through the entire circuit?
 c. What is the current through each branch of the parallel circuit?

10. A 12.0-Ω resistor and a 15.0-Ω resistor are connected in parallel and placed across the terminals of a 15.0-V battery.
 a. What is the equivalent resistance of the parallel circuit?
 b. What is the current through the entire circuit?
 c. What is the current through each branch of the parallel circuit?

CONCEPT DEVELOPMENT

CHECKING FOR UNDERSTANDING

Have students describe the way current divides in a parallel circuit. Which resistance has the largest current? [the smallest resistance] Which resistance has the smallest current? [the largest resistance] What is the same for all of the resistances in parallel? [the potential drop across each] Make sure students understand that two resistors in parallel have two points in common.

RETEACHING

Review common elements of a circuit by actually displaying wires, switches, resistors, power supplies, voltmeters, and ammeters. Point out that the simplest way of hooking up several things is in a series. Discuss branching as a lead into parallel circuits. Try to explain the geometrical arrangement first, then reintroduce electrical quantities: current, voltage, etc. Accompany these explanations with measurements on actual circuits.

EXTENSION

Enrichment Master. Prepare students for further work with electrical circuits by assigning the Enrichment Master for Chapter 23 from the Teacher Resource Package.

INDEPENDENT PRACTICE/ EXTENSION

Refer to the Assignment Guide below for additional questions and problems for independent practice.

Answers To
PRACTICE PROBLEMS

Have students refer to Appendix A of the Solutions Appendix for complete solutions to Practice Problems.

9. **a.** 5.0 Ω
 b. 6.0 A
 c. 2.0 *a*

10. **a.** 6.67 Ω
 b. 2.25 A
 c. 1.25 A, 1.00 A

23:1 ASSIGNMENT GUIDE

	PRACTICE	EXTENSION
CHAPTER REVIEW pp. 486–489		
· Reviewing Concepts	1–4, 6	
· Applying Concepts		1–9
· Problems*	1–11, 13–15	12
APPENDIX B PROBLEMS*		
· Chapter 23, pp. 704–705	1–3, 6, 7	4, 5, 8, 9

* Complete solutions to all Chapter Review and Appendix problems appear in the Problems and Solutions Manual.

LABORATORY MANUAL

Use Lab 23.2 with this section.

TRANSPARENCY

Use Transparency 33 with this section.

Answers To
PRACTICE PROBLEMS (cont)

11. a. 20.0 Ω
b. 0.600 A
c. 0.100 A, 0.200 A, 0.300 A

12. a. smaller
b. becomes larger
c. no

Guided Practice: After going over the Example Problem on page 477, have students work in class on the Practice Problems that follow. Spend time reviewing answers as a group.

Independent Practice: Assign the Concept Review questions on this page for homework and review them in class the next class period.

3 Close

CONVERGENT QUESTION

Ask students to describe the measurements you would have to make to determine the power rating of an unlabeled appliance. [Because you know that the potential difference is 120 V, you need only measure the current. Then calculate the product of current and voltage to get the power.]

CONCEPT REVIEW ANSWERS

1.1 Parallel, because you have seen a car with only one headlight functioning.

1.2 a. Series, so it can control the current through the lamp. **b.** Increase the resistance to reduce the current and dim the lamp.

1.3 a. 0 V. $V = IR$ with $R = 0$. **b.** 120 V. There is no current in the circuit, so the voltage across the bulb is 0. Since the sum of the voltages across the switch and bulb is 120 V, there must be 120 V across the switch.

1.4 Critical Thinking: The answer to each is "nothing." The potentials of points **A** and **B** are the same. Therefore, no current flows through the wire and nothing changes.

11. A 120.0-Ω resistor, a 60.0-Ω resistor, and a 40.0-Ω resistor are connected in parallel and placed across a potential difference of 12.0 V.
a. What is the equivalent resistance of the parallel circuit?
b. What is the current through the entire circuit?
c. What is the current through each of the branches of the parallel circuit?

▶ **12.** Suppose the 12.0-Ω resistor in Practice Problem 10 is replaced by a 10.0-Ω resistor.
a. Does the equivalent resistance become smaller, larger, or remain the same?
b. Does the amount of current through the entire circuit change? in what way?
c. Does the amount of current through the 15.0-Ω resistor change? in what way?

Which Light Lights Lighter? ▶

You learned in Chapter 22 that the resistance of a 60-watt bulb is greater than the resistance of a 100-watt bulb. The brightness of a bulb is directly proportional to the power dissipated by the filament of the bulb. In a series circuit, the same current flows through all elements in the circuit. Therefore, according to $P = I^2R$, the 60-watt bulb has a higher resistance, and for this reason, will dissipate more power and glow more brightly.

CONCEPT REVIEW

1.1 Are car headlights connected in series or parallel? Draw on your experience.

1.2 Lamp dimmers often contain variable resistors.
a. Would a dimmer be hooked in series or in parallel with the lamp to be controlled? Why?
b. Should the resistance of the dimmer be increased or decreased to dim the lamp?

1.3 A switch is connected in series with a 75-W bulb to a source of 120 V.
a. What is the potential difference across the switch when it is closed or on?
b. What is the potential difference across it when it is open or off? Explain.

1.4 Critical Thinking: The circuit in Figure 23–10 has four identical resistors. Suppose a wire is connected between points **A** and **B**. Answer each question, explaining your reasoning.
a. What current flows through the wire?
b. What happens to the current through each resistor?
c. What happens to the current drawn from the battery?
d. What happens to the potential difference across each resistor?

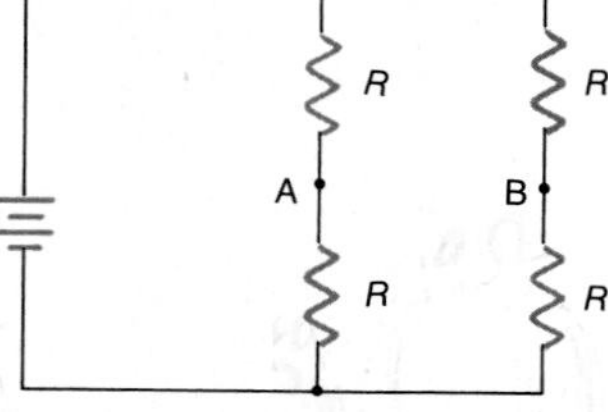

FIGURE 23–10. Use with Concept Review 1.4.

ENRICHMENT MASTER

Use the Enrichment master for Chapter 6 with this section.

LAB WORKSHEET

Use the Lab Worksheet for Chapter 23 with this Physics Lab.

PHYSICS LAB Circuits

Purpose

To construct series, parallel, and combination circuits.

Materials

- 0 - 12 V power supply
- 4 small lamps with sockets and connecting wires

Procedure

1. Turn the dial on the power supply to the off position. Use caution while working with line current electricity to prevent shocks.
2. Build a circuit with 2 lamps. Turn the power supply on so that both bulbs glow brightly. Record the setting on the power supply. This will be called the original setting.
3. Loosen one bulb from its socket and observe what happens to the other bulb. Turn the power supply off. If the other bulb goes out, you have made a series circuit. Go to the section marked SERIES CIRCUITS. If the other bulb stayed on you have made a parallel circuit. Go to the section marked PARALLEL CIRCUITS.

Series Circuits

1. Make a series circuit with three bulbs. Turn the power supply dial to the original setting and notice the brightness of the bulbs. Turn the power supply off.
2. Make a series circuit with four bulbs. Turn the power supply dial to the original setting and notice the brightness of the bulbs.
3. Try loosening one of the middle bulbs. What happens to the others? Sketch the circuit.
5. If you have not done the parallel circuits, try to make a circuit with 2 lamps so that when you loosen one bulb the other stays on. Then go to PARALLEL CIRCUITS.

Parallel Circuits

1. Make a parallel circuit with three bulbs.
2. Loosen one of the bulbs to verify that the other 2 stay on. Relight the bulbs.
3. Compare the brightness of the bulbs to the original brightness. Sketch the circuit.
4. If you have not already done series circuits, try to design a circuit with 2 bulbs so that when one is loosened the other will also go out. Then go to SERIES CIRCUITS.

Observations and Data

1. Describe what happens to the brightness of the bulbs as more are added in a series circuit and a parallel circuit.

Analysis

The brightness of each bulb depends on the current passing through the bulb.

1. Write a statement that compares the current through each bulb in the same series circuit.
2. What happens to the current as more lamps are added to the series circuit?

Applications

1. Design and construct a circuit with three lamps so that 1 is bright and 2 are dim. Draw the circuit.

ASSESSMENT

Critical Thinking: To further assess students' understanding of circuits, ask the following questions.

1. Suppose that you use a 9-V battery to light the lamps. Predict how the addition of more lamps in series would affect the life of the battery. Explain your reasoning. [Adding more lamps in series reduces the current so the battery would last longer. The energy flows out of the battery at a slower rate.]

2. You have used brightness as an indicator of current. Would you expect the lamps to be only half as bright when the current is half as much? Why? Reduce the voltage to half the previous value and note the change in the lamps. Record your results. [The relationship between the brightness and current is proportional, but not directly proportional. The lamps will be less than half as bright.]

PHYSICS LAB

Process Skills: defining operationally, questioning, observing, communicating, forming models.

MISCONCEPTIONS

Students lack the experience that is essential to understanding series and parallel circuits and therefore often confuse the two types.

Teaching Suggestions: Do not be too quick to jump in and help. Let students discover the basic ideas themselves.

Troubleshooting: Make sure that one student does not monopolize this activity. If one or two students have a background in electronics, encourage them to let others explore using the equipment.

Lab Worksheet, Teacher Resource Package. If desired, use the lab worksheet master provided for this chapter for students to record their data.

OBSERVATIONS

As more bulbs are added in series, they all become dimmer. Adding more bulbs in parallel has no effect on the brightness (unless the power supply is being heavily loaded, in which case they will dim).

ANALYSIS

1. Since the lamps become dimmer when more are added in series, this indicates that less current is flowing.

2. Each lamp stays the same brightness. The current through each bulb stays the same.

APPLICATIONS

Two lamps will be in parallel, and the third in series with the power supply. Parallel is the preferred choice. If one bulb burns out, the others will stay on.

23.2 APPLICATIONS OF CIRCUITS

Preparation

OBJECTIVES

The objectives are listed on the student page. Remind students to preview these objectives as a study guide to this major section.

OVERVIEW

This section builds directly on the first section, expanding the concepts introduced there. Safety devices such as fuses and circuit breakers are discussed for the first time in this section.

BRIDGING

This section relates most directly to the first section of this chapter.

1 Focus

Invite a local electrician to talk to the class about safety considerations in electrical circuits. Fuses and circuit breakers are only the beginning of this subject.

2 Teach

CONCEPT DEVELOPMENT

- The terms *open circuit, closed circuit,* and *short circuit* are often used in discussing circuits. They mean, respectively: complete, incomplete, and very low resistance path. Make sure that students are familiar with them.

Study Guide Master. To reinforce the concepts in this section, have the students complete the Study Guide Master for Section 23.2 from the Teacher Resource Package.

Enrichment: Some students might be interested in doing some research to find out how to wire a light that can be turned off or on from two different locations, such as at the top and bottom of a stairway. Then have them explain and demonstrate the circuit to the class.

Objectives

- describe a combination series-parallel circuit.
- calculate the equivalent resistance in a combination circuit.
- distinguish between voltmeters and ammeters and state the important characteristics of each.
- describe how each is wired into a circuit and explain why such a method is used.

23.2 APPLICATIONS OF CIRCUITS

Household wiring circuits are examples of the ideas we have examined in the earlier part of this chapter. We need to understand the requirements and limitations of these systems. Above all, it is important that we are aware of the safety measures that must be practiced to prevent accidents.

Safety Devices

In an electric circuit, fuses and circuit breakers are switches that act as safety devices. They prevent circuit overloads that can occur when too many appliances are turned on at the same time or a short circuit occurs in one appliance. When appliances are connected in parallel, each additional appliance placed in operation reduces the equivalent resistance in the circuit and causes more current to flow through the wires. The additional current may produce enough thermal energy (at the rate $P = I^2R$) to melt insulation on the wires, causing a short circuit in the wires or even a fire.

A fuse or circuit breaker protects against dangerously large currents.

A **fuse** is a short piece of metal that melts from the heating effect of the current. The thickness of the metal is adjusted to determine the current needed to melt the fuse. A circuit breaker, Figure 23–11, is an automatic switch that opens when the current reaches some set value. If current greater than the set value flows in the circuit, it will be overloaded. The circuit breaker will open stopping all current flow.

A ground-fault interrupter opens the circuit if a shock hazard exists.

A **ground-fault interrupter** is often required by law in electrical outlets in bathrooms. Current flows both through the wire bringing charges from the power source and in the wire returning the charges. If there is no other current path, the magnitude of these two currents is the same. Sometimes, when an appliance, such as a hair dryer, is used, the appliance or user might touch a cold water pipe or a sink full of water. Another current path, through the user, could exist—as little as 5 mA is serious. The ground-fault interrupter contains an electronic circuit that detects small differences in current caused by the extra current path and opens the circuit, preventing dangerous shocks.

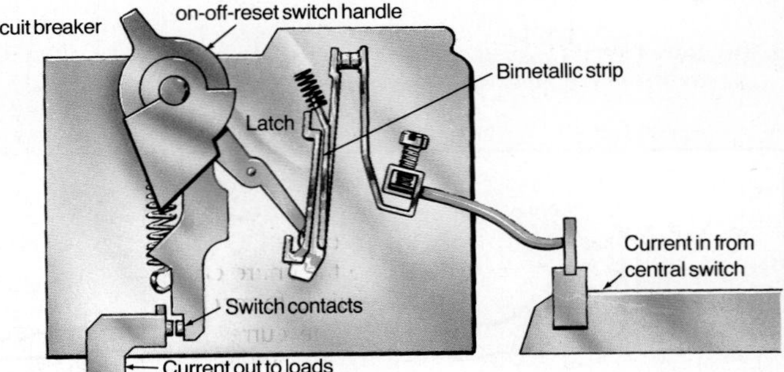

FIGURE 23–11. If too much current flows through the bimetallic strip, it will bend down, releasing the latch. The handle will move to the "off" position, opening the switch contacts. The handle will not stay in the "on" position with the switch contacts closed unless the bimetallic strip is cool and straight.

- Because our household circuits are parallel, students sometimes get the idea that series circuits are not important. This is not true; for example, a series portion is an essential part of the voltage divider that is found in the control circuits of many appliances.

STUDY GUIDE MASTER

Use the Study Guide master for section 23.2.

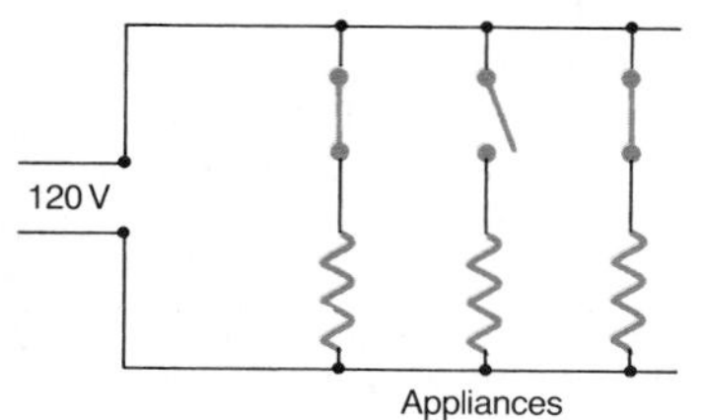

FIGURE 23–12. The wiring diagram for this house indicates the parallel nature of the circuit. This wiring arrangement will permit the use of one or more appliances.

Home wiring uses parallel circuits.

Electric wiring in a home uses parallel circuits, Figure 23–12, so that the current in any one circuit does not depend on the current in the other circuits. The current in a device that dissipates power, P, when connected to a voltage source, V, is given by $I = P/V$. Figure 23–13 shows a schematic diagram of the house circuit. Suppose, first, that a 240-W television is plugged into a 120-V outlet. The current that flows is given by I = (240 W)/(120 V) = 2 A. Then a 720-W curling iron is plugged in. The current through the iron is I = (720 W)/(120 V) = 6 A. Finally, a 1440-W hair dryer is added. The current through the hair dryer is I = (1440 W)/(120 V) = 12 A.

The current through these three appliances can be found by considering them as a parallel circuit where the currents are independent of each other. Each resistor represents an appliance. The value of the resistance is found by first calculating the current the appliance draws as above and then using the equation $R = V/I$. The equivalent resistance of the three appliances is

$$\frac{1}{R} = \frac{1}{10\ \Omega} + \frac{1}{20\ \Omega} + \frac{1}{60\ \Omega} = \frac{10}{60\ \Omega} = \frac{1}{6\ \Omega}$$

$$R = 6\ \Omega.$$

The 15-A fuse is connected in series with the power source so the entire current flows through it. The current flowing through the fuse is

$$I = \frac{V}{R} = \frac{120\ \text{V}}{6\ \Omega} = 20\ \text{A}.$$

The 20-A current exceeds the rating of the 15-A fuse, so the fuse will melt, or "blow," cutting off current to the entire circuit.

A **short circuit** occurs when a circuit is formed that has a very low resistance. The low resistance causes the current to be very large. If there were no fuse or circuit breaker, such a large current could easily

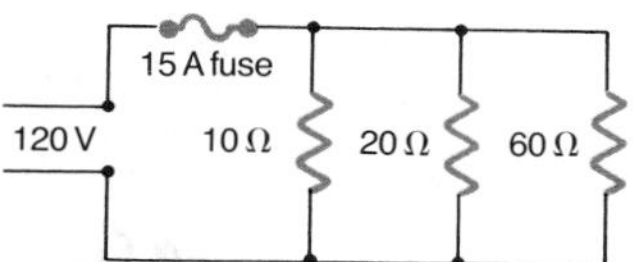

FIGURE 23–13. A 60-Ω, a 20-Ω, and a 10-Ω resistor are connected in parallel across a 120-V source. The current through the circuit will cause the fuse to melt.

CONCEPT DEVELOPMENT

- Continue to emphasize that a volt is a joule per coulomb. This will help keep the units more meaningful and make unit cancellation easier.
- If you have large demonstration ammeters and voltmeters, use them in your demonstrations of electrical circuits.
- You may have a broken electrical meter in the lab. If so, remove its back or bottom and pass it around for student inspection. You should be able to see at least the coil and some resistors in most meters.

ACTIVITY

Discovery: If you taught the resistor color code, here's an idea for a quick quiz. Obtain a supply of assorted resistors (you could remove them from a discarded radio or other appliance) and hand one out to each student. Have students completely identify their own resistor using the color code. Ask them to fasten the resistor to the corner of their paper so that you can check their work. Some teachers want students to memorize the code; others prefer to provide students copies to work from.

Enrichment: In the public mind, Edison is generally identified solely with the invention of the electric light bulb. He also pioneered the development of the system for distributing electrical power. Have interested students find out what this total electrical system was like.

Assessment

Portfolio

Make a survey of series and parallel circuits in your home. Present your results in a table. Consider both simple series and parallel circuits as well as more complex examples. For example, do you have two switches in series controlling one lamp? Is there one switch controlling several lamps? Consider also three-way lamps. Are they connected in series, parallel, or a combination?

TEACHER F.Y.I.

These are the calculations for the three resistances used in the text above.
Television: 120 V/2A = 60Ω
Curling iron: 120 V/6A = 20Ω
Hair dryer: 120 V/12A = 10Ω

CONCEPT DEVELOPMENT

ACTIVITY

Cooperative Learning: Have student groups hook up two bulbs in parallel using a battery and a switch but no meters. Check the circuits. Now have them place the ammeter in the circuit so it will measure the total current. Have them add a third bulb and observe the current increase. Students should then use the voltmeter to measure the voltage across the light bulbs so they can see that the voltage drops are all the same. In order to measure the current through each branch, students must open the circuit between the resistor and the junction and insert the ammeter, making sure the polarity is correct. Students will observe that the current through each branch is less than the circuit's total current. When the current in all the branches is added together, it equals the total current. Have students reduce the circuit to one bulb so they can see that the voltage is still the same, and that the total current is lower than when there were several bulbs.

Enrichment: Ask students if there are other ways of hooking up circuit devices besides series and parallel. Let them draw their suggestions. [Two other ways are the delta—three devices connected in a triangular arrangement; and the wye (or star)—three devices connected together at one point. These two arrangements are neither strictly series nor parallel.]

Critical Thinking: Ask students where you should place a fuse (called the main fuse) that would protect all the circuits in your house, not just one of the parallel circuits. [It should be placed on one of the main wires that bring electricity into the house so that the fuse would shut off everything.]

Critical Thinking Master, Teacher Resource Package. You may wish to have students complete the Critical Thinking Master, Breaking a Circuit, with this section.

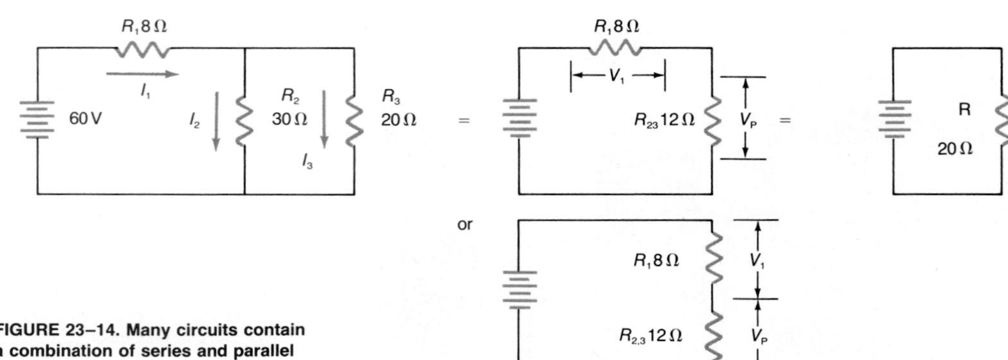

FIGURE 23–14. Many circuits contain a combination of series and parallel connections.

start a fire. A short circuit can occur if the insulation on a lamp cord becomes old and brittle. The two wires in the cord could accidentally touch. The resistance of the wire might be only 0.010 Ω. When placed across 120 V, this resistance would result in a current of

$$I = \frac{V}{R} = \frac{120\ \text{V}}{0.010\ \Omega} = 12\ 000\ \text{A}.$$

Such a current would cause a fuse or a circuit breaker to open the circuit immediately, preventing the wires from becoming hot enough to start a fire.

A short circuit is a very low resistance in a location where the resistance should be very high.

Combined Series-Parallel Circuits

Circuits often consist of combinations of series and parallel circuits, such as the three resistors in Figure 23–14. The circuits can be understood by analyzing them in steps.

1. If any resistors are connected in parallel, calculate the single equivalent resistance that can replace them.
2. If any equivalent resistances are now connected in series, calculate a single new equivalent resistance that can replace them.
3. By repeating steps 1 and 2, you can reduce the circuit to a single resistance. The total circuit current can now be found. The voltage drops and currents through individual resistors can then be calculated.

F.Y.I.

The largest voltages in your home are in your television set, where 15 000 V to 20 000 V are common. The largest currents are likely to be the 40 A in an electric range. In your car, voltages as high as 35 000 V are used in the spark plugs, and currents as large as 300 A are needed to turn the started motor.

PROBLEM SOLVING STRATEGY

1. How do you figure out which resistors are in parallel? Resistors in parallel have separate current paths. They are in parallel only if they have the same potential differences across them.
2. How do you figure out which resistors are in series? Remember that a simple series circuit has only one current path. Resistors are in series only if there is one and only one current path through them.

TEACHER F.Y.I.

Faulty electrical devices can deliver lethal shocks. An electric heater can be a potential hazard if the high voltage becomes connected to the case by frayed insulation on the wires. If a person who is grounded touches the case, he or she will complete a path for the current to the ground. This kind of hazard can be avoided by the use of a three-wire system. The third prong of a plug is connected by a wire to the case of the appliance. The third hole in the receptacle is connected to the ground. Therefore, if there is faulty wiring in the appliance, the current is routed through the ground and not the person because the case and the ground have essentially no resistance between them.

Example Problem

Series-Parallel Circuit

In Figure 23–14, a 30.0-Ω resistor is connected in parallel with a 20.0-Ω resistor. The parallel connection is placed in series with an 8.0-Ω resistor, and the entire circuit is placed across a 60.0-V difference of potential. **a.** What is the equivalent resistance ($R_{2,3}$) of the parallel portion of the circuit? **b.** What is the equivalent resistance of the entire circuit? **c.** What is the current in the entire circuit? **d.** What is the voltage drop across the 8.0-Ω resistor? **e.** What is the voltage drop across the parallel portion of the circuit? **f.** What is the current in each line of the parallel portion of the circuit?

Given: See Figure 23–14. **Unknowns:** $R_{2,3}$, R, I, V_1, V_p, I_2, I_3

Basic equations: $V = IR$

$R = R_1 + R_2 + \ldots$

$1/R = 1/R_1 + 1/R_2 + \ldots$

Solution:

a. R_2 and R_3 are connected in parallel. Their equivalent resistance is

$$\frac{1}{R_{2,3}} = \frac{1}{R_2} + \frac{1}{R_3} = \frac{1}{30.0\ \Omega} + \frac{1}{20.0\ \Omega} = \frac{5}{60.0\ \Omega}$$

$$R_{2,3} = 12.0\ \Omega$$

b. The circuit is equivalent to a series circuit with an 8.0-Ω resistor and a 12.0-Ω resistor in series, Figure 23–13.

$$R = R_1 + R_{2,3} = 8.0\ \Omega + 12.0\ \Omega = 20.0\ \Omega$$

c. The current in the circuit is

$$I = \frac{V}{R} = \frac{60.0\ \text{V}}{20.0\ \Omega} = 3.00\ \text{A}.$$

d. The voltage drop across the 8.0-Ω resistor is

$$V_1 = IR_1 = (3.00\ \text{A})(8.0\ \Omega) = 24\ \text{V}.$$

e. The parallel branch (R_2 and R_3) behaves as a 12.0-Ω resistor, with the sum of the currents through R_2 and R_3 flowing through it. Therefore, the voltage drop across it is

$$V_p = IR_{2,3} = (3.00\ \text{A})(12.0\ \Omega) = 36.0\ \text{V}.$$

f. The 36.0-V drop across the parallel portion of the circuit is the same across all parts of the parallel circuit. Therefore, the current through the 30.0-Ω resistor is

$$I_2 = \frac{V}{R_2} = \frac{36.0\ \text{V}}{30.0\ \Omega} = 1.20\ \text{A}.$$

The current through the 20.0-Ω resistor is

$$I_3 = \frac{V}{R_3} = \frac{36.0\ \text{V}}{20.0\ \Omega} = 1.80\ \text{A}.$$

The current through the parallel part of the circuit is

1.20 A + 1.80 A, or 3.00 A.

This value agrees with the value for the current calculated in Part **c.**

ECONOMICS CONNECTION

Thomas Edison did not invent the light bulb, but he did develop the first bulb that could be used in homes, and even more important, a commercially viable distribution system for electricity. Edison started with the basic assumption that each customer should be able to turn on and off his own light bulbs without affecting the other bulbs connected in the circuit. This meant that bulbs must be connected in parallel. Since only part of the circuit current flowed through each bulb, Edison had to design a high-resistance filament that required only a small current for a large heating effect. His assistants tried over 1600 materials including paper, cloth, thread, fishline, fiber, celluloid, boxwood, coconut shells, spruce, hickory, hay, maple shavings, rosewood, punk, cork, flax, bamboo, and the hair out of a redheaded Scotsman's beard before he developed a high vacuum-sealed bulb with a carbonized cotton.

CRITICAL THINKING

Use the Critical Thinking master for Chapter 23 with this section.

CONCEPT DEVELOPMENT

Discovery: After the discussion of short circuits, demonstrate a three-hole receptacle and a three-pronged plug properly wired to a piece of electric cable. Point out that a third wire connects the (metal) case of an appliance to the third prong in the plug. Have the students hypothesize what the third hole in the receptacle might be connected to. (Such a system will protect the operator of an appliance from receiving a dangerous shock should the high voltage in the appliance accidentally become connected to the case.)

CHECKING FOR UNDERSTANDING

On airplanes there are usually indicator lights that show whether or not the lavoratories are all in use. When all are occupied, the indicator lights up. Have students suggest one way of wiring such a circuit. [a series circuit through each of the door locks]

RETEACHING

There are two objectives to electrical circuit safety: preventing dangerously large currents and preventing currents from traveling out of control (resulting in shock or electrocution). Have students categorize safety devices in terms of what they prevent. [Fuses and circuit breakers prevent overly large currents; ground fault interrupters prevent currents from traveling in the wrong places.]

Reteaching Master. Use the Reteaching Master for Chapter 23 from the Teacher Resource Package.

Transparency Package. Reteach the concept of complex circuits using Transparency 34 and accompanying worksheet.

EXTENSION

There are rules for analyzing electrical circuits known as Kirchhoff's laws. They can be used to derive systems of simultaneous equations. Have interested students investigate these laws and present them to the class.

CONCEPT DEVELOPMENT

POCKET LAB

AMMETER RESISTANCE

Purpose: to determine if students understand the concept of resistance and electrical measurements.
Materials: power supply; voltmeter; ammeter; wires; 5 Ω or 10 Ω, 1% or 0.1% precision resistor.
Outcome: Students who understand the concept will build a series circuit with the power supply, ammeter, and resistor. They will then measure the voltage across the ammeter. It should be very, very small.

Guided Practice: After going over the Example Problems on page 483, have students work in class on the Practice Problems that follow.

INDEPENDENT PRACTICE/ EXTENSION

Refer to the Assignment Guide below for additional questions and problems for independent practice.

Answers To
PRACTICE PROBLEMS

Have students refer to Appendix A of the Solutions Appendix for complete solutions to Practice Problems.

13. **a.** Refer to Problems and Solutions Manual.
b. 30 Ω
c. 60 Ω
d. 2.0 A
e. 60 V
f. 60 V
g. 1.0 A
14. **a.** Refer to Problems and Solutions Manual.
b. 5.0 Ω
c. 15 Ω
d. 3.0 A
e. 30 V
15. 204 Ω, 23 Ω, 102 Ω

POCKET LAB

AMMETER RESISTANCE

Design an experiment using a power supply, a voltmeter, an ammeter, a resistor, and some wires to determine the resistance of the ammeter. Make a sketch of your set up and include measurements and equations. Be prepared to present your experiment to the rest of the class.

Practice Problems

13. Two 60-Ω resistors are connected in parallel. This parallel arrangement is connected in series with a 30-Ω resistor. The combination is then placed across a 120-V potential difference.
- **a.** Draw a diagram of the circuit.
- **b.** What is the equivalent resistance of the parallel portion of the circuit?
- **c.** What single resistance could replace the three original resistors?
- **d.** What is the current in the circuit?
- **e.** What is the voltage drop across the 30-Ω resistor?
- **f.** What is the voltage drop across the parallel portion of the circuit?
- **g.** What is the current in each branch of the parallel portion of the circuit?

14. Three 15-Ω resistors are connected in parallel. This arrangement is connected in series with a 10-Ω resistor. The entire combination is then placed across a 45-V difference in potential.
- **a.** Draw a diagram of the circuit.
- **b.** What is the equivalent resistance of the parallel portion of the circuit?
- **c.** What is the equivalent resistance of the entire circuit?
- **d.** What is the current in the entire circuit?
- **e.** What is the voltage drop across the 10-Ω resistor?

▶ **15.** Suppose you are given three 68-Ω resistors. You can use them in a series, parallel, or series-parallel circuit. Find the three different resistances you can produce in the circuit.

FIGURE 23–15. An ammeter measures current (a), and a standard laboratory voltmeter (b) measure potential differences. Ammeters are always placed in series within a circuit (c) and voltmeters are placed in parallel (d).

a

b

c

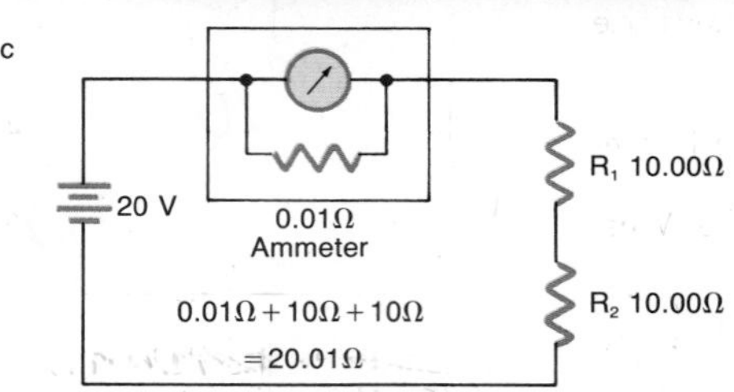

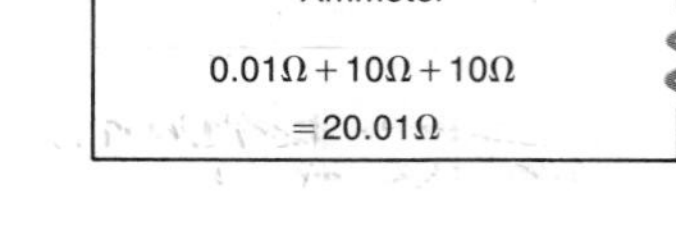

d

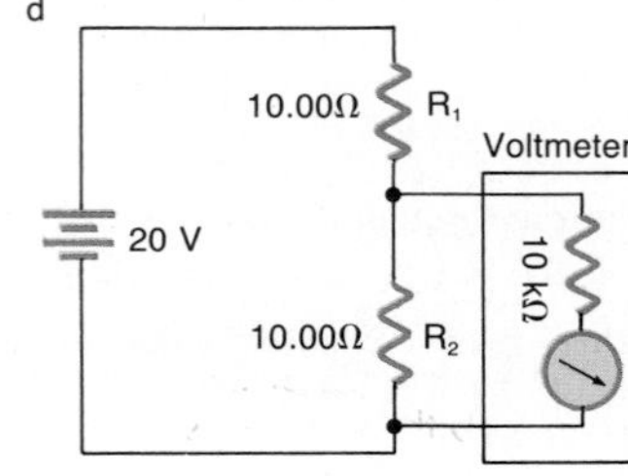

23:2 ASSIGNMENT GUIDE

	PRACTICE	EXTENSION
CHAPTER REVIEW pp. 486–489		
· Reviewing Concepts	5, 7–10	
· Applying Concepts		10
· Problems*	16–19	20
APPENDIX B PROBLEMS*		
· Chapter 23, p. 705	10–14	15

* Complete solutions to all Chapter Review and Appendix problems appear in the Problems and Solutions Manual.

Ammeters and Voltmeters

An **ammeter** is used to measure the current in any branch or part of a circuit. If, for example, we want to measure the current through a resistor, we would place an ammeter in series with the resistance. This requires opening a current path and inserting an ammeter. The use of an ammeter should not change the current in the circuit we are trying to measure. Because current would decrease if the ammeter increased the resistance in the circuit, the resistance of an ammeter should be as low as possible. Figure 23–15c shows a real ammeter as a meter placed in parallel with a 0.01-Ω resistor. The ammeter resistance is much smaller than the values of the resistors. The current decrease would be from 1.0 A to 0.9995 A, too small to notice.

A **voltmeter** is used to measure the voltage drop across some part of a circuit. To measure the potential drop across a resistor, connect the voltmeter in parallel with the resistor. To cause the smallest change in currents or voltages in the circuit, a voltmeter should have a very high resistance. Consider the circuit in Figure 23–15d. A typical real voltmeter consists of a meter in series with a 10-kΩ resistor. When it is connected in parallel with R_2, the equivalent resistance of the combination is smaller than R_2 alone. Thus, the total resistance of the circuit decreases, increasing the current. R_1 has not changed, but the current through it has increased, increasing the potential drop across it. The battery, however, holds the potential drop across R_1 and R_2 constant. Thus, the potential drop across R_2 must decrease. The result of connecting a voltmeter across a resistor is to lower the potential drop across it. The higher the resistance of the voltmeter, the smaller the voltage change. Using a voltmeter with a 10 000-Ω resistance changes the voltage across R_2 from 10 V to 9.9975 V, too small a change to detect. Modern electronic voltmeters, Figure 23–16, have even higher resistances, 10^7 Ω, and so produce even smaller changes.

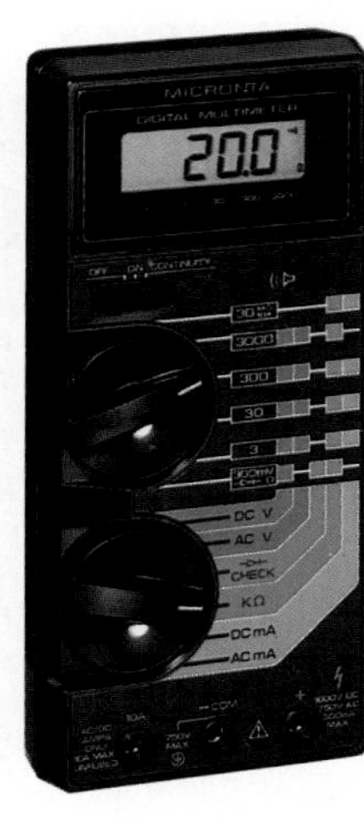

FIGURE 23–16. A modern digital multimeter can be used to measure a wide range of currents, voltages, and resistances in electrical circuits.

An ammeter is put in series with the circuit to be measured.

A voltmeter is connected in parallel with the element to be measured.

CONCEPT REVIEW

2.1 Home fires were often caused by people who replaced fuses with pennies. Why would this cause a problem?

2.2 Consider the circuit in Figure 23–17 made with identical bulbs.
- **a.** Compare the brightness of the three bulbs.
- **b.** What happens to the brightness of each bulb when bulb **1** is unscrewed from its socket? What happens to the three currents?
- **c.** Bulb **1** is screwed in again and bulb **3** is unscrewed. What happens to the brightness of each bulb? What happens to the three currents?

2.3 Consider again the circuit in Figure 23–17.
- **a.** What happens to the brightness of each bulb if a wire is connected between points **B** and **C**?
- **b.** A fourth bulb is connected in parallel with bulb **3** alone. What happens to the brightness of each bulb?

2.4 Critical Thinking: In the same circuit as 2.3, the wire at point **C** is broken and a small resistor is inserted in series with bulbs **2** and **3**. What happens to the brightness of the two bulbs? Explain.

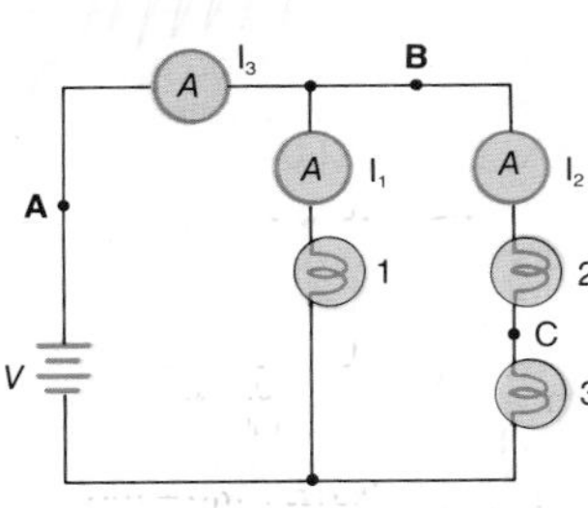

FIGURE 23–17. Use with Concept Review 2.2, 2.3, and 2.4.

3 Close

CONVERGENT QUESTION

Ask students to explain why an ammeter is hooked up in series and why a voltmeter is hooked up in parallel.

CONCEPT REVIEW ANSWERS

2.1 The penny is very thick and would not become hot enough to melt and open the circuit when dangerous currents had passed through it.

2.2 a. Bulbs **2** and **3** are equal in brightness, but dimmer than **1**. **b.** Bulb **1** goes out. The other two are not changed. Current I_1 goes to zero, current I_2 remains the same, and I_3 is reduced. **c.** Bulb **1** is its original brightness; the other two are out. Current I_1 returns to its original value, I_2 is zero, and I_3 is reduced.

2.3 a. Bulb **2** goes out (short circuited). Bulb **3** is now as bright as **1**; the brightness of **1** is unchanged. **b.** Bulb **1** is unchanged. The current in the end of the path increases, so bulb **2** brightens and bulb **3** dims.

2.4 Critical Thinking: Both dim equally. The current in each is reduced by the same amount.

TEACHER F.Y.I.

An ammeter is made by placing a low-resistance shunt across the terminals of the galvanometer so that it is parallel with the meter, providing a low resistance path through the meter. It can therefore be placed in series without affecting the circuit. The multiplier is placed in series with the galvanometer. When it is hooked into the circuit parallel with a component to be measured, very little current flows through it, although the voltage drop is the same. The resistance of a typical galvanometer is 100 Ω. See pages 505–506 for additional information about galvanometers.

Physics and technology

Student responses will vary. Applications for strain sensors range from the important job of monitoring stresses and potential flaws in aircraft and submarine skin, to measuring the forces of blows in contact sports, such as karate and football. Some cardiologists now use a microscopic strain gauge fitted to a tiny catheter to measure blood pressure at precise locations within the heart.

Teacher Resources: Time/Life Books. "Duplicating Dexterity and Touch." *Robotics* (One volume of a series: *Understanding Computers*), pages 90–99.
Amato, Ivan. "Getting a Feel for Atoms." *Science News,* April 7, 1990, pages 216–217, 220.
Amato, Ivan. "Fantastic Plastic." *Science News*, November 18, 1989, pages 328–329.
Stewart, Doug. "New Machines Are Smaller than a Hair, and Do Real Work." *Smithsonian,* November 1990, pages 84–96.

CLOSING CHAPTER 23

Review Summary statements and Key Terms with your students.

ASSESSMENT

Vocabulary Review Master, Teacher Resource Package. Use this master to check students' understanding of Key Terms.

Evaluation Masters. Use Parts A and B of the Chapter Evaluation Masters from the Teacher Resource Package to test qualitative chapter objectives. Use Parts C and D to test quantitative chapter objectives.

Physics and technology

ROBOTS AND OHM'S LAW

In 1854, the year that Georg Simon Ohm died, Lord Kelvin discovered that the resistance of a wire changes when it is strained (stretched).

Engineers first used this phenomenon to analyze stresses in structural surfaces. For example, by monitoring the current through a fine metal wire mounted alongside a bridge, machines can indicate strain on the bridge based on the wire's varying resistance. Such a device is called a strain gauge.

Researchers seeking ways to imitate the complex capabilities of the human hand have used a version of a strain gauge to give robots a sense of touch. As recently as 1985, robotic hands, equipped with superhuman strength, had the dexterity to gently crack an egg into a mixing bowl. However, a robot still needs some kind of tactile sensor in order to "see" with its hands.

One of the most promising sensor designs consists of an electronic chip printed with a fine metallic network and covered by a thin sheet of conducting rubber. Pressure on the rubber changes the resistance of the chip, transmitting a "picture" of the strain on the robotic skin.

· What might be some other valuable applications for strain gauge "sensors"?

CHAPTER 23 REVIEW

SUMMARY

23.1 Simple Circuits

- The current is the same everywhere in a simple series circuit.
- The equivalent resistance of a series circuit is the sum of the resistances of its parts.
- The sum of the voltage drops across resistors in series is equal to the potential difference applied across the combination.
- A voltage divider is a series circuit used to produce a voltage source from a higher voltage battery.
- The voltage drops across all branches of a parallel circuit are the same.
- In a parallel circuit, the total current is equal to the sum of the currents in the branches.
- The reciprocal of the equivalent resistance of parallel resistors is equal to the sum of the reciprocals of the individual resistances.
- If any branch of a parallel circuit is opened, there is no current in that branch. The current in the other branches is unchanged.

23.2 Applications of Circuits

- A fuse or circuit breaker, placed in series with appliances, creates an open circuit when dangerously high currents flow.
- A complex circuit is often a combination of series and parallel branches. Any parallel branch is first reduced to a single equivalent resistance. Then any resistors in series are replaced by a single resistance.
- An ammeter is used to measure the current in a branch or part of a circuit. An ammeter always has a low resistance and is connected in series.
- A voltmeter measures the potential difference (voltage) across any part or combination of parts of a circuit. A voltmeter always has a high resistance and is connected in parallel with the part of the circuit being measured.

RETEACHING MASTER
Use the Reteaching master for Chapter 23 with this section.

REVIEW MASTER
Use the Vocabulary Review master for Chapter 23 with this section.

TRANSPARENCY
Use Transparency 34 with this section.

EVALUATION MASTER
Use the Chapter Evaluation master for Chapter 23 with this section.

KEY TERMS

series circuit
equivalent resistance
voltage divider
parallel circuit
fuse
ground-fault interrupter
short circuit
ammeter
voltmeter

REVIEWING CONCEPTS

1. Why is it frustrating when one bulb burns out on a string of Christmas tree lights connected in series?
2. Why does the equivalent resistance decrease as more resistors are added to a parallel circuit?
3. Several resistors with different values are connected in parallel. The equivalent resistance will be less than which resistor?
4. Compare the amount of current entering a junction in a parallel circuit with that leaving the junction. Note: a junction is a point where three or more conductors are joined.
5. Why is household wiring done in parallel instead of in series?
6. Why is there a difference in total resistance between three 60-Ω resistors connected in series and three 60-Ω resistors connected in parallel?
7. Explain the function of a fuse in an electric circuit.
8. What is a short circuit? Why is a short circuit dangerous?
9. Why does an ammeter have a very low resistance?
10. Why does a voltmeter have a very high resistance?

APPLYING CONCEPTS

1. What happens to the current in the other two lamps if one lamp in a three-lamp series circuit burns out?
2. In the voltage divider in Figure 23–3, the resistor R_1 is a variable resistor. What happens to the voltage output, V_2 of the voltage divider if the resistance of the variable resistor is increased?
3. Circuit **A** contains three 60-Ω resistors in series. Circuit **B** contains three 60-Ω resistors in parallel. How does the current in the second 60-Ω resistor change if a switch cuts off the current to the first 60-Ω resistor in
   a. circuit **A?** **b.** circuit **B?**
4. What happens to the current in the other two lamps if one lamp in a three-lamp parallel circuit burns out?
5. An engineer needs a 10-Ω resistor and a 15-Ω resistor. But there are only 30-Ω resistors in stock. Must new resistors be purchased? Explain.
6. If you have a 6-V battery and many 1.5-V bulbs, how could you connect them so they light but do not have more than 1.5-V across each bulb ?
7. Two lamps have different resistances, one larger than the other.
   a. If they are connected in parallel, which is brighter (dissipates more power)?
   b. When connected in series, which is brighter?
8. Two 100-W light bulbs are connected in series to a 12-V battery and another two 100-W light bulbs are connected in parallel to a separate 12-V battery. Which battery will run out of energy first? Why?
9. For each part of this question, write the form of circuit that applies: series or parallel.
   a. The current is the same throughout.
   b. The total resistance is equal to the sum of the individual resistances.
   c. The voltage drop is the same across each resistor.
   d. The voltage drop is proportional to the resistance.
   e. Adding a resistor decreases the total resistance.
   f. Adding a resistor increases the total resistance.
   g. If the current through one resistor goes to zero there is no current in the entire circuit.
   h. If the current through one resistor goes to zero, the current through all other resistors remains the same.
   i. This form is suitable for house wiring.
10. Why is it dangerous to replace a 15-A fuse in a circuit with one of 30 A?

Answers To
REVIEWING CONCEPTS

1. When one bulb burns out, the circuit is incomplete and all of the bulbs go out.

2. Each new resistor provides an additional path for the electron flow.

3. The equivalent resistance will be less than any of the resistors.

4. The amount of current entering a junction is equal to the amount of current leaving.

5. Appliances in parallel can be run independently of one another.

6. In a series circuit, the current is opposed by each resistance in turn. The total resistance is the sum of the resistors. In a parallel circuit, each resistance provides an additional path for current flow. The result is a decrease in total resistance.

7. The purpose of a fuse is to prevent conductors from being overloaded with current, causing fires due to overheating. A fuse is simply a short length of wire that will melt from the heating effect if the current is over a certain maximum.

8. A short circuit is a formed circuit that has extremely low resistance. A short circuit is dangerous because a low resistance across any potential difference will draw a large current. The heating effect of the current can cause a fire.

9. An ammeter must have low resistance because it is placed directly in the circuit. If its resistance were high, it would change the total resistance of the circuit and thus serve to reduce the current flowing in the circuit, thereby defeating its own purpose.

10. A voltmeter is placed in parallel with the portion of the circuit whose difference in potential it is to measure. A voltmeter must have very high resistance for the same reason that an ammeter has low resistance. If the voltmeter had low resistance, it would lower the resistance of the portion of the circuit it is across and increase the current in the circuit. This would produce a higher voltage drop across the part of the circuit where the voltmeter is located, defeating its purpose.

Answers To

APPLYING CONCEPTS

1. If one of the lamp filaments burns out, the current will cease and all the lamps will go out.

2. $V_2 = \frac{VR_2}{R_1 + R_2}$. As R_1 increases, V_2 will decrease.

3. a. No current will flow in the resistor. **b.** The current in the resistor will remain the same.

4. If one of the filaments burns out, the resistance and the potential difference across the other lamps will not change, therefore their currents will remain the same.

5. No. The 30-Ω resistors can be used in parallel. Three 30-Ω resistors in parallel will give a 10-Ω resistance. Two 30-Ω resistors in parallel will give a 15-Ω resistance.

6. Connect four of the bulbs in series. The voltage drop across each will be 6 V/4 = 1.5 V.

7. a. The lamp with the lower resistance: $P = IV$ and $I = V/R$, so $P = V^2/R$. Smaller R means larger P. **b.** The lamp with the higher resistance: $P = IV$ and $V = IR$, so $P = I^2R$. Larger R means larger P.

8. The parallel circuit depletes the battery first. Its total current would be four times that of the series circuit, thus using the energy twice as fast.

9. a. series **b.** series **c.** parallel **d.** series **e.** parallel **f.** series **g.** series **h.** parallel **i.** parallel

10. The 30-A fuse allows more current to flow through the circuit, generating more heat, which can be harmful to objects included in the circuit.

Answers To

PROBLEMS

Complete solutions to all Chapter Review Problems can be found in the Problems and Solutions Manual accompanying this text.

1. a. 25.0 Ω
b. 2.0 A
c. 40 V; 10 V
d. 80 W; 20 W

2. 2.0 V

3. a. 60 Ω
b. 0.20 A

4. a. 60 Ω
b. 6.0 V

5. a. 1.5 A
b. 20 Ω

6. a. $2.3 \times 10^2\ \Omega$
b. 13 Ω
c. 3.6 W

PROBLEMS

23.1 Simple Circuits

1. A 20.0-Ω lamp and a 5.0-Ω lamp are connected in series and placed across a potential difference of 50 V. What is
   a. the equivalent resistance of the circuit?
   b. the current in the circuit?
   c. the voltage drop across each lamp?
   d. the power dissipated in each lamp?

2. Three identical lamps are connected in series to a 6.0-V battery. What is the voltage drop across each lamp?

3. The load across a 12-V battery consists of a series combination of three resistors of 15 Ω, 21 Ω, and 24 Ω.
   a. What is the total resistance of the load?
   b. What is the current in the circuit?

4. The load across a battery consists of two resistors, with values of 15 Ω and 45 Ω connected in series.
   a. What is the total resistance of the load?
   b. What is the voltage of the battery if the current in the circuit is 0.10 A?

5. A lamp having a resistance of 10 Ω is connected across a 15-V battery.
   a. What is the current through the lamp?
   b. What resistance must be connected in series with the lamp to reduce the current to 0.50 A?

6. A string of eighteen identical Christmas tree lights are connected in series to a 120-V source. The string dissipates 64.0 W.
   a. What is the equivalent resistance of the light string?
   b. What is the resistance of a single light?
   c. What power is dissipated by each lamp?

7. One of the bulbs in the previous problem burns out. The lamp has a wire that shorts out the lamp filament when it burns out. This drops the resistance of the lamp to zero.
   a. What is the resistance of the light string now?
   b. Find the power dissipated by the string.
   c. Did the power go up or down when a bulb burned out?

8. A 75.0-W bulb is connected to a 120-V source.
   a. What is the current through the bulb?
   b. What is the resistance of the bulb?
   c. A lamp dimmer puts a resistance in series with the bulb. What resistance would be needed to reduce the current to 0.300 A?

9. In the previous problem, you found the resistance of a lamp and a dimmer resistor.
   a. Assuming the resistances are constant, find the voltage drops across the lamp and the resistor.
   b. Find the power dissipated by the lamp.
   c. Find the power dissipated by the dimmer.

10. Amy needs 5.0 V for some integrated circuit experiments. She uses a 6.0-V battery and two resistors to make a voltage divider. One resistor is 330 Ω. She decides to make the other resistor smaller. What value should it have?

11. Pete is designing a voltage divider using a 12.0-V battery and a 100.0-Ω resistor as R_2. What resistor should be used as R_1 if the output voltage across R_2 is to be 4.00 V?

▶ **12.** A typical television dissipates 275 W when plugged into a 120-V outlet.
   a. Find the resistance of the television.
   b. The resistance of the wires between the outlet and fuse is 2.5 Ω. The television and wires form a series circuit that works like a voltage divider. Find the voltage drop across the television.
   c. A 12-Ω hair dryer is now plugged into the same outlet. Find the equivalent resistance of the two appliances.
   d. Find the voltage drop across the television and hair dryer combination. The lower voltage explains why the television picture sometimes shrinks when another appliance is turned on.

13. Three identical lamps are connected in parallel to each other and then connected to a 6.0-V battery. What is the voltage drop across each lamp?

14. A 16.0-Ω and a 20.0-Ω resistor are connected in parallel. A difference in potential of 40.0 V is applied to the combination.
   a. Compute the equivalent resistance of the parallel circuit.
   b. What is the current in the circuit?
   c. How large is the current through the 16.0-Ω resistor?

15. During a laboratory exercise, you are supplied with the following appartus: a battery of potential difference V, two heating elements of low resistance that can be placed in water, an ammeter of negligible resistance, a voltmeter of extremely high resistance, wires of negligible resistance, a beaker that is well-insulated and has negligible heat capacity, 100.0 g of water at 25° C.

a. By means of a diagram using standard symbols, show how these components should be connected to heat the water as rapidly as possible.

b. If the voltmeter reading holds steady at 50.0 V and the ammeter reading holds steady at 5.0 A, estimate the time in seconds required to completely vaporize the water in the beaker. Use 4200 J/kg·C° as the specific heat of water and 2.3×10^6 J/kg as the heat of vaporization of water.

23.2 Applications of Circuits

16. A circuit contains six 240-Ω lamps, 60-W bulbs, and a 10.0-Ω heater connected in parallel. The voltage across the circuit is 120 V. What is the current in the circuit

a. when four lamps are turned on?

b. when all lamps are on?

c. if six lamps and the heater are operating?

d. If the circuit has a fuse rated at 12 A, will it melt if everything is on?

17. Determine the reading of each ammeter and each voltmeter in Figure 23–18.

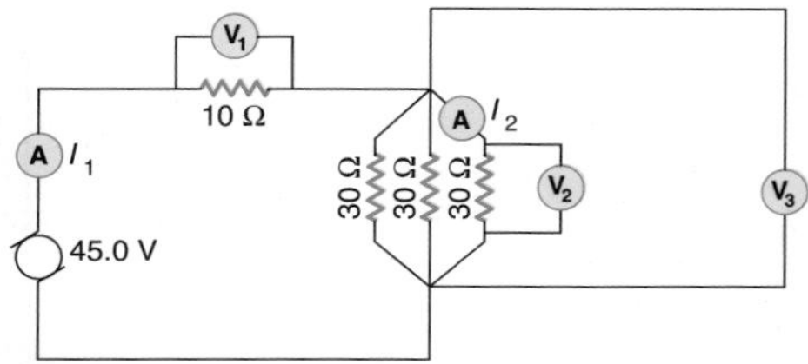

FIGURE 23–18. Use with Problem 17 and 18.

18. Determine the power used by each resistance shown in Figure 23–18.

19. A typical home circuit is diagrammed in Figure 23–19. Note that the lead lines to the kitchen lamp each have very low resistances of 0.25 Ω. The lamp has a resistance of 240.0 Ω. Although the circuit is a parallel circuit, the lead lines are in series with each of the components of the circuit.

a. Compute the equivalent resistance of the circuit consisting of just the light and the lead lines to and from the light.

b. Fina the current to the bulb.

c. Find the power rating of the bulb.

d. Since the current in the bulb is 0.50 A, the current in the lead lines must also be 0.50 A. Calculate the voltage drop due to the two leads.

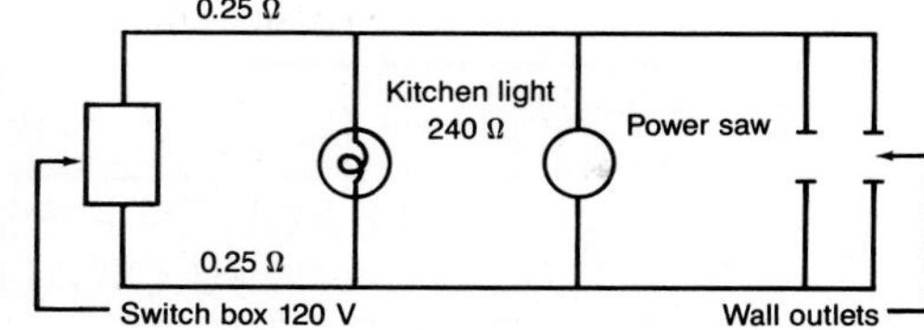

FIGURE 23–19. Use with Problem 19 and 20.

▶ **20.** A power saw is operated by an electric motor. When electric motors are first turned on, they have a very low resistance. Suppose that a kitchen light discussed in the previous problem is on and a power saw is turned on. The saw, light, and the lead lines have an initial total resistance of 6.0 Ω.

a. Compute the equivalent resistance of the light–saw parallel circuit.

b. What current flows to the light?

c. What is the total voltage drop across the two leads to the light?

d. What voltage remains to operate the light? Will this cause the light to dim temporarily?

USING LAB SKILLS

1. When you did the Pocket Lab on page 472, you found that adding more resistors in a series circuit caused the current to decrease. What happens to the voltage across each resistor as more are added in series? Use a voltmeter to find out. Describe your results.

THINKING PHYSIC-LY

A 50-200-250-W three-way bulb has three terminals on its base. Explain how to connect 120 V to the terminals to obtain a low, medium, and a high brightness.

7. a. 2.2×10^2 Ω
b. 66 W
c. It increased!
8. a. 0.625 A
b. 192 Ω
c. 208 Ω
9. a. 57.6 V, 62.4 V
b. 17.3 W
c. 18.7 W
10. 66 Ω
11. 200 Ω
12. a. 52.4 Ω
b. 115 V
c. 9.8 Ω
d. 96 V
13. 6.0 V
14. a. 8.89 Ω
b. 4.50 A
c. 2.50 A
15. a. Refer to Problems and Solutions Manual.
b. 1.0×10^3 s
16. a. 2.0 A
b. 3.0 A
c. 15 A
d. Yes
17. $I_1 = 2.25$ A; $V_1 = 22.5$ V; $V_2 = V_3 = 22.5$ V; $I_2 = 0.750$ A
18. $P_1 = 50.6$ W; $P = 16.9$ W
19. a. 240 Ω
b. 0.50 A
c. 60 W
d. 0.25 V
20. a. 6.4 Ω
b. 19 A
c. 9.5 V
d. 110 V
Yes. This will cause a momentary dimming.

Answer To
USING LAB SKILLS

1. The voltage across each resistor also decreases as more are added in series. Students should realize that the total voltage across all the resistors must equal the voltage of the power supply.

Answer To
THINKING PHYSIC-LY

Call the terminals A, B, and C. A 50-W filament is connected between A and B. A 200-W filament is between B and C. For low brightness, connect B and A across the 120 V. For medium brightness, connect B and C. For high brightness, connect the two filaments in parallel.

CHAPTER 24 Magnetic Fields

PLANNING GUIDE (7 class sessions)

CONTENTS	TEXT FEATURES	TEACHER RESOURCE PACKAGE	OTHER COMPONENTS
24.1 Magnets: Permanent and Temporary, pp. 492–500 (4 Class Sessions) • General Properties of Magnets • Magnetic Fields Around Permanent Magnets • Electromagnetism • Magnetic Field Near a Coil • A Microscopic Picture of Magnetic Materials	**Physics Lab:** Electric Motor, p. 501 **Pocket Lab:** Monopoles?, p. 494 **Pocket Lab:** Funny Balls, p. 498 **Concept Review,** p. 500	**Study Guide:** Magnets: Permanent and Temporary **Physics Lab Data Sheet:** Electric Motor **Critical Thinking Master:** The Doorbell	**Laboratory Manual:** Lab 24.1 The Nature of Magnetism Lab 24.2 Principles of Electromagnetism Lab 24.3 Magnetic Field About a Coil
24.2 Forces Caused by Magnetic Fields, pp. 502–509 (3 Class Sessions) • Forces on Currents in Magnetic Fields • Measuring the Force on a Wire Due to a Magnetic Field • Galvanometers • Electric Motors • The Force on a Single Charged Particle	**Physics and Technology:** Maglev Trains, p. 509 **Pocket Lab:** Jumping Wires, p. 504 **Concept Review,** p. 509	**Study Guide:** Forces Caused by Magnetic Fields **Reteaching Master:** Magnetic Force and Distance **Enrichment Master:** A Simple Meter **Transparency Worksheet:** Electric Motor/DC Generator	**Transparency 35:** Electric Motor/DC Generator
Chapter Review, pp. 510–513	Summary Key Terms Reviewing Concepts Applying Concepts Problems Thinking Physic-ly	**Vocabulary Review** **Chapter Test**	**Test Bank**

SUPPLEMENTARY MATERIALS

SOFTWARE	AUDIOVISUAL	BOOKS/MAGAZINES
Introduction to General Physics, Disk VI: Magnetism, COMPress/Queue, Inc. (Apple II, IBM PC, Macintosh). *Magnets and Electromagnetism,* Queue, Inc. (Apple II, IBM PC, Macintosh).	Video: *The Mechanical Universe and Beyond: Magnetic Fields* and *Vector Fields and Hydrodynamics,* Films Inc.	Chasnov, Robert, and Overcast, Louis. "Magnet Symmetry and Newton's Third Law." *The Physics Teacher,* February 1990, p. 112. Sandoval, J.L., Porta, A., and Segarra, P. "Measuring Magnetic Force and Magnetic Field of Small Permanent Magnets." *The Physics Teacher,* February 1990, p. 124. Turner, Raymond. "A Physics Toy: Magnetic Seal and Ball." *The Physics Teacher,* December 1987, pp. 568–569. Wolsky, A.M., Giese, R. F., and Daniels, E. J. "The New Superconductors: Prospects for Applications." *Scientific American,* February 1989, p. 60.

PROBLEM CORRELATION

CONCEPTS	CHAPTER REVIEW			PROBLEMS APPENDIX
	Reviewing Concepts	Applying Concepts	Problems	
24.1 Magnets: Permanent and Temporary				
General Properties of Magnets	1,2,3,6	1,2		
Magnetic Fields; Permanent Magnets	4,5	3,4	**2**	
Electromagnetism	7		3,4	1,2,3
Magnetic Field Near a Coil	8,9	5	5	4
A Microscopic Picture	10,11	6		
24.2 Forces Caused by Magnetic Fields				
Forces on Currents in Magnetic Fields	12	7,8,9	6,**7**	5
Measuring the Force on a Wire Due to a Magnetic Field	13		1,8,9,10,11,12, 13,14,15,**16,17**	6,7,8,9,10,**11**
Galvanometers	14	10	18,19	
Electric Motors				
The Force on a Single Charged Particle		11,12,13	20,21,22,23,**24,25**, 26,27,28,**29**	12,13,14,15,16

ACTIVITY AND DEMONSTRATION MATERIALS

PHYSICS LAB

Page 501
- low-voltage power supply
- small disk magnet
- 1-m length of #26 or #28 magnet wire
- 2 paper clips
- cellophane tape
- sandpaper
- clay

POCKET LAB

Pages 494, 498, 504
- 2 disk magnets
- two 3-mm steel balls
- magnetic compass
- 0–5 variable DC power supply
- ammeter
- horseshoe magnet
- 1-m length of insulated stranded wire

DEMONSTRATIONS

Pages 494, 495, 496, 497, 505
- magnets, assorted
- iron filings
- thin sheet of glass or transparent plastic container
- tube
- compass
- insulated 20-gauge stranded copper wire
- 1.5-V battery
- flicker bulb, light socket
- strip of aluminum foil
- variable, low-power DC power supply
- oscilloscope

EXTENSION PROJECTS

LIBRARY RESEARCH

1. Hysteresis
Through library research, find out what hysteresis is. What does the hysteresis loop indicate?

HANDS-ON

2. Demagnetizer
Obtain a demagnetizer and use it to demagnetize the head on a VCR or tape player. Why is this beneficial to the operation of these devices?

STUDENT READINGS

Bloxham, Jeremy, and Gubbins, David. "The Evolution of the Earth's Magnetic Field." *Scientific American,* December 1989.

Monforte, John. "The Digital Reproduction of Sound." *Scientific American,* December 1984.

Peterson, I. "Galactic Magnetism on a Gigantic Scale." *Science News,* June 16, 1990.

Spoonseller, Michael. "Magnetic Train." *Popular Science,* December 1988.

Timmons, D.L. "Finding Magnetic North the Hard Way." *The Physics Teacher,* May 1988.

Chapter 24

Magnetic Fields

CHAPTER OVERVIEW

Theme Development: The field line concept models magnetism and the mechanisms associated with it. Another conceptual model—the right-hand rule—develops this concept and leads into the topic of electric motors. The symmetry of an electromagnetic field contrasts with the necessary cyclic behavior of electromagnetism in motors.

MISCONCEPTIONS

Students need some help visualizing magnetic fields in 3-D space. Students will tend to confuse the direction of a magnetic field with the direction of magnetic force on moving charges.

KEY TERMS

domain
electromagnet
first right-hand rule
galvanometer
magnetic field
magnetic flux
magnetic induction
second right-hand rule
third right-hand rule

Laboratory Options

STUDENT EDITION

Physics Lab

Electric Motor	501

Pocket Labs

Monopoles?	494
Funny Balls	498
Jumping Wires	504

TEACHER EDITION

Activities

Demonstration	494, 495, 496, 497, 497, 505
Discovery	495
Cooperative Learning	499, 506

LABORATORY MANUAL

The Nature of Magnetism	Lab 24.1
Principles of Electromagnetism	Lab 24.2
Magnetic Field About a Coil	Lab 24.3

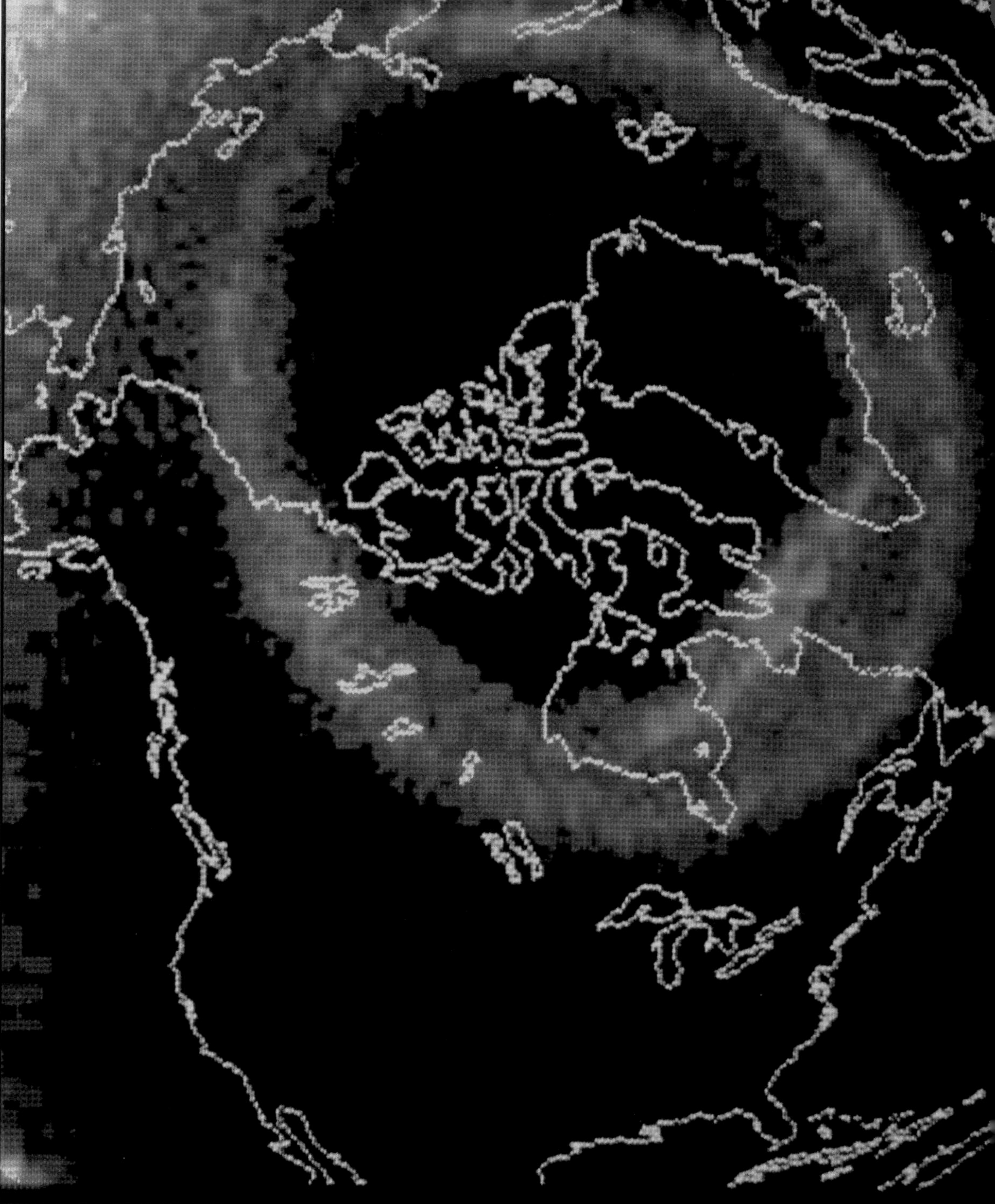

CHAPTER

24 Magnetic Fields

Earth's Halo

The Dynamics Explorer-1 satellite took this photo of Earth and a computer added the outline of the continents. But what is the band that circles the north polar region like a halo? It is the aurora borealis, the northern lights. The satellite detected ultraviolet radiation from oxygen atoms high in Earth's atmosphere and displayed it in yellow. How do charged particles from the sun and Earth's magnetic field combine to produce the flickering lights that thrill people who live in northern latitudes?

The displays of the aurora borealis have fascinated and mystified people for centuries. Story tellers and poets have found inspiration in the luminous streaks and patches of color in the night sky. According to ancient myths, the lights were caused by ghostly spirits. More recent observers believed the lights could be reflections from arctic ice or even from large schools of fish in arctic waters. Scientific studies tell us that the lights result from interaction between the solar wind and Earth's magnetic field.

Magnets are not new. The properties of naturally occurring magnetic rocks (lodestones) have been known for over 2000 years. The Chinese were using magnets as compasses when the first European explorers reached China in the 1500s. In 1600, the English physician William Gilbert wrote the first European book describing their properties. Today magnets are used in all the generators that supply us with electricity. In addition, motors, television sets, and tape recorders depend on the magnetic effects of electric currents. Thus, the study of magnetism is an important part of our investigation of electricity.

Chapter Outline

Concept Check

The following terms or concepts from earlier chapters are important for a good understanding of this chapter. If you are not familiar with them, you should review them before studying this chapter.

- force, Chapter 5
- circular motion, Chapter 7
- charged particles, charging by induction, Chapter 20
- electric fields, Chapter 21
- electric current, Chapter 22

Introducing The Chapter

Earth's Halo

The yellow light bathing Earth's atmosphere in the chapter opening photo is actually ultraviolet emitted by hydrogen atoms called "dayglow." Ultraviolet from hydrogen on the sun excites the hydrogen atoms in Earth's atmosphere, causing a diffuse glow. A computer has rendered this radiation as yellow. Students will find the answer to the question asked by the photo caption on page 508.

Concept Check

Make sure students have a clear understanding of the concepts covered in Chapters 5, 7, 20, and 21 that are listed in the Concept Check. Students familiar with forces, circular motion, charged particles, induction, and electric fields will be better prepared to master the principles of magnetic fields presented in this chapter.

Assessment Options

Portfolio Assessment
Extension 1, TWE, p. 490b
Portfolio Assessment, TWE, p. 493
Activity, TWE, p. 499
Enrichment, TWE, pp. 506, 508

Performance Assessment
Extension 2, TWE, p. 490b
Pocket Labs, pp. 494, 498, 504
Physics Lab, p. 501
Pocket Lab Assessment, TWE, p. 504
Using Lab Skills, p. 513

Content Assessment
Self Assessment: Practice Problems, pp. 496, 499, 504, 508
Critical Thinking, TWE, p. 494
Convergent Question, TWE, p. 500
Assessment, Critical Thinking, p. 501
Cooperative Learning, TWE, p. 506
Concept Reviews, pp. 500, 509
Chapter Review, pp. 510–513
Supplemental Problems, pp. 705–706

Group Assessment
Activities for group assessment occur with Cooperative Learning and lab activities.

24.1 MAGNETS: PERMANENT AND TEMPORARY

Preparation

OBJECTIVES

The objectives are listed on the student page. Remind students to preview these objectives as a study guide to this major section.

OVERVIEW

Magnetic fields, magnetic poles, and domains in magnets are the primary concepts introduced in this section.

BRIDGING

The field concept was introduced in Chapter 8 as an important part of the study of gravitation. It was studied again in Chapter 21 as an aspect of static electricity. Here we see the concept in connection with magnetism. The ideas of electrical currents and electrons are extended as well.

1 Focus

DISCREPANT EVENT

One of the best introductory activities is for students to play with magnets for five minutes or so. The strong ceramic magnets (most are about 2 × 3 cm) that are often used to fasten notes to the refrigerator door are most effective. They're available at electronics and hardware stores. Students will be able to observe magnetic attraction and repulsion with these magnets. Because of the way two magnets behave when placed together, students can begin to visualize that somehow a magnet changes the space around it—the magnet creates a field. Some students may even note that energy is stored by the position of the magnets when two like poles are pushed together. The potential energy can overcome gravitational forces as, for example, when one magnet is caused to hop up into the air.

Objectives

- summarize the properties of magnets.
- describe magnetic fields around permanent magnets and between like and unlike poles.
- describe the field around a current-carrying wire; explain the use of the right-hand rule in finding the direction of the field lines.
- explain the nature of the field due to both one and many wire loops; apply the right-hand rule to find direction.
- describe the origin of magnetism in materials.

24.1 MAGNETS: PERMANENT AND TEMPORARY

Have you ever played with magnets? Certainly you have picked up tacks or paper clips with a magnet. Perhaps you made an electromagnet by winding wire around a nail and connecting it to a dry cell. But, did you ever play with two magnets? Your study of this chapter will be greatly enhanced if you have two bar magnets or two small ceramic magnets, Figure 24–1, like those that are often sold in hardware stores.

General Properties of Magnets

A magnet has polarity. The two ends are called the north and south poles.

Suspend a magnet from a thread, Figure 24–2a. If it is a bar magnet, you may have to tie a yoke to keep it horizontal. What do you observe? When it comes to rest, the magnet will line up in a north-south direction. If you rotate it away from that direction, it will return. Put a mark on the magnet end that points north. Repeat this procedure for other magnets. From this simple experiment, you can conclude that a magnet has polarity. It has two ends, one of which is the north-seeking end, or north pole. The other is the south-seeking end or south pole. A compass is nothing more than a small magnet pivoted so it can turn.

Two like poles repel, two unlike poles attract.

While one magnet is suspended, bring a second magnet nearby, Figure 24–2b. Note that the two ends that pointed north, the north poles, repel each other, as do the two south poles. A north pole, however, will attract the south pole of the other magnet. That is, like poles repel, unlike poles attract.

If you consider these results, it may occur to you that Earth itself must be a giant magnet. The south pole of the Earth-magnet must be near Earth's geographic north pole.

Some metals can be polarized by being brought near a magnet. They become temporary magnets.

As you probably discovered as a child, a magnet will attract nails, tacks, paper clips, and other metal objects, not only other magnets. Unlike the case of two magnets, however, either end of the magnet will attract either end of the metal. What is happening? You can get a hint by touching the magnet to a nail and then touching the nail to smaller

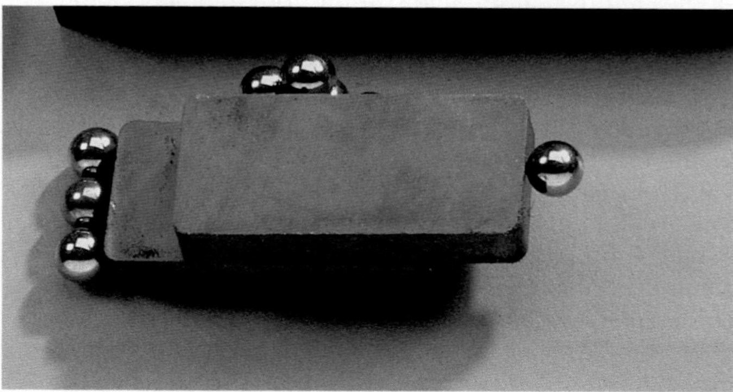

FIGURE 24–1. Inexpensive ceramic magnets are available in most hardware stores.

STUDY GUIDE MASTER

Use the Study Guide master for section 24.1.

a

b

FIGURE 24–2. A magnet suspended by a thread will align itself with Earth's magnetic field (a). When the N-pole of another magnet is brought close to the N-pole of the suspended magnet, the suspended N-pole moves away.

metal pieces. The nail has become a magnet itself, Figure 24–3. The nail has become polarized, and the direction of polarization of the nail depends on the polarization of the magnet. The nail is only temporarily magnetized; if you pull away the magnet, the nail's magnetism disappears. The polarization induced in the nail is similar to the polarization induced in a conductor by a nearby charged object.

You can separate a polarized neutral conductor into a positively-charged conductor and a negatively-charged conductor. Can you do the same with a magnet? It seems not. As far as it is known, poles always come in pairs. Scientists have tried "breaking" magnets, even on the microscopic level, into separated "monopoles," but no one has succeeded.

The magnetism of the permanent magnets you used was produced in the same way you created the magnetism of the nail. But, because of the microscopic structure of the magnet material, the induced magnetism became permanent. Many permanent magnets are made of ALNICO, an alloy of ALuminum, NIckel, and COBalt. A variety of rare-earth elements, such as neodymium, produce permanent magnets that are extremely strong for their size.

HELP WANTED

ELECTRONIC EQUIPMENT REPAIRERS

The ability to test, troubleshoot, and repair a variety of equipment requires knowledge of products, test equipment, safety measures, electrical schematics, and service manuals. In addition, you must be able to communicate effectively to represent the company to customers. Good manual dexterity and color vision, as well as vocational/technical school or military training, are also musts.

Your job performance will determine your advancement opportunities. For information contact: Electronic Technicians Association, 604 North Jackson Street, Greencastie, IN 46135

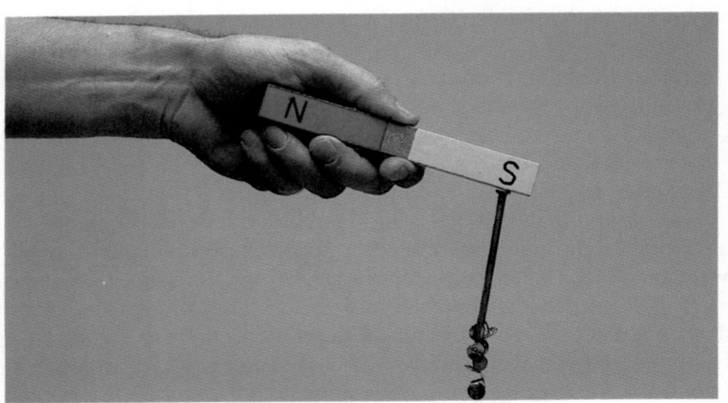

FIGURE 24–3. The nail has become a temporary magnet, attracting the tacks. If the bar magnet is removed, the nail will lose its magnetism.

2 Teach

CONCEPT DEVELOPMENT

- The attraction or repulsion interactions between magnetic poles are mutual forces. One pole exerts a force on a second pole, and the second pole exerts an equal and opposite force back on the first pole. In other words, they demonstrate Newton's third law.

Study Guide Master. To reinforce the concepts in this section, have students complete the Study Guide Master for Section 24.1 from the Teacher Resource Package.

- Gilbert was the first person to consider that Earth itself was a giant magnet. He made spherical lodestones that duplicated Earth's effect on a compass.

Assessment

Portfolio

Do library research on materials used in new, permanent magnets that are much stronger than the older ALNICO magnets. What materials and manufacturing methods are used to make them? What applications do they make possible that would be impossible with older materials.

Multicultural Connections

The Chinese were the first to make use of magnets to help navigate on land and sea. Their compasses used a spoon-shaped pointer to determine direction. The ladle portion of the spoon was made of lodestone (a naturally occurring, magnetic rock) and rested on a flat surface. Because the lodestone would always align with Earth's magnetic field, the handle of the spoon would always point south. So, where we look to the north using our compasses, the Chinese looked south.

CONCEPT DEVELOPMENT

Critical Thinking: Ask students to explain why the magnetic strength of a so-called permanent magnet eventually decreases. [Any piece of magnetized material represents a very ordered state. According to the entropy principle, things tend to go toward higher entropy states.]

Critical Thinking Master, Teacher Resource Package. You may wish to have students complete the Critical Thinking Master, The Doorbell, with this section.

Demonstration: Demonstrate field patterns with bar magnets and iron filings. Position a thin sheet of glass or a transparent plastic container on an overhead projector so the whole class can observe. Set the magnets beneath and the iron filings on the glass or container. Iron filings in a liquid encased in plastic may be used instead of loose filings.

POCKET LAB

MONOPOLES?

Purpose: to observe the interaction of disk magnets.
Materials: 2 disk magnets.
Outcome: If the disks remain flat on the paper, they will always attract or always repel. Rotating the disks will not change the polarity. The magnetic fields of the disks are vertically oriented.

a

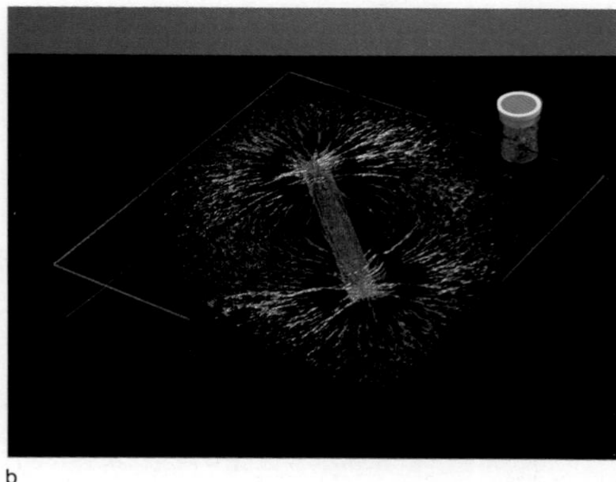

b

FIGURE 24–4. Iron filings suspended in glycerol give a 3-D representation of a magnetic field (a). Iron filings on a glass plate over a magnet show a 2-D model.

Charge and Field Conventions

- *Positive charges are red.*
- *Negative charges are blue.*
- *Electric field lines are red.*
- ***Magnetic field lines are blue.***
- *Ammeters are blue.*
- *Voltmeters are red.*

POCKET LAB

MONOPOLES?

Place a disk magnet flat on the center of your paper. Place another disk magnet flat at the top of your paper and slowly slide it toward the center magnet. Does it attract or repel? Rotate one of the magnets and note the effect on the other. Does each magnet only have one pole?

Magnetic Fields Around Permanent Magnets

The forces between magnets, both attraction and repulsion, occur not only when the magnets touch each other, but when they are at a distance. In the same way that electric and gravitational forces can be explained by electric and gravitational fields, magnetic forces can be explained by the existence of a **magnetic field** around a magnet.

The presence of a magnetic field around a magnet can be shown with iron filings. Each long, thin iron filing becomes a small magnet by induction. Just like a tiny compass needle, the filing rotates until it is tangent to the magnetic field at that point. Figure 24–4a shows filings in a glycerol solution surrounding a bar magnet. The three-dimensional shape of the field is visible. In Figure 24–4b, filings show a two-dimensional plot of the field. These lines of filings help you to visualize magnetic field lines.

Note that the magnetic field lines, like the electric field lines, are imaginary. They help, not only in visualizing the field, but also in providing a measure of its strength. The number of magnetic field lines passing through a surface is called the **magnetic flux**. The flux per unit area is proportional to the strength of the magnetic field. As you can see in Figure 24–4, the flux lines are most concentrated at the poles, where the flux per unit area, that is, the magnetic field, is the greatest.

The direction of the magnetic field lines is defined as the direction to which the N-pole of a compass points when it is placed in the magnetic field. Outside the magnet, the field lines come out of the magnet at its N-pole and enter the magnet at its S-pole, Figure 24–5. What happens inside the magnet? There are no isolated poles on which field lines can start or stop, so magnetic field lines always form closed loops.

What are the magnetic fields produced by pairs of bar magnets? You can visualize the fields by placing a sheet of paper over the poles of two magnets. Sprinkle the paper with iron filings. Figure 24–6a shows the field lines between two like poles. By contrast, two unlike poles (N and S) placed close together produce the pattern in Figure 24–6b. The filings show that the field lines between two unlike poles run directly from one magnet to the other.

CRITICAL THINKING

Use the Critical Thinking master for Chapter 24 with this section.

LABORATORY MANUAL

Use Lab 24.1 with this section.

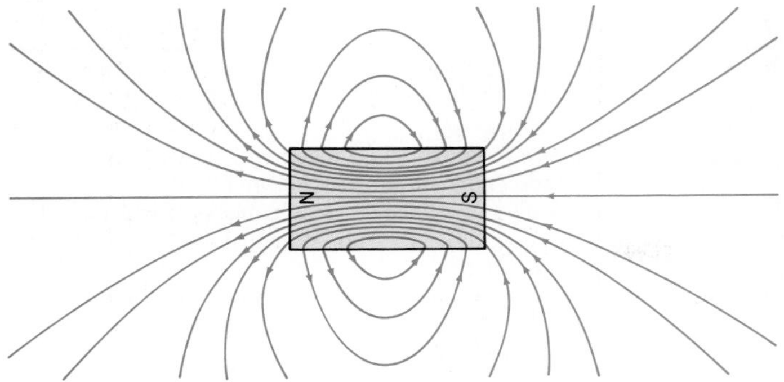

FIGURE 24–5. The magnetic field lines are closed loops leaving the N-pole of the bar magnet and entering the S-pole.

Magnetic fields exert forces on other magnets. The field produced by the N-pole of one magnet pushes the N-pole of a second magnet in the direction of the field line. The force exerted by the same field on the S-pole of the second magnet is in a direction opposite the field lines. The second magnet rotates, like the compass needle, to line up with the field. If the magnet field strength varies, it can also exert a net force, attractive or repulsive, on the second magnet.

When a sample made of iron, cobalt, or nickel is placed in the magnetic field of a permanent magnet, the field lines are concentrated in the sample. Lines leaving the N-pole of the magnet enter one end of the sample, pass through it, and leave the other end. Thus the end of the sample closest to the N-pole magnet becomes the sample's S-pole. The sample is attracted to the magnet.

A temporary magnet concentrates magnetic field lines in it. It is attracted to a permanent magnet.

A superconductor, on the other hand, repels a magnet. Why? Superconductors, act in the opposite way. Magnetic field lines are expelled from a superconductor so there is no magnetic flux inside. The same result would occur if field lines from the permanent magnet not only went through the superconductor, but induced a new field in the opposite direction. Each line from the magnet would be balanced by an induced line in the opposite direction. Thus, there would be no net flux inside the superconductor. But the superconductor would act like a magnet with its N-pole near the N-pole of the permanent magnet. The superconductor and the magnet would repel each other.

A superconductor repels magnetic field lines from it. It is repelled from a permanent magnet.

F.Y.I.

Earth's magnetic field has flip-flopped, north and south, at least 171 times.

a

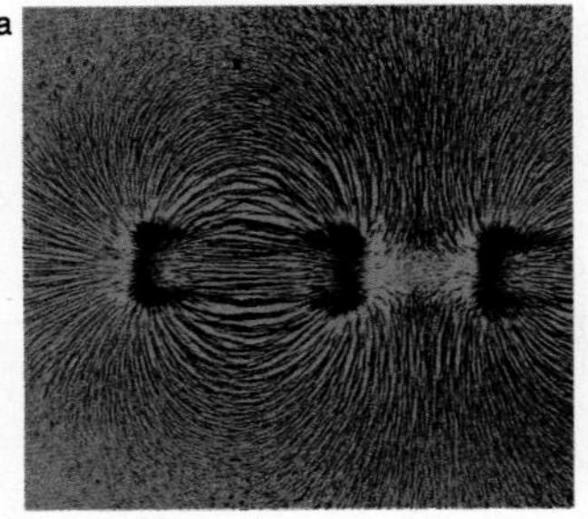

b

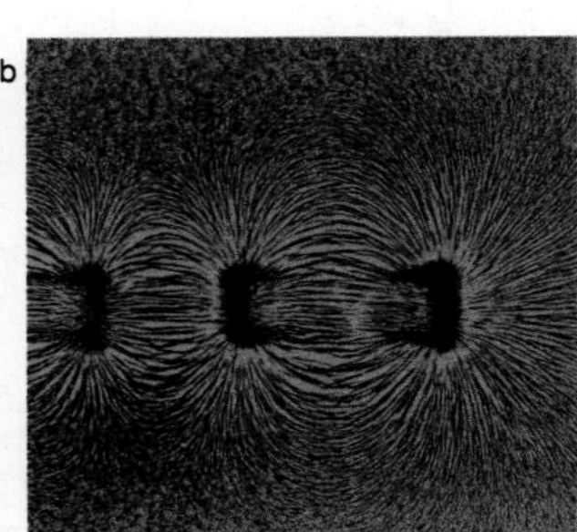

FIGURE 24–6. The field lines for like poles (a) and unlike poles (b).

CONCEPT DEVELOPMENT

Some students think all metals are attracted by a magnet. Demonstrate that metals such as aluminum are not.

ACTIVITY

Discovery: Demonstrate magnetizing an iron nail or a paper clip by rubbing it on a magnet. Rubbing in the same direction will be most effective. Allow students to observe a magnet's field by letting them experiment with iron filings.

Demonstration: Magnetize iron filings in a tube by stroking the tube with a permanent magnet. Use a compass to show students the magnetization. Shake the tube and show students that this makes the magnetization disappear.

Laboratory Manual. Give students additional experience with magnetism by doing Lab 24.1, The Nature of Magnetism, from the Laboratory Manual.

TEACHER F.Y.I.

According to Einstein's own reminiscences, he was filled with a sense of wonder when he played with a compass as a small boy. He credits this experience with inspiring his intensive study of physics.

Answers To
PRACTICE PROBLEMS

Have students refer to Appendix A of the Solutions Appendix for complete solutions to Practice Problems.

1. **a.** repulsive
   b. attractive
2. middle, S-pole; bottom, N-pole
3. From the top down, the top faces are N, S, N, S, N.
4. the bottom (the point)

CONCEPT DEVELOPMENT

• In SI units, the field of a current-carrying wire is kI/r, where the constant $k = 2 \times 10^{-7}$ Tm/A.

• For working out the units in problems it's very useful to remember that one tesla is one newton per ampere meter.

• Since the field of a coil of wire is proportional to the number of turns and the current, you will sometimes see a coil's field given as a number of ampere-turns.

Demonstration: Hang an insulated, flexible, 20-gauge stranded copper wire from two ring stands so it sags down to the table. Adjust the wire so it is hanging between the poles of a strong magnet. Place a 1.5-V battery and switch in the circuit. When you close the switch, the wire jumps. You can reverse the direction of the current or orientation of the magnet and observe the results.

Laboratory Manual. Give students additional experience with the principles of electromagnetism by doing Lab 24.2 from the Laboratory Manual.

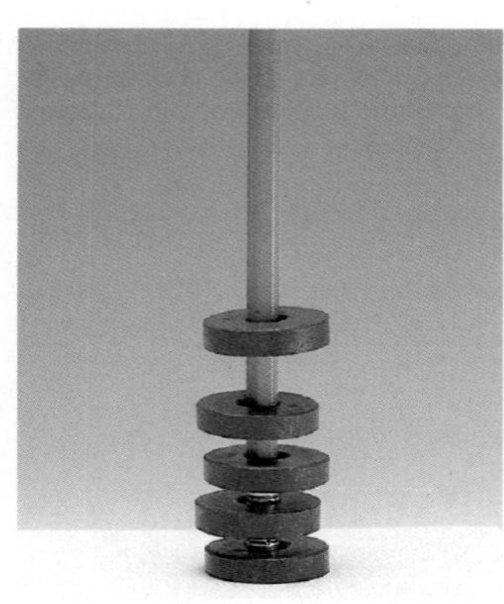

FIGURE 24–7. Use with Practice Problem 2.

Practice Problems

1. A student holds a bar magnet in each hand. If both hands are brought close together, will the force be attractive or repulsive if the magnets are held so that
   a. the two N-poles are brought close together?
   b. an N-pole and an S-pole are brought together?
2. Figure 24–7 shows five disk magnets floating above each other. The N-pole of the top-most disk faces up. Which poles are on the top side of the other magnets?
3. In the Chapter 1 opening photo, page 2, assume the N-pole is the bottom face of the floating magnet. Which is the direction of the induced field in the superconducting disk?
4. ▶ Figure 24–3 shows a magnet attracting a nail to it which, in turn, has attracted many small tacks to it. If the N-pole of the permanent magnet is the top face, which end of the nail is the N-pole?

Electromagnetism

Make a pair of Scotch-tape electrometers, Chapter 21, and bring the magnets near them. You will see no effect. There is no force exerted on the charges on the tapes by the magnets.

In 1820, the Danish physicist Hans Christian Oersted (1777–1851) was experimenting with electric currents in wires. Oersted laid one of his wires across the tip of a small compass, Figure 24–8. He had expected the needle to point toward the wire or along the wire, and was amazed to see that, instead, it rotated until it pointed perpendicular to the wire. The forces on the poles were perpendicular to the direction of current in the wire. Oersted also found that when the charges were stationary no magnetic forces existed, in agreement with the results of the tape-electrometer experiment.

If a compass needle turns, it must be the result of a magnetic field. The magnetic field around a current-carrying wire can easily be shown by placing a wire vertically through a horizontal piece of cardboard on which iron filings are sprinkled. When a current is flowing, tap the cardboard. The filings form a pattern of concentric circles around the wire, Figure 24–9. The center of each circle is the wire itself.

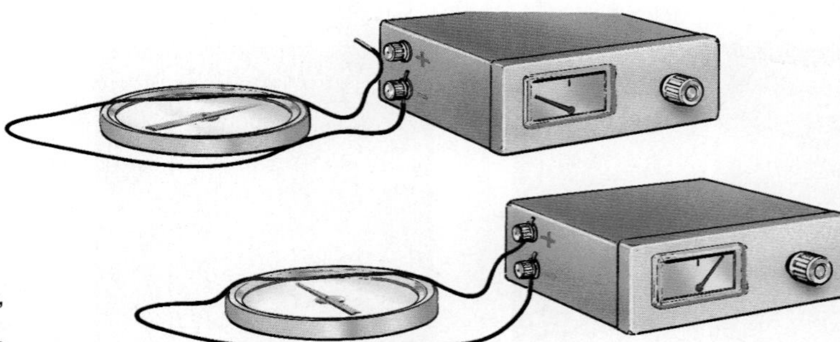

FIGURE 24–8. Using apparatus similiar to that shown on the right, Oersted showed a connection between electricity and magnetism.

LABORATORY MANUAL

Use Lab 24.2 with this section.

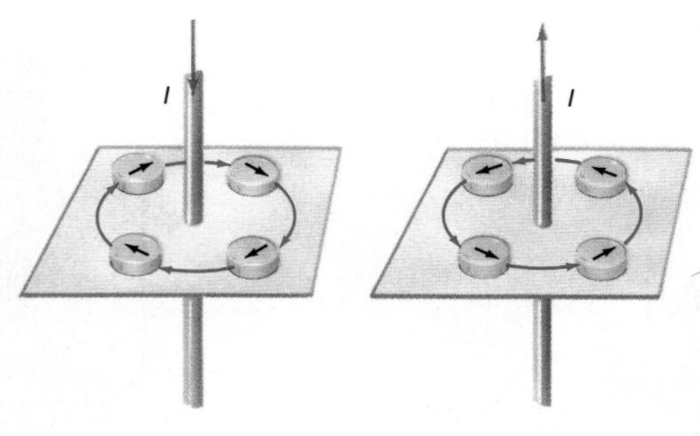

FIGURE 24–9. The magnetic field produced by current in a straight wire conductor reverses if the current in the wire is reversed.

The circular lines indicate that magnetic field lines form closed loops in the same way that field lines about permanent magnets form closed loops. The strength of the magnetic field around a long, straight wire is proportional to the current flowing in the wire. The strength also varies inversely with the distance from the wire.

A compass shows the direction of the field lines. If you reverse the direction of current flow, the compass needle also reverses its direction. You can find the direction of the field using the **first right-hand rule**. Grasp the wire with your right hand, Figure 24–10. Keep your thumb pointed in the direction of the conventional (positive) current flow. The fingers of your hand circle the wire and point in the direction of the magnetic field.

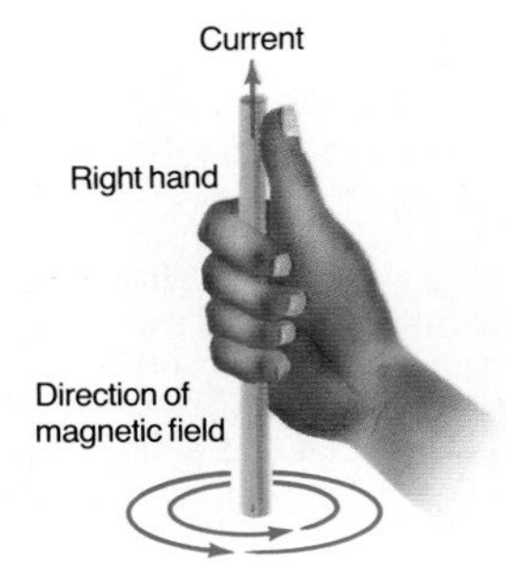

FIGURE 24–10. The right-hand rule for a current-carrying straight wire shows the direction of the magnetic field.

Magnetic Field Near a Coil

When an electric current flows through a single circular loop of wire, a magnetic field appears all around the loop. By applying the right-hand rule as in Figure 24–11 to any part of the wire loop, it can be shown that the direction of the field inside the loop is always the same. In the case shown in the diagram, the field is always up, out of the page. Outside the loop, it is always down, into the page.

Suppose wire is looped several times to form a coil. When a current flows through the coil, the field around all loops will be in the same direction. The field from each loop adds to the fields of the other loops.

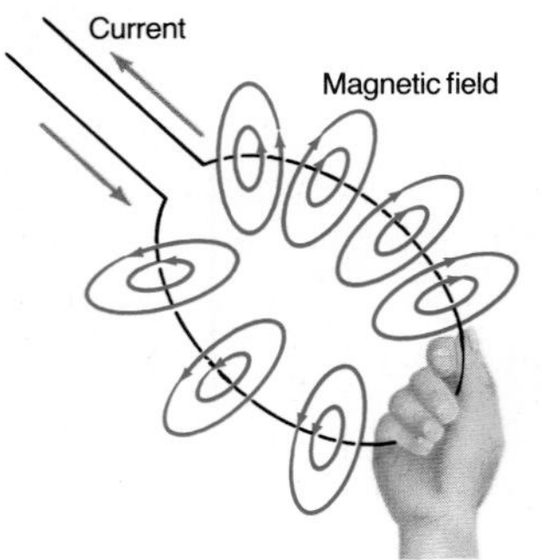

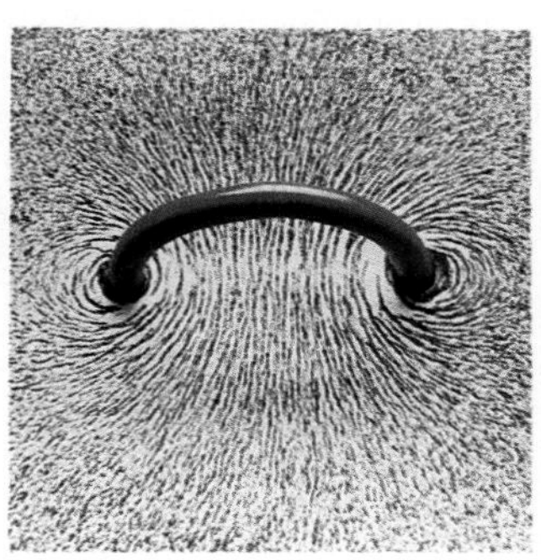

FIGURE 24–11. The magnetic field about a circular loop of current-carrying wire is shown.

CONCEPT DEVELOPMENT

Demonstration: Another demonstration to show the force on a current-carrying wire is to place a strip of very thin aluminum foil between the poles of horseshoe magnets. (Very thin foil can be obtained by unrolling a 0.02 microfarad paper capacitor, which may be obtained in an electronic supply store.) Stand up three strong horseshoe magnets about 10 cm apart so the poles alternate and form a kind of tunnel. Run the aluminum foil between the magnets. Attach the ends of the foil with wire to a variable, low-voltage DC power supply. Start at low current and increase slowly. The aluminum strip will arch in two places, showing there is a force on it. Reverse the current and observe.

Demonstration: A Flicker Bulb is available at very low cost from scientific supply houses and can be mounted in a standard light socket. The bulb will vibrate in a weak magnetic field because the current is oscillating at 60 Hz. Don't use a field so strong that it will cause the filament to break during its violent oscillations.

Connect to BIOLOGY

Certain bacteria, such as *Aquaspirillum* and *Magnetotacticum*, have been found to orient themselves in a magnetic field and to move along magnetic field lines. The bacteria contain several tiny crystals of the mineral magnetite, Fe_3O_4. These crystals respond to magnetic fields just like a compass needle. Evidently, the bacteria can sense the forces on the crystals and move in response.

Some scientists have reported finding evidence of these bacteria in the brains of homing pigeons. How might one test the hypothesis that these birds use Earth's magnetic field to find their way home? [Build a room in which you can create a magnetic field in any direction. See if the birds' flight is affected by the magnetic field.]

POCKET LAB

FUNNY BALLS

Purpose: to observe the effect of more than one steel ball in the same magnetic field.

Materials: #1 disk magnet; two 3-mm steel balls; magnetic compass (optional).

Outcome: The steel balls repel each other. Both steel balls will become magnetized with their axes pointing toward or away from the center of the bottom of the magnet. A small compass can be used to show that each ball really has a north and a south pole.

Guided Practice: Review electromagnetism and then have students work on the first two Practice Problems on page 499.

Independent Practice: Assign the remaining Practice Problems for homework and spend time going over them with students during the next class period.

Laboratory Manual. Give students additional experience with the magnetic field about a coil by doing Lab 24.3 from the Laboratory Manual.

FIGURE 24–12. Magnetic tools are useful when working ferromagnetic materials.

A current-carrying coil of wire is an electromagnet.

The field inside the coil is up, out of the page. The field outside the coil is in the opposite direction, into the page.

When an electric current flows through a coil of wire, the coil has a field like that of a permanent magnet. When this current-carrying coil is brought close to a suspended bar magnet, one end of the coil repels the north pole of the magnet. Thus, the current-carrying coil has a north and a south pole and is itself a magnet. This type of magnet is called an **electromagnet**.

POCKET LAB

FUNNY BALLS

Place a disk magnet flat on your paper. Roll a 3-mm steel ball at the magnet. Place a second steel ball on the paper, touching the magnet and the first steel ball. What happens? Why? Make a sketch to help explain your hypothesis. Devise a procedure to test your hypothesis.

The direction of the field produced by an electromagnet can be found by using a **second right-hand rule**. Grasp the coil with the right hand. Curl your fingers around the loops in the direction of the conventional (positive) current flow, Figure 24–13. Your thumb points toward the N-pole of the electromagnet.

The strength of an electromagnet can be increased by placing an iron rod or core inside the coil. The field inside the coil magnetizes the core by induction. The magnetic strength of the core adds to that of the coil to produce a much stronger magnet.

A right-hand rule shows the direction of the field produced by an electromagnet.

The strength of the magnetic field around a current-carrying wire is proportional to the current in the wire. The strength of the field of an electromagnet is also proportional to the current flowing through the coil. The magnetic field produced by each loop of a coil is the same as that produced by any other loop. These fields are in the same direction. Thus, increasing the number of loops in an electromagnet increases the strength of the magnetic field. The strength of the field of an electromagnet is proportional to the current and to the number of loops, and depends on the nature of the core.

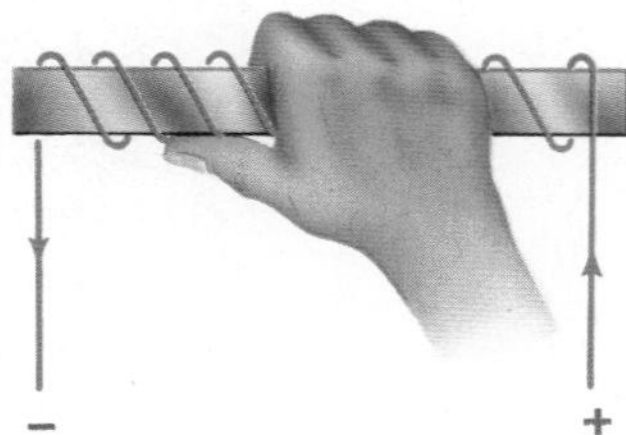

FIGURE 24–13. The second right-hand rule can be used to determine the polarity of an electromagnet.

LABORATORY MANUAL

Use Lab 24.3 with this section.

Practice Problems

5. A long, straight, current-carrying wire runs from north to south.
   a. A compass needle is placed above the wire points with its N-pole toward the east. In what direction is the current flowing?
   b. If a compass is put underneath the wire, in which direction will the needle point?
6. Suppose you measure the strength of the magnetic field 1 cm from a current-carrying wire. Compare this value with
   a. the strength of the field 2 cm from the wire.
   b. the strength of the field 3 cm from the wire.
7. The loop in Figure 24–11a has current running in a clockwise direction (from left to right above the cardboard). If a compass is placed on the cardboard beneath the loop, in which direction will the N-pole point?
8. ▶ A student makes a magnet by winding wire around a large nail as in Figure 24–14. The magnet is connected to the battery as shown. Which end of the nail, pointed end or head, will be the N-pole?

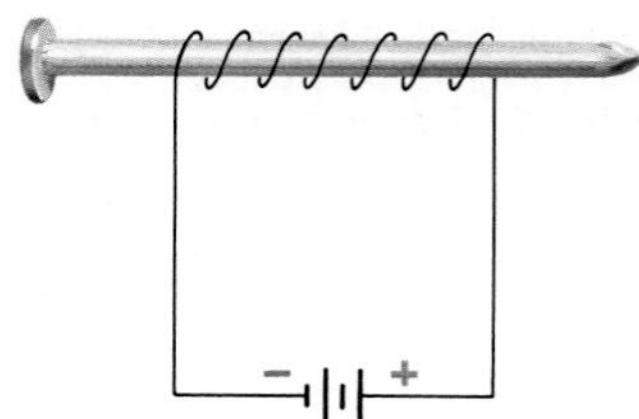

FIGURE 24–14. Use with Practice Problem 8.

A Microscopic Picture of Magnetic Materials

If you put a sample containing iron, nickel, or cobalt in a magnetic field, the sample will become magnetic. That is, north and south poles will be created. The polarity created depends on the direction of the external field. When you take away the external field, the sample will lose its magnetism.

Iron, nickel, and cobalt, three ferromagnetic elements, behave in many ways like an electromagnet. Why is this so? In the early 19th century, a theory of magnetism in iron was proposed by Andre Marie Ampere to explain this behavior. Ampere knew that the magnetic effects of an electromagnet are the result of electric current flowing through its loops. He reasoned that the effects of a bar magnet must result from tiny "loops" of current within the bar.

Magnetism in a permanent magnet is the result of magnetic fields of electrons.

Although the details of Ampere's reasoning were wrong, his basic idea was correct. Each electron in an atom acts like a tiny electromagnet. The magnetic fields of the electrons in a group of neighboring atoms can add together. Such a group is called a **domain**. Although domains may contain 10^{20} individual atoms, they are still very small. Thus, even a small sample of iron contains a huge number of domains.

When a piece of iron is not in a magnetic field, the domains point in random directions. Their magnetic fields cancel one another. If, however, the iron is placed in a magnetic field, the domains tend to align with the external field, as in Figure 24–15. In the case of a temporary magnet, after the external field is removed, the domains return to their random arrangement. In permanent magnets, the iron has been alloyed with other substances that keep the domains aligned after the external magnetic field is removed.

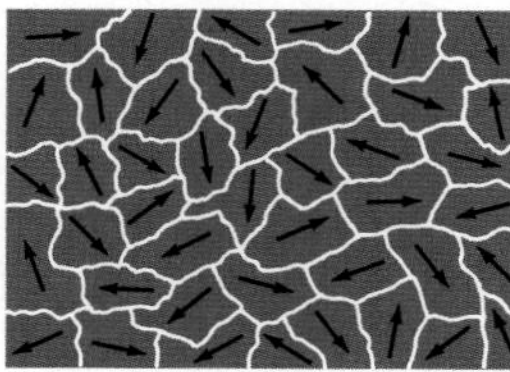

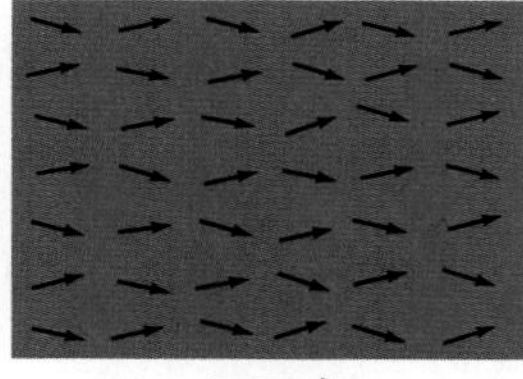

FIGURE 24–15. A piece of iron becomes a magnet only when its domains align.

Sound or video tape recorders create electric signals representing the sounds or pictures being recorded. The electric signals produce currents in an electromagnet called a recording head. Magnetic recording tape passes directly over the recording head. The tape has many very tiny

Answers To
PRACTICE PROBLEMS

Have students refer to Appendix A of the Solutions Appendix for complete solutions to Practice Problems.

5. a. from south to north
   b. west
6. a. half as strong
   b. one-third as strong
7. toward the top of the page
8. pointed end

CONCEPT DEVELOPMENT

ACTIVITY

Cooperative Learning: Have student groups find out all they can about Earth's magnetic field in their local region. Have other groups of students investigate the magnetic fields of other planets in the solar system.

CHECKING FOR UNDERSTANDING

Ask students to name the factors that determine magnetic field strength. [They include the magnet's material, the distance from the wire or magnet, the number of coils for an electromagnet, and the amount of current for current-produced fields.]

RETEACHING

Ask students how north and south poles are defined. Ask them to draw the magnetic field around a bar magnet. How does the field of a coil of wire compare to the bar magnet's field? What is the magnetic effect of a current moving down a wire?

EXTENSION

At the end of this section students learn that geologists have found that Earth's magnetic field has reversed several times in the geological past. Have interested students find out what is known about this phenomenon (called geomagnetic reversal). For example, how often has Earth's magnetic field reversed and is there evidence it may happen again in the near future? Some scientists have suggested this pole flipping has influenced the course of evolution. What's the connection between Earth's field and biology?

INDEPENDENT PRACTICE/ EXTENSION

Refer to the Assignment Guide below for additional questions and problems for independent practice.

3 Close

CONVERGENT QUESTION

Why does heating a magnet tend to weaken it? [The kinetic energy of the magnet's atoms increases, causing them to lose some of their alignment. This breaks down the domain structure.]

CONCEPT REVIEW ANSWERS

1.1 Field lines are not real, but help in visualization. The field is real.

1.2 If in the same direction, the field would be twice as large; if in opposite directions, it would be zero.

1.3 If you grasp the wire with your right hand, with your thumb pointing in the direction of the conventional current flow, your fingers will encircle the wire in the direction of the field.

1.4 Critical Thinking: a. The metal rods could be magnets with their axes parallel. If the top magnet is positioned so that its N- and S-poles are above the N- and S-poles of the bottom magnet, it will be repelled by the bottom magnet and "float" above it in the guides. If the top magnet is turned end-for-end, it will be attracted to the bottom magnet. **b.** If an ordinary iron bar is used on top or bottom, it will be attracted to the magnet in any orientation.

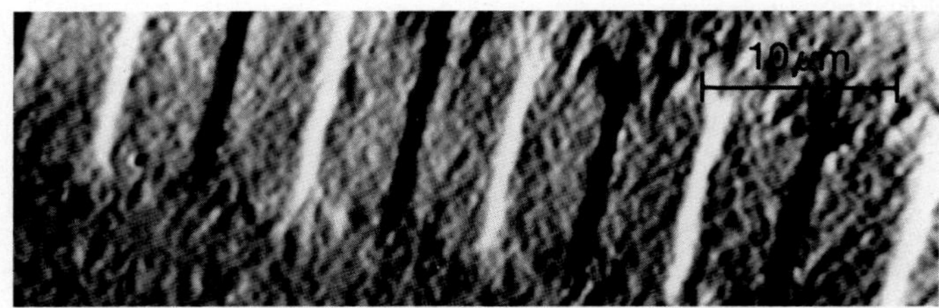

FIGURE 24–16. A scanning tunneling micrograph shows a pattern of magnetic fields on a recording disk.

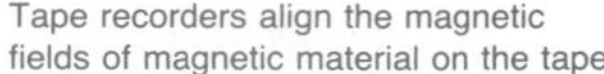

Tape recorders align the magnetic fields of magnetic material on the tape.

bits of magnetic material bonded to thin plastic. When the tape passes over the recording head, the domains of the bits are aligned by the magnetic fields of the head. The direction of the alignment depends on the direction of the current in the head. The directions of the magnetic fields of the tiny bits become a magnetic record of the sounds or pictures being recorded. The material on the tape is chosen so that the domains keep their alignment permanently. In Chapter 25, the method of playing back the recordings will be described. "Floppy disks" are magnetically-coated disks that record computer data in the same way. Figure 24–16 shows a pattern of magnetic fields on such a disk.

GEOLOGY CONNECTION

Rocks that contain iron have made a "tape recording" of the direction of Earth's magnetic field. Rocks on the seafloor were produced when molten rock poured out of cracks in the bottom of the oceans. As they cooled, they were magnetized in the direction of Earth's field at that time. The seafloor spreads, so rocks farther from the crack are older than those near the crack. When scientists examined these rocks, they were surprised to find that the direction of the magnetization varied. They concluded that the north and south magnetic poles of Earth have exchanged places many times in Earth's history. The origin of Earth's magnetic field is not well understood. How this field might reverse direction periodically is even more of a mystery.

The motion of electrons in superconductors produces magnetic fields that repel other magnets.

CONCEPT REVIEW

1.1 Are magnetic field lines real? Is the magnetic field real or just a convenience?

1.2 A wire is passed through a card on which iron filings are sprinkled. The filings show the magnetic field around the wire. A second wire is close to the first wire and parallel to it. An identical current flows through the second wire. If the two currents are in the same direction, how would the magnetic field be affected? What if the two currents were in opposite directions?

1.3 Explain the right-hand rule used to determine the direction of a magnetic field around a straight, current-carrying wire.

1.4 **Critical Thinking:** Lei has a toy containing two parallel metal rods.
- **a.** The top rod floats above the lower one. If the rod's direction is reversed, however, it falls down on to the lower rod. Explain what the rods could be.
- **b.** Lei once lost the top rod and replaced it with another bar. In this case, the top rod fell down no matter what the orientation. What type of rod must Lei have used?

LAB WORKSHEET

Use the Lab Worksheet for Chapter 24 with this Physics Lab.

24:1 ASSIGNMENT GUIDE

	PRACTICE	EXTENSION
CHAPTER REVIEW pp. 510–513		
· Reviewing Concepts	1–11	
· Applying Concepts		1–6
· Problems*	3–5	2
APPENDIX B PROBLEMS*		
· Chapter 24, p. 705	1–4	

* Complete solutions to all Chapter Review and Appendix problems appear in the Problems and Solutions Manual.

PHYSICS LAB : Electric Motor

Purpose

To construct an electric motor and to modify it for greater speed.

Materials

- low-voltage power supply
- small disk magnet
- 1 m length of #26 or #28 magnet wire
- 2 paper clips
- cellophane tape
- sandpaper
- 3 balls of clay

Procedure

1. Wrap the wire around the disk magnet leaving 2 cm of straight wire at each end. (See sketch.)
2. Remove the wire from the magnet and use thin strips of tape to keep it in a loop. (See sketch.)
3. Bend the paper clips as shown and use small balls of clay to hold the clips as shown.
4. Use another ball of clay to hold the magnet below the coil as shown in the sketch. The magnet should be close to the coil, but the coil needs to be able to rotate without hitting the magnet.
5. Place the straight ends of the wire on the paper clips. Adjust the straight ends so that the loop will turn without wobbling.
6. Use sandpaper to remove the coating on the top side only of the straight ends of the wire.
7. Place the loop back on the paper clips and give the coil a small spin.
8. Set the power supply at 1.5 V direct current and attach the alligator clips to the paper clips. The loop should spin.
9. Make fine adjustments on the loop, paper clips, and so on, to reduce friction until the motor works easily and spins quickly on its own.

Observations and Data

1. Will the loop turn in both directions?
2. Predict what will happen when the connections to the power supply are reversed. Try it. Describe your results.
3. List at least 3 ways that the experiment could be modified to give the coil a greater speed.
4. Try each of the ideas that you listed above and see if they work. Describe your results.

Analysis

1. Why does the loop rotate? (**Hint:** Start by describing the electrical path from the battery.)
2. Why might your motor work better in one direction than the other?

Applications

1. Look closely at the insides of a conventional electric motor. Identify the major components. Explain why it is so heavy for its size.

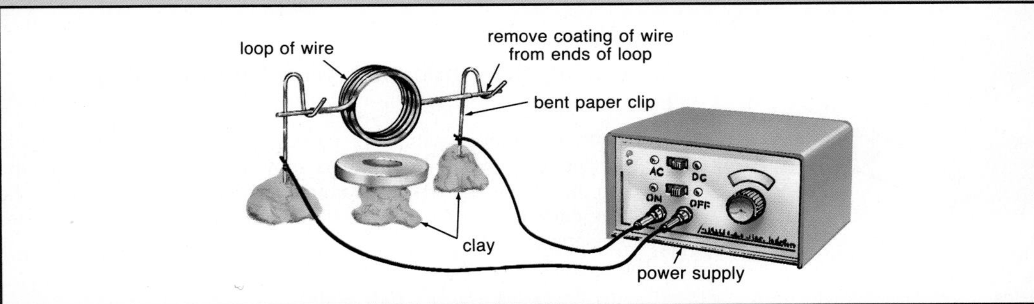

ASSESSMENT

Critical Thinking: To further assess students' understanding of electric motors, ask the following questions.

1. Suppose you hold a magnet directly above the coil to increase the speed of the coil. Should the poles of this magnet be the same as or the opposite of the bottom magnet? [The field between the two magnets should be the same as the original field. If the N-pole of the bottom magnet is pointing up, then the N-pole of the top magnet should be pointing up.]

2. Would you predict that alternating current would make the coil spin faster? Why? Try it, but don't use more than about 3.0 V. What happens to the energy supplied by the power supply? [The alternating current switches too fast (60 times /s) for this motor. The coil will just heat up. All the electrical energy goes to thermal energy.]

PHYSICS LAB

Process Skills: observing, questioning, inferring, predicting, hypothesizing, defining operationally, formulating models.

MISCONCEPTIONS

Students do not understand the fundamentals of an electric motor and often confuse electric and magnetic effects.

Teaching Suggestion: Build one before class and show it as an example. Then stand back and let the students have fun.

Lab Worksheet, Teacher Resource Package. If desired, use the lab worksheet master provided for this chapter for students to record their data.

OBSERVATIONS

1. Most motors will not work in both directions. Even those that work in both directions will work better in one direction.
2. The mirror will now run better in the opposite direction.
3. Students should list some of the following ideas: increase the voltage setting (this will increase the current in the coil); increase the number of magnets or use a stringer magnet; change the number of loops in the coil; hold a magnet directly above the coil in addition to the magnet under the coil.

ANALYSIS

1. Current flowing through the loop creates a magnetic field. The permanent magnet pushes (or pulls) on this, causing the loop to move.
2. The loop and straight wires are not perfectly balanced. As the loop rotates, it wobbles, which causes the electrical connections to change alternately—making and breaking the electrical circuit.

APPLICATIONS

Students should note the magnets, the brushes, and the coils. Motors are heavy for their size because they all have magnets (often in the form of electromagnets—coils of wire wrapped on an iron core) and lots of wire.

24.2 FORCES CAUSED BY MAGNETIC FIELDS

Preparation

OBJECTIVES

The objectives are listed on the student page. Remind students to preview these objectives as a study guide to this major section.

OVERVIEW

The forces on charges moving in magnetic fields in various situations are discussed. Since many of these situations are three-dimensional, students may need help visualizing them.

BRIDGING

Concepts from Section 24.1, including the magnetic field concept, the force that arises from the interaction of charges and magnetic fields, and the concept of a magnetic pole are expanded.

Objectives

- **define magnetic induction; explain the direction of the force on a current-carrying wire in a magnetic field.**
- **list the factors that determine the magnitude of the force on a wire; solve problems involving a wire in a magnetic field.**
- **explain the design, operation, and uses of a galvanometer.**
- **explain the design and operation of an electric motor.**
- **list the factors that determine the magnitude of the force on a moving charge in a magnetic field; solve problems involving this force.**

24.2 FORCES CAUSED BY MAGNETIC FIELDS

The test with Scotch-tape electrometers showed that a magnetic field exerts no force on an electric charge. Ampere noted that a moving charge, an electric current, produces a magnetic field like that of a permanent magnet. Since a magnetic field exerts forces on permanent magnets, Ampere suggested that there should be a force on a current-carrying wire placed in a magnetic field.

Forces on Currents in Magnetic Fields

A force is exerted on a current-carrying wire in a magnetic field.

The force on a wire in a magnetic field can be demonstrated using the arrangement shown in Figure 24–17. A battery produces the current that flows from left to right. The magnets have either the N-pole or S-pole facing out, and thus the field is either toward the camera or away from it. As you can see, the force on the wire either pushes it down or pulls it up. As discovered by Michael Faraday (1791–1867), the force on the wire is at right angles to the direction of the magnetic field. The force is also at right angles to the direction of the current.

The right-hand rule gives the direction of the force on a wire.

The direction of the force on a current-carrying wire in a magnetic field can be found by using a **third right-hand rule**, Figure 24–18. The magnetic field is indicated by the symbol B. Its direction is given by an arrow, but when a field is into or out of the page, its direction is indicated by crosses or dots, Figure 24–19. The crosses suggest the feathers at the end of an archery arrow, while the dot suggests the point. To use the right-hand rule, point the fingers of your right hand in the direction of the magnetic field. Point your thumb in the direction of the conventional (positive) current flow in the wire. The palm of your hand then faces in the direction of the force acting on the wire.

A week after the news of Oersted's discovery reached France, Ampere demonstrated the forces that current-carrying wires exert on each other. Figure 24–20a shows that the direction of the magnetic field around each of the current-carrying wires as given by the first right-hand rule. By applying the third right-hand rule to either wire you can show that the wires are forced together, or attract each other. In Figure 24–20b, we see the opposite situation. When currents are in opposite directions, the forces push the wires apart.

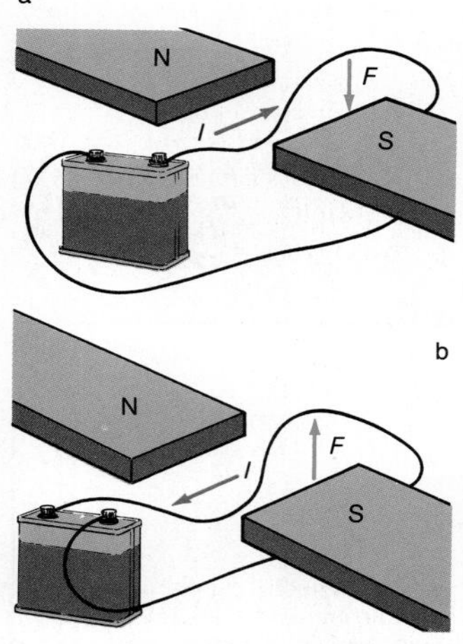

FIGURE 24–17. A representation of forces on currents in magnetic fields.

Measuring the Force on a Wire Due to a Magnetic Field

Imagine a current-carrying wire passing through a magnetic field at right angles to the wire. Experiments show that the magnitude of the force on the wire is proportional to three factors: the strength, B, of the field; the current, I, in the wire; and the length, L, of the wire that lies in the magnetic field.

The magnitude of the force is given by the expression

$$F = BIL.$$

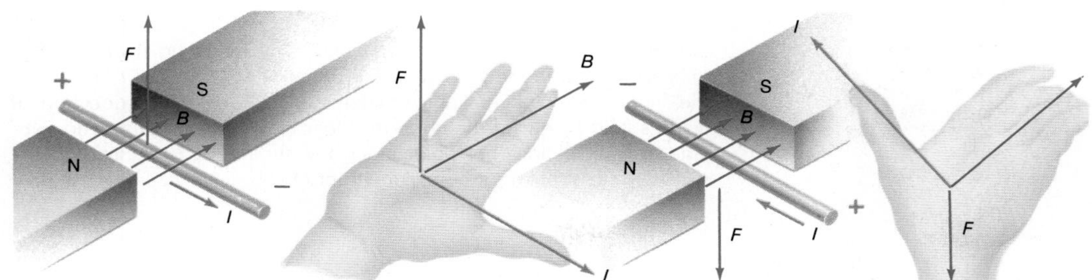

FIGURE 24–18. The third right-hand rule is used to determine the direction of force when the current and magnetic field are known.

We know how to measure force, current, and length, but not B. By rewriting the equation above, the strength of the field, B, can be calculated using the equation

$$B = \frac{F}{IL}.$$

The strength of a magnetic field is called **magnetic induction**, measured in teslas, represented by the symbol T. One tesla is equivalent to one newton per ampere-meter, N/A · m. Thus, the strength of a magnetic field is defined in terms of the force on a section of straight wire one meter long carrying one ampere of current.

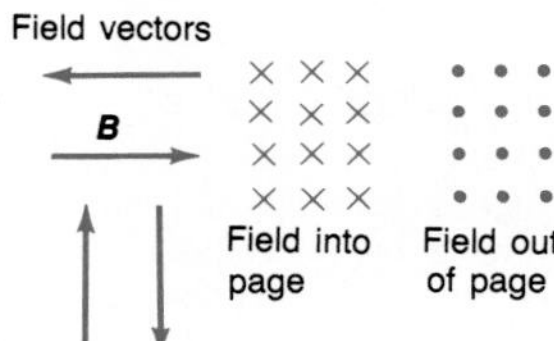

FIGURE 24–19. Directions of magnetic fields are indicated by directional arrows (a) when the field is in the same plane as the page, by crosses (b) when the field is into the page, and by dots (c) when the field is out of the page toward you.

Table 24-1

Typical Magnetic Field

Source and location	Strength (T)
surface of neutron star (predicted)	10^8
strong laboratory electromagnet	10
small bar magnet	0.01
Earth's magnetic field	5×10^{-5}

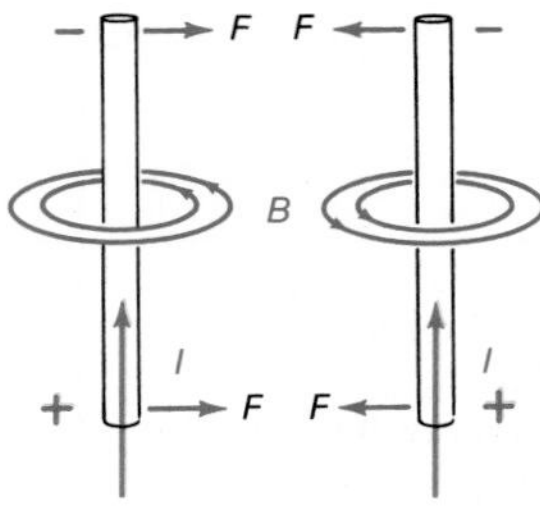

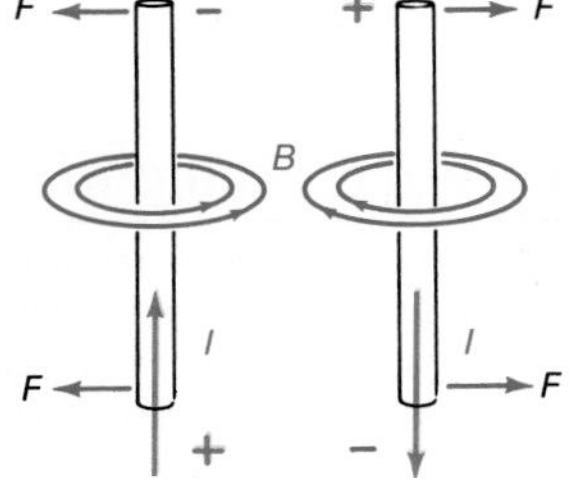

FIGURE 24–20. Two current-bearing conductors (a) are attracted when the currents are in the same direction, and (b) are repelled when the currents are in opposite directions.

1 Focus

DISCREPANT EVENT

Have a motor extravaganza. Some students will have old slot-car motors at home that can be brought in and taken apart. Others will use motors in different ways, which can be demonstrated or discussed. Simple motors can be constructed from kits or from various plans (such as in the note by Stuart McCausland "Make a Simple DC Motor," from the September 1990 issue of *The Science Teacher*, pages 80–81).

2 Teach

CONCEPT DEVELOPMENT

Students may ask about the derivation of the right-hand rules. The rules provide a convenient conceptual model for the way various facets of magnetism behave. They help especially with troublesome three-dimensional quantities.

Study Guide Master. To reinforce the concepts in this section, have the students complete the Study Guide Master for Section 24.2 from the Teacher Resource Package.

STUDY GUIDE MASTER

Use the Study Guide master for section 24.2.

CONCEPT DEVELOPMENT

- Nikola Tesla was a fascinating personality, with a talent for self-promotion. He tended to work outside the usual scientific and engineering channels, and the actual extent of his contributions is somewhat unclear. One source of information is *Tesla: Man Out of Time,* by Margaret Cheney.
- Closely wound coils of wire that carry heavy currents must be engineered to withstand the enormous repulsive forces within them; otherwise, such coils collapse.

POCKET LAB

JUMPING WIRES

Purpose: to apply the right-hand rule.
Materials: 0–5 A variable DC power supply; ammeter; horseshoe magnet; 1-m length of insulated stranded wire.
Outcome: The force on the moving charges can be predicted by the right-hand rule. The direction of the force can be reversed by either reversing the polarity of the magnet or reversing the direction of the current.

Answers To
PRACTICE PROBLEMS

Have students refer to Appendix A of the Solutions Appendix for complete solutions to Practice Problems.

9. 0.2 T
10. 1.6 N

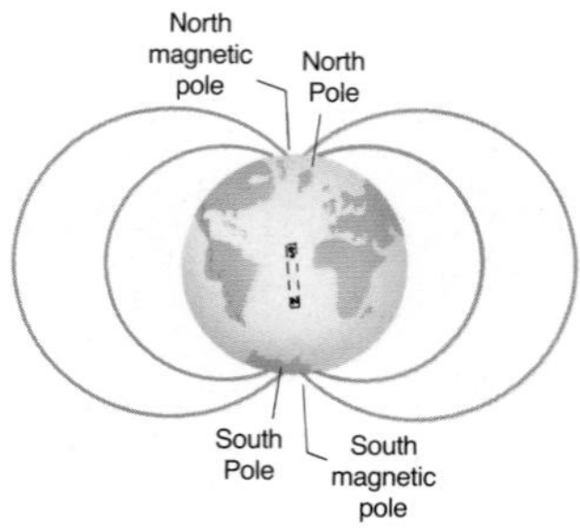

FIGURE 24–21. Earth's magnetic field lines run from the south magnetic pole to the north magnetic pole.

A magnetic field of 1 T (N/A · m) field strength is a very strong field, found only in powerful electromagnets. The magnetic fields of most magnets found in the laboratory are closer to 0.01 T. Earth's magnetic field has a strength of approximately 5×10^{-5} T. The direction of Earth's field is toward the north magnetic pole, which is in arctic Canada. The field does not point along the surface of Earth, but, in the northern hemisphere, it points down into Earth, Figure 24–21.

Example Problem

Calculating the Strength of the Magnetic Field

A wire 0.10 m long carries a current of 5.0 A. The wire is at right angles to a uniform magnetic field. The force on the wire is 0.20 N. What is the magnitude of the magnetic field, *B*?

Given: $F = 0.20$ N
$I = 5.0$ A
$L = 0.10$ m

Unknown: magnetic field strength, *B*
Basic equation: $B = F/IL$

Solution:

$$B = \frac{F}{IL} = \frac{0.20 \text{ N}}{(5.0 \text{ A})(0.10 \text{ m})} = 0.40 \frac{\text{N}}{\text{A} \cdot \text{m}} = 0.40 \text{ T}$$

POCKET LAB

JUMPING WIRES

Carefully position a horseshoe magnet so that its ends are hanging over the table. Attach one end of a 1 m long wire to your power supply through an ammeter. Hold the wire in your hand so that the wire hangs straight down between the poles of the magnet. Increase the power supply to 4 A as you watch the wire. **CAUTION:** *The wire can become very hot. Release the wire and turn off the power supply if it becomes too warm.* What happens? Why? Disconnect one end of the wire from the power supply. With the wire still hanging down between the poles, momentarily touch the free end of the wire to your power supply. Describe the results. Using the right-hand rule, verify that the wire moved in the direction of the force. Try two variations that will make the wire jump in opposite directions.

Example Problem

Force on a Current-Carrying Wire in a Magnetic Field

A wire 115 m long is at right angles to a uniform magnetic field. The field has a magnetic field strength of 5.0×10^{-5} T. The current through the wire is 400 A. Find the magnitude of the force.

Given: $L = 115$ m
$B = 5.0 \times 10^{-5}$ T
$I = 4.0 \times 10^{2}$ A

Unknown: *F*
Basic equation: $B = F/IL$

Solution:

$$\begin{aligned} F &= BIL \\ &= (5.0 \times 10^{-5} \text{ T})(4.0 \times 10^{2} \text{ A})(115 \text{ m}) \\ &= (5.0 \times 10^{-5} \text{ N/A} \cdot \text{m})(4.0 \times 10^{2} \text{ A})(115 \text{ m}) \\ &= 2.3 \text{ N} \end{aligned}$$

Practice Problems

9. A straight wire 0.10 m long carrying a current of 2.0 A is at right angles to a magnetic field. The force on the wire is 0.04 N. What is the strength of the magnetic field?

10. A wire 0.50 m long carrying a current of 8.0 A is at right angles to a 0.40 T magnetic field. How strong a force acts on the wire?

Assessment

Performance

To further assess students' understanding of forces on a current-carrying wire in a magnetic field, have them do the following. Note that they have seen how to change the direction of the force. Ask how they would change its magnitude. They might try rotating the magnet so that the field is partly in the direction of the wire, and check to see if the speed in which the wire jumps changes. They could use more magnets to increase the length of wire in the field. Ask what other parameters they might change. [When the field is not parallel to the wire, the force gets smaller, and the jump should be less evident. The force is proportional to the length of the wire in the field, so the more magnets, the greater the force. The force should also be proportional to the strength of the magnetic field and the amount of current in the wire.]

11. A wire 75 cm long carrying a current of 6.0 A is at right angles to a uniform magnetic field. The magnitude of the force acting on the wire is 0.60 N. What is the strength of the magnetic field?

▶ 12. A copper wire 40 cm long carries a current of 6.0 A and weighs 0.35 N. A certain magnetic field is strong enough to balance the force of gravity on the wire. What is the strength of the magnetic field?

One use of the force on a current-carrying wire in a magnetic field is a loudspeaker. A loudspeaker changes electrical energy to sound energy using a coil of fine wire mounted on a paper cone and placed in a magnetic field, Figure 24–22. The amplifier driving the loudspeaker sends a current through the coil. A force is exerted on the coil because it is in a magnetic field. The force pushes the coil either into or out of the magnetic field, depending on the direction of the current. The motion of the coil causes the cone to vibrate, creating sound waves in the air. An electric signal that represents a musical tone consists of a current that changes direction between 20 and 20 000 times each second, depending on the pitch of the tone.

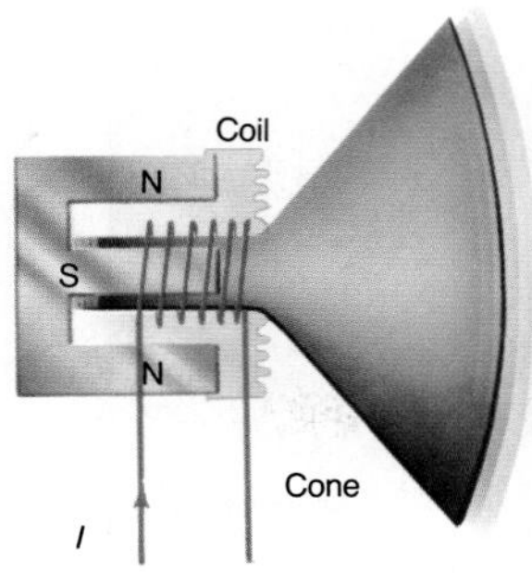

FIGURE 24–22. A schematic diagram of a loudspeaker.

Galvanometers

The **galvanometer** is a device to measure very small currents. For this reason, it is used in many voltmeters and ammeters. A galvanometer consists of a small coil of wire placed in the strong magnetic field of a permanent magnet. Each turn of wire in the coil is a wire loop. The current passing through such a loop in a magnetic field goes in one side of the loop and out the other side. Applying the third right-hand rule to each side of the loop, we find that one side of the loop is forced down while the other side of the loop is forced up. As a result, the loop has a torque on it and rotates.

Force on a wire in a galvanometer moves the needle, indicating the strength of the current.

The magnitude of the forces acting on the coil is proportional to the magnitude of the current. Figure 24–23 shows how the forces exerted on a loop of wire in a magnetic field can be used to measure current.

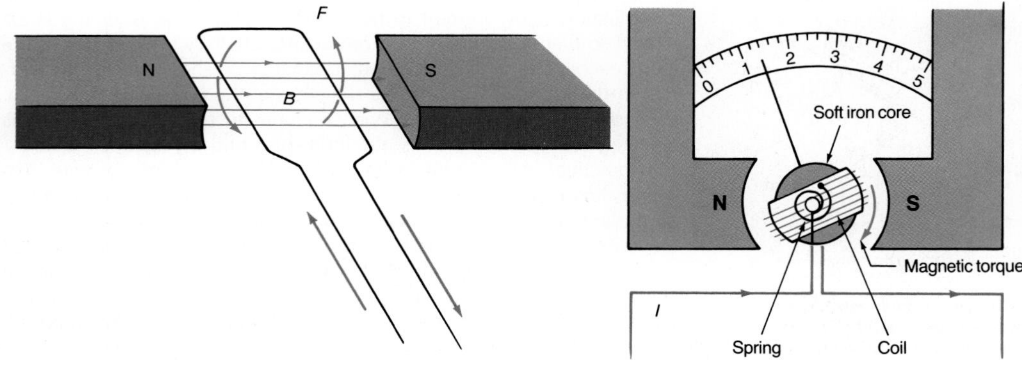

FIGURE 24–23. If a wire loop is placed in a magnetic field when current flows, the loop will rotate because of the torque exerted by the field.

11. 0.13 T
12. 0.15 T

Demonstration: Use your oscilloscope to show the effect of a magnetic field on a beam of electrons. Turn the oscilloscope on and use a fairly slow sweep speed. Bring a strong bar magnet carefully up to the scope face. You will see the electron beam deflect. Change the pole being brought up to the screen and you should see the deflection reverse in direction. Ask students to use the third right-hand rule to predict the direction of the force in each case.

• Use a St. Louis motor to show students the parts of a simple motor. (If other types of motors are available, show them as well.)

• Some teachers find it useful to make a gadget that shows the third right-hand rule. Stick three short sticks into a foam ball at right angles to each other. They represent *B*, *F*, and *v*. Leave it on display to remind students of the perpendicular orientation of these three quantities.

CONCEPT DEVELOPMENT

Cooperative Learning: Challenge student groups to brainstorm as many differences and similarities as they can between the motor and the galvanometer.

Enrichment: In the early days of electrical motors, one of the persistent problems was the brush contact point. Edison's notebooks are full of references to brushes wearing unevenly, not make good electrical contact, or wearing too fast. Have interested students find out how modern-day engineering handles this problem.

Enrichment Master. With this section, use the Enrichment Master, Making a Meter, from the Teacher Resource Package.

Transparency Package. Use Transparency 35 to help illustrate motors.

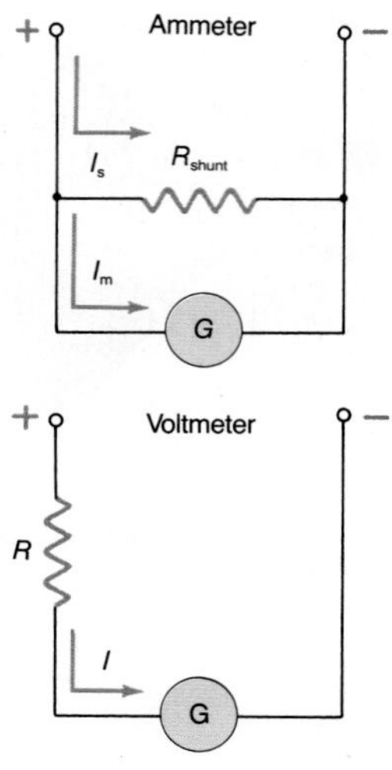

FIGURE 24–24. The components of an electric meter are shown.

The forces due to the current are opposed by a small spring. Thus, the amount of rotation is proportional to the current. The meter is calibrated by finding out how much the coil turns when a known current is sent through it. The galvanometer can then be used to measure unknown currents.

Many galvanometers produce a full-scale deflection with as little as 50 μA (50×10^{-6} A) current. The resistance of the coil of wire in a sensitive galvanometer is about 1000 Ω. Such a galvanometer can be converted into an ammeter by placing a resistor with resistance smaller than that of the galvanometer in parallel with the meter, Figure 24–24. Most of the current, I_S, flows through the resistor, called the shunt, because the current is inversely proportional to resistance, while only a few microamps, I_M, flow through the galvanometer.

A galvanometer can also be connected as a voltmeter. To make a voltmeter, a resistor, called the multiplier, is placed in series with the meter. The galvanometer measures the current through the multiplier. The current is given by $I = V/R$, where V is the voltage across the voltmeter and R is the effective resistance of the galvanometer and the multiplier resistor. Suppose you want a meter that reads full scale when 10 V are placed across it. The resistor is chosen so that at 10 V, the meter is deflected full scale by the current flowing through the meter and resistor.

Electric Motors

The force on a current-carrying wire in a magnetic field causes an electric motor to rotate.

The simple loop of wire used in a galvanometer cannot rotate more than 180°. As shown in Figure 24–23, the forces push the right side of the loop up and the left side of the loop down. The loop turns until it reaches the vertical position. The loop will not continue to turn because the forces are still up and down, now parallel to the loop, and can cause no further rotation.

For the loop to rotate 360° in the field, the current running through the loop must reverse direction just as the loop reaches its vertical position. This reversal allows the loop to continue rotating, Figure 24–25. To reverse current direction, a split-ring commutator is used. Brushes, pieces of graphite that make a rubbing or brushing contact with the commutator, allow current to flow into the loop. The split ring is arranged so that each half of the commutator changes brushes just as the loop reaches the vertical position. Changing brushes reverses the current in the loop. As a result, the direction of the force on each side of the loop is reversed and the loop continues to rotate. This process is repeated each half-turn. Thus, the loop spins in the magnetic field.

In practice, electric motors have several rotating loops of wire. Together they make up the armature of the motor. The total force acting on the armature is proportional to $nBIL$, where n is the total number of loops on the armature and L is the length of wire in each loop that moves through the magnetic field. The magnetic field can be produced either by permanent magnets or by an electromagnet called a field coil. The force on the armature, and as a result the speed of the motor, is controlled by varying the current flowing through the motor.

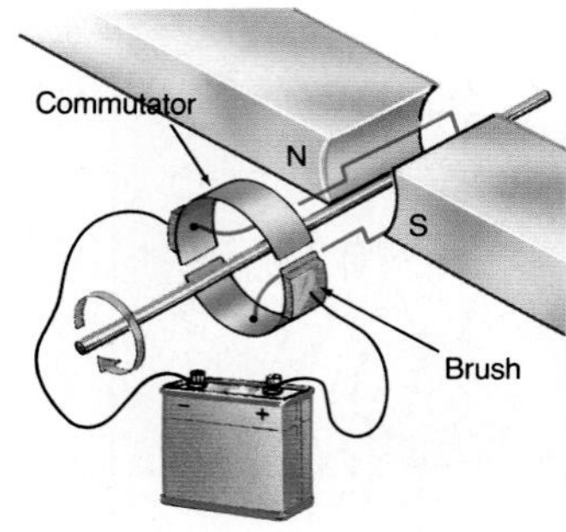

FIGURE 24–25. In an electric motor, split-ring commutators allow the wire loops in the motor to rotate 360°.

TEACHER F.Y.I.

The formulas $F = BIL$ and $F = Bqv$ are good only when the current or charge is moving at right angles to the magnetic field. The formulas are really cross-products: $F = qv \times B$ and $F = IL \times B$. Formulas for these relationships are $F = qvB \sin \theta$ and $F = ILB \sin \theta$, where θ is the angle between v and B, or the wire and B. These equations allow you to calculate the force on a charged particle or current-bearing wire regardless of the angle. You can also see that the force is a maximum at 90° where $\sin \theta = 1$, and is zero when v and B (or the wire and B) are parallel and $\sin \theta = 0$.

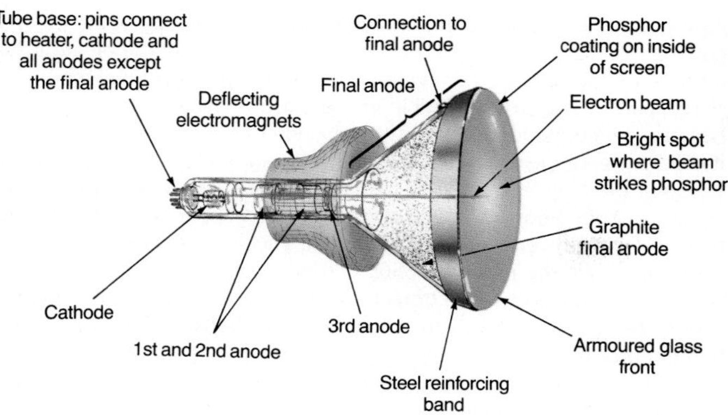

FIGURE 24–26. A television uses a cathode-ray tube to form pictures for viewing. The magnets shown deflect the electron beam vertically. There is another pair (not shown) that deflect the beam horizontally.

The Force on a Single Charged Particle

The force exerted by a magnetic field on a current-carrying wire is a result of the forces on the individual charges that make up the current flow. The charged particles do not have to be confined to a wire, but can move across any region as long as the air has been removed to prevent collisions with air molecules.

The picture tube, or cathode-ray tube, in a television set uses electrons deflected by magnetic fields to form the pictures on the screen, Figure 24–26. In the tube, electric fields pull electrons off atoms in the negative electrode, or cathode. Other electric fields gather, accelerate, and focus the electrons into a narrow beam. Magnetic fields are used to deflect the beam back and forth and up and down across the screen of the tube. The screen is coated with a phosphor that glows when struck by the electrons, producing the picture.

Magnetic fields change the direction of electrons in a television picture tube.

The force produced by a magnetic field on a single electron depends on the velocity of the electron, the strength of the field, and the angle between directions of the velocity and the field. It can be found by starting with the force on a current-carrying wire in a magnetic field, $F = BIL$. Consider a single electron moving in a wire of length L. The electron is moving perpendicular to the magnetic field. The current, I, is equal to the charge per unit time entering the wire, $I = q/t$. In this case, q is the charge of the electron and t is the time it takes to move the length of the wire, L. The time required for a particle with velocity v to travel a distance L is found by using the equation of motion, $d = vt$, or here, $t = L/v$. As a result, the equation for the current, $I = q/t$, can be replaced by $I = qv/L$. Therefore, the force on a single electron moving perpendicular to a magnetic field of strength B is

$$F = BIL = B\left(\frac{qv}{L}\right)L = Bqv.$$

The particle's charge is measured in coulombs, the velocity in m/s, and the strength of the magnetic field in teslas, T.

The direction of the force is perpendicular to both the velocity of the particle and the magnetic field. It is *opposite* that given by the third

F.Y.I.

Fritz Zwicky, an astronomer, and a minister were discussing the origin of the universe. The minister said that the universe began when God said, "Let there be light." Zwicky replied that he could buy this explanation only if God had said "Let there be light and a magnetic field."
—Letter from Emil Herzog

CONCEPT DEVELOPMENT

CHECKING FOR UNDERSTANDING

Draw various current-carrying wire and magnetic field situations on the board, asking students to predict the direction of the force on the charge. The phenomenon of moving-charge deflection is central to this section.

RETEACHING

Build your reteaching around the three right-hand rules. Use the rules to review the qualitative connections between moving charges and magnetic fields. Once these qualitative relationships have been established satisfactorily, move on to the proportionality statements about the strength of wire and coil magnetic fields. Finish by going over the equations $F = BIL$ and $F = qvB$, stressing their quantitative aspects.

Reteaching Master, Teacher Resource Package. Use the Reteaching Master for Chapter 24, Magnetic Force and Distance.

INDEPENDENT PRACTICE/ EXTENSION

Refer to the Assignment Guide on page 508 for additional questions and problems for independent practice.

ENRICHMENT MASTER

Use the Enrichment master for Chapter 24 with this section.

RETEACHING MASTER

Use the Reteaching master for Chapter 24 with this section.

TRANSPARENCY

Use Transparency 35 with this section.

CONCEPT DEVELOPMENT

- When a particle's velocity and magnetic field are not at right angles, then the path of the particle is not a circle but a helix.

Critical Thinking: Ask students to imagine that they are audio engineers trying to create a top-quality stereo speaker. Have them refer to the diagrams of loudspeaker design in this section as they write down some challenges they might face in their designs.

Enrichment: Have interested students investigate the phenomenon of the northern lights (aurora borealis). [Their basic cause is the interaction of charged particles coming from the sun and their interaction with Earth's magnetic field.]

Guided Practice: Go over the Example Problem on page 508 with students. Then have them work on the first two Practice Problems that follow, offering assistance where needed.

Independent Practice: Assign the remaining Practice Problems for homework. Go over them with students during the next class period.

Answers To
PRACTICE PROBLEMS

Have students refer to Appendix A of the Solutions Appendix for complete solutions to Practice Problems.

13. 3.2×10^{-13} N

right-hand rule with the thumb pointed along the velocity of the positive particle. The direction of the force is opposite because the electron has a negative charge and "conventional current" has a positive charge.

The path of a charged particle in a uniform magnetic field is circular because, since the force is always perpendicular to the particle's velocity, it is a centripetal force. The radius of the circle can be found by equating the magnetic force to the centripetal force, $Bqv = mv^2/r$. The circular motion allows charged particles to be trapped and held in magnetic fields. High energy nuclear particle accelerators, such as the one at Fermilab and the proposed SSC, use magnets to force the particles to travel in circular paths. Electrons trapped in the magnetic field of Earth, Figure 24–27, form the Van Allen radiation belts. Solar storms send tremendous numbers of high-energy charged particles toward Earth. They disturb Earth's magnetic field, dumping electrons out of the Van Allen belts. These electrons excite atoms of nitrogen and oxygen in Earth's atmosphere and cause them to emit the red, green, and blue called the northern lights. The "halo" circles the north magnetic pole.

Earth's Halo

Strong magnetic fields will be used in magnetic confinement fusion devices that are under development. The fields confine protons and other nuclei. The nuclei collide at high speed, producing large amounts of energy. The details are discussed in Chapter 31.

FIGURE 24–27. A representation of the Van Allen radiation belts around Earth.

Example Problem

Force on a Charged Particle in a Magnetic Field

A beam of electrons travels at 3.0×10^6 m/s through a 4.0×10^{-2}-T uniform magnetic field. **a.** The beam is at right angles to the magnetic field. What is the magnitude of the force acting on each electron? **b.** Compare the force acting on a proton moving at the same speed and in the same direction to the force acting on the electron in part **a.**

Given: $v = 3.0 \times 10^6$ m/s
$B = 4.0 \times 10^{-2}$ T
$q = 1.6 \times 10^{-19}$ C

Unknown: F
Basic equation: $F = Bqv$

Solution:

a. $F = Bqv$
$= (4.0 \times 10^{-2}\ \text{T})(1.6 \times 10^{-19}\ \text{C})(3.0 \times 10^6\ \text{m/s})$
$= (4.0 \times 10^{-2}\ \text{N/A} \cdot \text{m})(1.6 \times 10^{-19}\ \text{C})(3.0 \times 10^6\ \text{m/s})$
$= 1.9 \times 10^{-14}$ N

b. The magnitude of the force is exactly the same on a proton as it is on an electron, since the proton and the electron have exactly the same charge magnitude. Because the proton's charge is of the opposite sign, however, it is deflected in the opposite direction.

Practice Problems

13. An electron passes through a magnetic field at right angles to the field at a velocity of 4.0×10^6 m/s. The strength of the magnetic field is 0.50 T. What is the magnitude of the force acting on the electron?

24:2 ASSIGNMENT GUIDE		
	PRACTICE	EXTENSION
CHAPTER REVIEW pp. 510–513		
· Reviewing Concepts	12–14	
· Applying Concepts		7–13
· Problems*	1, 6, 8–15, 18–23, 26–28	7, 16, 17, 24, 25, 29
APPENDIX B PROBLEMS*		
· Chapter 24, pp. 705–706	5–10, 12–16	11

* Complete solutions to all Chapter Review and Appendix problems appear in the Problems and Solutions Manual.

14. A stream of doubly-ionized particles (missing two electrons and thus carrying a net charge of two elementary charges) moves at a velocity of 3.0×10^4 m/s perpendicular to a magnetic field of 9.0×10^{-2} T. What is the magnitude of the force acting on each ion?

15. Triply-ionized particles in a beam carry a net positive charge of three elementary charge units. The beam enters a 4.0×10^{-2}-T magnetic field. The particles have a velocity of 9.0×10^6 m/s. What is the magnitude of the force acting on each particle?

▶ 16. Doubly-ionized helium atoms (alpha particles) are traveling at right angles to a magnetic field at a speed of 4.0×10^{-2} m/s. The field strength is 5.0×10^{-2} T. What force acts on each particle?

F.Y.I.

The world's smallest electric motor weighs one half-millionth of a pound and is smaller than the head of a pin, measuring a sixty-fourth of an inch on all sides. It has thirteen parts, generates one millionth of a horsepower, and can be seen working only through a microscope. William McLellan, the inventor, built the motor using a toothpick, a microscope, and a watchmaker's lathe.

14. 8.6×10^{-16} N
15. 1.7×10^{-13} N
16. 6.4×10^{-22} N

CONCEPT REVIEW

2.1 A horizontal, current-carrying wire runs north-south through Earth's magnetic field. If the current flows north, in which direction is the force on the wire?

2.2 A beam of electrons in a cathode ray tube approaches the deflecting magnets. The N-pole is at the top of the tube, the S-pole on the bottom. If you are looking at the tube from the phosphor screen, in which direction are the electrons deflected?

2.3 When the plane of the coil in a motor is perpendicular to the magnetic field, the forces do not exert a torque on the coil. Does this mean the coil doesn't rotate? Explain.

2.4 Critical Thinking: How do you know that the forces on parallel current-carrying wires aren't due to electrostatics? **Hints:** 1. Consider what the charges would be like when the force is attractive. 2. Consider what the forces are if three wires carry currents in the same direction.

3 Close

CONVERGENT QUESTION

The magnetic deflection force depends directly on the velocity of the moving charge. Ask students if they can think of any other forces they've studied that depend on velocity. [air resistance]

CONCEPT REVIEW ANSWERS

2.1 Toward the west in the northern hemisphere; toward the east in the southern.
2.2 To the left side of the screen.
2.3 Not necessarily. If the coil is already in rotation, then rotational inertia will carry it past the point of zero torque. It is the acceleration that is zero, not the velocity.
2.4 Critical Thinking: If the currents are in the same direction, the force is attractive. If it were due to electrostatic forces, the like charges would make the force repulsive. Three wires would all attract each other, which could never happen in electrostatic charges.

Physics and technology

MAGLEV TRAINS

Trains that travel by means of magnets are known as maglev. Maglev is short for magnetic levitation. Maglevs are trains that "fly".

Germany is probably closer to building a high-speed intercity maglev system than its competitor, Japan. The German system utilizes conventional electromagnets that are attracted upwards to a metal rail lifting the maglev cars about one centimeter above the guideways.

The Japanese system uses pairs of electromagnets made of superconducting wire. The Japanese maglevs utilize the repulsion between like magnetic poles. Superconducting wire for the electromagnets has no resistance to current when it is in liquid helium at near-absolute-zero temperatures. Thus, no electric energy is needed to levitate the train.

· What might be a disadvantage of using superconductive magnets over conventional magnets.

Physics and technology

The superconducting magnets that are currently used must be cooled to near-absolute-zero temperatures. This requires costly liquid helium. Heavy compressors aboard the maglev trains reliquefy the helium after it evaporates.

Niobium-titanium magnet wires are now being used in the magnets, but new higher-temperature superconducting ceramic materials will probably be used in the future. Researchers continue to improve these new superconducting materials. Already, plans are underway to replace the costly liquid helium now used with much cheaper liquid nitrogen.

Teacher Resources: Benjamin, Daniel. "Floating Trains: What a Way to Go!" *Time.* August 22, 1988, pages 58–59.
Scott, David and Free, John. "310-mph Flying Trains—in the '90s—the U.S." *Popular Science.* Vol. 234, pages 132–135, 159.

CLOSING CHAPTER 24

Review Summary statements and Key Terms with your students.

ASSESSMENT

Vocabulary Review Master, Teacher Resource Package. Use this master to check students' understanding of Key Terms.

Evaluation Masters. Use Parts A and B of the Chapter Evaluation Masters from the Teacher Resource Package to test qualitative chapter objectives. Use Parts C and D to test quantitative chapter objectives.

Answers To
REVIEWING CONCEPTS

1. Like poles repel one another; opposite poles attract.
2. A temporary magnet is a magnet only while under the influence of another magnet. A permanent magnet needs no outside influence.
3. iron, cobalt, and nickel
4. Refer to Figure 24–5. Be sure students show field lines as closed loops.
5.

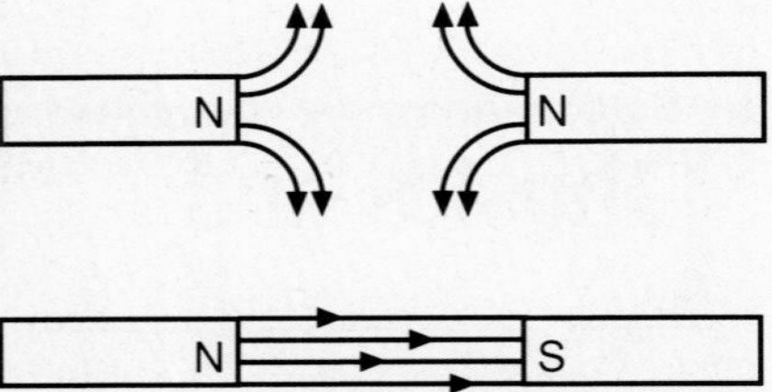

6. No. New poles would form on each of the broken ends.
7. Grasp wire with the right hand keeping thumb pointing in the direction of the conventional current flow. Fingers will encircle wire and point in the direction of the field.
8. The magnetic field lines are concentrated inside the loop.
9. Grasp the coil with the right hand keeping fingers encircling the coil in the direction of the conventional current flow through the loops. Thumb of right hand will point at the north-seeking pole of the electromagnet.
10. The electrons are not all oriented and moving in the same direction, and their magnetic fields, therefore, have a random direction.
11. The domains are jostled out of alignment.

CHAPTER 24 REVIEW

SUMMARY

24.1 Magnets: Permanent and Temporary

- The like magnetic poles of dipoles repel; the unlike magnetic poles attract.
- Magnetic fields run out from the north pole of a magnet and enter its south pole.
- Magnetic field lines always form closed loops.
- A magnetic field exists around any wire that carries current.
- A coil of wire through which a current flows also has a magnetic field. The field about the coil is like the field about a permanent magnet.

24.2 Forces Caused by Magnetic Fields

- When a current-carrying wire is placed in a magnetic field, there is a force on the wire that is perpendicular to the field and also to the wire. Galvanometers are based on this principle.
- The strength of a magnetic field is measured in teslas (newton per ampere-meter).
- An electric motor consists of a coil of wire placed in a magnetic field. When current flows in the coil, the coil rotates due to the force on the wire in the magnetic field.
- The force a magnetic field exerts on a charged particle depends on the velocity and charge of the particle and the strength of the field and is in a direction perpendicular to both.

KEY TERMS

magnetic field	domain
magnetic flux	third right-hand rule
first right-hand rule	magnetic induction
electromagnet	galvanometer
second right-hand rule	

REVIEWING CONCEPTS

1. State the rule for magnetic attraction and repulsion.
2. Describe how a temporary magnet differs from a permanent magnet.
3. Name the three most important common magnetic elements.
4. Draw a small bar magnet and show the magnetic field lines as they appear around the magnet. Use arrows to show the direction of the field lines.
5. Draw the magnetic field between two like magnetic poles and then between two unlike magnetic poles. Show the directions of the fields.
6. If you broke a magnet in two, would you have isolated north and south poles? Explain.
7. Describe how to use the right-hand rule to determine the direction of a magnetic field around a straight current-carrying wire.
8. If a current-carrying wire is bent into a loop, why is the magnetic field inside the loop stronger than the magnetic field outside?
9. Describe how to use the right-hand rule to determine the polarity of an electromagnet.
10. Each electron in a piece of iron is like a tiny magnet. The iron, however, is not a magnet. Explain.
11. Why will dropping or heating a magnet weaken it?
12. Describe how to use the right-hand rule to determine the direction of force on a current-carrying wire placed in a magnetic field.
13. A strong current is suddenly switched on in a wire. No force acts on the wire, however. Can you conclude that there is no magnetic field at the location of the wire? Explain.
14. Adding a shunt to a galvanometer makes the galvanometer what kind of meter?

APPLYING CONCEPTS

1. A small bar magnet is hidden in a fixed position inside a tennis ball. Describe an experiment you could do to find the location of the N-pole and the S-pole of the magnet.
2. A piece of metal is attracted to one pole of a large magnet. Describe how you could tell whether the metal is a temporary magnet or a permanent magnet.

REVIEW MASTER

Use the Vocabulary Review master for Chapter 24 with this section.

EVALUATION MASTER

Use the Chapter Evaluation master for Chapter 24 with this section.

3. Is the magnetic force Earth exerts on a compass needle less than, equal to, or greater than the force the compass needle exerts on Earth? Explain.
4. Iron, nickel, and cobalt are electrical conductors. So are superconductors. Do they behave the same way in magnetic fields?
5. You are lost in the woods but have a compass with you. Unfortunately, the red paint marking the N-pole has worn off. You do have a flashlight with a battery and a length of wire. How could you identify the N-pole?
6. A magnet can attract a piece of iron that is not a permanent magnet. A charged rubber rod can attract an uncharged insulator. Describe the different microscopic processes that produce these similar phenomena.
7. A bare current-carrying wire runs across a lecture table. Describe at least two ways you could find the direction of the current.
8. In what direction with respect to a magnetic field would you run a wire so that the force on it due to the field is minimized or even made zero?
9. Two wires carry equal currents and run parallel to each other.
   a. If the two currents are in the opposite direction, where will the magnetic field from the two wires be larger than the field from either wire alone?
   b. Where will the magnetic field be exactly twice as large?
   c. If the two currents are in the same direction, where will the magnetic field be exactly zero?
10. How is the range of a voltmeter changed when the resistor is increased?
11. A magnetic field can exert a force on a charged particle. Can it change the particle's kinetic energy? Explain.
12. A beam of protons is moving from the back to the front of a room. It is deflected upward by a magnetic field. What is the direction of the field causing the deflection?
13. As shown by the spacing of the field lines in Figure 24–21, Earth's magnetic field in space is stronger near the poles than over the equator. At what location would the circular paths followed by the charged particles around the magnetic field lines have larger radii? Explain.

PROBLEMS

24.1 Magnets: Permanent and Temporary

1. A wire 1.50 m long carrying a current of 10.0 A is at right angles to a uniform magnetic field. The force acting on the wire is 0.60 N. What is the induction of the magnetic field?
▶ 2. The repulsive force between two ceramic magnets was measured and found to depend on distance, as given in the table below.

Separation, d (mm)	Force, F (N)
10	3.93
12	0.40
14	0.13
16	0.057
18	0.030
20	0.018
22	0.011
24	0.0076
26	0.0053
28	0.0038
30	0.0028

   a. Plot the force as a function of distance.
   b. Does this force follow an inverse square law?
3. A conventional current flows in a wire as shown in Figure 24–28. Copy the wire segment and sketch the magnetic field the current generates.

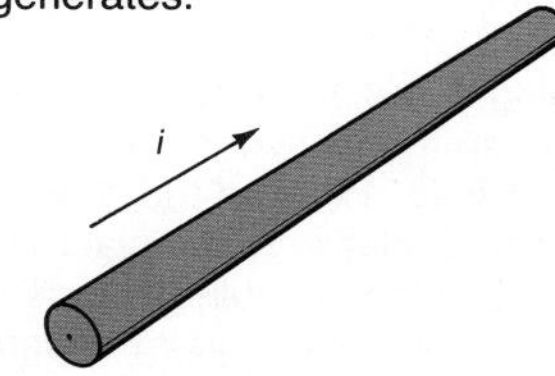

FIGURE 24–28. Use with Problem 3.

4. The current is coming straight out of the page in Figure 24–29. Copy the figure and sketch the magnetic field the current generates.

FIGURE 24–29. Use with Problem 4.

12. Point fingers of right hand in direction of magnetic field. Point thumb in direction of conventional current flow in wire. Palm of hand then faces in direction of force on wire.
13. No. If a field is parallel to the wire, no force would result.
14. an ammeter

Answers To
APPLYING CONCEPTS

1. Use a compass. The N-pole of the compass needle is attracted toward the S-pole and vice-versa.
2. Move it to the other pole. If the same end is attracted, it is a temporary magnet; if the other end is attracted, it is a permanent magnet.
3. The forces are equal by Newton's third law.
4. No. Superconductors expel all magnetic fields from them. They are not attracted as are ferro-magnetic elements.
5. Wrap the wire around the compass. Briefly connect the wire to the battery. Use the right-hand rule to identify the direction of the field produced by the current. The end of the compass needle that points in the direction of the field is the N-pole.
6. The magnet causes the domains in the iron to point in the same direction. The charged rod separates the positive and negative charges in the insulator.
7. Use a compass to find the direction of the magnetic field. Bring up a strong magnet and find the direction of the force on the wire, using the right-hand rule.
8. Run the wire parallel to the magnetic field.
9. a. The magnetic field will be larger anywhere between the two wires.

Answers To
APPLYING CONCEPTS (cont)

b. The magnetic field will be twice as large along a plane that is equal in distance from each wire. **c.** The magnetic field will be zero along a plane that is equal in distance from each wire.

10. The range of the voltmeter increases.

11. No. The force is always perpendicular to the velocity. No work is done. The energy is not changed.

12. The velocity is forward, the force is upward, and therefore *B* is to the left.

13. The radii of the paths would be larger over the equator. The field is weaker there, so the force is smaller. The velocity is the same, so, given $a = v^2/r$, the radius must be larger.

Answers To
PROBLEMS

Complete solutions for all Chapter Review Problems can be found in the Problems and Solutions Manual accompanying this text.

1. 0.040 T
2. **a.** Refer to Problems and Solutions Manual.
   b. no
3. Refer to Problems and Solutions Manual.
4. Refer to Problems and Solutions Manual.
5. Refer to Problems and Solutions Manual.
   a. into page
   b. out of page
6. Refer to Problems and Solutions Manual. Down. down.
7. The magnetic field is perpendicular to the plane of the coil. The right-hand rule would be used to find the direction of the field produced by the coil. The field in the room is in the same direction.
8. 0.10 T
9. 2.4 N
10. 0.45 N
11. 0.83 N
12. 7.2 mA
13. 3.0 kA
14. 0.60 m
15. **a.** 0.011 N/m
    b. north
    c. no
16. 5.7 N
17. **a.** 3.2 N **b.** 2.3 N **c.** 0

5. Figure 24–30 shows the end view of an electromagnet with the current as shown.
   a. What is the direction of the magnetic field inside the loop?
   b. What is the direction of the magnetic field outside the loop?

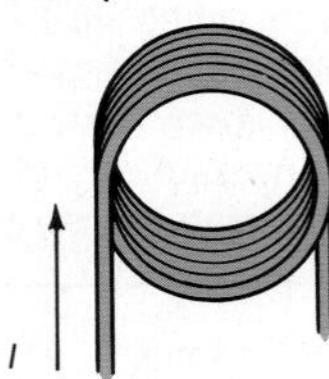

FIGURE 24–30. Use with Problem 5.

24.2 Forces Caused by Magnetic Fields

6. A current-carrying wire is placed between the poles of a magnet as shown in Figure 24–31. What is the direction of the force on the wire?

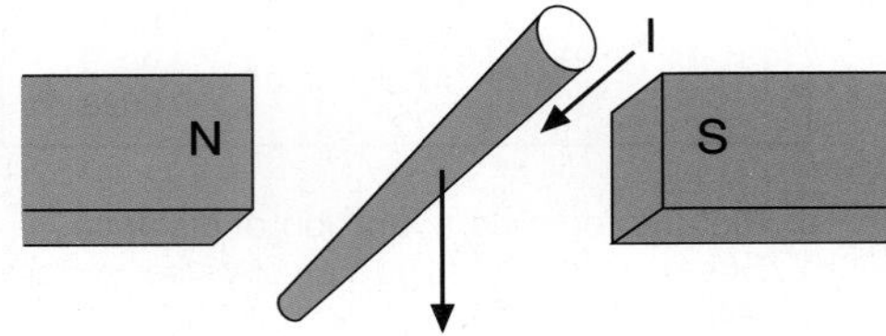

FIGURE 24–31. Use with Problem 6.

▶ **7.** A room contains a strong, uniform magnetic field. A loop of fine wire in the room has current flowing through it. You rotate the loop until there is no tendency for it to rotate as a result of the field. What is the direction of the magnetic field relative to the plane of the coil?

8. A wire 0.50 m long carrying a current of 8.0 A is at right angles to a uniform magnetic field. The force on the wire is 0.40 N. What is the strength of the magnetic field?

9. The current through a wire 0.80 m long is 5.0 A. The wire is perpendicular to a 0.60-T magnetic field. What is the magnitude of the force on the wire?

10. A wire 25 cm long is at right angles to a 0.30-T uniform magnetic field. The current through the wire is 6.0 A. What is the magnitude of the force on the wire?

11. A wire 35 cm long is parallel to a 0.53-T uniform magnetic field. The current through the wire is 4.5 A. What force acts on the wire?

12. A wire 625 m long is in a 0.40-T magnetic field. A 1.8-N force acts on the wire. What current is in the wire?

13. The force on an 0.80-m wire that is perpendicular to Earth's magnetic field is 0.12 N. What current flows through the wire?

14. The force acting on a wire at right angles to a 0.80-T magnetic field is 3.6 N. The current flowing through the wire is 7.5 A. How long is the wire?

15. A power line carries a 225-A current from east to west parallel to the surface of Earth.
   a. What is the magnitude of the force acting on each meter of the wire due to Earth's magnetic field?
   b. What is the direction of the force?
   c. In your judgment, would this force be important in designing towers to hold these power lines?

▶ **16.** The magnetic field in a loudspeaker is 0.15 T. The wire consists of 250 turns wound on a 2.5-cm diameter cylindrical form. The resistance of the wire is 8.0 Ω. Find the force exerted on the wire when 15 V is placed across the wire.

▶ **17.** A wire carrying 15 A of current has a length of 25 cm between a magnetic field of 0.85 T. The force on a current carrying wire in a uniform magnetic field can be found by $F = BIL \sin \theta$. Find the force on the wire if it makes an angle with the magnetic field lines of
   a. 90°. **b.** 45°. **c.** 0°.

18. A galvanometer deflects full scale for a 50.0-μA current.
   a. What must be the total resistance of the series resistor and the galvanometer to make a voltmeter with 10.0-V full-scale deflection?
   b. If the galvanometer has a resistance of 1.0 kΩ, what should be the resistance of the series (multiplier) resistor?

19. The galvanometer in the previous problem is used to make an ammeter that deflects full scale for 10 mA.
   a. What is the potential difference across the galvanometer (1.0 kΩ resistance) when 50 μA flows through it?
   b. What is the equivalent resistance of parallel resistors that have the potential difference calculated in part **a** for a circuit with a total current of 10 mA?

c. What resistor should be placed in parallel with the galvanometer to make the resistance calculated in part **b?**

20. A beam of electrons moves at right angles to a 6.0×10^{-2}-T magnetic field. The electrons have a velocity of 2.5×10^{6} m/s. What is the magnitude of the force on each electron?

21. A beta particle (high-speed electron) is traveling at right angles to a 0.60-T magnetic field. It has a speed of 2.5×10^{7} m/s. What size force acts on the particle?

22. The mass of an electron is 9.11×10^{-31} kg. What is the acceleration of the beta particle described in the previous problem?

23. A magnetic field of 16 T acts in a direction due west. An electron is traveling due south at 8.1×10^{5} m/s. What is the magnitude and direction of the force acting on the electron?

▶ **24.** In a nuclear research laboratory, a proton moves in a particle accelerator through a magnetic field of intensity 0.10 T at a speed of 3.0×10^{7} m/s.

a. If the proton is moving perpendicular to the field, what force acts on it?

b. If the proton continues to move in a direction that is consistently perpendicular to the field, what is the radius of curvature of its path? (mass of proton = 1.67×10^{-27} kg)

▶ **25.** An electron is accelerated from rest through a potential difference of 20 000 V, which exists between the plates $\mathbf{P_1}$ and $\mathbf{P_2}$, Figure 24–32. The electron then passes through a small opening into a magnetic field of uniform field strength *B*. As indicated, the magnetic field is directed into the page.

a. State the direction of the electric field between the plates as either $\mathbf{P_1}$ to $\mathbf{P_2}$ or $\mathbf{P_2}$ to $\mathbf{P_1}$.

b. In terms of the information given, calculate the electron's speed at plate $\mathbf{P_2}$.

c. Describe the motion of the electron through the magnetic field.

26. A muon (a particle with the same charge as an electron) is traveling at 4.21×10^{7} m/s at right angles to a magnetic field. The muon experiences a force of 5.00×10^{-12} N. How strong is the field?

27. The mass of a muon is 1.88×10^{-28} kg. What acceleration does the muon described in the previous problem experience?

28. A singly-ionized particle experiences a force of 4.1×10^{-13} N when it travels at right angles through a 0.61-T magnetic field. What is the velocity of the particle?

▶ **29.** A force of 5.78×10^{-16} N acts on an unknown particle traveling at a 90° angle through a magnetic field. If the velocity of the particle is 5.65×10^{4} m/s and the field is 3.20×10^{-2} T, how many elementary charges does the particle carry?

USING LAB SKILLS

1. You found that the steel balls repel each other when touching the disk magnet. Would you expect the same results with a horseshoe magnet? a bar magnet? Why? Try it. Describe your results.

THINKING PHYSIC-LY

A current is sent through a vertical spring as shown in Figure 24–33. The end of the spring is in a cup filled with mercury. What will happen? Why?

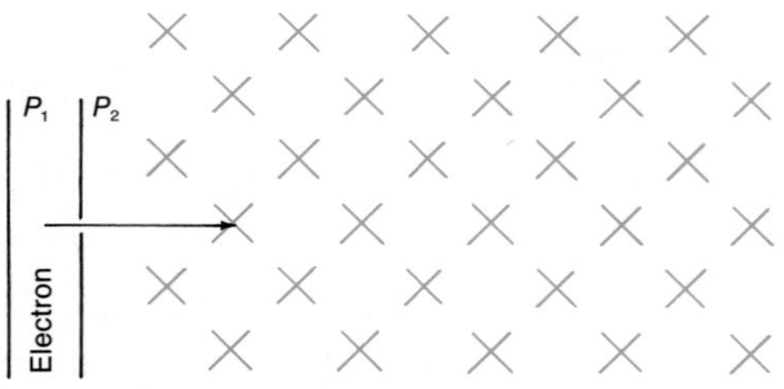

P_1 P_2 Electron

FIGURE 24–32.

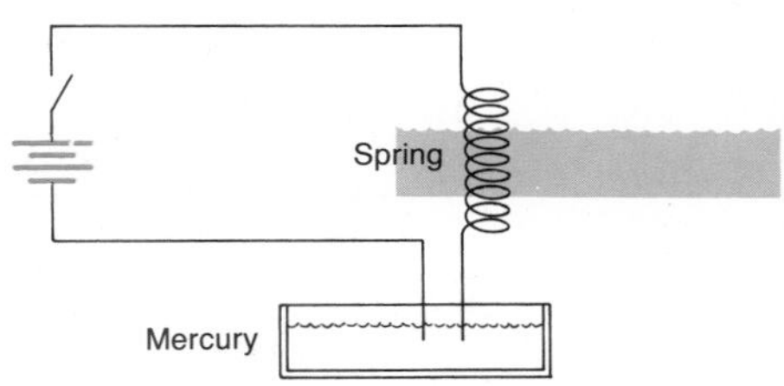

FIGURE 24–33. Use with Thinking Physic-ly.

18. **a.** 200 kΩ
b. 199 kΩ

19. **a.** 5.0×10^{-2} V
b. 5.0 Ω
c. 5.0 Ω

20. 2.4×10^{-14} N

21. 2.4×10^{-12} N

22. 2.6×10^{18} m/s^2

23. 2.1×10^{-12} N, upward

24. **a.** 4.8×10^{-13} N
b. 3.1 m

25. **a.** from P_2 to P_1
b. 8.4×10^{7} m/s
c. clockwise

26. 0.742 T

27. 2.66×10^{16} m/s^2

28. 4.2×10^{6} m/s

29. 2 charges

Answer To
USING LAB SKILLS

1. The results should be the same for all types of magnets. The magnetic field lines will flow through the steel balls in a parallel direction, causing the steel balls to become magnetized in the same orientation. The parts of the steel balls touching the magnet will be the same pole, and the parts of the steel balls farthest from the magnet will be the opposite pole.

Answer To
THINKING PHYSIC-LY

When the current passes through the coil, the magnetic field increases and the spring compresses. The wire comes out of the mercury, the circuit opens, the magnetic field decreases, and the spring drops down. The spring will oscillate up and down.

CHAPTER 25 Electromagnetic Induction

PLANNING GUIDE (6 class sessions)

CONTENTS	TEXT FEATURES	TEACHER RESOURCE PACKAGE	OTHER COMPONENTS
25.1 Creating Electric Current From Changing Magnetic Fields, pp. 516–523 (3 Class Sessions) • Faraday's Discovery • Electromotive Force • Electric Generators • Alternating Current Generator	**Physics Lab:** The Pick Up, p. 522 **Pocket Lab:** Making Currents, p. 518 **Pocket Lab:** Motor and Generator, p. 521 **Concept Review,** p. 523	**Study Guide:** Creating Electric Current From Changing Magnetic Fields **Physics Lab Data Sheet:** The Pick Up **Transparency Worksheet:** Right-Hand Rules **Transparency Worksheet:** AC Generator	**Laboratory Manual:** Lab 25.1 Electromagnetic Induction 1 **Transparency 36:** Right-Hand Rules **Transparency 37:** AC Generator
25.2 Effects of Changing Magnetic Fields: Induced *EMF,* pp. 523–528 (3 Class Sessions) • Lenz's Law • Self-Inductance • Transformers	**Physics and Society:** Weak Electromagnetic Fields—A Health Concern? p. 529 **Pocket Lab:** Slow Magnets, p. 524 **Pocket Lab:** Slow Motor, p. 526 **Concept Review,** p. 528	**Study Guide:** Effects of Changing Magnetic Fields: Induced *EMF* **Reteaching Master:** Induced Current **Critical Thinking Master:** The Electric Generator **Enrichment Master:** The Induction Coil	**Laboratory Manual:** Lab 25.2 Electromagnetic Induction 2
Chapter Review, pp. 530–533	Summary Key Terms Reviewing Concepts Applying Concepts Problems Thinking Physic-ly	**Vocabulary Review** **Chapter Test**	**Test Bank**

SUPPLEMENTARY MATERIALS

SOFTWARE	AUDIOVISUAL	BOOKS/MAGAZINES
Magnets and Electromagnetism, Queue, Inc. (Apple II, IBM PC, Macintosh). *Introduction to General Physics, Disk VI: Magnetism,* COMPress/Queue, Inc. (Apple II, IBM PC, Macintosh).	*The Mechanical Universe and Beyond: Electromagnetic Induction* and *Alternating Current,* Films Inc.	Clack, Jhules A. M., and Toepker, Terrence P. "Magnetic Induction Experiment." *The Physics Teacher,* April 1990, p. 236. Delinger, W. G. "Magnetic Field Inside a Hole in a Conductor." *The Physics Teacher,* April 1990, p. 234. Harrich, Lloyd. "AC Made Visible." *The Physics Teacher,* October 1984, p. 448. Zhong, An. "Determine the Magnetic Induction of a Coil with a Hall Element." *The Physics Teacher,* February 1990, p. 123.

PROBLEM CORRELATION

CONCEPTS	CHAPTER REVIEW			PROBLEMS APPENDIX
	Reviewing Concepts	Applying Concepts	Problems	
25.1 Creating Electric Current From Changing Magnetic Fields				
Faraday's Discovery	1,2	1,8,10,15		1
Electromotive Force	3	2,3,14	1,2,3,4,**5,6,7,**8, 9	2,3,4,5,6,**7**
Electric Generators	4,5,6			
Alternating Current Generator	7,8,9	5,6,7	10,11,12,**13**	8,9,10,11,**12**
25.2 Effects of Changing Magnetic Fields: Induced *EMF*				
Lenz's Law	10,11,12	4,9,16,17		**13**
Self–Inductance	13,14	18		
Transformers	15	11,12,13	14,15,16,17,18,19, **20,21,22**	14,**15**

ACTIVITY AND DEMONSTRATION MATERIALS

PHYSICS LAB	POCKET LAB	DEMONSTRATIONS
Page 522 telephone pickup coil (Radio Shack #44–533 or similar) mini audio amplifier (Radio Shack #277–1008 or similar) strong permanent magnet iron or air core solenoid supply 9–V battery low-voltage AC power supply battery-powered car 1 meter of string masking tape	Pages 518, 521, 524, 526 galvanometer (or microammeter) 1-m length of wire #26 or #28 2 neodymium or strong horseshoe magnets coil of wire solenoid Genecon (or efficient DC motor) miniature lamp and socket ammeter 1-m length of copper tubing (1/2 inch) stopwatch 9-mm steel marble variable DC power supply, motor voltmeter	Pages 517, 519, 524, 525 coil of heavy-gauge copper wire AG1B flashbulb strong horseshoe magnet 2 galvanometers 2 aluminum rings strong cylindrical magnet large AC induction coil 1.5-V flashlight bulb

EXTENSION PROJECTS

LIBRARY RESEARCH

1. Electromagnetic Induction in the Subway
Do some research into the braking systems on subway cars. How do they make use of eddy currents and electromagnetic induction?

DISPLAY MODEL

2. Electromagnet
Build an electromagnet using insulated wire, a core, and a source of potential difference. Demonstrate to the class how it works.

STUDENT READINGS

Parker, E. N. "Magnetic Fields in the COSMOS." *Scientific American,* August 1983.

Pool, R. "Electromagnetic Fields: The Biological Evidence." *Science,* September 21, 1990.

Pool, R. "A New Standard Volt." *Science,* April 29, 1988.

Raloff, Janet. "EPA Suspects ELF Fields Can Cause Cancer." *Science News,* June 30, 1990.

Slesin, Louis. "Power Lines and Cancer: The Evidence Grows." *Technology Review,* October 1987.

Chapter 25

Electromagnetic Induction

CHAPTER OVERVIEW

Theme Development: The conservation theme is reintroduced in Lenz's law, an example of energy conservation applied to electricity. In generating alternating current, output current and voltage change cyclically.

MISCONCEPTIONS

Students may need help conceptualizing how a wire cutting across magnetic field lines causes an induced voltage. To many students a transformer is a magic device that puts out more energy than is put into it.

KEY TERMS

electric generator
electromagnetic induction
electromotive force
Lenz's law
mutual inductance
primary coil
secondary coil
self-inductance
step-down transformer
step-up transformer
transformer

Laboratory Options

STUDENT EDITION

Physics Lab	
The Pick Up	522
Pocket Labs	
Making Currents	518
Motor and Generator	521
Slow Magnets	524
Slow Motor	526

TEACHER EDITION

Activities	
Demonstration	517, 519, 524, 525
Cooperative Learning	520, 526

LABORATORY MANUAL

Electromagnetic Induction 1	Lab 25.1
Electromagnetic Induction 2	Lab 25.2

CHAPTER 25 Electromagnetic Induction

Introducing The Chapter

Go With the Flow

Using The Photo: If at all possible, you should set up this jumping ring demonstration. It never fails to amuse and amaze students. Some teachers practice until they can "make a basket" with the jumping ring. You might also want to experiment with rings of different materials. Their behavior will vary because of their different resistances and masses. For an explanation of the chapter opener question, refer students to page 525.

Concept Check

Make sure students have a clear understanding of the concepts taught in Chapters 22 and 24 that are listed in the Concept Check. Students with a good grasp of potential difference, electron pumps, current resistance, the right-hand rules, and electric motors will find it easier to master the principles of electromagnetic induction discussed in this chapter.

Go With the Flow

Aluminum is classified as a non-magnetic substance. Two aluminum rings, one with a slit and one a continuous ring, are placed over a magnetic field generator that is producing a constantly-changing magnetic field. Why does one ring float but the other one does not?

Chapter Outline

25.1 CREATING ELECTRIC CURRENT FROM CHANGING MAGNETIC FIELDS
- Faraday's Discovery
- Electromotive Force
- Electric Generators
- Alternating Current Generator

25.2 EFFECTS OF CHANGING MAGNETIC FIELDS: INDUCED *EMF*
- Lenz's Law
- Self-Inductance
- Transformers

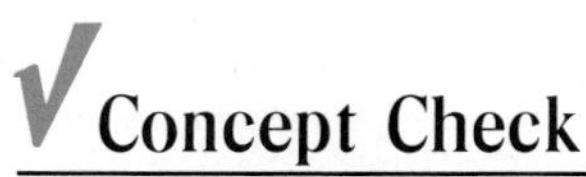

Concept Check

The following terms or concepts from earlier chapters are important for a good understanding of this chapter. If you are not familiar with them, you should review them before studying this chapter.
- potential difference, electron pump, current, resistance, Chapter 22
- right-hand rules, electric motor, Chapter 24

Levitation? There is no superconductor or permanent magnet in this photograph. The ring is made of aluminum, a non-magnetic conductor. The coil of wire around the central rod produces a continually changing magnetic field. You may never have seen such a floating ring, but the physical principle that explains why it is levitated also explains how the modern electrical distribution system works.

Assessment Options

Portfolio Assessment
Extension 1, TWE, p. 514b
Enrichment, TWE, p. 520
Portfolio Assessment, TWE, p. 528
Physics and Society, Developing a Viewpoint, p. 529

Performance Assessment
Extension 2, TWE, p. 514b
Pocket Labs, pp. 518, 521, 524, 526
Physics Lab, p. 522
Using Lab Skills, p. 533

Content Assessment
Self Assessment, Practice Problems, pp. 518, 521, 527
Critical Thinking, TWE, p. 520
Assessment, Critical Thinking, TWE, p. 522
Cooperative Learning, TWE, p. 526
Concept Reviews, pp. 523, 528
Chapter Review, pp. 530–533
Supplemental Problems, p. 706

Group Assessment
Activities for group assessment occur with Cooperative Learning and lab activities.

25.1 CREATING ELECTRIC CURRENT FROM CHANGING MAGNETIC FIELDS

Preparation

OBJECTIVES

The objectives are listed on the student page. Remind students to preview these objectives as a study guide to this major section.

OVERVIEW

The basic idea introduced is current production by moving wires in a magnetic field. An understanding of alternating current generators involves the concepts of effective and maximum currents.

BRIDGING

The material in this section relates to the fundamental concepts of electricity and magnetism, including current, magnetic fields, potential difference, circuits, the third right-hand rule, brushes, armature, and power. In addition, the concepts of velocity, relative motion, and sound waves are basic to the material in this section.

1 Focus

DISCREPANT EVENT

A simple demonstration can set the stage for this section. Take a piece of wire of almost any kind that is reasonably flexible and about a meter or two in length. Connect it to the terminals of a sensitive galvanometer. Quickly move the wire across the poles of a strong magnet. The galvanometer should register a small current. Moving the wire even faster should produce a bigger current. Make part of the wire into a coil of four or five loops that can be easily moved through the magnetic field. You should see a much increased current. Make sure students see that if the wire stays motionless in the magnetic field, no current is produced. Urge students to appreciate the beauty and simplicity of this phenomenon. Students should also have the opportunity to do this for themselves.

Objectives

- explain how a changing magnetic field produces an electric current.
- define *EMF*; show an ability to calculate *EMF* of wires moving in a magnetic field and know the limitations of the equation.
- explain how an electric generator works and how it differs from a motor.
- explain the difference between peak and effective voltage and current; use both in solving problems.

25.1 CREATING ELECTRIC CURRENT FROM CHANGING MAGNETIC FIELDS

In 1822, Michael Faraday wrote a goal in his notebook: "Convert Magnetism into Electricity." After nearly ten years of unsuccessful experiments, he was able to show that a changing magnetic field could produce electric current. In the same year, Joseph Henry, an American high school teacher, made the same discovery.

Faraday's Discovery

To induce current, there must be relative motion of a wire and the magnetic field.

Oersted had discovered that an electric current produces a magnetic field. Faraday tried all combinations of field and wire without success until he found he could induce current by *moving* the wire in a magnetic field. Figure 25–1 shows one of Faraday's experiments. A wire loop that is part of a closed circuit is placed in a magnetic field. If the wire moves up through the field, the current moves in one direction. When the wire moves down through the field, the current moves in the opposite direction. If the wire is held stationary or is moved parallel to the field, no current flows. An electric current is generated in a wire only when the wire cuts magnetic field lines.

To generate current, either the conductor can move through a magnetic field, or the magnetic field can move past a conductor. It is the relative motion between the wire and the magnetic field that produces the current. The process of generating a current through a circuit in this way is called **electromagnetic induction**.

In what direction does the current move? To find the force on the charges in the wire, use the third right-hand rule described in Chapter 24. Hold your right hand so that your thumb points in the direction in which the wire is moving and your fingers point in the direction of the magnetic field. The palm of your hand will point in the direction of the conventional (positive) current flow, Figure 25–2.

F.Y.I.

Michael Faraday left school at age 14 to become an apprentice to a bookbinder. He read most of the books in the shop. Joseph Henry left school at age 13 to work for a watch maker. Later in life, Faraday became director of the Royal Institution in London, founded by the American Benjamin Thomson (Count Rumford). Henry became the director of the Smithsonian Institution in Washington DC, founded by the Englishman James Smithson.

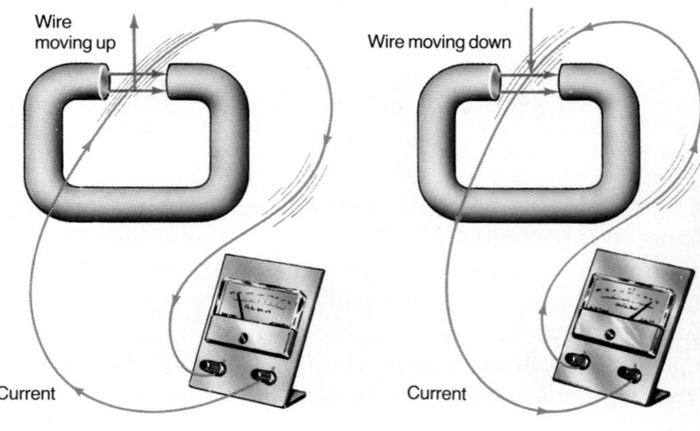

FIGURE 25–1. When a wire is moved in a magnetic field, an electric current flows in the wire, but only while the wire is moving. The direction of the current flow depends on the direction the wire is moving through the field. The arrows indicate the direction of conventional current flow.

LABORATORY MANUAL

Use Lab 25.1 with this section.

TRANSPARENCY

Use Transparency 36 with this section.

STUDY GUIDE MASTER

Use the Study Guide master for section 25.1.

TRANSPARENCY

Use Transparency 37 with this section.

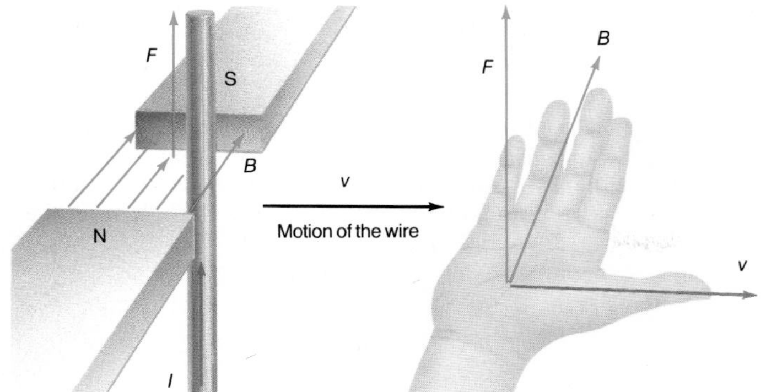

FIGURE 25–2. The right-hand rule can be used to find the direction of the forces on the charges in a conductor that is moving in a magnetic field.

Electromotive Force

When we studied electric circuits, we learned that a charge pump is needed to produce a continuous current flow. The potential increase, or voltage, given to the charges by the pump is called the **electromotive force**, or *EMF*. *Electromotive force, however, is not a force; it is a potential increase and is measured in volts.* Thus the term *EMF* is misleading. Like many other historical terms still in use, it originated before electricity was well understood.

Electromotive force is measured volts.

What creates the increase in potential that can cause an induced current to flow? When a wire is moved through a magnetic field, a force acts on the charges and they move in the direction of the force. Work is done on the charges. Their electrical potential energy, and thus their potential, is increased. The increase in potential is called the induced *EMF*. The *EMF*, measured in volts, depends on the magnetic field strength, *B*, the length of the wire in the magnetic field, *L*, and the velocity of the wire in the field, *v*. If *B*, *v*, and the direction of the length of the wire are mutually perpendicular,

The *EMF* depends on magnetic field strength, the length of the wire, and its velocity perpendicular to the field.

$$EMF = BLv.$$

If the moving wire is part of a closed circuit, the *EMF* will cause a current to flow in the circuit in the direction of the *EMF*.

If a wire moves through a magnetic field at an angle to the field, only the component of the wire's velocity that is perpendicular to the direction of the field generates *EMF*.

A microphone is a simple application that depends on an induced *EMF*. The "dynamic" microphone is similar in construction to a loudspeaker. The microphone in Figure 25–3 has a diaphragm attached to a coil of wire that is free to move in a magnetic field. Sound waves vibrate the diaphragm, which moves the coil in the magnetic field. The motion of the coil, in turn, induces an *EMF* across the ends of the coil. The voltage generated is small, typically 10^{-3} V, but it can be increased, or amplified, by electronic devices.

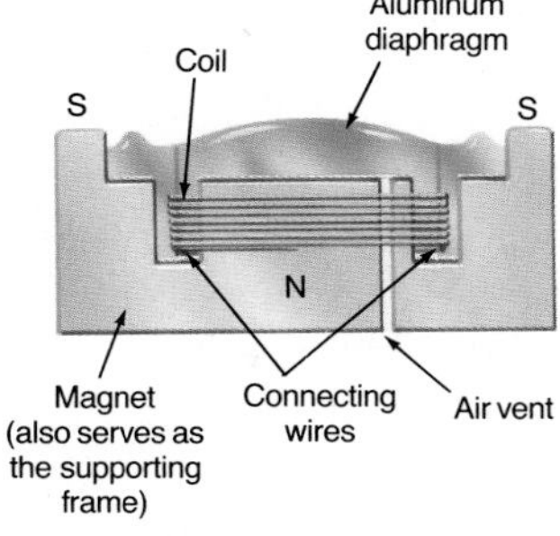

FIGURE 25–3. Schematic of a moving coil microphone. The aluminum diaphragm is connected to a coil in a magnetic field. When sound waves vibrate the diaphragm, the coil moves in the magnetic field, generating a current proportional to the sound wave.

2 Teach

CONCEPT DEVELOPMENT

- Emphasize the importance of relative motion. Moving either the magnetic field or the wire (or both) will produce an effect.

Laboratory Manual. Give students additional experience with electromagnetic induction by doing Lab 25.1 from the Laboratory Manual.

Transparency Package. Use Transparency 36 to review the right-hand rules.

- Often there is confusion between an induced *EMF* and an induced current. If one produces an induced *EMF*, an induced current will flow only when the circuit is complete. They are different ways of talking about the same induction effect.

Demonstration: Make a coil of heavy-gauge copper wire about 12 cm in diameter with about 60 loops of wire. Attach the ends of the wire to a flashbulb (AG1B flashbulbs work well). Now slowly put the bottom half of the coil through the poles of a very strong horseshoe magnet. Pull the coil out rapidly, and the bulb will flash. This demonstration shows the generation of an *EMF* by movement of a wire in a magnetic field.

Study Guide Master. To reinforce the concepts in this section, have the students complete the Study Guide Master for Section 25.1 from the Teacher Resource Package.

TEACHER F.Y.I.

Joseph Henry, the co-discoverer of electromagnetic induction, was an American high school teacher in Albany, New York. Insulated wire was not available at the time, so he spent hours winding cloth insulation onto miles of wire for his experiments. Surviving remnants of this wire show that he even used some of his wife's petticoats as insulation!

POCKET LAB

MAKING CURRENTS

Purpose: to investigate the effects of moving magnets near wires and coils.

Materials: galvanometer (or microammeter); 1-m length of wire #26 or #28; neodymium or strong horseshoe magnet; coil of wire or solenoid.

Outcome: Current is produced when there is relative motion between the magnet and the wire. The current direction depends on the direction of motion. The current is increased when the relative speed is greater, when the number of loops is increased, and when the distance is smaller. The current is much greater when the coil is used.

Answers To

PRACTICE PROBLEMS

Have students refer to Appendix A of the Solutions Appendix for complete solutions to Practice Problems.

1. **a.** 4 V
   b. 0.7 A
2. 0.16 V
3. bottom pole
4. **a.** 60 V
   b. 4.0 A

CONCEPT DEVELOPMENT

Student experiments with generators have been made much less expensive and simpler by the availability of a plastic hand-cranked generator that looks like a water pistol with a crank in the back. One version is called the Genecon. A manual included with the device should provide several activity ideas.

POCKET LAB

MAKING CURRENTS

Hook the ends of a 1 m length of wire to the binding posts of a galvanometer (or microammeter). Make several overlapping loops in the wire. Watch the readings on the wire as you move a pair of neodymium magnets (or a strong horseshoe magnet) near the loops. Record your observations. What can you do to increase the current? Replace the 1 m length of wire with a pre-formed coil and see how much current you can produce. Describe your results.

Example Problem

Induced *EMF*

A straight wire 0.20 m long moves perpendicularly through a magnetic field of magnetic induction 8.0×10^{-2} T at a speed of 7.0 m/s. **a.** What *EMF* is induced in the wire? **b.** The wire is part of a circuit that has a resistance of 0.50 Ω. What current flows in the circuit?

Given: $L = 0.20$ m, $B = 8.0 \times 10^{-2}$ T, $v = 7.0$ m/s, $R = 0.50\ \Omega$

Unknowns: **a.** *EMF* **b.** I

Basic equations: **a.** $EMF = BLv$ **b.** $I = V/R$

Solution: **a.** $EMF = BLv$

$$= (8.0 \times 10^{-2}\ \text{T})(0.20\ \text{m})(7.0\ \text{m/s})$$

$$= (8.0 \times 10^{-2}\ \text{N/A·m})(0.20\ \text{m})(7.0\ \text{m/s})$$

$$EMF = 0.11\left(\frac{\text{N}}{\text{A}\cdot\text{m}}\right)(\text{m})\left(\frac{\text{m}}{\text{s}}\right) = 0.11\ \frac{\text{W}}{\text{A}} = 0.11\ \text{V}$$

b. $$I = \frac{V}{R} = \frac{0.11\ \text{V}}{0.50\ \Omega} = 0.22\ \text{A}$$

Practice Problems

1. A straight wire, 0.5 m long, is moved straight up through a 0.4-T magnetic field pointed in the horizontal direction at a speed of 20 m/s.
   a. What *EMF* is induced in the wire?
   b. The wire is part of a circuit of total resistance of 6.0 Ω. What is the current in the circuit?
2. A straight wire, 25 m long, is mounted on an airplane flying at 125 m/s. The wire moves perpendicularly through Earth's magnetic field ($B = 5.0 \times 10^{-5}$ T). What *EMF* is induced in the wire?
3. A permanent horseshoe magnet is mounted so that the magnetic field lines are vertical. If a student passes a straight wire between the poles and pulls it toward herself, the current flow through the wire is from right to left. Which is the N-pole of the magnet?
4. ▶ A straight wire, 30.0 m long, moves at 2.0 m/s perpendicularly through a 1.0-T magnetic field.
   a. What *EMF* is induced in the wire?
   b. The total resistance of the circuit of which the wire is a part is 15.0 Ω. What is the current?

Electric Generators

The **electric generator**, invented by Michael Faraday, converts mechanical energy to electric energy. An electric generator consists of a number of wire loops placed in a strong magnetic field. The wire is wound around an iron form to increase the strength of the field. The iron and wires are called the armature, similar to that of an electric motor.

TEACHER F.Y.I.

Faraday demonstrated that electric forces could produce motion. His work led him to describe magnetism in terms of a field that expanded from a point of origin and weakened with distance. Imaginary lines could thus be drawn, connecting points of equal intensity. This method of describing forces in terms of fields became fundamental to describing the physical universe!

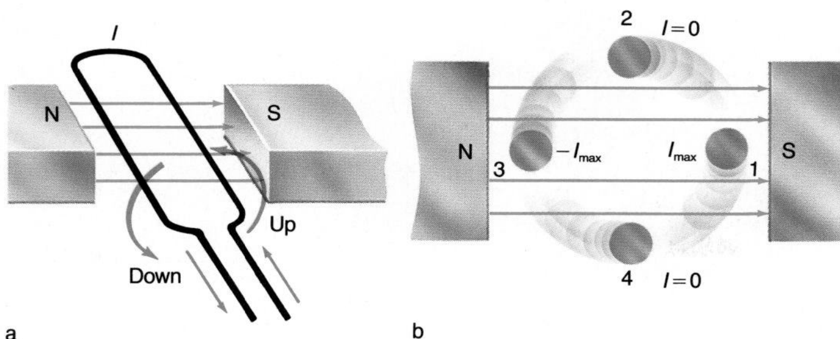

FIGURE 25–4. An electric current is generated in a wire loop as the loop rotates (a). The cross-sectional view (b) shows the position of the loop when maximum current is generated. The numbered positions correspond to the numbered points on the graph in Figure 25–5.

The armature is mounted so that it can rotate freely in the field. As the armature turns, the wire loops cut through the magnetic field lines, inducing an *EMF*. The *EMF,* commonly called the voltage, developed by the generator depends on the magnetic induction, B, the length of wire rotating in the field, L, and v, the speed of the loops perpendicular to the magnetic field. Increasing the number of loops in the armature increases the wire length, L, increasing the induced *EMF*.

When a generator is connected in a closed circuit, current flows that is proportional to the induced *EMF*. Figure 25–4 shows a single loop generator. The direction of the induced current can be found from the third right-hand rule. As the loop rotates, the strength and direction of the current change. The current is greatest when the component of the loop's velocity perpendicular to the field is largest. This occurs when the motion of the loop is perpendicular to the magnetic field—when the loop is in the horizontal position. As the loop rotates from the horizontal to the vertical position, it moves through the magnetic field lines at an ever-increasing angle and current decreases. When the loop is in the vertical position, the wire segments move parallel to the field and the current is zero. As the loop continues to turn, the segment that was moving up begins to move down, reversing the direction of the current in the loop. This change in direction takes place each time the loop turns through 180°. The current changes smoothly from zero to some maximum value and back to zero during each half-turn of the loop. Then it reverses direction. The graph of current versus time is shown in Figure 25–5.

The strength and direction of the induced current change as the armature rotates.

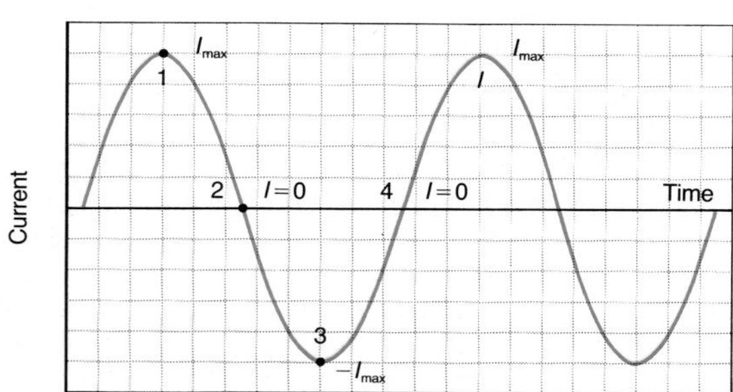

FIGURE 25–5. This graph shows the variation of current with time as the loop in Figure 25–4b rotates. The variation of *EMF* with time is given by a similar graph.

CONCEPT DEVELOPMENT

• Compare the loudspeaker and the microphone. The loudspeaker changes electrical energy into sound energy; the microphone changes sound energy into electrical energy. In fact, some home intercommunication devices use a loudspeaker for both functions. This is a good example of the symmetry of many electromagnetic effects. Simply put, wires moving in a magnetic field produce currents, and currents through wires in magnetic fields produce motion of those wires.

Demonstration: You can also demonstrate the motor-generator with two galvanometers. Connect two identical galvanometers. Pick up one and wiggle it. You are providing mechanical energy and making the coil rotate in the magnetic field. An *EMF* is induced in the coil. The first galvanometer acts as a generator. The second galvanometer converts the electric energy from the first galvanometer into mechanical energy, and the needle moves. The second galvanometer acts as a motor.

• If you have an oscilloscope, connect it to a low-voltage AC power supply to show the waveform of the voltage. Math students should recognize this as a sine curve. If you can turn up the voltage, the amplitude will increase, but the frequency will not. This is another example of how trigonometry applies naturally in many areas of physics.

• Introduce students to a way of visualizing the way the induced *EMF* depends on the angles between the field and velocity. The *EMF* is proportional to the rate at which the wire passes through, or cuts, magnetic field lines. When the wire moves perpendicular to the field, it cuts lines most rapidly. When it moves parallel to the field, no lines are cut.

James West is an African American experimental physicist who is the co-inventor of the foil electret. This device uses a paper-thin piece of plastic, which is coated with metal on one side to convert sound into electrical signals. It is used in hearing aids, small microphones, and portable tape recorders. As a result of this development, all the devices mentioned above can be made much smaller and still be effective. West continues to work at Bell Labs investigating directional sound perception using foil electret microphones.

CONCEPT DEVELOPMENT

Students may ask why 60 Hertz (cycles per second) was the value chosen for the frequency of alternating current. Part of the reason is simply what was mechanically possible at the time. Another reason has to do with human vision: If the alternating frequency is too low, the eye can detect flickering of the light source. Many European countries chose to make this value 50 Hz, which works just as well.

ACTIVITY

Cooperative Learning: Have your class develop a list of the energy sources for the generation of electricity. Most people, including your students, have a limited knowledge of the energy needed to produce electricity. (The list should include coal, oil, natural gas, uranium, falling water (hydroelectricity), wood, wind, and sunlight.)

Critical Thinking: Ask students to explain how the basic construction of motors and generators is similar. How do the two differ?

Enrichment: Michael Faraday was a very clear writer who tended to describe most of his experiments with vivid images and clear diagrams. Have interested students look up some of his original research papers and report on them.

Transparency Package. Use Transparency 37 to help illustrate AC generators.

Guided Practice: Review the Example Problem on page 521 with students, then have them work on the first two Practice Problems that follow.

Independent Practice: Assign the remaining Practice Problems for homework and spend time reviewing them with students during the next class period.

FIGURE 25–6. Alternating current generators transmit current to an external circuit by way of a brush-slip-ring arrangement (a). The alternating current varies with time (b).

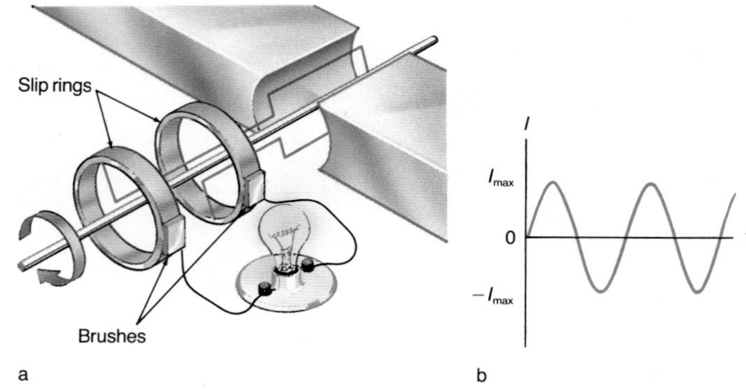

Generators and motors are almost identical in construction but convert energy in opposite directions. A generator converts mechanical energy to electric energy while a motor converts electric energy to mechanical energy. In a generator, mechanical energy turns an armature in a magnetic field. The induced voltage causes current to flow. In a motor, a voltage is placed across an armature coil in a magnetic field. The voltage causes current to flow in the coil and the armature turns, producing mechanical energy from electrical energy.

The direction of current produced by generators in electric utility companies alternates from one direction to the other and back 60 times each second.

Alternating Current Generator

An energy source turns the armature of a generator in a magnetic field at a fixed number of revolutions per second. In the United States, electric utilities use a 60-Hz frequency. The current goes from one direction, to the other, and back to the first, 60 times a second.

Figure 25–6 shows how an alternating current in an armature is transmitted to the rest of the circuit. The brush-slip-ring arrangement permits the armature to turn freely while still allowing the current to pass into the external circuit. As the armature turns, the alternating current varies between some maximum value and zero. If the armature is turning rapidly, the light in the circuit does not appear to dim or brighten because the changes are too fast for the eye to detect.

The power produced by a generator is the product of the current and the voltage. Power is always positive because either I and V are both positive or both negative. Because I and V vary, however, the power associated with an alternating current varies and its average value is less than the power supplied by a direct current with the same I_{max} and V_{max}. In fact, the average AC power is

$$P_{AC} = \tfrac{1}{2}P_{ACmax} = \tfrac{1}{2}P_{DC}.$$

It is common to describe alternating currents and voltages in terms of effective currents and voltages. Recall that $P = I^2R$. Thus, the average AC power can be written in terms of the effective current,

$$P_{AC} = I^2_{eff}R.$$
$$P_{AC} = \tfrac{1}{2}P_{DC}$$
$$I^2_{eff}R = \tfrac{1}{2}(I^2_{max})R$$

Connect to LIFESTYLE

The *EMFs* generated by changing magnetic fields have been used for illegal purposes. The Physics Lab on page 522 illustrates the principles of a pickup coil. This coil can be used to amplify a telephone conversation, but it can also be used to listen to phone conversations of others without their permission. Similarly, antennas can allow others to listen to conversations on portable and cellular phones.

How could you use the principles of this chapter to reduce the ability of pickup coils to listen to conversations? When might they not work? [Reduce the changing magnetic fields leaving the instrument by enclosing them in containers of magnetic materials (steel or nickel). Fiber optic cables can eliminate the possibility of detecting the changing fields in the wires connecting the phones. Shielding would not work for portable or cellular phones, where the changing magnetic fields are required for them to work.]

$$I_{eff} = \sqrt{1/2 I^2_{max}}$$

$$I_{eff} = 0.707 I_{max}$$
$$V_{eff} = 0.707 V_{max}$$

The voltage generally available at wall outlets is described as 120 V, where 120 is the magnitude of the effective voltage, not the maximum voltage.

Example Problem

Effective Voltage and Effective Current

An AC generator develops a maximum voltage of 34 V and delivers a maximum current of 0.17 A to a circuit. **a.** What is the effective voltage of the generator? **b.** What effective current is delivered to the circuit? **c.** What is the resistance of the circuit?

Given: $V_{max} = 34$ V, $I_{max} = 0.17$ A

Unknowns: **a.** V_{eff} **b.** I_{eff} **c.** R

Basic equations: **a.** $V_{eff} = 0.707\ V_{max}$ **b.** $I_{eff} = 0.707\ I_{max}$ **c.** $R = \frac{V_{eff}}{I_{eff}}$

Solution: **a.** $V_{eff} = 0.707(V_{max}) = 0.707(34\text{ V}) = 24\text{ V}$

b. $I_{eff} = 0.707(I_{max}) = 0.707(0.17\text{ A}) = 0.12\text{ A}$

c. $R = \frac{V_{eff}}{I_{eff}} = \frac{24\text{ V}}{0.12\text{ A}} = 200\ \Omega = 2.0 \times 10^2\ \Omega$

Practice Problems

5. A generator in a power plant develops a maximum voltage of 170 V.
   a. What is the effective voltage?
   b. A 60-W light bulb is placed across the generator. A maximum current of 0.70 A flows through the bulb. What effective current flows through the bulb?
   c. What is the resistance of the light bulb when it is working?
6. The effective voltage of a particular AC household outlet is 117 V.
   a. What is the maximum voltage across a lamp connected to the outlet?
   b. The effective current through the lamp is 5.5 A. What is the maximum current in the lamp?
7. An AC generator delivers a peak voltage of 425 V.
   a. What is the effective voltage in a circuit placed across the generator?
   b. The resistance of the circuit is $5.0 \times 10^2\ \Omega$. What is the effective current?
8. ▶ If the average power dissipated by an electric light is 100 W, what is the peak power?

F.Y.I.

In an incandescent bulb, the filament temperature cannot change fast enough to keep up with the changing voltage. However, a fluorescent lamp can. Look at the blades of a fan in the light of a fluorescent lamp. You will see blue-looking blades from the 120-Hz blue flashes of excited mercury vapor. The overall yellowish light is from the phosphors on the inner surface of the tube, which emit a more slowly changing light.

POCKET LAB

MOTOR AND GENERATOR

Make a series circuit with a Genecon (or efficient DC motor), a miniature lamp, and ammeter. Rotate the handle (or motor shaft) to try to light the lamp. Describe your results. Predict what might happen if you connect your Genecon to the Genecon from another lab group and crank yours. Try it. Describe what happens. Can more than two be connected?

CONCEPT DEVELOPMENT

CHECKING FOR UNDERSTANDING

Ask students how an alternating current generator works. In particular, why are there times during a complete cycle when the output of the generator is zero?

RETEACHING

Like many of the early experimenters, many students think that it is only the strength of the magnetic field that determines the amount of electromagnetic induction. However, motion is actually the key factor. Present this concept as an application of conservation of energy; the more kinetic energy put into the generator, the more electrical energy will come out! The principle of energy conservation was not yet established when electromagnetic induction was discovered. In electricity, as elsewhere in physics, you don't get something for nothing—there is no free lunch!

INDEPENDENT PRACTICE/ EXTENSION

Refer to the Assignment Guide on page 523 for additional questions and problems for independent practice.

POCKET LAB

MOTOR AND GENERATOR

Purpose: to observe how motors and generators work.
Materials: Genecon (or efficient DC motor); miniature lamp and socket; ammeter.
Outcome: Turning the handle of the Genecon (or shaft of the motor) will light the lamp. Turning faster makes the lamp brighter. When the Genecons are connected together, one acts as a generator and the other acts as a motor.

Answers To
PRACTICE PROBLEMS

Have students refer to Appendix A of the Solutions Appendix for complete solutions to Practice Problems.

5. **a.** 120 V
   b. 0.49 A
   c. 240 Ω
6. **a.** 165 V
   b. 7.8 A
7. **a.** 300 V
   b. 0.60 A
8. 200 W

PHYSICS LAB

Process Skills: observing, formulating models, communicating, predicting, inferring, questioning, defining operationally.

MISCONCEPTIONS

The concepts of magnetic flux, changing magnetic flux, and induced voltage are abstract and often confused.

Teaching Suggestions: Students need to be patient if they do not hear anything at first. The pickup coil may need to have its position changed.

OBSERVATIONS

1. The amplifier only makes sounds when the coil moves relative to the magnet. The loudness of the sound increases as the distance between the magnet and the coil decreases.
2. The amplifier makes a sound with a steady pitch. The loudness increases near the ends of the coil, but the frequency stays the same.

ANALYSIS

1. The pickup coil responds to changes in the magnetic field. When the coil is stationary, the magnetic flux is not changing.
2. The AC power produces a changing magnetic flux. When the pickup coil is perpendicular to the magnetic field lines, the sound is loud. When the coil is parallel to the field, no flux lines cut the area of the loop and the sound is quiet.
3. Connecting the solenoid coil to a battery would create a constant current in the circuit. This would create a constant magnetic field. No sound would be heard when the pickup coil was stationary.

APPLICATIONS

The amplifier will produce a whining sound when the coil is brought near the motor in the battery-powered car. In some cases, when the car is put in high speed, the sound will be the same. (The motor does not run at a higher speed, but the gear ratio is higher.) In other cases, the motor speed will increase and the whine will increase in frequency.

PHYSICS LAB: The Pick Up

Purpose

To investigate changing magnetic fields with a telephone pickup coil.

Materials

- telephone pickup coil (Radio Shack #44-533 or similar)
- mini audio amplifier (Radio Shack #277-1008 or similar)
- strong permanent magnet
- iron or air core solenoid coil
- 9-V battery
- low-voltage AC power supply
- battery-powered car
- 1 meter of string
- masking tape

Procedure

1. Put the 9-V battery into the amplifier and plug in the telephone pickup coil.
2. Place the strong permanent magnet on the table. Slowly bring the pickup coil near the magnet.
3. Use the suction cup to stick the pickup coil on the table. Attach the magnet to a string so that it hangs just above the pickup coil.
4. Swing the magnet like a pendulum. Twist the string so that as it untwists it will spin the magnet.
5. Attach the low-voltage AC power supply to the solenoid coil. Turn the power supply to about 2–3 V.
6. Hold the pickup coil near the solenoid coil to find where the sound is loudest. Listen to the amplifier as the pickup coil is rotated.

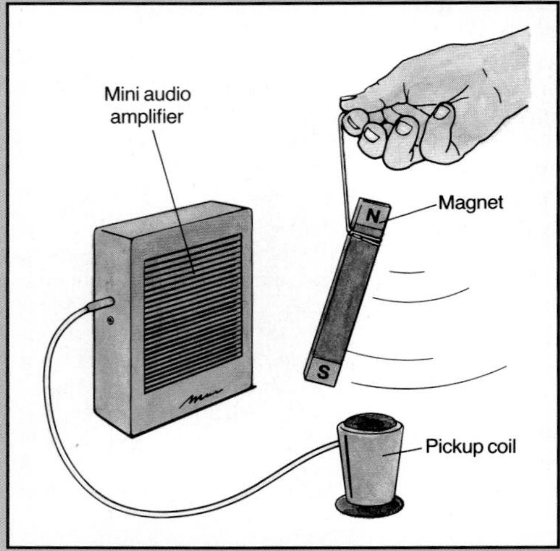

Observations and Data

1. When does the pickup coil and amplifier make a sound in Procedure 2–4?
2. Describe the sound as the pickup coil and amplifier approaches the solenoid coil.

Analysis

1. The pickup coil produces no signal when it is held stationary near the permanent magnet. Explain this.
2. Explain why rotating the pickup coil (Procedure 6) changes the loudness of the signal.
3. Predict the sound that you would hear if the solenoid coil was connected to a battery. Explain your prediction.

Applications

1. Turn the battery-powered car on low speed and bring the pickup coil near to "hear" the changing magnetic fields. Predict how the sound will be different when the battery-powered car is on high speed. Try it. What happened? Why?

ASSESSMENT

Critical Thinking: To further assess students' understanding of pickup coils, ask the following questions.

1. The pickup coil allows you to detect changing magnetic fields. Would you expect to hear anything when you bring the coil near a computer screen or TV? Why? Try it. [Students may be surprised to hear a strong signal when the pickup is brought close to a TV or computer monitor.]

2. As you change the distance from the computer screen, the loudness of the signal changes. What does this suggest about sitting directly in front of a computer monitor for extended periods of time? [The loudness increases as the distance decreases. This suggests that you can reduce your exposure by increasing your distance. The long-term biological effects of exposure to low-frequency electromagnetic waves is still unknown.]

CONCEPT REVIEW

1.1 Could you make a generator by mounting permanent magnets on the rotating shaft and having the coil stationary? Explain.

1.2 A bike generator lights the headlamp. What is the source of the energy for the bulb when the rider travels along a flat road?

1.3 Consider the microphone shown in Figure 25–3. When the diaphragm is pushed in, what is the direction of the current in the coil?

1.4 **Critical Thinking:** A student asks: "Why doesn't AC dissipate any power? The energy going into the lamp when the current is positive is removed when the current is negative. The net is zero." Explain why this argument is wrong.

25.2 EFFECTS OF CHANGING MAGNETIC FIELDS: INDUCED *EMF*

Objectives

- **state Lenz's law; explain back-*EMF* and how it affects the operation of motors and generators.**
- **explain the nature of self-inductance and its effects in circuits.**
- **describe the transformer; explain the connection of turns ratio to voltage ratio; solve transformer problems.**

In a generator, current flows when the armature turns through a magnetic field. We learned in Chapter 24 that when current flows through a wire in a magnetic field, a force is exerted on the wire. Thus, a force is exerted on the wires in the armature. In a sense, then, a generator is, at the same time, a motor.

Lenz's Law

In what direction is the force on the wires of the armature? The direction of the force on the wires opposes the original motion of the wires. That is, the force acts to slow down the rotation of the armature. The direction of the force was first determined in 1834 by H. F. E. Lenz and is called Lenz's law.

According to Lenz's law, the direction of the induced current is such that the current's magnetic effects oppose the changes that produced the current.

Lenz's law states: *The direction of the induced current is such that the magnetic field resulting from the induced current opposes the change in the field that caused the induced current.* Note that it is the *change* in the field and not the field itself that is opposed by the induced magnetic effects.

Figure 25–7 is a simple example of how Lenz's law works. The N-pole of a magnet is moved toward the right end of a coil. To oppose the approach of the N-pole, the right end of the coil must also become

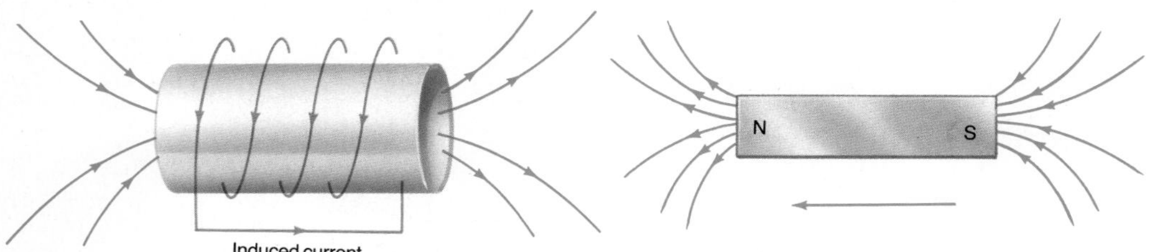

FIGURE 25–7. The magnet approaching the coil causes an induced current to flow. Lenz's law predicts the direction of flow shown.

3 Close

CONVERGENT QUESTION

Have students name the factors determining the size of the *EMF* produced by an alternating-current generator. [the size (area) of the armature, the number of turns of wire on the armature, the strength of the magnetic field, and the rate at which the generator is turned]

CONCEPT REVIEW ANSWERS

1.1 Yes. Only relative motion between coil and magnetic field is important.

1.2 the stored chemical energy of the bike rider

1.3 around the coil from left to right

1.4 Critical Thinking: Power is the rate at which energy is transferred. Power is the product of I and V. When I is positive, so is V, and therefore P is positive. When I is negative, so is V, thus P is again positive. Energy always flows into the lamp.

25.2 EFFECTS OF CHANGING MAGNETIC FIELDS: INDUCED *EMF*

Preparation

OBJECTIVES

The objectives are listed on the student page. Remind students to preview these objectives as a study guide to this major section.

OVERVIEW

This section introduces Lenz's law, which summarizes one way in which the conservation of energy principle applies to electricity. It also extends the application of electromagnetic induction to the study of transformers.

25:1 ASSIGNMENT GUIDE

	PRACTICE	EXTENSION
CHAPTER REVIEW pp. 530–533		
· Reviewing Concepts	1–9	
· Applying Concepts		1–3, 5–8, 10, 14, 15
· Problems*	1–4, 8–12	5–7, 13
APPENDIX B PROBLEMS*		
· Chapter 25, p. 706	1–6, 8–11	7, 12

* Complete solutions to all Chapter Review and Appendix problems appear in the Problems and Solutions Manual.

BRIDGING

Magnetic flux, resistance, and energy are previously introduced concepts that are basic to the material in this section.

LAB WORKSHEET

Use the Lab Worksheet for Chapter 25 with this Physics Lab.

POCKET LAB

SLOW MAGNETS

Purpose: to observe Lenz's law.
Materials: pair of neodymium magnets; 1-m length of copper tubing (1/2 inch); stopwatch; 9-mm steel marble.
Outcome: The magnets will take more than 10 seconds to fall, while the marble takes about 0.5 second. The moving magnets induce a current in the copper. The current in the copper creates a magnetic field that acts opposite to the field of the magnets. Students can test this hypothesis by dropping magnets through a coil hooked to an ammeter.

1 Focus

DISCREPANT EVENT

- Several apparatuses are available for demonstrating Lenz's law. One consists of two aluminum rings and a strong cylindrical magnet. The two aluminum rings are identical, except that one ring is solid and the other has a slot cut through it. Hang the two rings side by side from a ring stand, using two strings for each. Use heavy string that will cover up the slot in the one ring. Thrust the magnet into the solid ring and then pull the magnet back out. As you approach resonance, the ring will start swinging. When you do the same for the ring with the slot, it will not swing. This is Lenz's law in action; the motion of the magnet induces a current in the ring whose magnetic field opposes the cause (thrusting the magnet into the ring). Thus, the magnet and ring repel each other. Since the slotted ring is not a complete circuit, its induced current is zero. Be sure to show students that the magnet does not attract the rings magnetically.
- Lenz's law also can be demonstrated by swinging each ring through the poles of a strong magnet. The solid ring will be damped drastically.

POCKET LAB

SLOW MAGNETS

Lay the 1 m length of copper tube on the lab table. Try to pull the copper with a pair of neodymium magnets. Can you feel any force on the copper? Hold the tube by one end so that it hangs straight down. Drop a small steel marble through the tube. Use a stopwatch to measure the time needed for the marble and then for the pair of magnets to fall through the tube. Catch the magnets in your hand. If they hit the table or floor they will break. Devise a hypothesis that would explain the strange behavior and suggest a method of testing your hypothesis.

an N-pole. In other words, the magnetic field lines must emerge from the right end of the coil. Use the second right-hand rule you learned in Chapter 24. You will see that if Lenz's law is correct, the induced current must flow in a counterclockwise direction. Experiments have shown that this is so. If the magnet is turned so an S-pole approaches the coil, the induced current will be in a clockwise direction.

If a generator produces only a small current, then the opposing force on the armature will be small, and the armature will be easy to turn. If the generator produces a larger current, the force on the larger current will be larger, and the armature will be more difficult to turn. A generator supplying a large current is producing a large amount of electrical energy. The opposing force on the armature means that an armature of mechanical energy must be supplied to the generator to produce the electrical energy, consistent with the law of conservation of energy.

Lenz's law also applies to motors. When a current-carrying wire moves in a magnetic field, an *EMF* is generated. This *EMF*, called the back-*EMF*, is in a direction that opposes the current flow. When a motor is first turned on, a large current flows because of the low resistance of the motor. As the motor begins to turn, the motion of the wires across the magnetic field induces the back-*EMF* that opposes the current flow. Therefore, the net current flowing through the motor is reduced. If a mechanical load is placed on the motor, slowing it down, the back-*EMF* is reduced and more current flows. If the load stops the motor, current flow can be so high that wires overheat.

The heavy current required when a motor is started can cause voltage drops across the resistance of the wires that carry current to the motor. The voltage drop across the wires reduces the voltage across the motor. If a second device, such as a light bulb, is near the motor in a parallel circuit with it, the voltage at the bulb will also drop when the motor is started. The bulb will dim. As the motor picks up speed, the voltage will rise again and the bulb will brighten.

When the current to the motor is interrupted by turning off a switch in the circuit or by pulling the motor's plug from a wall outlet, the sudden change in the magnetic field generates a back-*EMF* that can be large enough to cause a spark across the switch or between the plug and the wall outlet.

A sensitive balance, Figure 25–8, such as the kind used in chemistry laboratories, uses Lenz's law to stop its oscillation when an object is placed on the pan. A piece of metal attached to the balance arm is

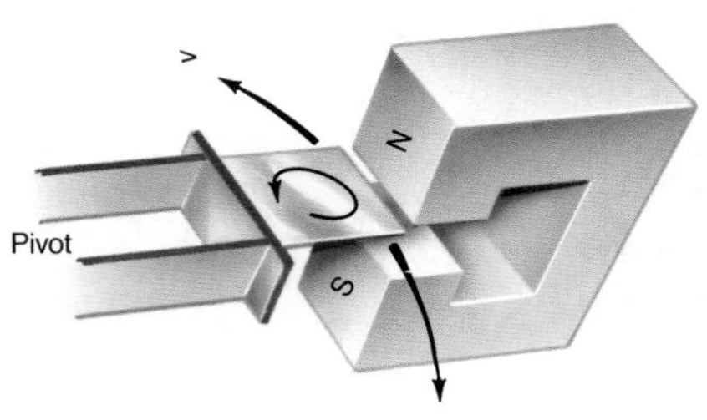

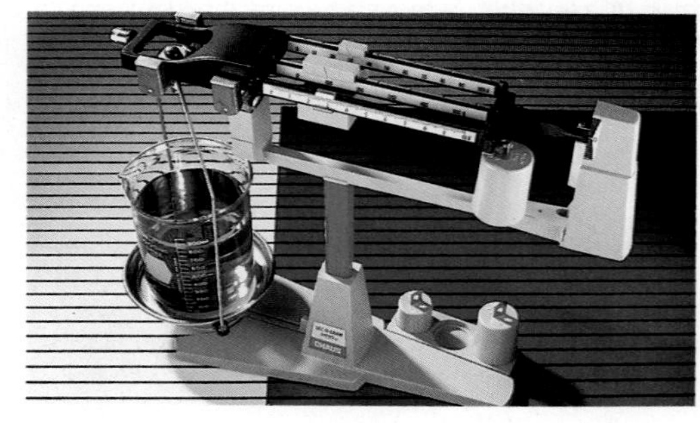

FIGURE 25–8. Sensitive balances use eddy current damping to control oscillations of the balance beam (a). As the metal plate on the end of the beam moves through the magnetic field, a current is generated in the metal. This current, in turn, produces a magnetic field that opposes the motion that caused it, and the motion of the beam is dampened (b).

TEACHER

Motional *EMF* and Lenz's law are both special cases of the more general Faraday's law. You can picture the magnetic flux as the total number of magnetic field lines passing through the surface. Faraday's law states that an *EMF* is generated around the edge of the surface proportional to the rate of change of flux through the surface. In the case of the generator (Figure 25–7), the surface is bounded by the wire loop. As the loop rotates, the number of field lines through it goes from a maximum through zero to a maximum in the opposite direction. The *EMF* is proportional to the rate at which this change occurs. In Figure 25–7, the surface is the opening in the coil. As the magnet approaches, more lines pass through that opening, and *EMF* is generated in the wire loops. The faster the magnet moves, the larger the *EMF* and the induced current.

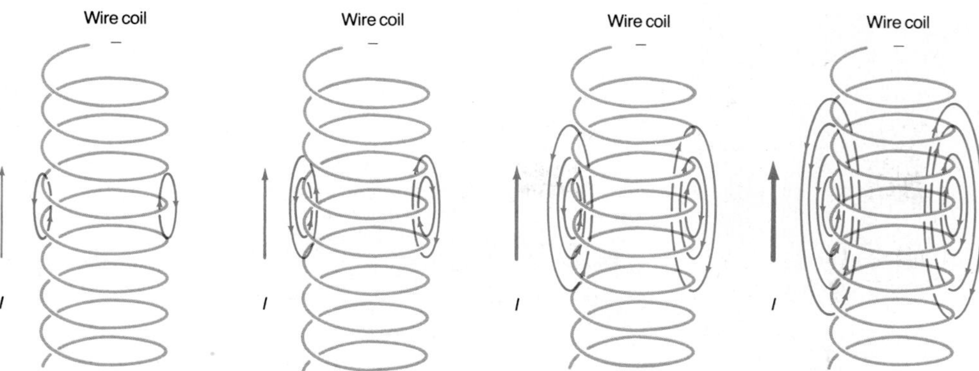

FIGURE 25–9. As the current in the coil increases from left to right, the *EMF* generated by the current also increases.

located between the poles of a horseshoe magnet. When the balance arm swings, the metal moves through the magnetic field. Currents, called eddy-currents, are generated in the metal. These currents produce a magnetic field that acts to oppose the motion that caused the currents. Thus the metal piece is slowed down. The force opposes the motion of the metal in either direction, but does not act if the metal is still. Thus it does not change the mass read by the balance. This effect is called "eddy-current damping."

The magnetic field caused by the induced *EMF* causes the ring in the chapter-opening photo to float. The coil is driven by AC, so the magnetic field is constantly changing, and this change induces an *EMF* in the ring. The resulting ring current produces a magnetic field that opposes the change in the generating field, the ring is pushed away. The lower ring has been sawed through. There is an *EMF* generated, but no current flow, and hence no magnetic field is produced by the ring.

Go With The Flow

Self-Inductance

Back-*EMF* can be explained another way. As Faraday showed, *EMF* is induced whenever a wire cuts magnetic field lines. Consider the coil of wire shown in Figure 25–9. The current through the wire increases as we move from left to right. Current generates a magnetic field, shown by magnetic field lines. As the current and magnetic field increase, new lines are created. As the lines expand, they cut through the coil wires, generating an *EMF* to oppose the current changes. This induction of *EMF* in a wire carrying changing current is called **self-inductance**. The size of the *EMF* is proportional to the rate at which field lines cut through the wires. The faster you try to change the current, the larger the opposing *EMF*, and the slower the current change. If the current reaches a steady value, the magnetic field is constant, and the *EMF* is zero. When the current is decreased, an *EMF* is generated that tends to prevent the reduction in magnetic field and current.

Because of self-inductance, work has to be done to increase the current flowing through the coil. Energy is stored in the magnetic field. This is similar to the way a charged capacitor stores energy in the electric field between its plates.

F.Y.I.

Many modern automobiles have an electronic ignition system that varies the magnetic field. An aluminum armature with 4, 6, or 8 protrusions (depending on the number of spark plugs) spins. Each protrusion in turn passes through the magnetic field, causing it to vary.

2 Teach

CONCEPT DEVELOPMENT

• The term *transformer* often brings smiles to students' faces because they are thinking of the toy that can be changed into many different forms!

• Students are familiar with transformers, whether they know the word or not. Electric trains, slot cars, and other toys use step-down transformers. Part of what the low-voltage AC/DC adapter does is to step down the voltage. Perhaps students could bring in examples.

• Note the limitation here on our treatment of transformers. We assume that there is no power loss, which is not true of any actual transformer.

• The unit for inductance is called the henry in honor of Joseph Henry. In a coil with an inductance of one henry, a change of current of one ampere per second produces a back-*EMF* of one volt.

Study Guide Master. To reinforce the concepts in this section, have the students complete the Study Guide Master for Section 25.2 from the Teacher Resource Package.

Demonstration: There are several demonstrations that can be done with a large AC induction coil. First make two coils with some heavy copper wire, and close the circuit with a 1.5-V flashlight bulb. With the AC current in the induction coil, bring the coil with the bulb over the iron core. As you approach it, the bulb glows and gets brighter the closer you come. The bulb can burn out if you are not careful.

• Note the analogy here between coils and capacitors. One involves energy storage in a magnetic field, and the other energy storage in an electric field.

• If you have an expendable transformer, dissect it to demonstrate the various forms of the transformer.

TEACHER F.Y.I.

The formula $EMF = BLv$ is used only when B and v are at right angles to each other. In Chapter 24, this was discussed for the equations $F = BIL$ and $F = Bqv$. The general form of the equation for EMF is $EMF = BLv \sin \theta$, where θ is the angle between v and B. EMF is a maximum when θ is 90 and minimum when $\theta = 0$, or the wire is moving parallel to the field. This can help students to understand the fluctuation in the magnitude of the current as the coil of wire is turned in the magnetic field.

POCKET LAB

SLOW MOTOR

Purpose: to observe the results of back-*EMF* in a motor.

Materials: variable DC power supply; miniature DC motor; ammeter; voltmeter; wires.

Outcome: The running motor creates a back-*EMF*. When the shaft of the motor is held, the back-*EMF* is reduced and the current increases.

CONCEPT DEVELOPMENT

Critical Thinking: Ask students if a transformer would work if connected to a DC source. [No, because the DC would not produce the changing magnetic field necessary to produce electromagnetic induction in the coils of the transformer.]

Critical Thinking Master, Teacher Resource Package. You may wish to have students complete the Critical Thinking Master, Induced Current, with this section.

ACTIVITY

Cooperative Learning: Challenge student groups to figure out an expression for the efficiency of a transformer involving the power input and the power output. [Efficiency = (Power out ÷ Power in) × 100%, or an equivalent expression using IV for power.]

Guided Practice: Go over the Example Problem on page 527, then have students work on the first two Practice Problems that follow.

INDEPENDENT PRACTICE/ EXTENSION

Refer to the Assignment Guide on page 527 for additional questions and problems for independent practice.

POCKET LAB

SLOW MOTOR

Make a series circuit with a miniature DC motor, an ammeter, and a DC power supply. Hook up a voltmeter in parallel across the motor. Adjust the setting on the power supply so that the motor is running at medium speed. Make a data table to show the readings on the ammeter and voltmeter. Predict what will happen to the readings on the circuit when you hold the shaft and keep it from turning. Try it. Explain the results.

Transformers

Inductance between coils is the basis for the operation of a transformer. A **transformer** is a device used to increase or decrease AC voltages. Transformers are widely used because they change voltages with essentially no loss of energy.

Self-inductance produces an *EMF* when current changes in a single coil. A transformer has two coils, electrically insulated from each other, but wound around the same iron core. One coil is called the **primary coil**. The other coil is called the **secondary coil**. When the primary coil is connected to a source of AC voltage, the changing current creates a varying magnetic field. The varying magnetic field is carried through the core to the secondary coil. In the secondary coil, the varying field induces a varying *EMF*. This effect is called **mutual inductance**.

The *EMF* induced in the secondary coil, called the secondary voltage, is proportional to the primary voltage. The secondary voltage also depends on the ratio of turns on the secondary to turns on the primary.

$$\frac{\text{secondary voltage}}{\text{primary voltage}} = \frac{\text{number of turns on secondary}}{\text{number of turns on primary}}$$

$$\boxed{\frac{V_s}{V_p} = \frac{N_s}{N_p}}$$

$$V_s = \frac{N_s}{N_p} V_p$$

A transformer uses two coupled coils to increase or decrease the voltage in an AC circuit.

If the secondary voltage is larger than the primary voltage, the transformer is called a **step-up transformer**. If the voltage out of the transformer is smaller than the voltage put in, then it is called a **step-down transformer**.

In an ideal transformer, the electric power delivered to the secondary circuit equals the power supplied to the primary. An ideal transformer dissipates no power itself. Since $P = VI$,

$$V_p I_p = V_s I_s.$$

The current that flows in the primary depends on how much current is required by the secondary circuit.

$$\frac{I_s}{I_p} = \frac{V_p}{V_s} = \frac{N_p}{N_s}$$

FIGURE 25–10. For a transformer, the ratio of input voltage to output voltage depends upon the ratio of the number of turns on the primary to the number of turns on the secondary.

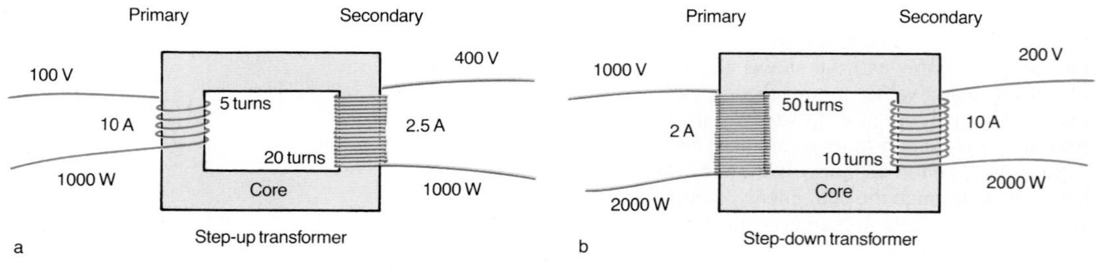

Assessment

Critical Thinking

To further assess your students' understanding of motors, have them do the following activity. Remind them that the power dissipated by the motor is the product of the current through it and the voltage across it. If the power increases, then the motor is doing more work per unit time. Thus, more electrical energy is being converted into another form of energy. Have them use the data from their tables to calculate the power for each of the measurements. Ask where the electrical energy goes. [It goes into thermal energy. They may feel the increase in temperature as the shafts rub against their fingers.]

A step-up transformer increases voltage; the current in the primary circuit is greater than that in the secondary. In a step-down transformer, the current is greater in the secondary circuit than it is in the primary.

FIGURE 25–11. If the input voltage is connected to the coils on the left, with the larger number of turns, the transformer functions as a step-down transformer. If the input voltage is connected at the right, it is a step-up transformer.

Example Problem

Step-Up Transformer

A certain step-up transformer has 2.00×10^2 turns on its primary coil and 3.00×10^3 turns on its secondary coil. **a.** The primary coil is supplied with an alternating current at an effective voltage of 90.0 V. What is the voltage in the secondary circuit? **b.** The current flowing in the secondary circuit is 2.00 A. What current flows in the primary circuit? **c.** What is the power in the primary circuit? in the secondary circuit?

Given: $N_p = 2.00 \times 10^2$, $N_s = 3.00 \times 10^3$, $V_p = 90.0$ V, $I_s = 2.00$ A

Unknowns: **a.** V_s **b.** I_p **c.** P

Basic equations:
a. $\frac{V_s}{V_p} = \frac{N_s}{N_p}$
b. $V_pI_p = V_sI_s$

Solution:

a. $\frac{V_p}{V_s} = \frac{N_p}{N_s}$ or $V_s = \frac{V_pN_s}{N_p}$

$$= \frac{(90.0 \text{ V})(3.00 \times 10^3)}{2.00 \times 10^2} = 1.35 \times 10^3 \text{ V}$$

b. $V_pI_p = V_sI_s$ or $I_p = \frac{V_sI_s}{V_p} = \frac{(1350 \text{ V})(2.00 \text{ A})}{90.0 \text{ V}} = 30.0 \text{ A}$

c. $P_p = V_p\,I_p = (90.0 \text{ V})(30.0 \text{ A}) = 2.70 \times 10^3 \text{ W}$

$P_s = V_s\,I_s = (1350 \text{ V})(2.00 \text{ A}) = 2.70 \times 10^3 \text{ W}$

Practice Problems

In all problems, effective currents and voltages are indicated.

9. A step-down transformer has 7500 turns on its primary and 125 turns on its secondary. The voltage across the primary is 7200 V.
  a. What voltage is across the secondary?
  b. The current in the secondary is 36 A. What current flows in the primary?

10. The secondary of a step-down transformer has 500 turns. The primary has 15 000 turns.
  a. The *EMF* of the primary is 3600 V. What is the *EMF* of the secondary?
  b. The current in the primary is 3.0 A. What current flows in the secondary?

F.Y.I.

The transformers with the largest power rating in the world changes 765 kV to 345 kV. Their power handling capacity is 1 500 000 W.

CHECKING FOR UNDERSTANDING

In this chapter we have assumed that transformers are 100% efficient. Ask students if they can cite some firsthand evidence that this is not the case. [Transformers get hot in use because electrical energy is being changed to thermal energy.]

RETEACHING

Use the idea of concept mapping to correlate and connect the topics in the first section with their applications in the second section.

Reteaching Master, Teacher Resource Package. Use the Reteaching Master, Electromotive Force, for Chapter 25.

Laboratory Manual. Give students additional experience with electromagnetic induction by doing Lab 25.2 from the Laboratory Manual.

Enrichment Master. With this section, use the Enrichment Master, A Transformer, from the Teacher Resource Package.

EXTENSION

Have interested students try to figure out several factors that determine the self-inductance of a coil of wire. [the size and shape of the coil, the number of turns of wire it has, whether or not it has a core, for example]

Answers To
PRACTICE PROBLEMS

Have students refer to Appendix A of the Solutions Appendix for complete solutions to Practice Problems.

9. **a.** 120 V
  b. 0.60 A
10. **a.** 120 V
  b. 90 A

CRITICAL THINKING
Use the Critical Thinking master for Chapter 25 with this section.

ENRICHMENT MASTER
Use the Enrichment master for Chapter 25 with this section.

RETEACHING MASTER
Use the Reteaching master for Chapter 25 with this section.

LABORATORY MANUAL
Use Lab 25.2 with this section.

Answers To
PRACTICE PROBLEMS (cont.)

11. a. 3.60×10^3 V
b. 90 A
c. 1.1×10^4 W
12. a. 1.80×10^4 V
b. 1.5×10^2 A

3 Close

CONVERGENT QUESTION

Ask students to imagine a real transformer connected to a source of alternating current. What is the one factor that is always common to both the primary and secondary coils? [the frequency of the alternating current]

CONCEPT REVIEW ANSWERS

2.1 Away from the magnet: The changing magnetic field induces a current in the coil, producing a magnetic field. This field opposes the field of the magnet, and thus the force between coil and magnet is repulsive.
2.2 The inductance of the motor creates a back-*EMF* that causes the spark. The bulb has very low self-inductance, so there is no back-*EMF*.
2.3 More current flows through the winding with fewer turns, so the resistance must be kept low to prevent voltage drops and I^2R power loss and heating.
2.4 Critical Thinking: No. The induced voltage depends on a changing magnetic field through the core. Permanent magnets are "permanent" because they are made of materials that resist such changes in magnetic field.

FIGURE 25–12. Transformers are used to reduce voltages to consumer levels at the points of use.

11. An ideal step-up transformer's primary circuit has 500 turns. Its secondary circuit has 15 000 turns. The primary is connected to an AC generator having an *EMF* of 120 V.
a. Calculate the *EMF* of the secondary.
b. Find the current in the primary if the current in the secondary is 3.0 A.
c. What power is drawn by the primary? What power is supplied by the secondary?

▶ **12.** A step-up transformer has 300 turns on its primary and 90 000 (9.000×10^4) turns on its secondary. The *EMF* of the generator to which the primary is attached is 60.0 V.
a. What is the *EMF* in the secondary?
b. The current flowing in the secondary is 0.50 A. What current flows in the primary?

As was discussed in Chapter 23, long-distance transmission of electric energy is economical only if low currents and very high voltages are used. Step-up transformers are used at power sources to develop voltages as high as 480 000 V. The high voltage reduces the current flow required in the transmission lines, keeping I^2R losses low. When the energy reaches the consumer, step-down transformers provide appropriately low voltages for consumer use.

There are many other important uses of transformers. Television picture tubes require up to 25 kV, developed by a transformer within the set. The spark or ignition coil in an automobile is a transformer designed to step up the 12 V from the battery to thousands of volts. The "points" interrupt the DC current from the battery to produce the changing magnetic field needed to induce *EMF* in the secondary coil. Some arc welders require currents of 10^4 A. Large step-down transformers are used to provide these currents, which can heat metals to 3000°C or more.

HISTORY CONNECTION

In the late 1800s, there was much debate in the United States over the best way to transmit power from power plants to consumers. The existing plants transmitted direct current (DC), but DC had serious limitations. A key decision was made to use alternating current (AC) in the new hydroelectric power plant at Niagara Falls. With the first successful transmission of AC to Buffalo, New York in 1896, the Niagara Falls plant paved the way for the development of AC power plants across the country. It literally provided the spark for the rapid growth of United States cities and industries that followed.

CONCEPT REVIEW

2.1 You hang a coil of wire with its ends joined so it can swing easily. If you now plunge a magnet into the coil, the coil will swing. Which way will it swing with respect to the magnet and why?
2.2 If you unplug a running vacuum cleaner from the wall outlet, you are much more likely to see a spark than if you unplug a lighted lamp from the wall. Why?
2.3 Frequently, transformer windings that have only a few turns are made of very thick (low-resistance) wire, while those with many turns are made of thin wire. Why is this true?
2.4 **Critical Thinking:** Would permanent magnets make good transformer cores? Explain.

Assessment

Portfolio

Students should develop a table of transformers they find in their everyday lives. The table should indicate whether the transformers are step-up or step-down, and, if possible, the input and output voltages. Students may find that the small transformers plugged into walls and used for battery chargers or power supplies for small electronic devices may list the output voltages as DC and not AC. In this case, the transformers contain electronic circuits to convert AC to DC. This should be noted in the table.

Physics and society

WEAK ELECTROMAGNETIC FIELDS—A HEALTH CONCERN?

Alternating currents, such as those in household wiring, produce electric and magnetic fields. The very low AC frequency is call Extremely Low Frequency, or ELF. The many sources of ELF electric and magnetic fields include power lines, home wiring, electric clocks, electric blankets, televisions and computer terminals. Twenty years ago, most scientists would have claimed that very weak electric and magnetic fields produced by ELFs could not affect living systems. Electric fields do exert forces on the ions in cellular fluids, and changing magnetic fields can induce such electric fields. Fields normally present in cells, however, are much larger than fields induced by ELFs, and, unlike ultraviolet radiation, ELFs can't break chemical bonds.

Recently, however, experiments have shown that cells are sensitive to even very weak ELF fields. They can affect flow of ions across cell membranes, synthesis of DNA, and the response of cells to hormones. Abnormal development of chick embryos has been seen. The experimental results, however, are very complex. Some effects of ELFs occur only at certain frequencies or amplitudes. Others occur only if the fields are turned on or off abruptly. Finally, for most environmental health hazards the larger the exposure, or dose, the larger the effect. For ELFs, there is no clear way to define or measure dose.

Some action has already been taken to reduce ELF fields. Electric blankets producing much lower magnetic fields are now sold. Several computer manufacturers sell terminals that produce smaller fields. Without knowing how to measure dose, however, it is not clear if such changes are enough to solve the problem.

Is there an association between cancer and exposure to ELF? Some studies found small increases in leukemia, breast cancer, and brain cancer. Studies of users of electric blankets have shown no effects on men, but increases in cancers and brain tumors in children whose mothers slept under electric blankets while pregnant. Studies to find the causes will take years and may not have conclusive results. In the meantime, what should be done?

DEVELOPING A VIEWPOINT

Read articles about ELFs and come to class ready to discuss the following questions.

1. What do you think should be done? Should no action be taken until there is conclusive evidence of health hazards of ELFs? Or, is there enough reason for concern to take measures to limit exposure to ELFs?
2. Suppose a study finds many cancer cases among people who live near power lines. Would this prove that ELF fields from power lines cause cancer?
3. What steps could you take to reduce exposure to ELF?
4. What could utility companies do to reduce ELF fields?

SUGGESTED READINGS

Noland, David. "Power Play." *Discover* 10 (12), 62–68, December, 1989.

Pool, Robert. "Electromagnetic Fields: The Biological Evidence." *Science* 249, 1378–1381, September 21, 1990.

Raloff, Janet. "EPA Suspects ELF Fields Can Cause Cancer." *Science News* 137, 404–405, June 30, 1990.

Physics and society

The review by Morgan is recommended as a balanced summary.

1. There is no correct answer at this time. Emphasize that in the realm of science, something is not true until it is clearly demonstrated to be so, but that in the realm of public health, action must sometimes be taken when evidence is suggestive, even though not yet conclusive. On the other hand, some claim that suspected hazards should be assumed risky until proven safe.

2. Because there are many other environmental factors, a high incidence of cancer in people who live near power lines does not prove they cause cancer. Effects of heredity are also not easily removed.

3. Don't use older electric blankets, keep away from TV's, computer terminals, and electric clocks.

4. Develop shielded home wiring, keep power lines farther away from people.

Manufacturers of video-display monitors are currently working to reduce the ELFs that these monitors produce. Such efforts to control ELFs may also be going on with other electrical-appliance manufacturers in possible anticipation of government regulations.

Teacher Resources: Decker, C. "ELF-zapped Genes Speed DNA Transcription." *Science News*, April 14, 1990, pages 137, 229. McGinnis, Bill. "Of Monitors and Emissions." *Byte* 15 (9), September 1990, pages 445–452.

25:2 ASSIGNMENT GUIDE

	PRACTICE	EXTENSION
CHAPTER REVIEW pp. 530–533		
· Reviewing Concepts	10–15	
· Applying Concepts		4, 9, 11–3, 16–18, 20, 22
· Problems*	14–19	20–22
APPENDIX B PROBLEMS*		
· Chapter 25, p. 706	14	13, 15

* Complete solutions to all Chapter Review and Appendix problems appear in the Problems and Solutions Manual.

CLOSING CHAPTER 25

Review Summary statements and Key Terms with your students.

ASSESSMENT

Vocabulary Review Master, Teacher Resource Package. Use this master to check students' understanding of Key Terms.

Evaluation Masters. Use Parts A and B of the Chapter Evaluation Masters from the Teacher Resource Package to test qualitative chapter objectives. Parts C and D to test quantitative chapter objectives.

Answers To
REVIEWING CONCEPTS

1. They are similar in that they each show a relationship between electricity and magnetism. They are different in that a steady electric current produces a magnetic field, but a change in magnetic field is needed to produce an electric current.
2. Either move the magnet in or out through the coil, or move the coil up and down over the end of the magnet.
3. ElectroMotive Force
It is not a force but an electric potential (energy per unit charge).
4. The armature of an electric generator consists of a number of wire loops wound around an iron core and placed in a strong magnetic field. As it rotates in the magnetic field, the loops cut through magnetic field lines and an electric current is induced.
5. Iron is used in an armature to increase the strength of the magnetic field.
6. In a generator, mechanical energy turns an armature in a magnetic field. The induced voltage causes current to flow, thus producing electrical energy. In a motor, a voltage is placed across an armature coil in a magnetic field. The voltage causes current to flow in the coil and the armature turns, producing mechanical energy.
7. An AC generator consists of a permanent magnet, an armature, a set of brushes, and a slip-ring.
8. In an alternating current generator, as the armature turns, the alternating current varies between some maximum value and zero. Since the current varies, the effective value of the current delivered by an alternating current generator is less than its maximum value.

CHAPTER 25 REVIEW

SUMMARY

25.1 Creating Electric Current from Changing Magnetic Fields

- Michael Faraday and Joseph Henry discovered that if a wire moves through a magnetic field, an electric current can be induced in the wire.
- The direction that current flows in a wire moving through a magnetic field depends upon the direction of the motion of the wire and the direction of the magnetic field.
- The current produced depends upon the angle between the velocity of the wire and the magnetic field. Maximum current occurs when the wire is moving at right angles to the field.
- Electromotive force, *EMF*, is the increased potential of charges in the moving wire. *EMF* is measured in volts.
- The *EMF* in a straight length of wire moving through a uniform magnetic field is the product of the magnetic induction, B, the length of the wire, L, and the component of the velocity of the moving wire, v, perpendicular to the field.
- An electric generator consists of a number of wire loops placed in a magnetic field. Because each side of the coil moves alternately up and down through the field, the current alternates direction in the loops. The generator develops alternating voltage and current.
- A generator and a motor are similar devices. A generator converts mechanical energy to electric energy; a motor converts electric energy to mechanical energy.

25.2 Effects of Changing Magnetic Fields: Induced *EMF*

- Lenz's law states: *An induced current is always produced in a direction such that the magnetic field resulting from the induced current opposes the change in the field that is causing the induced current.*
- A transformer has two coils wound about the same core. An AC current through the primary coil induces an alternating *EMF* in the secondary coil. The voltages in alternating current circuits may be increased or decreased by transformers.

KEY TERMS

electromagnetic induction
electromotive force
electric generator
Lenz's law
self-inductance
transformer
primary coil
secondary coil
mutual inductance
step-up transformer
step-down transformer

REVIEWING CONCEPTS

1. How are Oersted's and Faraday's results similar? How are they different?
2. Matt has a coil of wire and a bar magnet. Describe how Matt could use them to generate an electric current.
3. What does *EMF* stand for? Why is the name inaccurate?
4. What is the armature of an electric generator?
5. Why is iron used in an armature?
6. What is the difference between a generator and a motor?
7. List the major parts of an AC generator.
8. Why is the effective value of an AC current less than the maximum value?
9. Water trapped behind Hoover Dam turns turbines that rotate generators. List the forms of energy between the stored water and the final electricity produced.
10. State Lenz's law.
11. What produces the back-*EMF* of an electric motor?
12. Why is there no spark when you close a switch, putting current through an inductor, but there is a spark when you open the switch?
13. Why is the self-inductance of a coil a major factor when the coil is in an AC circuit but a minor factor when the coil is in a DC circuit?
14. Explain why the word "change" appears so often in this chapter.
15. Upon what does the ratio of the *EMF* in the primary of a transformer to the *EMF* in the secondary of the transformer depend?

REVIEW MASTER

Use the Vocabulary Review master for Chapter 25 with this section.

EVALUATION MASTER

Use the Chapter Evaluation master for Chapter 25 with this section.

APPLYING CONCEPTS

1. What is the difference between the current generated in a wire when the wire is moved up through a horizontal magnetic field and the current generated when the wire is moved down through the same field?
2. Substitute units to show that the unit of BLv is volts.
3. If the strength of a magnetic field is fixed, in what three ways can you vary the size of the *EMF* you can generate?
4. When a wire is moved through a magnetic field, resistance of the closed circuit affects
   a. current only. **c.** both.
   b. *EMF* only. **d.** neither.
5. As Logan slows his bike, what happens to the *EMF* produced by his bike's generator?
6. A hand-cranked generator is dropped, weakening the permanent magnet. How does this affect the speed at which the generator must be cranked to keep the same *EMF?*
7. The direction of AC voltage changes 120 times each second. Does that mean a device connected to an AC voltage alternately delivers and accepts energy?
8. A wire segment is moved horizontally between the poles of a magnet as shown in Figure 25–13. What is the direction of the induced current?

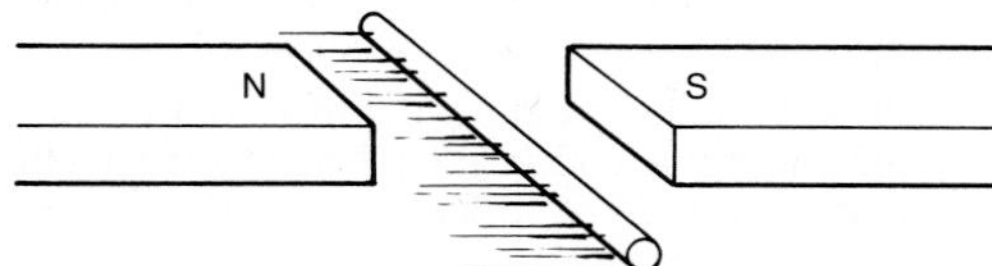

FIGURE 25–13. Use with Applying Concept 8.

9. Martha makes an electromagnet by winding wire around a large nail. If she connects the magnet to a battery, is the current larger just after she makes the connection or several tenths of seconds after the connection is made? Or is it always the same? Explain.
10. A wire segment is moving downward through the poles of a magnet as shown in Figure 25–14. What is the direction of the induced current?
11. Thomas Edison proposed distributing electrical energy using constant voltages (DC). George Westinghouse proposed using the present AC system. What are the reasons the Westinghouse system was adopted?
12. A transformer is connected to a battery through a switch. The secondary circuit contains a light bulb. Which of these statements best describes when the lamp will be lighted?
    a. as long as the switch is closed
    b. only the moment the switch is closed
    c. only the moment the switch is opened
    Explain.
13. An inventor claims that a very efficient transformer will step up power as well as voltage. Should we believe this? Explain.
14. Suppose a magnetic field is directed vertically downward. You move a wire at constant speed, first horizontally, then downward at 45°, then directly down.
    a. Compare the induced *EMF* for the three motions.
    b. Explain the variations in voltage.
15. The direction of Earth's magnetic field in the northern hemisphere is downward and to the north. If an east-west wire moves from north to south, in which direction does the current flow?
16. Steve is moving a loop of copper wire down through a magnetic field B, as shown in Figure 25–16.
    a. Will the induced current move to the right or left in the wire segment in the diagram?
    b. As soon as the wire is moved in the field, a current appears in it. Thus, the wire segment is a current-carrying wire located in a magnetic field. A force must act on the wire. What will be the direction of the force acting on the wire due to the induced current?

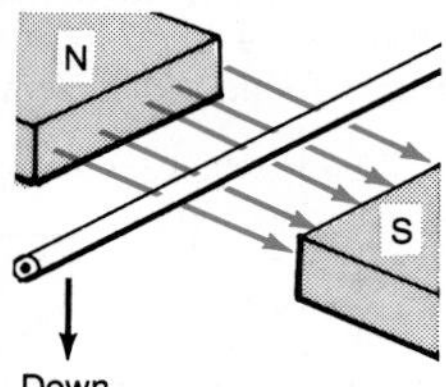

FIGURE 25–14. Use with Applying Concepts 10 and 16.

17. Steve, a physics instructor, drops a magnet through a copper pipe, Figure 25–15. The magnet falls very slowly and the class concludes that there must be some force opposing gravity.

9. There is potential energy in the stored water, kinetic energy in the falling water and turning turbine, and electric energy in the generator.
10. An induced current always acts in such a direction that its magnetic properties oppose the change by which the current is induced.
11. This is Lenz's law. Once the motor starts turning, it behaves as a generator and will generate current in opposition to the current being put into the motor.
12. The spark is from the back-*EMF* that tries to keep the current flowing. The *EMF* is very large because the current has very quickly dropped to zero. When closing the switch, the current increase isn't so fast because of resistance in the wires.
13. An alternating current is always changing in magnitude and direction. Therefore, self-induction is a constant factor. A direct current becomes steady quite rapidly and thus after a short time there is no changing magnetic field.
14. As Faraday discovered, only a *changing* magnetic field induces *EMF,* and thus current flow.
15. The ratio of number of turns of wire in the primary to the number of turns of wire in the secondary determines the *EMF* ratio.

Answers To
APPLYING CONCEPTS

1. The direction of the current is reversed.
2. The unit of BLv is $T \cdot m \cdot \frac{m}{s}$,
and $T = \left(\frac{N}{A \cdot m}\right)\left(\frac{A}{C/s}\right) = \frac{N \cdot s}{C \cdot m}$,
so $\left(\frac{T \cdot m \cdot m}{s}\right) = \left(\frac{N \cdot s}{C \cdot m}\right)\left(\frac{m \cdot m}{s}\right)$
$= \frac{N \cdot m}{C} = \frac{J}{C} = V.$

Answers To
APPLYING CONCEPTS (cont)

3. (1) Change the length of the wire; (2) change the speed the wire moves through the magnetic field; (3) change the direction of motion of the wire.
4. current only
5. As Logan slows his bike, the velocity of the wire in the magnetic field of the generator slows, and the *EMF* is reduced.
6. If the permanent magnet is weakened, *B* becomes smaller. To keep the same *EMF, V* must increase or the generator must be cranked at a faster speed.
7. No. The signs or the current and voltage reverse at the same time, and, therefore, the product of the current and the voltage is always positive.
8. No current is induced because the velocity is parallel to the magnetic field.
9. It is larger a moment after the connection is made. The back-*EMF* opposes current flow just after the current starts to flow.
10. The direction is downward.

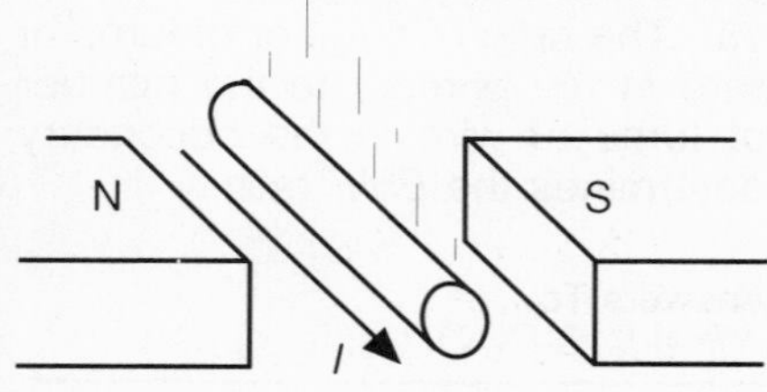

11. Transformers allow distributing the energy at high potential, using it at low voltages, and reducing losses in transmission.
12. The bulb will light because the current flows in the secondary circuit. This will happen whenever the primary current changes; so the bulb will glow when either the switch is closed or when it is opened.
13. No. The transformer would violate the law of conservation of energy.
14. a. Voltage is greatest when the motion of the wire is horizontal, or perpendicular (90°) to the magnetic field lines. It decreases as the angle decreases between the motion of the wire and the magnetic field lines. Voltage is zero when the motion of the wire and the magnetic field lines are parallel. **b.** The largest voltage is generated when the motion of the wire is horizontal and fully perpendicular to the magnetic field lines.
15. The current flows from west to east.
16. a. The right-hand rule will show the current moving left. **b.** The force will act in an upward direction.
17. a. Induced *EMF* is perpendicular to both the field and velocity, so the field must be circumferential. Field lines move in toward the S-pole, out from the N-pole. By the right-hand rule, current is clockwise near the S-pole, counterclockwise near the N-pole. **b.** Near the S-pole, the field inside the pipe is down, near the N-pole, it is up. **c.** Induced field exerts an upward force on both poles.

a. What is the direction of the current induced in the pipe by the falling magnet if the S-pole is toward the bottom?
b. The induced current produces a magnetic field. What is the direction of the field?
c. How does this field reduce the acceleration of the falling magnet?

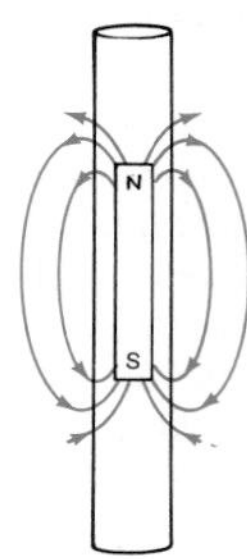

FIGURE 25–15. Use with Applying Concepts 17.

18. Why is a generator more difficult to rotate when it is connected to a circuit and supplying current than it is when it is standing alone?

PROBLEMS

25.1 Creating Electric Current From Changing Magnetic Fields

1. A wire segment, 31 m long, moves straight up through a 4.0×10^{-2}-T magnetic field at a speed of 15.0 m/s. What *EMF* is induced in the wire?
2. A wire, 20.0 m long, moves at 4.0 m/s perpendicularly through a 0.50-T magnetic field. What *EMF* is induced in the wire?

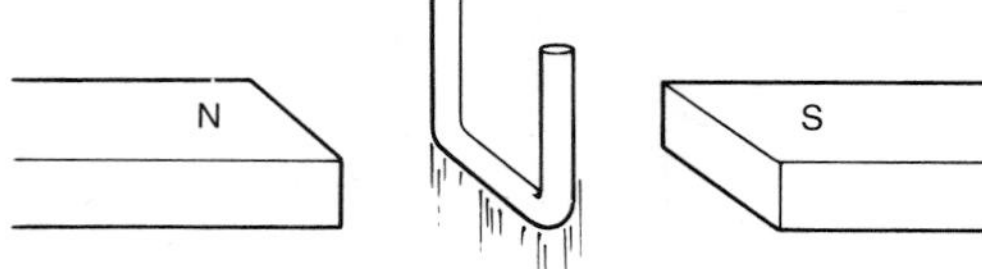

FIGURE 25–16. Use with Problem 2.

3. An airplane traveling at 950 km/h passes over a region where Earth's magnetic field is 4.5×10^{-5} T and is nearly vertical. What voltage is induced between the plane's wing tips, which are 75 m apart?
4. A straight wire, 0.75 m long, moves upward through a horizontal 0.30-T magnetic field at a speed of 16 m/s.
a. What *EMF* is induced in the wire?
b. The wire is a part of a circuit with a total resistance of 11 Ω. What current flows in the circuit?
▶ **5.** A 40-cm wire is moved perpendicularly through a magnetic field of 0.32 T with a velocity of 1.3 m/s. If this wire is connected into a circuit of 10-Ω resistance, how much current is flowing?
▶ **6.** Jennifer connects both ends of a copper wire, total resistance 0.10 Ω, to the terminals of a galvanometer. The galvanometer has a resistance of 875 Ω. Jennifer then moves a 10.0-cm segment of the wire upward at 1.0 m/s through a 2.0×10^{-2}-T magnetic field. What current will the galvanometer indicate?
▶ **7.** The direction of a 0.045-T magnetic field is 60° above the horizontal. A wire, 2.5 m long, moves horizontally at 2.4 m/s.
a. What is the vertical component of the magnetic field?
b. What *EMF* is induced in the wire?
8. An *EMF* of 0.0020 V is induced in a 10-cm wire when it is moving perpendicularly across a uniform magnetic field at a speed of 4.0 m/s. What is the size of the magnetic field?
9. At what speed would a 0.2-m length of wire have to move across a 2.5-T magnetic field to induce an *EMF* of 10 V?
10. An AC generator develops a maximum *EMF* of 565 V. What effective *EMF* does the generator deliver to an external circuit?
11. An AC generator develops a maximum voltage of 150 V. It delivers a maximum current of 30.0 A to an external circuit.
a. What is the effective voltage of the generator?
b. What effective current does it deliver to the external circuit?
c. What is the effective power dissipated in the circuit?
12. An electric stove is connected to an AC source with effective voltage of 240 V.
a. Find the maximum voltage across one of the stove's elements when it is operating?

b. The resistance of the operating element is 11 Ω. What effective current flows through it?

▶ **13.** A generator at Hoover Dam can supply 375 MW (375×10^6 W) of electrical power. Assume that the turbine and generator are 85% efficient.
  a. Find the rate which falling water must supply energy to the turbine.
  b. The energy of the water comes from a change in potential energy, *mgh*. What is the needed change in potential energy each second?
  c. If the water falls 22 m, what is the mass of the water that must pass through the turbine each second to supply this power?

25.2 Effects of Changing Magnetic Fields: Induced *EMF*

14. The primary of a transformer has 150 turns. It is connected to a 120-V source. Calculate the number of turns on the secondary needed to supply these voltages.
  a. 625 V **b.** 35 V **c.** 6.0 V

15. A step-up transformer has 80 turns on its primary. It has 1200 turns on its secondary. The primary is supplied with an alternating current at 120 V.
  a. What voltage is across the secondary?
  b. The current in the secondary is 2.0 A. What current flows in the primary circuit?
  c. What is the power input and output of the transformer?

16. A portable computer requires an effective voltage of 9.0 volts from the 120 -V line.
  a. If the primary of the transformer has 475 turns, how many does the secondary have?
  b. A 125-mA current flows through the computer. What current flows through the transformer's primary?

17. In a hydroelectric plant, electricity is generated at 1200 V. It is transmitted at 240 000 V.
  a. What is the ratio of the turns on the primary to the turns on the secondary of a transformer connected to one of the generators?
  b. One of the plant generators can deliver 40.0 A to the primary of its transformer. What current is flowing in the secondary?

18. A hair dryer uses 10 A at 120 V. It is used with a transformer in England, where the line voltage is 240 V.
  a. What should be the ratio of the turns of the transformer?
  b. What current will it draw from the 240-V line?

19. A step-up transformer is connected to a generator that is delivering 125 V and 95 A. The ratio of the turns on the secondary to the turns on the primary is 1000 to 1.
  a. What voltage is across the secondary?
  b. What current flows in the secondary?

▶ **20.** A 150-W transformer has an input voltage of 9.0 V and an output current of 5.0 A.
  a. Is this a step-up or step-down transformer?
  b. What is the ratio of output voltage to input voltage?

▶ **21.** A transformer has input voltage and current of 12 V and 3.0 A respectively, and an output current of 0.75 A. If there are 1200 turns on the secondary side of the transformer, how many turns are on the primary side?

▶ **22.** Scott connects a transformer to a 24-V source and measures 8.0 V at the secondary. If the primary and secondary were reversed, what would the new output voltage be?

USING LAB SKILLS

1. After doing the Pocket Lab on page 518, predict what will happen if the magnet is kept stationary and the coil moves. Try it. What happens if the coil and magnet move together? Try it.

THINKING PHYSIC-LY

1. A bike's headlamp is powered by a generator that rubs against a wheel. Why is it harder to pedal when the generator is lighting the lamp?

2. Suppose an "anti-Lenz's law" existed that meant a force was exerted to increase the change in magnetic field. Thus, when more electrical energy was demanded from a generator, the force needed to turn it would be reduced. What conservation law would be violated by this new "law"? Explain.

18. When the armature of a generator is rotated, a force that opposes the direction of rotation is produced.

Answers To
PROBLEMS

Complete solutions for all Chapter Review Problems can be found in the Problems and Solutions Manual.

1. 19 V
2. 40 V
3. 0.89 V
4. **a.** 3.6 V
   b. 0.33 A
5. 17 mA
6. 2.3 μA
7. **a.** 0.039 T
   b. 0.23 V
8. 0.0050 T
9. 20 m/s
10. 399 V
11. **a.** 106 V
    b. 21.2 A
    c. 2.25 kW
12. **a.** 340 V
    b. 22 A
13. **a.** 441 MW input
    b. 4.41×10^8 J/s
    c. 2.0×10^6 kg/s
14. **a.** 781 turns
    b. 44 turns
    c. 7.5 turns
15. **a.** 1.8 kV
    b. 30 A
    c. 3.6 kW; 3.6 kW
16. **a.** 36 turns
    b. 9.4 mA
17. **a.** 1 to 200
    b. 0.200 A
18. **a.** 2 to 1
    b. 5.0 A
19. **a.** 125 kV
    b. 95 mA
20. **a.** step up
    b. 10 to 3
21. 300 turns
22. 72 V

Answer To
USING LAB SKILLS

1. The current is caused by the relative motion between the magnet and coil. Moving either one produces the same effect. If the coil and magnet are moved together, however, then the relative motion is zero and no current is produced in the coil.

Answers To
THINKING PHYSIC-LY

1. Energy is needed to light the lamp and it comes from your pedaling.
2. It would violate the law of conservation of energy. More energy would come out than went in. A generator would create energy, not just change it from one form to another.

CHAPTER
26 Electric and Magnetic Fields

PLANNING GUIDE (5 class sessions)

CONTENTS	TEXT FEATURES	TEACHER RESOURCE PACKAGE	OTHER COMPONENTS
26.1 Action of Electric and Magnetic Fields on Matter, pp. 536–542 (3 Class Sessions) • Mass of the Electron • The Mass Spectrometer	**Pocket Lab:** Rolling Along, p. 537 **Concept Review,** p. 542	**Study Guide:** Action of Electric and Magnetic Fields on Matter **Enrichment Master:** Radio Waves **Transparency Worksheet:** Mass Spectrometer	**Laboratory Manual:** Lab 26.1 Mass of an Electron **Transparency 39:** Mass Spectrometer
26.2 Electric and Magnetic Fields in Space, pp. 542–551 (2 Class Sessions) • Electromagnetic Waves • Production of Electromagnetic Waves • Reception of Electromagnetic Waves • X Rays	**Physics Lab:** Homemade Mass Spectrometer, p. 543 **Physics and Society:** The Greenhouse Effect, p. 548 **Pocket Lab:** Catching the Wave, p. 549 **Concept Review,** p. 551	**Study Guide:** Electric and Magnetic Fields in Space **Physics Lab Data Sheet:** Homemade Mass Spectrometer **Critical Thinking Master:** The Microwave Oven **Reteaching Master:** Electromagnetic Waves **Transparency Worksheet:** Representative Examples of Electromagnetic Radiation **Transparency Worksheet:** Mass Spectrometer	**Transparency 38:** Representative Examples of Electromagnetic Radiation **Transparency 22:** Electromagnetic Spectrum
Chapter Review, pp. 551–553	Summary Key Terms Reviewing Concepts Applying Concepts Problems Thinking Physic-ly	**Vocabulary Review** **Chapter Test**	**Test Bank**

SUPPLEMENTARY MATERIALS

SOFTWARE	AUDIOVISUAL	BOOKS/MAGAZINES
Laboratory Simulations In Atomic Physics, Queue, Inc. (Apple II). *Mass Spectrometer,* Queue, Inc. (Apple II).	Video: *The Mechanical Universe and Beyond: Maxwell's Equations* and *Optics,* Films Inc.	Fritz, Ron. "Calibration and Efficiency of Microwave Ovens." *The Physics Teacher,* November 1990, p. 564. Jui-ming, Zhao. "A Simulation of the Hydrogen Spectrum." *The Physics Teacher,* December 1990, p. 596. Steyn-Ross, Alistair, and Riddell, Alister. "Standing Waves in a Microwave Oven." *The Physics Teacher,* October 1990, p. 474. Young, Hugh D. "Radio and TV Reception." *The Physics Teacher,* March 1984, p. 180.

PROBLEM CORRELATION

CONCEPTS	CHAPTER REVIEW			PROBLEMS APPENDIX
	Reviewing Concepts	Applying Concepts	Problems	
26.1 Action of Electric and Magnetic Fields on Matter				
Mass of the Electron	1	1,2,3	**1,2,3,4,5**	1,2,3,4,5,6,7, 8,9,10,**11**
The Mass Spectrometer	2	4,5,6	**6,**7,8,**9,**10,11,12, 13,**14,15**	
26.2 Electric and Magnetic Fields in Space				
Electromagnetic Waves	3,5,6			
Production of Electromagnetic Waves	7	7	**16**	12
Reception of Electromagnetic Waves	4,8,9	8,9	**17,**18	13
X Rays				

ACTIVITY AND DEMONSTRATION MATERIALS

PHYSICS LAB	POCKET LAB	DEMONSTRATIONS
Page 543 ball of clay grooved ruler 6-mm steel ball glass marble 2 permanent magnets cafeteria tray or glass wave tank graph paper masking tape	Pages 537, 549 ball of clay 30-cm ruler with center groove 6-mm steel ball strong magnet telephone pickup coil mini audio amplifier 9-V battery common household appliances	Page 544 small battery-powered radio light bulb and socket

EXTENSION PROJECTS

LIBRARY RESEARCH

1. Magnetic Fields in Electron Microscopes
Do some research to find out how magnetic fields are used in electron microscopes. What are magnetic lenses? Where and why are they used?

DISPLAY MODEL

2. Telegraph
Build a working model of the telegraph and demonstrate how it works.

STUDENT READINGS

Fox, B. "High Frequencies Relieve Radio Traffic Jams." *New Scientist,* April 21, 1988.

Langone, John. "X-Raying Egyptian Mummies." *Discover,* November 1984.

Monastersky, R. "Global Warming: Politics Muddle Policy." *Science News,* June 23, 1990.

Peterson, Ivars. "Stellar X-Ray Burst Brings Theory Shock." *Science News,* October 20, 1990.

White, Robert M. "The Great Climate Debate." *Scientific American,* July 1990.

Chapter 26

Electric and Magnetic Fields

CHAPTER OVERVIEW

Theme Development: Once more the field model of electric and magnetic fields is important. Strongly symmetrical patterns are shown by some electromagnetic waves, and the cyclic nature of electromagnetic waves is emphasized. While mainly the radio, microwave, and gamma regions of the electromagnetic spectrum are stressed, the range of wavelength and frequency values outside of human experience is vast.

MISCONCEPTIONS

Since most electromagnetic waves are not visible, there is a general abstractness to the topic. Some students have the idea that sound waves travel through the air, citing radio and TV broadcasts.

KEY TERMS

antenna
charge-to-mass ratio
electromagnetic radiation
electromagnetic wave
gamma rays
isotopes
mass spectrometer
piezoelectricity
receiver
X rays

Laboratory Options

STUDENT EDITION
Physics Lab
Homemade Mass Spectrometer 543

Pocket Lab
Rolling Along 537
Catching the Wave 549

TEACHER EDITION
Activities
Cooperative Learning 538
Demonstration 544

LABORATORY MANUAL
Mass of an Electron Lab 26.1

CHAPTER **26**

Electric and Magnetic Fields

Big Ears

These parabolic dish antennas are used to detect radio-frequency radiation having short wavelengths. Why are dish-style antennas used rather than normal television or radio antennas for detecting radio signals from deep space?

These huge parabolic dish antennas detect radio waves from space. They are used to receive information sent from space probes that pass close to Uranus and Neptune and to pick up signals from distant galaxies. They have the same function as television antennas on the roofs of homes, but are very different in form.

Chapter Outline

Concept Check

The following terms or concepts from earlier chapters are important for a good understanding of this chapter. If you are not familiar with them, you should review them before studying this chapter.

- transverse waves, Chapter 14
- electric fields, Chapter 21
- magnetic fields, Chapter 24
- magnetic induction, Chapter 25

535

Introducing The Chapter

Big Ears

Using The Photo: Instead of capturing visible light waves, this antenna captures radio wavelengths. Nevertheless, the antenna operates over a portion of the electromagnetic spectrum. Since the wavelengths are different, the dimensions of the antenna differ as well. A very close inspection of the antenna would reveal that it is not solid metal. Compared to the relatively large radio wavelengths, however, the antenna functions as if it were solid.

For an explanation of the chapter opener question, refer students to page 550.

Concept Check

Make sure students have a clear understanding of the concepts covered in Chapters 14, 21, 24, and 25 that are listed in the Concept Check. Students familiar with transverse waves, electric and magnetic fields, and magnetic induction will more easily understand the interactions of changing electric and magnetic fields, and electromagnetic waves.

Assessment Options

Portfolio Assessment
Extension 1, TWE, p. 534b
Physics and Society, Developing a Viewpoint, p. 548
Portfolio Assessment, TWE, p. 550
Thinking Physic-ly, p. 553

Performance Assessment
Extension 2, TWE, p. 534b
Pocket Labs, pp. 537, 549
Physics Lab, p. 543
Pocket Lab Assessment, TWE, p. 549

Content Assessment
Self assessment: Practice Problems, pp. 539, 541
Cooperative Learning, TWE, p. 538
Assessment, Critical Thinking, TWE, p. 543
Concept Reviews, pp. 542, 551
Chapter Review, pp. 551–553
Supplemental Problems, p. 707

Group Assessment
Activites for group assessment occur with Cooperative Learning and lab activities.

26.1 ACTION OF ELECTRIC AND MAGNETIC FIELDS ON MATTER

Preparation

OBJECTIVES

The objectives are listed on the student page. Remind students to preview these objectives as a study guide to this major section.

OVERVIEW

This section relies on students' knowledge of electric and magnetic fields to teach measuring the mass of the electron and the operation of the mass spectrometer.

BRIDGING

Students will need to recall the following concepts in this section: electric and magnetic fields, especially the details of how they exert forces on charged particles; the acceleration of charged particles by potential differences; and the behavior of objects in circular motion, including centripetal acceleration.

1 Focus

Speaker: Contact someone from a scientifically-related industry in your vicinity, or perhaps a nearby college or university, who uses a mass spectrometer in their everyday work. Invite them to explain the device's capabilities to your students.

Objectives

- **describe Thomson's measurement of the charge-to-mass ratio of the electrons; solve problems associated with this experiment.**
- **show an understanding of the mass spectrometer as an analytical tool; solve problems involving this instrument.**

26.1 ACTION OF ELECTRIC AND MAGNETIC FIELDS ON MATTER

The source of radio and television waves is usually accelerating electrons. It is their charge that results in electric fields, and their motion that produces magnetic fields. Electrons are also part of every atom that makes up the dish antennas. Therefore it is important to understand some of the properties of electrons. The same techniques used to study electrons can be extended to study the properties of positive ions, atoms stripped of one or more electrons.

Mass of the Electron

The mass of the electron is found indirectly from its charge, q, and its charge-to-mass ratio, q/m.

The charge of the electron was first measured by Robert Millikan using the force of an electric field on the charge on an oil drop. The mass of an electron is too small to measure on an ordinary balance. It is possible, however, to find the **charge-to-mass ratio**, q/m, by balancing the forces of an electric and a magnetic field acting on an electron. From this ratio and the charge, the mass can be found.

The ratio of charge-to-mass of the electron was first measured in 1897 by the British physicist J. J. Thomson (1856–1940). He used a cathode-ray tube similar to the one in Figure 26–1. All air is removed from the glass tube. An electric field pulls electrons out of the negatively-charged cathode and accelerates them toward the positively-charged anode. Some of the electrons pass through a hole in the anode and travel in a narrow beam toward a fluorescent screen. The screen glows at the point where the electrons hit.

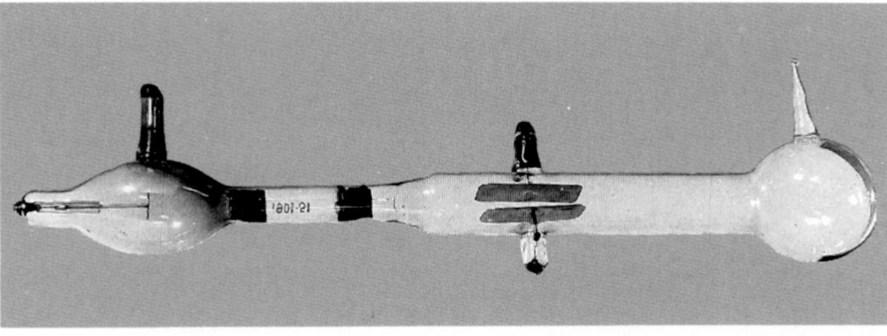

a

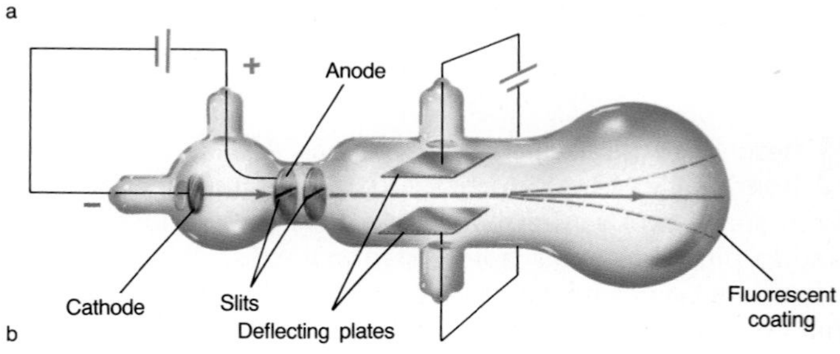

b

FIGURE 26–1. The Thomson q/m tube (a) is diagrammed in (b). The electromagnets have been moved forward to show the deflection plates. When the tube is in use, the electromagnets and the deflection plates lie in the same plane.

Electric and magnetic fields in the center of the tube exert forces on the electrons. Charged parallel plates produce a uniform electric field perpendicular to the beam. The electric field intensity, E, produces a force, qE, on the electrons that deflects them upward. Two coils produce a magnetic field at right angles to both the beam and the electric field. Remember that the force exerted by a magnetic field is perpendicular to the field and to the direction of motion of the particles. The magnitude of the force exerted by the magnetic field is equal to Bqv. Here, B is the magnetic field strength, and v is the electron velocity. The magnetic force acts downward.

Crossed electric and magnetic fields exert forces in opposite directions on the electrons.

The electric and magnetic fields are adjusted until the beam of electrons follows a straight, or undeflected, path. Then the forces due to the two fields are equal in magnitude and opposite in direction.

For electrons of a selected velocity, the two forces are exactly balanced.

$$Bqv = Eq$$

Solving this equation for v, we obtain the expression

$$v = \frac{Eq}{Bq} = \frac{E}{B}.$$

If the electric field is turned off, only the force due to the magnetic field remains. The magnetic force acts perpendicular to the direction of motion of the electrons, causing a centripetal acceleration. The electrons follow a circular path with radius r. Newton's second law gives

With only the magnetic force, electrons follow a circular path.

$$Bqv = m\frac{v^2}{r}.$$

Solving for q/m gives

$$\boxed{\frac{q}{m} = \frac{v}{Br}.}$$

Thomson calculated the velocity, v, using the measured values of E and B. Next, he measured the distance between the undeflected spot and the position of the spot when only the magnetic field acted on the electrons. Using this distance, he calculated the radius of the circular path of the electron, r. This allowed Thomson to calculate q/m. The average of many experimental trials gave the value $q/m = 1.759 \times 10^{11}$ C/kg. Using the value, $q = 1.602 \times 10^{-19}$ C, gives the mass of the electron, m.

$$m = \left(\frac{q}{q/m}\right) = \frac{1.602 \times 10^{-19}\ \text{C}}{1.759 \times 10^{11}\ \text{C/kg}} = 9.107 \times 10^{-31}\ \text{kg}$$
$$= 9.11 \times 10^{-31}\ \text{kg to 3 significant digits.}$$

Positively-charged particles bend the opposite way when in either an electric field or a magnetic field, Figure 26–2. Thomson found q/m for positive ions in the same way he measured the quantity for electrons. A

POCKET LAB

ROLLING ALONG

Place a small ball of clay under one end of a grooved ruler to make a ramp. Roll a 6-mm diameter steel ball down the ramp and along the table top. Place a strong magnet near the path of the ball so that the ball will curve, but not hit the magnet. Predict what will happen to the path when the ball is started higher or lower on the ramp. Try it. Is this consistent for a charged particle moving through a magnetic field?

STUDY GUIDE MASTER

Use the Study Guide master for section 26.1.

2 Teach

CONCEPT DEVELOPMENT

- Robert Millikan won the Nobel Prize in 1923 for his work on measuring the charge on the electron and his experiments with the photoelectric effect.
- There were earlier attempts than Millikan's to measure the charge on the electron that were unsuccessful because they were imprecise. One such attempt involved measuring the settling rates of ionized clouds of water vapor.
- Thomson arrived at the same value for the charge-to-mass ratio whether the "carriers of electricity" (the name *electron* came later) were from air, hydrogen, or carbonic acid. He realized his results suggested that these "carriers" were the same regardless of their source.
- Thomson used the value of the average charge on a large number of electrons from early experiments done in electrochemistry as an estimate of the electron's mass.

Study Guide Master. To reinforce the concepts in this section, have the students complete the Study Guide Master for Section 26.1 from the Teacher Resource Package.

POCKET LAB

ROLLING ALONG

Purpose: to see how the radius of curvature depends on the speed of the particle.

Materials: ball of clay; 30-cm ruler with center groove; 6-mm steel ball; strong magnet.

Outcome: When the ball moves faster, it curves less. The curvature depends on the time interval in which the force is acting. When the ball moves faster, the magnet is pulling on it for a smaller amount of time.

CONCEPT DEVELOPMENT

Laboratory Manual. Give students additional experience with the mass of an electron by doing Lab 26.1 from the Laboratory Manual.

ACTIVITY

Cooperative Learning: Write down the expression for the radius of a charged particle in a magnetic field from the second Example Problem on this page. Divide the class into four groups and assign mass, velocity, magnetic field, and charge—one to each group. Now ask how changing each of these quantities would change the radius. Ask further how each of these quantities could be changed. [Increasing the mass would increase the radius, because larger masses are harder to bend into a curved path. The mass can be changed by using a different element. Increasing the velocity would increase the radius. The velocity could be increased or decreased by changing the accelerating voltage. Increasing the magnetic field would decrease the radius because more force on the ionized atom would bend it into a tighter circle. The magnetic field could be increased by changing the magnet or increasing the current through the magnet if it were an electromagnet. Increasing the charge would decrease the radius because that increases the magnetic force again. The charge could be increased by increasing the original ionizing voltage.]

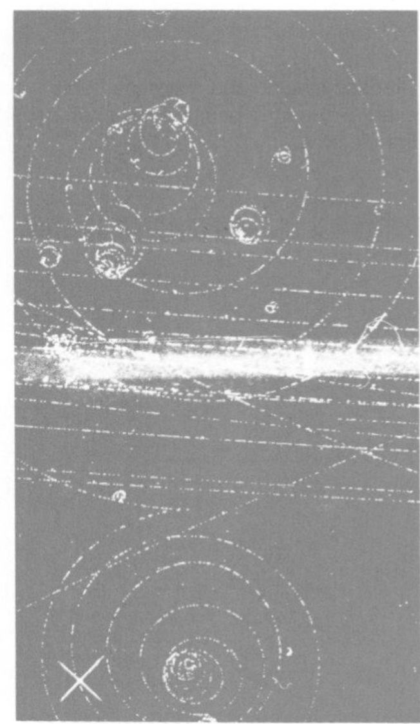

FIGURE 26–2. This photograph shows the circular tracks of two electrons (e^-) and a positron (e^+) moving through the magnetic field in a bubble chamber. Note that the electrons and positron curve in opposite directions.

positive ion is produced by removing one or more electrons from an atom. To accelerate positively-charged particles into the deflection region, he reversed the direction of the field between the cathode and anode. A small amount of a gas, such as hydrogen, was put into the tube. The field pulled the electrons off the hydrogen atoms and accelerated the positively-charged protons through a tiny hole in the negatively-charged electrode. The proton beam then passed through the electric and magnetic deflecting fields to the fluorescent screen of the Thomson q/m tube. The mass of the proton was determined in the same manner as was the mass of the electron. The mass of the proton was found to be 1.67×10^{-27} kg. Heavier ions produced by stripping an electron from gases such as helium, neon, or argon were measured by a similar method.

Example Problem

Balancing Electric and Magnetic Fields in a q/m Tube

A beam of electrons travels an undeflected path in a q/m tube. E is 7.0×10^3 N/C. B is 3.5×10^{-2} T. What is the speed of the electrons as they travel through the tube?

Given: $E = 7.0 \times 10^3$ N/C, $B = 3.5 \times 10^{-2}$ T

Unknown: v

Basic equation: $v = \frac{E}{B}$

Solution:

$$v = \frac{E}{B} = \frac{7.0 \times 10^3 \text{ N/C}}{3.5 \times 10^{-2} \text{ N/A} \cdot \text{m}} = 2.0 \times 10^5 \text{ m/s}$$

Example Problem

Path of an Electron in a Magnetic Field

An electron of mass 9.11×10^{-31} kg moves with a speed 2.0×10^5 m/s across and perpendicular to a 8.0×10^{-5}-T magnetic field. What is the predicted radius of the circular path followed by the electrons?

Given: $m = 9.11 \times 10^{-31}$ kg, $v = 2.0 \times 10^5$ m/s, $B = 8.0 \times 10^{-5}$ T, $q = 1.6 \times 10^{-19}$ C

Unknown: r

Basic equation: $Bqv = \frac{mv^2}{r}$

Solution:

$$Bqv = \frac{mv^2}{r}$$

$$r = \frac{mv}{Bq} = \frac{(9.11 \times 10^{-31} \text{ kg})(2.0 \times 10^5 \text{ m/s})}{(8.0 \times 10^{-5} \text{ N/A} \cdot \text{m})(1.6 \times 10^{-19} \text{ C})}$$

$$r = 1.4 \times 10^{-2} \text{ m}$$

F.Y.I.

Sir Joseph John Thomson was awarded the Nobel Prize in physics in 1906 for his work on the electron. Eventually, seven of his research assistants won Nobel Prizes. In 1908 he was knighted.

538 Electric and Magnetic Fields

TEACHER 

The cathode-ray tube, now called CRT, is the forerunner of the television tube. An evacuated tube with metal plates sealed into the ends is connected to a battery or induction coil. A glow emerges from the negative plate and disappears into the positive plate. If the positive plate takes the form of a cylinder and is sealed into the middle of the tube, a beam can be projected through the tube. Covering the tube with phosphors makes the beam easily visible and is the essence of current television tube design.

Practice Problems

Assume the direction of all moving charged particles is perpendicular to the uniform magnetic field.

1. Protons passing without deflection through a 0.6-T magnetic field are balanced by a 4.5×10^3-N/C electric field. What is the speed of the moving protons?
2. A proton moves at a speed of 7.5×10^3 m/s as it passes through a 0.6-T magnetic field. Find the radius of the circular path. The charge carried by the proton is equal to that of the electron, but it is positive.
3. Electrons move through a 6.0×10^{-2}-T magnetic field balanced by a 3.0×10^3-N/C electric field. What is the speed of the electrons?
4. ▶ Calculate the radius of the circular path the electrons in Practice Problem 3 follow in the absence of the electric field.

The Mass Spectrometer

A mass spectrometer can make precision measurements of the mass of ions.

When Thomson put neon gas into his tube, he found two dots on the screen, and thus two values of q/m. This meant that atoms could have the same chemical properties but have different masses. Thus Thomson had shown the existence of **isotopes**, a possibility first proposed by the chemist Frederick Soddy.

The masses of positive ions can be measured precisely using a **mass spectrometer**, an adaptation of the Thomson tube. The type of mass spectrometer used by K. T. Bainbridge is shown in Figure 26–3. It uses either a gas or a material that can be heated to form a gas. In the ion source, accelerated electrons strike the gas atoms, knocking off electrons to form positive gas ions. A potential difference, V, between the electrodes produces an electric field that accelerates the ions.

FIGURE 26–3. The mass spectrometer is used extensively as an analytical tool. Inside the spectrometer, a magnet (a) causes the positive ions to be deflected according to their mass. In the vacuum chamber (b), the process is recorded on a photographic plate or a solid-state detector.

a

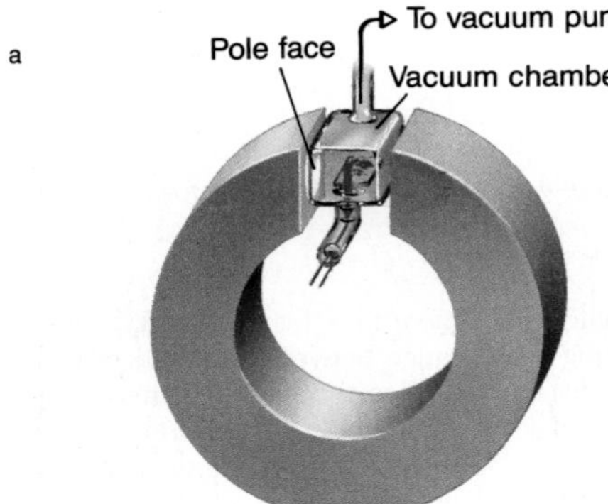

b

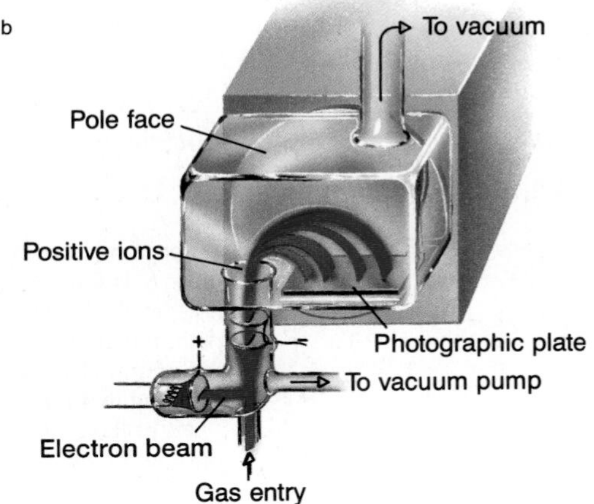

Answers To
PRACTICE PROBLEMS

Have students refer to Appendix A of the Solutions Appendix for complete solutions to Practice Problems.

1. 8×10^3 m/s
2. 1×10^{-4} m
3. 5.0×10^4 m/s
4. 4.7×10^{-6} m

CONCEPT DEVELOPMENT

- The mass spectrometer is a real workhorse of scientific analysis, used not only in physics but in chemistry, biology, or wherever the identification of the mass of small concentrations of elements is needed.
- The major point here is that the use of electric and magnetic fields is our primary way of controlling electrons, atoms, and other charged particles. Whether we are talking of moving a charge through electric or electronic circuits or guiding charged particles in huge accelerators, fields provide the forces.
- A very promising young British physicist, Francis Aston, did much early exploratory work with the mass spectrometer, only to be killed in the First World War.

Transparency Package. Use Transparency 39 to illustrate the operation of the mass spectrometer.

Enrichment Master. With this section, use the Enrichment Master, Motors, from the Teacher Resource Package.

LABORATORY MANUAL

Use Lab 26.1 with this section.

ENRICHMENT MASTER

Use the Enrichment master for Chapter 26 with this section.

TRANSPARENCY

Use Transparency 39 with this section.

CONCEPT DEVELOPMENT

- Use Newton's second law, $F = ma$, where the centripetal force is provided by the magnetic force so $Bqv = mv^2/r$. Now rearrange and solve for m/q to arrive at the final form.

Critical Thinking: When an electron moves in a uniform magnetic field, its path is circular. That means the electron has been accelerated by the field. Ask students if the electron has gained kinetic energy. Why or why not? [It has not. Because the direction of the magnetic force is always at right angles to the direction of motion, no work is done. Remember that work involves the force times cosine of the angle between the force and the direction of motion; the cosine of 90° is zero.]

- In Concept Review 1.3 on page 542, the bending radius of the atoms must stay more or less constant because of the way the spectrometer is built. Since voltage and charge have a constant value, mass, m, and magnetic field, B, must change in such a way to keep the radius value, r, constant. Therefore, the square root of the mass times one over the magnetic field must be equal to one. If, for example, mass increases by a factor of 25, the square root of that is five, so the magnetic field also must increase by a factor of five.

Guided Practice: Go over the Example Problem on page 541 in class, then have students work on the Practice Problems that follow.

INDEPENDENT PRACTICE/ EXTENSION

Refer to the Assignment Guide on page 541 for additional questions and problems for independent practice.

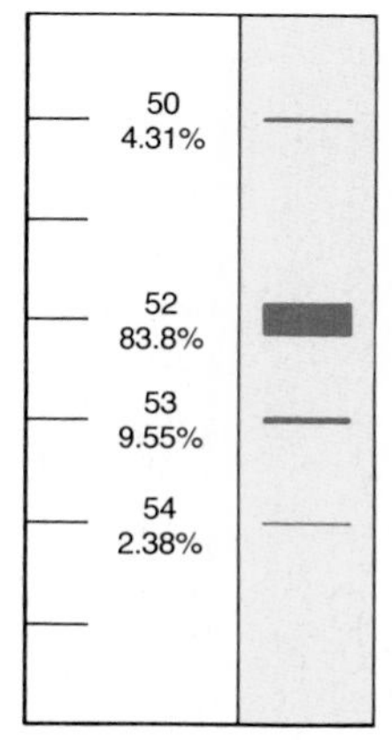

FIGURE 26–4. The mass spectrometer is widely used to determine relative concentrations of various isotopes of an element. Marks are left on a film by ^{50}Cr, ^{52}Cr, ^{53}Cr, and ^{54}Cr. Note that the weight of the mark is proportional to the percentage of the isotope.

To select ions with a specific velocity, the ions pass through electric and magnetic deflecting fields as in the Thomson tube. The ions that go through undeflected move into a region with a uniform magnetic field. There they follow a circular path with a radius found from Newton's second law, $Bqv = mv^2/r$. Solving for r yields

$$r = \frac{mv}{qB}.$$

The velocity of the ion can be found from the equation for the kinetic energy of ions accelerated from rest through a known potential difference V,

$$KE = \tfrac{1}{2}mv^2 = qV$$

$$v = \sqrt{\frac{2qV}{m}}.$$

Substituting this expression for v in the previous equation gives the radius of the circular path,

$$r = \frac{1}{B}\sqrt{\frac{2Vm}{q}}.$$

From this equation, the charge-to-mass ratio of the ion is found to be

$$\frac{q}{m} = \frac{2V}{B^2r^2}.$$

The location where ions hit is marked on photographic film.

The ions hit a photographic film, where they leave a mark. The radius, r, is found by measuring the distance between the mark and the hole in the electrode. This distance is twice the radius of the circular path. Figure 26–4 shows marks on film from the isotopes of the element chromium. The isotope with mass number 52 makes the darkest mark, showing that most chromium atoms have this mass.

All of the chromium ions have the same charge. The charge depends on how many electrons were removed in the ion source. It takes more-energetic electrons to remove a second electron from the gas atoms. For

TEACHER F.Y.I.

In 1943, Ernest Lawrence conceived the idea of separating two isotopes, U-235 and U-238, using an enormous mass spectrometer. This huge device was called the calutron. The scale of this device caused consternation in scientific circles at first, but the success of a series of increasingly large test devices demonstrated that he was indeed on the right track. The ability to separate these two isotopes was important in the Manhattan project. More recently, updated calutrons were built by Iraq. Those found were destroyed by United Nations inspection teams.

low electron energies, only one electron is removed from an atom. When the energy is increased, however, both singly- and doubly-charged ions are produced. In this way, the operator of the mass spectrometer can choose the charge on the ion.

Mass spectrometers can be used to separate isotopes of atoms such as uranium. Instead of film, cups are used to collect the separated isotopes. A mass spectrometer (often called an MS) is used by chemists as a very sensitive tool to find small amounts of molecules in samples. Amounts as small as one molecule in 10 billion molecules can be identified. Investigators detect the ions using electronic devices and are able to separate ions with mass differences of one ten-thousandth of one percent. Many dangerous contaminants in the environment have been detected with this device.

HELP WANTED

METEOROLOGIST

A crystal ball is not needed. What is needed is solid professional preparation, a sincere interest in the thorough study of data, and the ability to arrive at logical conclusions. Most of all, you must be willing to make predictions, even when the data provide much less than a 100% probability. A "thick skin" is also essential for anyone working for The National Weather Service.

A bachelor's degree from an accredited meteorology program is the minimum preparation needed, and advanced work will be considered a definite plus. Willingness to work your way up the ladder and take your turn with irregular shifts and possible relocation will help your career climb. For information contact:

American Meteorological Society, 45 Beacon Street, Boston, MA 02108

Example Problem

The Mass of a Neon Atom

The operator of a mass spectrometer produces a beam of doubly-ionized neon atoms (charge $q = 2(1.60 \times 10^{-19}\text{ C})$). The accelerating voltage is $V = 34$ V. In a 0.050-T magnetic field, the radius of the path of the ions is $r = 0.053$ m. **a.** Calculate the mass of a neon atom. **b.** How many proton masses are in the neon atom? (The mass of a proton is 1.67×10^{-27} kg.)

Given: $V = 34$ V, $B = 0.050$ T, $r = 0.053$ m, $q = 3.2 \times 10^{-19}$ C

Unknown: m

Basic equation: $\frac{q}{m} = \frac{2V}{B^2r^2}$

a. $m = \frac{qB^2r^2}{2V}$

$= \frac{(3.2 \times 10^{-19}\text{ C})(0.050\text{-T})^2(0.053\text{ m})^2}{2(34\text{ V})}$

$= 3.3 \times 10^{-26}$ kg

b. number of protons $= \frac{3.3 \times 10^{-26}\text{ kg}}{1.67 \times 10^{-27}\text{ kg/proton}}$

$= 20$ protons

Practice Problems

5. A stream of singly-ionized lithium atoms is not deflected as it passes through a 1.5×10^{-3}-T magnetic field perpendicular to a 6.0×10^2-V/m electric field.

a. What is the speed of the lithium atoms as they pass through the crossed fields?

b. The lithium atoms move into a 0.18-T magnetic field. They follow a circular path of radius 0.165 m. What is the mass of a lithium atom?

CHECKING FOR UNDERSTANDING

Choose suitable problems from the end of the chapter to go over with students to help assess their understanding of measuring the mass of the electron and the operation of the mass spectrometer. Make sure that they can explain their answers.

RETEACHING

Draw two oppositely charged, parallel plates on the board. Review with students how the electric field between them affects a charged particle. Do the same thing for a uniform magnetic field, reviewing the third right-hand rule. Now ask how these fields would have to be directed to make the electric and magnetic forces on the charged particle oppose each other. With this background, students should be able to understand the charge-to-mass ratio more easily.

EXTENSION

In order for the mass spectrometer to work correctly, it is necessary for all the charged particles that enter the bending magnet to have the same velocity and charge. Have interested students find out how this is accomplished.

Answers To

PRACTICE PROBLEMS

Have students refer to Appendix A of the Solutions Appendix for complete solutions to Practice Problems.

5. a. 4.0×10^5 m/s

b. 1.2×10^{-26} kg

26:1 ASSIGNMENT GUIDE

	PRACTICE	EXTENSION
CHAPTER REVIEW pp. 551–553		
· Reviewing Concepts	1–2	
· Applying Concepts		1–6
· Problems*	1–5, 7, 8, 10–13	6, 9, 14, 15
APPENDIX B PROBLEMS*		
· Chapter 24, p. 707	1–10	11

* Complete solutions to all Chapter Review and Appendix problems appear in the Problems and Solutions Manual.

Answers To

PRACTICE PROBLEMS (cont.)

6. 6.8×10^{-26} kg

7. 2.7×10^{-26} kg

8. 6 mm

3 Close

CONVERGENT QUESTION

Particle physicists often study charged particles in bubble chambers (see Chapter 30) that bend particles with a large uniform magnetic field. These physicists say that, for a given kind of particle, the radius is proportional to the particle's momentum. Ask students why this is correct. [In the equation $r = mv/qB$, q and B are constant, so r depends on mv, the momentum.]

CONCEPT REVIEW ANSWERS

1.1 a. No

b. For same r, v, and q, B is proportional to m, so B would have to be larger.

1.2 When the electric field was turned off, the ion beam's radius would have been half as much ($r = mv/qB$).

1.3 $r = \dfrac{1}{B}\sqrt{\dfrac{2Vm}{q}}$, so as m increases, so must B. If m is raised by a factor of about 10, B would have to go up a factor of about 3 because to keep r constant, B must increase as $\sqrt{m}$.

1.4 Critical Thinking: It must be only a single elementary charge.

26.2 ELECTRIC AND MAGNETIC FIELDS IN SPACE

Preparation

OBJECTIVES

The objectives are listed on the student page. Remind students to preview these objectives as a study guide to this major section.

OVERVIEW

The concepts introduced include antenna, receiver, gamma rays, X rays, piezoelectricity, and electromagnetic radiation.

BRIDGING

Previously discussed concepts include acceleration, resonance, frequency, thermal energy, speed of light, polarization, generator, capacitor, pendulum, potential and kinetic energy, voltage, nucleus, *EMF*, anode, and cathode. Much of electricity and magnetism is explained in terms of mechanical principles.

LAB WORKSHEET

Use the Lab Worksheet for Chapter 26 with this Physics Lab.

6. A mass spectrometer gives data for a beam of doubly-ionized argon atoms. The values are $B = 5.0 \times 10^{-2}$ T, $q = 2(1.6 \times 10^{-19}$ C), $r = 0.106$ m, and $V = 66.0$ V. Find the mass of an argon atom.

7. A beam of singly-ionized oxygen atoms is sent through a mass spectrometer. The values are $B = 7.2 \times 10^{-2}$ T, $q = 1.6 \times 10^{-19}$ C, $r = 0.085$ m, and $V = 110$ V. Find the mass of an oxygen atom.

▶ **8.** The Example Problem found the mass of a neon isotope. Another neon isotope has a mass of 22 proton masses. How far on the film from the first isotope would these ions land?

CONCEPT REVIEW

1.1 Consider what changes Thomson would have to make to change his q/m tube from electrons to protons. **a.** To select particles of the same velocity, would the ratio E/B have to be changed? **b.** To have the deflection caused by the magnetic field alone be the same, would the B field have to be made smaller or larger? Explain.

1.2 As Thomson raised the energy of the electrons producing the ions, he found ions with two positive elementary charges rather than just one. How would he have recognized this?

1.3 A modern mass spectrometer can analyze molecules having masses of hundreds of proton masses. If their singly-charged ions are produced using the same accelerating voltage, how would the magnetic field have to be changed for them to hit the film?

1.4 **Critical Thinking:** Thomson did not know the number of electrons in the atoms. He found with most atoms that, as he raised the energy of the electrons that produced ions, he would first get ions with one electron missing, then ions with two missing, and so on. With hydrogen, however, he could never remove more than one electron. What could he then conclude about the positive charge of the hydrogen atom?

Objectives

- describe formation of electric and magnetic fields without charges.
- describe the generation of electromagnetic waves by accelerated charges; recognize the use of resonance.
- know the frequency and wavelength of common electromagnetic waves.
- explain how electromagnetic waves can be detected.

26.2 ELECTRIC AND MAGNETIC FIELDS IN SPACE

Signals from galaxies, satellites, and television stations are electromagnetic waves. The properties of electric and magnetic fields were studied over most of the last century. In 1820 Oersted did his work on magnetic fields, and eleven years later Faraday discovered induction. In that year James Clerk Maxwell, a Scottish physicist, was born. In the 1860s, Maxwell predicted that even without wires, electric fields changing in time cause magnetic fields, and the magnetic fields changing in time produce electric fields. The result of this coupling is energy transmitted across empty space in the form of electromagnetic waves. Maxwell's theory led to a complete description of electricity and magnetism. It also gave us radio, television, and many other devices important to our lives.

PHYSICS LAB Homemade Mass Spectrometer

Purpose

To simulate the working parts of a mass spectrometer.

Materials

- ball of clay
- grooved ruler
- 6-mm steel ball
- glass marble
- 2 permanent magnets
- cafeteria tray or glass wave tank
- graph paper
- masking tape

Procedure

1. Build the apparatus as shown in the diagram below. Place a ball of clay under one side of the wave tank so that the tank is slightly sloped.
2. Make a test trial allowing the steel ball to roll down the track. The ball should follow a path similar to the one shown in the diagram when started one-half way up the ruler.
3. Starting from the same spot, roll the steel ball down the track three times. Mark the positions where the ball crosses the far side of the graph paper.
4. Place the permanent magnet(s) on the paper so they pull the ball slightly upward. Adjust the magnet(s) so that the ball crosses the far side of the graph paper on the same line as the end of the ramp.

Observations and Data

1. Describe the path of the ball in step 3.
2. What happens to the path as the magnet is brought closer to the path of the ball? Why?

Analysis

1. In this model, you used gravity to simulate the electric field of a mass spectrometer. How could the electric field in this model be varied?

Applications

1. Predict what would happen to a 6-mm ball that had the same mass, but less or no iron content. Explain your prediction. Test it.

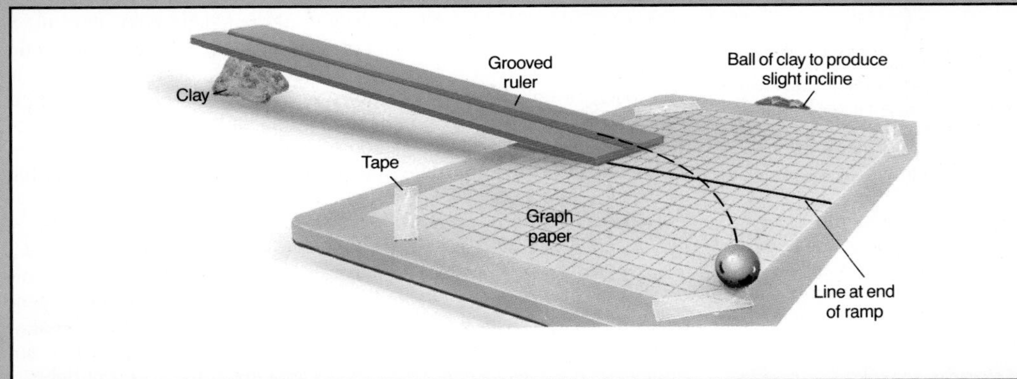

PHYSICS LAB

Process Skills: formulating models, observing, communicating, predicting, hypothesizing, questioning.

MISCONCEPTION

The concept of charged particles being deflected in electric and magnetic fields is often confusing.

Teaching Suggestion: Students should be asked to discuss the limitations of this model. For example, ask what path a neutral particle will follow. How could one simulate a particle that has more mass but the same charge?

Lab Worksheet, Teacher Resource Package. If desired, use the lab worksheet master for this chapter for students to record their data.

OBSERVATIONS

1. The ball follows a parabolic curve. It accelerates downward.
2. The magnetic force increases as the magnet is brought closer to the ball. If the ball gets too close to the magnet, the ball will move upward.

ANALYSIS

Increasing the slope of the wave tank would be similar to increasing the electric field.

APPLICATIONS

A ball with less iron content would not be affected as much by the magnets. A glass marble, for example, would not be affected by the magnets.

ASSESSMENT

Critical Thinking: To further assess students' understanding of mass spectrometers, ask the following questions.

1. If the ball leaves the ruler with more speed, then the path will curve less, even though the force on the ball is the same. Why? [A faster-moving ball curves less because the force acts for less time.]
2. Thomson adjusted the magnetic force to exactly cancel the electrical force. When this was done, the electrons moved without curving. Do you think it would be possible to place magnet(s) above the ball to make it travel straight across the ramp? Explain. [It is extremely unlikely that magnets could be placed so the balls did not curve. This would require that the ball move through an area where the magnetic effect on the ball was exactly equal to the gravitational effect. Thomson used electromagnets for his magnetic fields, not permanent magnets.]

1 Focus

Demonstration: Tune a small, battery-powered radio to an AM station. Let it play at one end of the demonstration desk, and at the other end, turn a light bulb off and on by unscrewing it in its socket. You'll be able to hear static (or clicks) in the radio because the light bulb has broadcast a signal to the radio. Sometimes it works better if you tune the radio in between stations.

2 Teach

CONCEPT DEVELOPMENT

Notice how Maxwell's theory encompassed optics. The theoretical framework allowed light to be understood as a particular kind of electromagnetic wave. The theory also predicted the existence of electromagnetic waves and that their speed should be the speed of light.

Study Guide Master. To reinforce the concepts in this section, have the students complete the Study Guide Master for Section 26.2 from the Teacher Resource Package.

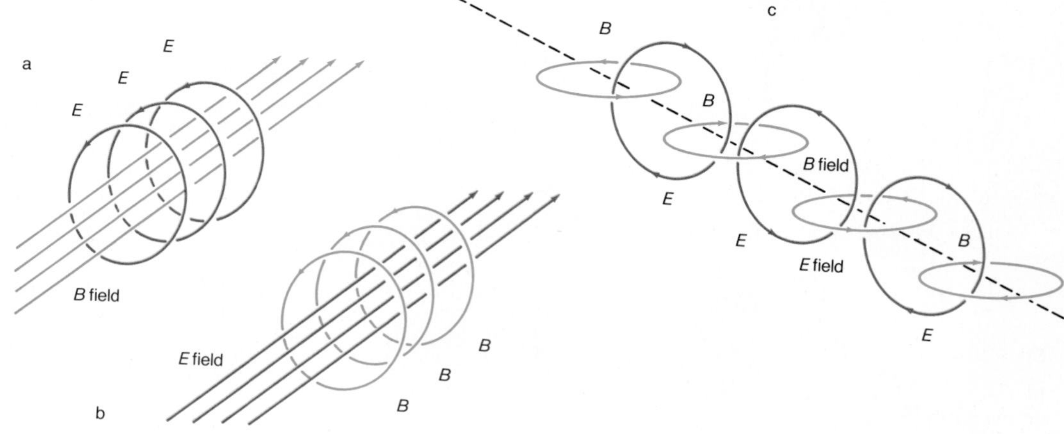

FIGURE 26–5. Representation of an induced electric field (a), magnetic field (b), and both electric and magnetic fields (c).

Electromagnetic Waves

Changing magnetic fields induce changing electric fields.

Oersted found that an electric current in a conductor produces a magnetic field. Changing the current changes the magnetic field, and, as Faraday discovered, changing the magnetic field can induce an electric current in a wire. Furthermore, the current-producing electric fields exist even without a wire, Figure 26–5a. Thus *a changing magnetic field produces a changing electric field.* The field lines of the induced electric field will be closed loops because, unlike an electrostatic field, there are no charges on which the lines begin or end.

Changing electric fields induce changing magnetic fields.

In 1860 Maxwell postulated that the opposite is also true. *A changing electric field produces a changing magnetic field,* Figure 26–5b. Maxwell suggested that charges were not necessary; the changing electric field alone would produce the magnetic field.

Maxwell then predicted that either accelerating charges or changing magnetic fields would produce electric and magnetic fields that move through space. The combined fields are called an **electromagnetic wave**. The speed at which the wave moves, calculated Maxwell, was the speed of light, 3.00×10^8 m/s, as measured by Fizeau in 1849. Not only were electricity and magnetism linked, but optics, the study of light, became a branch of the study of electricity and magnetism. Heinrich Hertz (1857–1894), a German physicist, demonstrated in 1887 that Maxwell's theory was correct.

Figure 26–6 shows the formation of an electromagnetic wave. A wire, called an **antenna**, is connected to an alternating current (AC) source. The source produces changing currents in the antenna that alternate at the frequency of the AC source. The changing currents generate a changing electric field that moves outward from the antenna. There is also a magnetic field perpendicular to the page that is not shown. The waves spread out in space, moving at the speed of light.

F.Y.I.

The Federal Communications Commission assigns each radio and TV station a carrier wave with a specific frequency. A station broadcasts talk or music by varying, or modulating, its carrier wave. When the wave is received by your radio or TV set, the carrier wave is stripped away and the "information" from the wave is processed so you can see or hear it.

TEACHER F.Y.I.

Maxwell's equations indicated that the wave velocities for both the electric and magnetic fields equal the speed of light. This led to his prediction that light waves are a form of electromagnetic radiation (EMR). In 1887, Hertz generated and detected EMR in the range of radio waves, instigating research into "wireless" communication which led to the development of radio and TV.

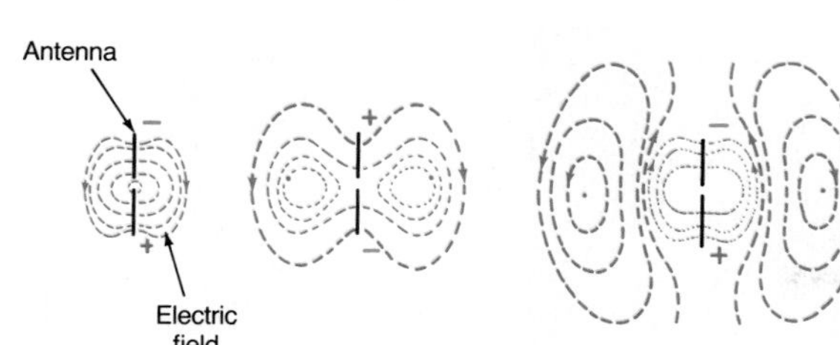

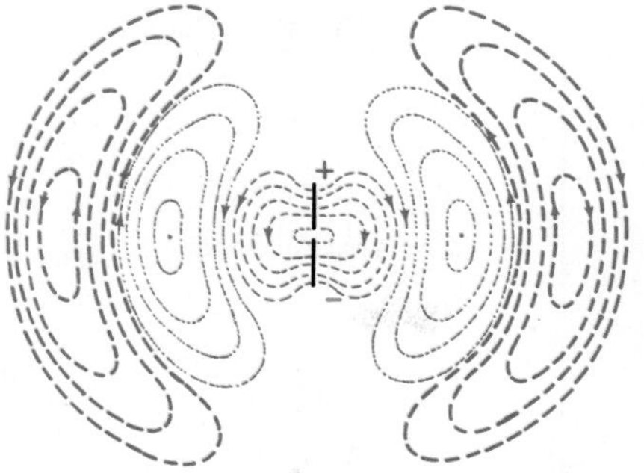

FIGURE 26–6. The changing current in the antenna generates a changing electric field. The changing electric field generates a changing magnetic field (not shown).

If you stood to the right of the antenna as the waves approached, you could visualize the electric and magnetic fields changing in time, Figure 26–7. The electric field oscillates, first up, then down. The magnetic field also oscillates at right angles to the electric field. The two fields are also at right angles to the direction of the motion of the wave. An electromagnetic wave produced by the antenna in Figure 26–6 is polarized. That is, the electric field is always parallel to the direction of the antenna wires.

The electric and magnetic fields are at right angles to each other and to the direction of motion of the wave.

Production of Electromagnetic Waves

Electromagnetic waves can be generated over a wide range of frequencies. Figure 26–8 shows the electromagnetic spectrum. One method of creating the oscillating fields in the antenna has already been described, the AC generator. Frequency can be changed by varying the speed at which the generator is rotated. The highest frequency that can be generated in this way is about 1000 Hz.

The most common method of generating higher frequencies is to use a coil and capacitor connected in a series circuit. If the capacitor is charged by a battery, the potential difference across the capacitor creates an electric field. When the battery is removed, the capacitor discharges, and the stored electrons flow through the coil, creating a magnetic field. After the capacitor has discharged, the magnetic field of the coil collapses. A back-*EMF* develops that recharges the capacitor, this

A coil-capacitor combination resonates at frequencies of radio and television waves.

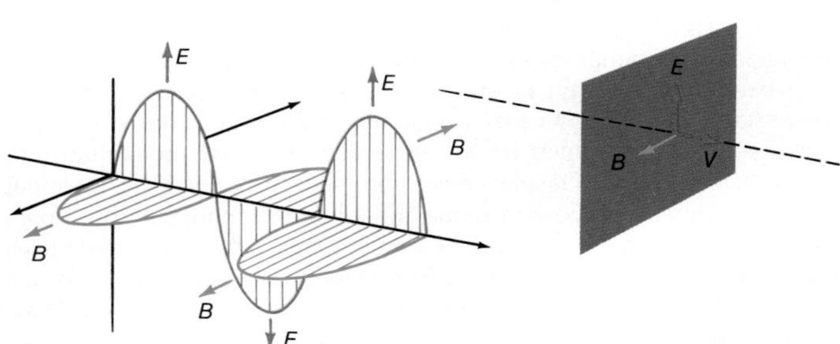

FIGURE 26–7. A look at portions of the electric and magnetic fields at an instant in time.

CONCEPT DEVELOPMENT

- In his researches with electromagnetic waves, Heinrich Hertz built a large (approximately 600 kg) prism made of asphalt to test whether or not such waves were refracted. He found that indeed they were, and that asphalt had an index of refraction of 1.69 for the 60-cm wavelength he was using.
- Magnetic fields circle around an electric current and around a changing electric field such as that of a capacitor.

STUDY GUIDE MASTER

Use the Study Guide master for section 26.2.

CONCEPT DEVELOPMENT

- The concepts behind electrical phenomena are often illustrated by analogy—usually to mechanical systems. The pendulum analogy here is but one of many examples.
- Notice on Figure 26–8 that as the wavelength becomes shorter, the size of the device producing the wave becomes smaller. We started with radio antennas that produce long radio waves and ended with the nuclei of atoms that produce very short gamma rays.

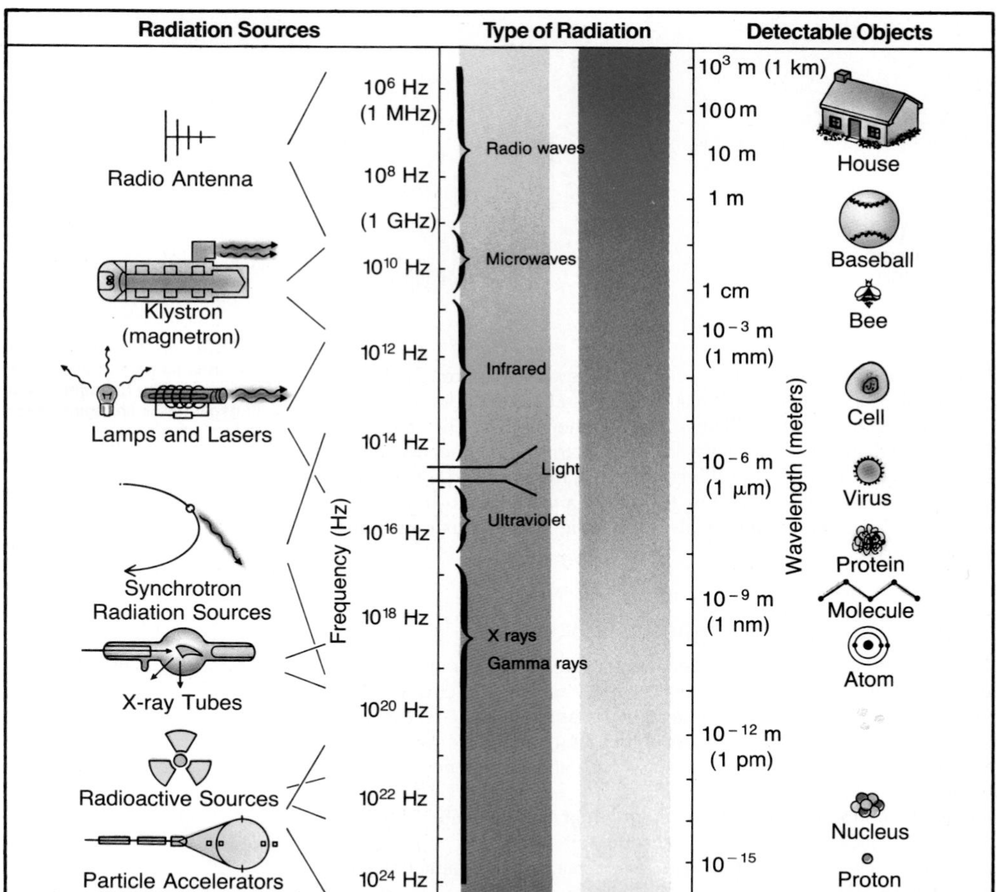

FIGURE 26–8. Representative examples of various types of electromagnetic radiation.

A pendulum is a good model of resonance in a coil-capacitor circuit.

time in the opposite direction. The capacitor again discharges, and so on. One complete oscillation cycle is seen in Figure 26–9. The number of oscillations each second is called the frequency, which depends on the size of the capacitor and the coil. The antenna, connected across the capacitor, extends the fields of the capacitor into space.

A pendulum analogy, Figure 26–10, is a good model to help you understand the coil and capacitor circuit. The electrons in the coil and capacitor are represented by the pendulum bob. The pendulum bob moves fastest when its displacement from vertical is zero. This is similar to the largest current flowing in the coil when the charge on the capacitor is zero. When the bob is at its greatest angle, its displacement from the vertical is largest, and it has a zero velocity. This position is like the instant when the capacitor holds the largest charge and the current through the coil is zero.

Multicultural Connections

A phenomenon that has yet to be explained was photographed by a Japanese scientist named Yasui in 1968 and again in 1971. Earthquake light has been seen as a faint red and white glow visible for hundreds of miles around a fault zone just before the ground starts to shake. Among the theories put forward to explain it is one by another Japanese scientist, Mitzutani. His idea is that the high pressure on the fault causes an electrical effect in quartz in the ground (called a piezoelectric effect) that creates a high electric field and results in a corona. Another corona theory is that hot, ionized gases escape from the ground just prior to the quake and cause the corona. Neither explanation has been proved or disproved, although Mitzutani's seems to require electrical fields that would generate much more heat than is observed.

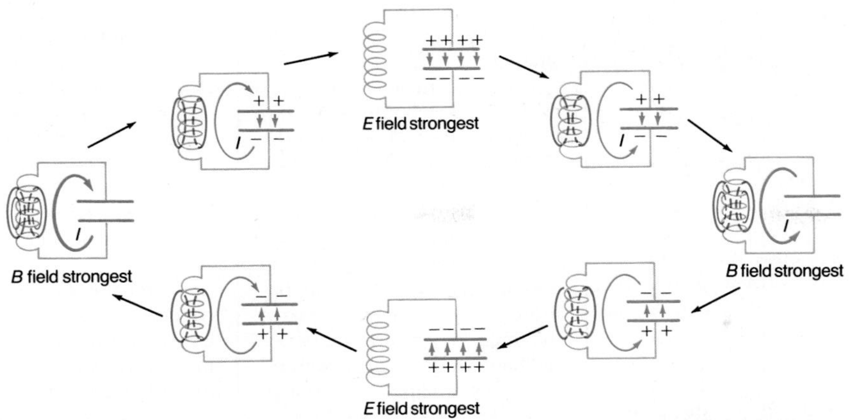

FIGURE 26–9. Production of electromagnetic waves.

The model can be used when considering energy. The potential energy of the pendulum is largest when its displacement is greatest. The kinetic energy is largest when the velocity is greatest. The sum of the potential and kinetic energies, the total energy, is constant. Both the magnetic field produced by the coil and the electric field in the capacitor contain energy. When the current is largest, the energy stored in the magnetic field is greatest. When the current is zero, the electric field of the capacitor is largest and all the energy is in the electric field. The total energy, the sum of magnetic field energy and electric field energy, is constant. The electromagnetic waves carry this energy through space in the form of electric and magnetic fields. Energy carried, or radiated, this way is frequently called **electromagnetic radiation**.

Energy must be added periodically to keep the oscillation going.

Just as the pendulum will eventually stop swinging if left alone, due to resistance in the circuit, the oscillations in a coil and capacitor will also die out if energy is not added to the circuit. Gentle pushes, applied at the correct times, will keep a pendulum moving. The largest amplitude swing occurs when the frequency of pushing is the same as the frequency of swinging. This is the condition of resonance discussed in

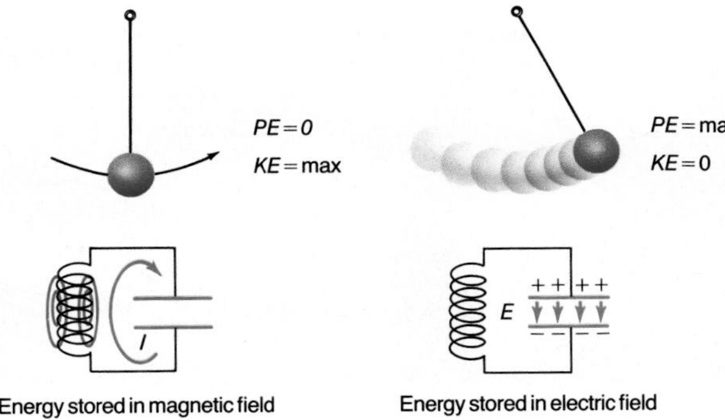

FIGURE 26–10. A pendulum is analogous to the action of electrons in a coil and capacitor combination.

CONCEPT DEVELOPMENT

- You may have students in your class who are ham radio operators. They can be a valuable resource on the details of radio transmission and reception. They may even be able to bring in equipment for demonstration purposes. Or, you may have a ham radio club in your school that you can use as a resource.
- Microwaves leave no residue of "radiation" in warmed food. In fact, microwaves don't have the energy necessary to ionize molecules in the way that alpha, beta, or gamma rays do.

Transparency Package. Use Transparency 38 to help illustrate electromagnetic radiation.

TRANSPARENCY

Use Transparency 38 with this section.

Physics and society

Answers To
DEVELOPING A VIEWPOINT

1. Probably not. The particles in the atmosphere are not desirable because they may block sunlight, create haze, or be the depositories of materials that may be hazardous when respired. Also, the concentration of particles may not be a constant and, therefore, cannot be counted on to balance the increasing carbon dioxide levels for a long period of time.
2. Where would crops be planted? Some presently arid regions might get more rainfall while the present crop-growing areas of the world could become extremely dry. The new crop-growing areas might have poor soils and might not be prepared to farm, store, and distribute large amounts of grain or other crops. This could lead to food shortages.
3. Students may suggest ways to decrease emissions of carbon dioxide and other gases, such as chlorofluorocarbons and methane, into the atmosphere. Cutting our combustion of fossil fuels and replacing these energy sources with alternative energy sources is one possibility. Using refrigerants other than chlorofluorocarbons is another possibility. Global planning to adapt to possibly inevitable climate changes may be a third possibility.

Teacher Resources: Bjerklie, David. "Greenhouse Initiatives." *Technology Review*, April 1990, pages 21–22.
Kerr, Richard A. "Greenhouse Skeptic Out in the Cold." *Science* 246 (4934), December 1, 1989, pages 1118–1119.
Ramanathan, V., Barkstrom, Bruce R., and Harrison, Edwin F. "Climate and the Earth's Radiation Budget." *Physics Today* 42 (5), May 1989, pages 22–32.

Critical Thinking Master, Teacher Resource Package. You may wish to have students complete the Critical Thinking Master, Interference, with this section.

Physics and society

THE GREENHOUSE EFFECT

For many people, the phrase "greenhouse effect" brings fears of polar ice caps melting and of coastal cities being flooded. For others, the words describe a simple, useful process that florists use to grow plants. Just what is the greenhouse effect?

The sun emits radiations of short wavelengths, most of which are transmitted through Earth's atmosphere. Earth radiates energy of longer wavelengths back into the atmosphere. This longer-wavelength radiation, infrared, is absorbed by atmospheric components such as carbon dioxide, water vapor, methane, chlorofluorocarbons, and nitrous oxide. These molecules reemit this radiation in all directions, some of the radiation going into space, some going back toward Earth's surface. The radiation that goes into space provides cooling that is necessary to maintain the thermal energy balance of Earth and its atmosphere.

This process is known as the greenhouse effect because a greenhouse that florists use also traps Earth's radiation. Glass is transparent to short-wavelength radiation but not to the longer wavelengths emitted by Earth; this warms a greenhouse. This analogy is only partly correct, because most of the warming inside a greenhouse occurs because air circulation is restricted.

The concern in recent years over the greenhouse effect has focused on carbon dioxide, (CO_2), because its concentration in the atmosphere is increasing. Since the beginning of the industrial revolution, CO_2 concentration has risen from 280 to 350 parts per million. More CO_2 molecules means that more of the surface-emitted radiation will be absorbed and less will escape into space, with the result that the thermal energy balance may be upset and the average temperature of Earth may increase.

Although the past few years have been warmer than normal, this might not be the result of the greenhouse effect. Scientists do not yet fully understand Earth's atmosphere. Predicting the future is also difficult.

DEVELOPING A VIEWPOINT

More research is needed to predict the effects of increased amounts of greenhouse gases on global temperature. Read as much as you can on the subject and come to class prepared to discuss the following questions.

1. Assume that the temperature increase caused by increased CO_2 in the atmosphere is balanced by the temperature decrease brought about by polluting particles reflecting infrared radiation into space. Do you see this situation as acceptable?
2. Probably one of the major effects of a warmer Earth would be shifts in rainfall patterns and in crop-growing regions. How might this be a problem?
3. What are your recommendations for dealing with the possibility that increasing levels of CO_2 may warm the planet several degrees over the next century?

SUGGESTED READINGS

Gushee, David E. "Global Climate Change." CHEMTECH 19 (8), August 1989, pp. 470–479.
Levi, Barbara Goss. "Climate Modelers Struggle to Understand Global Warming." *Physics Today* 43 (2), February 1990, pp. 17–19: "Scientific Perspectives on the Greenhouse Effect." *Consumers' Research* 73 (4), April 1990, pp. 22–24, 36.

CRITICAL THINKING
Use the Critical Thinking master for Chapter 26 with this section.

TRANSPARENCY
Use Transparency 22 with this section.

RETEACHING MASTER
Use the Reteaching master for Chapter 26 with this section.

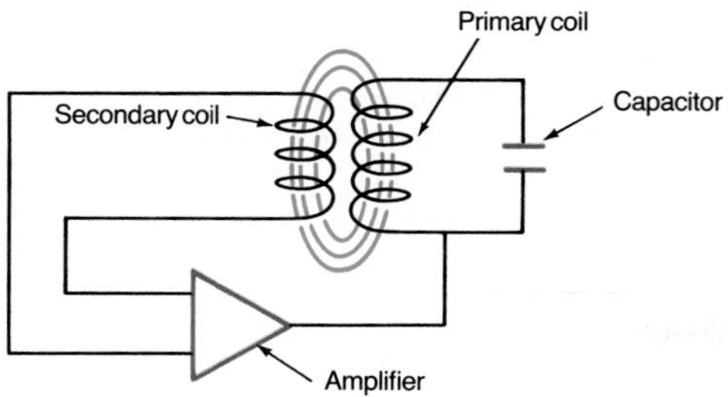

FIGURE 26–11. The amplified pulse from the secondary coil is in resonance with the coil-capacitor circuit and keeps the oscillations going.

Chapter 7. Voltage pulses applied to the coil-capacitor circuit at the right frequency keep the oscillations going. One way of doing this is to add a second coil to form a transformer, Figure 26–11. The AC induced in the secondary coil is increased by an amplifier and added back to the coil and capacitor. This type of circuit can produce frequencies up to approximately 100 MHz.

Coils and capacitors are not the only method of generating oscillation voltages. Quartz crystals have a property called **piezoelectricity**. They bend or deform when a voltage is applied across them. Just as a piece of metal will vibrate at a specific frequency when it is bent and released, so will a quartz crystal. A crystal can be cut so that it will vibrate at a specific desired frequency. An applied voltage bends it to start it vibrating. The piezoelectric property also generates an *EMF* when the crystal is bent. Since this *EMF* is produced at the vibrating frequency of the crystal, it can be amplified and returned to the crystal to keep it vibrating. Quartz crystals are used in wristwatches because the frequency of vibration is so constant. Frequencies in the range from 1 kHz to 10 MHz can be generated in this way.

To increase the oscillation frequency, the size of the coil and capacitor must be made smaller. Above 1000 MHz, individual coils and capacitors will not work. For these electromagnetic waves, called microwaves, a rectangular box, called a resonant cavity, acts as both a coil and a capacitor. The size of the box determines the frequency of oscillation. Such a cavity is in every microwave oven.

At frequencies of infrared waves, the size of resonant cavities would have to be reduced to the size of molecules. The oscillating electrons that produce infrared waves are in fact within the molecules. Visible and ultraviolet waves are generated by electrons within atoms.

X rays can be generated by electrons in heavy atoms. **Gamma rays** are the result of accelerating charges in the nucleus of an atom. Most electromagnetic waves arise from accelerated charges and travel at the speed of light.

Reception of Electromagnetic Waves

Electromagnetic waves are caused by the acceleration of electrons in an antenna. When the electric fields in these electromagnetic waves strike another antenna, Figure 26–12, they accelerate the electrons in it. The acceleration is largest when the antenna is turned in the direction

POCKET LAB

CATCHING THE WAVE

When you listen to your radio you are hearing the information that is carried by electromagnetic waves. Many electronic and electrical devices produce low frequency electromagnetic waves. Use the telephone pickup coil along with the amplifier to try to pick up signals from televisions, computers, lights, burning candles, coffee makers, vacuum cleaners, and so on. Describe your results.

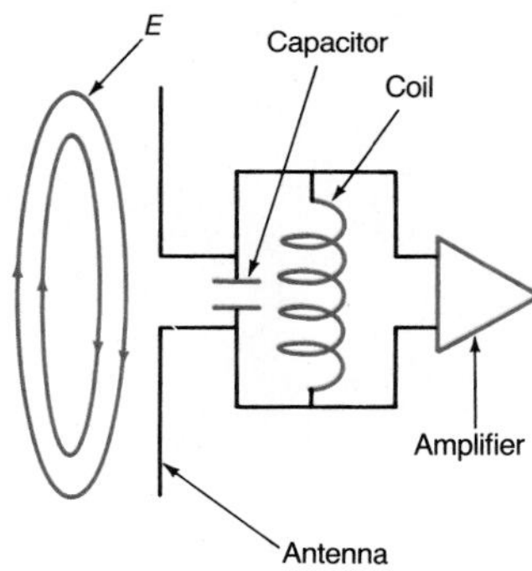

FIGURE 26–12. The changing electric fields from a radio station cause electrons in the antenna to accelerate.

Assessment

Performance

To further assess students' understanding of electromagnetic waves, have them do the following. When they have found a strong emitter of electromagnetic waves, have them find methods of blocking the waves. For example, they might try pieces of transparent plastic or opaque paper. Does aluminum foil work? In any case, is it enough to place a piece between the source and the pickup coil? Does thickness make any difference? Have them report their results. [They should find that only a metal blocks the waves. Although a piece put between sources and detector may have some effect, they usually must tightly wrap either the source or the detector to eliminate all transmission.

POCKET LAB

CATCHING THE WAVE

Purpose: to detect the electromagnetic waves that are produced by common appliances.

Materials: telephone pickup coil; mini audio amplifier; 9-V battery; common household appliances.

Outcome: Most appliances produce a humming sound at 60 Hz. Televisions produce a great deal of electromagnetic waves. Computers and electronic balances also produce many electromagnetic waves and will create a high-pitched whine. All the sounds are due to induced currents in the pickup coil.

CONCEPT DEVELOPMENT

CHECKING FOR UNDERSTANDING

In one of his experiments, Hertz beamed electromagnetic radiation onto a flat metal surface so that it was reflected back to the source. When he did this, he detected a series of nodes and antinodes. Ask students to explain the reason for this phenomenon. [He had set up a pattern of standing electromagnetic waves.]

RETEACHING

Reteaching Master, Teacher Resource Package. Use the Reteaching Master, Electromagnetic Waves, for Chapter 26.

Transparency Package. Reteach the electromagnetic spectrum using Transparency 22 and accompanying worksheet. Stress that the visible portion is only a very small part of the whole.

EXTENSION

It is thought that the piezoelectric phenomenon is involved in the growth and repair of human bones. Have interested students investigate this research claim.

CONCEPT DEVELOPMENT

Guided Practice: Go over the Concept Review Problems on page 551 in class. Have students provide explanations for their answers.

INDEPENDENT PRACTICE/ EXTENSION

Refer to the Assignment Guide below for additional questions and problems for independent practice.

3 Close

CONVERGENT QUESTION

Ask students to describe an electromagnetic wave. What are its two chief components? How do these two components influence each other?

Assessment

Portfolio

Interview personnel at a local dentist's office and a hospital to find out how X rays are generated, how operators are shielded, and how the dose of X rays is controlled.

Electromagnetic waves induce changing electric fields in a receiving antenna.

of the polarization of the wave. That is, when it is parallel to the direction of the electric fields in the wave. An *EMF* across the terminals of the antenna oscillates at the frequency of the electromagnetic wave. The *EMF* is largest if the length of the antenna is one half the wavelength of the wave. The antenna then resonates in the same way an open pipe one-half wavelength long resonates with sound waves. For that reason, an antenna designed to receive radio waves is much longer than one designed to receive microwaves.

While a simple wire antenna can detect electromagnetic waves, several wires can be used to increase the detected *EMF*. A television antenna often consists of two or more wires spaced about one-quarter wavelength apart. Electric fields generated in the individual wires form constructive interference patterns that increase the strength of the signal.

Big Ears ▶ At very short wavelengths, parabolic dishes reflect the waves just as parabolic mirrors reflect light waves. Giant parabolic dishes focus waves with wavelengths of 2- to 6-cm on the antennas held by the tripod above the dish.

A coil-capacitor circuit allows only the signal with the selected frequency to be amplified.

Radio and television waves are used to transmit information across space. There are many different radio and television stations producing electromagnetic waves at the same time. If the information being broadcast is to be understood, it must be possible to select the waves of a particular station. To select waves of a particular frequency and reject the others, a coil and capacitor circuit is connected to the antenna. The capacitance is adjusted until the oscillation frequency of the circuit equals the frequency of the desired wave. Only this frequency can cause significant oscillations of the electrons in the circuit. The information carried by the oscillations is then amplified and ultimately drives a loudspeaker. The combination of antenna, coil and capacitor circuit, and amplifier is called a **receiver**.

Waves carry energy as well as information. At microwave and infrared frequencies, the electromagnetic waves accelerate electrons in molecules. The energy of the electromagnetic waves is converted to thermal energy in the molecules. Microwaves cook foods in this way. Infrared waves from the sun produce the warmth we feel.

Light waves can transfer energy to electrons in atoms. In photographic film, this energy causes a chemical reaction. The result is a permanent record of the light reaching the camera from the subject. In the eye, the energy produces a chemical reaction that stimulates a nerve, resulting in a response in our brain that we call vision. At higher frequencies, UV radiation causes many chemical reactions to occur, including those that produce sunburn and tanning.

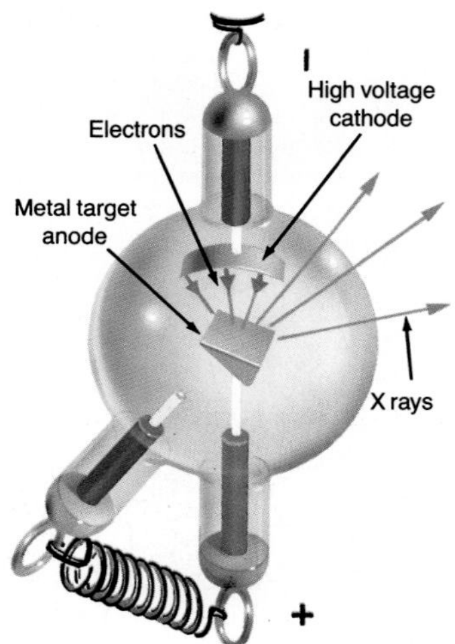

FIGURE 26–13. This tube is similar to the one used by Moseley in studying X rays. The metal target in the X-ray tube can be changed to produce X rays of different wavelengths.

X Rays

In 1895 in Germany, Wilhelm Roentgen (1845–1923) sent electrons through an evacuated glass tube. Roentgen used a very high voltage across the tube to give the electrons a large kinetic energy. The electrons struck the metal anode of the tube. When this happened, Roentgen noted a glow on a phosphorescent screen a short distance away. The glow continued even if a piece of wood was placed between the tube and the screen. He concluded that some kind of highly-penetrating rays were coming from the tube.

Connect to BIOLOGY

X rays that fall on human tissue, or any material, have enough energy to knock electrons from atoms. The energy of the X ray is given up to the potential energy of the electron, which frees it from the atom, and to the kinetic energy of the fast-moving electron that results. The more electrons on an atom, the greater the chance that the X ray will free an electron, and thus be blocked. Therefore, materials that are both dense and have a large number of electrons per atom absorb X rays most efficiently. The speeding electrons created by the X ray have the potential of removing electrons from other atoms. The ions created can undergo chemical reactions that damage the tissue. Although the body, over time, can repair the damage, frequent exposure to X rays can cause lasting damage. How might users protect themselves from X rays? [Build a shield of material that has high density and many electrons per atom. The best material is lead.]

Because Roentgen did not know what these strange rays were, he called them X rays. A few weeks later, Roentgen found that photographic plates were darkened by X rays. He also discovered that soft body tissue was transparent to the rays, but that bone blocked them. He produced an X-ray picture of his wife's hand. Within months, doctors recognized the medical uses of this phenomenon.

It is now known that X rays are high frequency electromagnetic waves. They are produced when electrons are accelerated to high speeds by means of potential differences of 20 000 volts or more, Figure 26–13. When the electrons crash into matter, their kinetic energies are converted into very-high frequency electromagnetic waves, or X rays.

Electrons are accelerated to these speeds in cathode-ray tubes, such as the picture tube in a television. When the electrons hit the faceplate, they cause the colored phosphors to glow. The sudden stopping of the electrons can also produce X rays. The faceplate glass contains lead to stop the X rays and protect viewers.

BIOLOGY CONNECTION

CONCEPT REVIEW

2.1 What was Maxwell's contribution to electromagnetism?

2.2 Television antennas normally have the metal rod elements horizontal. From that, what can you deduce about the directions of the electric fields in television signals?

2.3 Television Channels 2-6 have frequencies just below the FM radio band, while Channels 7-13 have much higher frequencies. Which signals would require a longer antenna, Channel 7 or Channel 6?

2.4 **Critical Thinking:** Most of the UV radiation from the sun is blocked by the ozone layer in Earth's atmosphere. Recently scientists have found "holes" in the ozone layer over both Antarctica and the Arctic Ocean. Why should we be concerned about this?

CHAPTER 26 REVIEW

SUMMARY

26.1 Action of Electric and Magnetic Fields on Matter

- The ratio of charge to mass of the electron was measured by J. J. Thomson using balanced electric and magnetic fields.
- The mass of the electron can be found by combining Thomson's result with Millikan's measurement of the electron charge.
- The mass spectrometer uses both electric and magnetic fields to measure the masses of atoms and molecules.

26.2 Electric and Magnetic Fields in Space

- An electric field changing in time generates a changing magnetic field.
- A changing magnetic field generates a changing electric field in space.
- Electromagnetic waves are coupled changing electric and magnetic fields that move through space.
- Changing currents in a transmitting antenna generate electromagnetic waves.
- The frequency of oscillating currents can be selected by a resonating coil and capacitor circuit.

CONCEPT REVIEW ANSWERS

2.1 He postulated that magnetic fields are produced by changing electric fields as well as by currents.

2.2 They must also be horizontal.

2.3 Channel 6

2.4 **Critical Thinking:** If the holes are an indication that the entire ozone layer is thinning, it would cause a decrease in the amount of UV from the sun that is absorbed by the ozone layer, allowing more UV to reach the surface of Earth. The resulting increase in UV to which humans would be exposed could increase the prevalence of skin cancer.

CLOSING CHAPTER 26

Review Summary statements and Key Terms with your students.

ASSESSMENT

Vocabulary Review Master, Teacher Resource Package. Use this master to check students' understanding of Key Terms.

Evaluation Masters. Use Parts A and B of the Chapter Evaluation Masters from the Teacher Resource Package to test qualitative chapter objectives, and Parts C and D to test quantitative chapter objectives.

26:2 ASSIGNMENT GUIDE

	PRACTICE	EXTENSION
CHAPTER REVIEW pp. 551–553		
· Reviewing Concepts	3–9	
· Applying Concepts		7–9
· Problems*	18	16, 17
APPENDIX B PROBLEMS*		
· Chapter 26, p. 707	12, 13	

* Complete solutions to all Chapter Review and Appendix problems appear in the Problems and Solutions Manual.

REVIEW MASTER

Use the Vocabulary Review master for Chapter 26 with this section.

EVALUATION MASTER

Use the Chapter Evaluation master for Chapter 26 with this section.

Answers To REVIEWING CONCEPTS

1. The mass of an electron is 9.11×10^{-31} kg and the charge on an electron is -1.60×10^{-19} C.
2. Isotopes are atoms of the same element that have different masses.
3. An induced magnetic field is always at right angles to the changing electric field.
4. Microwaves are reflected by metal, thus keeping the energy from the soup. The ceramic mug transmits microwaves, whereas the water of the soup absorbs them.
5. An AC generator supplies the changing electric field which in turn generates a changing magnetic field. A DC generator would only generate a changing electric field when turned on or off.
6.

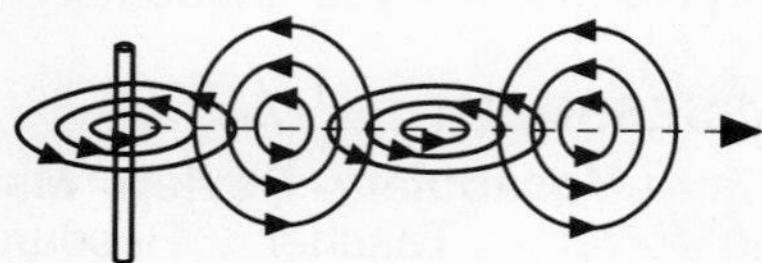

7. Quartz crystals bond or deform when a voltage is placed across them. The quartz crystal will then vibrate at a set frequency.
8. Electric fields are vertical and magnetic fields are horizontal.
9. By adjusting the capacitance of the antenna circuit, the oscillation frequency of the circuit equals the frequency of the desired radio waves. Resonance occurs, causing the electrons in the circuit to oscillate at that frequency.

Answers To APPLYING CONCEPTS

1. The top plate should be charged positively.
2. The magnetic field would be directed into the plane of the paper.
3. The unit for electric field intensity, E, is $\frac{\text{N}}{\text{C}}$ and the unit for magnetic induction, B, is T or $\frac{\text{N}}{\text{A} \cdot \text{m}}$.

Therefore, the unit for $\frac{E}{B}$ is

$$\frac{\frac{\text{N}}{\text{C}}}{\frac{\text{N}}{\text{A} \cdot \text{m}}} = \frac{\text{N}}{\text{C}} \cdot \frac{\text{A} \cdot \text{m}}{\text{N}} = \frac{\text{A} \cdot \text{m}}{\text{C}}$$

$$= \frac{\text{C/s} \cdot \text{m}}{\text{C}} = \text{m/s}.$$

- Electromagnetic waves can be detected by the *EMF* they produce in the antenna of a receiver. The length of the most efficient antenna is one-half wavelength.
- Microwave and infrared waves can accelerate electrons in molecules, producing thermal energy.
- When high-energy electrons strike an anode in an evacuated tube, their kinetic energies are converted to electromagnetic waves of very high energy called X rays.

KEY TERMS

charge-to-mass ratio	electromagnetic radiation
isotopes	piezoelectricity
mass spectrometer	X rays
electromagnetic wave	gamma rays
antenna	receiver

REVIEWING CONCEPTS

1. What is the mass of an electron and what is the charge of an electron?
2. What are isotopes?
3. The direction of an induced magnetic field is always at what angle to the changing electric field?
4. Like all waves, microwaves can be transmitted, reflected, and absorbed. Why can soup be warmed in a ceramic mug in a microwave but not in a metal pan? Why does the handle of the mug not get as hot as the soup?
5. Why must an AC generator be used to propagate electromagnetic waves? If a DC generator were used, when would it create electromagnetic waves?
6. A vertical antenna wire transmits radio waves. Sketch the antenna and the electric and magnetic fields it produces.
7. What happens to quartz crystals when a voltage is placed across them?
8. Car radio antennas are vertical. What is the direction of the electric fields they detect?
9. How does an antenna receiving circuit select electromagnetic radio waves of a certain frequency and reject all others?

APPLYING CONCEPTS

1. The electrons in a Thomson tube, like the one in Figure 26–1, travel from left to right. Which deflection plate should be charged positively to bend the electron beam up?
2. The electron beam in the previous question has a magnetic field to make the beam path straight. What would be the direction of the magnetic field needed to bend the beam down?
3. Show that the units of E/B are the same as the units for velocity.
4. A mass spectrometer operates on neon ions. What is the direction of the magnetic field needed to bend the beam in a clockwise semicircle?
5. Charged particles are moving through an electric field and a magnetic field that are perpendicular to each other. Suppose you adjust the fields so that a certain ion, with the correct velocity, passes without deflection. Now another ion with the same velocity, but a different mass, enters the fields. Describe the path of the second ion.
6. If the sign of the charge on the particle in the previous question is changed from positive to negative, do the directions of either or both of the two fields have to be changed to keep the particle undeflected? Explain.
7. Of radio waves, light, or X rays, which has the largest
   a. wavelength? **b.** frequency? **c.** velocity?
8. The frequency of television waves broadcast on channel 2 is about 58 MHz. The waves on channel 7 are about 180 MHz. Which channel requires a longer antenna?
9. Suppose the eyes of an alien being are sensitive to microwaves. Would you expect such a being to have larger or smaller eyes than ours? Explain.

PROBLEMS

26.1 Action of Electric and Magnetic Fields on Matter

1. A beam of ions passes through a pair of crossed electric and magnetic fields. E is 6.0×10^5 N/C and B is 3.0×10^{-3} T. What is the speed of the ions?

2. Electrons moving at 3.6×10^4 m/s pass through an electric field of intensity 5.8×10^3 N/C. How large a magnetic field must the electrons also experience for their path to be undeflected?

3. The electrons in a beam are moving at 2.8×10^8 m/s in an electric field of 1.4×10^4 N/C. What value must the magnetic field have if the electrons pass through the crossed fields undeflected?

4. A proton moves across a 0.36-T magnetic field in a circular path of radius 0.2 m. What is the speed of the proton?

5. Electrons move across a 4.0-mT magnetic field. They follow a circular path, radius 2.0 cm.
   a. What is their speed?
   b. An electric field is applied perpendicularly to the magnetic field. The electrons then follow a straight-line path. Find the magnitude of the electric field.

▶ 6. What energy must be given to an electron to transfer it across a potential difference of 4.0×10^5 V?

7. A proton enters a 6.0×10^{-2}-T magnetic field with a speed of 5.4×10^4 m/s. What is the radius of the circular path it follows?

8. A proton enters a magnetic field of 6.4×10^{-2}T with a speed of 4.5×10^4 m/s. What is the circumference of the circular path that it follows?

▶ 9. An alpha particle has a mass of approximately 6.6×10^{-27} kg and bears a double elementary positive charge. Such a particle is observed to move through a 2.0-T magnetic field along a path of radius 0.15 m.
   a. What speed does it have?
   b. What is its kinetic energy?
   c. What potential difference would be required to give it this kinetic energy?

10. A 3.0×10^{-2}-T magnetic field in a mass spectrometer causes an isotope of sodium to move in a circular path with a radius of 0.081 m. If the ions have a single positive charge and are moving with a speed of 1.0×10^4 m/s, what is the isotope's mass?

11. An alpha particle, a doubly-ionized helium atom, has a mass of 6.7×10^{-27} kg and is accelerated by a voltage of 1.0 kV. If a uniform magnetic field of 6.5×10^{-2} T is maintained on the alpha particle, what will be the particle's radius of curvature?

12. An electron is accelerated by a 4.5-kV potential difference. How strong a magnetic field must be experienced by the electron if its path is a circle of radius 5.0 cm?

13. A mass spectrometer yields the following data for a beam of doubly-ionized sodium atoms: $B = 8.0 \times 10^{-2}$ T; $q = 2(1.60 \times 10^{-19}$ C); $r = 0.077$ m; and $V = 156$ V. Calculate the mass of a sodium atom.

▶ 14. In a mass spectrometer, ionized silicon atoms have radii with curvatures of 16.23 cm and 17.97 cm. If the smaller radius corresponds to an atomic mass of 28 units, what is the atomic mass of the other silicon isotope?

▶ 15. A mass spectrometer is used to analyze a molecule with a mass of 175×10^3 proton masses. The operator wants to know whether the carbon in the molecule has mass 12 or 13 proton masses. What percent differentiation is needed?

26.2 Electric and Magnetic Fields in Space

▶ 16. The difference in potential between the cathode and anode of a spark plug is 1.0×10^4 V.
   a. What energy does an electron give up as it passes between the electrodes?
   b. One fourth of the energy given up by the electron is converted to electromagnetic radiation. The frequency of the wave is related to the energy by the equation $E = hf$, where h is Planck's constant, 6.6×10^{-34} J/Hz. What is the frequency of the waves?

▶ 17. Television Channel 6 broadcasts on a frequency of 85 MHz.
   a. What is the wavelength of the electromagnetic wave broadcast on Channel 6?
   b. What is the length of an antenna that will detect Channel 6 most easily?

18. The radio waves reflected by a parabolic dish are 2.0 cm long. How long is the antenna that detects the waves?

THINKING PHYSIC-LY

H.G. Wells wrote a science fiction book called *The Invisible Man,* in which a man drinks a potion and becomes invisible, although he retains all of his other faculties. If this could actually be accomplished, however, the subject would be blind. Explain.

4. The magnetic field is found by the right-hand rule and would be directed outside the plane of the semicircle.
5. The second ion also passes without deflection. The equation $V = E/B$ is independent of the mass or charge of the particle.
6. Change either both fields or neither field, never only one field.
7. a. Radio waves have the longest wavelength. **b.** X rays have the highest frequency. **c.** All travel at the same velocity, the speed of light.
8. Channel 2 waves have a lower frequency and a longer wavelength, so Channel 2 requires a longer antenna because the length of an antenna is directly proportional to wavelength.
9. Much larger, because the wavelength of microwave radiation is so much larger than that of visible light.

Answers To
PROBLEMS

1. 2.0×10^8 m/s
2. 0.16 T
3. 50 μT
4. 7×10^6 m/s
5. **a.** 1.4×10^7 m/s
   b. 5.6×10^4 N/C
6. 6.4×10^{-14} J
7. 9.6×10^{-3} m
8. 4.7×10^{-2} m
9. **a.** 1.5×10^7 m/s
   b. 7.4×10^{-13} J
   c. 2.3 MV
10. 3.9×10^{-26} kg
11. 0.10 m
12. 4.5×10^{-3} T
13. 3.9×10^{-26} kg
14. 34 units
15. one two-thousandth of one percent
16. **a.** 1.6×10^{-15} J
    b. 6.1×10^{17} Hz
17. **a.** 3.5 m
    b. 1.8 m
18. The antenna is 1 cm long.

Answer To
THINKING PHYSIC-LY

In order for a person to see, light must be absorbed by a retina after being focused through a lens. His eye would have to be visible as the light entered it. Completely invisible, light could not enter the eye, be focused by a lens, nor be captured by a retina.

CHAPTER

27 Quantum Theory

PLANNING GUIDE (5 class sessions)

CONTENTS	TEXT FEATURES	TEACHER RESOURCE PACKAGE	OTHER COMPONENTS
27.1 Waves Behave Like Particles, pp. 556–564 (3 Class Sessions) • Radiation From Incandescent Bodies • Photoelectric Effect • The Compton Effect	**Physics Lab:** Photoelectric Steel Balls, p. 562 **Pocket Lab:** See the Light, p. 559 **Concept Review,** p. 564	**Study Guide:** Waves Behave Like Particles **Physics Lab Data Sheet:** Photoelectric Steel Balls **Reteaching Master:** A Quantum Theory of Football **Transparency Worksheet:** Photoelectric Cell	**Laboratory Manual:** Lab 27.1 Planck's Constant Lab 27.2 The Photoelectric Effect **Transparency 40:** Photoelectric Cell
27.2 Particles Behave Like Waves, pp. 564–569 (2 Class Sessions) • Matter Waves • Particles and Waves	**Physics and Society:** Light Pollution and Observatories, p. 565 **Pocket Lab:** Glows in the Dark, p. 566 **Concept Review,** p. 569	**Study Guide:** Particles Behave Like Waves **Critical Thinking Master:** Step by Step **Enrichment Master:** Quantum Fireworks	
Chapter Review, pp. 569–571	Summary Key Terms Reviewing Concepts Applying Concepts Problems Thinking Physic-ly	**Vocabulary Review** **Chapter Test**	**Test Bank**

SUPPLEMENTARY MATERIALS

SOFTWARE	AUDIOVISUAL	BOOKS/MAGAZINES
Introduction to General Physics, Disk VIII: Waves and Light, COMPress/Queue, Inc. (Apple II, IBM PC, Macintosh). *Photoelectric Effect,* Queue, Inc. (Apple II).	Video: *The Mechanical Universe and Beyond: The Atom* and *Particles and Waves,* Films Inc. Filmstrips: *The Concept That Shook Physics—The Quantum Theory,* AVNA Media. *Light: The Wave That Wasn't,* AVNA Media. *Particles and Waves: Quantum Theory,* AVNA Media.	Bardeen, John. "Superconductivity and Other Macroscopic Quantum Phenomena." *Physics Today,* December 1990, pp. 25–31. Peterson, Ivars. "Linking Quantum Physics and Classical Chaos." *Science News,* October 6, 1990, p. 213. Schwarzschild, Bertram. "COBE Satellite Finds No Hint of Excess in the Cosmic Microwave Spectrum." *Physics Today,* March 1990, pp. 17–20. Sibers, Dennis, and Wilson, Alan. "Determining Planck's Constant Using a Light-Emitting Diode." *The Science Teacher,* February 1989, pp. 44–46.

PROBLEM CORRELATION

CONCEPTS	CHAPTER REVIEW			PROBLEMS APPENDIX
	Reviewing Concepts	Applying Concepts	Problems	
27.1 Waves Behave Like Particles				
Radiation From Incandescent Bodies	1,2	1,2	**1**	1,2
Photoelectric Effect	3,4,5,6	3,4	2,3,4,5,6,7,8,9, 10,**11,12**	3,4,5,6,7,8
The Compton Effect	7,8,10		13	9,10
27.2 Particles Behave Like Waves				
Matter Waves	9	5,6,7	14,15,16,17,18, **19,20,21**	11,12,**13**
Particles and Waves				

ACTIVITY AND DEMONSTRATION MATERIALS

PHYSICS LAB	POCKET LAB	DEMONSTRATIONS
Page 562 4 2-cm steel balls grooved channel (U channel or shelf bracket) red, orange, yellow, green, blue, violet colored marking pens or colored stickers	Pages 559, 566 120-W bulb electrical socket wired with dimmer switch 100-mL beaker 90 mL water 10 g fluorescein flashlight red, green, and blue filter material	

EXTENSION PROJECTS

LIBRARY RESEARCH

1. The Muon Experiments
Investigate the muon experiments done at CERN in 1976. What was the significance of the results of these experiments?

HANDS–ON

2. Electric Eye
Go to an electronics store and examine an electric eye. Ask for a demonstration of its capabilities. How does it work? What types of electric eyes are available?

STUDENT READINGS

Peterson, Ivars. "Shining a Bright Light on Quantum Darkness." *Science News,* September 29, 1990.

von Baeyer, Hans Christian. "One Quantum Step." *Discover,* June 1990.

Waldrop, M. M. "The Quantum Wave Function of the Universe." *Science,* December 2, 1988.

Walker, M. "Heisenberg, Goudsmit, and the German Atomic Bomb." *Physics Today,* January 1990.

Wheaton, Bruce. "Louis de Broglie and the Origins of Wave Mechanics." *The Physics Teacher,* May 1984.

Chapter 27

Quantum Theory

CHAPTER OVERVIEW

Theme Development: The quantum model of the submicroscopic world is introduced as an extension of the conservation of energy principle. Symmetry is found in the dual nature of waves and particles. The smallest physical scale at which human inquiry operates reveals a frontier on which new conceptual and mathematical models are constantly built.

MISCONCEPTIONS

Students often feel that this material is remote from their experience. There is a strong tendency to confuse the intensity of light with its frequency in the photoelectric effect. The idea that an invisible particle like an electron also has wave properties is difficult for students to grasp.

KEY TERMS

Compton effect
de Broglie wavelength
Heisenberg uncertainty principle
photoelectric effect
photons
threshold frequency
work function

Laboratory Options

STUDENT EDITION
Physics Lab

Photoelectric Steel Balls	562

Pocket Labs

See the Light	559
Glows in the Dark	566

TEACHER EDITION
Activities

Discovery	557
Cooperative Learning	559, 567

LABORATORY MANUAL

Planck's Constant	Lab 27.1
The Photoelectric Effect	Lab 27.2

CHAPTER
27 Quantum Theory

Red Hot or Not

Jann's class, visiting a steel plant, was watching a vat of molten steel being poured into molds. Jann commented that the molten red steel was very hot, but not as hot as the yellowish-white steel. Her friend disagreed, saying, "Everyone knows that red hot is supposed to be the hottest." How did Jann defend her statement?

In 1889, the experiments of Heinrich Hertz confirmed the predictions of Maxwell's theory. All of optics seemed to be explainable by electromagnetic theory. Only two small problems remained. Wave theory could not describe the spectrum of light emitted by a hot body, such as the hot steel in the photo. Also, as discovered by Hertz himself, ultraviolet light discharged electrically-charged metal plates. This effect, called the photoelectric effect, could not be explained by Maxwell's wave theory.

The solution of these two problems required a total change in our understanding of the structure of matter, and of electromagnetic radiation as well. It required development of the quantum theory and its experimental confirmation, one of the highlights of the history of the twentieth century.

Chapter Outline

✓ Concept Check

The following terms or concepts from earlier chapters are important for a good understanding of this chapter. If you are not familiar with them, you should review them before studying this chapter.

- momentum, Chapter 9
- conservation of energy, elastic scattering, Chapter 11
- wavelength, frequency, wave speed, Chapter 14
- diffraction, interference, diffraction gratings, Chapter 19
- electric potential and potential energy, Chapter 21
- electromagnetic waves, Chapter 26

Introducing The Chapter

Red Hot or Not

Using The Photo: You can easily duplicate the situation shown in the photo if you have a source of variable AC power (usually called a Variac or an autotransformer) that allows you to change the voltage from zero up to the normal value. Connect an ordinary light bulb of any size to the variable AC power source. As you increase the voltage, you'll see the filament begin glowing a dull red and change gradually to white. For an explanation of the chapter opener question, refer students to page 556.

✓ Concept Check

Make sure students have a clear understanding of the concepts covered in Chapters 9, 11, 14, 19, 21, and 26 that are listed in the Concept Check. Momentum, conservation of energy, and elastic scattering are particularly important for understanding the Compton and photoelectric effects. Knowledge of electromagnetic waves and familiarity with wave phenomena such as diffraction and interference are necessary for comprehension of wave-particle duality and the experiments that illustrate this duality. Electric potential and potential energy are used contextually in the discussion of the photoelectric effect.

Assessment Options

Portfolio Assessment
Extension 1, TWE, p. 554b
Extension, TWE, p. 563
Developing a Viewpoint, p. 565
Cooperative Learning, TWE, p. 567
Portfolio Assessment, TWE, p. 568

Performance Assessment
Extension 2, TWE, p. 554b
Pocket Lab, pp. 559, 566
Physics Lab, p. 562
Pocket Lab Assessment, TWE, p. 559

Content Assessment
Self Assessment: Practice Problems, pp. 561, 567
Assessment, Critical Thinking, TWE, p. 562
Checking for Understanding, TWE, p. 563
Critical Thinking, TWE, p. 568
Concept Reviews, pp. 564, 569
Chapter Review, pp. 569–571
Supplemental Problems, pp. 707–708

Group Assessment
Activities for group assessment occur with Cooperative Learning and lab activities.

27.1 WAVES BEHAVE LIKE PARTICLES

Preparation

OBJECTIVES

The objectives are listed on the student page. Remind students to preview these objectives as a study guide to this major section.

OVERVIEW

The concepts associated with the photoelectric effect, such as photons, work function, and threshold frequency, are introduced. In addition, the ideas of blackbody radiation and photon collisions with matter (Compton effect) are discussed.

BRIDGING

The following previously taught concepts are discussed as they relate to the Compton and photoelectric effects: prism, spectrum, frequency, infrared radiation, temperature, electron, electrodes (cathode and anode), current, electric field, kinetic energy, potential difference, electron volt, momentum.

1 Focus

DISCREPANT EVENT

Demonstrate the photoelectric effect by getting together an electroscope, a strip of zinc (approximately 2 cm × 10 cm), and a source of ultraviolet light. If your electroscope has a flat top, bend the zinc strip so that it will stand on the flat top. If you have a round-top electroscope, fasten the zinc strip onto it making good electrical contact. First, positively charge the electroscope with its attached zinc. Then, shine the UV light onto the strip. The electroscope will not discharge. Now charge the electroscope negatively and shine the UV light on the zinc strip. You'll see the leaves collapse. NOTE: The zinc strip must be cleaned of its oxide layer by steel wool just before you do the demonstration. Also remember that UV light is harmful to the eyes, so don't look directly into it.

Objectives

- understand the spectrum emitted by a hot body and the basics of the theory that explains this spectrum.
- define the photoelectric effect; recognize that the quantum theory can explain it while the wave theory can't; solve problems involving the photoelectric equation.
- define the Compton effect and explain in terms of the momentum and energy of the photon.
- describe experiments that demonstrate the particle-like properties of electromagnetic radiation.

27.1 WAVES BEHAVE LIKE PARTICLES

The radiation from hot bodies was a puzzle. Hot bodies contain vibrating particles, which radiate electromagnetic waves. Maxwell's theory should have no trouble with this, but it gave the wrong prediction. Why? What radiation do hot bodies emit?

Radiation From Incandescent Bodies

If you look through a prism at the light coming from an incandescent light bulb, you will see all the colors of the rainbow. The bulb also emits infrared radiation, which you cannot see. Figure 27–1 shows the spectrum of an incandescent body. A spectrum is a plot of the intensity of radiation emitted at various frequencies. Light and infrared radiation are produced by the vibration of the charged particles within the atoms of a body that is so hot it glows, or is incandescent.

The hotter the temperature, the more radiation at shorter wavelengths.

Suppose you put the light bulb on a dimmer control. You gradually turn up the voltage, increasing the temperature of the glowing filament. The color changes from deep red through orange to yellow and finally to white. The higher the temperature, the more radiation at frequencies of yellow, green, blue, and violet is produced, and the "whiter" the body appears. The color you see depends on the relative amounts of emission at various frequencies and the sensitivity of your eyes to those colors. Spectra of incandescent bodies at various temperatures are shown in Figure 27–1. The frequency at which the maximum amount of light is emitted is proportional to the Kelvin temperature.

Red Hot or Not

The total power emitted also increases with temperature. The amount of energy emitted every second in electromagnetic waves is proportional to the absolute temperature raised to the fourth power, T^4. Thus, as the figure shows, hotter sources radiate considerably more power than cooler bodies. The sun, for example, is a dense ball of gases heated to incandescence by the energy produced within it. It has a surface temperature of 5800 K and a yellow color. The sun radiates 4×10^{26} W, a truly enormous amount of power. Each square meter on Earth receives about one thousand joules of energy each second.

Planck explained the spectrum of an incandescent object by assuming atoms could vibrate only at specific frequencies.

FIGURE 27–1. This graph shows spectra of incandescent bodies at various temperatures.

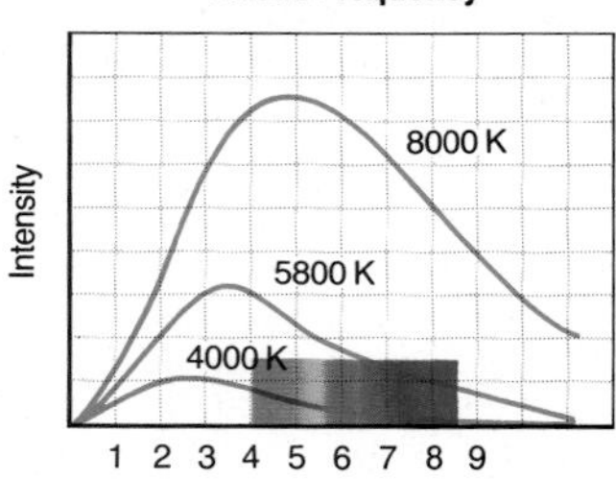

Why does the spectrum have the shape shown in Figure 27–1? Maxwell's theory could not account for it. Between 1887 and 1900, many physicists tried to predict the shape of this spectrum using existing physical theories, but all failed. In 1900, the German physicist Max Planck (1858–1947) found that he could calculate the spectrum only if he introduced a revolutionary hypothesis. Planck assumed that the energy of vibration of the atoms in a solid could have only the specific frequencies given by the equation

$$E = nhf.$$

Here f is the frequency of vibration of the atom, h is a constant, and n is an integer like 0, 1, 2, or 3. The energy, E, could have the values hf, $2hf$, $3hf$, and so on, but never, for example, $\frac{2}{3}hf$. This behavior is described by saying that energy is quantized. Energy only comes in packages of specific sizes.

TEACHER F.Y.I.

- A blackbody (as defined by Kirchhoff) is an object that re-emits all the radiant energy that is incident upon it. Planck's description of radiation being transmitted in quanta destroyed the idea that classical mechanics could be applied to the microscopic world.
- The assumption made by Planck given in the text above is not written as Planck wrote it in 1900, but as modified by Einstein a few years later.
- You may want to take this opportunity to discuss the background radiation of space. Nearly perfect blackbody spectra have been measured with the help of astrophysical instruments since 1990, and have been presented in various physics and astronomy journals.

Further, Planck proposed that atoms did not radiate electromagnetic waves all the time they were vibrating, as predicted by Maxwell. Instead, they could emit radiation *only when their vibration energy changed*. For example, when the energy changed from $3hf$ to $2hf$, the atom emitted radiation. The energy radiated was equal to the change in energy of the atom, hf.

Planck found that the constant h was extremely small, about 7×10^{-34} J/Hz. This meant that the energy-changing steps were too small to be noticeable in ordinary bodies. Still, the introduction of quantized energy was extremely troubling to physicists, especially Planck himself. It was the first hint that the physics of Newton and Maxwell might be valid only under certain conditions.

FIGURE 27–2. Max Planck, 1858-1947. Planck was awarded the Nobel Prize in 1918 for his discovery of the quantized nature of energy.

Photoelectric Effect

There was a second troubling experimental result unexplained by Maxwell. A negatively-charged zinc plate was discharged when ultraviolet radiation fell on it, but it remained charged when ordinary light fell on it. Furthermore, a positively-charged plate was never discharged. Further study showed that the zinc plate was discharged by emitting electrons. The emission of electrons when electromagnetic radiation falls on an object is called the **photoelectric effect**.

The photoelectric effect can be studied in a photocell like that in Figure 27–3. The cell contains two metal electrodes sealed in an evacuated tube. The air has been removed to keep the metal surface clean and to keep electrons from being stopped by air molecules. The large electrode, the cathode, is usually coated with cesium or another alkali metal. The second electrode, the anode, is made of a thin wire so it does not block any radiation. The tube is often made of quartz to permit ultraviolet wavelengths to pass through. A potential difference that attracts electrons to the anode is placed across the electrodes.

When no radiation falls on the cathode, current does not flow in the circuit. When radiation does fall on the cathode, however, a current, shown by the meter, flows in the circuit. Current is the result of electrons, called photoelectrons, being ejected from the cathode by the radiation. The electrons travel to the positive electrode, the anode.

The emission of electrons from metal as a result of electromagnetic radiation is the photoelectric effect.

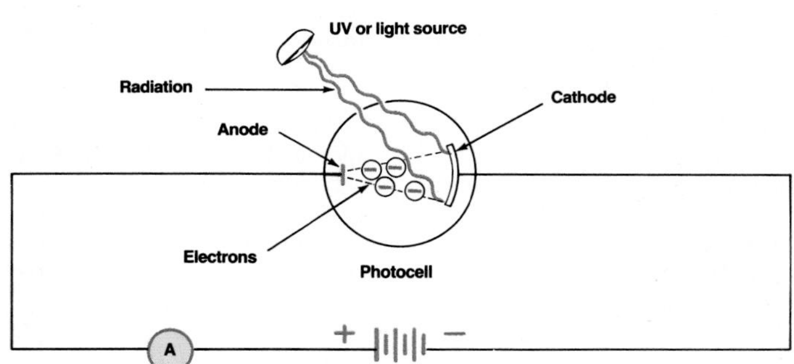

FIGURE 27–3. A diagram of a photocell circuit shows the ejection of electrons from a metal. Photocells are used to turn lights on automatically at dusk.

2 Teach

CONCEPT DEVELOPMENT

- Objects that are good absorbers of thermal energy are also good radiators of thermal energy. For example, black objects are excellent radiators.

Study Guide Master. To reinforce the concepts in this section, have the students complete the Study Guide Master for Section 27.1 from the Teacher Resource Package.

Discovery: Obtain a large carton (at least 0.5 m on one side) and paint the inside white or cover it with white paper. Make a hole about 3 cm in diameter in the center of one side. Have students look through the hole. Then ask them what color the box is on the inside. The box will appear to be black; the small amount of light that enters through the hole is reflected off the inside surfaces of the box many times. Some light is absorbed during each reflection, permitting only a minimal amount to come out. This is a model of a blackbody.

Laboratory Manual. Give students additional experience with Planck's constant by doing Lab 27.1 from the Laboratory Manual.

- In 1887, Heinrich Hertz discovered the photoelectric effect during his experiments on electromagnetic waves. He observed that a spark was more easily produced in two metal spheres separated by a small air gap when UV light shone on the negative terminal. However, he was preoccupied with the novel phenomenon of radio transmission and went no further with his discovery.

Connect to CHEMISTRY

Much of our knowledge of the structure of molecules has been obtained through infrared spectroscopy. A beam of infrared radiation from an incandescent source is projected onto a liquid solution of the material. A prism separates the wavelengths of the radiation that has passed through the solution. A detector is moved across the spectrum to record the wavelengths at which the solution absorbed energy. The energy absorbed by the molecules increased the energy of vibration of the atoms. The amount of energy depends on the mass of the atoms and the strength of the chemical bond joining them. Typically, wavelengths from 5 to 10 µm are used.

How hot should an incandescent source be so that the greatest intensity of blackbody radiation is emitted at 6 µm? Hint: Convert this wavelength to frequency and use the graph on page 556. [The frequency is 0.5×10^{14} Hz. The peak of the 8000 K graph is at 5×10^{14} Hz. Since the frequency is proportional to the temperature, the infrared emitter should be about 1/10 as hot, or about 800 K.]

CONCEPT DEVELOPMENT

- The discovery of the photoelectric effect was important for many reasons. One, it provided more information about electrons, helping to solidify the concept that electrons are separate particles. Two, it was another line of evidence that electrons are contained in many different metals. Three, it helped validate quantum theory.

Transparency Package. Use Transparency 40 to quiz students on details of the photoelectric cell.

- Remember that *Potential Difference = Energy / Charge*, or *V = Energy / q*. So, *Energy = qV*. Since the charge here is one elementary charge, 1.6×10^{-19} C, and one volt = 1 J/C, we have then *Energy* = $(1.6 \times 10^{-19}$ C$)$ (1 J/C) = 1.6×10^{-19} J. Therefore, one electron volt has this energy value.

- Note that we keep coming back to the conservation of energy and momentum, deep underlying principles in physics.

A portion of Einstein's original paper on the photoelectric effect is reproduced in Chapter 18 of the book *Project Physics*. It shows how clearly he wrote.

Multicultural Connections

Another example of the fact that all physicists work with and build on ideas from others in many cultures is the case of Bose-Einstein statistics. An Indian physicist, Satyendranath Bose (1894 to 1974), wrote a paper in 1924 dealing with quantum mechanics. Einstein read the paper and praised it highly, then he generalized Bose's techniques into a type of quantum statistics used to describe the behavior of some subatomic particles. Particles which behave predictably according to Bose-Einstein statistics are now called "bosons."

FIGURE 27–4. The kinetic energy of the ejected electrons can be measured with this device. An ammeter is used to measure the current flowing through the circuit.

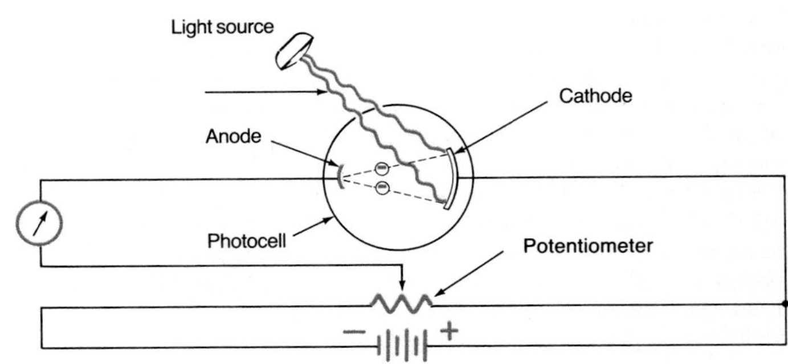

Only high frequency (short wavelength) radiation ejects electrons. The threshold frequency depends on the cathode material.

Not all radiation results in current flow. Electrons are ejected only if the frequency of the radiation is above a certain minimum value, called the **threshold frequency**, f_0. The threshold frequency varies with the metal. All wavelengths of light except red, for example, will eject electrons from cesium, while ultraviolet is needed with zinc. Radiation of a frequency below f_0 does not eject any electrons from the metal, no matter how bright it is. Even if it is very dim, radiation at or above the threshold frequency causes electrons to leave the metal immediately—the greater the intensity of radiation, the larger the flow of photoelectrons.

Maxwell's theory cannot explain the photoelectric effect.

The electromagnetic wave theory cannot explain these facts. In the wave theory, a more intense radiation, regardless of frequency, has stronger electric and magnetic fields. According to wave theory, the electric field accelerates and ejects the electrons from the metal. With very faint light shining on the metal, electrons would require a very long time before they gained enough energy to be ejected.

According to Einstein's photon theory, light and other forms of electromagnetic radiation consists of particles.

In 1905, Albert Einstein published a revolutionary theory that explained the photoelectric effect. According to Einstein, light and other forms of radiation consist of discrete bundles of energy, which were later called **photons**. The energy of each photon depends on the frequency of the light. The energy is given by the equation $E = hf$, where h is Planck's constant, 6.626×10^{-34} J/Hz.

It is important to note that Einstein's theory of the photon goes further than Planck's theory of hot bodies. While Planck had proposed that vibrating atoms emitted radiation with energy equal to hf, he did not suggest that light and other forms of radiation acted like particles. Einstein's theory of the photon reinterpreted and extended Planck's theory of hot bodies.

Einstein's photoelectric-effect theory explains the existence of a threshold frequency. A photon with a minimum energy, hf_0, is needed to eject an electron from the metal. If the photon has a frequency below f_0, it does not have the energy needed to eject an electron. Light with a frequency greater than f_0 has more energy than needed to eject an electron. The excess energy, $hf - hf_0$, becomes the kinetic energy of the electron. Thus,

$$KE = hf - hf_0.$$

F.Y.I.

If anybody says he can think about quantum problems without getting giddy, that only shows he has not understood the first thing about them.

—Niels Bohr

STUDY GUIDE MASTER

Use the Study Guide master for section 27.1.

LABORATORY MANUAL

Use Lab 27.1 with this section.

TRANSPARENCY

Use Transparency 40 with this section.

Einstein's equation is really little more than conservation of energy. The incoming photon has energy hf. An amount of energy, hf_0, is needed to free the electron from the metal. The remainder becomes the kinetic energy of the electron. Notice that an electron cannot simply accumulate photons until it has enough energy; only one photon interacts with one electron. In addition, hf_0 is actually the minimum energy needed to free an electron. Not all electrons in a solid have the same energy, so most need more than this minimum to escape. Thus, when we speak of the kinetic energy of the ejected electrons, we mean the maximum kinetic energy an ejected electron could have. Other electrons will have less *KE*.

How can Einstein's theory be tested? The kinetic energy of the ejected electrons can be measured indirectly by a device like the one pictured in Figure 27–4. A variable electric potential difference across the tube makes the anode negative. By analogy to gravity, the electrons must climb a hill to reach the anode. Only if they have enough kinetic energy at the cathode will they reach the anode before turning back. Light of the chosen frequency illuminates the cathode. An ammeter measures the current flowing through the circuit. The experimenter increases the opposing potential difference, making the anode more negative. Electrons must be ejected from the cathode with higher and higher kinetic energies to reach the anode. At some voltage, called the stopping potential, no electrons have enough energy to reach the anode, and the current falls to zero. The maximum kinetic energy of the electrons at the cathode equals their potential energy at the anode, $KE = -qV_0$. Here, V_0 is the magnitude of the stopping potential in volts (J/C) and q is the charge of the electron (-1.60×10^{-19} C).

The joule is too large a unit of energy to use with atomic systems. A more convenient energy unit is the electron volt (eV). One electron volt is the energy of an electron accelerated across a potential difference of one volt. That is,

$$1 \text{ eV} = (1.60 \times 10^{-19} \text{ C})(1 \text{ V}) = 1.60 \times 10^{-19} \text{ C} \cdot \text{V}$$
$$1 \text{ eV} = 1.60 \times 10^{-19} \text{ J}$$

Example Problem

Kinetic Energy of a Photoelectron

The stopping potential that prevents electrons from flowing across a certain photocell is 4.0 V. What is the kinetic energy given to the electrons by the incident light? Give the answer in both J and eV.

Given: stopping potential, $V_0 = 4.0$ V

Unknown: *KE*

Basic equation: $KE = -qV_0$

Solution:
$$\begin{aligned} KE &= -qV_0 \\ &= -(-1.60 \times 10^{-19} \text{ C})(4.0 \text{ J/C}) \\ &= +6.4 \times 10^{-19} \text{ J} \\ &= (6.4 \times 10^{-19} \text{ J})\left(\frac{1 \text{ eV}}{1.6 \times 10^{-19} \text{ J}}\right) \\ &= 4.0 \text{ eV} \end{aligned}$$

POCKET LAB

SEE THE LIGHT

Close the shades and turn off all the room lights. Look at a 120-W lamp as you slowly increase and decrease the voltage across the lamp with a dimmer switch. Describe your results. What would you expect to see if you repeat the experiment as you look through a diffraction grating? Why? Try it. Describe your results.

Part of the photon's energy frees the electron from the metal. The remainder becomes the kinetic energy of the electron.

The *KE* of the electrons can be determined by measuring the potential difference needed to stop them.

POCKET LAB

SEE THE LIGHT

Purpose: to observe how the intensity and range of colors depend on temperature.

Materials: 120-W bulb; electrical socket wired with dimmer switch.

Outcome: At low voltages, only red and orange are visible. At medium voltages, other colors become visible. At higher voltages, all colors can be seen.

CONCEPT DEVELOPMENT

• Einstein did not receive the Nobel Prize for the theory of relativity, as most people would guess. It was probably still considered too revolutionary, even though the photoelectric effect theory, though controversial, had been confirmed by Millikan's experiments.

Cooperative Learning: In the photoelectric effect phenomenon, the vast majority of incoming photons do not cause electron emission. Ask student groups to figure out what happens to the energy of all those photons not causing electron emission. [Some of the (light) photons are reflected and some transfer their energy in the form of thermal energy.]

• Increasing the intensity of the light source will increase the number of photoelectrons ejected (assuming the frequency is above threshold), but will not raise the energy of the electrons. Therefore, a dim blue light will emit electrons with more energy than those emitted by a bright red light. However, the red light will eject more photoelectrons.

Assessment

Performance

To further assess students' understanding of the relationship of the color and intensity of light to the temperature, have them do the following quantitative experiment. Connect both an ammeter and a voltmeter to the lamp so the electric power it consumes can be measured. Project the spectrum from the diffraction grating onto a piece of cardboard in which you have cut a slit wide enough for only one color to show through. Place a photoelectric meter behind the slit. Be sure to shield the cardboard from the direct light from the bulb. Start with the bulb at very low power and gradually increase the voltage while reading the meter. Plot the output of the photoelectric meter as a function of the power dissipated by the bulb. Try this first when the slit allows red light to reach the meter, then when it admits blue. Check to see if the meter will detect infrared by moving the slit to just beyond the red part of the spectrum.

CONCEPT DEVELOPMENT

In the equation photon energy $= hf$, notice that the new photon concept incorporates a major idea from waves—frequency. This exemplifies how quantum theory blends the ideas of particles and waves.

Laboratory Manual. Give students additional experience with the photoelectric effect by doing Lab 27.2 from the Laboratory Manual.

Guided Practice: Go over the Example Problem that begins on page 560, then have students work on the first two Practice Problems that follow.

Independent Practice: Assign the remaining Practice Problems for homework and spend time going over them with students during the next class period.

FIGURE 27–5. This graph shows the kinetic energy of ejected electrons versus frequency of incident radiation.

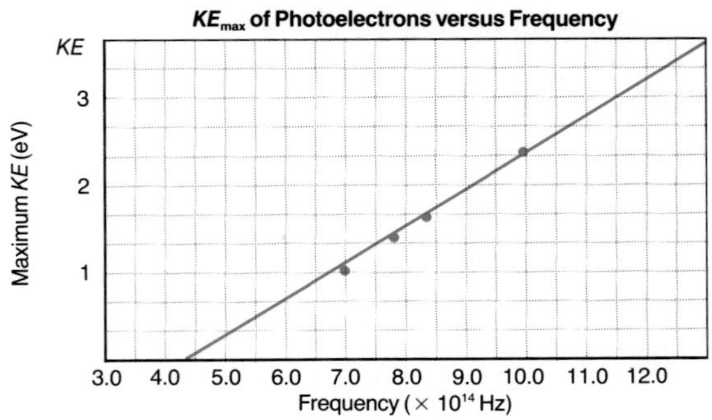

Planck's constant, h, is the slope of the graph of maximum KE of ejected electrons versus light frequency.

A graph of the kinetic energies of the electrons ejected from a metal versus the frequencies of the incident photons is a straight line, Figure 27–5. All metals have similar graphs with the same slope. The slope of all of the lines is Planck's constant, h.

$$h = \frac{\Delta KE}{\Delta f} = \frac{\text{change in maximum } KE \text{ of ejected electrons}}{\text{change in frequency of incident radiation}}$$

The work function is the energy needed to free an electron from a metal.

The graphs differ only in the threshold frequency that is needed to free electrons. The threshold frequency is related to the energy needed to free the most weakly-bound electron from a metal, called the **work function** of the metal. The work function is thus measured by hf_0.

Robert A. Millikan did the experiments that proved Einstein's photoelectric theory to be correct. Einstein won the Nobel Prize in 1921 for his work on the photoelectric effect. Millikan won the prize two years later.

Example Problem

Photoelectric Equation

The threshold frequency of sodium is 5.6×10^{14} Hz. **a.** What is the work function of sodium in J and eV? **b.** Sodium is illuminated by light of frequency 8.6×10^{14} Hz. What is the kinetic energy of the ejected electrons in eV?

Given: threshold frequency, $f_0 = 5.6 \times 10^{14}$ Hz; illumination frequency, $f = 8.6 \times 10^{14}$ Hz

Unknown: KE

Basic equation: $KE = hf - hf_0$

Solution:

a. work function $= hf_0$

$= (6.6 \times 10^{-34}\ \text{J/Hz})(5.6 \times 10^{14}\ \text{Hz})$

$= 3.7 \times 10^{-19}\ \text{J}$

$$\frac{3.7 \times 10^{-19}\ \text{J}}{1.6 \times 10^{-19}\ \text{J/eV}} = 2.3\ \text{eV}$$

TEACHER F.Y.I.

The photovoltaic cell is a device in which current flows when light of a given frequency falls on it. When the beam is broken, the current ceases. These cells are often used as electric eyes or alarm systems. Selenium was first used for this purpose but was replaced because of its inefficiency. (It converts only 1% of the light falling on it into electric energy.) Current technology converts up to 30%.

b. $hf = (6.6 \times 10^{-34}\ \text{J/Hz})(8.6 \times 10^{14}\ \text{Hz})(1\ \text{eV}/1.6 \times 10^{-19}\ \text{J})$
$= 3.5\ \text{eV}$
$KE = hf - hf_0$
$= 3.5\ \text{eV} - 2.3\ \text{eV}$
$= 1.2\ \text{eV}$

The wavelength of light is more easily measured than its frequency. If the wavelength is given in a problem, the frequency may be found using the equation $\lambda = c/f$, as discussed in Chapter 14. The energy (in eV) of a photon with wavelength λ is given by the formula

$$E = hf = \frac{hc}{\lambda}$$

$$= \frac{(6.6 \times 10^{-34}\ \text{J/Hz})(3.00 \times 10^{8}\ \text{m/s})(1\ \text{eV}/1.6 \times 10^{-19}\ \text{J})}{\lambda(10^{-9}\ \text{m/nm})}$$

$$E = \frac{1240}{\lambda}\ \text{eV} \cdot \text{nm}.$$

SOCIOLOGY CONNECTION

Many public buildings have doors that open automatically as people approach. These doors are often operated by so-called "electric eyes". A light beam shines across the door opening onto a photovoltaic cell, causing electrons to be given off and a current to flow in a circuit. When the beam is broken, the current stops, and a mechanism is triggered that opens the door. These devices have allowed easier access to many people who would otherwise find door-opening mechanisms difficult to use.

Practice Problems

1. The stopping potential to prevent current through a photocell is 3.2 V. Calculate the kinetic energy in joules of the photoelectrons as they are emitted.
2. The stopping potential for a photoelectric cell is 5.7 V. Calculate the kinetic energy in electron volts of the photoelectrons as they are emitted.
3. The threshold wavelength of zinc is 310 nm (310×10^{-9} m).
   - **a.** Find the threshold frequency of zinc.
   - **b.** What is the work function in eV of zinc?
   - **c.** Zinc in a photocell is irradiated by ultraviolet light of 240 nm wavelength. What is the kinetic energy of the photoelectrons in eV?
4. ▶ The work function for cesium is 1.96 eV.
   - **a.** Find the threshold wavelength for cesium.
   - **b.** What is the kinetic energy in eV of photoelectrons ejected when 425-nm violet light falls on the cesium?

The Compton Effect

The photoelectric effect demonstrates that, even though it has no mass, a photon has kinetic energy just as a particle does. In 1916, Einstein predicted that the photon should have another particle property, momentum. He showed that the momentum of a photon should be hf/c. Since $f/c = 1/\lambda$, the photon's momentum is

$$p = \frac{hf}{c} = \frac{h}{\lambda}.$$

Answers To
PRACTICE PROBLEMS

Have students refer to Appendix A of the Solutions Appendix for complete solutions to Practice Problems.

1. 5.1×10^{-19} J
2. 5.7 eV
3. **a.** 9.68×10^{14} Hz
   b. 4.0 eV
   c. 1.2 eV
4. **a.** 633 nm
   b. 0.96 eV

CONCEPT DEVELOPMENT

- The photoelectric effect and the Compton effect are the two major phenomena that reveal the particle (photon) properties of electromagnetic radiation.
- Compton was one of the leading scientists on the Manhattan Project, which developed the atomic bomb. He directed the research on methods of producing plutonium.
- As a mechanical analogy for the Compton effect, consider this: When the X-ray photon interacts with the atom as a whole and bounces off unchanged (as did the greater number of X-ray photons in Compton's experiment) it resembles a pea bouncing off a bowling ball—the bowling ball is barely affected by the collision. However, when an X-ray photon interacts with an electron, since they are closer in size, energy is more equally shared between them, leaving the photon with less energy and, hence, lower frequency—much like a collision between two billiard balls.

Critical Thinking: Sometimes the production of X rays is called the inverse photoelectric effect. Ask students to hypothesize about why that name was applied. [In the production of X rays, high speed electrons produce X-ray photons, the reverse of photons producing electrons as occurs in the photoelectric effect.]

LABORATORY MANUAL

Use Lab 27.2 with this section.

PHYSICS LAB

Process Skills: manipulating, measuring, observing, forming a hypothesis, predicting, inferring, describing.

MISCONCEPTIONS

Students live in a macroscopic world where physical phenomena appear in a classical way. They are not familiar with quantum phenomena, however, and frequently confuse the two.

Teaching Suggestion: Students should be asked to discuss the limitations of this model.

Lab Worksheet, Teacher Resource Package. If desired, use the lab worksheet master for this chapter for students to record their data.

OBSERVATIONS

1. Colors that have little energy per photon (red and yellow) will not remove an electron. Colors that have more energy per photon will push the electrons from the atom.
2. A single photon will not remove more than one electron.
3. Students should clearly state the following guidelines: (a) photons that start above a certain energy level will always remove a valence electron. (b) a single photon can remove only a single valence electron.

ANALYSIS

1. Most students will believe that two red photons should have enough energy to remove one electron. This is not correct.
2. Rolling two photons down the channel causes two electrons to move, but not enough to remove them from the atom.
3. The short end of the channel should be made longer or steeper to model a material that has a tighter grip on the valence electrons.

APPLICATIONS

Photographers use red light because red has low energy per photon. Blue light has more energy per photon and would cause a chemical change in the exposed film.

PHYSICS LAB: Photoelectric Steel Balls

Purpose

To simulate the photoelectric effect.

Materials

- 4 2-cm steel balls
- grooved channel (U channel or shelf bracket)
- red, orange, yellow, green, blue, violet colored marking pens or colored stickers

Procedure

1. Shape the grooved channel as shown in the diagram. Mark a point 4 cm above the table, on the channel, as "R" for red.
2. Mark a point 14 cm above the table, on the channel, with a "V" for violet. Place marks for B, G, Y, and O uniformly between them.
3. Place two steel balls at the lowest point on the channel. These steel balls represent valence electrons in the atom.
4. Try releasing a photon (steel ball) from various positions on the channel. Record the results of each trial.
5. Always make sure that two valence electrons start at the bottom of the channel.
6. Remove the steel ball that represents the photon from the lower part of the channel.
7. Repeat steps 4-6 for each color mark on the channel. Note: Always start with two electrons at the low point in the channel.

Observations and Data

1. Which color photons were able to remove the electrons?
2. Did one photon ever remove more than one electron?
3. Write at least two statements that summarize your results.

Analysis

1. Predict what would happen if two red photons could hit the electrons at the same time.
2. Start two steel balls (photons) at the red mark on the channel and see what happens. Describe the results.
3. Certain materials have a stronger grip on their valence electrons. How could the model be modified to show this?

Applications

1. Photographers often have a red light in their darkrooms. Explain why a red light is safe, but a blue light is not safe.

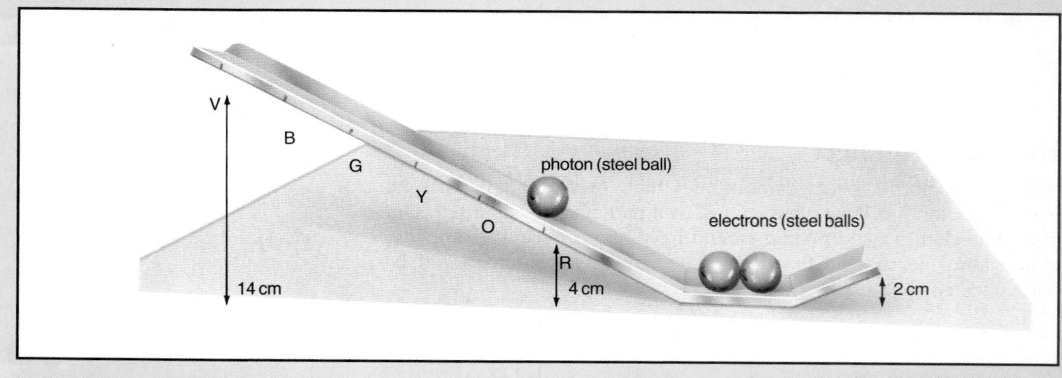

ASSESSMENT

Critical Thinking: To further assess students' understanding of the photoelectric effect, ask the following questions.

1. Look at your summary statements for step 3 in the Observations and Data section. How do they compare to the guideline statements for the photoelectric effect? [Students should get exactly the same rules as discovered during an experiment with real photoelectric equipment.]
2. In the model, if the potential energy of the photon on the channel was too small, then the energy was transferred into heat of the valence electrons. Compare this to an actual photoelectric experiment. [Again, the results of the model are identical with the real experiment. Low-energy photons are absorbed by the target metal and increase the temperature of the metal.]

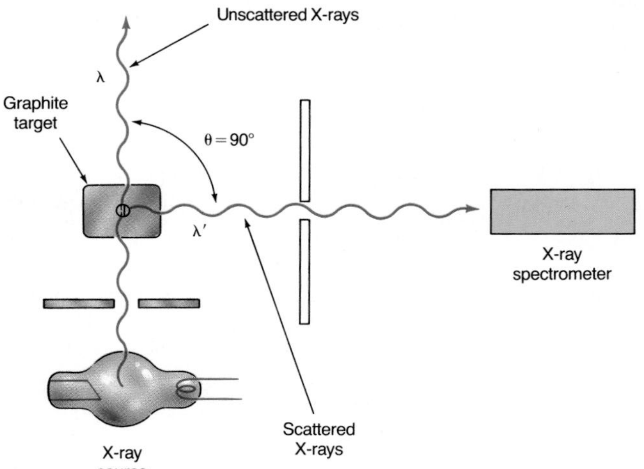

b

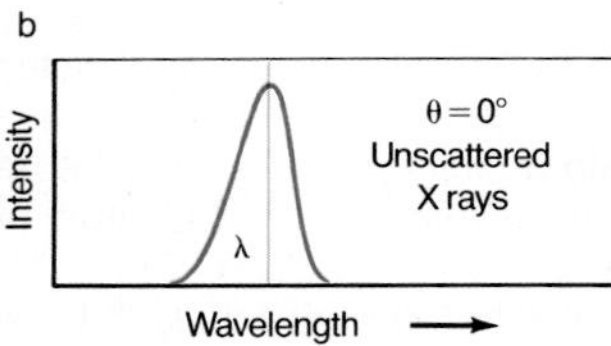

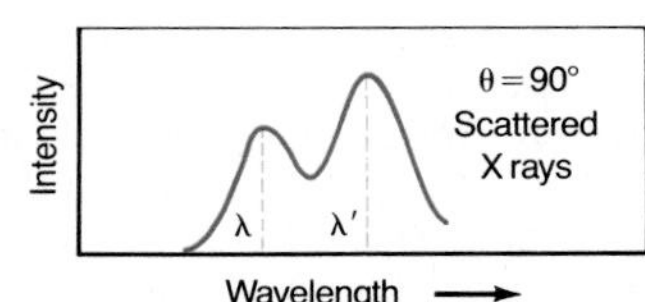

FIGURE 27–6. Diagram of apparatus used by Compton to study the nature of photons (a). An increased wavelength denotes that the X-ray photons have lost energy (b).

The American Arthur Holly Compton tested Einstein's theory in 1922. Compton directed X rays of known wavelength at a graphite target, Figure 27–6a, and measured the wavelengths of the X rays scattered by the target. He found that some of the X rays were scattered without change in wavelength. Other scattered X rays, however, had a longer wavelength than the original, as shown in Figure 27–6b. The energy of a photon is *hf*, given by

$$E = \frac{hc}{\lambda}.$$

Thus, an increased wavelength meant that the X-ray photons had lost both energy and momentum. The shift in energy of scattered photons is called the **Compton effect**. It is a tiny shift, about 10^{-3} nm, and so is measurable only when X rays, having wavelengths of 10^{-2} nm or smaller, are used. In later experiments, Compton observed that electrons were ejected from the graphite block during the experiment. He suggested that the X-ray photons collided with electrons in the graphite target and transferred energy and momentum. These collisions were similar to the elastic collisions experienced by two billiard balls, Figure 27–7. Compton tested this suggestion by measuring the energy of the ejected electrons. He found that the energy and momentum gained by the electrons equaled the energy and momentum lost by the photons. Photons obeyed the laws of conservation of momentum and energy.

The Compton effect is the increase in wavelength when X rays are scattered off of electrons.

Some X rays lose energy when they strike matter and are scattered with longer wavelengths.

CHECKING FOR UNDERSTANDING

Ask your students these questions: If the brightness of the light shining on a photosensitive surface increases, what happens to the photocurrent? [The current increases.] If you decrease the frequency of the light falling on the surface, what happens to the photocurrent? [At some frequency, referred to as the threshold frequency, the current falls abruptly to zero.] If you make the light very dim, do you have to wait longer for an electron to be ejected? [No, a photon-electron collision takes place just as quickly.]

RETEACHING

Use the principle of the conservation of energy to reteach the photoelectric effect. Start by stressing that input radiation is the cause and emission of photoelectrons is the effect. Then write down a statement such as the following: Energy input equals energy output. The energy input is the photon energy, *hf.* Now ask students where that photon energy goes. [The energy goes into ripping electrons loose from their atoms, into the work function, and into giving the loosened-up electrons kinetic energy.] This work statement can now be changed into the photoelectric equation.

Reteaching Master, Teacher Resource Package. Use the Reteaching Master, Quantized Energy, for Chapter 27.

EXTENSION

In studying the photoelectric effect, some students may have been reminded of the process of ionization in chemistry. It might seem that the first ionization energies of particular atoms would be the same as their work functions. Using a source like the *Handbook of Chemistry and Physics,* have interested students look up the ionization energies and work functions of several elements such as sodium, barium, copper, gold, and zinc. Ask them to compare the values and explain the differences. [The values are not the same. Ionization potentials are measured for gases, whereas atoms are acting more or less as individuals. Work functions are measured for elements in the solid state, hence the atoms are not acting like individuals and this changes their electron energy levels.]

LAB WORKSHEET

Use the Lab Worksheet for Chapter 27 with this Physics Lab.

RETEACHING MASTER

Use the Reteaching master for Chapter 27 with this section.

INDEPENDENT PRACTICE/ EXTENSION

Refer to the Assignment Guide below for additional questions and problems for independent practice.

3 Close

CONVERGENT QUESTION

In photographic darkrooms, the only light allowed usually has a red color. Ask students to explain, as fully as possible on the basis of a quantum theory, why this makes sense. [Since red has the lowest frequency of all visible light, it has the lowest photon energy ($E = hf$). These low energy photons are less likely to cause unwanted chemical reactions on the exposed film.]

CONCEPT REVIEW ANSWERS

1.1 It is zero at low frequencies, rises to a peak, then falls at high frequencies.

1.2 Both increase. The peak frequency increases as *T;* the total energy as T^4.

1.3 Photoelectric effect. In the Compton effect, the X rays are scattered, not absorbed.

1.4 Critical Thinking: No. A tennis ball can give a softball much more kinetic energy than it can give a bowling ball.

27.2 PARTICLES BEHAVE LIKE WAVES

Preparation

OBJECTIVES

The objectives are listed on the student page. Remind students to preview these objectives as a study guide to this major section.

OVERVIEW

The concepts of matter waves and wave-particle duality are introduced. These are difficult concepts to grasp, partly because we have little or no direct experience with them.

FIGURE 27–7. The energy and momentum gained by electrons equal the energy and momentum lost by photons.

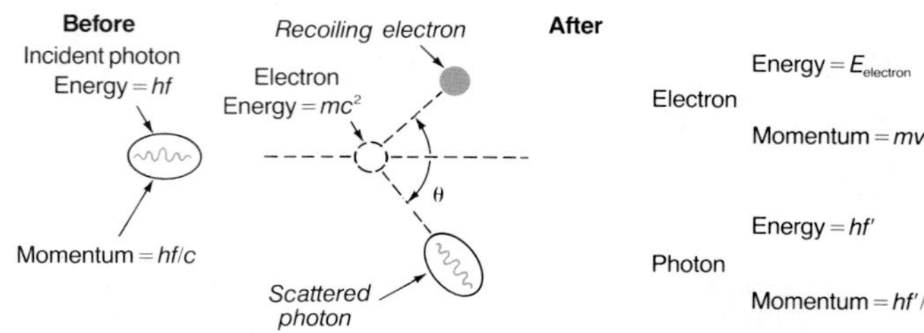

In the Compton effect, the incoming photon suffers an elastic collision with an atomic electron. Energy and momentum are transferred to the electron.

Compton's experiments further verified Einstein's theory of photons. A photon is a particle that has energy and momentum. Unlike matter, however, a photon has no mass and travels at the speed of light.

CONCEPT REVIEW

1.1 Describe, in general, how the intensity of a hot body at a fixed temperature varies with frequency of the radiation.

1.2 As the temperature of a body is increased, how does the frequency of peak intensity change? How does the total energy radiated change?

1.3 An experimenter sends an X ray into a target. An electron, but no other radiation, comes out. Was the event the photoelectric or Compton effect?

1.4 Critical Thinking: The photon and electron are treated as "billiard balls" in the Compton effect. Suppose the electron were replaced by the much more massive proton. Would the proton gain as much energy from the collision as the electron? Would the photon lose as much energy as it would colliding with the electron?

Objectives

- **describe evidence of the wave nature of matter; solve problems relating wavelength to particle momentum.**
- **recognize the dual nature of both waves and particles and the impact of the Heisenberg uncertainty principle.**

27.2 PARTICLES BEHAVE LIKE WAVES

The photoelectric effect and Compton scattering showed that electromagnetic waves had particle properties. The French physicist Louis-Victor de Broglie (di-BROY-lee) (1892–1987) suggested in 1923 that material particles have wave properties. His suggestions were ignored by other scientists until Einstein read his papers and supported his ideas.

Matter Waves

By analogy with the momentum of the photon, $p = h/\lambda$, de Broglie said that the momentum of a particle is given by the equation

$$p = mv = \frac{h}{\lambda}.$$

BRIDGING

Previously discussed concepts include momentum, diffraction, interference, and grating.

27:1 ASSIGNMENT GUIDE

	PRACTICE	EXTENSION
CHAPTER REVIEW pp. 569–571		
· Reviewing Concepts	1–8, 10	
· Applying Concepts		1–4
· Problems*	2–10, 13	1, 11, 12
APPENDIX B PROBLEMS*		
· Chapter 27, p. 707	1–10	

* Complete solutions to all Chapter Review and Appendix problems appear in the Problems and Solutions Manual.

Physics and society

LIGHT POLLUTION AND OBSERVATORIES

Depending upon where you live, you're probably only able to see a small percentage of the stars and planets at night. That's because in most industrially-developed countries, the sky is rarely completely dark at night. For years, scientists have been alerting us to a form of pollution that threatens our ability to learn about the rest of our universe: it's called light pollution.

Light pollution is a general glow in the night sky caused by thousands of unshielded lights along highways and in cities to make them safer for travelers. Most of these lights emit light over virtually the entire visible spectrum. "Skyglow" from large metropolitan areas can be seen for more than 100 miles. Scientists estimate that lighting has increased 40-fold in the past 20 years. As more light is generated on Earth, less light from the stars is visible to us with the naked eye.

Observatories must attempt to filter out skyglow from starlight. In recent years, new observatories have had to be located in remote locations to avoid light pollution from nearby communities. Today, there is almost no observatory on Earth where illumination from distant cities has not or will not become a problem. For example, a 100-inch telescope on Mt. Wilson in California was recently put out of use partly because of the severe skyglow from the Los Angeles area. The 200-inch reflector on Mt. Palomer is also threatened.

Earth's atmosphere causes problems of its own for astronomers: thick and dusty, it either blocks or smears much of the light from stars before the light can reach telescopes on Earth. The atmosphere also blocks almost all ultraviolet light, which due to its shorter wavelength, could be focused into much sharper images than visible light. The Hubble Space Telescope, orbiting 370 miles above Earth's surface, is designed to receive light of all wavelengths. The goal is for astronomers to be able to see five to ten times farther and more clearly than ever before.

DEVELOPING A VIEWPOINT

Read more about light pollution and observatories, and come to class to discuss the following questions.

1. When do you think is the best time for observing the stars and planets?
2. Can you suggest a solution to the growing problem of light pollution?

SUGGESTED READINGS

John Bortle, "A Bright Future? Perhaps Too Bright!" *Sky & Telescope,* Nov. 1988, p. 578.

Terry Dunkle, "The Big Glass," *Discover,* July '89, pp. 69–81.

David L. Crawford and Tim B. Hunter, "The Battle Against Light Pollution," *Sky & Telescope,* July 1990, pp. 23–29.

Physics and society

Background: In 1988, the International Dark-Sky Association (IDA) was formed to heighten public awareness of light pollution issues. Unlike residents of most cities, the citizens of Tucson, Arizona—which has adopted lighting control laws in the past decade—are able to see the Milky Way at night with the naked eye.

Answers To DEVELOPING A VIEWPOINT

1. Astronomers must wait until the moon "sets" to make most of their observations, because even moonlight can make the sky background too light. Also, there are fewer lights on after midnight.

2. The solution is twofold: First, we must change the way we light our world. The use of mercury vapor and low-pressure sodium lamps, which shine in discrete, narrow-wavelength bands, not only controls light pollution, but also saves money and energy. But, the yellow light from low-pressure sodium is not attractive. Also, outdoor lights should be shielded properly to prevent glare and light "trespass." Second, observatories should be located in remote locations or up in space, like the Hubble Space Telescope, which is set on a satellite circling Earth.

Teacher Resources: "Light pollution out West concerns optical astronomers." *Physics Today,* December 1984, pages 63–64.
The Space Telescope: A Study of NASA Science, Technology and Politics, Smith, Robert W. Cambridge University Press, 1989.

1 Focus

CONVERGENT QUESTION

Symmetry within principles, models, equations, and phenomena is a strong theme in the study of physics. In light of this, ask students the following question: Now that we have learned about waves possessing particle properties, what does symmetry suggest should also be true? [Particles should behave like waves.]

2 Teach

CONCEPT DEVELOPMENT

- In 1929, de Broglie won the Nobel Prize for his theoretical work on the wave nature of electrons.
- C.J. Davisson and G.P. Thomson (the son of J.J. Thomson, winner of the Nobel Prize in 1906) won the Nobel Prize in 1937 for their experimental work on the diffraction of electrons by crystals.
- Make sure that students notice that 10^{-34} m is much, much smaller than an atom.

Study Guide Master. To reinforce the concepts in this section, have students complete the Study Master for Section 27.2 from the Teacher Resource Package.

POCKET LAB

GLOWS IN THE DARK

Purpose: to observe the effects of different wavelengths of light on fluorescein.

Materials: 100-mL beaker; 90 mL water; 10 g fluorescein; flashlight; red, green, and blue filter material.

Outcome: Red will not cause the liquid to glow. Green will cause the liquid to glow. Blue light has more energy per photon than green light and will also cause the liquid to glow.

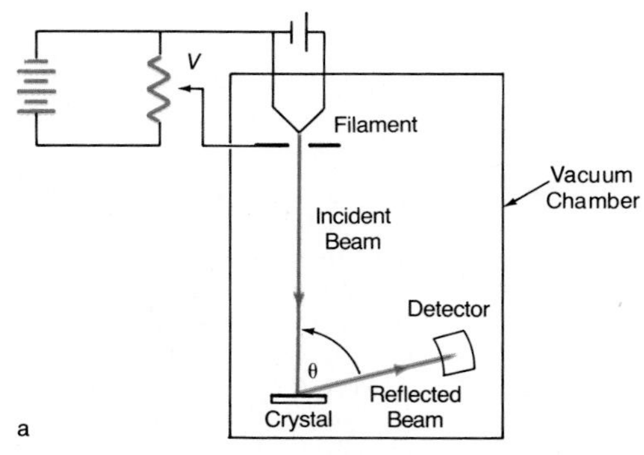

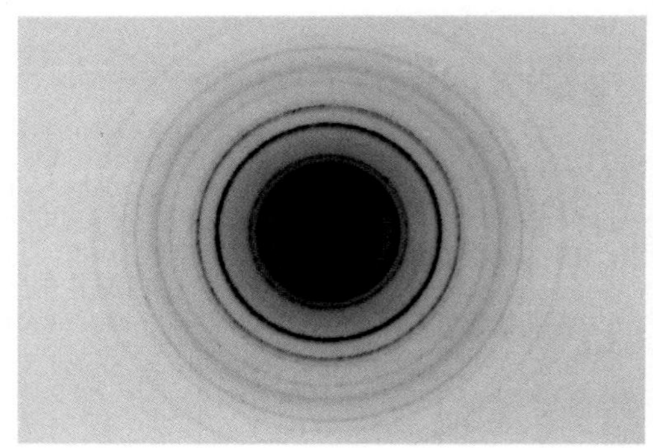

FIGURE 27–8. In the apparatus of Davisson and Germer, a beam of electrons from a hot cathode is directed at a crystal, and angles of the scattered electrons are detected (a). Electron diffraction patterns of aluminum produced by the method used by Thomson demonstrate the wave characteristics of particles (b).

Thus, the **de Broglie wavelength** of the particle is given by

$$\lambda = \frac{h}{p} = \frac{h}{mv}.$$

According to de Broglie, particles should have wavelike properties.

According to de Broglie, particles such as electrons or protons should show wavelike properties. Effects like diffraction and interference had never been observed, so de Broglie's work was greeted with considerable doubt. In 1927, the results of two different experiments showed the diffraction of electrons. One experiment was conducted by the Englishman G. P. Thomson, the son of J. J. Thomson, and the other by two Americans, C. J. Davisson and L. H. Germer. The experiments used a beam of electrons with a small crystal as a target. The atoms in the crystal formed a mesh-like pattern that acted as a diffraction grating. Electrons diffracted from the crystal formed the same patterns that X rays of a similar wavelength formed, Figure 27–8. The two experiments proved that material particles have wave properties.

The de Broglie wavelength of ordinary matter is far too small to produce observable effects.

The wave nature of ordinary matter is not obvious because the wavelengths are so extremely short that wavelike behaviors such as diffraction and interference are not observed. Consider the de Broglie wavelength of a 0.25-kg baseball when it leaves a bat with a speed of 20 m/s.

$$\lambda = \frac{h}{mv} = \frac{6.6 \times 10^{-34}\ \text{J} \cdot \text{s}}{(0.25\ \text{kg})(20\ \text{m/s})} = 1.3 \times 10^{-34}\ \text{m}$$

The wavelength is far too small to have effects that can be observed.

POCKET LAB

GLOWS IN THE DARK

Close the shades and turn off the room lights. Shine a flashlight at a beaker that contains fluorescein. Now place a red filter over the flashlight so that only red light hits the beaker. Describe the results. Repeat the experiment using a green filter. Explain the results. Would you expect the fluorescein to glow when a blue filter is used? Explain your prediction. Try it.

Example Problem

de Broglie Wavelength of an Electron

An electron is accelerated by a potential difference of 150 V. What is the de Broglie wavelength of this electron?

Given: potential difference, $V = 150$ V

Unknown: de Broglie wavelength, λ

Basic equations: $qV = \frac{1}{2}mv^2$, $\lambda = h/mv$

Solution: $qV = \frac{1}{2}mv^2$, so

TEACHER F.Y.I.

De Broglie waves account for the appearance of subatomic particles in unexpected places. For example, a heavy nucleus can emit an alpha particle even though the alpha particle does not have enough energy as a particle to overcome the nuclear force. As a wave, however, the alpha particle can leak through the barrier; it then has a statistically finite possibility of existing outside the nucleus.

$$v = \sqrt{\frac{2qV}{m}}$$

$$= \sqrt{\frac{2(1.6 \times 10^{-19}\ \text{C})(150\ \text{V})}{9.11 \times 10^{-34}\ \text{kg}}}$$

$$= 7.3 \times 10^{6}\ \text{m/s}$$

$$\text{Thus, } \lambda = \frac{h}{mv} = \frac{6.6 \times 10^{-34}\ \text{J} \cdot \text{s}}{(9.11 \times 10^{-31}\ \text{kg})(7.3 \times 10^{6}\ \text{m/s})}$$

$$= 9.9 \times 10^{-11}\ \text{m}$$

This wavelength is approximately the distance between the atoms in a crystal. For this reason, a crystal used as a grating produces diffraction and interference effects, making the wave properties of very small particles of matter observable.

HELP WANTED

COMPUTER PROGRAMMER

There are many different pathways of preparation for a career in computer programming. We are interested in what you know about programming (languages, hardware, software, and so on.), not what degree you have. However, a solid educational background will be a plus.

We want people whose vocabulary does not include the word "can't." Your ability to listen to a division's needs and persist imaginatively and analytically until you have developed a solution to a problem is important.

For information contact:

Your local state employment service

Practice Problems

5. a. Find the speed of an electron accelerated by a potential difference of 250 V.

b. What is the de Broglie wavelength of this electron?

6. A 7.0-kg bowling ball rolls down the alley with a velocity of 8.5 m/s.

a. What is the de Broglie wavelength of the bowling ball?

b. Why does the bowling ball show little wave behavior?

7. An X ray of wavelength 5.0×10^{-12} m is traveling in a vacuum.

a. Calculate the momentum associated with this X ray.

b. Why does the X ray show little particle behavior?

▶ **8. a.** In what ways are electrons and photons the same?

b. In what ways are they different?

Particles and Waves

When you think of a particle, you think of properties like mass, size, kinetic energy, and momentum. You can locate a particle at one point in space. You do not think of particles showing diffraction and interference effects.

Electromagnetic waves show particle-like properties.

The measures of a wave, on the other hand, are frequency, wavelength, and amplitude. A wave travels with a given velocity. A wave cannot be located at one point in space because it must be at least one wavelength long. Thus a wave must be spread out in space. It produces effects like diffraction and interference.

In this chapter, however, we have shown, as another example of the symmetry of the natural world, that light and other electromagnetic waves also have particle-like properties. We have also shown that matter, which is normally considered to be made of particles, can behave like a wave.

Particles show wavelike properties.

Is light a particle or a wave? In the years since the work of Einstein, de Broglie, and others, many physicists and philosophers have tried to work out a satisfactory answer to this question. Some have suggested

CONCEPT DEVELOPMENT

- Experiments obtaining photographs of electrons diffracting around the edge of a crystal and light diffracting at an edge show almost identical patterns.

ACTIVITY

Cooperative Learning: If you have other physics books in your classroom or available in the library, have students look up matter waves in other texts. Often a different way of expressing an idea can make it clearer. Have them pool the insights they've gained.

Guided Practice: Go over the Example Problem that begins on page 566, then have students work on the first two Practice Problems that follow.

Independent Practice: Assign the remaining Practice Problems for homework, and spend time going over them with students during the next class period.

Answers To

PRACTICE PROBLEMS

Have students refer to Appendix A of the Solutions Appendix for complete solutions to Practice Problems.

5. a. 9.4×10^{6} m/s

b. 7.7×10^{-11} m

6. a. 1.1×10^{-35} m

b. The wavelength is too small to show observable effects.

7. a. 1.3×10^{-22} kg · m/s

b. Its momentum is too small to affect objects of ordinary size.

8. a. They have momentum and energy, and can exhibit wave behavior.

b. An electron has mass and charge; a photon does not.

- Heisenberg's uncertainty principle, which won him the Nobel Prize in 1932, states that the product of the errors in measuring certain pairs of variables, such as momentum and position or energy and time, is approximately equal to Planck's constant. A bumper sticker, "Heisenberg May Have Slept Here," refers to this principle.

In 1913, W. Bragg and his father developed the Bragg equation, which indicates at what angle X rays will be most efficiently diffracted by a crystal when the wavelength and distance between the crystal atoms is known. X-ray diffraction is used to analyze crystal structure, and played a critical role in the discovery of the structure of DNA.

CONCEPT DEVELOPMENT

The uncertainty principle, as applied to photons, states that the narrower the slit used to determine the position of the photon, the wider the diffraction pattern becomes due to a spread in photon momentum.

Critical Thinking: Ask students the following questions: In detecting the diffraction of electrons, why was it necessary to find a grating with a very small spacing? [Because the matter wave of the electron is so very small. Diffraction gratings are most effective when their spacing is about the same as the wavelength being used.] What was eventually used? [Crystals, where the interatomic spacing is tiny.]

Critical Thinking Master, Teacher Resource Package. You may wish to have students complete the Critical Thinking Master, Photons, with this section.

Enrichment: Have interested students look up the probability wave interpretation of matter waves in an encyclopedia or college textbook.

Enrichment Master. With this section, use the Enrichment Master, Quantum Fireworks, from the Teacher Resource Package.

CHECKING FOR UNDERSTANDING

Ask students why we don't observe matter waves all around us. [The size of matter waves is so tiny that their effects are totally invisible unless revealed by very specialized measuring equipment.]

RETEACHING

Contact a local college or university to see if they have an electron diffraction apparatus that they would demonstrate for your class. Perhaps they also have an X-ray diffraction apparatus that they could demonstrate.

INDEPENDENT PRACTICE/ EXTENSION

Refer to the Assignment Guide on page 569 for additional questions and problems for independent practice.

F. Y. I.

How are waves and particles alike? They both carry momentum and energy. Particles carry these quantities in their mass, waves in their fields.

that the nature of light depends on the experiment. In the Compton effect, for example, the X ray acts like a particle when it is scattered from the graphite target. It is being treated like a wave when its wavelength is measured using a crystal like a diffraction grating. Most physicists share a belief that the particle and wave aspects of light show complementary views of the true nature of light. They must be taken together. Either picture alone, particle or wave, is incomplete.

The particle and wave properties complement each other to produce a more complete picture of both particles and waves.

Most physicists hold that the properties of an object can only be defined by thinking of an experiment that can measure them. One cannot simply say that a particle is at a certain location moving with a specific speed. Rather, an experiment must be described that will locate the particle and measure its speed.

Properties of an object cannot be defined in the abstract. A means of measuring them must be described.

How can you find the location of a particle? You must touch it or reflect light from it, Figure 27–9. The reflected light then must be collected by an instrument or the human eye. Because of diffraction effects, light spreads out, making it impossible to locate the particle exactly. You can reduce the spreading by decreasing the wavelength of the light. Thus the shorter the wavelength, the more precisely you can measure the location.

The Compton effect, however, proves that when light of short wavelengths strikes a particle, the momentum of the particle is changed. Therefore, the act of precisely measuring the location of an object changes its momentum, and the more precisely we try to measure its location, the larger the likely change in its momentum.

In the same way, if the momentum of the particle is measured, the position of the particle will be changed. *The position and momentum of a particle cannot both be precisely known at the same time.* This fact is called the **Heisenberg uncertainty principle** after the German physicist Werner Heisenberg. It is the result of the dual wave and particle description of light and matter.

The Heisenberg uncertainty principle states that a particle's momentum and position cannot both be known precisely at the same time.

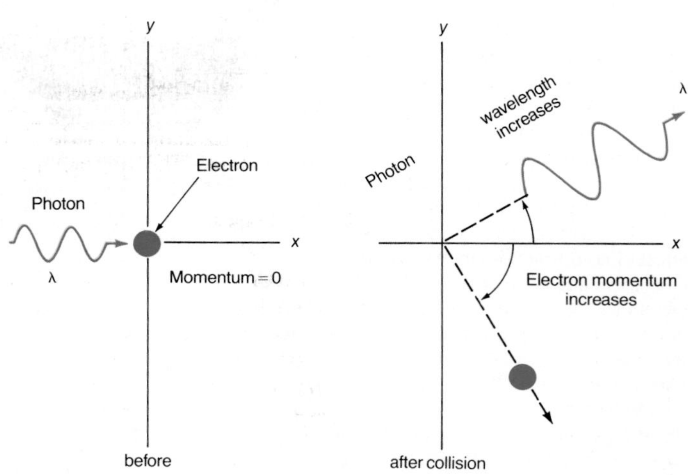

FIGURE 27–9. A particle can be seen only by scattering light off of it. The scattering changes the electron momentum.

Assessment

Portfolio

Make a table of the properties of waves and particles. For each property, briefly describe an experiment that could be used to measure this property.

CONCEPT REVIEW

2.1 If Davisson and Germer had wanted to increase the wavelength of the electrons they used, should they have decreased or increased their energy?

2.2 If you want to increase the wavelength of a proton, you slow it down. If you want to increase the wavelength of a photon, what could you do?

2.3 If you try to find the location of a beam of light by having it pass through a narrow hole, why can you not tell much about the direction of the beam?

2.4 **Critical Thinking:** Physicists recently made a "diffraction grating" of standing waves of light. They sent atoms through this grating and observed interference. If the spacing of the "slits" in the grating was half a wavelength, 250 nm, roughly what would you expect that the de Broglie wavelength of the atoms should be?

CHAPTER 27 REVIEW

SUMMARY

27.1 Waves Behave Like Particles

- Objects hot enough to be incandescent emit light because of the vibrations of the charged particles inside their atoms.
- The spectrum of incandescent objects covers a wide range of wavelengths. The spectrum depends on their temperature.
- Planck explained the spectrum of an incandescent object by supposing that a particle can have only certain energies that are multiples of a small constant now called Planck's constant.
- The photoelectric effect is the emission of electrons when certain metals are exposed to light.
- Einstein explained the photoelectric effect by postulating that light came in bundles of energy called photons.
- The photoelectric effect allows the measurement of Planck's constant, h.
- The work function, the energy with which electrons are held inside metals, is measured by the threshold frequency in the photoelectric effect.
- The Compton effect demonstrates the momentum of photons, first predicted by Einstein.
- Photons, or light quanta, are massless and travel at the speed of light. Yet they have energy, hf, and momentum, $p = h/\lambda$.

27.2 Particles Behave Like Waves

- The wave nature of material particles was suggested by de Broglie and verified experimentally by diffracting electrons off crystals.
- The particle and wave aspects are complementary parts of the complete nature of both matter and light.
- The Heisenberg uncertainty principle states that the position and momentum of a particle (light or matter) cannot both be known precisely at the same time.

KEY TERMS

photoelectric effect
threshold frequency
photons
work function
Compton effect
de Broglie wavelength
Heisenberg uncertainty principle

3 Close

CONVERGENT QUESTION

Matter waves are perhaps the most abstract concept we've learned about so far in physics. Discuss with students what makes them so abstract.

CONCEPT REVIEW ANSWERS

2.1 They should have decreased the energy because the momentum will also decrease and, hence, the wavelength, $\lambda = h/p$, will increase.

2.2 Lower its energy by scattering the photon off an electron (Compton effect). When it does lose energy, it doesn't slow down but its frequency is decreased ($f = E/h$), so its wavelength, $\lambda = c/f = hc/E$, is increased.

2.3 Diffraction causes the light coming through the hole to spread, therefore causing its direction to spread.

2.4 Critical Thinking: Since $\lambda = d \sin \theta$, the value of λ would be a few tens of nanometers.

CLOSING CHAPTER 27

Review Summary statements and Key Terms with your students.

ASSESSMENT

Vocabulary Review Master, Teacher Resource Package. Use this master to check students' understanding of Key Terms.

Evaluation Masters. Use Parts A and B of the Chapter Evaluation Masters from the Teacher Resource Package to test qualitative chapter objectives. Use Parts C and D to test quantitative chapter objectives.

27:2 ASSIGNMENT GUIDE

	PRACTICE	EXTENSION
CHAPTER REVIEW pp. 569–571		
· Reviewing Concepts	9	
· Applying Concepts		5–7
· Problems*	14–18	19–21
APPENDIX B PROBLEMS*		
· Chapter 27, pp. 707–708	11, 12	13

* Complete solutions to all Chapter Review and Appendix problems appear in the Problems and Solutions Manual.

STUDY GUIDE MASTER

Use the Study Guide master for section 27.2.

CRITICAL THINKING

Use the Critical Thinking master for Chapter 27 with this section.

ENRICHMENT MASTER

Use the Enrichment master for Chapter 27 with this section.

Answers To
REVIEWING CONCEPTS

1. *Quantized* means a quantity can only have a multiple of some minimum value.
2. the energy of vibration of the atoms that make up the walls of the hot body
3. a photon
4. Each photon ejects a photoelectron. More intense light has more photons per second, thus it ejects more photoelectrons per second.
5. Each electron requires one photon with more than some minimum energy to eject it. In this case, each photon lacks the energy needed to eject an electron.
6. Red photons do not have enough energy to cause the chemical reaction that exposes film.
7. Elastic collisions transfer both momentum and energy. Only if photons have momentum can the equations be satisfied.
8. No. Momentum would be zero, because the mass of a photon is zero.
9. a. Balance force of gravity against force of electric field on charge. (Millikan experiment)
b. Balance force of electric field against that of magnetic field to find *m/q,* then use measured value of *q.* (J.J. Thomson) **c.** Scatter off crystal, measuring angles of diffraction. (Bragg defraction)
10. a. Measure the kinetic energy of electron ejected from a metal for at least two different wavelengths. Or, measure *KE* from known metal for only one wavelength.
b. Measure change in wavelength of X ray scattered from matter.
c. Measure angle diffracted by two slits, grating, width of single-slit pattern, or angle bent through prism.

Answers To
APPLYING CONCEPTS

1. See Figure 27–1 on page 556. The intensity increases about seven times.
2. a. the rod glowing bright orange **b.** the rod glowing bright orange
3. Not necessarily. The number of ejected electrons is proportional to the number of incident photons or the brightness of the light, not the frequency of light.

REVIEWING CONCEPTS

1. Define the word *quantized.*
2. What is quantized in Planck's blackbody radiation theory?
3. What is a quantum of light called?
4. Light above the threshold frequency shines on the metal cathode in a photocell. How does Einstein's theory explain that, as the light intensity is increased, the current of photoelectrons increases?
5. Explain how Einstein's theory accounts for the fact that light below the threshold frequency of a metal produces no photoelectrons, no matter how intense it is.
6. Certain types of black-and-white film are not sensitive to red light. They can be developed with a red "safelight" on. Explain this on the basis of the photon theory of light.
7. How does the Compton effect demonstrate that photons have momentum as well as energy?
8. The momentum of a material particle is *mv.* Can you calculate the momentum of a photon using *mv?* Explain.
9. Describe how the following properties of the electron could be measured. Explain in each case what is to be done.
   a. charge **b.** mass **c.** wavelength
10. Describe how the following properties of a photon could be measured. Explain in each case what is to be done.
    a. energy **b.** momentum **c.** wavelength

APPLYING CONCEPTS

1. What is the change in the intensity of red light given off by blackbody radiation if the temperature increases from 4000 K to 8000 K?
2. Two iron rods are held in a fire. One glows dark red while the other is glowing bright orange.
   a. Which rod is hotter?
   b. Which rod is radiating more energy?
3. Will high frequency light eject a greater number of electrons from a photo-sensitive surface than low frequency light, assuming both frequencies are above the threshold frequency?
4. Potassium in a photocell emits photoelectrons when struck by blue light. Tungsten emits them only when ultraviolet light is used.
   a. Which metal has a higher threshold frequency?
   b. Which metal has a larger work function?
5. Electrons in one electron beam have a greater speed than those in another. Which electrons have the longer de Broglie wavelength?
6. As the speed of a particle increases, does its associated wavelength increase or decrease?
7. Compare the de Broglie wavelength of a baseball moving 20 m/s with the size of the baseball.

PROBLEMS

27.1 Waves Behave Like Particles

▶ 1. A home uses about 4×10^{11} J of energy each year. In many parts of the United States, there are about 3000 h of sunlight each year.
   a. How much energy from the sun falls on one square meter each year?
   b. If the solar energy can be converted to useful energy with an efficiency of 20%, how large an area of converters would produce the energy needed by the home?
2. The stopping potential of a certain metal is 5.0 V. What is the maximum kinetic energy of the photoelectrons in
   a. electron volts? **b.** joules?
3. To block the current in a photocell, a stopping potential of 3.8 V is used. Find the kinetic energy of the photoelectrons in J.
4. What potential difference is needed to stop electrons having a maximum kinetic energy of 4.8×10^{-19} J?
5. The threshold frequency of sodium is 4.4×10^{14} Hz. How much work must be done to free an electron from the surface of the sodium?
6. If light with a frequency of 1.00×10^{15} Hz falls on the sodium in the previous problem, what is the maximum kinetic energy of the photoelectrons?
7. Barium has a work function of 2.48 eV. What is the longest wavelength of light that will cause electrons to be emitted from barium?

REVIEW MASTER

Use the Vocabulary Review master for Chapter 27 with this section.

EVALUATION MASTER

Use the Chapter Evaluation master for Chapter 27 with this section.

8. A photocell is used by a photographer to measure the light falling on the subject to be photographed. What should be the work function of the cathode if the photocell is to be sensitive to red light (λ = 680 nm) as well as the other colors?

9. The threshold frequency of tin is 1.2×10^{15} Hz.
   a. What is the threshold wavelength?
   b. What is the work function of tin?
   c. Electromagnetic radiation of 167 nm wavelength falls on tin. What is the kinetic energy of the ejected electrons in eV?

10. The threshold frequency of a given metal is 6.7×10^{14} Hz. Calculate the kinetic energy in eV of the electrons ejected when the surface is illuminated with light of wavelength
   a. 350 nm. b. 550 nm.

▶ 11. The work function of iron is 4.7 eV.
   a. What is the threshold wavelength of iron?
   b. Iron is exposed to radiation of wavelength 150 nm. What is the maximum kinetic energy of the ejected electrons in eV?

▶ 12. Suppose a 5.0-g object, such as a nickel, vibrates while connected to a spring. Its maximum velocity is 1.0 cm/s.
   a. Find a maximum kinetic energy of the vibrating object.
   b. The object emits energy in the form of light of frequency 5.0×10^{14} Hz and its energy is reduced by one step. Find the energy lost by the object.
   c. How many step reductions would this object have to make to lose all its energy?

13. What is the momentum of a photon of yellow light whose wavelength is 600 nm?

27.2 Particles Behave Like Waves

14. Find the de Broglie wavelength of a deuteron of mass 3.3×10^{-27} kg that moves with a speed of 2.5×10^4 m/s.

15. What is the de Broglie wavelength of a proton moving with a speed of 1.00×10^6 m/s? The mass of a proton is 1.67×10^{-27} kg.

16. An electron is accelerated across a potential difference of 54 V.
   a. Find the maximum velocity of the electron.
   b. Calculate the de Broglie wavelength of the electron.

17. A neutron is held in a trap with a kinetic energy of only 0.025 eV.
   a. What is the velocity of the neutron?
   b. Find the de Broglie wavelength of the neutron.

18. The kinetic energy of the hydrogen atom electron is 13.65 eV.
   a. Find the velocity of the electron.
   b. Calculate the de Broglie wavelength of this electron.
   c. Compare your answer with the radius of the hydrogen atom, 5.19 nm.

▶ 19. An electron has a de Broglie wavelength of 400 nm, the shortest wavelength of visible light.
   a. Find its velocity.
   b. Calculate the energy of this electron in eV.

▶ 20. An electron microscope is useful because the de Broglie wavelength of electrons can be made smaller than the wavelength of visible light. What energy in eV has to be given to an electron for it to have a de Broglie wavelength of 20 nm?

▶ 21. An electron has a de Broglie wavelength of 0.18 nm.
   a. How large a potential difference did it experience if it started from rest?
   b. If a proton has a de Broglie wavelength of 0.18 nm, how large of a potential difference did it experience if it started from rest?

USING LAB SKILLS

1. When you did the Pocket Lab on page 566, you found that only certain colors caused the fluorescein to glow. Would ultraviolet light cause the dye to glow? Would infrared? Explain your prediction.

THINKING PHYSIC-LY

Sun tanning produces cell damage in the skin. Why is ultraviolet light capable of producing this damage while infrared radiation is not?

4. **a.** Blue has a lower frequency; tungsten has a higher threshold frequency. **b.** Tungsten has a larger work function.
5. $\lambda = h/mv$, so the electrons with the slower speed will have the longer de Broglie wavelength.
6. As the speed increases, the particle's momentum increases and this decreases the wavelength.
7. The size of the baseball is about 0.10 m, whereas the de Broglie wavelength is 10^{-34} m, a factor of 10^{33} difference.

Answers To
PROBLEMS

Complete solutions for all Chapter Review Problems can be found in the Problems and Solutions Manual accompanying this text.

1. **a.** 1×10^{10} J/m^2
   b. 2×10^2 m^2
2. **a.** 5.0 eV
   b. 8.0×10^{-19} J
3. 6.1×10^{-19} J
4. 3.0 V
5. 2.9×10^{-19} J
6. 3.7×10^{-19} J
7. 501 nm
8. 1.8 eV
9. **a.** 2.5×10^{-7} m
   b. 8.0×10^{-19} J
   c. 2.4 eV
10. **a.** 0.81 eV
   b. No electrons are ejected.
11. **a.** 2.6×10^2 nm
   b. 3.6 eV
12. **a.** 2.5×10^{-7} J
   b. 3.3×10^{-19} J
   c. 7.6×10^{11} "steps"
13. 1.10×10^{-27} kg·m/s
14. 8.0×10^{-12} m
15. 3.97×10^{-13} m
16. **a.** 4.4×10^6 m/s
   b. 0.17 nm
17. **a.** 2.2×10^3 m/s
   b. 1.8×10^{-10} m
18. **a.** 2.19×10^6 m/s
   b. 3.32×10^{-10} m
   c. 1/16 the radius of the atom
19. **a.** 1.83×10^3 m/s
   b. 9.43×10^{-6} eV
20. 3.8×10^{-3} eV
21. **a.** 46 V
   b. 2.6×10^{-2} V

Answer To
USING LAB SKILLS

1. The ultraviolet source will cause a brilliant and beautiful glow, but the infrared will not work. The ultraviolet has much more energy per photon than the infrared.

Answer To
THINKING PHYSIC-LY

The ultraviolet light has a higher frequency and therefore a greater energy.

CHAPTER

28 The Atom

PLANNING GUIDE (6 class sessions)

CONTENTS	TEXT FEATURES	TEACHER RESOURCE PACKAGE	OTHER COMPONENTS
28.1 The Bohr Model, pp. 574–584 (4 Class Sessions) • The Nuclear Model • Atomic Spectra • The Bohr Model of the Atom • Predictions of the Bohr Model	**Physics Lab:** Shots in the Dark, p. 579 **Pocket Lab:** Nuclear Bouncing, p. 575 **Concept Review,** p. 584	**Study Guide:** The Bohr Model **Physics Lab Data Sheet:** Shots in the Dark **Critical Thinking Master:** Star Spectra **Enrichment Master:** The Lyman, Balmer, and Paschen Series **Reteaching Master:** The Hydrogen Atom **Transparency Worksheet:** Gas Spectra **Transparency Worksheet:** Rutherford's Gold Foil	**Laboratory Manual:** Lab 28.1 Spectra **Transparency 41:** Gas Spectra **Transparency 42:** Rutherford's Gold Foil
28.2 The Present Model of the Atom, pp. 584–591 (2 Class Sessions) • A Quantum Model of the Atom • Lasers	**Physics and Technology:** Scanning Tunneling Microscope, p. 590 **Pocket Lab:** Bright Lines, p. 585 **Concept Review,** p. 591	**Study Guide:** The Present Model of the Atom **Transparency Worksheet:** Electron Cloud	**Transparency 43:** Electron Cloud
Chapter Review, pp. 591–593	Summary Key Terms Reviewing Concepts Applying Concepts Problems Thinking Physic-ly	**Vocabulary Review** **Chapter Test**	**Test Bank**

SUPPLEMENTARY MATERIALS

SOFTWARE	AUDIOVISUAL	BOOKS/MAGAZINES
Atomic Structure 1, Queue, Inc. (Apple II). *Hydrogen Spectrum,* Queue, Inc. (Apple II). *Molecules & Atoms: Exploring the Essence of Matter,* Queue, Inc. (Apple II, IBM PC).	Videos: *The Mechanical Universe and Beyond: The Atom* and *Particles and Waves,* Films Inc. *Lasers,* National Geographic. Filmstrips: *The Amazin' Laser,* Educational Dimensions. *Atoms and Atomic Energy,* Clearvue. *Models of the Atom,* AVNA Media.	Balykin, V. I., and Letokhov, V. S. "Laser Optics of Neutral Atomic Beams." *Physics Today,* April 1989, p. 23. Chiaverina, Chris. "A Laser Spirograph for Under $3 (Laser Not Included)." *The Physics Teacher,* December 1990, p. 606. Schmidt, Ellen. "Laser Light Gets Everyone's Attention." *The Physics Teacher,* January 1989, pp. 30–31. Zewail, Ahmed H. "The Birth of Molecules." *Scientific American,* December 1990, pp. 76–82.

PROBLEM CORRELATION

CONCEPTS	CHAPTER REVIEW			PROBLEMS APPENDIX
	Reviewing Concepts	Applying Concepts	Problems	
28.1 The Bohr Model				
The Nuclear Model	1		1	
Atomic Spectra		1,2		
The Bohr Model of the Atom	2,3	3,4,5	2,3,4,5	1,2,3,**4**
Predictions of the Bohr Model	4,5	6,7	6,7,8,9,10,11,12,13, **14,15,16,**17,**18**	5,6,7,8
28.2 The Present Model of the Atom				
A Quantum Model of the Atom		8		
Lasers	6,7,8	9	**19,**20	

ACTIVITY AND DEMONSTRATION MATERIALS

PHYSICS LAB

Page 579
- 3 dozen #0 rubber stoppers
- bed sheet (or blanket)
- goggles
- atomic model (see diagram)
- blindfold (or darkened goggles)

POCKET LAB

Pages 575, 585
- 9-in aluminum pie pan
- four 12-mm diameter glass marbles
- four 12-mm diameter steel balls
- grooved ruler
- gas discharge tubes
- gas discharge power supply
- diffraction gratings

DEMONSTRATIONS

Pages 578, 581
- spectrum discharge tubes
- prism
- high-voltage source
- good quality diffraction grating
- 35-mm slide-sized piece of cardboard
- slide projector
- movie screen
- long strip of flexible corrugated plastic (5 cm wide)

EXTENSION PROJECTS

LIBRARY RESEARCH

1. Water Drop Model of the Atom
Read about the water drop model of the atom. Describe the model in your own words.

DISPLAY MODEL

2. Particle Chart
Make a chart of the primary particles that have been identified by particle physicists.

STUDENT READINGS

Amato, Ivan. "Getting a Feel for Atoms." *Science News,* April 7, 1990.

Ansley, David. "Have Laser, Will Travel." *Discover,* December 1990.

Bromberg, J.L. "The Birth of the Laser." *Physics Today,* October 1988.

Jones, Edwin. "Observational Evidence for Atoms." *The Physics Teacher,* September 1984.

Peltz, James F. "Bright Lights, Big Money." *Discover,* March 1988.

Trefil, James. "Seeing Atoms." *Discover,* June 1990.

Chapter 28

The Atom

CHAPTER OVERVIEW

Theme Development: Understanding the evolving atomic model requires an appreciation of the stability and equilibrium theme. The spectral lines of each element represent a phenomenon consistent with this constancy theme. Quantum mechanics, a science derived from the conceptual quantum atomic model, has influenced all branches of inquiry and has led to numerous technical applications.

MISCONCEPTIONS

The abstract nature of atomic theories gives students difficulty. One misconception about lasers is that somehow lasers are exempt from the conservation of energy principle and put out much more energy than is put into them.

KEY TERMS

absorption spectrum
alpha (α) particle
Bohr model
electron cloud
emission spectrum
energy levels
excited state
ground state
laser
nuclear model
quantized
quantum mechanics
quantum model
quantum number
spectroscope
stimulated emission

Laboratory Options

STUDENT EDITION

Physics Lab

Shots in the Dark	579

Pocket Labs

Nuclear Bouncing	575
Bright Lines	585

TEACHER EDITION

Activities

Demonstration	578, 578, 581
Cooperative Learning	581, 587

LABORATORY MANUAL

Spectra	Lab 28.1

CHAPTER

28 The Atom

Atomic Secrets

The mercury and sodium street lamps and the car headlights in this photograph were photographed with a diffraction grating over the camera lens. Why are the images of the lights different, and how could these differences be used to identify the types of lights?

Chapter Outline

Concept Check

The following terms or concepts from earlier chapters are important for a good understanding of this chapter. If you are not familiar with them, you should review them before studying this chapter.

- Newton's laws of motion, Chapter 5
- centripetal acceleration, Chapter 7
- energy, Chapter 11
- light spectrum, Chapter 16
- Coulomb's law, Chapter 20
- quantization, photons, Chapter 27

As you have learned, both prisms and diffraction gratings separate white light into its component colors. Different sources of light look very different through diffraction gratings. While some sources emit continuous spectra, others give off only certain colors. Why is this so? How can the light emitted by atoms be used to help unravel their structure? Today the answers are known, but at the end of the last century these important questions were unsolved.

Introducing The Chapter

Atomic Secrets

Using The Photo: Novelty stores sell various types of diffraction grating glasses. A cheaper version comes in a cardboard frame, while the more expensive kind comes in a plastic frame of various colors. These glasses give the diffraction grating view without the squinting needed for the single, slide-mounted grating. Students will enjoy seeing the world distorted this way. For an explanation of the chapter opener question, refer students to page 577.

Concept Check

Make sure students have a clear understanding of the concepts taught in Chapters 5, 7, 11, 16, 20, and 27 that are listed in the Concept Check. Students with a fresh understanding of Newton's laws of motion, centripetal acceleration, energy, light spectrum, Coulomb's law, quantization, and photons will be prepared to learn the fundamental principles of the atom presented in this chapter.

Assessment Options

Portfolio Assessment
Extension 1, TWE, p. 572b
Portfolio Assessment, TWE, p. 580
Cooperative Learning, TWE, p. 581
Extension, TWE, p. 582
Extension, TWE, p. 588

Performance Assessment
Pocket Labs, pp. 575, 585
Physics Lab, p. 579
Enrichment, TWE, p. 575
Pocket Lab Assessment, TWE, p. 585

Content Assessment
Self Assessment: Practice Problems, p. 583
Assessment, Critical Thinking, TWE, p. 579
Critical Thinking, TWE, p. 582
Checking for Understanding, TWE, p. 588
Concept Reviews, pp. 584, 591
Chapter Review, pp. 591–593
Supplemental Problems, p. 708

Group Assessment
Activities for group assessment occur with Cooperative Learning and lab activities

28.1 THE BOHR MODEL

Preparation

OBJECTIVES

The objectives are listed on the student page. Remind students to preview these objectives as a study guide to this major section.

OVERVIEW

New concepts include absorption and emission spectra; energy levels, especially excited states and ground states; the Bohr model of the atom; and the nuclear (Rutherford) model. Alpha particles are introduced.

BRIDGING

The idea of quantization is extended. Other previously taught terms and concepts include spectroscope, diffraction grating, electron, electrode, wavelength, acceleration, oscillation, amplitude, kinetic and potential energy, proton, and angular momentum.

1 Focus

DISCREPANT EVENT

Get students to imagine they are living in a time before people believed in atoms. Have them give some commonplace evidence that atoms exist. [Students will probably mention such things as the evaporation of a liquid from a surface, the spreading of odors (diffusion), the boiling of liquids, and perhaps the regular structure of crystals as strongly suggesting microscopic substructure. Others may offer evidence from chemistry such as the law of combining volumes or the results of electrolysis experiments.]

Objectives

- **explain the method Rutherford and co-workers used to determine the structure of the atom; describe the nuclear model.**
- **distinguish continuous from line spectra; contrast emission and absorption spectra.**
- **list Bohr's assumptions; define energy levels, ground and excited states; understand the connection between photon energy and energy level differences.**
- **referring to the text, use the orbital radius and energy level equations to solve problems using the Bohr model.**

28.1 THE BOHR MODEL

By the end of the nineteenth century, most scientists agreed that atoms exist. Furthermore, as a result of the discovery of the electron by J. J. Thomson (1856 – 1940), the atom could not be an indivisible particle. All the atoms Thomson tested contained electrons. Yet atoms were known to be electrically neutral and much more massive than electrons. Therefore, atoms must contain not only electrons, but a massive, positively-charged part as well. It took three decades to work out how the parts of the atom are arranged.

The Nuclear Model

Discovering the nature of the massive part of the atom and the arrangement of the electrons was a major challenge. Physicists and chemists from many countries both cooperated and competed in searching for the solution to this puzzle. The result provided not only knowledge of the structure of the atom, but a totally new approach to both physics and chemistry. The story of this work is one of the most exciting stories of the twentieth century.

J. J. Thomson believed that a massive, positively-charged substance filled the atom. He pictured the electrons arranged within this substance like raisins in a muffin. Ernest Rutherford, who was working in England at the time, performed a series of brilliant experiments that showed that the atom was very different.

Rutherford's group studied atomic structure by bombarding metal foils with alpha particles.

Rutherford probed atoms with high speed particles emitted by uranium. In 1896 the French physicist Henri Becquerel (1852–1908) found that compounds containing the element uranium emitted penetrating rays. Some of the emissions were found to be massive, positively-charged particles moving at high speed. These were later named **alpha (α) particles**. The α particles could be detected by a screen coated with zinc sulfide that emitted a small flash of light, or scintillation (sint uhl AY shuhn), each time an α particle hit it, Figure 28–1.

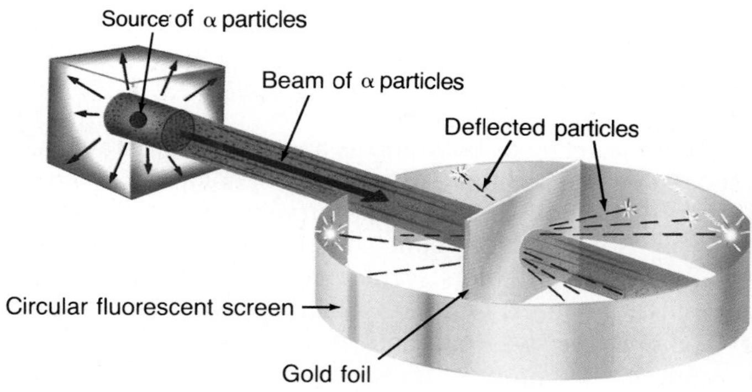

FIGURE 28–1. After bombarding metal foil with alpha particles, Rutherford's team concluded that most of the mass of the atom was concentrated in the nucleus.

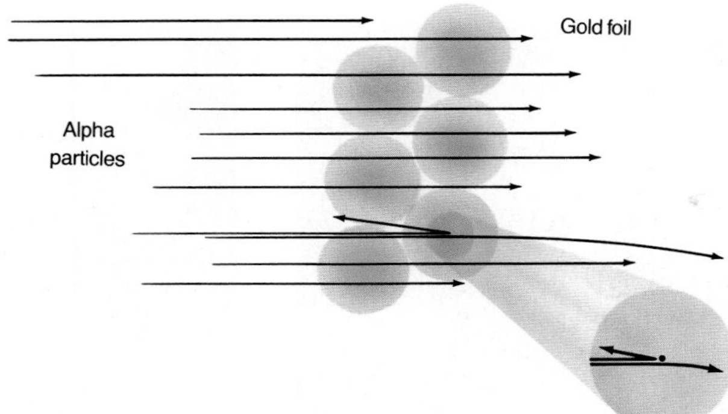

FIGURE 28–2. Most of the alpha particles went through the foil without deflection. A few, however, were deflected at large angles.

Rutherford directed a beam of α particles at a thin sheet of metal only a few atoms thick. He noticed that while most of the α particles passed through the sheet, the beam was spread slightly by the metal. Two members of Rutherford's team, Hans Geiger and Ernest Marsden, made detailed studies of the deflection of α particles by metal sheets. In 1910, they found that a few of the particles were deflected at large angles, even larger than 90°, Figure 28–2. Rutherford was amazed because he had assumed that the mass was spread throughout the atom. He commented that it was as surprising as if you had fired a 15-inch cannon shell at tissue paper and the shell had bounced back and hit you.

The nucleus contains all the positive charge and almost all the mass of the atom.

Rutherford, using Coulomb's force law and Newton's laws of motion, found that the results could be explained only if all the positive charge of the atom were concentrated in a tiny, massive central core, now called the nucleus. Rutherford's model is, therefore, called a **nuclear model** of the atom. All the positive charge and essentially all the mass of the atom are in its nucleus. Electrons are outside the nucleus and do not contribute a significant amount of mass. The electrons are far away from the nucleus; the atom is 10 000 times larger than the nucleus. So the atom is mostly empty space.

Atomic Spectra

How are the electrons arranged around the nucleus of the atom? One of the clues to answering this question came from studying the light emitted by atoms. The set of light wavelengths emitted by an atom is called the atom's **emission spectrum**.

You know that the continuous spectrum of an incandescent blackbody does not depend on the type of atom that makes up the body. The properties of individual atoms become apparent only when they are not packed together. Many substances can be vaporized by heating them in a flame. Then they can emit light that is characteristic of the atoms of the elements that make up the substance. For example, if sodium chloride is put on a wire and held in a flame, the sodium atoms will emit a bright yellow light. Similarly, lithium salts emit red light, and barium salts, green light.

POCKET LAB

NUCLEAR BOUNCING

What will happen when an alpha particle "hits" a proton? Place a 9" aluminum pie pan on the table. Gently press four glass marbles (protons) into the pie pan so that they make small indentations near the center of the pan. Roll a 12-mm steel ball (alpha particle) down a grooved ruler to see if you can hit the marbles. Does the steel ball change its path? Does the steel ball ever bounce "back"? Now put the steel marbles into the indentations (each steel ball represents a nucleus) in the pie pan and roll a marble (alpha particle) down the grooved ruler. How are the results different? Why are the results different?

TEACHER F.Y.I.

The fact that most of the alpha particles in Rutherford's experiments passed through the foil undeflected demonstrates that the atom is mostly empty space and that the nucleus is very small.

2 Teach

CONCEPT DEVELOPMENT

- The discovery of the neutron led to the idea that the nucleus might be made up of protons and neutrons rather than protons and electrons.

Enrichment: One quantitative experiment that can be done on the atom itself is the measurement of the diameter of an atom by using a monomolecular film. It uses quite simple equipment.

Study Guide Master. To reinforce the concepts in this section, have the students complete the Study Guide Master for Section 28.1 from the Teacher Resource Package.

POCKET LAB

NUCLEAR BOUNCING

Purpose: to compare how the alpha particle behaves when it hits lighter versus heavier targets.

Materials: 9″ aluminum pie pan; four 12-mm diameter glass marbles; four 12-mm diameter steel balls; grooved ruler.

Outcome: The steel ball is only slightly deflected when it hits the lighter glass marbles. The glass marble changes direction by large angles when it hits the more massive steel balls.

Transparency Package. Use Transparency 42 to quiz students on the details of Rutherford's experiment.

CONCEPT DEVELOPMENT

In the late nineteenth century, there was opposition to the development of the atomic theory. One chief opponent was Ernst Mach, whose ideas later led to the Vienna school of philosophy known as logical positivism.

Williamina Paton Stevens Fleming was an American physicist who lived from 1857 to 1911. She was born in Scotland and became a pupil-teacher at age 14. After marrying in 1877, she and her husband moved to the United States and settled in Boston. Her marriage failed and she started working for the director of Harvard College Observatory as a maid. He was impressed by her intellectual abilities and offered her part-time work doing clerical and computing tasks at the observatory. She took the opportunity to assume more duties and was made a permanent member in 1881. In 1886, she took charge of the new program to classify stars based on their spectra. In addition to administering the program, Williamina analyzed many of the photographs and supervised a staff of women research assistants. In 1898, she was named curator of the astronomical photographs and became the first woman to receive a corporation appointment at Harvard. In 1906, she was elected a member of the Royal Astronomical Society, one of the few women selected.

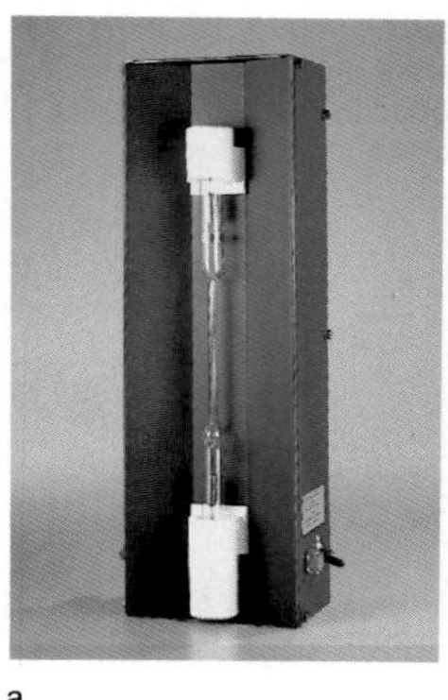

a

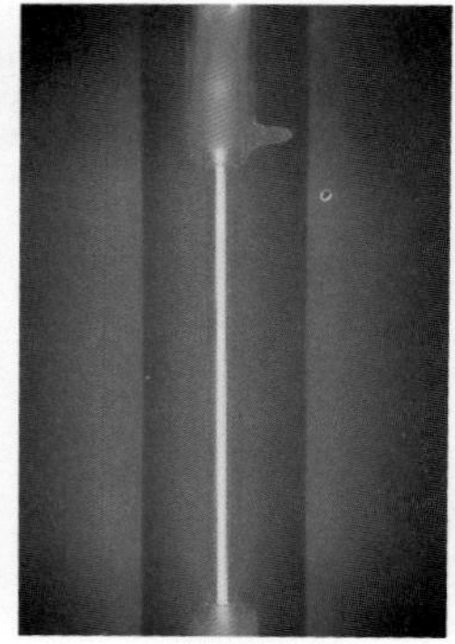

b

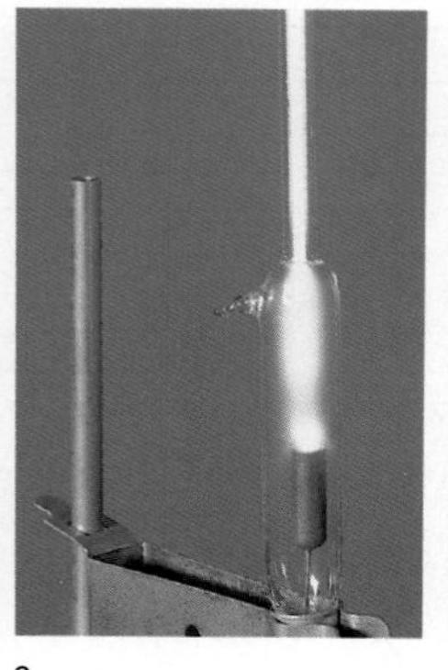

c

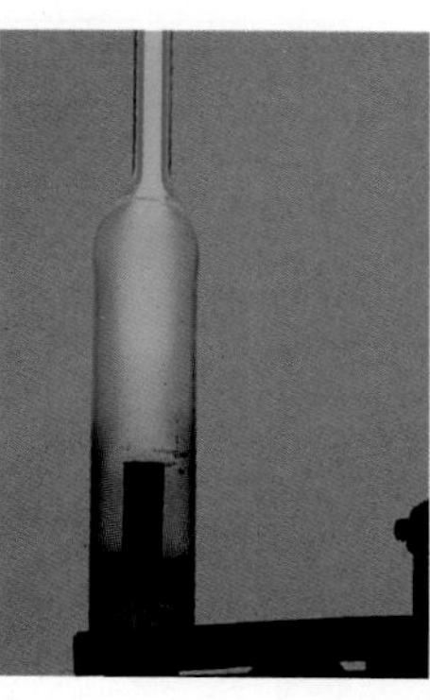

d

FIGURE 28–3. A gas discharge tube apparatus (a). Neon (b), argon (c), mercury (d) gases glow when high voltage is applied.

Gas atoms can be made to emit their characteristic colors by a method shown in Figure 28–3. A glass tube containing neon gas at low pressure has metal electrodes at each end. When a high voltage is applied across the tube, electrons pass through the gas. The electrons collide with the neon atoms, transferring energy to them. The atoms then give up this extra energy, emitting it in the form of light. The light emitted by neon is red. Nitrogen and argon emit a bluish color, and mercury a greenish blue.

The emission spectrum of an atom can be seen by looking at the light through a diffraction grating or prism or by putting a grating in front of a camera lens, as was done in the opening photo. The spectrum can be studied in greater detail using the instrument shown in Figure 28–4b. In this **spectroscope,** the light passes through a slit and is then dis-

FIGURE 28–4. A prism spectroscope can be used to observe emission spectra (a, b). The emission spectra of neon (c) and molecular hydrogen (d) show characteristic lines.

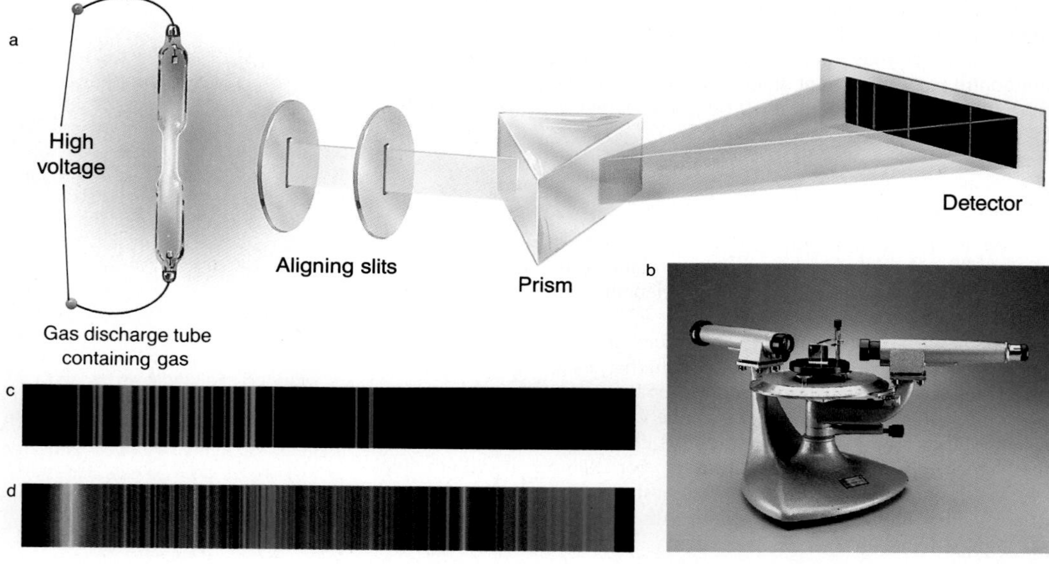

576 The Atom

STUDY GUIDE MASTER

Use the Study Guide master for section 28.1.

TRANSPARENCY

Use Transparency 42 with this section.

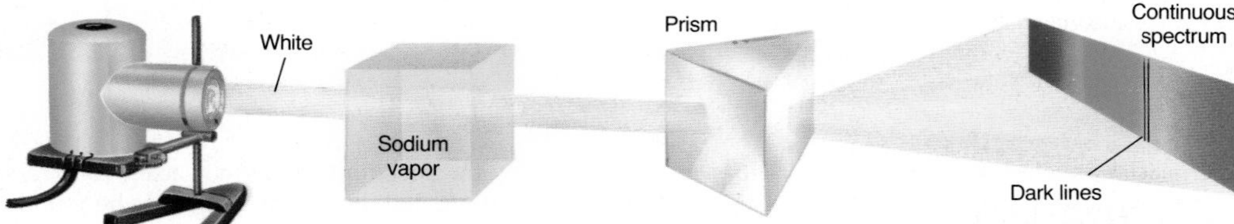

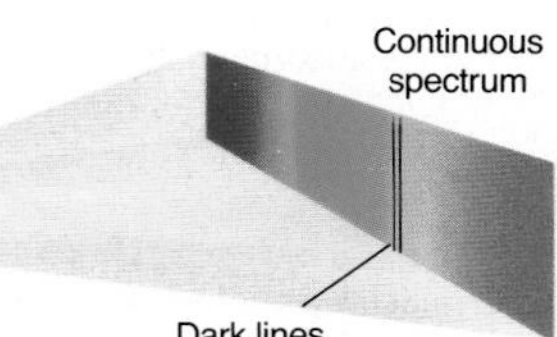

FIGURE 28–5. This apparatus is used to produce the absorption spectrum of sodium.

persed, passing through a prism or diffraction grating. A lens system collects the dispersed light for viewing through a telescope or for recording on a photographic plate. Each wavelength of light forms an image of the slit. The spectrum of an incandescent solid is a continuous band of colors from red through violet. The spectrum of a gas, however, is a series of lines of different colors. Each line corresponds to a particular wavelength of light emitted by the atoms of the gas. Suppose an unidentified gas, perhaps mercury, argon, or nitrogen, is contained in a tube. When excited, the gas will emit light at wavelengths characteristic of the atoms of that gas. Thus, the gas can be identified by comparing its wavelengths with the lines present in the spectrum of a known sample. Some emission spectra are shown in Figure 28–4c, d.

A spectroscope is used to study the wavelength of light emitted by atoms.

When the emission spectrum of a combination of elements is photographed, analysis of the lines on the photograph can indicate both the elements present and their relative amounts. If the substance being examined contains a large amount of any particular element, the lines for that element are more intense on the photograph. By comparing the intensities of the lines, the percentage composition of the substance can be determined. An emission spectrum is a useful analytic tool.

A gas that is cool and does not emit light will absorb light at characteristic wavelengths. This set of wavelengths is called an **absorption spectrum**. To obtain an absorption spectrum, white light is sent through a sample of gas and then through a spectroscope, Figure 28–5. The normally continuous spectrum of the white light now has dark lines in it. These lines show that light of some wavelengths has been absorbed. It has been found that often the bright lines of the emission spectrum of a gas and the dark lines of the absorption spectrum occur at the same wavelengths. Thus, cool gaseous elements absorb the same wavelengths that they emit when excited, Figure 28–6. Suppose white light shines through a cool gas. The spectrum will be continuous, but there will be a few dark lines in it. Analysis of the wavelengths of the missing lines can indicate the composition of the gas.

Atomic Secrets

F.Y.I.

It was absolutely marvelous working for Wolfgang Pauli. You could ask him anything. There was no worry that he would think a particular question was stupid, since he thought all questions were stupid.

—Victor Weisskopf

Gaseous atoms can also absorb light. The wavelength absorbed is the same as that emitted by excited, hot atoms.

FIGURE 28–6. The emission spectrum (a) and the absorption spectrum (b) of sodium.

CONCEPT DEVELOPMENT

Critical Thinking Master, Teacher Resource Package. You may wish to have students complete the Critical Thinking Master, Star Spectra, with this section.

Enrichment Master. With this section, use the Enrichment Master, The Lyman, Balmer, and Paschen Series, from the Teacher Resource Package.

Laboratory Manual. Give students additional experience with atomic spectra by doing Lab 28.1 from the Laboratory Manual.

- An excellent, low-cost spectrometer is available from Learning Technologies Inc., 59 Walden Street, Cambridge, MA 02140. It allows students to measure the wavelength of mercury lines in the spectrum of a fluorescent lamp and to see the Fraunhofer absorption lines in the sun's spectrum.

CRITICAL THINKING

Use the Critical Thinking master for Chapter 28 with this section.

LABORATORY MANUAL

Use Lab 28.1 with this section.

ENRICHMENT MASTER

Use the Enrichment master for Chapter 28 with this section.

CONCEPT DEVELOPMENT

Demonstration: Allow students to view emission spectra by setting up a demonstration using spectrum discharge tubes, a prism, and a high-voltage source. (Refer to Figure 28–4a.)

Demonstration: Use a good quality diffraction grating to perform a quantitative experiment. Find the wavelength value for a particular spectral line or a color in the continuous spectrum. Cut a 35-mm, slide-sized piece of cardboard and put a 2-mm slit in it. Place the cardboard slide in a slide projector, then put the diffraction grating over the front of the lens. This will produce a large spectrum on the screen. It works best, of course, in a darkened room.

Transparency Package. Use Transparency 41 to quiz students on the details of gas spectra.

Connect to ASTRONOMY

Spectroscopy has frequently been used to determine the constitution of planets and stars. Light from telescopes is directed to a spectroscope instead of to the observer's eye or film. Helium, for example, was identified by its emission spectrum in light from the sun before it was discovered on Earth. The spectrum of the sun's light reflected from Jupiter showed that its atmosphere contained methane long before space probes approached the giant planet. The Hubble Space Telescope can record ultraviolet and infrared spectra as well as visible because it is above the atmospheric gases that absorb these wavelengths.

Spectroscopy can even be used to detect the motion of planets, stars, and galaxies. As most stars contain hydrogen, a frequent component of stellar spectra are the four lines in Figure 28–8, as well as other emission spectra from this simple atom. Early observers of distant galaxies found two lines at 615 nm and 651 nm that they didn't recognize. It was shortly recognized that these were the two shortest wavelength lines of the hydrogen spectrum shifted to the red. Astronomers suggested that the change was a Doppler shift due to the motion of the galaxy away from Earth. The Doppler shift multiplies each wavelength by the same factor. Where should astronomers look for the two lines with longer wavelengths? [615/410 = 1.5, so look at 1.5 × 486 nm = 729 nm and 1.5 × 656 = 984 nm.]

TRANSPARENCY

Use Transparency 41 with this section.

LAB WORKSHEET

Use the Lab Worksheet for Chapter 28 with this Physics Lab.

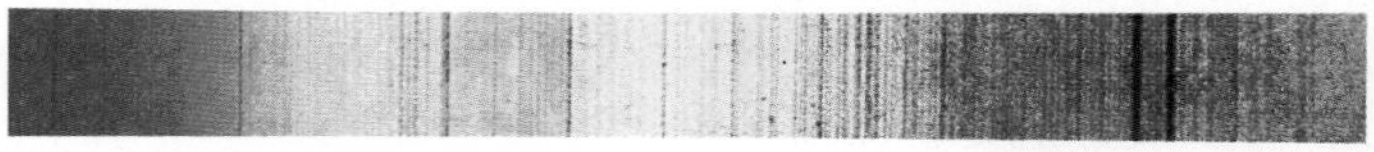

FIGURE 28–7. Fraunhofer lines appear in the absorption spectrum of the sun.

ASTRONOMY CONNECTION

In 1814, while examining the spectrum of sunlight, Josef von Fraunhofer (1787–1826) noticed some dark lines. The dark lines he found in the sun's spectrum are now called Fraunhofer lines, Figure 28–7. To account for these lines, he assumed that the sun has a relatively cool atmosphere of gaseous elements. As light leaves the sun, it passes through these gases. The gases absorb light at their characteristic wavelengths. As a result, these wavelengths are missing from the sun's absorption spectrum. By comparing the missing lines with the known lines of the various elements, the composition of the atmosphere of the sun was determined. In this manner, the element helium was discovered in the sun before it was found on Earth. Spectrographic analysis has made it possible to determine the composition of stars.

Helium was found on the sun by means of spectroscopy before it was found on Earth.

Both emission and absorption spectra are valuable scientific tools. As a result of the characteristic spectrum emitted by each element, chemists are able to analyze unknown materials by observing the spectra they emit. Not only is this an important research tool, it is important in industry as well. For example, steel mills reprocess large quantities of scrap iron of varying compositions. The exact composition of a sample of scrap can be determined in minutes by spectrographic analysis. The composition of the steel can then be adjusted to suit commercial specifications. Aluminum, zinc, and other metal processing plants employ the same method.

Analysis of spectra allows the identification of the elements that make up a mixture.

The study of spectra is a branch of science known as spectroscopy. Spectroscopists are employed throughout the research and industrial communities.

The Bohr Model of the Atom

In the nineteenth century many physicists tried to use atomic spectra to determine the structure of the atom. Hydrogen was studied extensively because it is the lightest element and has the simplest spectrum. The visible spectrum of hydrogen consists of four lines: red, green, blue, and violet, Figure 28–8. The Swedish scientist A. J. Ångstrom (1814–1874) made very careful measurements of the wavelengths of these lines. Any theory that explained the structure of the atom would have to account for these wavelengths.

FIGURE 28–8. The emission spectrum of hydrogen in the visible range has four lines.

578 The Atom

PHYSICS LAB: Shots in the Dark

Purpose

To study atomic scattering by investigating the "size" of a target through use of a model.

Materials

- 3 dozen # 0 rubber stoppers
- bed sheet (or blanket)
- goggles
- atomic model (see diagram)
- blindfold (or darkened goggles)

Procedure

Each student must wear goggles while using the model.

1. Construct the model according to the diagram. Set up a data table with columns for student, number of shots, and number of hits.
2. Each student will be blindfolded and led to a position 3 meters directly in front of the target area.
3. Each student will be allowed to toss 10 rubber stoppers (1 at a time) into the target area. If a rubber stopper does not strike within the target area, the shooter should be told "too high", "too low", etc. and given an extra rubber stopper.
4. Students will be able to hear the a nuclear "hit". After a hit, the guide should instruct the shooter that another hit cannot be counted on the same target and the shots should be moved around.
5. After a student finishes her throws, she will be the guide for the next student "shooter".
6. After serving as guide, each student should record her initials and the number of hits on the chalkboard.

Observations and Data

1. Record each student, the number of shots, and the number of hits.
2. Did the students with more hits have better data?

Analysis

There are six circular targets within the target area. The ratio of hits/shots is given by the following:

$$\frac{\text{hits}}{\text{shots}} = \frac{\text{target area}}{\text{total model area}} = \frac{6\pi r^2}{\text{width} \times \text{height}}$$

1. Find the class total for the number of shots and hits. Use the totals to calculate the total area for the six targets. Divide the total area by 6 to estimate the area for each target. Then calculate the radius for each target.
2. The uncertainty for this type of experiment decreases with more shots. The percent uncertainty is given by the following:

$$\%\ \text{uncertainty} = \frac{(\text{shots})^{\frac{1}{2}}}{\text{shots}} \times 100\%$$

Find the uncertainty for your class.

Applications

1. A recent phone poll sampled 800 people. What is the estimate of uncertainty in the poll?

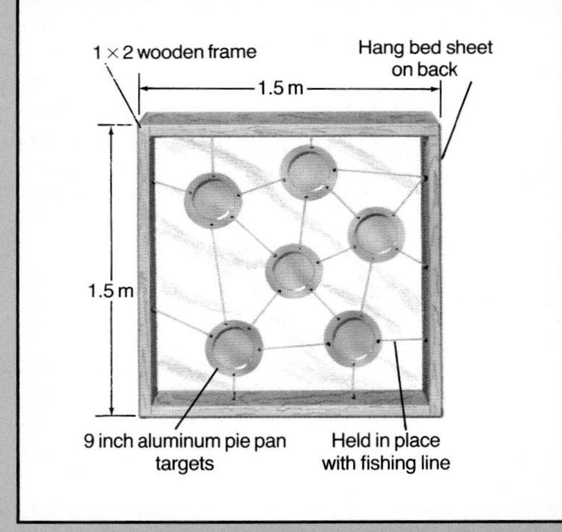

PHYSICS LAB

Process Skills: formulating models, observing, communicating, measuring, using numbers, hypothesizing, defining operationally.

Misconceptions: Students live in a macroscopic world. The idea of "knowing" the size of something that has never been seen seems paradoxical.

Teaching Suggestions: 1. An adjacent storage room would be the best place for this activity. This lab seems to work better if students do not see the targets until after they make their throws.
2. Use nine-inch aluminum pie pans for targets.

Lab Worksheet, Teacher Resource Package. If desired, use the lab worksheet master for this chapter for students to record their data.

OBSERVATIONS

1. Student data will vary.
2. Some students might get two or three hits while others get none. Since the shots were made blindfolded, there is no reward for hitting more targets.

ANALYSIS

1. Students should use the equation:

$$\frac{\text{hits}}{\text{shots}} = \frac{6\pi r^2}{\text{height} \times \text{width}}$$

2. For 25 students with 10 shots each, $\%\ \text{uncertainty} = \frac{(250)^{\frac{1}{2}}}{250} \times 100\% = 6.3\%$.

APPLICATIONS

The percent uncertainty in the telephone poll is

$$\frac{(800)^{\frac{1}{2}}}{800} \times 100\% = 3.5\%.$$

ASSESSMENT

Critical Thinking: To further assess students' understanding of the structure of the atom, ask the following questions.

1. When estimating the radius of the targets, you did not consider the size of the rubber stoppers. Is it reasonable to neglect their size? Would you expect fewer hits had you thrown BBs? Would BBs be more accurate? [The rubber stoppers were not measured because they were small compared to the size of the targets. Fewer hits would probably occur when throwing BBs. Because the size of the thrown objects was not measured, the BBs should give a slightly more accurate prediction.]

2. It was certainly possible for you to have a large fraction of misses with the pie plates. Would it be possible for Rutherford to shoot an alpha particle through a solid piece of gold foil and miss? [Because the foil is mostly empty spaces, most of the alpha particles went through without hitting a nucleus.]

CONCEPT DEVELOPMENT

- Scientists currently have the ability to work with *single* atoms! Some of this work is described in Chapter 5, "Atoms," in *The Ring of Truth,* by Philip and Phylis Morrison.
- In their study of semiconductors, students will learn about energy *bands* rather than energy levels. The addition of new degrees of freedom—including rotation and vibration—means additional energy levels for electrons in semiconductors; thus, levels become bands.

Assessment

Portfolio

Students should write a short essay on the subject "The Bohr Model: Should It Be Taught Today?". They should choose to argue on either side of the question.

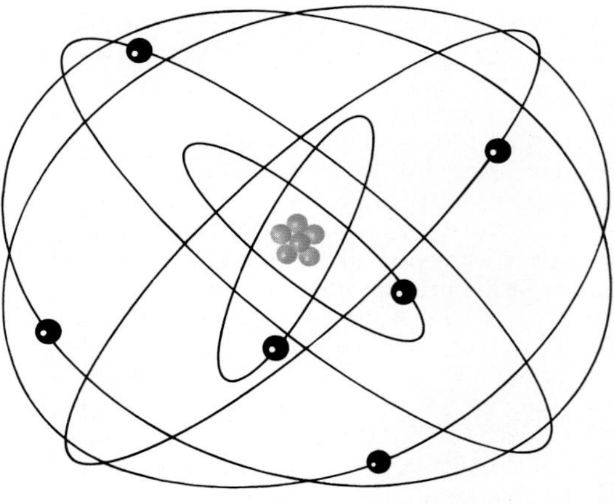

FIGURE 28–9. Bohr's planetary model of the atom postulated that electrons moved in fixed orbits around the nucleus.

Rutherford's model did not account for (1) the lack of emission of radiation as electrons move about the nucleus, and (2) the emission of light at only certain wavelengths.

Any valid theory of the structure of the atom would also have to fit Rutherford's nuclear model. Rutherford had suggested that electrons orbited the nucleus much as the planets orbit the sun. There was, however, a serious problem with this planetary model. An electron in an orbit is constantly accelerated toward the nucleus. As discussed in Chapter 27, accelerated electrons radiate energy by emitting electromagnetic waves. At the rate an electron would lose energy, it would spiral into the nucleus in only 10^{-9} seconds. Atoms are known to be stable, however, and to last for long times. Thus, the planetary model was not consistent with the laws of electromagnetism. In addition, if the planetary theory were true, the accelerated electron should radiate energy at all wavelengths. But, as we have seen, the light emitted by atoms is radiated only at specific wavelengths.

Bohr assumed that electrons in a stable orbit around the nucleus did not radiate energy.

The Danish physicist Niels Bohr (1885–1962) went to England in 1911 and soon joined Rutherford's group to work on the problem of the atom. He tried to unite the nuclear model with Einstein's quantum theory of light. This was a courageous idea because in 1911 Einstein's revolutionary theory of the photoelectric effect had not yet been confirmed by experiment and was not widely accepted.

Bohr started with the planetary arrangement of electrons, Figure 28–9, but made the bold hypothesis that the laws of electromagnetism do not operate inside atoms. He postulated that an electron in a stable orbit does not radiate energy, even though it is accelerating.

FIGURE 28–10. The energy of the emitted photon is equal to $E_f - E_i$.

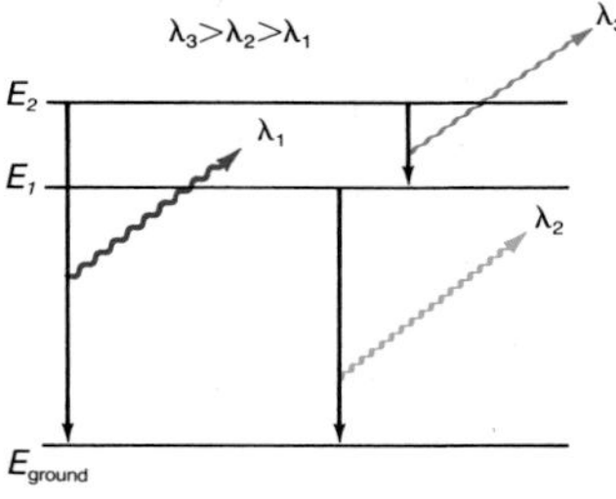

If energy was not radiated when electrons were in stable orbits, when was it radiated? Bohr suggested light was emitted when the electron's energy *changed,* Figure 28–10. According to Einstein, the energy of a photon of light is given by the equation $E = hf = hc/\lambda$. Thus, said Bohr, if the emission spectrum contains only certain wavelengths, then an electron can emit or absorb only specific amounts of energy. Therefore, the atomic electrons can have only certain amounts of energy. That is, the energy of an electron in an atom is **quantized**.

The quantization of energy in atoms is unlike everyday experience. For example, if the energy of a pendulum were quantized, it could oscillate only with certain amplitudes, such as 10 cm or 20 cm, but not, for example, 11.3 cm.

TEACHER

Bohr's quantized atom theory does not explain the groups of narrow, closely spaced lines that make up the dark spectrum because he assumed circular electron orbits based on a planetary model. A. J. W. Sommerfeld used Einstein's theory of relativity to provide a mathematical description of elliptical orbits and then proceeded to demonstrate that only certain types of ellipses were possible using quantum theory. This combination of circular and elliptical electron orbits successfully explains some of the fine details of the spectrum.

The atomic electron is allowed to have different amounts of energy called **energy levels**. When an electron has the smallest allowable amount of energy, it is in the lowest energy level, called the **ground state**. If an electron absorbs energy, it can make a transition to a higher energy level, called an **excited state**. Atomic electrons usually remain in excited states only a very small fraction of a second before returning to the ground state and emitting energy.

The energy of an orbiting electron in an atom is the sum of the kinetic energy of the electron and the potential energy resulting from the attractive force between the electron and the nucleus. The energy of an electron in an orbit near the nucleus is less than that of an electron in an orbit farther away because work must be done to move an electron to orbits farther away from the nucleus. The electrons in excited states have larger orbits and correspondingly higher energies.

Einstein's theory says the light photon has an energy hf. Bohr postulated that the change in the energy of an atomic electron when a photon is absorbed is equal to the energy of the photon. That is:

$$hf = E_{excited} - E_{ground}.$$

When the electron makes the return transition to the ground state, a photon is emitted. The energy of the photon is equal to the energy difference between the excited and ground states. Molecules have additional discrete energy levels. For example, they can rotate and vibrate, which individual atoms cannot do. As a result, molecules can emit a much wider variety of light frequencies than can atoms, Figure 28–4d.

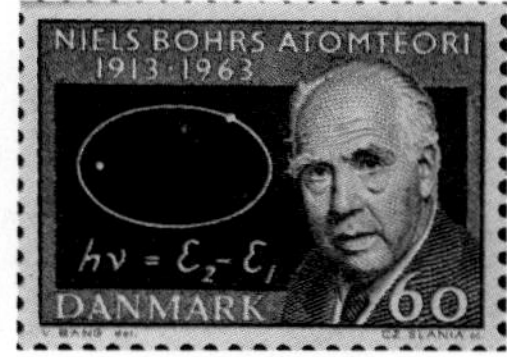

FIGURE 28–11. Ernest Rutherford and Niels Bohr devised the planetary model of the atom.

Predictions of the Bohr Model

A scientific theory must do more than present postulates; it must allow predictions to be made that can be checked against experimental data. A good theory can also be applied to many different problems, and ultimately provides a simple, unified explanation of some part of the physical world.

Bohr's theory correctly predicts the emission wavelengths of hydrogen.

Bohr was able to show that his two postulates could be used with the known laws of physics to calculate the wavelengths of light emitted by hydrogen. The calculations were in excellent agreement with the values measured by Ångstrom. As a result, Bohr's model was widely accepted. Unfortunately, the model could not predict the spectrum of the next simplest element, helium. In addition, there was no reason to suggest that the laws of electromagnetism should work everywhere *but* inside the atom. Not even Bohr believed that his model was a complete theory of the structure of the atom.

Despite its shortcomings, the Bohr model describes the energy levels and wavelengths of light emitted and absorbed by hydrogen atoms remarkably well. We will outline the method used by Bohr to calculate the wavelengths of light emitted by an atom. Bohr's calculations start with Newton's law, $F = ma$, applied to an electron of mass m and charge $-q$, in a circular orbit of radius r about a massive particle, a proton, of charge q.

$$F_c = ma_c$$

$$Kq^2/r^2 = mv^2/r$$

K is the constant $9.0 \times 10^9\ \mathrm{N \cdot m^2/C^2}$ from Coulomb's law.

CONCEPT DEVELOPMENT

Demonstration: Demonstrate the quantum number concept by obtaining a long strip of flexible corrugated plastic about 5 cm wide and bending it to form a circle. Mark off the distance between two crests or valleys in the corrugation to represent one wavelength of an electron. Show that the plastic strip can fit together when you wrap it around in a circle only if the overlap is one wavelength long, or multiples of a wavelength.

Remind students that an excited electron emitting a photon as it returns to a lower energy level is demonstrating the conservation of energy principle.

By Newton's second law, $F = ma$; a (for circular motion) $= v^2/r$. Thus $F = mv^2/r$. The force is provided by Coulomb's law, where $F = k\,qq/r^2$.

So, by substitution, $kq^2/r^2 = mv^2/r$. Now substitute $nh/2\pi$ for mvr and then solve for r to get the form shown on page 582.

ACTIVITY

Cooperative Learning: Have students, individually or in small groups, use their artistic talents to draw representations of Rutherford's nuclear model, atomic spectra, and the Bohr model and its predictions.

TEACHER F.Y.I.

- Shakespeare on atoms: In Act III, Scene II of *As You Like It*, Celia says, "It is as easy to count atomies as to resolve the propositions of a lover."
- In the 1920s and 1930s, Niels Bohr headed an institute for atomic studies which was funded by Carlsberg brewery.

CONCEPT DEVELOPMENT

In the discussion of quantum number, below, not: When the electron is removed from the atom, it has zero energy with respect to the nucleus. Since positive work must be done to free the electron, the initial energy state is made negative so that this occurs.

Critical Thinking: In science-fiction stories there's sometimes a gadget that makes it possible for one solid object to slip through another solid object. Based on what they have learned in this chapter, ask students why this invention seems next to impossible. [When atoms get close to each other, the enormous repulsive forces of their nuclei prevent the nuclei from getting close enough to slip by one another.]

CHECKING FOR UNDERSTANDING

Have students describe the postulates of the Bohr model of the atom and its successful predictions.

RETEACHING

Reteaching Master in the Teacher Resource Package. Use the Reteaching Master for Chapter 28, The Hydrogen Atom, with this section.

EXTENSION

Several lines of evidence helped lead to the concept of discrete electron energy levels. One famous source of data was the Franck-Hertz experiment, which involved a detailed look at the conductivity of gases. Have interested students look up this experiment and report on how it provides evidence for quantized electron energy levels.

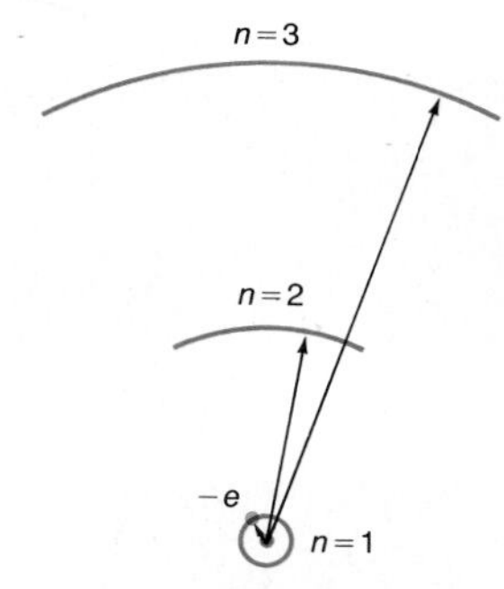

FIGURE 28–12. Radii of electron orbits for the first three energy levels of hydrogen according to the Bohr model.

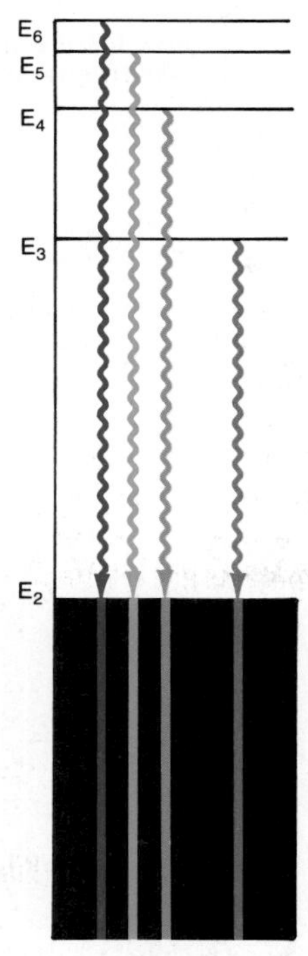

FIGURE 28–13. Bohr's model of the hydrogen atom showed that a definite amount of energy is released when an electron moves from a higher to a lower energy level. The energy released in each transition corresponds to a definite line in the hydrogen spectrum.

Bohr proposed a third postulate. The angular momentum, the product of the momentum of the electron and the radius of its circular orbit, *mvr*, can have only certain values. These values are given by the equation $mvr = nh/2\pi$, where h is Planck's constant and n is an integer. Because the quantity *mvr* can have only certain values, the angular momentum is said to be quantized.

The result of combining Newton's law with the quantization of angular momentum gives the predicted radii of the orbits of the electrons in the hydrogen atom.

$$r_n = \frac{h^2}{4\pi^2 Kmq^2} n^2$$

If we substitute SI values for the quantities into the equation, we can calculate the radius of the innermost orbit of the hydrogen atom, where $n = 1$.

$$r_n = \frac{(6.626 \times 10^{-34}\ \text{J} \cdot \text{s})^2}{4\pi^2(9.00 \times 10^9\ \text{N} \cdot \text{m}^2/\text{C}^2)(9.11 \times 10^{-31}\ \text{kg})(1.60 \times 10^{-19}\ \text{C})^2}$$

$$= 5.3 \times 10^{-11} \frac{\text{J}^2 \cdot \text{s}^2}{\text{N} \cdot \text{m}^2 \cdot \text{kg}}$$

$$= 5.3 \times 10^{-11}\ \text{m, or } 0.053\ \text{nm}$$

A little more algebra shows that the total energy of the electron in its orbit, the sum of the potential and kinetic energy of the electron, is given by

$$E_n = \frac{-2\pi^2 K^2 mq^4}{h^2} \times \frac{1}{n^2}$$

By substituting numerical values for the constants, we can calculate the energy of the electron.

$$E_n = -2.17 \times 10^{-18}\ \text{J}(1/n^2)$$

or, using the electron volt as the unit of energy,

$$E_n = -13.6\ \text{eV}(1/n^2).$$

Both the radius of an orbit and the energy of the electron can have only certain values. That is, both are quantized. The integer n is called the principal **quantum number**. The number n determines the values of r and E. The radius increases as the square of n, as shown in Figure 28–12. The energy depends on $1/n^2$. The energy is negative because the energy has to be added to the electron to free it from the attractive force of the nucleus, that is, to ionize the atom. The energy levels of hydrogen are shown in Figure 28–13.

Example Problem

Orbital Energy of Electrons in the Hydrogen Atom

For the hydrogen atom, determine **a.** the energy of the innermost energy level ($n = 1$), **b.** the energy of the second energy level, **c.** the energy difference between the first and second energy levels.

Given: $n = 1$, $n = 2$

Unknowns: E_1, E_2, ΔE

Basic equation: $E_n = -13.6\ \text{eV}(1/n^2)$

RETEACHING MASTER

Use the Reteaching master for Chapter 28 with this section.

Solution:

a. $E_1 = \frac{-13.6 \text{ eV}}{(1)^2} = -13.6 \text{ eV}$

b. $E_2 = \frac{-13.6 \text{ eV}}{(2)^2} = -3.4 \text{ eV}$

c. $\Delta E = E_f - E_i = E_2 - E_1$
$= -3.4 \text{ eV} - (-13.6 \text{ eV}) = 10.2 \text{ eV}$

This is the energy that must be added to the atom to raise the electron from its ground state to its first energized state.

FIGURE 28–14. Wolfgang Pauli and Niels Bohr, both Nobel laureates for their contributions to the understanding of atomic structure, watch the motions of a spinning top.

Example Problem

Frequency and Wavelength of Emitted Photons

An electron in an excited hydrogen atom drops from the second energy level to the first energy level. **a.** Determine the energy of the photon emitted. **b.** Calculate the frequency of the photon emitted. **c.** Calculate the wavelength of the photon emitted.

Given: initial quantum number, $n = 2$; final quantum number, $n = 1$

Unknowns: hf, f, λ

Basic equations: $hf = E_i - E_f$, $\lambda = c/f$

a. $hf = E_i - E_f = E_2 - E_1$
$= -3.4 \text{ eV} - (-13.6 \text{ eV}) = 10.2 \text{ eV}$

b. $f = \frac{(10.2 \text{ eV})(1.6 \times 10^{-19} \text{ J/eV})}{6.63 \times 10^{-34} \text{ J/Hz}} = 2.46 \times 10^{15} \text{ Hz}$

c. $\lambda = \frac{c}{f} = \frac{3.00 \times 10^{8} \text{ m/s}}{2.46 \times 10^{15} \text{ Hz}} = 1.22 \times 10^{-7} \text{ m}$

Practice Problems

1. According to the Bohr model, how many times larger is the orbit of hydrogen in the second level than in the first?
2. The discussion on page 582 shows how to calculate the radius of the innermost orbit of the hydrogen atom. Note that all factors in the equation are constants with the exception of n^2. Use the solution to the Example Problem to find the radius of the orbit of the second, third, and fourth allowable energy levels in the hydrogen atom.
3. Calculate the energies of the second, third, and fourth energy levels in the hydrogen atom.
4. ▶ Calculate the energy difference between E_3 and E_2 in the hydrogen atom. Do the same for E_4 and E_3.

CONCEPT DEVELOPMENT

Guided Practice: Go over the Example Problems beginning on page 582, then have students work in class on the Practice Problems that follow.

INDEPENDENT PRACTICE/ EXTENSION

Refer to the Assignment Guide on page 584 for additional questions and problems for independent practice.

Answers To
PRACTICE PROBLEMS

Have students refer to Appendix A of the Solutions Appendix for complete solutions to Practice Problems.

1. four times as large
2. 2.1×10^{-10} m; 4.8×10^{-10} m; 8.5×10^{-10} m
3. -3.4 eV; -1.5 eV; -0.85 eV
4. 1.9 eV; 0.7 eV

3 Close

CONVERGENT QUESTION

Have students list some reasons that the Bohr model of the atom is a limited representation.

TEACHER F.Y.I.

1. $E = KE - PE$ where $KE = 1/2mv^2$ and $PE = \frac{kq^2}{r}$.

2. To keep the electron in orbit the centripetal force must equal the electrical force, so: $\frac{mv^2}{r} = \frac{kq^2}{r^2}$.
Thus $\frac{kq^2}{r} = mv^2$ and $E = \frac{1/2kq^2}{r} - \frac{kq^2}{r}$, so $E = \frac{-1/2kq^2}{r}$.

3. For a circular orbit, angular momentum $p = mvr$, so $mvr = \frac{nh}{2(\pi)}$ and $v = \frac{nh}{2mr(\pi)}$.

4. $\frac{kq^2}{r} = \frac{n^2h^2}{4(\pi)^2r^2}$. 5. $r = \frac{n^2h^2}{4(\pi)^2mkq^2}$.

6. Since $E = -1/2kq^2/r$ and $r = \frac{n^2h^2}{4(\pi)^2mkq^2}$, then $E = \frac{-2(\pi)^2k^2mq^4}{h^2n^2}$.

CONCEPT REVIEW ANSWERS

1.1 Height is not, number of siblings and mass of gas are. Mass is always an integer times the mass of a gas atom.
1.2 They are bound to the nucleus by an attractive electric force.
1.3 The initial sum of the energy of the electron in the atom plus the energy of the incident photon equals the final energy of the electron in the atom.
1.4 The Rutherford atom was unstable because there was no mechanism to prevent the electrons from radiating energy and spiraling into the nucleus. Bohr introduced the postulate of stable orbits, each corresponding to a discrete energy level of the atom. The Bohr atom radiates only when its electron jumps from a higher to a lower energy level. There is a lowest possible energy level (orbit) corresponding to the ground state of the atom.
1.5 Critical Thinking: No. Atoms do not remain very long in the excited state, so there are few, if any, atoms in the second level to absorb light.

28.2 THE PRESENT MODEL OF THE ATOM

Preparation

OBJECTIVES

The objectives are listed on the student page. Remind students to preview these objectives as a study guide to this major section.

OVERVIEW

Many new ideas are introduced in this section, such as electron clouds, quantum mechanics, quantum model, quantum number, stimulated emission, and, with particular emphasis, lasers.

BRIDGING

Previously introduced concepts such as angular momentum, particle wavelength, and absorption and emission of light, help illustrate quantum concepts in this section.

CONCEPT REVIEW

1.1 Which of these quantities are quantized: your height, number of siblings, mass of a sample of gas?
1.2 Why can't the electrons in Rutherford's nuclear model fly away from the nucleus?
1.3 Explain how energy is conserved when an atom absorbs a photon of light.
1.4 How does the Bohr model differ from the Rutherford nuclear model?
1.5 **Critical Thinking:** An emission spectrum can contain wavelengths produced when an electron goes from the third to the second level. Could you see this line in the absorption spectrum? Why?

Objectives

- describe the shortcomings of the Bohr model.
- describe the quantum model of the atom.
- describe a laser and the properties of laser light; display an understanding of the operation of the laser.

28.2 THE PRESENT MODEL OF THE ATOM

The **Bohr model** of the atom was a major contribution to the understanding of the structure of the atom. In addition to calculating the emission spectrum, Bohr and his students were able to calculate the ionization energy of a hydrogen atom. The ionization energy of an atom is the energy needed to free an electron completely from an atom. The calculated value was in good agreement with experimental data. Using spectrographic data for many elements, they were able to determine the energy levels of the elements, even though they could not predict these levels as they could the levels of hydrogen. The Bohr model also provided an explanation of some of the chemical properties of the elements. The idea that atoms have electron arrangements unique to each element is the foundation of much of our knowledge of chemical reactions and bonding.

The postulates Bohr made, however, could not be explained on the basis of known physics. Electromagnetism required that accelerated particles radiate energy, causing the rapid collapse of the atom. In addition, the reason for the quantization of angular momentum was not known. How could Bohr's work be put on a firm foundation?

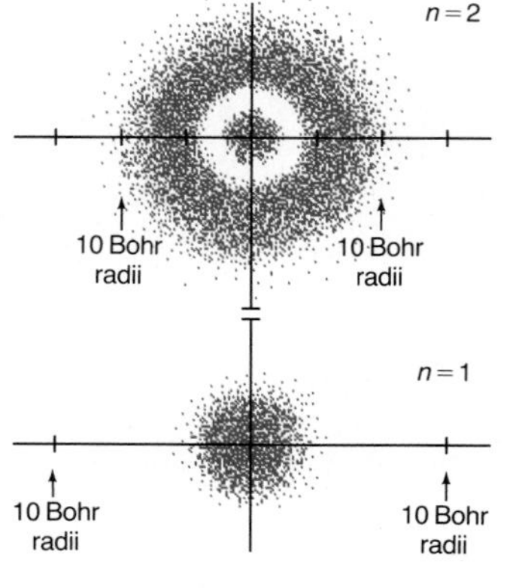

FIGURE 28–15. These plots show the probability of finding the electron in a hydrogen atom at any given location. The denser the points, the higher the probability of finding the electron.

A Quantum Model of the Atom

The first hint to the solution of these problems was provided by de Broglie. As you recall from Chapter 27, he proposed that particles have wave properties just as light waves have particle properties. The wavelength of a particle with momentum mv is given by $\lambda = h/mv$. Therefore, the angular momentum is given by $mvr = hr/\lambda$. The Bohr quantization condition, $mvr = nh/2\pi$, can be written as

$$\frac{hr}{\lambda} = \frac{nh}{2\pi}$$

or

$$n\lambda = 2\pi r.$$

28:1 ASSIGNMENT GUIDE	PRACTICE	EXTENSION
CHAPTER REVIEW pp. 591–593		
· Reviewing Concepts	1–5	
· Applying Concepts		1–7
· Problems*	1–13, 17	14–16, 18
APPENDIX B PROBLEMS*		
· Chapter 28, p. 708	1–3, 5–8	4

* Complete solutions to all Chapter Review and Appendix problems appear in the Problems and Solutions Manual.

FIGURE 28–16. The exact location of these moving cars cannot be pinpointed. Likewise, only the most probable location of an electron can be determined.

Note that the circumference of the Bohr orbit, $2\pi r$, is equal to a whole number multiple, n, of the wavelength of the electron, λ.

In 1926, the German physicist Erwin Schroedinger (1887–1961) used de Broglie's wave model to create a quantum theory of the atom based on waves. Further work by Werner Heisenberg, Wolfgang Pauli, Max Born, and others developed this theory into a complete description of the atom. The theory does not provide a simple planetary picture of an atom as in the Bohr model. In particular, the radius of the electron orbit is not like the radius of the orbit of a planet about the sun. The wave-particle nature of matter means that it is impossible to know both the position and momentum of an electron at the same time. Thus, the modern **quantum model** of the atom predicts only the *probability* that an electron is at a specific location. The most probable distance of the electron from the nucleus in hydrogen is found to be the same as the radius of the Bohr orbit. The probability that the electron is at any radius can be calculated, and a three-dimensional plot can be constructed that shows regions of equal probability. The region in which there is a high probability of finding the electron is called the **electron cloud**. Figure 28–15 shows a slice through the cloud for the two lowest states of hydrogen.

Schroedinger created a quantum theory of the atom based on Bohr's atomic model and de Broglie's wave model.

The quantum model of the atom predicts the probability of finding the electron at a specific location.

Even though the quantum model of the atom is difficult to visualize, **quantum mechanics**, which uses this model, has been extremely successful in predicting many details of the structure of the atom. These details are very difficult to calculate exactly for all but the simplest atoms. It takes large computers to make highly accurate approximations for the heavier atoms. Quantum mechanics also allows the structure of many molecules to be calculated, allowing chemists to determine the arrangement of atoms in the molecules. Guided by quantum mechanics, chemists have been able to create new and useful molecules not otherwise available.

Quantum mechanics also allows calculations of the details of the emission and absorption of light by atoms. As a result of this theory, a new source of light has been developed.

POCKET LAB

BRIGHT LINES

Turn on a gas discharge tube power supply attached to a gas tube so that the tube glows. **CAUTION:** *Do not touch any exposed metal when the power supply is turned on. Dangerous high voltages are present. Always turn off the power supply before changing gas tubes.* Turn off the room lights. Describe the color. Now look through a diffraction grating at the tube. Make a sketch of the results. Repeat the activity with a different gas tube. Explain the differences.

1 Focus

The laser is one of the technological wonders of our age. If you have a laser, demonstrate it for students. The instruction booklet that comes with your laser is an excellent source of both background information on its operation and possible demonstrations.

2 Teach

Amplification of stimulated emission was first achieved with microwaves, an effect called MASER. A running joke in the scientific community then was that MASER stood for Money Acquisition Scheme for Expensive Research!

POCKET LAB

BRIGHT LINES

Purpose: to observe the bright line spectra with gas tubes.
Materials: gas discharge tubes; gas discharge power supply; diffraction gratings.
Outcome: Each type of gas will have a characteristic set of bright lines. The colors and spacing of the lines depend on the electron energy levels within the gas.

Assessment

Performance

To further assess students' understanding of bright line spectra, have them make quantitative measurements. Use either commercial spectrometers or the equipment described in the laboratory in Chapter 19, page 399. Have students report the wavelengths of the light from the discharge tube they observed.

TRANSPARENCY

Use Transparency 43 with this section.

Transparency Package. Use Transparency 43 to quiz students on the electron cloud atomic model.

CONCEPT DEVELOPMENT

Study Guide Master. To reinforce the concepts in this section, have the students complete the Study Guide Master for Section 28.2 from the Teacher Resource Package.

- The tiny solid-state lasers used as light sources for optical fibers are about the size of a grain of salt!
- Stress the fact that lasers are not very efficient devices. Students often get the impression that lasers multiply energy, putting out more energy than they are supplied.

FIGURE 28–17. Waves of incoherent light (a) and coherent light (b).

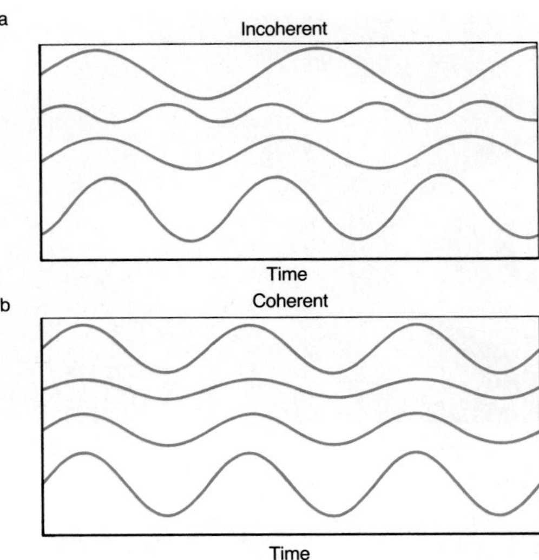

Lasers

Ordinary light sources emit waves of different wavelengths that are not in step with each other.

Light is emitted by an incandescent source at many wavelengths and in all directions. Light produced by an atomic gas consists of only a few different wavelengths, but is also emitted in all directions. The light waves emitted by atoms at one end of a discharge tube are not necessarily in step with the waves from the other end. That is, the waves are not necessarily all at the same point in their cycle, Figure 28–17. Some will be in step, others out of step. Such light is called incoherent.

Light is emitted by atoms that have been excited. So far we have discussed two ways in which atoms can be excited, thermal excitation and electron collision. Atoms can also be excited by collisions with photons of exactly the right energy.

Einstein predicted that when an atom in an excited state is struck by a photon with the correct energy, the atom is stimulated to emit another photon.

What happens when an atom is in an excited state? After a very short time, it normally returns to the ground state, giving off a photon of the same energy that it had absorbed. This is called spontaneous emission. In 1917, Einstein considered what would happen to an atom already in

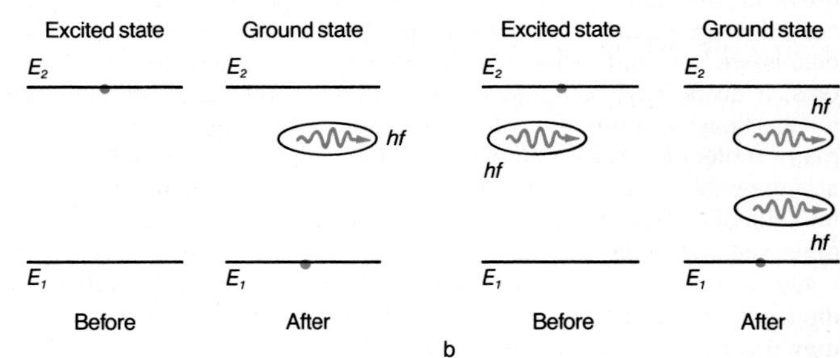

FIGURE 28–18. The spontaneous emission of a photon with energy hf when an electron in a atom drops from an excited state E_2 to the ground state E_1 (a). The stimulated emission of a photon when an excited atom is struck by a photon with energy hf (b). In both (a) and (b) $hf = E_2 - E_1$.

STUDY GUIDE MASTER

Use the Study Guide master for section 28.2.

FIGURE 28–19. A laser produces a beam of coherent light.

an excited state that is struck by another photon of the same energy as the original photon. He showed that the atom will emit a photon (of the same energy) and go to a lower state. The photon that caused, or stimulated, the emission will not be affected. This process is called **stimulated emission**. The two photons leaving the atom will not only have the same wavelength, they will also be in step, Figure 28–18b.

Photons produced by stimulated emission are all in step, that is, they are coherent.

Either of the two photons can now strike other excited atoms, producing additional photons that are in step with the original photons. This process can continue, producing an avalanche of photons, all of the same wavelength and having their maxima and minima at the same times. To get this process to happen, certain conditions must be met. First, of course, there must be other atoms in the excited state. Second, the photons must be collected so that they strike the excited atoms. A device that fulfills both these conditions was invented in 1959 and is called a **laser**. The word laser is an acronym. It stands for **L**ight **A**mplification by **S**timulated **E**mission of **R**adiation. An atom that emits light when stimulated in a laser is said to *lase*.

A laser contains atoms that have been put into their excited states. It has mirrors that reflect light emitted by the atoms so more atoms are stimulated to emit.

The atoms in a laser can be put into the excited state, or pumped, in different ways. An intense flash of light with a wavelength shorter (more energetic) than that of the laser can pump the atoms. The more energetic photons produced by the flash collide with and excite the lasing atoms. One atom decays to a lower energy state, starting the avalanche. As a result, a brief flash or pulse of laser light is emitted. Alternatively, a continuous electric discharge like that in a neon sign can be used to put atoms in the excited state. The laser light resulting from this process is continuous rather than pulsed. The helium-neon lasers often seen in science classrooms, Figure 28–19, are continuous lasers. An electric discharge excites the helium atoms. They collide with the neon atoms, pumping them to an excited state causing them to lase.

HELP WANTED

GEOLOGIST

Major oil company seeks geologist or geophysicist to work on a team for a major, new exploration effort aimed at discovering new and better oil sources.

The ideal candidate has a master's degree, with a specialty in areas relating to our industry, and an intense drive to succeed. He or she will persist when the average persons says "It can't be done." He or she must be able to "think big", communicate well, have the stamina and desire to do field work around the world. For information contact:
American Geological Institute, 4220 King Street, Alexandria, VA 22302

CONCEPT DEVELOPMENT

You may find the term "in phase" used instead of "in step" in other explanations of laser action. Both expressions refer to constructive interference, which was discussed earlier.

Cooperative Learning: Have various student groups look up the latest applications of lasers in periodical literature. Refer them to sources such as *Science News, Discover, Popular Science,* and *Scientific American.* Then have them report to the class on their findings.

Critical Thinking: Ask students the following question: Since a laser beam is so powerful, how can it be that such a beam is drastically reduced when it passes through air? [Basically, the air molecules scatter the beam in different directions.]

CHECKING FOR UNDERSTANDING

Ask students these questions: Where does the energy come from that causes a substance to "lase"? [some external source, such as a flash tube] Where does this energy go? [The energy goes into the laser beam itself, into light given off from the lasing medium that is not in the direct laser beam, and into heating the medium.]

RETEACHING

Use the idea of electron energy level changes as a framework for reteaching the process of laser action. Begin with the process of raising the atoms of the lasing medium into an excited state and work through the steps until the electron goes back to its ground state in the process of stimulated emission. Also stress that some energy is going somewhere other than into production of the beam.

EXTENSION

The Apollo astronauts left a mirror (more technically, a retro-reflector) on the moon. The mirror has been used in lunar ranging projects to determine a significantly more accurate value for the moon's distance from Earth. Have interested students look up the details of these experiments.

FIGURE 28–20. A photon striking an atom in the excited state stimulates it to make a transition to a lower state and emit a second coherent photon.

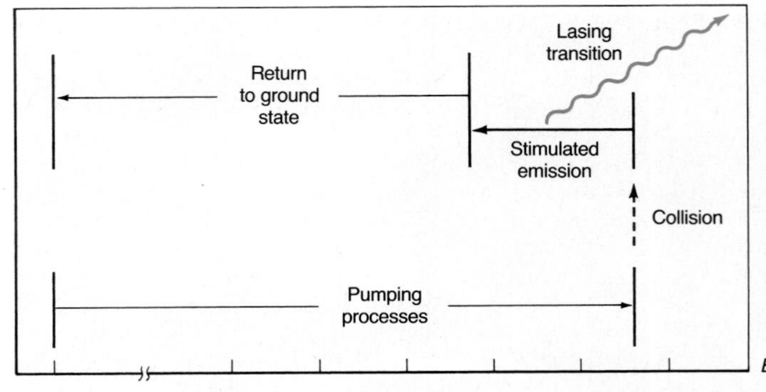

The photons emitted by the atoms are collected by placing the glass tube containing the atoms between two parallel mirrors. One mirror reflects all the light hitting it while the other allows about 1% to pass through. When a photon strikes an atom in the excited state, it stimulates the atom to make a transition to the lower state. Thus, two photons leave the atom. These photons can strike other atoms and produce more photons starting the avalanche. Photons that are directed toward the ends will be reflected back into the gas by the mirrors. Some of the photons will exit the tube through the partially reflecting mirror, producing the laser beam.

Laser light is directional, monochromatic, intense, and coherent.

Laser light is highly directional because of the parallel mirrors. The light beam is very small, typically about 1/2 mm in diameter, so the light is very intense. The light is all one wavelength, or monochromatic, because the transition of electrons between only one pair of energy levels in one type of atom is involved. Finally, laser light is coherent because all the stimulated photons are emitted in step with the photons that struck the atoms.

Table 28–1

Common Lasers

Medium	Wavelength (nm)	Type
Nitrogen	337 (UV)	Pulsed
Helium-cadmium	441.6	Continuous
Argon ion	476.5, 488.0	Continuous
Krypton ion	524.5	Continuous
Neon	632.8	Continuous
Ruby	694.3	Pulsed
Gallium arsenide	840-930 (IR)	Continuous
Neodymium	1040 (IR)	Pulsed
Carbon dioxide	10 600 (IR)	Continuous

(The wavelength of gallium arsenide depends on temperature.)

TEACHER

The mirrors in a laser form a resonating cavity that can amplify light with a wavelength such that an integer number of wavelengths is equal to the length of the cavity. (A typical wavelength for a laser is much, much less than the length of a laser.) This is similar to the way a closed tube resonator amplifies selected wavelengths of sound. If the lasing medium has a number of excited states with only slightly different energies, then the spacing between the mirrors can be adjusted to utilize the single excited state that will participate in the lasing process.

Many substances, solids, liquids, or gases, can be made to lase in this way. Most produce laser light at only one wavelength. For example, red is produced by a neon laser, blue by argon, and green by helium-cadmium. The light from some lasers, on the other hand, can be tuned, or adjusted, over a range of wavelengths.

All lasers are very inefficient. No more than 1% of the electrical energy delivered to the laser is converted to light energy. Despite this inefficiency, the unique properties of laser light have led to many applications. The laser beam is narrow and highly directional. It does not spread out over long distances. Surveyors use laser beams for this reason. A laser beam is used to check the straightness of long tunnels or pipes.

Laser light can be directed into a tiny glass fiber. The fiber uses total internal reflection to transmit light over many kilometers with little loss. The laser is switched on and off rapidly, transmitting information through the fiber. In many cities, optical fibers are replacing copper wires for the transmission of telephone calls, computer data, and even television pictures.

The single wavelength of light emitted by lasers makes lasers valuable in spectroscopy. The laser light is used to excite other atoms. The atoms then return to the ground state, emitting characteristic spectra. Samples with extremely small numbers of atoms can be analyzed in this way. In fact, single atoms have been detected by means of laser excitation and have even been held almost motionless by laser beams!

Holograms are made possible by the coherent nature of laser light. A hologram, Figure 28–21, is a photographic recording of the phase as well as the intensity of the light. Holograms form realistic three-dimensional images and can be used in industry to study the vibration of sensitive parts.

F.Y.I.

Sign on the door of a laser laboratory: "Optics is light work. We just lase around."

Lasers are used to send telephone, computer, and television signals through optical fibers.

Holograms use the coherent nature of laser light.

FIGURE 28–21. When a hologram is made on film, a laser beam is split in two parts by a half-silvered mirror. Interference occurs on the film as the direct laser light meets laser light reflected off an object. The interference of both beams of light allows the film to record both intensity and phase of light from the object.

CONCEPT DEVELOPMENT

The much higher frequency of laser light waves allows more information to be transmitted than does low frequency electromagnetic radiation, such as radio and TV waves.

Guided Practice: Go over the Concept Review Problems on page 591, then select several Chapter Review Problems for students to work on in class.

INDEPENDENT PRACTICE/ EXTENSION

Refer to the Assignment Guide below for additional questions and problems for independent practice.

3 Close

CONVERGENT QUESTION

Ask students to look into the future and predict applications of the laser that haven't been developed yet.

28:2 ASSIGNMENT GUIDE

	PRACTICE	EXTENSION
CHAPTER REVIEW pp. 591–593		
· Reviewing Concepts	6–8	
· Applying Concepts		8, 9
· Problems*		19, 20
APPENDIX B PROBLEMS*		
· Chapter 28, p. 708	7, 8	

* Complete solutions to all Chapter Review and Appendix problems appear in the Problems and Solutions Manual.

Physics and technology

Possible applications could include making ultra-small electric circuits, logic circuits, and electronic devices. Atomic-scale data storage could produce storage densities one million times greater than those possible today. Molecules could be custom-manufactured to meet specific needs—to produce a particular drug, for example.

Since the STM depends on electron tunneling, it does not work well with nonconducting materials. Another device, the atomic force microscope (AFM), can be used to study both conductors and nonconductors. It also scans the surface with a very fine tip, but it is in actual contact with the material. The sensing tip is mounted on a cantilever spring that deflects in response to the minute interatomic forces sensed at the tip. The AFM can measure a force as small as 10^{-8} N. The AFM has shown how friction between metal surfaces occurs and has been used to study the magnetic fields in materials used to make floppy disks for computers.

Teacher Resources: Amato, Ivan. "Getting a Feel for Atoms." *Science News.* April 7, 1990, pages 216–217, 220.

Fisher, Arthur. "Seeing Atoms." *Popular Science.* April 1989, pages 102–107.

Pool, Robert. "A Small, Small, Very Small Diode." *Science.* December 8, 1989, page 1251.

Powell, Corey S. "Science Writ Small." *Scientific American.* June 1990, page 26.

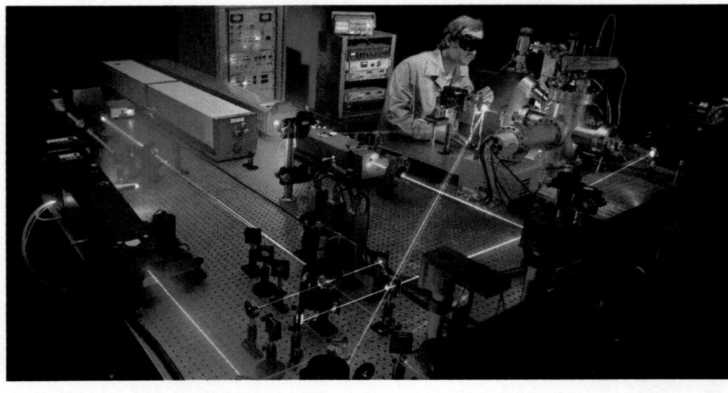

FIGURE 28–22. Because laser light is so concentrated and directed, laser technology has become indispensable to modern society.

The high power of lasers is used in cutting and welding metal as well as surgery.

The concentrated power of laser light is used in a variety of ways. In medicine, lasers can be used to repair the retina in an eye. Lasers can also be used in surgery in place of a knife to cut flesh with little loss of blood. In industry, lasers are used to cut steel and to weld materials together. In the future, lasers may produce nuclear fusion for an almost inexhaustible energy source.

Physics and technology

SCANNING TUNNELING MICROSCOPE

A powerful new instrument, the scanning tunneling microscope (STM), produces pictures of the arrangements of atoms on solid surfaces. With it, scientists can even see bonds between atoms.

An STM uses a very sharp metal "finger" which is brought near, but not touching, the surface to be examined. Because the point of the finger and the surface are not touching, they are insulated from each other. But if a small voltage is applied, some electrons flow (tunnel) across the gap between the surface and the point as a result of the wave nature of electrons. The number of electrons that cross the gap depends on how close the point is to the surface. In this way, the STM maps out the "hills and valleys" of a surface. Each hill is a single atom and each valley is the space between neighboring atoms. STMs and related instruments, especially the atomic force microscope (AFM), have been used to study the surfaces of metals, semiconductors, and biological systems. By dragging its sharp tip across graphite, the AFM investigated friction on an atomic level. In one demonstation, scientists carefully placed xenon atoms on a metal surface to spell out the letters "IBM."

• What practical applications might arise from the ability of the STM to manipulate individual atoms in a controlled manner?

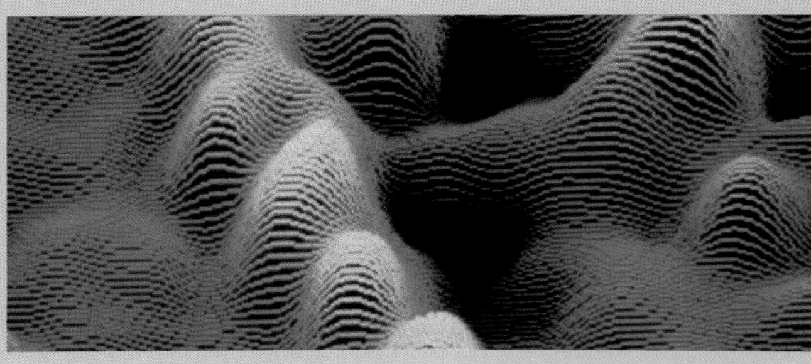

CONCEPT REVIEW

2.1 Which of the lasers in Table 28–1 emits the reddest (visible) light? Which emits in the blue?
2.2 Why could red light not be used to pump a green laser?
2.3 Why does the Bohr model conflict with the uncertainty principle while the quantum model does not?
2.4 **Critical Thinking:** Suppose the electron cloud were to get so small that the atom were almost the size of the nucleus. Use the uncertainty principle to explain why this would take a tremendous amount of energy.

CHAPTER 28 REVIEW

SUMMARY

28.1 The Bohr Model

- Ernest Rutherford directed positively-charged, high-speed alpha particles at thin metal foils. By studying the paths of the reflected particles, he showed that atoms are mostly empty space with a tiny, massive, positively-charged nucleus at the center.
- The spectra produced by atoms of an element can be used to identify that element.
- If white light passes through a gas, the gas absorbs the same wavelengths it would emit if excited. If light leaving the gas goes through a prism, an absorption spectrum is seen.
- In the model of the atom developed by Niels Bohr, the electrons are allowed to have only certain energy levels.
- In the Bohr model, electrons can make transitions between energy levels. As they do, they emit or absorb electromagnetic radiation.
- The frequency and wavelength of the absorbed and emitted radiation can be calculated using the Bohr model. The calculations agree with experiments.

28.2 The Present Model of the Atom

- The quantum mechanical model of the atom cannot be visualized easily. Only the probability that an electron is at a specific location can be calculated.
- Quantum mechanics is extremely successful in calculating the properties of atoms, molecules, and solids.
- Lasers produce light that is directional, powerful, monochromatic, and coherent. Each property gives the laser useful applications.

KEY TERMS

alpha (α) particles
nuclear model
emission spectrum
spectroscope
absorption spectrum
quantized
energy levels
ground state
excited state
quantum number
Bohr model
quantum model
electron cloud
quantum mechanics
stimulated emission
laser

REVIEWING CONCEPTS

1. Describe how Rutherford determined that the positive charge in an atom is concentrated in a tiny region rather than spread throughout the atom.
2. How does the Bohr model explain why the absorption spectrum of hydrogen contains exactly the same frequencies as its emission spectrum?
3. What are some of the problems with a planetary model of the atom?

REVIEW MASTER

Use the Vocabulary Review master for Chapter 28 with this section.

EVALUATION MASTER

Use the Chapter Evaluation master for Chapter 28 with this section.

CONCEPT REVIEW ANSWERS

2.1 Ruby is the reddest. Helium-cadmium and argon ions emit in the blue.
2.2 Red photons have less energy than green ones. You can't pump the laser because the red photons do not have enough energy to put the atoms in energy levels high enough to enable them to emit green photons.
2.3 The uncertainty principle doesn't allow a particle to have a precisely known position, such as a Bohr orbit. The quantum model predicts only the probability that the radius of the electron orbit will have any given value.
2.4 Critical Thinking: The smaller the electron cloud, the more precisely we know the position of the electrons. If a particle's position is well known, its momentum must be very uncertain. The uncertainty of the momentum can be large only if momentum itself is large. Therefore, the kinetic energy of the electron must also be large, and it takes lots of energy to do this.

CLOSING CHAPTER 28

Review Summary statements and Key Terms with your students.

ASSESSMENT

Vocabulary Review Master, Teacher Resource Package. Use this master to check students' understanding of Key Terms.

Evaluation Masters. Use Parts A and B of the Chapter Evaluation Masters from the Teacher Resource Package to test qualitative chapter objectives, Parts C and D test quantitative chapter objectives.

Answers To
REVIEWING CONCEPTS

1. He directed a beam of charged alpha particles at a thin metal sheet and measured the number of particles deflected at various angles.
2. Bohr said the energy of an emitted photon or an absorbed photon is equal to the change in energy of the atom, which can have only specific values.

Answers To
REVIEWING CONCEPTS (cont)

3. As the electrons undergo centripetal acceleration, they would lose energy and spiral into the nucleus. In addition, all atoms should radiate at all wavelengths, not discrete wavelengths.

4. (1) Energy levels are quantized. (2) Electrons do not radiate while they are in an allowed energy level. (3) Photons are emitted or absorbed when an electron changes energy levels. Energy of a photon is equal to the difference in energy levels.

5. Photon wavelengths are determined by the difference in energies of allowed levels.

6. Laser light is coherent and directional, thus it is more concentrated.

7. Microwave Amplification by Stimulated Emission of Radiation

8. Lasers are directional and coherent.

Answers To
APPLYING CONCEPTS

1. Line spectrum—the light comes from a diluted gas.

2. No. As white light passed through Earth's atmosphere, certain energies would be absorbed by the gases composing the atmosphere. Its spectrum, therefore, would have black lines in it.

3. Money—it comes in only certain discrete values, while water seems to come in any possible quantity.

4. No. It takes 5.43 eV to raise the electron to the E_4 level, and 6.67 eV to raise the electron to the E_5 level. The atom can absorb only photons that have exactly the right energy.

5. Six lines are possible. E_4–E_1 has the largest energy level.

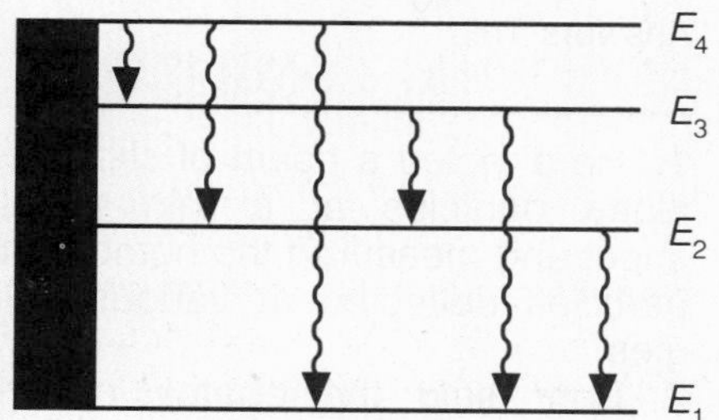

6. The maximum energy is 13.6 eV. This is also the ionization energy for hydrogen. The electron would have enough energy to leave the nucleus.

7. All transitions from higher energy levels to the third energy level in hydrogen atoms yield photons with wavelengths greater than visible light. Therefore, the protons emitted are infrared.

8. The Bohr mdoel has fixed orbital radii. The present model gives a probability of finding an electron at a location. The Bohr model allows for calculation of only hydrogen atoms. The present model can be used for all elements.

9. Blue light has a higher frequency and, therefore, higher energy.

4. What three assumptions did Bohr make in developing his model of the atom?

5. How does the Bohr model account for the spectra emitted by atoms?

6. A laboratory laser has a power of only 0.8 mW (8×10^{-4} W). Why does it seem stronger than the light of a 100-W lamp?

7. A device like a laser, that emits microwave radiation, is called a maser. What words are likely to make up this acronym?

8. What properties of the laser led to its use in light shows?

APPLYING CONCEPTS

1. The northern lights are the result of high energy particles coming from the sun striking atoms high in Earth's atmosphere. If you looked at the light through a spectrometer, would you expect to see a continuous or line spectrum? Explain.

2. If white light were emitted from Earth's surface and observed by someone in space, would its spectrum be continuous? Explain.

3. Suppose you wanted to explain quantization to a younger brother or sister. Would you use money or water as an example? Explain.

4. A photon with an energy of 6.2 eV enters a mercury atom in the ground state. Will it be absorbed by the atom? See Figure 28–23. Explain.

5. A certain atom has energy levels, Figure 28–24. If an electron can make transitions between any two levels, how many spectral lines can the atom emit? Which transition gives the photon with the highest energy?

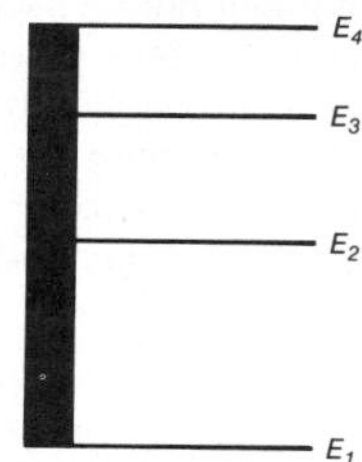

FIGURE 28–24. Use with Applying Concepts 5.

6. A photon is emitted when an electron drops through energy levels within an excited hydrogen atom. What is the maximum energy the photon can have? If this same amount of energy were given to an electron in ground state in a hydrogen atom, what would happen?

7. When electrons fall from higher energy levels to the third energy level within hydrogen atoms, are the photons emitted infrared, visible, or ultraviolet light? Explain.

8. Compare the quantum mechanical theory of the atom with the Bohr model.

9. Does a laser that emits red light, green light, or blue light produce photons with the highest energy?

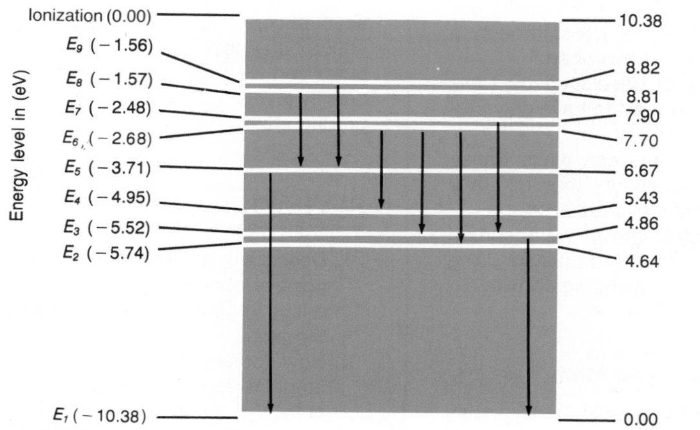

FIGURE 28–23. Use with Applying Concepts 4 and Problems 3, 4, and 5.

PROBLEMS

28.1 The Bohr Model

1. The diameter of hydrogen nucleus is 2.5×10^{-15} m; the distance between the nucleus and the first electron is about 5×10^{-9} m. If you use a baseball to represent the nucleus, how far away would the electron be?
2. A mercury atom drops from 8.82 eV to 6.67 eV above its ground state.
   a. What is the energy of the photon emitted by the mercury atom?
   b. What is the frequency of the photon?

See Figure 28–23 for Problems 3, 4, and 5.

3. A mercury atom is in an excited state when its energy level is 6.67 eV above the ground state. A photon of energy 2.15 eV strikes the mercury atom and is absorbed by it. To what energy level is the mercury atom raised?
4. A mercury atom is in an excited state at the E_6 energy level.
   a. How much energy would be needed to ionize the atom?
   b. How much energy would be released if the electron dropped down to the E_2 energy level instead?
5. A mercury atom is in an excited state that has an energy of -4.95 eV. It absorbs a photon that raises it to the next higher energy level.
   a. What is the energy of the photon?
   b. What is the photon's frequency?
6. A photon with an energy of 14.0 eV enters a hydrogen atom in the ground state and ionizes it. With what kinetic energy will the electron be ejected from the atom?
7. Calculate the radius of the orbital associated with the energy levels E_5 and E_6 of the hydrogen atom.
8. What energies are associated with hydrogen atom energy levels E_2, E_3, E_4, E_5, and E_6?
9. Using the values calculated in Problem 8, calculate the following energy differences for a hydrogen atom.
   a. $E_6 - E_5$ **c.** $E_4 - E_2$ **e.** $E_5 - E_3$
   b. $E_6 - E_3$ **d.** $E_5 - E_2$
10. Use the values from Problem 9 to determine the frequencies of the photons emitted when an electron in a hydrogen atom makes the level changes listed.
11. Determine the wavelengths of the photons of the frequencies calculated in Problem 10.
12. Determine the frequency and wavelength of the photon emitted when an electron drops
    a. from E_3 to E_2 in an excited hydrogen atom.
    b. from E_4 to E_3 in an excited hydrogen atom.
13. What is the difference between the energies of the E_4 and E_1 energy levels of the hydrogen atom?
14. ▶ By what amount does the mass of a hydrogen atom decrease when its electron makes a down transition from E_4 to E_1, in an excited hydrogen atom?
15. ▶ From what energy level did an electron fall if it emits a photon of 9.38×10^{-8} m wavelength when it reaches ground state within a hydrogen atom?
16. ▶ For a hydrogen atom in the $n = 3$ Bohr orbital, find
    a. the radius of the orbital.
    b. the electric force acting on the electron.
    c. the centripetal acceleration of the electron.
    d. the orbital speed of the electron. Compare this speed with the speed of light.
17. A hydrogen atom has its electron in the $n = 2$ level.
    a. If a photon with a wavelength of 332 nm strikes the atom, show that the atom will be ionized.
    b. When the atom is ionized, assume the electron receives the excess energy from the ionization. What will be the kinetic energy of the electron in joules?
18. ▶ How many orders of magnitude larger is the electrical force between the electron and proton in a hydrogen atom than the gravitational force between them?

28.2 The Present Model of the Atom

19. ▶ Gallium arsenide lasers are used in CD (compact disk) players. If the temperature is chosen so the laser emits at 840 nm, what is the difference in eV between the two lasing energy levels?
20. ▶ The carbon dioxide laser emits very high power infrared radiation. What is the energy difference in eV between the two lasing energy levels?

THINKING PHYSIC-LY

Often, posters that look rather dull under ordinary light glow brilliantly under black (UV) light. How is this effect achieved?

Answers To
PROBLEMS

Complete solutions to all Chapter Review Problems can be found in the Problems and Solutions Manual accompanying this text.

1. about 200 km
2. **a.** 2.15 eV
   b. 5.19×10^{14} Hz
3. E_9
4. **a.** 2.68 eV
   b. 3.06 eV
5. **a.** 1.24 eV
   b. 2.99×10^{14} Hz
6. 0.4 eV
7. $r_5 = 1.32 \times 10^{-9}$ m
   $r_6 = 1.91 \times 10^{-9}$ m
8. $E_2 = -3.40$ eV
   $E_3 = -1.51$ eV
   $E_4 = -0.85$ eV
   $E_5 = -0.54$ eV
   $E_6 = -0.38$ eV
9. **a.** 0.16 eV
   b. 1.13 eV
   c. 2.55 eV
   d. 2.86 eV
   e. 0.97 eV
10. **a.** 3.9×10^{13} Hz
    b. 2.70×10^{14} Hz
    c. 6.14×10^{14} Hz
    d. 6.89×10^{14} Hz
    e. 2.3×10^{14} Hz
11. **a.** 7.7×10^{-6} m
    b. 1.11×10^{-6} m
    c. 489 nm
    d. 435 nm
    e. 13 nm
12. **a.** $f = 4.6 \times 10^{14}$ Hz
    $\lambda = 6.5 \times 10^{-7}$ m
    b. $f = 1.5 \times 10^{14}$ Hz
    $\lambda = 2.0 \times 10^{-6}$ m
13. 12.8 eV
14. 2.26×10^{-35} kg
15. $n = 6$
16. **a.** 4.77×10^{-10} m
    b. 1.01×10^{-9} N
    c. 1.11×10^{21} m/s^2
    d. 7.28×10^{5} m/s or 0.2% of c
17. **a.** yes
    b. $0.3 \text{ eV} = 5 \times 10^{-20}$ J
18. 10^{40}
19. 1.48 eV
20. 0.117 eV

Answer To
THINKING PHYSIC-LY

Certain pigments absorb the ultraviolet photons and then emit the energy at lower frequencies, often in the visible range.

CHAPTER

29 Solid State Electronics

PLANNING GUIDE (5 class sessions)

CONTENTS	TEXT FEATURES	TEACHER RESOURCE PACKAGE	OTHER COMPONENTS
29.1 Conduction in Solids, pp. 596–603 (3 Class Sessions) • Band Theory of Solids • Conductors • Insulators • Semiconductors • Doped Semiconductors	**Physics Lab:** The Stoplight, p. 604 **Pocket Lab:** All Aboard!, p. 603 **Concept Review,** p. 603	**Study Guide:** Conduction in Solids **Physics Lab Data Sheet:** The Stoplight **Critical Thinking Master:** Remote Control **Reteaching Master:** The Vacuum Tube Diode **Transparency Worksheet:** Energy Levels/Energy Bands	**Transparency 44:** Energy Levels/Energy Bands
29.2 Electronic Devices, pp. 605–611 (2 Class Sessions) • Diodes • Transistors and Integrated Circuits	**Physics and Society:** Computer Viruses, p. 608 **Pocket Lab:** Red Light, p. 607 **Concept Review,** p. 611	**Study Guide:** Electronic Devices **Enrichment Master:** The Hall Effect	**Laboratory Manual:** Lab 29.1 Semiconductor Properties Lab 29.2 Integrated Circuit Logic Devices
Chapter Review, pp. 611–613	Summary Key Terms Reviewing Concepts Applying Concepts Problems Thinking Physic-ly	**Vocabulary Review** **Chapter Test**	**Test Bank**

SUPPLEMENTARY MATERIALS

SOFTWARE	AUDIOVISUAL	BOOKS/MAGAZINES
Step by Step, PDI (Apple II).	Video: *Miniature Miracle: The Computer Chip,* National Geographic.	Amato, Ivan. "A Hard Step Toward Diamond Circuitry." *Science News,* September 29, 1990, p. 197. Auston, D. H. "Probing Semiconductors with Femtosecond Pulses." *Physics Today,* February 1990, p. 46. Langreth, R. N. "Atom Clusters Act Bigger Than Their Britches." *Science News,* November 3, 1990, p. 279. Weart, S. R. "The Birth of the Solid-State Physics Community." *Physics Today,* July 1988, p. 38.

PROBLEM CORRELATION

CONCEPTS	CHAPTER REVIEW			PROBLEMS APPENDIX
	Reviewing Concepts	Applying Concepts	Problems	
29.1 Conduction in Solids				
Band Theory of Solids	1		1,2	1
Conductors			3,4	2
Insulators		2,3		
Semiconductors	2	1,4		
Doped Semiconductors	3	5,6,7	**5**,**6**	
29.2 Electronic Devices				
Diodes	4	8,9	**7**,8,9,10,11,12,13,14	3,4,5
Transistors and Integrated Circuits	5,6	10		

ACTIVITY AND DEMONSTRATION MATERIALS

PHYSICS LAB	POCKET LAB	DEMONSTRATIONS
Page 604 0–12 V variable power supply red LED green LED bi-color LED wires 470-Ω resistor voltmeter	Pages 603, 607 thermistor low-voltage DC power supply ammeter wires 0–12 V DC variable power supply 470-Ω resistor red LED	Page 605 LED (of any kind) 200–400 Ω resistor flashlight battery

EXTENSION PROJECTS

LIBRARY RESEARCH

1. UNIVAC
What was the UNIVAC? What advancements in technology made it possible?

HANDS–ON

2. Rectifier

STUDENT READINGS

McKenzie, A. "Chip Mimics Hearing." *Science News,* January 6, 1990.

Penrose, Roger. *The Emperor's New Mind: Concerning Computers, Minds, and the Laws of Physics.* New York: Oxford University Press, 1989.

Sze, S. M. *Semiconductor Devices, Physics and Technology.* New York: John Wiley & Sons Inc., 1985.

Thomsen, D. E. "Transistor Sensitive to One Electron." *Science News,* March 12, 1988.

Zuboff, Shoshana. *In the Age of the Smart Machine.* New York: Basic Books, 1988.

Chapter 29

Solid State Electronics

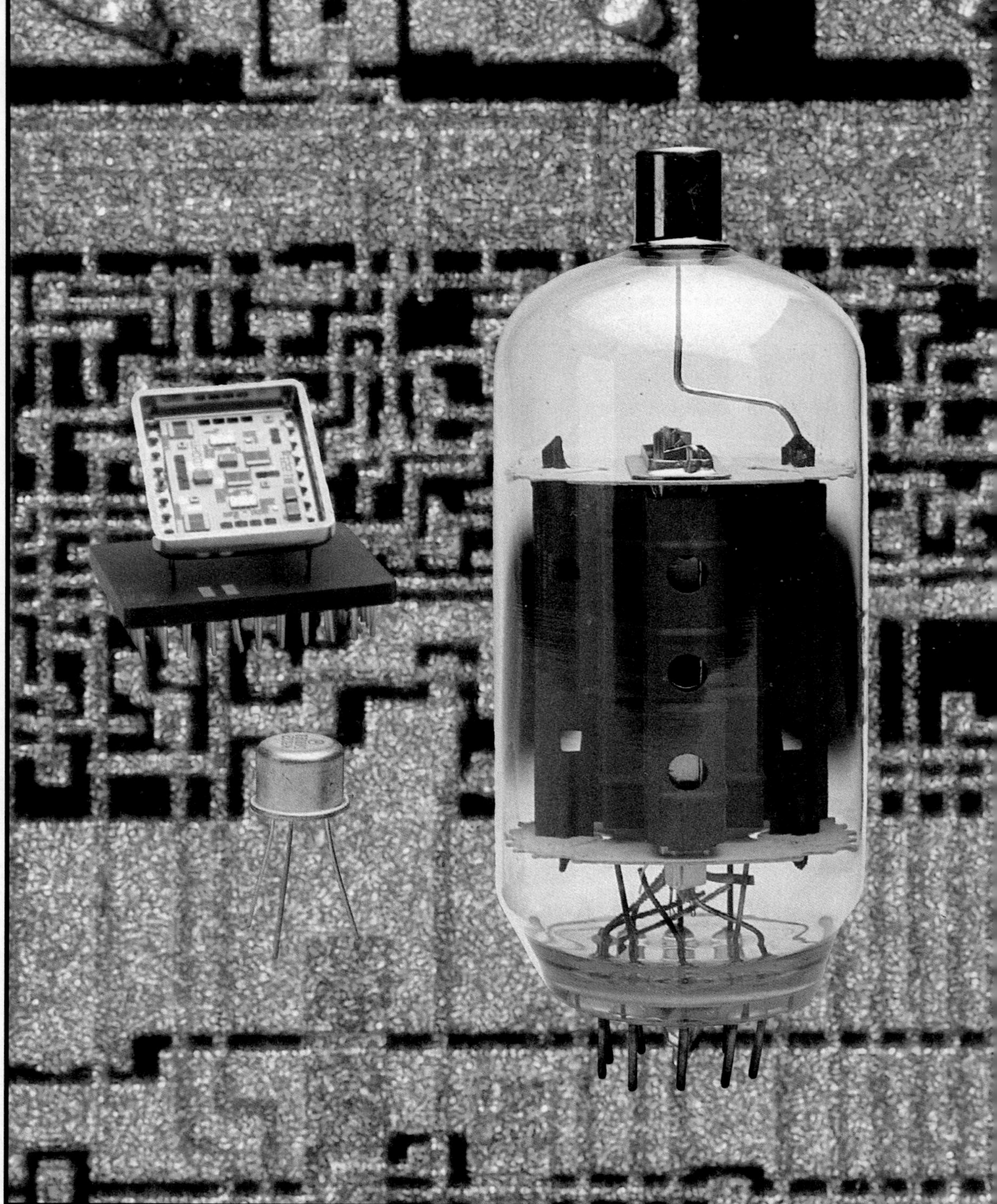

CHAPTER OVERVIEW

Theme Development: A new conceptual model for solids—band theory—is introduced, by which the quantum model may be extended to explain electron motion in conductors, insulators, and semiconductors. Understanding of physics at this subatomic scale is applied to microelectronics, one of today's most wide-ranging technologies.

MISCONCEPTIONS

This chapter takes an abstract submicroscopic point of view with electrons and holes moving through a solid crystal. The concept of a hole is a student stumbling block. Students will have trouble visualizing how semiconductor devices work.

KEY TERMS

bands
band theory
base
collector
conduction band
depletion layer
diode
donor electron
dopants
electron acceptor
electron gas model
emitter
extrinsic semiconductor
forbidden gaps
forward-biased diode
hole
intrinsic semiconductor
npn transistor
n-type semiconductor
pn-junction diode
pnp transistor
p-type semiconductor
reverse-biased diode

CHAPTER 29 Solid State Electronics

◀ The Inside Dope

How are conductors, resistors, diodes, and transistors that are the size of a human hair created on this crystal of pure silicon?

Chapter Outline

In our society we use electronic devices every day. From transistor radios and televisions to microcomputer-controlled microwave ovens and CD players, the results of solid-state physics and electrical engineering surround us. In the 1950s, the pencil-eraser sized transistor began to replace the much larger vacuum tube that had given birth to the field of electronics in the 1920s. In the 1960s, engineers found ways of putting many individual transistors on a single crystal of silicon. This integrated circuit, or microchip, was the key invention leading to today's technologies. Currently, circuits containing thousands of transistors are about the same size and cost as a single early transistor. Thus, designers can put systems as complex as a computer on your wrist.

✓ Concept Check

The following terms or concepts from earlier chapters are important for a good understanding of this chapter. If you are not familiar with them, you should review them before studying this chapter.
- conductors and insulators, Chapter 20
- current, potential difference, resistance, Chapter 22
- quantum theory, Chapter 27
- atomic structure, Chapter 28

Introducing The Chapter

The Inside Dope

Using The Photo: The process of manufacturing semiconductor devices involves technological marvels, whether we look at the purity of the substances required, the tiny dimensions of the chips, or the incredible machines used in their fabrication. Great ingenuity and hard work by tens of thousands of people have made these devices possible. Our description of the manufacturing process only hints at the many seemingly impossible mass-production techniques developed over the past thirty years. For an explanation of the chapter opener question, refer students to page 610.

✓ Concept Check

Make sure students have a clear understanding of the concepts taught in Chapters 20, 22, 27, and 28 that are listed in the Concept Check. Students with a good basic knowledge of conductors and insulators, current, potential difference, resistance, quantum theory, and atomic structure will be prepared to master the principles of solid state electronics discussed in this chapter.

Laboratory Options

STUDENT EDITION
Physics Lab
The Stoplight 604
Pocket Labs
All Aboard! 603
Red Light 607

TEACHER EDITION
Activities
Cooperative Learning 601
Demonstration 605

LABORATORY MANUAL
Semiconductor Properties
Diode Characteristics Lab 29.1
Integrated Circuit
Logic Devices Lab 29.2

Assessment Options

Portfolio Assessment
Extension 1, TWE, p. 594b
Extension, TWE, p. 602
Portfolio Assessment, TWE, p. 606
Developing a Viewpoint, p. 608
Enrichment, TWE, p. 609

Performance Assessment
Pocket Labs, pp. 603, 607
Physics Lab, p. 604
Pocket Lab Assessment, TWE, p. 602
Portfolio Assessment, TWE, p. 606

Content Assessment
Self Assessment: Practice Problems, pp. 598, 601, 603, 607
Checking for Understanding, TWE, p. 602
Assessment, Critical Thinking, p. 604
Checking for Understanding, TWE, p. 610
Concept Reviews, pp. 603, 611
Chapter Review, pp. 611–613
Supplemental Problems, p. 708

Group Assessment
Activites for group assessment occur with Cooperative Learning and lab activities.

29.1 CONDUCTION IN SOLIDS

Preparation

OBJECTIVES

The objectives are listed on the student page. Remind students to preview these objectives as a study guide to this major section.

OVERVIEW

Major concepts presented in this section include band theory, the electron gas model, types of semiconductors, and dopants.

BRIDGING

Previously discussed concepts, including conductor, insulator, current, potential difference, and resistance are expanded.

1 Focus

Pass around electronic components for students to look at. In particular, emphasize their small size.

Objectives

- **describe electron motion in conductors as the result of a partially-filled band of allowed energy levels.**
- **understand that electrons in metals have a very fast random motion, and that current flow results from a slow drift velocity when a potential difference is applied.**
- **describe insulators as having electrons bound to atoms, requiring more energy to move than is available.**
- **recognize that conduction in semiconductors is usually the result of doping with small numbers of impurity atoms.**
- **describe n-type semiconductors as conducting by means of free electrons and p-type semiconductors as conducting by means of "holes."**

29.1 CONDUCTION IN SOLIDS

Electronic devices depend not only on natural conductors and insulators, but even more on materials designed and produced by many scientists and engineers working together. We start our brief investigation into electronics by examining how materials conduct electricity.

Band Theory of Solids

We have previously divided materials into electrical conductors and insulators. In conductors, electrical charges can move easily, but in insulators, charges remain where they are placed. On the microscopic level, how does a conductor differ from an insulator?

As you learned in Chapter 13, crystalline solids consist of atoms bound together in regular arrangements. From Chapters 27 and 28, you know that an atom consists of a heavy, positively-charged nucleus, surrounded by a cloud of light, negatively-charged electrons. Atoms can have only certain specific energies. This means that energy changes must also be in specific amounts—energy is said to be quantized. The allowed atomic energies are called energy levels. Under most conditions, atoms are in their lowest possible energy level. The lowest energy level is said to be filled, and the other levels are empty.

Each electron in a solid must have its own energy level. These individual levels are very close together in a band.

Suppose we could construct a solid by assembling atoms together, one by one. We start with all the atoms in their lowest energy states. If two of the atoms are now brought together, the electric field of each atom affects the other atom, changing its energy levels. The energy levels of one atom are raised slightly, while those of the other are lowered, Figure 29–1a. There are two atoms, and there are two different sets of energy levels. Now consider what happens when many atoms are brought closely together, as in a solid. No two atoms can have exactly the same energy levels. There are now so many energy levels that they can no longer be identified as unique levels. Rather, the levels are spread into broad **bands**, Figure 29–1c. The bands are separated by values of energy that electrons are not allowed to have. These energies are called **forbidden gaps**. Electrical conduction in solids explained in terms of these bands is called the **band theory**.

FIGURE 29–1. The splitting of atomic energy levels when 2 hydrogen atoms are brought together (a); where 4 hydrogen atoms are brought together (b); and the formation of an energy band when many hydrogen atoms are brought together (c).

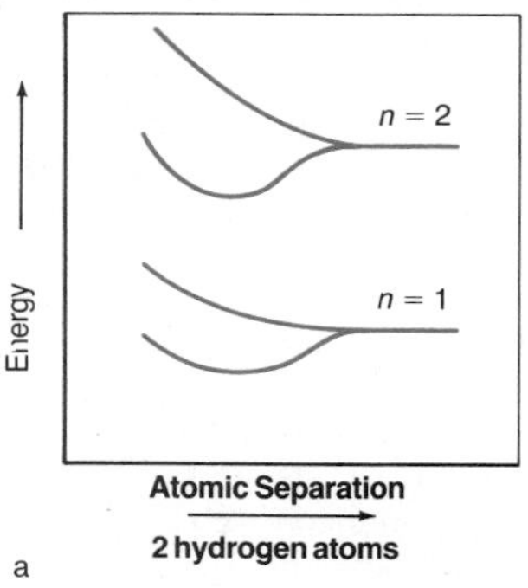

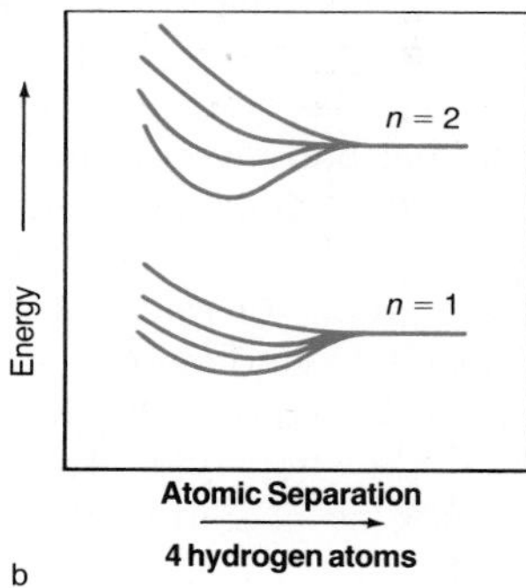

Allowed energy band
Forbidden energy gap
Allowed energy band
Energy
Atomic Separation
many hydrogen atoms
c

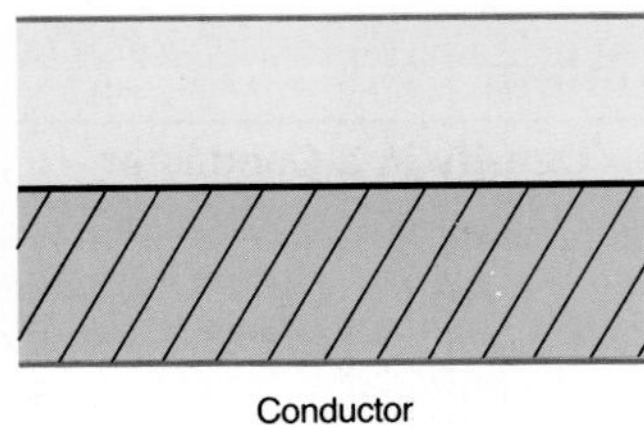

FIGURE 29–2. The allowed energy band in a conductor is half-filled with electrons. The blue-shaded region shows the lower energies occupied by electrons. Adding only an infinitesimal amount of energy to an electron puts it into the yellow region where it is free to move and conduct electricity.

Recall that any system will adjust itself until its energy is minimized. In a solid, electrons settle into states of lowest energy. No two electrons can have the same energy. In some materials there are more spaces in the lowest band than there are electrons to fill them. Empty states remain, Figure 29–2. Materials with partially-filled bands are conductors.

In conductors, the lowest band is only partially filled.

Conductors

Why do materials with partially-filled bands, such as the metals aluminum and copper, conduct electricity? When a potential difference is placed across a material, the resulting electric field exerts a force on the charged particles. They accelerate, the field does work on them, and they gain energy. But their energy can increase only if there is a higher energy level into which they can move. If the bands are only partially filled, then there are available energy levels only slightly higher than their present levels. As a result, the electrons can gain energy from the field and move from one atom to the next, or "conduct electricity."

In a conductor, the higher energy level is only a little above the normal level.

The free electrons in conductors act like atoms in an ordinary gas or water molecules in the sea. They move rapidly about in a random way, changing directions when they collide with the cores of the atoms. If an electric field is put across a length of wire, there will be a net force pushing the electrons to one end. Their overall motion is not greatly changed, however. As shown in Figure 29–3, they continue to move rapidly (speeds of 10^6 m/s) in random directions, but now they also drift very slowly (10^{-5} m/s or less) toward the positive end of the wire. This model of conductors is called the **electron gas model.** If the temperature is increased, the electron speeds increase, but they collide more frequently with atomic cores. Thus, the conductivity of metals is reduced as the temperature rises. Conductivity is the reciprocal of resistivity. As conductivity is reduced, the material's resistance rises.

Electrons in a conductor have very high random speeds like atoms in a gas.

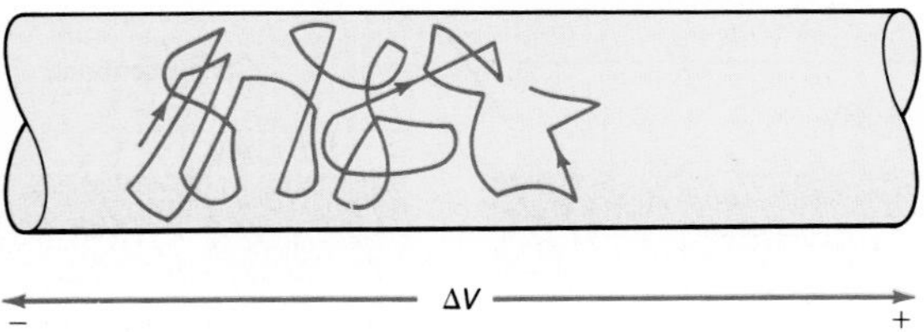

FIGURE 29–3. Electron motion in a conductor. The electrons move rapidly and randomly. If a field is applied across the wire, the electrons drift toward one end.

2 Teach

CONCEPT DEVELOPMENT

- A chemist might say that there are close to one mole of free electrons per cubic centimeter of copper. That's a lot of electrons. The number makes sense when you remember that there is one free electron per atom in copper and one gram of copper is about 2% of a mole. This number of electrons represents about the maximum for a good conductor.

Study Guide Master. To reinforce the concepts in this section, have the students complete the Study Guide Master for Section 29.1 from the Teacher Resource Package.

Transparency Package. Use Transparency 44 to quiz students on energy levels and energy bands.

- The band theory of conduction uses several abstract concepts that are difficult to understand. The abcissa of a graph of energy levels is energy, not distance. It may help students to think of objects obtaining energy as being lifted up against gravity so that their potential energy is proportional to their height. Be sure to emphasize, however, that levels with larger energies and levels with smaller energies are not located in different parts of space.

STUDY GUIDE MASTER

Use the Study Guide master for section 29.1.

TRANSPARENCY

Use Transparency 44 with this section.

CONCEPT DEVELOPMENT

Guided Practice: Go over the Example Problem on this page as a class exercise.

Independent Practice: Assign the Practice Problem on this page for homework, and spend time the following class period discussing it.

Answers To
PRACTICE PROBLEMS

Have students refer to Appendix A of the Solutions Appendix for complete solutions to Practice Problems.

1. 1.31×10^{23} free e^-/cm^3

F.Y.I.

Only science can hope to keep technology in some sort of moral order.
—Edgar Z. Friedenberg,
"The Impact of the School,"
The Vanishing Adolescent

Example Problem

The Free-Electron Density in a Conductor

If each copper atom contributes one electron, how many free electrons exist in a cubic centimeter of copper? The density of copper is 8.96 g/cm^3. Copper's atomic mass is 63.54 g/mole and Avogadro's number is 6.02×10^{23} atoms/mole.

Given: Copper:
1 free electron/atom
atomic mass, M = 63.54 g/mole
density, ρ = 8.96 g/cm^3
Avogadro's number, $A_V = 6.02 \times 10^{23}$ atoms/mole

Unknown: free electrons/cm^3

Solution: By dimensional analysis,

$$\frac{\text{free e}^-}{\text{cm}^3\text{ Cu}} = \left(\frac{1\text{ free e}^-}{1\text{ atom}}\right)\left(\frac{6.02 \times 10^{23}\text{ atoms}}{1\text{ mole}}\right)\left(\frac{1\text{ mole Cu}}{63.54\text{ g Cu}}\right)\left(\frac{8.96\text{ g}}{1\text{ cm}^3\text{ Cu}}\right)$$
$$= 8.49 \times 10^{22}\text{ free e}^-/\text{cm}^3\text{ Cu}$$

Practice Problem

1. Zinc, density 7.13 g/cm^3, atomic mass 65.37 g/mole, has two free electrons per atom. How many free electrons are there in each cubic centimeter of zinc?

Insulators

In insulators, all levels in the lowest band, the valence band, are filled.

We have discussed the properties of materials with partially-filled energy bands. In some materials, all energy levels in the lowest band are filled. The next lowest available level is in the higher band. An electron must either gain a very large amount of energy or none at all. If an electric field is put across such a material, the electrons cannot gain enough energy to reach the next available energy level. Thus, the electrons remain on their "home" atoms. The filled band is called the valence band because, in chemical terms, the electrons are the valence electrons of the atoms. Such a material is an insulator; charges remain in place. Examples are sulfur, common table salt, and glass.

An electric field cannot normally give an electron enough energy to reach the conduction band in insulators.

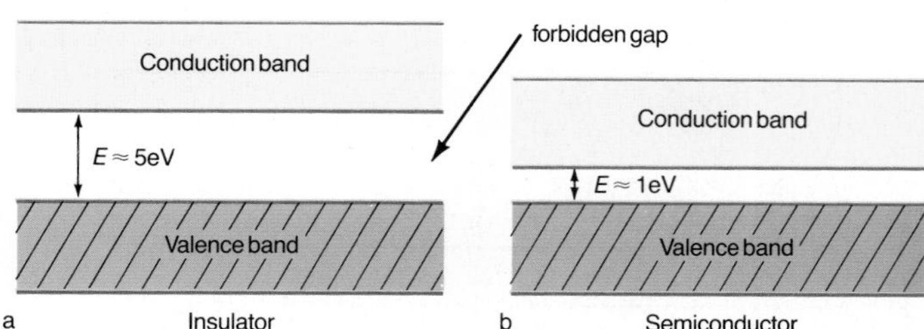

FIGURE 29–4. Valence and conduction bands in an insulator (a) and in a semiconductor (b). Notice that the forbidden gap is wider in (a) than in (b).

TEACHER F.Y.I.

The Avagadro constant, 6.02×10^{23} particles per mole of any substance, is an accepted SI standard. It is represented by the symbol N_A. If there were 1 mole of people, it would take 120 trillion (1.20×10^{14}) Earths, each with today's population, to accommodate them.

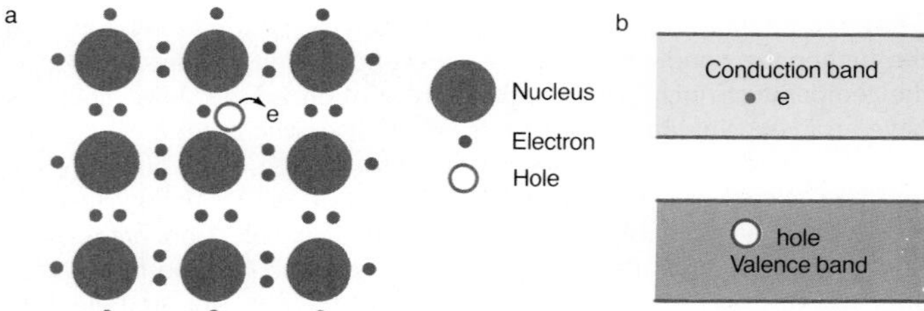

FIGURE 29–5. Some electrons in semiconductors have enough thermal energy to break free and wander through the crystal as shown in the crystal structure (a) and band (b).

If electrons are to move from atom to atom, that is, to conduct electricity, they will have to be given more energy than available from the electric field. The energy levels electrons would have to be in if they were to move are in a band called the **conduction band**, Figure 29–4.

How much energy would an electron need to gain to reach the next empty level? Recall from Chapter 27 that an electron volt (eV) is a convenient energy unit when discussing energy changes in atomic systems.

$$1 \text{ eV} = 1.6 \times 10^{-19} \text{ J}$$

One electron volt is 1.6×10^{-19} J of energy.

In an insulator, the lowest energy level in the *conduction* band is between 5 and 10 eV above the highest energy level in the *valence* band, Figure 29–4a. There is a 5 to 10-eV gap of energies that no electrons can have. Of course, electrons have some kinetic energy as a result of their thermal energy. But the average thermal energy of electrons at room temperature is only 0.025 eV, hardly enough to jump the forbidden gap. If an electric field is placed across an insulator, almost no electrons gain enough energy to reach the conduction band, so no current flows. That is, electrons in an insulator must be given a large amount of energy if they are to be pulled free from one atom and moved to the next. As a result, the electrons in an insulator remain in place, and the material does not conduct electricity.

The forbidden gap in insulators is 5 to 10 eV wide.

Semiconductors

Electrons can move more freely in semiconductors than in insulators, but not as easily as in conductors, Figure 29–4b. Thus, semiconductors have very high resistance. How does the microscopic structure of semiconductors explain this? Atoms of the most common semiconductors, silicon (Si) and germanium (Ge), each have four valence electrons. These four electrons are involved in binding the atoms together into the solid crystal. As a result, they are held, or bound, to an individual atom. The valence electrons form a filled band, as in an insulator, but the forbidden gap between the valence and conduction bands is much smaller. Not much energy is needed to pull one of the electrons from a silicon atom and put it into the conduction band, Figure 29–5. Indeed, the gap is so small that some electrons reach the conduction band due to their thermal energy. That is, the random motion of atoms and electrons gives some electrons enough energy to break free of their "home" atoms and wander around the silicon crystal. If an electric field is applied, these electrons can move through the solid. The higher the tem-

Semiconductors are usually made of atoms with four valence electrons.

The forbidden gap in semiconductors is only approximately 1 eV wide.

CONCEPT DEVELOPMENT

Enrichment: The idea that two electrons cannot occupy the same energy level is known as the Pauli Exclusion Principle. Some of your students may want to look up information about it and report to the class.

- The equation $E = qV$ was covered in Chapter 22 with the concept of potential.
- Someone may ask if insulators ever conduct. The answer is yes. Extremely large electric fields can be applied to give electrons the energy needed to jump across forbidden gaps and cause conduction. This is known as dielectric breakdown.
- The most common example of an insulator acting as a conductor is air. It is an insulator but it conducts electricity, for example lighting, when the potential difference across a distance is so large that a spark can jump across it.

Multicultural Connections

Shirley Jackson's interest in science began with stories her mother read her about African-American scientist Benjamin Banneker. Although her initial interest as a young girl was in biology, she later demonstrated significant skills in mathematics, which led her into physics. When she entered MIT in 1964, she was one of two African American women in a group of not more than 30 to 40 women in the whole school—she was a pioneer for both women and African Americans. She worked to help others by helping to found the Black Student Union. This group was instrumental in initiating MITs active recruitment of minority students. In 1973, she became the first African American to receive a doctoral degree in physics from MIT. Her current area of interest is in theoretical explanations for the behavior of semiconductors.

CONCEPT DEVELOPMENT

- The distinctions between conductors, semiconductors, and insulators are arbitrary; one classification just shades into another. Because the range of conductivities is enormous, there is extremely wide latitude in the engineering of various materials.

- About one atom in five billion contributes a free electron when a material is doped. One way of talking about dopant atoms is to think about peer pressure. If you were surrounded by five billion neighbors who were all alike, as are the silicon and germanium atoms, you would feel tremendous pressure to become just like them. Thus you would give away your extra electron (or hole) to conform.

HELP WANTED

SYSTEMS ANALYST

If you can analyze a problem, select the best hardware, software, and support system to solve it, and then work with the staff to implement that solution, we are looking for you to fill systems-analyst positions.

A B.S. or an advanced degree in such areas as business, scientific engineering, and so on will determine your position within this booming computer service company. Your sense of logic, ability to keep up with advances in our industry, communicative skills, and willingness to work hard will determine your success. For information contact:

Association for Systems Management, 24587 Bagley Road, Cleveland, OH 44138

perature, the more electrons are able to reach the conduction band, and the higher the conductivity. This is the opposite in metals, where, as the temperature increases, conductivity is reduced because electrons have an increasing number of collisions with atomic cores.

An atom from which an electron has broken free is missing an electron and is said to contain a hole. A **hole** is an empty energy level in the valence band. It has a positive charge. If an electron breaks free from another atom, it can land on a hole, becoming bound to an atom once again. This process can also be seen as the hole and free electron recombining, eliminating each other. The electron, however, left behind a hole on its previous atom. Thus, as in a game of musical chairs, the negatively-charged, free electrons move in one direction and the positively-charged holes move in the other. The energy of the electrons is in the conduction band while the holes have energies in the valence band. Pure semiconductors that conduct as a result of thermally freed electrons and holes are called **intrinsic semiconductors**. Because so few electrons or holes are available to carry charge, conduction in intrinsic semiconductors is very small; their resistance is very large.

Example Problem

The Fraction of Free Electrons in an Intrinsic Semiconductor

Find the fraction of atoms that has free electrons in silicon. At room temperature, thermal energy frees 1×10^{13} e^-/cm^3 in pure silicon. The density of silicon is 2.33 g/cm^3 and the atomic mass of silicon is 28.09 g/mole. **a.** How many silicon atoms are there in one cubic centimeter? **b.** What is the fraction of silicon atoms that have free electrons? That is, what is the ratio of free e^-/cm^3 to atoms/cm^3 in silicon?

Given: silicon: density, $\rho = 2.33$ g/cm^3
atomic mass, $M = 28.09$ g/mole
free $e^-/cm^3 = 1 \times 10^{13}$ e^-/cm^3
Avogadro's number, $A_V = 6.02 \times 10^{23}$ atoms/mole

Unknowns: **a.** Si atoms/cm^3
b. free e^-/atom Si

Solution:

a. By dimensional analysis,

$$\left(\frac{2.33\text{ g}}{1\text{ cm}^3}\right)\left(\frac{1\text{ mole}}{28.09\text{ g Si}}\right)\left(\frac{6.02 \times 10^{23}\text{ atoms}}{1\text{ mole}}\right)$$

$$= 4.99 \times 10^{22}\text{ atoms/cm}^3$$

b. $$\frac{\text{free e}^-}{\text{atom Si}} = \left(\frac{1 \times 10^{13}\text{ free e}^-}{\text{cm}^3}\right)\left(\frac{1\text{ cm}^3}{4.99 \times 10^{22}\text{ atoms Si}}\right)$$

$$= 2 \times 10^{-10}\text{ (fraction of Si atoms with free electrons)}$$

or 5×10^9 atoms of Si for every free e^-

Thus, there are many fewer free electrons in an intrinsic semiconductor than in a metal like copper.

TEACHER 

The range between excellent conductors such as copper, with 10^{22} free electrons per cubic centimeter, and good insulators with very few free electrons per cubic centimeter, represents over twenty orders of magnitude. To put this in more dramatic form, a rod of copper one centimeter square and a billion times as long as the distance from Earth to the sun would have less resistance than a thin sheet of fused quartz one centimeter square and one-tenth of a millimeter thick!

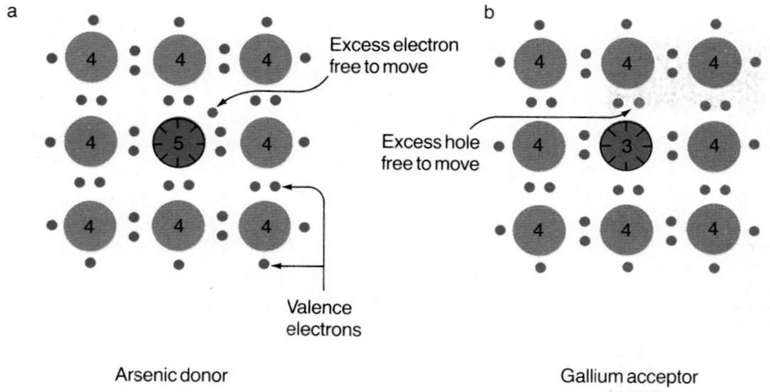

a

b

FIGURE 29–6. Donor and acceptor ions in a silicon crystal.

Practice Problem

2. In pure germanium, density 5.23 g/cm^3, atomic mass 72.6 g/mole, there are 2×10^{16} free electrons/cm^3 at room temperature. How many free electrons are there per atom?

Doped Semiconductors

While conductivity does not depend only on the number of free electrons, a material with fewer than one free electron per million atoms can't conduct electricity well. To make a practical device, the conductivity of semiconductors must be increased greatly. This can be done by adding certain other atoms, or impurities, creating **extrinsic semiconductors**. Impurity atoms, often called **dopants**, increase conductivity by adding either electrons or holes. A few dopant atoms replace silicon atoms in the crystal. Arsenic (As) atoms that have five valence electrons can be used, Figure 29–6a. Four of the five electrons bind to neighboring silicon atoms. The fifth electron is not needed in bonding and so can move relatively freely. Another way to say this is that the energy of this **donor electron** is so close to the conduction band that thermal energy can easily remove it from the impurity atom, putting an electron in the conduction band, Figure 29–7a. A semiconductor that conducts by means of electrons is called an **n-type semiconductor** because conduction is by means of negatively-charged particles.

FINE ARTS CONNECTION

You can see the fantastic creations of computer art whenever you turn on your television or see a film. These colorful, fast-paced pieces are created on computer screens by a skillful group of artists who use the electromagnetic spectrum as their paint and canvas. Their creations are then stored on videotape or reproduced on paper or film.

These artists need only to touch a stylus to a pad to produce a brilliant palette of colors on their screen. Any effect from water colors to oils, from pointillism to airbrush, can be produced.

The next time you watch Monday Night Football or tune in the national election returns, check out the opening sequences for a blitz of these computer art creations.

CRITICAL THINKING

Use the Critical Thinking master for Chapter 29 with this section.

Answers To
PRACTICE PROBLEMS

Have students refer to Appendix A of the Solutions Appendix for complete solutions to Practice Problems.

2. 5×10^{-7}

CONCEPT DEVELOPMENT

- It's important for students to realize that semiconductors as a whole remain neutral. If you look at only certain regions of the semiconductor, such as the depletion layer, you may find a net charge; however, taken as a complete unit, the semiconductor has no net charge. Put another way, adding dopant atoms to a crystal does not add any excess electrons or holes and therefore does not charge the crystal.
- The concentration of dopants in semiconductors is so low that a hundred years ago they would have seemed like magic even under sophisticated chemical analysis. Nevertheless, it's those small amounts of impurities that allow semiconductors to operate.

ACTIVITY

Cooperative Learning: Divide students into small groups and have them consult a periodic table. Point out that silicon and germanium are in Group 4. Have them list the nearby Group 3 elements that can be electron acceptors and the Group 5 elements that can be electron donors.

Critical Thinking: Ask students to explain why Group 5 elements such as bismuth are not used to dope silicon. [An atom of bismuth is so large in comparison with silicon that it causes dislocations in the crystal structure of the semiconductor, interfering with its conduction.]

Critical Thinking Master, Teacher Resource Package. You may wish to have students complete the Critical Thinking Master, The Hall Effect, with this section.

CHECKING FOR UNDERSTANDING

Ask students to describe the process of doping. Suggest that they refer only to electron donor materials in their descriptions in order to avoid getting into the hole concept.

RETEACHING

Reteach semiconductors by explaining their essential purpose as controllers of resistance. Semiconductors are substances engineered to have very carefully tailored resistances by manipulating the number of electrons and holes in the material. This control of resistance can exist over very short distances and be changed very abruptly so that even a single tiny structure can have widely differing resistances.

Reteaching Master, Teacher Resource Package. Use the Reteaching Master, for Chapter 29.

EXTENSION

Ask students why the original silicon or germanium used in manufacturing semiconductors has to be of such high purity. [To allow control over the kinds and numbers of impurities (dopants).] The process for achieving such high purity is called zone refining. Have interested students investigate this process.

INDEPENDENT PRACTICE/ EXTENSION

Refer to the Assignment Guide on page 603 for additional questions and problems for independent practice.

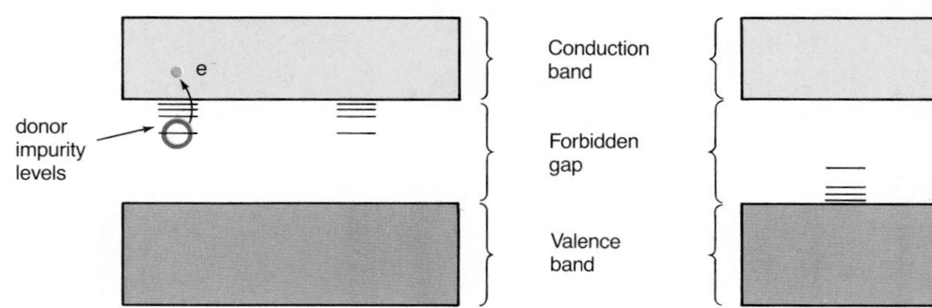

FIGURE 29–7. Donor and acceptor energy levels in a semiconductor.

Atoms in group three of the periodic table produce extra holes, resulting in p-type semiconductors.

A gallium (Ga) atom has only three valence electrons. If a gallium atom replaces a silicon atom, one binding electron is missing, Figure 29–6b. That is, the gallium atom creates a hole. Only thermal energy is needed to excite electrons from the valence band into this hole, creating a hole on a silicon atom that is free to move. The gallium atom is called an **electron acceptor**. A semiconductor that conducts by means of holes is called a **p-type semiconductor**. Conduction is the result of the motion of positively-charged holes in the valence band, Figure 29–7b. Whether p-type or n-type, the semiconductor is still neutral. Adding dopant atoms of either type does not add any net charge to the semiconductor. If there are free electrons, then there are the same number of positively-charged atoms. When a semiconductor conducts electricity by means of holes, there is a corresponding number of negatively-charged atoms.

F. Y. I.

Electronic calculators can solve problems which the man who made them cannot solve; but no government-subsidized commission of engineers and physicists could create a worm.
—Joseph Wood Krutch
"March,"
The Twelve Seasons

Silicon is doped by putting a silicon crystal in a vacuum with a sample of the impurity. The impurity material is heated to vaporize it, and the atoms condense on the cold silicon. The silicon is gently warmed so the impurities diffuse into the material. Only a few impurity atoms per million silicon atoms are needed to increase the conductivity by a factor of 1000 or more. Thus, the electrical properties of the semiconductor can be chosen by carefully controlling the number of impurity atoms. Finally, a thin layer of aluminum or gold is evaporated on the crystal and a wire is welded to the conductor. The wire allows the user to put current into and bring it out of the doped silicon.

Only a few dopant atoms can produce large increases in conductivity.

The electrical conductivity of both intrinsic and extrinsic semiconductors is sensitive to both temperature and light. An increase in temperature allows more electrons to reach the conduction band. Thus, the conductivity increases; the resistance decreases. One semiconductor device, the thermistor, is specially designed so its resistance depends very strongly on temperature. Thus, the thermistor can be used as a sensitive thermometer.

Thermometers use the variation of conductivity of semiconductors with temperature.

Other useful applications of semiconductors depend on their light sensitivity. When light falls on a semiconductor, the light can excite electrons from the valence band to the conduction band just as light excites atoms. Thus, the resistance decreases as the light intensity increases. Materials such as silicon and cadmium sulfide are used as light-dependent resistors in cameras and light meters.

Light detectors use the increase of conductivity of semiconductors exposed to light.

Assessment

Performance

To further assess students' understanding of the relationship between conductivity and temperature, explore how the resistance of several devices depends on temperature. Use the thermistor, a 1000-Ω composition or carbon resistor, and a wire-wound 1000-Ω resistor. Connect insulated wires to each of them and wrap them in waterproof electrical tape. To provide three different temperatures, use a beaker of ice water, one of very hot or boiling water, and a thermos bottle containing a mixture of dry ice and alcohol. To measure the resistance, use the series circuit used for the thermistor. For the two resistors, use a milliammeter capable of reading about 10 mA.

Place each object first in the dry ice, then the ice water, and finally the boiling water. Adjust the power supply voltage so that the current is the same at all three temperatures, but use a 50 mA current for

Example Problem

The Conductivity of Doped Silicon

Silicon is doped with arsenic so that one in every 10^6 Si atoms is replaced by an As atom. Assume that each As atom donates one electron to the conduction band. **a.** What is the density of free electrons in this extrinsic semiconductor? **b.** By what ratio is this density greater than that of intrinsic silicon of the Example Problem on page 600? **c.** Is conduction mainly by the thermally-freed electrons of the intrinsic silicon or by the arsenic-donated electrons?

Given: As atom density = 1 As atom /10^6 Si atom
free e^-/As atom = 1 free e^-/As atom
Si atom/cm^3 = 4.99×10^{22} Si atoms /cm^3
free e^-/cm^3 in intrinsic Si = $1 \times 10^{13}/cm^3$

Unknowns: a. As-donated free e^-/cm^3
b. ratio of result **a** to $1 \times 10^{13}/cm^3$

Solution: a. By dimensional analysis,

$$\frac{\text{free } e^-}{cm^3} = \left(\frac{1 \text{ free } e^-}{1 \text{ As atom}}\right)\left(\frac{1 \text{ As atom}}{1 \times 10^6 \text{ Si atom}}\right)\left(\frac{4.99 \times 10^{22} \text{ Si atoms}}{1 \text{ cm}^3}\right)$$
$$= 4.99 \times 10^{16} \text{ free } e^-/cm^3.$$

b. Ratio is

$$\frac{4.99 \times 10^{16} \text{ free } e^-/cm^3 \text{ in doped Si}}{1 \times 10^{13} \text{ free } e^-/cm^3 \text{ in pure Si}} = 4.99 \times 10^3$$

c. Since there are 5000 arsenic-donated electrons for every intrinsic one, conduction is mainly by the arsenic-donated ones.

Practice Problem

3. If you wanted to have 5×10^3 as many electrons from As doping as thermally-free electrons in the germanium semiconductor described in Practice Problem 2, how many As atoms should there be per Ge atom?

CONCEPT REVIEW

1.1 In which type of material, conductor, semiconductor, or insulator, are electrons more likely to remain with the same atom?

1.2 Magnesium oxide has a forbidden gap of 8 eV. Is this material a conductor, insulator, or semiconductor?

1.3 You are designing an integrated circuit using a single crystal of silicon. You want to have a region with relatively good insulating properties. Should you dope this region or leave it an intrinsic semiconductor?

1.4 **Critical Thinking:** If the temperature increases, the number of free electrons in an intrinsic semiconductor increases. For example, raising the temperature by 10°C doubles the number of free electrons. Which is likely to have a conductivity that depends more on temperature, an intrinsic or doped semiconductor? Explain.

POCKET LAB

ALL ABOARD!

Metals become better conductors when they are cooled. Semiconductors become better conductors when they are heated. Does a thermistor act like a metal or a semiconductor?

Make a series circuit with a low-voltage DC power supply, a thermistor, and an ammeter (0-100 microamp scale). Slowly turn up the power supply until the needle is in the middle of the scale (50 microamps). The voltage will be about 0.6 V. Watch what happens to the current when you hold the thermistor between your fingers. Describe the results. List several possible advantages of thermistors over standard thermometers.

POCKET LAB

ALL ABOARD!

Purpose: to discover how the conductivity of a thermistor changes with temperature.
Materials: thermistor; low-voltage DC power supply; ammeter; wires.
Outcome: The conductivity will increase as the temperature is increased. The thermistor is a semiconductor! Thermistors are smaller, cheaper, more durable, and can be directly connected into electronic circuits.

Answers To
PRACTICE PROBLEMS

Have students refer to Appendix A of the Solutions Appendix for complete solutions to Practice Problems.

3. 2×10^{-3} As atom/Ge atom

3 Close

CONVERGENT QUESTION

An n-type semiconductor has more free electrons than holes, yet it is electrically neutral. Ask students why this is the case. [Any dopant atom that is added is neutral; therefore, no net charge is added to the crystal.]

CONCEPT REVIEW ANSWERS

1.1 insulator
1.2 insulator
1.3 Leave it intrinsic so it has very few free electrons.
1.4 Critical Thinking: An intrinsic one, because all its conduction is from thermally freed electrons, while the doped semiconductor depends on the charges from the dopants that depend little on temperature.

the thermistor and a 10 mA current for the two resistors. Make a table of the temperature, voltage, current, and calculated resistances for the three objects. Graph the resistance of each device as a function of temperature. How are they similar? different? [The thermistor and carbon resistor both increase in resistance as the temperature drops, but the wire-wound resistor's resistance decreases. The resistance of the thermistor changes more rapidly than that of the carbon resistor.]

29:1 ASSIGNMENT GUIDE

	PRACTICE	EXTENSION
CHAPTER REVIEW pp. 611–613		
· Reviewing Concepts	1–3	
· Applying Concepts		1–7
· Problems*	1–4	5–6
APPENDIX B PROBLEMS*		
· Chapter 29, p. 708	1, 2	

* Complete solutions to all Chapter Review and Appendix problems appear in the Problems and Solutions Manual.

PHYSICS LAB

Process Skills: observing, formulating models, classifying, communicating, hypothesizing, questioning, designing experiments.

MISCONCEPTIONS

Although they are surrounded by solid state devices, most students will have very little familiarity with their fundamental structures. Students typically confuse filament lamps with LEDs.

Teaching Suggestions:

1. Be sure not to omit the current limiting resistor. Students can destroy the LEDs with excessive currents.
2. Let students discover that their stoplight needs to have the red and green LEDs in parallel.
3. If your LEDs and power supply only light the LEDs moderately, change your current limiting resistor to 330 Ω.

OBSERVATIONS

1. The LEDs will begin to glow around 1.8 V and be bright at 2.2 V (measured across the LED).
2. Reversing the current caused both LEDs to go out.

ANALYSIS

1. The stoplight circuit will have the LEDs in parallel branches and reversed in polarity.
2. By reversing the polarity of the LEDs, only one color can be *on* at a time. Reversing the leads at the power supply will change the color of the stoplight.

APPLICATIONS

The bi-color LED will be green when the current flows in one direction and red when the current flows in the opposite direction.

As a post-lab demonstration, you might ask students to predict what would happen with AC. When the bi-color LED is attached to AC, the lamp will appear yellow from the end. By rapidly moving the LED, red and green will flash alternately.

PHYSICS LAB: The Stoplight

Purpose

To investigate light emitting diodes (LEDs) by constructing a stoplight circuit.

Materials

- 0 - 12 V variable power supply
- red LED
- green LED
- bi-color LED
- wires
- 470-Ω resistor
- voltmeter

Procedure

1. Put the bi-color LED off to the side.
2. Connect a series circuit with the power supply, the resistor, and the colored LEDs to light them both. Do not bypass or omit the resistor with an LED. Always have the resistor between an LED and one side of the power supply.
3. Reverse the direction of the current in the circuit and note the result. Measure the voltage across an LED.
4. Design a circuit so that changing the direction of the current will change the color that lights up.
5. Test your circuit.

Observations and Data

1. What voltage was needed to light the LEDs?
2. Describe what happened when the current was reversed in Procedure 3.

Analysis

1. Make a drawing to show your stoplight circuit [red on (green off), then green on (red off)].
2. Explain why your stoplight circuit works.

Applications

1. Design and conduct experiments to discover what type of LED the bi-color LED is. Remember to leave the resistor connected to the power supply.

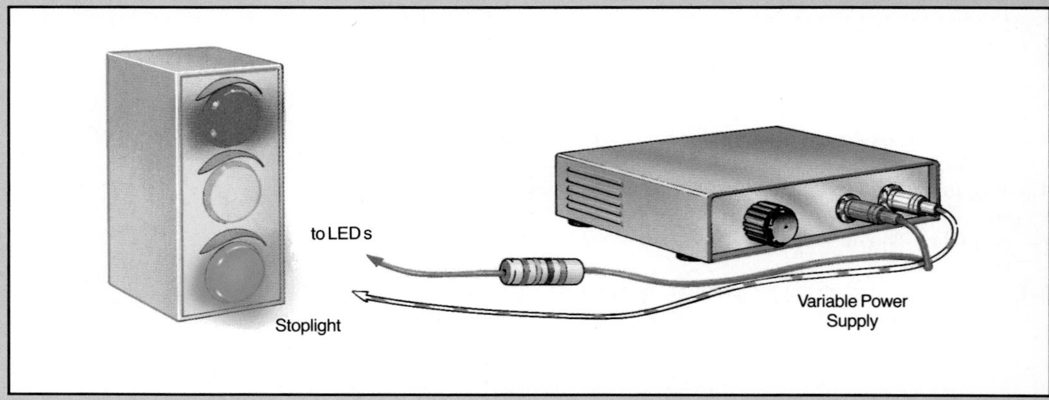

ASSESSMENT

Critical Thinking: To further assess students' understanding of LEDs, ask the following questions.

1. The current through the LED depends on the voltage. Use a multimeter on the 100 mA scale to measure the current when the voltage across the LED is 0.5 V, 1.0 V, and 1.5 V. Sketch the graph of the current (*y*-axis) and voltage (*x*-axis).
2. Describe the relationship between the current and the voltage.

V	amps
0.5	0.001
1.0	0.002
1.5	0.030

What does the graph indicate about the resistance of the LED at 1.0 V and also at 1.5 V? Use $R = V/I$. [The relationship is not linear. The resistance of the LED is not constant. At 1.0 V: 1.0 V/0.002 A = 500 Ω; at 1.5 V: 1.5 V/0.03 A = 50 Ω.]

29.2 ELECTRONIC DEVICES

Today's electronic instruments use many semiconductor devices, usually combined on "chips" of semiconducting silicon a few millimeters on a side. The chips contain not only regions of doped silicon that act as wires or resistors, but areas where two or three differently doped regions are in contact, forming diodes and transistors. In these devices, current and voltage vary in ways much more complex than described by Ohm's law. Because the variation is not linear, the devices can change current from AC to DC and amplify voltages. The integrated circuit contains several thousand diodes and transistors, connected together on a single chip, to perform the complex functions demanded by radios, televisions, tape and CD players, and microcomputers.

Objectives

- **understand why diodes conduct charges in one direction only.**
- **describe how diodes can be used to produce current that flows in one direction only.**
- **recognize how a transistor is constructed and how it can amplify or increase voltage changes.**

Diodes

The simplest semiconductor device is the diode. A **diode** consists of joined regions of p-type and n-type semiconductors. Rather than joining two separate pieces of doped silicon, a single sample of intrinsic silicon is treated first with a p-dopant, then with an n-dopant. Metal contacts are coated on each region so wires can be attached, Figure 29–8. The boundary between the p-type and n-type regions is called the junction. Thus, the resulting device is called a **pn-junction diode**.

A diode consists of adjacent n- and p-type semiconductors.

The holes and electrons in the p- and n-regions are affected by the junction. There are forces on the free charge carriers in the two regions near the junction. The free electrons on the n-side are attracted to the positive holes on the p-side. The electrons readily move into the p-side and recombine with the holes. Holes from the p-side similarly move into the n-side where they recombine with electrons. As a result of this flow, the n-side has a net positive charge, the p-side a net negative charge. These charges produce forces in the opposite direction that stop further movement of charge carriers. The region around the junction is left with neither holes nor free electrons. This area, depleted of charge carriers, is called the **depletion layer**. Because it has no charge carriers, it is a poor conductor of electricity. Thus, a junction diode consists of relatively good conductors at the ends surrounding a poor conductor.

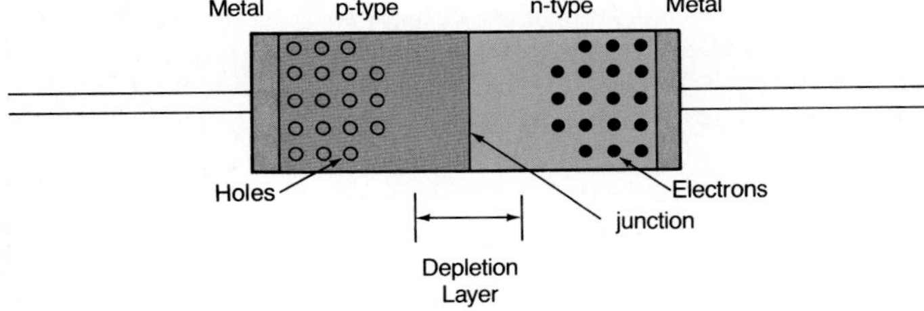

FIGURE 29–8. A junction diode showing the depletion layer.

29.2 ELECTRONIC DEVICES

Preparation

OBJECTIVES

The objectives are listed on the student page. Remind students to preview these objectives as a study guide to this major section.

OVERVIEW

The technique of putting n-type and p-type layers together to form diodes or transistors, and the concept of amplification are both discussed.

BRIDGING

The material in this section extends the concepts covered in Section 29.1.

1 Focus

Demonstration: Obtain a light-emitting diode (LED) of any kind, put it in series with a resistor of 200–400 ohms, and connect the combination to a flashlight battery or other source of about three volts DC. One way of hooking up the diode will cause it to light, the other way will not allow the diode to light. Explain to the class that this is an example of the one-way nature of conduction in a diode.

LAB WORKSHEET

Use the Lab Worksheet for Chapter 29 with this Physics Lab.

2 Teach

- In terms of the water analogy discussed in past chapters, a diode is like a flap valve that only allows water to go one way through a pipe.
- The arrow on a diode or transistor schematic symbol points in the direction of conventional (positive) current flow.
- The transistor is a current amplifier in which a small input current controls a much larger output current. The energy for the larger output current is provided by a battery or other source of potential difference in the circuit.
- The behavior of charges at a junction between different types of semiconductors is the key to the operation of a diode or transistor.
- Because diodes conduct well in only one direction, they are used for changing alternating current into direct current. This process is called rectification. Many types of circuits can do this; a particularly important type is known as a bridge rectifier.

Study Guide Master. To reinforce the concepts in this section, have the students complete the Study Guide Master for Section 29.2 from the Teacher Resource Package.

Laboratory Manual. Give students additional experience with diode characteristics by doing Lab 29.1 from the Laboratory Manual.

Assessment

Portfolio

Have students make a series circuit of a variable power supply (0 to about 12 V), a 220-Ω resistor, and a LED. Vary the output of the power supply from 1 to 12 V. Measure the current through the LED and the voltage across it for currents between 0 and 40 mA. Plot the results. Different students should use different colored LEDs and compare their results.

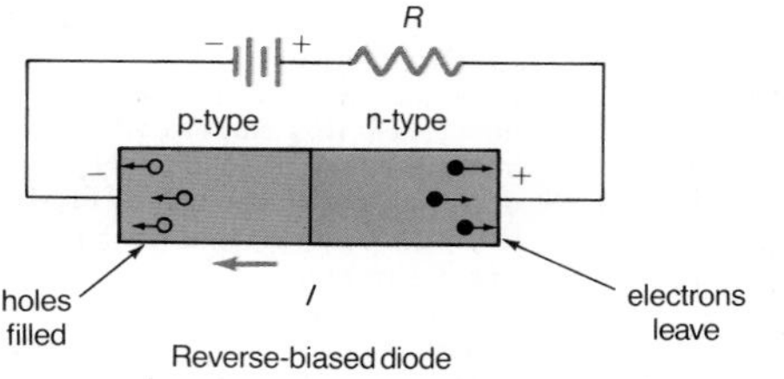

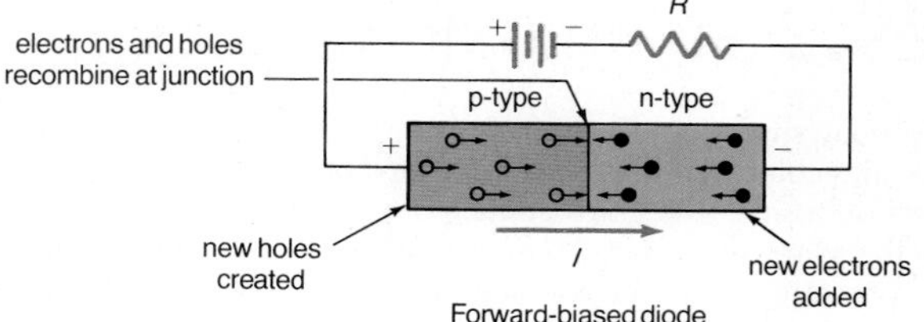

FIGURE 29–9. A reverse-biased diode (a); a forward-biased diode (b).

A diode with its n-type end connected to the positive battery terminal is reverse-biased. Almost no current flows.

When a diode is connected into a circuit in the way it is in Figure 29–9a, both the free electrons in the n-type semiconductor and the holes in the p-type semiconductor are attracted toward the battery. The width of the depletion layer is increased and no charge carriers meet. Almost no current flows through the diode—it acts like a very large resistor, almost an insulator. The diode is a **reverse-biased diode**.

If the battery is connected in the opposite direction, Figure 29–9b, charge carriers are pushed toward the junction. If the voltage of the battery is large enough, 0.6 V for a silicon diode, electrons reach the p-end and fill the holes. The depletion layer is eliminated and a current flows. The battery continues to supply electrons for the n-end. It removes electrons from the p-end, which is the same as supplying holes. With further increases in voltage from the battery, the current increases. The diode is a **forward-biased diode**.

Diodes can convert AC voltage to voltage with only one polarity.

Figure 29–10 shows the current through a silicon diode as a function of voltage. If the applied voltage is negative, the reverse-biased diode acts like a very high resistance; only a tiny current flows (about 10^{-11} A for a silicon diode). If the voltage is positive, the diode is forward-biased and acts like a small resistance, but not, however, one that obeys Ohm's law. One major use of a diode is to convert AC voltage to a voltage that has only one polarity. When a diode is used in a circuit such as that in Figure 29–12, it is called a rectifier. The arrow in the symbol for the diode shows the direction of conventional current flow.

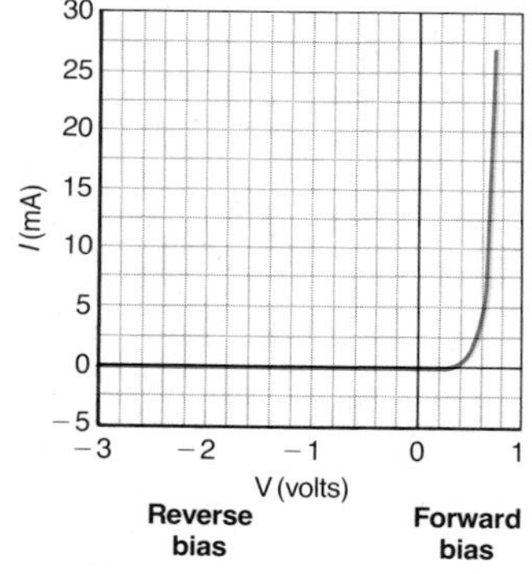

FIGURE 29–10. Current-voltage characteristics for a silicon junction diode.

Example Problem

A Diode in a Simple Circuit

A silicon diode, whose I/V characteristics are shown in Figure 29–10, is connected to a battery through a 470-Ω resistor. The battery forward-biases the diode and its voltage is adjusted until the diode current is 12 mA. **a.** Draw a schematic diagram of the circuit. **b.** What is the battery voltage?

Given: graph of V_d versus I, $R = 470\ \Omega$

Unknown: battery voltage, V

Basic equation: $V = V_d + IR$

Solution: At $I = 12$ mA, $V_d = 0.7$ V (from the graph)

$V = V_d + IR = 0.7\text{ V} + (470\ \Omega)(1.2 \times 10^{-2}\text{ A}) = 6.3\text{ V}.$

STUDY GUIDE MASTER

Use the Study Guide master for section 29.2.

LABORATORY MANUAL

Use Lab 29.1 with this section.

FIGURE 29–11. Light-emitting diodes (LEDs) are doped diodes that emit light when they are forward-biased.

Practice Problems

4. What battery voltage would be needed to have a current of 2.5 mA in the diode above?
5. A Ge diode has a voltage drop of 0.4 V when 12 mA flows through it. If the same 470-Ω resistor is used, what battery voltage is needed?

Diodes can do more than provide one-way paths for current. Diodes made from combinations of gallium and aluminum with arsenic and phosphorus emit light when they are forward-biased. When electrons reach the holes in the junction, they recombine and release the excess energy at the wavelengths of light. These diodes are called light-emitting diodes, or LEDs. Certain semiconductor crystals can be cut with parallel faces so the light waves reflect back and forth in the crystal. The result is a diode laser that emits a narrow beam of coherent, monochromatic light or infrared radiation. Diode lasers are used in CD players and supermarket bar-code scanners. They are compact, powerful light sources.

LEDs and semiconductor lasers are diodes that emit light.

Both CD players and supermarket scanners must detect the laser light reflected from the CD or bar-code. Diodes can detect light as well as emit it. A reverse-biased pn-junction diode is usually used as a light detector. Light falling on the junction creates pairs of electrons and holes. These are pulled toward the ends of the diode, resulting in a current flow that depends on the light intensity.

POCKET LAB

RED LIGHT

Make a series circuit with the power supply, 470-Ω resistor, and the red LED. Connect the short lead of the LED to the negative side of the power supply. Attach the other lead to the resistor. Hook the remaining resistor lead to the positive of the power supply. Slowly increase the voltage until the LED glows. Note the voltage setting on the power supply. What would happen if you reverse the direction of current? Why? Try it. Explain what happened.

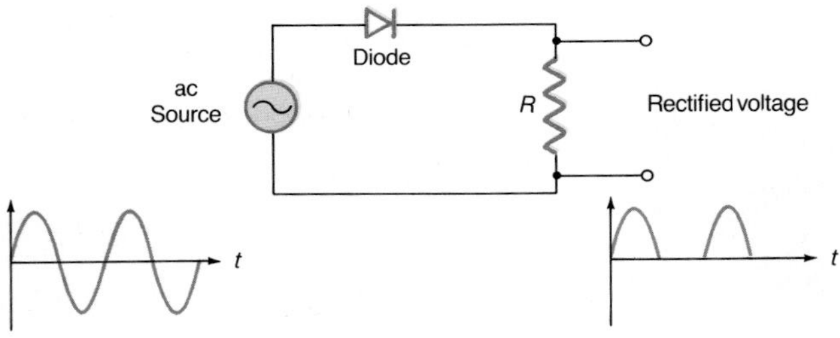

FIGURE 29–12. A diode used as a rectifier in a circuit.

Answers To
PRACTICE PROBLEMS

Have students refer to Appendix A of the Solutions Appendix for complete solutions to Practice Problems.

4. 1.8 V
5. 6.0 V

CONCEPT DEVELOPMENT

- Looking at the shape of the diode conduction curve, a diode conducts very poorly at voltages below about 0.6 V (the actual number depends on the construction of the diode) and then conducts very well after that. In effect, the diode has an "off" region and an "on" region as far as the passage of current is concerned. This makes the diode (and the transistor) ideal for representing the "off" and "on" of the binary number system used in computers.
- One of the best ways of fostering student understanding of diodes is to actually hook them up in circuits. The Radio Shack "200-in-1" Electronic Project Kit is excellent for this purpose. It uses flashlight batteries for power and has all needed meters and wires. Its possible circuits range from simple series circuits to signal generators.

POCKET LAB

RED LIGHT

Purpose: to discover the electrical property of a diode.
Materials: 0–12 VDC variable power supply; 470-ohm resistor; red LED; wires.
Outcome: The light will not glow when the current is reversed. The LED will only allow current to flow in one direction.

Physics and society

Answers To
DEVELOPING A VIEWPOINT

1. Most students would probably say that they do not think friendly computer viruses should be tolerated. They waste valuable computer time and the user's time. They can be quite costly for these reasons. But, by learning to destroy friendly viruses, a person can gain the expertise needed to destroy unfriendly viruses.

2. Banks could send their data over protected communication lines so that people cannot put foreign programs into the banks' computers. They could also make several back-up copies of their data so that if one copy is damaged, the others are available.

Teacher Resources: Dewdney, A. K. "Of Worms, Viruses, and Core War." *Scientific American* 260, March 1989, pages 110–113.
Greenberg, Ross M. "Know Thy Viral Enemy." *Byte* 14, June 1989, pages 275–280.
Stoll, Clifford. *The Cuckoo's Egg.* Doubleday, 1989.

Physics and society

COMPUTER VIRUSES—DANGEROUS ENEMIES OR HARMLESS PRANKS?

One of the most common uses of solid-state electronic devices is in microcomputers that are used almost everywhere in today's society. We depend on these computers in school, home, industry, and government. While most software designers write programs that do useful things, a few have used their skills to write computer viruses.

In biology, you learned that a virus requires a host cell in order to carry out its functions. In the course of using that cell, the virus frequently destroys the host cell. In the same way, a computer virus is a program that includes itself in other programs. A computer that contains a virus is said to be infected. The virus uses the host program to move from computer to computer. It can be written to destroy data or even the programs themselves. Some viruses even damage the mechanical components of the computer itself.

A computer virus is often spread by a floppy disk that is used on more than one computer. A virus on an infected computer might be copied onto any floppy used in that computer. When the floppy is used in another computer, the virus may be copied into the program on that computer. Most viruses infect only programs, not data files, so there is no danger in carrying data-like word-processing documents from one machine to another. Another common method for viruses to spread is by computer bulletin board systems (BBS). Internet, the world-wide network used to exchange messages and programs, has also been used to distribute viruses.

Some computer viruses have been called "friendly." For example, in 1987 a German student developed a program that sent a Christmas message over a German computer network. The virus displayed a greeting on the person's computer screen and then forwarded a copy of itself to everyone on the person's computer mailing list.

Some viruses have been designed to destroy data and programs on the infected computers. Some of these viruses cause no trouble until the computer's built in clock-calendar shows it is a certain date. Then the virus goes into action, destroying data and programs.

Programmers have designed virus detection programs that inspect programs and data files for every known virus. Floppies put into a computer protected by such a program are checked before they can do any damage. An operator of a BBS uses these programs to keep viruses from spreading. As soon as a new strain of virus is detected, the detection program can be updated to increase its protection. It is always possible, however, for a clever virus creator to do great damage before the protective "serum" can be devised.

DEVELOPING A VIEWPOINT

Read about computer viruses and come to class with answers to the following questions.

1. In your opinion, should friendly computer viruses be tolerated? Why or why not?

2. Suppose that an unfriendly computer virus were produced that could destroy all the data in the computers at your bank. How could your bank safeguard its financial data against such a virus?

SUGGESTED READINGS

Greenberg, Ross M. "Know Thy Viral Enemy." *Byte* 14, 275–280, June 1989.
Kerr, Susan. "A Secret No More." *Datamation* 35 (13), 53–55, July 1, 1989.
Marshall, Eliot. "The Scourge of Computer Viruses." *Science* 240, 133–134, April 8, 1988.

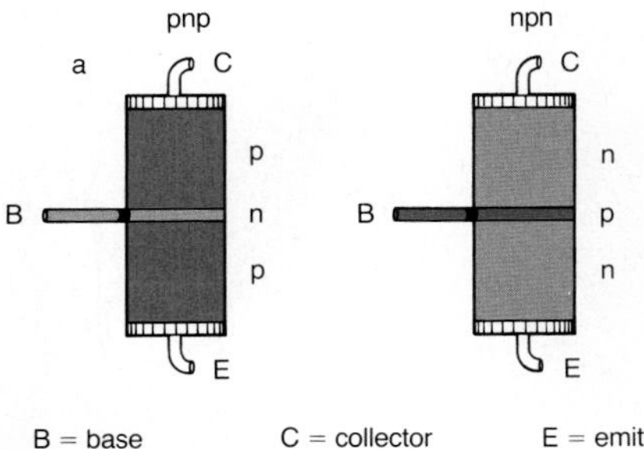

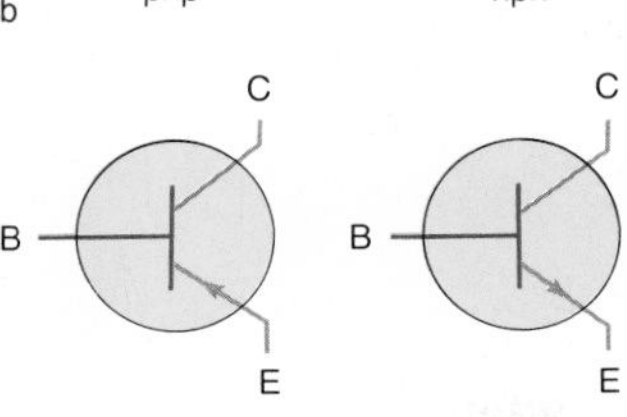

FIGURE 29–13. A pnp and an npn transistor (a); their circuit symbols (b).

Transistors and Integrated Circuits

A junction transistor consists of a region of one type of doped semiconductor sandwiched between layers of the opposite type. An **npn transistor** consists of n-type semiconductors surrounding a thin p-type layer. If the region in the center is n-type, then the device is called a **pnp transistor**. In either case, the central layer is called the **base**. The two surrounding regions are the **emitter** and the **collector**. The schematic symbols for the two transistor types are shown in Figure 29–13. The arrow is on the emitter and shows the direction of conventional current flow.

A transistor consists of three alternating n- and p-type layers called the collector, base, and emitter.

The operation of an npn transistor can be described using Figure 29–14. The pn-junctions in the transistor can be thought of as two back-to-back diodes. The battery on the right keeps the potential difference between collector and emitter, V_{CE}, positive. The base-collector diode is reverse-biased, so no current flows. The battery on the left is connected so that the base is more positive than the emitter. That is, the base-emitter diode is forward-biased. Conventional current flows in the direction of the arrow from the base into the emitter. Thus, electrons flow from the emitter into the base. But the base layer is very thin, often less than 10^{-6} m wide. As a result, most of the electrons pass through the base to the collector. The current through the collector, I_C, is much larger than the current through the base, I_B. The collector current causes a voltage drop across resistor R_C. Small changes in the voltage on the base produce large changes in the collector current, and thus changes in the voltage drop across R_C. As a result, the transistor amplifies small voltage changes into much larger changes. A pnp transistor works the same way, except the potentials of both batteries are reversed and holes carry the current in the transistor. The energy for amplification comes from battery V_C.

A small current through the base-emitter junction causes a large current from the collector to the emitter.

Transistors are used as amplifiers in almost every electronic instrument. In a tape player, the small voltage variations from the voltage induced in a coil by magnetized regions on the tape are amplified to move the speaker coil. In computers, small currents in the base-emitter circuits can turn on or turn off large currents in the collector-emitter circuits. Several transistors can be connected together to perform logic operations or to add numbers together. In this case, they act as fast switches, not amplifiers.

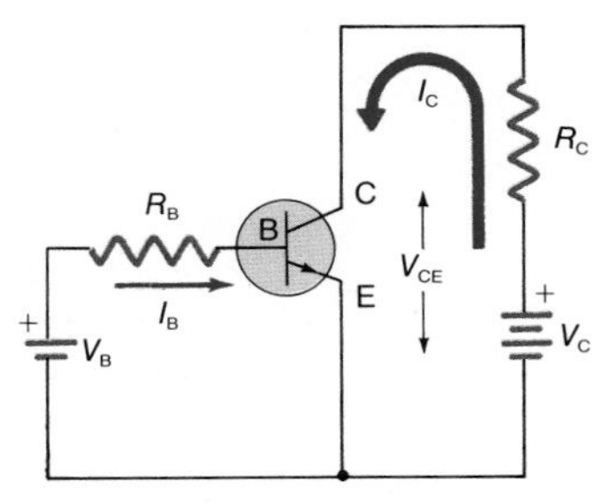

FIGURE 29–14. A transistor amplifying circuit.

CONCEPT DEVELOPMENT

Critical Thinking: Ask students why the base region in a transistor is made so thin. [So that charge can move more easily between the emitter and collector and the emitter and base.]

Enrichment: Have interested students investigate how diodes and transistors are used in the simplest of computer devices known as adders and half-adders. Students may first need to do some research into logic truth tables. (One good source is the sixth edition of *PSSC Physics*, D.C. Heath, especially Chapter 13.)

Enrichment Master. With this section, use the Enrichment Master, Diodes, from the Teacher Resource Package.

Guided Practice: Go over the Concept Review Problems on page 611 as a class exercise.

Independent Practice: Assign some appropriate Chapter Review Problems for homework, then spend time discussing them during the next class period.

ENRICHMENT MASTER

Use the Enrichment master for Chapter 29 with this section.

CHECKING FOR UNDERSTANDING

Initiate a discussion by posing the following questions to students: How is the construction of a transistor similar to a diode? [A transistor can be thought of as two back-to-back diodes.] What's the difference between an npn and a pnp transistor? [The former has two n regions separated by a thin p region and the latter has two p regions separated by a thin n region.]

RETEACHING

Review the idea of a depletion layer in a diode. Now go over the typical transistor structure in which the behavior of charge in the base is the primary controlling factor. Stress that the base is thinner and more lightly doped than the two surrounding semiconductors. Go over Figure 29–14, emphasizing the difference in the size of the two currents.

INDEPENDENT PRACTICE/ EXTENSION

Refer to the Assignment Guide below for additional questions and problems for independent practice.

Laboratory Manual. Give students additional experience with integrated circuit logic devices by doing Lab 29.2 from the Laboratory Manual.

3 Close

CONVERGENT QUESTION

Ask students to explain why free electrons in an npn transistor can flow from the emitter to the collector without many of them falling into holes in the base (a p region). [The base is very thin and lightly doped, so not many holes are there. Further, some electrons that fall into holes in the base are pulled out by the base-to-emitter voltage.]

FIGURE 29–15. A piece of ultra pure silicon (a) forms the basis for an integrated circuit chip (b).

a

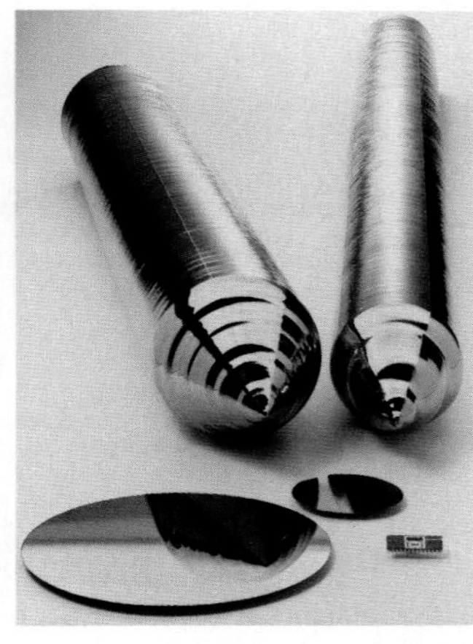

b

The Inside Dope

An integrated circuit, or a microchip, consists of thousands of transistors, diodes, resistors, and conductors each no more than a few micrometers across. All these components can be made by doping silicon in the proper way. A microchip starts with an extremely pure single crystal of silicon, 10 cm in diameter and half a meter long. It is sliced by a diamond-coated saw into wafers less than a millimeter thick. The circuit is then built layer by layer on the surface of this wafer. By a photographic process, most of the wafer's surface is covered by a protective layer, with a pattern of selected areas left uncovered so it can be doped appropriately. The wafer is placed in a chamber out of which almost all the air has been pumped. Vapors of a dopant such as arsenic enter the machine, doping the wafer in the unprotected regions. By controlling the amount of exposure, the engineer can control the conductivity of the exposed regions of the chip. This process creates resistors, as well as one of the two layers of a diode or one of the three layers of a transistor. The protective layer is removed, and another one with a different pattern of exposed areas is applied. Now the wafer is exposed to another dopant, often gallium, producing pn junctions. If a third layer is added, npn transistors are formed. The wafer may also be exposed to oxygen to produce areas of silicon dioxide insulation. A layer exposed to aluminum vapors can produce a pattern of thin conducting pathways between the resistors, diodes, and transistors. Hundreds of identical circuits, usually called chips, are produced on a single 10-cm diameter wafer at one time. The chips are then sliced apart and tested, have wires attached, and are mounted in a plastic protective body. They are sold for a few dollars or even less.

An integrated circuit is constructed on a slice of a single crystal of silicon.

A single exposure to dopants produces resistors. Two exposures result in diodes, three in transistors.

Semiconductor electronics illustrates how the sciences and engineering work together. Physicists gain an understanding of the motion of electrons and holes in semiconductors. Physicists and chemists together learn how to add precisely-controlled amounts of impurities to extremely pure silicon. Engineers develop means of mass producing chips containing thousands of miniaturized diodes and transistors. Together their efforts have revolutionized our world.

Connect to CHEMISTRY

In the process of making semiconductors, chemists and materials scientists are challenged to produce materials purer than previously thought possible. Traditional chemical methods leave impurities at the part per thousand (ppt) level. Semiconductors must be purified to the part per billion (ppb) level. One method used to reach these levels is to melt a region of a crystal and let it slowly recrystallize. Crystallization is a natural means of purification. If a crystal forms slowly, it pushes impurities to its edge. Thus, if a short length of the rod-like crystal of silicon shown in Figure 29–15 is heated in a vacuum and allowed to cool slowly, any remaining impurities will migrate to the surface of the rod where they can be removed.

The large rod in Figure 29–15b has a mass of 915 g. If the fraction of atoms that are not silicon is 1.0 ppb, how many impurity atoms are there in the rod? [The molecular weight of Si is 28.1 g/mole, so the rod contains 32.6 moles, or 1.96×10^{25} atoms. Since 1.0 ppb is one atom in 19^9, there are 1.96×10^{16} impurity atoms.]

CONCEPT REVIEW

2.1 Compare the resistance of a pn-junction diode when it is forward-biased to when it is reverse-biased.

2.2 Does a light-emitting diode produce light no matter which battery terminal is connected to the p-end of the diode? If not, which terminal should be connected to make the diode light?

2.3 If the diode of Figure 29–10 is forward-biased by a battery and a series resistor so that more than about 10 mA of current flows, the voltage drop is always about 0.7 V. If the battery voltage is increased by one volt,

a. does the voltage across the diode or the voltage across the resistor increase? by how much?

b. does the current through the resistor increase? by how much?

2.4 **Critical Thinking:** Could you replace an npn transistor with two separate diodes with their p-terminals connected together? Explain.

CHAPTER 29 REVIEW

SUMMARY

29.1 Conduction in Solids

- Electrical conduction in materials is explained by the band theory of solids.
- Electrons can have only certain values of energy called allowed energy levels.
- In solids, the allowed energy levels are spread into broad bands. The bands are separated by values of energies that electrons may not have called the forbidden gap.
- In conductors, electrons can move because the band of allowed energy levels is only partially filled.
- Electrons in metals have a very fast random motion. A potential difference across the metal causes a very slow drift of the electrons.
- In insulators, electrons are bound to atoms. More energy is needed to move them than is available.
- Conduction in semiconductors is usually the result of doping pure crystals with small numbers of impurity atoms.
- N-type semiconductors conduct by means of free electrons, while in p-type semiconductors, conduction is by means of "holes."

29.2 Electronic Devices

- Diodes conduct charges in one direction only and can be used to produce current that flows in one direction only.
- A transistor is constructed of three alternate layers of n- and p-type semiconductors and can amplify or increase current changes.

KEY TERMS

bands
forbidden gaps
band theory
electron gas model
conduction band
hole
intrinsic semiconductor
extrinsic semiconductor
dopants
donor electron
n-type semiconductor
electron acceptor
p-type semiconductor
diode
pn-junction diode
depletion layer
reverse-biased diode
forward-biased diode
npn transistor
pnp transistor
base
emitter
collector

CONCEPT REVIEW ANSWERS

2.1 It conducts much better when forward-biased, so its resistance is much smaller when forward-biased than when reverse-biased.

2.2 The LED must be forward-biased, so the + terminal should be connected to the p-end.

2.3 **a.** Because the voltage across the diode is always 0.7 V, the voltage across the resistor increases by 1 V. **b.** The current increases by $I = (1\text{ V})/R$.

2.4 **Critical Thinking:** No. The p-region of an npn transistor must be very thin so that electrons can pass through. When p-terminals of two diodes are connected, this common p-region acts as the p-region of an npn transistor in regard to biasing only. The necessary wires and terminals make the region too thick for electrons to pass through.

CLOSING CHAPTER 29

Review Summary statements and Key Terms with your students.

ASSESSMENT

Vocabulary Review Master, Teacher Resource Package. Use this master to check students' understanding of Key Terms.

Evaluation Masters. Use Parts A and B of the Chapter Evaluation Masters from the Teacher Resource Package to test qualitative chapter objectives. Use Parts C and D to test quantitative chapter objectives.

29:2 ASSIGNMENT GUIDE

	PRACTICE	EXTENSION
CHAPTER REVIEW pp. 611–613		
· Reviewing Concepts	4–6	
· Applying Concepts		8–10
· Problems*	8–14	7
APPENDIX B PROBLEM*		
· Chapter 29, p. 708	3–5	

* Complete solutions to all Chapter Review and Appendix problems appear in the Problems and Solutions Manual.

LABORATORY MANUAL

Use Lab 29.2 with this section.

REVIEW MASTER

Use the Vocabulary Review master for Chapter 29 with this section.

EVALUATION MASTER

Use the Chapter Evaluation master for Chapter 29 with this section.

Answers To

REVIEWING CONCEPTS

1. The energy levels of a single atom have discrete and unique values. The energy levels in a crystal have a small range around the values found in a single atom.
2. A higher temperature gives electrons additional energy, permitting more electrons to reach the conductive band.
3. positively-charged holes
4. Yes. One way, you forward-bias the diode; the other way, you reverse-bias it.
5. The arrowhead shows the direction of the conventional current flow.
6.

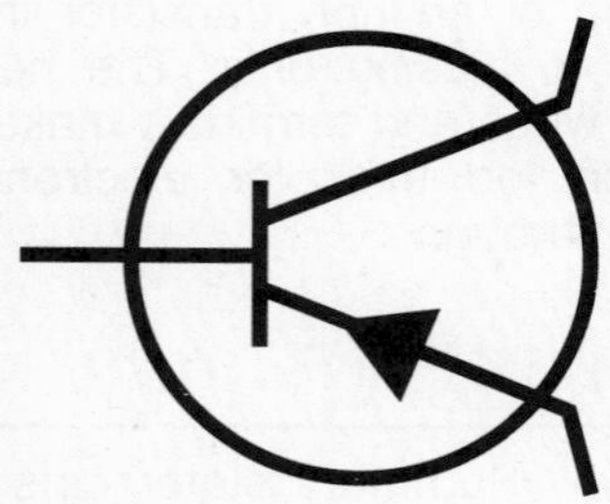

Answers To

APPLYING CONCEPTS

1. Graphite behaves like silicon.
2. a material with an 8 eV wide gap
3. The 8 eV-gap would require 8 eV of energy.
4. If the gap is small, the solid will be a semiconductor. If the gap is large, it will be an insulator.
5. Intrinsic semiconductors have lower conductivity, and therefore are better insulators.
6. The phosphorus will be a donor and the conduction will occur with electrons.
7. Holes can move around freely and because there are about a million silicon atoms per gallium atom, most will be on silicon.
8. The diode will have a lower resistance when it is forward-biased.
9. higher potential, more positive
10. You make a resistor, because there is no junction.

REVIEWING CONCEPTS

1. How do the energy levels in a crystal of an element differ from the energy levels in a single atom of that element?
2. Why does heating a semiconductor increase its conductivity?
3. What is the main current carrier in a p-type semiconductor?
4. An ohmmeter is an instrument that places a potential difference across a device to be tested, measures the current flow, and displays the resistance of the device. If you connect an ohmmeter across a diode, will the current you measure depend on which end of the diode was connected to the positive terminal of the ohmmeter? Explain.
5. What is the significance of the arrowhead at the emitter in a transistor circuit symbol?
6. Redraw Figure 29–14 as a pnp transistor.

APPLYING CONCEPTS

1. The resistance of graphite decreases as the temperature rises. Does graphite conduct electricity like copper or like silicon?
2. Which of the following materials would make a better insulator: one with a forbidden gap 8 eV wide, 3 eV wide, or one with no gap?
3. In which of the three materials in the previous problem would it be most difficult to remove an electron from an atom?
4. How does the size of the gap between the conduction band and the next lower energy band determine whether a solid will be a semiconductor or an insulator?
5. Which would make a better insulator, an extrinsic or an intrinsic semiconductor? Explain.
6. Silicon is doped with phosphorus. Will the dopant atoms be donors or acceptors? Will the semiconductor conduct with holes or electrons?
7. Doping silicon with gallium produces a p-type semiconductor. Why are there holes mainly on silicon atoms rather than on the gallium atoms that caused the holes to be produced?
8. Carol uses an ohmmeter to measure the resistance of a pn-junction diode. Would the meter show a higher resistance when the diode is forward-biased or reverse-biased?
9. If the ohmmeter in the previous problem shows the lower resistance, is the ohmmeter lead connected to the arrow side of the diode at a higher or lower potential than the lead connected to the other side?
10. If you dope pure germanium with gallium alone, do you produce a resistor, a diode, or a transistor?

PROBLEMS

29.1 Conduction in Solids

1. The forbidden gap in silicon is 1.1 eV. Electromagnetic waves striking the silicon cause electrons to move from the valence band to the conduction band. What is the longest wavelength of radiation that could excite an electron in this way?
   Chapter 27 gives $E = \frac{1240 \text{ eV·nm}}{\lambda}$, where the energy is in eV and the wavelength in nm.
2. A light-emitting diode (LED) produces green light with a wavelength of 550 nm when an electron moves from the conduction band to the valence band. Find the width of the forbidden gap in eV in this diode.
3. How many free electrons exist in a cubic centimeter of sodium? Its density is 0.971 g/cm^3, atomic weight is 22.99 g/mole, and there is one free electron per atom.
4. At a temperature of 0°C, thermal energy frees 1.1×10^{12} e$^-$/cm^3 in pure silicon. The density of silicon is 2.33 g/cm^3 and the atomic weight of silicon is 28.09 g/mole. What is the fraction of atoms that have free electrons?
5. ▶ Use a periodic table to determine which of the following elements could be added to germanium to make a p-type semiconductor: B, C, N, P, Si, Al, Ge, Ga, As, In, Sn, Sb.
6. ▶ Which of the elements listed in the previous problem would produce an n-type semiconductor?

29.2 Electronic Devices

7. ▶ Which element or elements could be used as the second dopant when making a diode, if the first dopant was boron?

8. The potential drop across a glowing LED is about 1.2 V. In Figure 29–16, the potential drop across the resistor is the difference between the battery voltage and LED potential drop, 6.0 V − 1.2 V = 4.8 V. What is the current through **a.** the LED? **b.** the resistor?

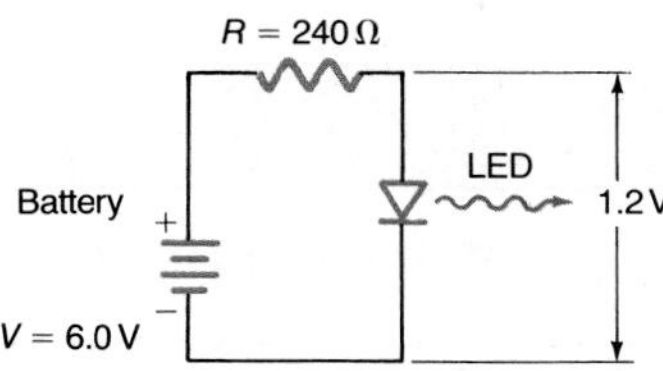

FIGURE 29–16. Use with Problems 8 and 9.

9. Jon wanted to raise the current through the LED in the previous problem to 30 mA so that it would glow brighter. Assume that the potential drop across the LED is still 1.2 V. What resistor should be used?

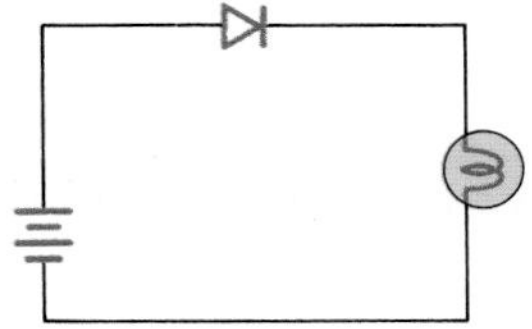

FIGURE 29–17. Use with Problem 10.

10. Figure 29–17 shows a battery, diode, and bulb connected in series so that the bulb lights. Note that the diode is forward-biased. Describe whether the bulb in each of the pictured circuits is lighted.

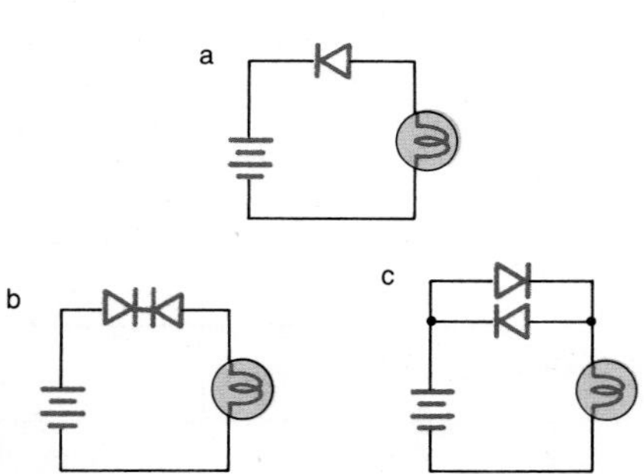

11. For each pictured circuit, tell whether lamp L_1, lamp L_2, both, or neither, is lighted.

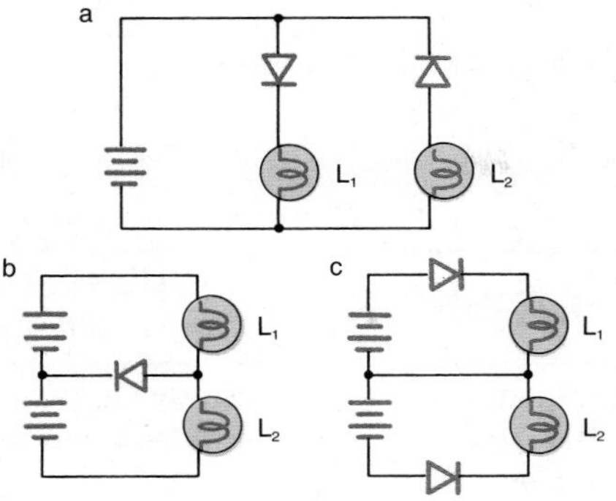

12. Draw a circuit having one 6.0-V battery, two LEDs, and two resistors. One LED should have a current of 30 mA, the other 20 mA.
13. A silicon diode whose I/V characteristics are shown in Figure 29–10 is connected to a battery through a 270-Ω resistor. The battery forward-biases the diode and its voltage is adjusted until the diode current is 15 mA. What is the battery voltage?
14. What bulbs are lighted in the circuit of Figure 29–18 when
    a. switch 1 is closed and switch 2 is open?
    b. switch 2 is closed and switch 1 is open?

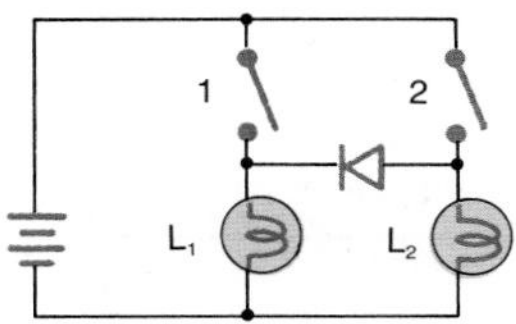

FIGURE 29–18. Use with Problem 14.

THINKING PHYSIC-LY

A silicon solar cell consists of a thin, about 0.5 μm, n-type layer formed over a p-type base. Suggest a reason for the exposed layer being so thin that most of the light will penetrate the layer and be absorbed by atoms in or very near the pn junction.

Answers To
PROBLEMS

Complete solutions for all Chapter Review Problems can be found in the Problems and Solutions Manual.

1. 1.1 μm (infrared)
2. 2.25 eV
3. 2.54×10^{22} free e^-/cm^3
4. 2.2×10^{-11} e^-/atom
5. B, Al, Ga, In
6. N, P, As, Sb
7. N, P, As, Sb
8. **a.** 20 mA
b. 20 mA
9. 160 Ω
10. **a.** no
b. no
c. yes
11. **a.** L_1 is on.
b. Both lamps are on.
c. L_1 is on.
12. Refer to Problems and Solutions Manual.
13. 4.8 V
14. **a.** light 1 only
b. both lights 1 and 2

Answer To
THINKING PHYSIC-LY

A greater number of atoms receive energy from the light, improving the conductivity.

CHAPTER

30 The Nucleus

PLANNING GUIDE (6 class sessions)

CONTENTS	TEXT FEATURES	TEACHER RESOURCE PACKAGE	OTHER COMPONENTS
30.1 Radioactivity, pp. 616–624 (3 Class Sessions) • Description of the Nucleus • Isotopes • Radioactive Decay • Nuclear Reactions and Equations • Half-Life	**Physics Lab:** Heads Up, p. 623 **Pocket Lab:** Background Radiation, p. 618 **Concept Review,** p. 624	**Study Guide:** Radioactivity **Physics Lab Data Sheet:** Heads Up **Enrichment Master:** Half-Life **Critical Thinking Master:** Distance and Radioactivity **Reteaching Master:** One Element Changes into Another **Transparency Worksheet:** α, β, γ Particles	**Laboratory Manual:** Lab 30.1 Radiation Properties **Transparency 45:** α, β, γ Particles
30.2 The Building Blocks of Matter, pp. 624–635 (3 Class Sessions) • Nuclear Bombardment • Linear Accelerators • The Synchrotron • Particle Detectors • The Fundamental Particles • Particles and Antiparticles • The Quark Model of Nucleons	**Physics and Society:** A Daily Dose of Radon, p. 632 **Pocket Lab:** Follow the Tracks, p. 627 **Concept Review,** p. 635	**Study Guide:** The Building Blocks of Matter **Transparency Worksheet:** Subatomic Particles	**Transparency 46:** Subatomic Particles
Chapter Review, pp. 635–637	Summary Key Terms Reviewing Concepts Applying Concepts Problems Using a Graphing Calculator Thinking Physic-ly	**Vocabulary Review** **Chapter Test**	**Test Bank**

SUPPLEMENTARY MATERIALS

SOFTWARE	AUDIOVISUAL	BOOKS/MAGAZINES
Atomic Physics, Cross (Apple II, IBM PC). *Atomic Structure 2,* Queue Inc. (Apple II). *Radioactive Decay,* Queue, Inc. (Apple II).	Video: *The Mechanical Universe and Beyond: From Atoms to Quarks* and *The Quantum Mechanical Universe,* Films Inc. Filmstrip: *Atoms and Atomic Energy,* Clearvue. *Models of the Atom,* AVNA Media.	Boslough, John. "Worlds Within the Atom." *National Geographic,* May 1985, pp. 634–663. Brown, L. M., Dresden, M., and Hoddeson, L. "Pions to Quarks: Particle Physics in the 1950s." *Physics Today,* November 1988, p. 56. "Fundamental Particles and Interactions, A Wall Chart of Modern Physics, By the Fundamental Particles and Interactions Chart Committee." *The Physics Teacher,* December 1988, pp. 556–565. Garrett, John S. "Modification of the Classic M & M® Decay Experiment." *The Physics Teacher,* December 1990, p. 611. Peterson, Ivars. "Beyond the Z." *Science News,* September 29, 1990, pp. 204–206.

PROBLEM CORRELATION

CONCEPTS	CHAPTER REVIEW			PROBLEMS APPENDIX
	Reviewing Concepts	Applying Concepts	Problems	
30.1 Radioactivity				
Description of the Nucleus	1	3	1,2	
Isotopes		2	3,4	1,2,3
Radioactive Decay	2,3,4,5	1,4,5		
Nuclear Reactions and Equations	6		5,6,7,8,9,10,**11**	4,5,6,7,**8,9,**10,11,**12**
Half-Life		6,7	12,13,14,**15,16,17**	
30.2 The Building Blocks of Matter				
Nuclear Bombardment				
Linear Accelerators	7			
The Synchrotron			**18**	
Particle Detectors	8			
The Fundamental Particles	9		19	
Particles and Antiparticles	10,11	8	20,21	**13,14**
The Quark Model of Nucleons				15,16

ACTIVITY AND DEMONSTRATION MATERIALS

PHYSICS LAB	POCKET LAB	DEMONSTRATIONS
Page 623 20 pennies graph paper	Pages 618, 627 Geiger counter paper tape simple cloud chamber alcohol 2 pounds dry ice alpha source on needle small neodymium magnet (optional)	

EXTENSION PROJECTS

LIBRARY RESEARCH

1. Boltwood Method
Investigate the Boltwood Method. How has a knowledge of radioactivity made estimates of the age of Earth more accurate?

HANDS–ON

2. Radiology Lab
Make an appointment to visit a radiology lab. Find out what types of tests (X rays, radioisotopes, etc.) are run and what safety precautions are taken by technicians.

STUDENT READINGS

Guillen, Michael. “The Paradox of Antimatter.” *Science Digest,* February 1985.

McGeachy, Frank. “Radioactive Decay—An Analog.” *The Physics Teacher,* January 1988.

Monastersky, Richard. “Coral Corrects Carbon Dating Problems.” *Science News,* June 9, 1990.

Myers, Stephen, and Picasso, Emilio. “The LEP Collider.” *Scientific American,* July 1990.

Nash, J. Madeleine. “Real Gone Neutrinos.” *Time,* September 10, 1990.

Rees, John R. “The Stanford Linear Collider.” *Scientific American,* October 1989.

Chapter 30

The Nucleus

CHAPTER OVERVIEW

Theme Development: Mathematical models are extended from the conceptual quantum models introduced in previous chapters. Explaining atomic structures and relationships in terms of numbers reveals themes of randomness, scale, symmetry, and conservation among fundamental particles during nuclear reactions: how half-lives describe radioactive decay; the vast scale of significant energy quantities over which quantum research operates; particle-antiparticle symmetry; conservation principles apparent in balancing nuclear equations.

MISCONCEPTIONS

Students often believe that a radioactive substance will be gone in two half-lives, that atoms disappear as a result of radioactive decay, and that all radioisotopes decay in the same time.

KEY TERMS

activity
α (alpha) decay
antiparticle
atomic mass unit
atomic number
baryon
β (beta) decay
bubble chamber
γ (gamma) decay
Geiger-Mueller tube
gluon
graviton
half-life
isotope
lepton
linear accelerator
mass number
meson
neutrino
neutron
nuclear reaction
nuclide
pair production
positron
proton
quark
radioactive
radioactive decay
spark chamber
synchrotron
transmutation
weak boson
Wilson cloud chamber

CHAPTER

30 The Nucleus

◀ Phantom Tracks

In the highlighted box are two particles moving in opposite spiral paths in a magnetic field. The curvatures are about the same, so their momenta must be equal. What might cause this pair of paths?

Chapter Outline

Rutherford not only established the existence of the nucleus, but he did some of the early experiments to discover its structure. Modern accelerators and detectors have given physicists the ability to study nuclei and the particles that compose them with much greater precision. The chapter-opening photo shows trails of subatomic particles moving to the left in a bubble chamber. These charged particles are bent by a magnetic field. The direction of the curve shows their charge. The faster they are moving, the less the bend. Thus their momentum can be determined as well. We will see how this and other tools have enlarged our knowledge of the ultimate building-blocks of matter.

✓ Concept Check

The following terms or concepts from earlier chapters are important for a good understanding of this chapter. If you are not familiar with them, you should review them before studying this chapter.

- conservation of energy, Chapter 11
- electric force on charged particles, Chapter 20
- magnetic force on charged particle, Chapter 24
- Rutherford scattering, structure of the atom, Chapter 28

615

Introducing The Chapter

Phantom Tracks

Using The Photo: Charged subatomic particles can be detected in a bubble chamber. When a charged particle passes through the liquid it leaves a trail of tiny bubbles that can be photographed. You might give students a hint about the photo question by reviewing the force on a charged particle in a magnetic field, page 597. For a detailed explanation of the photo question, refer students to page 631.

✓ Concept Check

Make sure students have a clear understanding of the concepts taught in Chapters 11, 20, 24, and 28 that are listed in the Concept Check. Students with a good knowledge of conservation of energy, electric and magnetic force on charged particles, Rutherford scattering, and atomic structure will be prepared to assimilate the principles of the nucleus discussed in this chapter. While not required, the supplemental lesson on Special Relativity will give background information that will help students gain a deeper understanding of the content of this chapter and Chapter 31.

Assessment Options

Portfolio Assessment
Extension 1 and 2, TWE, p. 614b
Enrichment, TWE, p. 628
Portfolio Assessment, TWE, p. 629
Developing a Viewpoint, p. 632

Performance Assessment
Pocket Labs, pp. 618, 627
Physics Lab, p. 623
Pocket Lab Assessment, TWE, p. 618
Activity, TWE, p. 621

Content Assessment
Self Assessment: Practice Problems, pp. 618, 621, 622, 631
Critical Thinking, TWE, p. 621
Assessment, Critical Thinking, TWE, p. 623
Checking for Understanding, TWE, p. 633
Convergent Question, TWE, p. 634
Concept Reviews, pp. 624, 635
Chapter Review, pp. 635–637
Supplemental Problems, pp. 708–709

Group Assessment
Activities for group assessment occur with Cooperative Learning and lab activities.

Laboratory Options

STUDENT EDITION
Physics Lab
Heads Up 623
Pocket Labs
Background Radiation 618
Follow the Tracks 627

TEACHER EDITION
Activities
Cooperative Learning 620, 621, 628

LABORATORY MANUAL
Radiation Properties Lab 30.1

30.1 RADIOACTIVITY

Preparation

OBJECTIVES

The objectives are listed on the student page. Remind students to preview these objectives as a study guide to this major section.

OVERVIEW

Many details of the nucleus are discussed, including particles in the nucleus, differences in nuclei of the same element (isotopes), spontaneous breakdown of nuclei, nuclear reactions, and notation for identifying nuclei.

BRIDGING

Topics from preceding chapters include mass spectrometer, charge and its conservation, and mass and its conservation.

1 Focus

Emphasize to students that the variety of nuclei is much greater than that of elements, which is only about 100. In fact, there are almost 2000 different nuclides. Display a wall chart version of the chart of the nuclides to help illustrate.

2 Teach

CONCEPT DEVELOPMENT

- Older books or references may refer to the new unified atomic mass unit (u) as the atomic mass unit (amu). For all practical purposes they are the same.
- It might be helpful to compare nuclear reactions that give off energy and nuclear reactions that require the addition of energy to the chemical definitions of exothermic and endothermic, respectively.

Objectives

- **define atomic number and mass number; find the charge and mass of a nucleus.**
- **define an isotope and a nuclide; calculate the number of neutrons, protons, and electrons in an isotope.**
- **describe three modes of radioactive decay; explain the changes in atomic number or mass number for each mode; write equations for the three forms of radioactive decay.**
- **define half-life; calculate the amount of material and its activity remaining after a given number of half-lives.**

30.1 RADIOACTIVITY

After the discovery of radioactivity by Becquerel in 1896, many scientists studied this new phenomenon. In Canada, Ernest Rutherford and Frederick Soddy discovered that uranium atoms were changed, or transmuted, to other atoms. The French scientists Marie and Pierre Curie discovered the new elements polonium and radium in samples of radioactive uranium. One of the first results of radioactivity studies was an understanding of the composition of the atomic nucleus.

Description of the Nucleus

Rutherford's analysis of his scattering experiments predicted that the number of α particles deflected through a given angle should be proportional to the square of the charge of the nucleus of the atom. At that time, only the mass of an atom was known. The number of electrons, and thus the charge of the nucleus, was unknown.

Rutherford and his co-workers experimented with sheets of carbon, aluminum, and gold. In each case, the charge of the nucleus was found to be roughly half the atomic mass times the elementary unit of charge. Since each electron carries one elementary charge, the number of electrons in an atom is equal to roughly half the atomic mass number. The carbon nucleus has a charge of 6, so the carbon atom must contain 6 electrons. Using a similar argument, aluminum contains 13 electrons and gold 79 electrons.

Protons are the positively-charged particles in a nucleus.

The atom is neutral, so the nucleus must contain positive charge. The **proton** is the name given to the nucleus of the hydrogen atom. The proton is positively charged with one unit of elementary charge. Its mass is approximately one **atomic mass unit**, u. The number of protons in a nucleus, which, in a neutral atom, is equal to the number of electrons surrounding the nucleus, is called the atom's **atomic number**, Z. All atoms of a given element contain the same number of protons. Thus carbon always has 6 protons and aluminum 13. Their atomic numbers are $Z = 6$ for carbon and $Z = 13$ for aluminum.

The atomic number is the number of protons in the nucleus.

FIGURE 30–1. Many countries have issued commemorative stamps documenting the history of radioactivity.

TEACHER F.Y.I.

Rutherford always needed to visualize his work. After his gold foil experiment, which contradicted atomic theory of the day, Rutherford had a large model made to demonstrate the deflection of the alpha particles by the nucleus. A heavy electromagnet was suspended on 30 feet of wire to function as a pendulum, and another electromagnet was placed on a table. When the suspended magnet grazed the surface of the stationary magnet and matched polarities, it was deflected into a parabolic path according to the angle of approach and velocity, as had the alpha particles in his experiment.

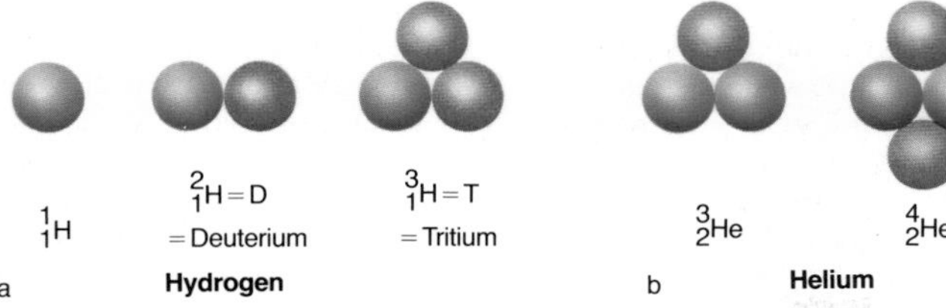

FIGURE 30–2. The isotopes of hydrogen (a) and helium (b). Protons are blue and neutrons are red.

The mass of the carbon atom, however, is the mass of 12 protons, not 6. To account for the excess mass in the nucleus, Rutherford postulated the existence of a neutral particle with a mass of a proton. In 1932 James Chadwick, a student of Rutherford, demonstrated the existence of this particle, called the neutron. A **neutron** is a particle with no charge and with a mass almost equal to that of the proton.

Neutrons are uncharged particles in the nucleus.

The nucleus of every atom except hydrogen contains both neutrons and protons. The sum of the numbers of protons and neutrons is equal to the **mass number**, *A*. The mass of the nucleus is approximately equal to the mass number, *A*, multiplied by the atomic mass unit (u), 1.66×10^{-27} kg. The mass of the nucleus in atomic mass units is approximately equal to the atomic mass number. The mass number of carbon is 12, while that of aluminum is 27. Elements with 20 or fewer protons have roughly equal numbers of protons and neutrons. Heavier elements, however, contain more neutrons than protons.

The mass number is the sum of the numbers of protons and neutrons in a nucleus.

How large is the nucleus? Rutherford had found that the nucleus is a very small body in the center of the atom. Today it is known that the nucleus is almost spherical and has a diameter ranging from 2.6 fm (2.6×10^{-15} m) in hydrogen to 16 fm in uranium.

Atoms with the same atomic number but different mass numbers are called isotopes.

Isotopes

Careful measurements of the mass of boron atoms consistently yielded 10.8 u. If, as was thought, the nucleus is made up of protons and neutrons, each with a mass of approximately 1 u, then the total mass of any atom should be near a whole number.

The puzzle of atomic masses that were not integral numbers of atomic mass units was solved with the mass spectrometer. The mass spectrometer demonstrated that an element could have atoms with different masses. For example, when analyzing a pure sample of neon, not one, but two spots appeared on the film of the spectrometer. The two spots were produced by neon atoms of different masses. One variety of neon atom was found to have a mass of 20 u, the second type a mass of 22 u. All neon atoms have 10 protons in the nucleus and 10 electrons in the atom. One kind of neon atom, however, has 10 neutrons in its nucleus, while the other has 12 neutrons. The two kinds of atoms are called **isotopes** of neon. The nucleus of an isotope is called a **nuclide**. All nuclides of an element have the same number of protons, but different numbers of neutrons, Figure 30–2. All isotopes of an element have the same number of electrons around the nucleus and behave the same chemically.

HELP WANTED

NUCLEAR ENGINEER

Several federal departments need bright, conscientious nuclear engineers to continue to work on refining the production and distribution process of nuclear energy to make it the world's best and safest energy source. The key word is safety.

If you have an advanced degree, a creative yet logical approach to problem solving, a desire to be part of an exciting team, and the ability to help convince the public about the future of our industry, Uncle Sam wants you! For information contact:
American Nuclear Society, 555 North Kensington Avenue, La-Grange Park, IL 60525

CONCEPT DEVELOPMENT

- The recently launched NASA satellite GRO (Gamma Ray Observatory) is observing gamma rays from quasars, pulsars, and black holes.
- The term *isotopes* comes from the Greek words meaning *same place*, since they are at the same place in the periodic table.

Study Guide Master. To reinforce the concepts in this section, have the students complete the Study Guide Master for Section 30.1 from the Teacher Resource Package.

TEACHER 

Rutherford and most other physicists first thought that the nucleus consisted of protons and electrons. This hypothesis was supported by the emission of electrons from the nucleus in beta decay. Rutherford suggested in 1920 that the proton and electron were so tightly bound that they could be considered a single particle, which he named the neutron. This model was given up for several reasons. Among them are that wave mechanics and the uncertainty principle show that an electron confined to a region the size of a proton has much greater kinetic energy than that exhibited by beta particles. Also, the angular momentum and magnetic moments of nuclei cannot be explained with a proton-electron model. The discovery of the neutron in 1932 laid this hypothesis to rest. Hans Bethe remarked that everything before 1932 was "the prehistory of nuclear physics, and from 1932 on, the history of nuclear physics."

POCKET LAB

BACKGROUND RADIATION

Purpose: to demonstrate that we live in a sea of radiation.

Materials: Geiger counter; paper; tape.

Outcome: The count rate is random, with an uncertainty equal to the square root of the number of counts recorded. Thus, two counts are statistically different only if they differ by several multiples of the uncertainty in each count. You may have to count for an hour or more to determine if you have a difference. Background radiation consists primarily of gamma rays.

Answers To

PRACTICE PROBLEMS

Have students refer to Appendix A of the Solutions Appendix for complete solutions to Practice Problems.

1. 7 neutrons
2. 142 neutrons; 143 neutrons; 146 neutrons
3. 120 neutrons
4. $^{1}_{1}H$, $^{2}_{1}H$, $^{3}_{1}H$

CONCEPT DEVELOPMENT

• Marie Curie gave the phenomenon of radioactivity its name. For a while the rays were called Becquerel rays.

• The theory of radioactivity can predict what happens to a large number of atoms; that is, a certain fraction of them will decay. However, the theory cannot tell us *which* particular atoms will decay. In other words, we have collective certainty but individual ignorance.

POCKET LAB

BACKGROUND RADIATION

Place a Geiger counter on the lab table far away from any sources of radiation. Turn the counter on and record the number of counts for a three-minute interval. Tape a piece of paper around the tube and repeat the measurements. Did the count go down? What type of radiation could the counter be receiving? Explain.

The measured mass of neon gas is 20.183 u. This figure is now understood to be the average mass of the naturally occurring isotopes of neon. Thus, while the mass of an individual atom of neon is close to a whole number of mass units, the atomic mass of an average sample of neon atoms is not. Most elements have many isotopic forms that occur naturally. The mass of the isotope of carbon, $^{12}_{6}C$, is now used to define the mass unit. One u is defined to be 1/12 the mass of the $^{12}_{6}C$ isotope.

A special method of notation is used to describe an isotope. A subscript representing the atomic number, Z, is written to the lower left of the symbol for the element. A superscript written to the upper left of the symbol is the mass number, A. This notation takes the form $^{A}_{Z}X$, where X is any element. For example, the two isotopes of neon, with atomic number 10, are written as $^{20}_{10}Ne$ and $^{22}_{10}Ne$.

Practice Problems

1. An isotope of oxygen has a mass number of 15. The atomic number of oxygen is 8. How many neutrons are in the nuclei of this isotope?
2. Three isotopes of uranium have mass numbers of 234, 235, and 238 respectively. The atomic number of uranium is 92. How many neutrons are in the nuclei of each of these isotopes?
3. How many neutrons are in an atom of the mercury isotope $^{200}_{80}Hg$?
4. ▶ Write the symbols for the three isotopes of hydrogen in Figure 30–2 with 0, 1, and 2 neutrons in the nucleus.

Radioactive Decay

Nuclei that decay are radioactive.

In 1896 Henri Becquerel was working with compounds containing the element uranium. To his surprise, he found that photographic plates covered to keep out light, became fogged, or partially exposed, when these uranium compounds were anywhere near the plates. This fogging suggested that some kind of ray had passed through the plate coverings. Several materials other than uranium or its compounds were also found to emit these penetrating rays. Materials that emit this kind of radiation are said to be **radioactive** and to undergo **radioactive decay**.

The decay of nuclei can produce α-, β-, or γ-particles.

In 1899 Rutherford discovered that uranium compounds produce three different kinds of radiation. He separated the radiations according to their penetrating ability and named them α (alpha), β (beta), and γ (gamma) radiation.

The α radiation can be stopped by a thick sheet of paper. Rutherford later showed that an α particle is the nucleus of a helium atom, $^{4}_{2}He$. Beta particles were later identified as high speed electrons. Six millimeters of aluminum are needed to stop most β particles. Several centimeters of lead are required to stop γ rays, which proved to be high energy photons. Alpha particles and γ rays are emitted with a specific energy that depends on the radioactive isotope. Beta particles, however, are emitted with a wide range of energies.

The emission of an α particle is a process called **α decay**. Since α particles contain protons and neutrons, they must come from the nucleus of an atom. The nucleus that results from α decay will have a mass and charge different from those of the original nucleus. A change in nuclear charge means that the element has been changed, or transmuted, into a different element. The mass number, A, of an α particle,

F.Y.I.

. . . science is awash with serendipity; science is hard work when done properly, but in the hard work there is joy and in the discovery there is abundant reward. . . .

Sherwin B. Nuland
Doctors: The Biography of Medicine, 1988

Assessment

Performance

To further assess students' understanding of background radiation, have them do the following experiment. They have found that alpha particles are not an important part of background radiation. Then have them test for beta particles by surrounding the counter with aluminum plates at least 6 mm thick. Record the number of counts over three three-minute intervals without the aluminum and then over a second set of intervals with the aluminum. Was there any change? Next surround the counter with lead plates or bricks. If possible, place 5 cm of lead on all sides of the counter. Again, check for a change in the count rate. What can you conclude about the source of background radiation? [Students should find only a tiny change after adding aluminum shielding, but a measurable change when the counter was surrounded with lead because most of the background radiation consists of gamma rays.]

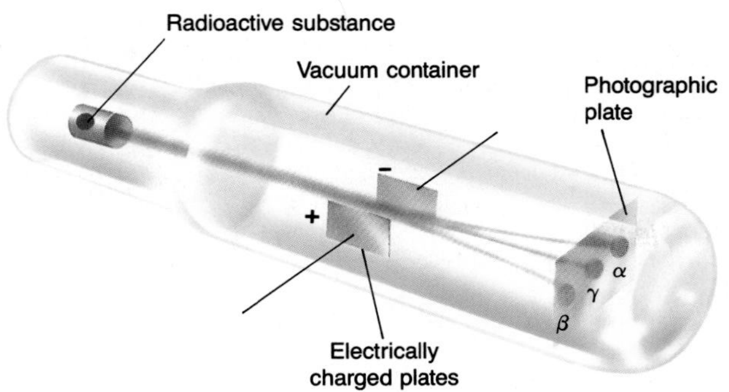

FIGURE 30–3. Alpha, beta, and gamma emissions behave differently in an electric field. Alpha and beta particles are deflected because of their charge.

$^4_2$He, is four, so the mass number, A, of the decaying nucleus is reduced by four. The atomic number, Z, of $^4_2$He is two, and therefore the atomic number of the nucleus, the number of protons, is reduced by two. For example, when $^{238}_{92}$U emits an α particle, the atomic number, Z, changes from 92 to 90. From Table D–5 of the Appendix, we find that $Z = 90$ is thorium. The mass number of the nucleus is $A = 238 - 4 = 234$. A thorium isotope, $^{234}_{90}$Th, is formed. The uranium isotope has been transmuted into thorium.

In α decay, the nucleus loses two charge units and four mass units.

Beta particles are negative electrons emitted by the nucleus. Since the mass of an electron is a tiny fraction of an atomic mass unit, the atomic mass of a nucleus that undergoes **β decay** is changed only a tiny amount. The mass number is unchanged. The nucleus contains no electrons. Rather, β decay occurs when a neutron is changed to a proton within the nucleus. An unseen neutrino accompanies each β decay. Neutrinos will be discussed later. The number of protons, and thus the atomic number, is increased by one. For example, the isotope $^{234}_{90}$Th, produced by the α decay of $^{238}_{92}$U, is unstable and emits a β particle. The $^{234}_{90}$Th then becomes a protactinium isotope, $^{234}_{91}$Pa.

β particles are high speed electrons.

In β-decay, the atomic number is increased by one while the mass number is not changed.

Gamma radiation results from the redistribution of the charge within the nucleus. The γ ray is a high energy photon. Neither the mass number nor the atomic number is changed when a nucleus emits a γ ray in **γ decay**.

Radioactive elements often go through a series of successive decays, or **transmutations**, until they form a stable nucleus. For example, $^{238}_{92}$U undergoes fourteen separate transmutations before the stable lead isotope $^{206}_{82}$Pb is produced.

In gamma decay, neither the atomic number nor the mass number is changed.

Nuclear Reactions and Equations

A **nuclear reaction** occurs whenever the number of neutrons or protons in a nucleus changes. Just as in chemical reactions, some nuclear reactions occur with a release of energy; others occur only when energy is added to a nucleus.

One form of nuclear reaction is the emission of particles by radioactive nuclei. The reaction releases excess energy in the form of the kinetic energy of the emitted particles.

CONCEPT DEVELOPMENT

Various experiments with radioactivity can be carried out with a small device containing a tiny amount of a low-level radioactive isotope (usually barium) called a minigenerator. They are available from various scientific supply houses.

Enrichment Master. With this section, use the Enrichment Master, Half-Life, from the Teacher Resource Package.

Transparency Package. Use Transparency 45 to quiz students on α, β, and γ particles.

STUDY GUIDE MASTER

Use the Study Guide master for section 30.1.

ENRICHMENT MASTER

Use the Enrichment master for Chapter 30 with this section.

TRANSPARENCY

Use Transparency 45 with this section.

CONCEPT DEVELOPMENT

- Point out that the balance of mass numbers in nuclear reactions represents approximate conservation of mass (small mass discrepancies will be treated in Chapter 31) and that the balance of atomic numbers in nuclear reactions is a consequence of charge conservation.
- Since these are *nuclear* reactions, electrons are not included in the equations. Electrons have very little influence on nuclear reactions.
- Emphasize that decayed atoms do not disappear, but change into atoms of different elements.
- The presence of gamma rays usually indicates some sort of nuclear rearrangement. Only in the nucleus is there enough energy to produce the high energy of gamma rays.

Critical Thinking Master, Teacher Resource Package. You may wish to have students complete the Critical Thinking Master, Distance and Radioactivity, with this section.

Cooperative Learning: Using the Chart of the Nuclides, have student groups investigate various aspects of nuclear decays. For example, one group might investigate alpha decays, another beta decays, still another artificially radioactive substances, and so on.

Guided Practice: Go over the Example Problems that begin on this page, then have students work on the Practice Problems that follow as an in-class exercise.

INDEPENDENT PRACTICE/ EXTENSION

Refer to the Assignment Guide on page 624 for additional questions and problems for independent practice.

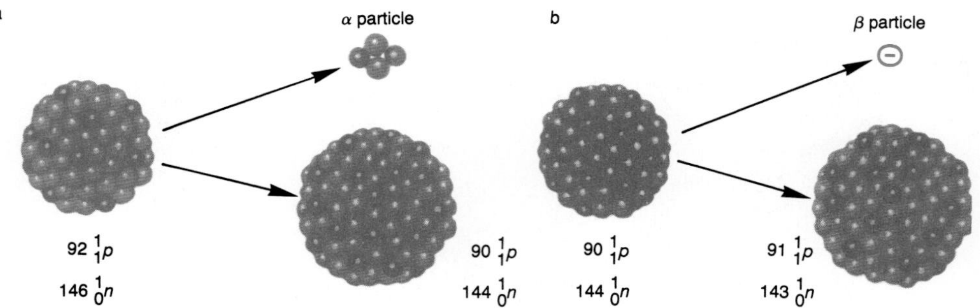

FIGURE 30–4. The emission of an alpha particle (a) by uranium-238 results in the formation of thorium-234. The emission of a beta particle (b) by thorium-234 results in the formation of protactinium-234.

While nuclear reactions can be described in words, or in pictures, such as Figure 30–4a, they can be written more easily in equation form. The symbols used for the nuclei in nuclear equations make the calculation of atomic number and mass number in nuclear reactions simpler. For example, the word equation for the change of uranium to thorium due to α decay is: uranium 238 yields thorium 234 plus an α particle. The nuclear equation for this reaction is

$$^{238}_{92}\text{U} \rightarrow {}^{234}_{90}\text{Th} + {}^{4}_{2}\text{He}.$$

When writing nuclear equations, be sure the atomic numbers and mass numbers are the same before and after the reaction.

No nuclear particles are destroyed during the nuclear reaction. Thus, the sum of the superscripts on the right side of the equation must equal the sum of the superscripts on the left side of the equation. The sum of the superscripts on both sides of the equation is 238. Electric charge is also conserved. Thus, the sum of the subscripts on the right is equal to the sum of the subscripts on the left.

Example Problem

Nuclear Equations—Alpha Decay

Write the nuclear equation for the transmutation of a radioactive radium isotope, $^{226}_{88}\text{Ra}$, into a radon isotope, $^{222}_{86}\text{Rn}$, by the emission of an α particle.

Solution: $^{226}_{88}\text{Ra} \rightarrow {}^{222}_{86}\text{Rn} + {}^{4}_{2}\text{He}$

Since a β particle is a negative electron, it is represented by the symbol $_{-1}^{0}\text{e}$. This indicates that the electron has one negative charge and an atomic mass number of zero. The transmutation of a thorium atom by the emission of a β particle is shown in Figure 30–4b. Its equation is

$$^{234}_{90}\text{Th} \rightarrow {}^{234}_{91}\text{Pa} + {}_{-1}^{0}\text{e} + {}^{0}_{0}\bar{\nu}$$

The symbol $^{0}_{0}\bar{\nu}$ represents an antineutrino that is emitted with the β particle. The sum of the superscripts on the right side of the equation equals the sum of the superscripts on the left side of the equation. Also, the sum of the subscripts on the right side of the equation equals the sum of the subscripts on the left side of the equation.

Connect to CHEMISTRY

The radioactive isotope carbon-14 is used to date organic materials. Carbon-14 is formed high in the atmosphere as the result of the bombardment of Earth by cosmic rays, predominantly protons. When the protons crash into atoms high in the atmosphere they create a variety of debris including neutrons. Neutrons that strike the nuclei of nitrogen atoms cause the following reaction: $^{1}_{0}\text{n} + {}^{14}_{7}\text{N} \rightarrow {}^{14}_{6}\text{C} + {}^{1}_{1}\text{p}$. This reaction occurs at a relatively steady rate. The carbon atoms can combine with oxygen to produce CO_2. About one molecule in each trillion contains carbon-14 instead of carbon-12. The carbon-14 decays radioactively with a half-life of 5730 years. As long as a plant (or animal) lives, its organic material contains the same fraction of carbon-14 as does the atmosphere. When the organism dies, however, it no longer exchanges carbon with the atmosphere, and the carbon-14 lost to radiation is not replaced. So, the fraction of carbon-14 to carbon-12 can be used to determine the time of death of the organism.

Example Problem

Nuclear Equations—Beta Decay

Write the nuclear equation for the transmutation of a radioactive lead isotope, $^{209}_{82}\text{Pb}$, into a bismuth isotope, $^{209}_{83}\text{Bi}$, by the emission of a β particle and an antineutrino.

Solution: $^{209}_{82}\text{Pb} \rightarrow {}^{209}_{83}\text{Bi} + {}^{0}_{-1}\text{e} + {}^{0}_{0}\bar{\nu}$

Practice Problems

5. Write the nuclear equation for the transmutation of a radioactive uranium isotope, $^{234}_{92}\text{U}$, into a thorium isotope, $^{230}_{90}\text{Th}$, by the emission of an α particle.
6. Write the nuclear equation for the transmutation of a radioactive thorium isotope, $^{230}_{90}\text{Th}$, into a radioactive radium isotope, $^{226}_{88}\text{Ra}$, by the emission of an α particle.
7. Write the nuclear equation for the transmutation of a radioactive radium isotope, $^{226}_{88}\text{Ra}$, into a radon isotope, $^{222}_{86}\text{Rn}$, by the emission of an α particle.
8. ▶ A radioactive lead isotope, $^{214}_{82}\text{Pb}$, can change to a radioactive bismuth isotope, $^{214}_{83}\text{Bi}$, by the emission of a β particle and an antineutrino. Write the nuclear equation.

Half-Life

The time required for half of the atoms in any given quantity of a radioactive isotope to decay is the **half-life** of that element. Each particular isotope has its own half-life. For example, the half-life of radium isotope $^{226}_{88}\text{Ra}$ is 1600 years. That is, in 1600 years, half of a given quantity of $^{226}_{88}\text{Ra}$ decays into another element. In a second 1600 years, half of the remaining sample will have decayed. Only one fourth of the original amount will remain after 3200 years.

In a time interval equal to one half-life, half the mass of the radioactive element decays.

Table 30–1

Half-Life of Selected Isotopes

Element	Isotope	Half-life	Radiation produced
hydrogen	$^{3}_{1}\text{H}$	12.3 years	β
carbon	$^{14}_{6}\text{C}$	5730 years	β
iodine	$^{131}_{53}\text{I}$	80.7 days	β
lead	$^{212}_{82}\text{Pb}$	10.6 hours	β
polonium	$^{194}_{84}\text{Po}$	0.7 seconds	α
polonium	$^{210}_{84}\text{Po}$	138 days	α
uranium	$^{227}_{92}\text{U}$	1.1 minutes	α
uranium	$^{235}_{92}\text{U}$	7.1×10^{8} years	α
uranium	$^{238}_{92}\text{U}$	4.51×10^{9} years	α
plutonium	$^{236}_{94}\text{Pu}$	2.85 years	α
plutonium	$^{242}_{94}\text{Pu}$	3.79×10^{5} years	α

Answers To

PRACTICE PROBLEMS

Have students refer to Appendix A of the Solutions Appendix for complete solutions to Practice Problems.

5. $^{234}_{92}\text{U} \rightarrow {}^{230}_{90}\text{Th} + {}^{4}_{2}\text{He}$
6. $^{230}_{90}\text{Th} \rightarrow {}^{226}_{88}\text{Ra} + {}^{4}_{2}\text{He}$
7. $^{226}_{88}\text{Ra} \rightarrow {}^{222}_{86}\text{Rn} + {}^{4}_{2}\text{He}$
8. $^{214}_{82}\text{Pb} \rightarrow {}^{214}_{83}\text{Bi} + {}^{0}_{-1}\text{e} + {}^{0}_{0}\bar{\nu}$

CONCEPT DEVELOPMENT

- Point out that half-life and activity have an inverse relationship. That is, something with a large half-life has a low activity (it decays slowly) and a nuclide with a short half-life has a high activity (it decays quickly).
- Rutherford named the time for half the material to decay the half-life.

ACTIVITY

Cooperative Learning: Divide the class into groups and give each group a box containing 100 pennies. Have each group place all the pennies heads up. Then have students shake the box vigorously. Have each group open their box and remove the pennies that are tails up. They shoud count and record the remaining "undecayed pennies." Have groups repeat this procedure five more times. Each shake represents a half-life. Instruct student groups to plot a graph of the number of half-lives on the *x*-axis versus the number of undecayed pennies on the *y*-axis. Discuss the shape of the curve. Ask students if a radioactive substance is radioactive forever. Ask: What would happen if you had a penny with two heads? [You would end up with one "atom" that refuses to decay.]

CRITICAL THINKING

Use the Critical Thinking master for Chapter 30 with this section.

Critical Thinking: Here's a sign posted at the proposed site of a low-level nuclear waste dump: "Think before you dump, nuclear waste is forever!!" Ask students to critique this statement. [Basically, the slogan is not true. For nuclides with short half-lives (say less than one year), activity decays to extremely low levels within ten years. Some longer half-life nuclides will be measurably radioactive for longer times. It is actually non-radioactive materials that are around forever! Nuclides with very long half-lives have quite low activity. The most troublesome part of the waste is those nuclides with half-lives in the tens of years. They have fairly high activity and remain active for a few hundred years.]

CHECKING FOR UNDERSTANDING

By way of discussing how the mass spectroscope works, ask students why it is easier to separate the isotopes of hydrogen than to separate other isotopes. [The mass ratios of the three most common hydrogen isotopes are 1 : 2 : 3—large percentage differences. Other isotopes don't differ from each other by that much.]

RETEACHING

Begin by reviewing the results of the mass spectrometer experiments from Chapter 26. They clearly indicate that atoms of a single element come in more than one mass variety. Follow this up by going over how our nuclear notation allows us to distinguish between isotopes. Choose some examples of naturally occurring radioactive elements to illustrate radioactive decay. Once these ideas are established, go on to the more quantitative idea of half-life. Be sure to use lots of examples with simple numbers to convey the idea of a half-life.

Reteaching Master, Teacher Resource Package. Use the Reteaching Master for Chapter 30, One Element Changes into Another.

EXTENSION

Over the past several years it has been discovered that radon, a colorless, odorless, radioactive gas, tends to concentrate in the basements of houses. The concentrations of radon are sometimes above what is considered safe. This radon comes from natural sources, mainly the soil and rocks. Have interested students investigate the problem and give a report to the class.

Answers To

PRACTICE PROBLEMS

Have students refer to Appendix A of the Solutions Appendix for complete solutions to Practice Problems.

9. 0.25 g
10. 0.25 g
11. $5 \times 10^5 \frac{\text{decays}}{\text{s}}$
12. about 11/16 of the original

FIGURE 30–5. Use this half-life graph with Practice Problems 9 through 12.

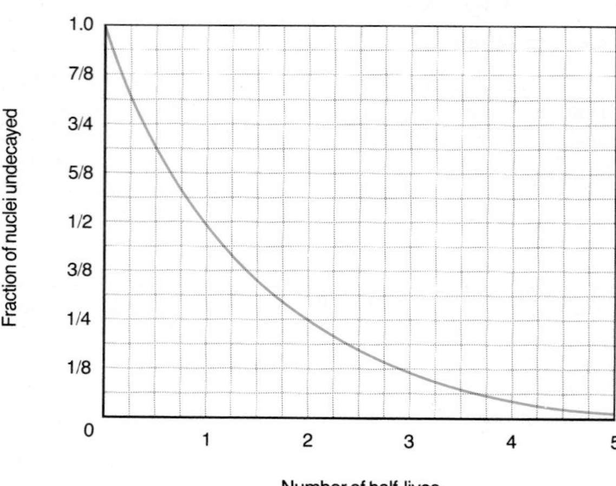

Activity, or decays per second, is proportional to the number of radioactive atoms.

The decay rate, or number of decays per second, of a radioactive substance is called its **activity**. Activity is proportional to the number of radioactive atoms present. Therefore, the activity of a particular sample is also reduced by one half in one half-life. Consider $^{131}_{53}I$ with a half-life of 8.07 days. If the activity of a certain sample is 8×10^5 decays per second when the $^{131}_{53}I$ is produced, 8.07 days later its activity will be 4×10^5 decays per second. After another 8.07 days, its activity will be 2×10^5 decays per second. The SI unit for decays per second is a Bequerel, Bq.

Practice Problems

These problems require the use of Figure 30–5 and Table 30–1.

9. A sample of 1.0 g of tritium, ^3_1H, is produced. What will be the mass of tritium remaining after 24.6 years?

10. The isotope $^{238}_{93}Np$ has a half-life of 2.0 days. If 4.0 g are produced on Monday, what will be the mass of neptunium remaining on Tuesday of the next week?

11. A sample of $^{210}_{84}Po$ is purchased for a physics class on September 1. Its activity is 2×10^6 decays per second. The sample is used in an experiment on June 1. What activity can be expected?

▶ **12.** Tritium, ^3_1H, was once used in some watches to produce a fluorescent glow so the watch could be read in the dark. If the brightness of the glow is proportional to the activity of the tritium, what would be the brightness of the watch, in comparison to its original brightness, when the watch is six years old?

LABORATORY MANUAL

Use Lab 30.1 with this section.

RETEACHING MASTER

Use the Reteaching master for Chapter 30 with this section.

LAB WORKSHEET

Use the Lab Worksheet for Chapter 30 with this Physics Lab.

PHYSICS LAB : Heads Up

Purpose

To formulate a model of radioactive decay.

Materials

- 20 pennies
- graph paper

Procedure

1. Set up a data table as shown below. Turn the pennies so that they are all heads. In this simulation, a heads indicates that the nucleus has not decayed.
2. Flip each coin separately and separate the heads and tails.
3. Record the number of heads on your data sheet. Remove the pennies that came up tails.
4. Flip all remaining coins and separate the heads and tails. Count the number of heads and record the value.
5. Repeat steps 2–4 one more time.
6. Share your data with four other students and copy their data onto your data sheet.

Observations and Data

Data Table

Student	1	2	3	4	5	Total
Beginning Number	20	20	20	20	20	100
After Trial 1						
After Trial 2						
After Trial 3						

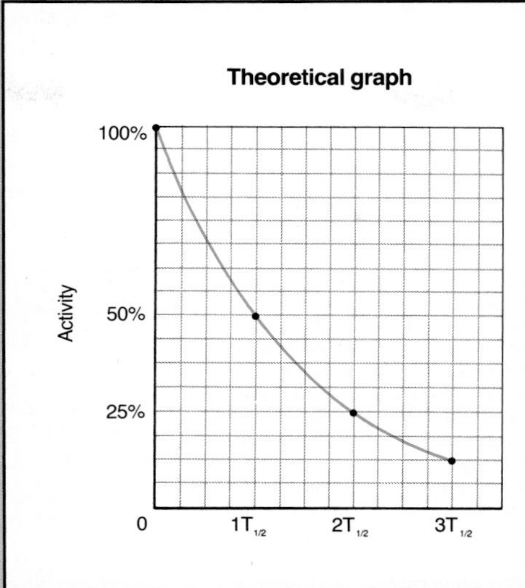

1. Did each person have the same number of heads after each trial?
2. Is the number of heads close to what you expected?

Analysis

1. Total the number of heads remaining for each trial. Make a graph of the number of heads (vertical) verses the trial (horizontal).
2. Compare your graph to the theoretical graph shown in the sketch above.

Applications

1. Laws mandate that hospitals keep radioactive materials for 10 half-lives before disposing of them. Calculate the fraction of the original activity left at the end of 10 half-lives.

PHYSICS LAB

Process Skills: questioning, measuring, defining operationally, communicating, formulating models.

MISCONCEPTION

Students frequently confuse the concept of exponential decay with reduction in a simple linear fashion.

Teaching Suggestion: Bring in several rolls of pennies for lab.

Lab Worksheet, Teacher Resource Package. If desired, use the lab worksheet master for this chapter for students to record their data.

OBSERVATIONS

Student data table

1. Student answers will vary.
2. Most students will get about half heads each trial, but a few may get large discrepancies.

ANALYSIS

1. Combining student data will likely smooth out individual variation.
2. The actual data will show the same type of curve as the theoretical graph.

APPLICATIONS

After 10 half-lives the activity will be 0.098% of the original rate.

Laboratory Manual. Give students additional experience with radiation properties by doing Lab 30.1 from the Laboratory Manual.

ASSESSMENT

Critical Thinking: To further assess students' understanding of half-life, ask the following questions.

1. Suppose that you make a graph of the data for the entire class. How would this new graph compare to your own? Why? [The new graph would be closer to the theoretical graph. Although the results for a single coin cannot be predicted, the results for hundreds of coins would be expected to be similar to the theoretical curve.
2. Radioactive materials are often used in medicine for diagnostic purposes. Suppose that your doctor recommended such a test for you. Would you expect the radioisotope to have a short or long half-life? Explain. [The radioisotope should have a very short half-life. You would want the radioactive material in your system for a very short time to reduce the harmful effects of the radiation.]

3 Close

CONVERGENT QUESTION

Ask students to compare the concepts of half-life and activity. [Half-life is a constant for any given nuclide. Activity decreases with time for any given nuclide. Activity is also proportional to the number of radioactive atoms present.]

CONCEPT REVIEW ANSWERS

1.1 The first pair has the same number of protons, but a different number of neutrons. The second pair has the same number of neutrons, but a different number of protons.
1.2 A neutron changes into a proton and an electron.
1.3 From the graph, it would be 1.4 half-lives, or 113 days.
1.4 Critical Thinking: The plate being struck by the α particles has the more positive potential since the positively charged α particles move positive charge from the emitter plate to the struck plate.

30.2 THE BUILDING BLOCKS OF MATTER

Preparation

OBJECTIVES

The objectives are listed on the student page. Remind students to preview these objectives as a study guide to this major section.

OVERVIEW

The two major concepts presented in this section are nuclear bombardment particle accelerators used to study nuclear structure; and particle detectors—which have been used in the last several decades to record and examine particles.

CONCEPT REVIEW

1.1 Consider the pairs of nuclei: first, ${}^{12}_{6}C$ and ${}^{13}_{6}C$; second, ${}^{11}_{5}B$ and ${}^{12}_{6}C$. In which way is the first pair like the second? In which way are they different?
1.2 How can an electron be expelled from a nucleus in β decay if the nucleus has no electrons?
1.3 Use Figure 30–5 and Table 30–1 to estimate in how many days a sample of ${}^{131}_{53}I$ would have 3/8 its original activity.
1.4 **Critical Thinking:** An α emitter is used in smoke detectors. The emitter is mounted on one plate of a capacitor, and the α particles strike the other plate. As a result there is a potential difference across the plates. Explain and predict which plate has the more positive potential.

Objectives

- balance nuclear equations showing the result of nuclear reactions.
- describe the operation of linear accelerators and synchrotrons and the operation of different particle detectors.
- define the two families of fundamental particles; explain the difference between particles and force carriers.
- define antiparticles; calculate the energy of γ rays emitted when particles annihilate with their antiparticles.
- describe the quark content of the proton and neutron; understand the place of additional quark and lepton families in the quark model.

30.2 THE BUILDING BLOCKS OF MATTER

Why are some isotopes radioactive while others are stable? What holds the nucleus together against the repulsive force of the charged protons? These questions and many more motivated many of the best physicists to study the nucleus. The tiny size of the nucleus meant that new tools had to be developed for this study. Studies of nuclei have also led to an understanding of the structure of the particles found in the nucleus, the proton and the neutron, and the nature of the forces that hold the nucleus together.

Nuclear Bombardment

Rutherford used α particles to cause nuclear reactions.

The first tool used was the result of radioactivity. Rutherford bombarded many elements with α particles, using them to cause a nuclear reaction. For example, when nitrogen gas was bombarded, Rutherford noted that high energy protons were emitted from the gas. A proton has a charge of one, while an α particle has a charge of two. Rutherford hypothesized that the nitrogen had been artificially transmuted by the α particles. The unknown results of the transmutation can be written ${}^{A}_{Z}X$, and the nuclear reaction can be written

$${}^{4}_{2}He + {}^{14}_{7}N \rightarrow {}^{1}_{1}H + {}^{A}_{Z}X.$$

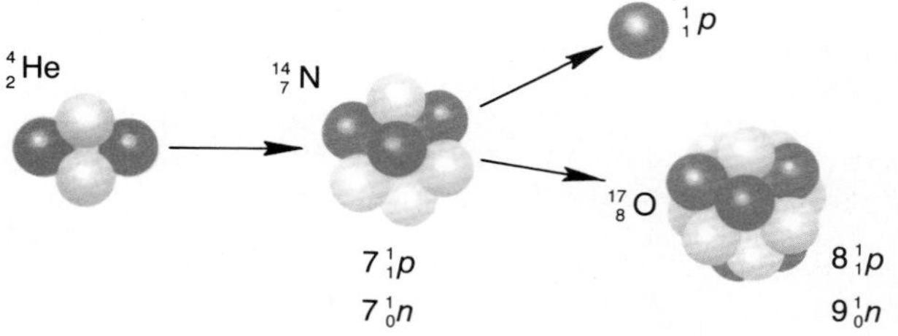

FIGURE 30–6. Production of oxygen-17 from the artificial transmutation of nitrogen.

TEACHER F.Y.I.

The mass spectrograph that Aston built in 1919 was a precision instrument. It charged a gas or coating until the gas was ionized into electrons and nuclei, and shot a beam of the nuclei through two slits that acted as collimators. This beam was then subjected to a strong electrostatic field that sorted the nuclei into separate beams that were further sorted by a magnetic field. The sorted beams struck a strip of calibrated film where they left a black mark that indicated the mass of the component nuclei.

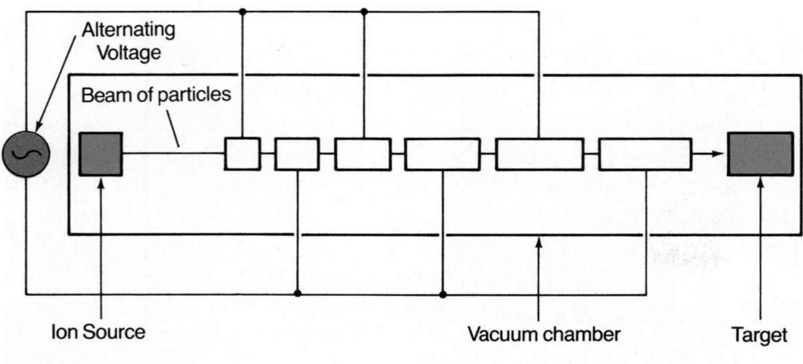

FIGURE 30–7. The linear accelerator at Stanford University is 3.3 km long (a). A proton is accelerated in a linear accelerator by changing the charges on the tubes as the proton moves (b). Not drawn to scale.

Simple arithmetic shows that the atomic number of the unknown isotope is $Z = 2 + 7 - 1 = 8$. The mass number is $A = 4 + 14 - 1 = 17$. From Appendix Table D–5, the isotope must be ${}^{17}_{8}\text{O}$, Figure 30–6. The identity of the ${}^{17}_{8}\text{O}$ isotope was confirmed with a mass spectrometer several years later.

Bombarding ${}^{9}_{4}\text{Be}$ with α particles produced a radiation more penetrating than any previously discovered. In 1932, Irene Curie (daughter of Marie and Pierre Curie) and her husband, Frederic Joliot, discovered that high speed protons were expelled from paraffin wax that was exposed to this new radiation from beryllium. In the same year, James Chadwick showed that the particles emitted from beryllium were uncharged, but had approximately the same mass as protons. That is, the beryllium emitted the particle Rutherford had theorized must be in the nucleus, the neutron. The reaction can be written using the symbol for the neutron, ${}^{1}_{0}n$.

Free neutrons can be produced in a nuclear reaction.

$$ {}^{4}_{2}\text{He} + {}^{9}_{4}\text{Be} \rightarrow {}^{12}_{6}\text{C} + {}^{1}_{0}n $$

Neutrons, being uncharged, are not repelled by the nucleus. As a result, neutrons are often used to bombard nuclei.

Alpha particles are useful in producing nuclear reactions. Alphas from radioactive materials, however, have fixed energies. In addition, sources that emit a large number of particles per second are difficult to produce. Thus methods of artificially accelerating particles to high energies are needed. Energies of several million electron volts are required to produce nuclear reactions. Several types of particle accelerators have been developed. The linear accelerator, cyclotron, and the synchrotron are the accelerator types in greatest use today.

Accelerators give more flexibility in producing nuclear reactions.

Linear Accelerators

A **linear accelerator** consists of a series of hollow tubes within a long evacuated chamber. The tubes are connected to a source of high frequency alternating voltage, Figure 30–7b. Protons are produced in an ion source similar to that described in Chapter 26. When the first tube has a negative potential, protons are accelerated into it. There is no electric field within the tube, so the proton moves at constant velocity. The length of the tube and the frequency of the voltage are adjusted so that when the protons have reached the far end of the tube, the poten-

Alternating voltages accelerate charged particles along a straight line in a linear accelerator.

BRIDGING

In this section, students will be working with numerous terms and concepts to which they have already been introduced: alpha, beta, and gamma rays; electric field; voltage; velocity; acceleration; electron volt; magnetic field; frequency; ionization; pressure; current; boiling point; conservation of energy and momentum; and the strong nuclear force.

1 Focus

Invite a scientist from a local college or university to share information about research on elementary particles. Or, invite a scientist from an accelerator laboratory to share her or his expertise with your class.

2 Teach

CONCEPT DEVELOPMENT

- Since 101 kPa is normal atmospheric pressure, 10 kPa is about one-tenth of an atmosphere.
- Remember that in Chapter 27 we showed mathematically that one electron volt is equal to 1.6×10^{-19} J.
- The presence of the nucleus is needed to conserve momentum.
- One facility planned for the future is the Advanced Photon Source (APS) that will produce UV radiation by accelerating positrons around a bend in a synchrotron. Located at Argonne National Laboratory, it will be used for materials research.

30:1 ASSIGNMENT GUIDE

	PRACTICE	EXTENSION
CHAPTER REVIEW pp. 635–637		
· Reviewing Concepts	1–6	
· Applying Concepts		1–7
· Problems*	1–10, 12–14	11, 15–17
APPENDIX B PROBLEMS*		
· Chapter 30, pp. 708–709	1–7, 10–11	8–9, 12

* Complete solutions to all Chapter Review and Appendix problems appear in the Problems and Solutions Manual.

CONCEPT DEVELOPMENT

- If you have a Geiger counter available, use it to demonstrate radioactivity to your students. A cloud chamber makes a fascinating display as well; the wispy tracks of atoms and atomic particles have a spooky effect.
- Be sure to point out that linear accelerators are related to circular accelerators. Accelerating methods are similar, but in the circular machine magnetic fields are used to bend the track of the particle into a circle. Circular accelerators are also more compact as a result.

Study Guide Master. To reinforce the concepts in this section, have the students complete the Study Guide Master for Section 30.2 from the Teacher Resource Package.

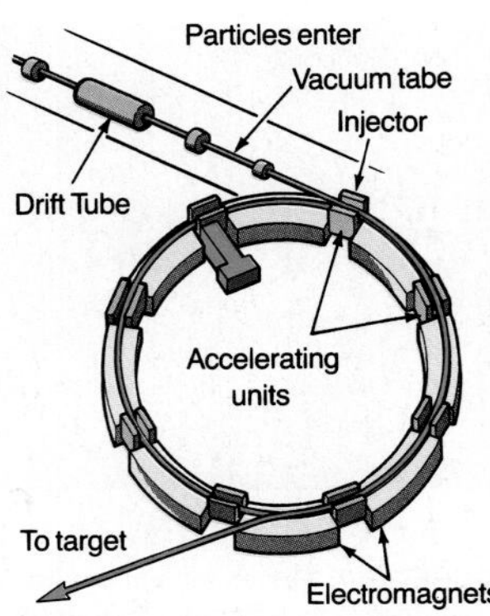

FIGURE 30–8. The synchrotron is a circular accelerator. Magnets are used to control the path and acceleration of the particles (a). Fermi Laboratory's synchrotron has a diameter of 2 km (b).

tial of the second tube is negative with respect to that of the first. The resulting electric field in the gap between the tubes accelerates the protons into the second tube. This process continues, with the protons receiving an acceleration between each pair of tubes. The energy of the protons is increased by 10^5 eV with each acceleration. The proton rides along the crest of an electric field wave much as a surfboard moves on the ocean. At the end of the accelerator, the protons can have energies of many millions or billions of electron volts.

Linear accelerators can be used with both electrons and protons. The largest linear accelerator is at Stanford University in California. It is 3.3 km long and accelerates electrons to energies of 20 GeV (2.0×10^{10} eV).

F.Y.I.

Superconductors are used in the bending magnets in both the final stage of the Fermilab accelerator and in the SSC. Magnets used in these machines are the largest superconducting magnets in regular use.

The Synchrotron

A synchrotron uses magnetic fields to bend charged particles into circular paths.

An accelerator may be made smaller by using a magnetic field to bend the path of the particles into a circle. In a device known as a **synchrotron**, the bending magnets are separated by accelerating regions. In the straight regions, high frequency alternating voltage accelerates the particles. The strength of the magnetic field and the length of the path are chosen so that the particles reach the location of the alternating electric field precisely when the field's polarity will accelerate them. One of the largest synchrotrons in operation is at the Fermi National Accelerator Laboratory near Chicago, Figure 30–8. Protons there reach energies of 1 TeV (1.0×10^{12} eV). The Superconducting Super Collider (SSC), presently under construction near Dallas, Texas, is a synchrotron with two particle beams traveling around an 88-km ring in opposite directions. The beams will collide in several interaction regions and the results studied.

Particle Detectors

Particles that ionize matter can be detected by several means.

Photographic films become "fogged," or exposed, when α particles, β particles, or γ rays strike them. Thus, photographic film can be used to detect these particles and rays. Many other devices are used to detect charged particles and γ rays. Most of these devices make use of the fact that a collision with a high speed particle will remove electrons from

STUDY GUIDE MASTER

Use the Study Guide master for section 30.2.

atoms. That is, the high speed particles ionize the matter that they bombard. In addition, some substances fluoresce when exposed to certain types of radiation. Thus, fluorescent substances can be used to detect radiation.

In the **Geiger-Mueller tube,** particles ionize gas atoms, Figure 30–9. The tube contains a gas at low pressure (10 kPa). At one end of the tube is a very thin "window" through which charged particles or gamma rays pass. Inside the tube is a copper cylinder with a negative charge. A rigid wire with a positive charge runs down the center of this cylinder. The voltage across the wire and cylinder is kept just below the point at which a spontaneous discharge, or spark, occurs. When a charged particle or gamma ray enters the tube, it ionizes a gas atom between the copper cylinder and the wire. The positive ion produced is accelerated toward the copper cylinder by the potential difference. The electron is accelerated toward the positive wire. As these new particles move toward the electrodes, they strike other atoms and form even more ions in their path.

Thus an avalanche of charged particles is created and a pulse of current flows through the tube. The current causes a potential difference across a resistor in the circuit. The voltage is amplified and registers the arrival of a particle by advancing a counter or producing an audible signal, such as a click. The potential difference across the resistor lowers the voltage across the tube so that the current flow stops. Thus the tube is ready for the beginning of a new avalanche when another particle or gamma ray enters it.

A device once used to detect particles was the **Wilson cloud chamber**. The chamber contains an area supersaturated with water vapor or ethanol vapor. When charged particles travel through the chamber, leaving a trail of ions in their paths, the vapor tends to condense into small droplets on the ions. In this way, visible trails of droplets, or fog, are formed. The **bubble chamber** was similar, except that trails of small vapor droplets formed in a liquid held just above the boiling point.

Modern experiments use **spark chambers** that are like giant Geiger-Mueller tubes. Plates several meters in size are separated by a few centimeters. The gap is filled with a low-pressure gas. A discharge is pro-

FOLLOW THE TRACKS

Prepare the cloud chamber by soaking the cloth ring in alcohol. Place the radioactive needle into the side of the cloud chamber and then place the chamber on a block of dry ice. After the chamber cools down, you should be able to observe the tracks of the radiations. Predict what might happen when you place a small neodymium magnet in the bottom of the center of the chamber. Explain. Try it. Describe the results.

In a cloud chamber, particles create tracks of condensed vapor.

In a bubble chamber, trails of bubbles show paths of particles.

A spark chamber uses computers to analyze the trail of ions left by the particles.

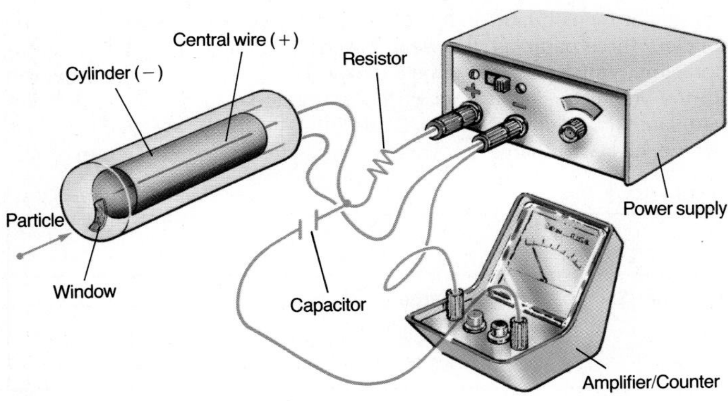

FIGURE 30–9. Gamma rays from a radioactive source ionize the low pressure gas in the tube, allowing a pulse of current to flow between the central wire and the copper tube.

POCKET LAB

FOLLOW THE TRACKS

Purpose: to observe the tracks of alpha radiation.
Materials: simple cloud chamber; alcohol; 2 pounds dry ice; alpha source on needle; small neodymium magnet (optional).
Outcome: Alpha particles will shoot outward from the needle, leaving momentary "jet trails" behind in the alcohol vapor. Students should form a lasting impression of this activity.

CONCEPT DEVELOPMENT

Cooperative Learning: Have student groups explore further details of the various types of accelerators and particle detectors covered in this section. Then let them share their findings with the rest of the class.

Critical Thinking: The usual source of protons used in accelerators is hydrogen gas, which is ionized. Suppose you wanted to use alpha particles in an accelerator. Ask students what a convenient source would be. [Doubly ionized helium gas.]

Enrichment: Have interested students investigate how scientists know when they have discovered a new particle. In particular, what is the evidence?

FIGURE 30–10. The spark chamber used at Lawrence Livermore Laboratory.

duced in the path of a particle passing through the chamber. A computer locates the discharge and records its position for later analysis. Neutral particles do not produce discharges, and thus no not leave tracks. The laws of conservation of energy and momentum in collisions can be used to tell if any neutral particles were produced. Other detectors measure the energy of the particles. The entire array of detectors used in high energy accelerator experiments, such as that in Figure 30–10, can be many meters in size, weigh 10 tons or more, and cost tens of millions of dollars.

Neutral particles cannot be detected directly. The laws of conservation of momentum and energy are used to find their paths.

The Fundamental Particles

The atom was once thought to be the smallest particle into which matter could be divided. Then Rutherford found that the atom had a nucleus surrounded by electrons. After the proton was discovered, it was also thought to be indivisible. Experiments have been done that bombard protons with other protons or electrons accelerated by accelerators to very high energies. The results of these experiments show that the proton is composed of yet smaller bodies. The neutron also appears to be composed of smaller bodies.

F.Y.I.

Rutherford discovered the tiny charged nucleus at the center of an atom by scattering charged particles. Similarly, physicists have found evidence of smaller charged particles within the proton by scattering charged particles off of it.

Physicists now believe that the particles out of which all matter is made are grouped into two families, quarks and leptons. **Quarks** make up protons and neutrons. **Leptons** are particles, like the electron and neutrino. In addition to quarks and leptons, there are also particles that carry, or transmit, forces between particles. The photon is the carrier of the electromagnetic force. Eight particles, called **gluons**, carry the strong force that binds quarks into protons and the protons and neutrons into nuclei. Three particles, the **weak bosons**, are involved in the weak interaction, which operates in beta decay. The **graviton** is the name given to the yet-undetected carrier of the gravitational force. These particles are summarized in Tables 30–2 and 30–3. Charges are given in units of the electron charge and masses are stated as energy equivalents,

Other particles like the photon carry, or transmit, forces.

All matter is composed of quarks and leptons.

Table 30–2

Quarks				Leptons			
Name	Symbol	Mass	Charge	Name	Symbol	Mass	Charge
down	d	330 MeV	−1/3 e	electron	e	0.511 MeV	−e
up	u	330 MeV	2/3 e	neutrino	ν_e	0	0

TEACHER F.Y.I.

Leptons are pointlike particles and antiparticles that do not respond to the strong nuclear force, but do respond to the gravitational, electromagnetic, and weak forces. The electron, neutrino, and muon are leptons.

Hadrons respond to the strong nuclear force and are subdivided into baryons and mesons. Examples of baryons are the proton and neutron. Examples of mesons are the pion and kaon. Hadrons are of measurable size and are thought to be composed of combinations of quarks.

Table 30–3

Force carriers				
Force	Name	Symbol	Mass	Charge
Electromagnetic	photon	γ	0	0
Weak	weak boson	W^+	80.6 GeV	+e
		W^-	80.6 GeV	−e
		Z^0	91.2 GeV	0
Strong	gluon (8)	g	0	0
Gravitational	graviton (?)	G	0	0

given by Einstein's famous formula, $E = mc^2$. The energy unit, the electron volt, was defined in Chapter 27. The energy equivalent of these particles is much larger, and so are shown in MeV (mega-electron volts, or 10^6 eV) and GeV (giga-electron volts, or 10^9 eV).

Each quark and each lepton also has its **antiparticle.** The antiparticles are identical with the particles except they have the opposite charge. When a particle and its antiparticle collide, they annihilate each other and are transformed into photons, or lighter particle-antiparticle pairs and energy, Figure 30–11. The total number of quarks and the total number of leptons in the universe are constant. That is, quarks and leptons are created or destroyed only in particle-antiparticle pairs. The number of charge carriers is not conserved; the total charge, however, is conserved. Gravitons, photons, gluons, and weak bosons can be created or destroyed if there is enough energy. After exploring the production and annihilation of antiparticles, we will return to the quark and lepton theory of matter.

Quarks and leptons cannot be created or destroyed individually, only in particle-antiparticle pairs.

Particles and Antiparticles

The α particles and γ rays emitted by radioactive nuclei have single energies that depend on the decaying nucleus. For example, the energy of the α particle emitted by $^{234}_{90}$Th is always 4.2 MeV. Beta particles, however, are emitted with a wide range of energies. One might expect the energy of the β particles to be equal to the difference between the energy of the nucleus before decay and the energy of the nucleus produced by the decay. In fact, the wide range of energies of electrons emitted during β decay suggested to Niels Bohr that energy might not be conserved in nuclear reactions. Wolfgang Pauli in 1931 and Enrico Fermi in 1934 suggested that an unseen neutral particle was emitted with the β particle. Named the **neutrino** ("little neutral one" in Italian) by Fermi, the particle (actually an antineutrino) was not directly observed until 1956.

A neutron decay is accompanied by emission of an antineutrino.

In a stable nucleus, the neutron does not decay. A free neutron, or one in an unstable nucleus, can decay by emitting a β particle. Sharing the outgoing energy with the β particle is an antinuetrino ($^0_0\bar{\nu}$). The antineutrino has zero mass and is uncharged, but like the photon, it carries momentum and energy. The neutron decay equation is written

$$^1_0n \rightarrow {}^1_1p + {}^{0}_{-1}e + {}^0_0\bar{\nu}.$$

FIGURE 30–11. The collision of a positron and an electron results in gamma ray production.

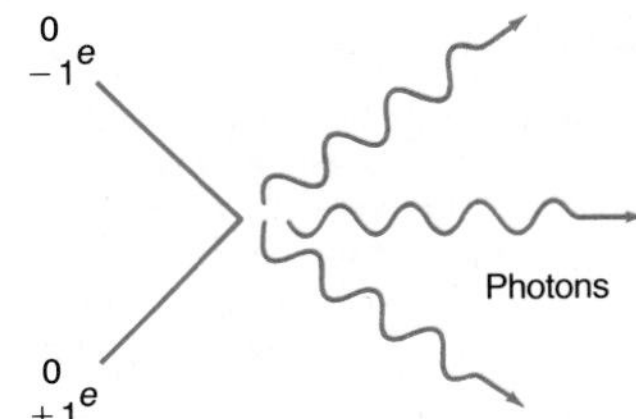

LITERATURE CONNECTION

In 1964, an American physicist, Murray Gell-Mann, suggested that particles with a charge equal to 1/3e or 2/3e might exist. He named these particles "quarks"–the word comes from James Joyce's novel *Finnegan's Wake.* Free quarks, not bound together with others into a hadron, have never been observed.

CONCEPT DEVELOPMENT

Transparency Package. Use Transparency 46 and accompanying worksheet to quiz students on subatomic particles.

Assessment

Portfolio

Students should design a poster showing quarks, lepton, and force carriers, and how they are assembled into observable particles (protons, neutrons, nuclei, and atoms).

TRANSPARENCY

Use Transparency 46 with this section.

CONCEPT DEVELOPMENT

Enrichment: Carbon-14 dating is used to find the age of various old organic samples. Recently the process has undergone close scrutiny, revealing that the dates may be incorrect for very old samples. The reason for the discrepancy has nothing to do with half-life changing over a long period of time. Have interested students investigate this subject. A good source is an article in the September 1990 issue of *Earth in Space*, titled "Accuracy of Radiocarbon Dating Improved."

FIGURE 30–12. Scientists identify the particles produced in high-energy collisions by the tracks they produce.

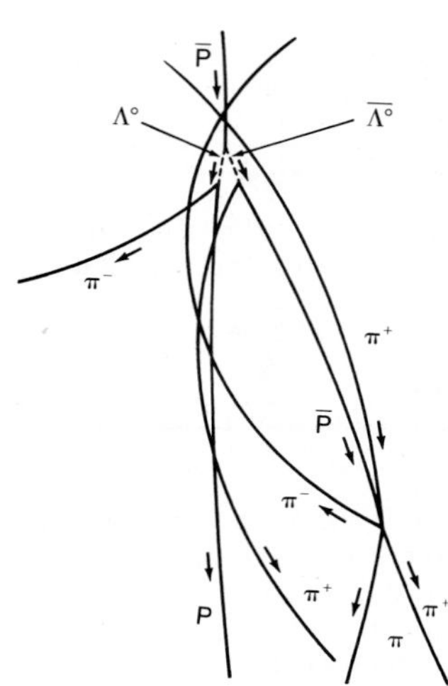

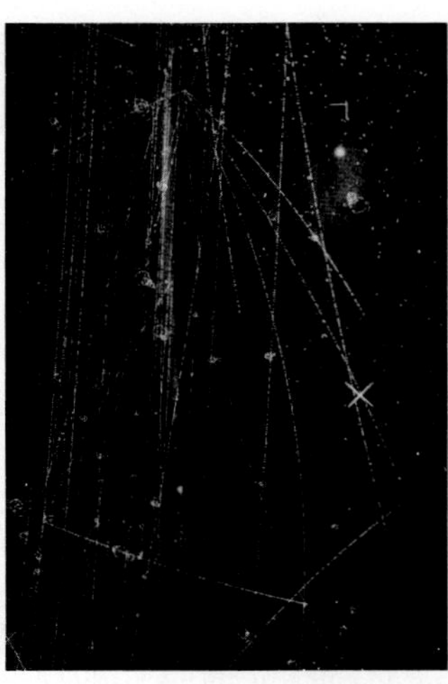

When an isotope decays by emission of a **positron** (antielectron), a process like β decay occurs. A proton within the nucleus changes into a neutron with the emission of a positron ($^{0}_{1}e$) and a neutrino ($^{0}_{0}\nu$). The decay reaction is written

$$^{1}_{1}p \rightarrow {}^{1}_{0}n + {}^{0}_{1}e + {}^{0}_{0}\nu.$$

The decay of neutrons into protons and protons into neutrons cannot be explained by the strong force. The existence of β decay indicates there must be another force or interaction, called the weak interaction, acting in the nucleus.

When an electron and positron annihilate, gamma rays are produced with total energy equal to the rest energy of the two particles.

The positron is an example of an antiparticle, or a particle of antimatter. When a positron and an electron collide, the two can annihilate each other, resulting in energy in the form of γ rays. Matter is converted directly into energy. The amount of energy can be calculated using Einstein's equation for the energy equivalent of mass

$$E = mc^2.$$

The mass of the electron is 9.11×10^{-31} kg. The mass of the positron is the same. Therefore, the energy equivalent of the positron and the electron together is

$$\begin{aligned} E &= 2(9.11 \times 10^{-31}\ \text{kg})(3.00 \times 10^{8}\ \text{m/s})^2 \\ &= (1.64 \times 10^{-13}\ \text{J})(1\ \text{eV}/1.60 \times 10^{-19}\ \text{J}) \\ &= 1.02 \times 10^{6}\ \text{eV or } 1.02\ \text{MeV}. \end{aligned}$$

When a positron and an electron at rest annihilate each other, the sum of the energies of the γ rays emitted is 1.02 MeV.

The inverse of annihilation can also occur. That is, energy can be converted directly into matter. If a γ ray with at least 1.02 MeV energy passes close by a nucleus, a positron and electron pair can be produced. This is called **pair production.** Reactions like $\gamma \rightarrow e^-$ or $\gamma \rightarrow e^+$, however, cannot occur because such an event would violate the law of conservation of charge. Matter and antimatter particles must always be produced in pairs.

F.Y.I.

The electromagnetic attraction of an electron and a positron is 42×10^{41} times stronger than their gravitational attraction.
—Isaac Asimov's *Book of Facts*

TEACHER F.Y.I.

"Every Monday night at 7:30 we turned the cyclotron off and met in the old LeConte library. Since most physicists find they don't really understand a subject until they've discussed it with their colleagues, talking physics is essential to doing physics."—Alvarez

The production of a positron-electron pair is shown in the chapter-opening bubble chamber photograph. A magnetic field around the bubble chamber causes the oppositely-charged particles to curve in opposite directions. The γ ray that produced the pair produced no track. If the energy of the γ ray is larger than 1.02 MeV, the excess energy goes into kinetic energy of the positron and electron. The positron soon collides with another electron and they are both annihilated, resulting in the production of two or three γ rays with a total energy of 1.02 MeV.

Antiprotons can also be created. An antiproton has a mass equal to that of the proton but is negatively charged. Protons have 1836 times as much mass as electrons. The energy needed to create proton-antiproton pairs is comparably larger. The first proton-antiproton pair was produced and observed at Berkeley, California in 1955.

Phantom Tracks

Gamma rays of sufficient energy can produce particle-antiparticle pairs.

Practice Problem

13. The mass of a proton is 1.67×10^{-27} kg.

a. Find the energy equivalent of the proton's mass in joules.

b. Convert this value to eV.

c. Find the smallest total γ ray energy that could result in a proton-antiproton pair.

The Quark Model of Nucleons

The quark model describes the proton and the neutron as an assembly of quarks. The nucleons are each made up of three quarks. The proton has two up quarks (charge $+2/3$ e) and one down quark (charge $-1/3$ e). A proton is described as $p = (uud)$. The charge on the proton is the sum of the charges of the three quarks, $(2/3 + 2/3 + -1/3)e = +e$. The neutron is made up of one up quark and two down quarks, $n = (udd)$. The charge of the neutron is zero, $(2/3 + -1/3 + -1/3)e = 0$.

Individual quarks cannot be observed because the strong force that holds them together becomes larger as the quarks are pulled farther apart. In this sense, the strong force acts like the force of a spring. It is unlike the electric force, which becomes weaker as charged particles are moved farther apart. In the quark model, the strong force is the result of the emission and absorption of gluons that carry the force.

The weak interaction involves three force carriers: W^+, W^-, and Z^0 bosons. The weak interaction exhibits itself in beta decay, the decay of a neutron into a proton, electron, and antineutrino. As was shown before, only one quark in the neutron and the proton is different. Beta decay occurs in two steps. First, one d quark in a neutron changes to a u quark with the emission of a W^- boson,

$$d \rightarrow u + W^-.$$

Then the W^- boson decays into an electron and an antineutrino,

$$W^- \rightarrow e^- + \bar{\nu}.$$

Similarly, in the decay of a proton, a neutron and a W^+ boson are emitted. The weak boson then decays into a positron and a neutrino.

The emission of a Z^0 boson is not accompanied by a change from one quark to another. The Z^0 boson produces an interaction between

FIGURE 30–13. Characteristic sizes of the structures of matter, given in meters, from the smallest "living" thing, a virus. It is not yet known whether quarks are measurable and have some internal structure, or whether they are really point-like objects.

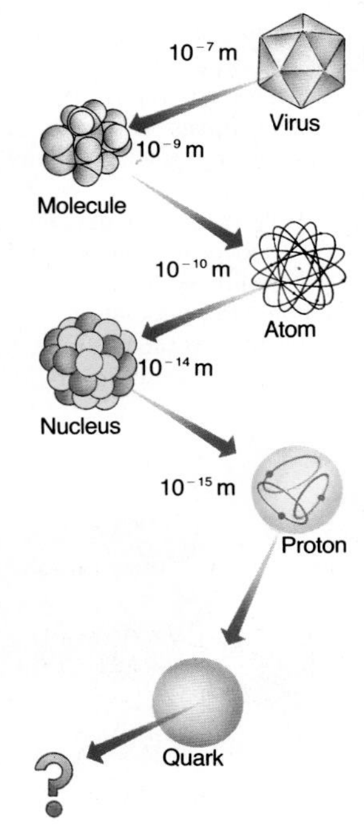

CONCEPT DEVELOPMENT

Guided Practice: Go over the Practice Problem on this page as a class exercise.

Independent Practice: Assign an appropriate problem from the Chapter Review as homework and spend time discussing it during the next class period.

Answers To
PRACTICE PROBLEMS

Have students refer to Appendix A of the Solutions Appendix for complete solutions to Practice Problems.

13. a. 1.50×10^{-10} J

b. 9.38×10^{8} eV = 938 MeV

c. 1.88 GeV

Multicultural Connections

A theory to explain the weak interaction force was developed by a Pakistani physicist named Abdul Salam about the same time as two American physicists, Sheldon Glashow and Steven Weinberg. As often happens in theoretical work, physicists in different parts of the world work out very similar theories at about the same time. In this case, once their theories were experimentally verified, all three physicists were awarded a shared Nobel Prize in 1979. Their work provided a way to combine the weak force with the electromagnetic force.

Physics and society

The following information is provided by The National Radon Association: "Homes with basements or slab-on-grade construction may have a greater chance for radon entry due to the direct contact to soil. On the other hand, homes with ventilated crawl spaces allow radon to dilute with proper ventilation.

"Studies show a strong interaction between a home's indoor air and the geology, or soil and rock types, beneath the house.

"Indoor air pressure relative to the pressure of gas in the underlying soil also appears to be very important. If the gas pressure in the soil is sufficiently greater than the indoor air pressure in the house, the radon gas will be forced upward into the house. If an underpressurized house tends to draw radon in, it stands to reason that an overpressurized house could impede radon entry. An overpressurized house might sit like a tight bottle over water, forcing radon out and around it. This suggests that an energy-efficient house, with an appropriate pressure differential to its underlying soil, could actually inhibit the entry of radon.

"Just mixing a home's indoor air with fans—without exchanging the air—can reduce the concentration of radon progeny in indoor air. Scientists theorize that fans push radon progeny closer to walls, floors, ceilings and ductwork, encouraging attachment to household surfaces.

"Recent research also indicates that the water supply of homes in the Northwest is not as big a radon source as it was once thought to be. The level of radon in household water would have to be extremely high to have any significant impact on air quality within a home. The same seems to be true of natural gas and building materials, which were once more suspect as radon-bearers than they are today."

Physics and society

A DAILY DOSE OF RADON

The radioactive isotopes $^{226}_{88}$Ra (radium) and $^{222}_{86}$Rn (radon) are two elements formed in the series of radioactive elements as uranium decays to a stable form of lead.

Radon occurs in trace amounts in various rocks throughout Earth's crust. As radium decays, it produces gaseous radon. Radon is present in high concentrations in soils containing shale, granite, phosphate, and pitchblende. Radon moves out of the soil and into air, water, and buildings. Radon gas moves into houses through cracks in floors or walls, or any opening around water or gas pipes and drains. Radon mixes with the air in houses and is then inhaled by the occupants.

Within the last decade, serious concerns have arisen over the health effects of radon on the general population.

Health problems from radon are due mainly to its decay products, which are chemically active and become attached to particles in the air. If these particles are inhaled, they become deposited in the bronchi.

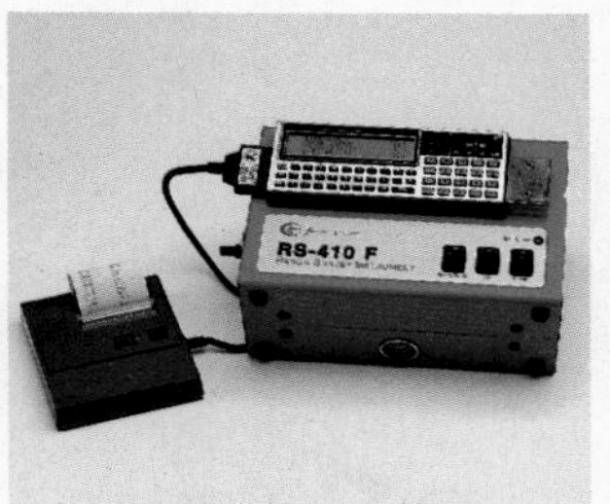

In outdoor air, radon is usually diluted and poses no health hazard. In a tightly-closed house, however, radon concentrations can build up to dangerous levels. Average indoor concentrations may be from five to ten times greater than average outdoor concentrations. Because radon is colorless and odorless, and causes no acute health effects, it is undetectable without special testing equipment. Reliable radon monitoring devices are widely available.

The EPA has set 4 picocuries per liter as the acceptable level. One picocurie is equal to 0.15 decays/second/liter. If radioactivity from radon is found to be present in a house at unacceptable levels, there are ways to reduce a person's exposure. Simply opening windows in basements can help. Sealing cracks and plugging up openings in floors yield only low to moderate reductions in radon. Most radon gas is drawn into a house by slight reductions in air pressure caused by air being driven from the house by such things as clothes dryers, fireplaces, exhaust-only fans, and by the chimney, or stack, effect. The stack effect occurs as warm air rises, moves out through openings at the top of the house, and draws air into the lower part of the structure. This effect can be counteracted by installation of a sub-slab venting system. In this method, a fan and pipe system is used to reverse the pressure difference between the soil and the house by continuously pumping out air from below the substructure. Such a system can bring about huge reductions in indoor radon concentrations.

DEVELOPING A VIEWPOINT

1. Scientists do not agree on the risks associated with radon exposure. Some think EPA estimates of deaths from radon-induced lung cancer are too high. Others believe that radon poses an extremely serious long-term threat to health.

Study recent references on radon in houses. Come to class prepared to discuss the following questions.

1. What are the risks of living with radon and the pros and cons of using expensive methods to decrease radon concentrations? 2. Find out what you can about the type of soil on which your school is built. Predict whether your school will have a low, moderate, or high radon concentration. 3. Obtain radon testing equipment and measure the radon concentration. How well did you predict the outcome?

SUGGESTED READINGS

Cole, Leonard A. "Much Ado About Radon." *The Sciences,* January/February 1990, pp. 19–23.

Moeller, Dade W. Moeller. "Radon Zapper." *Popular Science,* 235 (4), October 1989, pp. 78–80.

Teacher Resources: Bodner, George M. and Tony A. Rhea. "Natural Sources of Ionizing Radiation." *Journal of Chemical Education.* August 1984, pages 687–689.

Nazaroff, William W. and Nero, Anthony V., Jr., eds. *Radon and Its Decay Products in Indoor Air.* John Wiley and Sons, Inc., 1988.

The National Radon Association, Inc., Suite 240, 2786 North Decatur Road, Decatur, Georgia 30033, (404) 292-1113.

the nucleons and the electrons in atoms that is similar to, but much weaker than, the electromagnetic force holding the atom together. The interaction was first detected in 1979. The W^+, W^-, and Z^0 bosons were first observed directly in 1983.

The force between charged particles, the electromagnetic interaction, is carried by photons in much the same way as weak bosons carry the weak force. The electric force acts over a long range because the photon has zero mass, while the weak force acts over short distances because the *W* and *Z* bosons are so relatively massive. The mathematical structures of the theories of the weak interaction and electromagnetic interaction, however, are similar. In the high energy collisions produced in accelerators, the electromagnetic and weak interactions have the same strength and range.

Astrophysical theories of supernovae indicate that during massive stellar explosions, the two interactions are identical. Present theories of the origin of the universe suggest that the two forces were identical during the early moments in the life of the cosmos as well. For this reason, the electromagnetic and weak forces are said to be unified by this theory into a single force, called the electroweak force.

Bombardment of particles at high energies creates many particles of medium and large mass that have very short lifetimes. Some of these particles are combinations of two or three *u* or *d* quarks or a quark-antiquark pair. Particles composed of quark-antiquark pairs are called **mesons;** those composed of three quarks are called **baryons.** Combinations of the *u* and *d* quarks, however, cannot account for all the particles produced. Combinations of three other quarks are necessary to form all known baryons and mesons. A fourth additional quark, the top quark, has not been found, but the theories that work very well predict its existence. Two additional pairs of leptons are also produced in high energy collisions. The additional quarks and leptons are listed in Table 30–4. No one knows why there are six quarks and six leptons or if there are still other undiscovered particles. One reason for building the Superconducting Super Collider is to attempt to answer this question.

Table 30–4

Additional Quarks

Name	Symbol	Mass	Charge
strange	*s*	510 MeV	−1/3 e
charm	*c*	1.6 GeV	+2/3 e
bottom	*b*	5.2 GeV	−1/3 e
top	*t*	>100 GeV	+2/3 e

Additional Leptons

Name	Symbol	Mass	Charge
muon	μ	105 MeV	−e
muon neutrino	ν_μ	0	0
tau	τ	1.8 GeV	−e
tau neutrino	ν_τ	0	0

FIGURE 30–14. A battery of devices is waiting to detect the decay of a proton in a water molecule in this subterranean lake.

A total of six quarks and six leptons are needed to account for all particles produced by high-energy accelerators.

F.Y.I.

If I could remember the names of all these particles, I'd be a botanist.

Enrico Fermi

CONCEPT DEVELOPMENT

• Experiments underway in 1993 give hints that the top quark will soon be observed. Its mass is approximately that of an entire silver atom!

CHECKING FOR UNDERSTANDING

Have students explain how the velocity of particles in accelerators is controlled. [By electric and magnetic fields. The electric fields are used to give the particles linear acceleration and the magnetic fields are used to bend the particles into curved paths.]

RETEACHING

Review the behavior of charged particles in electric and magnetic fields. Stress that it is the charged nature of particles that allows us to control them. Give a review of the third right-hand rule, then ask how a charged particle would move in a region of uniform magnetic field. Finally, apply this to the operation of particle accelerators.

INDEPENDENT PRACTICE/ EXTENSION

Refer to the Assignment Guide on page 633 for additional questions and problems for independent practice.

CONCEPT DEVELOPMENT

Students or teachers who wish to pursue the topic of elementary particles may find the following books useful:

The Hunting of the Quark: A True Story of Modern Physics, Michael Riordan, Simon and Schuster, 1987.

Story of the W and Z, Peter Watkins, Cambridge University Press, 1986.

Quarks: The Stuff of Matter, Harald Fritzsch, Basic Books, 1983.

The Particle Explosion, Close, Frank, Marten, Michael; and Sutton, Christine; Oxford University Press, 1987.

3 Close

CONVERGENT QUESTION

Ask students why it is necessary to accelerate particles to such a high velocity for bombarding nuclei. [The charged bombarding particle must be able to overcome the tremendous electric repulsive force due to the charge on the nucleus.]

In the same way that the electromagnetic and weak forces were unified into the electroweak force during the 1970s, physicists are presently trying to create a Grand Unified Theory that includes the strong force as well. Work is still incomplete. One prediction of current theories is that the proton should not exist forever, but decay into leptons and photons. The proton half-life should be 10^{31} years. Experiments to test this prediction took data continuously for three years, but found no decays. Theories are being revised and new experiments planned. A fully unified theory that includes gravitation requires even more work.

The field of physics that studies these particles is called elementary particle physics. The field is very exciting because new discoveries occur almost every week. Each new discovery seems to raise as many questions as it answers. The question of what makes up the universe does not yet have a complete answer.

FIGURE 30–15. The known quarks and leptons are divided into three families. The everyday world is made from particles in the bottom family. Particles in the middle group are found in cosmic rays and are routinely produced in particle accelerators. Particles in the top families are believed to have existed briefly during the earliest moments of the Big Bang and are created in high-energy collisions.

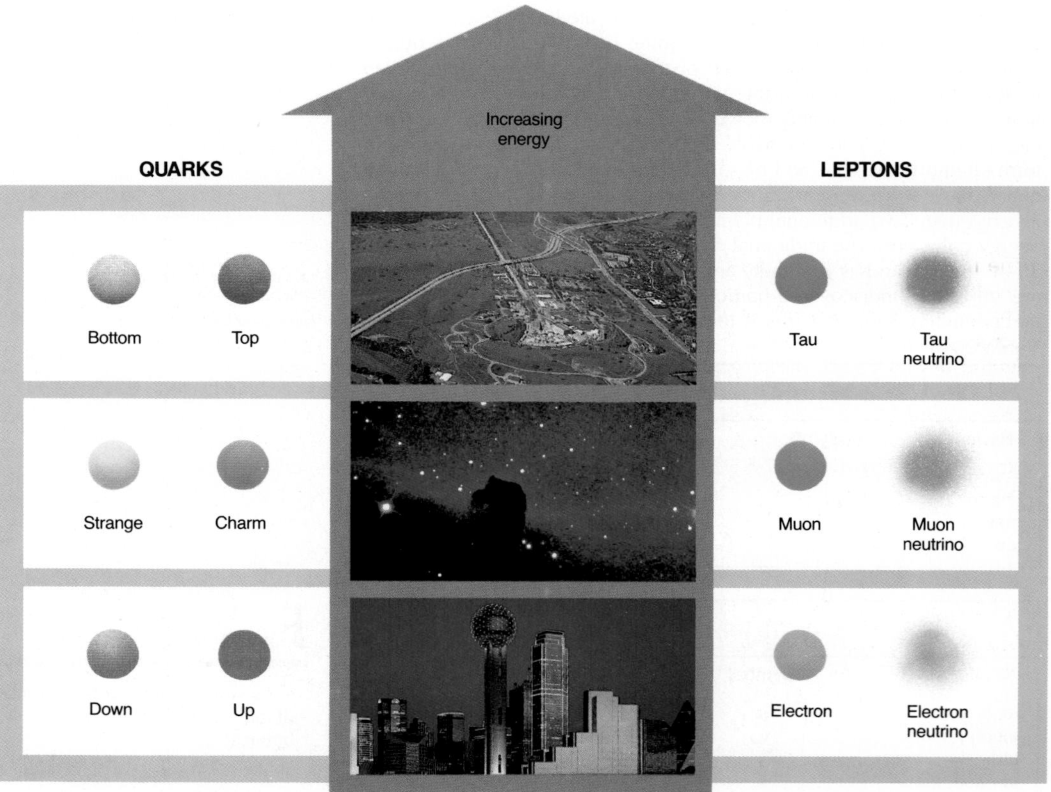

30:2 ASSIGNMENT GUIDE	PRACTICE	EXTENSION
CHAPTER REVIEW pp. 635–637		
· Reviewing Concepts	7–11	
· Applying Concepts		8
· Problems*	19–21	18
APPENDIX B PROBLEMS*		
· Chapter 30, p. 709	15–16	13–14

* Complete solutions to all Chapter Review and Appendix problems appear in the Problems and Solutions Manual.

CONCEPT REVIEW

2.1 Why would it require a more energetic proton than a neutron to produce a nuclear reaction?

2.2 Protons in the FermiLab accelerator, Figure 30–8, move counterclockwise. In what direction is the magnetic field of the bending magnets?

2.3 Figure 30–12 shows the collision of an antiproton coming from the bottom of the photo with a proton in the liquid-hydrogen bubble chamber. The track moving upward and leaving the right-hand edge of the photo is a negatively-charged "pion." What is the charge of the particles producing the spirals seen in many locations?

2.4 **Critical Thinking:** Write an equation for beta decay in which you write the quarks comprising both the neutron and the proton. Include both steps in the decay.

F. Y. I.

I have long held an opinion, amounting almost to conviction, in common, I believe, with many other lovers of natural knowledge, that the various forms under which the forces of matter are made manifest have one common origin.

Michael Faraday

CONCEPT REVIEW ANSWERS

2.1 The proton and nucleus are both positive, so they repel each other. Therefore, the proton must have enough kinetic energy to overcome the potential energy caused by the repulsion. The uncharged neutron feels no repulsive force.

2.2 down, into Earth

2.3 Negative. The direction of bending is the same.

2.4 Critical Thinking: udd $\rightarrow$ uud + W^- and $W^- \rightarrow e^- + \bar{\nu}$.

CLOSING CHAPTER 30

Review Summary statements and Key Terms with your students.

ASSESSMENT

Vocabulary Review Master, Teacher Resource Package. Use this master to check students' understanding of Key Terms.

Evaluation Masters. Use Parts A and B of the Chapter Evaluation Masters from the Teacher Resource Package to test qualitative chapter objectives. Use Parts C and D to test quantitative chapter objectives.

CHAPTER 30 REVIEW

SUMMARY

30.1 Radioactivity

- The number of protons in a nucleus is given by the atomic number.
- The sum of the numbers of protons and neutrons in a nucleus is equal to the mass number.
- Atoms having nuclei with the same number of protons but different numbers of neutrons are called isotopes.
- An unstable nucleus undergoes radioactive decay, transmuting into another element.
- Radioactive decay produces three kinds of particles. Alpha (α) particles are helium nuclei; beta (β) particles are high speed electrons; and gamma (γ) rays are high energy photons.

30.2 The Building Blocks of Matter

- In nuclear reactions, the sum of the mass number, *A*, and the total charge is not changed.
- The half-life of a radioactive isotope is the time required for half of the nuclei to decay.
- The number of decays of a particle per second, the activity, is also reduced by a factor of two in a time equal to the half-life.
- Bombardment of nuclei by protons, neutrons, alpha particles, electrons, gamma rays, or other nuclei can produce a nuclear reaction.
- Linear accelerators and synchrotrons produce the high energy protons and electrons.
- The Geiger counter and other particle detectors use the ionization of charged particles passing through matter.
- In beta decay, an uncharged, massless antineutrino is emitted with the electron.
- A positron (antimatter electron) and a neutrino are emitted by radioactive nuclei in a process called positron decay.
- When antimatter and matter combine, all mass is converted into energy or lighter matter-antimatter particle pairs.
- By pair production, energy is transformed into a matter-antimatter particle pair.
- The weak interaction, or weak force, operates in beta decay. The strong force binds the nucleus together.
- Protons and neutrons, together called nucleons, are composed of still smaller particles called quarks.
- All matter appears to be made up of two families of particles, quarks and leptons.

REVIEW MASTER

Use the Vocabulary Review master for Chapter 30 with this section.

EVALUATION MASTER

Use the Chapter Evaluation master for Chapter 30 with this section.

Answers To
REVIEWING CONCEPTS

1. u

2. Transmutation is the change of one element into another by means of a nuclear reaction caused by radioactive decay or nuclear bombardment. For example, uranium-238 decays into thorium-234 and an alpha particle.

3. a helium nucleus, an electron, and a high-energy photon

4. The atomic number is reduced by 2, and the mass number is reduced by 4.
$Z \rightarrow Z - 2; A \rightarrow A - 4$

5. The atomic number is increased by 1, and there is no change in the mass number.
$Z \rightarrow Z + 1; A \rightarrow A$

6. the atomic number, to conserve charge; the mass number, to conserve mass

7. It accelerates particles using electrical force, and the neutron has no charge.

8. The gamma ray or high-speed charged particle hits an atom. The atom becomes excited. When the electron returns to its ground state, the atom emits a photon.

9. a. electromagnetic, weak, gravitational; **b.** strong, electromagnetic, gravitational; **c.** weak

10. The atomic number decreases by 1, and there is no change in the mass number.
$Z \rightarrow Z - 1; A \rightarrow A$

11. a. $^{1}_{1}p$ or $^{1}_{1}H$; **b.** $^{1}_{0}n$; **c.** $^{0}_{1}e(e^{+})$; **d.** $^{0}_{-1}e(e^{-})$; **e.** α or $^{4}_{2}He$

Answers To
APPLYING CONCEPTS

1. Large nuclei, because the protons are farther apart and the neutrons are able to decay.

2. Uranium-238 has 146 neutrons compared to 143 in uranium-235.

3. *A*, because it is the sum of the number of neutrons plus *Z*.

4. Gamma radiation, since they are both photons.

5. No. Both *Z* and *A* are smaller than that of the α.

6. The material with the shorter half-life is more active and will give a higher reading on the detector.

7. Carbon is present in skeletons but not in metal armor.

8. It would annihilate with an equivalent amount of matter, producing an extremely large amount of energy.

KEY TERMS

proton
atomic mass unit
atomic number
neutron
mass number
isotope
nuclide
radioactive
radioactive decay
α decay
β decay
γ decay
transmutation
nuclear reaction
half-life
activity
linear accelerator
synchrotron
Geiger-Mueller tube
Wilson cloud chamber
bubble chamber
spark chamber
quark
lepton
gluon
weak boson
graviton
antiparticle
neutrino
positron
pair production
meson
baryon

REVIEWING CONCEPTS

1. What is the symbol for the atomic mass unit?
2. Define the term *transmutation* as used in nuclear physics and give an example.
3. What are the common names for an α particle, β particle, and γ radiation?
4. What happens to the atomic number and mass number of a nucleus that emits an alpha particle?
5. What happens to the atomic number and mass number of a nucleus that emits a beta particle?
6. What two quantities must always be conserved in any nuclear equation?
7. Why would a linear accelerator not work with a neutron?
8. Explain how a scintillation counter detects gamma rays and high-speed charged particles.
9. In which of the four interactions (strong, weak, electromagnetic, gravitational) does the following particle take part?
   a. electron **b.** proton **c.** neutrino
10. What happens to the atomic number and mass number of a nucleus that emits a positron?
11. Give the symbol, mass, and charge of the following particles.
    a. proton **c.** positron **e.** α particle
    b. neutron **d.** electron

APPLYING CONCEPTS

1. Which are generally more unstable, small or large nuclei?
2. Which isotope has the greater number of neutrons, uranium-235 or uranium-238?
3. Which is usually larger, *A* or *Z*? Explain.
4. Which is most like an X ray, alpha particles, beta particles, or gamma radiation?
5. Could a deuteron, $^{2}_{1}H$, decay via alpha decay? Explain.
6. Which will give a higher reading on a radiation detector: equal amounts of a radioactive substance that has a short half-life or a radioactive substance that has a long half-life?
7. Why is carbon dating useful in establishing the age of campfires but not the age of a set of knight's armor?
8. What would happen if a meteorite made of antiprotons, antineutrons, and positrons landed on Earth?

PROBLEMS

30.1 Radioactivity

1. An atom of an isotope of magnesium has an atomic mass of about 24 u. The atomic number of magnesium is 12. How many neutrons are in the nucleus of this atom?
2. An atom of an isotope of nitrogen has an atomic mass of about 15 u. The atomic number of nitrogen is 7. How many neutrons are in the nucleus of this isotope?
3. List the number of neutrons in an atom of each of these isotopes.
   a. $^{112}_{48}Cd$ **c.** $^{208}_{83}Bi$ **e.** $^{1}_{1}H$
   b. $^{209}_{83}Bi$ **d.** $^{80}_{35}Br$ **f.** $^{40}_{18}Ar$
4. Find the symbol for the elements that are shown by the following symbols, where X replaces the symbol for the element.
   a. $^{18}_{9}X$ **b.** $^{241}_{95}X$ **c.** $^{21}_{10}X$ **d.** $^{7}_{3}X$
5. A radioactive bismuth isotope, $^{214}_{83}Bi$, emits a β particle. Write the complete nuclear equation, showing the element formed.
6. A radioactive polonium isotope, $^{210}_{84}Po$, emits an α particle. Write the complete nuclear equation, showing the element formed.
7. An unstable chromium isotope, $^{56}_{24}Cr$, emits a β particle. Write a complete equation, showing the element formed.

8. During a reaction, two deuterons, ${}^{2}_{1}H$, combine to form a helium isotope, ${}^{3}_{2}He$. What other particle is produced?

9. On the sun, the nuclei of four ordinary hydrogen atoms combine to form a helium isotope, ${}^{4}_{2}He$. What type of particles are missing from the following equation for this reaction?

$$4{}^{1}_{1}H \rightarrow {}^{4}_{2}He + ?$$

10. Write a complete nuclear equation for the transmutation of a uranium isotope, ${}^{227}_{92}U$, into a thorium isotope, ${}^{223}_{90}Th$.

▶ 11. ${}^{238}_{92}U$ decays by α emission and two successive β emissions back into uranium again. Show the three nuclear decay equations and predict the atomic mass number of the uranium formed.

12. In an accident in a research laboratory, a radioactive isotope with a half-life of three days is spilled. As a result, the radiation is eight times the maximum permissible amount. How long must workers wait before they can enter the room?

13. If the half-life of an isotope is two years, what fraction of the isotope remains after six years?

14. The half-life of strontium-90 is 28 years. After 280 years, how would the intensity of a sample of strontium-90 compare to the original intensity of the sample?

▶ 15. A Geiger counter registers an initial reading of 3200 counts, measuring a radioactive substance and 100 counts 30 hours later. What is the half-life of this substance?

▶ 16. A 14-g sample of ${}^{14}_{6}C$ contains Avogadro's number, 6.02×10^{23}, nuclei. A 5.0 g-sample of ${}^{14}_{6}C$ will have how many nondecayed nuclei after 11 460 years?

▶ 17. A 1.00-μg sample of a radioactive material contains 6.0×10^{14} nuclei. After 48 hours, 0.25 μg of the material remains.
   a. What is the half-life of the material?
   b. How could one determine the activity of the sample at 24 hours using this information?

30.2 The Building Blocks of Matter

▶ 18. The synchrotron at FermiLab has a diameter of 2.0 km. Protons circling in it move at approximately the speed of light.
   a. How long does it take a proton to complete one revolution?
   b. The protons enter the ring at an energy of 8.0 GeV. They gain 2.5 MeV each revolution. How many revolutions must they travel before they reach 400 GeV energy?
   c. How long does it take the protons to be accelerated to 400 GeV?
   d. How far do the protons travel during this acceleration?

19. What would be the charge of a particle composed of three *u* quarks?

20. The charge of an antiquark is opposite that of a quark. A pion is composed of a *u* quark and an *anti-d* quark. What would be the charge of this pion?

21. Find the charges of the following pions made of
   a. *u* and *anti-u* quark pair.
   b. *d* and *anti-u* quarks.
   c. *d* and *anti-d* quarks.

USING A GRAPHING CALCULATOR

An archaeological expedition in Jerusalem finds three wooden bowls, each in a different part of the city. An analysis of the levels of carbon-14 reveals that the three bowls have 90%, 75%, and 60% of the carbon-14 one would expect to find in a similar bowl made today. The equation for the decay of carbon-14 is $y = 100 \cdot 2^{(-x/5730)}$, where *y* is the percentage of carbon-14 remaining and *x* is the age of the object in years. Graph this equation on a graphing calculator with axes scaled from 0 to 5000 years and from 100% to 50%. Trace along the equation to find the age of the three objects.

USING LAB SKILLS

1. In the Pocket Lab on page 627, you were able to see that the magnet caused the short, wide tracks to curve. What does this indicate about the radiation? You may have also noticed that the long thin track did not curve. Suggest a possible reason.

THINKING PHYSIC-LY

Why is a sample of radioactive material always a little warmer than its surrounding?

Answers To
PROBLEMS

Complete solutions for all Chapter Review Problems can be found in the Problems and Solutions Manual accompanying this text.

1. 12 neutrons
2. 8 neutrons
3. **a.** 64 **e.** 0
   b. 126 **f.** 22
   c. 125
   d. 45
4. **a.** F **b.** Am **c.** Ne **d.** Li
5. ${}^{214}_{83}Bi \rightarrow {}^{214}_{84}Po + {}^{0}_{-1}e$
6. ${}^{210}_{84}Po \rightarrow {}^{206}_{82}Pb + {}^{4}_{2}He$
7. ${}^{56}_{24}Cr \rightarrow {}^{56}_{25}Mn + {}^{0}_{-1}e$
8. ${}^{2}_{1}H + {}^{2}_{1}H \rightarrow {}^{3}_{2}He + {}^{1}_{0}n$
9. $4{}^{1}_{1}H \rightarrow {}^{4}_{2}He + 2{}^{0}_{1}e$
10. ${}^{227}_{92}U \rightarrow {}^{223}_{90}Th + {}^{4}_{2}He$
11. ${}^{238}_{92}U \rightarrow {}^{234}_{90}Th + {}^{4}_{2}He$
    ${}^{234}_{90}Th \rightarrow {}^{234}_{91}Pa + {}^{0}_{-1}e$
    ${}^{234}_{91}Pa \rightarrow {}^{234}_{92}U + {}^{0}_{-1}e$
    $A = 234$
12. 9 days
13. $\frac{1}{8}$
14. 0.098%
15. 6 h
16. 5.4×10^{22} nuclei
17. Refer to Problems and Solutions Manual.
    a. 24 h
    b. the slope of the line of a graph of remaining nuclei versus time; slope $= 9 \times 10^{12}$ nuclei/s
18. **a.** 2.1×10^{-5} s
    b. 1.6×10^{5} revolutions
    c. 3.4 s
    d. 1.0×10^{9} m
19. + 2 elementary charges
20. + 1 elementary charge
21. **a.** 0 charge
    b. −1 charge
    c. 0 charge

Answers To
USING A GRAPHING CALCULATOR

1. Set the range values (RANGE 0 5000 1000 50 100 10)
2. Clear the graph (Cls EXE)
3. Graph the equation (GRAPH 100* 2 SHIFT X^Y (X/ −5730)EXE)
4. Trace along the graph to the three x's and find the y's (TRACE −> X<−>Y)

Answers: The bowls are 850, 2400, and 4200 years old.

Answer To
USING LAB SKILLS

1. The short wide tracks were alpha particles with a charge of +2. The massive alpha is not very penetrating, but curves in the strong magnetic field. The long thin tracks were made by faster, less charged particles. Possibilities are beta particles with a charge of −1 or even gamma radiation with zero charge.

Answer To
THINKING PHYSIC-LY

Radioactive decay gives off energy that warms the sample.

CHAPTER

31 Nuclear Applications

PLANNING GUIDE (6 class sessions)

CONTENTS	TEXT FEATURES	TEACHER RESOURCE PACKAGE	OTHER COMPONENTS
31.1 Holding the Nucleus Together, pp. 640–643 (2 Class Sessions) • The Strong Nuclear Force • Binding Energy of the Nucleus	**Pocket Lab:** Binding Energy, p. 641 **Concept Review,** p. 643	**Study Guide:** Holding the Nucleus Together	
31.2 Using Nuclear Energy, pp. 643–653 (4 Class Sessions) • Artificial Radioactivity • Nuclear Fission • Nuclear Reactors • Nuclear Fusion • Controlled Fusion	**Physics Lab:** Hot Stuff, p. 650 **Physics and Society:** Nuclear Waste Disposal, p. 646 **Pocket Lab:** Power Plant, p. 647 **Concept Review,** p. 653	**Study Guide:** Using Nuclear Energy **Physics Lab Data Sheet:** Hot Stuff **Critical Thinking Master:** The Penetrating Power of Radiation **Enrichment Master:** Carbon Dating **Reteaching Master:** A Debate About Nuclear Power Plants **Transparency Worksheet:** Fission/Fusion	**Laboratory Manual:** Lab 31.1 Radioactive Shielding **Transparency 47:** Fission/Fusion
Chapter Review, pp. 653–655	Summary Key Terms Reviewing Concepts Applying Concepts Problems Thinking Physic-ly	**Vocabulary Review** **Chapter Test**	**Test Bank**

SUPPLEMENTARY MATERIALS

SOFTWARE	AUDIOVISUAL	BOOKS/MAGAZINES
Atomic Structure 2, Queue, Inc. (Apple II). *Three Mile Island,* Queue, Inc. (Apple II).	Videos: *Alternative Energy Sources: Nuclear Power,* Queue, Inc. *Nuclear Power—In France It Works,* Films Inc. Filmstrip: *Nuclear Energy: Too Hot to Handle?,* Current Affairs.	Golay, Michael W., and Todreas, Neil E. "Advanced Light-Water Reactors." *Scientific American,* April 1990, p. 82. Hewitt, Paul. "Why Is the Hot Spring Hot?" *The Physics Teacher,* May 1987, p. 339. Marzewski, Robert. "Chain Reaction Model." *The Physics Teacher,* November 1988, p. 514. Segrè, E. G. "The Discovery of Nuclear Fission." *Physics Today,* July 1989, p. 38.

PROBLEM CORRELATION

CONCEPTS	CHAPTER REVIEW			PROBLEMS APPENDIX
	Reviewing Concepts	Applying Concepts	Problems	
31.1 Holding the Nucleus Together				
The Strong Nuclear Force	1			
Binding Energy of the Nucleus	2	1,2	1,2,3,4,**5,6**	1,2,3,**4,13**
31.2 Using Nuclear Energy				
Artificial Radioactivity	3	3	7,8,9,10,11,12, 13,14,**15,16**	5,6,7,8,**9**
Nuclear Fission	4,5,6		**17,**18,19,20	10,11,12
Nuclear Reactors	7,8,9	4,6,7	**23**	
Nuclear Fusion	10,11	5	21,**22**	**14,**15
Controlled Fusion	12	8		

ACTIVITY AND DEMONSTRATION MATERIALS

PHYSICS LAB	POCKET LAB	DEMONSTRATIONS
Page 650 photocell voltmeter ammeter electrical leads ruler	Pages 641, 647 disk magnets wood or plastic disks contact or rubber cement telephone	Page 647 dominoes

EXTENSION PROJECTS

LIBRARY RESEARCH

1. Cold Fusion
Investigate cold fusion. Why did the initial findings cause such a stir in the scientific community?

HANDS–ON

2. Energy Technology
Make a chart of mankind's advancements in energy technology beginning with the discovery of fire and moving chronologically to recent developments such as nuclear power.

STUDENT READINGS

Amato, Ivan. "Hot Fusion Research Reaches a Milestone." *Science News,* October 13, 1990.

Boyd, Derek A. "Taking the Temperature of a Tokamak." *The Physics Teacher,* January 1987.

Eliot, Marshall. "Hanford's Radioactive Tumbleweed." *Science,* June 26, 1987.

Fischetti, Mark A. "Inherently Safe Reactors: They'd Work If We'd Let Them." *IEEE Spectrum,* April 1987.

Häfele, Wolf. "Energy From Nuclear Power." *Scientific American,* September 1990.

Raloff, Janet. "Fallout Over Nevada's Nuclear Destiny." *Science News,* January 6,1990.

Chapter 31

Nuclear Applications

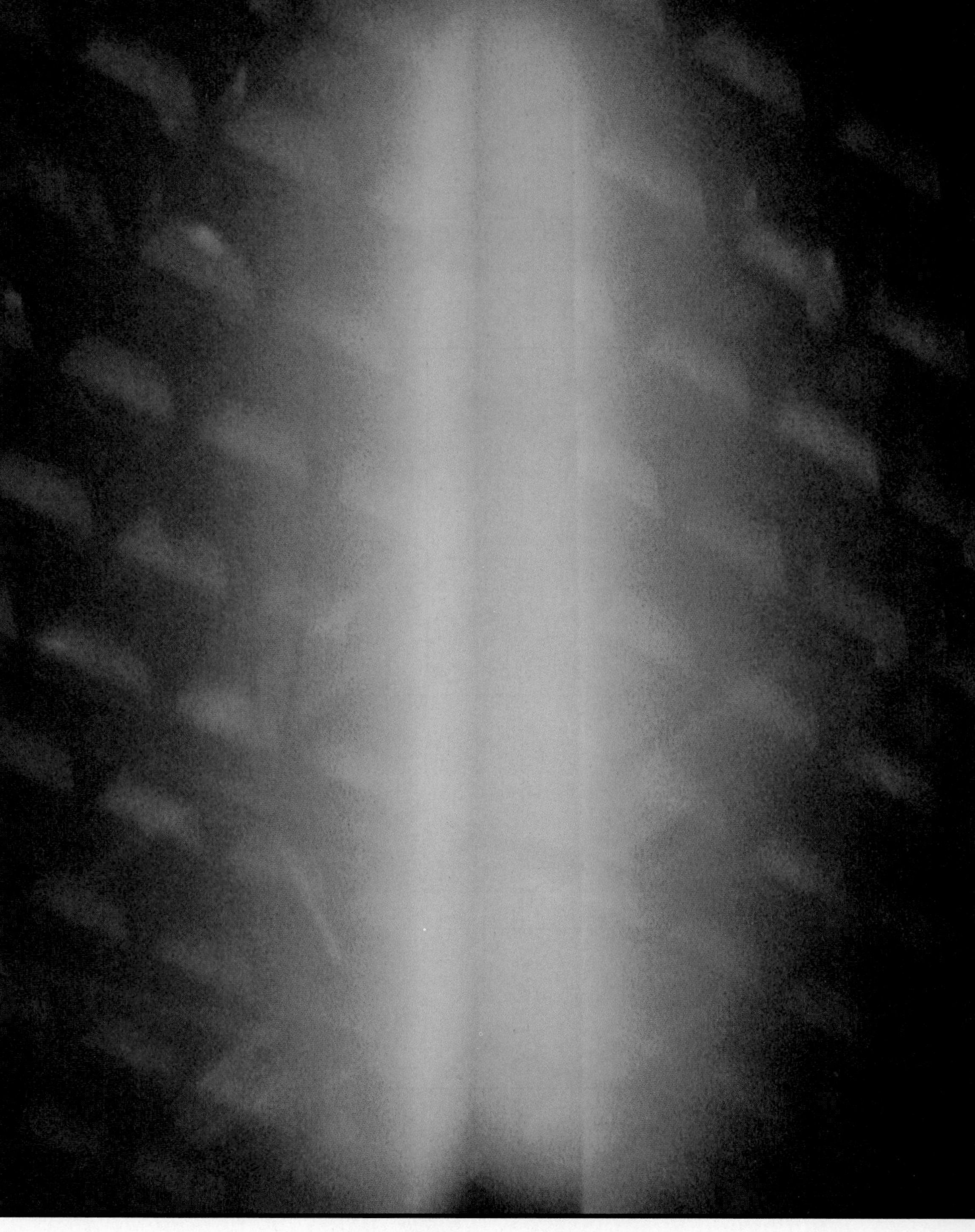

CHAPTER OVERVIEW

Theme Development: Chapter 31 continues to reveal the power of numbers in describing chaotic interactions over an immense scale, as equations are applied to nuclear binding energy, isotope formation and decay, fission reactions, chain reactions, and controlled nuclear fusion.

MISCONCEPTIONS

Without question the subtlest, trickiest concept here is binding energy. Because none of us have direct experience with mass turning to energy, we find the concept very abstract. In addition, most students are under the impression that radioactivity is a man-made phenomenon. On the contrary, natural radioactivity has been around as long as Earth has, as far as we know.

KEY TERMS

binding energy
breeder reactor
chain reaction
controlled fusion
control rod
fission
fusion
inertial confinement fusion
mass defect
moderator
nucleon
strong nuclear force
thermonuclear reaction

Laboratory Options

CHAPTER 31

Nuclear Applications

Shock Waves

One of the more familiar photos of a nuclear reactor is this picture of a bundle of uranium-filled fuel rods in water. What causes the blue glow surrounding the assembly?

Chapter Outline

31.1 HOLDING THE NUCLEUS TOGETHER
- The Strong Nuclear Force
- Binding Energy of the Nucleus

31.2 USING NUCLEAR ENERGY
- Artificial Radioactivity
- Nuclear Fission
- Nuclear Reactors
- Nuclear Fusion
- Controlled Fusion

Few areas of physics are in the news more than nuclear physics. Whether it is nuclear weapons, the storage of waste from medical applications, or nuclear power reactors such as the one shown in the photograph, it seems nuclear physics is always in the news. Unfortunately, most of the publicity is negative. Seldom interviewed are people whose lives have been saved by nuclear medicine or people who can breathe more easily because of the lack of pollution from coal-burning electrical plants. An informed citizen must understand some of the science and technology before passing judgment.

✓ Concept Check

The following terms or concepts from earlier chapters are important for a good understanding of this chapter. If you are not familiar with them, you should review them before studying this chapter.
- nuclear reaction; nuclear particles, Chapter 30

Introducing The Chapter

Shock Waves

Using The Photo: The blue glow in the photograph is called the Cerenkov effect. Contrary to popular belief, the effect is not produced by radioactivity. For further details, refer to page 648.

✓ Concept Check

Make sure students have a clear understanding of the concepts covered in Chapter 30 that are listed in the Concept Check. A basic knowledge of nuclear reactions and nuclear particles is essential for conceptualizing the nuclear applications discussed in this chapter.

Assessment Options

Portfolio Assessment
Extension 1 and 2, TWE, p. 638b
Extension, TWE, p. 642
Developing a Viewpoint, p. 646
Portfolio Assessment, TWE, p. 652

Performance Assessment
Pocket Labs, pp. 641, 647
Physics Lab, p. 650
Pocket Lab Assessment, TWE, p. 641
Activity, TWE, p. 648

Content Assessment
Self Assessment: Practice Problems, pp. 642, 645, 652
Critical Thinking, TWE, p. 641
Assessment, Critical Thinking, TWE, p. 650
Checking for Understanding, TWE, p. 651
Concept Reviews, pp. 643, 653
Chapter Review, pp. 653–655
Supplemental Problems, p. 709

Group Assessment
Activities for group assessment occur with Cooperative Learning and lab activities.

31.1 HOLDING THE NUCLEUS TOGETHER

Preparation

OBJECTIVES

The objectives are listed on the student page. Remind students to preview these objectives as a study guide to this major section.

OVERVIEW

Two major concepts are developed here, the strong nuclear force and the binding energy with its equivalent, mass defect.

BRIDGING

For this section, students will rely on several previously taught terms: repulsive electric force, neutrons, protons, nuclei, work, energy, mass, atomic number, electron volt, and electromagnetic radiation.

1 Focus

DISCREPANT EVENT

Challenge students to recall or figure out the energy involved in a typical chemical reaction. [Broadly speaking, chemical reactions involve the energy needed to rearrange electrons, which is approximately the same energy needed for ionization. Although the electron volt unit may not have been used in chemistry, it turns out that typical ionization energies are a few electron volts.] Now compare that number with the energies involved in nuclear reactions. [This is calculated at a few *million* electron volts in the Example Problem on page 641. So, reaction-for-reaction, nuclear reactions are about a million times more energetic than chemical ones. This factor of a million marks the difference between the atomic and the pre-atomic era!]

2 Teach

CONCEPT DEVELOPMENT

- Remember from the last chapter that 1 eV $= 1.6 \times 10^{-19}$ J.
- The strong nuclear force acts when particles are closer than about 10^{-15} m.

Objectives

- **recognize the role and nature of the strong nuclear force; define the binding energy.**
- **relate the energy released in a nuclear reaction to change in binding energy before and after the reaction.**

31.1 HOLDING THE NUCLEUS TOGETHER

The negatively-charged electrons that surround the positively-charged nucleus of an atom are held in place by the attractive electric force. The nucleus consists of positively-charged protons and neutral neutrons. The repulsive electric force between the protons might be expected to cause them to fly apart. This does not happen because an even stronger attractive force exists within the nucleus.

The Strong Nuclear Force

The strong force acts the same between neutrons and protons or between protons and protons or neutrons and neutrons.

The force that overcomes the mutual repulsion of the charged protons is called the **strong nuclear force**. The strong force acts between protons and neutrons that are very close together, as they are in a nucleus. The range of the strong force is very short, only about the radius of a proton, 1.3×10^{-15} m. It is attractive and is of the same strength between protons and protons, protons and neutrons, and neutrons and neutrons. As a result of this equivalence, both neutrons and protons are called **nucleons**.

The strong force holds the nucleons in the nucleus. If a nucleon were to be pulled out of a nucleus, work would have to be done to overcome the attractive force. Doing work adds energy to the system. Thus, the assembled nucleus has less energy than the separate protons and neutrons that make it up. The difference is the **binding energy** of the nucleus. Thus, the binding energy is negative.

Binding Energy of the Nucleus

The binding energy of a nucleus is proportional to the difference between the mass of the nucleus and the masses of the nucleons from which it is assembled.

Binding energy can be expressed in the form of an equivalent amount of mass, according to the equation $E = mc^2$. The unit of mass used in nuclear physics is the atomic mass unit, u. One atomic mass unit is 1/12 the mass of the $^{12}_{6}$C nucleus.

Because energy has to be added to take a nucleus apart, the mass of the assembled nucleus is less than the sum of the masses of the nucleons that compose it. For example, the helium nucleus, $^{4}_{2}$He, consists of 2 protons and 2 neutrons. The mass of a proton is 1.007825 u. The mass of a neutron is 1.008665 u. The mass of the nucleons that make up the helium nucleus is equal to the sum of the masses of the two protons and the two neutrons. Thus, if it weren't for the binding energy, the mass of the nucleus would be 4.032980 u. Careful measurement, however, shows the mass of a helium nucleus is only 4.002603 u. The mass of the helium nucleus is less than the mass of its constituent parts by 0.0030377 u. The difference, 0.0030377 u is called the **mass defect.** The binding energy can be calculated from the experimentally-determined mass defect by using $E = mc^2$ to compute the energy equivalent of the missing mass.

F.Y.I.

Science is inherently neither a potential for good nor for evil. It is a potential to be harnessed by man to do his bidding.

Glenn T. Seaborg
1951 Nobel Laureate

TEACHER F.Y.I.

When a radioactive nuclide decays, mass is lost and energy is generated, primarily in the form of kinetic energy of the emitted particle and nucleus. This energy is generally dissipated in the form of heat as these energetic particles collide with atoms and molecules in the area.

The electrons of the surrounding atoms are excited in some instances and give up the excess energy as electromagnetic radiation, usually in the form of X rays, visible light, or ultraviolet light. Early in this century luminescent paint was made of an alpha emitter such as radium and a substance such as zinc sulfide to which small amounts of silver had been added. In this paint, electrons could be easily excited by the alphas. Workers who painted watch dials with this paint suffered radiation sickness when they licked the paint brushes. Now luminescent paint contains no radioactive material.

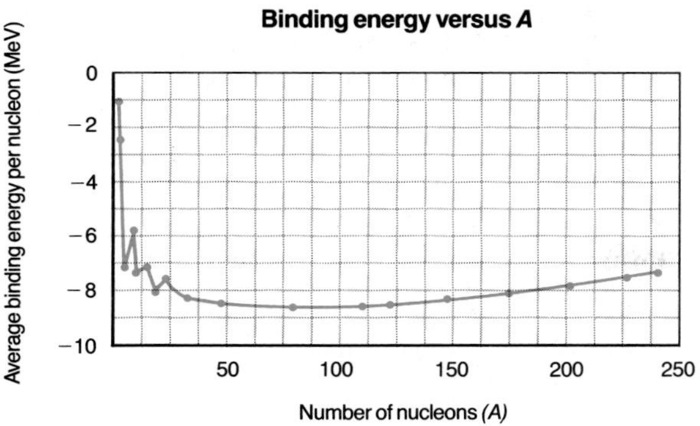

FIGURE 31–1. A graph of the binding energy per nucleon.

Masses are normally measured in atomic mass units. It will be useful, then, to determine the energy equivalent of 1 u (1.6605×10^{-27} kg). The most convenient unit of energy to use is the electron volt. To five significant digits,

$$\begin{aligned} E &= mc^2 \\ &= (1.6605 \times 10^{-27}\ \text{kg})(2.9979 \times 10^{8}\ \text{m/s})^2 \\ &= (14.923 \times 10^{-11}\ \text{J})(1\ \text{eV}/1.6022 \times 10^{-19}\ \text{J}) \\ &= 9.3149 \times 10^{8}\ \text{eV} \\ E &= 931.49\ \text{MeV}. \end{aligned}$$

The energy equivalent of one atomic mass unit is 931.5 MeV.

A useful relationship is shown by the graph of binding energy per nucleon in Figure 31–1.

Example Problem

Calculating Mass Defect and Nuclear Binding Energy

The mass of a proton is 1.007825 u. The mass of a neutron is 1.008665 u. The mass of the nucleus of the radioactive hydrogen isotope tritium, ${}^{3}_{1}\text{H}$, is 3.016049 u. **a.** What is the nuclear mass defect of this isotope? **b.** What is the binding energy of tritium?

Solution:

a. As indicated by the superscript and subscript in the symbol for tritium, its nucleus contains 1 proton and 2 neutrons.

mass of 1 proton =	1.007825 u
mass of 2 neutrons = (2)(1.008665 u) =	2.017330 u
total mass of nucleons =	3.025155 u
mass of tritium nucleus =	3.016049 u
less total mass of nucleons	−3.025155 u
mass defect =	−0.009106 u

b. Since 1 u is equivalent to 931.49 MeV, the binding energy of the tritium nucleus can be calculated.

binding energy of ${}^{3}_{1}\text{H}$ nucleus,

$E = (-0.009106\ \text{u})(931.49\ \text{MeV/u})$

$= -8.482$ MeV

POCKET LAB

BINDING ENERGY

Particles within the nucleus experience the strong force as well as the electric force. Use a few disk magnets (to represent protons) and an equal number of plastic or wood disks the same size (to represent neutrons). Orient the magnets so the same pole faces upward. The magnetic force represents the electric repulsion between the charged particles. Coat the edges of the disks with rubber cement to represent the strong force that is felt only when particles touch. Start by building a hydrogen nucleus, then a deuterium (${}^{2}_{1}\text{H}$), then a tritium (${}^{3}_{1}\text{H}$). Now add a second proton to form helium (${}^{4}_{2}\text{He}$). Describe the forces you feel. When does the strong force act?

CONCEPT DEVELOPMENT

In larger nuclei, each nucleon only "feels" the nuclear attraction of its neighbors because of the limited range of interaction of the nuclear force. Scientists have not found a simple equation that can express the strong nuclear force.

Study Guide Master. To reinforce the concepts in this section, have the students complete the Study Guide Master for Section 31.1 from the Teacher Resource Package.

Critical Thinking: Ask students why there is an end to the periodic table. [Broadly speaking, with the strong nuclear force affecting only neighboring nucleons and the repulsive electric force acting between all nucleons, the electric force dominates. Large nuclei tend to be unstable, with very short half-lives.]

Guided Practice: Go over the Example Problem on this page as a class exercise, then have students work on the Practice Problems that follow.

INDEPENDENT PRACTICE/ EXTENSION

Refer to the Assignment Guide on page 642 for additional questions and problems for independent practice.

POCKET LAB

BINDING ENERGY

Purpose: to model the electrostatic and strong forces within the nucleus.

Materials: several disk magnets, wood or plastic disks the same diameter, contact or rubber cement.

Outcome: No repulsive electric force is felt until the second proton is added. Then work has to be done to overcome the repulsion. The strong force holding this nucleus together acts only when the particles are touching.

Assessment

Performance

To further assess students' understanding of nuclear binding energy, have them use their models to explore such nuclei as lithium-7 (${}^{7}_{3}\text{Li}$) and beryllium-7 (${}^{7}_{4}\text{Be}$). These two are called mirror nuclei because they have the same number of nuclear particles (7), but one has more protons, while the other has more neutrons. Which would you expect to be more stable? Ask how the model helps make this prediction. [Lithium-7 would be more stable because the repulsive force is smaller because there are only three protons out of the seven particles. The strong force is the same in both cases. Students can feel this extra repulsive force as they assemble their model nuclei.]

Answers To
PRACTICE PROBLEMS

Have students refer to Appendix A of the Solutions Appendix for complete solutions to Practice Problems.

1. a. −0.098940 u
   b. −92.162 MeV
2. a. −0.0025 u
   b. −2.3 MeV
3. a. −0.12399 u
   b. −115.50 MeV
4. a. −0.13701 u
   b. −127.62 MeV

CONCEPT DEVELOPMENT

Make sure that students understand the difference between fission and fusion.

CHECKING FOR UNDERSTANDING

Ask students how energy can be liberated or absorbed in nuclear reactions. [By radiation (usually X rays or gamma rays), kinetic energy of the nuclei or particles involved, or a change in potential energy (mass defect).]

RETEACHING

Under the influence of only the repulsive electrostatic force, the nucleus should fly apart. However, since most nuclei are stable, some other force must be present. This force is known as the strong nuclear force. Point out that in a nuclear reaction, as in any reaction, the total energy is conserved. The mass of the assembled nucleus is not equal to the sum of the masses of its parts. The difference in mass is called the mass defect and can be considered as a form of potential energy. If the nucleus is more massive than its parts, then the extra mass can be released in the form of kinetic energy when the nucleus undergoes radioactive decay of fission. If the nucleus is less massive than its parts, then fusing the parts releases energy.

EXTENSION

Refer to the graph of binding energy per nucleon in Figure 31–1 on page 641. Note that iron is at the peak of the chart. Have interested students investigate how this curve of binding energy influences the production of elements in the stars.

F. Y. I.

Idealists maintain that all nations should share the atomic bomb. Pessimists maintain they will.

—Punch

Practice Problems

Use these values in the following problems: mass of proton = 1.007825 u; mass of neutron = 1.008665 u; 1 u = 931.49 MeV.

1. The carbon isotope, $^{12}_{6}C$, has a nuclear mass of 12.0000 u.
   a. Calculate its mass defect.
   b. Calculate its binding energy in MeV.
2. The isotope of hydrogen that contains 1 proton and 1 neutron is called deuterium. The mass of its nucleus is 2.0140 u.
   a. What is its mass defect?
   b. What is the binding energy of deuterium in MeV?
3. A nitrogen isotope, $^{15}_{7}N$, has 7 protons and 8 neutrons. Its nucleus has a mass of 15.00011 u.
   a. Calculate the mass defect of this nucleus.
   b. Calculate the binding energy of the nucleus.
4. ▶ An oxygen isotope, $^{16}_{8}O$, has a nuclear mass of 15.99491 u.
   a. What is the mass defect of this isotope?
   b. What is the binding energy of its nucleus?

Iron-56 has the most negative binding energy per nucleon.

When you worked the Practice Problems you found that the heavier nuclei were bound more strongly than lighter nuclei. Except for a few nuclei, the binding energy per nucleon becomes more negative as A increases to a value of 56, iron, Fe. $^{56}_{26}Fe$ is the most tightly bound nucleus. Nuclei larger than iron are less strongly bound.

A nuclear reaction will occur naturally if energy is released by the reaction. Energy will be released if the nucleus that results from the reaction is more tightly bound than the original nucleus. When a heavy nucleus, such as $^{238}_{92}U$, decays by releasing an alpha particle, the binding energy per nucleon of the resulting $^{234}_{90}Th$ is larger than that of the uranium. The excess energy of the $^{238}_{92}U$ nucleus is transferred into the kinetic energy of the alpha particle. At low atomic numbers, reactions that add nucleons to a nucleus make the binding energy of the nucleus more negative. Thus the energy of the larger nucleus is less than the sum of the energies of the two smaller ones. Energy is released when the reaction occurs. In the sun and other stars, the production of heavier nuclei like helium and carbon from hydrogen releases energy that eventually becomes the electromagnetic radiation by which we see the stars.

FIGURE 31–2. The strawberries in the two cartons are identical except that those in the carton on the left have been treated with gamma radiation to destroy the bacteria causing spoilage.

STUDY GUIDE MASTER

Use the Study Guide master for section 31.1.

31:1 ASSIGNMENT GUIDE

	PRACTICE	EXTENSION
CHAPTER REVIEW pp. 653–655		
· Reviewing Concepts	1–2	
· Applying Concepts		1–2
· Problems*	1–4	5–6
APPENDIX B PROBLEMS*		
· Chapter 31, p. 709	1–3	4, 13

* Complete solutions to all Chapter Review and Appendix problems appear in the Problems and Solutions Manual.

CONCEPT REVIEW

1.1 When tritium, ${}^3_1H$, decays, it emits a β particle and becomes ${}^3_2He$. Which nucleus would you expect to have a more negative binding energy?

1.2 Which of the two nuclei above would have the larger mass defect?

1.3 The range of the strong force is so short that only nucleons that touch each other feel the force. Use this fact to explain why in very large nuclei the repulsive electric force can overcome the strong attractive force and make the nucleus unstable.

1.4 Critical Thinking: In old stars, not only are helium and carbon produced by joining more tightly-bound nuclei, but so are oxygen ($Z = 8$) and silicon ($Z = 14$). What would be the atomic number of the heaviest nucleus that could be formed this way? Explain.

31.2 USING NUCLEAR ENERGY

Objectives

- define artificially produced radioactive isotopes; describe their medical uses; solve nuclear equations involving the formation and decay of radioactive isotopes.
- define nuclear fission and a chain reaction; understand the source of energy in fission.
- describe the operation of one or more types of nuclear reactors; understand the formation of plutonium in a reactor.
- describe the fusion process and the formation of helium in the sun.
- describe two approaches to controlled nuclear fusion.

In no other area of physics has basic knowledge led to applications as quickly as in the field of nuclear physics. The medical use of the radioactive element radium began within 20 years of its discovery. Proton accelerators were tested for medical applications less than one year after being invented. In the case of nuclear fission, the military application was under development before the basic physics was even known. Peaceful applications followed in less than 10 years. The question of the uses of nuclear science in our society is an important one for all citizens today.

Artificial Radioactivity

Radioactive isotopes not found in nature can be produced by bombarding nuclei.

Marie and Pierre Curie had noted as early as 1899 that substances placed close to radioactive uranium became radioactive themselves. In 1934, Irene Joliot-Curie and Frederic Joliot bombarded aluminum with alpha particles, producing neutrons by the reaction

$$ {}^4_2He + {}^{27}_{13}Al \rightarrow {}^{30}_{15}P + {}^1_0n. $$

In addition to neutrons, the Curies found another particle coming from the aluminum, a positively-charged electron, or positron. The positron, a particle with the same mass as the electron but with a positive charge, had been discovered two years earlier by American Carl Anderson. The most interesting result of the Curies' experiment was that positrons continued to be emitted after the alpha bombardment stopped. The positrons were found to come from the phosphorus isotope ${}^{30}_{15}P$. The Curies had produced a radioactive isotope not previously known.

Radioactive isotopes can be formed from stable isotopes by bombardment with alpha particles, protons, neutrons, electrons, or gamma rays. The resulting unstable nuclei emit radiation until they are transmuted into stable isotopes. The radioactive nuclei may emit alpha, beta, and gamma radiation as well as positrons.

Multicultural Connections

Hideki Yukawa was the first Japanese to receive the Nobel Prize. He accomplished this by developing a theory about what holds the nucleus of the atom together. He reasoned that there must be a nuclear force which involved the transfer of some entity other than a proton or neutron. His theory also stated that this force must be stronger over short distances than electromagnetic forces in order to overcome the repulsion beween protons. When he published his theory in 1935, no particle had been discovered which matched the exchange particle his ideas required. Although a particle was discovered the next year which appeared close, it was not until 1947 that the particle Yukawa predicted was actually found. As a result of the verification of his theory, Yukawa was awarded the Nobel Prize in 1949.

3 Close

CONVERGENT QUESTION

Discuss with students how the two conservation principles of mass and energy have been combined into one principle of mass plus energy conservation by the equation $E = mc^2$.

CONCEPT REVIEW ANSWERS

1.1 The tritium nucleus, because tritium emits a particle with mass and kinetic energy in its decay.

1.2 the tritium nucleus

1.3 The electric force is long range and one proton repels every other proton in the nucleus, but attracts, via the strong force, only those nucleons touching it. The repulsive force grows, with increasing nuclear size, faster than the strong force. Eventually, the repulsive force on some of the nucleons becomes larger than the nuclear force.

1.4 Critical Thinking: Iron, because its binding energy is largest.

31.2 USING NUCLEAR ENERGY

Preparation

OBJECTIVES

The objectives are listed on the student page. Remind students to preview these objectives as a study guide to this major section.

OVERVIEW

Energy production from nuclear reactions and the production of various radioactive materials by means of artifical radioactivity are the main ideas presented in this section.

BRIDGING

Previously taught terms and concepts important to this section are: accelerator; alpha, beta, and gamma radiation; position; electron; neutron; isotope; Geiger-Mueller counter; temperature; generator; thermal kinetic energy; and magnetic field.

1 Focus

Power companies often have people available who can come to your class to discuss the operation of the nuclear power plant. Or, if possible, set up a field trip to a nearby nuclear power plant.

2 Teach

CONCEPT DEVELOPMENT

- Some say the chain reaction was the beginning of the atomic age.
- France gets a very high percentage of its electric energy from nuclear power plants. They have standardized reactor designs.
- Natural radioactive decay of atomic nuclei in Earth's interior releases thermal energy. Among other things, this energy warms up hot springs and may drive volcanic action.

Study Guide Master. To reinforce the concepts in this section, have the students complete the Study Guide Master for Section 31.2 from the Teacher Resource Package.

Laboratory Manual. For practice with radioactive emission concepts, assign Lab 31.1, Radioactive Shielding.

FIGURE 31–3. PET scanner results.

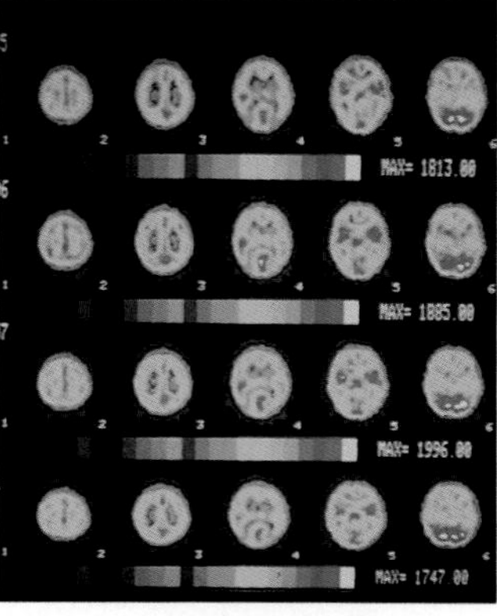

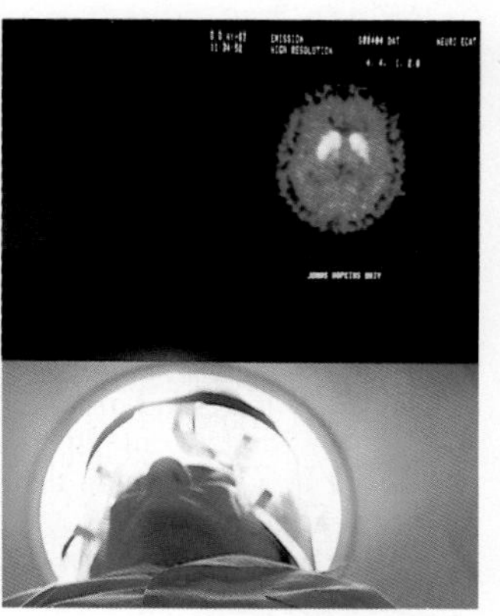

Tracer isotopes allow doctors to follow the path of molecules through the body.

Artificially produced radioactive isotopes have many uses, especially in medicine. In many medical applications, patients are given radioactive isotopes that are absorbed by specific parts of the body. The detection of the decay products of these isotopes allows doctors to trace the movement of the isotopes, and of the molecules to which they are attached, through the body. For that reason, these isotopes are called tracer isotopes. Iodine, for example, is primarily used in the thyroid gland. A patient is given an iodine compound containing radioactive $^{131}_{53}I$. The iodine concentrates in the thyroid gland. A physician uses a Geiger-Mueller counter to monitor the activity of $^{131}_{53}I$ in the region of the thyroid. The amount of iodine taken up by this gland is a measure of its ability to function.

MEDICINE CONNECTION

A new instrument, the Positron Emission Tomography Scanner, or PET scanner, Figure 31–3, uses isotopes that emit positrons. Such an isotope is included in a solution injected into the patient's body. In the body, the isotope decays, releasing a positron. The positron annihilates an electron, emitting two gamma rays. The PET scanner detects the gammas and pinpoints the location of the positron-emitting isotope. A computer is then used to make a three-dimensional map of the isotope distribution. By this means, details such as the use of nutrients in particular regions of the brain can be traced. For example, if a person in a PET scanner were solving a physics problem, more nutrients would flow to the part of the brain being used to solve the problem. The decay of the positrons in this part of the brain would increase, and the PET scanner could map this area.

A PET scanner makes a three-dimensional map of the distribution of decaying nuclei in the body.

Another use of radioactivity in medicine is the destruction of cells. Often gamma rays from the isotope $^{60}_{27}Co$ are used to treat cancer patients. The ionizing radiation produced by radioactive iodine can be used to destroy cells in a diseased thyroid gland, with minimal harm to the rest of the body. Another method of reducing damage to healthy cells is to use unstable particles produced by particle accelerators like the synchrotron. These unstable particles pass through body tissue without doing damage. When they decay, however, the emitted particles destroy cells. The physician adjusts the accelerator so the particles decay only in the cancerous tissue.

Ionizing radiation can destroy cells.

TEACHER

Ionization is the knocking-out of electrons from atoms to form charged atoms. Alpha rays, beta rays, gamma rays, X rays, neutrons, and protons all cause ionization, excitation, and chemical changes in plant and animal cells that may include somatic (structural) changes in the genes of an organism. Low-level ionizing radiation was once thought to be only minimally dangerous. Today, there is increasing concern over its long-term effects.

Practice Problems

5. Use Table D–5 of the Appendix to complete the following nuclear equations.
   a. ${}^{14}_{6}C \rightarrow ? + {}^{0}_{-1}e$
   b. ${}^{55}_{24}Cr \rightarrow ? + {}^{0}_{-1}e$
6. Write the nuclear equation for the transmutation of a uranium isotope, ${}^{238}_{92}U$, into a thorium isotope, ${}^{234}_{90}Th$, by emission of an alpha particle.
7. A radioactive polonium isotope, ${}^{214}_{84}Po$, undergoes alpha decay and becomes lead. Write the nuclear equation.
8. Write the nuclear equations for the beta decay of these isotopes.
   a. ${}^{210}_{82}Pb$ **b.** ${}^{210}_{83}Bi$ **c.** ${}^{234}_{90}Th$ **d.** ${}^{239}_{93}Np$

F. Y. I.

Whatever nature has in store for mankind, unpleasant as it may be, men must accept, for ignorance is never better than knowledge.

—Enrico Fermi

Nuclear Fission

The possibility of obtaining useful forms of energy from nuclear reactions was discussed in the 1930s. The most promising results came from bombarding substances with neutrons. In Italy, in 1934, Enrico Fermi and Emilio Segré produced many new radioactive isotopes by bombarding uranium with neutrons. They believed they had formed new elements with atomic numbers larger than 92, that of uranium.

German chemists Otto Hahn and Fritz Strassmann made careful chemical studies of the results of bombardment of uranium by neutrons. In 1939, their analyses showed that the resulting atoms acted chemically like barium. The two chemists could not understand how barium, with an atomic number of 56, could be produced from uranium. One week later, Lise Meitner and Otto Frisch proposed that the neutrons had

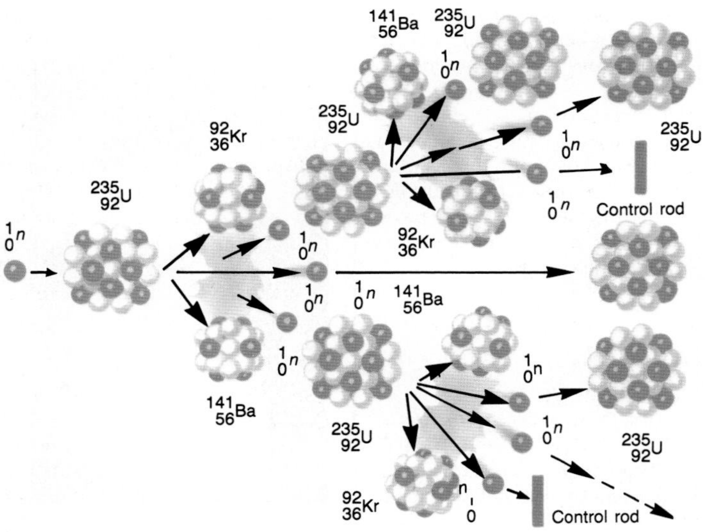

Fission is the splitting of a nucleus into two or more fragments of roughly equal size. It is accompanied by the release of a large amount of energy.

FIGURE 31–4. The nuclear fission chain reaction of uranium-235 takes place in the core of a nuclear reactor.

Answers To
PRACTICE PROBLEMS

Have students refer to Appendix A of the Solutions Appendix for complete solutions to Practice Problems.

5. **a.** ${}^{14}_{6}C \rightarrow {}^{14}_{7}N + {}^{0}_{-1}e$
   b. ${}^{55}_{24}Cr \rightarrow {}^{55}_{25}Mn + {}^{0}_{-1}e$
6. ${}^{238}_{92}U \rightarrow {}^{234}_{90}Th + {}^{4}_{2}He$
7. ${}^{214}_{84}Po \rightarrow {}^{210}_{82}Pb + {}^{4}_{2}He$
8. **a.** ${}^{210}_{82}Pb \rightarrow {}^{210}_{83}Bi + {}^{0}_{-1}e$
   b. ${}^{210}_{83}Bi \rightarrow {}^{210}_{84}Po + {}^{0}_{-1}e$
   c. ${}^{234}_{90}Th \rightarrow {}^{234}_{91}Pa + {}^{0}_{-1}e$
   d. ${}^{239}_{93}Np \rightarrow {}^{239}_{94}Pu + {}^{0}_{-1}e$

CONCEPT DEVELOPMENT

- The kinetic energy of the fast moving fission fragments given off in a fission reaction are made to collide with water molecules, producing pressurized hot water or steam.
- Students will probably come to you with a biological meaning of the word fission in mind. In biology, fission usually means division into two roughly equal parts. That is rarely the case in nuclear fission.
- The fission reaction can take place in several different combinations. That is, the two fission fragments do not have to be barium and krypton. About two dozen possiblities exist.
- If a student asks where the neutron comes from that starts the chain reaction, explain that a new nuclear reactor has to be "started up" by an external source of neutrons, usually an element that decays by neutron emission.

TEACHER 

An open pit mine in Oklo, West Africa is considered to be the first nuclear reactor. Approximately 1.7 billion years ago, the uranium-rich ore began to fission. The water of crystallization acts as a moderator.

Physics and society

Background: In 1989, an international accord signed by leaders from 105 countries spelled out worldwide limitations on hazardous industrial wastes. An important provision of this pact—negotiated at the behest of the United Nations Environmental Program (UNEP)—is that nations shall no longer export hazardous wastes. Program officials had no trouble arguing the urgency of their cause. With waste-dumping costs as high as $250 per ton in the United States, hazardous-waste disposal has offered handsome financial dividends to those developing countries willing to accept the contracts. Unfortunately, in the case of nuclear waste, even the preferred alternative of reprocessing results in a bonus for landfill contractors. Reprocessing technology leaves a radioactive liquid waste that, currently, is stored in heavy cannisters after being dried and mixed with molten glass. This enhances the physical bulk of the waste being contracted for. Only by banning international hazardous waste shipments, officials argue, can abuses of waste shipping and disposal safety codes be entirely prevented.

Answers To
DEVELOPING A VIEWPOINT

1. Fission released energy from heavy nuclei, fusion from light ones. It would take a huge amount of energy to overcome the repulsion between the two nuclei that resulted from fission. In addition, the excess neutrons released would have to be added to create the original nucleus. For this reason, for all practical purposes, nuclear fission cannot be reversed.
2. Proponents could suggest that it might be possible to send a rocket containing nuclear waste on a trajectory toward the sun, from which it could not return. Opponents could argue that rocket launches often fail, and a failure of a rocket containing nuclear waste could endanger very large numbers of people.

Physics and society

NUCLEAR WASTE DISPOSAL

Uranium fuel rods used to power nuclear reactors are useful for about one year before they must be replaced. In addition, some experts believe that entire nuclear facilities must be dismantled or sealed up after about 30 years due to high levels of radioactivity and resulting structural damage.

Although radiation has many useful applications, such as the treatment of cancer, it must be carefully monitored. Exposure to too much radiation can result in the destruction of body cells and eventual death. Unfortunately, all the materials in nuclear waste are still extremely radioactive and cannot be discarded using conventional waste disposal methods.

In the United States alone, approximately 1500 metric tons of spent fuel are produced every year, enough to form a radioactive chain of paper clips that would wrap around our planet. By the year 2000, the United States will have accumulated approximately three times this much.

So far, there is only one way to deal with nuclear waste. Spent fuel is stored at nuclear reactor storage facilities (resembling large swimming pools) or at remote sites for at least 100 years. Liquid radioactive waste can be "vitrified" or turned into glass, resulting in a solid that minimizes the chance of releasing radioactivity into the environment. The safety of these solids is now being tested. If proven safe, they would be stored underground in giant vaults. As you might expect, however, national and local governments are hesitant to compete for the seemingly lucrative right to become nuclear waste disposal sites because of health and environmental concerns.

The original concept for nuclear power was that scientists would be able to devise a way to reprocess spent fuel, chemically separating it into uranium, plutonium, and waste fission products, with the uranium going back into the fuel cycle. It was also assumed that modern technology would soon devise ways to dispose of the small amount of spent fuel that could not be reprocessed.

Fuel reprocessing technology, however, has not kept up with nuclear waste production, and nations around the world are faced with the problem of storing spent fuel until a more permanent solution is developed.

Those countries involved in the use of nuclear energy face a difficult problem in the disposal of nuclear waste. They must decide whether or not the problems of nuclear energy outweigh the benefits.

DEVELOPING A VIEWPOINT

Read further concerning nuclear waste disposal. Come to class prepared to discuss the following questions.

1. You have learned about physical changes, such as freezing water. Physical changes can be reversed. That is, ice can be melted. You might think of nuclear fission and fusion as being like melting and freezing. Why can't nuclear fission be reversed by fusing the fission products back into the original nucleus, thus eliminating much of the nuclear waste?
2. What are the pros and cons of sending nuclear waste into space?

SUGGESTED READINGS

Wolf Häfele, "Energy from Nuclear Power," *Scientific American,* September 1990, p. 144.
George E. Brown, Jr. "U.S. Nuclear Waste Policy: Flawed but Feasible," *Environment,* Vol 29 (No. 8) October 1987, pp. 6–7.

Teacher Resources: Quigg, Catherine Thiel. "Buried Alive: Doomed Nuclear Reactors Will Require Perpetual Care." *The Progressive,* December 1983, pages 23–25.
World Book Encyclopedia, "Nuclear Energy: Hazards of Nuclear Power," pages 511w–x.
Bryan, Richard H. "The Politics and Promises of Nuclear Waste Disposal: The View from Nevada," *ibid,* pages 14–17, 32–38.

STUDY GUIDE MASTER

Use the Study Guide master for section 31.2.

LABORATORY MANUAL

Use Lab 31.1 with this section.

caused a division of the uranium into two smaller nuclei, with a large release of energy. A division of a nucleus into two or more fragments is called **fission.** The possibility that fission could be not only a source of energy, but an explosive weapon, was immediately realized by many scientists.

The uranium isotope $^{235}_{92}U$ undergoes fission when bombarded with neutrons. The elements barium and krypton are typical results of fission, Figure 31–4. The reaction is

$$^{1}_{0}n + ^{235}_{92}U \rightarrow ^{92}_{36}Kr + ^{141}_{56}Ba + 3\,^{1}_{0}n + 200 \text{ MeV}.$$

The energy released by each fission can be found by calculating the masses of the atoms on each side of the equation. In the uranium-235 reaction, the total mass on the right side of the equation is 0.215 u smaller than that on the left. The energy equivalent of this mass is 3.21×10^{-11} J, or 200 MeV. This energy is transferred to the kinetic energy of the products of the fission.

Once the fission process is started, the neutron needed to cause the fission of additional $^{235}_{92}U$ nuclei can be one of the three neutrons produced by an earlier fission. If one or more of the neutrons causes a fission, that fission releases three more neutrons, each of which can cause more fission. This process is called a **chain reaction.**

POCKET LAB

POWER PLANT

Call your local electric company and ask the following questions: 1. Where is the nearest nuclear power plant? 2. What fraction (or percentage) of electrical power is supplied by nuclear power in your area?

In a chain reaction, neutrons released by one fission induce other fissions.

Nuclear Reactors

Most of the neutrons released by the fission of $^{235}_{92}U$ atoms are moving at high speed and are unable to cause the fission of another $^{235}_{92}U$ atom. In addition, naturally occurring uranium consists of less than 1% $^{235}_{92}U$ and more than 99% $^{238}_{92}U$. When a $^{238}_{92}U$ nucleus absorbs a fast neutron, it does not undergo fission, but becomes a new isotope, $^{239}_{92}U$. The absorption of neutrons by $^{238}_{92}U$ keeps most of the neutrons from reaching the fissionable $^{235}_{92}U$ atoms.

A slow neutron is more effective in causing fission than is a fast neutron.

Fermi suggested that a chain reaction would occur if the uranium were broken up into small pieces and placed in a material that can slow down, or moderate, the fast neutrons. When a neutron collides with a light atom, it transfers momentum and energy to the atom. In this way, the neutron loses energy. The **moderator** creates many slow neutrons, which are more likely to be absorbed by $^{235}_{92}U$ than by $^{238}_{92}U$. The larger number of slow neutrons greatly increases the probability that a neutron released by a fissioning $^{235}_{92}U$ nucleus will cause another $^{235}_{92}U$ nucleus to fission. If there is enough $^{235}_{92}U$ in the sample, a chain reaction can occur.

The lightest atom, hydrogen, would be an ideal moderator. Fast neutrons, however, cause a nuclear reaction with normal hydrogen nuclei, $^{1}_{1}H$. For this reason, when Fermi produced the first controlled chain reaction on December 2, 1942, he used graphite (carbon) as a moderator.

Heavy water, in which the hydrogen, $^{1}_{1}H$, is replaced by the isotope deuterium, $^{2}_{1}H$, does not absorb fast neutrons. As a result, heavy water is used as a moderator with natural uranium in the Canadian CANDU reactors.

Ordinary water can be used as a moderator if the number of $^{235}_{92}U$ nuclei in the uranium sample is increased. The process that increases the number of fissionable nuclei is called enrichment. Enrichment of

F.Y.I.

The energy produced by the breaking down of the atom is a very poor kind of thing. Anyone who expects a source of power from the transformation of these atoms is talking moonshine.

—Ernest Rutherford
retold in *Physics Today*, 1970

POCKET LAB

POWER PLANT

Purpose: to increase your awareness of nuclear power plants in your region.
Materials: telephone or other reference materials.
Outcome: Answers will vary depending on the region of the country and the electric company serving your region.

CONCEPT DEVELOPMENT

Demonstration: To demonstrate a chain reaction, stand one domino up and place two behind it in such a way that when the first domino falls, it will knock down the others. Then set 4 dominoes behind the 2, 8 behind the 4, and so on. Space the dominoes so they will all fall in succession after you knock over the first one.

CONCEPT DEVELOPMENT

ACTIVITY

Cooperative Learning: To demonstrate a chain reaction and critical mass, give each student two corks. Turn your back to the class and toss a cork over your head toward the students. The student who gets hit should close his or her eyes and throw up in the air the two corks received earlier (not at another student). Other students who get hit should repeat the procedure. Then have students move closer together so they are taking up about half the space as before and repeat the procedure. Repeat the procedure a third time, having students move very close together. The closer together the students are, the faster the reaction. Almost everyone will get hit. Discuss the results. Students should observe that when people are spread out, it takes longer to get the chain reaction going. Compact groups start faster and react faster. Use the following statement to initiate a class discussion about public opinion of nuclear energy: If the electric chair had been invented before the electric light bulb, people would feel the same way about electrical energy as they do about nuclear energy.

FIGURE 31–5. In a nuclear power plant, the thermal energy released in nuclear reactions is converted to electric energy.

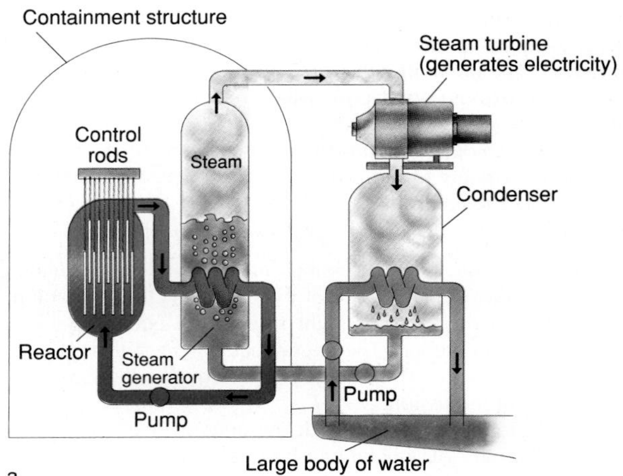

uranium is difficult and requires large, expensive equipment. The United States government operates the plants that produce enriched uranium for most of the nuclear reactors in the western world.

The type of nuclear reactor used in the United States, the pressurized water reactor, contains about 200 metric tons of uranium sealed in hundreds of metal rods. The rods are immersed in water. Water not only is the moderator, but also transfers thermal energy away from the fissioning uranium. Between the uranium rods are placed rods of cadmium metal. Cadmium absorbs neutrons easily. The cadmium rods are moved in and out of the reactor to control the rate of the chain reaction. Thus the rods are called **control rods**. When the control rods are inserted completely into the reactor, they absorb enough neutrons to prevent the chain reaction. As they are removed from the reactor, the rate of energy release increases.

Energy released by the fission heats the water surrounding the uranium rods. The water itself doesn't boil because it is under high pressure, which increases its boiling temperature. As shown in Figure 31–5, this water is pumped to a heat exchanger, where it causes other water to boil, producing steam that turns turbines. The turbines are connected to generators that produce electrical energy. At present about 10% of the electricity used in the United States is produced by nuclear energy.

Shock Waves ▶

Some of the fission energy goes into kinetic energy of electrons and neutrons, giving them speeds near the speed of light in vacuum. When these particles enter the water, they exceed the speed of light in the water. As a result, a blue glow is emitted when fuel rods are placed in water. The glow is called the Cerenkov effect. It is not the result of radioactivity in the water; radioactive objects do not emit a blue glow.

Fission of ${}^{235}_{92}U$ nuclei produces Kr, Ba, and other atoms in the fuel rods. Most of these atoms are radioactive. About once a year, some of the uranium fuel rods must be replaced. The old rods can no longer be used in the reactor, but they are still extremely radioactive and must be stored in safe locations. Research is now being done on methods of

TEACHER F.Y.I.

A 1000-megawatt nuclear power plant uses 25 tons of fuel per year, producing 25 tons of used fuel. An equivalent coal-burning plant uses 2 500 000 tons of fuel per year. In addition to producing large quantities of ash, the coal plant produces 6 500 000 tons of CO_2, 9000 tons of SO_2, and 4500 tons of NO_x. It should be noted that the total weight of the waste products is greater than the weight of the fuel because the fuel combines with oxygen from the atmosphere in the combustion process.

safe, permanent storage of these radioactive waste products. Among the products of fission is an isotope of plutonium, $^{239}_{94}Pu$. This isotope is fissionable when it absorbs neutrons and can also be used in nuclear weapons. It is also very toxic. As a result, plutonium-containing materials are all stored in safe, temporary locations, never in "waste dumps." There is hope that in the future this fissionable isotope might be removed from radioactive waste and recycled to fuel other reactors.

The world's supply of uranium is limited. If nuclear reactors are used to supply a large fraction of the world's energy, uranium will become scarce. Even though the plutonium produced by normal reactors might be recovered to fuel other reactors, there is still a net loss of fuel. In order to extend the supply of uranium, **breeder reactors** have been developed. When a reactor contains both plutonium and $^{238}_{92}U$, the plutonium will undergo fission just as $^{235}_{92}U$ does. Many of the free neutrons from the fission are absorbed by the $^{238}_{92}U$ to produce additional $^{239}_{94}Pu$. For every two plutonium atoms that undergo fission, three new ones are formed. More fissionable fuel can be recovered from this reactor than was originally present. Breeder reactors are operating only in France, but research is underway in the United States and the Soviet Union.

HELP WANTED

RADIOLOGIC TECHNOLOGIST

Do you have an associate degree and professional certification in radiological technology? We are looking for a person who is compassionate, conscientious, and cooperative. You must have a penchant for perfection when it comes to safety regulations and procedures. A large hospital offers excellent opportunity for advancement with increased training. For information contact:
American Society of Radiologic Technologists, 15000 Central Avenue, S.E., Albuquerque, NM 87123

Nuclear Fusion

In nuclear **fusion**, nuclei with small masses combine to form a nucleus with a larger mass, Figure 31–6. In the process energy is released. The larger nucleus is more tightly bound, Figure 31–1, so its mass is less than the sum of the masses of the smaller nuclei. A typical example of fusion is the process that occurs in the sun. Four hydrogen nuclei (protons) fuse in several steps to form one helium nucleus. The mass of the four protons is greater than the mass of the helium nucleus that is produced. The energy equivalent of this mass difference is transferred to the kinetic energy of the resultant particles. The energy released by the fusion of one helium nucleus is 25 MeV. In comparison, the energy released when one dynamite molecule reacts chemically is about 20 eV, almost one million times smaller.

Fusion is the union of small nuclei to form larger ones. It is accompanied by the release of a large amount of energy.

Fusion in the sun is believed to occur in steps. The most important process is expected to be the proton-proton chain.

Fusion in the sun converts four protons to one helium nucleus.

$$^{1}_{1}H + ^{1}_{1}H \rightarrow ^{2}_{1}H + ^{0}_{+1}e + ^{0}_{0}\nu$$
$$^{1}_{1}H + ^{2}_{1}H \rightarrow ^{3}_{2}He + \gamma$$
$$^{3}_{2}He + ^{3}_{2}He \rightarrow ^{4}_{2}He + 2\,^{1}_{1}H$$

The first two reactions must occur twice in order to produce the two $^{3}_{2}He$ particles needed for the final reaction. The net result is that four protons produce one $^{4}_{2}He$, two positrons, and two neutrinos.

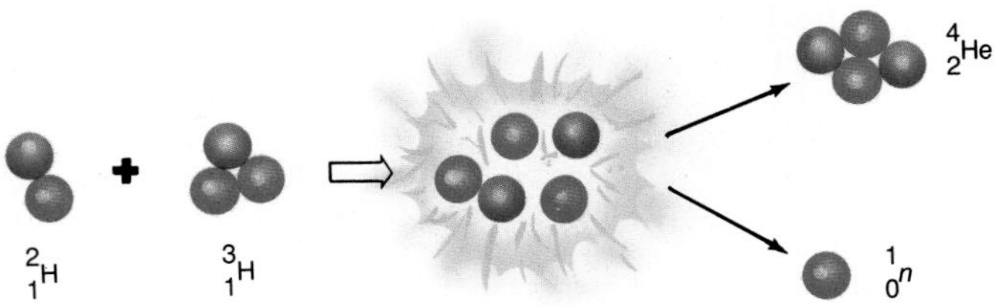

FIGURE 31–6. The fusion of deuterium and tritium produces helium. Protons are blue and neutrons are red in the figure.

CONCEPT DEVELOPMENT

ACTIVITY

Cooperative Learning: Have student groups investigate the environmental and economic pros and cons of solar, fossil fuel, and nuclear energy. Encourage them to explore the issues thoroughly before drawing their conclusions. You may want to organize a debate once students have done their research.

Critical Thinking: Ask students what makes it possible to use radioisotopes as tracer elements [The low levels of radiation produced by these isotopes can be well located in the body so that the body's use of them can be carefully followed and analyzed.]

Critical Thinking Master, Teacher Resource Package. You may wish to have students complete the Critical Thinking Master, The Penetrating Power of Radiation, with this section.

Enrichment: By using the Chart of the Nuclides, ask students if they can explain why cadmium is often used in nuclear reactor control rods. [Cadmium has several stable isotopes that enable it to absorb many neutrons without becoming very radioactive.]

Enrichment Master. With this section, use the Enrichment Master, Carbon Dating, from the Teacher Resource Package.

Transparency Package. Use Transparency 47 to quiz students on fission and fusion.

TEACHER F.Y.I.

Enrico Fermi was trying to induce radioactivity in elements when he discovered that placing a piece of paraffin between the neutron source and the sample demonstrates a strong activation. Why? Scientists had assumed that fast neutrons would work better in the same way that fast protons and alpha particles do. However, a charged particle has to push through the electrical barrier of the nucleus, whereas the neutron does not. Slowing down a neutron puts it in the vicinity of the nucleus for a greater period of time, improving the probability of its capture.

PHYSICS LAB

Process Skills: using numbers; observing; communicating; measuring; predicting; defining operationally.

MISCONCEPTION

Most students do not recognize the vast potential of solar power.

Teaching Suggestions: Encourage students to keep an open mind about the possibilities of solar power.

Lab Worksheet, Teacher Resource Package. If desired, use the lab worksheet master for this chapter for students to record their data.

OBSERVATIONS

Student readings will vary depending on the solar cell and the relative angle between the path of sunlight and the solar cell.

ANALYSIS

1. The typical power for a 4-cm × 10-cm solar cell is 0.45 watts. Student answers will vary depending on the time of day. If the sun strikes the window directly, nearly all the power will pass through. If the sun hits the window at a very oblique angle, the window may stop up to 80% of the power.
2. The typical cell could produce about 110 watts for each square meter.
3. The efficiency of most readily available solar cells should be in the range of 10% to 15%.

APPLICATIONS

Fifteen square meters of solar cells could collect 15 000 watts of sunlight. At 15% efficiency, the electrical output would be 2.3 kilowatts.

PHYSICS LAB : Hot Stuff

Purpose

To measure the local power output from the nearest continuous running fusion reaction.

Materials

- photocell
- voltmeter
- ammeter
- electrical leads
- ruler

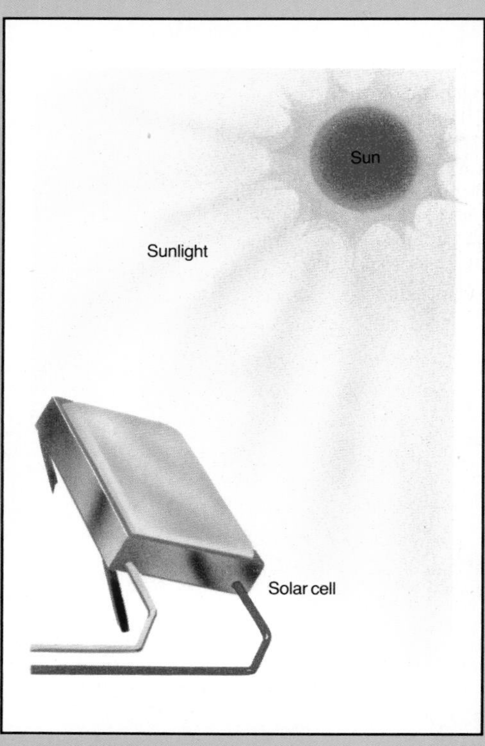

Procedure

1. With no load attached, measure the voltage output of a solar cell when the cell is outdoors and directly facing the sun.
2. Measure the current from the solar cell when the cell is outdoors and directly facing the sun.
3. Measure the length and width of the solar cell and determine its surface area.
4. Remeasure the voltage and current when the sunlight passes through a window.

Observations and Data

1. Record your voltage and current readings for outdoor and indoor readings.

Analysis

1. Using $P = IV$, calculate the power for the solar cell outdoors and indoors. What percentage of power did the window stop?
2. Calculate the amount of power that could be produced by a cell that had an area of 1.0 square meter.
3. The sun supplies about 1000 W of power per square meter to the earth. Calculate the efficiency of your solar cell.

Applications

1. Suppose that you installed 15 square meters of solar cells on your roof. How much power could they produce?

ASSESSMENT

Critical Thinking: To further assess students' understanding of solar cells, ask the following questions.

1. Predict what the power would be when you cover half of the area of the solar cell with your hand. Measure the volts and amps with half of the cell covered. What is the new power? [Surprisingly, the voltage will be about the same as before. The voltage depends on the material in the cell. The new current will be roughly half of the original measurement.]

2. Suppose that you surround an incandescent lamp with many solar cells and connect the solar cells to the lamp. Could the energy collected from the lamp by the solar cells be reused to light the lamp? Explain your reasoning. [The situation described is a perpetual motion machine. Most of the energy that operates an incandescent lamp goes into heat. The solar cells could not absorb all this energy. Further, the efficiency of the solar cell is not 100%. Only a small fraction of the light energy gets converted back into electrical energy.]

The repulsive force between the charged nuclei requires the fusing nuclei to have high energies. Thus, fusion reactions take place only when the nuclei have large amounts of thermal energy. For this reason, fusion reactions are often called **thermonuclear reactions.** The proton-proton chain requires temperatures of about 2×10^7 K, temperatures found in the center of the sun. Fusion reactions also occur in a "hydrogen," or thermonuclear, bomb. In this device, the high temperature necessary to produce the fusion reaction is produced by exploding a uranium, or "atomic," bomb.

Controlled Fusion

Could the huge energy available from fusion be used safely on Earth? Safe energy requires control of the fusion reaction. One reaction that might produce **controlled fusion** is

$$^{2}_{1}\text{H} + ^{3}_{1}\text{H} \rightarrow ^{4}_{2}\text{He} + ^{1}_{0}n + 17.6\text{ MeV}.$$

Deuterium, $^{2}_{1}\text{H}$, is available in large quantities in seawater, and tritium, $^{3}_{1}\text{H}$, is easily produced from deuterium. Therefore, controlled fusion would give the world an almost limitless source of energy. In order to control fusion, however, some very difficult problems must be solved.

Fusion reactions require that the atoms be raised to temperatures of millions of degrees. No material we now have can withstand temperatures even as high as 5000 K. In addition, the atoms would be cooled if they touched confining material. Magnetic fields, however, can confine charged particles. Energy is added to the atoms, stripping away electrons and forming separated plasmas of electrons and ions. A sudden increase in the magnetic field will compress the plasma, raising its temperature. Electromagnetic fields and fast moving neutral atoms can also increase the energy of the plasma. Using this technique, hydrogen nuclei have been fused into helium. The energy released by the reaction becomes the kinetic energy of the neutron and helium ion. This energy would be used to heat some other material, possibly liquified lithium. The lithium, in turn, would boil water, producing steam to turn electric generators.

FIGURE 31–7. The Tokamak is an experimental controlled fusion reactor.

CHECKING FOR UNDERSTANDING

Ask students the following questions: Where does the energy released in a fission reaction come from? [The mass of the fission products is smaller than the mass of the original nucleus. This difference in mass is the mass defect, which takes the form of kinetic energy.] Why is it so difficult to control a fusion reaction for the production of useful power? [Since these fusion reactions only occur at very high temperatures, containment of the reaction is quite difficult. The proposed answer, magnetic confinement, turns out to be technically quite complex.]
Why is the total mass of a nucleus as a whole not equal to the sum of the separate masses of the neutrons and protons that compose it? [The nucleus is bound together. This binding energy must be supplied to the nucleus to break it apart, and subsequently shows up as increased mass of the pieces.]

RETEACHING

Build your reteaching around the idea of energy conservation. In the process of nuclear fission, the binding energy of the uranium nucleus appears mainly as the kinetic energy of the fission fragments. Mass can be considered a form of potential energy that can be converted into kinetic energy when the nucleus fissions. In a nuclear reactor, the increased thermal energy of the water in the primary coolant loop is then transferred to the water in the secondary coolant loop. Comparing the amount of energy of the fission reaction to the final amount of electricity produced, a typical nuclear reactor has an efficiency of 30–35%.

Reteaching Master, Teacher Resource Package. Use the Reteaching Master for Chapter 31, A Debate About Nuclear Power Plants, with this section.

INDEPENDENT PRACTICE/ EXTENSION

Refer to the Assignment Guide on page 652 for additional questions and problems for independent practice.

CRITICAL THINKING

Use the Critical Thinking master for Chapter 31 with this section.

TRANSPARENCY

Use Transparency 47 with this section.

ENRICHMENT MASTER

Use the Enrichment master for Chapter 31 with this section.

RETEACHING MASTER

Use the Reteaching master for Chapter 31 with this section.

Guided Practice: Go over the Practice Problems on this page as a class exercise.

Independent Practice: Assign the Concept Review Problems that follow as homework and spend time discussing them during the next class period.

3 Close

CONVERGENT QUESTION

Ask students what some of the differences are between alpha decay and nuclear fission, both examples of a nucleus splitting up. [Most alpha decays occur naturally without any bombardment, while (in the case of uranium) nuclear fission usually needs a slow neutron to be initiated. Furthermore, fission splits the nucleus into two more equal-sized parts.]

Answers To
PRACTICE PROBLEMS

Have students refer to Appendix A of the Solutions Appendix for complete solutions to Practice Problems.

9. a. -0.018883 u
b. -17.589 MeV
10. 25.710 MeV

Assessment

Portfolio

Students should develop posters showing fission and fusion reactions. The posters should show the reactants, products, and energy released. Sources of the material should be shown, as well as uses of these reactions.

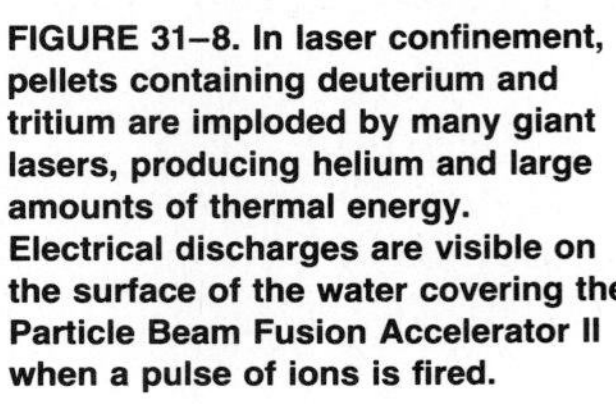

FIGURE 31–8. In laser confinement, pellets containing deuterium and tritium are imploded by many giant lasers, producing helium and large amounts of thermal energy. Electrical discharges are visible on the surface of the water covering the Particle Beam Fusion Accelerator II when a pulse of ions is fired.

Laser beams are used to implode tiny glass spheres containing liquified deuterium and tritium. The compression creates temperatures high enough to produce fusion.

A useful reactor must produce more energy than it consumes. So far, the energy produced by fusion has been only a tiny fraction of the energy required to create and hold the plasma. The confinement of plasma is a very difficult problem because instabilities in the magnetic field allow the plasma to escape. One of the most promising fusion reactors under development is the Tokamak reactor, Figure 31–7. The Tokamak provides a doughnut-shaped magnetic field in which the plasma is confined. Research has led to the confinement of larger amounts of plasma for longer periods of time. The next large Tokamak built should produce as much energy as it consumes.

A second approach to controlled fusion is called **inertial confinement fusion**. Deuterium and tritium are liquified under high pressure and confined in tiny glass spheres. Multiple laser beams, Figure 31–8a, are directed at the spheres. The energy deposited by the lasers causes forces that make the pellets implode, squeezing their contents. The tremendous compression of the hydrogen that results raises the temperature to levels needed for fusion.

Practice Problems

9. a. Calculate the mass defect for the deuterium-tritium fusion reaction used in the Tokamak, ${}^{2}_{1}H + {}^{3}_{1}H \rightarrow {}^{4}_{2}He + {}^{1}_{0}n$.
b. Find the energy equivalent of the mass defect.

▶ **10.** Calculate the energy released for the overall reaction in the sun where four protons produce one ${}^{4}_{2}He$, two positrons, and two neutrinos.

Connect to ASTRONOMY

Fusion reactions release energy in the formation of nuclei from ^{4}He through ^{56}Fe. How were the elements heavier than iron formed? It is believed that the production of all heavier elements occurred in the tremendous explosions that occur when massive stars exhaust all their nuclear fuel. When the outward pressure provided by the thermonuclear reactions ends, the gravitational force pulls all the atoms together. The resulting pressure and temperature is sufficient to cause the nuclear reactions that produce elements to plutonium and beyond. These theories were tested in the widely observed supernova SN1987a. While the heavy elements have not been directly observed, the drop in light intensity from the explosion matches that predicted by the theories.

How might scientists detect elements like uranium in a star in another galaxy? [They would examine the spectrum of light from the star and look for emission lines given off by the elements.]

CONCEPT REVIEW

2.1 What happens to the energy released in a fusion reaction in the sun?
2.2 One fusion reaction involves two deuterium nuclei. A deuterium molecule contains two deuterium atoms. Why doesn't this molecule undergo fusion?
2.3 How does a breeder reactor differ from a normal one?
2.4 Critical Thinking: Fusion powers the sun. The temperatures are hottest, and the number of fusion reactions greatest, in the center of the sun. What confines the fusion reaction?

CHAPTER 31 REVIEW

SUMMARY

31.1 Holding the Nucleus Together

- The strong force binds the nucleus together.
- The energy released in a nuclear reaction can be calculated by finding the mass defect, the difference in mass of the particles before and after the reaction.
- The binding energy is the energy equivalent of the mass defect.

31.2 Using Nuclear Energy

- Bombardment can produce radioactive isotopes not found in nature. These are called artificial radioactive nuclei and are often used in medicine.
- In nuclear fission, the uranium nucleus is split into two smaller nuclei with a release of neutrons and energy.
- Nuclear reactors use the energy released in fission to generate electrical energy.
- The fusion of hydrogen nuclei into a helium nucleus releases the energy that causes stars to shine.
- Development of a process for controlling fusion for use on Earth might provide large amounts of energy safely.

KEY TERMS

strong nuclear force
nucleon
binding energy
mass defect
fission
chain reaction
moderator
control rod
breeder reactor
fusion
thermonuclear reaction
controlled fusion
inertial confinement fusion

REVIEWING CONCEPTS

1. What force inside a nucleus acts to tear the nucleus apart? What force inside the nucleus acts in a way to hold the nucleus together?
2. Define the mass defect of a nucleus. To what is it related?
3. List three medical uses of radioactivity.
4. What sequence of events must occur for a chain reaction to take place?
5. In a fission reaction, binding energy is converted into thermal energy. Objects with thermal energy have random kinetic energy. What objects have kinetic energy after fission?
6. A newspaper claims that scientists have been able to cause iron nuclei to undergo fission. Is the claim likely to be true? Explain.

31:2 ASSIGNMENT GUIDE

	PRACTICE	EXTENSION
CHAPTER REVIEW pp. 653–655		
· Reviewing Concepts	3–12	
· Applying Concepts		3–8
· Problems*	7–14, 18–21	15–17, 22–23
APPENDIX B PROBLEMS*		
· Chapter 31, p. 709	5–8, 10–12, 15	9, 14

* Complete solutions to all Chapter Review and Appendix problems appear in the Problems and Solutions Manual.

REVIEW MASTER

Use the Vocabulary Review master for Chapter 31 with this section.

EVALUATION MASTER

Use the Chapter Evaluation master for Chapter 31 with this section.

CONCEPT REVIEW ANSWERS

2.1 It goes into the kinetic energy of the helium nucleus, the positrons, and the neutrinos.
2.2 In order for the positively-charged nuclei to fuse, they must overcome the strong repulsive force between them. Enough energy for this is not available in the deuterium molecule.
2.3 The breeder reactor produces more fissionable material than it consumes. A normal reactor produces much less.
2.4 Critical Thinking: The gravitational attraction holds all the particles together.

CLOSING CHAPTER 31

Review Summary statements and Key Terms with your students.

ASSESSMENT

Vocabulary Review Master, Teacher Resource Package. Use this master to check students' understanding of Key Terms.

Evaluation Masters. Use Parts A and B of the Chapter Evaluation Masters from the Teacher Resource Package to test qualitative chapter objectives. Use Parts C and D to test quantitative chapter objectives.

Answers To
REVIEWING CONCEPTS

1. The repulsive electric force between the positive protons acts to tear the nucleus apart. The strong nuclear force acts to hold the nucleus together.
2. The mass defect is the difference between the sum of the mass of the individual particles of the nucleus and the mass of the nucleus. It is related to binding energy through $E = mc^2$.
3. PET scanner, tracer isotopes, destroying diseased cells
4. Many neutrons must be released by a fissioned nucleus and absorbed by neighboring nuclei causing them to fission.
5. the fission fragments and neutrons
6. Not true. Iron is the most tightly bound element, and thus the most stable nucleus. It cannot decay by either fission or fusion.

Answers To
REVIEWING CONCEPTS (cont)

7. The moderator slows the fast neutrons, increasing their probability of being absorbed.

8. Graphite is used as a moderator to slow neutrons in order to increase the probability of their being absorbed by $^{235}_{92}U$.

9. No. In a breeder reactor, U-238, which is not fissionable, is converted to Pu-239, which is fissionable.

10. The nuclei that combine in the fusion process of stars require the high kinetic energy that comes from the high temperatures to overcome the repulsive electrical forces among them.

11. When a large atom, such as uranium, undergoes fission, the mass of the products is less than that of the original nucleus. An amount of energy equivalent to the difference in mass is relased. However, when small nuclei fuse into a larger nucleus, the mass of the more tightly-bound, large nucleus is less, and the extra mass appears as energy.

12. Plasma confinement by magnetic fields and inertial confinement or laser implosion are under study.

Answers To
APPLYING CONCEPTS

1. As the average binding energy per nucleon increases, the nucleus becomes more stable.

2. The incoming binding energy is less than the outgoing binding energy and, therefore, the reaction is possible.

3. A natural radioactive material is one that is found to exist normally in ores and displays radiations, for example, U-238. Artificially radioactive material displays radiations only after being subjected to bombardment by particles, for example, I-131.

4. The water in the heat exchanger is radioactive, and it cannot be used to generate steam. Therefore, a second loop is needed to carry the non-radioactive water that produces steam.

5. a. fission of 1 uranium nucleus = 200 MeV, fusion of 4 hydrogen nuclei = 50 MeV **b.** The fusion of a kilogram of deuterium produces much more energy.
c. Although the fission of one uranium nucleus produces more energy than the fusion of two hydrogen nuclei, there are over 100 times as many deuterium nuclei in a kilogram than there are uranium nuclei.

6. Fissionable plutonium in a reactor produces more plutonium than is used. Such reactors are called breeder reactors.

7. the rate of fission

8. Fusion does not produce plutonium and results in fewer radioactive wastes than fission.

7. What role does a moderator play in a fission reactor?
8. The reactor at the Chernobyl power station that exploded and burned used blocks of graphite. What was the purpose of the graphite blocks?
9. Breeder reactors generate more fuel than they consume. Is this a violation of the law of conservation of energy? Explain.
10. Scientists think Jupiter might have become a star, but temperatures inside the planet are too low. Why must stars have a very high internal temperature?
11. Fission and fusion are opposite processes. How can each release energy?
12. What two processes are being studied to control the fusion process?

APPLYING CONCEPTS

1. What is the relationship between the average binding energy per nucleon and the degree of stability of a nucleus?
2. Use the graph of binding energy per nucleon to determine if the reaction $^{2}_{1}H + ^{1}_{1}H \rightarrow ^{3}_{2}He$ is energetically possible.
3. Give an example of a naturally and an artifically produced radioactive isotope. Explain the difference.
4. In a nuclear reactor, water that passes through the core of the reactor flows through one loop while the water that produces steam for the turbines flows through a second loop. Why are there two loops?
5. The fission of a uranium nucleus and the fusion of four hydrogen nuclei both produce energy.
  a. Which produces more energy?
  b. Does the fission of a kilogram of uranium nuclei or the fusion of a kilogram of deuterium produce more energy?
  c. Why are your answers to parts **a** and **b** different?
6. Explain how it might be possible for some fission reactors to produce more fissionable fuel than they consume. What are such reactors called?
7. What is the difference between the fission process in an atomic bomb and in a reactor?
8. Why might a fusion reactor be safer than a fission reactor?

PROBLEMS

31.1 Holding the Nucleus Together

1. A carbon isotope, $^{13}_{6}C$, has a nuclear mass of 13.00335 u.
  a. What is the mass defect of this isotope?
  b. What is the binding energy of its nucleus?
2. A nitrogen isotope, $^{14}_{7}N$, has a nuclear mass of approximately 14.00307 u.
  a. What is the mass defect of the nucleus?
  b. What is the binding energy of this nucleus?
  c. What is the binding energy per nucleon?
3. A nitrogen isotope, $^{12}_{7}N$, has a nuclear mass of 12.0188 u.
  a. What is the binding energy per nucleon?
  b. Does it require more energy to separate a nucleon from a $^{14}_{7}N$ nucleus or from a $^{12}_{7}N$ nucleus? Refer to the previous problem.
4. The two positively-charged protons in a helium nucleus are separated by about 2.0×10^{-15} m. Use Coulomb's law to find the electric force of repulsion between the two protons. The result will give you an indication of the strength of the strong nuclear force.
▶ **5.** A $^{232}_{92}U$ nucleus, mass = 232.0372 u, decays to $^{228}_{90}Th$, mass = 228.0287 u, by emitting an α particle, mass = 4.0026 u, with a kinetic energy of 5.3 MeV. What must be the kinetic energy of the recoiling thorium nucleus?
▶ **6.** The binding energy for $^{4}_{2}He$ is 28.3 MeV. Calculate the mass of a helium nucleus in atomic mass units.

31.2 Using Nuclear Energy

7. The radioactive nucleus indicated in each equation disintegrates by emitting a positron. Complete each nuclear equation.
  a. $^{21}_{11}Na \rightarrow ? \; ^{0}_{1}e + ?$
  b. $^{49}_{24}Cr \rightarrow ? \; ^{0}_{1}e + ?$
8. Complete the nuclear equations for these transmutations.
  a. $^{30}_{15}P \rightarrow ? + ^{0}_{1}e + ?$
  b. $^{205}_{82}Pb \rightarrow ? + ^{0}_{1}e + ?$
9. A mercury isotope, $^{200}_{80}Hg$, is bombarded with deuterons, $^{2}_{1}H$. The mercury nucleus absorbs the deuteron and then emits an α particle.

a. What element is formed by this reaction?
b. Write the nuclear equation for the reaction.

10. When bombarded by protons, a lithium isotope, ${}^{7}_{3}\mathrm{Li}$, absorbs a proton and then ejects two α particles. Write the nuclear equation for this reaction.

11. Each of the nuclei given below can absorb an α particle, assuming that no secondary particles are emitted by the nucleus. Complete each equation.
a. ${}^{14}_{7}\mathrm{N} + {}^{4}_{2}\mathrm{He} \rightarrow ?$
b. ${}^{27}_{13}\mathrm{Al} + {}^{4}_{2}\mathrm{He} \rightarrow ?$

12. In each of these reactions, a neutron is absorbed by a nucleus. The nucleus then emits a proton. Complete the equations.
a. ${}^{65}_{29}\mathrm{Cu} + {}^{1}_{0}\mathrm{n} \rightarrow ? + {}^{1}_{1}\mathrm{H}$
b. ${}^{14}_{7}\mathrm{N} + {}^{1}_{0}\mathrm{n} \rightarrow ? + {}^{1}_{1}\mathrm{H}$

13. When a boron isotope, ${}^{10}_{5}\mathrm{B}$, is bombarded with neutrons, it absorbs a neutron and then emits an α particle.
a. What element is also formed?
b. Write the nuclear equation for this reaction.

14. When a boron isotope, ${}^{11}_{5}\mathrm{B}$, is bombarded with protons, it absorbs a proton and emits a neutron.
a. What element is formed?
b. Write the nuclear equation for this reaction.
c. The isotope formed is radioactive, decaying by emitting a positron. Write the complete nuclear equation for this reaction.

▶ **15.** The isotope most commonly used in PET scanners is ${}^{18}_{9}\mathrm{F}$.
a. What element is formed by the positron emission of this element?
b. Write the equation for this reaction.
c. The half-life of ${}^{18}_{9}\mathrm{F}$ is 110 min. A solution containing 10.0 mg of this isotope is injected into a patient at 8:00 A.M. How much remains at 3:30 P.M.?

▶ **16.** The basements of many homes contain the rock granite or are built over granite. Granite contains small amounts of radioactive uranium and thorium. Uranium-238 goes through a series of decays before reaching a stable lead isotope. ${}^{238}_{92}\mathrm{U}$ emits an α, leaving an isotope that decays by emitting a β. The next decay is again a β, followed by three α decays. The result is the gas radon that can seep into the basement. Write the equations for these decays.

▶ **17.** The first atomic bomb released an energy equivalent of 20 kilotons of TNT. One kiloton of TNT is the equivalent of 5.0×10^{12} J. What was the mass of the uranium-235 that was fissioned to produce this energy?

18. Complete the following fission reaction.
${}^{239}_{94}\mathrm{Pu} + {}^{1}_{0}\mathrm{n} \rightarrow {}^{137}_{52}\mathrm{Te} + ? + 3{}^{1}_{0}\mathrm{n}$

19. Complete the following fission reaction.
${}^{235}_{92}\mathrm{U} + {}^{1}_{0}\mathrm{n} \rightarrow {}^{92}_{36}\mathrm{Kr} + ? + 3{}^{1}_{0}\mathrm{n}$

20. Plutonium is formed in two steps. First U-238 absorbs a neutron which then becomes unstable U-239. The U-239 emits a β particle forming a new element and this new element emits a second β particle forming plutonium. Complete the following reaction. ${}^{238}_{92}\mathrm{U} + {}^{1}_{0}\mathrm{n} \rightarrow {}^{239}_{92}\mathrm{U} \rightarrow$

21. Complete each of the following fusion reactions.
a. ${}^{2}_{1}\mathrm{H} + {}^{2}_{1}\mathrm{H} \rightarrow ? + {}^{1}_{0}\mathrm{n}$
b. ${}^{2}_{1}\mathrm{H} + {}^{2}_{1}\mathrm{H} \rightarrow ? + {}^{1}_{1}\mathrm{H}$
c. ${}^{2}_{1}\mathrm{H} + {}^{3}_{1}\mathrm{H} \rightarrow ? + {}^{1}_{0}\mathrm{n}$

▶ **22.** One fusion reaction is ${}^{2}_{1}\mathrm{H} + {}^{2}_{1}\mathrm{H} \rightarrow {}^{4}_{2}\mathrm{He}$.
a. What energy is released in this reaction?
b. Deuterium exists as a diatomic, two-atom molecule. One mole of deuterium contains 6.02×10^{23} molecules. Find the amount of energy released, in joules, in the fusion of one mole of deuterium molecules.
c. When one mole of deuterium burns, it releases 2.9×10^{6} J. How many moles of deuterium molecules would have to burn to release just the energy released by the fusion of one mole of deuterium molecules?

▶ **23.** The energy released in the fission of one atom of ${}^{235}_{92}\mathrm{U}$ is 2.00×10^{2} MeV. One mole of uranium atoms, 6.02×10^{23} atoms, has a mass of 0.235 kg.
a. How many atoms are in 1.00 kg of ${}^{235}_{92}\mathrm{U}$?
b. How much energy would be released if all of the atoms in 1.00 kg of ${}^{235}_{92}\mathrm{U}$ underwent fission?
c. A typical large nuclear reactor produces fission energy at a rate of 3600 MW. How many kilograms of ${}^{235}_{92}\mathrm{U}$ are used each second?
d. How much ${}^{235}_{92}\mathrm{U}$ would be used in one year?

THINKING PHYSIC-LY

If a uranium nucleus were to split into three pieces of approximately the same size instead of two, would more or less energy be released?

Answers To PROBLEMS

1. a. -0.10426 u
b. -97.1 MeV
2. a. -0.11236 u
b. -105 MeV
c. -7.5 MeV/nucleon
3. a. -6.15 MeV
b. more energy
4. 58 N
5. 0.2 MeV
6. 4.0026 u
7. a. ${}^{21}_{11}\mathrm{Na} \rightarrow {}^{21}_{10}\mathrm{Ne} + {}^{0}_{+1}e + {}^{0}_{0}\nu$
b. ${}^{49}_{24}\mathrm{Cr} \rightarrow {}^{49}_{23}\mathrm{V} + {}^{0}_{+1}e + {}^{0}_{0}\nu$
8. a. ${}^{30}_{15}\mathrm{P} \rightarrow {}^{30}_{14}\mathrm{Si} + {}^{0}_{+1}e + {}^{0}_{0}\nu$
b. ${}^{205}_{82}\mathrm{Pb} \rightarrow {}^{205}_{81}\mathrm{Tl} + {}^{0}_{+1}e + {}^{0}_{0}\nu$
9. a. gold
b. ${}^{200}_{80}\mathrm{Hg} + {}^{2}_{1}\mathrm{H} \rightarrow {}^{198}_{79}\mathrm{Au} + {}^{4}_{2}\mathrm{He}$
10. ${}^{7}_{3}\mathrm{Li} + {}^{1}_{1}\mathrm{H} \rightarrow 2{}^{4}_{2}\mathrm{He}$
11. a. ${}^{14}_{7}\mathrm{N} + {}^{4}_{2}\mathrm{He} \rightarrow {}^{18}_{9}\mathrm{F}$
b. ${}^{27}_{13}\mathrm{Al} + {}^{4}_{2}\mathrm{He} \rightarrow {}^{31}_{15}\mathrm{P}$
12. a. ${}^{65}_{29}\mathrm{Cu} + {}^{1}_{0}n \rightarrow {}^{65}_{28}\mathrm{Ni} + {}^{1}_{1}\mathrm{H}$
b. ${}^{14}_{7}\mathrm{N} + {}^{1}_{0}n \rightarrow {}^{14}_{6}\mathrm{C} + {}^{1}_{1}\mathrm{H}$
13. a. lithium
b. ${}^{10}_{5}\mathrm{B} + {}^{1}_{0}n \rightarrow {}^{7}_{3}\mathrm{Li} + {}^{4}_{2}\mathrm{He}$
14. a. carbon
b. ${}^{11}_{5}\mathrm{B} + {}^{1}_{1}p \rightarrow {}^{11}_{6}\mathrm{C} + {}^{1}_{0}n$
c. ${}^{11}_{6}\mathrm{C} \rightarrow {}^{11}_{5}\mathrm{B} + {}^{0}_{1}e + {}^{0}_{0}\nu$
15. a. oxygen
b. ${}^{18}_{9}\mathrm{F} \rightarrow {}^{18}_{8}\mathrm{O} + {}^{0}_{1}e + {}^{0}_{0}\nu$
c. 0.63 mg
16. ${}^{238}_{92}\mathrm{U} \rightarrow {}^{234}_{90}\mathrm{Th} + {}^{4}_{2}\mathrm{He}$
${}^{234}_{90}\mathrm{Th} \rightarrow {}^{234}_{91}\mathrm{Pa} + {}^{0}_{-1}e + {}^{0}_{0}\bar{\nu}$
${}^{234}_{91}\mathrm{Pa} \rightarrow {}^{234}_{92}\mathrm{U} + {}^{0}_{-1}e + {}^{0}_{0}\bar{\nu}$
${}^{234}_{92}\mathrm{U} \rightarrow {}^{230}_{90}\mathrm{Th} + {}^{4}_{2}\mathrm{He}$
${}^{230}_{90}\mathrm{Th} \rightarrow {}^{226}_{88}\mathrm{Ra} + {}^{4}_{2}\mathrm{He}$
${}^{226}_{88}\mathrm{Ra} \rightarrow {}^{222}_{86}\mathrm{Rn} + {}^{4}_{2}\mathrm{He}$
17. 1.2 kg
18. ${}^{239}_{94}\mathrm{Pu} + {}^{1}_{0}n \rightarrow {}^{137}_{52}\mathrm{Te} + {}^{100}_{42}\mathrm{Mo} + 3{}^{1}_{0}n$
19. ${}^{235}_{92}\mathrm{U} + {}^{1}_{0}n \rightarrow {}^{92}_{36}\mathrm{Kr} + {}^{141}_{56}\mathrm{Ba} + 3{}^{1}_{0}n$
20. ${}^{238}_{92}\mathrm{U} + {}^{1}_{0}n \rightarrow ({}^{239}_{92}\mathrm{U}) \rightarrow {}^{239}_{93}\mathrm{Np} + {}^{0}_{-1}e + {}^{0}_{0}\bar{\nu}$
${}^{239}_{93}\mathrm{Np} \rightarrow {}^{239}_{94}\mathrm{Pu} + {}^{0}_{-1}e + {}^{0}_{0}\bar{\nu}$
21. ${}^{2}_{1}\mathrm{H} + {}^{2}_{1}\mathrm{H} \rightarrow {}^{3}_{2}\mathrm{He} + {}^{1}_{0}n$
${}^{2}_{1}\mathrm{H} + {}^{2}_{1}\mathrm{H} \rightarrow {}^{3}_{1}\mathrm{H} + {}^{1}_{1}\mathrm{H}$
${}^{2}_{1}\mathrm{H} + {}^{3}_{1}\mathrm{H} \rightarrow {}^{4}_{2}\mathrm{He} + {}^{1}_{0}n$
22. a. 23.8 MeV
b. 2.29×10^{12} J/mole
c. 7.9×10^{5} moles
23. a. 2.56×10^{24} atoms
b. 8.2×10^{13} J
c. 4.4×10^{-5} kg/s
d. 1.4×10^{3} kg/y

Answers To THINKING PHYSIC-LY

For nuclei larger than the ${}^{56}_{26}\mathrm{Fe}$ nucleus, the binding energy per nucleon decreases as the nucleus gets larger. The three pieces are larger than the ${}^{56}_{26}\mathrm{Fe}$ nucleus but smaller than the two pieces would be. Therefore, the binding energy per nucleon is larger for the three pieces, and more energy is released when uranium splits into three pieces.

Appendix A
Solutions for Practice Problems

There are no Practice Problems in Chapter 1.

Chapter 2

1. a. 5.8×10^3 m
b. 4.5×10^5 m
c. 3.02×10^8 m
d. 8.6×10^{10} m

2. a. 5.08×10^{-4} kg
b. 4.5×10^{-7} kg
c. 3.600×10^{-3} kg
d. 4×10^{-3} kg

3. a. 3×10^8 s
b. 1.86×10^5 s
c. 9.3×10^7 s

4. a. $(1.1 \text{ cm})\dfrac{(1 \times 10^{-2} \text{ m})}{(1 \text{ cm})} = 1.1 \times 10^{-2}$ m

b. $(76.2 \text{ pm})\dfrac{(1 \times 10^{-12} \text{ m})}{(1 \text{ pm})} = 76.2 \times 10^{-12}$ m
$= 7.62 \times 10^{-11}$ m

c. $(2.1 \text{ km})\dfrac{(1 \times 10^3 \text{ m})}{(1 \text{ km})} = 2.1 \times 10^3$ m

d. $(0.123 \text{ Mm})\dfrac{(1 \times 10^6 \text{ m})}{(1 \text{ Mm})} = 0.123 \times 10^6$ m
$= 1.23 \times 10^5$ m

5. a. $1 \text{ kg} = 1 \times 10^3 \text{ g so } 147 \text{ g}\left[\dfrac{1 \text{ kg}}{1 \times 10^3 \text{ g}}\right]$
$= 147 \times 10^{-3}$ kg
$= 1.47 \times 10^{-1}$ kg

b. $1\ \mu\text{g} = 1 \times 10^{-6}$ g and 1 kg
$= 1 \times 10^3$ g so
$11\ \mu\text{g}\left[\dfrac{1 \times 10^{-6} \text{ g}}{1\ \mu\text{g}}\right]\left[\dfrac{1 \text{ kg}}{1 \times 10^3 \text{ g}}\right]$
$= 11 \times 10^{-6} \times 10^{-3}$ kg
$= 1.1 \times 10^{-8}$ kg

c. $7.23 \text{ Mg}\left[\dfrac{1 \times 10^6 \text{ g}}{1 \text{ Mg}}\right]\left[\dfrac{1 \text{ kg}}{1 \times {}^3 \text{ g}}\right]$
$= 7.23 \times 10^3$ kg

d. $478 \text{ mg}\left[\dfrac{1 \times 10^{-3} \text{ g}}{1 \text{ mg}}\right]\left[\dfrac{1 \text{ kg}}{1 \times 10^3 \text{ g}}\right]$
$= 4.78 \times 10^{-4}$ kg

6. a. 8×10^{-7} kg
b. 7×10^{-3} kg
c. 3.96×10^{-19} kg
d. 4.6×10^{-12} kg

7. a. 2×10^{-8} m^2
b. -1.52×10^{-11} m^2
c. 3.0×10^{-9} m^2
d. 0.46×10^{-18} m^2 $= 4.6 \times 10^{-19}$ m^2

8. a. 5.0×10^{-7} mg $+ 4 \times 10^{-8}$ mg
$= 5.0 \times 10^{-7}$ mg $+ 0.4 \times 10^{-7}$ mg
$= 5.4 \times 10^{-7}$ mg
b. 6.0×10^{-3} mg $+ 2 \times 10^{-4}$ mg
$= 6.0 \times 10^{-3}$ mg $+ 0.2 \times 10^{-3}$ mg
$= 6.2 \times 10^{-3}$ mg
c. 3.0×10^{-2} pg $- 2 \times 10^{-6}$ ng
$= 3.0 \times 10^{-2} \times 10^{-12}$ g $- 2 \times 10^{-6} \times 10^{-9}$ g
$= 3.0 \times 10^{-14}$ g $- 0.2 \times 10^{-14}$ g
$= 2.8 \times 10^{-14}$ g
d. 8.2 km $- 3 \times 10^2$ m
$= 8.2 \times 10^3$ m $- 0.3 \times 10^3$ m
$= 7.9 \times 10^3$ m

9. a. $(2 \times 10^4 \text{ m})(4 \times 10^8 \text{ m}) = 8 \times 10^{4+8} \text{ m}^2$
$= 8 \times 10^{12}$ m^2
b. $(3 \times 10^4 \text{ m})(2 \times 10^6 \text{ m}) = 6 \times 10^{4+6} \text{ m}^2$
$= 6 \times 10^{10}$ m^2
c. $(6 \times 10^{-4} \text{ m})(5 \times 10^{-8} \text{ m}) = 30 \times 10^{-4-8} \text{ m}^2$
$= 3 \times 10^{-11}$ m^2
d. $(2.50 \times 10^{-7} \text{ m})(2.50 \times 10^{16} \text{ m})$
$= 6.25 \times 10^{-7+16}$ m^2
$= 6.25 \times 10^9$ m^2

10. a. $\dfrac{6 \times 10^8 \text{ kg}}{2 \times 10^4 \text{ m}^3} = 3 \times 10^{8-4} \text{ kg/m}^3$
$= 3 \times 10^4$kg/m^3
b. $\dfrac{6 \times 10^8 \text{ kg}}{2 \times 10^{-4} \text{ m}^3} = 3 \times 10^{8-(-4)} \text{ kg/m}^3$
$= 3 \times 10^{12}$ kg/m^3
c. $\dfrac{6 \times 10^{-8} \text{ m}}{2 \times 10^4 \text{ s}} = 3 \times 10^{-8-4} \text{ m/s}$
$= 3 \times 10^{-12}$ m/s
d. $\dfrac{6 \times 10^{-8} \text{ m}}{2 \times 10^{-4} \text{ s}} = 3 \times 10^{-8-(-4)} \text{ m/s}$
$= 3 \times 10^{-4}$ m/s

656

11. a. $\frac{(3 \times 10^4\ \text{kg})(4 \times 10^4\ \text{m})}{6 \times 10^4\ \text{s}} = \frac{12 \times 10^{4+4}\ \text{kg·m}}{6 \times 10^4\ \text{s}}$

$= 2 \times 10^{8-4}\ \text{kg·m/s}$
$= 2 \times 10^4\ \text{kg·m/s}$

The evaluation may be done in several other ways. For example,

$\frac{(3 \times 10^4\ \text{kg})(4 \times 10^4\ \text{m})}{6 \times 10^4\ \text{s}}$

$= (0.5 \times 10^{4-4}\ \text{kg/s})(4 \times 10^4\ \text{m})$
$= (0.5\ \text{kg/s})(5 \times 10^4\ \text{m}) = 2 \times 10^4\ \text{kg·m/s}$.

b. $\frac{(2.5 \times 10^6\ \text{kg})(6 \times 10^4\ \text{m})}{5 \times 10^{-2}\text{s}^2}$

$= \frac{15 \times 10^{6+4}\ \text{kg·m}}{5 \times 10^{-2}\text{s}^2}$

$= 3 \times 10^{10-(-2)}\ \text{kg·m/s}^2$
$= 3 \times 10^{12}\ \text{kg·m/s}^2$

12. a. 4 **b.** 3 **c.** 2
d. 4 **e.** 2 **f.** 3

13. a. 2 **b.** 4 **c.** 4
d. 3 **e.** 4 **f.** 3

14. 26.3 cm (rounded from 26.281 cm)

15. a. 2.5 g (rounded from 2.536 g)
b. 475 m (rounded from 474.5832 m)

16. a. $3.0 \times 10^2\ \text{cm}^2$ (the result 301.3 cm² expressed to two significant digits. Note that the expression in the form 300 cm² would not indicate how many of the digits are significant.)
b. 13.6 km² (the result 13.597335 expressed to three significant digits)

17. a. 2.73 cm/s (the result 2.726045 . . . cm/s expressed to three significant digits)
b. 0.253 cm/s (the result 0.253354 . . . cm/s expressed to three significant digits)

18. $mx + b = y,\ b = y - mx$

19. a. $vt = d,\ v = \frac{d}{t}$

b. $t = \frac{d}{v},\ tv = d,\ v = \frac{d}{t}$

c. $\frac{v^2}{2d} = a,\ v^2 = 2ad,\ v = \pm\sqrt{2ad}$

d. $\frac{v}{a} = \frac{b}{c},\ v = \frac{ab}{c}$

20. a. $\frac{E}{s} = f,\ E = fs$

b. $\frac{2E}{v^2} = m,\ 2E = mv^2,\ E = \frac{mv^2}{2}$

c. $\frac{E}{c^2} = m,\ E = mc^2$

21. $v_0^2 + 2ad = v^2,\ 2ad = v^2 - v_0^2,\ d = \frac{(v^2 - v_0^2)}{2a}$

22. a. $at = v - v_0;\ a = \frac{v - v_0}{t}$

b. $\frac{1}{2}at^2 = y - v_0t;\ a = \frac{2(y - v_0t)}{t^2}$

c. $2ay = v^2 - {v_0}^2;\ a = \frac{v^2 - {v_0}^2}{2y}$

d. $v = \sqrt{2as};\ v^2 = 2as;\ a = \frac{v^2}{2s}$

23. a. $A = (0.2\ \text{cm})(30\ \text{cm}) = 6\ \text{cm}^2$
b. $P = 0.25\ \text{m} + 0.25\ \text{m} + 2.00\ \text{m} + 2.00\ \text{m}$
$= 4.50\ \text{m}$

24. a. incorrect since area has units m^2 and (length)(width)(height) has units m^3

b. correct since $\frac{\text{distance}}{\text{speed}}$ has units $\frac{\text{m}}{(\text{m/s})} = \text{s}$

c. incorrect since (speed)(time)² has units $(\text{m/s})(\text{s})^2 = \text{m·s}$

Chapter 3

1. $\bar{v} = \frac{\Delta d}{\Delta t} = (1.00 \times 10^2\ \text{m})/(12.20\ \text{s})$

$= 8.20\ \text{m/s}$
$(8.20\ \text{m/s})(1\ \text{km}/1000\ \text{m})(3600\ \text{s}/1\ \text{h})$
$= 29.5\ \text{km/h}$
or $(8.20\ \text{m/s})(3600\ \text{s/h})/1000\ \text{m/km})$
$= 29.5\ \text{km/h}$

2. $\bar{v} = \frac{\Delta d}{\Delta t} = (13\ \text{km})/(2.0\ \text{h})$

$= 6.5\ \text{km/h}$;
$(6.5\ \text{km/h})(1\ \text{h}/3600\ \text{s})(1000\ \text{m}/1\ \text{km})$
$= 1.8\ \text{m/s}$
or $(6.5\ \text{km/h})(1000\ \text{m/km})/(3600\ \text{s/h}) = 1.8\ \text{m/s}$

3. Slowest between 0.0 and 1.0 s (0 m/s). Fastest between 3.0 and 4.0 s (15 m/s).

657

4. $\bar{v} = (d_2 - d_1)/(t_2 - t_1)$
$= (35\text{ m} - 30\text{ m})/(2.0\text{ s} - 0.0\text{ s})$
$= 2.5\text{ m/s}$

5. Using $d = vt$ with $v = 10$ m/s:

t	d
1 h = 3600 s	3.6×10^4 m
1 min = 60 s	6.0×10^2 m
1 s	10 m
1 ms = 10^{-3} s	10×10^{-3} m = 10 mm
1 μs = 10^{-6} s	10×10^{-6} m = 10 μm
1 ns = 10^{-9} s	10×10^{-9} m = 10 nm

6. a. $v = \frac{d}{t}$, so $t = \frac{d}{v} = (1620.0\text{ m})/(36.0\text{ m/s})$
$= 45.0\text{ s}$

b. $v = (36.0\text{ m/s})(1\text{ km}/1000\text{ m})(3600\text{ s}/1\text{ h})$
$= 130\text{ km/h}$

7. $\bar{v} = (d_2 - d_1)/(t_2 - t_1)$ with $t_2 - t_1 = 2.5$ h
$d_2 = d_1 + \bar{v}(t_2 - t_1)$
$= 17\text{ km} + (94\text{ km/h})(2.5\text{ h})$
$= 252$ km west of school

8. a. Same displacement, but position is $-17\text{ km} + 235\text{ km} = 218$ km west of school.

b. $\Delta t = \frac{\Delta d}{\bar{v}} = (17\text{ km})/(94\text{ km/h}) = 11$ min, so

$t = $ 1:11 P.M.

9. a. Starting at High St., walking east at a constant velocity.
b. Starts west of High St., walking east at slower constant velocity.
c. Walks west from High St., first fast, but slowing to a stop.
d. Starts east of High St., walking west at constant velocity.

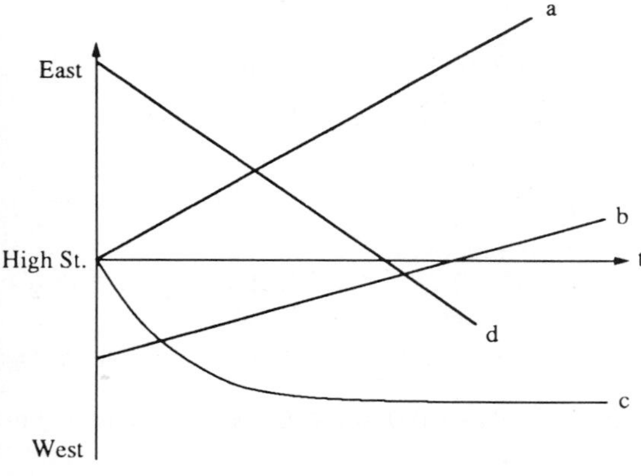

10.

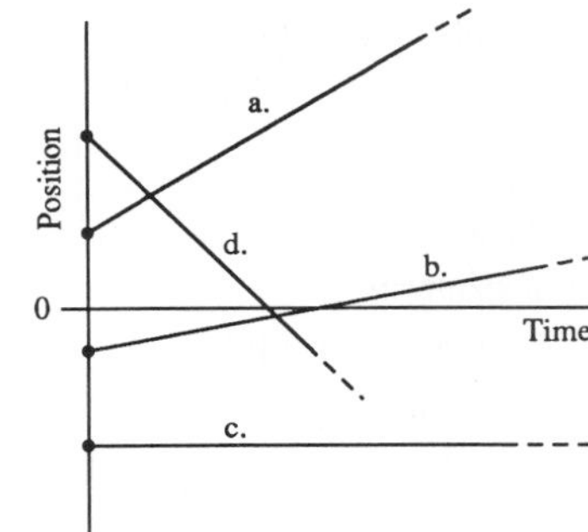

11. a. $\bar{v} = \frac{\Delta d}{\Delta t} = \frac{+5\text{ m}}{2\text{ s}} = 2.5\text{ m/s}$

b. $\bar{v} = \frac{\Delta d}{\Delta t} = \frac{0\text{ m}}{4\text{ s}} = 0\text{ m/s}$

c. $\bar{v} = \frac{\Delta d}{\Delta t} = \frac{-15\text{ m}}{4\text{ s}} = -3.75\text{ m/s}$

d. $\bar{v} = \frac{\Delta d}{\Delta t} = \frac{+5\text{ m}}{4\text{ s}} = 1.25\text{ m/s}$

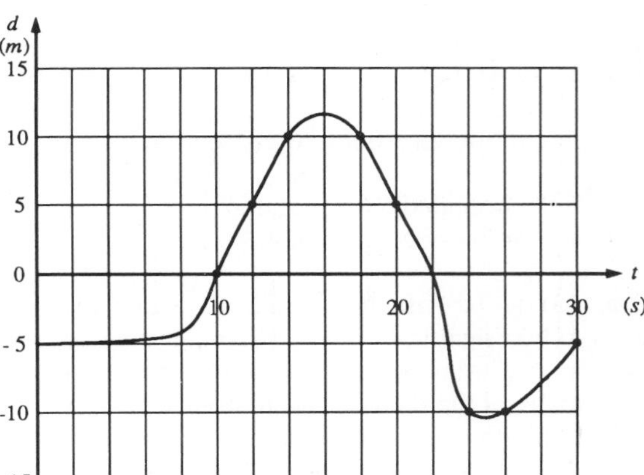

12.

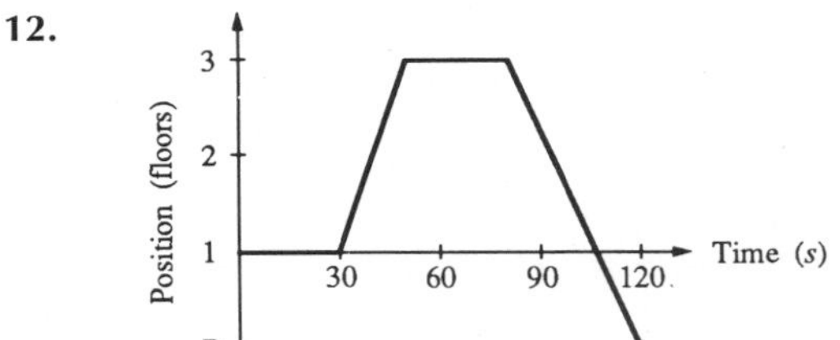

13.

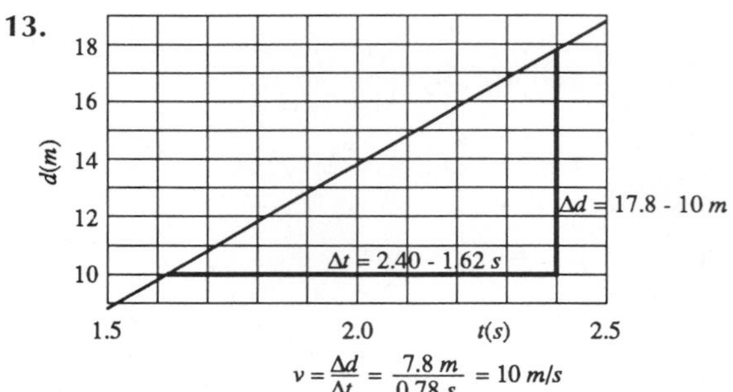

658

14. a. Moves to right at constant speed.

b. Moves to right from rest at constantly increasing speed.

c. Has an initial non-zero velocity to the right and continues to move to right at constantly increasing speed.

15. a. 10 m/s

b. 20 m/s

c. 30 m/s

16. Each second it increases 10 m/s.

17.

v

b and c

0

a

t

18. a.

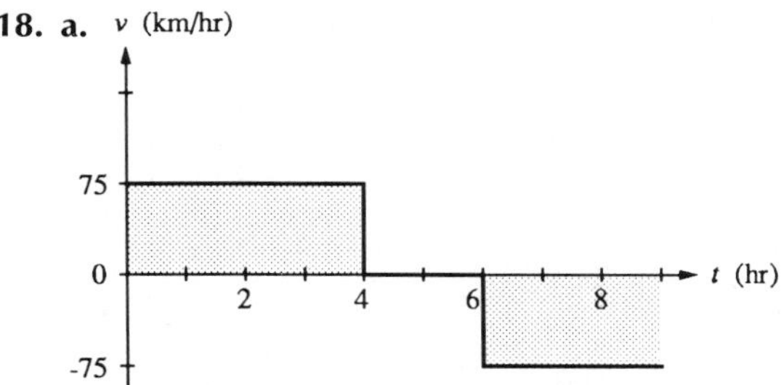

b. Area is (75 km/h)(4 h) = 300 km, the distance traveled in that time.

c. Find total area under curve for all three segments of trip, which is
300 km + 0 km + (−225 km) = 75 km.

19. a.

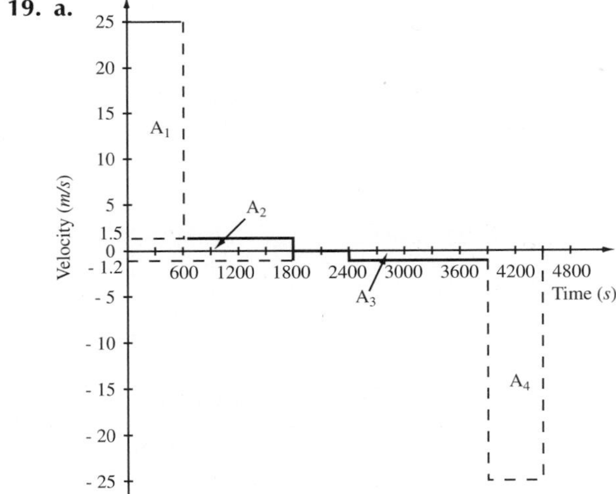

Distance walked to station
= (1.5 m/s)(20.0 min)(60 s/min)
= 1800 m.
Time for walk back to car
= (1800 m)/(1.2 m/s)
= 1500 s.

b.

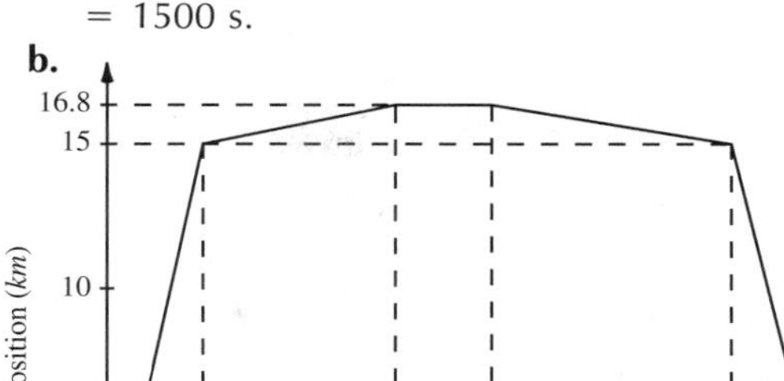

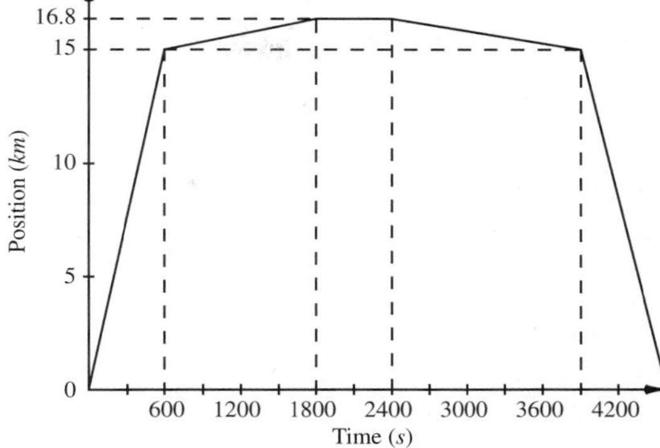

From the graph in part **a,** the changes in position are

$\Delta d_1 = A_1 = (25 \text{ m/s})(600 \text{ s})$
$= 15\,000 \text{ m} = 15 \text{ km}$

$\Delta d_2 = A_2 = (1.5 \text{ m/s})(1200 \text{ s})$
$= 1800 \text{ m} = 1.8 \text{ km}$

$\Delta d_3 = A_3 = (-1.2 \text{ m/s})(1500 \text{ s})$
$= -1800 \text{ m} = -1.8 \text{ km}$

$\Delta d_4 = A_4 = (-25 \text{ m/s})(600 \text{ s})$
$= -15\,000 \text{ m} = -15 \text{ km}$

20. If $v_B = v_A + v_{BA}$, where v_A, v_B are velocities relative to Earth and v_{BA} is the velocity of B relative to A, then $v_{BA} = v_B - v_A$.

a. $v_{tc} = v_t - v_c = 105 \text{ km/h} - 92 \text{ km/h}$
$= 13 \text{ km/h}$

b. $v_{ct} = v_c - v_t = 92 \text{ km/h} - 105 \text{ km/h}$
$= -13 \text{ km/h}$

21. The relative speed is (3.5 m)/(1.8 s) = 1.9 m/s = 7.0 km/h, so its speed is 102 km/h.

Chapter 4

1. $a = \dfrac{\Delta v}{\Delta t} = (36 \text{ m/s} - 4.0 \text{ m/s})/(4.0 \text{ s}) = 8.0 \text{ m/s}^2$

2. $a = (v_2 - v_1)/(t_2 - t_1) = (15 \text{ m/s} - 36 \text{ m/s})/(3.0 \text{ s})$
$= -7.0 \text{ m/s}^2$

3. $a = (v_2 - v_1)/(t_2 - t_1)$
$= (4.5 \text{ m/s} - (-3.0 \text{ m/s}))/(2.5 \text{ s})$
$= 3.0 \text{ m/s}^2$

659

4. **a.** $a = (v_2 - v_1)/(t_2 - t_1)$
$= (0 \text{ m/s} - 25 \text{ m/s})/(3.0 \text{ s})$
$= -8.3 \text{ m/s}^2$
b. half as great (-4.2 m/s^2)

5. Starting from rest, it accelerates to 10 m/s in the first 5 s. It remains at this speed for 10 s, before slowing to 4 m/s over the last 5 s.

6. **a.** 5 to 15 s and 21 to 28 s
b. 0 to 6 s
c. 15 to 20 s, 28 s to 40 s
d. 16 to 19 s

7. **a.** 2 m/s^2
b. 1 m/s^2
c. -1.2 m/s^2
d. 0 m/s^2

8. **a.** 10

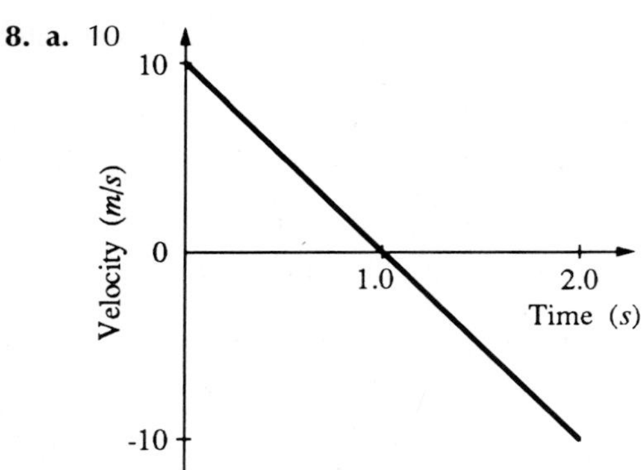

b. $a = \frac{\Delta v}{\Delta t} = (-10 \text{ m/s} - 10 \text{ m/s})/(2 \text{ s})$
$= -10 \text{ m/s}^2$

c. the same, -10 m/s^2

9. **a.** $v_f = v_i + at = 2.0 \text{ m/s} + (-5.0 \text{ m/s}^2)(2.0 \text{ s})$
$= 1.0 \text{ m/s}$
b. $v_f = v_i + at = 2.0 \text{ m/s} + (-0.50 \text{ m/s}^2)(6.0 \text{ s})$
$= -1.0 \text{ m/s}$
c. The ball velocity simply decreased in the first case. In the second case, the ball slowed to a stop and then began rolling down the hill.

10. $a = (3.5 \text{ m/s}^2)(1 \text{ km}/1000 \text{ m})(3600 \text{ s}/1 \text{ h})$
$= 12.6 \text{ (km/h)/s}$
$v_f = v_i + at = 30 \text{ km/h} + (12.6 \text{ (km/h)/s})(6.8 \text{ s})$
$= 30 \text{ km/h} + 86 \text{ km/h} = 116 \text{ km/h}$

11. $v_f = v_i + at$, so $t = (v_f - v_i)/a$
$= (28 \text{ m/s} - 0 \text{ m/s})/(5.5 \text{ m/s}^2)$
$= 5.1 \text{ s}$

12. $v_f = v_i + at$, so
$t = (v_f - v_i)/a$
$= (3 \text{ m/s} - 22 \text{ m/s})/(-2.1 \text{ m/s}^2)$
$= 9.0 \text{ s}$

13. $d = \frac{1}{2}(v_f + v_i)t = \frac{1}{2}(22 \text{ m/s} + 44 \text{ m/s})(11 \text{ s})$
$= 3.6 \times 10^2 \text{ m}$

14. $d = \frac{1}{2}(v_f + v_i)t = \frac{1}{2}(132 \text{ m/s} + 88 \text{ m/s})(15 \text{ s})$
$= 1.7 \times 10^3 \text{ m}$

15. $d = \frac{1}{2}(v_f + v_i)t$, so
$t = 2d/(v_f + v_i)$
$= 2(125 \text{ m})/(25 \text{ m/s} + 15 \text{ m/s})$
$= 6.3 \text{ s}$

16. $d = \frac{1}{2}(v_f + v_i)t$, so
$v_i = 2d/t - v_f$
$= 2(19 \text{ m})/(4.5 \text{ s}) - 7.5 \text{ m/s}$
$= 0.94 \text{ m/s}$

17. $d = v_i t + \frac{1}{2}at^2$
$= (0 \text{ m/s})(30.0 \text{ s}) + \frac{1}{2}(3.00 \text{ m/s}^2)(30.0 \text{ s})^2$
$= 0 \text{ m} + 1350 \text{ m} = 1.35 \times 10^3 \text{ m}$

18. Using $d = v_i t + \frac{1}{2}at^2$ with $v_i = 0$,
$a = 2d/t^2 = 2(110 \text{ m})/(5.0 \text{ s})^2 = 8.8 \text{ m/s}^2$.

19. **a.** $a = (v_2 - v_1)/(t_2 - t_1)$
$= (0 \text{ m/s} - 22 \text{ m/s})/(2.0 \text{ s})$
$= -11 \text{ m/s}^2$
b. $d = v_i t + \frac{1}{2}at^2$
$= (22 \text{ m/s})(2.0 \text{ s}) + \frac{1}{2}(-11 \text{ m/s}^2)(2.0 \text{ s})^2$
$= 44 \text{ m} - 22 \text{ m} = 22 \text{ m}$

20. $d = v_i t + \frac{1}{2}at^2$
$= (4.5 \text{ m/s})(12 \text{ s}) + \frac{1}{2}(0.40 \text{ m/s}^2)(12 \text{ s})^2$
$= 54 \text{ m} + 29 \text{ m} = 83 \text{ m}$

660

21. $v_f^2 = v_i^2 + 2ad$
$= (21\ \text{m/s})^2 + 2(3.0\ \text{m/s}^2)(535\ \text{m})$
$= 3651\ \text{m}^2/\text{s}^2$
$v_f = 60\ \text{m/s}$

22. $v_f^2 = v_i^2 + 2ad$, so
$v_i^2 = v_f^2 - 2ad$
$= (0\ \text{m/s})^2 - 2(-8.0\ \text{m/s}^2)(484\ \text{m})$
$= 7744\ \text{m}^2/\text{s}^2$
$v_i = 88\ \text{m/s}$

23. Using $v_f^2 = v_i^2 + 2ad$ with
$v_i = 101\ \text{km/h} = 28.1\ \text{m/s}$ and $v_f = 0$,
$d = (v_f^2 - v_i^2)/2a$
$= ((0\ \text{m/s})^2 - (28.1\ \text{m/s})^2)/2(-300\ \text{m/s}^2)$
$= 1.32\ \text{m}$.

24. Convert speeds to m/s.
$v_i = -6.9\ \text{m/s}$, $v_f = 9.7\ \text{m/s}$,
$d = (v_f^2 - v_i^2)/2a$, so
$a = (v_f^2 - v_i^2)/2d$
$= ((9.7\ \text{m/s})^2 - (-6.9\ \text{m/s})^2)/2(3.2\ \text{m})$
$= 7.3\ \text{m/s}^2$

25. a. $v_f = v_i + gt$
$= 0\ \text{m/s} + (-9.80\ \text{m/s}^2)(4.0\ \text{s})$
$v_i = -39\ \text{m/s}$, downward

b. $d = v_it + \frac{1}{2}gt^2$
$= 0 + \frac{1}{2}(-9.80\ \text{m/s}^2)(4.0\ \text{s})^2$
$= \frac{1}{2}(-9.81\ \text{m/s}^2)(16\ \text{s}^2)$
$d = -78\ \text{m}$, downward

26. Using $d = \frac{1}{2}gt^2$, the reaction time can be calculated from $t = \sqrt{2\frac{d}{g}}$.

27. $d = v_it + \frac{1}{2}gt^2 = 0 + \frac{1}{2}(-9.80\ \text{m/s}^2)(0.50\ \text{s})^2$
$= -1.2\ \text{m}$

28. $v_f = v_i + at = 1210\ \text{m/s} + (-150\ \text{m/s}^2)(8.68\ \text{s})$
$= 1210\ \text{m/s} - 1300\ \text{m/s}$
$= -90\ \text{m/s}$
Spacecraft slows to a stop then reverses motion.

29. a. Using $d = v_it + \frac{1}{2}gt^2$ with $v_i = 0$,
$t = \sqrt{\frac{2d}{g}} = \sqrt{2(-1.0\text{m})/(-9.80\ \text{m/s}^2)} = 0.45\ \text{s}$.

b. $v_f = v_i + gt = 0\ \text{m/s} + (-9.80\ \text{m/s}^2)(0.45\ \text{s})$
$= -4.4\ \text{m/s}$

30. a. $v_i = 0\ \text{m/s}$, so
$v_f = gt = (0.2)(9.80\ \text{m/s}^2)(2.0\ \text{s}) = 3.9\ \text{m/s}$

b. $d = \frac{1}{2}at^2 = \frac{1}{2}(0.2)(9.8\ \text{m/s}^2)(4.0\ \text{s})^2 = 16\ \text{m}$

31. a. Since $v_f = 0$ at high point, $v_f = v_i + gt$ becomes $t = -v_i/g$
$= -(27\ \text{m/s})/(-9.80\ \text{m/s}^2)$
$= 2.8\ \text{s}$

b. $d = v_it + \frac{1}{2}gt^2$
$= (27\ \text{m/s})(2.8\ \text{s}) + \frac{1}{2}(-9.80\ \text{m/s}^2)(2.8\ \text{s})^2$
$= 75.6\ \text{m} - 38.4\ \text{m} = 37\ \text{m}$

32. a. 46 m/min/s can be interpreted as a speed change of either 46 m/min each second or 46 m/s each minute.

b. $v_f = v_i + at$
$= 0\ \text{m/min} + (46\ \text{m/min/s})(2.0\ \text{s})$
$= 92\ \text{m/min}$

c. Speeds before 2.0 s are given by $v_f = at$; speeds after are 92 m/min.

t (s)	v_f (m/min)
0.5	23
1.0	46
1.5	69
2.0	92
3.0	92
4.0	92
5.0	92

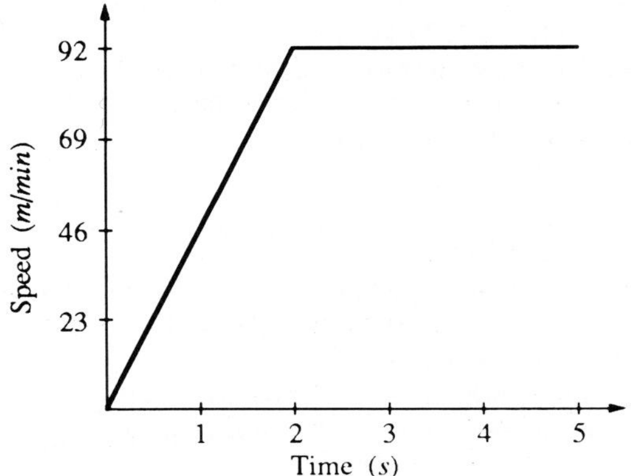

661

d. For first 2 seconds $d = \frac{1}{2}at^2$, where

$a = (46 \text{ m/min/s})(1 \text{ min}/60 \text{ s}) = 0.767 \text{ m/s}^2$
and after 2 seconds it continues to rise
$(92 \text{ m/min})(1/60 \text{ min}) = 1.5$ m each second.

t (s)	d (m)
1.0	0.4
2.0	1.5
3.0	3.0
4.0	4.5
5.0	6.0

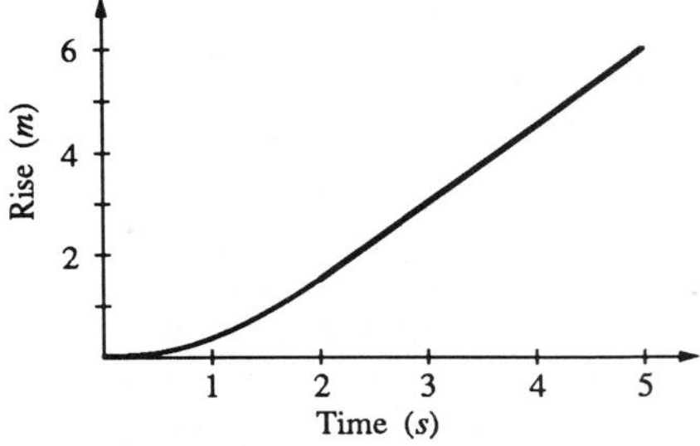

Chapter 5

1. $m = \frac{F}{a} = \frac{+140 \text{ N}}{+19 \text{ m/s}^2} = 7.4 \text{ kg}$

2. $F = ma = (275 \text{ kg})(-4.50 \text{ m/s}^2)$
$= -1.24 \times 10^3 \text{ N}$
The negative sign of the acceleration slowing down the motor bike tells us that the motor bike has a velocity in the positive direction. The negative sign on the force indicates that it is directed opposite to the motor bike velocity.

3. Given: $v_i = 105 \text{ km/h} = 29.2 \text{ m/s}$,
$v_f = 0$, $d = 53$ m,

$$a = \frac{(v_f^2 - v_i^2)}{2d} = -8.0 \text{ m/s}^2$$

$F = ma = (1225 \text{ kg})(-8.0 \text{ m/s}^2) = -9.8 \times 10^3 \text{ N}$
The force is directed opposite to the car motion and is provided by the road surface pushing against the car tires.

4. a. $a = \frac{F}{m} = \frac{(+1.2 \times 10^{-4} \text{ N})}{(7.0 \times 10^{-5} \text{ kg})} = +1.7 \text{ m/s}^2$

b. The upward force being given as a positive number means that the downward motion of the spider is represented as a negative velocity. The positive acceleration is opposed to this negative velocity and gives rise to a slowing down of the spider.

5. a. $W = mg = (0.113 \text{ kg})(9.8 \text{ m/s}^2) = 1.11 \text{ N}$
b. $W = mg = (108 \text{ kg})(9.80 \text{ m/s}^2)$
$= 1.06 \times 10^3 \text{ N}$
c. $W = mg = (870 \text{ kg})(9.80 \text{ m/s}^2)$
$= 8.50 \times 10^3 \text{ N}$

6. a. $m = \frac{W}{g} = \frac{98 \text{ N}}{9.80 \text{ m/s}^2} = 10 \text{ kg}$

b. $m = \frac{W}{g} = \frac{80 \text{ N}}{9.80 \text{ m/s}^2} = 8.2 \text{ kg}$

c. $m = \frac{W}{g} = \frac{0.98 \text{ N}}{9.80 \text{ m/s}^2} = 0.10 \text{ kg}$

7. 20 N, upward

8. a. $W = mg = (75 \text{ kg})(9.80 \text{ m/s}^2) = 7.4 \times 10^2 \text{ N}$
b. $W = mg = (75 \text{ kg})(3.8 \text{ m/s}^2) = 2.9 \times 10^2 \text{ N}$
c. $g = \frac{W}{m} = \frac{683 \text{ N}}{75 \text{ kg}} = 9.1 \text{ m/s}^2$

9. a. 625 N, upward
b. 675 N
c. Since $F_{\text{father on Joe}} + F_{\text{scale on Joe}} = W_{\text{Joe}}$.
$F_{\text{scale on Joe}} = W_{\text{Joe}} - F_{\text{father on Joe}}$
$= 625 \text{ N} - 72 \text{ N} = 553$ N, upward.

10. a. $F_f = \mu F_N$ with $F_N = W$, so

$$\mu = \frac{F_f}{F_N} = \frac{36 \text{ N}}{52 \text{ N}} = 0.69$$

b. The force must equal the friction force.
$F_f = \mu F_N = \mu(W + W_1)$
$= (0.12)(52 \text{ N} + 650 \text{ N}) = 84 \text{ N}$

11. a. $F_f = \mu F_N$ where $F_N = W = mg$, so
$F_f = -(0.50)(750 \text{ kg})(9.80 \text{ m/s}^2)$
$= -3.7 \times 10^3 \text{ N}$
The negative sign has been used to indicate that the friction force is opposite the car velocity.

b. $a = \frac{F_f}{m} = \frac{(-3.7 \times 10^3 \text{ N})}{750 \text{ kg}} = -4.9 \text{ m/s}^2$

directed opposite car velocity and constant because F_f is constant
c. $v_f^2 = v_i^2 + 2ad$, so

$$d = \frac{(v_f^2 - v_i^2)}{2a} = \frac{(0 - (30 \text{ m/s})^2)}{-9.8 \text{ m/s}^2}$$

$= 92$ m

12. larger, since F_f is proportional to μ; shorter distance since, from the solution to Practice Problem 11, d is inversely proportional to a, and a is proportional to F_f

662

13. a. $m = \frac{W}{g} = \frac{49\ \text{N}}{9.80\ \text{m/s}^2} = 5.0\ \text{kg}$

b. $ma = F_{net} = F_{appl} + W = 69\ \text{N} + (-49\ \text{N})$
$= 20\ \text{N}$

So, $a = \frac{F_{net}}{m} = \frac{20\ \text{N}}{5.0\ \text{kg}}$
$= 4.0\ \text{m/s}^2$

14. a. $m = \frac{W}{g} = \frac{14.7\ \text{N}}{9.80\ \text{m/s}^2} = 1.50\ \text{kg}$

b. $ma = F_{net} = F_{appl} + W$
$= 10.2\ \text{N} + (-14.7\ \text{N})$
$= -4.50\ \text{N}$

Thus, $a = \frac{F_{net}}{m} = \frac{-4.50\ \text{N}}{1.5\ \text{kg}} = -3.00\ \text{m/s}^2$

15. a. $W = mg = (2 \times 10^6\ \text{kg})(9.80\ \text{m/s}^2)$
$= 20 \times 10^6\ \text{N}$

b. $ma = F_{net} = F_{appl} + W$
$= 30 \times 10^6\ \text{N} + (-20 \times 10^6\ \text{N})$
$= 10 \times 10^6\ \text{N}$

Thus, $a = \frac{F_{net}}{m} = \frac{(10 \times 10^6\ \text{N})}{(2 \times 10^6\ \text{kg})} = 5.0\ \text{m/s}^2$

c. $v = at = (13\ \text{m/s}^2)(600\ \text{s})$
$= 7.8 \times 10^3\ \text{m/s} = 7.8\ \text{km/s}$

d. It would increase.

$a = \frac{F}{m}$ F is constant, m decreases, so a increases.

16. $F_{net} = ma = (1354\ \text{kg})(3.0\ \text{m/s}^2) = 4.1 \times 10^3\ \text{N}$
$F_{net} = F_{appl} + F_{drag}$, so
$F_{appl} = F_{net} - F_{drag}$
$= 4.1 \times 10^3\ \text{N} - (-280\ \text{N}) = 4.4 \times 10^3\ \text{N}$

Chapter 6

1. a. 11 km + 11 km = 22 km

b. 16 km

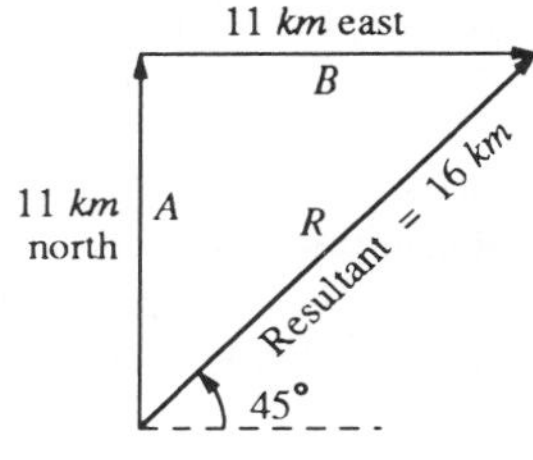

2. 207 N, 53°, north of east

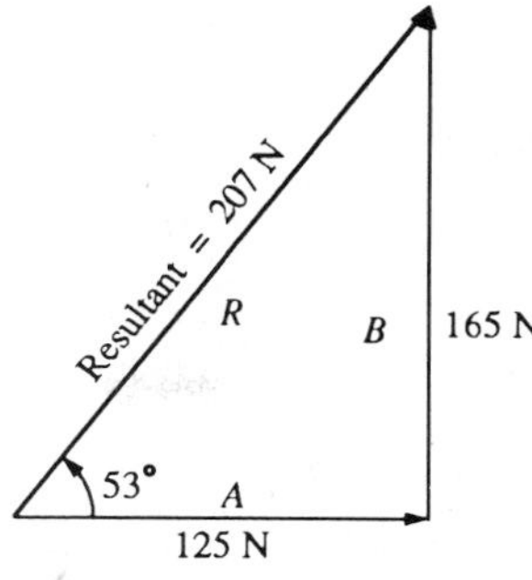

3. a. 13 km + 18 km + 3 km = 34 km

b. 21 km, 61°, north of east

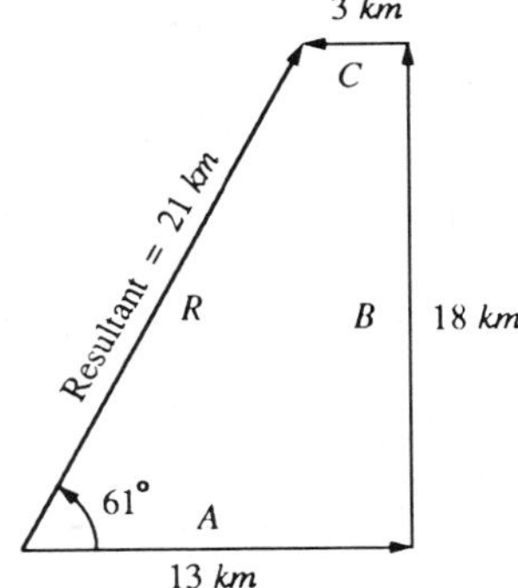

4. a. 18 m/s, 29°, north of east

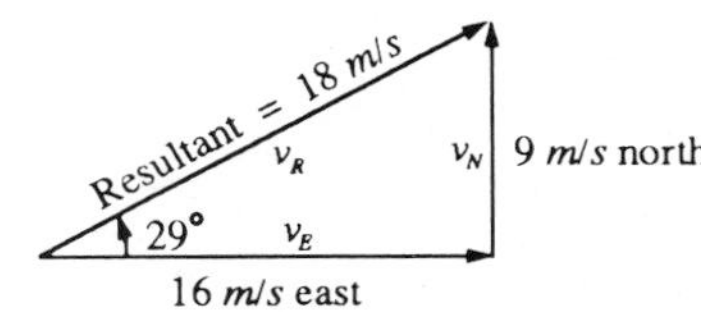

b. $t = \frac{d}{v_E} = \frac{136\ \text{m}}{16\ \text{m/s}} = 8.5\ \text{s}$

c. $d = v_N t = (9.0\ \text{m/s})(8.5\ \text{s}) = 77\ \text{m}$

5. 130 km/h, 21°, north of east

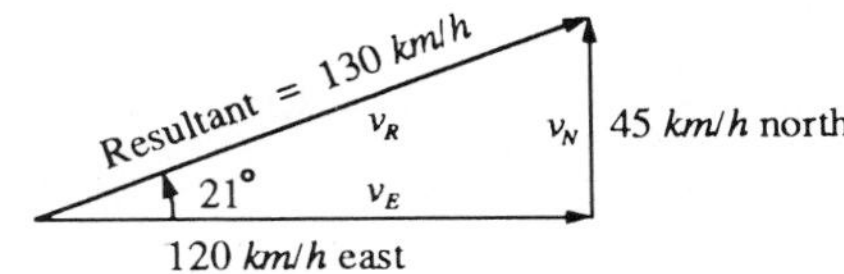

6. 434 N, 11.5°, south of east

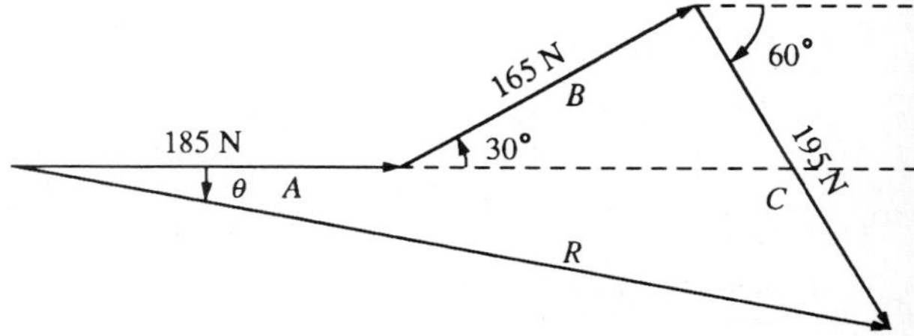

663

7. 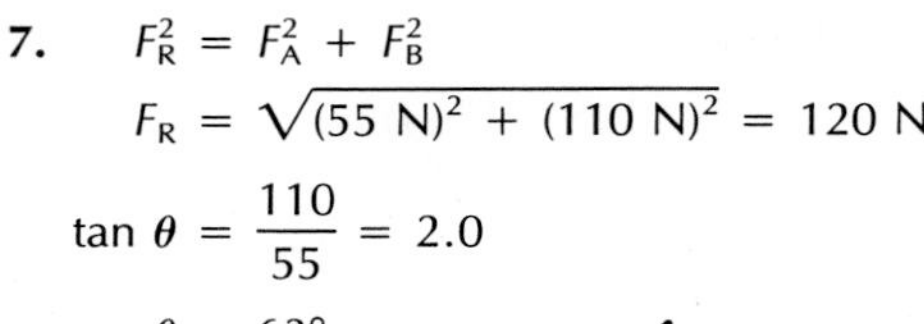

$$F_R^2 = F_A^2 + F_B^2$$

$$F_R = \sqrt{(55\ \text{N})^2 + (110\ \text{N})^2} = 120\ \text{N}$$

$$\tan\theta = \frac{110}{55} = 2.0$$

$$\theta = 63°$$

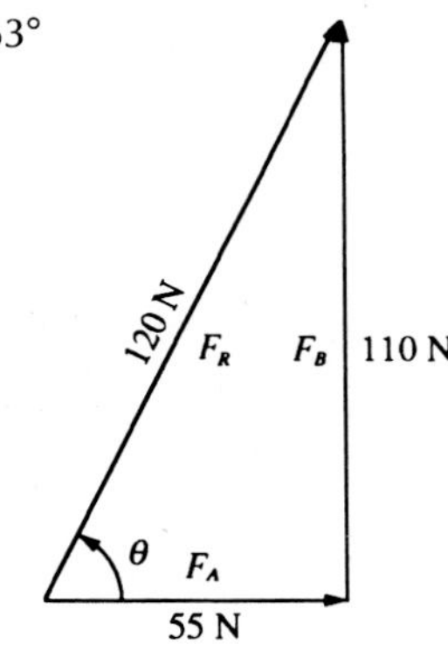

8. a. $v_R = \sqrt{(8.5\ \text{m/s})^2 + (3.8\ \text{m/s})^2} = 9.3\ \text{m/s}$

$$\tan\theta = \frac{3.8}{8.5} = 0.45,\ \theta = 24°$$

$$v_R = 9.3\ \text{m/s at } 24°$$

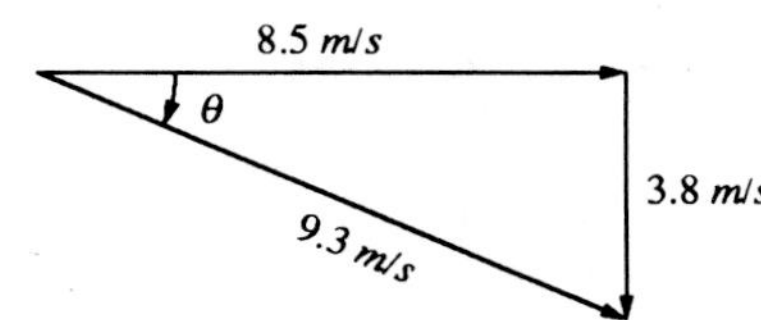

b. $t = \frac{d}{v} = \frac{110\ \text{m}}{8.5\ \text{m/s}} = 13\ \text{s}$

9. a. $v_R = \sqrt{(3.8\ \text{m/s})^2 + (2.2\ \text{m/s})^2} = 4.4\ \text{m/s}$

$$\tan\theta = \frac{2.2}{3.8} = 0.58,\ \theta = 30°$$

$$v_R = 4.4\ \text{m/s at } 30°$$

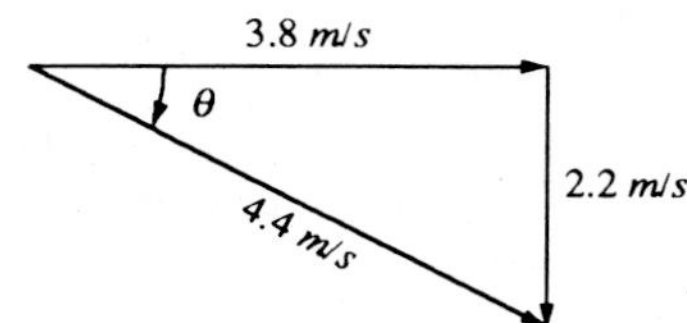

b. $t = \frac{d}{v} = \frac{41\ \text{m}}{3.8\ \text{m/s}} = 11\ \text{s}$

c. $d = vt = (2.2\ \text{m/s})(11\ \text{s}) = 24\ \text{m}$

10. $v_R = \sqrt{(152\ \text{km/h})^2 + (42\ \text{km/h})^2} = 160\ \text{km/h}$

$$\tan\theta = \frac{42}{152} = 0.276$$

$$\theta = 15°$$

$$\theta_R = 125° + 15° = 140°$$

$$v_R = 160\ \text{km/h at } 140°$$

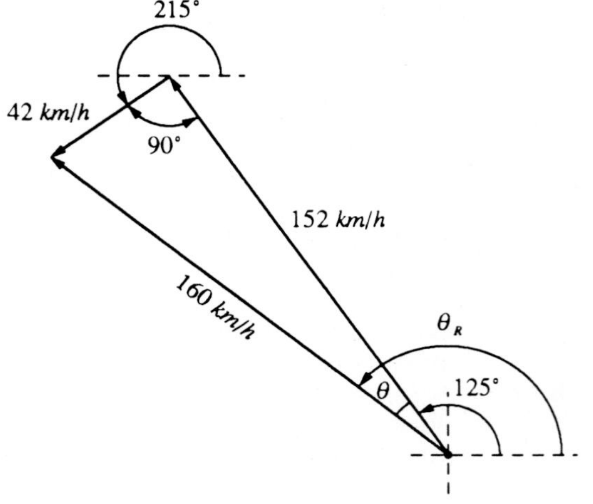

11. $F_h = (75\ \text{N}) \cos 60° = 37.5\ \text{N}$

12.

$\theta = 180° - 149° = 31°$

a. $v_{90} = v \sin\theta = (525\ \text{km/h}) \sin 31°$
$= 270\ \text{km/h}$

b. $v_{180} = -v\cos\theta = -(525\ \text{km/h}) \cos 31°$
$= -450\ \text{km/h}$

13. a. $F_h = (72\ \text{N}) \cos 60° = 36\ \text{N}$

b. $F_h = (72\ \text{N}) \cos 40° = 55\ \text{N}$

c. $F_h = (72\ \text{N}) \cos 30° = 62\ \text{N}$

14. $\theta = 360° - 305° = 55°$ south of east

east − west component = (14.7 km) cos 55°
= 8.43 km, east

north − south component = (14.7 km) sin 55°
= 12.0 km, south

664

15. $F_{1x} = (12.0 \text{ N}) \cos 10.0° = 11.8 \text{ N}$
$F_{1y} = (12.0 \text{ N}) \sin 10.0° = 2.0 \text{ N}$
$F_{2x} = (14.0 \text{ N}) \cos 310.0° = 9.0 \text{ N}$
$F_{2y} = (14.0 \text{ N}) \sin 310.0° = -10.7 \text{ N}$,
where $\cos 310.0° = \cos(-50.0°) = \cos 50.0°$
$\sin 310.0° = \sin(-50.0°) = -\sin 50.0°$

$$F_{net} = \sqrt{(F_{1x} + F_{2x})^2 + (F_{1y} + F_{2y})^2}$$
$$= \sqrt{(11.8 \text{ N} + 9.0 \text{ N})^2 + (2.0 \text{ N} - 10.7 \text{ N})^2}$$
$$= \sqrt{(20.8 \text{ N})^2 + (-8.7 \text{ N})^2} = 22.5 \text{ N}$$
$$\tan\theta = \frac{F_y}{F_x} = \frac{-8.7 \text{ N}}{20.8 \text{ N}} = -0.418$$
$$\theta = -22.7° \text{ or } 337.3°$$

16. $F_{1x} = (15 \text{ N}) \cos 65.0° = 6.3 \text{ N}$
$F_{1y} = (15 \text{ N}) \sin 65.0° = 13.6 \text{ N}$
$F_{2x} = (16 \text{ N}) \cos 135° = -11.3 \text{ N}$
$F_{2y} = (16 \text{ N}) \sin 135° = 11.3 \text{ N}$
$F_{3x} = (11 \text{ N}) \cos 195° = -10.6 \text{ N}$
$F_{3y} = (11 \text{ N}) \sin 195° = -2.8 \text{ N}$
$F_x = F_{1x} + F_{2x} + F_{3x}$
$= 6.3 \text{ N} + (-11.3 \text{ N}) + (-10.6 \text{ N})$
$= -15.6 \text{ N}$
$F_y = F_{1y} + F_{2y} + F_{3y}$
$= 13.6 \text{ N} + 11.3 \text{ N} + (-2.8 \text{ N}) = 22.1 \text{ N}$

$$F_{net} = \sqrt{F_x^2 + F_y^2}$$
$$= \sqrt{(-15.6 \text{ N})^2 + (22.1 \text{ N})^2} = 27.1 \text{ N}$$
$$\tan\theta = \frac{F_y}{F_x} = \frac{22.1 \text{ N}}{-15.6 \text{ N}} = -1.42$$

Since, from signs of F_x and F_y, θ is second quadrant, angle $\theta = 180° - 54.8° = 125°$.

17. 55 N, due east

18.

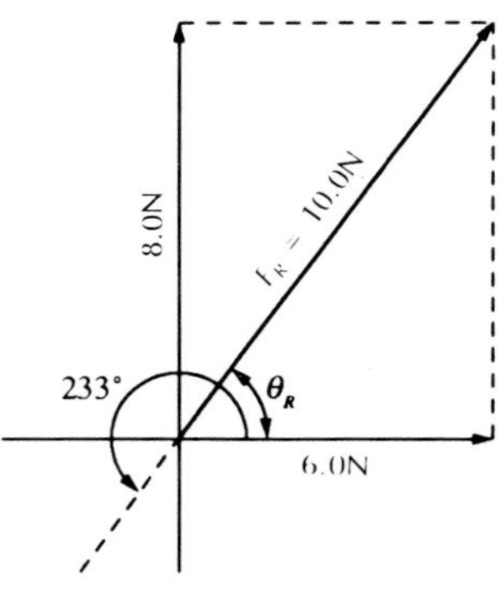

a. $F_R = \sqrt{(6.0 \text{ N})^2 + (8.0 \text{ N})^2}$
$= 10.0 \text{ N}$
$\tan\theta_R = \frac{8.0}{6.0} = 1.33$
$\theta_R = 53°$
$F_R = 10.0 \text{ N at } 53°$

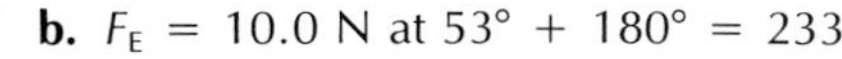

b. $F_E = 10.0 \text{ N at } 53° + 180° = 233°$

19.

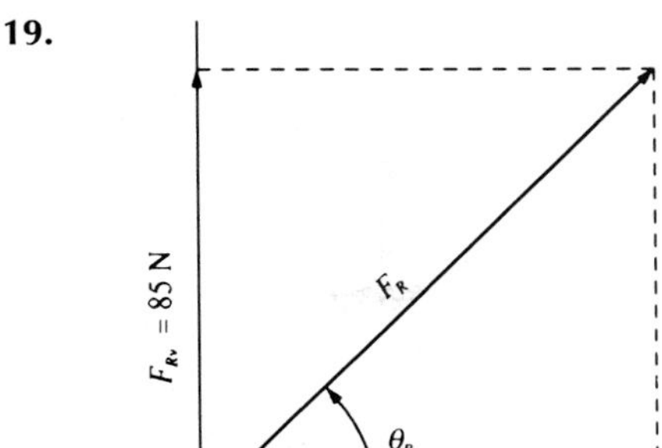

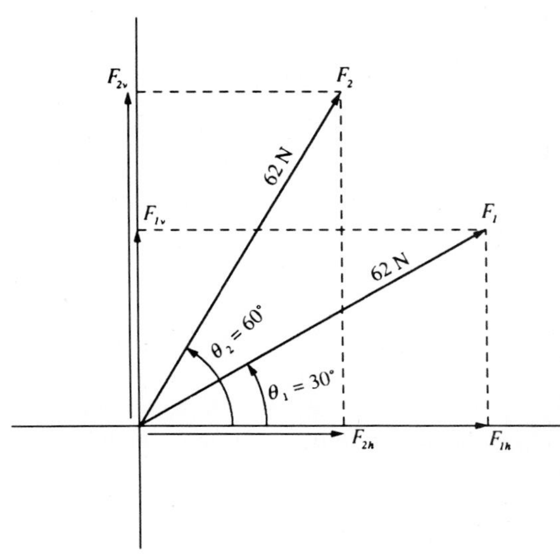

a. Vector addition is most easily carried out by using the method of addition by components. The first step in this method is the resolution of the given vectors into their horizontal and vertical components.
$F_{1h} = F_1 \cos\theta_1 = (62 \text{ N}) \cos 30° = 54 \text{ N}$
$F_{1v} = F_1 \sin\theta_1 = (62 \text{ N}) \sin 30° = 31 \text{ N}$

$F_{2h} = F_2 \cos\theta_2 = (62 \text{ N}) \cos 60° = 31 \text{ N}$
$F_{2v} = F_2 \sin\theta_2 = (62 \text{ N}) \sin 60° = 54 \text{ N}$

At this point, the two original vectors have been replaced by four components, vectors that are much easier to add. The horizontal and vertical components of the resultant vector are found by simple addition.

$F_{Rh} = F_{1h} + F_{2h} = 54 \text{ N} + 31 \text{ N} = 85 \text{ N}$
$F_{Rv} = F_{1v} + F_{2v} = 31 \text{ N} + 54 \text{ N} = 85 \text{ N}$

665

The magnitude and direction of the resultant vector are found by the usual method.

$$F_R = \sqrt{(F_{Rh})^2 + (F_{Rv})^2}$$
$$= \sqrt{(85\ N)^2 + (85\ N)^2}$$
$$= 120\ N$$

$$\tan \theta_R = \frac{F_{Rv}}{F_{Rh}} = \frac{85\ N}{85\ N} = 1,\ \theta_R = 45°$$

$F_R = 120$ N at 45°

b. $F_E = 120$ N, 225°

20.

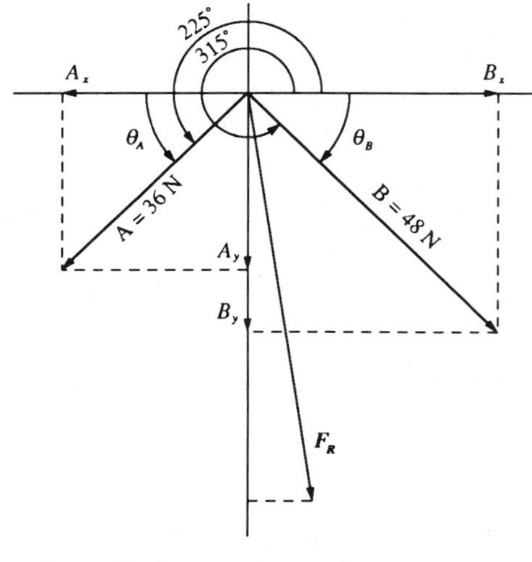

$\theta_A = 225° - 180° = 45°$
$\theta_B = 360° - 315° = 45°$
$A_x = -A \cos \theta_A = -(36\ N) \cos 45° = -25$ N
$A_y = -A \sin \theta_A = (-36\ N) \sin 45° = -25$ N
$B_x = B \cos \theta_B = (48\ N) \cos 45° = 34$ N
$B_y = -B \sin \theta_B = -(48\ N) \sin 45° = -34$ N
$F_x = A_x + B_x = -25\ N + 34\ N = 9$ N
$F_y = A_y + B_y = -25\ N - 34\ N = -59$ N
$F_R = \sqrt{F_x^2 + F_y^2} = \sqrt{(-9\ N)^2 + (-59\ N)^2}$
$= 60$ N

$\tan \theta_R = \frac{9}{59} = 0.153,\ \theta = 9°$

$\theta_R = 270° + 9° = 279°$
$F_R = 60$ N at 279°
$F_E = 60$ N
$\theta_E = 279° - 180° = 99°$

21. Following the method of the Example Problem, the vertical component of the force exerted by each rope must support half of the sign weight.

$$A_v = B_v = \frac{168\ N}{2} = 84\ N$$

$$\frac{A_v}{\sin 42°} = A = \frac{84\ N}{\sin 42°} = 126\ N$$

$B = A = 126$ N

22. Since $A_v = A \sin \theta$, and $A_v = 84$ N and $A = 575$ N,

$$\sin \theta = \frac{84}{575} = 0.146$$

$\theta = 8.4°$.

23. a. $F_\perp = (562\ N) \cos 66° = 229$ N
$F_\parallel = (562\ N) \sin 66° = 513$ N

b. The perpendicular force is less and the parallel force is greater on the 66° incline than in the case of the 30° incline.

24. a. $F_\parallel = (1.2 \times 10^4\ N) \sin 36° = 7.1 \times 10^3$ N
b. $F_\perp = (1.2 \times 10^4\ N) \cos 36° = 9.7 \times 10^3$ N

25. a. $a = \frac{F}{m} = \frac{F_\parallel}{m} = \frac{mg \sin \theta}{m}$

$g \sin \theta = 5.8\ m/s^2$

b. $v^2 = 2ad = 2(5.8\ m/s^2)(30\ m)$, so
$v = 19$ m/s

c. No. A sprinter can run about 10 m/s.

26. $F_\parallel = W \sin \theta$, where we find θ from $\tan \theta = (1.00\ m)/(3.50\ m) = 0.286$, so $\theta = 16.0°$.
$W = (71.0\ kg)(9.80\ m/s^2) = 969$ N,
so $F_\parallel = 191$ N

Chapter 7

1. a. Since $v_y = 0$, $y = v_y t + \frac{1}{2}gt^2$ becomes

$y = \frac{1}{2}gt^2$, or

$$t^2 = \frac{2y}{g} = \frac{2(-78.4\ m)}{-9.80\ m/s^2} = 16.0\ s^2,$$

$t = \sqrt{16.0\ s^2} = 4.00$ s.

b. $x = v_x t = (5.0\ m/s)(4.00\ s) = 20$ m

c. $v_x = 5.0$ m/s. This is the same as the initial horizontal speed because the acceleration of gravity influences only the vertical motion. For the vertical component, use $v_f = v_i + gt$ with $v_f = v_y$ and v_i, the initial vertical component of velocity zero. At $t = 4.00$ s, $v_y = gt = (-9.80\ m/s^2)(4.00\ s) = -39.2$ m/s.

2. a. (a) no change; 4.00 s
(b) twice the previous distance; 40 m
(c) v_x doubles; 10 m/s
no change in v_y; -39.2 m/s

b. (a) increases by $\sqrt{2}$, since $t = \sqrt{\frac{2y}{g}}$ and y doubles; 5.66 s

(b) increases by $\sqrt{2}$, since t increases by $\sqrt{2}$; 28 m

(c) no change in v_x; 5.0 m/s
v_y increases by $\sqrt{2}$, since t increases by $\sqrt{2}$; -55.4 m/s

3. Since $v_y = 0$, $y = \frac{1}{2}gt^2$ and the time to reach the ground is

$$t = \sqrt{\frac{2y}{g}} = \sqrt{\frac{2(-0.950 \text{ m})}{-9.80 \text{ m/s}}} = 0.440 \text{ s.}$$

From $x = v_x t$,

$$v_x = \frac{x}{t} = \frac{0.352 \text{ m}}{0.440 \text{ s}} = 0.800 \text{ m/s.}$$

4. Following the method of Practice Problem 3,

a. $t = \sqrt{\frac{2y}{g}} = \sqrt{\frac{2(-43.9 \text{ m})}{-9.80 \text{ m/s}^2}} = 2.99 \text{ s.}$

b. $v_x = \frac{x}{t} = \frac{87.7 \text{ m}}{2.99 \text{ s}} = 29.3 \text{ m/s}$

$= 29.3 \text{ m/s}\left[\frac{1 \text{ km}}{1000 \text{ m}}\right]\left[\frac{3600 \text{ s}}{1 \text{ h}}\right]$

$= 105 \text{ km/h}$

c. $g = -9.80 \text{ m/s}^2$ at all times.

5. a. $v_x = v_i \cos\theta = (27.0 \text{ m/s}) \cos 30.0°$
$= 23.4 \text{ m/s}$
$v_y = v_i \sin\theta = (27.0 \text{ m/s}) \sin 30.0°$
$= 13.5 \text{ m/s}$

When it lands, $y = v_y t + \frac{1}{2}gt^2 = 0$.

Therefore,

$$t = \frac{-2v_y}{g} = \frac{-2(13.5 \text{ m/s})}{-9.8 \text{ m/s}^2} = 2.76 \text{ s.}$$

b. $x = v_x t = (23.4 \text{ m/s})(2.76 \text{ s}) = 64.6 \text{ m}$

c. Maximum height occurs at half the "long time," or 1.38 s. Thus,

$y = v_y t + \frac{1}{2}gt^2$

$= (13.5 \text{ m/s})(1.38 \text{ s})$

$+ \frac{1}{2}(-9.80 \text{ m/s}^2)(1.38 \text{ s})^2$

$= 18.6 \text{ m} - 9.3 \text{ m} = 9.3 \text{ m.}$

6. Following the method of Practice Problem 5,

a. $v_x = v_i \cos\theta = (27.0 \text{ m/s}) \cos 60.0°$
$= 13.5 \text{ m/s}$
$v_y = v_i \sin\theta = (27.0 \text{ m/s}) \sin 60.0°$
$= 23.4 \text{ m/s}$

$$t = \frac{-2v_y}{g} = \frac{-2(23.4 \text{ m/s})}{-9.80 \text{ m/s})^2} = 4.78 \text{ s.}$$

b. $x = v_x t = (13.5 \text{ m/s})(4.78 \text{ s}) = 64.5 \text{ m}$

c. at $t = \frac{1}{2}(4.78 \text{ s}) = 2.39 \text{ s}$,

$y = v_y t + \frac{1}{2}gt^2$

$= (23.4 \text{ m/s})(2.39 \text{ s})$

$+ \frac{1}{2}(-9.80 \text{ m/s}^2)(2.39 \text{ s})^2 = 27.9 \text{ m.}$

7. For two projectiles with the same initial velocity and complementary launch angles, the projectile with the higher trajectory has the longest flight time and the greatest maximum height. The ranges are the same.

8. a. $v_y = 0$ and $y = -17.0 \text{ m} =$ ground level.

Therefore, $y = v_y t = \frac{1}{2}gt^2$ becomes

$y = \frac{1}{2}gt^2$ or $t = \sqrt{\frac{2y}{g}} = \sqrt{\frac{2(-17.0 \text{ m})}{-9.80 \text{ m/s}^2}}$

$= 1.86 \text{ s.}$

b. $v_x = 7.0 \text{ m/s}$, so $x = v_x t = (7.0 \text{ m/s})(1.86 \text{ s})$
$= 13 \text{ m}$

c. Now $v_y = 8.5 \text{ m/s}$ and $y = v_y t + \frac{1}{2}gt^2$

becomes $-17.0 \text{ m} = (8.5 \text{ m/s})t$

$+ \frac{1}{2}(-9.80 \text{ m/s})t^2$,

or $(4.90 \text{ m/s}^2)t^2 - (8.5 \text{ m/s})t - 17.0 \text{ m} = 0$.
Using the quadratic formula to solve for t,

$$t = \frac{8.5 \text{ m/s} \pm \sqrt{(8.5 \text{ m/s})^2 - 4(4.90 \text{ m/s}^2)(-17.0 \text{ m})}}{2(4.90 \text{ m/s})^2}$$

$$= \frac{8.50 \text{ m/s} \pm 20.1 \text{ m/s}}{9.80 \text{ m/s}^2}.$$

Choosing the + sign to make flight time positive $t = 2.92$ s.

d. $v_x = 7.0 \text{ m/s}$, so $x = v_x t = (7.0 \text{ m/s})(2.92 \text{ s})$
$= 20 \text{ m}$

9. a. Since r and T remain the same,

$v = \frac{2\pi r}{T}$ and $a = \frac{v^2}{r}$ remain the same. The new value of the mass is $m' = 2m$. The new force is $F' = m'a = 2ma = 2F$, double the original force.

667

b. The new radius is $r' = 2r$, so the new velocity is $v' = \frac{2\pi r'}{T} = \frac{2\pi(2r)}{T} = 2v$, twice the original velocity. The new acceleration is $a' = \frac{(v')^2}{r'} = \frac{(2v)^2}{2r} = 2a$, twice the original.

The new force is $F' = ma' = m(2a) = 2F$, twice the original.

c. new velocity, $v' = \frac{2\pi r}{T'} = \frac{2\pi r}{\left[\frac{1}{2}T\right]} = 2v$, twice the original;

new acceleration, $a' = \frac{(v')^2}{r} = \frac{(2v)^2}{r} = 4a$, four times original;

new force, $F' = ma' = m(4a) = 4F$, four times original

10. a. $a_c = \frac{v^2}{r} = \frac{(8.8\ \text{m/s})^2}{25\ \text{m}} = 3.1\ \text{m/s}^2$

b. the track friction force acting on the runner's shoes

11. a. $a_c = \frac{v^2}{r} = \frac{(32\ \text{m/s})^2}{56\ \text{m}} = 18\ \text{m/s}^2$

b. Recall $F_f = \mu F_N$. The friction force must supply the centripetal force so $F_f = ma_c$. The normal force is $F_N = -W = -mg$. The coefficient of friction must be at least

$$\mu = \frac{F_f}{F_N} = \frac{ma_c}{-mg} = \frac{a_c}{-g} = \frac{18\ \text{m/s}^2}{-(-9.80\ \text{m/s}^2)} = 1.8.$$

12. a.

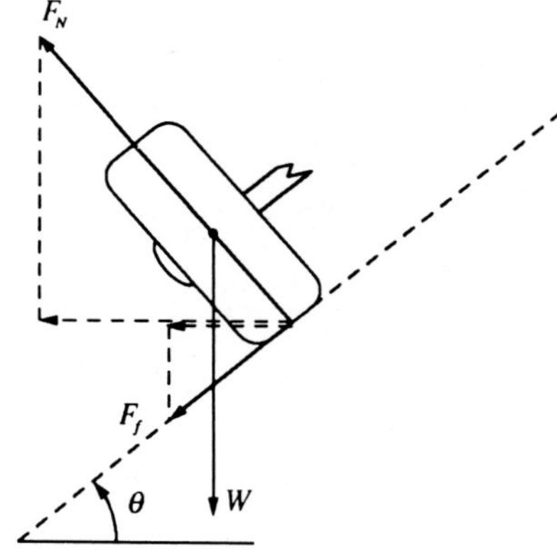

b. the horizontal component of the normal force and the horizontal component of the friction force; These component forces, $F_N \sin\theta$ and $F_f \cos\theta$ are shown by dotted lines in the figure.

13. From $T = 2\pi\sqrt{\frac{l}{g}}$, we obtain

$$l = \frac{gT^2}{4\pi^2} = \frac{(9.80\ \text{m/s}^2)(1.00\ \text{s})^2}{4\pi^2} = 0.248\ \text{m}.$$

14. From $T = 2\pi\sqrt{\frac{l}{g}}$, we obtain

$$g = \frac{4\pi^2 l}{T^2} = \frac{4\pi^2(0.65\ \text{m})}{(2.85\ \text{s})^2} = 3.3\ \text{m/s}^2.$$

Chapter 8

1. $\left[\frac{T_a}{T_E}\right]^2 = \left[\frac{r_a}{r_E}\right]^3$ with $r_a = 2r_E$.

Thus, $T_a^2 = \left[\frac{r_a}{r_E}\right]^3 T_E^2$

$= \left[\frac{2r_E}{r_E}\right]^3 (1\ \text{yr})^2 = 8\ \text{yr}^2,\ T_a = 2.8\ \text{yr}$

2. $\left[\frac{T_M}{T_E}\right] = \left[\frac{r_M}{r_E}\right]^3$, with $r_M = 1.52 r_E$.

Thus, $T_M^2 = \left[\frac{r_M}{r_E}\right]^3 T_E^2 = \left[\frac{1.52 r_E}{r_E}\right]^3 (365\ \text{days})^2$

$= 4.679 \times 10^5\ \text{days}^2,\ T_M = 684\ \text{days}$

3. $\left[\frac{T_s}{T_m}\right]^2 = \left[\frac{r_s}{r_m}\right]^3,\ T_s^2 = \left[\frac{r_s}{r_m}\right]^3 T_m^2$

$= \left[\frac{6.70 \times 10^3\ \text{km}}{3.90 \times 10^5\ \text{km}}\right]^3 (27.3\ \text{days})^2$

$= 3.779 \times 10^{-3}\ \text{days}^2,\ T_s$
$= 6.15 \times 10^{-2}\ \text{days} = 88.5\ \text{min}$

4. $\left[\frac{T_s}{T_m}\right]^2 = \left[\frac{r_s}{r_m}\right]^3$, so $r_s^3 = r_m^3 \left[\frac{T_s}{T_m}\right]^2$

$= (3.90 \times 10^5\ \text{km})^3 \left[\frac{1.00}{27.3}\right]^2$

$= 7.96 \times 10^{13}\ \text{km}^3$, so $r_s = 4.30 \times 10^4\ \text{km}$

5. a. $v = \sqrt{\frac{GM_E}{r}}$, with $r = r_E + 150\ \text{km}$

$r = 6.37 \times 10^6\ \text{m} + 0.150 \times 10^6\ \text{m}$
$= 6.52 \times 10^6\ \text{m}$

$$v = \sqrt{\frac{(6.67 \times 10^{-11})(5.98 \times 10^{24})}{6.52 \times 10^6}} = 7.82 \times 10^3\ \text{m/s}$$

b. $T = 2\pi\sqrt{\dfrac{r^3}{GM_E}}$

$= 2\pi\sqrt{\dfrac{(6.52 \times 10^6 \text{ m})^3}{(6.67 \times 10^{-11} \text{ Nm}^2/\text{kg}^2)(5.98 \times 10^{24} \text{ kg})}}$

$= 5.24 \times 10^3 \text{ s} = 87.3 \text{ min}$

6. a. $v = \sqrt{\dfrac{GM_m}{r}}$, with $r = r_m + 265$ km

$= 2.43 \times 10^6 \text{ m} + 0.265 \times 10^6 \text{ m}$

$= 2.70 \times 10^6 \text{ m}$

$v = \sqrt{\dfrac{(6.67 \times 10^{-11} \text{ Nm}^2/\text{kg}^2)(3.2 \times 10^{23} \text{ kg})}{2.70 \times 10^6 \text{ m}}}$

$= 2.8 \times 10^3 \text{ m/s}$

b. $T = 2\pi\sqrt{\dfrac{r^3}{GM_m}}$

$= 2\pi\sqrt{\dfrac{(2.70 \times 10^6 \text{ m})^3}{(6.67 \times 10^{-11} \text{ Nm}^2/\text{kg}^2)(3.2 \times 10^{23} \text{ kg})}}$

$= 6.03 \times 10^3 \text{ s} = 1.0 \times 10^2 \text{ min}$

7. a. $v = \sqrt{\dfrac{GM}{r}}$, where here M is the mass of the sun.

$v = \sqrt{\dfrac{(6.67 \times 10^{-11} \text{ Nm}^2/\text{kg}^2)(1.991 \times 10^{30} \text{ kg})}{(5.80 \times 10^{10} \text{ m})}}$

$= 4.79 \times 10^4 \text{ m/s}$

b. $v = \sqrt{\dfrac{(6.67 \times 10^{-11} \text{ Nm}^2/\text{kg}^2)(1.991 \times 10^{30} \text{ kg})}{(1.427 \times 10^{12} \text{ m})}}$

$= 9.65 \times 10^3$ m/s, about 1/5 as fast as Mercury

8. a. Using $T = 2\pi\sqrt{\dfrac{r^3}{GM}}$, with

$T = 2.5 \times 10^8 y = 7.9 \times 10^{15} \text{ s}$

$M = \dfrac{4\pi^2 r^3}{GT^2}$

$= \dfrac{4\pi^2(2.2 \times 10^{20} \text{ m})^3}{(6.67 \times 10^{-11} \text{ Nm}^2/\text{kg}^2)(7.9 \times 10^{15} \text{ s})^2}$

$= 1.0 \times 10^{41} \text{ kg}$

b. number of stars $= \dfrac{\text{total galaxy mass}}{\text{mass per star}}$

$= \dfrac{1.0 \times 10^{41} \text{ kg}}{2.0 \times 10^{30} \text{ kg}}$

$= 5.0 \times 10^{10}$

c. $v = \sqrt{\dfrac{GM}{r}}$

$= \sqrt{\dfrac{(6.67 \times 10^{-11} \text{ Nm}^2/\text{kg}^2)(1.0 \times 10^{41} \text{ kg})}{2.2 \times 10^{20} \text{ m}}}$

$= 1.7 \times 10^5 \text{ m/s} = 6.1 \times 10^5 \text{ km/h}$

Chapter 9

1. a. 100 km/h = 27.8 m/s,

$p = mv = (725 \text{ kg})(27.8 \text{ m/s})$
$= 2.02 \times 10^4 \text{ kg·m/s}$

b. $v = p/m = \dfrac{(2.02 \times 10^4 \text{ kg·m/s})}{(2175 \text{ kg})}$

$= 9.29 \text{ m/s} = 33.4 \text{ km/h}$

2. a. $\Delta p = m(v_f - v_i)$
$= (250 \text{ kg})(28.0 \text{ m/s} - 6.0 \text{ m/s})$
$= 5.50 \times 10^3 \text{ kg·m/s}$

b. $F = \Delta p/\Delta t = \dfrac{(5.50 \times 10^3 \text{ kg·m/s})}{(60.0 \text{ s})} = 91.7 \text{ N}$

3. a. $m = W/g = \dfrac{(15\,680 \text{ N})}{(9.80 \text{ m/s}^2)} = 1.60 \times 10^3 \text{ kg}$

b. $p_i = mv_i = (1600 \text{ kg})(20.0 \text{ m/s})$
$= 3.20 \times 10^4 \text{ kg·m/s}$

c. $\Delta p = p_f - p_i = 0 - 3.20 \times 10^4 \text{ kg·m/s}$
$= -3.20 \times 10^4 \text{ kg·m/s}$

d. $F\Delta t = \Delta p$, $\Delta t = \Delta p/F$

$= \dfrac{(-3.20 \times 10^4 \text{ kg·m/s})}{(-6.40 \times 10^2 \text{ N})}$

$= 50.0 \text{ s}$

4. a. The area under the curve is 52.5 squares. Each square represents 0.100 N·s, so the impulse is

$F\Delta T$ = Area
= (52.5 squares)(0.100 N·s/square)
= 5.25 N·s.

b. $\Delta p = m\Delta v$ with $\Delta p = F\Delta t$, so

$\Delta v = \dfrac{\Delta p}{m} = \dfrac{F\Delta t}{m} = \dfrac{(5.25 \text{ N·s})}{(2.4 \text{ kg})} = 2.2 \text{ m/s}$

5. $p_h + p_g = p'_h + p'_g$ or $m_h v_h + m_g v_g$
$= m_h v'_h + m_g v'_g$

Since $v_g = 0$, $m_h v_h = (m_h + m_h)v'$
where $v' = v'_h = v'_g$ is the common final speed of goalie and puck.

$v' = \dfrac{m_h v_h}{(m_h + m_g)}$

$= (0.105 \text{ kg})(48 \text{ m/s})(0.105 \text{ kg} + 75 \text{ kg})$
$= 0.067 \text{ m/s}$

669

6. $m_b v_b + m_w v_w = (m_b + m_w)v'$ where v' is the common final velocity of bullet and wooden block. Since $v_w = 0$, $v_b = (m_b + m_w)v'/m_b$

$$= \frac{(0.035 \text{ kg} + 5.0 \text{ kg})(8.6 \text{ m/s})}{(0.035 \text{ kg})}$$

$$= 1.2 \times 10^3 \text{ m/s}$$

7. $m_b v_b + m_w v_w = m_b v_b' + m_w v_w'$ with $v_w = 0$

$$v_w' = \frac{(m_b v_b - m_b v_b')}{m_w} = \frac{m_b(v_b - v_b')}{m_w}$$

$$= \frac{(0.035 \text{ kg})(475 \text{ m/s} - 275 \text{ m/s})}{(2.5 \text{ kg})}$$

$$= 2.8 \text{ m/s}$$

8. $m_A v_A + m_B v_B = m_A v_A' + m_B v_B'$, so v_B'

$$= \frac{(m_A v_A + m_B v_B - m_A v_A')}{m_B}$$

$= [(0.50 \text{ kg})(6.0 \text{ m/s}) + (1.00 \text{ kg})(-12.0 \text{ m/s}) - (0.50 \text{ kg})(-14 \text{ m/s})]/(1.00 \text{ kg})$

$= -2.0 \text{ m/s}$

9. $p_r + p_f = p_r' + p_f'$, where $p_r + p_f = 0$.
If the initial mass of the rocket (including fuel) is $m_r = 4.00$ kg, then the final mass of the rocket is
$m_r' = 4.00 \text{ kg} - 0.050 \text{ kg} = 3.95 \text{ kg}$.
$0 = m_r' v_r' + m_f v_f'$,

$$v_r' = \frac{-m_f v_f'}{m_r'}$$

$$= \frac{-(0.050 \text{ kg})(-625 \text{ m/s})}{(3.95 \text{ kg})}$$

$$= 7.91 \text{ m/s}$$

10. $p_A + p_B = p_A' + p_B'$ with $p_A + p_B = 0$,
$m_B v_B' = -m_A v_A'$,

$$\text{so } v_B = \frac{-m_A v_A}{m_B} = \frac{-(1.5 \text{ kg})(-27 \text{ cm/s})}{(4.5 \text{ kg})}$$

$= 9.0$ cm/s, or 9.0 cm/s to the right.

11. $p_A + p_B = p_A' + p_B'$ with $p_A + p_B = 0$,

$$m_A v_A' = -m_B v_B', \text{ so } v_B' = \frac{-m_A v_A'}{m_B}$$

$$= \frac{-(80.0 \text{ kg})(4.0 \text{ m/s})}{(110 \text{ kg})}$$

$= -2.9$ m/s, or 2.9 m/s in the opposite direction.

12. a. Both the cannon and the ball fall to the ground in the same time from the same height. In that fall time, the ball moves 215 m, the cannon an unknown distance we will call x.

$$\text{Now } t = \frac{d}{v}, \text{ so } \frac{(215 \text{ m})}{v_{ball}} = \frac{x}{v_{cannon}},$$

$$\text{so } x = \left[\frac{v_{cannon}}{v_{ball}}\right](215 \text{ m})$$

related by conservation of momentum;
$(4.5 \text{ kg})v_{ball} = -(225 \text{ kg})v_{cannon}$, so

$$\left[\frac{v_{cannon}}{v_{ball}}\right] = \frac{(4.5 \text{ kg})}{(225 \text{ kg})}.$$

$$\text{Thus, } x = \left[\frac{4.5}{225}\right](215 \text{ m}) = 4.3 \text{ m}.$$

b. While on top, the cannon moves with no friction, and its velocity doesn't change, so it can take any amount of time to reach the back edge.

13.

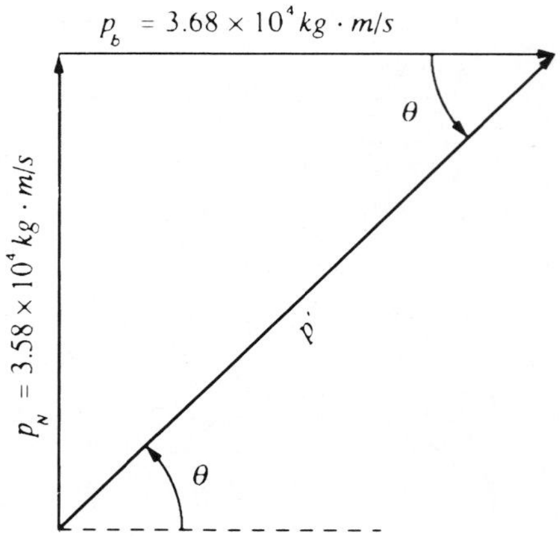

$p_E = 3.68 \times 10^4 \, kg \cdot m/s$
$p_N = 3.58 \times 10^4 \, kg \cdot m/s$
p'
θ

$p_N = p_E = p'$ (vector sum)
$p_N = m_N v_N = (1325 \text{ kg})(27.0 \text{ m/s})$
$= 3.58 \times 10^4 \text{ kg·m/s}$
$p_E = m_E v_E = (2165 \text{ kg})(17.0 \text{ m/s})$
$= 3.68 \times 10^4 \text{ kg·m/s}$

$$\tan\theta = \frac{p_N}{p_E} = \frac{3.58 \times 10^4 \text{ kg·m/s}}{3.68 \times 10^4 \text{ kg·m/s}} = 0.973,$$

$\theta = 44.2°$, north of east
$(p')^2 = (p_N)^2 + (p_E)^2$
$= (3.58 \times 10^4 \text{ kg·m/s})^2 + (3.68 \times 10^4 \text{ kg·m/s})^2$
$= 2.64 \times 10^9 \text{ kg}^2 \text{ m}^2/\text{s}^2$,
$p' = 5.13 \times 10^4 \text{ kg·m/s}$
$p' = m'v' = (m_N + m_E)v'$,

$$v' = \frac{p'}{(m_N + m_E)}$$

$$= \frac{(5.13 \times 10^4 \text{ kg·m/s})}{(1325 \text{ kg} + 2165 \text{ kg})}$$

$$= 14.7 \text{ m/s}$$

670

14.

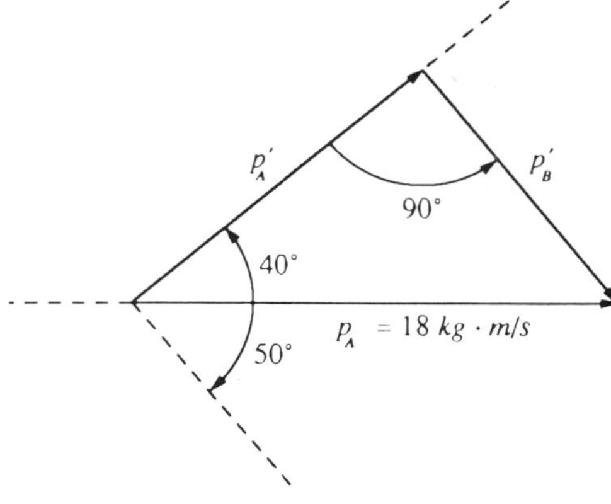

a. $p_A + p_B = p'_A + p'_B$ (vector sum)
with $p_B = 0$
$p_A = m_A v_A = (6.0\text{ kg})(3.0\text{ m/s}) = 18\text{ kg·m/s}$
$p'_A = p_A \cos 40° = (18\text{ kg·m/s}) \cos 40°$
$= 14\text{ kg·m/s}$
$p'_B = p_A \sin 40° = (18\text{ kg·m/s}) \sin 40°$
$= 12\text{ kg·m/s}$

b. $p'_A = m_A v'_A$,
$v'_A = \frac{p'_A}{m_A} = \frac{(14\text{ kg·m/s})}{(6.0\text{ kg})}$
$= 2.3$ m/s, 40° to left
$p'_B = m_B v'_B$,
$v'_B = \frac{p'_B}{m_B} = \frac{(12\text{ kg·m/s})}{(6.0\text{ kg})}$
$= 2.0$ m/s, 50° to right

15.

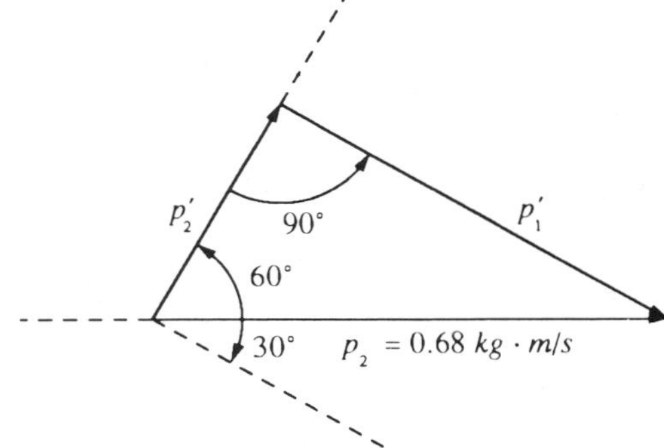

$p_1 + p_2 = p'_1 + p'_2$ (vector sum) with $p_1 = 0$
$m_1 = m_2 = m = 0.17$ kg
$p_2 = m_2 v_2 = (0.17\text{ kg})(4.0\text{ m/s}) = 0.68\text{ kg·m/s}$
$p'_1 = p_2 \sin 60°$, $mv'_1 = mv_2 \sin 60°$,
$v'_1 = v_2 \sin 60° = (4.0\text{ m/s}) \sin 60°$
$= 3.5$ m/s, 30° to right
$p'_2 = p_2 \cos 60°$, $mv'_2 = mv_2 \cos 60°$,
$v'_2 = v_2 \cos 60° = (4.0\text{ m/s}) \cos 60°$
$= 2.0$ m/s, 60° to left

Chapter 10

1. a. $W = Fd = (825\text{ N})(35\text{ m}) = 2.9 \times 10^4\text{ J}$
b. The work doubles; when displacement remains the same, work is directly proportional to force.

2. $W = Fd = (34\text{ N})(15\text{ m}) = 510\text{ J}$

3. $W = Fd = mgd = (583\text{ kg})(9.80\text{ m/s}^2)(1.2\text{ m})$
$= 6.9 \times 10^3\text{ J}$

4. Both do the same amount of work. Only the height lifted and the vertical force exerted count.

5. Both the force and displacement are in the same direction, so
$W = Fd = (25\text{ N})(3.5\text{ m}) = 88\text{ J}$.

6. a. Since gravity acts vertically, only the vertical displacement needs to be considered.
$W = Fd = (215\text{ N})(4.20\text{ m}) = 903\text{ J}$
b. Force is upward, but vertical displacement is downward, so
$W = Fd \cos \theta = Fd \cos 180°$
$= (215\text{ N})(4.20\text{ m})(-1) = -903\text{ J}$.

7. $W = Fd \cos \theta = (628\text{ N})(15.0\text{ m})(\cos 46.0°)$
$= 6.54 \times 10^3\text{ J}$

8. a. Displacement in direction of force is 4.0 m, so $W = (85\text{ N})(4.0\text{ m}) = 340\text{ J}$.
b. Displacement in direction of force is -3.0 m, so $W = (93\text{ N})(-3.0\text{ m}) = -279\text{ J}$ (work done against gravity).
c. $W = \mu F_N d$
$= 0.20\left[85\text{ N} \cdot \frac{3}{5} + 93\text{ N} \cdot \frac{4}{5}\right]5.0\text{ m}$
$= 1.3 \times 10^2\text{ J}$

9. $P = \frac{W}{t} = \frac{Fd}{t} = \frac{(575\text{ N})(20.0\text{ m})}{10.0\text{ m}}$
$= 1.15 \times 10^3\text{ W} = 1.15\text{ kW}$

10. a. $W = mgd = (750\text{ kg})(9.80\text{ m/s}^2)(8.2\text{ m})$
$= 6.0 \times 10^2\text{ J}$
b. $W = Fd + 6.0 \times 10^2\text{ J}$
$= (645\text{ N})(8.2\text{ m}) + 6.0 \times 10^2\text{ J}$
$= 5.9 \times 10^3\text{ J}$
c. $P = \frac{W}{t} = \frac{5.9 \times 10^3\text{ J}}{(30\text{ min})(60\text{ s/min})}$
$= 3.3\text{ W}$

671

11. $P = \frac{W}{t}$, and $W = Fd$,

$$\text{so } F = \frac{Pt}{d} = \frac{(65 \times 10^3 \text{ W})(35.0 \text{ s})}{17.5 \text{ m}}$$

$$= 1.3 \times 10^5 \text{ N}$$

12. a. forward: force of road on cart; rearward: force of air on car; These forces are equal in magnitude when the car moves with constant speed.

b. Car exerts a rearward force on road and a forward force on air.

c. $P = \frac{W}{t}$ and $W = Fd$, so $P = \frac{Fd}{t}$,

$$\text{so } F = \frac{Pt}{d} = \frac{P}{v}$$

For sports car,

$$F = \frac{35 \times 10^3 \text{ W}}{29.2 \text{ m/s}} = 1.2 \times 10^3 \text{ N;}$$

for other,

$$F = \frac{65 \times 10^3 \text{ W}}{29.2 \text{ m/s}} = 2.2 \times 10^3 \text{ N.}$$

d. from the chemical energy in the gasoline

13. a. $IMA = \frac{d_e}{d_r} = \frac{20 \text{ cm}}{5.0 \text{ cm}} = 4.0$

b. $MA = \frac{F_r}{F_e} = \frac{1.9 \times 10^4 \text{ N}}{9.8 \times 10^3 \text{ N}} = 1.9$

c. $$Efficiency = \left[\frac{MA}{IMA}\right] \times 100\%$$

$$= \left[\frac{1.9}{4.0}\right] \times 100\% = 48\%$$

14. a. $MA = \frac{F_r}{F_e} = \frac{225 \text{ N}}{129 \text{ N}} = 1.74$

b. $Efficiency = \left[\frac{MA}{IMA}\right] \times 100\%$, where

$$IMA = \frac{d_e}{d_r} = \frac{33.0 \text{ m}}{16.5 \text{ m}} = 2.00, \text{ so}$$

$$efficiency = \frac{1.74}{2.00} \times 100\% = 87\%$$

15. $$eff = \frac{W_o}{W_i} \times 100\% = \frac{F_r d_r}{F_e d_e} \times 100\%, \text{ so}$$

$$d_e = \frac{F_r d_r (100\%)}{F_e(eff)}$$

$$= \frac{(125 \times 10^3 \text{ N})(0.13 \text{ m})(100\%)}{(225 \text{ N})(88.7\%)}$$

$$= 0.81 \text{ m}$$

16. $IMA = \frac{8.00 \text{ cm}}{35.6 \text{ cm}} = 0.224$

$$MA = (95\%)\frac{0.224}{100\%} = 0.214 \text{ (both doubled)}$$

The force exerted by the distance the chain moved, d_e, would also be doubled to 3.14 cm.

Chapter 11

1. a. 50 km/h is 14 m/s, so

$$KE = \frac{1}{2}mv^2 = \frac{1}{2}(750 \text{ kg})(14 \text{ m/s})^2$$

$$= 7.4 \times 10^4 \text{ J}$$

b. $W = \Delta KE = KE_f - KE_i$
$= 0.74 \times 10^5 \text{ J} - 2.94 \times 10^5 \text{ J}$
$= -2.20 \times 10^5 \text{ J}$

c. $W = \Delta KE = 0 - 7.4 \times 10^4 \text{ J}$
$= -7.4 \times 10^4 \text{ J}$

d. $W = Fd$, so distance is proportional to work. The ratio is $(-2.2 \times 10^5 \text{ J})/(-7.4 \times 10^4 \text{ J}) = 3$. It takes three times the distance to slow the car to half its speed than it does to a complete stop.

2. a. $KE = \frac{1}{2}mv^2 = \frac{1}{2}(0.00420 \text{ kg})(965 \text{ m/s})^2$
$= 1.96 \times 10^3 \text{ J}$

b. $W = \Delta KE = 1.96 \times 10^3 \text{ J}$

c. $W = Fd$, so
$F = W/d = (1.96 \times 10^3 \text{ J})/(0.75 \text{ m})$
$= 2.6 \times 10^3 \text{ N}$

d. $F = W/d = KE/d = (1.96 \times 10^3 \text{ J})/(0.015 \text{ m})$
$= 1.3 \times 10^5 \text{ N}$

3. a. $KE = \frac{1}{2}mv^2$

$$= \frac{1}{2}(7.85 \times 10^{11} \text{ kg})(2.5 \times 10^4 \text{ m/s})^2$$

$$= 2.5 \times 10^{20} \text{ J}$$

b. The work is that of 60 000 100-megaton bombs.

4. a. Since $W = \Delta KE = \frac{1}{2}mv^2$, then $v = \sqrt{2W/m}$.

If $W' = \frac{1}{2}W$,

$$v' = \sqrt{2W'/m}$$

$$= \sqrt{2\left(\frac{1}{2}W\right)/m} = \sqrt{\frac{1}{2}}\,v$$

$$= (0.707)(100 \text{ km/h}) = 71 \text{ km/h}$$

b. If $W' = 2W$,

$$v' = \sqrt{2}\,(100 \text{ km/h})$$

$$= 140 \text{ km/h}$$

672

5. $PE = mgh$. At the edge,
$PE = (90 \text{ kg})(9.8 \text{ m/s}^2)(+45 \text{ m})$
$= +4.0 \times 10^4$ J.
At bottom,
$PE = (90 \text{ kg})(9.8 \text{ m/s}^2)(+45 \text{ m} - 85 \text{ m})$
$= -3.5 \times 10^4$ J.

6. a. $PE = mgh = (50.0 \text{ kg})(9.80 \text{ m/s}^2)(400 \text{ m})$
$= 1.96 \times 10^5$ J

b. $\Delta PE = mgh_f - mgh_i = mg(h_f - h_i)$
$= (50.0 \text{ kg})(9.80 \text{ m/s}^2)(200 \text{ m} - 400 \text{ m})$
$= -9.80 \times 10^4$ J

7. a. $W = Fd = Fh = (630 \text{ N})(5.0 \text{ m}) = 3200$ J

b. $\Delta PE = (mg)h = (630 \text{ N})(5.0 \text{ m}) = 3200$ J
The increase in gravitational potential energy is equal to the work done.

c. Directly from the work done by the person. Indirectly from the chemical energy stored in the person's body.

8. a.

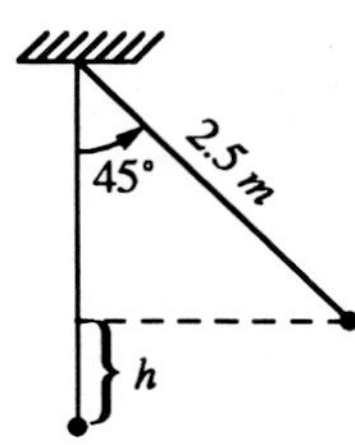

$h = (2.5 \text{ m})(1 - \cos\theta) = 0.73$ m
$PE = mgh = (7.26 \text{ kg})(9.80 \text{ m/s}^2)(0.73 \text{ m})$
$= 52$ J

b. the height of the ball when the rope was vertical

9. a. $KE = \frac{1}{2}mv^2$

$= \frac{1}{2}(85 \text{ kg})(8.5 \text{ m/s})^2 = 3.1 \times 10^3$ J

b. $KE_i + PE_i = KE_f + PE_f$

$\frac{1}{2}mv^2 + 0 = 0 + mgh$

$h = v^2/2g = (8.5 \text{ m/s})^2/(2)(9.8 \text{ m/s}^2) = 3.7$ m

c. No. It cancels because both KE and PE are proportional to m.

10. a. $KE_i + PE_i = KE_f + PE_f$

$0 + mgh = \frac{1}{2}mv^2 + 0$

$v^2 = 2gh = 2(9.8 \text{ m/s}^2)(4.0 \text{ m}) = 78.4 \text{ m}^2/\text{s}^2$
$v = 8.9$ m/s

b. No

c. No

11. a. $KE_i + PE_i = KE_f + PE_f$

$0 + mgh = \frac{1}{2}mv^2 + 0$

$v^2 = 2gh = 2(9.8 \text{ m/s}^2)(45 \text{ m}) = 880 \text{ m}^2/\text{s}^2$
$v = 30$ m/s

b. $KE_i + PE_i = KE_f + PE_f$

$0 + mgh_i = \frac{1}{2}mv^2 + mgh_f$

$v^2 = 2g(h_i - h_f)$
$= 2(9.8 \text{ m/s}^2)(45 \text{ m} - 40 \text{ m}) = 98 \text{ m}^2/\text{s}^2$
$v = 10$ m/s

12. a. The system Earth, bike, and rider remains the same but now the energy involved is not mechanical energy alone. The rider must be considered as having stored energy, some of which is converted to mechanical energy.

b. Energy came from chemical potential energy stored in the rider's body.

13. a. From conservation of momentum,
$mv = (m + M)V$, so
$V = mv/(m + M)$

$= \dfrac{(0.002 \text{ kg})(538 \text{ m/s})}{(0.002 \text{ kg} + 0.250 \text{ kg})} = 4.27$ m/s.

b. $KE_i = \frac{1}{2}mv^2 = \frac{1}{2}(0.002 \text{ kg})(538 \text{ m/s})^2 = 289$ J

c. $KE_f = \frac{1}{2}(m + M)V^2$

$= \frac{1}{2}(0.002 \text{ kg} + 0.250 \text{ kg})(4.27 \text{ m/s})^2$

$= 2.30$ J

d. $\Delta KE = KE_i - KE_f = 289 \text{ J} - 2 \text{ J} = 287$ J

e. % KE lost $= (\Delta KE/KE_i) \times 100$
$= (287 \text{ J}/298 \text{ J}) \times 100$
$= 99.3\%$

14. Conservation of momentum, $mv = (m + M)V$, or
$v = (m + M)V/m$
$= (0.008 \text{ kg} + 9.00 \text{ kg})(0.10 \text{ m/s})/(0.008 \text{ kg})$
$= 1.1 \times 10^2$ m/s.

15. We have conservation of momentum $mv + MV = mv' + MV'$ and conservation of energy $\frac{1}{2}mv^2 + \frac{1}{2}MV^2 = \frac{1}{2}mv'^2 + \frac{1}{2}MV'^2$ where m, v, v' refer to bullet, M, V, V' to Superman, and $V = 0$. v' may be eliminated from these equations by solving the momentum equation for $v' = (mv - MV')/m$ and substituting this into the energy equation $mv^2 = mv'^2 + MV'^2$. This gives a quadratic equation for V' which, in factored form, is $MV'[(M + m)V' - 2mv] = 0$. We are not interested in the

673

solution $V' = 0$ which corresponds to the case where the bullet does not hit Superman. We want the other,

$$V' = 2mv/(M + m) = \frac{2(0.0042\ \text{kg})(835\ \text{m/s})}{(104\ \text{kg} + 0.0042\ \text{kg})}$$

$$= 6.7 \times 10^{-2}\ \text{m/s}.$$

16. Only momentum is conserved in the inelastic dart-target collision, so $mv_i + MV_i = (m + M)V_f$ where $V_i = 0$, since the target is initially at rest and V_f is the common velocity just after impact. As the dart-target combination swings upward, energy is conserved, so $\Delta PE = \Delta KE$ or, at the top of the swing, $(m + M)gh = \frac{1}{2}(m + M)V_f^2$. Solving this for V_f and inserting into the momentum equation gives

$$v_i = (m + M)\sqrt{2gh}/m$$

$$= \frac{(0.025\ \text{kg} + 0.73\ \text{kg})\sqrt{2(9.8\ \text{m/s}^2)(0.12\ \text{m})}}{(0.025\ \text{kg})}$$

$$= 46\ \text{m/s}.$$

Chapter 12

1. a. K = °C + 273 = 0 + 273 = 273 K
b. °C = K − 273 = 0 − 273 = −273°C
c. K = °C + 273 = 273 + 273 = 546 K
d. °C = K − 273 = 273 − 273 = 0°C

2. a. K = 27°C + 273 = 300 K
b. K = 560°C + 273 = 833 K
c. K = −184°C + 273 = 89 K
d. impossible temperature − below absolute zero

3. a. °C = 110 − 273 = −163°C
b. °C = 22 − 273 = −251°C
c. °C = 402 − 273 = 129°C
d. °C = 323 − 273 = 50°C

4. Answers will vary:
a. 68 − 72°F = 20 to 22°C, 293 − 295 K
b. about 40°F is about 4°C, 277 K
c. about 86°F is 30°C, 303 K
d. about 0°F, −18°C, 255 K

5. $Q = mC\Delta T$
$= (0.0600\ \text{kg})(385\ \text{J/kg} \cdot \text{K})(80.0°\text{C} - 20.0°\text{C})$
$= 1.39 \times 10^3\ \text{J}$

6. $Q = mC\Delta T$
$= (38\ \text{kg})(130\ \text{J/kg} \cdot \text{K})(180°\text{C} - (-26°\text{C}))$
$= 1.0 \times 10^6\ \text{J}$

7. a. $Q = mC\Delta T$
$\Delta T = Q/mC$

$$= \frac{(836 \times 10^3\ \text{J})}{(20.0\ \text{kg})(4180\ \text{J/kg} \cdot \text{K})}$$

$= 10.0°\text{C}$

b. Using 1L = 1000 cm³, the mass of methanol required is
$DV = (0.80\ \text{g/cm}^3)(20\ \text{L})(1000\ \text{cm}^3/\text{L})$
$= 16{,}000$ g or 16 kg.

$$\Delta T = Q/mC = \frac{(836 \times 10^3\ \text{J})}{(16\ \text{kg})(2450\ \text{J/kg} \cdot \text{K})}$$

$= 21°\text{C}$

c. Water is the better coolant since its temperature increase is less than half that of methanol when absorbing the same amount of heat.

8. a. Iron: $Q = mC\Delta T$
$= (0.565\ \text{kg})(450\ \text{J/kg} \cdot \text{K})(100°\text{C} - 20°\text{C})$
$= 2.0 \times 10^4\ \text{J}$

b. Water: $Q = mC\Delta T$, so

$$m = Q/C\Delta T = \frac{(2.0 \times 10^4\ \text{J})}{(4180\ \text{J/kg} \cdot \text{K})(20°\text{C})}$$

$= 0.24$ kg

9. $m_A C_A(T_f - T_{A,i}) + m_B C_B(T_f - T_{B,i}) = 0$
Since $m_A = m_B$ and $C_A = C_B$, there is cancellation in this particular case so that

$$T_f = \frac{(T_{A,i} + T_{B,i})}{2} = \frac{(80.0° + 10.0°\text{C})}{2} = 45.0°\text{C}.$$

10. $m_a C_a(T_f - T_{a,i}) + m_w C_w(T_f - T_{w,i}) = 0$
Since, in this particular case, $m_a = m_w$, the masses cancel and

$$T_f = \frac{C_a T_{a,i} + C_w T_{w,i}}{C_a + C_w}$$

$$= \frac{(2450\ \text{J/kg} \cdot \text{C°})(16.0\ °\text{C}) + (4180\ \text{J/kg} \cdot \text{C°})(85.0°\text{C})}{2450\ \text{J/kg} \cdot \text{C°} + 4180\ \text{J/kg} \cdot \text{C°}}$$

$= 59.5°\text{C}.$

11. $m_b C_b(T_f - T_{b,i}) + m_w C_w(T_f - T_{w,i}) = 0$

$$T_f = \frac{m_b C_b T_{b,i} + m_w C_w T_{w,i}}{m_b C_b + m_w C_w}$$

$$= \frac{(0.100\ \text{kg})(376\ \text{J/kg} \cdot \text{C°})(90.0°\text{C}) + (0.200\ \text{kg})(4180\ \text{J/kg} \cdot \text{C°})(20.0°\text{C})}{(0.100\ \text{kg})(376\ \text{J/kg} \cdot \text{C°}) + (0.200\ \text{kg})(4180\ \text{J/kg} \cdot \text{C°})}$$

$= 23.0°\text{C}$

674

12. $m_aC_a(T_f - T_{a,i}) + m_wC_w(T_f - T_{w,i}) = 0$
Since $m_a = m_w$, the masses cancel and
$C_a = -C_w(T_f - T_{w,i})/(T_f - T_{a,i})$

$$= \frac{-(4180 \text{ J/kg} \cdot \text{K})(25° \text{ C} - 10°\text{C})}{(25°\text{C} - 100°\text{C})} = 8.4 \times 10^2 \text{ J/kg} \cdot \text{K}.$$

13. To warm the ice to 0°C, Q_w
$= mC\Delta T = (0.100 \text{ kg})(2060 \text{ J/kg} \cdot \text{C°})(0 - (-20.0°\text{C}))$
$= 4120$ J.
To melt the ice, $Q_m = mH_f$
$= (0.100 \text{ kg})(3.34 \times 10^5 \text{ J/kg}) = 3.34 \times 10^4$ J.
Total heat required $= Q_w + Q_m$
$= 0.41 \times 10^4 + 3.34 \times 10^4 \text{ J} = 3.75 \times 10^4$ J.

14. To heat the water from 60°C to 100°C:
$Q = mC\Delta T = (0.200 \text{ kg})(4180 \text{ J/kg} \cdot \text{C°})(40°\text{C})$
$= 0.334 \times 10^5$ J
To change the water to steam:
$Q = mH_v = (0.200 \text{ kg})(2.26 \times 10^6 \text{ J/kg})$
$= 4.52 \times 10^5$ J
To heat the steam from 100°C to 140°C:
$Q = mC\Delta T = (0.200 \text{ kg})(2020 \text{ J/kg} \cdot \text{C°})(40°\text{C})$
$= 0.162 \times 10^5$ J
$Q_{total} = 5.02 \times 10^5$ J

15. Warm ice from −30°C to 0°C:
$Q = mC\Delta T = (0.300 \text{ kg})(2060 \text{ J/kg} \cdot \text{C°})(30.0°\text{C})$
$= 0.185 \times 10^5$ J
Melt ice:
$Q = mH_f = (0.300 \text{ kg})(3.34 \times 10^5 \text{ J/kg})$
$= 1.00 \times 10^5$ J
Heat water 0°C to 100°C:
$Q = mC\Delta T = (0.300 \text{ kg})(4180 \text{ J/kg} \cdot \text{C°})(100°\text{C})$
$= 1.25 \times 10^5$ J
Vaporize water:
$Q = mH_v = (0.300 \text{ kg})(2.26 \times 10^6 \text{ J/kg})$
$= 6.78 \times 10^5$ J
Heat steam 100°C to 130°C:
$Q = mC\Delta T = (0.300 \text{ kg})(2020 \text{ J/kg} \cdot \text{C°})(30°\text{C})$
$= 0.18 \times 10^5$ J
$Q_{total} = 9.40 \times 10^5$ J

16. a. To freeze, lead must absorb
$Q = -mH_f = -(0.175 \text{ kg})(2.04 \times 10^4 \text{ J/kg})$
$= -3.57 \times 10^3$ J.
This will heat the water.

$$\Delta T = Q/mC = \frac{(3.57 \times 10^3 \text{ J})}{(0.055 \text{ kg})(4180 \text{ J/kg} \cdot \text{K})}$$

$= 16°\text{C to } 36°\text{C}$

b. Now, $T_f = \dfrac{(m_AC_AT_{A,i} + m_BC_BT_{B,i})}{(m_AC_A + m_BC_B)}$

$$= \frac{(0.175 \text{ kg})(130 \text{ J/kg} \cdot \text{K})(327°\text{C}) + (0.55 \text{ kg})(4180 \text{ J/kg} \cdot \text{K})(35.5°\text{C})}{(0.175 \text{ kg})(130 \text{ J/kg} \cdot \text{K}) + (0.055 \text{ kg})(4180 \text{ J/kg} \cdot \text{K})}$$

$= 62°\text{C}$

Chapter 13

1. $p = F/A$, so
$F = pA = (1.0 \times 10^5 \text{ Pa})(1.52 \text{ m})(0.76 \text{ m})$
$= 1.2 \times 10^5$ N

2. $F = mg = (925 \text{ kg})(9.80 \text{ m/s}^2) = 9.07 \times 10^3$ N
$A = 4(0.12 \text{ m})(0.18 \text{ m}) = 0.0864 \text{ m}^2$
$p = F/A = (9.07 \times 10^3 \text{ N})/(0.0864 \text{ m}^2)$
$= 1.0 \times 10^5$ Pa

3. $F = (11.8 \text{ gm/cm}^3)(10^{-3} \text{ kg/g})(5.0 \text{ cm})(10 \text{ cm}) \times (20 \text{ cm})(9.8 \text{ m/s}^2)$
$= 116$ N
$A = (0.05 \text{ m})(0.10 \text{ m}) = 0.005 \text{ m}^2$
$p = F/A = (116 \text{ N})/(0.005 \text{ m}^2) = 23$ kPa

4. $F_{net} = F_{outside} - F_{inside}$
$= (p_{outside} - p_{inside})A$
$= (0.85 \times 10^5 \text{ Pa} - 1.00 \times 10^5 \text{ Pa}) \times (1.82 \text{ m})(0.91 \text{ m})$
$= -2.5 \times 10^4$ N (toward the outside)

5. $F_1/A_1 = F_2/A_2$ with $A_2 = 0.400 \text{ m}^2$, since the circular area is proportional to the diameter squared and the original diameter has been doubled.
$F_2 = A_2F_1/A_1 = (0.400 \text{ m}^2)(20.0 \text{ N})/(0.0500 \text{ m}^2)$
$= 160$ N

6. $F_1/A_1 = F_2/A_2$
$F_1 = F_2A_1/A_2$
$= (1600 \text{ N})(72 \text{ cm}^2)/(1440 \text{ cm}^2) = 80$ N

7. $F_{weight} = F_{buoyant} = \rho_{water}Vg$
$V = F_{weight}/\rho_{water}g$
$= (600 \text{ N})/(1000 \text{ kg/m}^3)(9.8 \text{ m/s}^2)$
$= 0.06 \text{ m}^3.$
This volume does not include that portion of her head that is above the water.

8. $T + F_{buoyant} = W$, where W is the air weight of the camera.
$T = W - F_{buoyant} = W - \rho_{water}Vg$
$= 1250 \text{ N} - (1000 \text{ kg/m}^3)(0.083 \text{ m}^3)(9.8 \text{ m/s}^2)$
$= 4.4 \times 10^2$ N

9. $\Delta L = \alpha L_i\Delta T = (25 \times 10^{-6} \text{ °C}^{-1})(3.66 \text{ m})(67°\text{C})$
$= 6.1 \times 10^{-3}$ m, or 6.1 mm

10. $L_f = L_i + \alpha L_i(T - T_i) = (11.5 \text{ m})$
$+ (11 \times 10^{-6} \text{ °C}^{-1})(11.5 \text{ m})(1221°\text{C} - 22°\text{C})$
$= 11.7$ m

11. a. For water, $\beta = 210 \times 10^{-6} \text{ °C}^{-1}$, so $\Delta V = \beta V\Delta T$
$= (354 \text{ mL})(210 \times 10^{-6} \text{ °C}^{-1})(30.1°\text{C})$
$= 2.24$ mL

675

b. For Al $\beta = 75 \times 10^{-6}\,°C^{-1}$, so
$\Delta V = \beta V \Delta T$
$= (354\text{ mL})(75 \times 10^{-6}\,°C^{-1})(30.1°C)$
$= 0.80\text{ mL}$

c. The difference will spill.
$2.24\text{ mL} - 0.80\text{ mL} = 1.44\text{ mL}$

12. a. $V = V_i + \beta V_i(T - T_i)$
$= 45\,725\text{ L} + (950 \times 10^{-6}\,°C^{-1})(45\,725\text{ L}) \times (-18.0°C - 32.0°C)$
$= 45\,725\text{ L} - 2170\text{ L}$
$= 43\,555\text{ L} = 43\,560\text{ L}$

b. Its volume has decreased because of temperature change.

Chapter 14

1. a. $v = d/t = (515\text{ m})/(1.5\text{ s}) = 343\text{ m/s}$
b. $T = 1/f = 1/(436\text{ Hz}) = 2.29 \times 10^{-3}\text{ s}$
$= 2.29\text{ ms}$
c. $\lambda = v/f = (343\text{ m/s})/(436\text{ Hz}) = 0.787\text{ m}$

2. a. $v = d/t = (685\text{ m})/(2.0\text{ s}) = 343\text{ m/s}$
b. $f = v/\lambda = (342\text{ m/s})/(0.750\text{ m}) = 457\text{ Hz}$
c. $T = 1/f = 1/(456\text{ Hz}) = 2.19 \times 10^{-3}\text{ s}$
$= 2.19\text{ ms}$

3. $\lambda = v/f = (3.00 \times 10^8\text{ m/s})/(99.5 \times 10^6\text{ Hz})$
$= 3.02\text{ m}$

4. a. $\lambda = (580\text{ nm})(1 \times 10^{-9}\text{ m/nm})$
$= 5.8 \times 10^{-7}\text{ m}$
b. $f = v/\lambda = (3.0 \times 10^8\text{ m/s})/(5.8 \times 10^{-7}\text{ m})$
$= 5.2 \times 10^{14}\text{ Hz}$

5. a. The pulse is partially reflected, partially transmitted.
b. Erect, since reflection is from a less dense medium.
c. It is almost totally reflected from the wall.
d. Inverted, since reflection is from a more dense medium.

6. Pulse inversion means rigid boundary: attached to wall.

7. at a lower frequency because wavelength varies inversely with frequency

8. a. The pulse is partially reflected, partially transmitted.
b. Inverted, since reflection is from a more dense medium.
c. It is almost totally reflected from the wall.
d. Inverted, since reflection is from a more dense medium.

Chapter 15

1. $v = \lambda f$, so $\lambda = \dfrac{v}{f} = \dfrac{1435\text{ m/s}}{261.6\text{ Hz}} = 5.485\text{ m}$

2. $v = \lambda f$, so $f = \dfrac{v}{\lambda} = \dfrac{343\text{ m/s}}{0.667\text{ m}} = 514\text{ Hz}$

3. From $v = \lambda f$, the largest wavelength is

$\lambda = \dfrac{v}{f} = \dfrac{343\text{ m/s}}{20\text{ Hz}} = 17\text{ m}$; the smallest is

$\lambda = \dfrac{v}{f} = \dfrac{343\text{ m/s}}{16\,000\text{ Hz}} = 0.021\text{ m}.$

4. Woofer diameter 38 cm,
$f = v/\lambda = (343\text{ m/s})/(0.38\text{ m}) = 0.90\text{ kHz}$
Tweeter diameter 7.6 cm,
$f = v/\lambda = (343\text{ m/s})/(0.076\text{ m}) = 4.5\text{ kHz}$

5. Resonance spacing is $\lambda/2$, so using $v = \lambda f$, the resonance spacing is $\dfrac{\lambda}{2} = \dfrac{v}{2f}$

$= \dfrac{343\text{ m/s}}{2(440\text{ Hz})} = 0.390\text{ m}.$

6. Resonance spacing $= \dfrac{\lambda}{2} = 1.10\text{ m}$, so $\lambda = 2.20\text{ m}$

and $v = f\lambda = (440\text{ Hz})(2.20\text{ m}) = 968\text{ m/s}.$

7. From the previous Example Problem, $v = 347\text{ m/s}$ at 27°C and the resonance spacing gives

$\dfrac{\lambda}{2} = 0.392\text{ m}$ or $\lambda = 0.784\text{ m}$. Using $v = \lambda f$,

$f = \dfrac{v}{\lambda} = \dfrac{347\text{ m/s}}{(0.784\text{ m})} = 443\text{ Hz}.$

8. $l = \lambda/4$, $v = \lambda f$, so
$f = v/4l = (343\text{ m/s})/(4 \times 0.03\text{ m}) = 2.9\text{ kHz}$

9. The lowest resonant frequency of an open pipe corresponds to the wavelength λ_1, where

$\dfrac{\lambda_1}{2} = L$ = length of pipe. Further resonances are

676

spaced $\frac{\lambda}{2}$ apart giving the series of resonant wavelengths $L = \frac{\lambda_1}{2}, 2\left(\frac{\lambda_2}{2}\right), 3\left(\frac{\lambda_3}{2}\right), \ldots$.

a. $\lambda_1 = 2L = 2(2.65 \text{ m}) = 5.30 \text{ m}$, so that the lowest frequency is

$$f_1 = \frac{v}{\lambda_1} = \frac{343 \text{ m/s}}{5.30 \text{ m}} = 64.7 \text{ Hz}.$$

b. $f_2 = \frac{v}{\lambda_2} = \frac{v}{L} = \frac{343 \text{ m/s}}{2.65 \text{ m}} = 129 \text{ Hz}$

$$f_3 = \frac{v}{\lambda_3} = \frac{3v}{2L} = \frac{3(343 \text{ m/s})}{2(2.65 \text{ m})} = 194 \text{ Hz}$$

10. The lowest resonant frequency corresponds to the wavelength given by $\frac{\lambda}{2} = L$, the length of the pipe.

$\lambda = 2L = 2(0.65 \text{ m}) = 1.30 \text{ m}$, so $f = \frac{v}{\lambda}$

$= \frac{343 \text{ m/s}}{1.30 \text{ m}} = 260 \text{ Hz}$

Since the saxophone is an open pipe,
$\lambda_{max} = 2 \times (\text{pipe length}) = 2(0.65 \text{ m}) = 1.30 \text{ m}$.
$f_{min} = v/\lambda_{max} = (343 \text{ m/s})/(1.30 \text{ m}) = 260 \text{ Hz}$

11. Beat frequency $= |f_2 - f_1|$
$= |333 \text{ Hz} - 330 \text{ Hz}|$
$= 3 \text{ Hz}$

12. The frequency of the second fork could be either
$f_2 = f_1 + f_{beat} = 349 \text{ Hz} + 3 \text{ Hz} = 352 \text{ Hz}$ or
$f_2 = f_1 - f_{beat} = 349 \text{ Hz} - 3 \text{ Hz} = 346 \text{ Hz}$.

Chapter 16

1. $c = \lambda f$, so
$f = c/\lambda = (3.00 \times 10^8 \text{ m/s})/(556 \times 10^{-9} \text{ m})$
$= 5.40 \times 10^{14} \text{ Hz}$

2. $d = ct = (3.00 \times 10^8 \text{ m/s})(1.0 \times 10^{-9} \text{ s})$
$= 0.30 \text{ m}$

3. a. $d = ct = (3.00 \times 10^8 \text{ m/s})(6.0 \times 10^{-15} \text{ s})$
$= 1.8 \times 10^{-6} \text{ m}$

b. Number of wavelengths $= \frac{\text{pulse length}}{\lambda_{violet}}$

$$= \frac{1.8 \times 10^{-6} \text{ m}}{4.0 \times 10^{-7} \text{ m}}$$

$= 4.5$

4. $d = ct = (299\,792\,458 \text{ m/s})(1/2)(2.562 \text{ s})$
$= 3.840 \times 10^8 \text{ m}$

5. $v = d/t = (3.0 \times 10^{11} \text{ m})/(16 \text{ min})(60 \text{ s/m})$
$= 3.1 \times 10^8 \text{ m/s}$

6. $\frac{E_{after}}{E_{before}} = \frac{P/4\pi d_{after}^2}{P/4\pi d_{before}^2} = \frac{d_{before}^2}{d_{after}^2} = \frac{(30 \text{ cm})^2}{(90 \text{ cm})^2} = \frac{1}{9}$

7. $E = \frac{P}{4\pi d^2} = \frac{2275 \text{ lm}}{4\pi(3.0 \text{ m})^2} = 20 \text{ lx}$

8. Illuminance of a 150-watt bulb
$P = 2275$, $d = 0.5, 0.75 \ldots 5$

$E(d) = \frac{P}{4\pi d^2}$

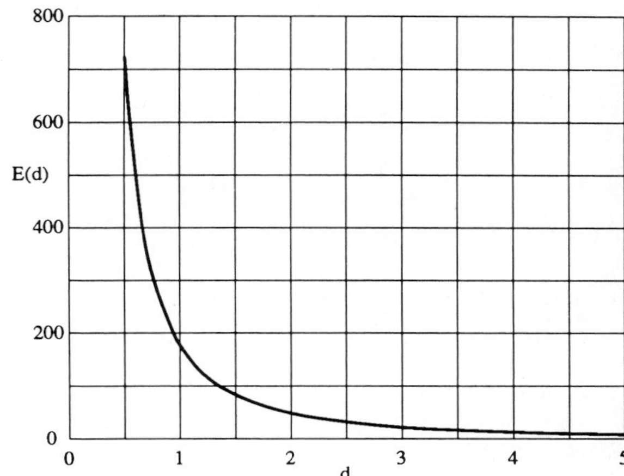

9. $P = 4\pi I = 4\pi(64 \text{ cd}) = 256\pi \text{ lm}$,

so $E = \frac{P}{4\pi d^2} = \frac{256\pi \text{ lm}}{4\pi(3.0 \text{ m})^2} = 7.1 \text{ lx}$

10. From $E = \frac{P}{4\pi d^2}$,

$P = 4\pi d^2 E = 3\pi(4.0 \text{ m})^2(2.0 \times 10^1 \text{ lx})$
$= 1280\pi \text{ lm}$,

so $I = \frac{P}{4\pi} = \frac{1280\pi \text{ lm}}{4\pi} = 320 \text{ cd}$

Chapter 17

1. Assume the light is incident from air.
From $n_i \sin \theta_i = n_r \sin \theta_r$,

$\sin \theta_r = \frac{n_i \sin \theta_i}{n_r} = \frac{(1.00) \sin 45.0°}{1.52}$

$= 0.465$, or $\theta_r = 27.7°$.

2. $n_i \sin \theta_i = n_r \sin \theta_r$ so,

$\sin \theta_r = \frac{n_i \sin \theta_i}{n_r} = \frac{(1.00) \sin 30.0°}{1.33} = 0.376$,

or $\theta_r = 22.1°$

677

3. a. Assume the light is incident from air.
$n_i \sin \theta_i = n_r \sin \theta_r$ gives

$$\sin \theta_r = \frac{n_i \sin \theta_i}{n_r} = \frac{(1.00) \sin 45.0°}{2.42} = 0.292,$$

or $\theta_r = 17.0°$

b. Diamond bends the light more.

4. $n_1 \sin \theta_1 = n_2 \sin \theta_2$, so
$n_2 = n_1 \sin \theta_1 / \sin \theta_2 = (1.33)(0.515)/(0.454) = 1.5$

5. a. $$v_{ethanol} = \frac{c}{n_{ethanol}} = \frac{3.00 \times 10^8 \text{ m/s}}{1.36}$$
$= 2.21 \times 10^8$ m/s

b. $$v_{quartz} = \frac{c}{n_{quartz}} = \frac{3.00 \times 10^8 \text{ m/s}}{1.54}$$
$= 1.95 \times 10^8$ m/s

c. $$v_{flint\ glass} = \frac{c}{n_{flint\ glass}} = \frac{3.00 \times 10^8 \text{ m/s}}{1.61}$$
$= 1.86 \times 10^8$ m/s

6. $$n = \frac{c}{v} = \frac{3.00 \times 10^8 \text{ m/s}}{2.00 \times 10^8 \text{ m/s}} = 1.50$$

7. $n = 1.5$, so $$v = \frac{c}{n} = \frac{3.00 \times 10^8 \text{ m/s}}{1.5}$$
$= 2.0 \times 10^8$ m/s

8. $t = d/v = dn/c$
$\Delta t = d(n_{air} - n_{vacuum})/c$
$= d(1.0003 - 1.0000)/3.00 \times 10^8$ m/s
$= d(1 \times 10^{-12}$ s/m)
Thus, $d = \Delta t/(1 \times 10^{-12}$ s/m)
$= 1 \times 10^{-8}$ s$/1 \times 10^{-12}$ s/m
$= 10^4$ m $= 10$ km.

Chapter 18

1.

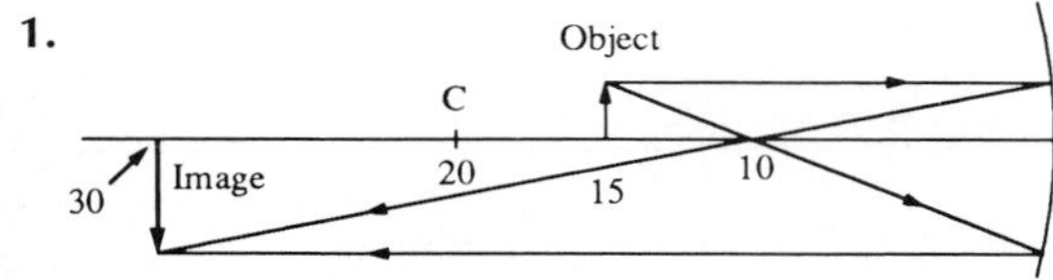

2. a.

b. $$\frac{1}{f} = \frac{1}{d_o} + \frac{1}{d_i}, \text{ so}$$
$d_i = d_o f/(d_o - f)$
$= (10 \text{ cm})(6.0 \text{ cm})/(10 \text{ cm} - 6.0 \text{ cm})$
$= 15$ cm

c. $m = -d_i/d_o = -(15 \text{ cm})/(10.0 \text{ cm}) = -1.5$

d. $m = h_i/h_o$, so
$h_i = mh_o = (-1.5)(3.0 \text{ mm}) = -4.5$ mm

3. $f = r/2 = (20.0 \text{ cm})/2 = 10.0$ cm,
$1/d_o + 1/d_i = 1/f$, so
$d_o = fd_i/(d_i - f)$
$= (10.0 \text{ cm})(30.0 \text{ cm})/(30.0 \text{ cm} - 10.0 \text{ cm})$
$= 15.0$ cm

4. If $d_o = d_i$, then $1/f = 2/d_o$, or $f = \frac{1}{2}d_o$

Now, $r = 2f = d_o = 25$ cm

5. $f = r/2 = (12.0 \text{ cm})/2 = 6.0$ cm
$1/d_o + 1/d_i = 1/f$, so
$d_i = fd_o/(d_o - f)$
$= (6.0 \text{ cm})(4.0 \text{ cm})/(4.0 \text{ cm} - 6.0 \text{ cm})$
$= -12$ cm

6. a. $1/d_o + 1/d_i = 1/f$, so
$d_i = fd_o/(d_o - f)$
$= (9.0 \text{ cm})(6.0 \text{ cm})/(6.0 \text{ cm} - 9.0 \text{ cm})$
$= -18$ cm

b. $m = h_i/h_o = -d_i/d_o = -(-18 \text{ cm})/(6.0 \text{ cm})$
$= +3.0$, so
$h_i = mh_o = (3.0)(15 \text{ mm}) = 45$ mm

7. a. $1/d_o + 1/d_i = 1/f$, so
$d_i = fd_o/(d_o - f)$
$= (16.0 \text{ cm})(10.0 \text{ cm})/(10.0 \text{ cm} - 16.0 \text{ cm})$
$= -27$ cm

b. $m = h_i/h_o = -d_i/d_o$
$= -(-27 \text{ cm})/(10.0 \text{ cm}) = +2.7$, so
$h_i = mh_o = (2.7)(4.0 \text{ cm}) = 11$ cm

8. $m = -d_i/d_o = 3$, so
$d_i = -75$ cm
$1/f = 1/d_o + 1/d_i$, so
$f = d_o d_i/(d_o + d_i)$
$= (25 \text{ cm})(-75 \text{ cm})/(25 \text{ cm} + (-75 \text{ cm}))$
$= 37.5$ cm and $r = 2f = 75$ cm

9. a.

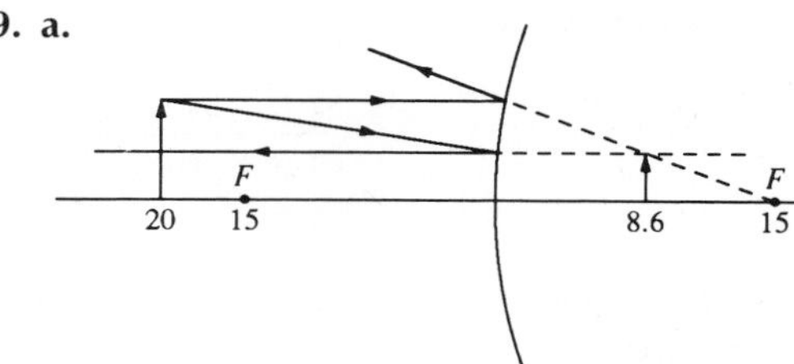

678

b. $1/d_o + 1/d_i = 1/f$, so

$d_i = fd_o/(d_o - f)$

$$= \frac{(-15.0 \text{ cm})(20.0 \text{ cm})}{(20.0 \text{ cm} - (-15.0 \text{ cm}))}$$

$= -8.57$ cm

10. a. $1/d_o + 1/d_i = 1/f$, so

$d_i = fd_o/(d_o - f)$

$$= \frac{(-12 \text{ cm})(60.0 \text{ cm})}{(60.0 \text{ cm} - (-12 \text{ cm}))}$$

$= -10$ cm

b. $m = h_i/h_o = -d_i/d_o$

$= -(-10 \text{ cm})/(60.0 \text{ cm}) = +0.17$, so

$h_i = mh_o = (0.17)(6.0 \text{ cm}) = 1.0$ cm

11. $1/d_o + 1/d_i = 1/f$, so

$d_i = fd_o/(d_o - f)$

$= (-0.40 \text{ m})(6.0 \text{ m})/(6.0 \text{ m} - (-0.40 \text{ m}))$

$= -0.38$ m

12. $1/f = 1/d_o + 1/d_i$, so $f = d_od_i/(d_o + d_i)$ and $m = -d_i/d_o$, so $d_o = -d_i/m$.

Since $d_i = -24$ cm and $m = 0.75$,

$$d_o = \frac{-(-24 \text{ cm})}{0.75} = 32 \text{ cm and}$$

$$f = \frac{(32 \text{ cm})(-24 \text{ cm})}{32 \text{ cm} + (-24 \text{ cm})} = -96 \text{ cm.}$$

13.

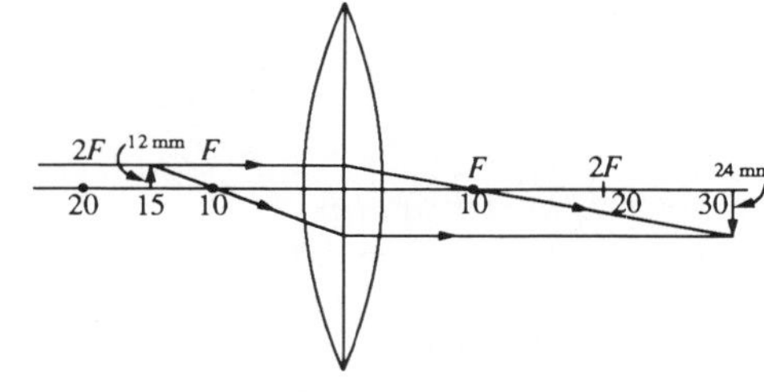

14. $1/d_o + 1/d_i = 1/f$, so

$d_i = fd_o/(d_o - f)$

$= (5.5 \text{ cm})(8.5 \text{ cm})/(8.5 \text{ cm} - 5.5 \text{ cm})$

$= 16$ cm

$h_i = -d_ih_o/d_o = -(16 \text{ cm})(2.25 \text{ mm})/(8.5 \text{ cm})$

$= -4.2$ mm

15. $1/d_o + 1/d_i = 1/f$ with $d_o = d_i$, since $m = -d_i/d_o$ and $m = -1$. Therefore, $2/d_o = 1/f$, $d_o = d_i = 2f = 50$ mm.

16. $m = -d_i/d_o$,

so $d_i = -md_o = -(-2)(7.0 \text{ cm}) = 14$ cm

$1/f = 1/d_o + 1/d_i$, so

$f = d_od_i/(d_o + d_i)$

$= (7.0 \text{ cm})(14 \text{ cm})/(7.0 \text{ cm} + 14 \text{ cm})$

$= 4.7$ cm

17. $1/d_o + 1/d_i = 1/f$, so

$d_i = fd_o/(d_o - f)$

$= (20.0 \text{ cm})(6.0 \text{ cm})/(6.0 \text{ cm} - 20.0 \text{ cm})$

$= -8.6$ cm

18. a. $1/d_o + 1/d_i = 1/f$, so

$d_i = fd_o/(d_o - f)$

$= (12 \text{ cm})(3.4 \text{ cm})/(3.4 \text{ cm} - 12 \text{ cm})$

$= -4.7$ cm

b. $h_i = -h_od_i/d_o$

$= -(2.0 \text{ cm})(-4.7 \text{ cm})/(3.4 \text{ cm})$

$= 2.8$ cm

19. $m = -d_i/d_o$, so

$d_i = -md_o = -(4.0)(3.5 \text{ cm}) = -14$ cm

$1/f = 1/d_o + 1/d_i$, so

$f = d_od_i/(d_o + d_i)$

$= (3.5 \text{ cm})(-14 \text{ cm})/(3.5 \text{ cm} + (-14 \text{ cm}))$

$= 4.7$ cm

20. From Figure 18–17, you can increase image size by making $(d_o - f)$ as small as possible. Thus, increase d_o until it is almost f, which is the limit.

Chapter 19

1. $\lambda = xd/L$

$= (13.2 \times 10^{-3} \text{ m})(1.90 \times 10^{-5} \text{ m})/(0.600 \text{ m})$

$= 4.18 \times 10^{-7}$ m

$= 418$ nm

2. $x = \lambda L/d$

$= (5.96 \times 10^{-7} \text{ m})(0.600 \text{ m})/(1.90 \times 10^{-5} \text{ m})$

$= 0.0188$ m

$= 18.8$ mm

3. $d = \lambda L/x$

$= (6.328 \times 10^{-7} \text{ m})/(1.000 \text{ m})(65.5 \times 10^{-3} \text{ m})$

$= 9.66 \times 10^{-6}$ m

4. $\lambda = xd/L$

$= (55.8 \times 10^{-3} \text{ m})(9.66 \times 10^{-6} \text{ m})/(1.000 \text{ m})$

$= 5.39 \times 10^{-7}$ m

$= 539$ nm

5. $x = \lambda L/w$

$= (5.46 \times 10^{-7} \text{ m})(0.75 \text{ m})/(9.5 \times 10^{-5} \text{ m})$

$= 4.3 \times 10^{-3}$ m

$= 4.3$ mm

679

6. $w = \frac{\lambda L}{x}$

$= (6.328 \times 10^{-7}\text{ m})(1.15\text{ m})/(7.5 \times 10^{-3}\text{ m})$
$= 9.7 \times 10^{-5}\text{ m}$

7. $\lambda = \frac{wx}{L}$

$= (2.95 \times 10^{-5}\text{ m})(1.20 \times 10^{-2}\text{ m})/(0.600\text{ m})$
$= 5.90 \times 10^{-7}\text{ m}$
$= 590\text{ nm}$

8. a. Red, because central peak width is proportional to wavelength.
b. Width $= 2x = 2\lambda L/w$
for blue,

$$2x = \frac{2(4.41 \times 10^{-7}\text{ m})(1.00\text{ m})}{(5.0 \times 10^{-5}\text{ m})}$$
$= 18\text{ mm}$

for red,

$$2x = \frac{2(6.22 \times 10^{-7}\text{ m})(1.00\text{ m})}{(5.0 \times 10^{-5}\text{ m})}$$
$= 25\text{ mm}$

Chapter 20

1. $F = \frac{Kqq'}{d^2}$

$$= \frac{(9.0 \times 10^9\text{ N} \cdot \text{m}^2/\text{C}^2)(6.0 \times 10^{-6}\text{ C})(6.0 \times 10^{-6}\text{ C})}{(0.5\text{m})^2}$$
$= 1.3\text{ N}$

2. $F = \frac{Kqq'}{d^2}$

$$= \frac{(9.0 \times 10^9\text{ N} \cdot \text{m}^2/\text{C}^2)(-2.0 \times 10^{-4}\text{ C})(8.0 \times 10^{-4}\text{ C})}{(0.30\text{ m})^2}$$
$= -1.6 \times 10^4\text{ N}$

3. $F = \frac{Kqq'}{d^2}$

$q' = \frac{Fd^2}{Kq}$

$$= \frac{(65\text{ N})(0.05\text{ m})^2}{(9.0 \times 10^9\text{ N} \cdot \text{m}^2/\text{C}^2)(6.0 \times 10^{-6}\text{ C})}$$
$= 3.0 \times 10^{-6}\text{ C}$

4.

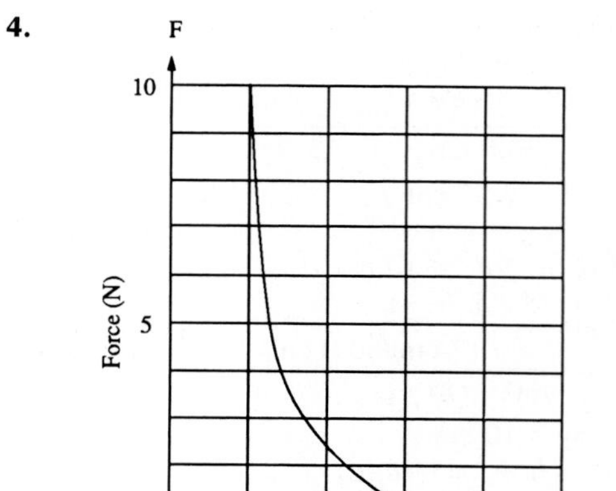

5. Magnitudes of all forces remain the same. The direction changes to 42° above the $-x$ axis, or 138°.

Chapter 21

1. $E = \frac{F}{q'} = \frac{0.060\text{ N}}{2.0 \times 10^{-8}\text{ C}}$
$= 3.0 \times 10^6$ N/C, directed to the left

2. $E = \frac{F}{q'} = \frac{2.5 \times 10^{-4}\text{ N}}{5.0 \times 10^{-4}\text{ C}} = 0.50\text{ N/C}$

3. $F_2/F_1 = (Kqq'/d_2{}^2)/(Kqq'/d_1{}^2)$
$= (d_1/d_2)^2$ with $d_2 = 2d_1$
$F_2 = (d_1/d_2)^2F_1 = (d_1/2d_1)^2(2.5 \times 10^{-4}\text{ N})$
$= 6.3 \times 10^{-5}\text{ N}$

4. a. No. The force on the 2.0 μC charge would be twice that on the 1.0 μC charge.
b. Yes. You would divide the force by the strength of the test charge, so the results would be the same.

5. $V = Ed = (8000\text{ N/C})(0.05\text{ m}) = 400\text{ J/C}$
$= 4 \times 10^2\text{ V}$

6. $V = Ed$

$E = \frac{V}{d} = \frac{500\text{ V}}{0.02\text{ m}} = 2.5 \times 10^4\text{ N/C}$

7. $V = Ed = (2.50 \times 10^3\text{ N/C})(0.500\text{ m})$
$= 1.25 \times 10^3\text{ V}$

8. $W = qV = (5.0\text{ C})(1.5\text{ V}) = 7.5\text{ J}$

680

9. a. Gravitational force (weight), downward; frictional force of air, upward

b. The two are equal in magnitude.

10. a. $F = Eq$

$$q = \frac{F}{E} = \frac{1.9 \times 10^{-15}\ \text{N}}{6.0 \times 10^{3}\ \text{N/C}} = 3.2 \times 10^{-19}\ \text{C}$$

b. $\#\ \text{electrons} = \frac{q}{q_e} = \frac{3.2 \times 10^{-19}\ \text{C}}{1.6 \times 10^{-19}\ \text{C/electron}}$

$= 2$ electrons

11. a. $F = Eq$

$$q = \frac{F}{E} = \frac{6.4 \times 10^{-13}\ \text{N}}{4.0 \times 10^{6}\ \text{N/C}} = 1.6 \times 10^{-19}\ \text{C}$$

b. $\#\ \text{electrons} = \frac{q}{1.6 \times 10^{-19}\ \text{C/electron}}$

$= 1$ electron

12. $E = \frac{F}{q} = \frac{6.4 \times 10^{-13}\ \text{N}}{(4)(1.6 \times 10^{-19}\ \text{C})} = 1.0 \times 10^{6}\ \text{N/C}$

13. $q = CV = 27\ \mu\text{F}(25\ \text{V}) = 6.8 \times 10^{-4}\ \text{C}$

14. $q = CV$, so the larger capacitor has a greater charge.
$q = 1.0 \times 10^{-4}\ \text{C}$

15. $V = q/C$, so the smaller capacitor has the larger potential difference.
$V = (2.5 \times 10^{-4}\ \text{C})/(3.3 \times 10^{-6}\ \text{F}) = 76\ \text{V}$

16. $q = CV$, so $\Delta q = C\Delta V$;
$\Delta q = (2.2\ \mu\text{F})(15.0\ \text{V} - 6.0\ \text{V}) = 2.0 \times 10^{-5}\ \text{C}$

Chapter 22

1. $P = VI = (120\ \text{V})(0.5\ \text{A}) = 60\ \text{J/s} = 60\ \text{W}$

2. $P = VI = (12\ \text{V})(2.0\ \text{A}) = 24\ \text{W}$

3. $P = VI,\ I = \frac{P}{V} = \frac{75\ \text{W}}{120\ \text{V}} = 0.63\ \text{A}$

4. $P = VI = (12\ \text{V})(210\ \text{A}) = 2500\ \text{W}$
In 10 s, $E = Pt = (2500\ \text{J/s})(10\ \text{s})$
$= 25\ 000\ \text{J} = 2.5 \times 10^{4}\ \text{J}$.

5. $I = \frac{V}{R} = \frac{12\ \text{V}}{30\ \Omega} = 0.40\ \text{A}$

6. $V = IR = (3.8\ \text{A})(32\ \Omega) = 120\ \text{V}$

7. $R = \frac{V}{I} = \frac{3\ \text{V}}{2 \times 10^{-4}\ \text{A}} = 1.5 \times 10^{4}\ \Omega$
$= 2 \times 10^{4}\ \Omega$

8. a. $R = \frac{V}{I} = \frac{120\ \text{V}}{0.5\ \text{A}} = 240\ \Omega = 200\ \Omega$

b. $P = VI = (120\ \text{V})(0.5\ \text{A}) = 60\ \text{W}$

9. a. $I = P/V = (75\ \text{W})/(120\ \text{V}) = 0.63\ \text{A}$

b. $R = V/I = 120\ \text{V}/0.63\ \text{A} = 190\ \Omega$

10. a. The new value of the current is
$0.63\ \text{A}/2 = 0.315\ \text{A}$, so
$V = IR = (0.315\ \text{A})(190\ \Omega) = 60\ \text{V}$.

b. The total resistance of the circuit is now
$R_{total} = V/I = (120\ \text{V})/(0.315\ \text{A}) = 380\ \Omega$.
Therefore, $R_{res} = R_{total} - R_{lamp}$
$= 380\ \Omega - 190\ \Omega = 190\ \Omega$.

c. $P = VI = (60\ \text{V})(0.315\ \text{A}) = 19\ \text{W}$

11. $I = \frac{V}{R} = \frac{60\ \text{V}}{12.5\ \Omega} = 4.8\ \text{A}$

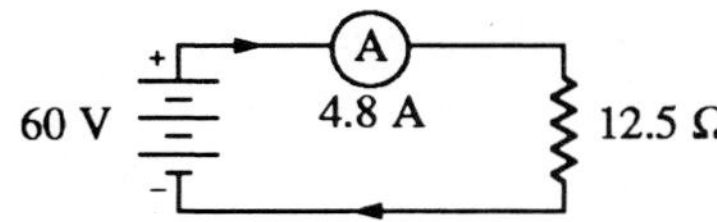

12. $R = V/I = (4.5\ \text{V})/(0.090\ \text{A}) = 50\ \Omega$

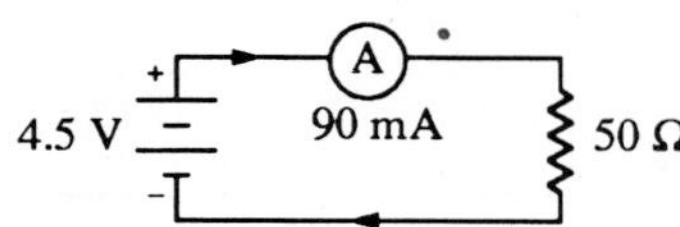

13. Both circuits will take the form

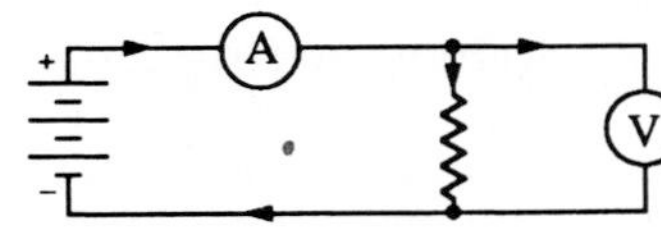

Since the ammeter resistance is assumed zero, the voltmeter readings will be
Practice Problem 11 60 V.
Practice Problem 12 4.5 V.

14. a. $I = V/R = (120\ \text{V})/(15\ \Omega) = 8.0\ \text{A}$

b. $E = I^2Rt = (8.0\ \text{A})^2(15\ \Omega)(30.0\ \text{s})$
$= 2.9 \times 10^{4}\ \text{J}$

c. 2.9×10^{4} J, since all electrical energy is converted to thermal energy.

15. a. $I = V/R = (60\ \text{V})/(30\ \Omega) = 2.0\ \text{A}$

b. $E = I^2Rt = (2.0\ \text{A})^2(30\ \Omega)(5\ \text{min})(60\ \text{s/min})$
$= 3.6 \times 10^{4}\ \text{J}$

681

16. a. $E = (0.200)(100.0\ \text{J/s})(60.0\ \text{s})$
$= 1.20 \times 10^3\ \text{J}$
b. $E = (0.800)(100.0\ \text{J/s})(60.0\ \text{s})$
$= 4.80 \times 10^3\ \text{J}$

17. a. $I = V/R = (220\ \text{V})/(11\ \Omega) = 20\ \text{A}$
b. $E = I^2Rt = (20\ \text{A})^2(11\ \Omega)(30.0\ \text{s})$
$= 1.3 \times 10^5\ \text{J}$
c. $Q = mC\Delta T$ with $Q = 0.70\ E$
$\Delta T = 0.70\ E/mC$
$$= \frac{(0.70)(1.3 \times 10^5\ \text{J})}{(1.20\ \text{kg})(4180\ \text{J/kg}\cdot{}^\circ\text{C})} = 18^\circ\text{C}$$

18. a. $P = IV = (15.0\ \text{A})(120\ \text{V})$
$= 1800\ \text{W} = 1.80\ \text{kW}$
b. $E = Pt = (1.8\ \text{kW})(5\ \text{h/day})(30\ \text{days})$
$= 270\ \text{kWh}$
c. Cost $= (0.11\ \$/\text{kWh})(270\ \text{kWh}) = \$29.70$

19. a. $I = \dfrac{V}{R} = \dfrac{(115\ \text{V})}{(12\ 000\ \Omega)} = 9.6 \times 10^{-3}\ \text{A}$
b. $P = VI = (115\ \text{V})(9.6 \times 10^{-3}\ \text{A}) = 1.10\ \text{W}$
c. Cost $= (1.10 \times 10^{-3}\ \text{kW})(\$0.09/\text{kWh}) \times$
$(30\ \text{days})(24\ \text{h/day}) = \$0.07$

Chapter 23

1. a. $R = R_1 + R_2 + R_3$
$= 20\ \Omega + 20\ \Omega + 20\ \Omega$
$= 60\ \Omega$
b. $I = V/R = (120\ \text{V})/(60\ \Omega) = 2.0\ \text{A}$

2. a. $R = 10\ \Omega + 15\ \Omega + 5\ \Omega = 30\ \Omega$
b. $I = V/R = (90\ \text{V})/(30\ \Omega) = 3.0\ \text{A}$

3. a. It will increase.
b. $I = V/R$, so it will decrease.
c. No. It does not depend on the resistance.

4. a. $R = V/I = (120\ \text{V})/(0.06\ \text{A}) = 2000\ \Omega$
b. $2000\ \Omega/10 = 200\ \Omega$

5. a. $R = 20.0\ \Omega + 30.0\ \Omega = 50.0\ \Omega$
b. $I = V/R = (120\ \text{V})/(50.0\ \Omega) = 2.40\ \text{A}$
c. $V = IR$. Across 20.0-Ω resistor,
$V = (2.40\ \text{A})(20.0\ \Omega) = 48.0\ \text{V}$
Across 30.0-Ω resistor,
$V = (2.40\ \text{A})(30.0\ \Omega) = 72.0\ \text{V}$.
d. $V = 48.0\ \text{V} + 72.0\ \text{V} = 120\ \text{V}$

6. a. $R = 3.0\ \text{k}\Omega + 5.0\ \text{k}\Omega + 4.0\ \text{k}\Omega = 12.0\ \text{k}\Omega$
b. $I = V/R = (12\ \text{V})/(12.0\ \text{k}\Omega)$
$= 1.0\ \text{mA} = 1.0 \times 10^{-3}\ \text{A}$
c. $V = IR$,
so $V = 3.0\ \text{V}$, $5.0\ \text{V}$, and $4.0\ \text{V}$
d. $V = 3.0\ \text{V} + 5.0\ \text{V} + 4.0\ \text{V}$
$= 12.0\ \text{V}$

7. $V_2 = VR_2/(R_1 + R_2)$
$= (45\ \text{V})(235\ \text{k}\Omega)/(475\ \text{k}\Omega + 235\ \text{k}\Omega) = 15\ \text{V}$

8. a. $V_2 = VR_2/(R_1 + R_2)$
$= (9.0\ \text{V})(475\ \Omega)/(500\ \Omega + 475\ \Omega)$
$= 4.4\ \text{V}$
b. $V_2 = VR_2/(R_1 + R_2)$
$= (9.0\ \text{V})(4.0\ \text{k}\Omega)/(0.50\ \text{k}\Omega + 4.0\ \text{k}\Omega)$
$= 8.0\ \text{V}$
c. $V_2 = VR_2/(R_1 + R_2)$
$$= \frac{(9.0\ \text{V})(4.0 \times 10^5\ \Omega)}{(0.005 \times 10^5\ \Omega + 4.0 \times 10^5\ \Omega)}$$
$= 9.0\ \text{V}$

9. a. $1/R = 1/R_1 + 1/R_2 + 1/R_3$
$= 3/15\ \Omega$, $R = 5.0\ \Omega$
b. $I = V/R = (30\ \text{V})/(5.0\ \Omega) = 6.0\ \text{A}$
c. $I = V/R = (30\ \text{V})/(15.0\ \Omega) = 2.0\ \text{A}$

10. a. $1/R = 1/15.0\ \Omega + 1/12.0\ \Omega$, so
$R = 6.67\ \Omega$
b. $I = V/R = (15.0\text{V})/(6.67\ \Omega) = 2.25\ \text{A}$
c. $I = V/R$
$= (15.0\text{V})/(15.0\ \Omega)$
$= 1.00\ \text{A}$,
$(15.0\ \text{V})/(12.0\ \Omega)$
$= 1.25\ \text{A}$

11. a. $1/R = 1/120.0\ \Omega + 1/60.0\ \Omega + 1/40.0\ \Omega$,
$R = 20.0\ \Omega$
b. $I = V/R$
$= (12.0\ \text{V})/(20.0\ \Omega)$
$= 0.600\ \text{A}$
c. $I = V/R$
$= (12.0\ \text{V})/(120.0\ \Omega)$
$= 0.100\ \text{A}$,
$(12.0\ \text{V})/(60.0\ \Omega)$
$= 0.200\ \text{A}$,
$(12.0\ \text{V})/(40.0\ \Omega)$
$= 0.300\ \text{A}$

12. a. smaller
b. gets larger
c. No. It remains the same. Currents are independent.

682

13. a.

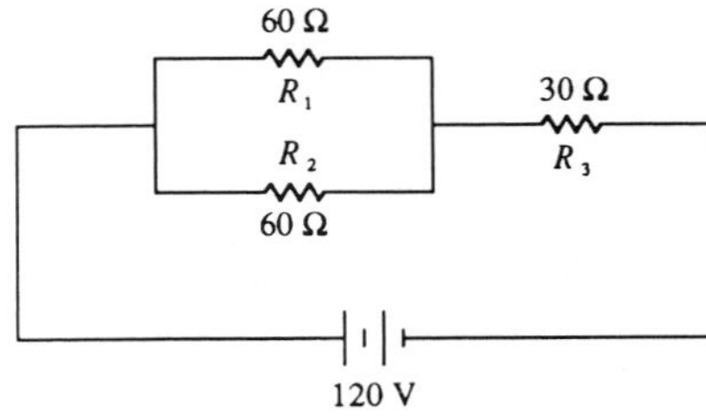

b. $\frac{1}{R} = \frac{1}{60\ \Omega} + \frac{1}{60\ \Omega} = \frac{2}{60\ \Omega}$

$R = \frac{60\ \Omega}{2} = 30\ \Omega$

c. $R_{eff} = 30\ \Omega + 30\ \Omega = 60\ \Omega$

d. $I = \frac{V}{R} = \frac{120\ V}{60\ \Omega} = 2.0\ A$

e. $V_3 = IR_3 = (2.0)(30\ \Omega) = 60\ V$

f. $V = IR = (2.0\ A)(30\ \Omega) = 60\ V$

g. $I = \frac{V}{R_1} = \frac{V}{R_2} = \frac{60\ V}{60\ \Omega} = 1.0\ A$

14. a.

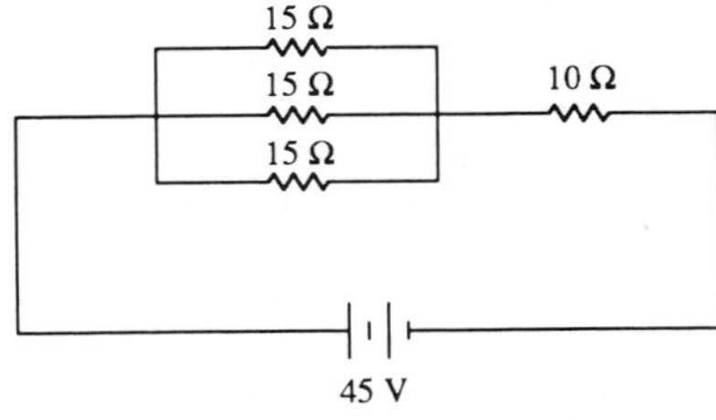

b. $\frac{1}{R} = \frac{1}{15\ \Omega} + \frac{1}{15\ \Omega} + \frac{1}{15\ \Omega} = \frac{3}{15\ \Omega}$

$R = \frac{15\ \Omega}{3} = 5.0\ \Omega$

c. $R_{eff} = 5\ \Omega + 10\ \Omega = 15\ \Omega$

d. $I = \frac{V}{R_{eff}} = \frac{45\ V}{15\ \Omega} = 3.0\ A$

e. $V = IR = (3.0\ A)(10\ \Omega) = 30\ V$

15. Series: $68\ \Omega + 68\ \Omega + 68\ \Omega = 204\ \Omega$
Parallel: $68\ \Omega/3 = 23\ \Omega$
Series parallel: $68\ \Omega + 68\ \Omega/2 = 102\ \Omega$

Chapter 24

1. a. repulsive **b.** attractive

2. south, north, south, north

3. The top face of the disk is the N-pole, so the direction of the field is up out of the N-pole.

4. the bottom (the point)

5. a. from south to north **b.** west

6. Since magnetic field strength varies inversely with the distance from the wire, it will be
a. half as strong.
b. one-third as strong.

7. It will point toward the top of the page.

8. the pointed end

9. $F = BIL$,

$B = \frac{F}{IL} = \frac{0.04\ N}{(2.0\ A)(0.10\ m)} = 0.2\ T$

10. $F = BIL = (0.40\ N/A \cdot m)(8.0\ A)(0.50\ m)$
$= 1.6\ N$

11. $B = \frac{F}{IL} = \frac{0.60\ N}{(6.0\ A)(0.75\ m)} = 0.13\ T$

12. $F = BIL$, $F =$ weight of wire

$B = \frac{F}{IL} = \frac{0.35\ N}{(6.0\ A)(0.40\ m)} = 0.15\ T$

13. $F = Bqv$
$= (0.50\ T)(1.6 \times 10^{-19}\ C)(4.0 \times 10^{6}\ m/s)$
$= 3.2 \times 10^{-13}\ N$

14. $F = Bqv$
$= (9.0 \times 10^{-2}\ T)\ (2)\ (1.6 \times 10^{-19}\ C)$
$(3.0 \times 10^{4}\ m/s)$
$= 8.6 \times 10^{-16}\ N$

15. $F = Bqv$
$= (4.0 \times 10^{-2}\ T)(3)(1.6 \times 10^{-19}\ C)$
$(9.0 \times 10^{6}\ m/s)$
$= 1.7 \times 10^{-13}\ N$

16. $F = Bqv$
$= (5.0 \times 10^{-2}\ T)(2)(1.6 \times 10^{-19}\ C)$
$(4.0 \times 10^{-2}\ m/s)$
$= 6.4 \times 10^{-22}\ N$

Chapter 25

1. a. $EMF = BLv$
$= (0.4\ N/A \cdot m)(0.5\ m)(20\ m/s) = 4\ V$

b. $I = \frac{V}{R} = \frac{4\ V}{6.0\ \Omega} = 0.7\ A$

2. $EMF = BLv$
$= (5.0 \times 10^{-5}\ T)(25\ m)(125\ m/s) = 0.16\ V$

683

3. Using the right-hand rule, the north pole is at the bottom.

4. a. $EMF = BLv = (1.0\ \text{T})(30.0\ \text{m})(2.0\ \text{m/s}) = 60\ \text{V}$

b. $I = \frac{V}{R} = \frac{60\ \text{V}}{15.0\ \Omega} = 4.0\ \text{A}$

5. a. $V_{eff} = (0.707)V_{max} = (0.707)(170\ \text{V}) = 120\ \text{V}$

b. $I_{eff} = (0.707)I_{max} = (0.707)(0.70\ \text{A}) = 0.49\ \text{A}$

c. $R = \frac{V_{eff}}{I_{eff}} = \frac{120\ \text{V}}{0.49\ \text{A}} = 240\ \Omega$

6. a. $V_{max} = \frac{V_{eff}}{0.707} = \frac{117\ \text{V}}{0.707} = 165\ \text{V}$

b. $I_{max} = \frac{I_{eff}}{0.707} = \frac{5.5\ \text{A}}{0.707} = 7.8\ \text{A}$

7. a. $V_{eff} = (0.707)V_{max} = (0.707)(425\ \text{V}) = 300\ \text{V}$ or $3.00 \times 10^2\ \text{V}$

b. $I_{eff} = V_{eff}/R = (300\ \text{V})/(5.0 \times 10^2\ \Omega) = 0.60\ \text{A}$

8. Since $P = V_{eff}I_{eff} = (0.707\ V_{max})(0.707\ I_{max})$

$$= \frac{1}{2}P_{max},$$

$$P_{max} = 2P = 2(100\ \text{W}) = 200\ \text{W}$$

9. a. $\frac{V_s}{V_p} = \frac{N_s}{N_p}$

$$V_s = \frac{V_pN_s}{N_p} = \frac{(7200\ \text{V})(125)}{7500} = 120\ \text{V}$$

b. $V_pI_p = V_sI_s$

$$I_p = \frac{V_sI_s}{V_p} = \frac{(120\ \text{V})(36\ \text{A})}{7200\ \text{V}} = 0.60\ \text{A}$$

10. a. $V_s = \frac{V_pN_s}{N_p} = \frac{(3600\ \text{V})(500)}{15\ 000} = 120\ \text{V}$

b. $I_s = \frac{V_pI_p}{V_s} = \frac{(3600\ \text{V})(3.0\ \text{A})}{120\ \text{V}} = 90\ \text{A}$

11. a. $\frac{V_p}{V_s} = \frac{N_p}{N_s}$

$$V_s = \frac{V_pN_s}{N_p} = \frac{(120\ \text{V})(15\ 000)}{500} = 3.60 \times 10^3\ \text{V}$$

b. $V_pI_p = V_sI_s$

$$I_p = \frac{V_sI_s}{V_p} = \frac{(3600\ \text{V})(3.0\ \text{A})}{120\ \text{V}} = 90\ \text{A}$$

c. $V_pI_p = (120\ \text{V})(90\ \text{A}) = 1.1 \times 10^4\ \text{W}$

$V_sI_s = (3600\ \text{V})(3.0\ \text{A}) = 1.1 \times 10^4\ \text{W}$

12. a. $V_s = \frac{V_pN_s}{N_p} = \frac{(60.0\ \text{V})(90\ 000)}{300} = 1.80 \times 10^4\ \text{V}$

b. $I_p = \frac{V_sI_s}{V_p}$

$$= \frac{(1.80 \times 10^4\ \text{V})(0.50\ \text{A})}{60.0\ \text{V}} = 1.5 \times 10^2\ \text{A}$$

Chapter 26

1. $Bqv = Eq,$

$$v = \frac{E}{B} = \frac{4.5 \times 10^3\ \text{N/C}}{0.6\ \text{T}} = 8 \times 10^3\ \text{m/s}$$

2. $Bqv = \frac{mv^2}{r},$

$$r = \frac{mv}{Bq} = \frac{(1.7 \times 10^{-27}\ \text{kg})(7.5 \times 10^3\ \text{m/s})}{(0.6\ \text{T})(1.6 \times 10^{-19}\ \text{C})} = 1 \times 10^{-4}\ \text{m}$$

3. $Bqv = Eq,$

$$v = \frac{E}{B} = \frac{3.0 \times 10^3\ \text{N/C}}{6.0 \times 10^{-2}\ \text{T}} = 5.0 \times 10^4\ \text{m/s}$$

4. $Bqv = \frac{mv^2}{r},$

$$r = \frac{mv}{Bq} = \frac{(9.11 \times 10^{-31}\ \text{kg})(5.0 \times 10^4\ \text{m/s})}{(6.0 \times 10^{-2}\ \text{T})(1.6 \times 10^{-19}\ \text{C})} = 4.7 \times 10^{-6}\ \text{m}$$

5. a. $Bqv = Eq,$

$$v = \frac{E}{B} = \frac{6.0 \times 10^2\ \text{N/C}}{1.5 \times 10^{-3}\ \text{T}} = 4.0 \times 10^5\ \text{m/s}$$

b. $Bqv = \frac{mv^2}{r},$

$$m = \frac{Bqr}{v} = \frac{(0.18\ \text{T})(1.6 \times 10^{-19}\ \text{C})(0.165\ \text{m})}{4.0 \times 10^5\ \text{m/s}} = 1.2 \times 10^{-26}\ \text{kg}$$

6. $m = \frac{B^2r^2q}{2V}$

$$= \frac{(5.0 \times 10^{-2}\ \text{T})^2(0.106\ \text{m})^2(2)(1.6 \times 10^{-19}\ \text{C})}{2(66.0\ \text{V})} = 6.8 \times 10^{-26}\ \text{kg}$$

7. $m = B^2r^2q/2V$

$$= \frac{(7.2 \times 10^{-2}\ \text{T})^2(0.085\ \text{m})^2(1.6 \times 10^{-19}\ \text{C})}{2(110\ \text{V})} = 2.7 \times 10^{-26}\ \text{kg}$$

684

8. Use $r = \frac{1}{B}\sqrt{\frac{2Vm}{q}}$ to find the ratio of radii of the two isotopes. If M represents number of proton masses, then $\frac{r_{22}}{r_{20}} = \sqrt{\frac{M_{22}}{M_{20}}}$, so $r_{22} = r_{20}(22/20)^{1/2} = 0.056$ m. Separation then is 2(0.056 m − 0.053 m) = 6 mm.

Chapter 27

1. $KE = -qV_0 = -(-1.6 \times 10^{-19}$ C)(3.2 J/C) $= 5.1 \times 10^{-19}$ J

2. $KE = -qV_0 = \frac{-(-1.6 \times 10^{-19} \text{ C})(5.7 \text{ J/C})}{(1.6 \times 10^{-19} \text{ J/eV})}$ = 5.7 eV

3. a. $c = f_0\lambda$

$f_0 = \frac{c}{\lambda} = \frac{3.00 \times 10^8 \text{ m/s}}{310 \times 10^{-9} \text{ m}} = 9.68 \times 10^{14}$ Hz

b. $hf_0 = (6.6 \times 10^{-34}$ J/Hz)$(9.67 \times 10^{14}$ Hz)
$= (6.4 \times 10^{-19}$ J)(1 eV/1.6×10^{-19} J)
= 4.0 eV

c. $KE_{max} = \frac{hc}{\lambda} - hf_0$

$= \frac{(6.6 \times 10^{-34} \text{ J/Hz})(3.00 \times 10^8 \text{ m/s})(1 \text{ eV}/1.6 \times 10^{-19} \text{ J})}{240 \times 10^{-9} \text{ m}} - 4.0$ eV

= 5.2 eV − 4.0 eV = 1.2 eV

4. a. E = work function $= hf_0 = \frac{1240 \text{ eV} \cdot \text{nm}}{\lambda_0}$ where λ_0 has units of nm and E has units of eV.

λ_0 = (1240 eV · nm)/E
= (1240 eV · nm)/(1.96 eV) = 633 nm

b. $KE_{max} = hf - hf_0 = E_{photon} - hf_0$
= (1240 eV · nm)/λ − hf_0
= (1240 eV · nm)/(425 nm) − 1.96 eV
= 2.92 eV − 1.96 eV = 0.96 eV

5. a. $\frac{1}{2}mv^2 = qV_0$,

$v^2 = 2qV_0/m$
$= 2(1.60 \times 10^{-19}$ C)(250 J/C)/$(9.11 \times 10^{-31}$ kg)
$= 8.78 \times 10^{13}$ m²/s²
$v = 9.4 \times 10^6$ m/s

b. $\lambda = h/mv$
$= (6.6 \times 10^{-34}$ J · s)/$(9.11 \times 10^{-31}$ kg) ×
$(9.4 \times 10^6$ m/s)
$= 7.7 \times 10^{-11}$ m

6. a. $\lambda = \frac{h}{mv}$

$= \frac{6.6 \times 10^{-34} \text{ J} \cdot \text{s}}{(7.0 \text{ kg})(8.5 \text{ m/s})} = 1.1 \times 10^{-35}$ m

b. The wavelength is too small to show observable effects.

7. a. $p = \frac{h}{\lambda} = \frac{6.6 \times 10^{-34} \text{ J} \cdot \text{s}}{5.0 \times 10^{-12} \text{ m}}$
$= 1.3 \times 10^{-22}$ kg · m/s

b. Its momentum is too small to affect objects of ordinary size.

8. a. They have momentum and energy, and they show wave behavior.

b. An electron has mass and charge, a photon does not.

Chapter 28

1. Four times as large since orbit radius is proportional to n^2, where n is the integer labeling the level.

2. $r_n = n^2k$, where $k = 5.3 \times 10^{-11}$ m
$r_2 = (2)^2(5.3 \times 10^{-11}$ m) $= 2.1 \times 10^{-10}$ m
$r_3 = (3)^2(5.3 \times 10^{-11}$ m) $= 4.8 \times 10^{-10}$ m
$r_4 = (4)^2(5.3 \times 10^{-11}$ m) $= 8.5 \times 10^{-10}$ m

3. $E_n = \frac{-13.6 \text{ eV}}{n^2}$

$E_2 = \frac{-13.6 \text{ eV}}{(2)^2} = -3.4$ eV

$E_3 = \frac{-13.6 \text{ eV}}{(3)^2} = -1.5$ eV

$E_4 = \frac{-13.6 \text{ eV}}{(4)^2} = -0.85$ eV

4. Using the results of Practice Exercise 3,
$E_3 - E_2 = (-1.5$ eV) − (−3.4 eV) = 1.9 eV
$E_4 - E_3 = (-0.85$ eV) − (−1.5 eV) = 0.7 eV

Chapter 29

1. free e⁻/cm³

$= \frac{(2 \text{ e}^-/\text{atom})(6.02 \times 10^{23} \text{ atoms/mole})(7.13 \text{ g/cm}^3)}{(65.37 \text{ g/mole})}$

$= 1.31 \times 10^{23}$ free e⁻/cm³

685

2. atoms/cm^3

$$= \frac{(6.02 \times 10^{23} \text{ atoms/mole})(5.23 \text{ g/cm}^3)}{(72.6 \text{ g/mole})}$$

$$= 4.34 \times 10^{22} \text{ atoms/cm}^3$$

$$\text{free e}^-/\text{atom} = \frac{(2 \times 10^{16} \text{ free e}^-/\text{cm}^3)}{(4.34 \times 10^{22} \text{ atoms/cm}^3)}$$

$$= 5 \times 10^{-7}$$

3. There were 5×10^{-7} free e$^-$/Ge atoms, so we need 5×10^3 as many As dopant atoms, or 2×10^{-3} As atoms/Ge atoms.

4. At $I = 2.5$ mA, $V_d = 0.6$ V, so
$V = V_d + IR$
$= 0.6 \text{ V} + (2.5 \times 10^{-3} \text{ A})(470\ \Omega) = 1.8 \text{ V}.$

5. $V = V_d + IR$
$= 0.4 \text{ V} + (1.2 \times 10^{-2} \text{ A})(470\ \Omega) = 6.0 \text{ V}$

Chapter 30

1. $A - Z = 15 - 8 = 7$ neutrons

2. $A - Z =$ neutrons
$234 - 92 = 142$ neutrons
$235 - 92 = 143$ neutrons
$238 - 92 = 146$ neutrons

3. $A - Z = 200 - 80 = 120$ neutrons

4. ${}^1_1\text{H}$, ${}^2_1\text{H}$, ${}^3_1\text{H}$

5. ${}^{234}_{92}\text{U} \rightarrow {}^{230}_{90}\text{Th} + {}^4_2\text{He}$

6. ${}^{230}_{90}\text{Th} \rightarrow {}^{226}_{88}\text{Ra} + {}^4_2\text{He}$

7. ${}^{226}_{88}\text{Ra} \rightarrow {}^{222}_{86}\text{Rn} + {}^4_2\text{He}$

8. ${}^{214}_{82}\text{Pb} \rightarrow {}^{214}_{83}\text{Bi} + {}^{0}_{-1}\text{e} + {}^{0}_{0}\bar{\nu}$

9. 24.6 years = 2(12.3 years) which is 2 half-lives.
Since $\frac{1}{2} \times \frac{1}{2} = \frac{1}{4}$, there will be
$(1.0 \text{ g})\left(\frac{1}{4}\right) = 0.25$ g remaining.

10. Amount remaining = (original amount)$\left(\frac{1}{2}\right)^N$, where N is the number of half-lives elapsed.
Since $N = 8$ days/2.0 days $= 4$,
amount remaining $= (4.0 \text{ g})\left(\frac{1}{2}\right)^4 = 0.25$ g.

11. The half-life of ${}^{210}_{84}\text{Po}$ is 138 days.
There are 273 days or about 2 half-lives between September 1 and June 1.
So the activity is

$$= \left(2 \times 10^6 \frac{\text{decays}}{\text{s}}\right)\left(\frac{1}{2}\right)\left(\frac{1}{2}\right) = 5 \times 10^5 \frac{\text{decays}}{\text{s}}$$

12. From Table 30–1, 6 years is approximately 0.5 half-life for tritium. Since Figure 30–5 indicates that approximately $\frac{11}{16}$ of the original nuclei remain after 0.5 half-life, the brightness will be about $\frac{11}{16}$ of the original.

13. a. $E = mc^2$
$= (1.67 \times 10^{-27} \text{ kg})(3.00 \times 10^8 \text{ m/s})^2$
$= 1.50 \times 10^{-10}$ J

b. $E = \dfrac{1.50 \times 10^{-10} \text{ J}}{1.60 \times 10^{-19} \text{ J/eV}}$
$= 9.38 \times 10^8$ eV
$= 938$ MeV

c. The pair will be (2)(938 MeV) = 1.88 GeV.

Chapter 31

1. a.

6 protons = (6)(1.007825 u) =	6.046950 u
6 neutrons = (6)(1.008665 u) =	6.051990 u
total	12.098940 u
mass of carbon nucleus	−12.000000 u
mass defect	−0.098940 u

b. −(0.098940 u)(931.49 MeV/u) = −92.162 MeV

2. a.

1 proton =	0.007825 u
1 neutron =	1.008665 u
	2.016490 u
mass of deuterium nucleus =	−2.0140 u
mass defect	−0.0025 u

b. −(0.0025 u)(931.49 MeV/u) = −2.3 MeV

3. a.

7 protons = 7(1.007825 u) =	7.054775 u
8 neutrons = 8(1.008665 u) =	8.069320 u
total	15.124095 u
mass of nitrogen nucleus	−15.00011 u
mass defect	−0.123985 u
=	−0.12399 u

b. −(0.12399 u)(931.49 MeV/u) = −115.50 MeV

686

4. a. 8 protons = 8(1.007825 u) = 8.062600 u
8 neutrons = 8(1.008665 u) = 8.069320 u
total 16.131920 u
mass of oxygen nucleus −15.99491 u
mass defect −0.13701 u

b. −(0.13701 u)(931.49 MeV/u) = −127.62 MeV

5. a. $^{14}_{6}C \rightarrow ^{14}_{7}N + ^{0}_{-1}e$
b. $^{55}_{24}Cr \rightarrow ^{55}_{25}Mn + ^{0}_{-1}e$

6. a. $^{238}_{92}U \rightarrow ^{234}_{90}Th + ^{4}_{2}He$

7. $^{214}_{84}Po \rightarrow ^{210}_{82}Pb + ^{4}_{2}He$

8. a. $^{210}_{82}Pb \rightarrow ^{210}_{83}Bi + ^{0}_{-1}e$
b. $^{210}_{83}Bi \rightarrow ^{210}_{84}Po + ^{0}_{-1}e$
c. $^{234}_{90}Th \rightarrow ^{234}_{91}Pa + ^{0}_{-1}e$
d. $^{239}_{93}Np \rightarrow ^{239}_{94}Pu + ^{0}_{-1}e$

9. a. Input masses 2.014102 u + 3.016049 u
= 5.030151 u
Output masses 4.002603 u + 1.008665 u
= 5.011268 u
Difference is −0.018883 u

b. −(0.018883 u)(931.49 MeV/u) = −17.589 MeV

10. Positron mass

$$= (9.109 \times 10^{-31}\ \text{kg})\left(\frac{1\ \text{u}}{1.661 \times 10^{-27}\ \text{kg}}\right)$$

= 0.000548 u
Input mass: 4 protons = 4(1.007825 u)
= 4.031300 u
Output mass:
$^{4}_{2}He$ + 2 positrons = 4.002603 u + 2(0.000548 u)
= 4.003699
Mass difference = 0.027601 u
Energy released = (0.027601 u)(931.49 MeV/u)
= 25.710 MeV

687

Answers to
SUPPLEMENTAL PROBLEMS

Complete solutions for all Supplemental Problems can be found in the Problems and Solutions Manual accompanying this text.

Chapter 2

1. a. 8.1×10^5 g
   b. 6.34×10^{-4} g
   c. 6×10^7 g
   d. 1.0×10^{-6} g
2. a. 5.8×10^{-8} s
   b. 4.6×10^7 s
   c. 9.27 s
   d. 1.23×10^4 s
3. a. 6.32×10^{-3} m
   b. 8.36×10^8 km
   c. 1.69×10^4 cm^2
   d. 6.45×10^{-13} m/s
4. a. 4
   b. 5
   c. 3
   d. 3
5. a. 3
   b. 5
   c. 2
   d. 4
6. a. 90.0 g
   b. 1.68 km
   c. 128.6 kg
   d. 47.9 s
7. a. 2×10^{16} m^2
   b. 1.4×10^{-7} km^2
   c. 2.8 kg/m^3
   d. 1.7×10^{-3} m/s
8. a. 22.2 m
   b. 21 m^2
9. a. Refer to Problems and Solutions Manual.
   b. The curve is parabolic, concave, upward.
   c. $d = 5t^2$
10. a. Refer to Problems and Solutions Manual.
    b. straight line
    c. linear relationship
    d. 0.30 m/s
    e. $d = 0.30t$
11. a. $m = \frac{Fr}{v^2}$
    b. $r = \frac{mv^2}{F}$
    c. $v = \sqrt{\frac{Fr}{m}}$
12. $d_o = \frac{d_i f}{d_i - f}$
13. a. 160 cm^2
    b. 140 cm^3
14. 19 m/s
15. 120 g

Appendix B
Supplemental Problems

There are no supplemental problems for Chapter 1.

Chapter 2

1. Express the following numbers in scientific notation.
   a. 810 000 g
   b. 0.000634 g
   c. 60 000 000 g
   d. 0.0000010 g

2. Convert each of the following time measurements to its equivalent in seconds.
   a. 58 ns
   b. 0.046 Gs
   c. 9270 ms
   d. 12.3 ks

3. Solve the following problems. Express your answers in scientific notation.
   a. 6.2×10^{-4} m $+ 5.7 \times 10^{-3}$ m
   b. 8.7×10^8 km $- 3.4 \times 10^7$ km
   c. $(9.21 \times 10^{-5}$ cm$)(1.83 \times 10^8$ cm$)$
   d. $(2.63 \times 10^{-6}$ m$) \div (4.08 \times 10^6$ s$)$

4. State the number of significant digits in the following measurements.
   a. 3218 kg
   b. 60.080 kg
   c. 801 kg
   d. 0.000534 kg

5. State the number of significant digits in the following measurements.
   a. 5.60×10^8 m
   b. 3.0005×10^{-6} m
   c. 8.0×10^{10} m
   d. 9.204×10^{-3} m

6. Add or subtract as indicated and state the answer with the correct number of significant digits.
   a. 85.26 g + 4.7 g
   b. 1.07 km + 0.608 km
   c. 186.4 kg − 57.83 kg
   d. 60.08 s − 12.2 s

7. Multiply or divide as indicated using significant digits correctly.
   a. $(5 \times 10^8$ m$)(4.2 \times 10^7$ m$)$
   b. $(1.67 \times 10^{-2}$ km$)(8.5 \times 10^{-6}$ km$)$
   c. $(2.6 \times 10^4$ kg$) \div (9.4 \times 10^3$ m$^3)$
   d. $(6.3 \times 10^{-1}$ m$) \div (3.8 \times 10^2$ s$)$

8. A rectangular room is 8.7 m by 2.41 m.
   a. What length of baseboard molding must be purchased to go around the perimeter of the floor?
   b. What area must be covered if floor tiles are laid?

▶ 9. The following data table was established showing the total distances an object fell during various lengths of time.

Time (s)	Distance (m)
1.0	5
2.0	20
3.0	44
4.0	78
5.0	123

   a. Plot distance vs time from the values given in the table and draw a curve that best fits all points.
   b. Describe the resulting curve.
   c. According to the graph, what is the relationship between distance and time for a free-falling object?

▶ 10. The total distance a lab cart travels during specified lengths of time is given in the following table.

Time (s)	Distance (m)
1.0	0.32
2.0	0.60
3.0	0.95
4.0	1.18
5.0	1.45

   a. Plot distance vs time from the values given in the table and draw the curve that best fits all points.
   b. Describe the resulting curve.
   c. According to the graph, what type of relationship exists between the total distance traveled by the lab cart and the time?
   d. What is the slope of this graph?
   e. Write an equation relating distance and time for this data.

11. Solve the equation

$$F = \frac{mv^2}{r}$$

   a. for *m*. b. for *r*. c. for *v*.

▶ 12. Solve the equation for d_o.

$$\frac{1}{f} = \frac{1}{d_o} + \frac{1}{d_i}$$

13. A cube has an edge of length 5.2 cm.
   a. Find its surface area.
   b. Find its volume.

14. A truck is traveling at a constant velocity of 70 km/h. Convert the velocity to m/s.

15. The density of gold is 19.3 g/cm^3. A gold washer has an outside radius of 4.3 cm and an inside radius of 2.1 cm. Its thickness is 0.14 cm. What is the mass of the washer?

Chapter 3

1. Bob walks 80 m and then he walks 125 m.
   a. What is Bob's displacement if he walks east both times?
   b. What is Bob's displacement if he walks east then west?
   c. What distance does Bob walk in each case?

2. A cross-country runner runs 5.0 km east along the course, then turns around and runs 5.0 km west along the same path. She returns to the starting point in 40 min. What is her average speed? her average velocity?

3. 0.30 s after seeing a puff of smoke rise from the starter's pistol, the sound of the firing of the pistol is heard by the track timer 100 m away. What is the velocity of sound?

4. The radius of the tires on a particular vehicle is 0.62 m. If the tires are rotating 5 times per second, what is the velocity of the vehicle?

5. A bullet is fired with a speed of 720.0 m/s.
   a. What time is required for the bullet to strike a target 324 m away?
   b. What is the velocity in km/h?

6. Light travels at 3.0×10^8 m/s. How many seconds go by from the moment the starter's pistol is shot until the smoke is seen by the track timer 100 m away?

7. You drive your car from home at an average velocity of 80 km/h for 3 h. Halfway to your destination, you develop some engine problems, and for 5 h you nurse the car the rest of the way. What is your average velocity for the entire trip?

8. The total distance a ball is off the ground when thrown vertically is given for each second of flight by the following table.

Time (s)	Distance (m)
0.0	0.0
1.0	24.5
2.0	39.2
3.0	44.1
4.0	39.2
5.0	24.5
6.0	0.0

   a. Draw a position-time graph of the motion of the ball.
   b. How far off the ground is the ball at the end of 0.5 s? When would the ball again be this distance from the ground?

9. Use the following position-time graph to find how far the object travels between
   a. t = 0 s and t = 5 s.
   b. t = 5 s and t = 10 s.
   c. t = 10 s and t = 15 s.
   d. t = 15 s and t = 20 s.
   e. t = 0 s and t = 20 s.

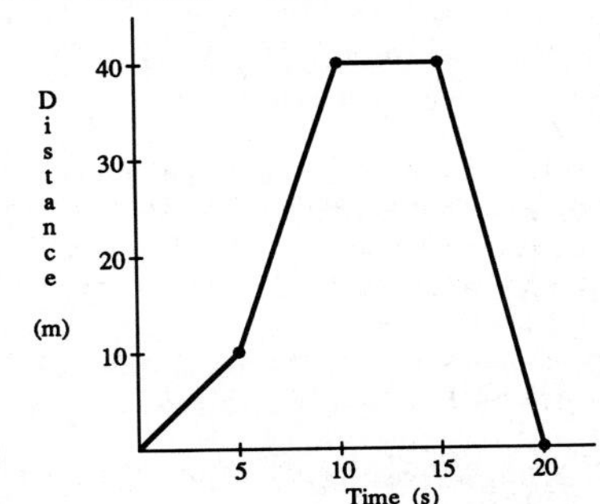

10. Use the position-time graph from problem 9 to find the object's velocity between
   a. t = 0 s and t = 5 s.
   b. t = 5 s and t = 10 s.
   c. t = 10 s and t = 15 s.
   d. t = 15 s and t = 20 s.

11. Two cars are headed in the same direction; one traveling 60 km/h is 20 km ahead of the other traveling 80 km/h.
   a. Draw a position-time graph showing the motion of the cars.
   b. Use your graph to find the time when the faster car overtakes the slower one.

12. Use your graph from Problem 8 to calculate the ball's instantaneous velocity at
   a. t = 2 s. b. t = 3 s. c. t = 4 s.

Answers to
SUPPLEMENTAL PROBLEMS

Chapter 3

1. a. 205 m
   b. −45 m
   c. 205 m
2. 15 km/h; 0
3. 330 m/s
4. 20 m/s
5. a. 0.450 s
   b. 2592 km/h
6. 3.3×10^{-7} s
7. 60 km/h
8. a. Refer to Problems and Solutions Manual.
   b. 13.5 m, 5.5 s
9. a. 10 m
   b. 30 m
   c. 0 m
   d. −40 m
   e. 80 m distance, but 0 displacement
10. a. 2 m/s
   b. 6 m/s
   c. 0 m/s
   d. −8 m/s
11. a. Refer to Problems and Solutions Manual.
   b. 1 h
12. a. ≈ 10 m/s
   b. 0 m/s
   c. ≈ −10 m/s

Answers to
SUPPLEMENTAL PROBLEMS
Chapter 3 (continued)

13. a.

Clock Reading (s)	Position (m)
0	0
1	75
2	150
3	225
4	300
5	375
6	450
7	525
8	600
9	675
10	750

b. Refer to Problems and Solutions Manual.
c. 75 m/s
d. Refer to Problems and Solution Manual.
e. 300 m

14. a. Refer to Problems and Solutions Manual.
b. 3600 m
c. 9000 m
d. 0 m

15. a. 25 km/h
b. 145 km/h

Chapter 4

1. -3.3×10^3 m/s^2
2. a. The car is moving at a constant velocity of 10 m/s.
b. The car is slowing down to a stop.
c. 0 m/s^2
d. -5 m/s^2
3. a. Refer to Problems and Solutions Manual.
b. no; no
c. $\approx$30 m/s^2
4. 8.00 s
5. 34 m/s
6. 160 m
7. a. -8.0 m/s^2
b. 480 m
8. a. 4.9×10^{-3} s
b. 3.3×10^2 m/s
9. a. 2.8 m/s^2
b. 35 m
10. 26 m/s
11. -81 m/s^2
12. 35 m/s = 130 km/h; yes

▶ **13.** A plane flies in a straight line at a constant speed of +75 m/s. Assume that it is at the reference point when the clock reads t = 0.
a. Construct a table showing the position or displacement of the plane at the end of each second for a 10-s period.
b. Use the data from the table to plot a position-time graph.
c. Show that the slope of the line is the velocity of the plane. Use at least two different sets of points along the line.
d. Plot a velocity-time graph of the plane's motion for the first 6 s of the 10-s interval.
e. From the velocity-time graph, find the displacement of the plane between the second and the sixth period.

▶ **14.** Mary jogs for 15 min at 240 m/min, walks the next 10 min at 90 m/min, rests for 5 min, and jogs back to where she started at -180 m/min.
a. Plot a velocity-time graph for Mary's exercise run.
b. Find the area under the curve for the first 15 min. What does this represent?
c. What is the total distance traveled by Mary?
d. What is Mary's displacement from start to finish?

15. Car A is traveling at 85 km/h while car B is at 60 km/h. What is the relative velocity of car A to car B
a. if they both are traveling in the same direction?
b. if they are headed towards each other?

Chapter 4

1. From the moment a 40 m/s fastball touches the catcher's mitt until it is completely stopped takes 0.012 s. Calculate the average acceleration of the ball as it is being caught.

2. The following velocity-time graph describes a familiar motion of a car traveling during rush-hour traffic.
a. Describe the car's motion from t = 0 s to t = 4 s.
b. Describe the car's motion from t = 4 s to t = 6 s.
c. What is the average acceleration for the first 4 s?
d. What is the average acceleration from t = 4 s to t = 6 s?

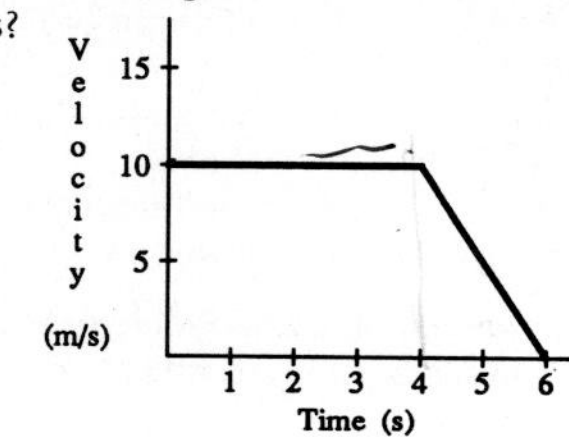

▶ **3.** Given the following table:

Time (s)	Velocity (m/s)
0.0	0.0
1.0	5.0
2.0	20.0
3.0	45.0
4.0	80.0

a. Plot a velocity-time graph for this motion.
b. Is this motion constant velocity? uniform acceleration?
c. Calculate the instantaneous acceleration at t = 3.0 s.

4. Top-fuel drag racers are able to uniformly accelerate at 12.5 m/s^2 from rest to 100 m/s before crossing the finish line. How much time elapses during the run?

5. A race car accelerates from rest at +7.5 m/s^2 for 4.5 s. How fast will it be going at the end of that time?

6. A race car starts from rest and is accelerated uniformly to +41 m/s in 8.0 s. What is the car's displacement?

7. A jet plane traveling at +88 m/s lands on a runway and comes to rest in 11 s.
a. Calculate its uniform acceleration.
b. Calculate the distance it travels.

8. A bullet accelerates at 6.8×10^4 m/s^2 from rest as it travels the 0.80 m of the rifle barrel.
a. How long was the bullet in the barrel?
b. What velocity does the bullet have as it leaves the barrel?

9. A car traveling at 14 m/s encounters a patch of ice and takes 5.0 s to stop.
a. What is the car's acceleration?
b. How far does it travel before stopping?

10. A motorcycle traveling at 16 m/s accelerates at a constant rate of 4.0 m/s^2 over 50 m. What is its final velocity?

11. A hockey player skating at 18 m/s comes to a complete stop in 2.0 m. What is the acceleration of the hockey player?

12. Police find skid marks 60 m long on a highway showing where a car made an emergency stop. Assuming that the acceleration was -10 m/s^2 (about the maximum for dry pavement), how fast was the car going? Was the car exceeding the 80 km/h speed limit?

13. An accelerating lab cart passes through two photo gate timers 3.0 m apart in 4.2 s. The velocity of the cart at the second timer is 1.2 m/s.
   a. What is the cart's velocity at the first gate?
   b. What is the acceleration?

14. A camera is accidentally dropped from the edge of a cliff and 6.0 s later hits the bottom.
   a. How fast was it going just before it hit?
   b. How high is the cliff?

▶ 15. A rock is thrown vertically with a velocity of 20 m/s from the edge of a bridge 42 m above a river. How long does the rock stay in the air?

▶ 16. A platform diver jumps vertically with a velocity of 4.2 m/s. The diver enters the water 2.5 s later. How high is the platform above the water?

Chapter 5

1. A towrope is used to pull a 1750-kg car, giving it an acceleration of 1.35 m/s². What force does the rope exert?

2. A racing car undergoes a uniform acceleration of 4.00 m/s². If the net force causing the acceleration is 3.00×10^3 N, what is the mass of the car?

▶ 3. A 5.2-kg bowling ball is accelerated from rest to a velocity of 12 m/s as the bowler covers 5.0 m of approach before releasing the ball. What force is exerted on the ball during this time?

▶ 4. A high jumper, falling at 4.0 m/s, lands on a foam pit and comes to rest, compressing the pit 0.40 m. If the pit is able to exert an average force of 1200 N on the high jumper in breaking the fall, what is the jumper's mass?

5. When a 20-kg child steps off a 3.0-kg stationary skateboard with an acceleration of 0.50 m/s², with what acceleration will the skateboard travel in the opposite direction?

6. On Planet X, a 50-kg barbell can be lifted by only exerting a force of 180 N.
   a. What is the acceleration of gravity on Planet X?
   b. If the same barbell is lifted on Earth, what minimal force is needed?

7. A proton has a mass of 1.672×10^{-27} kg. What is its weight?

8. A force of 20 N accelerates a 9.0-kg wagon at 2.0 m/s² along the sidewalk.
   a. How large is the frictional force?
   b. What is the coefficient of friction?

9. A 2.0-kg brick has a sliding coefficient of friction of 0.38. What force must be applied to the brick for it to move at a constant velocity?

10. In bench pressing 100 kg, a weight lifter applies a force of 1040 N. How large is the upward acceleration of the weights during the lift?

▶ 11. An elevator that weighs 3.0×10^3 N is accelerated upward at 1.0 m/s². What force does the cable exert to give it this acceleration?

▶ 12. A person weighing 490 N stands on a scale in an elevator.
   a. What does the scale read when the elevator is at rest?
   b. What is the reading on the scale when the elevator rises at a constant velocity?
   c. The elevator slows down at −2.2 m/s² as it reaches the desired floor. What does the scale read?
   d. The elevator descends, accelerating at −2.7 m/s². What does the scale read?
   e. What does the scale read when the elevator descends at a constant velocity?
   f. Suppose the cable snapped and the elevator fell freely. What would the scale read?

▶ 13. A 10.0-kg mass, m_1, on a frictionless table is accelerated by a 5.0-kg mass, m_2, hanging over the edge of the table. What is the acceleration of the mass along the table?

Chapter 6

1. Find θ if
   a. $\tan \theta = 9.5143$.
   b. $\sin \theta = .4540$.
   c. $\cos \theta = .8192$.
   d. $\tan \theta = .1405$.
   e. $\sin \theta = .7547$.
   f. $\cos \theta = .9781$.

2. Find the value of:
   a. tan 28°.
   b. sin 86°.
   c. cos 2°.
   d. tan 58°.
   e. sin 40°.
   f. cos 71°.

Answers to
SUPPLEMENTAL PROBLEMS
Chapter 4 (continued)

13. a. 0.23 m/s
    b. 0.24 m/s²
14. a. 59 m/s
    b. 1.8×10^2 m
15. 5.6 s
16. −20 m

Chapter 5

1. 2.36×10^3 N, in the direction of the acceleration
2. 750 kg
3. 75 N
4. 60 kg
5. 3.3 m/s²
6. a. 3.6 m/s²
   b. 4.9×10^2 N
7. 1.6×10^{-26} N
8. a. 2 N
   b. 0.02
9. 7.4 N
10. 0.60 m/s²
11. 3.3×10^3 N
12. a. 490 N
    b. 490 N
    c. 3.8×10^2 N
    d. 3.6×10^2 N
    e. 490 N
    f. 0
13. 3.3 m/s²

Chapter 6

1. a. $\theta = 84.000°$
   b. $\theta = 27.00°$
   c. $\theta = 35.00°$
   d. $\theta = 7.998°$
   e. $\theta = 49.00°$
   f. $\theta = 12.01°$
2. a. 0.53
   b. 1.0
   c. 1
   d. 1.6
   e. 0.64
   f. 0.33

Answers to

SUPPLEMENTAL PROBLEMS

Chapter 6 (continued)

3. Refer to Problems and Solutions Manual.

4. **a.** 140 N
b. 20 N
c. 100 N

5. 38.5 min

6. Refer to Problems and Solutions Manual.
a. 90 N
b. 87 N
c. 84 N
d. 79 N
e. 67 N
f. 30 N

7. Refer to Problems and Solutions Manual.
R = 42 m, 315°

8. Refer to Problems and Solutions Manual.
V = 112 m/s, 117°

9. Refer to Problems and Solutions Manual.
F = 820 N, 232°

10. Refer to Problems and Solutions Manual.
R = 48.1 m, 3.6° north of east

11. Refer to Problems and Solutions Manual.
1.93×10^2 km, north
2.30×10^2 km, east

12. 200 N

13. $V_x = -50.0$ km/h; $V_y = -86.6$ km/h

14. **a.** horizontal = 48 N, vertical = 82 N
b. horizontal = 82 N, vertical = 48 N

15. 0.71 m/s^2

16. **a.** 30 N
b. 29 N
c. 21 N
d. 15 N
e. 0 N

17. Refer to Problems and Solutions Manual; 580 km/h, 54° east of north

18. 74 N, 253°

19. 460 N

3. Solve for all sides and all angles for the following right triangles.

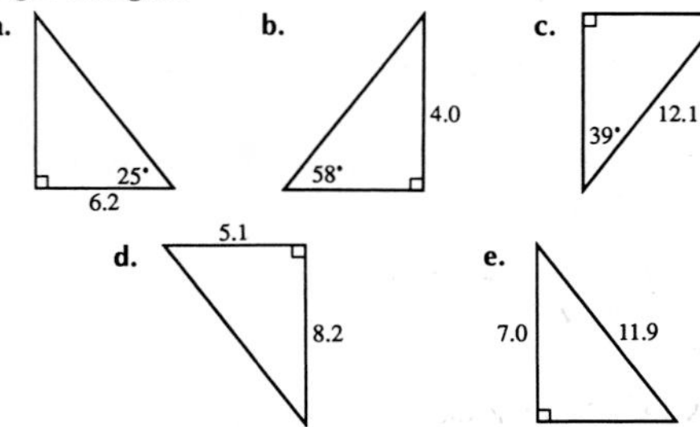

4. An 80-N and a 60-N force act concurrently on a point. Find the magnitude of the vector sum if the forces pull
a. in the same direction.
b. in opposite directions.
c. at a right angle to each other.

▶ **5.** You head downstream on a river in an outboard. The current is flowing at a rate of 1.50 m/s. After 30.0 min, you find that you have traveled 24.3 km. How long will it take you to travel back upstream to your original point of departure?

6. One force of 60 N and a second of 30 N act on an object at point **P.** Graphically add the vectors and find the magnitude of the resultant when the angle between them is as follows.
a. 0° **b.** 30° **c.** 45° **d.** 60° **e.** 90° **f.** 180°

7. You walk 30 m south and 30 m east. Draw and add vectors representing these two displacements.

8. A plane flying at 90° at 1.00×10^2 m/s is blown toward 180° at 5.0×10^1 m/s by a strong wind. Find the plane's resultant velocity and direction.

9. In tackling a running back from the opposing team, a defensive lineman exerts a force of 500 N at 180°, while a linebacker simultaneously applies a force of 650 N at 270°. What is the resultant force on the ball carrier?

▶ **10.** A hobo hops a freight car 15 m long and 3.0 m wide. The car is moving east at 2.5 m/s. Exploring the surroundings, the hobo walks from corner A to corner B in 20.0 s; then from corner B to corner C in 5.0 s as shown. With the aid of a vector diagram, compute the hobo's displacement relative to the ground.

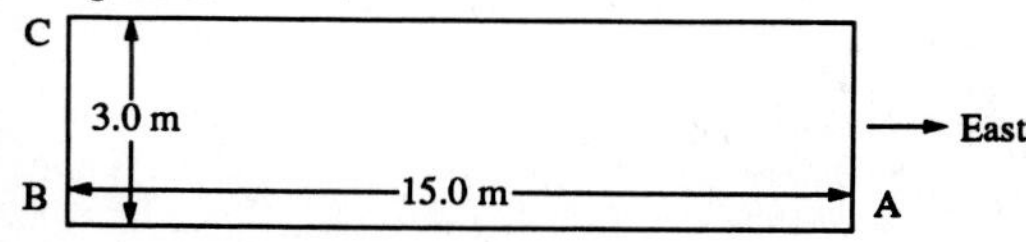

11. A plane travels on a heading of 40.0° for a distance of 3.00×10^2 km. How far north and how far east does the plane travel?

12. A water skier is towed by a speedboat. The skier moves to one side of the boat in such a way that the tow rope forms an angle of 55° with the direction of the boat. The tension on the rope is 350 N. What would be the tension on the rope if the skier were directly behind the boat?

13. What are the x and y components of a velocity vector of magnitude 100 km/h and direction of 240°?

14. Wendy pushes a lawn spreader across a lawn by applying a force of 95 N along the handle that makes an angle of 60.0° with the horizontal.
a. What are the horizontal and vertical components of the force?
b. The handle is lowered so it makes an angle of 30.0° with the horizontal. Now what are the horizontal and vertical components of the force?

▶ **15.** A brick layer applies a force of 100 N to each of two handles of a wheelbarrow. Its mass is 20 kg and it is loaded with 30 bricks, each of mass 1.5 kg. The handles of the wheelbarrow are 30° from the horizontal and the coefficient of friction is 0.20. What initial acceleration is given the wheelbarrow?

16. Two 15-N forces act concurrently on point **P**. Find the magnitude of their resultant when the angle between them is
a. 0.0°. **b.** 30.0°. **c.** 90.0°. **d.** 120.0°. **e.** 180.0°.

▶ **17.** You are a pilot on an aircraft carrier. You must fly to another aircraft carrier, now 1450 km at 45° of your position, moving at 56 km/h due east. The wind is blowing from the south at 72 km/h. Calculate the heading and air speed needed to reach the carrier 2.5 h after you take off. **Hint:** Draw a displacement vector diagram.

▶ **18.** A 33-N force acting at 90° and a 44-N force acting at 60° act concurrently on point **P**. What is the magnitude and direction of a third force that produces equilibrium at point **P?**

▶ **19.** A person weighs 612 N. If the person sits in the middle of a hammock that is 3.0 m long and sags 1.0 m below the points of support, what force would be exerted by each of the two hammock ropes?

▶ **20.** A bell ringer decides to use a bowling ball to ring the bell. He hangs the 7.3-kg ball from the end of a 2.0 m long rope. He attaches another rope to the

692 Appendix B

ball to pull the ball back, and pulls it horizontally until the ball has moved 0.60 m away from the vertical. How much force must he apply?

▶ **21.** A mass, M, starts from rest and slides down the frictionless incline, Figure 6–19. As it leaves the incline, its speed is 24 m/s.
   a. What is the acceleration of the mass while on the incline?
   b. What is the length of the incline?
   c. How long does it take the mass to reach the floor after it leaves the top of the incline?

Chapter 7

1. A ball falls from rest from a height of 490 m.
   a. How long does it remain in the air?
   b. If the ball has a horizontal velocity of 2.00×10^2 m/s when it begins its fall, what horizontal displacement will it have?

▶ **2.** An archer stands 40.0 m from the target. If the arrow is shot horizontally with a velocity of 90.0 m/s, how far above the bull's-eye must he aim to compensate for gravity pulling his arrow downward?

3. A bridge is 176.4 m above a river. If a lead-weighted fishing line is thrown from the bridge with a horizontal velocity of 22.0 m/s, how far has it moved horizontally when it hits the water?

4. A beach ball, moving with a speed of +1.27 m/s, rolls off a pier and hits the water 0.75 m from the end of the pier. How high above the water is the pier?

5. Pete has a tendency to drop his bowling ball on his release. Instead of having the ball on the floor at the completion of his swing, Pete lets go with the ball 0.35 m above the floor. If he throws it horizontally with a velocity of 6.3 m/s, what distance does it travel before you hear a "thud"?

6. A discus is released at an angle of 45° and a velocity of 24.0 m/s.
   a. How long does it stay in the air?
   b. What horizontal distance does it travel?

▶ **7.** A shot put is released with a velocity of 12 m/s and stays in the air for 2.0 s.
   a. At what angle with the horizontal was it released?
   b. What horizontal distance did it travel?

▶ **8.** A football is kicked at 45° and travels 82 m before hitting the ground.
   a. What was its initial velocity?
   b. How long was it in the air?
   c. How high did it go?

9. A golf ball is hit with a velocity of 24.5 m/s at 35.0° above the horizontal. Find
   a. the range of the ball.
   b. the maximum height of the ball.

▶ **10.** A carnival clown rides a motorcycle down a ramp and around a "loop-the-loop." If the loop has a radius of 18 m, what is the slowest speed the rider can have at the top of the loop to avoid falling? **Hint:** At this slowest speed, at the top of the loop, the clown's weight is equal to the centripetal force.

▶ **11.** A 75-kg pilot flies a plane in a loop. At the top of the loop, where the plane is completely upside-down for an instant, the pilot hangs freely in the seat and does not push against the seat belt. The airspeed indicator reads 120 m/s. What is the radius of the plane's loop?

▶ **12.** A 2.0-kg object is attached to a 1.5 m long string and swung in a vertical circle at a constant speed of 12 m/s.
   a. What is the tension in the string when the object is at the bottom of its path?
   b. What is the tension in the string when the object is at the top of its path?

13. A 60.0-kg speed skater with a velocity of 18.0 m/s comes into a curve of 20.0-m radius. How much friction must be exerted between the skates and ice to negotiate the curve?

14. A 20.0-kg child wishes to balance on a seesaw with a child of 32.0 kg. If the smaller child sits 3.2 m from the pivot, where must the larger child sit?

15. A pendulum has a length of 1.00 m.
   a. What is its period on Earth?
   b. What is its period on the moon where the acceleration due to gravity is 1.67 m/s²?

Answers to
SUPPLEMENTAL PROBLEMS
Chapter 6 (continued)

20. 22 N
21. Refer to Problems and Solutions Manual.
   a. 4.9 m/s²
   b. 59 m
   c. 1 s

Chapter 7

1. **a.** 10.0 s
   b. 2.00×10^3 m
2. 0.966 m
3. 132 m
4. 1.7 m
5. 1.7 m
6. **a.** 3.46 s
   b. 58.8 m
7. **a.** 55°
   b. 14 m
8. **a.** 28 m/s
   b. 4.1 s
   c. 20 m
9. **a.** 57.9 m
   b. 10.2 m
10. 13 m/s
11. 1.5×10^3 m
12. **a.** 2.1×10^2 N
   b. 1.7×10^2 N
13. 972 N
14. 2.0 m
15. **a.** 2.01 s
   b. 4.86 s

Answers to
SUPPLEMENTAL PROBLEMS
Chapter 7 (continued)

16. a. 0.10 kg
 b. 0.25 m
 c. No change is necessary for the harmonic oscillator. The pendulum must be shortened to 4.1 cm.

Chapter 8

1. 2.7×10^{12} m
2. a. 2.21×10^{15} m^2/s
 b. 2.0×10^{11} m^2/s
3. 4.2×10^{7} m
4. 1.0×10^{-47} N
5. 6.67×10^{-11} N
6. a. 1.6×10^{3} kg
 b. 1.3×10^{-10} m/s^2
7. 8.3×10^{-9} N
8. 7.2×10^{22} kg
9. a. 1.7×10^{-10} N
 b. 1.7×10^{-12} N
10. 6.0×10^{24} kg
11. 235 N
12. 79 days
13. $V = 3.47 \times 10^{3}$ m/s; $T = 6.45 \times 10^{3}$ s or 1.79 h
14. 19.6 m/s^2; 2.45 m/s^2; 4.9 m/s^2
15. 7.35 m/s^2
16. 1.60 m/s^2

16. The period of an object oscillating on a spring is

$$T = 2\pi\sqrt{\frac{m}{k}},$$

where m is the mass of the object and k is the spring constant which indicates the force necessary to produce a unit elongation of the spring. The period of a simple pendulum is

$$T = 2\pi\sqrt{\frac{l}{|g|}}.$$

a. What mass will produce a 1.0-s period of oscillation if it is attached to a spring with a spring constant of 4.0 N/m?
b. What length pendulum will produce a period of 1.0 s?
c. How would the harmonic oscillator and the pendulum have to be modified in order to produce 1.0-s periods on the surface of the moon where g is 1.6 m/s^2?

Chapter 8

1. Comet Halley returns every 74 years. Find the average distance of the comet from the sun.

2. Area is measured in m^2, so the rate at which area is swept out by a planet or satellite is measured in m^2/s.
a. How fast is area swept out by Earth in its orbit about the sun. See Table 8–1.
b. How fast is area swept out by the moon in its orbit about Earth. Use 3.9×10^8 m as the average distance between the Earth and the moon, and 27.3 days as the moon's period.

3. You wish to launch a satellite that will remain above the same spot on Earth's surface. This means the satellite must have a period of exactly one day. Calculate the radius of the circular orbit this satellite must have. **Hint:** The moon also circles Earth and both the moon and the satellite will obey Kepler's third law. The moon is 3.8×10^8 m from Earth and its period is 27.33 days.

4. The mass of an electron is 9.1×10^{-31} kg. The mass of a proton is 1.7×10^{-27} kg. They are about 1.0×10^{-10} m apart in a hydrogen atom. What gravitational force exists between the proton and the electron of a hydrogen atom?

5. Two 1.00-kg masses have their centers 1.00 m apart. What is the force of attraction between them?

6. Two satellites of equal mass are put into orbit 30 m apart. The gravitational force between them is 2.0×10^{-7} N.
a. What is the mass of each satellite?
b. What is the initial acceleration given to each satellite by the gravitational force?

7. Two large spheres are suspended close to each other. Their centers are 4.0 m apart. One sphere weighs 9.8×10^2 N. The other sphere has a weight of 1.96×10^2 N. What is the gravitational force between them?

8. If the centers of Earth and the moon are 3.9×10^8 m apart, the gravitational force between them is about 1.9×10^{20} N. What is the approximate mass of the moon?

9. a. What is the gravitational force between two spherical 8.00-kg masses that are 5.0 m apart?
b. What is the gravitational force between them when they are 5.0×10^1 m apart?

10. A satellite is placed in a circular orbit with a radius of 1.0×10^7 m a period of 9.9×10^3 s. Calculate the mass of Earth. **Hint:** Gravity supplies the needed centripetal force for such a satellite. Scientists have actually measured the mass of Earth this way.

11. If you weigh 637 N on Earth's surface, how much would you weigh on the planet Mars? (Mars has a mass of 6.37×10^{23} kg and a radius of 3.43×10^6 m.)

12. Using Newton's variation of Kepler's third law and information from Table 8–1, calculate the period of Earth's moon if the radius of orbit was twice the actual value of 3.9×10^8 m.

13. Use the data from Table 8–1 to find the speed and period of a satellite that would orbit Mars 175 km above its surface.

14. What would be the value of g, acceleration of gravity, if Earth's mass was double its actual value, but its radius remained the same? If the radius was doubled, but the mass remained the same? If both the mass and radius were doubled?

15. What would be the strength of Earth's gravitational field at a point where an 80.0-kg astronaut would experience a 25% reduction in weight?

16. On the surface of the moon, a 91.0-kg physics teacher weighs only 145.6 N. What is the value of the moon's gravitational field at its surface?

694 Appendix B

Chapter 9

1. Jim strikes a 0.058-kg golf ball with a force of 272 N and gives it a velocity of 62.0 m/s. How long was the club in contact with the ball?

2. A force of 186 N acts on a 7.3-kg bowling ball for 0.40 s.
   a. What is the bowling ball's change in momentum?
   b. What is its change in velocity?

3. A 5500-kg freight truck accelerates from 4.2 m/s to 7.8 m/s in 15.0 s by applying a constant force.
   a. What change in momentum occurs?
   b. How large of a force is exerted?

▶ 4. In running a ballistics test at the police department, officer Spears fires a 6.0-g bullet at 350 m/s into a container that stops it in 0.30 m. What average force stops the bullet?

5. A 0.24-kg volleyball approaches Jennifer with a velocity of 3.8 m/s. Jennifer bumps the ball giving it a velocity of −2.4 m/s. What average force did she apply if the interaction time between her hands and the ball is 0.025 s?

6. A 0.145-kg baseball is pitched at 42 m/s. The batter hits it horizontally to the pitcher at 58 m/s.
   a. Find the change in momentum of the ball.
   b. If the ball and bat were in contact 4.6×10^{-4} s, what would be the average force while they touched?

7. A 550-kg car traveling at 24.0 m/s collides head-on with a 680-kg pick-up truck. Both vehicles come to a complete stop upon impact.
   a. What is the momentum of the car before collision?
   b. What is the change in the car's momentum?
   c. What is the change in the truck's momentum?
   d. What is the velocity of the truck before collision?

8. A truck weighs four times as much as a car. If the truck coasts into the car at 12 km/h and they stick together, what is their final velocity?

9. A 50.0-g projectile is launched with a horizontal velocity of 647 m/s from a 4.65-kg launcher moving in the same direction at 2.00 m/s. What is the velocity of the launcher after the projectile is launched?

10. Two lab carts are pushed together with a spring mechanism compressed between them. Upon release, the 5.0-kg cart repels one way with a velocity of 0.12 m/s while the 2.0-kg cart goes in the opposite direction. What velocity does it have?

▶ 11. A 12.0-g rubber bullet travels at a velocity of 150 m/s, hits a stationary 8.5-kg concrete block resting on a frictionless surface, and ricochets in the opposite direction with a velocity of −100 m/s. How fast will the concrete block be moving?

12. A 6500-kg freight car traveling at 2.5 m/s c[illegible]es with an 8000-kg stationary freight car. If they interlock upon collision, find their velocity.

▶ 13. Tim, mass 42.00 kg, is riding a skateboard, mass 2.00 kg, traveling at 1.20 m/s. Tim jumps off and the skateboard stops dead in its tracks. In what direction and with what velocity did he jump?

▶ 14. A cue ball, mass 0.16 kg, rolling at 4.0 m/s, hits a stationary eight-ball of similar mass. If the cue ball travels 45° above its original path, and the eight-ball at 45° below, what is the velocity of each after collision?

▶ 15. Two opposing hockey players, one of mass 82.0 kg skating north at 6.0 m/s and the other of mass 70.0 kg skating east at 3.0 m/s, collide and become tangled.
   a. Draw a vector momentum diagram of the collision.
   b. In what direction and with what velocity do they move after collision?

Chapter 10

1. After scoring a touchdown, an 84.0-kg wide receiver celebrates by leaping 120 cm off the ground. How much work was done in the celebration?

2. During a tug-of-war, Team A does 2.20×10^5 J of work in pulling Team B 8.00 m. What force was Team A exerting?

3. To keep a car traveling at a constant velocity, 551 N of force is needed to overcome frictional forces. How much work is done against friction by the car in traveling from Columbus to Cincinnati, a distance of 161 km?

4. A weightlifter raises a 180-kg barbell to a height of 1.95 m. How much work was done by the weightlifter in lifting the barbells?

▶ 5. A wagon is pulled by a force of 38.0 N on the handle at an angle of 42° with the horizontal. If the wagon is pulled in a circle of radius 25.0 m, how much work is done?

Answers to
SUPPLEMENTAL PROBLEMS

Chapter 9

1. 0.013 s
2. a. 74 N · s
   b. 1.0×10^1 m/s
3. a. 2.0×10^4 kg · m/s
   b. 1.3×10^3 N
4. -1.2×10^3 N
5. -6.0×10^1 N
6. a. −14.5 kg · m/s
   b. -3.2×10^4 N
7. a. 1.32×10^4 kg · m/s
   b. -1.32×10^4 kg · m/s, since car stops on impact
   c. 1.32×10^4 kg · m/s, by conservation of momentum
   d. −19.4 m/s
8. 9.6 km/h
9. −4.94 m/s
10. 0.30 m/s
11. 0.35 m/s
12. 1.1 m/s
13. 1.26 m/s, in the same direction as he was riding
14. 2.8 m/s
15. a. Refer to Problems and Solutions Manual.
    b. 3.5 m/s, 67°

Chapter 10

1. 988 J
2. 2.75×10^4 N
3. 8.87×10^7 J
4. 3.44×10^3 J
5. 4.4×10^3 J

Answers to

SUPPLEMENTAL PROBLEMS

Chapter 10 (continued)

6. 3.4×10^3 J
7. 8.0×10^4 J
8. 36.2°
9. 3.4×10^4 W
10. 126 W
11. 2.04×10^3 W
12. 0.63 kW
13. a. 3.5
    b. 4.00
    c. 88%
14. 0.24 m
15. 31.5 cm

Chapter 11

1. 2.26×10^{-12} J
2. 0.90 J
3. a. 84 J
   b. 84 J
   c. 11 m/s
4. 5.2 m
5. a. 2.6×10^4 J
   b. 66 m
   c. 3.9×10^2 N
6. 2.1 J
7. 2.8×10^3 J
8. −2.0 J
9. 0.24 m
10. 72°
11. a. 1.17×10^3 J
    b. 3.00×10^3 J
    c. 3.00×10^3 J
    d. 4.17×10^3 J
    e. 23.6 m/s

▶ 6. A 185-kg refrigerator is loaded into a moving van by pushing it up a 10.0-m ramp at an angle of inclination of 11°. How much work is done?

7. A lawn mower is pushed with a force of 88.0 N along a handle that makes an angle of 41° with the horizontal. How much work is done in pushing the mower 1.2 km in mowing the yard?

▶ 8. A 17.0-kg crate is to be pulled a distance of 20.0 m requiring 1210 J of work being done. If the job is done by attaching a rope and pulling with a force of 75.0 N, at what angle is the rope held?

9. An elevator lifts a total mass of 1.1×10^3 kg, a distance of 40.0 m in 12.5 s. How much power does the elevator demonstrate?

10. A cyclist exerts a force of 15.0 N in riding a bike 251 m in 30.0 s. What is the cyclist's power?

▶ 11. A 120-kg lawn tractor goes up a 21° incline of 12.0 m in 2.5 s. What power is shown by the tractor?

▶ 12. What power does a pump develop to lift 35 L of water per minute from a depth of 110 m? (A liter of water has a mass of 1.00 kg.)

13. A force of 1.4 N is exerted through a distance of 40.0 cm on a rope in a pulley system to lift a 0.50-kg mass 10.0 cm.
    a. Calculate the *MA*.
    b. Calculate the *IMA*.
    c. What is the efficiency of the pulley system?

▶ 14. A student exerts a force of 250 N through a distance of 1.6 m on a lever in lifting a 150-kg crate. If the efficiency of the lever is 90%, how far is the crate lifted?

▶ 15. Karen pedals a bicycle with a gear radius of 5.00 cm and a wheel radius of 38.6 cm. What length of chain must be pulled through to make the wheel revolve once?

Chapter 11

1. Calculate the kinetic energy of a proton, mass 1.67×10^{-27} kg, traveling at 5.20×10^7 m/s.

2. What is the kinetic energy of a 3.2-kg pike swimming at 2.7 km/h?

3. A force of 30.0 N pushes a 1.5-kg cart, initially at rest, a distance of 2.8 m along a frictionless surface.
   a. Find the work done on the cart.
   b. What is its change in kinetic energy?
   c. What is the cart's final velocity?

4. A bike and rider, 82.0-kg combined mass, are traveling at 4.2 m/s. A constant force of −140 N is applied by the brakes in stopping the bike. What braking distance is needed?

▶ 5. A 712-kg car is traveling at 5.6 m/s when a force acts on it for 8.4 s, changing its velocity to 10.2 m/s.
   a. What is the change in kinetic energy of the car?
   b. How far did the car move while the force acted?
   c. How large is the force?

6. Five identical 0.85-kg books of 2.50-cm thickness are each laying flat on a table. Calculate the gain in potential energy of the system if they are stacked one on top of the other.

7. Each step of a ladder increases one's vertical height 40 cm. If a 90.0-kg painter climbs 8 steps of the ladder, what is the increase in potential energy?

8. A 0.25-kg ball is dropped from a height of 3.2 m and bounces to a height of 2.4 m. What is its loss in potential energy?

9. A 0.18-kg ball is placed on a compressed spring on the floor. The spring exerts an average force of 2.8 N through a distance of 15 cm as it shoots the ball upward. How high will the ball travel above the release spring?

▶ 10. A force of 14.0 N is applied to a 1.5-kg cart as it travels 2.6 m along an inclined plane. What is the angle of inclination of the plane?

11. A 15.0-kg model plane flies horizontally at a constant speed of 12.5 m/s.
    a. Calculate its kinetic energy.
    b. The plane goes into a dive and levels off 20.4 m closer to Earth. How much potential energy does it lose during the dive? Assume no additional drag.
    c. How much kinetic energy does the plane gain during the dive?
    d. What is its new kinetic energy?
    e. What is its new horizontal velocity?

12. A 1200-kg car starts from rest and accelerates to 72 km/h in 20.0 s. Friction exerts an average force of 450 N on the car during this time.
   a. What is the net work done on the car?
   b. How far does the car move during its acceleration?
   c. What is the net force exerted on the car during this time?
   d. What is the forward force exerted on the car as a result of the engine, power train, and wheels pushing backward on the road?

▶13. In an electronics factory, small cabinets slide down a 30.0° incline a distance of 16.0 m to reach the next assembly stage. The cabinets have a mass of 10.0 kg each.
   a. Calculate the speed each cabinet would acquire if the incline were frictionless.
   b. What kinetic energy would a cabinet have under such circumstances?

▶14. An average force of 8.2 N is used to pull a 0.40-kg rock, stretching a sling shot 43 cm. The rock is shot downward from a bridge 18 m above a stream. What will be the velocity of the rock just before it enters the water?

▶15. A 15-g bullet is fired horizontally into a 3.000-kg block of wood suspended by a long cord. The bullet sticks in the block. Compute the velocity of the bullet if the impact causes the block to swing 10 cm above its initial level.

Chapter 12

1. The boiling point of liquid chlorine is −34.60°C. Find this temperature in Kelvin.

2. Fluorine has a melting point of 50.28 K. Find this temperature in degrees Celsius.

3. Five kilograms of ice cubes are moved from the freezing compartment of a refrigerator into a home freezer. The refrigerator's freezing compartment is kept at −4.0°C. The home freezer is kept at −17°C. How much heat does the freezer's cooling system remove from the ice cubes?

4. How much heat must be added to 124 g of brass at 12.5°C to raise its temperature to 97.0°C?

5. 2.8×10^5 J of thermal energy are added to a sample of water and its temperature changes from 293 K to 308 K. What is the mass of the water?

6. 1420 J of thermal energy are added to a 100.0-g block of carbon at −20.0°C. What final temperature will the carbon reach?

7. A gold brick, mass 10.5 kg, requires 2.08×10^4 J of heat to change its temperature from 35.0°C to 50.0°C. What is the specific heat of gold?

▶8. An 8.00×10^2-g block of lead is heated in boiling water, 100.0°C, until the block's temperature is the same as the water's. The lead is then removed from the boiling water and dropped into 2.50×10^2 g of cool water at 12.2°C. After a short time, the temperature of both lead and water is 20.0°C.
   a. How much heat is gained by the cool water?
   b. On the basis of these measurements, what is the specific heat of lead?

▶9. 250.0 g of copper at 100.0°C are placed in a cup containing 325.0 g of water at 20.0°C. Assume no heat loss to the surroundings. What is the final temperature of the copper and water?

▶10. A 4.00×10^2-g sample of methanol at 30.0°C is mixed with a 2.00×10^2-g sample of water at 0.0°C. Assume no heat loss to the surroundings. What is the final temperature of the mixture?

11. How much heat is needed to change 50.0 g of water at 80.0°C to steam at 110°C?

▶12. The specific heat of mercury is 140 J/kg · C°. Its heat of vaporization is 3.06×10^5 J/kg. How much heat is needed to heat 1.0 kg of mercury metal from 10.0°C to its boiling point and vaporize it completely? The boiling point of mercury is 357°C.

▶13. 30.0 g of −3.0°C ice is placed in a cup containing 104.0 g of water at 62.0°C. All the ice melts. Find the final temperature of the mixture. Assume no heat loss to the surroundings.

▶14. Water flows over a falls 125.0 m high. If the potential energy of the water is all converted to thermal energy, calculate the temperature difference between the water at the top and the bottom of the falls.

▶15. During the game, the metabolism of basketball players often increases by as much as 30.0 W. How much perspiration must a player vaporize per hour to dissipate this extra thermal energy?

Answers to
SUPPLEMENTAL PROBLEMS
Chapter 11 (continued)

12. a. 2.4×10^5 J
    b. 2.0×10^2 m
    c. 1.2×10^3 N
    d. 1.7×10^3 N
13. a. 12.5 m/s
    b. 781 J
14. 19 m/s
15. 2.8×10^2 m/s

Chapter 12

1. 238.55 K
2. −222.87°C
3. 1.3×10^5 J removed
4. 3.94×10^3 J
5. 4.5 kg
6. 0°C
7. 132 J/kg · K
8. a. 8.2×10^3 J
   b. 1.3×10^2 J/kg · K
9. 25.2°C
10. T_f = 16.2°C
11. 1.18×10^5 J
12. 3.6×10^5 J
13. 30.0°C
14. 0.29°C
15. 47.8 g

Answers to
SUPPLEMENTAL PROBLEMS
Chapter 13

1. 0.760 m
2. 1.6×10^4 Pa
3. 36.5 kg
4. 4.0×10^3 Pa
5. a. 1.61×10^3 Pa
   b. 6.07×10^3 Pa
6. a. 412 N
   b. 4.20×10^{-2} m^3
7. 16.0
8. 875 N
9. 5.00×10^3 kg/m^3
10. 3.92×10^6 N
11. -2.7×10^{-1} m
12. 0.801 m^3
13. 5.3×10^3 cm^3
14. 4.5×10^{-2} cm
15. 719°C

Chapter 14

1. 5.00 m
2. a. 0.250 s
   b. 4.00 Hz
3. a. 0.244 s
   b. 4.10 Hz
4. 1.50 m/s
5. 0.330 m/s
6. 0.600 m/s
7. 8.00 m/s
8. 1.6 m
9. 3.00 m
10. 12.0 Hz
11. 24°

Chapter 13

1. How tall must a column of mercury, $\rho = 1.36 \times 10^4$ kg/m^3, be to exert a pressure equal to the atmosphere?
2. A dog, whose paw has an area of 12.0 cm^2, has a mass of 8.0 kg. What average pressure does the dog exert while standing?
3. A crate, whose bottom surface is 50.4 cm by 28.3 cm, exerts a pressure of 2.50×10^3 Pa on the floor. What is the mass of the crate?
4. ▶ The dimensions of a waterbed are 2.13 m by 1.52 m by 0.38 m. If the frame has a mass of 91.0 kg and the mattress is filled with water, what pressure does the bed exert on the floor?
5. ▶ A rectangular block of tin, $\rho = 7.29 \times 10^3$ kg/m^3, has dimensions of 5.00 cm by 8.50 cm by 2.25 cm. What pressure does it exert on a table top if it is laying on its side of
   a. greatest surface area?
   b. smallest surface area?
6. A rowboat, mass 42.0 kg, is floating on a lake.
   a. What is the size of the buoyant force?
   b. What is the volume of the submerged part of the boat?
7. A hydraulic lift has a large piston of 20.00-cm diameter and a small piston of 5.00-cm diameter. What is the mechanical advantage of the lift?
8. A lever on a hydraulic system gives a mechanical advantage of 5.00. The cross-sectional area of the small piston is 0.0400 m^2, and that of the large piston is 0.280 m^2. If a force of 25.0 N is exerted on the lever, what is the force given by the larger piston?
9. ▶ A piece of metal weighs 75.0 N in air and 60.0 N in water. What is the density of the metal?
10. ▶ A river barge with vertical sides is 20.0 m long and 10.0 m wide. It floats 3.00 m out of the water when empty. When loaded with coals the water is only 1.00 m from the top. What is the weight of the load of coal?
11. What is the change in the length of a 15.0-m steel rail as it is cooled from 1535°C to 20°C?
12. A concrete sidewalk section 8.000 m by 1.000 m by 0.100 m at exactly 0°C will expand to what volume at 35°C?
13. An air-filled balloon of 15.0-cm radius at 11°C is heated to 121°C. What change in volume occurs?
14. ▶ A circular, pyrex watch glass of 10.0-cm diameter at 21°C is heated to 501°C. What change will be found in the circumference of the glass?
15. ▶ A 200.0-cm copper wire and a 201-cm platinum wire are both at exactly 0°C. At what temperature will they both be of equal length?

Chapter 14

1. A periodic transverse wave that has a frequency of 10.0 Hz, travels along a string. The distance between a crest and either adjacent trough is 2.50 m. What is its wavelength?
2. A wave generator produces 16.0 pulses in 4.00 s.
   a. What is its period?
   b. What is its frequency?
3. A wave generator produces 22.5 pulses in 5.50 s.
   a. What is its period?
   b. What is its frequency?
4. What is the speed of a periodic wave disturbance that has a frequency of 2.50 Hz and a wavelength of 0.600 m?
5. One pulse is generated every 0.100 s in a tank of water. What is the speed of propagation of the wave if the wavelength of the surface wave is 3.30 cm?
6. ▶ Five pulses are generated every 0.100 s in a tank of water. What is the speed of propagation of the wave if the wavelength of the surface wave is 1.20 cm?
7. ▶ A periodic longitudinal wave that has a frequency of 20.0 Hz travels along a coil spring. If the distance between successive compressions is 0.400 m, what is the speed of the wave?
8. What is the wavelength of a water wave that has a frequency of 2.50 Hz and a speed of 4.0 m/s?
9. The speed of a transverse wave in a string is 15.0 m/s. If a source produces a disturbance that has a frequency of 5.00 Hz, what is its wavelength?
10. The speed of a transverse wave in a string is 15.0 m/s. If a source produces a disturbance that has a wavelength of 1.25 m, what is the frequency of the wave?

698 Appendix B

11. A wave has an angle of incidence of 24°. What is the angle of reflection?

Chapter 15

1. The echo of a ship's fog horn, reflected from an iceberg, is heard 5.0 s after the horn is sounded. How far away is the iceberg?

2. What is the speed of sound that has a frequency of 250 Hz and a wavelength of 0.600 m?

3. A sound wave has a frequency of 2000 Hz and travels along a steel rod. If the distance between successive compressions is 0.400 m, what is the speed of the wave?

4. What is the wavelength of a sound wave that has a frequency of 250 Hz and a speed of 400 m/s?

5. What is the wavelength of sound that has a frequency of 539.8 Hz?

6. What is the wavelength of sound that has a frequency of 320.0 Hz?

▶ 7. A stone is dropped into a mine shaft 250.0 m deep. How many seconds pass before the stone is heard to strike the bottom of the shaft?

▶ 8. A rifle is shot in a valley formed between two parallel mountains. The echo from one mountain is heard after 2.00 s and from the other mountain 2.00 s later. What is the width of the valley?

▶ 9. Sam, a train engineer, blows a whistle that has a frequency of 4.0×10^2 Hz as the train approaches a station. If the speed of the train is 25 m/s, what frequency will be heard by a person at the station?

▶ 10. Jane is on a train that is traveling at 95 km/h. The train passes a factory whose whistle is blowing at 288 Hz. What frequency does Jane hear as the train approaches the factory?

11. What is the sound level of a sound that has a sound pressure one tenth of 90 dB?

12. What is the sound level of a sound that has a sound pressure ten times 90 dB?

13. A tuning fork produces a resonance with a closed tube 19.0 cm long. What is the lowest possible frequency of the tuning fork?

14. How do the frequencies of notes that are an octave apart compare?

15. Two tuning forks of 320 Hz and 324 Hz are sounded simultaneously. What frequency of sound will the listener hear?

16. How many beats will be heard each second when a string with a frequency of 288 Hz is plucked simultaneously with another string that has a frequency of 296 Hz?

17. A tuning fork has a frequency of 440 Hz. If another tuning fork of slightly lower pitch is sounded at the same time, 5.0 beats per second are produced. What is the frequency of the second tuning fork?

Chapter 16

1. The wavelength of blue light is about 4.5×10^{-7} m. Convert this to nm.

2. As a spacecraft passes directly over Cape Kennedy, radar pulses are transmitted toward the craft and are then reflected back toward the ground. If the total time interval was 3.00×10^{-3} s, how far above the ground was the spacecraft when it passed over Cape Kennedy?

3. It takes 4.0 years for light from a star to reach Earth. How far away is this star from Earth?

4. The planet Venus is sometimes a very bright object in the night sky. Venus is 4.1×10^{10} m away from Earth when it is closest to Earth. How long would we have to wait for a radar signal to return from Venus and be detected?

5. The distance from Earth to the moon is about 3.8×10^8 m. A beam of light is sent to the moon and, after it reflects, returns to Earth. How long did it take to make the round trip?

6. A baseball fan in a ball park is 101 m away from the batter's box when the batter hits the ball. How long after the batter hits the ball does the fan see it occur?

7. A radio station on the AM band has an assigned frequency of 825 kHz (kilohertz). What is the wavelength of the station?

8. A short-wave, HAM, radio operator uses the 5-meter band. On what frequency does the HAM operate?

Answers to
SUPPLEMENTAL PROBLEMS

Chapter 15

1. 8.6×10^2 m
2. 150 m/s
3. 800 m/s
4. 1.60 m
5. 0.635 m
6. 1.07 m
7. 7.87 s
8. 1030 m
9. 430 Hz
10. 310 Hz
11. 70 dB
12. 110 dB
13. 451 Hz
14. The higher note has a frequency twice that of the lower note.
15. 4 Hz
16. 8 beats/s
17. 435 Hz

Chapter 16

1. 4.5×10^2 nm
2. 4.50×10^5 m
3. 3.8×10^{16} m
4. 2.7×10^2 s
5. 2.5 s
6. 3.37×10^{-7} s
7. 364 m
8. 60 MHz

Answers to
SUPPLEMENTAL PROBLEMS
Chapter 16 (continued)

9. 0.50 lx
10. 1.1×10^2 cd
11. 6.9 m
12. infrared
13. ultraviolet
14. The black object stands out from other objects that are not black. It is also illuminated by some diffuse reflection.
15. The dress appears black since red pigment absorbs green light.
16. black

Chapter 17

1. 28°
2. 1.37
3. 15.9°
4. 48.4°
5. 85.23560°
6. water
7. 49.5°
8. Refer to Problems and Solutions Manual. The reflected rays appear to intersect 9.0 cm below the surface. Apparent depth/true depth = 0.75. N_{air}/N_{water} = 0.75.
9. 2.26×10^8 m/s
10. 1.28×10^8 m/s
11. 1.71
12. None: This is impossible, since sin θ_r cannot exceed 1. Therefore, total internal reflection occurs.
13. 1.56
14. 29.8°
15. Refer to Problems and Solutions Manual. The path of the light ray is a diamond.
16. Refer to Problems and Solutions Manual.
17. 0.20
18. 2.0×10^6 m/s

9. Find the illumination 8.0 m below a 405-lm lamp.

▶ 10. Two lamps illuminate a screen equally. The first lamp has an intensity of 12.5 cd and is 3.0 m from the screen. The second lamp is 9.0 m from the screen. What is its intensity?

▶ 11. A 15-cd point source lamp and a 45-cd point source lamp provide equal illuminations on a wall. If the 45-cd lamp is 12 m away from the wall, how far from the wall is the 15-cd lamp?

12. What is the name given to the electromagnetic radiation that has a wavelength slightly longer than visible light?

13. What is the name given to the electromagnetic radiation that has a wavelength slightly shorter than visible light?

14. If a black object absorbs all light ray incident on it, how can we see it?

15. What is the appearance of a red dress in a closed room illuminated only by green light?

16. A shirt that is the color of a primary color is illuminated with the complement of that primary color. What color do you see?

Chapter 17

1. A ray of light strikes a mirror at an angle of incidence of 28°. What is the angle of reflection?

2. A ray of light passes from an unknown substance into air. If the angle in the unknown substance is 35.0° and the angle in air is 52.0°, what is the index of refraction of the unknown substance?

3. A ray of light has an angle of incidence of 25.0° upon the surface of a piece of quartz. What is the angle of refraction?

4. A beam of light passes from water into polyethylene, index of refraction = 1.50. If the angle in water is 57.5°, what is the angle in polyethylene?

5. Dave makes some hydrogen sulfide, index of refraction = 1.000644. If Karen measures an angle of 85.000000° in the hydrogen sulfide, what angle will Karen measure in air if the index of refraction of air is 1.0002926?

6. Sue submerged some ice in water and shined a laser beam through the water and into the ice. Sue found the angle in ice was larger than the angle in water. Which material has a larger index of refraction?

▶ 7. A ray of light enters a triangular crown glass prism perpendicular to one face and it emerges from an adjacent side. If the two adjacent sides meet at a 30.0° angle, what is the angle the light ray has in the air when it comes out?

8. Make a drawing, to scale, of the side of an aquarium in which the water is 12.0 cm deep. From a single point on the bottom, draw two lines upward, one vertical and the other 5.0° from the vertical. Let these two lines represent two light rays that start from the same point on the bottom of the tank. Compute the directions the refracted rays will travel above the surface of the water. Draw in these rays and continue them backward into the tank until they intersect. At what depth does the bottom of the tank appear to be if you look into the water? Divide the apparent depth into the true depth and compare it to the index of refraction.

9. Find the speed of light in water.

10. Find the speed of light in antimony trioxide if it has an index of refraction of 2.35.

11. The speed of light in a special piece of glass is 1.75×10^8 m/s. What is its index of refraction?

12. Glenn gently pours some acetic acid, index of refraction = 1.37, onto some antimony trioxide, index of refraction = 2.35. What angle will Glenn find in the acetic acid if the angle in the antimony trioxide is 42.0°?

13. Steve finds that a plastic has a critical angle of 40.0°. What is the index of refraction of the plastic?

14. Kathy decides to find the critical angle of arsenic trioxide, index of refraction = 2.01, which is very toxic. What angle did Kathy find?

15. A light source is in a cylindrical container of carbon dichloride, index of refraction = 1.500. The light source sends a ray of light parallel to the bottom of the container at a 45.0° angle from the radius to the circumference. What will the path of the light ray be?

▶ 16. With a square block of glass, index of refraction = 1.50, it is impossible, when looking into one side, to see out of an adjacent side of the square block of glass. It appears to be a mirror. Use your knowledge of geometry and critical angles to show that this is true.

17. The index of refraction for red light in arsenic trioxide is 2.010, while the index of refraction for blue light is 2.023. Find the difference between the angles of refraction if white light is incident at an angle of 65.0°.

18. The index of refraction for red light in a diamond is 2.410, while the index of refraction for blue light is 2.450. Find the difference in the speed of light in diamond.

Chapter 18

1. Sally's face is 75 cm in front of a plane mirror. Where is the image of Sally's face?

2. A concave mirror has a focal length of 10.0 cm. What is its radius of curvature?

3. Light from a distant star is collected by a concave mirror that has a radius of curvature of 150 cm. How far from the mirror is the image of the star?

4. An object is placed 25.0 cm away from a concave mirror that has a focal length of 5.00 cm. Where is the image located?

5. An object and its image as seen in a concave mirror are the same height when the object is 48.4 cm from the mirror. What is the focal length of the mirror?

6. An object placed 50.0 cm from a concave mirror gives a real image 33.3 cm from the mirror. If the image is 28.4 cm high, what is the height of the object?

7. An object, 15.8 cm high, is located 87.6 cm from a concave mirror that has a focal length of 17.0 cm.
a. Where is the image located?
b. How high is the image?

▶ **8.** The image of the moon is formed by a concave mirror whose radius of curvature is 4.20 m at a time when the moon's distance is 3.80×10^5 km. What is the diameter of the image of the moon if the diameter of the moon is 3480 km?

9. A shaving mirror has a radius of curvature of 30.0 cm. When a face is 10.0 cm away from the mirror, what is the magnification of the mirror?

10. A convex mirror has a focal length of −16 cm. How far behind the mirror does the image of a person 3.0 m away appear?

11. How far behind the surface of a convex mirror, focal length of −6.0 cm, does a car 10.0 m from the mirror appear?

12. A converging lens has a focal length of 25.5 cm. If it is placed 72.5 cm from an object, at what distance from the lens will the image be?

13. If an object is 10.0 cm from a converging lens that has a focal length of 5.00 cm, how far from the lens will the image be?

14. The focal length of a lens in a box camera is 10.0 cm. The fixed distance between the lens and the film is 11.0 cm. If an object is clearly focused on the film, how far must the object be from the lens?

15. An object 3.0 cm tall is placed 22 cm in front of a converging lens. A real image is formed 11 cm from the lens. What is the size of the image?

▶ **16.** An object 3.0 cm tall is placed 20 cm in front of a converging lens. A real image is formed 10 cm from the lens. What is the focal length of the lens?

▶ **17.** What is the focal length of the lens in your eye when you read a book that is 35.0 cm from your eye? The distance from the lens to the retina is 0.19 mm.

▶ **18.** When an object 5.0 cm tall is placed 12 cm from a converging lens, an image is formed on the same side of the lens as the object but the image is 61 cm away from the lens. What is the focal length of the lens?

▶ **19.** When an object 5.0 cm tall is placed 12 cm from a converging lens, an image is formed on the same side of the lens as the object but the image is 61 cm away from the lens. What is the size of the image?

Chapter 19

1. Monochromatic light passes through two slits that are 0.0300 cm apart and it falls on a screen 120 cm away. The first-order image is 0.160 cm from the middle of the center band. What is the wavelength of the light used?

Answers to
SUPPLEMENTAL PROBLEMS

Chapter 18

1. 75 cm behind the mirror
2. 20.0 cm
3. 75.0 cm
4. 6.25 cm in front of the mirror
5. 24.2 cm
6. 42.6 cm
7. **a.** 21.1 cm
b. −3.81 cm; inverted
8. −1.92 cm; inverted
9. 3.0
10. −0.15 m
11. −0.060 m
12. 39.3 cm
13. 10 cm
14. 1.1×10^2 cm
15. −1.5 cm; inverted
16. 6.7 cm
17. 0.19 mm
18. 15 cm
19. 25 cm; image is erect.

Chapter 19

1. 4.00×10^2 nm

Answers to

SUPPLEMENTAL PROBLEMS

Chapter 19 (continued)

2. 5.0×10^2 nm
3. 5.40 mm
4. 0.750 m
5. 6.00 km
6. 1.3×10^{-6} m
7. 1.62 m
8. 3.7 m
9. 5.7°
10. 2.35×10^{-3} mm/line
11. 16.7°
12. 524 nm
13. 0.360 m
14. 2.18×10^{-5} m

Chapter 20

1. $F/4$
2. $4F$
3. 1.0×10^{-5} N
4. 8.0×10^{-5} N
5. 6.25×10^{18} electrons
6. $+9.0 \times 10^3$ N
7. -1.1×10^2 N; the force is attractive.
8. $+44$ N. away

2. Green light passes through a double slit for which $d = 0.20$ mm and it falls on a screen 2.00 m away. The first-order image is at 0.50 cm. What is the wavelength of the light?

3. Yellow light that has a wavelength of 6.00×10^2 nm passes through two narrow slits that are 0.200 mm apart. An interference pattern is produced on a screen 180 cm away. What is the location of the first-order image?

4. Violet light that has a wavelength of 4.00×10^2 nm passes through two slits that are 0.0100 cm apart. How far away must the screen be so the first-order image is at 0.300 cm?

▶ 5. Two radio transmitters are 25.0 m apart and each one sends out a radio wave with a wavelength of 10.0 m. The two radio towers act exactly like a double-slit source for light. How far from the central band is the first-order image if you are 15.0 km away? (Yes, this really happens. Radio stations can and do fade in and out as you cross the nodals and the antinodals.)

6. Monochromatic light passes through a single slit, 0.500 mm wide, and falls on a screen 1.0 m away. If the distance from the center of the pattern to the first band is 2.6 mm, what is the wavelength of the light?

7. Red light that has a wavelength of 7.50×10^2 nm passes through a single slit that is 0.1350 mm wide. How far away from the screen must the slit be if the first dark band is 0.9000 cm away from the central bright band?

8. Microwaves with a wavelength of 3.5 cm pass through a single slit 0.85 cm wide and fall on a screen 91 cm away. What is the distance to the first-order band?

▶ 9. Radio waves that are emitted by two adjacent radio transmitters behave like light waves coming from a double slit. If two transmitters, 1500 m apart, each send out radio waves with a wavelength of 150 m, what is the diffraction angle?

10. What is the average distance between the lines of a diffraction grating if the number of lines per millimeter is 425?

11. A transmission grating with 5.85×10^3 lines/cm is illuminated by monochromatic light that has a wavelength of 492 nm. What is the diffraction angle for the first-order image?

12. Monochromatic light illuminates a transmission grating having 5900 lines/cm. The diffraction angle for a first-order image is 18.0°. What is the wavelength of the light in nanometers?

13. A transmission grating, 5.80×10^3 lines/cm, is illuminated by a monochromatic light source that has a wavelength of 495 nm. How far from the center line is the first-order image if the distance to the grating is 1.25 m?

14. A pinhole camera uses a 1.5-mm hole instead of a lens to form an image. What is the resolution of this camera for green light, 545-nm wavelength, if the film is 6.0 cm behind the pinhole?

Chapter 20

1. Two charges, q_1 and q_2, are separated by a distance, d, and exert a force on each other. What new force will exist if d is doubled?

2. Two charges, q_1 and q_2, are separated by a distance, d, and exert a force on each other. What new force will exist if q_1 and q_2 are both doubled?

3. Two identical point charges are separated by a distance of 3.0 cm and they repel each other with a force of 4.0×10^{-5} N. What is the new force if the distance between the point charges is doubled?

▶ 4. An electric force of 2.5×10^{-4} N acts between two small equally-charged spheres which are 2.0 cm apart. Calculate the force acting between the spheres if the charge on one of the spheres is doubled and the spheres move to a 5.0-cm separation.

5. How many electrons would be required to have a total charge of 1.00 C on a sphere?

6. If two identical charges, 1.000 C each, are separated by a distance of 1.00 km, what is the force between them?

7. Two point charges are separated by 10.0 cm. If one charge is $+20.00$ μC and the other is -6.00 μC, what is the force between them?

8. The two point charges in the previous problem are allowed to touch each other and are again separated by 10.00 cm. Now what is the force between them?

9. Determine the electrostatic force of attraction between a proton and an electron that are separated by 5.00×10^2 nm.

10. Find the force between two charged spheres 1.25 cm apart if the charge on one sphere is 2.50 μC and the charge on the other sphere is 1.75×10^{-8} C.

11. Two identical point charges are 3.00 cm apart. Find the charge on each of them if the force of repulsion is 4.00×10^{-7} N.

12. A charge of 4.0×10^{-5} C is attracted by a second charge with a force of 350 N when the separation is 10.0 cm. Calculate the size of the second charge.

▶ 13. Three particles are placed on a straight line. The left particle has a charge of $+4.6 \times 10^{-6}$ C, the middle particle has a charge of -2.3×10^{-6} C, and the right particle has a charge of -2.3×10^{-6} C. The left particle is 12 cm from the middle particle and the right particle is 24 cm from the middle particle. Find the total force on the middle particle.

▶ 14. The left particle in the problem above is moved directly above the middle particle, still 12 cm away. Find the force on the middle particle.

Chapter 21

1. How strong would an electric field have to be to produce a force of 1.00 N if the charge was 1.000×10^3 μC?

2. A positive charge of 7.0 mC experiences a 5.6×10^{-2}-N force when placed in an electric field. What is the size of the electric field intensity?

3. A positive test charge of 6.5×10^{-6} C experiences a force of 4.5×10^{-5} N. What is the magnitude of the electric field intensity?

4. A charge experiences a force of 3.0×10^{-3} N in an electric field of intensity 2.0 N/C. What is the magnitude of the charge?

5. What is the size of the force on an electron when the electron is in a uniform electric field that has an intensity of 1.000×10^3 N/C?

6. Sketch the electric field lines around a −1.0-μC charge.

7. It takes 8.00 mJ to move a charge of 4.00 μC from point **A** to point **C** in an electric field. What is the potential difference between the two points?

8. How much work is required to move a positive charge of 2.5 μC between two points that have a potential difference of 60 V?

▶ 9. A cloud has a potential difference relative to a tree of 9.00×10^2 MV. During a lighting storm, a charge of 1.00×10^2 C travels through this potential difference. How much work is done on this charge?

10. A constant electric field of 750 N/C is between a set of parallel plates. What is the potential difference between the parallel plates if they are 1.5 cm apart?

11. A spark will jump between two people if the electric field exceeds 4.0×10^6 V/m. You shuffle across a rug and a spark jumps when you put your finger 0.15 cm from another person's arm. Calculate the potential difference between your body and the other person's arm.

12. A potential difference of 0.90 V exists from one side to the other side of a cell membrane that is 5.0 nm thick. What is the electric field across the membrane?

▶ 13. An oil drop having a charge of 8.0×10^{-19} C is suspended between two charged parallel plates. The plates are separated by a distance of 8.0 mm, and there is a potential difference of 1200 V between the plates. What is the weight of the suspended oil drop?

14. A capacitor accumulates 4.0 μC on each plate when the potential difference between the plates is 100 V. What is the capacitance of the capacitor?

15. What is the voltage across a capacitor with a charge of 6.0 μC and a capacitance 7.0 pF?

16. How large is the charge accumulated on one of the plates of a 30-μF capacitor when the potential difference between the plates is 120 V?

Chapter 22

1. How many amperes of current flow in a wire through which 1.00×10^{18} electrons pass per second?

Answers to
SUPPLEMENTAL PROBLEMS

Chapter 20 (continued)

9. -9.2×10^{-16} N
10. +2.5 N
11. $\pm 2.0 + 10^{-10}$ C
12. -9.7×10^{-6} C
13. 7.4 N, to the left
14. 6.7 N at 7.2° to the left of vertical

Chapter 21

1. 1.00×10^3 N/C
2. 8.0 N/C
3. 6.9 N/C
4. 1.5 mC
5. -1.60×10^{-16} N
6. Refer to Problems and Solutions Manual.
7. 2.00×10^3 V
8. 0.15 mJ
9. 9.00×10^{10} J
10. 11 V
11. 6.0×10^3 V
12. 1.8×10^8 V/m
13. 1.2×10^{-13} N
14. 40 μF
15. 8.6×10^5 V
16. 3.6 mC

Chapter 22

1. 0.160 A

Answers to
SUPPLEMENTAL PROBLEMS
Chapter 22 (continued)

2. 1.00×10^2 C
3. 180 W
4. 83 W
5. a. 2.0 A
   b. 12 kJ
6. 4.00 Ω
7. 20.0 Ω
8. 0.400 V
9. a. 10.4 A
   b. greater
10. a. 0.500 A
    b. 0.522 A
11. 460 Ω
12. 133 Ω
13. a. 1.41 A
    b. 0.447 A
14. 24 W
15. 62¢/yr
16. a. 16.7 A
    b. 7.19 Ω
    c. $3.36

Chapter 23

1. a. 350 Ω
   b. 0.143 A
   c. 17.9 V
2. a. Refer to Problems and Solutions Manual.
   b. 60 Ω
   c. 0.20 A
3. a. 680 Ω
   b. 18 mA
   c. 2.2 V
4. a. 0.10 A
   b. 400 Ω
   c. 40 Ω
5. 153 Ω

2. A current of 5.00 A flowed in a copper wire for 20.0 s. How many coulombs of charge passed through the wire in this time?

3. What power is supplied to a motor that operates on a 120-V line and draws 1.50 A of current?

4. An electric lamp is connected to a 110-V source. If the current through the lamp is 0.75 A, what is the power consumption of the lamp?

5. A lamp is labeled 6.0 V and 12 W.
   a. What current flows through the lamp when it is operating?
   b. How much energy is supplied to the lamp in 1.000×10^3 s?

6. A current of 3.00 A flows through a resistor when it is connected to a 12.0-V battery. What is the resistance of the resistor?

7. A small lamp is designed to draw a current of 3.00×10^2 mA in a 6.00-V circuit. What is the resistance of the lamp?

8. What potential difference is required if you want a current of 8.00 mA in a load having a resistance of 50.0 Ω?

9. In common metals, resistance increases as the temperature increases. An electric toaster has a resistance of 12.0 Ω when hot.
   a. What current will flow through it when it is connected to 125 V?
   b. When the toaster is first turned on, will the current be more or less than during operation?

10. The resistance of a lamp is 230 Ω. The voltage is 115 V when the lamp is turned on.
    a. What is the current in the lamp?
    b. If the voltage rises to 120 V, what is the current?

11. What should the resistance of the lamp in part **a** of the previous problem be if the lamp is to draw the same current, but in a 230-V circuit?

12. A 110-W lamp draws 0.909 A. What is the lamp's resistance?

13. Each coil in a resistance box is capable of dissipating heat at the rate of 4.00 W. What is the maximum current that should be allowed across a coil to avoid overheating if the coil has a resistance of
    a. 2.00 Ω.
    b. 20.0 Ω.

14. What is the power supplied to a lamp that is operated by a battery having a 12-V potential difference across its terminals when the resistance of the lamp is 6.0 Ω?

15. How much does it cost to run a 2.00-W clock for one year (365.25 days) if it costs 3.53 cents/kWh?

16. A small electric furnace that expends 2.00 kW of power is connected across a potential difference of 120 V.
    a. What is the current in the circuit?
    b. What is the resistance of the furnace?
    c. What is the cost of operating the furnace for 24.0 h at 7.00 cents/kWh?

Chapter 23

1. The load across a 50.0-V battery consists of a series combination of two lamps with resistances of 125 Ω and 225 Ω.
   a. Find the total resistance of the circuit.
   b. Find the current in the circuit.
   c. Find the potential difference across the 125-Ω lamp.

2. The load across a 12-V battery consists of a series combination of three resistances that are 15 Ω, 21 Ω, and 24 Ω respectively.
   a. Draw the circuit diagram.
   b. What is the total resistance of the load?
   c. What is the magnitude of the circuit current?

3. The load across a 12-V battery consists of a series combination of three resistances R_1, R_2, and R_3. R_1 is 210 Ω, R_2 is 350 Ω, and R_3 is 120 Ω.
   a. Find the equivalent resistance of the circuit.
   b. Find the current in the circuit.
   c. Find the potential difference across R_3.

4. The load across a 40-V battery consists of a series combination of three resistances R_1, R_2, and R_3. R_1 is 240 Ω, and R_3 is 120 Ω. The potential difference across R_1 is 24 V.
   a. Find the current in the circuit.
   b. Find the equivalent resistance of the circuit.
   c. Find the resistance of R_2.

5. Pete is designing a voltage divider using a 12.0-V battery and a 100-Ω resistor as R_2. What resistor should be used as R_1 if the output voltage is 4.75 V?

6. Two resistances, one 12 Ω and the other 18 Ω, are connected in parallel. What is the equivalent resistance of the parallel combination?

7. Three resistances of 12 Ω each are connected in parallel. What is the equivalent resistance?

▶ 8. Two resistances, one 62 Ω and the other 88 Ω, are connected in parallel. The resistors are then connected to a 12-V battery.
   a. What is the equivalent resistance of the parallel combination?
   b. What is the current through each resistor?

▶ 9. A 35-Ω, 55-Ω, and 85-Ω resistor are connected in parallel. The resistors are then connected to a 35-V battery.
   a. What is the equivalent resistance of the parallel combination?
   b. What is the current through each resistor?

10. A 110-V household circuit that contains an 1800-W microwave, a 1000-W toaster, and an 800-W coffee maker is connected to a 20-A fuse. Will the fuse melt if the microwave and the coffee maker are both on?

11. Resistors R_1, R_2, and R_3 have resistances of 15.0 Ω, 9.0 Ω, and 8.0 Ω respectively. R_1 and R_2 are connected in series, and their combination is in parallel with R_3 to form a load across a 6.0-V battery.
   a. Draw the circuit diagram.
   b. What is the total resistance of the load?
   c. What is the magnitude of the circuit current?
   d. What is the current in R_3?
   e. What is the potential difference across R_2?

12. A 15.0-Ω resistor is connected in series to a 120-V generator and two 10.0-Ω resistors that are connected in parallel to each other.
   a. Draw the circuit diagram.
   b. What is the total resistance of the load?
   c. What is the magnitude of the circuit current?
   d. What is the current in one of the 10.0-Ω resistors?
   e. What is the potential difference across the 15.0-Ω resistor?

13. How would you change the resistance of a voltmeter to allow the voltmeter to measure a larger potential difference?

14. How would you change the shunt in an ammeter to allow the ammeter to measure a larger current?

▶ 15. An ohmmeter is made by connecting a 6.0-V battery in series with an adjustable resistor and an ideal ammeter. The ammeter deflects full-scale with a current of 1.0 mA. The two leads are touched together and the resistance is adjusted so 1.0-mA current flows.
   a. What is the resistance of the adjustable resistor?
   b. The leads are now connected to an unknown resistance. What external resistance would produce a reading of 0.50 mA, half full-scale?
   c. What external resistance would produce a reading of 0.25 mA, quarter-scale?
   d. What external resistance would produce a reading of 0.75 mA, three-quarter full-scale?

Chapter 24

1. Assume the current in the wire shown in Figure 24–28 goes in the opposite direction. Copy the wire segment and sketch the new magnetic field the current generated.

2. Assume the current shown in Figure 24–29 goes into the page instead of out of the page. Copy the figure with the new current and sketch the magnetic field.

3. What happens to the strength of a magnetic field around a wire if the current in the wire is doubled?

4. What happens to the magnetic field inside the coil of Figure 24–30 if the current shown was reversed?

5. What is the direction of the force on a current carrying wire in a magnetic field if the current is toward the left on a page and the magnetic field is down the page?

6. A 0.25 m long wire is carrying a 1.25 A current while the wire is perpendicular to a 0.35-T magnetic field. What is the force on the wire?

7. A 3.0 cm long wire lies perpendicular to a magnetic field with a magnetic induction of 0.40 T. Calculate the force on the wire if the current in the wire is 5.0 A.

8. What is the force on a 3.5 m long wire that is carrying a 12-A current if the wire is perpendicular to Earth's magnetic field?

9. A wire, 0.50 m long, is put into a uniform magnetic field. The force exerted upon the wire when the current in the wire is 20 A is 3.0 N. What is the magnetic induction of the field acting upon the wire?

10. What is the size of the current in a 35 cm long wire that is perpendicular to a magnetic field of 0.085 T if the force on the wire is 125 mN?

Answers to
SUPPLEMENTAL PROBLEMS
Chapter 23 (continued)

6. 7.2 Ω
7. 4.0 Ω
8. a. 36 Ω
   b. 0.19 A
   0.14 A
9. a. 17 Ω
   b. $I_1 = 1.0$ A; $I_2 = 0.64$ A; $I_3 = 0.41$ A
10. The fuse will melt.
11. a. Refer to Problems and Solutions Manual.
   b. 6.0 Ω
   c. 1.0 A
   d. 0.75 A
   e. 2.3 V
12. a. Refer to Problems and Solutions Manual.
   b. 20.0 Ω
   c. 6.00 A
   d. 3.00 A
   e. 90.0 V
13. increase
14. decrease
15. a. 6.0×10^3 Ω
   b. 6×10^3 Ω
   c. 1.8×10^4 Ω
   d. 2.0×10^3 Ω

Chapter 24

1. Refer to Problems and Solutions Manual.
2. Refer to Problems and Solutions Manual.
3. It doubles, since magnetic field strength is proportional to current.
4. The magnetic field is reversed.
5. out of the page
6. 0.11 N
7. 0.060 N
8. 2.1 mN
9. 0.30 T
10. 4.2 A

Answers to
SUPPLEMENTAL PROBLEMS
Chapter 24 (continued)

11. 599 KΩ
12. Refer to Problems and Solutions Manual.
13. down the page
14. Force is 9.6×10^{-16} N into the page.
15. 2.8×10^{-14} N
16. 1.9×10^{-12} N

Chapter 25

1. north
2. 0.20 mV
3. 5.0 mT
4. 20 m/s
5. 10 m/s
6. a. 6.4 V
   b. 1.0 A
7. 41 mA
8. 170 V
9. 3.5 A
10. 406 V
11. 15.0 A
12. 69.4 W
13. a. clockwise around the pipe, as viewed from above
    b. down the pipe
14. 1 to 545
15. a. 50 turns
    b. 0.40 A

▶ **11.** A galvanometer has a full-scale deflection when the current is 50.0 μA. If the galvanometer has a resistance of 1.0 kΩ, what should the resistance of the multiplier resistor be to make a voltmeter with a full-scale deflection of 30.0 V?

12. A charged particle is moving to the right in a magnetic field whose direction is up the page. Show by diagram the direction of the force exerted by the magnetic field upon the particle if the particle is a positive proton.

13. An electron beam moving horizontally away from you is deflected toward the right after passing through a certain region of space that contains a constant magnetic field. What is the direction of the magnetic field?

14. A beam of electrons moving left at 3.0×10^7 m/s passes at right angles to a uniform magnetic field that is down and in which the magnetic induction is 2.0×10^{-4} T. What force acts upon each electron in the beam?

15. The electrons in a beam in a cathode ray tube are moving horizontally at 5.0×10^7 m/s and pass through a vertical magnetic field of 3.5×10^{-3} T. What size force acts on each of the electrons in the beam?

16. An ion of oxygen having 2 elementary negative electric charges is moving at right angles to a uniform magnetic field for which B = 0.30 T. If its velocity is 2.0×10^7 m/s, what force is acting on the ion?

Chapter 25

1. A north-south wire is moved toward the east through a magnetic field that is pointing down, into Earth. What is the direction of the induced current?

2. A wire, 1.0 m long, is moved at right angles to Earth's magnetic field where the magnetic induction is 5.0×10^{-5} T at a speed of 4.0 m/s. What is the *EMF* induced in the wire?

3. An *EMF* of 2.0 mV is induced in a wire 0.10 m long when it is moving perpendicularly across a uniform magnetic field at a velocity of 4.0 m/s. What is the magnetic induction of the field?

4. With what speed must a 0.20-m long wire cut across a magnetic field for which B is 2.5 T if it is to have an *EMF* of 10 V induced in it?

5. At what speed must a wire conductor 50 cm long be moved at right angles to a magnetic field of induction 0.20 T to induce an *EMF* of 1.0 V in it?

6. A wire, 0.40 m long, cuts perpendicularly across a magnetic field for which *B* is 2.0 T at a velocity of 8.0 m/s.
a. What *EMF* is induced in the wire?
b. If the wire is in a circuit having a resistance of 6.4 Ω, what is the size of the current through the wire?

▶ **7.** A coil of wire, which has a total length of 7.50 m, is moved perpendicular to Earth's magnetic field at 5.50 m/s. What is the size of the current in the wire if the total resistance of the wire is 5.0×10^{-2} mΩ?

8. A house lighting circuit is rated at 120 V. What is the maximum voltage that can be expected from this circuit?

9. A toaster draws 2.5 A of alternating current. What is the maximum current that this toaster can draw?

10. The insulation of a capacitor will break down if the instantaneous voltage exceeds 575 V. What is the largest effective alternating voltage that may be applied to the capacitor?

11. A magnetic circuit breaker will open its circuit if the instantaneous current reaches 21.25 A. What is the largest effective current the circuit will carry?

▶ **12.** The peak value of the alternating voltage applied to a 144-Ω resistor is 1.00×10^2 V. What power must the resistor be able to handle?

▶ **13.** Steve drops a magnet, S-pole down, through a vertical copper pipe.
a. What is the direction of the induced current in the copper pipe as the bottom of the magnet passes?
b. The induced current produces a magnetic field. What is the direction of the induced magnetic field?

14. The electricity received at an electrical substation has a potential difference of 240 000 V. What should the ratio of the turns of the step-down transformer be to have an output of 440 V?

▶ **15.** The CRT in a television uses a step-up transformer to change 120 V to 48 000 V. The secondary side of the transformer has 20 000 turns and an output of 1.0 mA.
a. How many turns does the primary side have?
b. What is the input current?

Chapter 26

1. A beam of electrons travels through a set of crossed electric and magnetic fields. What is the speed of the electrons if the magnetic field is 85 mT and the electric field is 6.5×10^4 N/C?

2. Electrons, moving at 8.5×10^7 m/s, pass through crossed magnetic and electric fields undeflected. What is the size of the magnetic field if the electric field is 4.0×10^4 N/C?

3. What effect does increasing the magnetic induction of the field have on the radius of the particle's path for a given particle moving at a fixed speed?

4. An electron is moving at 2.0×10^8 m/s in a constant magnetic field. How strong should the magnetic field be to keep the electron moving in a circle of radius 0.50 m?

5. A positively-charged ion, having 2 elementary charges and a velocity of 5.0×10^7 m/s, is moving across a magnetic field for which $B = 4.0$ T. If the mass of the ion is 6.8×10^{-27} kg, what is the radius of the circular path it travels?

6. A beam of electrons, moving at 2.0×10^8 m/s, passes at right angles to a uniform magnetic field of 41 mT. What is the radius of the circular path in which this beam will travel through the magnetic field?

7. An unknown particle is accelerated by a potential difference of 150 V. The particle then enters a magnetic field of 50.0 mT, and follows a curved path with a radius of 9.80 cm. What is the ratio of q/m?

8. A beam of doubly-ionized oxygen atoms is accelerated by a potential difference of 232 V. The oxygen then enters a magnetic field of 75.0 mT, and follows a curved path with a radius of 8.3 cm. What is the mass of the oxygen atom?

9. If the atomic mass unit is equal to 1.67×10^{-27} kg, how many atomic mass units are in the oxygen atom in the previous problem?

10. A hydrogen ion is accelerated through an accelerating potential of 1.00×10^2 V and then through a magnetic field of 50.0 mT to standardize the mass spectrometer. What is the radius of curvature if the mass of the ion is 1.67×10^{-27} kg?

▶11. What is the change in the radius of curvature if a doubly-ionized neon atom, mass = 3.34×10^{-26} kg, is sent through the mass spectrometer in the previous problem?

12. Microwaves for a microwave oven are produced in a special tube, the klystron tube, which has a microwave antenna attached to it. What length antenna would produce 3.0-cm microwaves?

13. An FM radio station broadcasts on a frequency of 94.5 MHz. What is the antenna length that would give the best reception for this radio station?

Chapter 27

1. Consider an incandescent light bulb on a dimmer control. What happens to the color of the light given off by the bulb as the dimmer control is turned down?

2. What would the change in frequency of the vibration of an atom be according to Planck's theory if it gave off 5.44×10^{-19} J? Assume n = 1.

3. What is the maximum kinetic energy of photoelectrons ejected from the metal that has a stopping potential of 3.8 V?

4. The stopping potential needed to return all the electrons ejected from a metal is 7.3 V. What is the maximum kinetic energy of the electrons in J?

5. What is the potential difference needed to stop photoelectrons that have a maximum kinetic energy of 8.0×10^{-19} J?

6. The threshold frequency of a certain metal is 8.0×10^{14} Hz. What is the work function of the metal?

7. If light with a frequency of 1.6×10^{15} Hz falls on the metal in the previous problem, what is the maximum kinetic energy of the photoelectrons?

8. The threshold frequency of a certain metal is 3.00×10^{14} Hz. What is the maximum kinetic energy of the ejected photoelectrons when the metal is illuminated by light with a wavelength of 650 nm?

9. What is the momentum of a photon of violet light that has a wavelength of 4.00×10^2 nm?

10. What is the momentum of a photon of red light that has a wavelength of 7.00×10^2 nm?

11. What is the wavelength associated with an electron moving at 3.0×10^6 m/s?

Answers to
SUPPLEMENTAL PROBLEMS
Chapter 26

1. 7.6×10^5 m/s
2. 0.47 mT
3. It decreases the radius.
4. 2.3 mT
5. 0.27 m
6. 2.8 cm
7. 1.25×10^7 C/kg
8. 2.7×10^{-26} kg
9. 16 u
10. 2.89 cm
11. 6.25 cm
12. 0.75 cm
13. 0.794 m

Chapter 27

1. more red
2. 8.21×10^{14} Hz
3. 3.8 eV
4. 1.2×10^{-18} J
5. 5.0 V
6. 5.3×10^{-19} J
7. 5.3×10^{-19} J
8. 1.07×10^{-19} J
9. 1.66×10^{-27} kg · m/s
10. 9.47×10^{-28} kg · m/s
11. 0.24 nm

Answers to
SUPPLEMENTAL PROBLEMS
Chapter 27 (continued)

12. 2.4×10^6 m/s
13. a. 4.2×10^7 m/s
    b. 0.017 nm

Chapter 28

1. 5.38×10^{14} Hz
2. E_3
3. 2.23 eV
4. 1.15 eV
5. 0.848 nm
6. $E_1 = -0.278$ eV
   $E_2 = -3.40$ eV
7. 3.12 eV
8. 7.53×10^{14} Hz

Chapter 29

1. 1.55 eV
2. $4.63 \times 10^{22}\ e^-/cm^3$
3. 3.1 V
4. 20 Ω
5. zero

Chapter 30

1. 47 electrons, 47 protons, 62 neutrons
2. $^{40}_{20}Ca$
3. $^{64}_{30}Zn$
4. $^{210}_{84}Bi \rightarrow {}^{4}_{2}He + {}^{206}_{82}Pb$
5. $^{14}_{6}C \rightarrow {}^{0}_{-1}e + {}^{14}_{7}N + {}^{0}_{0}\bar{\nu}$
6. $^{225}_{89}Ac \rightarrow {}^{4}_{2}He + {}^{221}_{87}Fr$
7. $^{227}_{88}Ra \rightarrow {}^{0}_{-1}e + {}^{227}_{89}Ac + {}^{0}_{0}\bar{\nu}$
8. $^{65}_{29}Cu + {}^{1}_{0}n \rightarrow {}^{66}_{29}Cu \rightarrow {}^{1}_{1}p + {}^{65}_{28}Ni$
9. $^{235}_{92}U + {}^{1}_{0}n \rightarrow {}^{96}_{40}Zr + 3({}^{1}_{0}n) + {}^{137}_{52}Te$
10. a. 25% is left.
    b. 12.5% is left.
    c. 6.3% is left.

12. What velocity would an electron need to have a wavelength of 3.0×10^{-10} m associated with it?

▶ **13.** An electron is accelerated across a potential difference of 5.0×10^3 V in the CRT of a television.

a. What is the velocity of the electron if it started from rest?

b. What is the wavelength associated with the electron?

Chapter 28

1 A calcium atom drops from 5.16 eV above the ground state to 2.93 eV above the ground state. What is the frequency of the photon emitted by the atom?

2. A calcium atom is in an excited state when the energy level is 2.93 eV, E_2, above the ground state. A photon of energy 1.20 eV strikes the calcium atom and is absorbed by it. To what energy level is the calcium atom raised? Refer to diagram below.

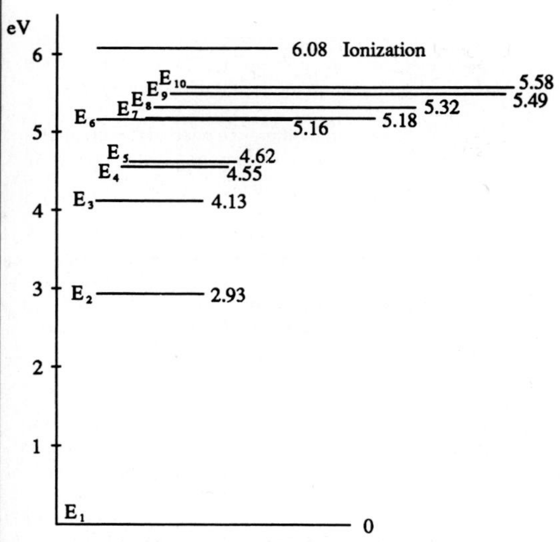

Energy Level Diagram for Calcium Atom

3. A calcium atom is in an excited state at the E_6 energy level. How much energy is released when the atom dropped down to the E_2 energy level?

▶ **4.** A photon of orange light, wavelength of 600 nm, enters a calcium atom in the E_6 excited state and ionizes the atom. What kinetic energy will the electron have as it is ejected from the atom?

5. Calculate the radius of the orbital associated with the energy level E_4 of the hydrogen atom.

6. Calculate the energy associated with the E_7 and the E_2 energy levels of the hydrogen atom.

7. Calculate the difference in energy levels in the previous problems.

8. What frequency photon is emitted from the hydrogen atom when the atom releases the energy found in the previous problem?

Chapter 29

1. An LED, light-emitting diode, produces infrared radiation wavelength, 800 nm, when an electron jumps from the conduction band to the valence band. Find the energy width of the forbidden gap in this diode.

2. How many free electrons exist in 1.00 cm^3 of lithium? Its density is 0.534 gm/cm^3, atomic weight is 6.941 g/mole, and there is one free electron per atom.

3. The voltage drop across a diode is 0.70 V when it is connected in series to a 210-Ω resistor and a battery, and there is a 11-mA current. If the LED has an equivalent resistance of 70 Ω, what potential difference must be supplied by the battery?

4. What resistor would replace the 210-Ω resistor in the previous problem if the current was changed to 30 mA?

5. What would the new current in the previous problem be if the leads on the battery were reversed?

Chapter 30

1. What particles, and how many of each, make up an atom of $^{109}_{47}Ag$?

2. A calcium ion has 20 protons and 20 neutrons. Write its isotopic symbol.

3. What is the isotopic symbol of a zinc atom composed of 30 protons and 34 neutrons?

708 Appendix B

4. Write the complete nuclear equation for the alpha decay of $^{210}_{84}Po$.

5. Write the complete nuclear equation for the beta decay of $^{14}_{6}C$.

6. Complete the nuclear reaction:
$^{225}_{89}Ac \rightarrow ^{4}_{2}He +$

7. Complete the nuclear reaction:
$^{227}_{88}Ra \rightarrow ^{\;\;0}_{-1}e +$

▶ **8.** Complete the nuclear reaction:
$^{65}_{29}Cu + ^{1}_{0}n \rightarrow$ ______ $\rightarrow ^{1}_{1}p +$

▶ **9.** Complete the nuclear equation:
$^{235}_{92}U + ^{1}_{0}n \rightarrow ^{96}_{40}Zr + 3(^{1}_{0}n) +$

10. An isotope has a half-life of 3.0 days. What percent of the original material will be left after
a. 6.0 days?
b. 9.0 days?
c. 12 days?

11. $^{211}_{86}Rn$ has a half-life of 15 h. What fraction of a sample would be left after 60 h?

▶ **12.** $^{209}_{84}Po$ has a half-life of 103 years. How long would it take for a 100-g sample to decay so only 3.1 g of Po-209 was left?

▶ **13.** The positron, $^{\;\;0}_{+1}e$, is the antiparticle to the electron and is the particle ejected from the nucleus in some nuclear reactions. Complete the nuclear reaction:
$^{17}_{9}F \rightarrow ^{\;\;0}_{+1}e +$

▶ **14.** Complete the nuclear reaction: $^{22}_{11}Na \rightarrow ^{\;\;0}_{+1}e +$

15. Find the charge of a π^{+} meson made of a *u* and *anti-d* quark pair.

16. Baryons are particles that are made of three quarks. Find the charge on each of the following baryons.
a. neutron; *d, d, u* quark triplet
b. antiproton; *anti-u, anti-u, anti-d* quark triplet

Chapter 31

1. The carbon isotope, $^{12}_{6}C$, has a nuclear mass of 12.000 000 u.
a. What is the mass defect of this isotope?
b. What is the binding energy of its nucleus?

2. The sulfur isotope, $^{32}_{16}S$, has a nuclear mass of 31.972 07 u.
a. What is the mass defect of this isotope?
b. What is the binding energy of its nucleus?

3. The sodium isotope, $^{22}_{11}Na$, has a nuclear mass of 21.994 434 u.
a. What is the mass defect of this isotope?
b. What is the binding energy of its nucleus?
c. What is the binding energy per nucleon?

▶ **4.** The binding energy for $^{7}_{3}Li$ is 39.25 MeV. Calculate the mass of the lithium-7 nucleus in atomic mass units.

5. Write the complete nuclear equation for the positron decay of $^{132}_{55}Cs$.

6. Complete the nuclear reaction:
$^{14}_{7}N + ^{1}_{0}n \rightarrow$ ______ $\rightarrow ^{1}_{1}p +$

7. Complete the nuclear reaction:
$^{65}_{29}Cu + ^{1}_{0}n \rightarrow$ ______ $\rightarrow ^{1}_{1}p +$

8. When a magnesium isotope, $^{24}_{12}Mg$, is bombarded with neutrons, it absorbs a neutron and then emits a proton. Write the complete nuclear equation for this reaction.

▶ **9.** When oxygen-17 is bombarded by neutrons, it absorbs a neutron and then emits an alpha particle. The resulting nucleus is unstable and it will emit a beta particle. Write the complete nuclear equation for this reaction.

10. Complete the following fission reaction:
$^{239}_{94}Pu + ^{1}_{0}n \rightarrow ^{137}_{52}Te + 3(^{1}_{0}n)$

11. Complete the following fission reaction:
$^{233}_{92}U + ^{1}_{0}n \rightarrow ^{134}_{55}Cs + 2(^{1}_{0}n) +$

12. Complete the following fission reaction:
$^{235}_{92}U + ^{1}_{0}n \rightarrow ^{90}_{38}Sr + 10(^{1}_{0}n) +$

▶ **13.** Strontium-90 has a mass of 89.907 747 u, xenon-136 has a mass of 135.907 221 u, and uranium-235 has a mass of 235.043 915 u.
a. Compute the mass defect in the previous problem.
b. Compute the amount of energy released.

▶ **14.** One of the simplest fusion reactions involves the production of deuterium, $^{2}_{1}H$ (2.014 102 u), from a neutron and a proton. Write the complete fusion reaction and find the amount of energy released.

15. The fusion reactions most likely to succeed in a fusion reactor are listed below. Complete each fusion reaction.
a. $^{2}_{1}H + ^{2}_{1}H \rightarrow ^{3}_{1}H +$
b. $^{2}_{1}H + ^{2}_{1}H \rightarrow ^{3}_{2}He +$
c. $^{2}_{1}H + ^{3}_{1}H \rightarrow ^{4}_{2}He +$
d. $^{3}_{1}H + ^{3}_{1}H \rightarrow ^{4}_{2}He + 2$

Answers to
SUPPLEMENTAL PROBLEMS
Chapter 30 (continued)

11. 1/16 is left.
12. 5 half-lives or 515 years
13. $^{0}_{1}e + ^{17}_{8}O + ^{0}_{0}\nu$
14. $^{0}_{1}e + ^{22}_{10}Ne + ^{0}_{0}\nu$
15. +1
16. **a.** 0
b. −1

Chapter 31

1. **a.** 0.098 940 u
b. 92.16 MeV
2. **a.** 0.291 77 u
b. 271.8 MeV
3. **a.** 0.186 96 u
b. 174.2 MeV
c. 7.916 MeV/nucleon
4. 7.01600 u
5. $^{132}_{55}Cs \rightarrow ^{0}_{1}e + ^{132}_{54}Xe + ^{0}_{0}\nu$
6. $^{15}_{7}N \rightarrow ^{1}_{1}p + ^{14}_{6}C$
7. $^{66}_{29}Cu \rightarrow ^{1}_{1}p + ^{65}_{28}Ni$
8. $^{24}_{12}Mg + ^{1}_{0}n \rightarrow ^{25}_{12}Mg \rightarrow ^{1}_{1}p + ^{24}_{11}Na$
9. $^{17}_{8}O + ^{1}_{0}n \rightarrow ^{18}_{8}O \rightarrow ^{4}_{2}He + ^{14}_{6}C \rightarrow ^{\;\;0}_{-1}e + ^{14}_{7}N + ^{0}_{0}\bar{\nu}$
10. $^{137}_{52}Te + 3(^{1}_{0}n) + ^{100}_{42}Mo$
11. $^{134}_{55}Cs + 2(^{1}_{0}n) + ^{98}_{37}Rb$
12. $^{90}_{38}Sr + 10(^{1}_{0}n) + ^{136}_{54}Xe$
13. **a.** 0.15096
b. 140.6 MeV
14. $^{1}_{1}p + ^{1}_{0}n \rightarrow ^{2}_{1}H$ 2.224 MeV
15. **a.** $^{2}_{1}H + ^{2}_{1}H \rightarrow ^{3}_{1}H + ^{1}_{1}H$
b. $^{2}_{1}H + ^{2}_{1}H \rightarrow ^{3}_{2}H + ^{1}_{0}n$
c. $^{2}_{1}H + ^{3}_{1}H \rightarrow ^{4}_{2}H + ^{1}_{0}n$
d. $^{3}_{1}H + ^{3}_{1}H \rightarrow ^{4}_{2}H_2 + 2(^{1}_{0}n)$

Appendix C
Equations

Chapter 3 Describing Motion: Velocity

$\bar{v} = \frac{\Delta d}{\Delta t}$

Chapter 4 Acceleration

$\bar{a} = \frac{\Delta v}{\Delta t}$

$v_f = v_i + at$

$d = \frac{1}{2}(v_f + v_i)t$

$d = v_i t + \frac{1}{2}at^2$

$v_f^2 = v_i^2 + 2ad$

Chapter 5 Forces

$F = ma$

$W = mg$

$F_f = \mu F_N$

Chapter 6 Vectors

$F_v = F \sin \theta$ $\quad F_h = F \cos \theta$

$F^2 = F_h^2 + F_v^2$

Chapter 7 Motion in Two Dimensions

$x = v_x t$ $\quad y = v_y t + \frac{1}{2}gt^2$

$a_c = \frac{v^2}{r}$ $\quad T = 2\pi\sqrt{\frac{l}{|g|}}$

Chapter 8 Universal Gravitation

$F = G\frac{m_1 m_2}{d^2}$

Chapter 9 Momentum and Its Conservation

$p = mv$

$F\Delta t = \Delta p$

$p_A + p_B = p'_A + p'_B$

Chapter 10 Work, Energy, and Simple Machines

$W = Fd$

$P = \frac{W}{t}$ $\quad MA = \frac{F_r}{F_e}$

$IMA = \frac{d_e}{d_r}$

$efficiency = \frac{W_o}{W_i} \times 100\%$

Chapter 11 Energy

$KE = \frac{1}{2}mv^2$

$W = \Delta KE$

$PE = mgh$

$KE_i + PE_i = KE_f + PE_f$

Chapter 12 Thermal Energy

$Q = mC\Delta T$

$Q = mH_f$

$Q = mH_v$

Chapter 13 States of Matter

$p = \frac{F}{A}$ $\quad \frac{F_1}{A_1} = \frac{F_2}{A_2}$

Chapter 14 Waves and Energy Transfer

$v = \lambda f$

Chapter 16 Light

$E = \frac{P}{4\pi d^2}$

Chapter 17 Reflection and Refraction

$n_i \sin \theta_i = n_r \sin \theta_r$

$n = \frac{c}{v}$

Chapter 18 Mirrors and Lenses

$\frac{1}{f} = \frac{1}{d_i} + \frac{1}{d_o}$

$m = \frac{h_i}{h_o} = -\frac{d_i}{d_o}$

Chapter 19 Diffraction and Interference of Light

$\lambda = \frac{xd}{L} = d \sin \theta$

Chapter 20 Static Electricity

$F = \frac{Kqq'}{d^2}$

Chapter 21 Electric Fields

$E = \frac{F}{q'}$ $\quad \Delta V = \frac{\Delta PE}{q'}$

$C = \frac{q}{V}$

Chapter 22 Current Electricity

$R = \frac{V}{I}$ $\quad P = VI$

Chapter 23 Series and Parallel Circuits

$R_{eq} = R_1 + R_2 + R_3$

$\frac{1}{R_{eq}} = \frac{1}{R_1} + \frac{1}{R_2} + \frac{1}{R_3}$

Chapter 24 Magnetic Fields

$B = \frac{F}{IL}$ $\quad F = Bqv$

Chapter 25 Electromagnetic Induction

$EMF = BLv$ $\quad I_{eff} = 0.707 I_{max}$

$V_{eff} = 0.707 V_{max}$

$\frac{V_s}{V_p} = \frac{N_s}{N_p}$

Chapter 26 Electric and Magnetic Fields

$\frac{q}{m} = \frac{v}{Br}$ $\quad \frac{q}{m} = \frac{2V}{B^2 r^2}$

Chapter 27 Quantum Theory

$E = nhf$ $\quad KE = hf - hf_o$

$p = \frac{h}{\lambda}$

Chapter 28 The Atom

$r_n = \frac{h^2}{4\pi^2 Kmq^2}n^2$

$E_n = \frac{-2\pi^2 K^2 mq^4}{h^2} \cdot \frac{1}{n^2}$

$hf = \Delta E$

Chapter 31 Nuclear Applications

$E = mc^2$

710

Appendix D
Tables

TABLE D–1
SI Base Units

Measurement	Unit	Symbol
length	meter	m
mass	kilogram	kg
time	second	s
electric current	ampere	A
temperature	kelvin	K
amount of substance	mole	mol
intensity of light	candela	cd

TABLE D–2
SI Prefixes

Prefix		Multiplication Factor	Prefix		Multiplication Factor
exa	E	1 000 000 000 000 000 000 = 10^{18}	deci	d	0.1 = 10^{-1}
peta	P	1 000 000 000 000 000 = 10^{15}	centi	c	0.01 = 10^{-2}
tera	T	1 000 000 000 000 = 10^{12}	milli	m	0.001 = 10^{-3}
giga	G	1 000 000 000 = 10^{9}	micro	μ	0.000 001 = 10^{-6}
mega	M	1 000 000 = 10^{6}	nano	n	0.000 000 001 = 10^{-9}
kilo	k	1 000 = 10^{3}	pico	p	0.000 000 000 001 = 10^{-12}
hecto	h	100 = 10^{2}	femto	f	0.000 000 000 000 001 = 10^{-15}
deka	da	10 = 10^{1}	atto	a	0.000 000 000 000 000 001 = 10^{-18}

TABLE D–3
Units with Special Names Derived from SI Base Units

Measurement	Unit	Symbol	Expressed in Base Units
energy, work	joule	J	$kg \cdot m^2/s^2$
force	newton	N	$kg \cdot m/s^2$
frequency	hertz	Hz	1/s
illuminance	lux	lx	$cd \cdot sr/m^2 (lm/m^2)$
luminous flux	lumen	lm	$cd \cdot sr$
potential difference	volt	V	$kg \cdot m^2/A \cdot s^3$ (W/A)
power	watt	W	$kg \cdot m^2/s^3$ (J/s)
pressure	pascal	Pa	$kg/m \cdot s^2$ (N/m^2)
quantity of electric charge	coulomb	C	$A \cdot s$
resistance	ohm	Ω	$m^2 \cdot kg/s^3 \cdot A^2$ (V/A)
magnetic field strength	tesla	T	$kg/C \cdot s$ ($1\ N/A \cdot m$)
capacitance	farad	F	$A^2 \cdot s^4/kg \cdot m^2$

711

TABLE D–4
Reference Data: Physical Constants, Conversion Factors, Useful Equations

Physical Constants

Absolute zero temperature: 0 K = −273.15°C

Acceleration due to gravity at sea level (Washington D.C.): 9.801 m/s^2

Avogadro's number: N_O = 6.022 × 10^{23} particles/mole

Charge of an electron: e = −1.6022 × 10^{-19} C

Constant in Coulomb's law: K = 8.988 × 10^9 N · m^3/C^2

Gravitational constant: G = 6.673 × 10^{-11} N · m^2/kg^2

Mass of an electron: m_e = 9.109 × 10^{-31} kg

Mass of a proton: m_p = 1.673 × 10^{-27} kg

Planck's constant: h = 6.626 × 10^{-34} J/Hz = 4.136 × 10^{-15} eV · s

Speed of light in a vacuum: c = 2.99792458 × 10^8 m/s (exact)

Conversion Factors

1 atomic mass unit = 1.661 × 10^{-27} kg = 931.5 MeV/c^2

1 electronvolt = 1.602 × 10^{-19} J

1 joule = 1 N · m

1 joule = 1 V · C

1 coulomb = 6.242 × 10^{18} elementary charge units

Useful Equations

Quadratic equation: A quadratic equation may be reduced to the form

$$ax^2 + bx + c = 0$$

then

$$x = \frac{-b \pm \sqrt{b^2 - 4ac}}{2a}$$

Remember that the sign immediately preceding the coefficient is carried with the coefficient in solving for the two values of x.

Circumference of a circle: $C = 2\pi r$ or $C = \pi d$

Area of a circle: $A = \pi r^2$

Volume of a cylinder: $V = \pi r^2 h$

Surface area of a sphere: $A = 4\pi r^2$

Volume of a sphere: $V = \dfrac{4\pi r^3}{3}$

712

TABLE D–5
International Atomic Masses

Element	Symbol	Atomic number	Atomic mass
Actinium	Ac	89	227.02777*
Aluminum	Al	13	26.98154
Americium	Am	95	243.06139*
Antimony	Sb	51	121.75
Argon	Ar	18	39.948
Arsenic	As	33	74.9216
Astatine	At	85	209.98704*
Barium	Ba	56	137.33
Berkelium	Bk	97	247.07032*
Beryllium	Be	4	9.01218
Bismuth	Bi	83	208.9804
Boron	B	5	10.81
Bromine	Br	35	79.904
Cadmium	Cd	48	112.41
Calcium	Ca	20	40.08
Californium	Cf	98	251.07961*
Carbon	C	6	12.011
Cerium	Ce	58	140.12
Cesium	Cs	55	132.9054
Chlorine	Cl	17	35.453
Chromium	Cr	24	51.996
Cobalt	Co	27	58.9332
Copper	Cu	29	63.546
Curium	Cm	96	247.07038*
Dysprosium	Dy	66	162.50
Einsteinium	Es	99	254.08805*
Erbium	Er	68	167.26
Europium	Eu	63	151.96
Fermium	Fm	100	257.09515*
Fluorine	F	9	18.998403
Francium	Fr	87	223.01976*
Gadolinium	Gd	64	157.25
Gallium	Ga	31	69.72
Germanium	Ge	32	72.59
Gold	Au	79	196.9665
Hafnium	Hf	72	178.49
Helium	He	2	4.00260
Holmium	Ho	67	164.9304
Hydrogen	H	1	1.0079
Indium	In	49	114.82
Iodine	I	53	126.9045
Iridium	Ir	77	192.22
Iron	Fe	26	55.847
Krypton	Kr	36	83.80
Lanthanum	La	57	138.9055
Lawrencium	Lr	103	256.099*
Lead	Pb	82	207.2
Lithium	Li	3	6.941
Lutetium	Lu	71	174.97
Magnesium	Mg	12	24.305
Manganese	Mn	25	54.9380
Mendelevium	Md	101	258*
Mercury	Hg	80	200.59
Molybdenum	Mo	42	95.94
Neodymium	Nd	60	144.24
Neon	Ne	10	20.179
Neptunium	Np	93	237.04819
Nickel	Ni	28	58.70
Niobium	Nb	41	92.9064
Nitrogen	N	7	14.0067
Nobelium	No	102	255.093*
Osmium	Os	76	190.2
Oxygen	O	8	15.9994
Palladium	Pd	46	106.4
Phosphorus	P	15	30.97376
Platinum	Pt	78	195.09
Plutonium	Pu	94	244.06424*
Polonium	Po	84	208.98244*
Potassium	K	19	39.0983
Praseodymium	Pr	59	140.9077
Promethium	Pm	61	144.91279*
Protactinium	Pa	91	231.03590*
Radium	Ra	88	226.0254
Radon	Rn	86	222*
Rhenium	Re	75	186.207
Rhodium	Rh	45	102.9055
Rubidium	Rb	37	85.4678
Ruthenium	Ru	44	101.07
Samarium	Sm	62	150.4
Scandium	Sc	21	44.9559
Selenium	Se	34	78.96
Silicon	Si	14	28.0855
Silver	Ag	47	107.868
Sodium	Na	11	22.98977
Strontium	Sr	38	87.62
Sulfur	S	16	32.06
Tantalum	Ta	73	180.9479
Technetium	Tc	43	96.90639*
Tellurium	Te	52	127.60
Terbium	Tb	65	158.9254
Thallium	Tl	81	204.37
Thorium	Th	90	232.0381
Thulium	Tm	69	168.9342
Tin	Sn	50	118.69
Titanium	Ti	22	47.90
Tungsten	W	74	183.85
Uranium	U	92	238.029
Vanadium	V	23	50.9414
Xenon	Xe	54	131.30
Ytterbium	Yb	70	173.04
Yttrium	Y	39	88.9059
Zinc	Zn	30	65.38
Zirconium	Zr	40	91.22
Element 104†		104	257*
Element 105†		105	260*
Element 106†		106	263*
Element 107†		107	258*
Element 108†		108	265*
Element 109†		109	266*

*The mass of the isotope with the longest known half-life.
†Names for elements 104 and 105 have not yet been approved by the IUPAC. The USSR has proposed Kurchatovium (Ku) for element 104 and Bohrium (Bh) for element 105. The United States has proposed Rutherfordium (Rf) for element 104 and Hahnium (Ha) for element 105.

713

TABLE D–6 Trigonometric Functions

Angle	sin	cos	tan	Angle	sin	cos	tan
0°	.0000	1.0000	.0000	**45°**	.7071	.7071	1.0000
1°	.0175	.9998	.0175	**46°**	.7193	.6947	1.0355
2°	.0349	.9994	.0349	**47°**	.7314	.6820	1.0724
3°	.0523	.9986	.0524	**48°**	.7431	.6691	1.1106
4°	.0698	.9976	.0699	**49°**	.7547	.6561	1.1504
5°	.0872	.9962	.0875	**50°**	.7660	.6428	1.1918
6°	.1045	.9945	.1051	**51°**	.7771	.6293	1.2349
7°	.1219	.9925	.1228	**52°**	.7880	.6157	1.2799
8°	.1392	.9903	.1405	**53°**	.7986	.6018	1.3270
9°	.1564	.9877	.1584	**54°**	.8090	.5878	1.3764
10°	.1736	.9848	.1763	**55°**	.8192	.5736	1.4281
11°	.1908	.9816	.1944	**56°**	.8290	.5592	1.4826
12°	.2079	.9781	.2126	**57°**	.8387	.5446	1.5399
13°	.2250	.9744	.2309	**58°**	.8480	.5299	1.6003
14°	.2419	.9703	.2493	**59°**	.8572	.5150	1.6643
15°	.2588	.9659	.2679	**60°**	.8660	.5000	1.7321
16°	.2756	.9613	.2867	**61°**	.8746	.4848	1.8040
17°	.2924	.9563	.3057	**62°**	.8829	.4695	1.8807
18°	.3090	.9511	.3249	**63°**	.8910	.4540	1.9626
19°	.3256	.9455	.3443	**64°**	.8988	.4384	2.0503
20°	.3420	.9397	.3640	**65°**	.9063	.4226	2.1445
21°	.3584	.9336	.3839	**66°**	.9135	.4067	2.2460
22°	.3746	.9272	.4040	**67°**	.9205	.3907	2.3559
23°	.3907	.9205	.4245	**68°**	.9272	.3746	2.4751
24°	.4067	.9135	.4452	**69°**	.9336	.3584	2.6051
25°	.4226	.9063	.4663	**70°**	.9397	.3420	2.7475
26°	.4384	.8988	.4877	**71°**	.9455	.3256	2.9042
27°	.4540	.8910	.5095	**72°**	.9511	.3090	3.0777
28°	.4695	.8829	.5317	**73°**	.9563	.2924	3.2709
29°	.4848	.8746	.5543	**74°**	.9613	.2756	3.4874
30°	.5000	.8660	.5774	**75°**	.9659	.2588	3.7321
31°	.5150	.8572	.6009	**76°**	.9703	.2419	4.0108
32°	.5299	.8480	.6249	**77°**	.9744	.2250	4.3315
33°	.5446	.8387	.6494	**78°**	.9781	.2079	4.7046
34°	.5592	.8290	.6745	**79°**	.9816	.1908	5.1446
35°	.5736	.8192	.7002	**80°**	.9848	.1736	5.6713
36°	.5878	.8090	.7265	**81°**	.9877	.1564	6.3138
37°	.6018	.7986	.7536	**82°**	.9903	.1392	7.1154
38°	.6157	.7880	.7813	**83°**	.9925	.1219	8.1443
39°	.6293	.7771	.8098	**84°**	.9945	.1045	9.5144
40°	.6428	.7660	.8391	**85°**	.9962	.0872	11.4301
41°	.6561	.7547	.8693	**86°**	.9976	.0698	14.3007
42°	.6691	.7431	.9004	**87°**	.9986	.0523	19.0811
43°	.6820	.7314	.9325	**88°**	.9994	.0349	28.6363
44°	.6947	.7193	.9657	**89°**	.9998	.0175	57.2900
45°	.7071	.7071	1.0000	**90°**	1.0000	.0000	∞

714

TABLE D–7
Safety Symbols

DISPOSAL ALERT This symbol appears when care must be taken to dispose of materials properly.	**LASER SAFETY** This symbol appears when care must be taken to avoid staring directly into the laser beam or at bright reflections.
BIOLOGICAL HAZARD This symbol appears when there is danger involving bacteria, fungi, or protists.	**RADIOACTIVE SAFETY** This symbol appears when radioactive materials are used.
OPEN FLAME ALERT This symbol appears when use of an open flame could cause a fire or an explosion.	**CLOTHING PROTECTION SAFETY** This symbol appears when substances used could stain or burn clothing.
THERMAL SAFETY This symbol appears as a reminder to use caution when handling hot objects.	**FIRE SAFETY** This symbol appears when care should be taken around open flames.
SHARP OBJECT SAFETY This symbol appears when a danger of cuts or punctures caused by the use of sharp objects exists.	**EXPLOSION SAFETY** This symbol appears when the misuse of chemicals could cause an explosion.
FUME SAFETY This symbol appears when chemicals or chemical reactions could cause dangerous fumes.	**EYE SAFETY** This symbol appears when a danger to the eyes exists. Safety goggles should be worn when this symbol appears
ELECTRICAL SAFETY This symbol appears when care should be taken when using electrical equipment	**POISON SAFETY** This symbol appears when poisonous substances are used.
PLANT SAFETY This symbol appears when poisonous plants or plants with thorns are handled.	**CHEMICAL SAFETY** This symbol appears when chemicals used can cause burns or are poisonous if absorbed through the skin.

715

Appendix E
Laws of Cosines and Sines

E:1 Law of Cosines

To use the trigonometry of the right triangle, two of the sides of a triangle must be perpendicular. That is, you must have a right triangle. But sometimes you will need to work with a triangle that is not a right triangle. The law of cosines applies to all triangles. Consider the two triangles shown in Figure E-1. They are not right triangles. When angle C is known, the lengths of the sides obey the following relationship.

$$c^2 = a^2 + b^2 - 2ab \cos C$$

If a, b, and angle C are known, the length of side c is

$$c = \sqrt{a^2 + b^2 - 2ab \cos C}.$$

In triangle 1 of Figure E-1, the length of side a is 4.00 cm, side b is 5.00 cm, and angle C is 60.0°. Substituting the values in the equation, side c is obtained. Substituting the appropriate values yields

$$a^2 = (4.0 \text{ cm})^2 = 16.0 \text{ cm}^2$$

$$b^2 = (5.0 \text{ cm})^2 = 25.0 \text{ cm}^2$$

$$\begin{aligned} 2ab \cos \theta &= 2(4.00 \text{ cm})(5.00 \text{ cm})(\cos 60.0°) \\ &= 2(4.00 \text{ cm})(5.00 \text{ cm})(0.500) \\ 2ab \cos \theta &= 20.0 \text{ cm}^2. \end{aligned}$$

Therefore,

$$\begin{aligned} c &= \sqrt{a^2 + b^2 - 2ab \cos \theta} \\ &= \sqrt{16.0 \text{ cm}^2 + 25.0 \text{ cm}^2 - 20.0 \text{ cm}^2} \\ &= \sqrt{21.0 \text{ cm}^2} \\ c &= 4.58 \text{ cm} \end{aligned}$$

If angle C is larger than 90°, its cosine is negative and is numerically equal to the cosine of its supplement. In triangle 2, Figure E-1, angle C is 120.0°. Therefore, its cosine is the negative of the cosine of (180.0° − 120.0°) or 60.0°. The cosine of 60.0° is 0.500. Thus, the cosine of 120.0° is −0.500.

E:2 Law of Sines

Just as the law of cosines applies to all triangles, the law of sines also applies to all triangles. The relationship is

$$\frac{a}{\sin A} = \frac{b}{\sin B} = \frac{c}{\sin C}.$$

Using the values for triangle 1 shown in Figure E-1, angle A can be calculated by the law of sines.

$$\frac{a}{\sin A} = \frac{c}{\sin C}$$

$$\sin A = \frac{a}{c} \sin C$$

$$\begin{aligned} \sin A &= \frac{4.00 \text{ cm}}{4.58 \text{ cm}} \sin (60.0°) \\ &= \frac{(4.00 \text{ cm})(0.867)}{(4.58 \text{ cm})} \\ &= 0.757 \\ A &= 49.2° \end{aligned}$$

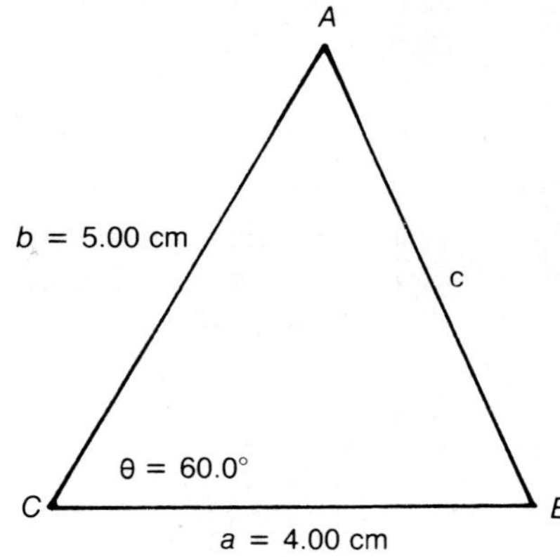

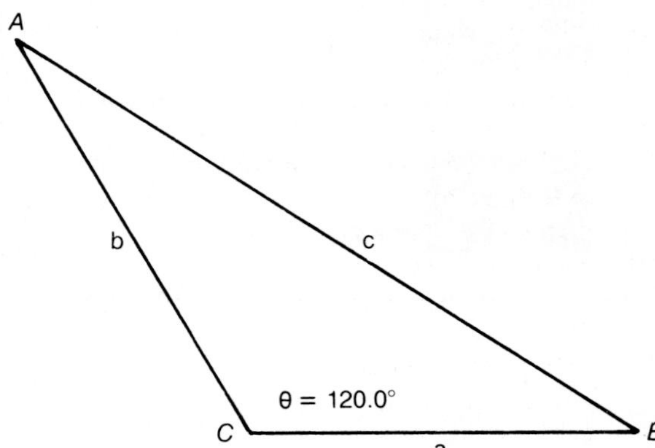

FIGURE E-1.

Appendix F
Physics Nobel Laureates

1901 **Wilhelm Roentgen**
discovered X rays

1902 **Hendrik A. Lorentz**
predicted the Zeeman effect

1902 **Pieter Zeeman**
discovered the Zeeman effect, the splitting of spectral lines in magnetic fields

1903 **Antoine-Henri Becquerel**
discovered radioactivity

1903 **Pierre and Marie Curie**
studied radioactivity

1904 **Lord Rayleigh**
studied the density of gases and discovered argon

1905 **Philipp Lenard**
studied cathode rays and electrons

1906 **J. J. Thomson**
studied electrical discharge through gases and discovered the electron

1907 **Albert A. Michelson**
invented optical instruments and measured the speed of light

1908 **Gabriel Lippmann**
made the first color photographic plate, using interference methods

1909 **Guglielmo Marconi** and **Carl Ferdinand Braun**
developed wireless telegraphy

1910 **Johannes D. van der Waals**
studied the equation of state for gases and liquids

1911 **Wilhelm Wien**
discovered Wien's law giving the peak of a blackbody spectrum

1912 **Nils Dalén**
invented automatic gas regulators for lighthouses

1913 **Heike Kamerlingh Onnes**
discovered superconductivity and liquefied helium

1914 **Max T. F. von Laue**
studied X rays from their diffraction by crystals, showing that X rays are electromagnetic waves

1915 **William Henry Bragg** and **William Lawrence Bragg**, (his son)
studied the diffraction of X rays in crystals

1917 **Charles Barkla**
studied atoms by X-ray scattering

1918 **Max Planck**
discovered energy quanta

1919 **Johannes Stark**
discovered the Stark effect, the splitting of spectral lines in electric fields

1920 **Charles-Édouard Guillaume**
discovered invar, a nickel-steel alloy with low coefficient of expansion

1921 **Albert Einstein**
explained the photoelectric effect and honored for his service to theoretical physics

1922 **Niels Bohr**
model of the atom and its radiation

1923 **Robert A. Millikan**
measured the charge on an electron and studied the photoelectric effect experimentally

1924 **Karl M. G. Siegbahn**
X-ray spectroscopy

1925 **James Franck** and **Gustav Hertz**
discovered the Franck-Hertz effect in electron-atom collisions

1926 **Jean-Baptiste Perrin**
studied Brownian motion to validate the discontinuous structure of matter and measure the size of atoms

1927 **Arthur Holly Compton**
discovered the Compton effect on X rays, and how they change in wavelength when they collide with matter

1927 **Charles T. R. Wilson**
invented the cloud chamber, used to study charged particles

1928 **Owen W. Richardson**
studied the thermionic effect and electrons emitted by hot metals

1929 **Louis Victor de Broglie**
discovered the wave nature of electrons

1930 **Chandrasekhara Venkata Raman**
studied Raman scattering, the scattering of light by atoms and molecules with a change in wavelength

1932 **Werner Heisenberg**
created quantum mechanics

1933 **Erwin Schrödinger** and **Paul A. M. Dirac**
developed wave mechanics and relativistic quantum mechanics

1935 **James Chadwick**
discovered the neutron

1936 **Carl D. Anderson**
discovered the positron in particular and antimatter in general

1936 **Victor F. Hess**
discovered cosmic rays

1937 **Clinton Davisson** and **George Thomson**
discovered the diffraction of electrons by crystals, confirming de Broglie's hypothesis

1938 **Enrico Fermi**
produced transuranic radioactive elements by neutron irradiation

1939 **Ernest O. Lawrence**
invented the cyclotron

717

1943 Otto Stern
developed molecular-beam studies and used them to discover the magnetic element of the proton

1944 Isidor I. Rabi
discovered nuclear magnetic resonance in atomic and molecular beams

1945 Wolfgang Pauli
discovered the exclusion principle

1946 Percy W. Bridgman
studied physics at high pressures

1947 Edward V. Appleton
studied the ionosphere

1948 Patrick M. S. Blackett
studied nuclear physics with cloud-chamber photographs of cosmic-ray interactions

1949 Hideki Yukawa
predicted the existence of mesons

1950 Cecil F. Powell
developed the method of studying cosmic rays with photographic emulsions and discovered new mesons

1951 John D. Cockcroft and **Ernest T. S. Walton**
transmuted nuclei in an accelerator

1952 Felix Bloch and **Edward Mills Purcell**
discovered nuclear magnetic resonance in liquids and gases

1953 Frits Zernike
invented the phase-contrast microscope

1954 Max Born
interpreted the wave function as a probability

1954 Walther Bothe
developed the coincidence method to study subatomic particles

1955 Willis E. Lamb, Jr.
discovered the Lamb shift in the hydrogen spectrum

1955 Polykarp Kusch
determined the magnetic moment of the electron

1956 John Bardeen, Walter H. Brattain, and **William Shockley**
invented the transistor

1957 T.-D. Lee and **C.-N. Yang**
predicted that parity is not conserved in beta decay

1958 Pavel A. Cerenkov
discovered Cerenkov radiation

1958 Ilya M. Frank and **Igor Tamm**
interpreted Cerenkov radiation

1959 Emilio G. Segre and **Owen Chamberlain**
discovered the antiproton

1960 Donald A. Glaser
invented the bubble chamber to study elementary particles

1961 Robert Hofstadter
discovered internal structure in protons and neutrons

1961 Rudolf L. Mössbauer
discovered the Mössbauer effect of recoilless gamma-ray emission

1962 Lev Davidovich Landau
studied liquid helium and other condensed matter theoretically

1963 Eugene P. Wigner
applied symmetry principles to elementary-particle theory

1963 Maria Goeppert Mayer and **J. Hans D. Jensen**
studied the shell model of nuclei

1964 Charles H. Townes, Nikolai G. Basov, and **Alexander M. Prokhorov**
developed masers and lasers

1965 Sin-itiro Tomonaga, Julian S. Schwinger, and **Richard P. Feynman**
developed quantum electrodynamics

1966 Alfred Kastler
optical methods of studying atomic energy levels

1967 Hans Albrecht Bethe
discovered the routes of energy production in stars

1968 Luis W. Alvarez
discovered resonance states of elementary particles

1969 Murray Gell-Mann
classified elementary particles

1970 Hannes Alfvén
developed magnetohydrodynamic theory

1970 Louis Eugène Félix Néel
discovered antiferromagnetism and ferrimagnetism

1971 Dennis Gabor
developed holography

1972 John Bardeen, Leon N. Cooper, and **John Robert Schrieffer**
explained superconductivity

1973 Leo Esaki
discovered tunneling in semiconductors

1973 Ivar Giaever
discovered tunneling in superconductors

1973 Brian D. Josephson
predicted the Josephson effect

1974 Anthony Hewish
discovered pulsars

1974 Martin Ryle
developed radio interferometry

1975 Aage N. Bohr, Ben R. Mottelson, and **James Rainwater**
discovered why some nuclei take asymmetric shapes

1976 Burton Richter and **Samuel C. C. Ting**
discovered the J/psi particle, the first charmed particle

1977 John H. Van Vleck, Nevill F. Mott, and **Philip W. Anderson**
studied solids in terms of quantum mechanics

1978 Arno A. Penzias and **Robert W. Wilson**
discovered the cosmic background radiation

718

1978 Pyotr Kapitsa
studies of liquid helium

1979 Sheldon L. Glashow, Abdus Salam, and **Steven Weinberg**
developed theory that unified the weak and electromagnetic forces

1980 Val Fitch and **James W. Cronin**
discovered **CP** (charge-parity) violation

1981 Nicolaas Bloembergen and **Arthur L. Schawlow**
developed laser spectroscopy

1981 Kai M. Siegbahn
developed high-resolution electron spectroscopy

1982 Kenneth G. Wilson
developed a method of constructing theories of phase transitions to analyze critical phenomena

1983 William A. Fowler
theoretical studies of astrophysical nucleosynthesis

1983 Subramanyan Chandrasekhar
studied physical processes of importance to stellar structure and evolution, including the prediction of white dwarf stars

1984 Carlo Rubbia
discovered the ***W*** and ***Z*** particles

1984 Simon van der Meer
developed the method of stochastic cooling of the CERN beam that allowed the discovery

1985 Klaus von Klitzing
quantized Hall effect, relating to conductivity in the presence of a magnetic field

1986 Ernst Ruska
invented the electron microscope

1986 Gerd Binnig and **Heinrich Rohrer**
invented the scanning-tunneling electron microscope

1987 J. Georg Bednorz and **Karl Alex Müller**
discovered high temperature superconductivity

1988 Leon M. Lederman, Melvin Schwartz, and **Jack Steinberger**
the development of a new tool for studying the weak nuclear force, which affects the radioactive decay of atoms

1989 Norman Ramsay
development of techniques for studying the structure of atoms, the hydrogen atom and hydrogen maser, and the development of the cesium atomic clock

1989 Hans Dehmelt and **Wolfgang Paul**
development of the ion-trap method for separating charged particles, especially the electron and ions

1990 Richard E. Taylor, Jerome I. Friedman, and **Henry W. Kendall**
"deep inelastic scattering" experiments that showed the quark structures of the proton and neutron

719

Glossary

The numbers in parentheses refer to the page on which the term is introduced.

A

absolute zero (246): Lowest possible temperature at which gas would have zero volume.
absorption spectrum (577): Spectrum of electromagnetic radiation absorbed by matter when radiation of all frequencies is passed through it.
acceleration (64): Change in velocity divided by time interval over which it occurred.
accuracy (22): Closeness of a measurement to the standard value of that quantity.
achromatic lens (384): Lens for which all light colors have the same focal length.
action-reaction forces (92): Pair of forces involved in an interaction that are equal in magnitude and opposite in direction.
activity (622): Number of decays per second of a radioactive substance.
adhesion (275): Force of attraction between two unlike materials.
air resistance (102): Force of air on objects moving through it.
alpha decay (618): Process in which a nucleus emits an alpha particle.
alpha particle (574): Positively-charged particles consisting of two protons and two neutrons emitted by radioactive materials.
ammeter (485): Device to measure electrical current.
amorphous solid (278): Solids that have no long-range order; no crystal structure.
ampere (A) (450): Unit of electric current. One ampere is the flow of one coulomb of charge per second.
amplitude (145): In any periodic motion, the maximum displacement from equilibrium.
angle of incidence (299): Angle between direction of motion of waves and a line perpendicular to surface the waves are striking.
angle of reflection (299): Angle between direction of motion of waves and a line perpendicular to surface the waves are reflected from.
angle of refraction (300): Angle between direction of motion of waves and a line perpendicular to surface the waves have been refracted from.
angular momentum (179): Quantity of rotational motion. For a rotating object, product of moment of inertia and angular velocity.
annihilation (629): Process in which a particle and its antiparticle are converted into energy.
antenna (544): Device used to receive or transmit electromagnetic waves.
antineutrino (620): Subatomic particle with no charge or mass emitted in beta decay.
antinode (298): Point of maximum displacement of two superimposed waves.
Archimedes' principle (270): Object immersed in a fluid has an upward force equal to the weight of the fluid displaced by the object.
artificial radioactivity (643): Radioactive isotope not found in nature.
atomic mass unit (u) (616): Unit of mass equal to 1/12 the atomic mass of the carbon-12 nucleus.
atomic number (Z) (616): Number of protons in the nucleus of the atom.
average acceleration (64): Acceleration measured over a finite time interval.
average velocity (44): Velocity measured over a finite time interval.

B

back-*EMF* (524): Potential difference across a conductor caused by change in magnetic flux.
band theory (596): Theory explaining electrical conduction in solids.
baryon (633): Subatomic particle composed of three quarks. Interacts with the strong nuclear force.
battery (448): Device that converts chemical to electrical energy consisting of two dissimilar conductors and an electrolyte.
beat (320): Slow oscillation in amplitude of a complex wave.
Bernoulli's principle (273): When a fixed quantity of fluid flows, the pressure is decreased when the flow velocity increases.
beta decay (619): Radioactive decay process in which an electron or positron and neutrino is emitted from a nucleus.
beta particle (619): High speed electron emitted by a radioactive nucleus in beta decay.
binding energy (640): Negative of the amount of energy needed to separate a nucleus into individual nucleons.
boiling point (253): Temperature at which a substance, under normal atmospheric pressure, changes from a liquid to a vapor state.
breeder reactor (649): Nuclear reactor that converts nonfissionable nuclei to fissionable nuclei while producing energy.
bubble chamber (627): Instrument containing superheated liquid in which the path of ionizing particles is made visible as trails of tiny bubbles.
buoyant force (270): Upward force on an object immersed in fluid.

C

calorimeter (250): Device that isolates objects to measure temperature changes due to heat flow.
candela (cd) (335): Unit of luminous intensity.
capacitance (441): Ratio of charge stored per increase in potential difference.
capacitor (441): Electrical device used to store charge and energy in the electric field.
capillary action (275): Rise of liquid in narrow tube due to surface tension.
Carnot efficiency (258): Ideal efficiency of heat engine or refrigerator working between two constant temperatures.
centripetal acceleration (143): Acceleration toward center of circular motion.
centripetal force (144): Force that causes centripetal acceleration.
chain reaction (647): Nuclear reaction in which neutrons are produced that can cause further reactions.
charged (408): Object that has an unbalance of positive and negative electrical charges.
charging by conduction (414): Process of charging by touching neutral object to a charged object.
charging by induction (414): Process of charging by bringing neutral object near charged object, then removing part of resulting separated charge.
chromatic aberration (383): Variation in focal length of lens with wavelength of light.
circular motion (142): Motion with constant radius of curvature caused by acceleration being perpendicular to velocity.
clock reading (43): Time between event and a reference time, usually zero.

closed, isolated system (180): Collection of objects such that neither matter nor energy can enter or leave the collection.
closed-pipe resonator (315): Cylindrical tube with one end closed and a sound source at other end.
coefficient of friction (μ) (97): Ratio of frictional force and the normal force between two surfaces.
coefficient of linear expansion (281): Change in length divided by original length and by temperature change.
coefficient of volume expansion (281): Change in volume divided by original volume and by temperature change.
coherent waves (392): Waves in which all are in step; are in phase.
cohesive force (274): Attractive force between similar substances.
complementary color (339): Two colors that, when added, produce white light. Two pigments, that when combined, produce black.
compound machine (207): Machine consisting of two or more simple machines.
Compton effect (563): Interaction of photons, usually X rays, with electrons in matter resulting in increased wavelength of X rays and kinetic energy of electrons.
concave lens (378): Lens thinner in center than edges; a diverging lens.
concave mirror (370): Converging mirror, one with center of curvature on reflecting side of mirror.
conduction band (599): Energies of charge carriers in a solid such that the carriers are free to move.
conductor (411): Materials (electrical) through which charged particles move readily; (heat) or heat flow readily.
conserved properties (180): Property (like energy or momentum) that is the same before and after an interaction.
consonance (321): Two or more sounds that, when heard together, sound pleasant.
constant acceleration (69): Acceleration that does not change in time.
constant velocity (47): Velocity that does not change in time.
constructive interference (297): Superposition of waves resulting in a combined wave with amplitude larger than the component waves.
convection (243): Heat transfer by means of motion of fluid.
conventional current (450): Motion of positive electrical current.
converging lens (378): Lens that causes light rays to converge; usually a convex lens.
convex lens (378): Lens that is thicker in center than at edges.
convex mirror (376): Diverging mirror. Center of curvature is on side opposite reflecting side of mirror.
cosine (113): The ratio of the adjacent side and the hypotenuse.
coulomb (C) (417): Unit of electrical charge. Charge caused by flow of one ampere for one second.
crest of wave (290): High point of wave motion.
critical angle (357): Minimum angle of incidence that produces total internal reflection.
crystal lattice (278): Structure of solid consisting of regular arrangement of atoms.

D

de Broglie wavelength (566): Length of de Broglie wave of particle; Planck's constant divided by momentum of particle.
decibel (dB) (311): Unit of sound level.
dependent variable (27): Variable that responds to change in manipulated variable.
derived units (15): Unit of a quantity that consists of combination of fundamental units.
destructive interference (297): Superposition of waves resulting in a combined wave with zero amplitude.
diffraction (301): Bending of waves around object in their path.
diffraction grating (400): Material containing many parallel lines very closely spaced that produces a light spectrum by interference.
diffuse reflection (348): Reflection of light into many directions by rough object.
dimensional analysis (45): Checking a derived equation by making sure dimensions are the same on both sides.
diode (605): Electrical device permitting only one way current flow.
dispersion of light (360): Variation with wavelength of speed of light through matter resulting in separation of light into spectrum.
displacement (d) (43): Change in position. A vector quantity.
dissonance (321): Two or more sounds that, when heard together, sound unpleasant.
distance (42): The separation between two points. A scalar quantity.
diverging lens (378): Lens that causes light rays to spread apart or diverge; usually a concave lens.
dopants (601): Small quantities of material added to semiconductor to increase electrical conduction.
Doppler shift (309): Change in wavelength due to relative motion of source and detector.
dynamics (87): Study of motion of particles acted on by forces.

E

effective current (AC) (520): DC current that would produce the same heating effects.
effective voltage (AC) (520): DC potential difference that would produce the same heating effects.
efficiency (206): Ratio of output work (or energy) to input work (or energy).
effort force (205): Force exerted on a machine.
elastic collision (231): Interaction between two objects in which the total energy is the same before and after the interaction.
elasticity (279): Ability of object to return to original shape after deforming forces are removed.
electric charge pump (449): Device, often battery or generator, that increases potential of electric charges.
electric circuit (449): Continuous path through which electric charges can flow.
electric current (450): Flow of charged particles.
electric field (426): Property of space around a charged object that causes forces on other charged objects.
electric field lines (428): Lines representing the direction of electric field.
electric field strength (426): Ratio of force exerted by field on a tiny test charge to that charge.
electric generator (518): Device converting mechanical energy to electrical energy.
electric potential (432): Ratio of electric potential energy to charge.
electric potential difference (432): Difference in electric potential between two points.
electric potential energy (432): Energy of a charged body in an electric field.
electromagnet (498): Device that uses an electric current to produce a concentrated magnetic field.
electromagnetic force (88): One of fundamental forces due to electric charges, both static and moving.
electromagnetic induction (516): Production of electric field or current due to change in magnetic flux.
electromagnetic radiation (547): Energy carried by electromagnetic waves through space.
electromagnetic waves (288): Wave consisting of oscillating electric and magnetic fields that move at speed of light through space.
electromotive force (*EMF*) (517): Potential difference produced by electromagnetic induction.
electron (410): Subatomic particle of small mass and negative charge found in every atom.
electron cloud (585): Region of high probability of finding an electron around an atom.
electron diffraction (566): Effects on electrons due to wave-like interference of electrons with matter.
electron gas model (597): Description of current flow through conductors.

electroscope (414): Device to detect electric charges.
electrostatics (408): Study of properties and results of electric charges at rest.
electroweak force (633): Unification of electromagnetic and weak forces.
elementary charge (418): Magnitude of the charge of an electron, 1.602×10^{-19} C.
emission spectrum (575): Spectrum produced by radiation from excited atoms.
energy (201): Non-material property capable of causing changes in matter.
energy levels (581): Amounts of energy an electron in an atom may have.
entropy (258): Measure of disorder in a system; ratio of heat added to temperature.
equilibrant force (121): Force needed to bring an object into translational equilibrium.
equilibrium (121): (translational) Condition in which net force on object is zero. (rotational) Condition in which net torque on object is zero.
equivalent resistance (471): Single resistance that could replace several resistors.
evaporation (276): Change from liquid to vapor state.
excited state (581): Energy level of atom higher than ground state.
external forces (186): Forces exerted from outside a system.
extrinsic semiconductor (601): Semiconductor in which conduction is primarily the result of added impurities (dopants).

F

factor-label method (45): Dimensional analysis.
farad (F) (441): Unit of capacitance. One coulomb per volt.
ferromagnetic materials (499): Materials in which large internal magnetic fields are generated by cooperative action of electrons.
first harmonic (321): In music, the fundamental frequency.
first law of thermodynamics (256): Change in internal or thermal energy is equal to heat added and work done on system. Same as law of conservation of energy.
fluid (266): Material that flows, i.e. liquids, gases, and plasmas.
focal length (371): Distance from the focal point to the center of a lens or vertex of a mirror.
focal point (370): Location at which rays parallel to the optical axis of an ideal mirror or lens converge to a point.
forbidden gap (596): Energy values that electrons in a semiconductor or insulator may not have.
force (88): Agent that results in accelerating or deforming an object.
frame of reference (42): Coordinate system used to define motion.
Fraunhofer lines (578): Absorption lines in the sun's spectrum due to gases in the solar atmosphere.
frequency (290): Number of occurrences per unit time.
friction (96): Force opposing relative motion of two objects that are in contact.
fundamental particles (628): Those particles (i.e. quarks and leptons) of which all matter is composed.
fundamental tone (321): Lowest frequency sound produced by a musical instrument.
fundamental units (14): Set of units on which a measurement system is based (i.e. meter, second, kilogram, ampere, candela).
fuse (480): Metal safety device in an electric circuit that melts to stop current flow when current is too large.
fusion (253): Combination of two nuclei into one with release of energy.

G

galvanometer (505): Device used to measure very small currents.
gamma decay (619): Process by which a nucleus emits a gamma ray.
gamma particle (619): High energy photon (very high frequency electromagnetic wave) emitted by a radioactive nucleus.
gas (266): State of matter that expands to fill container.
Geiger-Mueller tube (627): Device used to detect radiation using its ability to ionize matter.
general theory of relativity (169): Explanation of gravity and accelerated motion invented by Einstein.
gluon (628): Carrier of the strong nuclear force.
grand unified theories (GUTs) (88): Theories being developed that unify the strong and electroweak forces into one force.
gravitational field (168): Distortion of space due to the presence of a mass.
gravitational force (88): Attraction between two objects due to their mass.
gravitational mass (96): Ratio of gravitational force to object's acceleration.
gravitational potential energy (223): Change of energy of object when moved in a gravitational field.
graviton (628): Particle that carries the gravitational force. Not yet observed.
ground state (581): Lowest energy level of an electron in an atom.
grounding (439): Process of connecting a charged object to Earth to remove object's unbalanced charge.

H

half-life (621): Length of time for half of a sample of radioactive material to decay.
harmonics (321): Frequencies produced by musical instrument that are multiples of fundamental tone.
heat (Q) (247): Quantity of energy transferred from one object to another because of a difference in temperature.
heat engine (256): Device that converts thermal energy to mechanical energy.
heat of fusion (253): Quantity of energy needed to change a unit mass of a substance from solid to liquid state at the melting point.
heat of vaporization (253): Quantity of energy needed to change a unit mass of a substance from liquid to gaseous state at the boiling point.
heavy water (647): Deuterium oxide used mainly in CANDU nuclear reactors.
Heisenberg uncertainty principle (568): The more accurately one determines the position of a particle, the less accurately the momentum can be known, and vice versa.
hertz (Hz) (290): Unit of frequency equal to one event or cycle per second.
hole (600): Absence of an electron in a semiconductor.
Hooke's law (147): Deformation of an object is proportional to force causing it.
Huygens' wavelets (392): Model of spreading of waves in which each point on wavefront is source of circular or spherical waves.
hydraulic system (268): Machines using fluids to transmit energy.
hyperbola (31): Mathematical curve that describes an inverse relationship between two variables.
hypotenuse (113): Side opposite the right angle in a triangle.

I

ideal mechanical advantage (*IMA*) (206): In simple machine, the ratio of effort distance to resistance distance.
illuminance (333): Rate at which electromagnetic wave energy falls on a surface.
illuminated object (368): Object on which light falls.
image (368): Reproduction of object formed with lenses or mirrors.

impulse (177): Product of force and time interval over which it acts.
impulse-momentum theorem (177): Impulse given to an object is equal to its change in momentum.
incandescent body (556): Object that emits light because of its high temperature.
incident wave (295): Wave that strikes a boundary where it is either reflected or refracted.
incoherent light (586): Light consisting of waves that are not in step (not coherent).
independent variable (27): Variable that is manipulated or changed in an experiment.
index of refraction (350): Ratio of the speed of light in vacuum to its speed in a material.
inelastic collision (231): Collision in which some of the kinetic energy is changed into another form.
inertia (90): Tendency of object not to change its motion.
inertial mass (96): Ratio of net force exerted on object to its acceleration.
initial velocity (69): Velocity of object at time $t = 0$.
instantaneous acceleration (67): Acceleration at a specific time; slope of tangent to velocity-time graph.
instantaneous position (43): Position of object at specific time.
instantaneous velocity (53): Slope of the tangent to position-time graph.
insulator (411): Material through which the flow of electrical charge carriers or heat is greatly reduced.
interference fringes (392): Pattern of dark and light bands from interference of light waves.
interference of waves (297): Displacements of two or more waves, producing either larger or smaller waves.
internal forces (186): Forces between objects within a system.
intrinsic semiconductor (600): Semiconductor in which conduction is by charges due to host material, not impurities (of extrinsic semiconductor).
inverse relationship (31): Mathematical relationship between two variables, x and y, summarized by the equation $xy = k$, where k is a constant.
ionizing radiation (644): Particles or waves that can remove electrons from atoms, molecules, or atoms in a solid.
isolated system (180): A collection of objects not acted upon by external forces into which energy neither enters nor leaves.
isotope (617): Atomic nuclei having same number of protons but different numbers of neutrons.

J

joule (J) (198): SI unit of energy (or work or heat) equal to one newton-meter.
Joule heating (460): Increase in temperature of electrical conductor due to conversion of electrical to thermal energy.

K

Kelvin temperature scale (246): Scale with 0 K = absolute zero and 273.16 K = triple point of water.
Kepler's laws (157): Three laws of motion of bodies attracted together by the gravitational force.
kilogram (kg) (15): SI unit of mass.
kilowatt hour (kWh) (462): Amount of energy equal to 3.6×10^6 J. Usually used in electrical measurement.
kinematics (87): Study of motion of objects without regard to the causes of this motion.
kinetic energy (218): Energy of object due to its motion.
kinetic-molecular theory (242): Description of matter as being made up of extremely small particles in constant motion.

L

laser (587): Devise that produces coherent light by stimulated emission of radiation.
laser-induced fusion (652): Proposed method of creating nuclear fusion by using heating caused by intense laser beams to squeeze matter together.
law of conservation of energy (227): In a closed, isolated system, the total energy does not change.
law of conservation of momentum (183): In a closed, isolated system, the total momentum is constant.
law of reflection (299): Angle of incidence of a wave is equal to the angle of reflection.
law of universal gravitation (164): Gravitational force between two objects depends directly on the product of their masses and inversely on the square of their separation.
lens (378): Optical device designed to converge or diverge light.
lens equation (381): *See mirror equation.*
Lenz's law (523): Magnetic field generated by an induced current opposes the change in field that caused the current.
lepton (628): Particle (like electron) that interacts with other particles only by the electroweak and gravitational interactions.
lever arm (146): Component of the displacement of the force from the axis of rotation in the direction perpendicular to the force.
light (330): Electromagnetic radiation with wavelengths between 400 and 700 nm that is visible.
linear accelerator (625): Device to accelerate subatomic particles by applying successive electric fields.
linear relationship (29): Relationship between two variables, x and y, summarized by the equation $y = ax + b$, where a and b are constant.
linear restoring force (147): Force in direction toward equilibrium position that depends linearly on distance from that position.
liquid (274): Materials that have fixed volume but whose shape depends on the container.
lodestone (491): Naturally occurring magnetic rock.
longitudinal waves (288): Wave in which direction of disturbance is the same as the direction of travel of wave.
loudness (310): Physiological measure of amplitude of a sound wave; heard loudness depends on pitch and tone color as well as amplitude.
lumen (lm) (333): Unit of luminous flux.
luminance intensity (338): Measure of light emitted by source in candelas; luminous flux divided by 4π.
luminous flux (333): Flow of light from source measured in lumens.
luminous object (368): Object that emits light, as opposed to one that reflects light.
lux (lx) (333): Unit of luminous flux; one lumen per square meter.

M

machine (205): Device that changes force needed to do work.
magnetic field (494): Space around a magnet throughout which magnetic force exists.
magnification (373): Ratio of size of an optical image to the size of the object.
manipulated variable (27): Variable that the experimenter can change.
mass defect (640): Mass equivalent of the binding energy; $m = E/c^2$.
mass number (A) (617): Number of nucleons (protons plus neutrons) in the nucleus of an atom.
mass spectrometer (539): Device used to measure the mass of atoms or molecules.
matter wave (288): Wave-like properties of particles such as electrons.
mechanical advantage (*MA*) (205): Ratio of resistance force to effort force in a machine.
mechanical energy (227): Sum of potential and kinetic energy.
mechanical resonance (149): Condition at which natural oscillation frequency equals frequency of driving force; amplitude of oscillatory motion at a maximum.
mechanical wave (288): Wave consisting of periodic motion of matter; e.g. sound wave or water wave as opposed to electromagnetic wave.

melting point (253): Temperature at which substance changes from solid to liquid state.
meson (633): Medium mass subatomic particle consisting of combination of a quark and antiquark.
meter (m) (14): SI unit of length.
mirror equation (373): $1/d_o + 1/d_i = 1/f$, where d_o is object distance, d_i is image distance, f is focal length.
moderator (647): Material used to decrease speed of neutrons in nuclear reactor.
momentum (176): Product of object's mass and velocity.
monochromatic light (392): Light of a single wavelength.
mutual inductance (526): Measures the amount of overlap between the magnetic flux produced in one coil and that which passes through a second coil, thus the amount of *EMF* induced in a secondary coil by the varying flux in the primary coil.
myopia (384): Defect of eye, commonly called nearsightedness, in which distant objects focus in front of the retina.

N

n-type semiconductor (601): Semiconductor in which current is carried by electrons.
net force (89): Vector sum of forces on object.
neutral (410): Object that has no net electric charge.
neutrino (629): Chargeless, massless, subatomic particle emitted with beta particles; type of lepton.
neutron (617): Subatomic particle with no charge and mass slightly greater than that of proton; type of nucleon.
newton (N) (91): SI unit of force.
Newton's laws of motion (89, 90, 92): Laws relating force and acceleration.
node (298): Point where disturbances caused by two or more waves result in no displacement.
normal (299): Perpendicular to plane of interest.
normal force (97): Force perpendicular to surface.
nuclear equation (620): Equation representing a nuclear reaction.
nuclear fission (647): Reaction in which large nucleus splits into two parts, often approximately equal in mass.
nuclear fusion (649): Reaction in which two nuclei are combined into one.
nuclear reaction (619): Reaction involving the strong force in which the number of protons or neutrons in a nucleus changes.
nuclear reactor (647): Device in which nuclear fusion is used to generate electricity.
nuclear transmutation (619): Change of one nucleus into another as the result of a nuclear reaction.
nucleon (640): Either a proton or a neutron.
nuclide (617): Nucleus of an isotope.

O

object (optics) (368): Source of diverging light rays: either luminous or illuminated.
octave (311): Interval between two frequencies with a ratio of two to one.
ohm (Ω) (452): SI unit of resistance; one volt per ampere.
Ohm's law (452): Resistance of object is constant, independent of voltage across it.
opaque (336): Material that does not transmit light.
open-pipe resonator (318): Cylindrical tube with both ends closed and a sound source at one end.

P

p-type semiconductor (602): Semiconductor in which conduction is the result of motion of holes.
pair production (630): Formation of particle and antiparticle from gamma rays.
parabolic mirror (371): Mirror the shape of a paraboloid of revolution that has no spherical aberration.
parallel circuit (475): Circuit in which there are two or more paths for current flow.
parallel connection (455): Connection of two or more electrical devices between two points to provide more than one current path.
pascal (Pa) (267): SI unit of pressure; one neutron per square meter.
Pascal's principle (268): Pressure applied to a fluid is transmitted undiminished throughout it.
period (T) (143, 147): Time needed to repeat one complete cycle of motion.
periodic motion (141): Motion that repeats itself at regular intervals of time.
photoelectric effect (558): Ejection of electrons from surface of metal exposed to electromagnetic radiation.
photon (558): Quantum of electromagnetic waves; particle aspect of these waves.
photovoltaic cell (448): Device that converts electromagnetic radiation (light) into electrical energy.
physics (4): Study of matter and energy and their relationships.
piezoelectricity (549): Electric potential produced by deforming material.
pigment (339): Colored material that absorbs certain colors and transmits or reflects others.
pitch (310): Perceived sound characteristic equivalent to frequency.
Planck's constant (*h*) (558): ratio of energy of photon to its frequency.
plane mirror (368): Flat, smooth surface that reflects light regularly (specularly).
plasma (276): State of matter in which atoms are separated into electrons and positive ions or bare nuclei.
point object (42): Object idealized as so small to be located at only one position.
polarized light (342): Light in which electric fields are all in same plane.
position (42): Separation between object and a reference point.
position-time graph (48): Graph of object's motion that shows how its position depends on clock reading, or time.
positron (630): Antiparticle equivalent of electron.
potential difference (432): Difference in electric potential between two points.
potential energy (218): Energy of object due to its position or state.
potentiometer (453): Electrical device with variable resistance; rheostat.
power (202): Rate of doing work; rate of energy conversion.
precision (21): Degree of exactness in a measurement.
pressure (266): Force per unit area.
primary coil (526): Transformer coil that, when connected to voltage source, creates varying magnetic flux.
primary light colors (338): Red, green, or blue light.
primary pigment (339): Yellow, cyan, or magenta pigment.
principal axis (370): Line connecting center of curvature of spherical mirror with its geometric vertex. Line perpendicular to plane of lens passing through its center.
principle of superposition (297): Displacement due to two or more forces is equal to vector sum of forces.
projectiles (134): Motion of objects given initial velocity that then move only under force of gravity.
proton (616): Subatomic particle with positive charge that is nucleus of hydrogen atom.

Q

quantized (580): A quantity that cannot be divided into smaller and smaller increments forever, for which there exists a minimum, quantum increment.
quantum mechanics (585): Study of properties of matter using its wave properties.
quantum model of atom (585): Atomic model in which only probability of locating electron is known.

quantum number (582): Integer ratio of energy to its quantum increment.
quark (628): Basic building block of protons, neutrons, other baryons, and mesons.
quark model (631): Model in which all particles that interact via the strong interaction are composed of two or three quarks.

R

radiation (243): Electromagnetic waves that carry energy.
radioactive decay (618): Spontaneous change of unstable nuclei into other nuclei.
radioactive materials (618): Materials that undergo radioactive decay.
range of projectile (137): Horizontal distance between launch point of projectile and where it returns to launch height.
ray model of light (330): Light may be represented by straight line along direction of motion.
ray optics (330): Study of light using ray model.
Rayleigh criterion (401): Two optical images are separable if central bright spot of one image falls on first dark band of second.
real image (371): Optical image at which rays from object converge.
receiver (550): Device that detects electromagnetic waves.
reference level (223): Location at which potential energy is chosen to be zero.
reference point (42): Zero location in a coordinate system or frame of reference.
refraction (348): Change in direction of light ray when passing from one medium to another.
refractive index (351): Ratio of speed of light in vacuum to that in the medium.
resistance (451): Ratio of potential difference across device to current through it.
resistance force (205): Force exerted by a machine.
resistor (452): Device designed to have a specific resistance.
responding variable (27): Variable that changes as result of change in manipulated variable.
rest energy (229): Energy due to mass of object; $E = mc^2$.
resultant (110): Vector sum of two or more vectors.
right-hand rules (497, 498, 502): Used to find force on current or moving particle in magnetic field; used to find direction of magnetic field caused by current or of induced *EMF*.
Rutherford's model of atom (575): Nuclear model of atom; essentially all mass in compact, positively-charged object at center, surrounded by electrons.

S

scalar (42): Quantity, like distance, that has only a magnitude, or size.
schematic diagram (454): Representation of electric circuit using symbols.
scientific notation (15): Numbers expressed in form $M \times 10^n$, where $1 \leq M < 10$, and n is an integer.
scintillation (574): Flash of light emitted when substance is struck by radiation.
second (s) (14): SI unit of time.
second law of thermodynamics (258): Heat flow only from region of high temperature to region of lower temperature.
secondary coil (526): Transformer coil in which varying *EMF* is induced.
secondary light colors (338): Yellow, cyan, or magenta light.
secondary pigment (339): Red, green, or blue pigment.
self-inductance (525): Induced *EMF* produced in coil by changing current.
semiconductor (599): Material in which electrical conduction is smaller than that in a conductor, but more than in an insulator.
series circuit (470): Circuit in which electrical current flows through each component, one after another.
series connection (455): Arrangement of electrical devices so that there is only one path through which current can flow.
short circuit (481): Low resistance connection between two points, often accidental.
SI (14): Internationally agreed-upon method of using the metric system of measurement.
significant digit (22): Reliable digits reported in a measurement.
simple harmonic motion (147): Motion caused by linear restoring force that has a period independent of amplitude of motion.
simple machine (205): Machine consisting of only one lever, inclined plane, wedge, screw, pulley, or wheel and axle.
sine (113): The ratio of the opposite side and the hypotenuse.
sliding friction (97): Force between two surfaces in relative motion.
slope (29): Ratio of the vertical separation, or rise to the horizontal separation, or run.
solid (278): State of matter with fixed volume and shape.
sound level (311): Quantity measuring logarithm of sound intensity in decibels.
spark chamber (627): Device used to detect path of charged subatomic particles by a spark that jumps along path of ionization created in a gas.
specific heat (247): Thermal energy needed to change temperature of unit mass of substance one kelvin.
spectroscope (576): Device used to study spectrum of material.
spectrum (337): Collection of wavelengths in electromagnetic spectrum.
speed (v) (51): Ratio of distance traveled to time interval.
speed of light (332): In vacuum, 2.9979458×10^8 m/s.
spherical aberration (371): Inability of spherical mirror to focus all parallel rays to a single point.
standing wave (316): Wave with stationary nodes.
static friction (96): Force that opposes start of motion between two surfaces.
step-down transformer (526): Transformer with output voltage smaller than input voltage.
step-up transformer (526): Transformer with output voltage larger than input voltage.
stimulated emission (587): Emission of photon from excited atom caused by impact of photon of same energy.
strong nuclear force (88): Force of very short range that holds neutrons and protons in nucleus together.
superconductor (452): Electrical conductor that has no resistance and low temperatures.
surface wave (289): Wave on surface of liquid with characteristics of both longitudinal and transverse waves.
symmetry (75): Property that is now changed when operation or reference frame is changed.
synchrotron (626): Device to accelerate particles in which particles move in circular path.
system (180): Defined collection of objects.

T

tangent (113): The ratio of the opposite side and the adjacent side.
temperature (244): Measure of hotness of object on a quantitative scale. In gases, proportional to average kinetic energy of molecules.
terminal velocity (102): Velocity of falling object reached when force of air resistance equals weight.
test charge (426): Charge used, in principle, to measure electric field.
thermal energy (243): Internal energy. Sum of kinetic and potential energy of random motion of particles making up object.
thermal equilibrium (244): State between two or more bodies where temperatures do not change.
thermal expansion (279): Increase in length or volume of object due to change in temperature.

thermometer (244): Device used to measure temperature.
thermonuclear reaction (651): Nuclear fusion.
thin-film interference (340): Light interference caused by reflection from both front and rear surface of thin layer of liquid or solid.
timbre (320): Sound quality or tone color; spectrum of sound frequencies that produce a complex wave.
time interval (Δt) (43): Difference in time between two clock readings.
Tokamak (652): Type of fusion reactor.
tone color (320): Timbre or tone quality.
torque (τ) (146): Product of force and the lever arm.
trajectory (134): The path followed by projectile.
transformer (526): Device to transfer energy from one electrical circuit to another by means of mutual inductance between two coils.
transistor (609): Semiconductor device that controls large current by means of small voltage changes.
translucent (336): Material transmitting light but distorting its path.
transmutation (619): Nuclear change from one element to another.
transparent (336): Material transmitting light without distorting directions of rays.
transverse wave (288): Wave in which disturbance is perpendicular to direction of travel of wave.
traveling wave (289): Moving, periodic disturbance in a medium or field.
trigonometry (113): Branch of math that deals with the relationships among angles and sides of triangles.
trough of wave (290): Low point of wave motion, where displacement is most negative.

U

uniform acceleration (69): constant acceleration.
uniform circular motion (142): Motion in a circle of constant radius with constant speed.

V

valence band (598): In a solid, the range of energies of electrons that are bound to atoms.
vector quantity (110): Quantity having both magnitude (size) and direction.
vector resolution (116): Process of finding the effective value of a component in a given direction.
velocity (v) (51): Ratio of change in position to time interval over which change takes place.
velocity-time graph (54): Plot of velocity of object as a function of time.
virtual image (368): Point from which light rays appear to diverge without actually doing so.
viscous fluid (278): Fluid that creates force that opposes motion of objects through it. The force is proportional to object's speed.
volatile liquid (276): Liquid that is easily vaporized.

W

watt (W) (202): Unit of power, one joule per second.
wavelength (λ) (290): Distance between corresponding points on two successive waves.
wave pulse (289): Single disturbance moving through a medium or field.
weak boson (628): Particle that carries or transmits the weak interaction or force.
weak interaction (631): Force involved in beta decay of the neutron and atomic nuclei; one aspect of the electroweak force.
weight (94): Force of gravity on an object.
weightlessness (166): Object in freefall, on which only the gravitational force acts.
Wilson cloud chamber (627): Chamber containing supersaturated vapor through which ionizing radiation leaves trails of visible droplets.
work (198): Product of force and displacement in the direction of the force.
work function (560): Energy needed to remove an electron from metal.
work-energy theorem (220): Work done on object is equal to the change in its kinetic energy.

X

X ray (551): High-energy photons; high-frequency, short-wavelength electromagnetic waves.

Index

A

B

C

F

G

H

I

J

K

L

M

N

O

P

Q

R

S

T

U

V

W

X

Y

Z

Photo Credits

Cover, **i,** Richard Megna, Fundamental Photographs; **iii,** Tim Courlas; **v,** courtesy The Children's Museum, Indianapolis; **vii,** Tim Courlas; **viii,** Steven Trank Photography; **ix,** Jeff Gnass/The Stock Market; **x,** Ralph Wetmore/Photo Researchers, Inc.; **xi,** Bud Fowle Photography; **2,** Makoto Iwafuji/The Stock Market; **3,** courtesy Lawrence Berkeley National Lab; **4,** Andrew Sacks/Tony Stone Images; **5, (t)** Medichrome/The Stock Shop, Inc., **(b)** courtesy Argonne National Lab; **6,** © 1970 Sidney Harris, *American Scientist* magazine; **7,** courtesy Fermi National Accelerator Lab; **11,** Connolly/*New York Times*/University of Houston; **12,** Doug Martin; **14,** file photo; **15, (t)** courtesy The Children's Museum, Indianapolis, **(b)** Jean-Paul Ferrero; **16, (tl)** Roger K. Burnard, **(tc)** NASA, **(tr)** U.S. Naval Observatory, **(bl)** file photo, **(bc)** courtesy General Electric Company, **(br)** file photo; **19, (t)** courtesy IBM Corporation, **(b)** Grant Heilman Photography; **20,** Tom McGuire; **21,** Tim Courlas; **22, (l)** Doug Martin, **(r)** courtesy Fisher Scientific; **24,** Tim Courlas; **27,** Doug Martin; **33,** Roger-Viollet; **40,** Paul J. Sutton/DUOMO; **44, (top to bottom)** file photo, NASA, Doug Martin, Aaron Haupt, Alvin E. Staffan, William D. Popejoy; **46,** German Information Center; **47,** courtesy Acculab Products Group; **48,** Cessna Aircraft Company; **56,** Carnival Cruise Lines; **62,** Cedar Point photo by Dan Feicht; **67,** Aaron Haupt; **68,** National Highway Safety Administration; **69,** Peticolas/Megna/Fundamental Photographs; **71,** Robert Estall/Tony Stone Images; **74,** First Image; **76,** Peticolas/Megna/Fundamental Photographs; **77,** Aaron Haupt; **78,** Tim Courlas; **79,** NASA; **86,** © 1990 Photri/The Stock Market; **88,** StudiOhio; **89,** David T. Dennison; **90,** StudiOhio; **91,** Jean-Marc Loubat/Agence Vandystadt/Photo Researchers; **93,** Lance Jeffrey/Leo deWys, Inc.; **95,** Doug Martin; **96,** courtesy Lawrence Livermore National Lab; **103,** bicycle design by Leigh Sargent & Ralph Ray, photo R. Spencer; **108,** Joan Baron/The Stock Market; **116,** Robert Winslow; **117,** Aaron Haupt/Glencoe photo; **120,** Mindy Paderewsky; **123, (t)** Color artwork by Folon © 1966 The New Yorker Magazine, Inc. Reprinted by special permission. All rights reserved., **(b)** First Image; **124-126,** First Image; **132,** Andrew Graham, Department of Physics and Astronomy, Appalachian State University; **134,** PSSC Physics, D. C. Heath & Co., Lexington, 1965; **137,** Susan Rhodes-Martin; **138,** Kodansha; **139,** Al Tielemans/DUOMO; **141, 142,** First Image; **143,** NASA; **144,** David Madison/DUOMO; **146,** First Image; **149,** Forest McMullin Photography; **154,** NASA; **156,** Historical Pictures/Stock Montage, Inc.; **159, 160,** NASA; **162,** Historical Pictures/Stock Montage, Inc.; **163,** Reprinted by permission from Nature, Vol. 311, No. 5983, cover © 1984 Macmillan Journals Ltd.; **165,** file photo; **167, (t)** Center for Astrophysics/Smithsonian Astrophysical Observatory, **(b)** NASA; **169,** Arthur Selby; **174,** courtesy National Highway Safety Administration; **177,** First Image; **179,** NASA; **184, (t)** Johnny Johnson, **(b)** courtesy Daedalon Corporation; **187,** First Image; **188,** The Telegraph Colour Library/FPG; **191,** Lewis Portnoy/Spectra-Action, Inc.; **196,** David Stoecklein/The Stock Market; **198,** E.R. Degginger/Color-Pic, Inc.; **200, 202,** First Image; **203,** StudiOhio; **208,** Reprinted with special permission of King Features Syndicate; **216,** Photo Researchers; **218,** Joe Strunk; **219, (t)** Tim Courlas, **(b)** Robert Winslow; **222,** StudiOhio; **223, (l)** Frank Cezus, **(r)** Jim Bradshaw; **224,** Aaron Haupt; **226,** E.R. Degginger/Color-Pic, Inc.; **228,** StudiOhio; **232,** Carsand-Mosher; **234,** Cobalt Productions; **235,** Superman and related indicia is trademark DC Comics Inc. All rights reserved. Used by permission.; **240,** Tim Courlas; **245, (l)** Mary Lou Uttermohlen, **(r)** StudiOhio; **246, (l)** Anglo-Australian Telescope Board, **(cl)** Tracy I. Borland, **(cr)** NASA, **(r)** U.S. DOE; **248,** courtesy Texas Gulf Chemical Company; **250,** Phil Degginger/Color-Pic, Inc.; **253,** Doug Martin; **259, (t)** Doug Martin, **(b)** StudiOhio; **260,** Doug Martin; **264,** Chris Collins/The Stock Market; **266, (l)** Tim Courlas, **(c)** J. F. Towers/The Stock Market, **(r)** Doug Martin; **267,** Don C. Nieman; **268,** Joey Jacques; **269,** courtesy Central Scientific Company; **270, (t)** Diana Davet, **(b)** James L. Amos/Photo Researchers; **272,** StudiOhio; **273, (l)** NASA, **(r)** © 1973, Estate of Harold Edgerton, courtesy Palm Press, Inc.; **274, (l)** file photo, **(r)** Hickson-Bender Photogra phy; **275,** Hickson-Bender Photography; **276,** John Barger; **277, (t)** Aaron Haupt, **(b)** courtesy Simpson Race Products; **278, (t)** From *Computers in Physics*, "How Do Crystals Melt?", courtesy Argonne National Lab/U.S.DOE/S.R.Phillpot, S.Yip, D.Wolf, **(b)** Roger K. Burnard; **279,** First Image; **280, (t)** Wide World Photos, **(b)** courtesy Lawrence Livermore Lab; **281, (t)** First Image, **(b)** Doug Martin; **284,** Tim Courlas; **286,** Brian Bielman/Preferred Stock Photography; **288,** StudiOhio; **289, (t)** David Lawrence/The Stock Market, **(b)** Doug Martin; **295, (t)** KS Studios, **(b)** StudiOhio; **296,** Doug Martin; **298,** Kodansha; **299,** Runk/Schoenberger from Grant Heilman Photography; **300, (tl)** Richard Megna/Fundamental Photographs, **(tr)** file photo, **(b)** Kodansha; **301,** Kodansha; **302,** Reprinted from *Popular Science* with permission © 1988 Time Mirror Magazines; **306,** Russ Kinne/Comstock; **308,** courtesy AT&T Archives; **310,** Kodansha; **311,** Roy Morsch/The Stock Market; **312, (tl)** Aaron Haupt, **(tr)** David R. Frazier, **(cl)** Allen Zak, **(cr)** Doug Martin, **(bl)** StudiOhio, **(br)** Doug Martin; **315,** Tim Courlas; **319,** Disario/The Stock Market; **322, (l)** Tim Courlas, **(c,r)** Doug Martin; **323,** KS Studios; **327,** StudiOhio; **328,** Steven Trank Photography; **331,** AIP/Niels Bohr Library/W. F. Meggers Collection; **332, (l)** Larry Hamill, **(r)** George Anderson; **336,** Doug Martin; **337, (t)** courtesy Eastman Kodak Company, **(b)** Doug Martin; **338, (t)** courtesy Central Scientific Company, **(b)** StudiOhio; **339,** Tim Courlas; **340,** E.R. Degginger/Color-Pic, Inc. **342,** Henry Leap and Jim Lehman; **346,** Jeff Gnass/The Stock Market; **348,** Doug Martin; **349-351,** Henry Leap and Jim Lehman; **357,** Tim Courlas; **358,** Runk/Schoenberger from Grant Heilman Photography; **359,** Robert Greenler; **360, (t)** Eric Lessing/Magnum, **(b)** file photo; **362,** Illustration by Thomas C. Moore, from "Optical Fibers in Medicine," by Abraham Katzier, May 1989. © 1989 by Scientific American, Inc. All rights reserved. Photo by Olympus Corporation, Medical Instruments Division; **366,** Tim Courlas; **370, (l)** AGE Fotostock/Peter Arnold, Inc, **(r)** Henry Leap and Jim Lehman; **375,** Latent Image; **377,** Allen Zak; **380, (t,c)** David Parker/Photo Researchers, **(b)** Craig Kramer; **390,** Kjell B. Sandved; **393,** Kodansha; **396, (l)** D.C.H. Plowes, **(r)** courtesy J.V. Sanders CSIRO, Division of Materials Science, Parkville, Victoria, Australia; **398,** Kodansha; **400,** courtesy Central Scientific Company; **401, (tl,bl)** Kodansha, **(r)** courtesy Central Scientific Company; **402, (t)** From M. Cagnet, M. Francon and J.C Thierr, ATLAS OF OPTICAL PHENOMENA, Berlin, Springer-Verlag 1962, plate 16, **(b)** Philippe Plailly/Science Photo Library/Photo Researchers; **405,** NASA; **406,** Ralph Wetmore/Photo Researchers; **408,** Comstock; **409,** StudiOhio; **410, (t)** Bruce Terris/IBM Almaden Research Center, **(b)** Tim Courlas; **416,** file photo; **417,** courtesy Xerox Corporation; **424,** file photo; **429-433,** Kodansha; **435,** University of California/Berkeley/Peter Arnold, Inc.; **439,** Tim Courlas; **441, (t)** Aaron Haupt, **(b)** Tim Courlas; **446,** Doug Martin; **450, (l)** Andrew Rakoczy, **(c)** David R. Frazier, **(r)** courtesy General Motors/Hughes Aircraft AeroVironment; **453,** Matt Meadows; **459,** Mary Lou Uttermohlen; **461, (t)** file photo, **(b)** David R. Frazier; **462, (l)** Mark Burnett/Glencoe photo, **(r)** First Image; **463,** file photo; **464,** Manfred Danegger/Peter Arnold, Inc; **467,** Bud Fowle Photography; **468,** Craig Kramer; **473,** First Image; **480,** Mary Lou Uttermohlen; **481,** Elaine Shay; **484,** courtesy Central Scientific Company; **485,** courtesy Radio Shack, Inc; **486,** file photo; **490,** Dr. Louis A. Frank, University of Iowa; **492,** courtesy Central Scientific Company; **493,** Doug Martin; **494,** courtesy Arbor Scientific; **495,** Kodansha; **496,** Doug Martin; **497,** Kodansha; **498,** Paul Brown; **500,** courtesy IBM Almaden Research Center; **509,** German Information Center; **514,** Craig Kramer; **524, 527,** courtesy Central Scientific Company; **528,** E.R. Degginger/Color-Pic, Inc.; **529,** Gerard Photography; **534,** Kay Chernush/The Image Bank; **536,** The Science Museum London; **538,** courtesy Brookhaven National Lab; **540,** Doug Martin; **554,** file photo; **557, (t)** Historical Pictures/Stock Montage, Inc., **(b)** Bud Fowle Photography; **565,** Lawrence Migdale; **566,** E.R. Degginger/Color-Pic, Inc.; **572,** Aaron Haupt; **576, (tl)** courtesy Central Scientific Company, **(tr)** Richard Megna/Fundamental Photographs, **(tcl)** Rich Treplow/Photo Researchers, **(tcr)** Doug Martin, **(bl)** Kodansha, **(br)** courtesy Central Scientific Company; **577,** Kodansha; **578,** file photo; **581,** Stamps from the collection of Prof. C.M. Lang, photography by Gary Shulfer, University of Wisconsin-Stevens Point: New Zealand 487 (1971) and Denmark 410 (1971); **583,** AIP/Niels Bohr Library/Margrethe Bohr Collection; **585,** David R. Frazier; **587,** D. Hamann Hailes/Peter Arnold, Inc; **589,** courtesy Central Scientific Company; **590, (t)** courtesy Battelle Pacific Northwest Labs, **(b)** courtesy Lawrence Livermore National Lab, **(background and inset)** Bruce Iverson; **607,** Charles Falco/Photo Researchers; **610,** Company Wacker-Chemitronic, Burghausen, Germany; **614,** Patrice Loiez, CERN/Science Library/Photo Researchers; **616,** Bud Fowle Photography; **625,** courtesy Stanford Linear Accelerator Center, Stanford University; **626,** courtesy Fermilab; **628,** courtesy Stanford Linear Accelerator Center; **630,** courtesy Brookhaven National Lab; **632,** Matt Meadows; **633,** courtesy University of Tokyo; **634, (t)** courtesy Stanford Linear Accelerator Center, Stanford University, **(c)** file photo, **(b)** The Telegraph Colour Library/FPG; **638,** Craig Kramer; **642,** Dan Guravich; **644, (l)** Tsiaras/Medichrome/The Stock Shop, Inc., **(r)** Howard Sochurek/Medichrome/The Stock Shop, Inc; **646,** Doug Martin; **651,** Gordon Gahar, Lawrence Livermore Lab; **652, (l)** Phototake, **(r)** Sandia National Lab/Walter Dickenman.